Technical Drawing and Design

Louis Gary Lamit
DeAnza College

Illustrations
Manual Illustrations—John J. Higgins
CAD Illustrations—John I. Shull
Assistant CAD Illustrator—Victor E. Valenzuela
Technical Assistance—Vernon Paige, Dennis Wahler

WEST PUBLISHING COMPANY
MINNEAPOLIS/ST. PAUL   NEW YORK   LOS ANGELES   SAN FRANCISCO

DEDICATION

In memory of Walter Brown, one of the most dedicated engineering drawing instructors I have ever known. A sincere coworker, a dependable coauthor, and most importantly an excellent friend.

and to

my children Corina, Jamie, and Angie.
Louis Gary Lamit

Copyediting: Loretta Palagi
Text Design: Roslyn Stendahl/Dapper Design
Layout: Geri Davis, Quadrata
Composition: Carlisle Communications, Inc.
Proofreading: Lynn Reichel
Illustration and photo credits follow the index.
Production, Prepress, Printing and Binding by West Publishing
   Company.

WEST'S COMMITMENT TO THE ENVIRONMENT

In 1906, West Publishing Company began recycling materials left over from the production of books. This began a tradition of efficient and responsible use of resources. Today, up to 95 percent of our legal books and 70 percent of our college and school texts are printed on recycled, acid-free stock. West also recycles nearly 22 million pounds of scrap paper annually—the equivalent of 181,717 trees. Since the 1960s, West has devised ways to capture and recycle waste inks, solvents, oils, and vapors created in the printing process. We also recycle plastics of all kinds, wood, glass, corrugated cardboard, and batteries, and have eliminated the use of styrofoam book packaging. We at West are proud of the longevity and the scope of our commitment to the environment.

Library of Congress Cataloging in Publication Data
Lamit, Louis Gary, 1949–
   Technical drawing and design / Louis Gary Lamit.
      p.   cm.
   Includes index.
   ISBN 0-314-01264-8
   1. Mechanical drawing.   I. Title.
T353.L265   1994
604.2--dc20   92-43902
                                     CIP

Contents in Brief

Contents

Preface

The drafting and design process has been in a state of perpetual change for the last 12 years. The transition from traditional manual methods of graphics communication to CAD-based graphics has been fast-paced and uneven at best. Many of the excellent older texts on the subject have simply added a paragraph at the end of each existing chapter and included one or two chapters introducing CAD to the beginning student. Instructors have tried a variety of instructional methodologies including all manual drafting, manual first then CAD, and only CAD. Each school has had to proceed along this path unguided. It is hoped that this text will ease the transition process, enabling you to choose a unique chapter sequence, the proper combination of CAD and manual methods, and a series of exercises and problems that allow your school to meet its requirements for educating the prospective drafter, designer, or engineer.

One of the greatest difficulties I encountered while writing this text during the last 10 years was not what to *include,* but what to *exclude.* You will note that charts and graphs are lightly covered in Chapter 17 instead of having a complete chapter devoted to them. Engineer-based subjects such as graphical analysis, empirical equations, and other math-engineering oriented subjects have been left to other books where they more properly belong.

The most important reason for including a wide variety of current industry drawings in the text relates to my guiding philosophy about drafting: Drafting is not a field of study or a field in and of itself. *Drafting is a process, a tool used to communicate manufacturing and construction information from the engineering design office to the manufacturing department.* It is not a subject to be studied and mastered for its own sake; the purpose of a drawing is to give manufacturing the technical data required to make a part or produce a product. Technical illustrations, artwork, and artistic renderings are the only types of drawings that are used as the actual product. The product of a technical drawing, however, is the efficiently manufactured, economically produced, and profitable item that is created for a consumer or for the government. The part itself is the goal, not the drawing of the part. Without proper part definition (graphics and dimensions), the drawing is useless and the part cannot be manufactured. Many of the existing texts include drawings of parts that were last manufactured before World War II and some are even from World War I! The goal of this text is to bring drafting and design into the twenty-first century by covering the time-proven basics, yet also extending our abilities with new technology made available by the computer.

ILLUSTRATIONS IN THE TEXT

Unlike many of the traditional texts that have only one style of drawing throughout, this text is dedicated to letting the student see what the real world of drafting, design, and engineering is like. No drawing in this text is over 15 years old as far as when the part was last manufactured. Most projects are from industry and have been manufactured within the last 5 years. Drawings in the text include a range of manually drawn illustrations and engineering details, CAD-plotted projects using pen, electrostatic, and laser plotters, and professional technical illustrations. The variety of drawing types and styles found in the text include the following:

■ *Instructional drawings* were created by professional illustrators to introduce a concept or guide a student through a series of steps to accomplish a specific construction or lay out a part. These are done with CAD and manual technical illustration techniques.
■ *Industry drawings* are directly from a company source, and no changes have been made. Some are CAD and some are manual drawings.
■ *Example art* illustrates a concept and is normally redrawn from an industry source.
■ *Exercises* are placed at the end of each chapter. Each exercise is on an $8\frac{1}{2} \times 11$ in. "A" size sheet with a $\frac{1}{4}$ in. grid.
■ *Problems* are found at the end of most chapters and include a variety of CAD, sketch quality projects, and manually drawn instrument drawings. Problems range from simple "A" size one-view drawings to multiple-view "D" size projects. Problems can be completed as 2D or 3D CAD, instrument, or sketch assignments.

TEXT ORGANIZATION

The text is organized to introduce the student to graphic communication in the traditional sequence, with the addition of new innovations in the design process and technological advances using computers. Chapter 1 (Section 1.14) covers the text's specific organization. As a drafting instructor for the last 23 years, I feel that I have gained a wealth of information on how and what to teach, but it would be presumptuous of to give other instructors advice on how to teach their courses. What suggestions I do have I have left to the instructor's manual and I do hope that they will aid in your communication of this changing field.

TEXT FEATURES

A variety of traditional and unique features have been provided in the text including the following:

■ Performance-based learning *objectives* begin each chapter.

■ *Design-for-manufacturability* (DFM) and *computer-integrated manufacturing* (CIM) applications are presented throughout the text to allow the student to learn about recent innovations, new procedures, and technological advances as they affect engineering and design.

■ CAD commands (usually AutoCAD and sometimes Computervision- Personal Designer), CAD procedures, and concepts are included within and at the end of each chapter to show how a particular procedure or construction would be accomplished on the computer.

■ Industry-based drawings and company examples of *recent* designs are shown.

■ *Sketching* has been integrated into many, if not most, of the chapters, since it is my firm belief that this skill will become even more indispensable as CAD is adopted by all industry and education. Chapter 6 is devoted entirely to sketching. Other chapters in the text have many sketching examples, problems, or exercises. In fact, all of the exercises could be assigned as sketching projects.

■ A number of chapters are unique in their presentation and depth of coverage:

1. Chapter 13 is a very comprehensive coverage of *geometric tolerancing* as provided by Sam Levy (a member of the ANSI Y14 committee) and myself. A 16-page *reference guide* is provided within the chapter for quick reference to a specific geometric tolerancing concept or procedure.

2. Chapter 17 covers the *design process* and design-for-manufacturability in great depth.

3. Chapter 18 covers *assemblies* along with an introduction to *tooling fixtures* using standard off-the-shelf hardware available on computer disk as 3D models.

4. Chapters 19, 20, and 21 are devoted to descriptive geometry, intersections, and developments, respectively, which should allow the instructor to teach a full-length *descriptive geometry* class.

5. Chapter 22 covers *piping drafting and specifications* to such a sufficient depth that it could be used for a one-term course.

6. Chapter 23 on *electronic drafting* is comprehensive enough to be used in an introductory electronic drafting class.

■ Industrial-based *interest boxes* (by Pat Courington) focus on career opportunities, historical information, and specific engineering concepts as they relate to each chapter's material. Interest boxes are meant to increase the student's understanding of the applications of the chapter as they relate to the real world. Interest boxes contain photographs or illustrations to present visually the concept or explain the historical significance of the material.

■ Full color has been added to the text to enhance the graphics. Two chapters are in full color (Chapters 1 and 3). A 16-page full-color section is also included that has more than 100 color plates provided by industry. The full-color sections and chapters reflect the increasing use of color graphics by industry for illustrations that are generated on CAD systems.

■ *Chapter exercises* are provided at the end of each chapter. The exercises are designed to be assigned at specific intervals in the chapter. The exercises allow the student to complete portions of the chapter and understand the material incrementally, piece-by-piece and step-by-step, rather than being required to complete the chapter before doing a problem. The exercises are suggested at logical stopping points within each chapter so as to test the students' mastery of the material before continuing.

■ *Chapter review questions* include eight true and false, eight fill-in-the-blank, and eight short answer questions for Chapters 2 through 23. The 24 questions will aid the student in understanding and retaining the ideas, concepts, and technical information provided in the chapter. The quiz should also force the student into reading the chapter! Answers to all quiz questions are given in the solutions manual.

■ *End-of-chapter problems* close every appropriate chapter. Problems are numerous and of sufficient level of difficulty to provide real-world examples of industrial projects or to teach instructional concepts. Simple to advanced projects are provided in most chapters.

■ The text ends with a comprehensive *appendix,* which includes a series of application-oriented glossaries; mathematical formulas; conversion charts; mechanical, piping, and electronic components; and symbol references. The appendix was designed to be used in industry as a reference on the job.

SUPPLEMENTS

In addition to the text, a series of ancillaries is available to make transition to a new text as comfortable as possible:

■ *Transparency acetates* (about 200) and *transparency masters* (about 200) provide the instructor with a comprehensive set of lecture materials that can be used to display the chapter concepts on an overhead projector.

■ The *solutions manual* (by James Wilson, Georgia Southern College) offers answers to all text quiz questions and solutions to many of the exercises and problems found at the end of each chapter. The solutions manual is also available on an AutoCAD disk.

■ A selection of *workbooks* offer additional drawing exercises with worksheets for students taking manual or CAD-based classes.

■ An *instructor's manual* by the author offers teaching suggestions for a variety of different programs.

Acknowledgments

There is no way a project of this magnitude could be done alone. The gratitude I feel for the many hours of effort put in by others knows no bounds. Without these people, this project simply could not have happened.

First and foremost, I would like to thank Debra Pratt, Rachael Svit, Elena Verne, Irene Guerrero, Valarie Prouty, Jaime Guerrero, Dennis Wahler, Vern Paige, and Sam Levy for contributions to specific chapters of the text; Pat Courington for the chapter objectives and interest boxes; the preparers of the solutions manual and workbooks whose names will become familiar to everyone; Kathleen Kitto for improving the pedagogy and reviewing page and art proofs; and Lou Moegenburg for going into the West office in Eagan and spending countless hours accuracy-checking the art and manuscript, in the process finding errors that had eluded many other pairs of eyes.

At De Anza College I would like to thank the following people: John Allan, Lorn Beall, and Mike Engle for contributions to Chapter 11 on machine tools, Vernon Paige for technically editing the complete manuscript, Bob De Hart who was the president of the college during this project and who encouraged my efforts, and Bob Hubbs, my favorite (and former) administrator for hiring me and providing unlimited support. Many thanks to the present administrators—Oscar Ramirez and Jorge Guevara—for listening to my complaints and providing me with school assistance. And many thanks to John Shull, my trusted assistant, friend, and CAD illustrator.

John Higgins completed all of the manual illustrations (except the sketches, which were my own doing). I particularly wish to thank John Higgins for staying with the project (without pay) for most of 10 years and John Shull for the last 6 years of assistance.

Next, concerning equipment and software donations, I would like to thank Houston Instruments for donating the use of a plotter and digitalizer and Kurta Corporation for use of a digitizer tablet. T & W Systems donated CADAPPLE and VersaCAD software, and Autodesk donated copies of Auto-CAD. Many of the illustrations were completed on AutoCAD and a Computervision system (and Personal Designer) that was donated to De Anza College.

The publishers of my earlier texts deserve a special acknowledgment because without the experience derived and the drawings developed for these more specialized projects, I could not have considered undertaking a work of the present magnitude. Similarly, I must thank the anonymous reviewers, survey respondents, employees, and agencies originally hired by my first publisher on this present project, because their contribution gave this text its necessary beginning. The detail West's reviewers provided was essential to the finished product:

Steven R. Bailes—Kentucky Tech–Daviess County Campus
Brian Bennett—Morrison Institute of Technology (IL)
James R. Brock—Mesa State College (CO)
Richard L. Burns, Ed.D., CMfgE—Indiana State University
Richard Ciocci—Harrisburg Area Community College (PA)
Pat Courington—Valencia Community College and Central Florida Technical Institute (FL)
Harold Craven—University of Maryland
James C. Culbertson—Venango County Area Vocational Technical School (PA)
Joseph P. DiLiberto—Island Drafting and Technical Institute (NY)
John Frostad—Green River Community College (WA)
David D. Gloyeski—Dickson Tennessee Area Vo Tech
Larry D. Goss—University of Southern Indiana
Rhonda Housley—Spartanburg Technical College (SC)
Steven F. Horton—San Jacinto College (TX)
Kathleen L. Kitto—Western Washington University
Thaddeus Kranz—Cuyahoga Community College (OH)
Edward P. Maruggi—Rochester Institute of Technology (NY)
Mark Miller—New England Institute of Technology (RI)
Louis Moegenburg—University of Wisconsin–Stout
William E. Moore—Tidewater Community College (VA)
David G. Price—Orange Coast College (CA)
Arthur J. Reinking—Texas State Technical Institute
J. Pat Spicer—Western Illinois University
Ken Stibolt—Anne Arundel Community College (MD)
Joseph Tuholsky—West Virginia Institute of Technology
James Wilson—Visual Solutions Associates

Specifically, at West, I wish to express appreciation to Cliff Kallemeyn, Holly Henjum, Sheila Hatzenbeller, Mélina Brown, John Lindley, Liz Riedel, and others who increased their knowledge of drafting books while contributing to my knowledge of publishing while working on this; to Christine Hurney for the enormous job of coordinating a project of almost unimaginable complexity; and, finally, to Chris Conty, who managed to give this author the unusual experience of starting and ending a 10-year project with the same editor!

L. Gary Lamit
Cupertino, California

About the Author

Louis Gary Lamit is the former department head of drafting and CAD facility manager and is currently an instructor at De Anza College in Cupertino, California, where he teaches computer-aided drafting and design as well as basic drafting.

Mr. Lamit has worked as a drafter, designer, numerical control (NC) programmer, and engineer in the automotive, aircraft, and piping industries. A majority of his work experience is in the area of mechanical and piping design. Mr. Lamit started as a drafter in Detroit (as a job shopper) working for the automobile industry doing tooling, dies, jigs and fixture layout, and detailing at Koltanbar Engineering, Tool Engineering, Time Engineering, and Premier Engineering for Chrysler, Ford, AMC, and Fisher Body. Mr. Lamit has worked at Remington Arms and Pratt & Whitney Aircraft as a designer, and at Boeing Aircraft and Kollmorgen Optics as an NC programmer and aircraft engineer.

Since leaving industry, Mr. Lamit has taught at all levels (Melby Jr. High, Warren, Michigan; Carroll County Vocational Technical School, Carrollton, Georgia; Heald Engineering College, San Francisco, California; Cogswell Polytechnical College, San Francisco, California, and Cupertino, California; Mission College, Santa Clara, California; Santa Rosa Junior College, Santa Rosa, California; Northern Kentucky University, Highland Heights, Kentucky; and De Anza College, Cupertino, California).

Mr. Lamit has written a number of textbooks including *Industrial Model Building* (1981), *Piping Drafting and Design* (1981), *Descriptive Geometry* (1983), and *Pipefitting and Piping Handbook* (1984) for Prentice-Hall; *Electronic Drafting and Design* (1985; 2e 1993), and *CADD* (1987) were published by Charles Merrill (Macmillan). Mr. Lamit has also written a number of articles, booklets, and workbooks, and presented papers and tutorials in technical areas associated with physical modeling, piping, electronics, and descriptive geometry.

Mr. Lamit received a BS degree from Western Michigan University in 1970 and did masters work at Michigan State University. He has done graduate work at Wayne State University in Michigan and University of California at Berkeley and holds an NC programming certificate from Boeing Aircraft.

PART I

Background

Viewing-plane Line

Extension Line

Dimension Line

2.875

Center Line

Hidden Line

Break Line

B

B

tting-plane Line

ble Line

ter Line
th of motion)

Leader

Chain Line

Phantom Line

Section Line

SECTION A-A

VIEW B-B

1

Introduction to Design and Drafting

Learning Objectives

Upon completion of this chapter you will be able to accomplish the following:

1. Recognize design and drafting as tools that allow graphical representation of ideas.
2. Compare possible career fields and sequences that use technical drawing.
3. Define common terms used in the drafting profession.
4. Understand transitions in technical drawing that have taken place from ancient Roman construction projects to modern computer-aided design and drafting.
5. Develop familiarity with and identify technical drawing types and stages in the design process.
6. Define the role of descriptive geometry in solving three-dimensional problems.
7. Identify the various standards of practice used in drafting and design.

1.1   Introduction

Technical design and drawing—commonly referred to as *drafting*—use a graphic language to communicate ideas. This language, developed and used by engineers, designers, and drafters, serves as an essential tool from the beginning of a product's development to production. But how do we communicate ideas graphically? What are the components of this graphic language? What constitutes a good drawing? This text will answer these questions by covering technical drawing basics, as well as more advanced topics in design.

Technical drawing is basically a *tool* and not a specialized field or subject matter. Industry uses this tool to create and produce a variety of items. Technical drawings play an essential role in design, manufacturing, processing, and production. Every industrial nation employs a large number of drafters. In the United States, more than 400,000 drafters are at work.

Technical drawings are graphical representations of an idea or product that must be processed, manufactured, or constructed. Engineers, designers, and drafters use the drawing and design process to define, establish, create, and transfer technical information. All machines, devices, and products are graphically designed before they can be manufactured and used. The cost, the intricacy, and the manufacturability of the item are considered during the design stage. After the design has been refined, standardized graphics are used to communicate the design data.

You should not consider drafting and design an end in itself or an island of information. The design drawings are only the first step in the long and complicated process of product development, production, and construction.

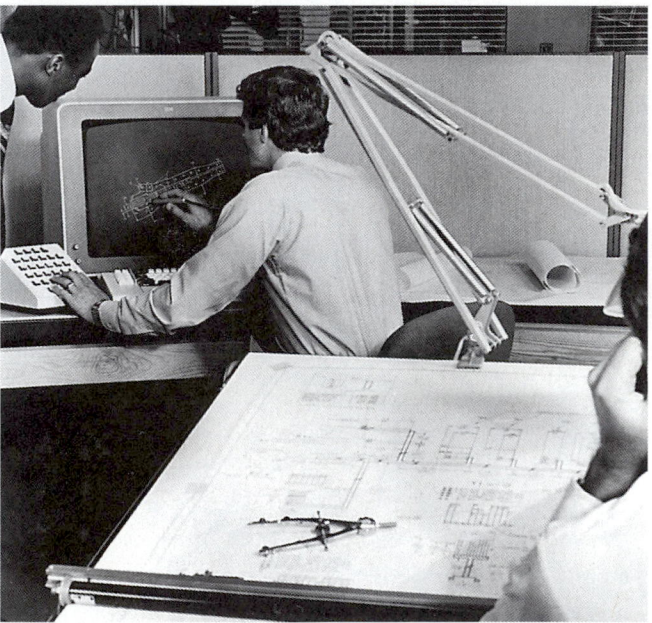

FIGURE 1.1   Drafting and Design in Industry

Drawings are prepared on drafting boards using traditional drafting tools and instruments and on computers. Computer-aided design and drafting (CAD) is a tool found in many companies. It is not uncommon to see CAD systems interspersed among drafting tables (Fig. 1.1). Some small companies use traditional drafting exclusively. Many large companies such as IBM, General Motors, Hewlett Packard (Fig. 1.2), and Ford have converted entirely to CAD for engineering, design, and drafting.

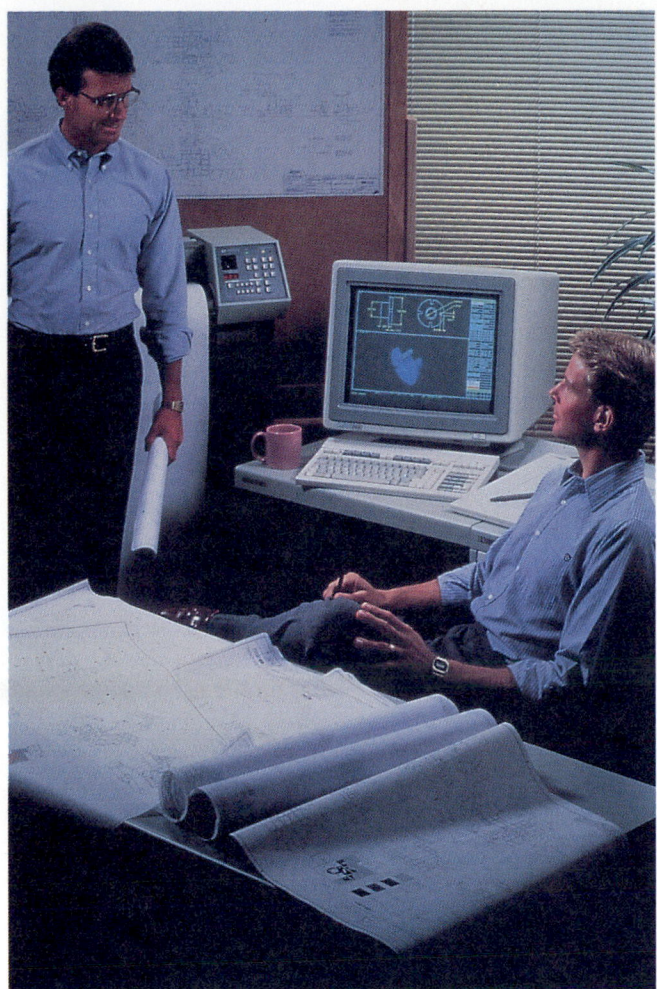

FIGURE 1.2 CAD System

The traditional starting point for a career in drafting is the *drafting trainee*. The drafting trainee normally has had high school or beginning level college courses in drafting, math, and related technical subjects. Some drafting trainees start at the apprentice level, with no drafting experience.

More typically, the path for starting a career in drafting would be to obtain a certificate at a technical school or a one- to two-year associate degree at a community or technical college that offers a drafting and design degree. With this education you would enter the job market as a *drafter/detailer* or a *junior drafter*. The entry level depends on the quality of the degree program and the graduate's experience. The junior drafter is required to know considerably more than the drafting trainee. A junior drafter must have mastered the use of instruments, materials, and drafting techniques including lettering, geometric construction, freehand sketching, projection techniques, sectioning, dimensioning, and tolerancing. The primary responsibility of the junior drafter is to prepare detail drawings.

1.2 Drafting Careers

You can follow many possible paths in a career that uses technical drawing. Figure 1.3 shows the traditional job categories and the path from drafting trainee to design supervisor. The list that follows shows the job categories and responsibilities in drafting and design:

Job Category	Responsibility
Chief engineer	Management
Engineer	Conceptual design
	Ideas
	Calculations
Designer	Design ideas
	Physical layout
Layout designer	Assemblies
	Finalizes design
Detailer	Basic drawings
	Details
	Dimensioning
Checker	Checks all drawings and design
Technical illustrator	Presentation drawings
	Manuals
	Publication quality art

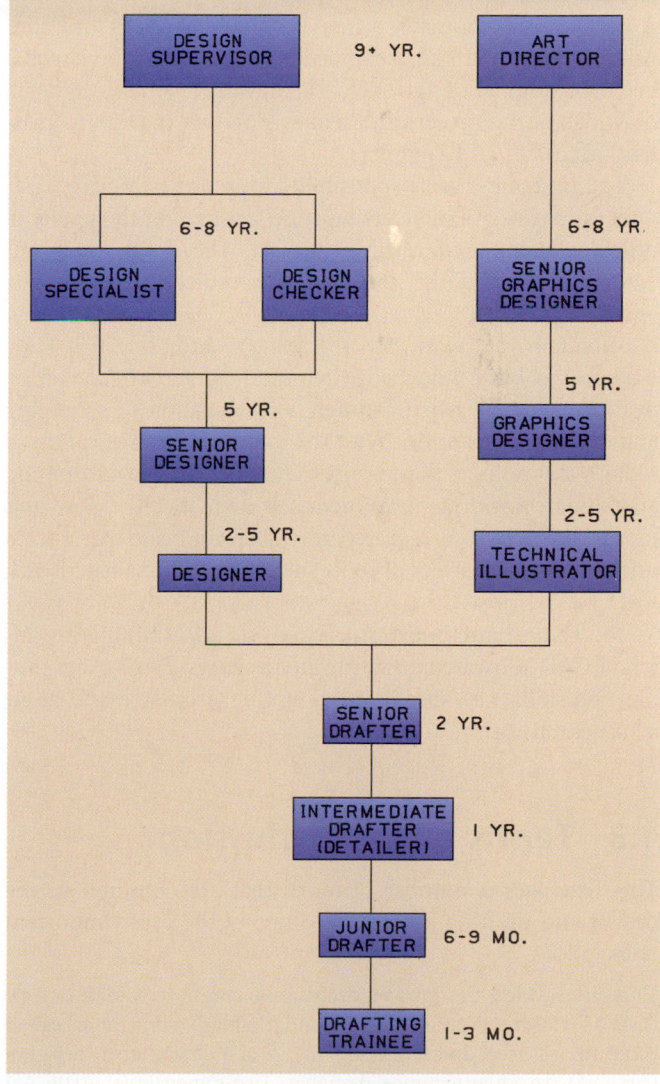

FIGURE 1.3 Flow Chart for a Career in Drafting and Design

The *senior drafter* position requires a minimum of two to five years of experience in a particular engineering discipline. Sometimes this position is called a *layout designer*. Layout designers refine the engineer's and designer's sketches. This includes investigating alternate design possibilities. Layout designers are required to understand drafting conventions and standards, to know how to determine clearances and fits, and to complete the calculations necessary for an accurate design. Knowledge and understanding of machine shop practices, procedures, manufacturing techniques, and basic production methods are important. After two to seven years of experience, you may qualify as a *junior designer* or *designer*. A designer is called on to refine designs established by engineers.

Senior designers are normally in charge of a design group. The senior designer has between six and twenty years of experience as a designer in a particular field. The senior designer works directly with engineers and checkers.

The *checker* is responsible for the accuracy of the finished drawings. They review the drawings for clarity, completeness, production feasibility, and cost effectiveness. Checkers review all mathematical computations required to make the product. A checker is thoroughly schooled in all standards and conventions for a particular engineering discipline. The checker takes the original design sketches, drawing layouts, and detail drawings of the project and makes sure that they are consistent, accurate, and complete.

The ultimate legal responsibility for a project always rests with the *engineer*. Engineers must be *registered* in their state in order to stamp and certify a project. The *design supervisor* (sometimes called the *room boss*) coordinates, supervises, and assigns work.

Whether you work on a drafting board, or on a CAD system, the basic knowledge required for a particular engineering field is learned through a combination of schooling and on-the-job training. With the increased sophistication of today's technology, the requirements for entry-level drafting and design positions have increased dramatically. More and more, designers are required to understand and be able to utilize a greater variety of tools such as those associated with CAD.

You should attempt to gain exposure and training on different CAD software and hardware packages. Strong communication skills, i.e., speaking and writing, are also essential for a successful technical career.

1.3   Terms of the Profession

This text uses a number of terms that are common in the design and drafting profession. Some of the most important ones follow:

Computer-aided design and drafting or computer-aided design (CAD)   Computer-aided design and drafting (sometimes called computer-assisted drafting) refers to use of a computer to design a part and to produce technical drawings. Two-dimensional (2D) CAD is confined to the layout and graphic representation of parts using

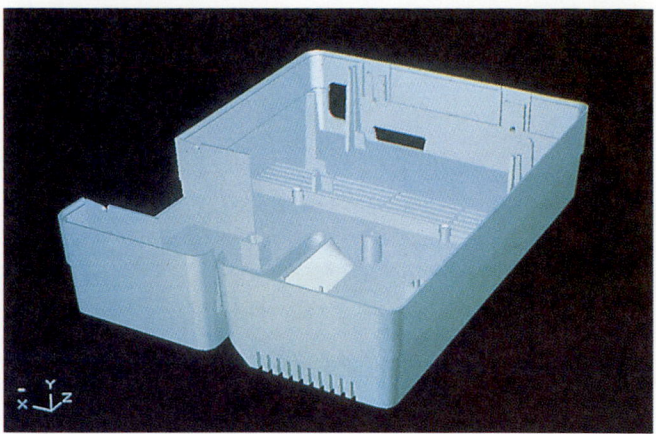

FIGURE 1.4   **3D Mold Design**

traditional standard industry conventions. Drawings are *representations* of the product plotted on paper. 2D CAD is limited to the detailing and drafting aspects of technical drawing. Three-dimensional (3D) CAD (Fig. 1.4) is normally the starting point for the design.

Engineering graphics   Engineering graphics is an all-encompassing term used to describe the use of graphical means of communication in the design process. Engineering graphics refers basically to the use of drawings to represent design ideas, configurations, and specifications, and to the analyses required for an engineering project.

Manual drafting (instrument drawing)   Manual drafting is accomplished on a drafting board using paper, pencil, and drawing instruments. Each chapter of the text covers a specific area of drafting and the manual and CAD procedures and techniques associated with it. In this text, the term *manual drafting* is confined to the creation of drawings by a drafter using traditional instruments, not a computer.

Modeling   The term *modeling* is used throughout the text to describe the design stage of constructing a 3D physical model or an electronic 3D model of a part. A model can be created by physical modeling (Figs. 1.5 and 1.6) or by computer modeling (Fig. 1.7) using a 3D CAD system. With 3D CAD models, you can investigate a variety of designs, test the designs on the system, and perform engineering analyses with the computer (Fig. 1.8). Physical modeling is used to create a lifelike scale model of a part.

Technical drawing   Technical drawing encompasses all of the forms of graphic communication—manual, mechanical, freehand, instrument, and computer generated—used by the engineer, designer, or drafter to express and to develop technical designs for manufacturing, production, or construction.

Technical illustration   Technical illustrations use artistic methods and pictorial techniques to represent a part or system for use by nontechnical personnel. Technical illustrations are widely used in service, parts, owners, and other types of manuals. Sales and advertising also use technical illustrations.

Technical sketching   Technical sketching is the use of freehand graphics. It is one of the most important tools available to the engineer, designer, and drafter to express creative ideas and preliminary design solutions.

FIGURE 1.5   Models of Cranes

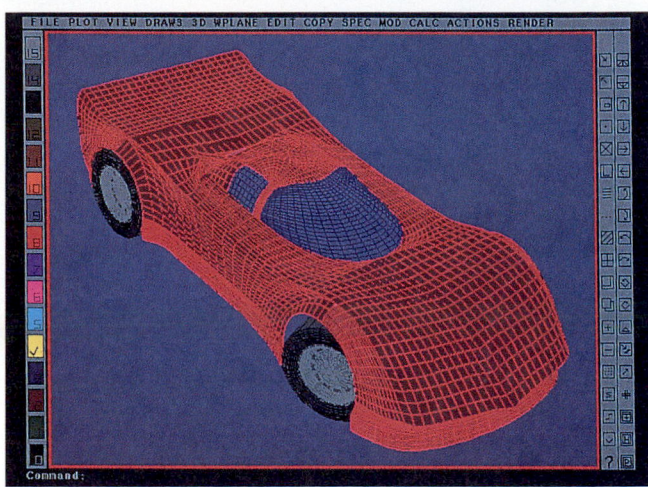

FIGURE 1.7   3D CAD Model

FIGURE 1.6   Power Plant Model

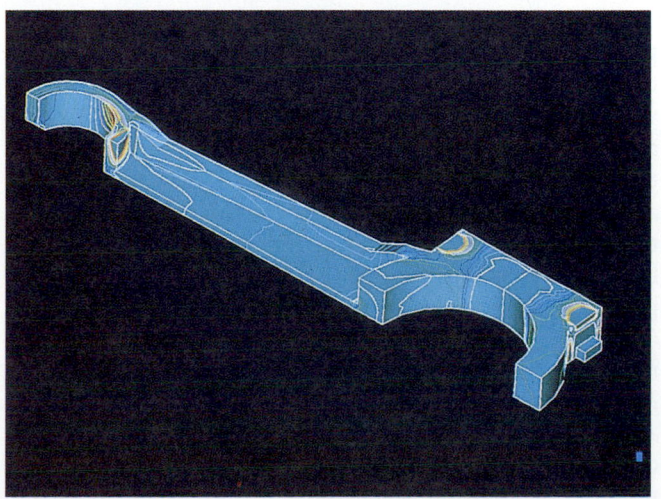

FIGURE 1.8   3D Design Model Used for Engineering Analysis

1.4 The History of Technical Drawing

Technical drawing has been used throughout history. Some of the earliest evidence of the use of drawings comes from the construction of the ancient pyramids and temples. Evidence of the use of technical drawings exists as far back as 1400 B.C. Drawings were used in ancient Rome to display bridge designs and other construction projects. Leonardo da Vinci used pictorial sketches to develop and explore different inventions and designs.

The beginning of modern technical drawing dates back to the early 1800s. Until then, graphic communication had been more artistic in nature and used a pen, ink, and color washes to display pictorial graphic images of a product or construction project. By the 1900s, drawings were used for the production and manufacture of a wide variety of industrial products. As the world became more industrialized, the career of the drafter became a major job category.

As the use of the graphic language became standardized, a series of standards and conventions was established. Standardization aided the transfer of information between the engineering/design department and manufacturing/production or construction. Communication between companies, industries, and countries was also made easier by standardization. Today, we have a very strict, standardized method of displaying graphic information, which is continually evolving.

At one time, before the mid-1800s, the instruments for graphical representation were limited to measuring scales, the compass, dividers, paper, and ink. The use of inking was replaced by the pencil. The T-square was the first standard mechanical drawing board item. It eventually evolved into the parallel bar and then the drafting machine. The newest *tool* in design and drafting is the CAD system.

1.5 Types of Drawings: Artistic and Technical

Drawing is a tool used by people to design a product, solve a problem, or transfer an idea into reality. Almost everything that exists in the world today was drawn first. Look around you. The buildings in which you live and work; the appliances in your home—dishwashers, can openers, dryers, toasters; the methods of transportation—cars, trains, boats, airplanes; the systems that support your life—plumbing, electricity; even what you wear was conceived and brought into being by means of drawings. Few items get manufactured or produced without a drawing.

In general, the two types of drawings are *artistic* and *technical*. Artistic drawings are well outside the scope of this text. An artistic drawing has many techniques and expressions that are not used in technical drawings. First of all, a technical drawing must communicate the same thing to every user or reader of the drawing, whereas the artistic drawing is usually interpreted differently by everyone who sees it. Imagine if a

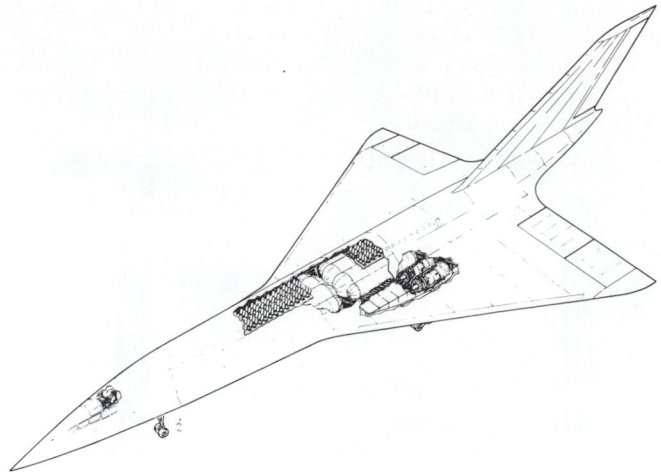

FIGURE 1.9   **Technical Illustration of an Airplane**

technical drawing meant something different to each user! Some drawings of a technical nature, however, incorporate the use of artistic techniques. These are referred to as technical illustrations (Fig. 1.9).

To limit the interpretation to only one possible conclusion, the technical drawing is controlled by accepted standards, drawing "conventions," and projection techniques. The user of a technical drawing understands the exact intent of the drawing. Whether the drawing is completed using sketching techniques, drafting machines, or CAD, the end result is a concise, standardized representation of a part.

Technical drawings are meant to be used to transfer technical information. The drawing must contain all information required to bring the concept, product, or idea into reality. Dimensions, notes, views, and specifications are required for a complete drawing. The user of the drawing may be a great distance from the person who completed it. Therefore, technical drawings must contain everything needed for proper interpretation of the design.

1.6 Types of Technical Drawings

This text is primarily concerned with drawings of mechanical parts—machined parts, castings, and weldments. Various types of drawings are associated with mechanical design and drafting. The following are considered standard types of drawings in this field:

Design sketches   Sketches of initial design ideas, requirements, calculations, and concepts. Sketches are used to convey the design parameters to the layout designer.

Layout drawings   Layout drawings are made to develop the initial design of a unit or machine. A layout drawing must show all the information necessary to make an assembly or a detail drawing.

Assembly drawings   Assembly drawings show a number of detail parts or subassemblies that are joined together to perform a specific function. These parts, when joined together, are usually recognized as a unit.

Detail drawings   A detail drawing shows all information necessary to determine the final form or to purchase a part. The detail drawing must show a complete and exact description of the part including shapes, dimensions, tolerances, surface finish, and heat treatment, either specified or implied.

Casting drawings   Separate casting drawings are usually not required. Normal practice is to show the necessary casting dimension along with the machining dimensions on the detail drawing. When a casting drawing is used, it contains only information needed to cast it. Dimensions for machining and finishing are not contained in this document.

Fabrication drawings   Fabrication drawings are made for parts with permanently fixed pieces. The method of fastening is called out on the drawing with symbols or other standard methods. Welded and riveted parts are examples of projects that require fabrication drawings.

1.7   The Design Process

The design process (Fig. 1.10) starts with someone formulating a concept or idea. The *first stage* of a project begins with the identification of a particular need for a product. The product or situation is often identified by a need in industry, government, the military, or the private sector.

The *second stage* involves the creation of a variety of options or design ideas. These ideas may be in the form of sketches and include mathematical computations. The *third stage* is the refinement of the preliminary designs. At this point in the process, possible solutions to problems are iden-

tified. Various design solutions could be pursued at the same time.

The *fourth stage* involves refinement and selection of a particular design. Here, the project coalesces into a more formal, finalized state using assembly drawings and models. This stage requires close attention to be paid to how the part is manufactured and produced. **Design for manufacturability (DFM)** is an important concept that has gained wide acceptance throughout industry.

In the *fifth stage* detail drawings are prepared. These drawings are prepared using manual drafting or are completed on a CAD system. The result is a complete set of working drawings. The drawings would be very similar regardless of whether they were developed manually or with the use of CAD.

The *sixth stage* in the design process is the manufacturing and production of a product, or the construction of a system. In manufacturing, design and layout time is allocated for producing dies, tools, jigs, and fixtures. In fact, the time and drawing requirements needed for product development may be extremely small when compared to the design of manufacturing and production aids.

During the design process, the designer and drafter encounter many situations where traditional visualization techniques and a mastery of the principles of projection are used in the solution of complex engineering and technical problems. The ability to analyze a specific problem, visualize its spatial considerations, and translate the problem into a viable graphic projection is essential for the designer. Descriptive geometry is an important technique in this process.

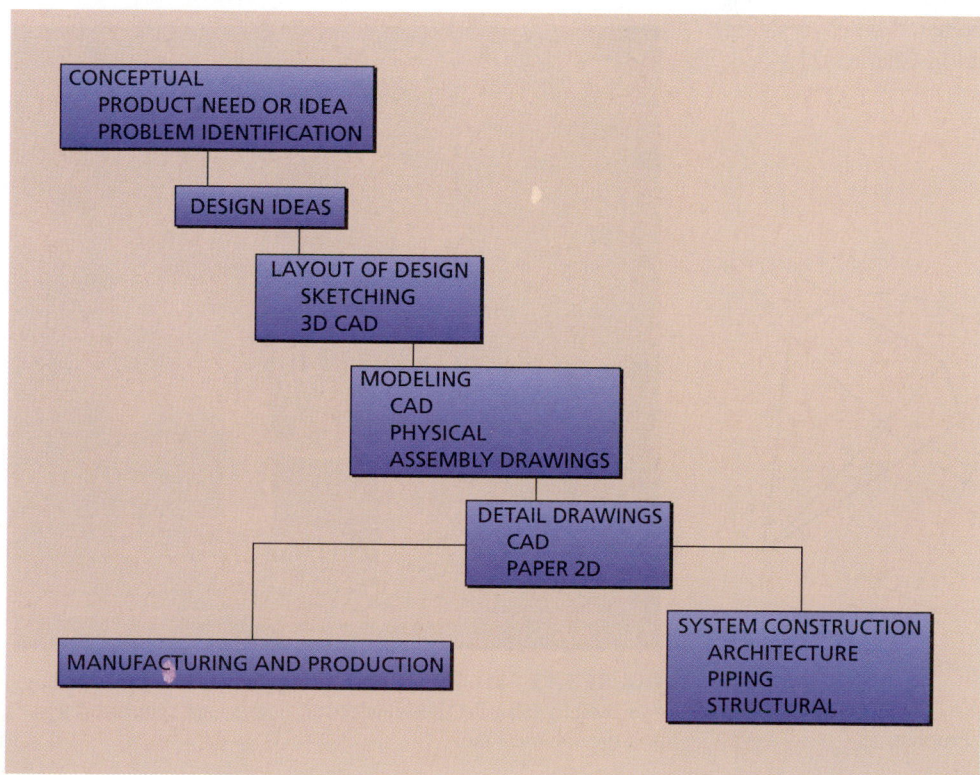

FIGURE 1.10   The Design Process

1.8 Descriptive Geometry

Descriptive geometry (Chapter 19) is the use of orthographic projection to solve 3D problems with a 2D graphics procedure. Descriptive geometry applications are used to establish the proper representation and relationships of geometric features on a drawing. These views provide an accurate graphic method to establish information such as the determination of true shape and true length. Figure 1.11 shows a descriptive geometry solution to the angle formed by two intersecting planes. The relationship of elements to one another, such as the distance between a line and a point or the angle between two planes, is a typical descriptive geometry problem.

Engineering graphics, technical drawing, and descriptive geometry share many of the same techniques and are not distinctly different, since each includes and encompasses much of the other. 2D mechanical drawing is actually elementary descriptive geometry. Constructions in descriptive geometry are done using orthographic projection techniques. Descriptive geometry has been part of a drafter's and a mechanical, structural, or civil engineer's education for a great many years. Gaspard Monge developed the principles of descriptive geometry as a set of projection methods and techniques that is the basis of technical drawing education. A text on technical drawing, therefore, is a book based on the principles of descriptive geometry.

The study of descriptive geometry includes intersections and developments. *Intersections* are covered in depth in Chapter 20. Intersections can be accomplished manually as in Figure 1.12, or on a CAD system using surface models (Fig. 1.13) or solid models. All three solutions are provided in Chapter 20. *Developments* are constructed manually as in Figure 1.14, or the process can be automated when designing with CAD. Developments are covered in Chapter 21.

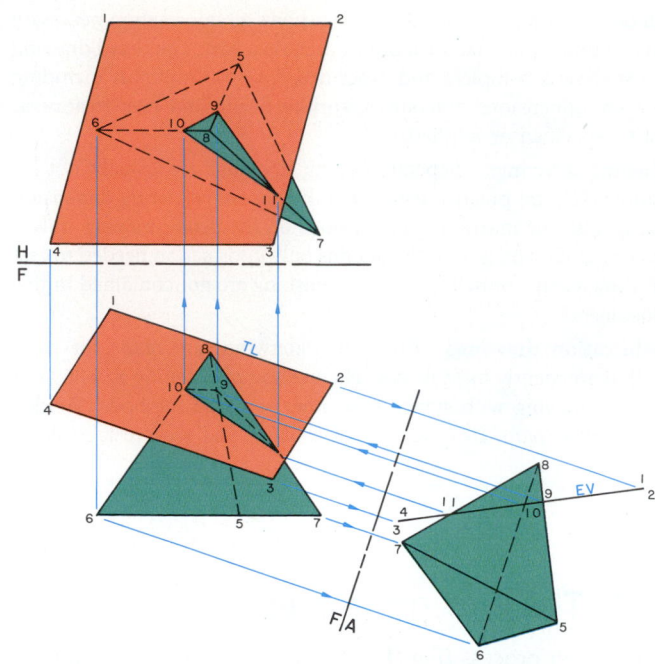

FIGURE 1.12   **Intersection Problem**

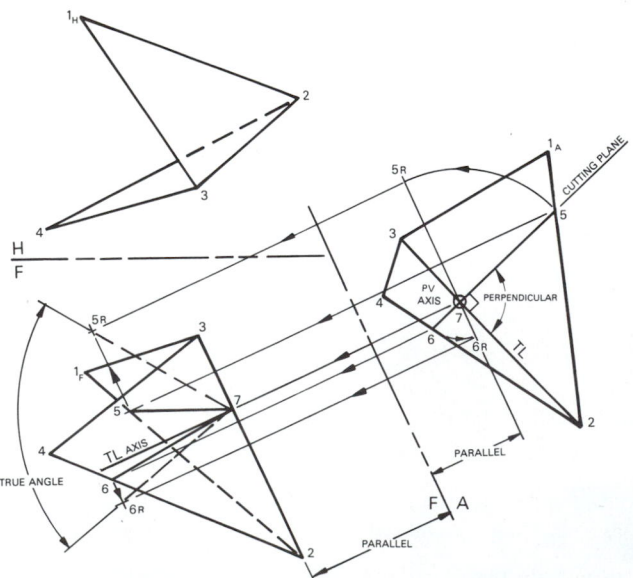

FIGURE 1.11   **Descriptive Geometry Problem**

FIGURE 1.13   **3D Design of Holding Tank.**   Surface modeling was used to solve for the intersection of the four cylindrical legs and the spherical tank.

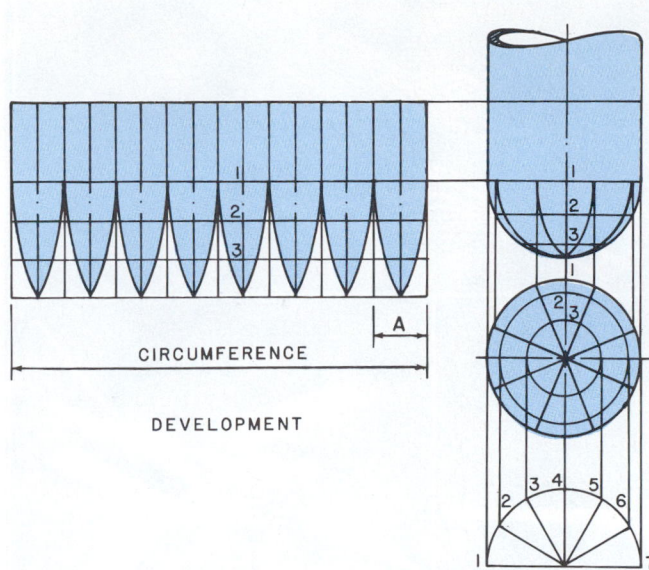

FIGURE 1.14   Development Problem

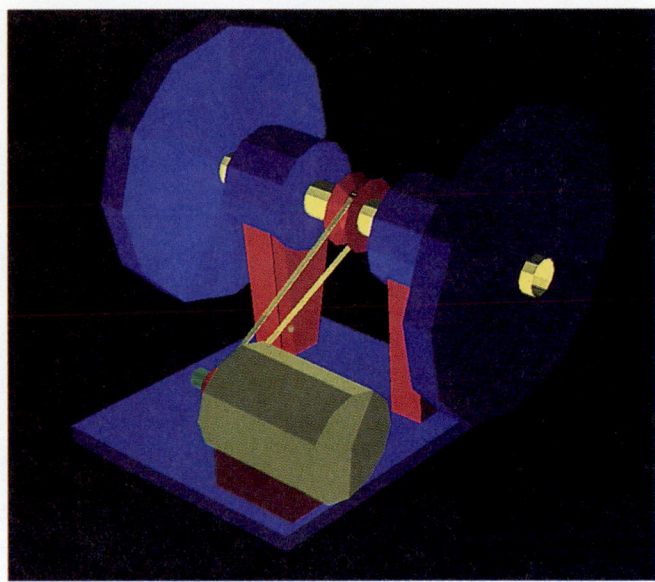

FIGURE 1.15   3D Mechanical Design

1.9   Career Fields in Industry

The educated engineer, designer, or drafter finds employment in a wide variety of industries. You may enter such diverse fields as civil engineering, electronic engineering, chemical engineering, ceramic engineering, mechanical engineering, nuclear engineering, solar engineering, petrochemical engineering, mining engineering, or metallurgical engineering. Each of these areas has a different set of requirements and design solutions. All engineering fields employ designers and drafters to refine ideas and bring the design to fruition. The following list provides an overview of the possible fields of employment for engineers, designers, and drafters:

Mechanical
Product design
Manufacturing design: jigs, fixtures, dies, assemblies, and details

Electronic-Electrical
Circuits, printed circuit boards
Integrated circuits
Electrical, electro-mechanical, computers
Applications for electronic and mechanical design
Marine
Aerospace
Transportation
Mining

Architectural, Engineering, and Construction (AE&C)
Civil: facilities, dams, airports, roads, mapping
Structural: buildings, plants, power generation
Piping: solar, nuclear, chemical, process, power, hydroelectric
Architecture: commercial, residential, landscape

Technical Illustration
Product literature: advertising, sales, presentation, service manuals, display.

In mechanical engineering, designers and drafters make assembly drawings and models of jigs, fixtures, dies, and other types of manufacturing aids to create and produce machine parts and new machinery (Fig. 1.15). This is one of the largest areas for employment for a designer or drafter. The mechanical engineer is concerned with the conceptual development and the calculations involved in creating and developing mechanical devices including items to be used in machinery, automobiles, mechanical equipment (Fig. 1.16), and aerospace products such as airplanes (Fig. 1.17) and helicopters.

FIGURE 1.16   Earthmover Tractor

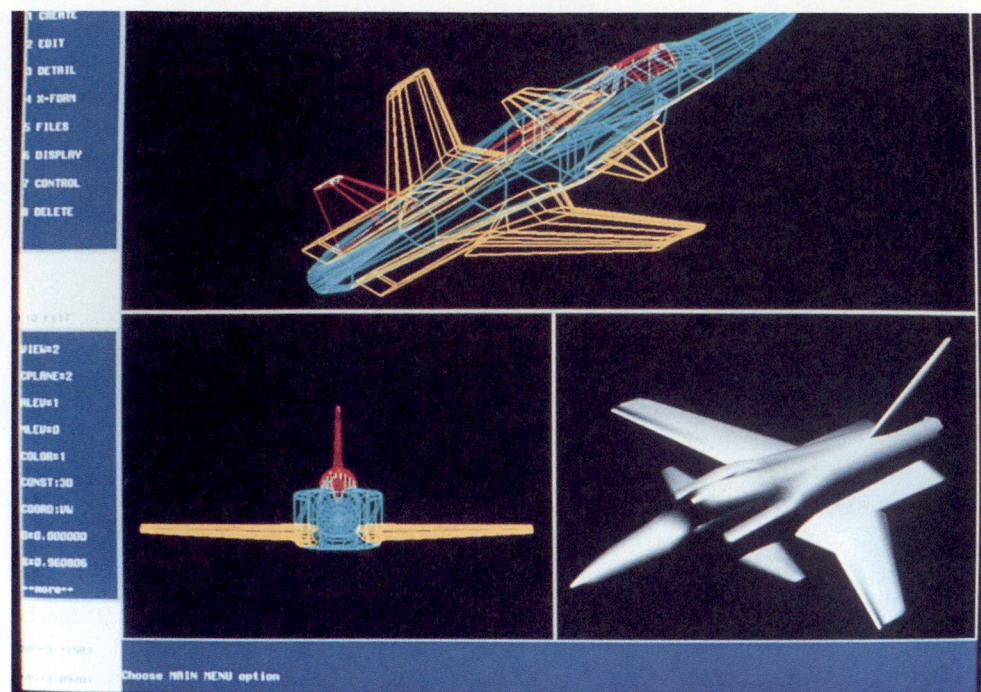

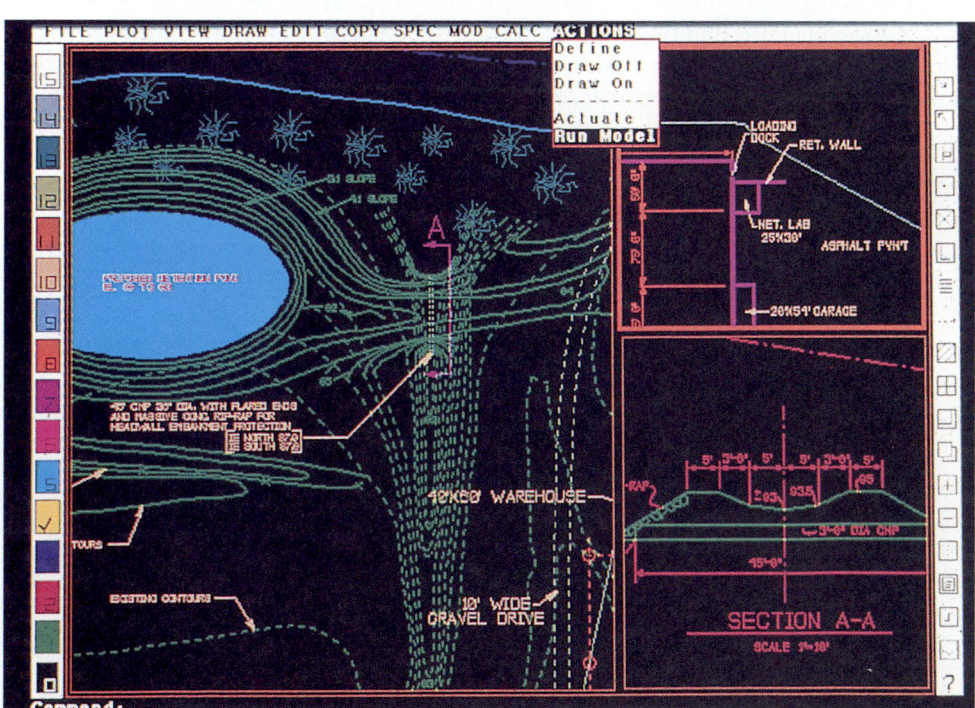

FIGURE 1.19 Petrochemical Facility

FIGURE 1.20 Diablo Canyon Nuclear Power Plant

Architecture, engineering, and construction are major areas of employment for designers and drafters. This area is comprised primarily of civil engineering, structural design, piping design, and architecture. The civil engineering and mapping industries (Fig. 1.18) employ a number of drafters and designers to develop highways, roads, railways, and airports. Sewage treatment plants, water systems, and dams are also designed in this discipline. Piping design includes such diverse fields as fossil fuel power plant design (Fig. 1.19), nuclear power plants (Fig. 1.20), solar power, and a wide range of other areas that require industrial piping systems used in the production of chemicals, petrochemical products, food, and beverages. Piping design includes equipment and vessel design (Fig. 1.13) and detailing (Fig. 1.21). Chapter 22 covers piping drafting and design.

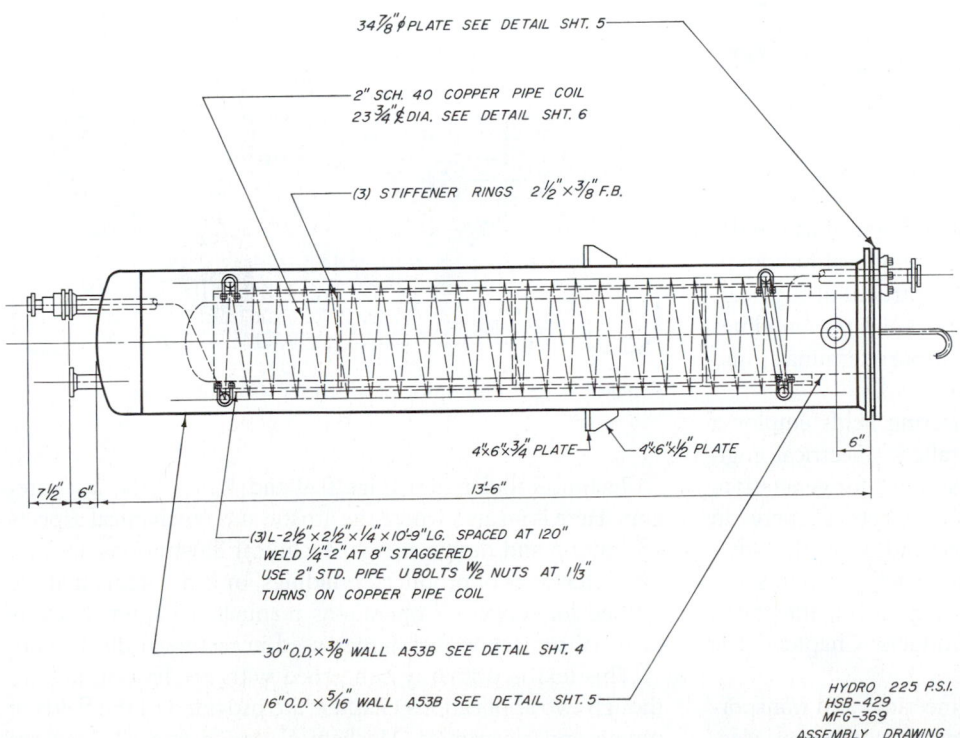

FIGURE 1.21 Piping Fabrication Drawing

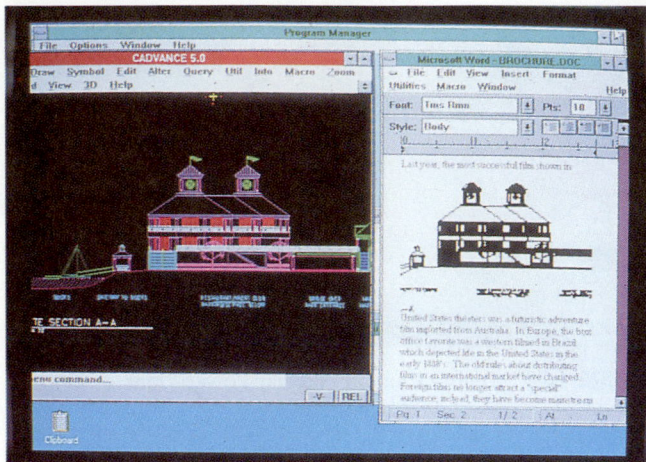

FIGURE 1.22 Architectural Design

FIGURE 1.24 Power Transmission Lines

FIGURE 1.23 Construction of a Corporate Office Facility

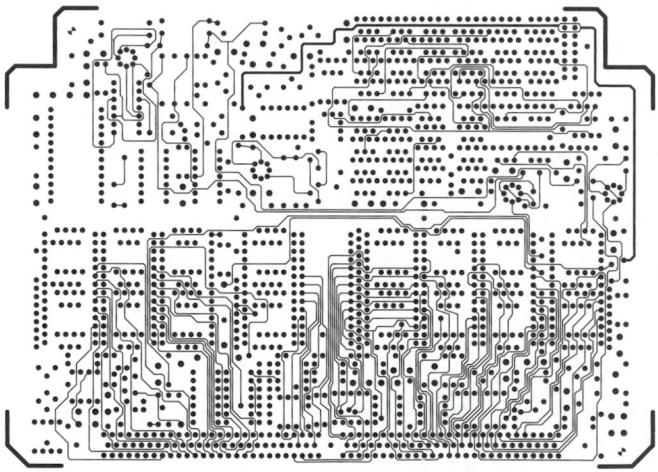

FIGURE 1.25 Photoplot of a Printed Circuit Board

Architecture (Fig. 1.22) is normally thought of as the design and construction of residential or commercial buildings, though larger structures can be included. Structural engineering includes the design and construction of large buildings (Fig. 1.23), manufacturing facilities, airport terminals, and power plants to name a few.

The electronic and electrical engineering fields employ a growing number of designers and drafters. Electrical engineering includes the layout of power systems for generation, transmission (Fig. 1.24), and utilization of electrical energy in industry and in the public sector. Electronics, on the other hand, is concerned with smaller devices, such as circuits and the design of printed circuit boards (Fig. 1.25), integrated circuits (Fig. 1.26), and computer products. Chapter 23 is devoted to electronic drafting.

Mining engineering, aerospace engineering, and transportation engineering all use combinations of mechanical, electronic, and electrical designs.

Technical illustration (Figs. 1.9 and 1.27) is the last category. Here is an area where the artistic and mechanical aspects of drafting and design merge. Technical illustrations are pictorial drawings of products, buildings, or other items that are needed for service or operations manuals. Chapter 8 covers pictorial projection techniques used in technical illustration.

This text is primarily concerned with mechanical design, though two applications chapters are provided in the fields of piping and electronics. Mechanical design and drafting are important because they involve the production of devices and

The Design Process

Even as you read this text, new ideas to give you new sources of pleasure or new sources of frustration are being conceived. Engineers create systems, devices, and processes useful to and sought after by our society. The process by which these goals are achieved in engineering design is a planned sequence of events.

It has been said that "necessity is the mother of invention." Need is the motivating factor in most designs. When Levi Strauss first made what became known as blue jeans, they didn't have the rivets at the pockets. In 1872, Levi was contacted

by a tailor from Reno, Nevada who had started riveting the pants he made for his customers. The two men decided to patent this new innovation and in 1873 were awarded the first patent for pocket rivets.

Some design is an accident. In 1878, a Procter & Gamble worker forgot to turn off the machine that stirred the soap. The soap that resulted had a lot of air bubbles and was so light it could float. He had just invented Ivory soap, by accident!

Curiosity sometimes drives design. The design of the microwave oven came about because Percy Spencer was curious about the amount of heat that was generated from magnetrons, the tubes used in radar during World War II. He could warm his hands by holding them close to the magnetrons. It was not until he found candy melted in his coat pocket that the idea of using the microwave to cook entered his mind. Many experiments later, the *high-frequency dielectric heating apparatus*—a microwave oven!—was invented. Spencer obtained a patent for it in 1953. Today, microwave ovens are an integral part of home, work, and school—all because Spencer was curious.

For years, we have dreamed about "smart homes." Imagine all the electric appliances in your home connected so they electronically communicate with each other. As you return home, your house "senses" your arrival, opens the garage door, unlocks the house, turns on the

lights, and turns on the television to your favorite program. As we approach the age when this is indeed possible, it is also easy to imagine the amount of information and technology that is needed to produce such a system.

If a design is to be a success and not a frustration, it must be simple and easy to operate, no matter how much information or technology is used. The designer must be able to transmit precise, clear instructions to the user. Much of our technology today makes devices simpler to use, but requires reams of documentation in the development stage. Information management and our ability to communicate will determine whether our future designs are a joy or a frustrating mess of words and wires.

The Microwave Was Born Out of Curiosity

The Patent Certificate for Rivets on Jeans

FIGURE 1.26   Integrated Circuit Design

FIGURE 1.27   Technical Illustration Using AutoCAD

FIGURE 1.28 **Ship Model**

(a)

FIGURE 1.29 **CAD 3D Design of a Wheel** (a) Wheel (b) 3D design of a wheel using CAD

designs for a variety of applications. Marine engineering, including the design and manufacture of marine vessels (Fig. 1.28) and similar products, uses a variety of standard and unique mechanical parts in their designs. Aerospace engineering includes the design of engines and other mechanical devices. Transportation engineering includes the design of automobiles, trucks, buses, trains, and their individual components and requires extensive mechanical design (Fig. 1.29).

1.10 Computers and Technical Drawing

Computer-integrated manufacturing (CIM) refers to the integration of all phases of production, from design to manufacturing using the computer. Anyone wishing to enter industry as a drafter, designer, or engineer must be familiar with how the computer is profoundly altering the factory floor and engineering office. Computer-aided engineering (CAE), computer-aided manufacturing (CAM), and CAD are collectively called CIM. The term CAD/CAM refers to the use of computers to integrate the design and production process to improve productivity. CAM includes numerical control (NC), computer numerical control (CNC), machining (Fig. 1.30), and the use of robotics in manufacturing.

Although this text is primarily concerned with manual technical drawing and CAD, the integration of computers in all phases of the design-through-production process is extremely important to the future engineer, designer, or drafter. Descriptive geometry, projection techniques, drafting conventions, and dimensioning standards apply to drawings completed manually and to those created with the aid of a computer.

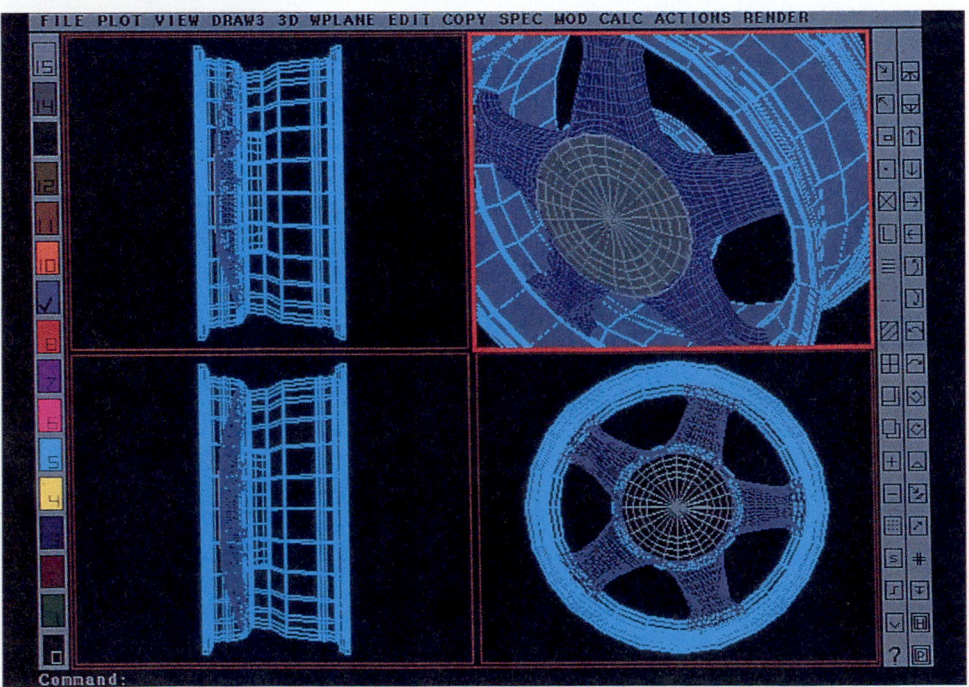

(b)

1.11 Computer-Aided Design

CAD involves any type of design activity that uses the computer to develop, analyze, modify, or enhance an engineering design. CAD systems are based on interactive computer graphics. The drafter creates an image on the CRT screen by entering commands on the computer (Fig. 1.31). In most systems, the image is constructed from basic geometric elements/entities—points, lines, circles, arcs, splines, and 3D shapes such as surfaces and solids. The graphics can be modified according to the commands of the operator—enlarged or reduced in size, moved to another location on the screen, rotated, etc. Through these various manipulations, the required details of the graphic image are formulated.

In terms of CAD, *design* refers to the establishment and definition of the 3D database; *drafting* primarily involves defining, refining, and manipulating the database to provide certain kinds of information. CAM and CIM apply and utilize the *same* database created on the CAD system.

As a designer or drafter using a CAD system you must be able to understand the system's *hardware* configuration and its *software* capabilities. Programming ability is not required for operation of today's CAD/CAM systems. As a CAD drafter or designer, you should be familiar with the following:

1. drafting standards
2. specific engineering field conventions
3. a particular industrial application; mechanical, piping, electrical, electronic, electromechanical, civil, structural, or architecture
4. software characteristics of your CAD system.

It must be stressed that CAD is a drafting and design *tool*. As a drafter or designer you are required to create the necessary graphics. The method of creating engineering graphics has changed, not the content. Regardless of the type of system, the most common form of output remains the "drawing." In addition to teaching manual drafting techniques and drafting standards, this text is meant to acquaint you with some of today's CAD systems. In most cases where specific CAD commands are provided in the text, the commands given are from AutoCAD to demonstrate a command sequence and a capability.

FIGURE 1.31 **Personal Computer CAD System**

1.12 Standards

Many different agencies control the standards of practice used in drafting and design. The **American National Standards Institute (ANSI)** standards, the **Department of Defense (DOD)** standards, and the **military standards (MIL)** are the three most used standards in the United States. The **International Standards Organization (ISO)** standards and **Japanese standards (JIS)** are also used in certain companies.

ANSI standards are normally available to drafters and designers at their place of employment. It is important to become familiar with these standards. ANSI-Y14 contains information on drafting practices, dimensioning, projection, descriptive geometry, geometric tolerancing, and a wide variety of other areas associated with drafting and design.

Why are standards used? Drawings are used as a form of communication between departments and companies. They are used to communicate design requirements among companies and different branches of industry and science, and among branches of the government. Through the use of standards, each drawing will mean the same thing to everyone who reads it.

Some companies have not adopted ANSI standards or are using older standards and have not updated to the latest issue of ANSI-Y14. This text uses ANSI standards as a basis for its drawings, conventions, practices, and instructional methodology. All projects completed from the book (including exercises, drawings, and problems) are to be drawn using the latest revision of ANSI standards, conventions, and drawing practices.

Technical drawing and drafting specifications are covered in appropriate chapters and sections throughout the text. References are made to ANSI-Y14 where appropriate.

FIGURE 1.30 **CNC Machining**

1.13 Standards of Measurement

The United States is the only country in the world still using feet, inches, and decimal equivalents. However, many large corporations such as Ford, IBM, International Harvester, John Deere, General Motors, Honeywell, and most electronic, medical instrument, and computer manufacturers have completely converted to the metric system of units that is called the **Système Internationale (SI).** The English system is now called the **U.S. customary unit.**

Because you may encounter both measurement systems on the job, this text uses a balanced approach and applies both systems. Since the majority of the text is devoted to mechanical drafting and design, the use of metric units is more typical than that found in piping, architectural, and structural drafting and design fields, which use units of feet, inches, and fractions, in most cases. Mechanical engineering and design, on the other hand, have become far more oriented toward the metric system even though decimal-inch units are still in use.

The standard of measurement for metric drawings is the millimeter. The U.S. decimal-inch unit is on many of the text's illustrations and in the exercise and problem sections at the end of each chapter. In some cases, your instructor may wish for you to convert the units of measurement from one system to another.

1.14 Organization of the Text

The text is divided into five parts. Part I presents the background techniques and procedures used in all fields of drafting and design. This part introduces instruments, materials, and techniques (Chapter 2), CAD (Chapter 3), lettering (Chapter 4), geometric construction (Chapter 5), and sketching techniques (Chapter 6).

Part II provides the basics for drawing including multiview projection (Chapter 7), pictorial projection (Chapter 8), sections (Chapter 9), auxiliary projections (Chapter 10), shop processes (Chapter 11), dimensioning (Chapter 12), and tolerancing (Chapter 13).

Part III covers types of mechanical parts and procedures including welding (Chapter 14), threads, fasteners, and springs (Chapter 15), and gears, shafts, bearings, and cams (Chapter 16).

Part IV presents design concepts and procedures for the drafter and designer, including product design and development (Chapter 17), working drawings (Chapter 18), descriptive geometry (Chapter 19), intersections (Chapter 20), and developments (Chapter 21).

Part V provides examples of technical drawing applications in Chapter 22 on piping and Chapter 23 on electronics.

The last section of the text contains the appendixes. Here, you will find a number of glossaries, abbreviations, standards, conversion charts, and catalog items such as nuts, bolts, washers, bearings, keys, pins, valves, and fittings. You will also find welding, electronic, and piping symbols used on drawings. Consult the appendixes when working on projects from the text.

Each chapter in the text has the same sequence. Chapters start with an introduction and an explanation of the material to be covered. Exercises are found at the end of the chapter, but are designed to be completed at specific intervals. You will be prompted at intervals within each chapter to complete exercises designed to test your knowledge of the material just covered. Exercises are on a grid format, using .25 in. units, and can be transferred directly without the use of dimensions to an $8\frac{1}{2} \times 11$ in. "A" size grid lined sheet of paper. If metrics are preferred, use metric grid paper with appropriate divisions.

Each chapter (except Chapter 1) has a quiz at the end composed of eight true or false, eight fill in the blanks, and eight answer the following questions. After the quiz, problems are provided for you to complete. These problems can be completed in many different ways—either as sketches, ink drawings, manual drafting, or CAD projects. Unlike the exercises, which are confined to an $8\frac{1}{2} \times 11$ in. "A" size format, the size of paper is dependent on the project requirements.

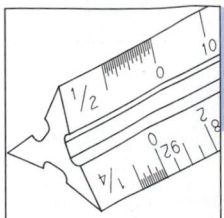

CHAPTER 2

Equipment, Instruments, Materials, and Techniques

Learning Objectives

Upon completion of this chapter you will be able to accomplish the following:

1. Identify equipment and general drafting tools used in technical drawing.
2. Produce drawings using various drafting instruments and appropriate scales.
3. Exhibit knowledge of drafting media and drawing formats.
4. Develop the ability to produce ANSI standard line types while recognizing preferred line precedence.
5. Master techniques for drawing construction and printable lines and curves.
6. Prepare drawings in ink using technical pens.

2.1 Introduction

Drafting tools (Fig. 2.1) are used in all fields of engineering and design. Although CAD systems are increasingly found in industry, traditional (manual) drafting techniques and tools are still used and will continue to be used in the foreseeable future. Therefore, as an aspiring drafter, designer, or engineer, you must thoroughly understand these procedures and be familiar with drafting tools and techniques. Every engineering office uses—with varying degrees of sophistication—the equipment described in this chapter. The simple lead holder and the complex electronic pen are both important in the drafting and design process and share the same purpose.

This chapter covers drafting equipment, instruments, and materials and will introduce you to the techniques of using them. **Equipment** includes drafting boards, drafting machines, print machines, T-squares, triangles, templates, and computer-aided design hardware. **Instruments** are precision-manufactured drawing tools, such as the compass and dividers, in all their variations. Drafting **materials** comprise drawing media (vellum and drafting film) and related support items, such as grid underlays, preprinted title blocks, transfer drafting aids, and print paper.

Techniques are the methods used by the drafter to complete a drawing and are covered at the end of this chapter. This chapter's primary focus is on equipment and tools and on the methods and techniques of creating a drawing manually. Drafters and designers must know how to use their equipment, instruments, and materials to communicate effectively. Both the originator and the user of a drawing must understand the procedures, conventions, and concepts used in the drawing. In all fields of technical drawing and design, symbols, linework, projection procedures, and notation must be used in accordance with standard *drafting conventions*.

2.2 Equipment

The most important and conspicuous piece of equipment found in any drafting room is the **drafting table.** Originally, all drafting was done on flat-surfaced wood drawing boards. Normally, one or more edges were cut as straight and square as possible, creating a "straight edge" that the drafter could use to guide a T-square. Today, board sizes range from hand-carried versions to the large-format, stand-alone tables

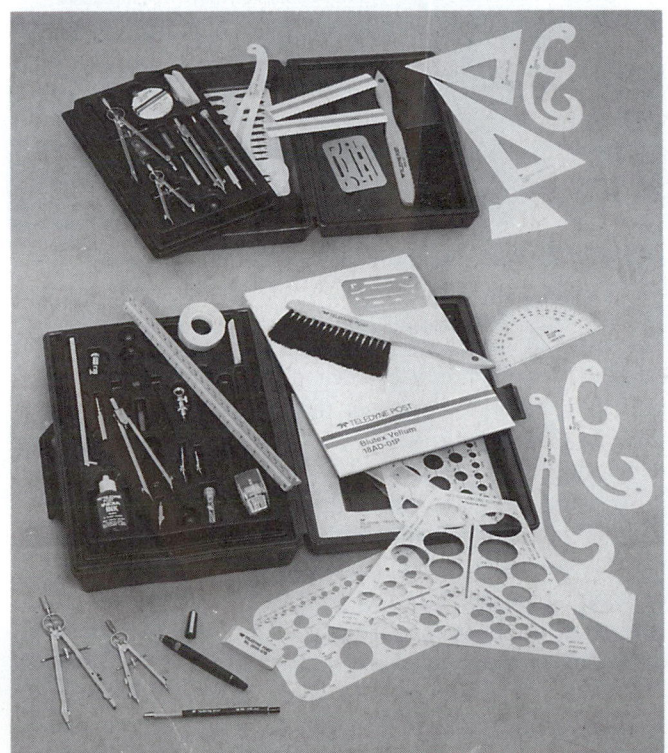

FIGURE 2.1 Drafting Tools

FIGURE 2.2   Metal Drafting Table

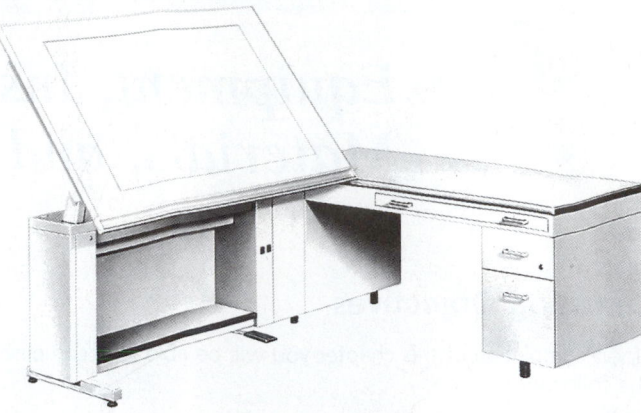

FIGURE 2.3   Light Table and Reference Table

commonly found in industry and the classroom. The table in Figure 2.2 is vertically adjustable and can be tilted to any comfortable angle. Modern tables may be power operated. Whatever the size or material used for a drafting table, the table surface must have a pliable cover. This surface can be Borco vinyl (or linoleum) or some other plastic or vinyl covering that permits drafting without destroying the table surface or marring the drawing medium.

Light tables are also used throughout industry to prepare printed circuit artwork, draw pictorial illustrations, and do tracing. Normally, the drawing surface is an opaque glass or plastic sheet that scatters the rays from the light source. Figure 2.3 shows a modern light table and reference desk. Here the table top and the light mechanism are an integral part of the drawing surface.

2.2.1   Storage and Reproduction Equipment

After a project is drawn, regardless of the method, it must be *stored* and *reproduced*. Frequently, drawings are stored as paper originals and prints in multiple-drawer cabinets and in tube storage systems. Because drawings must be cataloged and available for several departments, this method of storage is time-consuming and requires considerable office space, but it is still widely used.

Drawings can also be stored on **microfilm** and **microfiche.** Computer graphics systems enable the user to reproduce almost instantaneously design data stored on disk or tape. Another form of reprographics uses 35 mm micrographic **aperture cards** or **design data cards** (Fig. 2.4). Design data systems are used with manually produced drawings or with CAD drawings. These systems provide access to more than 1,000 design drawings in less than $7\frac{1}{2}$ inches of space. When a new or revised drawing is checked and ready for release, it is taken to a processor camera (Fig. 2.5). In seconds, a master data

FIGURE 2.4   Aperture Card Viewing System

card (an accurately reduced version of the original drawing) is produced. Multiple copies of the data card are then made from the original for distribution. You can review the drawing with a display device (Fig. 2.4).

Aperture data cards enable the user to make prints quickly with several reduction and enlargement printout options. The manually operated copier shown in Figure 2.6 can copy a drawing on various kinds of paper and instantly switch enlargement sizes. The copy paper is manually fed into the front of the copier and the viewing screen allows easy monitoring.

Traditionally, the **blueprint machine** was used to make multiple prints of drawings. However, the term "blueprint" is no longer accurate since the prints are actually white, or what are sometimes called blueline prints. **Whiteprint machine** would

FIGURE 2.5   Microfilm Processor Camera

FIGURE 2.6   Aperture Card Drawing Reproduction System

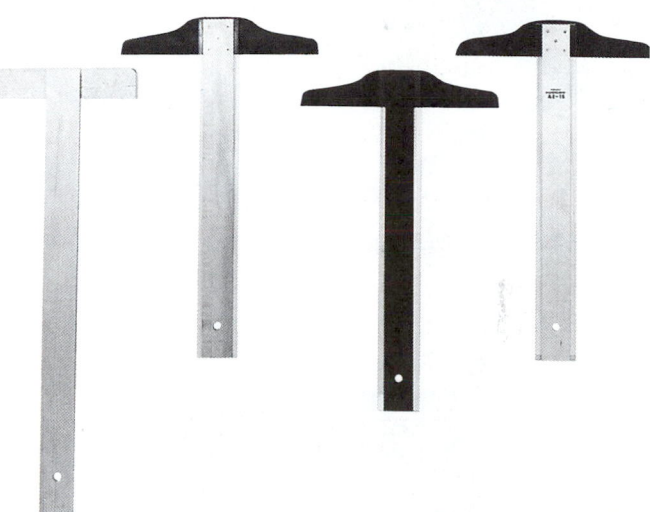

FIGURE 2.7   T-Squares

be a more accurate term because most, if not all, reproduction with this method involves developing a print with blue lines and white background, not the opposite. Printing is covered in Chapter 18.

When a drawing is completed on a CAD system, the user must be able either to reproduce the drawing from a hardcopy device such as a photocopier or plot the drawing on a pen plotter. The pen plotting method allows the reproduction of an accurate original every time the drawing is plotted. Multiple copies can then be made from a whiteprinter or from input to a data card system.

2.2.2   Straightedges

Originally, the primary horizontal straightedge device used in drafting was the **T-square** (Fig. 2.7). This piece of equipment is still found in a few drafting classes and for personal drafting. Because the T-square is the most difficult to manage of all straightedge drawing devices, it is said that "if you can draw with a T-square you can draw with anything." If you must learn by using a T-square, you will be glad to know that once you master it, other straightedges will be easier. Using a T-square is difficult because it is the easiest to misalign of all straightedge devices. The bar portion of the T is placed along the edge of a drafting board or table. Parallel horizontal lines are drawn with the length of the T-square, and parallel vertical lines are drawn with a triangle placed against the top edge of the horizontal length. Obviously, if the T-square and the table edge are not aligned properly, your linework will be inconsistent.

Since it is an excellent tool for drawing long horizontal lines, the **parallel straightedge** (Fig. 2.8) is found throughout

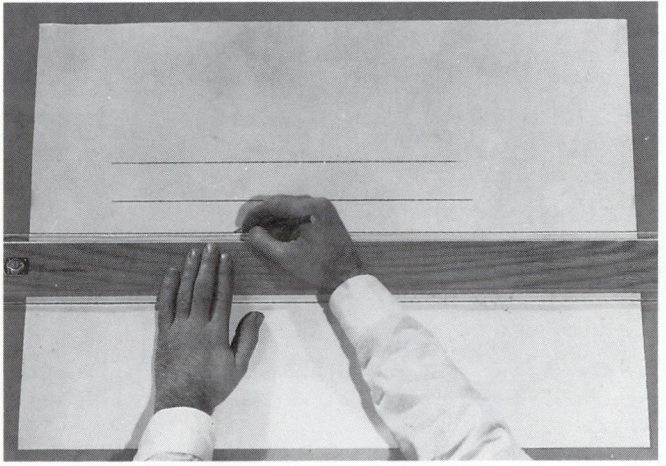

FIGURE 2.8   Parallel Straightedge

industry, especially for large drawings such as those required in the construction trades—architecture, piping design, and civil engineering. The parallel straightedge is attached to the drafting table by a series of cables and pulleys. It remains parallel or at a preset angle to the drafting table as it is moved up or down on the table surface. Parallel straightedges are excellent tools to use when the drawing consists of long, straight, parallel horizontal lines.

The **drafting machine** comes in two standard versions: the drafting arm type (Fig. 2.9) and the track type (Fig. 2.10).

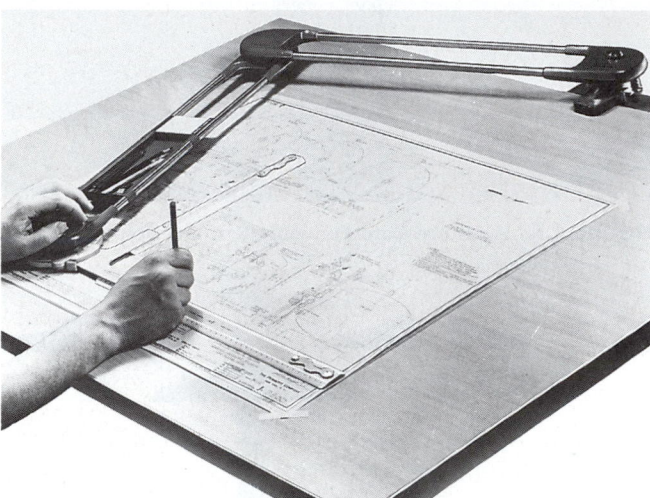

FIGURE 2.9   **Arm Drafting Machine**

FIGURE 2.10   **Track Drafting Machine**

The track type is the most accurate. Drafting machines are mounted on drafting tables, as shown in these figures. The control head on the drafting machine can be rotated to any angle and set by pushing a button to lock at increments of 15°. It must be hand-locked for intermediate angles. When you use the drafting machine, or any drafting straightedge, avoid dragging the equipment across the drawing.

Drafting machines take the place of triangles, protractors, and scales, but you must still know how to use all types of equipment and instruments.

Regardless of the type of drafting table and straightedge, proper lighting is also essential for relaxed, unstrained work with manual drafting techniques. Since the CRT screen is easier to read if it is shaded from external light sources, lighting requirements are different when a CAD system is used.

2.3   General Drafting Tools

Traditional manual drafting requires a variety of small tools and equipment (Fig. 2.1). For example, special templates, triangles, pencils, lead holders, and technical inking pens are used throughout industry. The quality of your drafting is directly influenced by the range and quality of the tools and equipment used. This is not to say that expensive, high-quality tools themselves draw the project, but good quality tools are beneficial for fast, efficient, and precise linework and projection.

TABLE 2.1 Equipment	
Essential Items	**Optional Items**
Pencils (grades 4H, 3H, 2H, H, HB)	Lead holders
Sandpaper block	Thin-line pencil
Erasers	Electric eraser
Dusting pad or powder	Adjustable triangle
Erasing shield	Symbol templates
Drafting tape	Lettering guide
Drafting brush	Lettering template
Scales (metric, architect, mechanical, civil)	Drop compass
Protractor	Beam compass
30/60° triangle	Compass inking attachment
45° triangle	Technical inking pens
Irregular curves	Ink
Templates (circle and ellipse)	Ink eraser
Bow compass	Lettering set
Dividers	Grid paper
Drafting board	Drafting table
Straightedge (T-square, parallel straightedge)	Flexible curve
Calculator	Drafting machine
Paper (vellum, drawing film)	

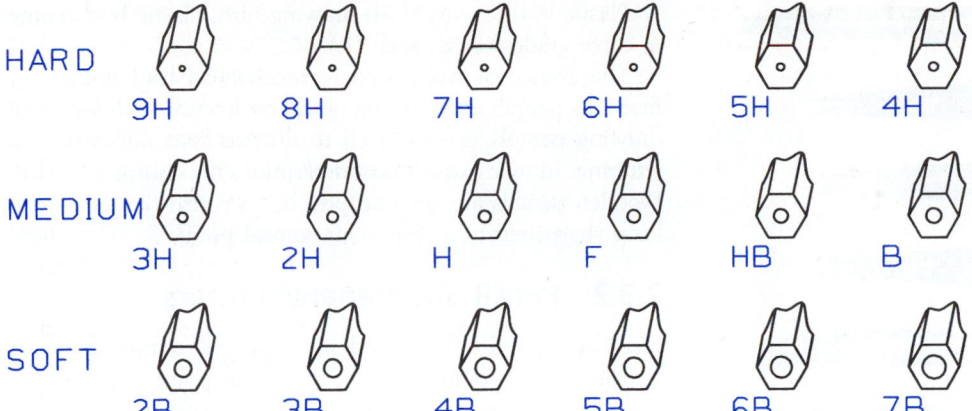

FIGURE 2.11   Pencil Types

Drafting kits are available from a variety of reputable companies. These kits are sufficient for most classes in drafting. However, precision high-quality tools and instruments can be purchased individually, either at a drafting supply store or through a drafting equipment catalog. Table 2.1 lists standard drafting tools you can buy. Essential items are distinguished from optional items, which can be added as needed.

2.3.1   Pencil Leads and Pencils

Drafting **pencils** are graded by the hardness of their lead. The hardness of the lead determines the kind of line that can be drawn. A hard lead can make a very sharp, thin line, but it will lack the darkness and density necessary to make a good print. A soft lead will make dark lines, but they are very difficult to keep sharp. "H" lead grades are used for drafting on vellum. The "H" grades are, from hardest to softest: 9H, 8H, 7H, 6H, 5H, 4H, 3H, 2H, H, F, and HB (Fig. 2.11). The recommended hardnesses for lead used on vinyl-topped drafting boards with a good grade of paper are:

1. 6H–3H for layout and construction lines
2. H–HB for reproducible (printable) lines
3. H for lettering.

The appropriate hardnesses of lead, combined with proper drafting techniques, will help produce good reproducible drawings with sharp dense lines that make good prints. The skills required to use drafting tools and equipment come only through constant practice. Drafting is a skill that must be cultivated throughout your career, not just in school.

Drafting pencils are made in three types; the familiar wood pencil (Fig. 2.12), the mechanical lead holder (Fig. 2.13), which uses drafting leads, and the fine-line mechanical pencil. The wood pencil is the least expensive, but is not as convenient to use as mechanical pencils. With the lead holder, the lead is sharpened with a pencil pointer that sharpens only the lead; the wood pencil must have the wood cut away before it is sharpened with a drafting pencil sharpener or a knife (Fig. 2.14). Fine-line pencils do not need sharpening.

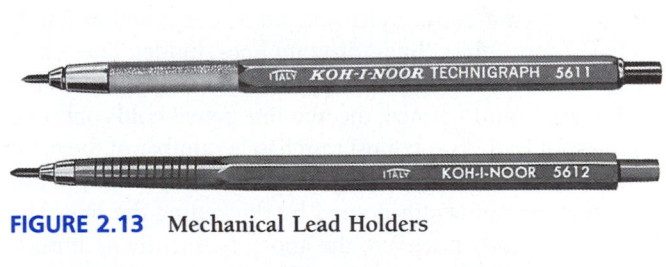

FIGURE 2.13   Mechanical Lead Holders

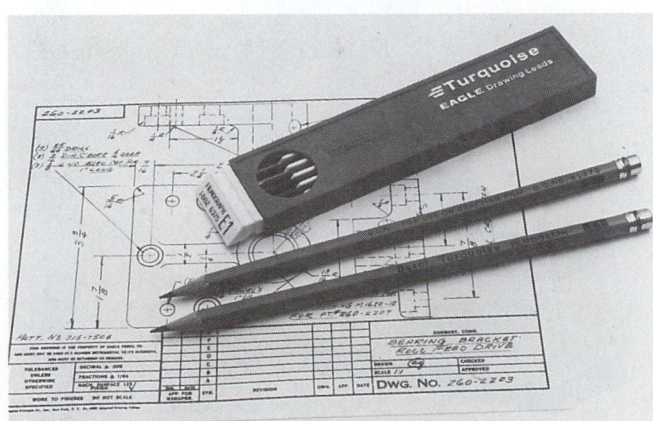

FIGURE 2.12   Drawing Pencils and Leads

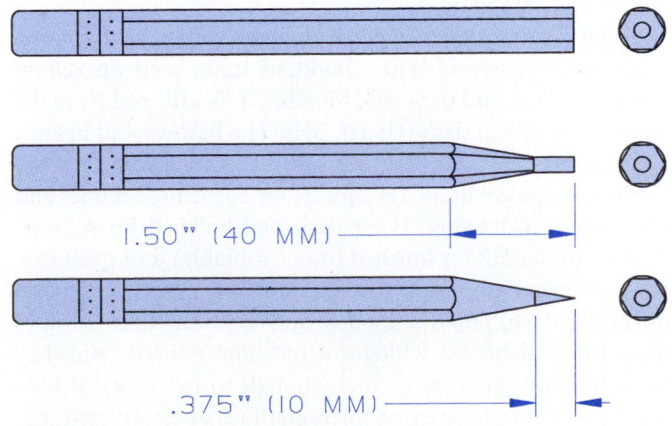

1.50" (40 MM)

.375" (10 MM)

FIGURE 2.14   Sharpening Pencils

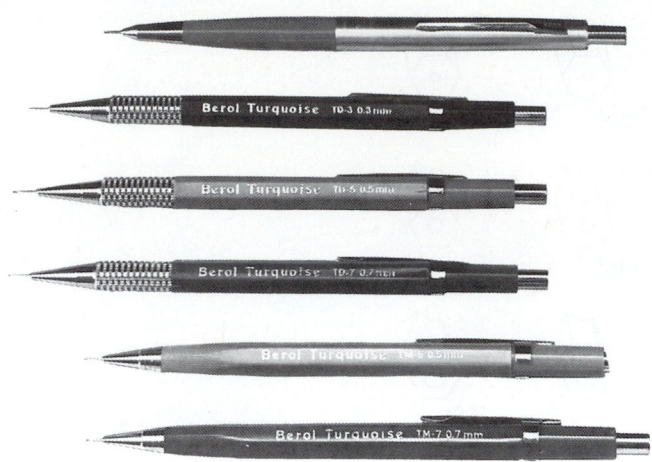

FIGURE 2.15 Fine-Line Mechanical Pencils

The **mechanical lead holder** (Fig. 2.13) has essentially replaced the wood pencil. It holds a single piece of lead. Having more than one lead holder available with leads of various hardness makes it easy to change line weights. This drawing tool is easily sharpened and increases the speed, consistency, and ease of drafting. The mechanical pencil allows the length of exposed lead to be adjusted both for sharpening and for drawing without decreasing the length of the holder, which is what happens when sharpening a wood pencil.

The automatic drawing pencil (**fine-line pencil**) is an excellent tool for drawing lines and letters of consistent width. It never requires sharpening. Automatic drawing pencils come in metric sizes: 0.3, 0.5, 0.7, and 0.9 mm (Fig. 2.15). These sizes are used to draw the typical line weights, 0.25 to 0.35 mm (centerlines, dimension lines, construction lines), 0.5 to 0.7 mm (object lines, diagram lines, hidden lines), and 0.7 to 0.9 mm (cutting plane lines, border lines). Unlike the mechanical drafting pencil, the fine-line pencil holds only one thickness of lead, so you must purchase a number of them. Of course, if you are using a small-width fine-line pencil, you can make the line any width desired by thickening the line. The thinner the lead, however, the more frequently it breaks. Fine-line pencils are sometimes difficult to use with lettering guides and templates.

Regardless of which type of drawing pencil you choose, purchase a variety of leads. Standard leads used on vellum range from soft and dark (6B, 5B, 4B, 2B, B, HB, and F) to the medium hard and dark (H, 2H, 3H). The hardest and lightest types are 4H, 5H, 6H, 7H, 8H, and 9H. In general, only the medium leads are used: 2H and 3H for construction lines and blocking in a drawing, H for darkened finished lines. Some drafters prefer HB for finished lines (printable), but great care must be taken to ensure that the drawing is kept clean and unsmudged. To attain a good-quality reproduction, all lines must block light if a whiteprint machine is used, and they must be dark, crisp, and thick enough to be recorded by a camera if a photocopier or micrographics aperture card machine is used.

Plastic leads are used on drawing film. Plastic leads come in three grades (E, K, and CF).

The choice of wood pencil, mechanical lead holder, or fine-line pencil depends on your preference. All forms of drawing pencils can be used to do excellent linework and lettering. In many cases, cost determines the choice of pencil. Wooden pencils are the cheapest but are also the hardest to keep sharpened to a consistent conical point.

2.3.2 Pencil Sharpeners/Pointers

Mechanical lead holders and wood pencils require frequent sharpening or pointing. A sharp conical point is needed to make the thin erasable lines required for construction lines. For darkened finished linework, the pencil point is slightly dulled on scrap paper to avoid frequent breaking and to draw wide lines. *To maintain the line thickness, the pencil or lead holder should be rotated as the line is drawn.* A sharpened, then slightly dulled, lead point is required for lettering. The advantage of using a fine-line pencil is that the lead never needs sharpening.

The **pencil pointer** sharpens by cutting away only the lead and produces a uniform conical shape with a rather long taper. The taper should be three to four times the diameter of the lead. Several good pointers are available that use a ribbed cylindrical metal cutter. The pencil or lead holder (Fig. 2.16)

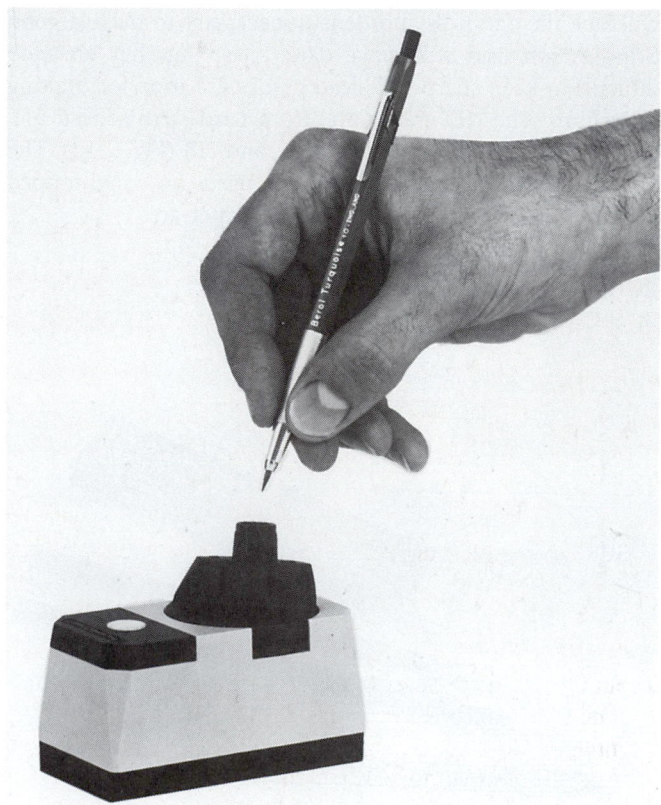

FIGURE 2.16 Mechanical Pencil Sharpener

FIGURE 2.17   **Sharpener**

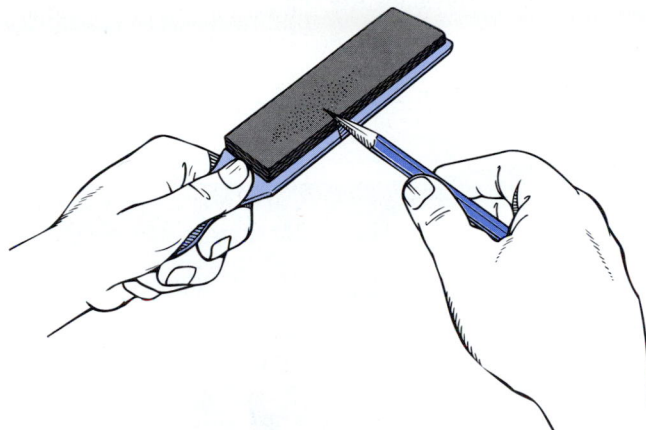

FIGURE 2.18   **Sharpening a Pencil with a Sandpaper Block**

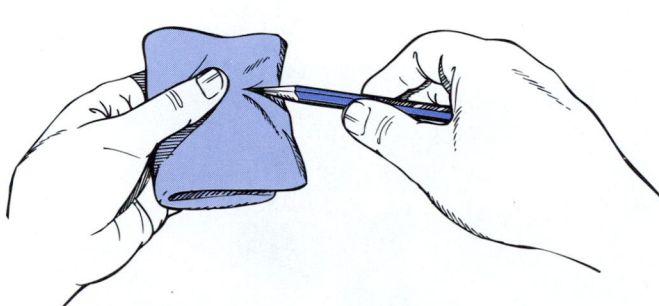

FIGURE 2.19   **Cleaning Pencil Tip**

paper pad can also sharpen lead points on compasses. Compass leads are sharpened as wedge shapes instead of conical points in order to keep the edge sharper longer. After sanding the lead, wipe it clean with a soft cloth or tissue (Fig. 2.19).

2.3.3   Erasers and Erasing Shields

Erasing is a necessary part of drafting and, when done properly, enables you to improve and correct drawings easily (Fig. 2.20). The **eraser** should have good "pick-up" power without smudging. Eraser selection is based primarily on the drafting media you are using (vellum, film, etc.).

To protect adjacent areas of the drawing that are to remain, most erasing is done through the perforations of a stainless steel **erasing shield** (Fig. 2.21). The erasing shield is firmly held in place on the drawing with one hand while the other hand erases through a selected opening (Fig. 2.22). Care must be taken not to erase other areas through adjacent openings.

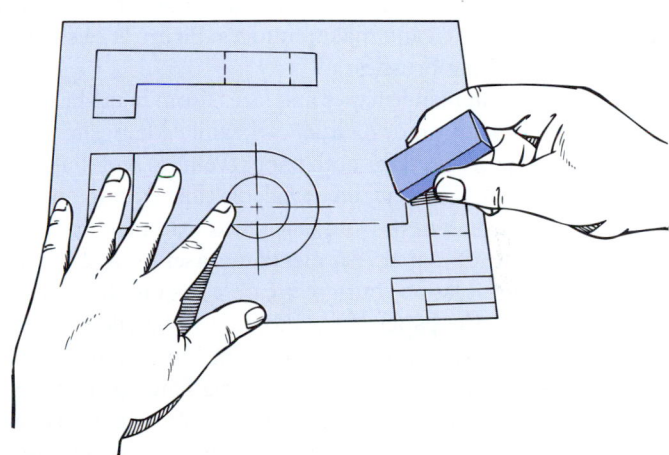

FIGURE 2.20   **Eraser**

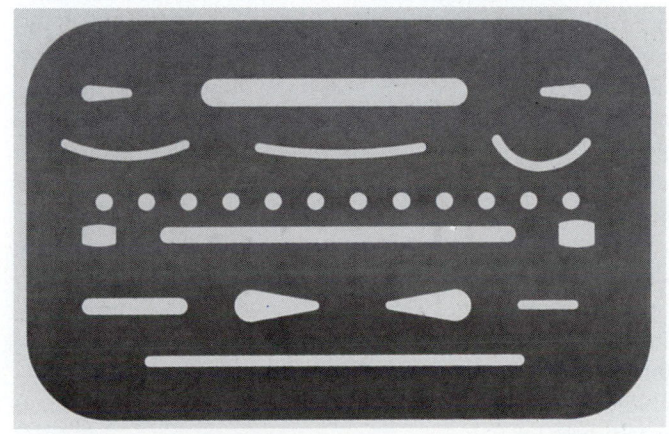

FIGURE 2.21   **Erasing Shield**

is put into a hole in the cover of the cutter and rotated around the cutter. Figure 2.17 shows an inexpensive hand-held pointer.

Another sharpening device used for wood pencils and lead holders is the **sandpaper pad/block.** The pencil or lead holder is rotated as the point is sanded (Fig. 2.18). A sand-

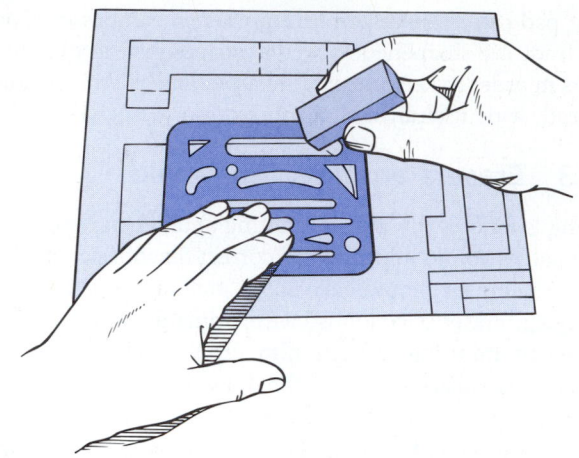

FIGURE 2.22 Using an Erasing Shield

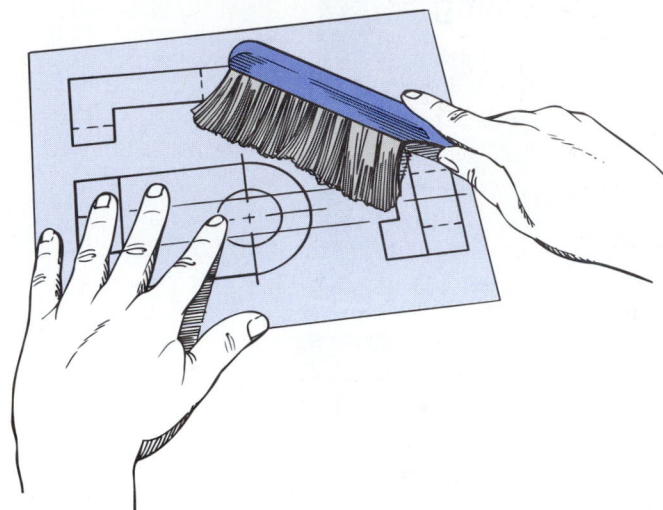

FIGURE 2.23 Brushing the Drawing

Eraser crumbs should be immediately swept from the drawing with the **drafting brush** (Fig. 2.23). The crumbs should not be rubbed with the hand—each graphite-laden crumb will act as a dull pencil and make smudges. Figure 2.24 shows two sizes of drafting brushes.

Erasers come in many shapes and sizes, from hand-held to electric, and in many grades. Pink Pearl, white composite, and Art Gum erasers are used for both paper (vellum) and drafting film. Special vinyl erasers are available for erasing inked drawings on drafting film. Note that ink is extremely hard to erase when used on paper. An **electric eraser** (Fig. 2.25) is essential in this situation, but great care is required to avoid rubbing holes in the paper. Care should also be taken when using an electric eraser on drafting film since it tends to destroy the tooth, or surface, of the drafting film. To erase ink drawings completed on film, the best technique is to use a small amount of moisture applied to a vinyl eraser and carefully rub the area to be erased.

A **dry cleaning pad** (an erasing dust pad) is another item used to keep drawings clean and unsmudged. Dry cleaning pads contain finely ground eraser pieces and powder. They are used to remove dirt and leftover crumbled graphite deposited from drawing and lettering. When you use a dry cleaning pad, do not drag it across the drawing. Instead, after a small portion of the drawing is complete, lightly pat the linework and lettering. Then use a drafting brush to sweep the drawing clean of powder and dirt. Although you must be careful not to lighten the lines and lettering too much by rubbing, frequent patting and dusting ensure a higher quality drawing. Never use a dry cleaning pad when inking with technical pens. Some drafters prefer to cover the entire drawing with a very light layer of erasing powder while lettering and drawing, others find this method messy and uncomfortable. Try a variety of methods in order to discover which works best for you.

FIGURE 2.24 Drafting Brushes

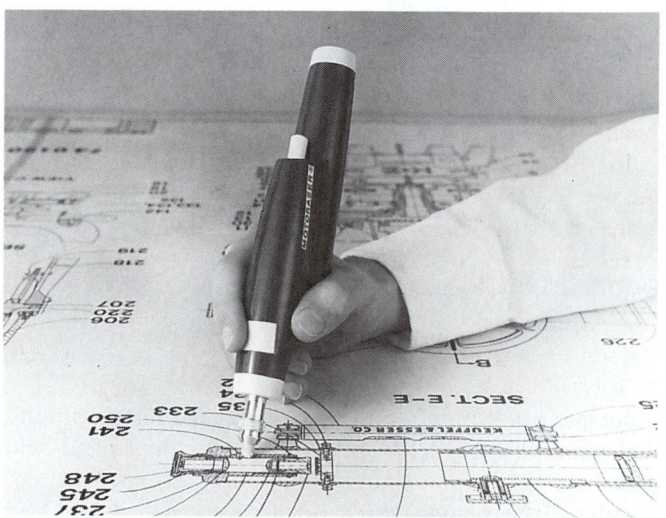

FIGURE 2.25 Battery-Operated Erasing Machine

2.4   Drawing Scales

All instrument drawings are drawn accurately at one size, which may be a reduced size, so that all features of the part are in proportion. Such a drawing is said to be drawn *"to scale."* Drawings can be drawn full size or to an enlarged or reduced size. CAD drawings are 1:1 (full size).

Since construction projects—piping, structural, architecture, and civil—are large and the paper size is small, all of these drawings are done at a reduced scale. Some mechanical drawings are also drawn to a reduced size. The instrument used to measure these reduced-size drawings is called a **scale** (not a ruler). A ruler makes only full-size measurements.

Certain scales are used in construction work: the civil engineer's scale, the architect's scale, and the metric scale for SI projects. The engineer's scale is used to draw very large objects, for example, earthworks, roads, and surveys of property. The architect's scale is used to make drawings of buildings and structures. Generally, the basic shape of each of these scales is either two-sided and flat or triangular (Figs. 2.26 and 2.27), and each is about twelve inches long. The triangular shape makes six surfaces available for the different sized scales. Figure 2.28 shows five types of scales that are found in industry.

The markings on scales are arranged in two ways: *fully divided* and *open divided*. Fully divided scales have each main unit of measurement throughout the length of the scale completely divided, like the familiar foot ruler on which each inch is divided into sixteenths. The engineer's and the metric scale are normally fully divided. Open divided scales have each main unit of the scale undivided, except for a fully divided extra main unit at the 0 end of the scale. The architect's scale is open divided.

The scale is a precision instrument and, with proper use, will produce consistent drawings. Remember, the scale is a measuring instrument not a drawing instrument; do not draw with the scale (unless it is one of the two scales of the drafting machine). Scales do not have edges designed for drawing.

2.4.1   The Civil Engineer's Scale

The **engineer's scale** (triangular) normally has six scales that are fully divided. Three-sided civil engineering scales are divided into 10, 20, 30, 40, 50, and 60 divisions per inch and are numbered at each tenth division along the length of each scale. The number of divisions per inch is marked at the 0 end of each scale. Although, in normal usage each division equals one foot, you can assign any unit to the scale divisions. This is designated on a drawing as 1″ = 20′, where one inch on the scale represents twenty feet of real size. This scale can also be used as a decimal scale, where 1″ = 2′ and each division represents one-tenth of a foot on the 20 scale or 1″ = 200′ and each division represents ten feet on the 20 scale. The other scales can be similarly used. Figure 2.29 shows measurements taken along the civil engineer's scale. Here, .50, 3.60, and 4.90 in. are shown measured on the full-size inch

FIGURE 2.26   Triangular and Flat Scales

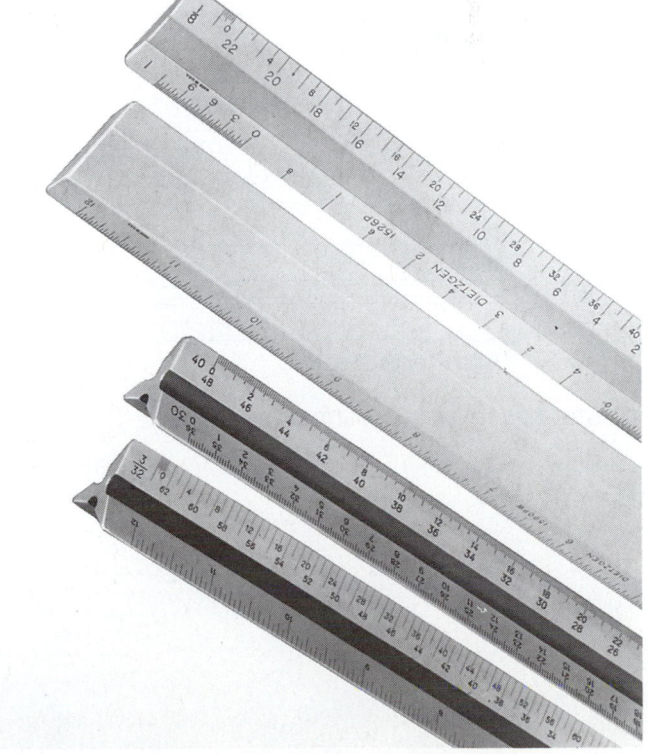

FIGURE 2.27   Scales

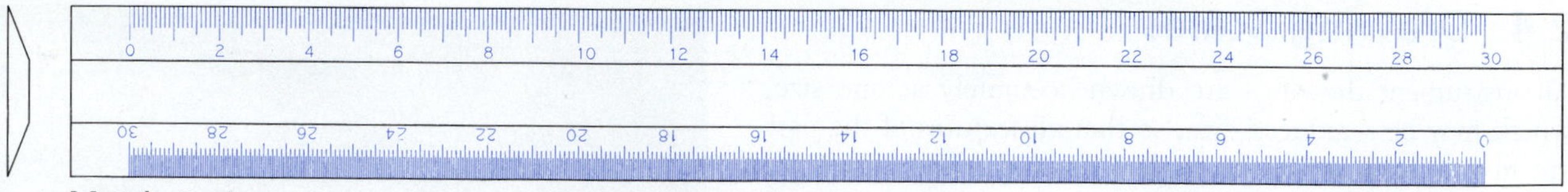

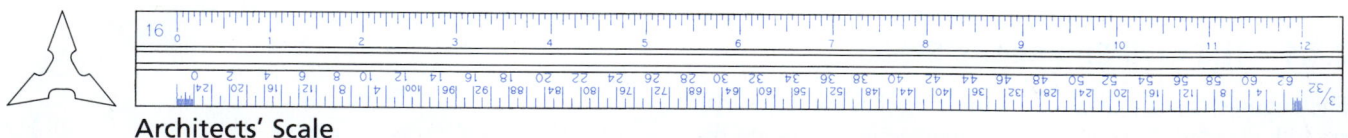

Metric Scale

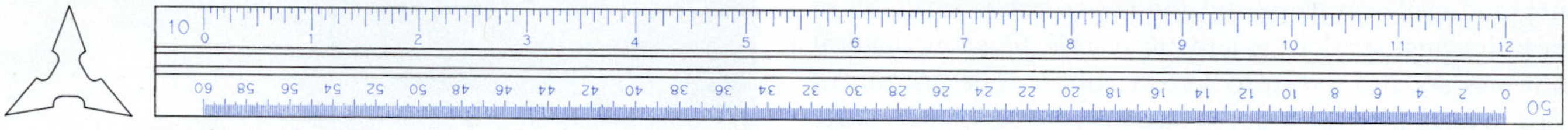

Engineers' Scale

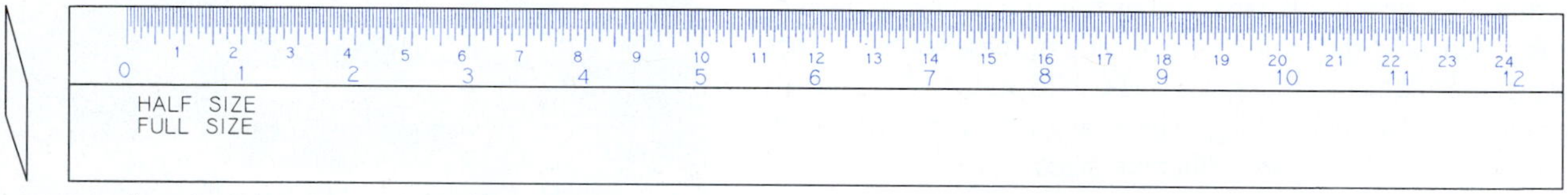

Mechanical Engineers' Scale

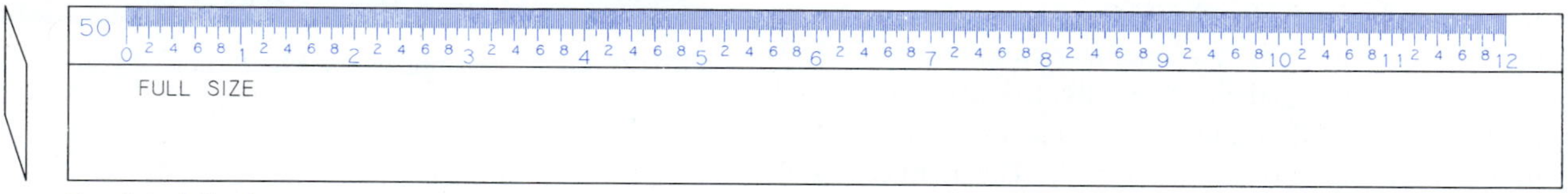

Decimal Scale

Architects' Scale

FIGURE 2.28   Five Types of Drawing Scales

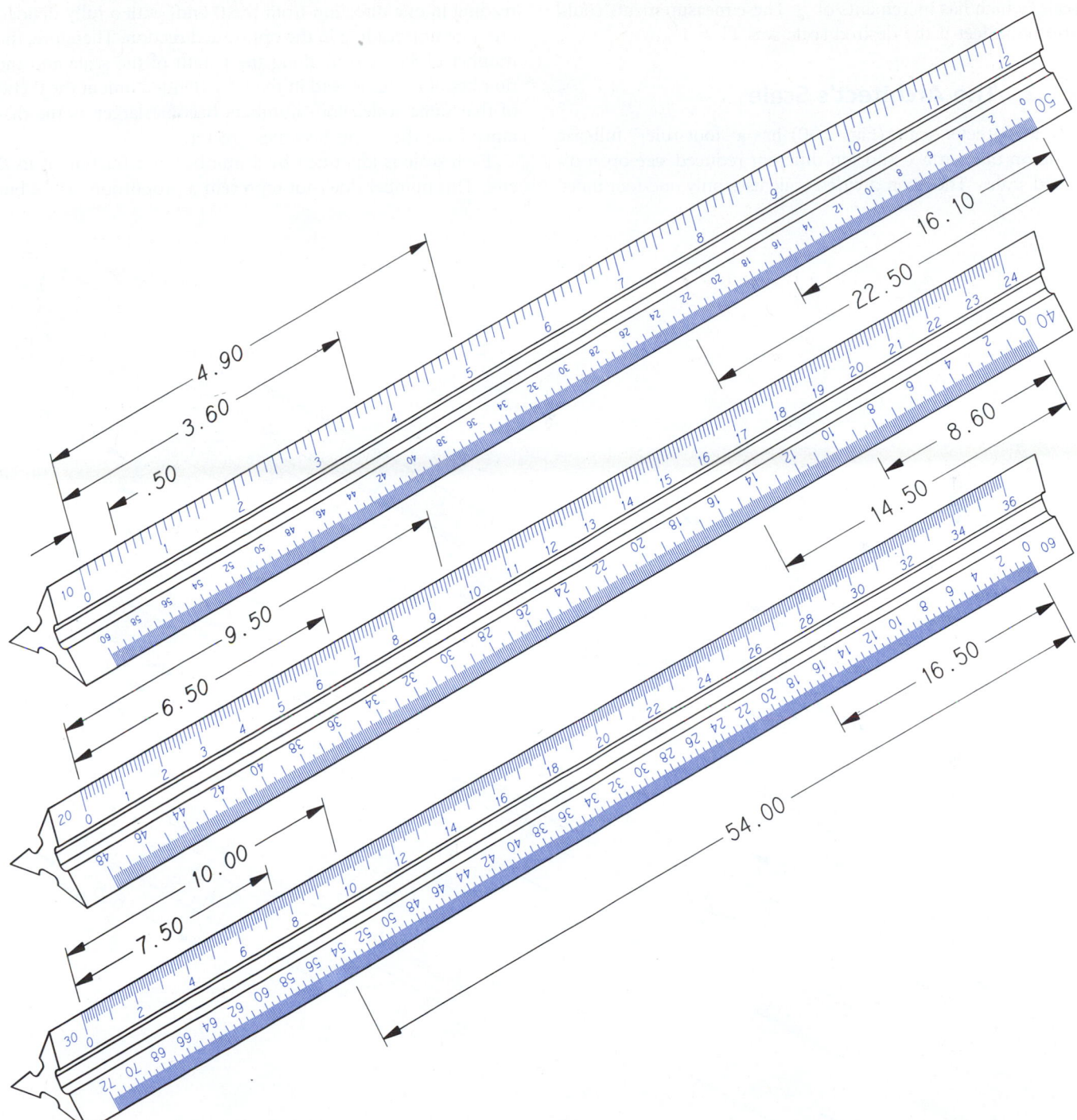

FIGURE 2.29   Civil Engineer's Scale

scale, which has increments of $\frac{1}{10}$. These measurements could also be in feet if the desired scale was $1'' = 1'$.

2.4.2 The Architect's Scale

The **architect's scale** (Fig. 2.30) has a "foot ruler" full-size scale on one surface and ten different reduced-size open divided scales. The open divided scale uses only one-foot units, reading in one direction from the 0 end, with a fully divided one-foot unit reading in the opposite direction. Therefore, the number of feet is read along the length of the scale and the number of inches is read in the fully divided unit at the 0 end of that same scale. Both numbers become larger as the distance from the 0 end becomes greater.

Each scale is identified by a number or a fraction at its 0 end. This number does not represent a proportion of size but

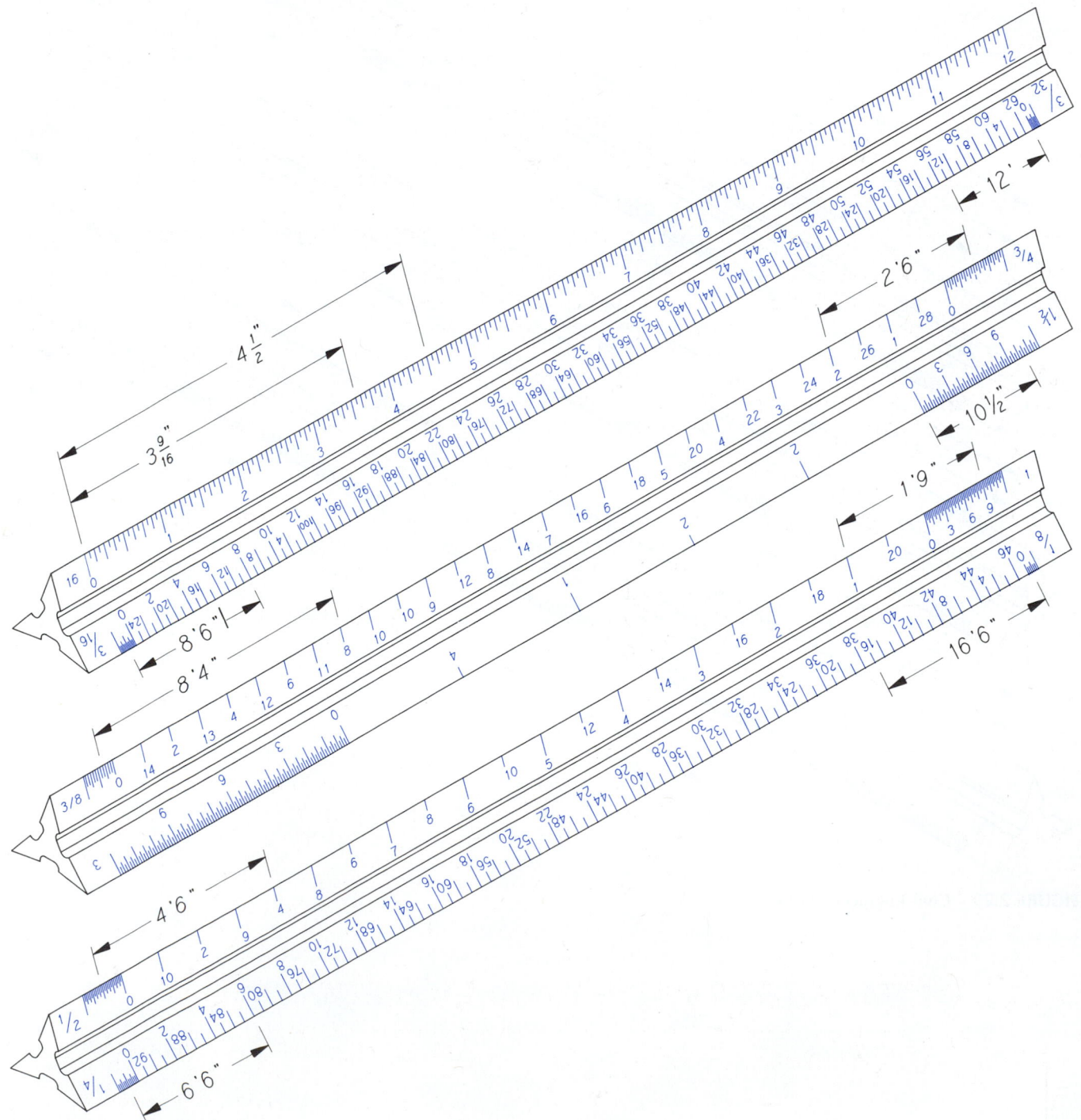

FIGURE 2.30 Architect's Scale

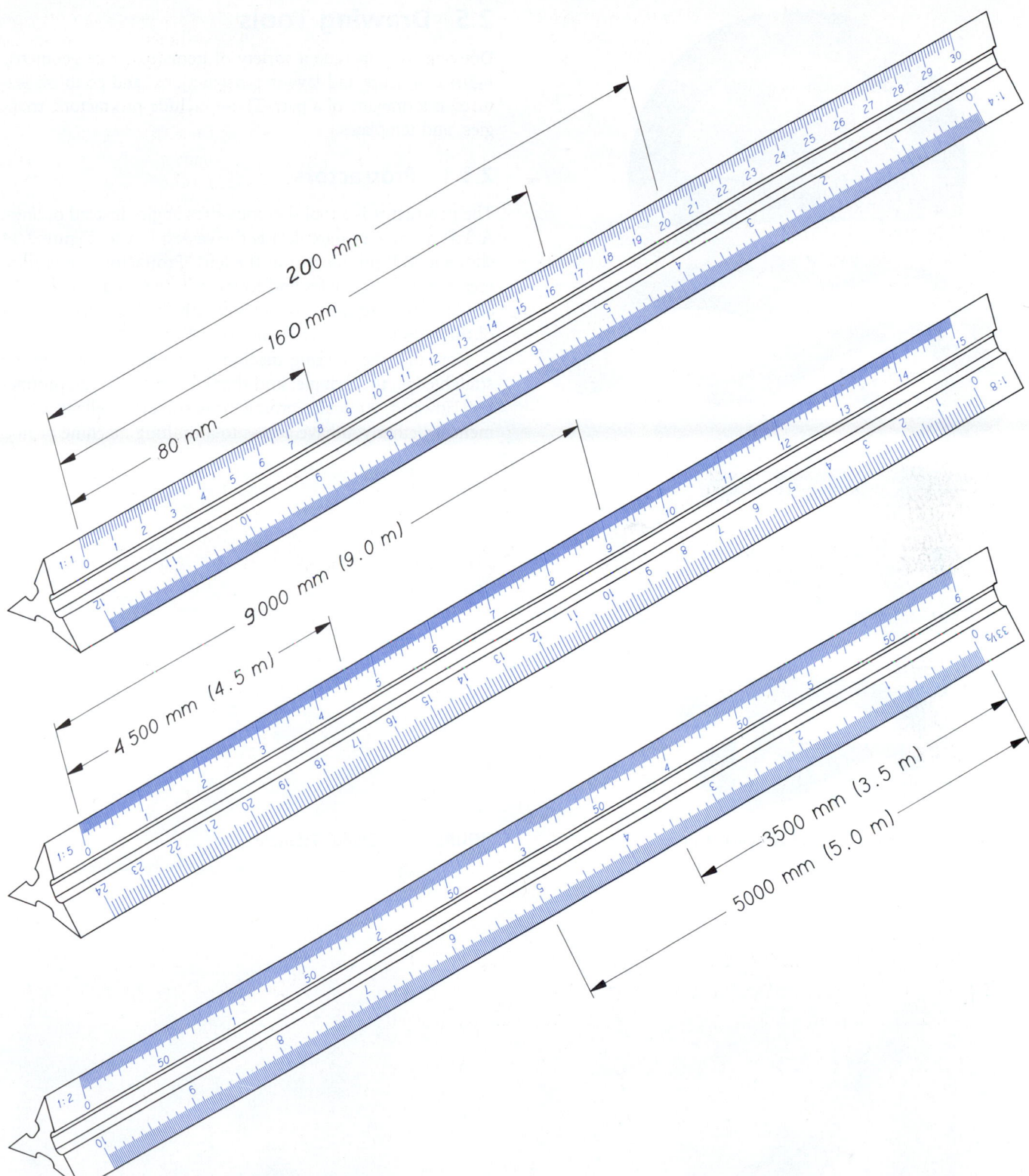

FIGURE 2.33   Triangular Metric Scale

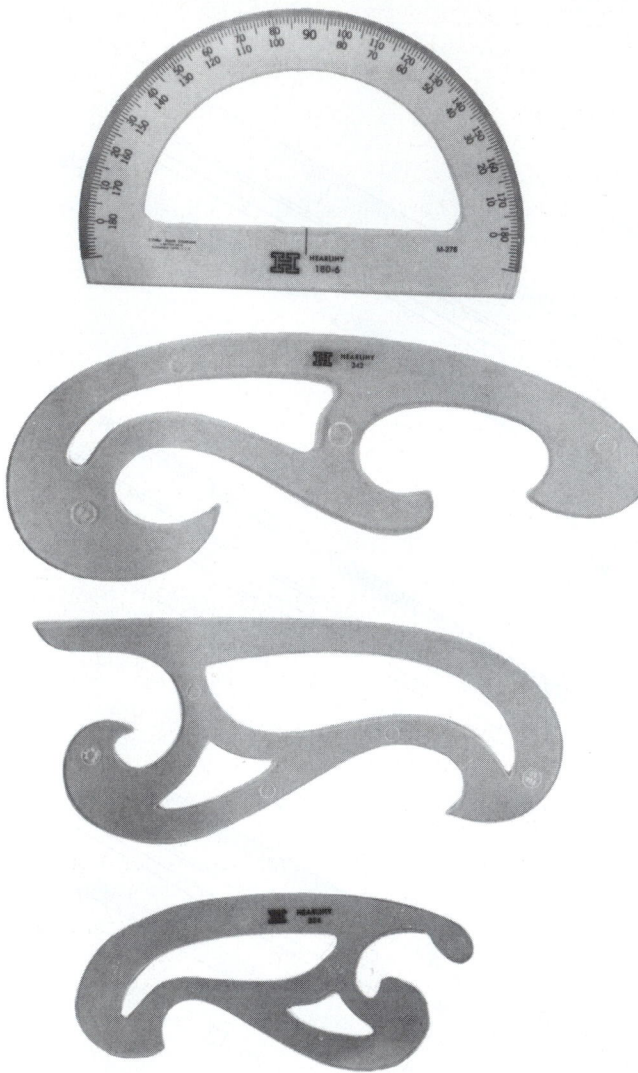

FIGURE 2.34 Protractor and Irregular Curves

FIGURE 2.35 45° Triangle

2.5 Drawing Tools

Drawing tools include a variety of items to create geometric figures, measure and layout constructions, and establish features as a drawing of a part. These include protractors, triangles, and templates.

2.5.1 Protractors

The **protractor** is a tool that measures angles instead of lines. A 360° protractor (circular) is the easiest to use. Figure 2.34 shows a 180° protractor (on the left). Protractors are used to measure existing angles and to lay out lines at an angle. The center of the protractor is aligned with the intersecting point of the lines to be drawn or measured.

Note that the drafting machine can replace not only the straightedge, the triangle, and the scale, but also the protractor. However, a circular protractor is still an excellent investment, whether you have access to a drafting machine or not.

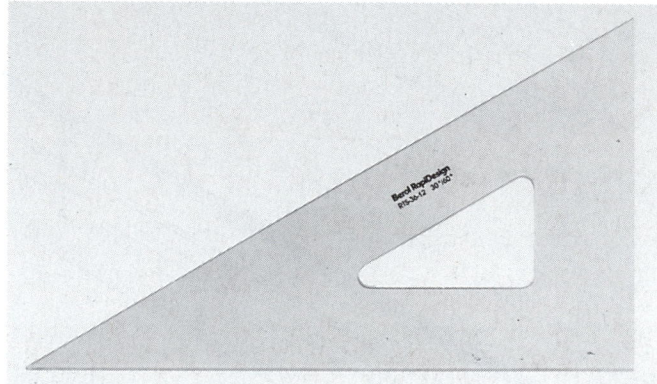

FIGURE 2.36 30/60° Triangle

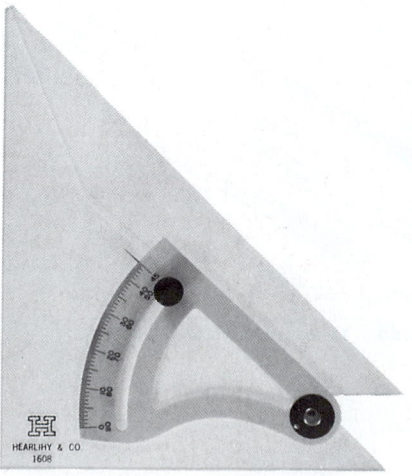

FIGURE 2.37 Adjustable Triangle

Since beginning drafters tend to misread angle measurements when drawing with a drafting machine or an adjustable triangle, use of a protractor is recommended. Features of a part drawn at angles, regardless of the method of construction, should always be checked with a protractor.

2.5.2   Triangles

The standard **triangles** are the 45° triangle, the 30/60° triangle, and the adjustable triangle. Triangles are used with a straightedge forming a horizontal baseline, and each can be used to draw a vertical line. When a drafting machine is available, triangles are unnecessary, but for productivity, triangles are extremely useful in conjunction with a drafting machine. The vertical scale of a drafting machine is difficult to keep 90° (perpendicular) to the horizontal scale; triangles used with drafting machines eliminate this problem.

The **45° triangle** (Fig. 2.35) is used to draw lines at an angle of 45° with the baseline. The **30/60° triangle** (Fig. 2.36) is used to create lines at 30° or 60° with the baseline. Together the two triangles create angles of 15° and 75°. Combinations of the 45° and the 30/60° triangle divide the 360° of a full circle into twenty-four 15° segments. Other angles are drawn with an adjustable triangle or with the aid of a protractor.

The **adjustable triangle** (Fig. 2.37) is the same as a 45° triangle when closed, but it can be opened to form two parallel edges. The amount of opening of the triangle is measured by a protractor scale that reads from 0° to 45° and then doubles back from 45° to 90°. Zero to 45° angles are formed by the two edges at the "open" corner of the triangle. Forty-five to 90° angles are formed by the sides at the "hinge" corner. By rotating the adjustable triangle into position, you can draw all angles. Check all measurements and constructions made with an adjustable triangle with a protractor because it is very easy to make a mistake with an adjustable triangle. For example, 40° and 50° have the same setting, so the angle you establish depends on which side of the triangle is touching the straightedge.

2.5.3   Templates

A **template** is a tool for drafting shapes of all sizes. Standard templates (Fig. 2.38) are essential for the quick, easy construction of circular, square, rectangular, triangular, elliptical, and symbolic shapes. In general, templates are better than a compass for small-diameter circles.

Circle templates (Fig. 2.39), one of the most common types of templates used in drafting, come in all standard sizes for U.S. and metric units. After you master the essentials of linework and compass work, you will use templates for all standard shape construction. Templates are discussed further in chapters on electronic, piping, welding, and for other drawing applications.

2.6   Instruments

Instruments include all forms of *compasses, dividers,* and *inking tools.* The drafting instrument set (Fig. 2.40) consists of one or two sizes of compasses, a divider, and accessories. The

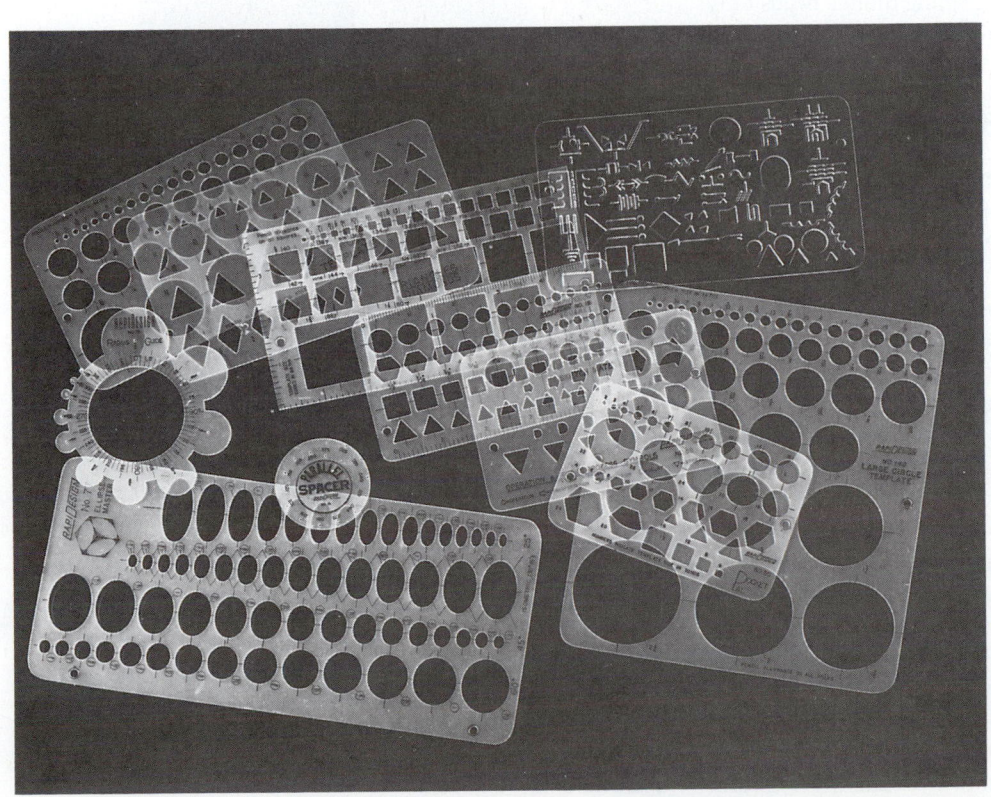

FIGURE 2.38   Templates

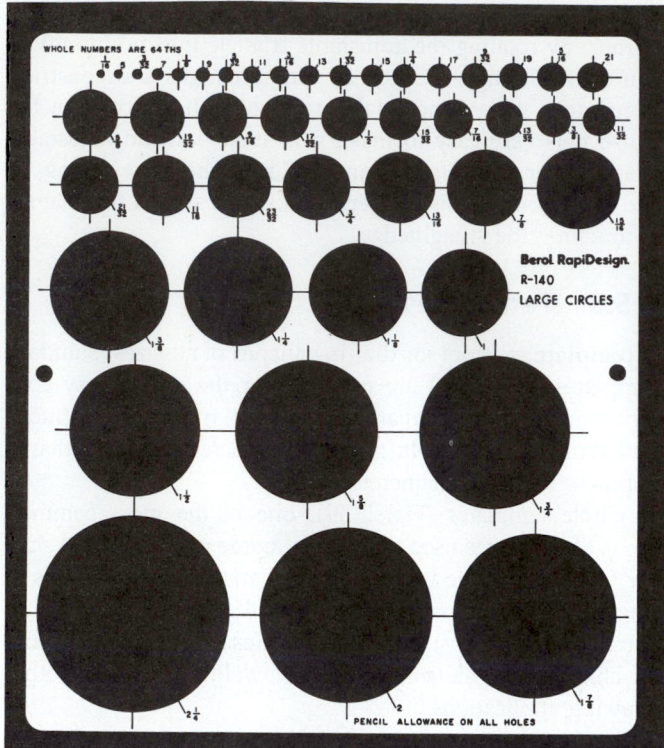

FIGURE 2.39   Circle Template

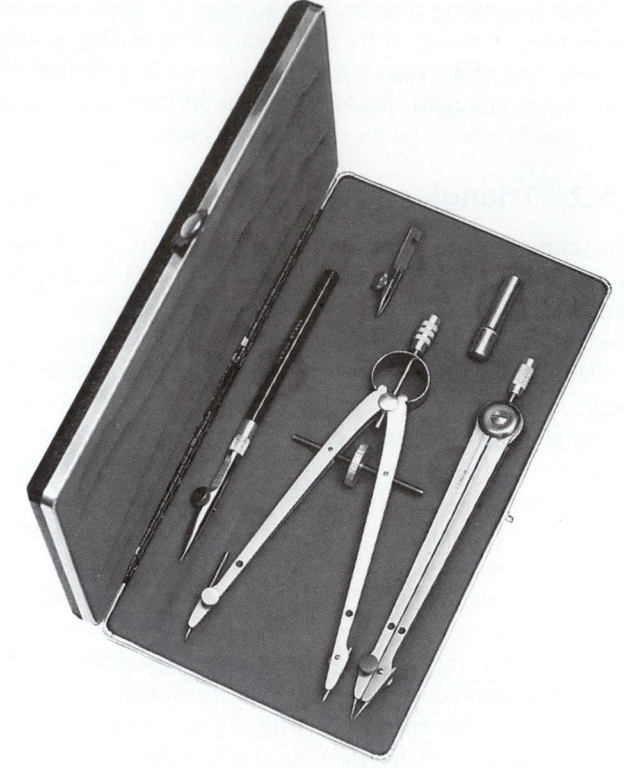

FIGURE 2.40   Drafting Instruments

compass is used to draw circles and circular arcs. Although many types of drafting sets are available, they normally contain such obsolete items as the ruling pen. This item has been replaced by the technical pen. A beginning drafter needs only to purchase a medium-sized, high-quality bow compass and medium-sized dividers.

2.6.1   Bow Compass and Dividers

A good **bow compass** and **dividers** are essential to the accurate construction of all forms of engineering drawings. A bow compass (Fig. 2.41) has a center thumb wheel that is used to set and hold the spacing between the center point and the lead. Compasses without a center thumb set wheel and compasses that do not rigidly hold the spacing between point and lead are not recommended for drafting. Dividers (Fig. 2.42) do not have a center wheel and are used to quickly set off measurements from one view to another. This is extremely useful in the construction of mechanical drawings and for descriptive geometry (Chapter 19).

The centering point for the compass is either a tapered point or a short needle point projecting from a wider shaft that creates a "shoulder." The shoulder acts as a limit to the point's penetration into the paper and board. To restrict the compass point from penetrating the drawing medium and to provide a stable secure centering point from which to swing an arc or a circle, you can place a small piece of drafting tape (or dot) on the drawing at the center of the arc or circle to be drawn. Draw construction centerlines over the tape. Circles

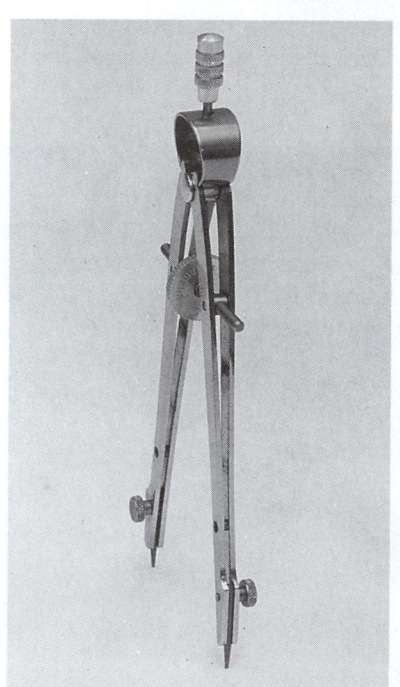

FIGURE 2.41   Bow Compass

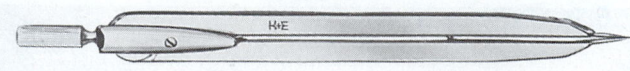

FIGURE 2.42   Dividers

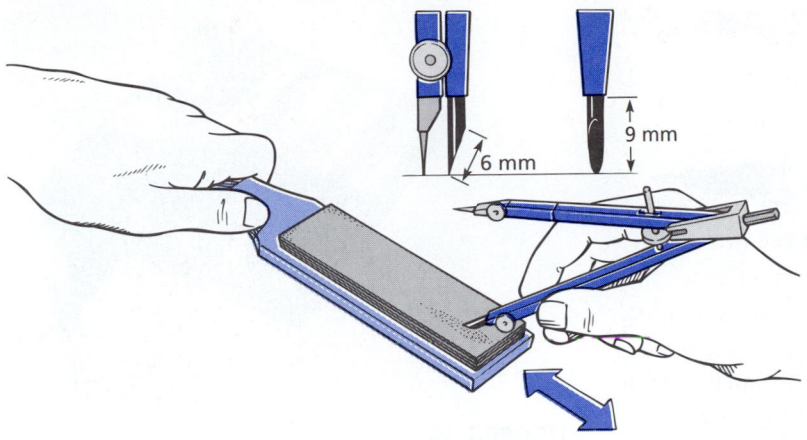

FIGURE 2.43   Sharpening the Lead of a Compass

smaller than .50 in. (12 mm) are much easier to draw with a template or a drop bow compass than with a large- or medium-sized compass. Use templates whenever possible. A compass is best for odd-sized and large circles and for construction techniques.

The compass lead should be a piece of the drafting pencil lead (same grade lead or softer). Then both straight and curved lines will be drawn with the same lead and it will be easier to maintain uniformity. The lead is secured in the compass with about $\frac{3}{8}$ in. (9 mm) exposed and is sharpened with a sandpaper block (Fig. 2.43). Use care when sharpening the lead to keep the line through the point and the lead perpendicular to the sandpaper. Make a flat cut that leaves an oval surface, called a *bevel*. The bevel should be about three times as long as the diameter of the lead. The resulting point is chisel-shaped and should have about the same taper, when viewed from the side, as the drafting pencil. Do not try to adjust the lead in the compass after it is sharpened because it is almost impossible to reposition the chisel shape properly. The centering point is adjusted so that the midpoint of the needle point is even with the end of the lead. The beveled end can be on either side of the lead (Fig. 2.44) though most drafters put it on the outside. To create a thin, dark curve, both sides of the lead may be beveled, which also creates a longer lasting point, but is harder to maintain.

Dividers come with two identical tapered metal points. Some drafters prefer to replace one metal point with a piece of 4H lead. The lead point can be used to set off dimensions (especially for descriptive geometry) instead of using the two metal points, which tend to mar the drafting medium.

For special drawing needs, three expensive but extremely useful tools are available: the *drop compass* (Fig. 2.45) for very small, accurate circles; the *beam compass* (Fig. 2.46) for very large circles and arcs; and *proportional dividers* (Fig. 2.47) for reductions and enlargements.

2.6.2 Inking Instruments

Most compasses have inking-pen or technical-pen attachments. When you purchase a compass set, attempt to find one

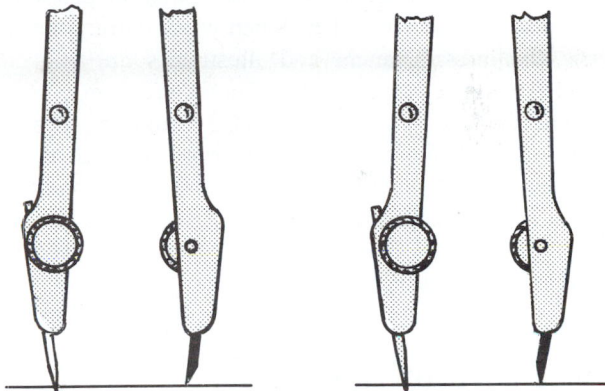

FIGURE 2.44   Positioning Compass Leads

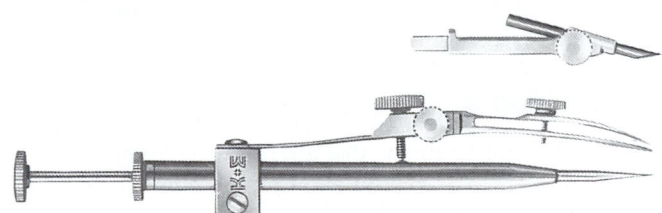

FIGURE 2.45   Drop Compass

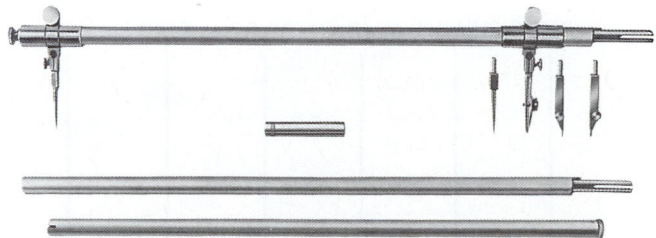

FIGURE 2.46   Beam Compass

FIGURE 2.47   Proportional Dividers

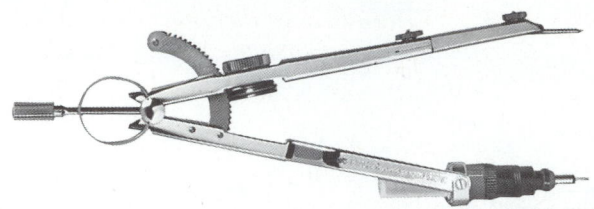

FIGURE 2.48   Bow Compass with Technical Pen Attachment

equipped with an attachment for holding a *technical pen* (Fig. 2.48), not a **ruling pen** (Fig. 2.45). Although many drafting sets contain ruling pens (Fig. 2.40), they are rarely used in industry, so we will limit our discussion to technical pens.

Technical pens, like the sets shown in Figure 2.49, although expensive, have replaced all other forms of inking tools. Technical pens come in a wide range of pen widths (diameters) (Fig. 2.50), and each pen width corresponds to a metric thickness. Drafters and illustrators are frequently asked to complete projects in ink. Such projects may include diagrams and pictorials for technical manuals, sales brochures, and graph and chart presentations. In general, technical pens in 0.25, 0.35, 0.45, 0.50, and 0.70 mm widths are used for such drafting. *Though it is a poor practice, manual inking is also used by some companies to make minor corrections on CAD plotted drawings.*

2.7   Drafting Materials

Drafting materials include drawing media (vellum, film, grid sheets) and preprinted transfer items (title blocks, lettering, symbols). A wide variety of materials is available for manually drawn and CAD plotted drawings.

2.7.1   Media

Traditional drafting media that are transparent enough to be whiteprinted include vellum and drafting film. Drawing **vellum** is a high-quality, translucent paper. Paper used for the diazo reproduction process must allow light to shine through

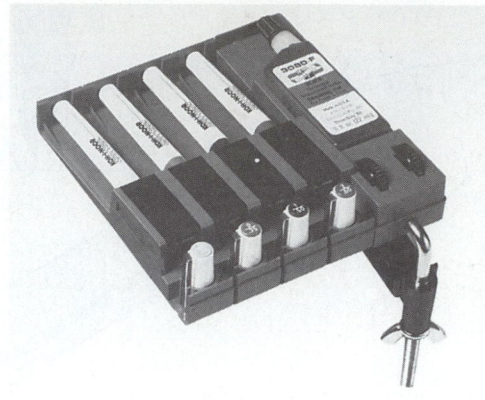

FIGURE 2.49   Technical Pens

(i.e., be translucent). In addition, pencil on vellum is easily erasable, and vellum also takes ink well.

Drafting film is made of durable, high-quality, polyester sheets. This drafting medium is excellent for ink and also for plastic and combination leads. Special leads and erasers are available for use on drafting film. Although film is expensive compared to vellum, you should have some experience drawing on it with graphite lead, plastic lead, and with ink. Vellum and drafting film are available in a plain version or a version with fine, blue nonreproductive grids.

Drafting media are secured to the drafting table with drafting tape. **Drafting tape** (or drafting dots) is a high-quality version of masking tape that is designed not to pull the finish off the paper surface.

2.7.2   Drawing Sheet Size and Format

Drafting media come in standard sheet sizes and rolls. Table 2.3 compares International and ANSI drawing sizes. Rolls of drafting paper and film are available in widths of 30, 36, 42, and 54 inches and in lengths of 25 feet or more. International standards establish a series of paper sizes based on width-to-length proportions. Figure 2.51 illustrates the various ANSI

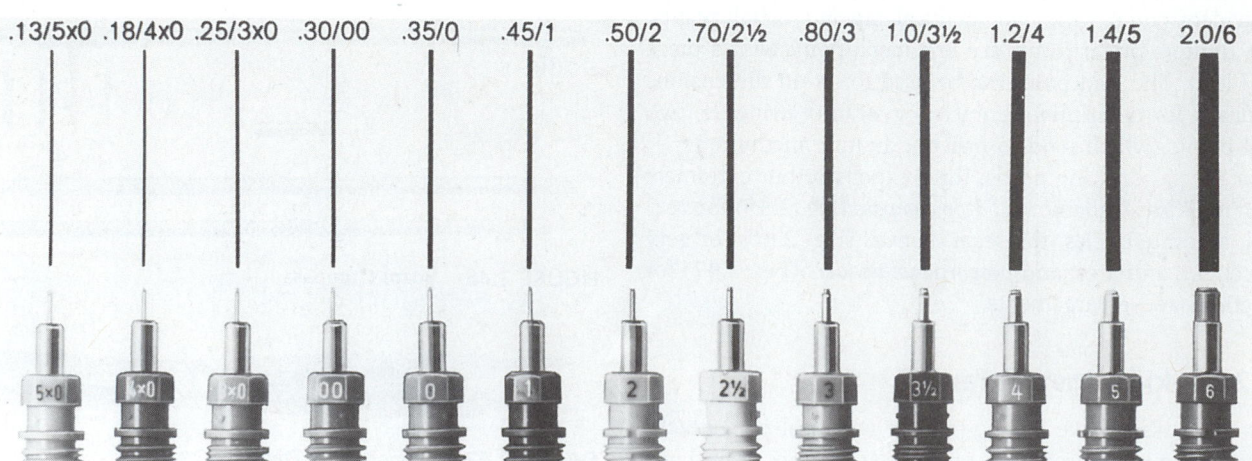

FIGURE 2.50   Pen Sizes

TABLE 2.3 Drawing Sheet Sizes

American National Standard Y14.1, in.	International Standard, mm
A–$8\frac{1}{2}$ × 11	A4–210 × 297
B–11 × 17	A3–297 × 420
C–17 × 22	A2–470 × 594
D–22 × 34	A1–594 × 841
E–34 × 44	A0–841 × 1189
F–28 × 40	

sheet sizes. The margins shown in Figure 2.51 produce net drawing areas that are well within the sheet sizes of both standards. Drawing formats made to this standard can be reproduced on either U.S. or international sheet sizes by contact printing and microfilm projection methods. Most U.S. companies purchase preprinted standard sheets in ISO or ANSI specifications. Figure 2.52 compares the ISO and ANSI drawing formats.

Standardization of drawing size and location of format features on drawing forms provides definite advantages for the design office in the areas of readability, handling, filing, and reproduction. If companies are to share drawings successfully, similar items of information must be in the same location on all drawings and the information must be recorded in the same manner. Sheet size and format are covered in ANSI Standard Y14.1-1980.

2.7.3   Drawing Formats

The size and style of lettering on **drawing formats** is to be in accordance with ANSI Y14.2M (see Chapter 4). To provide contrasting divisions between major elements of the format, the following guide should be used on all projects taken from the text:

Thick lines: 0.7 to 0.9 mm (approximately .03 in.)

1. borderline
2. outline of principal blocks
3. main division of blocks.

Medium lines: 0.45 to 0.5 mm (approximately .02 in.)

1. Minor divisions of the title block.

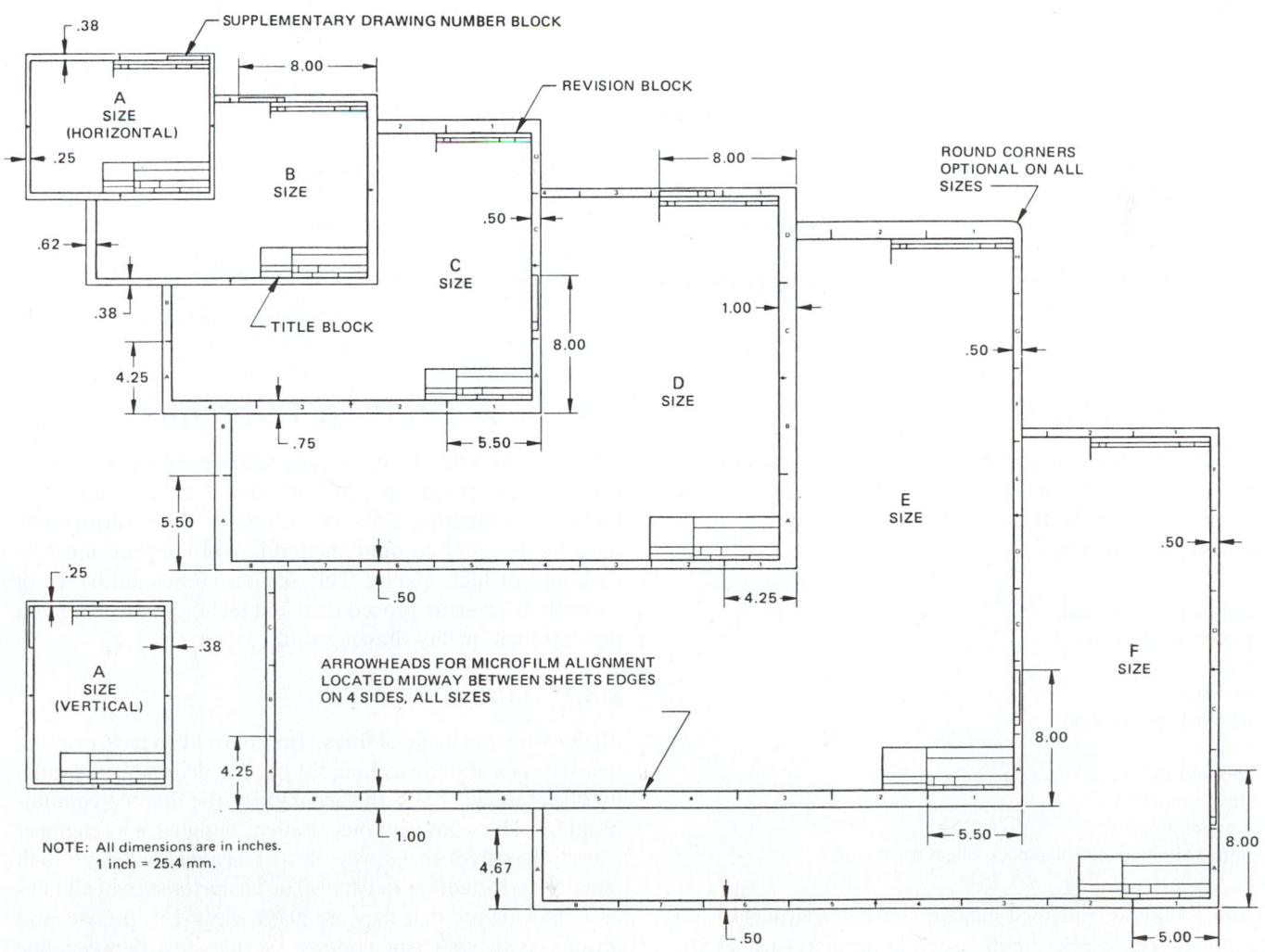

FIGURE 2.51 Flat Size Formats, A through F

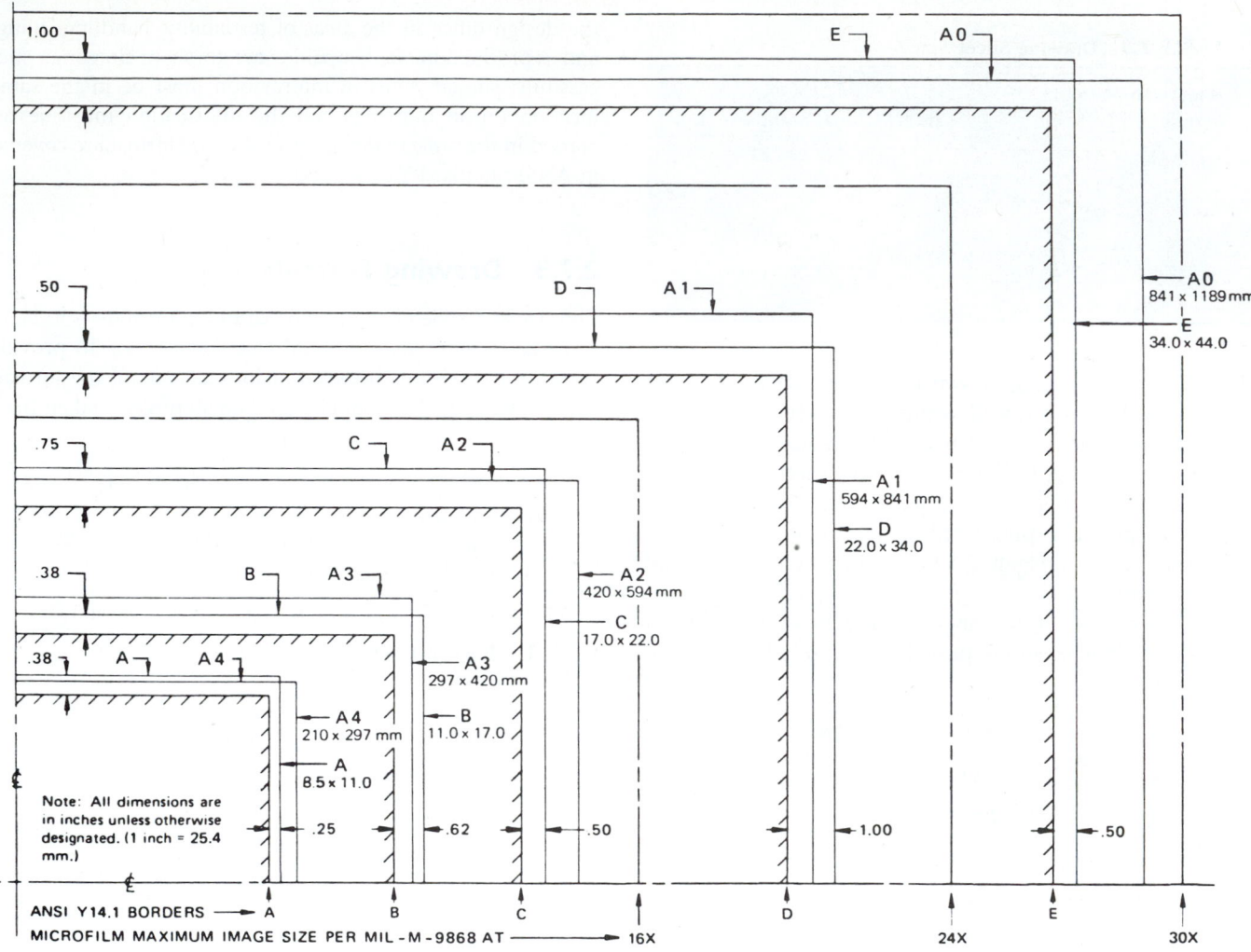

FIGURE 2.52   Comparison of ANSI Y14.1 Drawing Format Sizes with ISO Paper Sizes

2.7.4   Title Blocks

The **title block** is one of the most important parts of the drawing. The title block is located in the lower right corner of the format. Normally, the title block includes spaces for the following information:

- company/school name
- project title/part name
- scale
- drawn by
- material specification
- date
- checked by
- sheet number
- drawing number
- standard company tolerances (sheet tolerance).

Figure 2.53 shows the ANSI standard title block layouts for A–K sheet sizes. Title blocks are discussed in detail in Chapter 18.

2.8   Basic Drafting Techniques

Whatever the field of engineering, when graphics are used to communicate design, production, and manufacturing data, high-quality drafting skills are essential. Also, calculations must be neat and accurate. Lettering and linework must be dark and of high quality. This section covers the basics of *linework*. It presents procedures, and techniques to help you develop high-quality drawing skills.

2.8.1   Lines

All drawings are made of **lines**. The control you have over the pencil or pen and the techniques you use determine the quality of the drawing and the accuracy of the graphic communication. The conscientious drafter, designer, or engineer constantly strives to improve his or her technique through practice and attention to detail. The characteristics of all lines on a drawing are that they are black, clean-cut, precise, and opaque, with sufficient contrast in thickness between line

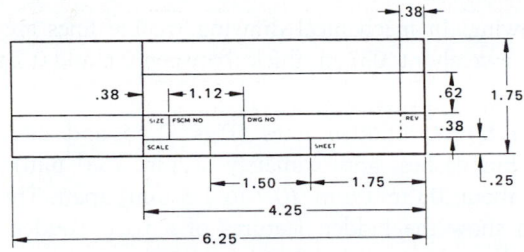

NOTE: All dimensions are in inches. 1 inch = 25.4 mm.
TITLE BLOCK FOR A, B, C, AND G – SIZES

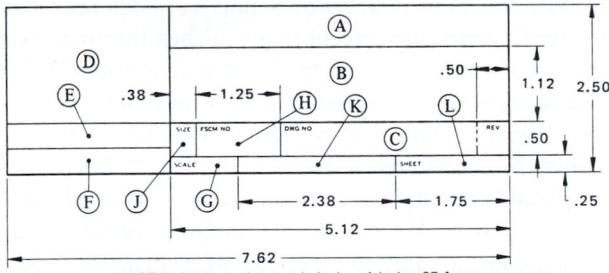

NOTE: All dimensions are in inches. 1 inch = 25.4 mm.
TITLE BLOCK FOR D, E, F, H, J, AND K – SIZES

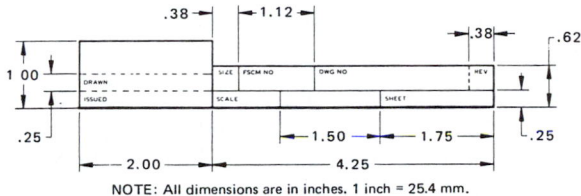

NOTE: All dimensions are in inches. 1 inch = 25.4 mm.
CONTINUATION SHEET TITLE BLOCK FOR A, B, C, and G – SIZES

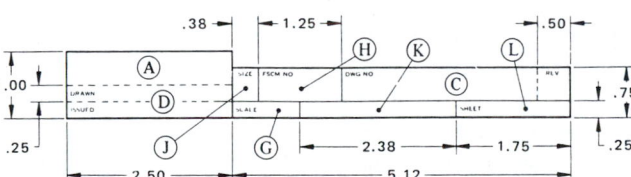

NOTE: All dimensions are in inches. 1 inch = 25.4 mm.
CONTINUATION SHEET TITLE BLOCK FOR D, E, F, H, J, AND K – SIZES

FIGURE 2.53   ANSI Title Block Dimensions

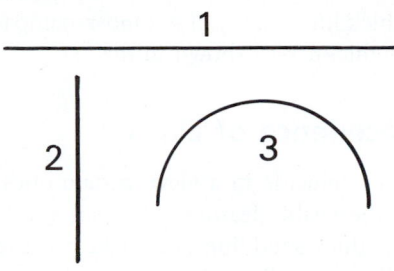

Lines, 1 (horizontal), 2 (vertical), 3 (curved).

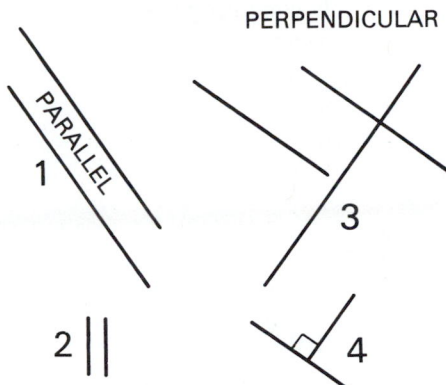

Parallel and perpendicular lines.

FIGURE 2.54   Line Types

types. The most important aspect of your job as a drafter is the understanding of the process, the intent, and the content of a drawing. Understanding how lines function and what they mean is particularly important.

Lines (Fig. 2.54) and their relationships are important concerns of engineering graphics. A *line* is considered to have length but no width. A straight line is the shortest distance between two points and is the type of line implied by the word "line." A line that bends is called a *curve*.

Parallel lines are equally spaced along their entire length, becoming neither closer together nor farther apart. The symbol for parallel line is // (Fig. 2.54). *Perpendicular lines* are at an angle of 90 degrees to each other and can be intersecting or nonintersecting (Fig. 2.54). The symbol for a perpendicular line is ⊥.

The lines in engineering drawings are drawn with different widths to provide specific information. Each line type is ac-

tually a symbol that represents a function or idea or communicates a special situation. The thickness of any line is determined by what it represents and the smallest size to which it will be reduced. To avoid confusion, lines representing the same function must be the same thickness throughout a single drawing. The minimum spacing between parallel lines is determined by how much the drawing will be reduced. Two parallel lines that are placed too close will merge when the drawing is reduced—this is called *fill-in*, a situation that must be avoided. Normally .06 in. (1.5 mm) minimum parallel spacing meets reduction requirements for most drawings.

The following list describes traditional line thicknesses used on engineering drawings:

1. Fine lines   Thin, black lines used to provide information about the drawing or to construct the drawing. These include dimension lines, leader lines, extension lines, centerlines, and construction lines.

2. Medium lines   Medium width, solid, black lines used to outline planes, lines, surfaces, and solid shapes. Medium lines are also used for hidden (dashed) lines.

3. Heavy lines   Solid, thick, black lines used for the border, cutting plane lines, and break lines.

The newest ANSI standard suggests only two line thicknesses— thin and thick. All lines listed under 1 and 2 from the list above are now drawn with thin lines and all lines listed under 3 are drawn with thick lines. Many, if not most, companies still use the three line thicknesses shown in the list.

2.8.2 Precedence of Lines

Whenever lines coincide in a view, certain ones take precedence. Since the visible features of a part (object lines) are represented by thick solid lines, they take precedence over all other lines. If a centerline and cutting plane coincide, the more important one should take precedence. Normally the cutting plane line, drawn with a thicker weight, will take precedence. The following list gives the preferred *precedence of lines* on your drawing:

1. Visible (object) lines
2. Hidden (dashed) lines
3. Cutting plane lines
4. Centerlines
5. Break lines
6. Dimension and extension lines
7. Section lines

2.8.3 Line Types

Line types and conventions for mechanical drawings are covered in ANSI Standard Y14.2M (Fig. 2.55). Figure 2.56 provides examples of each type of line. Every line on your drawing has a meaning. In other words, lines are symbols that mean a specific thing. The line type determines if the line is part of the part or conveys information about the part. A visible object line represents the visible edges of the part. A hidden line is a dashed line that represents an edge that does not show because it is behind another feature of the part. Part description is composed of these two types of lines.

Other lines convey information about the part but are not lines of the part itself. In this category are section lines, cutting plane lines, centerlines, dimension and extension lines, and phantom lines.

Besides having different configurations such as dashes and spaces, each line type has a weight thickness (Figs. 2.55 and 2.56). The following list gives the suggested weight (thickness) of lines used on your drawing:

Visible object line	0.60 to 0.70 mm
Hidden line	0.45 to 0.50 mm
Section line	0.25 to 0.30 mm
Centerline	0.30 to 0.35 mm
Dimension line	0.30 to 0.35 mm
Cutting plane line	0.70 to 0.90 mm
Phantom line	0.45 to 0.50 mm
Border line	0.70 to 0.90 mm
Break line	0.45 to 0.70 mm

Visible Object Lines   Visible object lines (Figs. 2.55 and 2.56) are thick lines used to represent the visible edges and contours of a part. Since visible lines are the most important lines, they must stand out from all other secondary lines on

the drawing. In mechanical drawing, visible lines are normally drawn about .032 in. thick (between 0.6 and 0.7 mm).

Hidden Lines   Hidden lines (Figs. 2.55 and 2.56) are short, thin dashes, approximately .12 in. (3.0 mm) long, spaced about .03 to .06 in. (0.7 to 1.5 mm) apart. They are used to show the hidden features of a part. Hidden lines should always begin and end with a dash, except when a dash would form a continuation of a visible line.

Dashes always meet at corners, and a hidden arc should start with dashes at the tangent points. When the arc is small, the length of the dash may be modified to maintain a uniform and neat appearance. Excessive hidden lines are difficult to follow. Therefore, only lines or features that add to the clearness and the conciseness of the drawing are shown. Confusing and conflicting hidden lines should be eliminated. If hidden lines do not adequately define a part's configuration, a section should be taken (see Chapter 9). Whenever possible, hidden lines are eliminated from the sectioned portion of a drawing. Hidden lines are drawn approximately .017 in. (0.45 to 0.50 mm) thick (see Chapter 7).

Centerlines   Centerlines (Figs. 2.55 and 2.56) are thin, long and short dashes, alternately and evenly spaced, with long dashes placed at each end of the line. The long dash is dependent on the size of the drawing and normally varies in length from .75 to 2 in. (20 to 50 mm). Short dashes, depending on the length of the required centerline should be approximately .06 to .12 in. (1.5 to 3.0 mm). Very short centerlines may be unbroken with dashes at both ends.

Centerlines are used to indicate the axes of symmetrical parts of features, bolt circles, paths of motion, and pitch circles. They should extend about .12 in. (3 mm) beyond the outline of symmetry, unless they are used as extension lines for dimensioning. Every circle, and some arcs, should have two centerlines that intersect at their center of the short dashes. Centerlines are usually drawn about .012 in. (0.3 mm) thick.

Dimension Lines   Dimension lines (Figs. 2.55 and 2.56) are thin lines used to show the extent and the direction of dimensions. Space for a single line of numerals is provided by a break in the dimension line. However, on horizontal line dimensions, when two lines of numerals are used in the form of limits, one may be placed above and the other below an unbroken dimension line.

If possible, dimension lines are aligned and grouped for uniform appearance and ease of reading. For example, parallel dimension lines should be spaced not less than .25 in. (6 mm) apart, and no dimension line should be closer than .38 in. (10 mm) to the outline of a part feature [.50 in. (12 mm) is the preferred distance].

All dimension lines terminate with an arrowhead in mechanical drafting; a slash, or a dot in architecture. The preferred ending is the arrowhead. Arrowheads are drawn with a

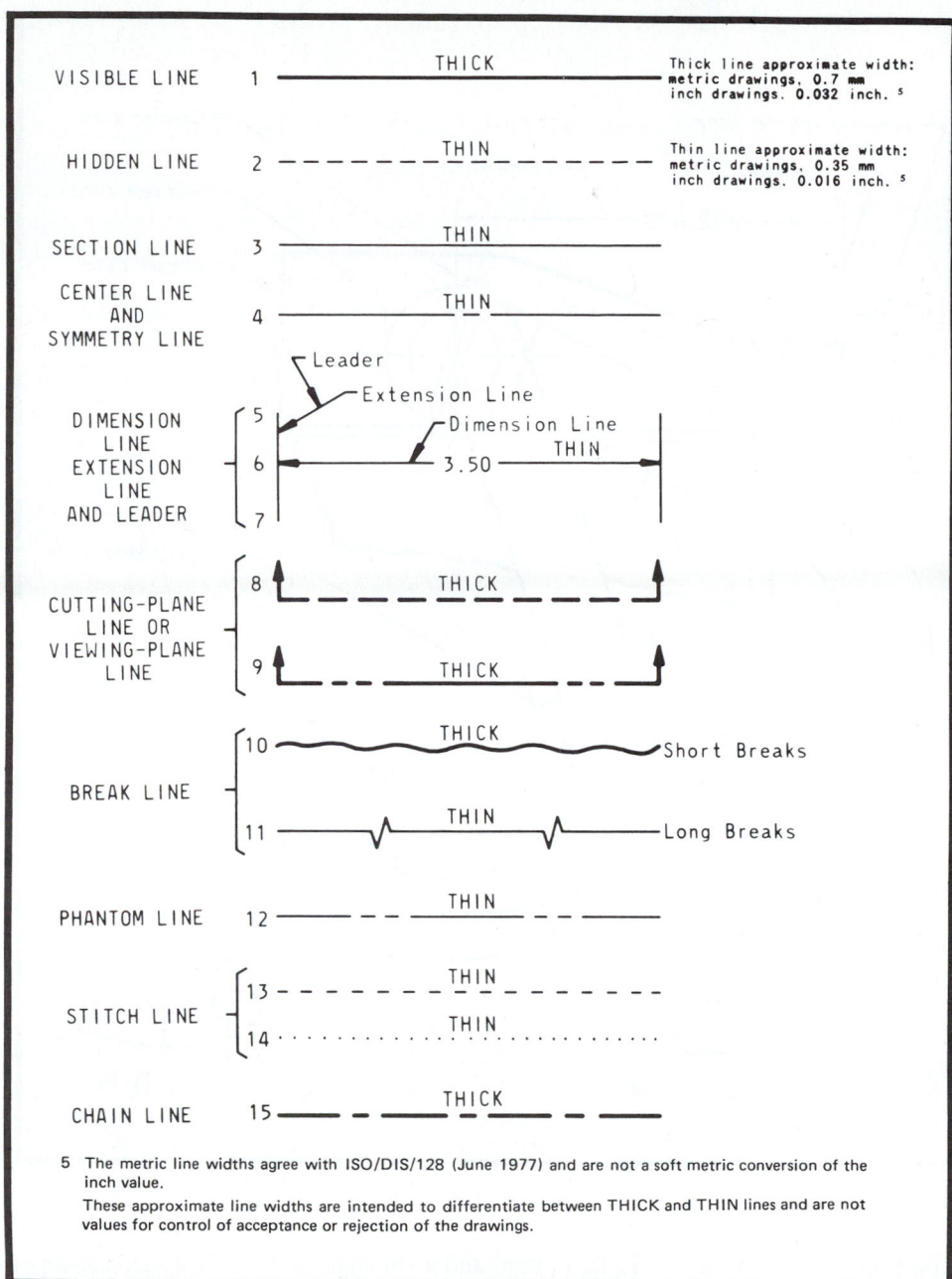

FIGURE 2.55 Standard Line Types and Thicknesses

1:3 ratio (width is $\frac{1}{3}$ the length). The actual size is determined by the drawing scale, the total drawing size and area used, and the reduction requirements. You should avoid large elaborate arrowheads. Dimension lines are drawn the same thickness as centerlines, .012 in. (0.3 mm). See Chapter 12 for complete information on dimensions.

Extension Lines   Extension lines (Figs. 2.55 and 2.56) are used to indicate the termination of a dimension. An extension line must not touch the feature from which it extends, but should start approximately .04 to .06 in. (2 mm) from the feature being dimensioned and extended the same amount beyond the arrow side of the last dimension line. When ex-

tension lines cross other extension lines, dimension lines, leader lines, or object lines, they are usually not broken, unless this is the company's accepted practice. When extension lines cross dimension lines close to an arrowhead, breaking the extension line is recommended for clarity. Extension lines are drawn at the same thickness as dimension lines and centerlines, .012 in. (0.3 mm).

Leader Lines   A leader line (Figs. 2.55 and 2.56) is a continuous straight line that extends at an angle from a note, a dimension, or other reference to a feature. An arrowhead touches the feature at that end of the leader. At the note end, a horizontal bar .25 in. (6 mm) long terminates the leader

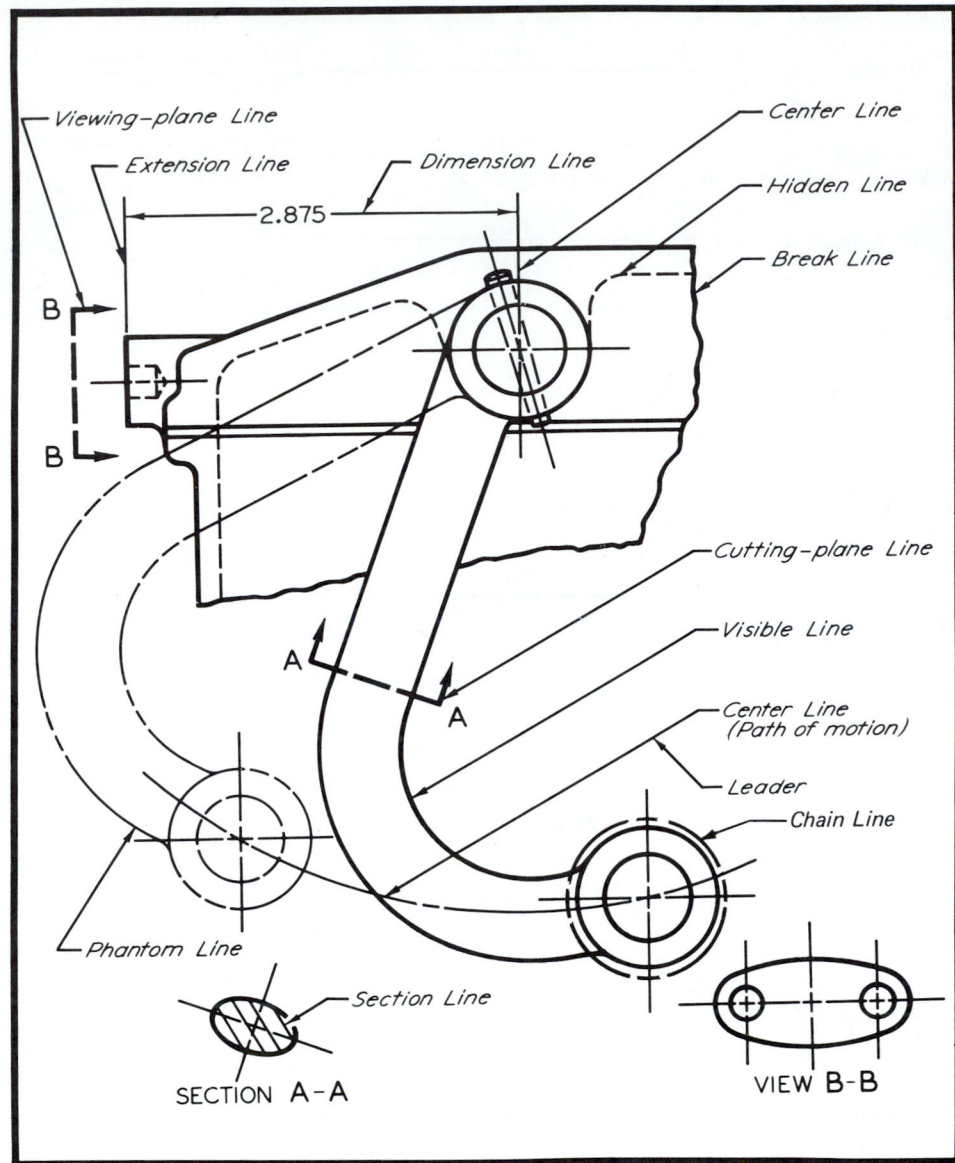

FIGURE 2.56 **Application of Line Types**

approximately .12 in. (3 mm) away from midheight of the note's lettering, either at the beginning or end of the first line. Leaders should not be bent to underline the note or dimension. Unless unavoidable, leaders should not be bent in any way except to form the horizontal terminating bar at the note end of the leader.

Leaders usually do not cross. Leaders or extension lines may cross an outline of a part or extension lines if necessary, but they usually remain continuous and unbroken at the point of intersection. When a leader is directed to a circle or a circular arc, its direction should be radial. Leader lines are drawn the same thickness as centerlines, dimension lines, and extension lines, .12 in. (0.3 mm).

Section Lines Section lines (Figs. 2.55 and 2.56) are thin, uniformly spaced lines that indicate the exposed cut surfaces of a part in a sectional view. Spacing should be approximately .10 in. (3 mm) and at an angle of 45°. The spacing is dependent on the reduction percentage of the drawing. Section lines are drawn slightly thinner than centerlines and dimension lines, .01 in. (0.25 mm) (see Chapter 9).

Phantom Lines Phantom lines (Figs. 2.55 and 2.56) consist of medium-thin, long and short dashes. They are used to indicate alternate positions of moving parts, adjacent positions of related parts, and repeated details. They are also used to show the cast, or the rough shape, of a part before machining. The line starts and ends with the long dash of .60 in. (15 mm) with about .06 in. (1.5 mm) space between the long and short dashes. A phantom line is drawn approximately as thick as a hidden line, .016 in. (0.45 mm). Phantom lines are drawn similar to centerlines except they have two short dashes between each long dash. The short dashes are drawn approximately .12 in. (0.3 mm) or longer depending on the size of the drawing and the reduction requirements. In some cases, as when showing alternative or related positions of parts, or when a part is the *workpiece* on a *jig and fixture* assembly, the phantom line is drawn in *red*.

Cutting Plane Lines and Viewing Plane Lines   Cutting plane lines and viewing plane lines (Figs. 2.55 and 2.56) consist of thick long and short dashes. These lines are used to indicate the location of cutting planes for sectional views and the viewing positions for removed partial views. These lines start and stop with long dashes—.60 in. (15 mm) or longer. The short dashes are approximately .25 in. (6 mm) long, with about .12 in. (3 mm) of space between them. An alternative method uses medium-length [.38 in. (9 mm)] dashed lines for the total cutting plane. Both methods are acceptable. Cutting plane lines are normally drawn with a thickness of about .032 in. (0.70 mm) and are the thickest lines on a drawing (see Chapter 9 on sectioning).

Break Lines   Break lines (Figs. 2.55 and 2.56) are thick, freehand, continuous, ragged lines that are used to limit a broken view, a partial view, or a broken section. For long breaks, where space is limited, a neat break may be made with long, medium thickness, ruled dashes joined by freehand zigzags. For short breaks, the lines are drawn thicker, the same as cutting plane lines, .03 in (0.7 mm). Long break lines are about as thick as hidden lines, .017 in. (0.45 to 0.50 mm) (see Chapter 9).

Construction Lines   Construction lines are used to lay out the part's features and to locate dimensions. They are very thin, light gray lines. Normally 6H–3H grade lead is used for construction lines. In most cases, excess construction lines are erased before the part is darkened. When construction lines are drawn with blue nonreproducible lead they do not require erasing.

2.8.4   Placing the Paper or Drafting Film on the Board

Drafting paper is placed on the board in a position that will allow you to use the drawing tools properly and to be comfortable while drawing. This position is approximately halfway up on the board and near the working edge of the board or centered.

When using a T-square, the working edge of the board is the side against which the head of the T-square rests (normally the left side). With the paper positioned near it, the head of the T-square will make full contact with the working edge of the board in all necessary drawing positions. In addition, the blade of the T-square is slightly flexible and "gives" as pressure is applied when drawing. Placing the paper near the working edge of the board allows the T-square to be used with minimum bending of the blade.

When using a parallel straightedge or a drafting machine, the bottom of the paper is aligned first and the corners are then taped.

Unless standard format preprinted sheets are available, the piece of drawing paper is always about one inch larger in width and height than the size of the final sheet. This excess paper is trimmed off when the sheet is complete. (A completed sheet is called a drawing.)

After it is cut from the roll, the paper is placed on the board with its curl down (unless the paper has a "tooth" side that cannot be reversed) to keep the edges of the paper from being accidentally torn—for instance, by a triangle corner. The paper is square with the board and taped down with small strips of drafting tape—$\frac{1}{2} \times 1$ in. is sufficient, or you can use drafting dots. One-half of each strip of tape is attached to the paper first, and then, after the paper is pulled snug (but not stretched), the tape is pressed onto the drawing board. You can hold the paper in position by laying the straightedge across it and holding the straightedge down with the left arm while taping with the right hand. After the two top corners are taped, the straightedge can be released. Then tape the bottom corners. When properly taped down, the paper clings tightly to the board without wrinkles, loose edges, or signs of stretching. Rubbing the edges of the masking tape with your fingernail will make it stick better and make it less likely to roll up under the straightedge and triangles.

Once the paper is taped in position, trim lines are drawn using a straightedge and triangles (corresponding to a standard drawing format). Upon completion of the drawing, the excess paper is trimmed. The trim lines will be the edges of the completed drawing. Standard sheet sizes do not need trimming.

2.9   Instrument Drawings

Drawings with straight lines that have been drawn with the aid of a T-square, a straightedge, or a drafting machine and triangle are known as **instrument drawings**. These drawings are carefully drawn to an accurate size. Lines of each type are uniform in width and density. The lines begin and end so as to form square corners and intersections.

You should first find the exact center of the sheet by drawing diagonals (connecting opposite corners). This will help center the work on a layout drawing.

Drafting a line in an instrument drawing is a two-step process that requires two different kinds of lines to be drawn. First, the position and the length of the line are determined, and then the line is drawn with correct width and density. The first line, for positioning, is drawn thin and light gray and is called a **construction line.** You may prefer to lay out your work with a blue nonreproducible lead. After the line's position has been verified and its length measured (Fig. 2.57) and marked, a second line is drawn exactly over the first line. This second line is drawn dense and uniform and is called a **printable line.** The part or project being drawn is completely blocked-in (laid out) before darkening any lines.

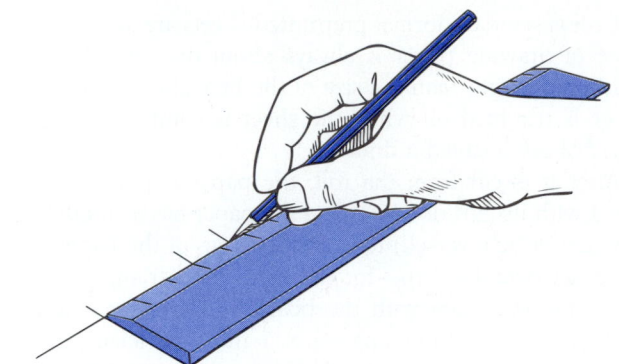

FIGURE 2.57 Measuring with a Scale

Construction lines are used to construct or lay out the drawing. Construction lines may extend somewhat beyond corners and intersections of the part's outline. Construction lines are thin and gray, and they are cleaned up after the drawing is complete if they will print. Blue nonreproducible lines do not require erasing since they will not reproduce when the drawing is printed using a whiteprint machine. Printable lines are drawn using a 2H, H, or HB lead and are drawn with different widths to show different kinds of information.

Unless company (or school) practice allows construction lines to remain on the finished drawing, any extra lines used for construction purposes are erased before the drawing is darkened. Ask your instructor which method to follow before you complete a project.

2.9.1 Techniques for Drawing Lines

All drafters use triangles and/or some form of straightedge. Vertical lines are constructed with a straightedge and triangle or a drafting machine. Horizontal lines are drawn with a straightedge that will give consistent parallel lines. Curved lines are drawn with a compass, a template, or an irregular curve. Lines are not formed freehand. Only lettering is drawn freehand.

A properly drawn line is uniform for its entire length. When using a wood pencil or a lead holder, you can make a line consistent in two ways:

1. Incline the pencil or the lead holder so that it makes an angle of about 60° with the surface of the paper, and then pull it in the direction in which it is leaning (Fig. 2.58). Keep the pencil at a consistent angle as you draw the line.
2. Rotate the pencil or the lead holder slowly as the line is drawn to maintain a semisharp conical point. This will enable you to control the thickness and the quality of the line.

These techniques take practice but will soon become automatic. Your lines will be uniform from end to end and from one line to another. Fine-line pencils are held straight (vertical to the board) instead of at an angle and usually do not need to be rotated.

Since most drawings are reduced or enlarged, the correct use of line weights and line techniques is essential. Since even

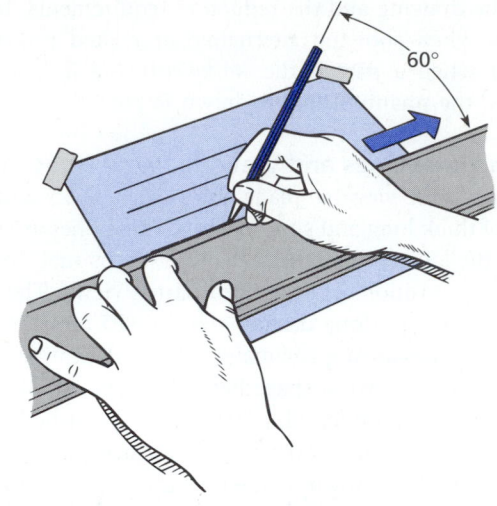

(a)

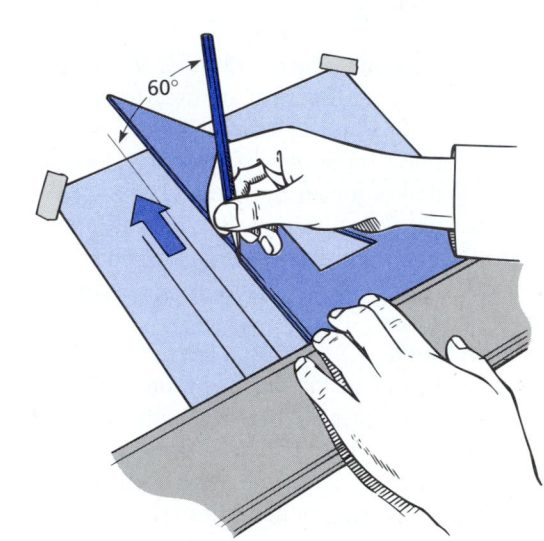

(b)

FIGURE 2.58 Angling the Pencil While Drawing

the smallest mistake can be magnified, special care must be taken on drawings that are to be enlarged. In other words, the mistake will also be enlarged. On drawings that are to be reduced—for example, printed circuit artwork drawings that are normally drawn at 2:1 or 4:1 enlargements—reduction will clean up and minimize any small problems. However, accuracy is still important regardless of the scale that is used. Do not rely on reduction to hide any poorly constructed areas of your drawing.

How well lines print is determined by their density—that is, their ability to block light. Density is controlled by the hardness/softness of the lead and by the pressure applied while the line is being drawn. The width and the sharpness of the line are determined by the size of the point touching the paper. A sharpened pencil point should be smoothed and rounded on scratch paper after being repointed. It can also be resharpened on scratch paper. Uniform lines require uniform point preparation.

Fine-line lead holders are available in different lead thicknesses. A 0.5 and 0.7 mm lead holder with H or 2H leads are good for lettering and linework. Construction lines can be drawn with 0.3 and 0.4 mm fine-line pencils with 3H or 6H leads or nonreproducible blue leads. These instruments require no sharpening and help maintain a high-quality consistently uniform line.

Construction lines are drawn with the greatest accuracy possible. To achieve accuracy, place the pencil point on the paper where the line is to be drawn. Then carefully move the straightedge or triangle up to it so as to just touch the pencil point without moving it. Draw a construction line with the pencil point riding along the top edge of the straightedge. Tilt the pencil slightly away from the straightedge. Always pull the pencil; do not push it, except when using a fine-line pencil.

2.9.2   Pencil Position for Printable Lines

Once the lines, corners, and intersections have been positioned and verified using construction lines, the figure must be redrawn using printable lines. These lines are drawn exactly over the construction lines even though they will not extend the full length of the construction lines. Printable lines will make sharp corners and intersections.

Drawing one line exactly over another is not difficult if the proper technique is used. Let the pencil lead ride along the top edge of the straightedge (or triangle) by tilting the pencil slightly toward the straightedge. This will move the point slightly away from the straightedge so that both edges of the line are visible as it is being drawn. Also, the construction line is completely visible ahead of the point, so it is easy to see that it has been completely covered by the printable line. It is usually necessary to go over a printable line a couple of times in order to build up enough density to make sharp clear prints. Again, the wood pencil and the lead holder are pulled (never pushed—it may tear the paper). A consistent line width is maintained by touching up the lead point as often as necessary.

Drawing a straight line while guiding the lead along the top edge of the straightedge requires practice and technique. First, if the point is to stay the same distance from the straightedge as it is being rotated, the pencil point must be prepared with a smooth cone shape—no flat spots. Second, the angle that the pencil tilts over the straightedge, as seen when viewed parallel to the straightedge, must be kept uniform by proper wrist and arm action. This technique will become automatic with a little practice.

2.9.3   Drawing Horizontal Lines

Horizontal lines are drawn with the T-square, the parallel bar, or the drafting machine. Place the pencil point at the desired position of the horizontal line and move the straightedge up to the point, just touching it. When the straightedge is positioned, hold it with the free hand and forearm. This will minimize the deflection of the blade (when using the T-square or a drafting machine) as the line is drawn. Using

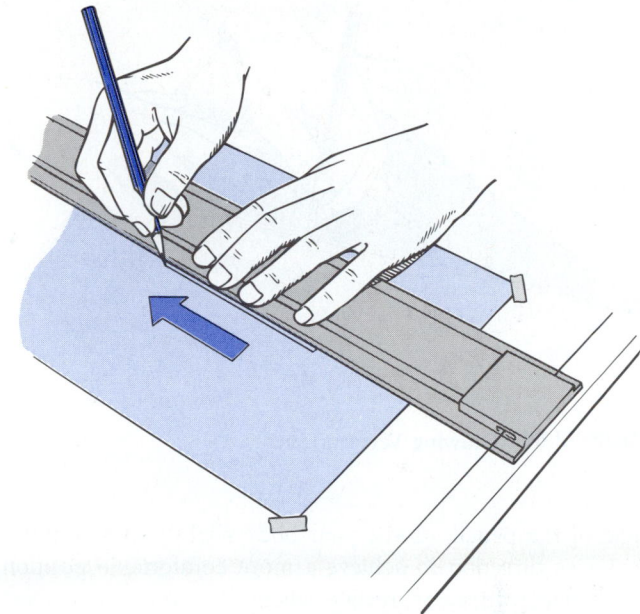

FIGURE 2.59   Drawing Horizontal Lines

the techniques that have been previously discussed, draw the line from left to right (Fig. 2.59). Horizontal lines are always drawn along the top edge of the straightedge. This places the straightedge between the hand and the paper and helps keep the drawing clean.

As any line is drawn, some graphite "chalks" off the point and lies as dust on the drawing. To avoid smearing this graphite dust, frequently blow or brush the dust off the drawing. Always use a drafting brush, never your hand. Graphite dust is the source of almost all "dirt" on drawings. All drawing equipment is lifted from the board before being moved. If you drag the equipment or instruments across the drawing you will smear the linework and dirty the drawing. Keep the board, your hands, equipment, and instruments clean to minimize smearing your linework.

2.9.4   Drawing Vertical Lines

Vertical lines are drawn with the vertical edge of any triangle (or the vertical scale of the drafting machine). Position the straightedge and the triangle at the desired spot with the vertical edge of the triangle to the left (Fig. 2.60). Then place the pencil point at the desired position of the vertical line and move the triangle up to the point, just touching it. This is done by holding the straightedge with the left hand and forearm and positioning the triangle with the fingers of the left hand (reverse this process if you are left-handed). Draw the line from bottom to top using the construction line or printable line technique.

Vertical lines are usually drawn with an upward motion along the left edge of the triangle. This places the triangle between the hand and the paper and helps keep the drawing clean. When drawing a construction line, change only the

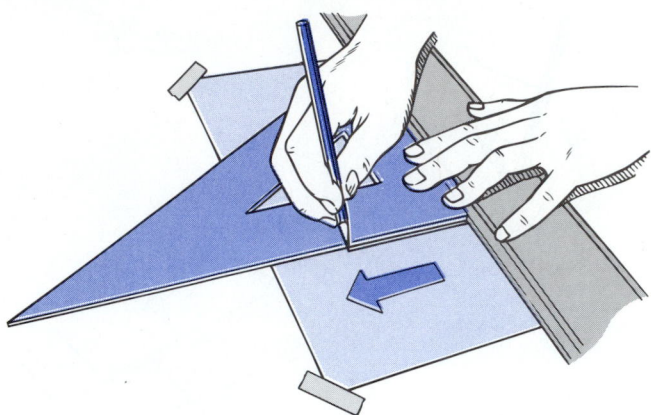

FIGURE 2.60   Drawing Vertical Lines

angle of the pencil. (Twist your body slightly in a counter-clockwise direction to achieve a more comfortable position for printable lines.) In reality, when it is convenient, most drafters will use this method. They will also draw on the right side of the triangle, pulling the pencil toward them. The goal is a clean, accurate, and quickly constructed drawing. Your method of achieving this may differ slightly.

2.9.5   Drawing Sloping Lines

Sloping lines are drawn much like vertical lines except that the sloping edge of the triangle, adjustable triangle, or drafting machine is used. Lines that slope toward the upper right corner of the board are easily drawn. Sloping lines must first be accurately measured and laid out with construction lines. Check the angle with a protractor before darkening.

2.9.6   Drawing Curved Lines

Arcs, **circles**, and other **curved lines** require special line-work techniques. The compass lead is fixed in the compass and cannot be rotated, therefore it requires frequent repointing. Noncircular curves are drawn with a **French curve** or **irregular curve** (Fig. 2.34) or a **flexible curve** as a guide, but the guide fits the curve only for a short distance. Moreover, curves must be drawn equal in width to the straight lines to produce a uniform drawing.

The use of the compass and the irregular curve to create dark, consistent linework is typically one of the most frustrating aspects of mastering drafting. Circle, ellipse, and other curved templates are available in standard sizes. These excellent tools can be used for many constructions, though they are somewhat limited in sizes and shapes and are relatively expensive if you need to purchase more than a few. You should wait to practice curves with templates until you have mastered the compass and the irregular curve.

2.9.7   Using the Bow Compass

As mentioned in the section on instruments, the compass lead in a bow compass should be a short piece of the *same lead* used in the drafting pencil. The lead that comes with the compass is usually unsatisfactory and should be discarded. By using the same lead, both straight and curved lines will be drawn uniformly. Recall that the lead is secured in the compass with about $\frac{3}{8}$ in. (0.9 mm) exposed, and it is sharpened with a sandpaper pad (Fig. 2.43). (Remember, sandpaper pads are very messy and should be kept off of the drawing board and in a plastic bag.) Care should be used in sharpening the lead to keep the line through the point and the lead perpendicular to the sandpaper and to make a flat cut that gives an oval surface. This surface should be about three times as long as the diameter of the lead. The sides of this oval can be lightly sanded. When viewed from the side, the resulting "point" is chisel shaped and should have about the same taper as the cone-shaped taper of the drafting pencil. Because it is almost impossible to reposition the chisel shape properly, the lead in the compass is not adjusted after it has been sharpened. The chisel point should be touched up on scratch paper, and the centering point should be adjusted so that the midpoint of the needle point portion is even with the end of the lead. This adjustment assures that the point makes proper contact with the paper. The compass can now be adjusted to the required radius and used to draw an arc or a circle.

On a construction line drawn on scratch paper, a distance equal to the radius of the circle or arc to be drawn is measured. The compass is set to this distance and a construction circle is drawn. When the diameter of the circle is measured, the reading should be twice that of the given radius. To get an accurate diameter reading, the measurement must be taken along a line that passes through the center point of the circle (Fig. 2.61). Any difference between the measured diameter and twice the given radius is twice the error of the compass setting. In Figure 2.62, the compass is being set by using the scale. This is not the easiest or most accurate method, but it is faster.

The width of the line drawn is determined by the thickness of the lead at the bevel. As a circle is drawn, the point shortens and the line widens. Therefore, a circle is started with a line somewhat narrower than desired. The line is redrawn until it is the correct width and density. A longer taper will hold a line width longer than a short stubby taper.

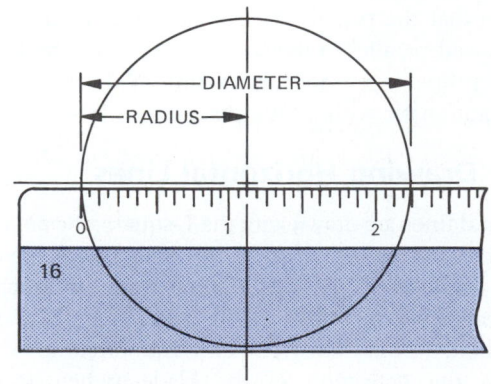

FIGURE 2.61   Measuring a Circle

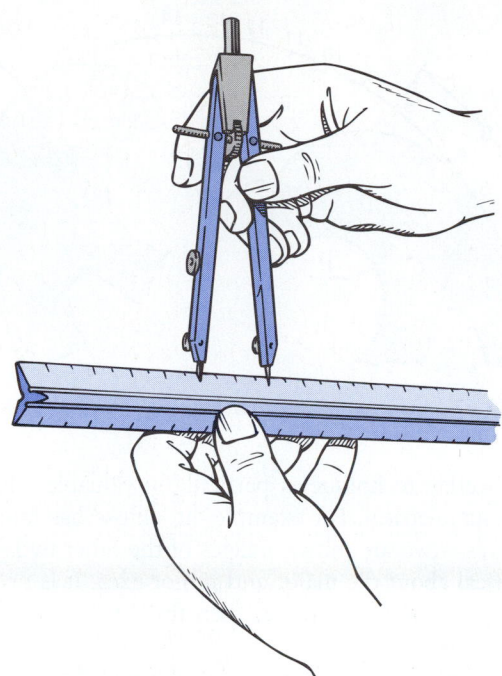

FIGURE 2.62   Setting the Compass Radius

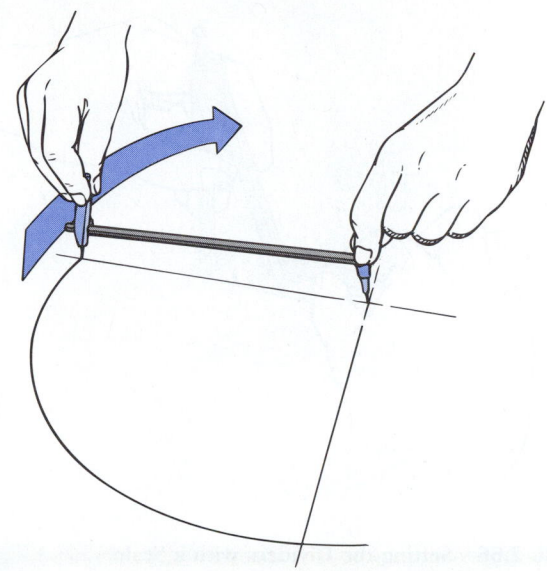

FIGURE 2.64   Using the Beam Compass

2.9.8   Using Dividers

Dividers are used to transfer dimensions and measurements. Dividers are not used to set off distances when cumulative errors could result. The scale is used to measure divisions in these cases.

Figure 2.65 provides an example of how to use dividers. Dividers are held, adjusted, and manipulated with one hand. Measurements can be taken from an existing view or from a scale (Fig. 2.66). Dividers are one of the most important instruments for quick construction of accurate drawings and are essential for solving descriptive geometry problems.

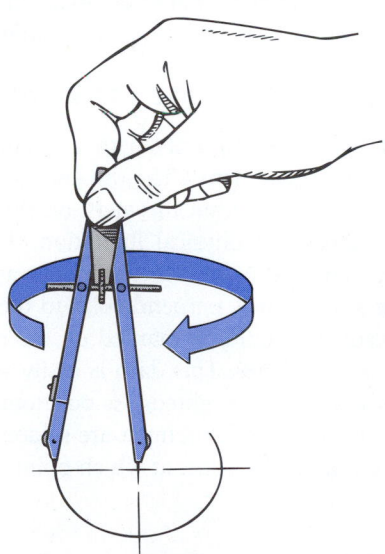

FIGURE 2.63   Using the Bow Compass

Figure 2.63 shows the proper method of constructing a circle with a **bow compass.** First, draw the circle with a thin dark line. Then thicken it by resetting the radius slightly and drawing another curve touching the first one. This method ensures crisp black lines with the appropriate thickness. Of course, this method is of no use for drawing a hidden (dashed) line. Dashed curves are drawn with a slightly dulled compass lead point and only one pass to complete the circle.

The **beam compass** (Fig. 2.64) is used when a large-diameter circle or arc is required. Both hands are required to draw a circle with this instrument.

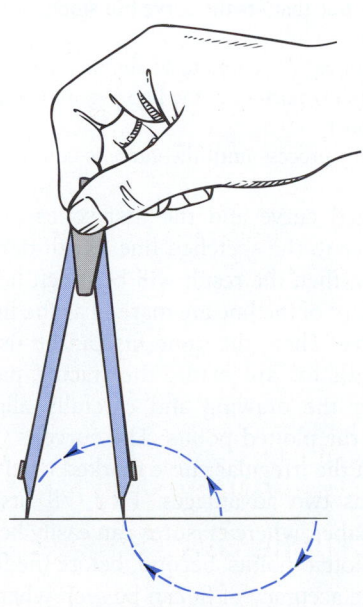

FIGURE 2.65   Using the Dividers

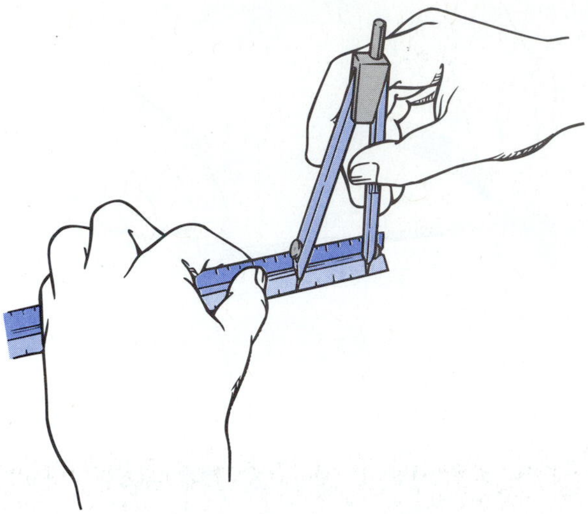

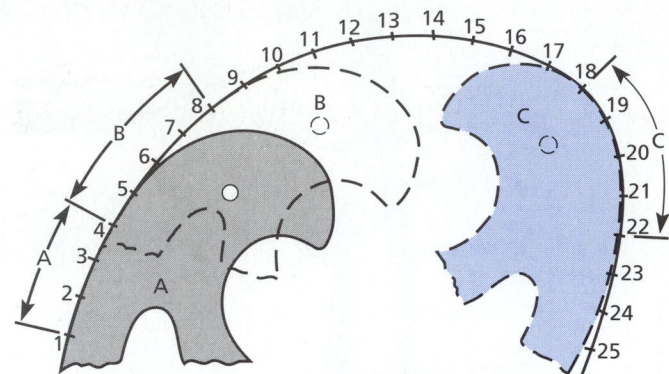

FIGURE 2.66   Setting the Dividers with a Scale

2.9.9   Using the Irregular Curve

Noncircular curves require the use of the **irregular curve** (Fig. 2.34) to make smooth printable lines. Examples of such curves are the ellipse—an angular view of a circle—the helix, and spirals. Irregular curves are manufactured in many shapes and sizes.

Curves that are drawn using the irregular curve are usually determined by first plotting a series of points that are known to lie on the curve. Then, a curve is drawn that includes all of these points. Figure 2.67 illustrates the use of the irregular curve. Good results can be obtained by following these steps:

1. Lightly sketch a smooth line freehand to include the plotted points. It is easier to set the irregular curve to a line than it is to match a series of points.
2. Set the irregular curve so that it matches a part of the line.
3. Draw the line that fits the curve but stop a little before the end of the fit.
4. Reset the irregular curve to fit the next part of the curve and draw the next portion of the line. Again, the last portion of fit is not drawn.
5. Repeat this process until the curve is complete.

If the sketched curve and the first series of matching the irregular curve to the sketched line are all done on a tracing paper overlay, then the result will be much neater. The ends of each segment of the line are marked as the line matches the irregular curve. Then, the same fits can be used in the next step. When all fits are made, the tracing paper overlay is placed under the drawing and carefully aligned with the curve under the plotted points. The curve is traced onto the drawing with the irregular curve marked on the overlay. This technique has two advantages. First, all fits are made on throwaway paper, where erasures can easily be made without erasing the plotted points. Second, before the final drawing of the curve, the accuracy of fit can be seen when the overlay is positioned under the drawing.

FIGURE 2.67   Using the Irregular Curve

The overlay technique is particularly valuable when the curve is symmetrical. For example, an ellipse has four identical curves—two are mirror images of the other two. All are symmetrical about the major and minor axes. It is necessary to fit only one of these curves, then this fit is duplicated on the other three.

If a smooth curve is desired, the plotting of the points of an irregular curve is particularly important. A small error in the position of a point can easily cause irregularities in the curve. The spacing of plotted points should be small where the curve is sharpest and long where the curve is the straightest.

2.9.10   Making Accurate Measurements

Accurate drafting is possible only with accurate use of the scale in marking measurements. The thickness of the edge of the scale and the distance from the mark on the scale to the surface of the paper is a physical limitation of your scale's accuracy. The most accurate measurements are made by sighting along a line that is perpendicular to the paper.

All scale readings should be marked on the paper with a short, thin dash (Fig. 2.68). This dash is easily seen after the scale is removed and the straightedge is positioned to use the measurement. Errors in measurement are seldom discovered until much work has been done, at which point the only way

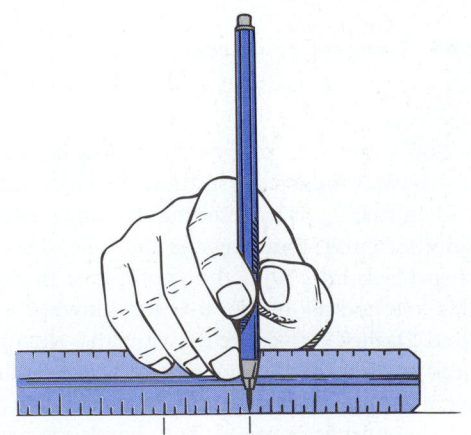

FIGURE 2.68   Measurements with a Scale

ITEMS OF INTEREST

Reproduction Equipment

You have probably heard the term *blueprint* to describe an engineering drawing. Blueprinting is a reproduction technique that was, for many years, the only way to duplicate engineering drawings. It is a photographic process in which the original drawing is the negative. The paper for the duplicate print is treated with chemicals that are sensitive to light. After the paper is exposed, it passes through a developing or fixing bath and is then rinsed and dried. The end product is a print (the same size) with blue background paper and white lines.

As more and more engineering drawings were created, it became evident that a new reproduction process that was fast, exact, cost effective, and simple was needed. Considering the number of hours invested in engineering drawings, it seems reasonable that people would also invest many hours trying to create the best reproduction process for those valuable drawings.

The *diazo process* was the answer. This process produces a positive print with dark lines on a white background. Light is transmitted through the original onto chemically treated paper. Developing is completed by one of three processes: dry (utilizing an ammonia vapor), moist, (transferring an ammonia solution to the print), or pressure (a thin film of activator is deposited on the exposed paper). You can easily read marks and notations made directly on the print with this method. Unfortunately, the prints soil easily and the life of a print is relatively short.

The next evolution in reproduction equipment was developed from an idea that originated in 1937. In 1937, a young

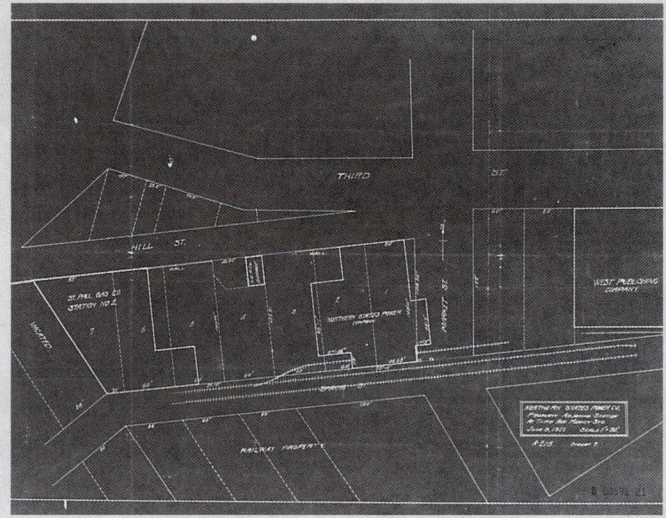

Early Reproduction Processes (Blueprint)

law student named Chester Carlson developed a method called *xerography* to make copies. (The word *xerography* comes from the Greek words for "dry" and "writing.") A copy made by this method became known as a Xerox. No doubt you have also heard of Xerox, the company that developed and marketed this process throughout the world. Of course, it was only a matter of time until reproduction equipment was made large enough for copying drawings. This process can produce a copy not only from an original, but also from a copy. Enlarged or reduced size copies are also possible.

Today, a copy of a computer-generated drawing can be produced with a laser printer/plotter. A laser plotter uses a laser to form areas of static charge to attract metallic powder to the paper. The process

produces sharp, clear prints, is extremely fast, and is inexpensive enough to be used in small engineering offices. Laser printers have become an integral part of the engineering workplace.

When you walk into an engineering firm today, you could see a diazo print, a Xerox print, or a print produced with a laser plotter. Regardless of the method used to produce the print, many engineers, designers, and drafters ask for a "blueprint" of the latest product or assembly even though blue paper with white lines hasn't been around for many years.

Whatever the next evolution is in reproduction equipment, it will probably be faster, more accurate, easier to use, and more economical—just like all the other versions—yet whatever process we use, we will probably call the print a "blueprint."

---

to correct them is to erase and redraw. Measurements put down as dots are too often lost, and many incorrect lines have been drawn from specks of dust.

If a number of measurements are to be put down end-to-end, all of them should be measured from the same point. If the measurements are put down by moving the scale for each measurement to the end of the previous one, an accumulation of errors may result in a large error. Remember, a series of successive dimensions is equal to the dimensions' arithmetic total and must be drawn that way.

2.9.11   Keeping Your Drawings Clean

All drawings attract dirt. How much dirt is determined by your habits as a drafter. Cleanliness does not just happen, it is the result of developing correct habits. Procedures and techniques that will keep your drawings clean include the following:

1. **Clean hands**   Periodically wash your hands to remove accumulations of graphite, perspiration, body oils, and dirt.
2. **Equipment**   Periodically wash with soap and water all tools that

touch the paper. Tools that contain wood or metal should be cleaned with a damp sponge. When they become soiled, they must also be scrubbed. The drawing surface should be cleaned regularly.

3. **Graphite**   Most dirt on a drawing is actually graphite. Repeated and consistent use of the drafting brush and the dust pad to remove this graphite dust, before other tools smear it around, will contribute significantly to cleaner drawings. Always brush after erasing.

4. **Pencil pointer**   The pencil pointer leaves dust clinging to the lead. Some pointers also push shavings up into the pencil's jaws. If the dust and the shavings are not removed before drawing starts, they will drop onto the drawing. Thus, after each sharpening, lightly tap the pencil on the side of the desk to dislodge any shavings and then wipe the lead on a piece of tissue. Poking the lead point into a piece of Styrofoam also works well.

5. **Equipment use**   Proper use of the straightedge and triangle always places these instruments between your hands and the paper. Even clean hands will put body oils onto the paper; this has a magnetic effect on dirt. When lettering, place a sheet of clean paper under your hands to keep the drawing cleaner.

2.9.12   Inking Drawings

Ink is frequently used on drafting film or vellum. Drawings used in product literature, technical manuals, and pictorial illustrations are normally inked to get good photographic quality (all drawings in this text are ink drawings).

Ink drawings must first be laid out with construction lines and then inked. It is very difficult to ink a drawing while laying it out. Light tables are excellent for inking and tracing drawings. Because ink tends to flow between surfaces and to smear lines, triangles and templates must be raised from the drawing when inking a line. Specially designed equipment with a ledge or with inking risers prevents the equipment from being flush with the paper.

Ink drawings are prepared with technical pens. Keeping the technical pen almost vertical helps prevent uneven and

ragged linework (Fig. 2.69). If possible, no more than one pass should be made for thin and medium lines. Extremely thick lines are drawn with an appropriate pen size. If a thinner pen is used to thicken the line in stages, better results may be obtained.

The ink should be completely dry before you start another portion of the drawing. Some drafters prefer to ink all horizontal lines from the top of the sheet downward and then from left to right. Ink lines should be erased very carefully, especially on vellum or other types of paper. You can easily erase ink from drafting film with the proper type of eraser and a small amount of moisture. As in pencil drawings, the surrounding lines should be protected while erasing.

You May Complete Exercises 2.1 Through 2.12 at This Time

QUIZ

True or False

1. Plastic leads are used on vellum.
2. 5H and 6H leads are used to darken the final drawing.
3. Construction lines drawn with blue nonreproducible lead do not require erasing before the drawing is darkened.
4. The title block is always placed in the lower left-hand corner of the sheet.
5. Hidden lines always take precedence over centerlines.
6. Object lines are thin, black, and approximately 0.35 mm.
7. Break lines are normally drawn freehand.
8. A dry cleaning pad is used to remove graphite from a newly sharpened pencil.

Fill in the Blanks

9. A sandpaper pad is used to _____ .
10. Dry cleaning pads are used to _____ and _____ a drawing.
11. An architect's scale is _____ divided.
12. _____ and _____ curves are used to draw odd-sized circular curves and arcs.
13. Technical pens should be held _____ .
14. A mechanical engineer's scale is _____ divided.
15. Always draw on the _____ side of the straightedge.
16. Incline lead holders at _____ degrees to the drafting board when drawing.

Answer the Following

17. Describe the process of drawing a vertical instrument line.
18. Describe three ways to keep your drawing clean.
19. Explain how to sharpen and prepare a wooden pencil for drawing an instrument line.
20. Describe the process of drawing an irregular curve.
21. Describe the two primary types of drawing media used in drafting.
22. What does the term *precedence of lines* mean?
23. What line widths are used on a drafting format and title block?
24. Name five types of information included in a title block.

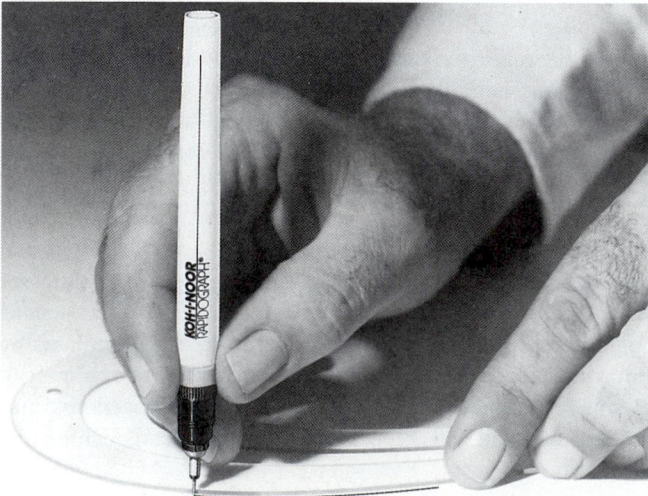

FIGURE 2.69   **Inking with a Technical Pen and an Irregular Curve**

EXERCISES

Transfer the given information to an "A" size sheet of .25 in. grid paper. Complete all views and solve for proper visibility, including centerlines, object lines, and hidden lines. Exercises that are not assigned by the instructor can be sketched in the text to provide practice and understanding for the preceding instructional material.

After Completing the Chapter You May Draw the Assigned Exercises

Exercise 2.1 Draw the given design as shown.

Exercise 2.2 Draw the cover plate as shown.

Exercise 2.3 Draw the gage plate as shown.

Exercise 2.4 Draw the design as shown.

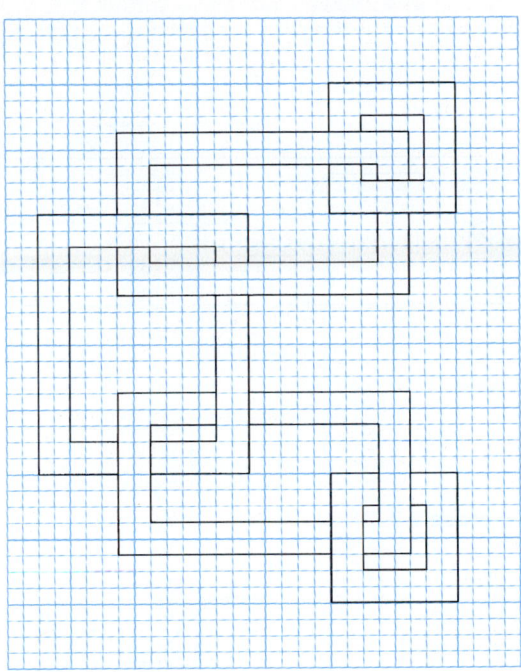

Exercise 2.1

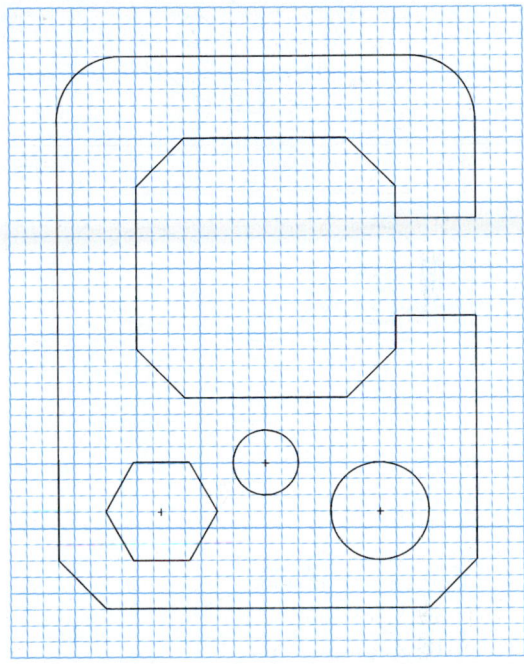

Exercise 2.3

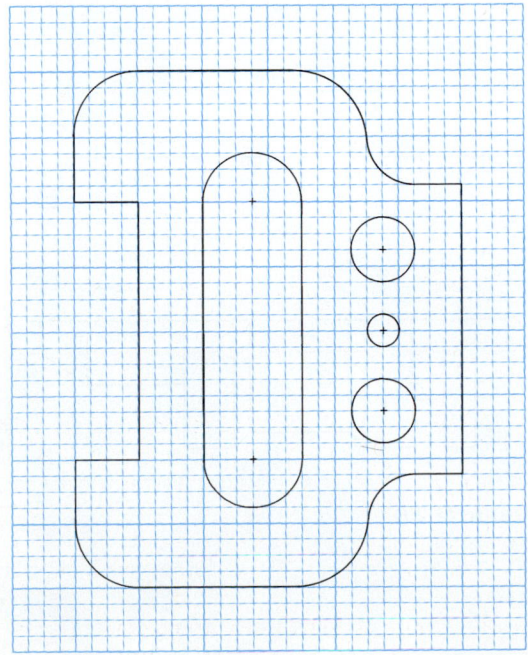

Exercise 2.2

Exercise 2.4

Exercise 2.5   Draw the two gaskets as shown.

Exercise 2.6   Draw the two cover plates as shown.

Exercise 2.7   Draw the complete cone check and guide.

Exercise 2.8   Draw the two guides.

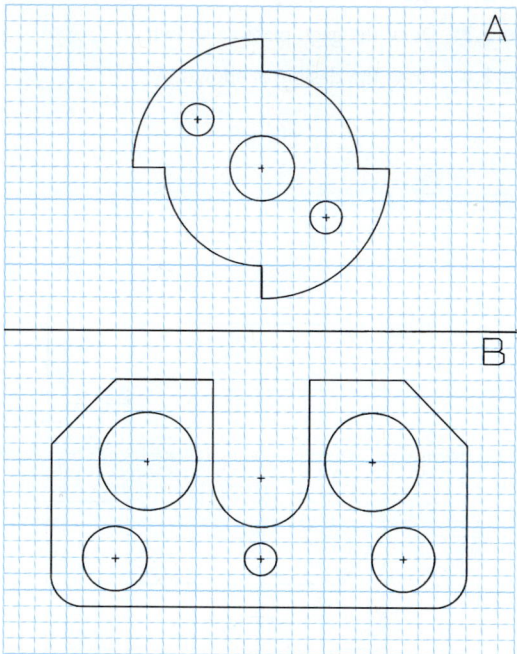

Exercise 2.5

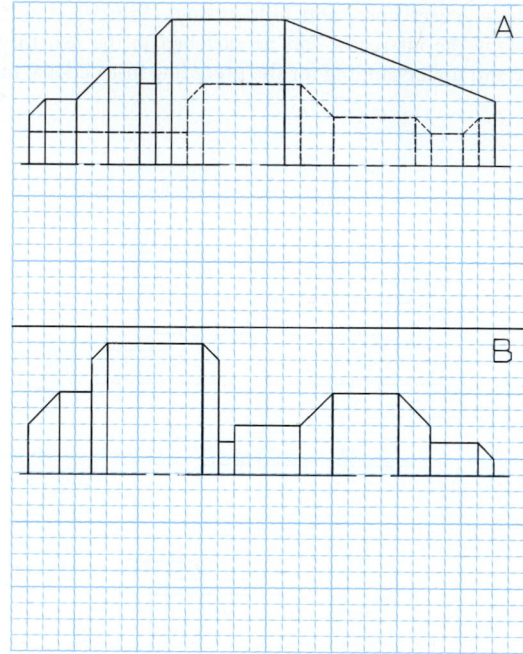

Exercise 2.7

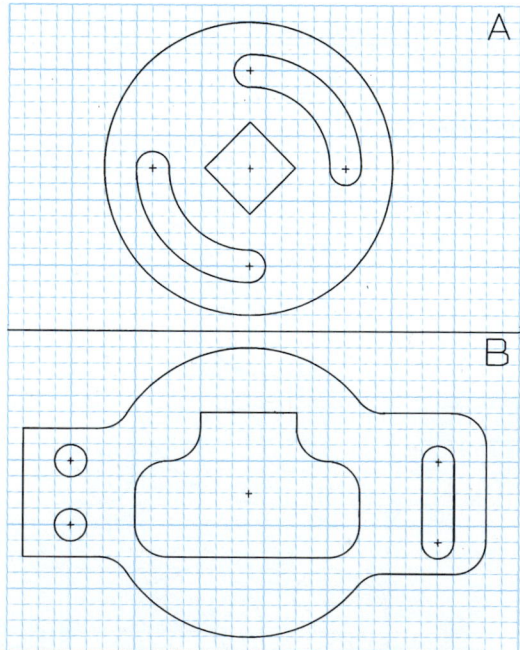

Exercise 2.6

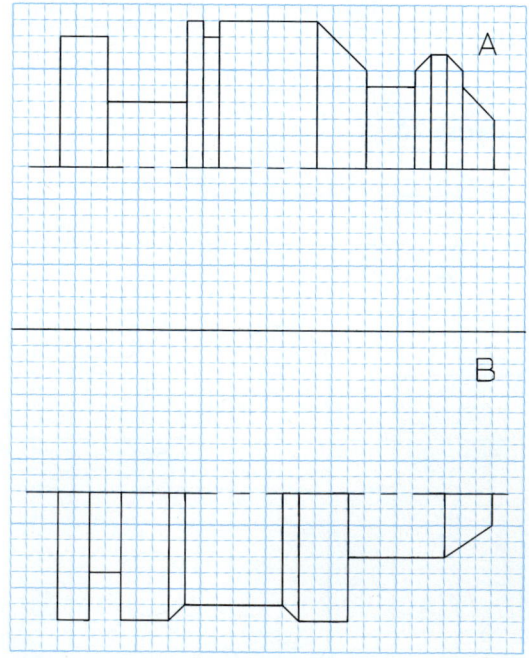

Exercise 2.8

Exercise 2.9   Draw the control plate as shown.

Exercise 2.10   Draw the disk guide as shown.

Exercise 2.11   Draw the mount surface as shown.

Exercise 2.12   Draw the tube gasket as shown.

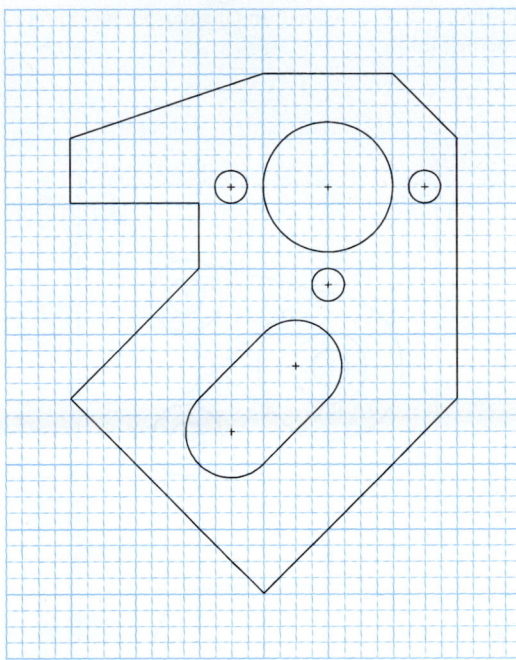

Exercise 2.9

Exercise 2.11

Exercise 2.10

Exercise 2.12

PROBLEMS

Problems 2.1(A) Through (K) Draw each problem assigned by the instructor on an "A" size sheet, one drawing per sheet. Establish measurements by using one of the three scales provided. Your instructor may request enlarged or reduced drawings as needed.

Problem 2.2 An "A" size drawing format is called for in this project. Redraw the object as shown at the top of page 55. Do not dimension.

Problem 2.3 Using a "B" size sheet, redraw the part on page 55. This is an ISO standard drawing using metric dimensions (millimeters). Do not dimension.

Problem 2.4 Using a "C" size sheet, draw the part as shown on page 56. Dimension only if assigned by the instructor. (This project is difficult; information contained in Chapter 5 concerning tangent arcs may be helpful.)

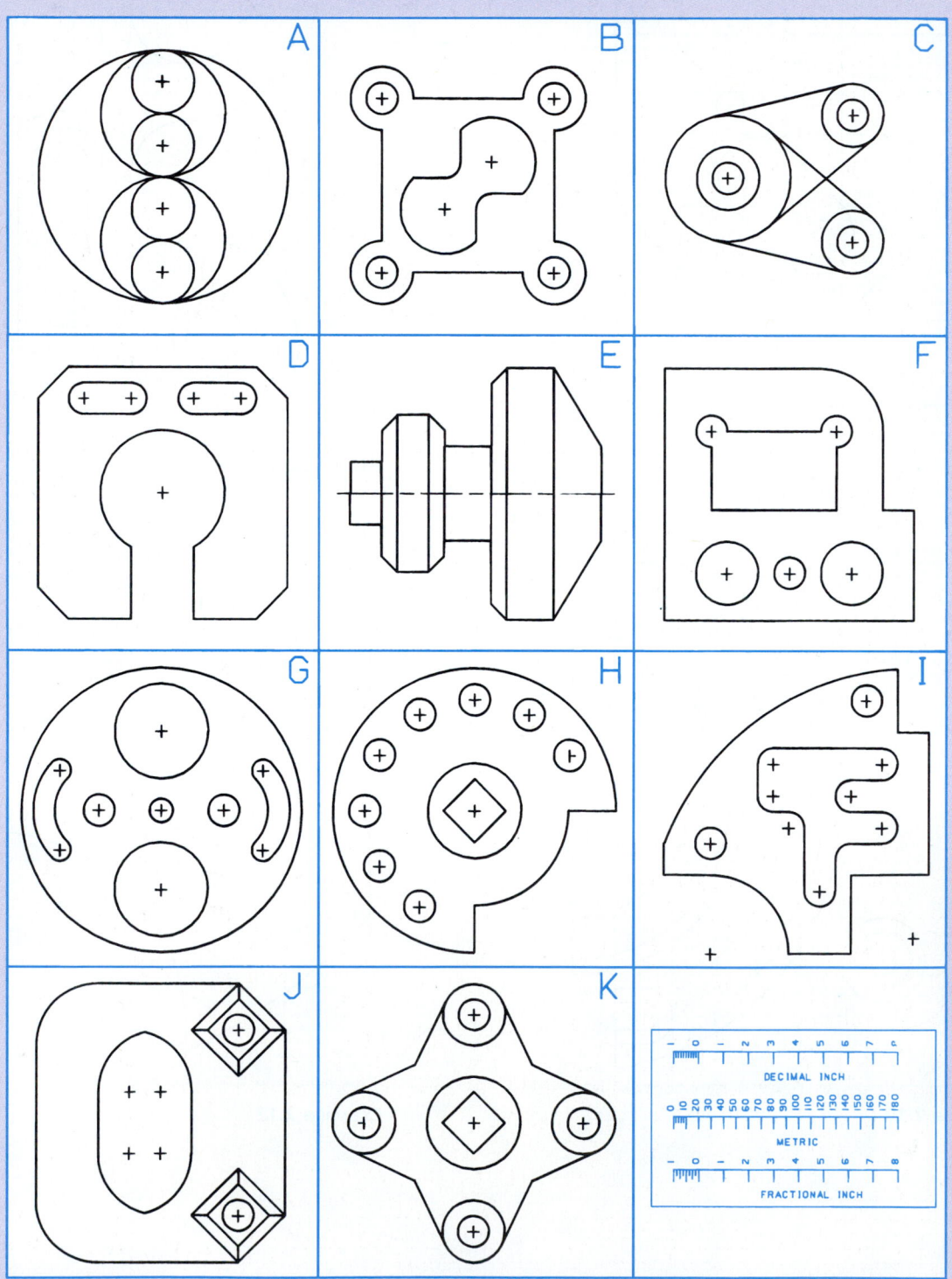

Problem 2.1

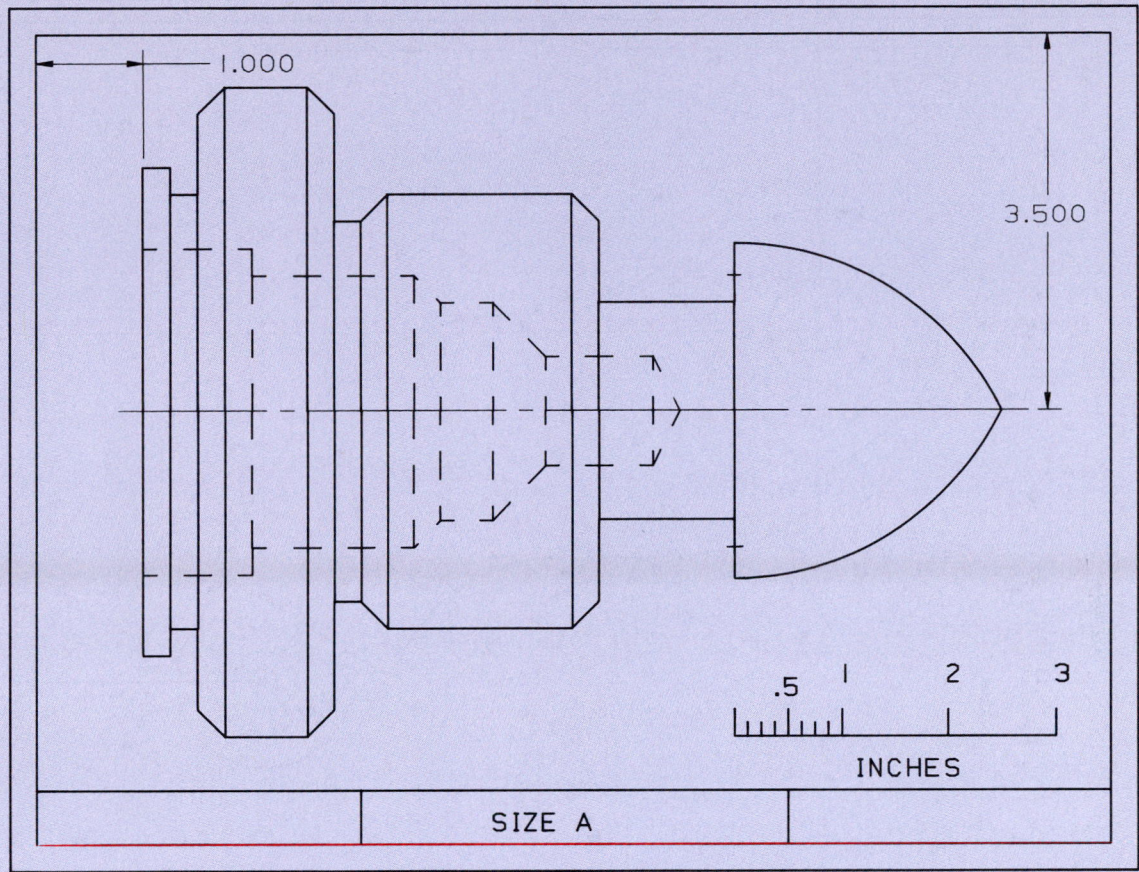

Problem 2.2 Cone Check

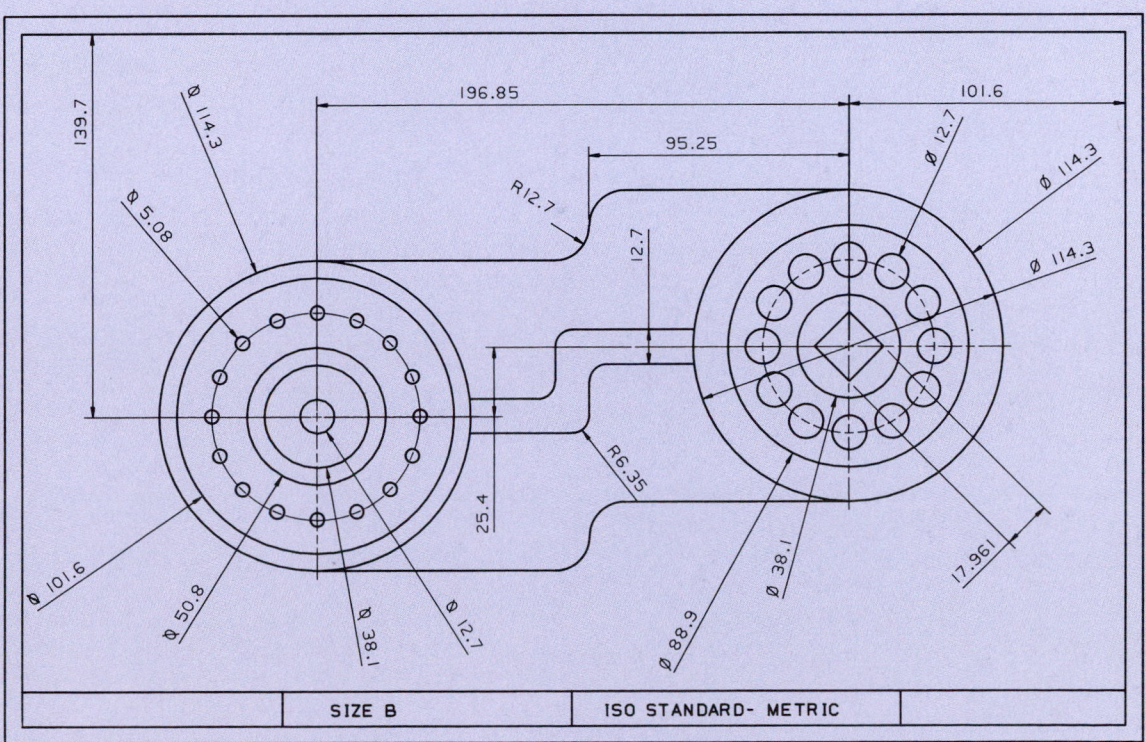

Problem 2.3 Assembly Plate

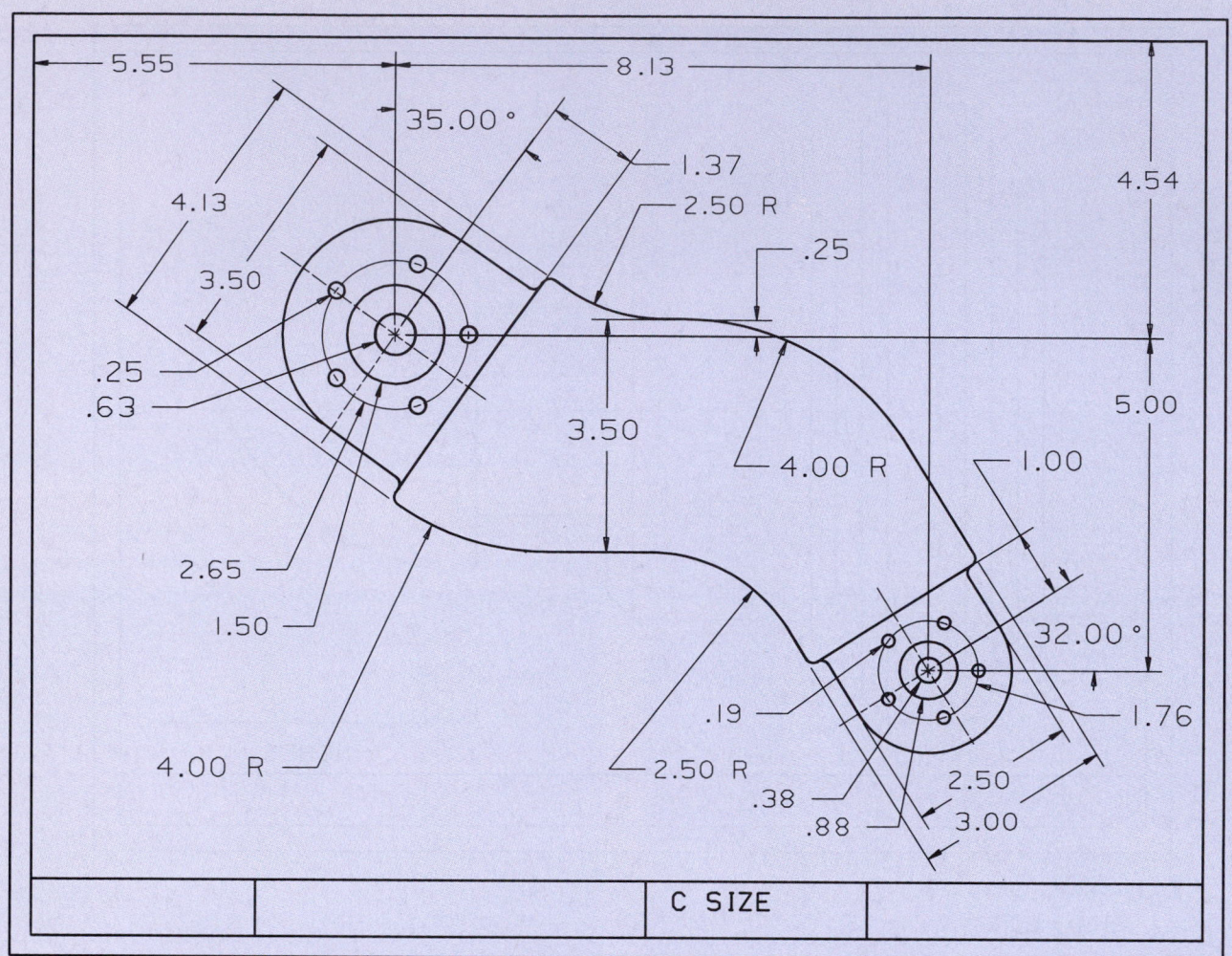

Problem 2.4 Arm

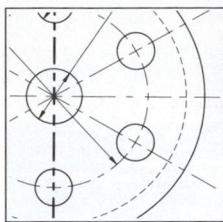

CHAPTER 3

Computers in the Design and Manufacturing Process

Learning Objectives

Upon completion of this chapter you will be able to accomplish the following:

1. Recognize the significance of computer-integrated manufacturing (CIM) in modern production.
2. Define CAD/CAM hardware and software as well as their respective configurations and capabilities.
3. Differentiate between ROM and RAM.
4. Demonstrate an understanding of how data is stored on magnetic disk, magnetic tape, or on the computer itself.
5. Identify the components of a CAD workstation and their functions.
6. Develop a broad concept of applications software.
7. Demonstrate knowledge of computer numerical control (CNC) part programming and robotic integration into the manufacturing production process.

3.1 Introduction

Anyone wishing to enter industry as a drafter, designer, or engineer must be familiar with how the computer is profoundly altering the factory floor and the engineering office (Fig. 3.1). **Computer-aided engineering (CAE), computer-aided manufacturing (CAM),** and **computer-aided design** and drafting **(CAD)** are collectively called **computer integrated manufacturing (CIM).** CIM refers to the integration of all phases of production, from design to manufacturing, using the computer. The term **CAD/CAM** refers to the use of computers to integrate the design and production process to improve productivity. CAM includes **computer numerical control (CNC)** machining (Fig. 3.2) and the integration of *robotics* in manufacturing and production.

As we move into the 1990s, the role of CAM in a CAD/CAM environment takes on increased importance, especially as an integrator in helping firms achieve the benefits of

FIGURE 3.1 Design and Engineering Office

FIGURE 3.2 CNC Machining Center

computer-integrated manufacturing. The CIM concept encompasses many manufacturing, computer-based automation applications. CIM can be thought of as a closed-loop feedback system whose primary inputs are product requirements and whose primary outputs are finished products. CIM is comprised of a combination of software and hardware for product design, production planning/control, and manufacturing processes.

CAD/CAM is the primary CIM integrator for computer-based applications in manufacturing. CAD/CAM's integration ability rests on a foundation of common engineering and manufacturing information. This allows engineering to define a part model (Fig. 3.3) and manufacturing to use that same definition to produce the product.

Product design simplification and other factory simplifications such as **just-in-time (JIT)** programs are normally completed before large-scale integration is used in a company. JIT programs are developed to bring the correct part or material to the appropriate place at the required time. This eliminates excessive and costly warehousing of material and parts and streamlines the production and materials/parts handling process. JIT programs depend on parts standardization. The fewer the part variations and types of parts, the simpler the flow of material and parts within the factory. JIT programs therefore reduce the **work-in-progress (WIP)** inventory. This is why **design for manufacturability (DFM)** is usually the first step when initiating a CIM program. DFM simplifies designs, reduces the number of part types, and therefore streamlines the flow of parts in a factory. The method of design determines how well the design fits into a CIM environment. CAD easily flows into CAM, but once the factory is dependent on CAD input, it will not be able to accept manual designs.

FIGURE 3.4   Flexible Manufacturing System

CIM also encompasses **flexible manufacturing** processes and procedures. Flexible manufacturing depends on **parts commonality programs**, which strive to minimize the number of part types and maximize commonality throughout the product line. If a factory is to be flexible, each manufacturing work station must be able to work on a wide range of products. This is possible only when the parts are common enough to be always available where they are needed. **Standardization of design features** is also required for flexible manufacturing. Different parts will be traveling along the same materials handling systems and will be built by the same tools and equipment. Figure 3.4 shows a factory using a flexible manufacturing system for production. Here, a number of manufacturing work stations are linked by a *materials handling system that moves the part from station to station where one or more machining or processing operations are performed.*

Design for manufacturability, just-in-time programs, flexible manufacturing, and other automation concepts are driven by the original CAD input. Automation using CIM places constraints on the design for which DFM accounts. Because the trend is toward more sophisticated factories, good DFM practices will be required by the designer and should be understood by the drafter. The extensive use and integration of the computer in the design and manufacturing process will continue to increase throughout your career in industry.

3.2   CAD Technology

Drafters and designers create their designs electronically with a CAD system, view the designs on a display (Fig. 3.5), make quick and easy revisions, and then command the system to draw the design using a plotter. The completed parts [Figs. 3.5(a) and (b)] can be combined in an assembly [Fig. 3.5(c)] and displayed as shaded models [Fig. 3.5(d)]. **Interactive**

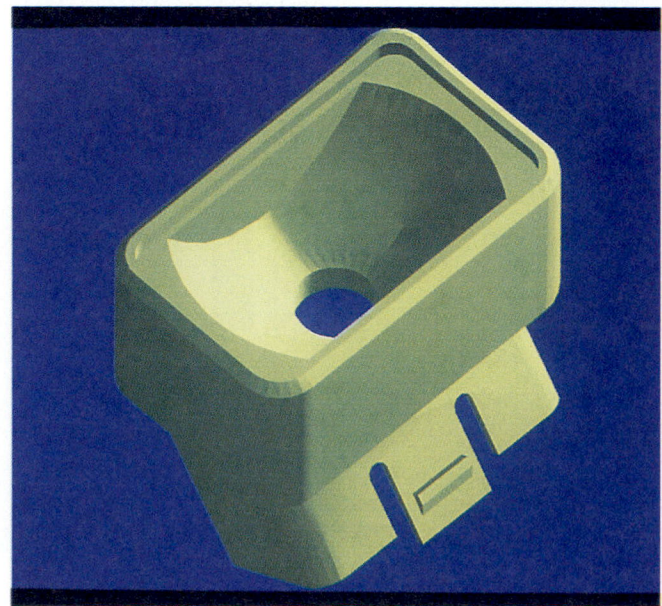

FIGURE 3.3   3D Part Design

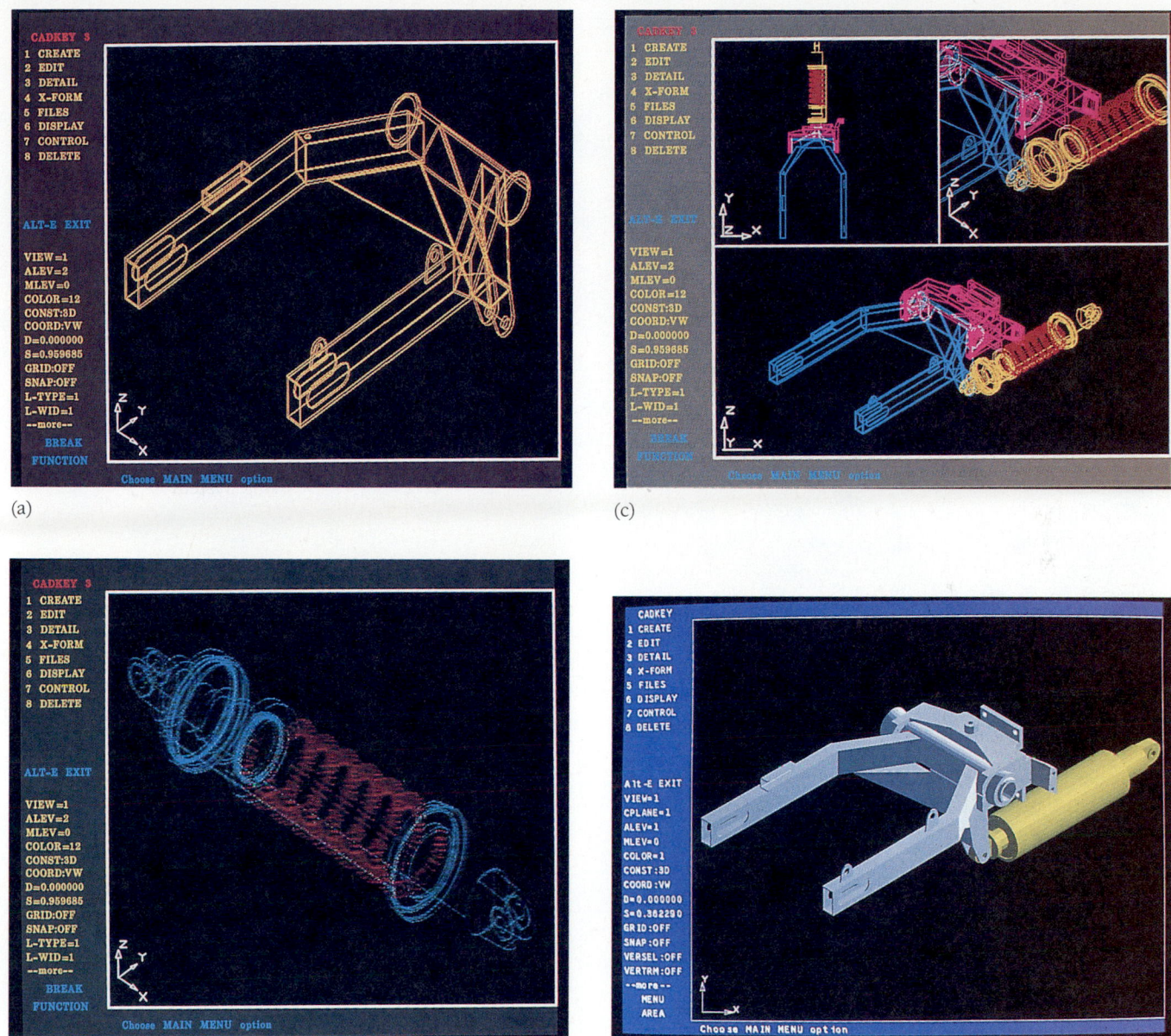

FIGURE 3.5 **Part Design and Assemblies**   (a) 3D part design (wire frame) (b) Wire frame model of subpart (c) Wire frame assembly (d) Shaded assembly

graphics is the ability to perform graphics operations directly on the computer with immediate feedback. You need not be a computer programmer or typist to use a CAD system effectively. However, typing skills do improve command input, and programming using built-in programming of some CAD programs such as EDLIN and AUTOLISP is also helpful.

The CAD drafter also has constant access to processors and storage units that provide all the capabilities of a calculator and all the reference information of a library: Data is supplied for both trigonometric and geometric construction. Symbols, patterns, drawing segments, minidrawings, and even complete drawings can be stored and reused. You can electronically erase selected portions, shrink or enlarge a part's geom-

etry, copy and edit portions of existing parts, and mirror, copy, and rotate complete parts or selected geometry. To accomplish this, a combination of hardware and software is required.

Hardware includes tablets, display devices, keyboards, input devices, processors, data storage components, plotters, printers, and all the other physical parts of a complete system. The hardware itself does nothing unless directed to do so by a set of instructions.

Software includes the sets of instructions that control the hardware. Software is usually provided by the CAD manufacturer and is already stored on the computer or available on disks, ready for use.

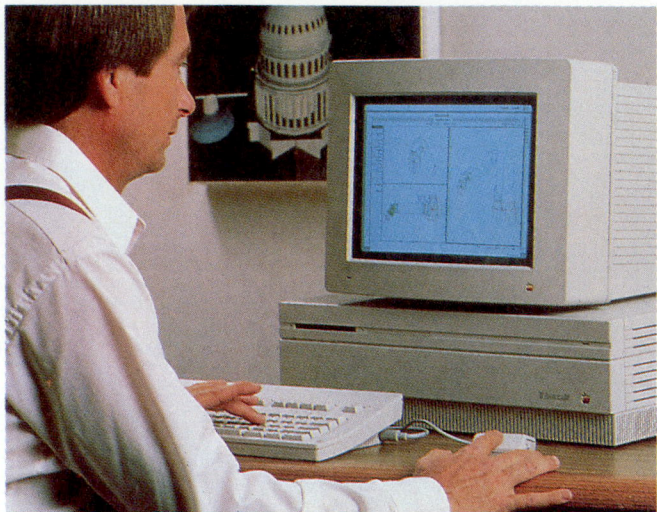

FIGURE 3.6   PC-based CAD System

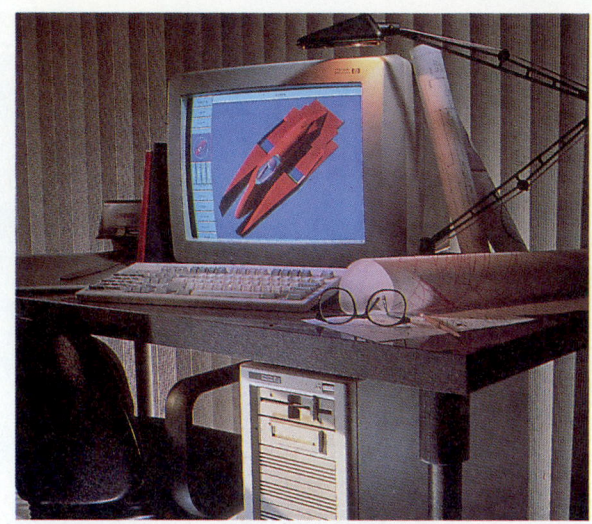

FIGURE 3.7   Engineering Workstation with Tower CPU

The input, processing, output, and storage hardware elements are interconnected via cables or telecommunications. Interactive CAD is either a stand-alone system or a processor with remote input/output units attached, such as on a PC-based CAD system (Fig. 3.6). System configuration and component terminology vary between CAD manufacturers.

An operator of a CAD system must be able to understand the system's *hardware* configuration and its *software* capabilities. The following is essential for you to understand and use a CAD system effectively in engineering design and drafting:

1. knowledge of drafting standards and procedures
2. specific engineering field conventions
3. actual industrial applications
4. software language for a particular CAD system package.

Software programs are available for all areas of engineering and design. Most systems can be mastered with training, but the specifics of the design area (piping, architecture, electronics, mechanical, structural, etc.) must be learned through a combination of education and experience.

The heart of any CAD system is the design **terminal** or **workstation** (Figs. 3.7 and 3.8). Here, the drafter/designer interacts with the system to develop a part design in detail, monitoring the work constantly on a display screen. By issuing commands to the system and responding to messages from the system, you create a design by manipulating, modifying, and refining it. Once the design is final, a command to the system will make a *hardcopy* or guide computer-controlled machine tools in manufacturing and testing the part. Hardcopy can be any level of graphics, from a simple check copy to a full-scale ink plot of the drawing on vellum paper. The PC-based system in Figure 3.8 is linked to a pen plotter for outputting drawings.

As a design is developed, the software accumulates and stores product-related data—identifying the precise location,

FIGURE 3.8   Drafting Station Including CAD System and Plotter

dimensions, descriptive text, and other properties of every element that helps define the new part. Using the design data, the system can be used to do complex engineering analyses, generate special lists and reports, and detect and flag (note/indicate) design flaws before the part is manufactured.

3.3   Hardware and Software

CAD systems vary in size, ability, and cost. Engineering firms select the computers and software based on their needs and funds available to buy them. The range is from personal computers (PC) to large mainframes. Some companies need the systems for drafting and design. Others use the systems for CAD/CAM, analysis, fabrication, and testing.

The stand-alone personal computers (Fig. 3.8) have an integral **central processing unit (CPU).** The CPU for the

CAD system in Figure 3.7 is housed in a separate floor cabinet. The CPU is the brain, which figures out what the software directions are telling it to do. Inside the brain is a section for **read-only memory (ROM)**. The ROM cannot be changed or edited easily. There is also a **random access memory (RAM)** section. This is where the data gets changed and edited. The CPU, ROM, and RAM are on the inside. On the outside are the various devices used to put data into the CPU. The monitor looks like a TV screen. The function keys on the keyboard (F1, F2, etc.) are shorthand versions of commands. The keyboard is another way to input commands—by typing. A digitizer is a table or tablet with pictures, words, or icons of items from which to choose.

RAM is also called volatile because it can remember the data stored in it only as long as power is applied. Once the power has been removed, the memory promptly forgets, and the next time power is applied it must be taught all over again. This is like having a series of lights, each controlled by a button. When you press down any combination of buttons, the corresponding lights come on. When you release the button, the lights go off. All data is stored in the RAM as a series of 1's and 0's called **bits.** This is again like the light bulbs, where a 1 is on and a 0 is off. Eight bits make up a **byte,** which is the smallest unit used to describe a letter or number. The amount of memory in a computer is measured in bytes. 64 Mbytes would represent $64 \times 1,024,000$ bytes, or 65,536,000 letters, or about 100,000 typewritten pages. An **M** is shorthand notation for 1,024,000. The typical PC CAD system requires 4 to 8 Mbytes of RAM.

ROM is like RAM, but the data is not lost when the power is turned off. ROM has many uses. After the power is turned on, the computer must be given a detailed instruction, that is, where to get the incoming data (from which peripheral device). It must then be fed specific information; that is, what to do with the incoming data—what kind of calculation or other process is going to be done. These instructions can be in the ROM and thus never erased.

On a **networked system**, several people can work simultaneously on a part (drawing or model), each providing information from his or her own terminal (Fig. 3.1). It is not uncommon to have eight or more people working on different aspects of the project, each on a different phase of development—such as design, engineering analysis, drafting, or manufacturing—for a single product or for many different products all tied together by the network.

The most common type of CAD system is PC-based. Macintosh (Fig. 3.6), IBM 386–486 PCs, or clones now compete with workstation-based or terminal systems (Fig. 3.7). Auto-CAD, CADKEY, VersaCAD, and Personal Designer software packages are PC-based systems typically found in schools and throughout industry.

3.3.1   Operation

A typical CAD system makes possible simple yet powerful interaction between you and the computer. Just by pointing an electronic pen, puck, or mouse to a premarked, touch-sensitive drawing tablet or by picking an option from a pulldown menu, you can give the system drafting commands, such as **DRAW** or **ERASE** . You can create, modify, and refine the design interactively, viewing the emerging work on a graphics display. With a single stroke of the pen or keyboard input, you can move, magnify, mirror, rotate, copy, stretch, or otherwise manipulate the entire design or any portion of it.

The system lets you know, by a message on the screen, if there is a procedural error. Using the keyboard, electronic pen, and drawing tablet, you can ask the system to retrieve automatically any previously completed drawing needed for reference, as well as the standard design symbols expected to be used. Symbols and completed designs are all stored in the computer's data bank (memory or database), where they are instantly available. The on-line library speeds up the design process by eliminating unnecessary redrafting of commonly used components and subassemblies.

3.3.2   Documentation

As a part is designed on the system, its physical dimensions are defined along with the attributes of its various components. This data, filed in the computer's memory, can later serve many other nongraphical needs. For example, the part-number data of materials can be used to help generate bills of materials for the production control.

The CAD database can be used directly by CNC machine tools and equipment for quality control and product testing. Other computer programs can help engineers check for interferences or tolerances; generate models for engineering analyses; and calculate areas, volumes, and weights for the product under development. All these nongraphic capabilities are automatic by-products of the CAD/CAM design process.

3.3.3   Memory/Storage

On mainframe computers and minicomputers, data may be stored in three ways:

1. **Magnetic disks** (which are configured like stacked long-playing records but have much more storage capacity) contain data in a form quickly accessible to the system.
2. **Magnetic tapes** (resembling reel-to-reel audiotapes) are used for semi-active storage.
3. The **computer** itself has a storage capacity, although data is seldom stored there for extended periods.

System commands, utility instructions, and computational procedures are usually stored on disks. Seldom-used reference data is usually stored on magnetic tape. On PC-based systems, storage is accomplished with internal or external hard drives, WORM optical disks, tape drives, or on $3\frac{1}{2}$ in. or $5\frac{1}{4}$ in. floppy disks. Figure 3.9 shows a variety of PC disk drives and hard drives.

Symbol libraries, drawing segments, whole drawings, design models, and submodels complete with text are stored on magnetic tape (if inactive or waiting for scheduled revisions) or on disks (if needed for reference at an adjoining workstation or another CAD system). A completed drawing is placed

FIGURE 3.9 Floppy and Hard Disk Drives

FIGURE 3.10 IC Design on a Calma Workstation Using Dual Screens

on a portion of disk storage where it can be found rapidly by the system.

3.3.4 CAD Workstations

The **drafting workstation** (Fig. 3.10) may include a **digitizer** (which converts graphics to digits) and a monitor with **alphanumeric keyboard**. This is the control center for active work input. If a mouse is used, the system may not have a digitizer tablet (Fig. 3.8).

The digitizer is wired so that the location of each place on its surface can be sent electronically to the processor by pushing the input button on the crosshair device to indicate a particular point. In the processor, all information is in digits (0 or 1); the digitizer changes graphics (lines and points) to digits. The processor then uses its calculating power to change the lines as the designer or drafter indicates and then reproduce them on the monitor. A typical interactive CAD workstation provides several functions:

1. interface to the host computer, either a large mainframe or local minicomputer
2. digital descriptions of a drawing, possibly stored locally
3. generation of a steady image on the display through its own local memory or by other means
4. translation of computer instructions into operating functions and routing of commands for the various function generators
5. operator input devices for communicating with the computer: data tablets, mouse, light pen, digitizer table, cursor controls, or function keys.

To carry out these functions, some form of display and an alphanumeric keyboard must be available.

3.3.5 Display Devices

All CAD systems use some kind of **display device**. There may be two screens, one alphanumeric (letters and numbers), the other graphic (pictures) (Fig. 3.10). This image can be produced by a number of available devices. One display device is the **cathode ray tube (CRT)**. It is similar to a television, oscilloscope, or radar. CRTs are available in many sizes and configurations and with various capabilities.

3.4 Input Devices

Input devices enable you to communicate with a computer without the need to learn programming. These devices are used to pick a function, to enter text and numerical data, to insert and manipulate geometry, to modify the graphics, and finally to detail the finished part. All CAD systems have at least one operator input device. Many systems have several such devices, each for a different function. Alphanumeric keyboards, function boxes, electronic pens, light pens, track balls, mice, joysticks, graphics tablets, and digitizing tables are used with CAD systems.

3.4.1 Keyboards and Function Boxes

In addition to the pen, mouse, or puck, you can communicate with the system through a **keyboard**. Using a combination of numbers and simple phrases, you can type **X, Y, Z** coordinates, enter text for drawing annotation, and initiate graphics processing commands. Several kinds of alphanumeric keyboards are commonly used with CAD/CAM graphics terminals. The conventional typewriter-like alphanumeric keyboard allows you to enter commands, symbols, and text as well as to request information. One of the most important uses of the keyboard is for annotation, the process of inserting text (words and numbers) on a drawing.

The keyboard is used to enter messages consisting of letters, numbers, mathematical computations, and other symbols into the computer storage. As the message or text is composed, it is displayed on the screen for verification or editing before the content is entered into the computer's main

FIGURE 3.11   CAD System Using a Keyboard and a Separate Function Box

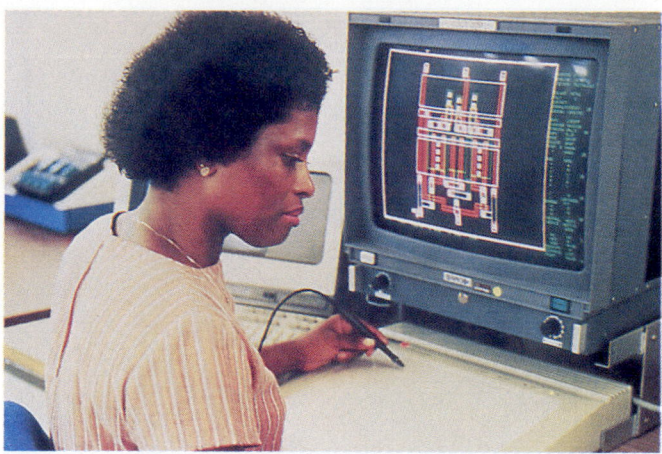

FIGURE 3.12   Drafter Using an Electronic Pen on a Graphics Tablet

storage. The keyboard also can control the screen location of a movable **cursor** symbol (dash, blinking box, small cross, fullscreen cross, or other marker) that is displayed where the next character will be entered. Keyboards may also include special graphics buttons called **function keys.**

In many cases, the CAD terminal is equipped with a separate box containing program-controlled push buttons (called a **function box** or **button box**). The function box can be integrated into the main keyboard or housed separately, as in Figure 3.11 (also see Fig. 3.17). The number of function keys varies from about 8 to 80. The function identified with each button is generally under computer control and can be changed as the program progresses or when a new application program is activated on the system. In some systems, the buttons can be labeled with an overlay, and the overlay can be changed with each application program. The use of function keys is easily mastered and quickly memorized. In other applications, the buttons are simply numbered and the function of each button is included in a user-selectable **menu.**

3.4.2 Graphics Tablet and Digitizing Tables

One common input device is the **graphics tablet** (Fig. 3.12). Graphics tablets and tables are electronic units that consist of a rectangular grid of horizontal and vertical lines integrated into a flat drafting table-like surface. Generators within the tablet pulse the lines, producing discrete code signals in response to an electronic pen, puck, or mouse device moved by the designer. The computer determines the location of the pointing device by decoding the signal. This decoded information is displayed on the CRT as **X** and **Y** coordinates. A line or spot (cursor symbol) corresponding to the input device position appears on the screen.

Most data tablets allow some separation between the pen and the tablet surface. That is, the pen need not be in contact with the tablet surface. Therefore, a paper drawing or other sheet can be placed on the data tablet, enabling you to trans-

late drawing coordinates into digital form. This process is called *digitizing*. This digitizing feature is very important in many computer-aided design and data analysis applications. Digitizers are devices that convert coordinate information into numeric form readable by a digital computer. Some CAD systems use a sheet overlay to develop unique menus for program control (Fig. 3.13).

Tablets without menu options are simply **data tablets** (Fig. 3.10). This type of graphics tablet has a surface area that corresponds to the display area of the CRT. By moving a hand-held puck with input buttons, you can position the display cursor symbol on the CRT. Instead of a tablet menu, a **display menu** appears on the CRT (Fig. 3.14). Menu commands are entered by positioning the symbol cursor over the desired menu function displayed on the screen and pressing an input button.

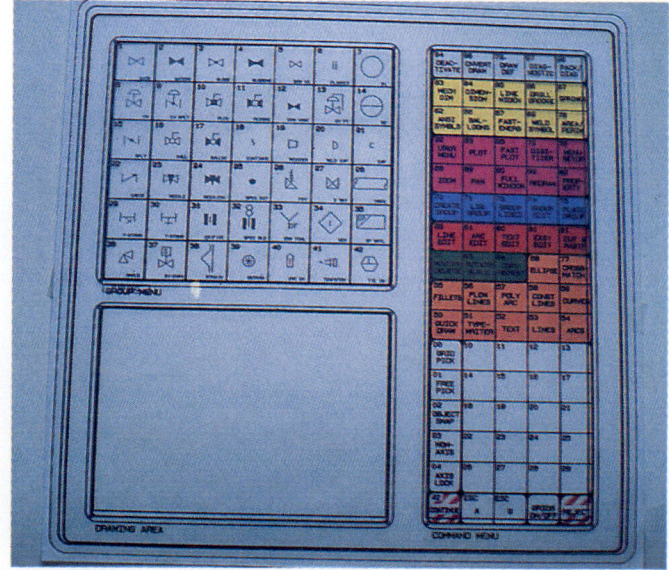

FIGURE 3.13   CAD Tablet Menu

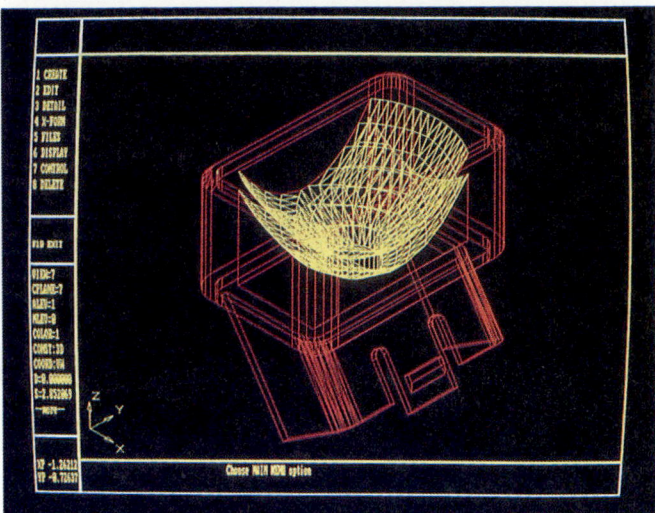

FIGURE 3.14 Screen Menu

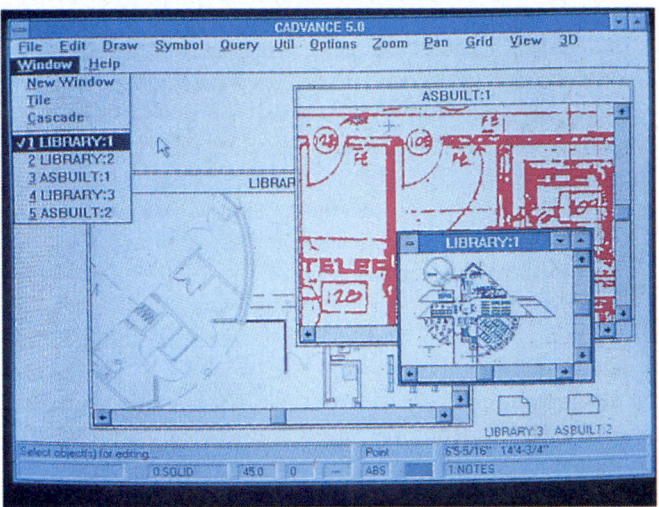

(a)

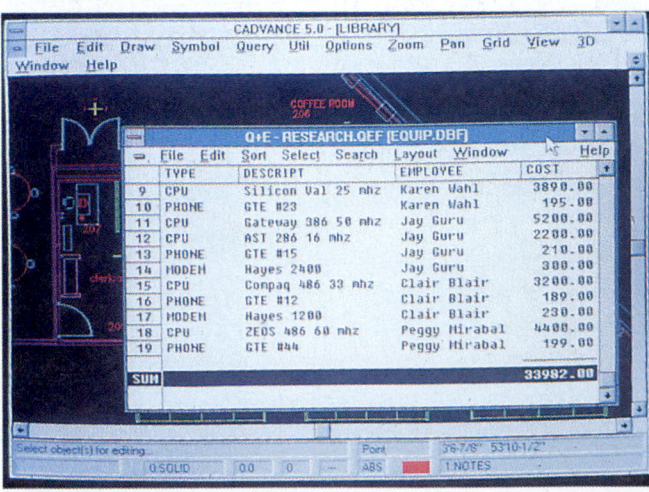

(b)

FIGURE 3.15 CADVANCE CAD System Using Windows
Software (a) Accessing part libraries using windows
(b) Equipment list for office (displayed with window)

Some CAD systems now run with Windows software as shown in Figure 3.15. These systems are normally equipped with a mouse-type input device for quick and simple selection of the window options.

Digitizing tables are used by some companies to directly input 2D sketches into the system (Fig. 3.16). This practice is limited to straight-line sketches of diagrams. Flow diagrams, block diagrams, schematic diagrams, logic diagrams for electronics, and piping diagrams for piping design lend themselves to direct digitizing.

3.4.3 Light Pen and Electronic Pen

The **light pen** is a pen-shaped electrophoto-optical device that allows you to identify a particular element directly on the display screen or to select a particular function from the menu. An **electronic pen** (Fig. 3.12) is restricted to coordinate input or menu selections and cannot be used to draw on the display device. A light pen can be used to *draw* on the CRT display surface. The original CADAM CAD workstation used a light pen (Fig. 3.17). Few systems today employ the use of a light pen. Most CAD stations input information with an electronic pen, a puck, or a mouse (using a screen menu).

3.4.4 Pointing Devices

Besides pens, various special **cursor controls** are available for CAD systems including the track ball, joystick, and the mouse. Figure 3.18 shows a variety of pointing devices available for use with a CAD system, including roller ball and mouse types. Each of these devices is a data entry device used by the drafter to enter coordinates manually in specific **X, Y,** and **Z** registers. The **track ball** is a device that mechanically couples a control element to both the **X** and **Y** generators so that a single motion can drive both transducers simultaneously (the operation as a mouse). The track ball uses a rolling ball to drive the transducers. The **joystick** is similar to the track ball except that it provides a small bat-like handle that the designer moves.

FIGURE 3.16 Large Digitizing Table Being Used to Input a Sketch

FIGURE 3.17   IBM CAD System Equipped with a Function Box for Inputting Commands

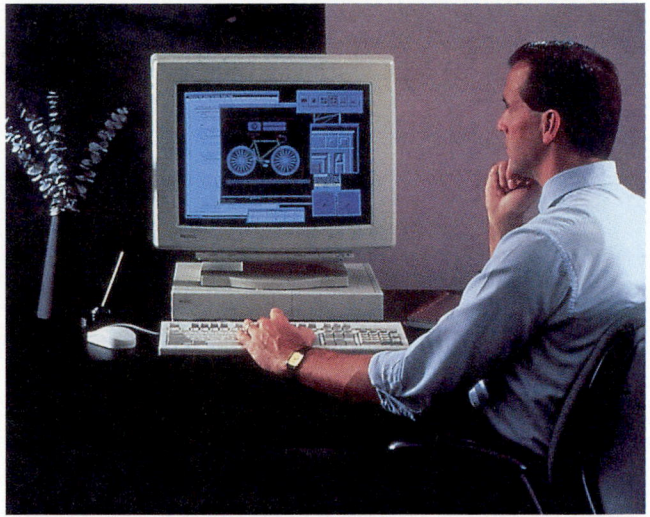

(a)

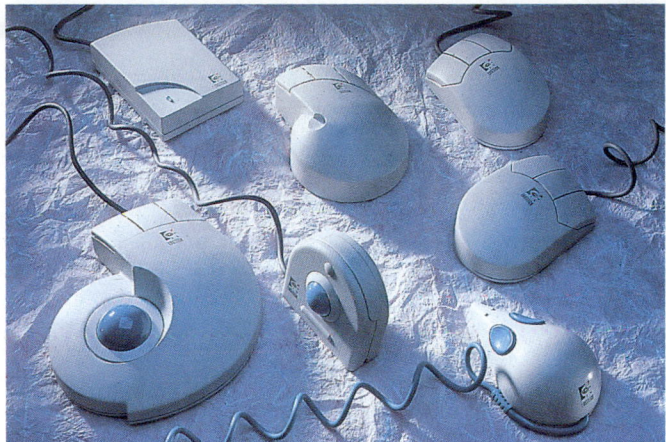

FIGURE 3.18   Pointing Devices

(b)

FIGURE 3.19   CAD Systems that Use a Mouse as the Only Input Device

Most PC-based CAD systems can be operated with a **mouse** as their primary means of input (Fig. 3.19). A mouse is moved along a flat surface (a pad or table); its movement controls the position of the screen cursor. Buttons on the mouse allow you to input the screen menu selections and to pick locations on the screen.

3.4.5   Menus

A **menu** is an input device consisting of command squares on a digitizing surface (such as a tablet or table) or on the screen. A menu eliminates the need to use the keyboard for entering graphical or common command data. A menu tablet allows the selection of the most commonly used tasks for a particular design field. General drawing menus are available for constructing simple to complex graphics. New menus can be changed or created as required.

To use a menu (Fig. 3.20), you simply place the pointing device over the desired command and press the cursor button or the function key (Fig. 3.21). Most systems have commands that allow frequently changed parameter options (such as

letter heights and slant) to be displayed on the alphanumeric screen for operator inspection or modification.

The menu shows the commonly used symbols and commands. Since not all symbols can be placed on a menu, a typical system has the capability to create and hold a large **drafting library**. A library contains all the needed symbols, drawings, or figures for a particular engineering field: nuts, bolts, screws, electrical symbols, welding symbols, or component outlines. It is basically an unlimited template. The drafting library can be added to or subtracted from as necessary. A drafter typically collects and customizes figures or symbols from the drafting library, creates any special figures that will be used repeatedly, and assembles them into special menus.

Although the number of figures may be limited because of size and space, the number of menus is unlimited. The typical menu item is inserted with a minimum of keystrokes. Each

FIGURE 3.20   Tablet and Pen

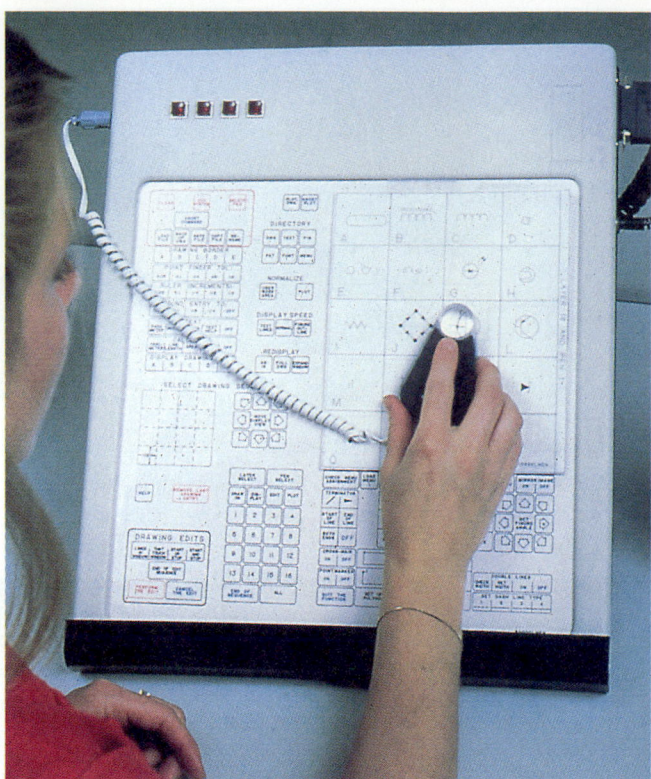

FIGURE 3.21   Graphics Tablet with Menu and Puck

symbol can be inserted at any angle or scale. The symbol or figure can be as simple as an electronic diagram symbol or as complex as a complete printed circuit board. Once the menu symbol or figure is created, it can be stored and used any number of times in other drawings.

3.5 Output/Hardcopy Devices

Output from CAD systems can be in many forms. The most common is a drawing just like the one created on a drafting board. This drawing is created by a plotter (Fig. 3.22). Output can also be a copy of what is on the screen, called a **hardcopy**. A hardcopy normally comes from a printer or plotter attached directly to the workstation. A drawing can not only be obtained from a plotter, but can also be drawn on microfilm. This is called **computer output microfilm (COM)**.

Hardcopy and output devices include printers, plotters, and photocopy equipment. Printers provide the user with alphanumeric readouts and material lists. The plotter allows you to produce ink drawings on paper, vellum, or drafting film in a multitude of colors. Some plotters are limited by the size of the plotting surface. Although they are limited to standard paper widths, others can plot drawings of any length. Pen plotters can use ballpoint pens, felt-tip pens, liquid ink pens or pencils. Check copies are normally run with inexpensive ballpoint pens. Original high-quality drawings are plotted with India ink and liquid ink pens. When plotting a drawing, you have a number of options: to scale the drawing, rotate it, select the colors to plot, or even substitute different line widths. Not all pen plotters have these options. Various plotters are available including drum plotters, flatbed plotters, electrostatic plotters, digitizer plotters, and laser plotters.

3.5.1 Plotters

In a CAD system, plotters and displays complement each other. A display is capable of rapidly presenting a picture so that you can react to it, perhaps making changes interactively. A **plotter**, on the other hand, can make large, highly accurate

FIGURE 3.22   **3D Models**   Three-dimensional models from a computer screen can easily be converted back to two dimensions to make hardcopy displays on the Draftmaster I plotter shown here.

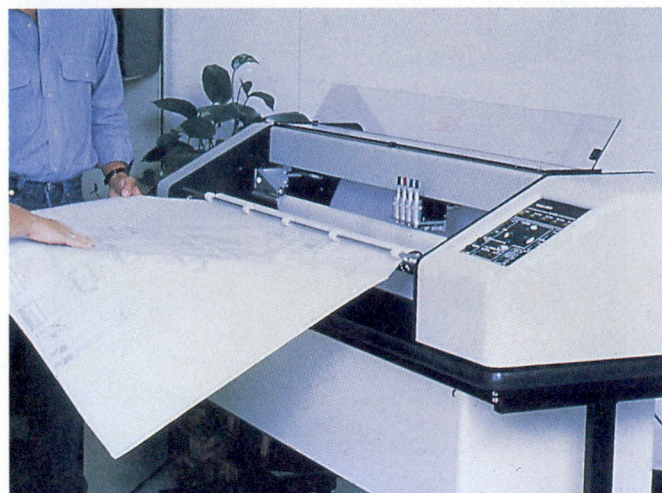

FIGURE 3.23 Drum Plotter

drawings, but more slowly (Fig. 3.23). Displays are used to make the initial decisions, while plotters make the record copies.

The accuracy of plotted output can be considerably higher than the apparent accuracy and quality of the image on the display. A computer defines all graphics as coordinate points. Therefore, all graphics on a CAD system are made of straight-line elements. The closer the points of a curve are spaced, the better a system's **resolution.** *Resolution is the smallest spacing between points on a graphic device at which the points can be detected as distinct.* The degree of resolution influences the quality of the drawing plot since curves appear as a series of straight lines if the resolution is poor.

3.5.2   Pen Plotters

Typical CAD systems use an electromechanical **pen plotter** to plot data and make engineering drawings. Two basic kinds of pen plotters are currently used. The earliest and perhaps most widely used type is the **drum plotter** (Figs. 3.22 and 3.23). Plotting paper is wrapped around the drum, and the drum is rotated by a digital stepping motor. The rotation provides one deflection axis while the pen, mounted on a gantry across the drum, provides the other deflection axis. The only other basic control, besides **X** and **Y** deflection, is the control to move the pen up and down. Drum plotters are available in sizes that range from $8\frac{1}{2}$ in. to more than 42 in. wide. They make plots quickly and of unlimited length. The smaller drum plotters make lines in incremental steps, approximately .005 to .01 in. apart, with plotting rates of around 5 in. per second. A typical drum plotter uses either ballpoint, felt-tip, or ink pens.

As the name suggests, a **flatbed plotter** has a flat horizontal drawing surface with the paper lying flat, suitable for highly accurate, top-quality drawings. On most flatbed plotters, the pens move and the paper remains stationary. Flatbed plotters were introduced to satisfy the need for high-quality images and large drawing sizes. Now plotters ranging from about $8\frac{1}{2} \times 11$ in. to as much as 4 ft wide $\times$ 12 ft long are available.

3.5.3   Electrostatic Plotters

In the past, **electrostatic plotters** were used primarily for a *quick look* capability. However, electrostatic plotters are now of such high quality that they are used as one of the primary output devices for CAD/CAM systems.

(a)

(b)

FIGURE 3.24   Electrostatic Plotters   (a) Electrostatic plotting (b) High-end electrostatic plotter

While it takes seconds (or even fractions of a second) to display an image on the CRT, the time required to plot that same drawing on a precision plotter may be several minutes. Plotting twenty to thirty times faster than pen plotters, electrostatic plotters can plot a square foot of data in a few seconds.

All electrostatic plotters (Fig. 3.24) share a similar operating principle. Voltage is applied to an array of densely spaced writing nibs embedded in a stationary writing head. The nibs selectively create minute electrostatic dots on the paper as the paper passes over the writing head. The paper is then exposed to liquid toner to produce a visible, permanent image.

The electrostatic plotter retains the advantage of the drum plotter in that drawings can be of unlimited length. Electrostatic plotters are available up to 6 ft in width. A further advantage is that the electrostatic plotter can be used very effectively as a high-speed line printer (up to 1200 lines per minute).

3.5.4   Photoplotter

Photoplotters are the most accurate type of plotter. Photoplotters are used where extreme accuracy takes precedence over the cost of the unit. Printed circuit board art masters are normally created with this type of plotter (see Chapter 23). A light beam is used to "plot" the drawing on light-sensitive film.

3.5.5   Scanners

Scanners are used to produce high-quality reproductions of photographs, line drawings, or technical illustrations (Fig. 3.25). This technology is used in desktop publishing, and to produce and merge graphics with word processing for technical reports, technical and service manuals, and various other output.

3.5.6   Printers

A **printer** is a computer-operated typewriter providing the user with hardcopy of alphanumeric data. Printers are used as a quick screen dump for reviewing graphics and for producing parts lists and other nongraphic output. Many types of

(a)

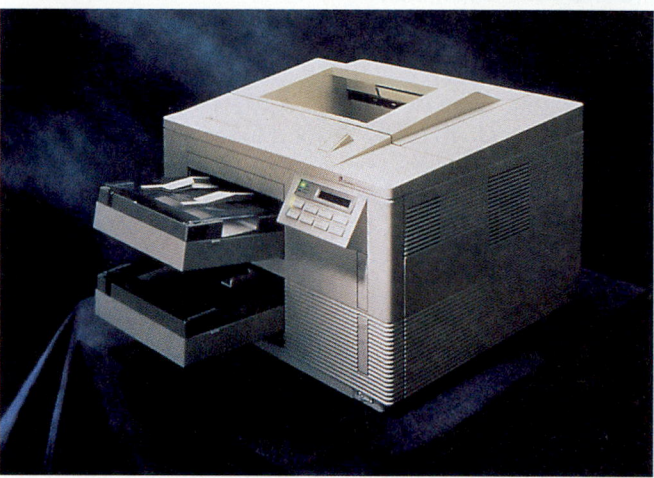

(b)

FIGURE 3.26   Printers   (a) HP DeskJet 500c printer (b) HP LaserJet IIIsi printer

printers are available. The quality of typeface and the speed of printing are two of the most important features of a printer. **Letter-quality printers** are slower and do not plot any type of graphics. Although the quality of the typeface is poor, **dot matrix printers** are extremely fast and plot limited quality graphics. **Jet ink printers** [Fig. 3.26(a)] and **laser jet printers** [Fig. 3.26(b)] are also available for high-quality printing needs as well as high-quality graphics. *Printers used with CAD systems as hardcopy devices must be able to process graphics.*

3.6   CAD/CAM Software

Software is the programmed instructions that tell the processor what to do. Programming that is built into the chips (integrated circuits) and printed circuit boards of the computer is called **firmware.**

Many CAD systems come from the manufacturer preprogrammed. Knowledge of programming is not needed to use a

FIGURE 3.25   Scanner

CAD system; you just turn it on and the system is ready to use. Software orders the computer to direct the flow of input data either into working storage or to the disk for instant recall. Software also helps the computer retrieve input data for processing.

3.6.1   Applications Software

A typical CAD **application software** package does not require that the designer be a computer programmer. CAD systems are designed to free the designers from the time-consuming task of programming so that they can concentrate on the design capabilities of the system. On the other hand, *any person using an application program must be familiar with the standards and the conventions used in that technical field.* It is very important for the beginning drafter to understand that, no matter what the level of sophistication, the hardware and the software are only there to aid the user in design and drafting tasks. As a drafter or designer, you must know about the application and what procedures are applicable to that area. Excellent software packages have been developed for civil and mapping, structural, architectural, piping, and mechanical engineering, electronics, technical illustration, and a variety of other areas. The use of CAD in these technical areas has enhanced design and streamlined drafting. But the drafter, designer, or engineer must still know all of the particulars of the application area. CAD is a tool that can only be cost-effective in the hands of a knowledgeable, well-educated user.

Generally, the manufacturer of the CAD/CAM system supplies programs for basic-level creation of 2D and 3D drawings. Additional programs may be supplied by the manufacturer to do engineering analysis or help the designers learn special system functions. A typical drawing software package allows the designer to construct all the traditional drafting graphics using standard conventions and practices. The difference lies in the automated capabilities imbedded in the system and the availability of specific applications programs. Some CAD vendors offer a general CAD software package that can be used to construct symbols, menus, standards, and conventions for any engineering area. This type of software allows other vendors of applications programs to write software for a technical area such as printed circuit board (PCB) design, architecture, etc., using the generic software as the base. Other CAD systems are totally dedicated to one or just a limited amount of applications. As an example, many CAE/CAD systems are dedicated to integrated circuit design. Other CAD software packages are limited to PCB design or mechanical drafting.

It would be an excellent exercise for you to investigate what other areas of industry and business utilize CAD capabilities. For instance, chemists are using CAD to create new drugs. This field is actually called Computer-Aided Drug Design. The 1985 Indy race winner drove a car that was designed on a CAD system. Once you start to look into the present-day uses of CAD, the future possibilities seem unlimited.

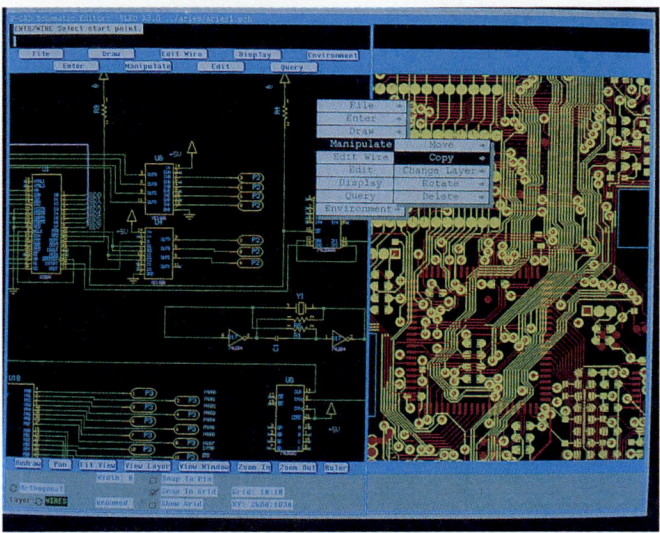

FIGURE 3.27   PCB Design

3.6.2   Electronic Applications

One of the most important applications for CAD is **integrated circuit** and **printed circuit board** design and documentation. All integrated circuit design is done on a computer (see Fig. 3.10). CAD increases productivity by automating and integrating the key steps in the design and production of integrated circuits and PCBs. The typical PCB program (Fig. 3.27) uses automatic and manual editing modes to design the entire board from the drawing of the schematic to the final manufacturing and testing stages (Figs. 3.28 and 3.29). Schematics, text, and board geometry are entered interactively into the system. Automatic assignment, placement, and routing routines are used to complete the design of the board. A variety of PCB sizes and types can be designed. Manual input can be used to override the automatic routines.

The automatic routing of PCBs is complemented by software to place components on the board automatically. Because of the increasing density of boards and complexity of circuits, this is an important feature for development. The CAD system also provides control tapes for numerically controlled drilling and insertion machines for use during the production and manufacturing of circuit boards.

For the development department, there are special problems both in design and in preparing the necessary documentation for manufacturing. Designing the printed board entails overcoming spatial restrictions and layout constraints. Designing the equipment housing requires consideration of cooling arrangements, protection against shocks or vibrations, provision of easy access for servicing, and, at the same time, satisfaction of styling requirements. This is called electronic packaging design.

CAD systems can automate and integrate the key steps in the design, documentation, and design rules checking of wiring diagrams. It reduces the time and expense required to

FIGURE 3.28   PCB Design on an Engineering Workstation

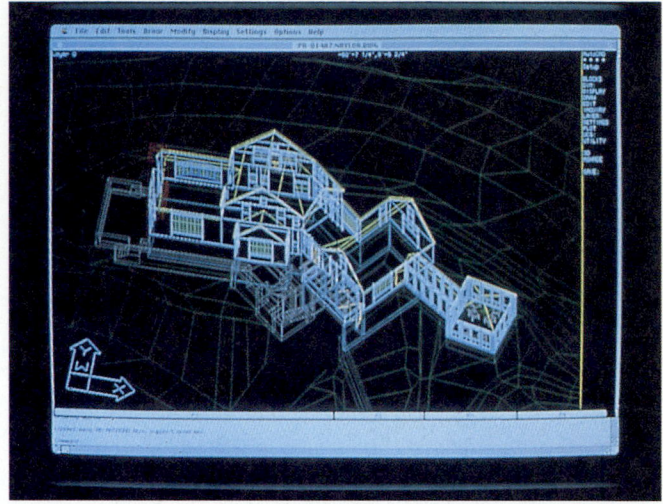

(a)

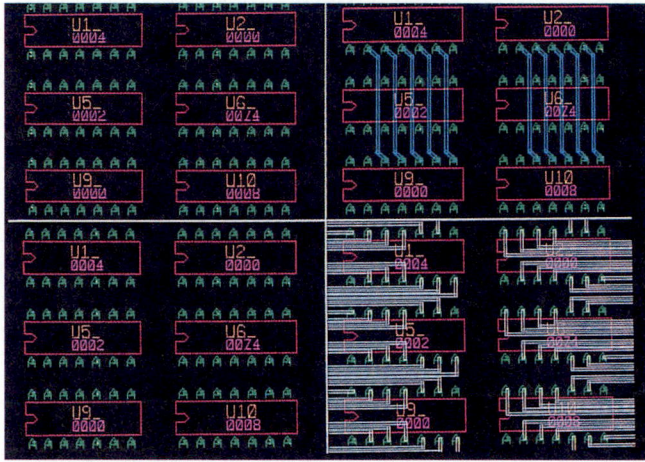

FIGURE 3.29   Printed Circuit Board Design and Editing

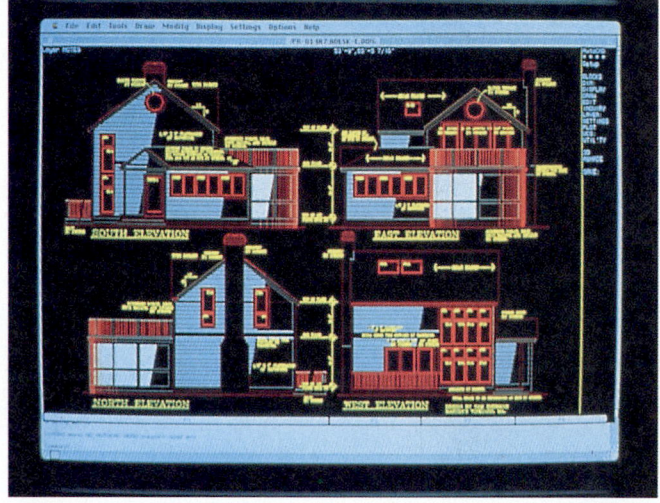

(b)

capture, check, update, and extract design information. This capability is applied to many types of diagrams: logic, schematic, wire harness, or interconnection.

3.6.3   Architecture and Construction Applications

Applications are available for building designs on a CAD system, including **architectural design** (Fig. 3.30). You can design the structure [Fig. 3.30(a)], display and detail the appropriate views [Fig. 3.30(b)], and use color shading to show how the building would appear realistically [Figure 3.30(c)]. This eliminates the need to model the building physically or do a rendering.

Space planning (Fig. 3.31), duct work, electrical layout, and plumbing (Fig. 3.32) can also be completed. The system allows the integration of such disciplines and permits you to

(c)

FIGURE 3.30   **Architectural Design**   (a) Architectural design using AutoCAD (b) Elevations (c) Shaded model

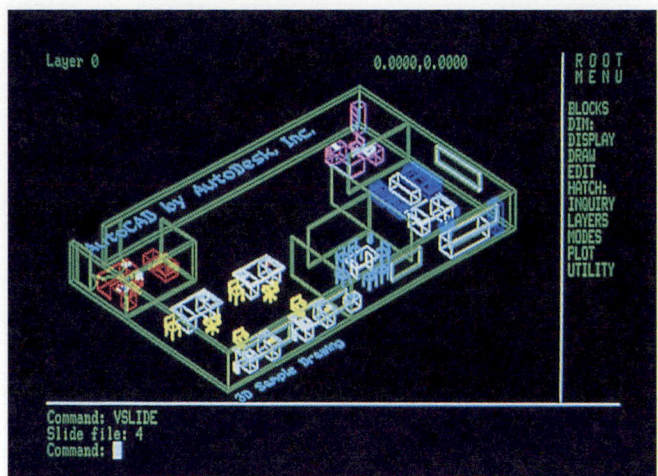

FIGURE 3.31 3D Space Planning on AutoCAD

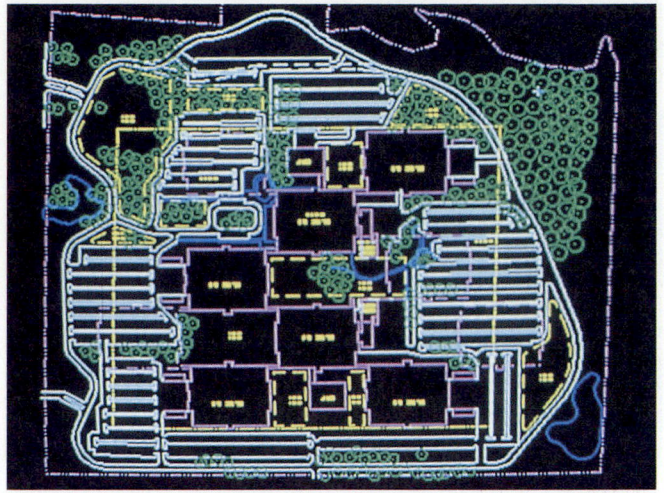

FIGURE 3.33 Site Plan and Landscaping Using DesignCAD

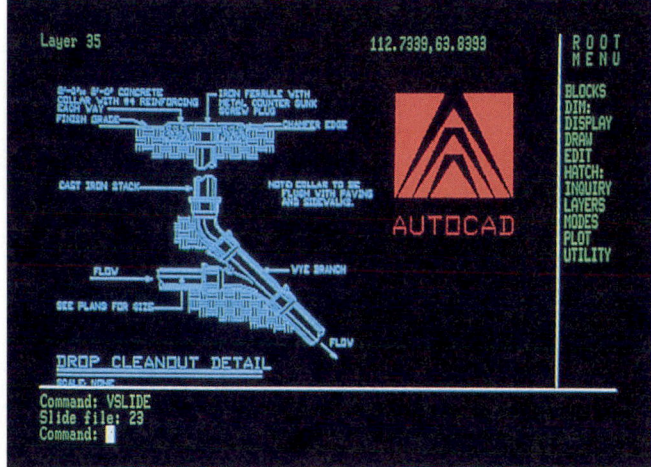

FIGURE 3.32 Sewage Piping Design and Detailing on AutoCAD

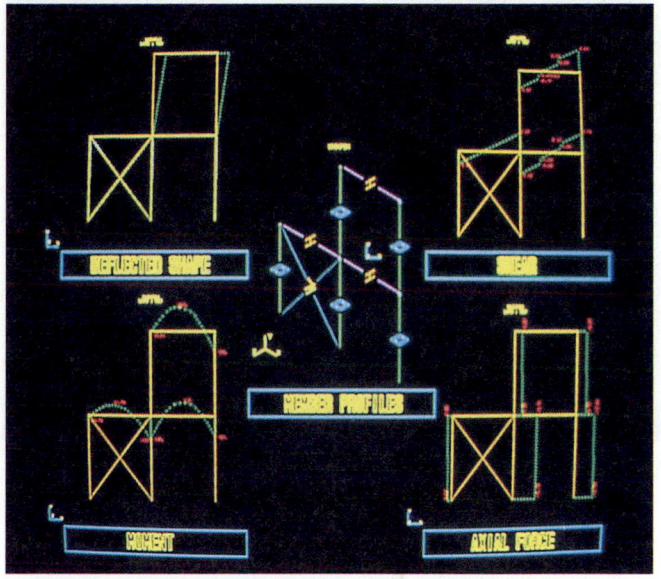

FIGURE 3.34 Structural Steel Design and Detailing

develop several design alternatives for a particular project including possible landscaping schemes (Fig. 3.33).

3.6.4 Structural Design and Engineering Applications

Structural design, layout, and detailing are important applications for which CAD has been used effectively in the building industry to improve design and decrease drafting time (Fig. 3.34). The designer inputs the structural grid, geometry, and member properties. The member profiles can then be graphically checked before analysis begins. After the structural analysis is performed, the results can be displayed using moment, sheer, axial force, and deflected shape diagrams. Color and layering capabilities are used for analysis and to differentiate between structural element types and sizes.

3.6.5 Civil Engineering and Mapping Applications

Civil engineering and **mapping** [Fig. 3.35(a)] features include site selection, site preparation, digital terrain modeling, earth work calculations, and contour mapping. Other mapping capabilities allow utility companies and municipalities to plan distribution networks and to manage accurately assets widely distributed throughout large geographic areas [Fig. 3.35(b)].

The CAD system provides a tool for analysis and design coupled with actual cost estimates. You can automatically design and estimate costs of a runoff water collection system by selecting the minimum pipe sizes required, minimum pipe slope, calculating flow line, elevation data, and segregating

(a)

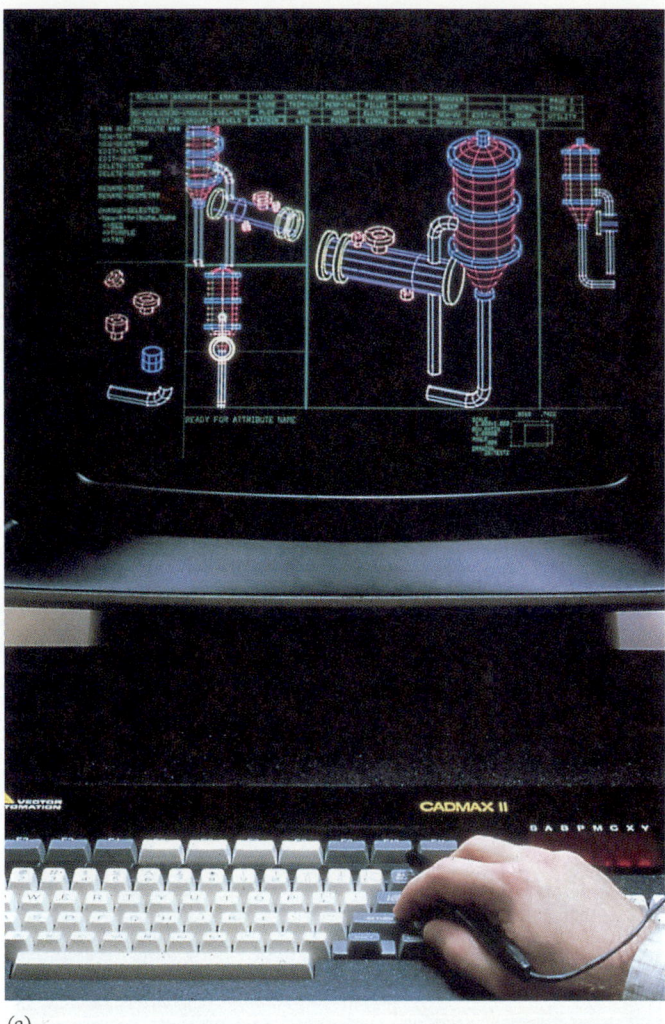

(a)

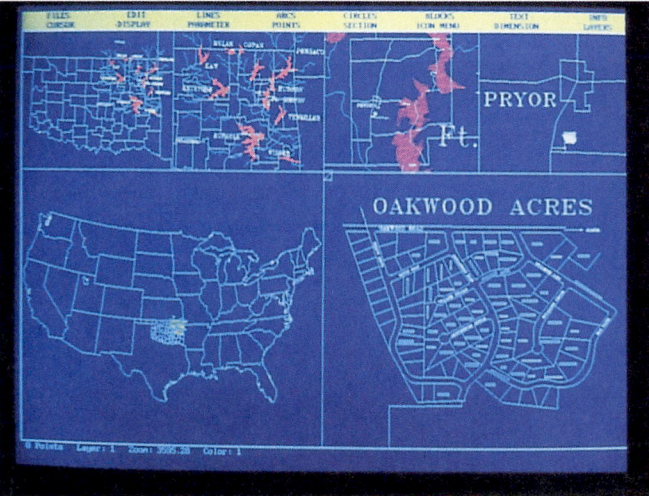

(b)

FIGURE 3.35 **Mapping Layout with DesignCAD**

the quantities into bid item costs for the specified layout and flow input to each manhole. This design tool allows the engineer to process several layouts and system modifications, including full cost estimates, in less time than would be spent to design one layout conventionally without cost estimates.

3.6.6   Piping and Plant Design

Plant design CAD programs permit the extraction of a wide range of drawings and reports directly from the stored information, including flow diagrams, isometrics, spools, pipe fabrication, pipe supports, plan, elevation, and section drawings, solid views, from–to lists, bills of materials, and formatted lists. With a 3D CAD system, designs for process and power plants can be created as a true 3D model on the system [Fig. 3.36(a)]. The 3D model facilitates revisions, graphics manipulations, and analysis such as piping interference checks.

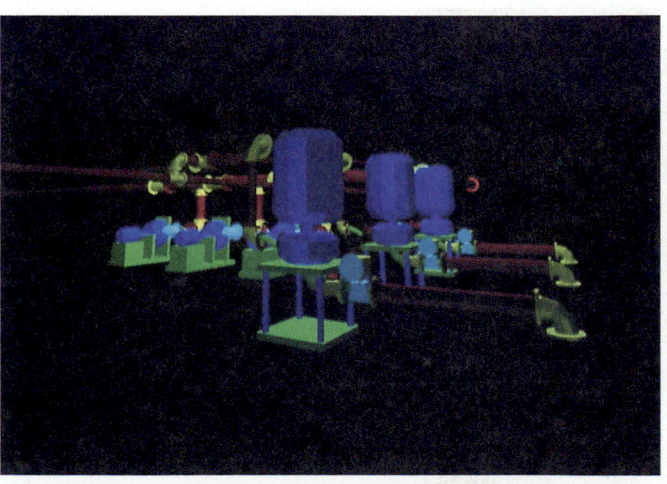

(b)

FIGURE 3.36 **3D Piping Design**   (a) Piping design (wire frame) (b) Piping design using 3D CAD (surface model with shading)

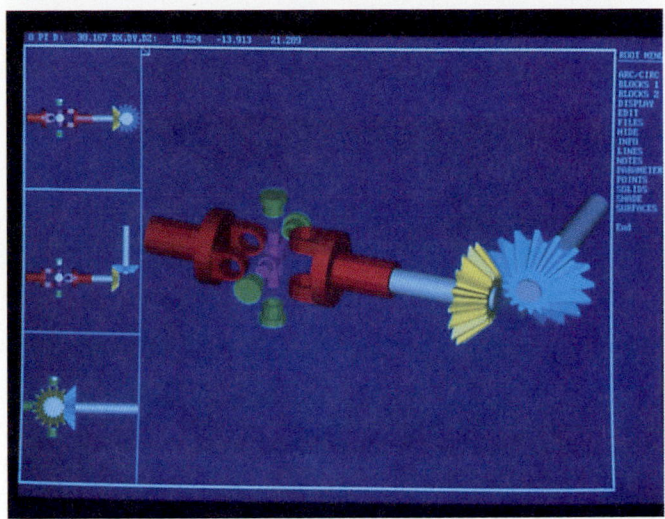

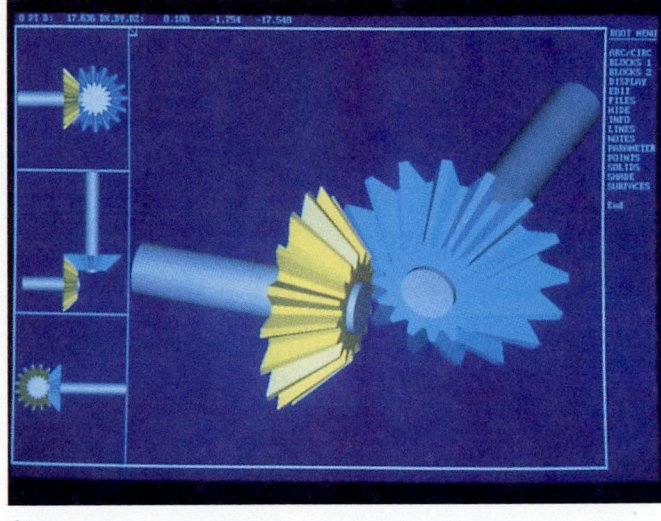

(a)   (b)

FIGURE 3.37   **Helical Gear Design and Assembly Using DesignCAD**   (a) Gear assembly (b) Helical gears

These checks pinpoint interferences between plant components early in the design cycle. The 3D model provides hidden line removal to enhance the visual representation of the model [Fig. 3.36(b)]. The designer can recognize and rectify potential plant problems early in the design phase, eliminating costly and time-consuming construction delays.

3.6.7   Mechanical Design Applications

A majority of CAD software packages have **mechanical design** and detailing capabilities. Besides 3D modeling of mechanical parts, mechanical software packages have many drafting and detailing capabilities to add dimensional information, notes, and labels to your drawings. You can also manipulate your drawings of the model for aesthetic reasons or for visual clar-

ification (Fig. 3.37). These manipulation features include choosing a variety of line fonts (patterns), erasing hidden lines, defining any type or number of views, inserting dual dimensions, defining ANSI, JIS, or ISO standards, sectioning, and crosshatching. One of the most important tasks handled by a CAD system is the updating of existing mechanical designs and drawings since it can be accomplished quickly and easily compared to manual methods.

Mechanical design includes a wide variety of products and machinery. Aerospace design is one of the most important uses of mechanical CAD and many of the software packages used in mechanical design were developed by aerospace companies such as Lockheed and McDonnell Douglas. McDonnell Douglas Unigraphics software running on HP 9000 computers is used in the design and manufacture of the NOTAR

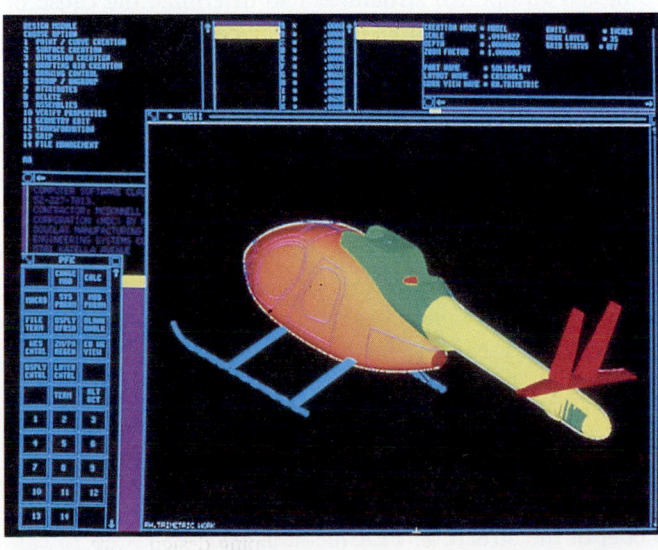

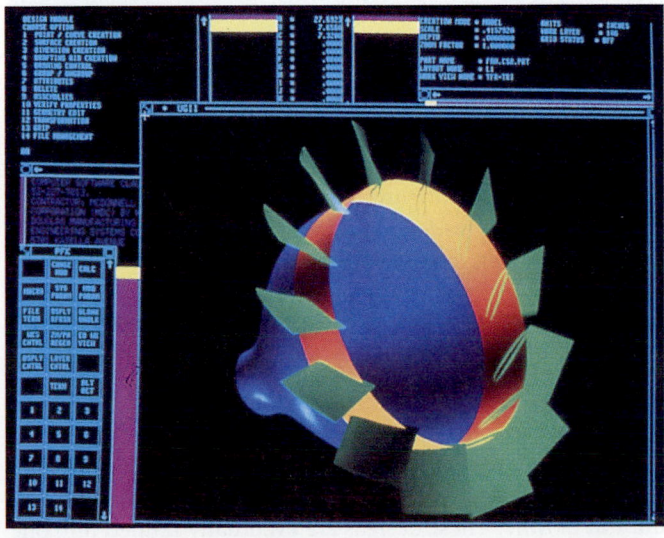

(a)   (b)

FIGURE 3.38   **3D Modeling**   (a) Helicopter design (b) Turbine design

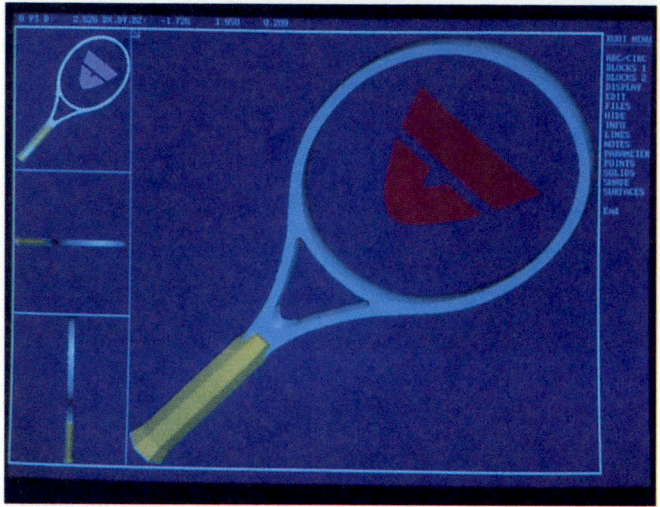

(a)   (b)

FIGURE 3.39   **Product Design Using 3D CAD**   (a) Racket (b) Telescope

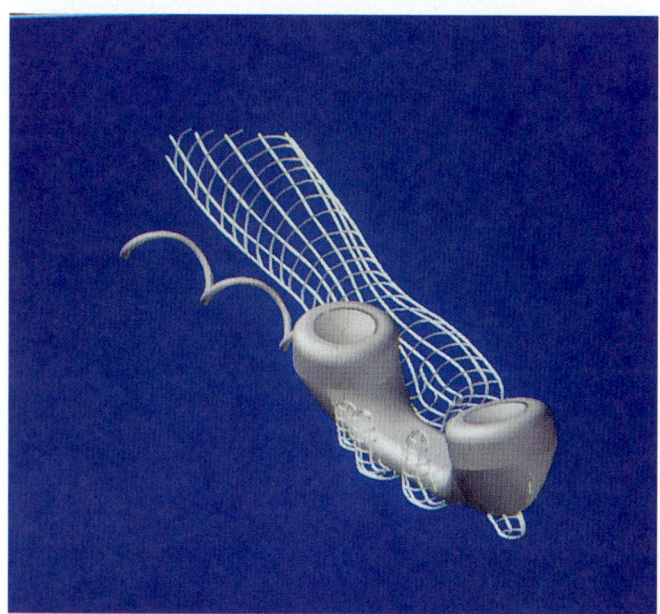

FIGURE 3.40   **Product Design and Display**

helicopter shown in Figure 3.38(a). McDonnell Douglas Helicopter Company uses DFM principles in the development of
turbine parts [Fig. 3.38(b)].

3.6.8   Product Design and Development

CAD systems provide a means to explore any number of
design ideas for new products, such as the racket in Figure
3.39(a) or the telescope in Figure 3.39(b). Since exploring
design alternatives with CAD systems is much faster than
manual methods, more exploration is possible in the same
amount of time. These designs are eventually refined into one
finished model. Figure 3.40 shows a product design of a
phone using CADAM software. The phone is shown as a solid
model with the arm and the hand of the user modeled so as

to study the product in relationship to the person using it.
The use of color and shading along with 3D models of the
proposed product also aids in rendering and illustrating the
product for consumer display.

3.6.9   Technical Illustration

Technical illustration can be done with a 2D or 3D system.
The fact that the original 3D model database can be used to
generate the illustration instead of redrawing the part is an
advantage of the 3D system (Fig. 3.41). The generation of
sales literature is also expedited with the use of CAD especially when the different departments within a company can
all share a common 3D model database.

3.6.10   FEM and FEA Applications

To design an optimal structure or to determine the cause of
failure after manufacture, design engineers commonly use
computerized design and analysis methods. CAD/CAM systems may have a **finite element modeling (FEM)** package
that allows you to create the model, prepare it for analysis,
and then graphically display the results of the analysis.

Finite element modeling [Fig. 3.42(a)] involves subdivid-
ing a structure into a network of simple elements that have
easily definable characteristics. A mesh, which is comprised
of associative grid points and elements, is generated. Then
you interactively define material properties, boundary conditions, and loads (such as forces/moments, pressures, and displacements) applied to the structure.

Most CAD systems significantly aid the design engineer in
design detailing and in the verification of the functionality
and mechanical resistance of complex parts by employing
finite element analysis (FEA) methods interfaced to the 3D
model of the structure. FEA methods may be set up to calculate thermal stresses [Fig. 3.42(b)] in addition to loads or to
model the behavior of the construction material (usually
steel) in its elastic or elastoplastic domain.

(a)

(b)

FIGURE 3.41   **Technical Illustration Using DesignCAD**   (a) Building illustration (b) Aircraft illustration

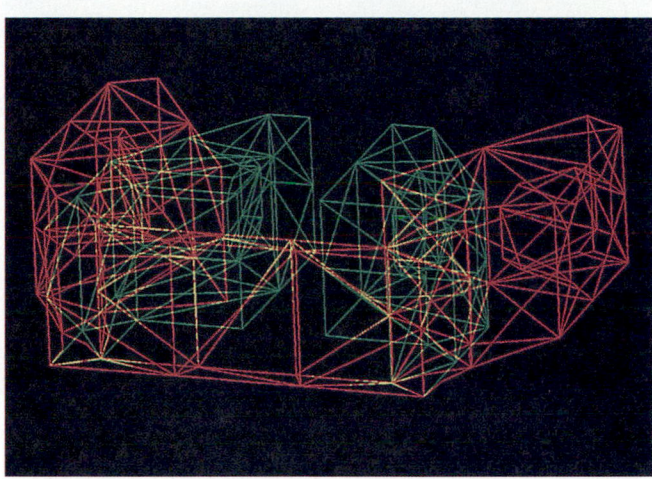

(a)

(b)

FIGURE 3.42   Engineering Analysis   (a) FEM (b) FEA

3.6.11   Computer-Aided Manufacturing Applications

CAD is the process that uses a computer to help create or modify a design. **CAM** is the process that uses a computer to manage and control the operations of a manufacturing facility. The integration of computer-aided design and computer-aided manufacturing eliminates duplication of effort by the engineering and manufacturing or production departments. An engineering model (Fig. 3.43) created on a graphics terminal simultaneously defines the source geometry (points, lines, planes, etc.) that otherwise must be manually derived from the drawing before the product is manufactured.

In an optimal CAD/CAM integrated system the production process is computerized from the original graphics input through to the manufacture of the part on a numerically controlled machine. Shop production drawings may at times be entirely eliminated with this process. By producing the source geometry directly from the engineering data, the programmer can extract accurate geometric data, replicating the definition of the part to be manufactured (Fig. 3.44).

CAM speeds the manufacturing process by using the same common information initially created in the design and drafting cycle. This information, representing the part (or model) design, is also used by the manufacturing group. The system serves all applications, promotes standardization to enhance management control, accumulates (rather than randomly collects) manufacturing information, and reduces redundancy and errors.

3.6.12   Computer Numerical Control Part Programming

Since the geometry of the part is defined in the CAD system, there is no need to go through the process of extracting the part geometry from the drawings. The geometry is already

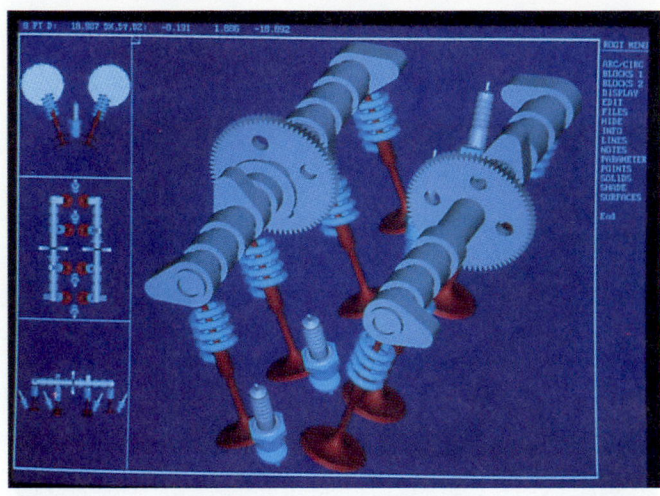 

(a) (b)

FIGURE 3.43 **3D Design of Cams** (a) Cam shaft assembly (b) 3D design of a cam shaft

 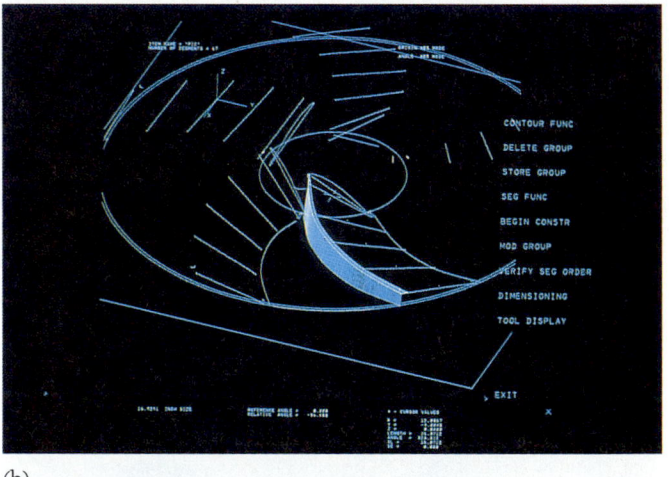

(a) (b)

FIGURE 3.44 **3D Mold Design** (a) Mold (b) Cutter paths

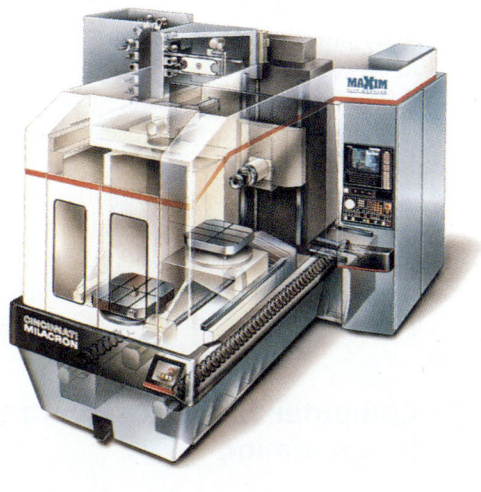 

(a) (b)

FIGURE 3.45 **Computer Numerical Control Machining** (a) Horizontal CNC machining center (b) Vertical CNC machining center

Computer-Integrated Manufacturing

Computer-integrated manufacturing (CIM) is a system in which all the functions needed in design, purchasing, manufacturing, inventory, and marketing of products are networked together. The computer information database is shared by everyone, eliminating duplication of information. The software that controls such a system must be refined and perfected, but many companies already have the key components of such a system in place.

One of the major components of CIM is the flexible manufacturing system (FMS), in which computer numerically controlled (CNC) machines are used with robots and part transfer vehicles to move a part from raw stock, through all machining steps and assembly, until it becomes a finished part. A software base controls the entire sequence.

The four major components of FMS are CNC machines, the coordinate measuring machines (CMM), robots, and part and tool transfer vehicles. This system can run unattended if it is supported properly. Worn tools are not a problem because of the on-line monitoring system. Inspection is completed with the CMM. Electronic gaging probes measure the features of the part and the computer compares the results with the limits stored in the database.

Robots load and unload materials and parts to the manufacturing cell. The tool and material transfer vehicles shuttle workpieces and tool magazines from in-

Manufacturing Cells

ventory and to specific machines. These vehicles can be automatic guided vehicles (AGVs) or wire guided, air cushion, or hardware guided vehicles.

AGVs are not connected to hardware and rely on onboard sensors and programs to establish their paths. A wire buried in the factory floor defines the path of travel for wire guided vehicles. The air cushion vehicle glides on an air cushion and is guided by external hardware. Unfortunately, any debris on the floor will stop the air cushion vehicle. The hardware guided vehicle runs on a track or rail. It is very reliable, but hardly flexible.

The American manufacturing industry has taken a hard look at what must be done to compete with ambitious programs under way in Japan and in Europe. Executives from a review program concluded that we need to make our factories "agile," link them together by computers and collaborate.

CIM will certainly play the key role as industry strives to eliminate paperwork, eliminate duplication of effort, reduce development to product cycle time, and improve quality and customer satisfaction. Much development is still needed before we have a true CIM environment.

---

given, precisely as specified. Since the designer is provided with a visual verification of every step in the process, the graphic display and interactive nature of the system eliminate the need to envision the cutter path. Many CAD systems provide this graphical approach to computer numerical control (CNC). CNC involves generating tool paths and producing machine control data for a variety of machining operations (Fig. 3.44). CNC machines (Fig. 3.45) perform their machining operations automatically by using the instructions contained on this punched tape or derived directly from the engineering database by the computers. Figure 3.45(a) shows an example of a horizontal CNC machining center and Figure 3.45(b) shows a vertical CNC machining center. In Figure 3.46, an example of a CNC turning center is provided. Each of these machines uses the CAD-generated engineering database for programming the part machining requirements.

The programmer (Fig. 3.46) defines cutting tools, creates a tool library, and retrieves these tools later to create tool path information. Because CAM packages support most cutting tool configurations, programmers can describe most types of generally used cutting tools. The system also prompts the user to define machining characteristics such as retract and clearance plane, cutting depth, feed rate (rate of travel), and spindle speed (rate of spindle rotation). The cutter position (X and Z positions in Fig. 3.47) and all other machining information are displayed on the CNC control center while the machining is in progress.

3.6.13 Robotic Applications and CAD

Robotics is the integration of computer-controlled robots in the manufacturing production process. Industrial robots are

FIGURE 3.46   CNC Turning Center

FIGURE 3.48   Industrial Robot

used to move, manipulate, position, weld, and machine. Robots are controlled by a microprocessor and are normally composed of a separate stand-alone computer station, the robot mechanism itself, and an electrical hydraulic power unit (Fig. 3.48).

A robot is a reprogrammable, multifunction manipulator designed to move material, parts, tools, or specialized devices through variable, programmed motions for the performance of a variety of tasks. This definition can be expanded to include the control and synchronization of the equipment with which the robot works. This is a capability that can eliminate the need for humans to work in an environment that may be hazardous.

The integration of CAD/CAM and robotics results in increased productivity for robotic implementation activities. The **robotic workcell** contains all the physical equipment needed to create a functioning robot application. In addition to the robot, a workcell can have special fixturing, other automated machines (CNC machines, coordinate measuring machines, or visual inspection equipment), materials handling devices, part-presentation equipment, and robot grippers.

The equipment in the workcell must be arranged so that the robot work envelope includes all required device areas. CAD/CAM is perfect for designing the equipment layout (Fig. 3.49). Libraries of workcell components can be stored on the CAD/CAM system and recalled when needed. For example, a

FIGURE 3.47   CNC Control Panel

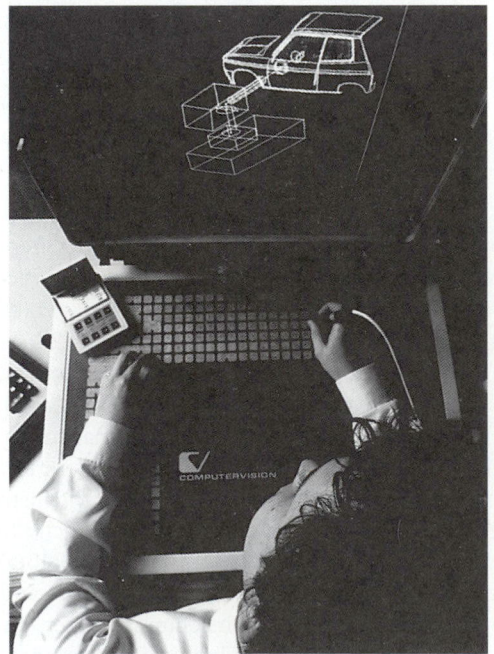

FIGURE 3.49   Off-line Robot Programming

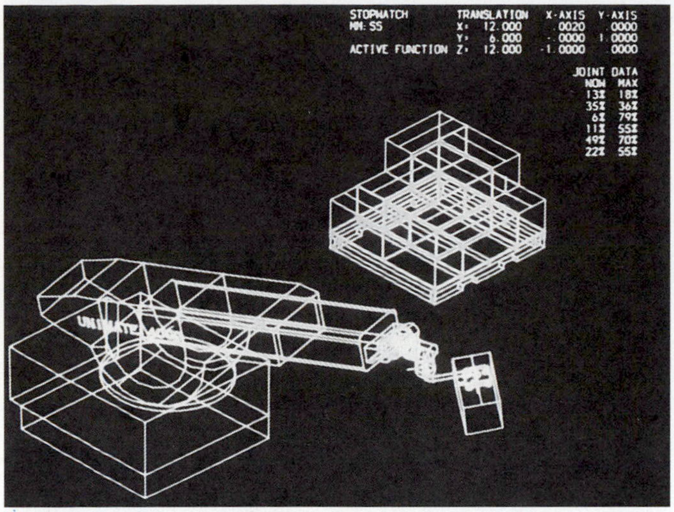

FIGURE 3.50   **Robotic Workcell Design**

robot library could contain commercial robots along with their work envelopes. Robot movement can be programmed, displayed, and checked directly on the CAD system (Fig. 3.50).

Robotics represents a stage in the engineering, design, drafting, manufacturing, and production sequence. As can be seen, the computer and its related technology play an important and essential part in the present and future of industrial design. From the days of T-squares and wooden pencils, the technology of engineering design techniques has been continually evolving, making the process of product design and manufacturing increasingly more creative and streamlined. The need for manual methods of drafting and drawing will never be totally replaced. But the use of computer-assisted methods will continue to influence the type, quality, and pace of industry.

QUIZ

True or False

1. Hardware includes instructions to do specific CAD commands to manipulate the display.
2. CAD systems require that the operator have programming ability.
3. The CPU of a CAD system performs all data manipulation required to construct, calculate, process, and store a drawing or engineering design.
4. Interactive CAD means that the system requires little or no input from the drafter-operator.
5. Resolution is the smallest spacing between points on a graphics display at which the points can be detected as distinct.
6. Robots can be viewed and controlled directly on a CAD/CAM system.
7. Electrostatic plotters are the most accurate hardcopy device.
8. Systems software allows the user to complete drawings in specific engineering fields such as piping and electronics.

Fill in the Blanks

9. _____ , _____ , _____ , and _____ are four applications areas of CAD software.
10. Industrial _____ are used to move, manipulate, position, weld, and assemble items in the manufacturing cycle.
11. A design workstation normally includes a _____ , _____ , _____ , and a _____ .
12. Electrostatic, _____ , _____ , _____ , and printers are hardcopy devices.
13. The CPU is shared by a number of _____ on a _____ CAD system.
14. The _____ is the movable screen "marker," usually a blinking box, crosshair, or other symbol.
15. Keyboards, _____ boxes, _____ balls, _____ sticks, _____ , and _____ tables are all types of operator input devices.
16. A _____ is an input device consisting of command spaces on a digitizing surface such as a data tablet, digitizing tablet, or digitizing table.

Answer the Following

17. Name six typical input devices.
18. Name five typical output devices.
19. What are function keyboards and how do they differ from terminal keyboards?
20. What is the difference between a printer and a plotter? What are the capabilities of both pieces of equipment?
21. Name three types of plotters and explain their uses.
22. What is applications software? Name five types.
23. What is the difference between a display menu (on-line menu) and a tablet menu?
24. Define "CIM" and how it relates to the total design-through-manufacturing cycle.

CHAPTER 4

Lettering

Learning Objectives

Upon completion of this chapter you will be able to accomplish the following:

1. Recognize the importance of freehand, mechanical, and machine lettering.
2. Differentiate between common lettering styles.
3. Develop the ability to use guidelines and lettering guides to determine proper lettering heights.
4. Produce standard single-stroke, uppercase Gothic characters with uniform size and spacing.
5. Identify and use mechanical lettering aids.
6. Identify machine lettering techniques.
7. Identify characteristics of CAD lettering.

4.1 Introduction

Line drawings are never complete until they are explained by labels, dimensions, notations, and titles (Fig. 4.1). This information is either carefully lettered freehand or inserted using a **TEXT** or **DIMENSION** command when done on a CAD system.

All drafters, designers, and engineers should master the art of freehand lettering. Through the study of letter forms and the direction of strokes, and with consistent practicing of lettering styles, an acceptable quality and style of lettering can be developed. The importance of good lettering cannot be overemphasized. Lettering can *make or break* an otherwise excellent drawing. In drafting and design, sloppy or misplaced lettering causes misconceptions and inaccurate communication of data.

CAD-generated drawings allow the drafter to access the database and therefore request the system to provide extra information, clarification, and verification of a part. Drawings generated on the board can only be "read." Therefore the written information about the part in the form of notes, labels, and dimensions is of great importance. This is not to say that the written information on a CAD drawing is any less important. But, with a CAD system you can recall the drawing and verify a location of a feature, check a dimension, or list out information about the part. The manually constructed and hand-lettered drawing must stand on its own.

4.2 Lettering Methods and Styles

Lettering can be divided into three separate methods: (1) manual (freehand), (2) mechanical, and (3) machine. Table 4.1 lists the three categories along with a few types of equipment and the techniques associated with each group.

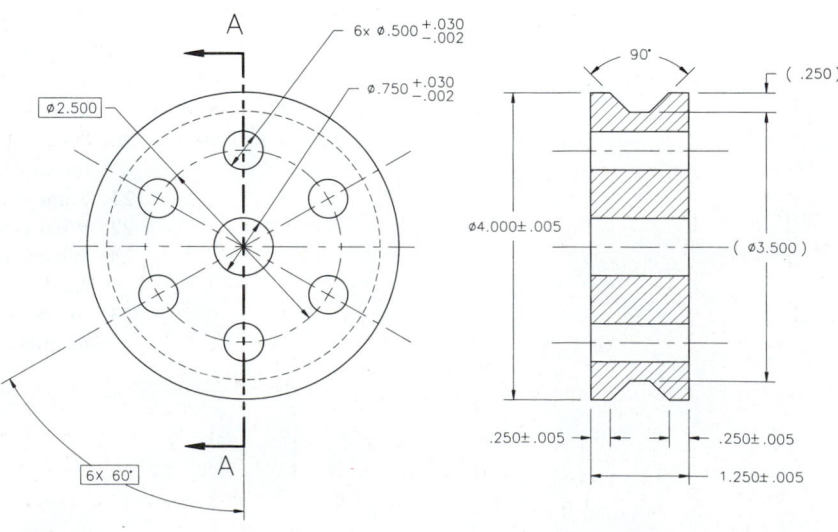

FIGURE 4.1 Engineering Drawing

SECTION A–A

TABLE 4.1 Lettering Methods

Types of Letters	Manual	Mechanical	Machine
Vertical	Freehand	Template	Typewriter
Inclined	Lettering aid	WRICO	Printer
Uppercase	(slot guide)	Leroy	Dry transfer
Lowercase		Letterguide	Phototypesetter
		Varigraph	CAD

A wide variety of lettering styles, or fonts, are available. A **font** is an assortment of type all of one size and style. For most drafting disciplines, the *single-stroke uppercase Gothic alphabet* is used. The Gothic alphabet does not have short bars, or **serifs**, at the ends of strokes as does the Roman alphabet. Figure 4.2 shows a few of the many fonts commercially available in phototypesetting and printing processes and in dry transfer letters. Note that the vertical uppercase DRAFTING STANDARD font is available.

Lettering of titles, subtitles, drawing numbers, and other uses may be made freehand, by typewriter, or with the aid of mechanical lettering devices such as templates and lettering machines. Regardless of the method used, all characters must conform, in general, with the recommended Gothic style and must be legible in full- or reduced-size copy by any accepted method of reproduction. The quality of your lettering after reduction will depend on the legibility of the lettering and its height. The recommended minimum freehand and mechanical lettering heights for various size drawings are given in Table 4.2.

Cooper Bl. Ital.
Cooper Blk. Out.
COPPERPLATE
DAVIDA
Dom Casual
Dom Diagonal
DRAFTING STANDARD
Eckmann
Egyptian Exp.
EMBOSS LIGHT
EMBOSS BOLD
Embrionic
Engravers Old Eng.
Eurostile Med. Ex.
Eurostile Bold Ext.
Fanfare
Folio Light
Folio Medium
Folio Bold
Folio Ex. Bold
Folio Bold Cond.

FIGURE 4.2 Examples of Typefaces

4.3 Manual Lettering

Many drawings are still made and revised with freehand lettering techniques. Both **vertical** (Fig. 4.3) and **inclined** (Fig. 4.4) lettering are found throughout industry. Vertical lettering is preferred since it reduces and microfilms better than inclined lettering. Still, inclined lettering is easier for some to master and normally is faster to complete. Some companies accept only vertical lettering.

Uppercase letters are used for all lettering on drawings unless lowercase letters are required to conform with other established standards, equipment nomenclature, or marking. Lowercase lettering is seldom found on engineering drawings except for the drawing *notes* since long columns of uppercase characters are not as pleasing to the eye and are harder to read. The use of lowercase lettering is specified in company standards when acceptable. In general, only uppercase Gothic lettering is required on mechanical and electronic drawings.

TABLE 4.2 Recommended Lettering Heights for Manual and Mechanical Lettering (Uppercase Letters)

Project	Size of Drawing	Height of Manual Letters, English (Metric) Units	Height of Mechanical Letters, English (Metric) Units
Numbers in a title block	A–C*	.250 in., $\frac{1}{4}$ in. (7 mm)	.240 in. (7 mm)
	D and above*	.312 in., $\frac{5}{16}$ in. (7 mm)	.290 in. (7 mm)
Title, section lettering	A–F	.250 in., $\frac{1}{4}$ in. (7 mm)	.240 in. (7 mm)
Zone letters and numerals in borders	A–F	.188 in., $\frac{3}{16}$ in. (5 mm)	.175 in. (5 mm)
Lettering in dimensions, tolerances, notes,	A–C	.125 in., $\frac{1}{8}$ in. (3.5 mm)	.120 in. (3.5 mm)
tables, limits	D and above	.156 in., $\frac{5}{32}$ in. (5 mm)	.140 in. (5 mm)

*Drawing sizes: A — $8\frac{1}{2} \times 11$ in., B — 11×17 in., C — 17×22 in., D — 22×34 in.

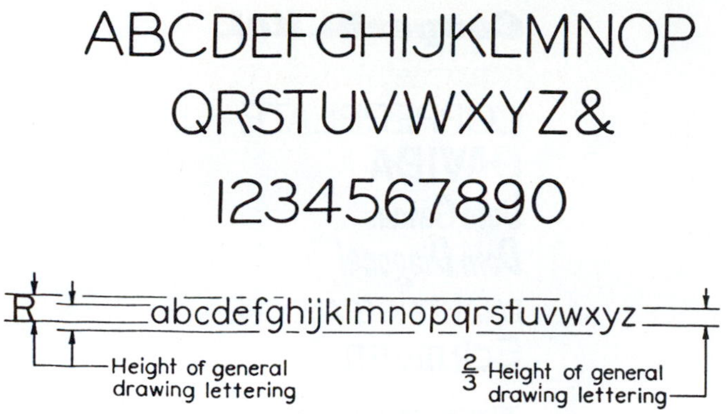

ABCDEFGHIJKLMNOP
QRSTUVWXYZ&
1234567890

R abcdefghijklmnopqrstuvwxyz
Height of general
drawing lettering   ⅔ Height of general
drawing lettering

FIGURE 4.3   ANSI Standard Vertical Upper- and Lowercase Lettering

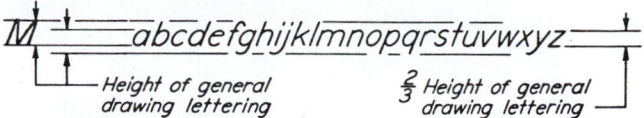

ABCDEFGHIJKLMNOP
QRSTUVWXYZ&
1234567890

M abcdefghijklmnopqrstuvwxyz
Height of general
drawing lettering   ⅔ Height of general
drawing lettering

FIGURE 4.4   ANSI Standard Inclined Upper- and Lowercase Lettering

Piping, architectural, structural, and civil drawings sometimes employ lowercase lettering.

Though the recommended font style is single-stroke Gothic, adaptations such as the **Gothic style Microfont alphabet** are also acceptable (Fig. 4.5). The Microfont alphabet is suggested for drawings requiring microfilm reproduction.

4.3.1   Guidelines and Lettering Heights

Freehand lettering, whether vertical or inclined, requires guidelines at the top and bottom of the letters to determine the height of lettering on the drawing. Guidelines are not necessary if you use grid underlays or fadeout grid paper, but you should avoid using grid underlays until you have gained some experience with lettering from hand-drawn guidelines.

Guidelines (Fig. 4.6) are very thin, sharp, light gray, and drawn with 6H–3H grade lead or with blue nonreproducible lead. Figure 4.7 has two labels specifying the required markings on a piece of electronic equipment, which is upside-

ABCDEFGHIJKLMNO

PQRSTUVWXYZ

1234567890

FIGURE 4.5   ANSI Standard Microfont Alphabet

down. The object and note were completed first and then the drawing was turned and lettered as required. Guidelines were used on all lettering. This is an actual industry drawing and shows the position of the instrument during a particular assembly operation. This figure demonstrates that some drawings require lettering from both sides.

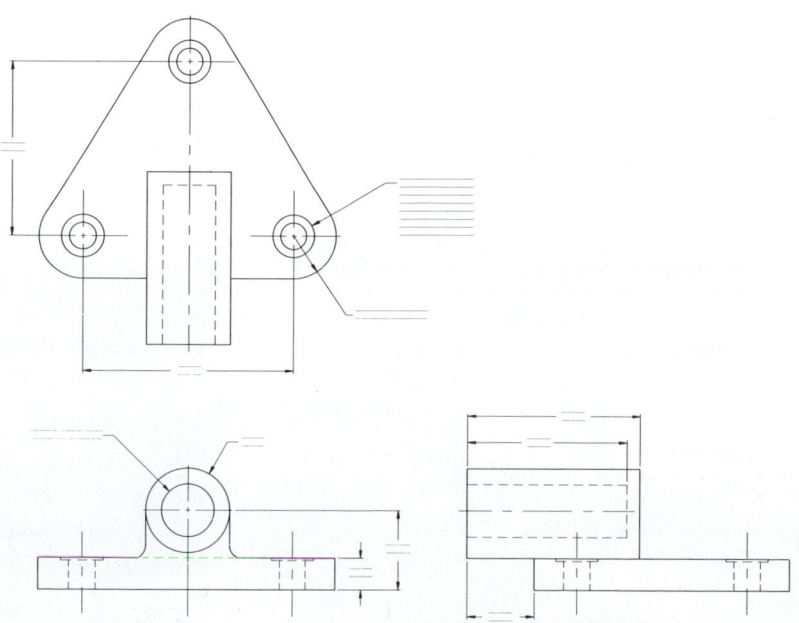

FIGURE 4.6   Mechanical Drawing with Guidelines

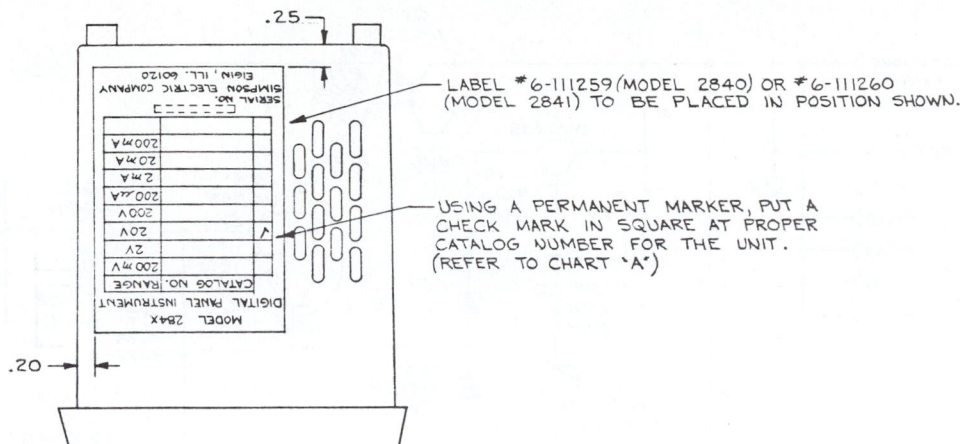

FIGURE 4.7 Freehand Lettering Using Guidelines

Since most lettering is done with capital letters and whole numbers, only two guidelines are necessary. Guidelines can be drawn with a straightedge or with the aid of a line spacing guide, such as the AMES lettering guide (Fig. 4.8) or the Braddock-Rowe triangle. For dimensions, notes, and labels, most lettering is between $\frac{1}{8}$ in. (.125 in.) and $\frac{5}{32}$ in. (.156 in.) high in U.S. units or 3.5 and 5 mm high in SI units. Lettering height is determined by the drawing format size. For all problems in the text, you should use the standards for lettering heights and guideline spacing shown in Table 4.2, which corresponds to *Conventions and Lettering* from the American National Standards Institute. (Metric sizes are not U.S. conversions.)

The distance between lines of lettering on manually drawn projects for notes and labels is equal to the full height of the letter being used. This spacing is best for reproducible, legible letters if they will be reduced and/or enlarged (for instance, when a microfilmed drawing is returned to its original size). When upper- and lowercase lettering is used on "D" size sheets and larger, the minimum uppercase height is a minimum of 5 mm for metric drawings and $\frac{5}{32}$ in. (.156 in.) for U.S. drawings. This will provide for legible enlargement for microfilmed drawings.

The **freehand lettering guide** shown in Figure 4.9 was used to letter the diagram in Figure 4.10. This device eliminates the need for guidelines since it limits the height of the lettering to the space within the slots. Lettering aids tend to flatten the upper and lower portions of some letters. Do not use lettering guides while attempting to learn and perfect freehand lettering. Guidelines are also unnecessary when you use vellum, or drafting film, with nonreproducible grid lines. The grid spacing (if the correct size) can be used as guidelines for the lettering. Guidelines are also unnecessary when you use a lettering template.

Many times a drafter is called on to complete or revise an existing drawing. If you are given such a project, try to match the existing lettering style. The lettering in Figure 4.11 is both vertical and horizontal, and guidelines were obviously not used. *Vertical and inclined lettering should never be mixed on one drawing.*

The lettering page provided in Figure 4.12 shows the use of both horizontal and vertical (or inclined) guidelines. You may wish to use vertical or inclined guidelines when practicing lettering until some consistency is achieved. Vertical or inclined guidelines are rarely used on drawings.

Except when special emphasis is required, lettering should not be underlined. If underlining is required, it should not be less than 1.5 mm (.06 in.) below the lettering.

FIGURE 4.8 AMES Lettering Guide

FIGURE 4.9 Freehand Lettering Aid

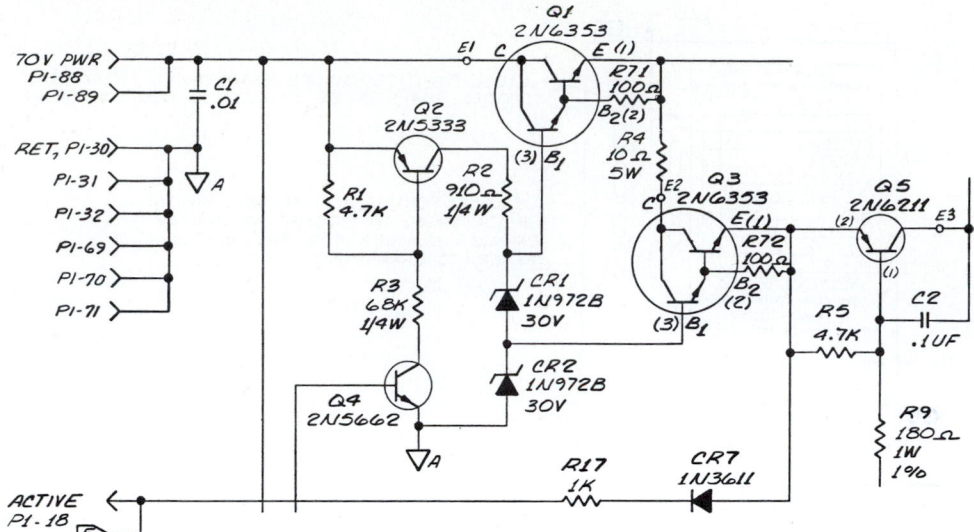

FIGURE 4.10 Inclined Lettering Using a Lettering Guide

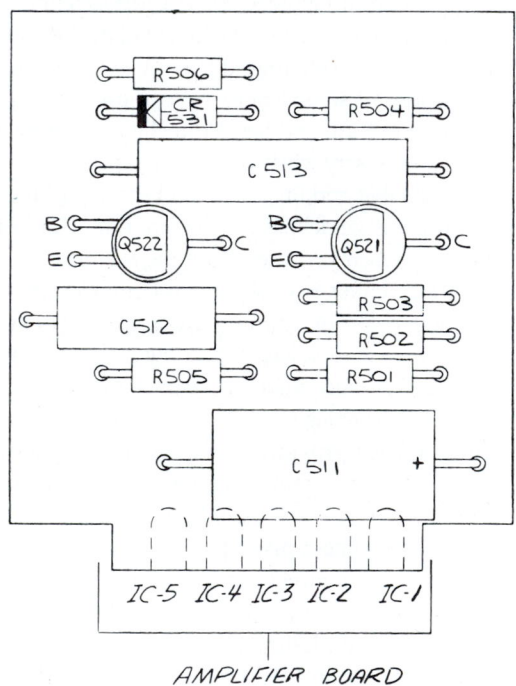

FIGURE 4.11 Mixed Vertical and Inclined Lettering on the Same Drawing   Guidelines are not used.

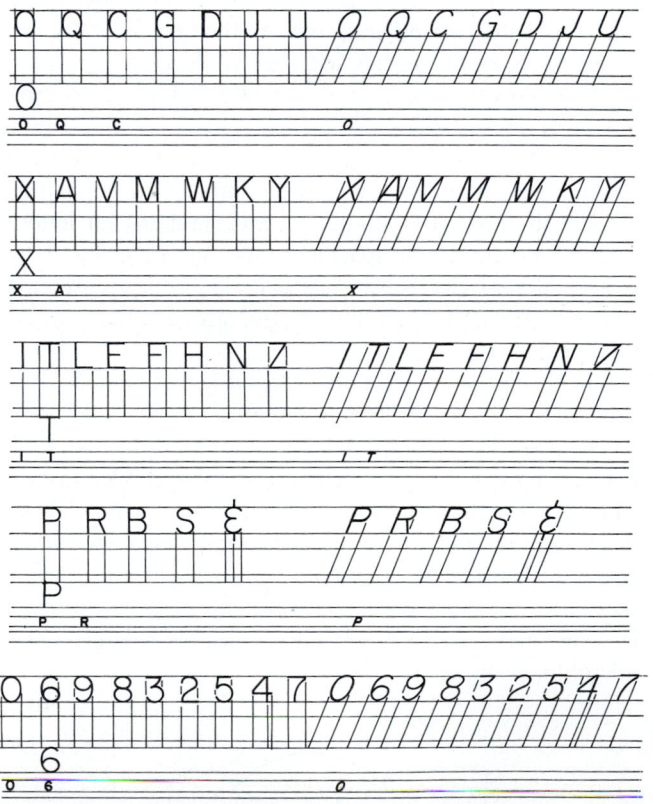

FIGURE 4.12 Using Horizontal and Vertical (or Inclined) Guidelines for Lettering Practice

4.3.2 Pencil Technique

Freehand lettering places a requirement on linework that is different from that possible with instrument lines. Instrument lines are made more dense when the construction line is traced, but for most drafters, it is impossible to trace freehand lettering consistently . Therefore, drafters must draw lettering of the proper density in only one stroke. To help get the proper density, a soft lead is used. Depending on your preference, the H, HB, or F lead can be used for all lettering with good results.

Soft lead contributes to the dirt on the drawing because it "chalks" more easily. Frequent use of the drafting brush is necessary. Due to its tendency to smear, lettering is usually the last step in the completion of a drawing. When lettering, do not let your hand come in contact with the drawing surface. Always place a sheet of clean paper between your hand

and the drawing medium. This will help keep the drawing free of body oils and dirt as well as prevent smearing of the linework (Fig. 4.13).

Since it requires no sharpening, the fine-line pencil is an excellent lettering device. A 0.5 or 0.7 mm fine-line pencil is used for lettering when available. Rotating your pencil or lead holder minimizes depletion of the point and helps maintain consistency of character width.

By now you have developed lifelong habits regarding how to hold a pencil and how to form each character. The suggested hand orientation (Fig. 4.13), stroke sequence, and stroke direction (Fig. 4.14) are provided to help guide you, but are not meant to be interpreted as the only method of

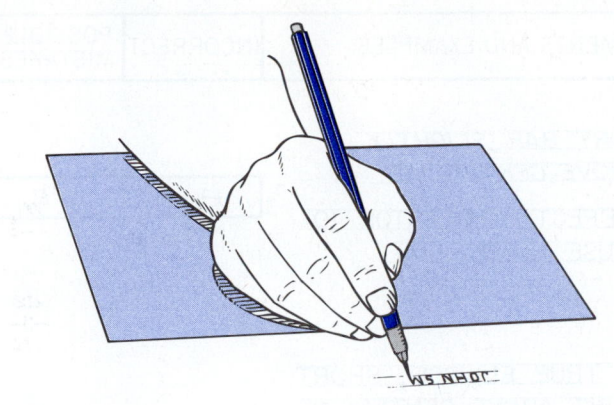

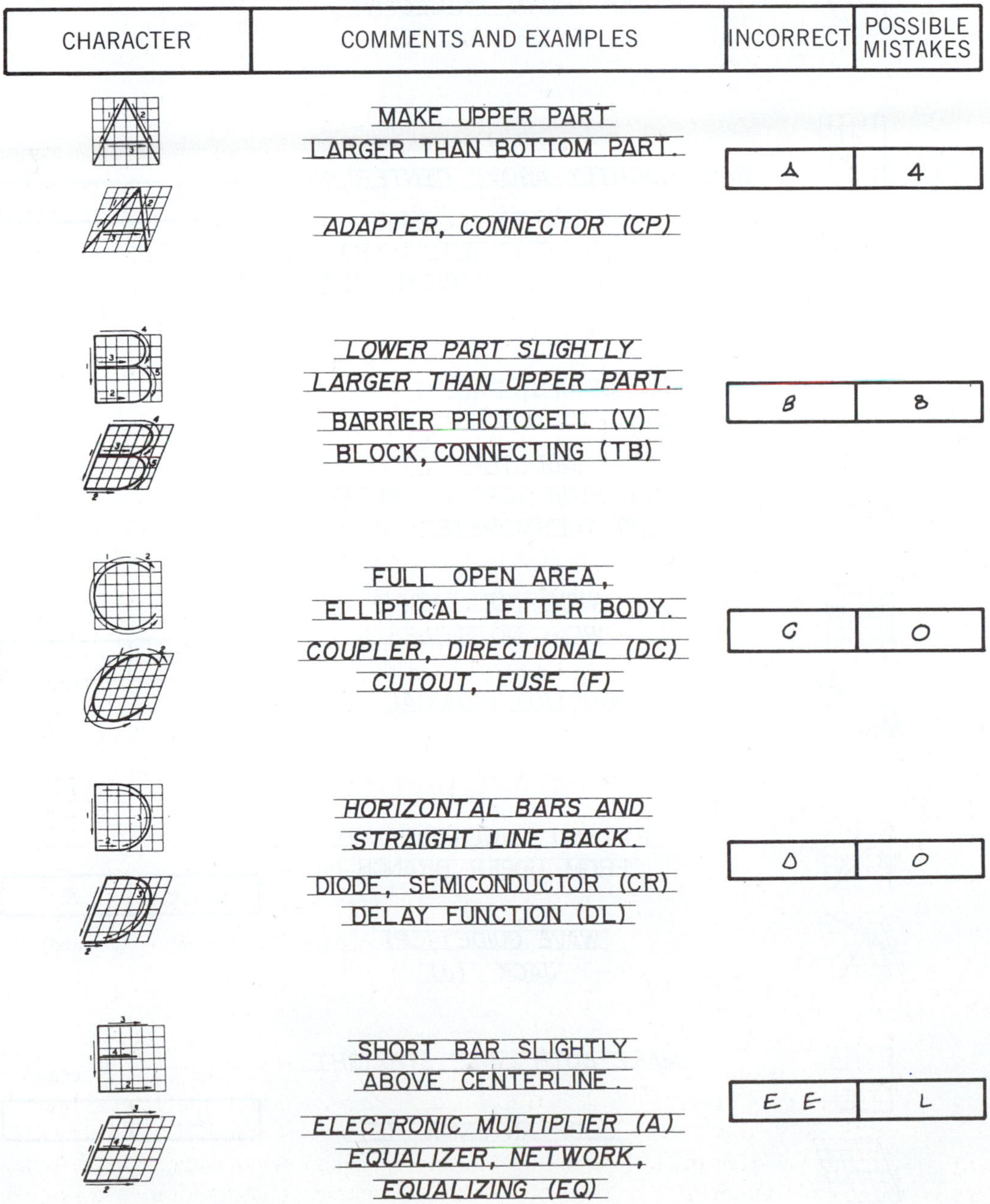

FIGURE 4.13 Hand Position When Lettering

CHARACTER	COMMENTS AND EXAMPLES	INCORRECT	POSSIBLE MISTAKES
	MAKE UPPER PART LARGER THAN BOTTOM PART. ADAPTER, CONNECTOR (CP)	A	4
	LOWER PART SLIGHTLY LARGER THAN UPPER PART. BARRIER PHOTOCELL (V) BLOCK, CONNECTING (TB)	B	8
	FULL OPEN AREA, ELLIPTICAL LETTER BODY. COUPLER, DIRECTIONAL (DC) CUTOUT, FUSE (F)	C	O
	HORIZONTAL BARS AND STRAIGHT LINE BACK. DIODE, SEMICONDUCTOR (CR) DELAY FUNCTION (DL)	D	O
	SHORT BAR SLIGHTLY ABOVE CENTERLINE. ELECTRONIC MULTIPLIER (A) EQUALIZER, NETWORK, EQUALIZING (EQ)	E E	L

FIGURE 4.14 Stroke Sequence, Comments, Examples, and Possible Errors in Lettering

Continues

CHARACTER	COMMENTS AND EXAMPLES	INCORRECT	POSSIBLE MISTAKES

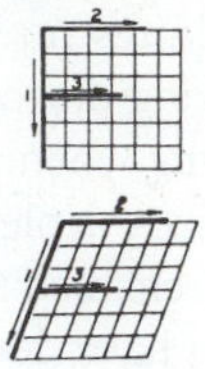

SHORT BAR SLIGHTLY ABOVE CENTERLINE.

FIELD EFFECT TRANSISTOR (Q)
FUSE HOLDER (X)

F F | T E

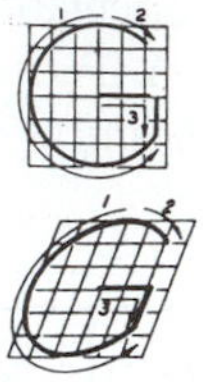

BASED ON TRUE ELLIPSE, SHORT HORIZONTAL LINE ABOVE CENTERLINE.

GENERATOR (G)
GAP (HORN, PROJECTIVE, OR SPHERE) (E)

G G G | C O G

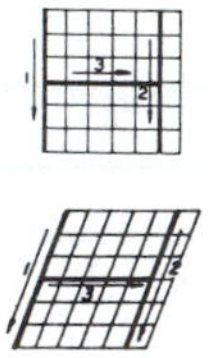

BAR SLIGHTLY ABOVE CENTERLINE.

HARDWARE (COMMON FASTENERS, ETC.) (H)
HEADSET, ELECTRICAL (HT)

H H

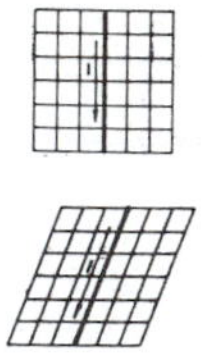

NO SERIFS, EXCEPT WHEN NEXT TO NUMBER ONE (1).

INDUCTOR (L)
INDICATOR (EXCEPT METER OR THERMOMETER) (DS)

I 1

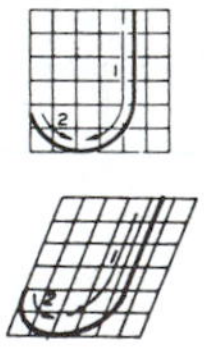

WIDE FULL HOOK WITH NO SERIFS.

JUNCTION (COAXIAL OR

J J

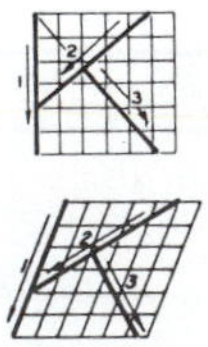

EXTEND LOWER BRANCH FROM UPPER BRANCH.

WAVE GUIDE) (CP)
JACK (J)

K K | R

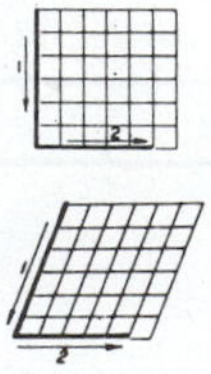

MAKE BOTH LINES STRAIGHT.

LOOP ANTENNA (E)

L

FIGURE 4.14 Stroke Sequence, Comments, Examples, and Possible Errors in Lettering *Continued*

CHARACTER	COMMENTS AND EXAMPLES	INCORRECT	POSSIBLE MISTAKES
M	NOT AS WIDE AS W : CENTER PART EXTENDS TO BOTTOM OF LETTER. MICROCIRCUIT (U) MULTIPLIER, ELECTRONIC (A)	M M	
N	DO NOT CRAM LINES TOGETHER. NETWORK, EQUALIZING (HY) DIODE, TUNNEL (CR)	N N	V U
O	FULL TRUE ELLIPSE. OSCILLOGRAPH (M) OSCILLOSCOPE (M)	0 O	C Q 6
P	MIDDLE BAR INTERSECTS AT LETTER'S MIDDLE. PHOTODIODE (CR) POTENTIOMETER (R)	P P	K T D
Q	BASED ON TRUE WIDE ELLIPSE. NETWORK, EQUALIZING (HY) SWITCH, SEMICONDUCTOR CONTROLLED (Q)	Q	O
R	MAKE UPPER PORTION LARGE. REGULATOR, VOLTAGE (V) RESISTOR, THERMAL (RT)	R R	K
S	BASED ON NUMBER 8; KEEP ENDS OPEN. SOLENOID, ELECTRICAL (L) SWITCH, INTERLOCK (S)	S	8

Continues

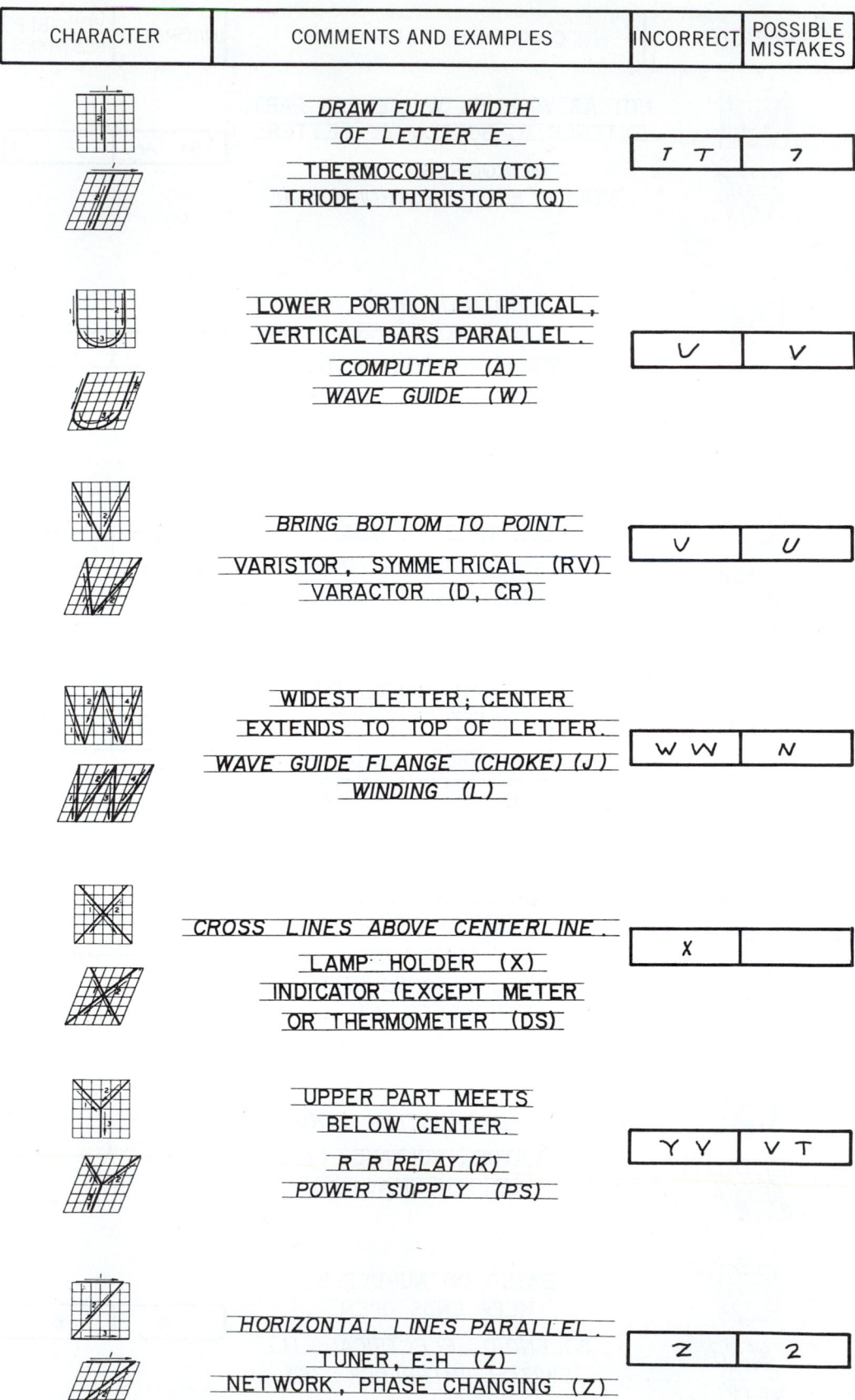

FIGURE 4.14 Stroke Sequence, Comments, Examples, and Possible Errors in Lettering *Continued*

CHARACTER	COMMENTS AND EXAMPLES	INCORRECT	POSSIBLE MISTAKES
	SAME AS LETTER I. 10,000 OHMS Q4 2N1011	1 1	7
	BASED ON NUMBER 8; OPEN HOOK. Q1 2N1925 1200 OHMS	2 2	Z
	BASED ON NUMBER 8; UPPER PART SMALLER THAN LOWER. VM103 1N673	3 3	8 5
	HORIZONTAL BAR BELOW CENTER OF FIGURE. TB1034 - 22G/R 2N38974	4 4 4	7 9 H
	BASED ON ELLIPSE; KEEP WIDE. XQ2-5 1.5 MS	5 5	6 3 S
	BASED ON ELLIPSE; OPEN. 42 - 020 - 6 68,000 OHMS	6	8
	KEEP AS WIDE AS LETTER E. 4.7 K 47,000 OHMS	7 7 7	I

Continues

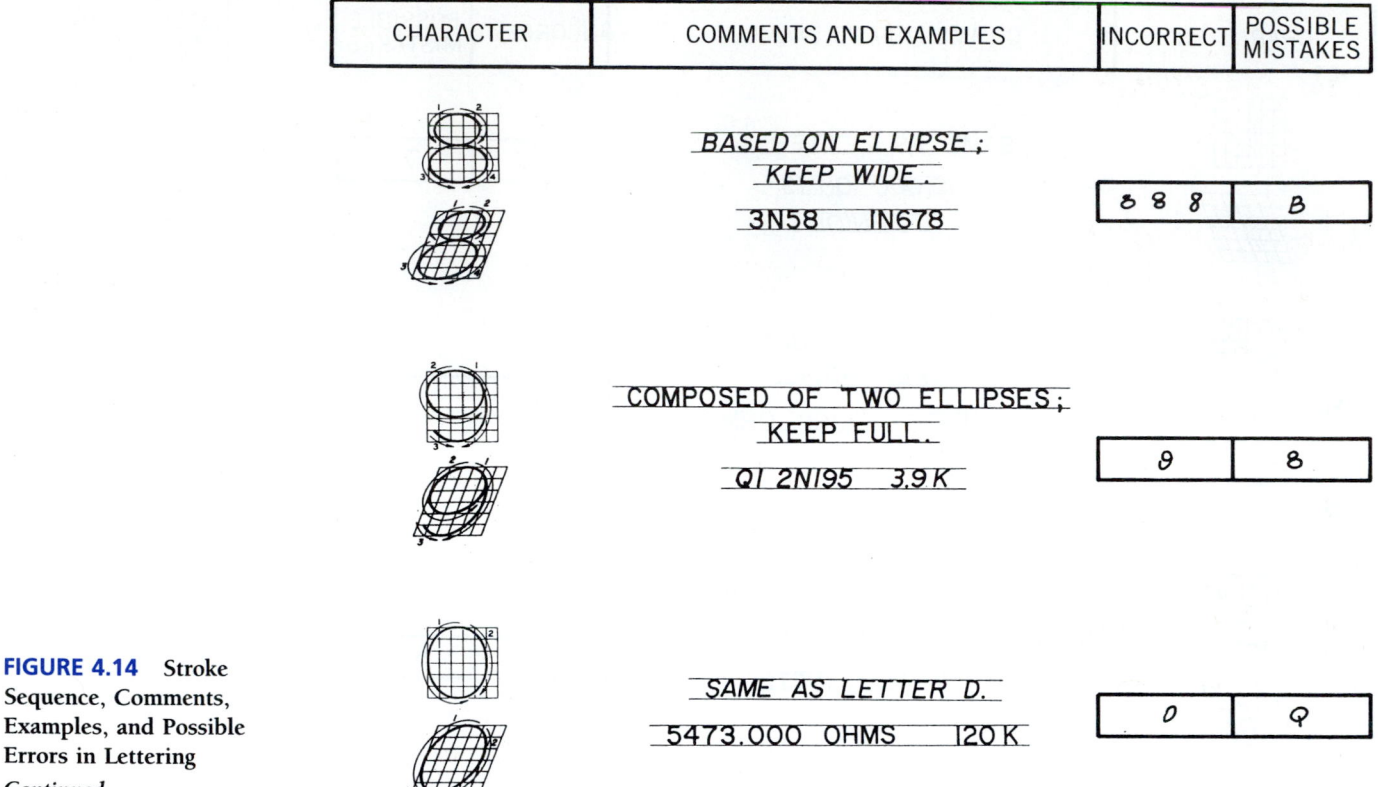

CHARACTER	COMMENTS AND EXAMPLES	INCORRECT	POSSIBLE MISTAKES
	BASED ON ELLIPSE; *KEEP WIDE.* 3N58 1N678	8 8 8	B
	COMPOSED OF TWO ELLIPSES; KEEP FULL. Q1 2N195 3.9K	0	8
	SAME AS LETTER D. 5473.000 OHMS 120 K	D	Q

FIGURE 4.14 Stroke Sequence, Comments, Examples, and Possible Errors in Lettering *Continued*

lettering. Left-handed and right-handed people have individualized methods, but the most important thing is that the end result must conform to the ANSI standard style and quality. To achieve this quality, *you must practice.*

4.3.3 Lettering Strokes, Uniformity, and Form

The strokes of your letters must be consistent in both width and density. Obviously, variation in the densities between lettering and linework must be avoided. You should strive for consistent, uniform, well-spaced letters. The stroke sequence is the same for both inclined and vertical lettering. In Figure 4.14, an alphabet of vertical and inclined lettering is shown along with a numbered suggested stroke sequence. This figure also highlights typical problems in forming letters. Lettering examples are also provided below each comment. The examples used are reference designations found on electronic drawings. Note that guidelines were used throughout.

The grid pattern shown in Figure 4.14 gives the ideal width and height relationship for single-stroke Gothic lettering. All characters are six units in height and vary in width from the 1 and l to the W and M. The six basic strokes used for freehand lettering are shown in Figure 4.15. Note that this suggested stroke sequence is only meant to be a general guide. Your lettering style, manner of holding the pencil, and whether you are right-handed or left-handed affect the choice of stroke sequence.

You should strive to develop a lettering style that is comfortable, a style that communicates the necessary engineering data without confusion and mistakes. It is very important to catch bad habits early in order not to ingrain them in your lettering style. Please note that in the beginning it is important to eliminate any individualized style, until your lettering becomes clear, concise, dark, and well formed. Through practice, a more attractive personal style will emerge and become *yours.*

In Figure 4.16, the typical slant angle used for inclined lettering is shown. Any angle between 90° (vertical) and 65° is acceptable unless an individual company has a preferred practice. Left-handed drafters sometimes slant their lettering backwards 1 to 5°. This method should only be used if it falls within your company's (or class's) standard practice (Fig. 4.7).

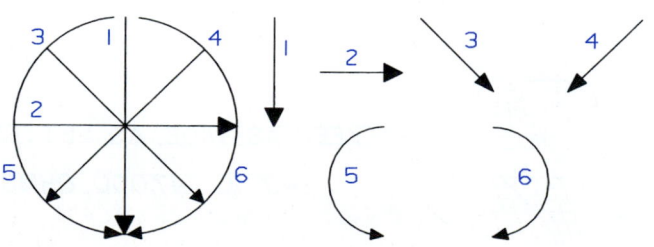

FIGURE 4.15   Basic Lettering Strokes

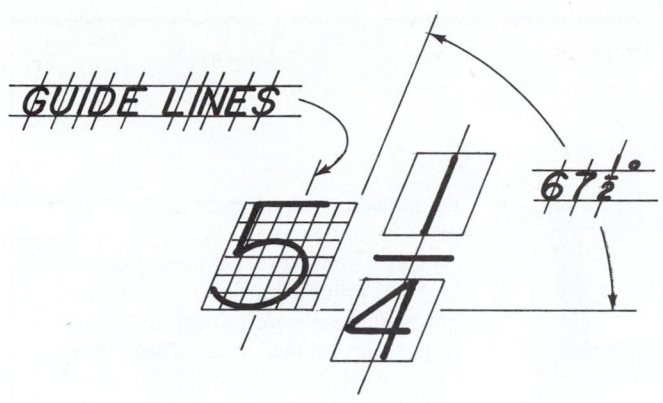

FIGURE 4.16   Using Guidelines for Inclined Lettering

4.3.4   Spacing

Spacing is done by eye to create a pleasing and orderly set of words or numbers. The spacing between letters in a word is as important as the spacing between words. The background area between characters should *appear* equal even though it's not. The spacing between words should be a minimum of six units wide, in other words, the width of the widest letter such as a W or M. The spacing between letters varies because the shape of the adjacent letters varies. Spacing for letters and words should correspond to the following specifications (Fig. 4.17):

- Background areas between letters in words are separated by approximately equal areas.
- Spacing for numerals separated by a decimal point (5.375, 2.54 mm, etc.) are a minimum of $\frac{2}{3}$ of the character height used.
- Spaces between words are approximately equal and a minimum of .06 in. (1.5 mm). A full character height for horizontal word spacing is suggested.
- The horizontal space between lines of lettering is at least $\frac{1}{2}$ of the height of the characters, but preferably one full character height of space is left between lines.
- Sentences are separated by at least one full character height and preferably two character heights if space permits.

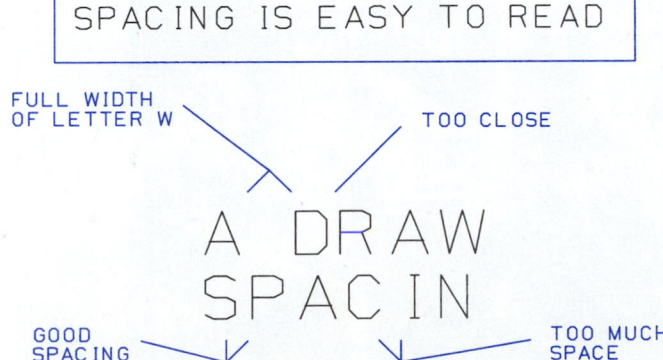

FIGURE 4.17   Spacing of Letters and Words

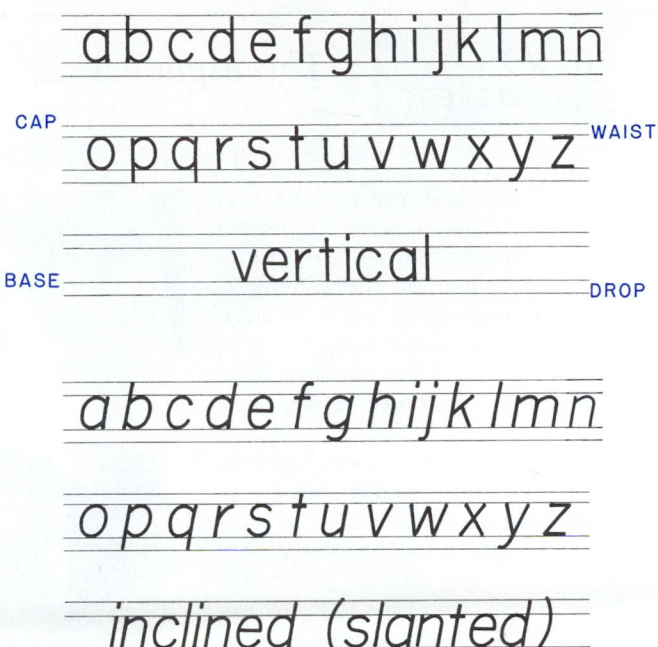

FIGURE 4.18   Lowercase Lettering

4.3.5   Lowercase Lettering

Lowercase lettering as shown in Figure 4.18 is seldom used on engineering work except for construction drawings. Lowercase lettering, whether inclined or vertical, requires extra guidelines. Guidelines for the *waistline* (top of main body of letter) and *baseline* (bottom of main body of letter), as well as for *ascender* and *descender lines*, should be added to the drawing before the letters are drawn. Ascender lines or *cap lines* designate the top of strokes for letters that extend above the waistline, such as b, d, f, h, k, and l. Descender lines or *drop lines* designate the bottom of strokes for letters below the baseline, such as g, j, p, and y.

4.3.6   Fractions on Drawings

Most drawings are dimensioned with decimal-inch or metric units. These methods are easier, more accurate, and quicker to draw since all numbers are placed between two equally spaced guidelines. For some drawings, the tolerance and accuracy required for manufacturing and construction is loose enough to permit fraction dimensioning, such as for sheet metal work. Fractions are also widely used in piping, civil, architectural, and structural design. In Figure 4.19, the height

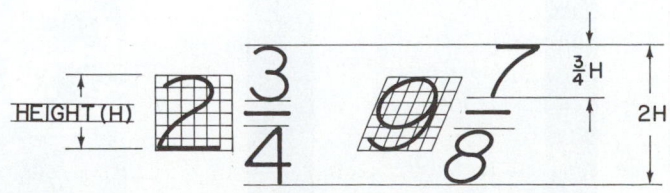

FIGURE 4.19   Fractions

The Alphabet

The alphabet developed as a result of man's need to record events. In fact, our modern alphabet had its origin in Egyptian hieroglyphics. The word *hieroglyphics* means "picture writing" and is the oldest and most primitive of all writing. Some of the letters of the Roman alphabet in use today can be traced back to these crude pictures.

The Greeks adopted symbology from the Phoenicians who had developed a 22-letter alphabet in about 1500 B.C. The adopted system evolved into two distinct alphabets in two parts of Greece. The Western type became the Latin alphabet (about 700 B.C.) and was used throughout the Old World. (The modern English word for *alphabet* comes from the first two letters of the Greek alphabet, *alpha* and *beta*.) The original Roman alphabet of twenty-three characters has remained unchanged except that characters have been added.

People began communicating with each other through all forms of written communication once the alphabet was accepted. Unfortunately, books, even from the earliest times, were prepared by the laborious method of hand copying onto papyrus, parchment, or vellum. The scribes cut quills and made ink from gum and lampblack. Before the fall of the Roman Empire, the copying of books was a thriving and important industry. When Rome fell, the rich patrons of literature were scattered and their libraries were left

A Gutenberg Printing Press

to be burned. Monks, fearful that all literature would be lost, took on as part of their religious duties, the task of copying classical and religious books.

About fifty years before Columbus discovered America, Johannes Gutenberg revolutionized graphic communications. Gutenberg, in Mainz, Germany, perfected a way to cast individual letters. As a young man, he had studied the arduous task of scribes and wanted to invent a mechanical printing process to make the scribes' work easier and make books more accessible. Until his time, all lettering was done by hand and it was left to

the individual as to how each letter was made or decorated.

Three years after he started, Gutenberg had printed 200 copies of the Bible. Thirty of these were printed on a paper made from animal skins. These thirty copies used the hides of about 10,000 calves!

During the Industrial Revolution, the printing press needed for production was invented. Now with the printing process, more books could be printed and more people could afford to own them. Gutenberg's dream was realized at last!

It seems inconceivable to not know an alphabet or to have printed books. Even though we don't think much about our alphabet, most of what we do to communicate with each other is based on standard alphabets and printed material.

The computer is now the basis for another revolution in communications. The operators of modern CAD systems have a variety of *fonts* to choose from when inserting text into their drawings. A font is a series of patterns created by the CAD program to represent specific letters in certain styles (roman, italic, or script, for example). The font of the text can be changed at will. Computers can virtually link offices together across the country and the world. Regardless of how fast or sophisticated the method or the style of the text, our modern alphabet remains the basis for the way we communicate in written form.

Hieroglyphics

A Modern Printing Shop

ratio of fraction number to whole number is provided. When a drawing is to be reduced, the size of lettering may need to be larger than normal for accurate enlargement (enlargement from reduction size). *The ANSI standard on lettering states that the height of the fraction number should be the same as that for the whole number.* Most drafting books, and many companies, however, suggest the relationship shown in Figure 4.19.

The division line of the common fraction is drawn parallel to the direction in which the dimension reads and is separated from the numerals by a minimum of 1.5 mm (.06 in.) of space. The numbers must not touch the fraction division bar. The division bar is normally drawn horizontally between the numbers and not at an angle, except in notes, when the angled division bar is acceptable. Some company standards require the angled division bar, but it is not an ANSI standard.

4.3.7   Lettering Composition

Various special circumstances affect the composition and placement of letters on a drawing. Expanded (extended), compressed, stopline, centered, and symmetrical lettering are found on many types of diagrams and drawings. Figure 4.20 shows examples of compressed and extended letters. Note that these variations are easily accomplished using a CAD system since the lettering font, height, width, slant, and justification can be selected by the drafter.

By practicing letters and numerals in groups, going from simple to complex, you will learn an easy way to practice on the forms that you need to improve without having to letter the whole alphabet. The following groupings can be used during practice:

- Straight lines only
  A, E, F, H, I, K, L, M, N, T, V, W, X, Y, Z, 1, 4,
- Straight and curved lines
  B, D, J, P, U, 2, 5, 7
- Curved lines only
  C, G, O, Q, S, 3, 6, 8, 9, 0

Stopline lettering is used on some drawings and charts. In most cases, lettering is *left-justified* (aligned on the left in a column). When lettering must stop along a given line or at a specific point it is called *right-justified*. Since the letters are normally drawn from the left toward the right, right-justified freehand lettering (stopline lettering) is somewhat difficult to do. The drafter may have to letter from the right toward the left to complete stopline lettering properly.

The stability of lettering construction is very important to lettering composition. How does the lettering or number look on the paper? The construction of each letter and number is extremely important. This includes proportion, stability, uniformity, balance, consistency, thickness, and density. The combination of these factors to make notes is called *composition*. The beauty of machine lettering lies in its ability to do all of the above variations automatically.

4.3.8   Lists and Notes

Traditionally, notes have been placed above the drawing's title block area on the far right. The newest ANSI standards have reversed the placement of notes. *Notes are now to be placed on the lower left or the upper left of the drawing.* However, many

CONDENSED LETTERING

NORMAL LETTERING

EXTENDED LETTERING

CONDENSED

NORMAL

EXTENDED

FIGURE 4.20   Condensed, Normal, and Extended Vertical and Inclined Lettering

REF NO	COMPONENT	PART NO
R-401	33K	216480
R-402	24K	216477
R-403	9.1K	216467
R-404	33	549978
R-405	100K	216491
R-406	430K	216731
R-407	7.5K	216465
R-408	100	595359
R-409	1K	216445
R-410	5.1K	216461
R-411	15K	216472
R-412	47K	216484
R-413	100K	216491
R-414	680	216442
J	JUMPER	1207833
C-421	.15/35 MFD	491255
C-422	150 PF DISC	1207587
C-423	3.3/35 MFD	1207585
C-424	.47/35 MFD	1208599
C-425	.33/35 MFD	1208591
C-426	2.2/35 MFD	1208601
C-427	.0068/100 MFD	492500
C-428	.0027/100 MFD	491309
C-429	150 PF DISC	1207587
Q-441	GREEN	1207577
Q-442	GREEN	1207577
Q-443	BLACK	1207601

FIGURE 4.21   Hand-Lettered Parts List

NOTES:

1. MARK PER MIL-STD-130 APPROXIMATELY WHERE SHOWN, .093 HIGH CHARACTERS USING ITEM 48

2. SOLDER IN ACCORDANCE WITH NHB5300.4 (3A-1)

3. PARTIAL REFERENCE DESIGNATIONS ARE SHOWN FOR COMPLETE DESIGNATIONS PREFIX WITH UNIT NUMBER AND SUBASSEMBLY DESIGNATIONS

4. ELECTROSTATIC DEVICE, HANDLE PER DOD-STD-1686

5. TORQUE 2-2.5 INCH LBS

6. FINISH: CONFORMAL COAT PER GEN-PS5205 EXCEPT CONNECTOR AND DESIGNATED AREAS SHOWN

7. BOND ITEM 67 TO ITEM 1 PRIOR TO POPULATION OF CARD ASSEMBLY PER GEN-PS5402 CLASS 7

8. APPLY FILLET TO COMPONENTS INDICATED AFTER CONFORMAL COATING PER GEN-PS5402 CL II

FIGURE 4.22 Hand-Lettered Notes Added to Preprinted Company Notes

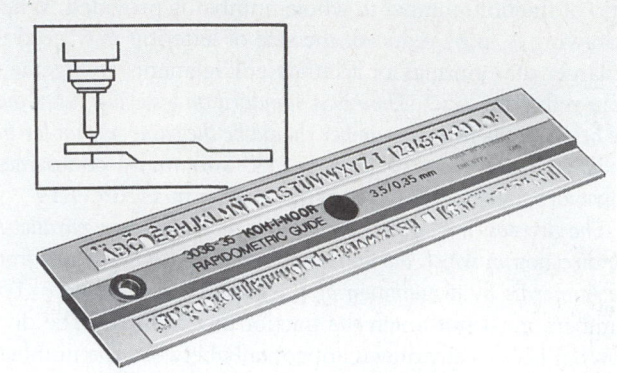

FIGURE 4.23 Lettering Guide Template

companies still follow the older practice of placing notes above the title block on the right side of the drawing. Hand-lettered lists (Fig. 4.21) and notes are time-consuming and tiring. The notes in Figure 4.22 are standard preprinted company notes; 7 and 8 were added using freehand lettering.

You May Complete Exercises 4.1 Through 4.4 at This Time

4.4 Mechanical Lettering Aids

One of the most common lettering devices found in any drafting room is the **template.** Although freehand lettering is the rule rather than the exception on manually drawn projects, templates are used on some drawings. Templates are available for almost any size and style of lettering, and can be adapted for ink as well as pencil use (Fig. 4.23). The beauty of a template lies in its ability to produce repeatable uniform letters and numerals. Template lettering, however, takes considerably more time than freehand lettering (Fig. 4.24).

With a template, guidelines are unnecessary, but a template must rest against a straightedge while in use so that all the letters are aligned properly. In general, template lettering is used on drawings that are inked, in title blocks, and for section letter identification. The major drawback of templates is that it is hard to ink perfectly formed letters without a great deal of practice. The pencil or inking pen must be kept almost perpendicular to the paper while the letters are drawn. The Koh-I-Noor Rapidometric Guide template in Figure 4.23 is an example of a template designed to be used for inking. Note that the inset drawing shows how the template shelf does not come in contact with the drawing surface. Thin stick-on pads may also be fastened to the bottom of templates and triangles. This eliminates potential smearing of the ink.

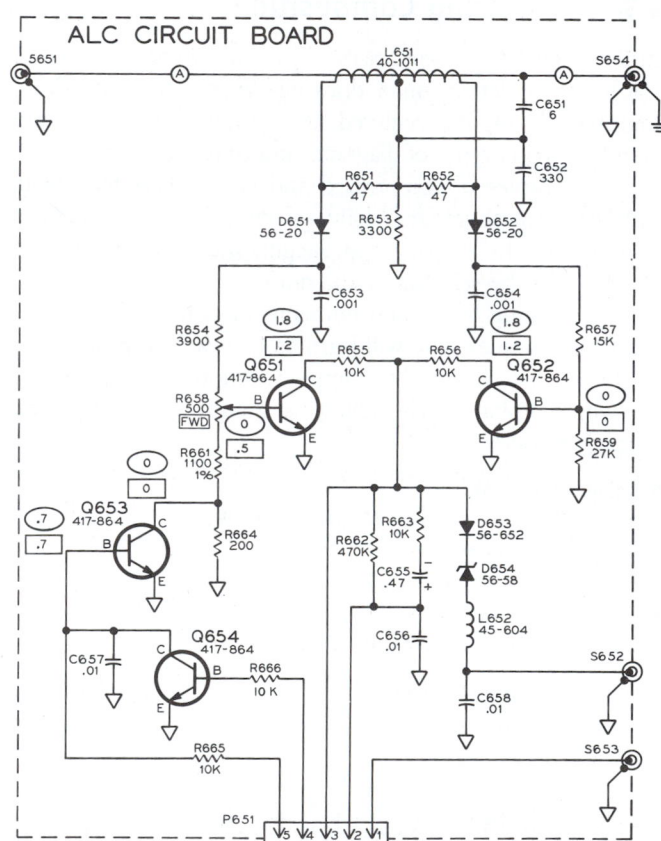

FIGURE 4.24 Template-Lettered Diagram

The **Leroy lettering set** uses a scriber and a template with a slot guide to produce close-to-perfect letters (Fig. 4.25). The scriber can be adjusted to alter the slant of the lettering. The drawing in Figure 4.26 was lettered with a Leroy set. Skill in using a lettering template and scriber can only be accomplished through practice. The most difficult part of lettering systems is the mastery of spacing the characters.

The **Letterguide** system shown in Figure 4.27 uses an adjustable scriber that can alter the slant of the characters and change the character size from 60 to 140% of the template size. When you use a lettering device, always place the template along a straightedge, as shown in this figure. The **Varigraph** lettering headline machine shown in Figure 4.28 uses the template system combined with a special holder and scriber mechanism. This device allows you to adjust the vertical and horizontal size and the inclination of the letters. Varigraphs are used for headings and graphic art productions.

All hand-operated lettering systems are expensive and take more time than traditional freehand lettering. Mechanical lettering devices and the inking of drawings are usually limited to drawings for publication. Manuals, catalogs, and sales literature require more precise lettering and linework than design, detailing, and assembly drawings.

Mechanical lettering devices enable you to make slightly smaller letters than manual techniques. (See Table 4.2 to compare sizes.) The variation in recommended minimum standard letter heights between freehand and mechanical devices is needed because freehand lettering does not reduce and enlarge as accurately as mechanically drawn characters.

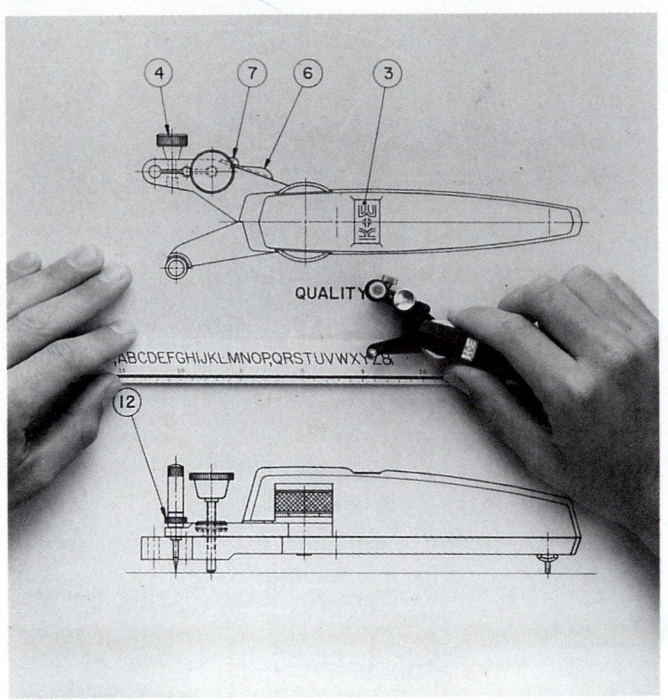

FIGURE 4.25   **Lettering with a Leroy Set**

4.5   Machine Lettering Devices

In the past, typewriters with specially designed carriages and Gothic typefaces were sometimes used on A, B, and C sized

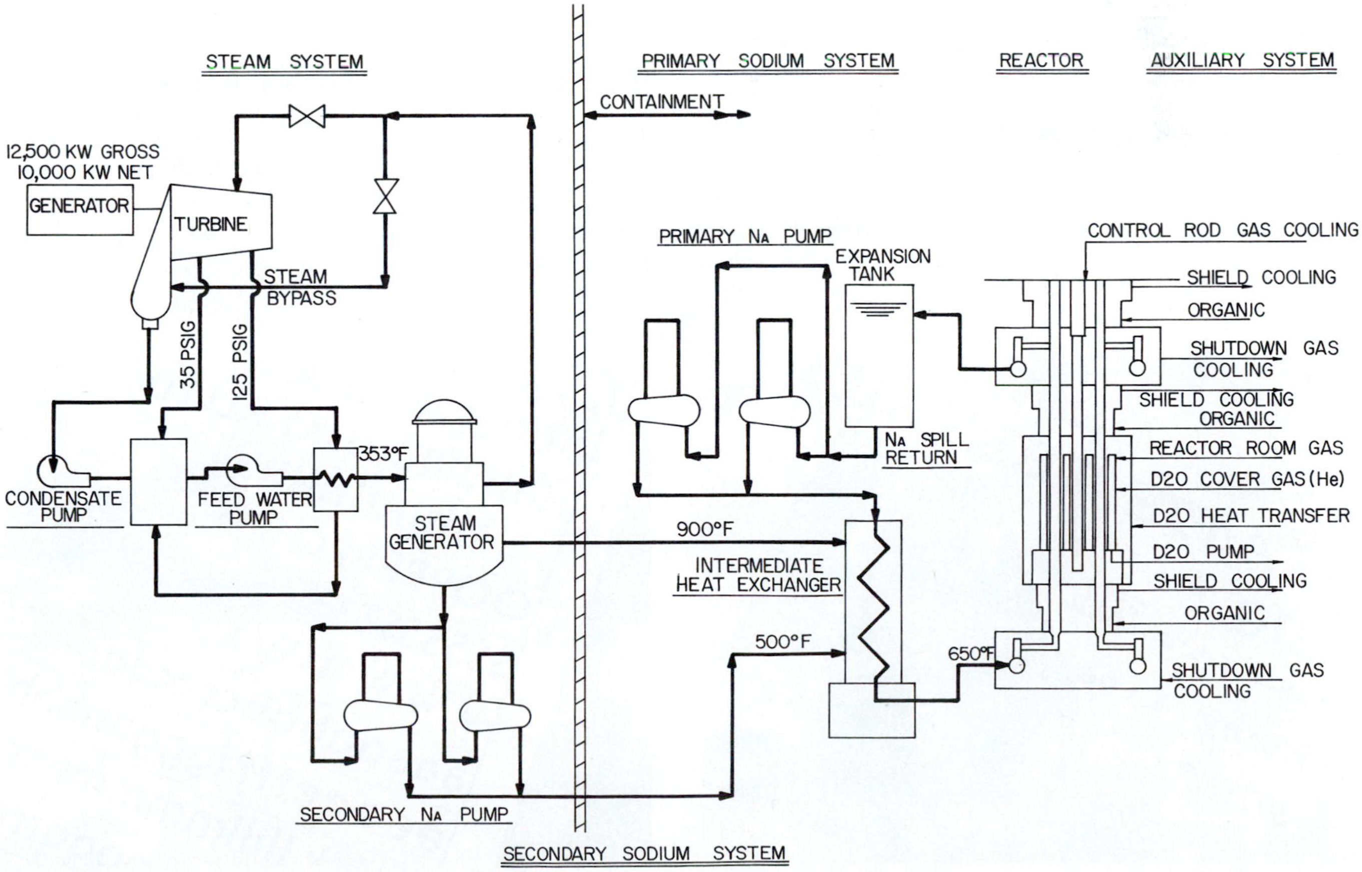

FIGURE 4.26   **Drawing Lettered with a Leroy Set**

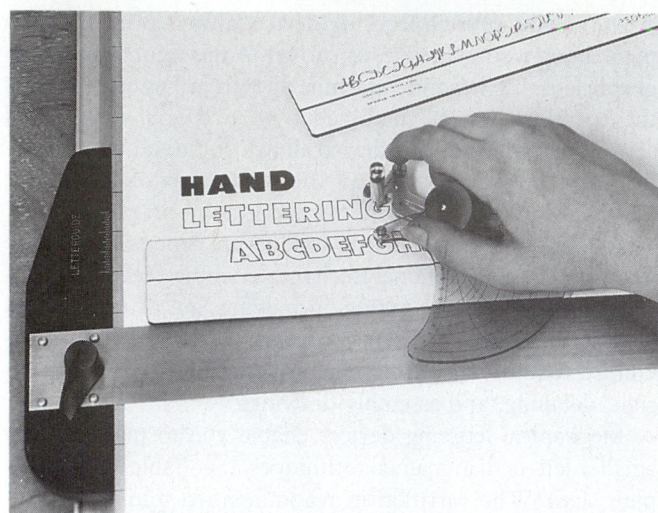

FIGURE 4.27   Letterguide

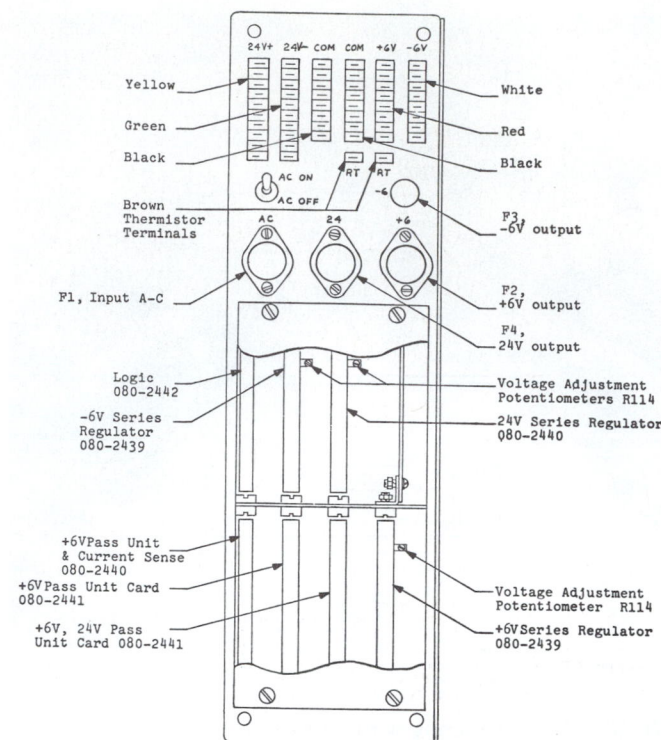

FIGURE 4.29   Typed Lettering on Panel Drawing

sheets. Figure 4.29 shows a panel drawing where the labels have been typed on the drawing. Oddly enough, freehand lettering was used for markings on the panel itself. When using the typewriter for lettering, a special inking ribbon must be used so that the characters do not smear.

Dry transfer lettering and **appliques** are normally confined to artwork or headings (Fig. 4.30). It is time-consuming to apply each letter or number separately. The Kroy or Merlin lettering systems allows you to dial a sequence of letters or numbers as required (Fig. 4.31). The result is a dry adhesive-backed strip for easy attachment to the drawing. Notes, headings, and titles are easy to apply with this system (Fig. 4.32). The drawing in Figure 4.33 was lettered with a Kroy system.

Phototypesetting and **printing** are used for publication-level artwork and drawings when quality is extremely impor-

tant. Figure 4.34 is an example of phototypeset lettering on an illustration of a pressure vessel module.

4.6   Lettering with a CAD System

The speed of lettering with a CAD system is only limited by the efficiency and speed of the drafter entering the data on the terminal keyboard. CAD systems allow for almost unlimited lettering fonts and sizes. Figure 4.35 shows examples of CAD fonts and character modification.

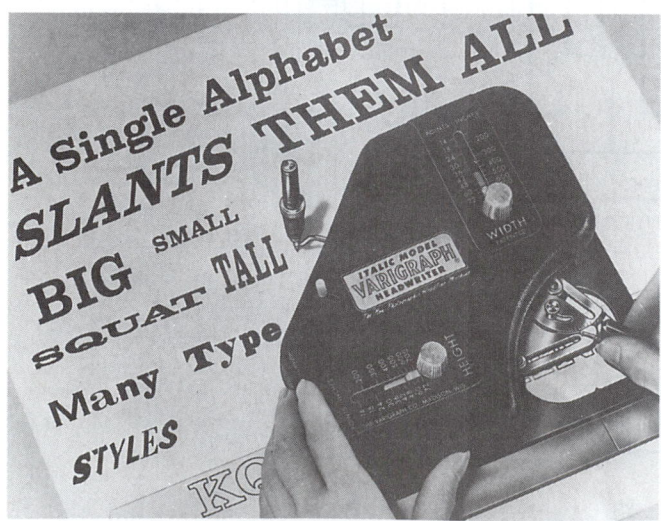

FIGURE 4.28   Varigraph Lettering Device

FIGURE 4.30   Transfer Lettering

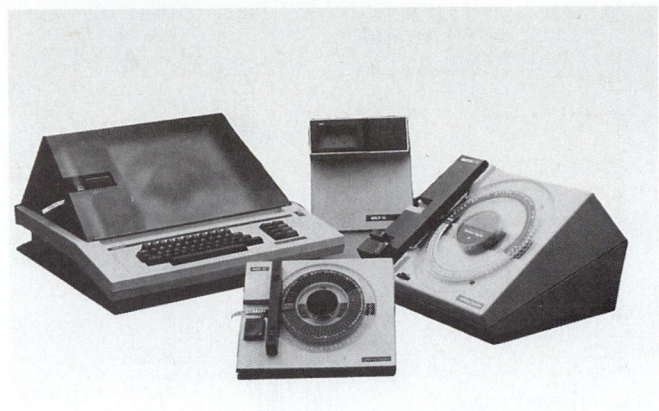

FIGURE 4.31 Kroy Lettering Systems

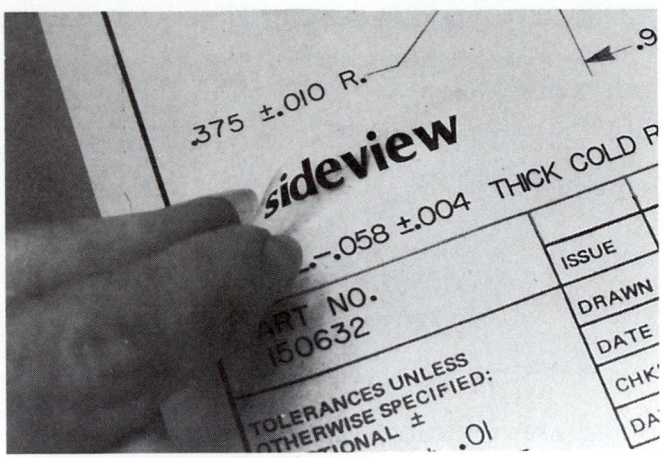

FIGURE 4.32 Kroy Lettering Being Applied to a Drawing

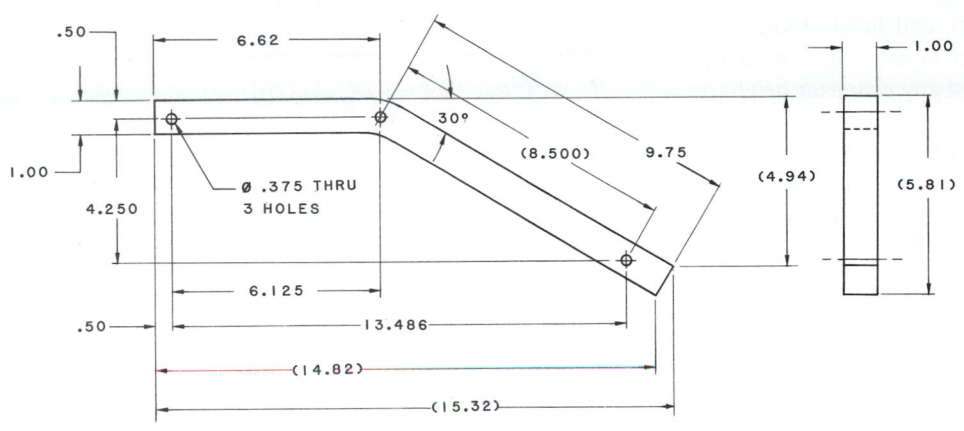

FIGURE 4.33 Kroy Lettered Drawing

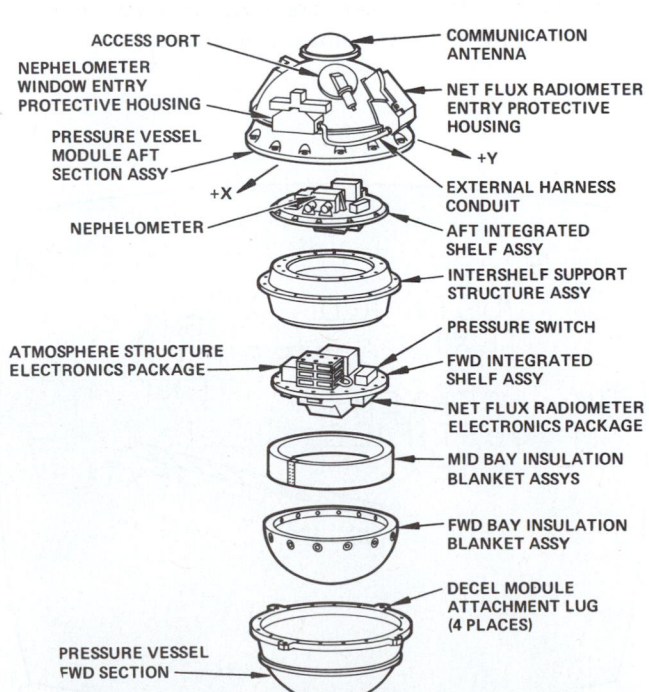

FIGURE 4.34 Typeset Lettering Used on Vessel Illustration

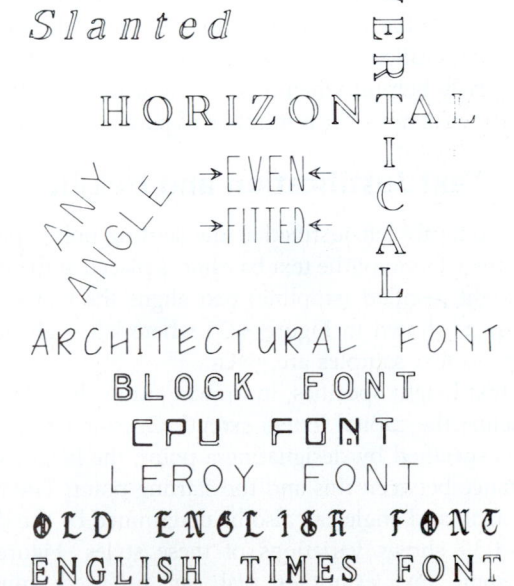

FIGURE 4.35 CAD Fonts and Character Modification

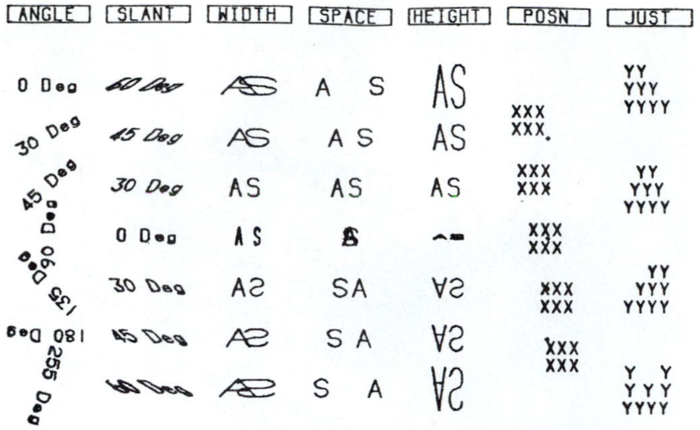

ANGLE	SLANT	WIDTH	SPACE	HEIGHT	POSN	JUST

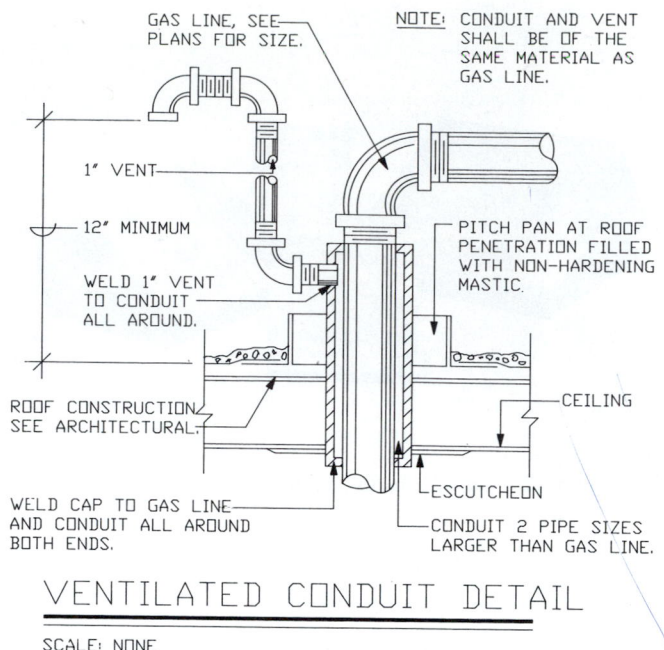

FIGURE 4.36 Character Modification Using a CAD System

Figure 4.36 shows seven lettering characteristics: angle, slant, width, space, height, position, and justification. CAD systems have the capability to letter at any angle, with any inclination to the vertical, and almost any character height or width. The character spacing, position, and justification (right, left, or center) are easily selected as default parameters (**SET-VARS** command in AutoCAD). In Figure 4.37 the conduit detail was drawn and annotated using an AutoCAD system.

4.6.1 Annotation

Annotation is the process of placing words and numbers (text) on a drawing. You can add text to a drawing by means of the **TEXT** command in AutoCAD. Text entities can be drawn with a variety of character patterns, or fonts, and can be stretched, compressed, obliqued, angled, slanted, thickened, or mirrored. A **text string** is one or more characters forming one unit or block. A text string can have just one text character or could be composed of many lines or paragraphs of text. Some systems allow text to be saved in the same manner used to file a part or drawing. The **text file** (or block) can then be recalled and reused on any drawing. This ability is particularly helpful when a company uses the same set of notes or instructions for a number of parts.

4.6.2 Text Justification and Height

Text is ordinarily left-justified at the starting point specified. That is, the left end of the text baseline is placed at the starting point. Right-justified (stopline) text aligns the text with the right side as shown in Figure 4.38 where left, right, center, and aligned text samples are given.

The text height specifies, in drawing units, how far above the baseline the capital letters extend. On some systems the height is specified by designating a point; the height will be the distance between this and the starting point. The height, width, slant, and angle can also be determined by the drafter. Figure 4.39 shows variations of these styles. Figure 4.40 shows some text examples that can be used: mirrored, curved, block, and backwards. Lowercase lettering must be

FIGURE 4.37 Conduit Detail

specified before inserting the text because the default for many systems is uppercase characters.

4.6.3 Text Styles and Fonts

A text **font** defines the pattern used to draw text characters. Fonts are referred to as **STYLES** in AutoCAD. Text entities can be drawn using any number of character fonts. Several such fonts are supplied with most CAD software; samples of six of AutoCAD styles are shown in Figure 4.41.

FIGURE 4.38 Text Justification

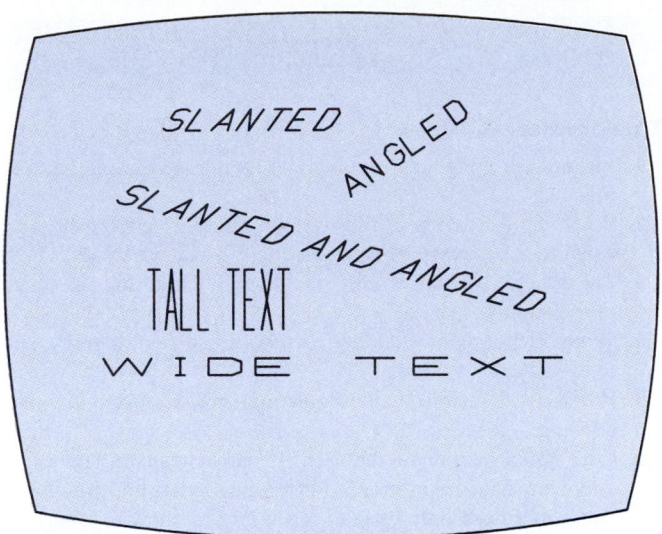

FIGURE 4.39 Slanted, Angled, Tall, and Wide Text

FIGURE 4.42 Text Tablet Menu

Many systems have a variety of text fonts available on the screen or tablet menu for quick and easy insertion on the drawing. Figure 4.42 shows a tablet menu used for selecting a text font, changing the font style of an existing text string, and inserting text with variations of height, width, thickness, angle, slant, and justification.

On many systems the default values have been set for standard drafting text and the drafter can change the values before adding text to the drawing. The **TEXT STYLE** command in AutoCAD affects all text including the parameters for the text characters used in dimensions. The **STYLE** command prompts you for the specific information that will set the defaults for the text. The following **STYLE** command was used to set the text parameters for Figure 4.43.

```
Command: STYLE
Text Style (or ?) <Default>: MONOTEXT
Existing Style.
Font file <default>: <RETURN>
Height <default>: .250
Width factor <default>: <RETURN>
Obliquing factor <default>: <RETURN>
Backwards? <N>: <RETURN>
Upside-down <N>: <RETURN>
Vertical? <N>: <RETURN>
(MONOTEXT is now the current text style)
```

FIGURE 4.40 Text Variations

ROMAN SIMPLEX   1 2 3 4 5

ITALIC TRIPLEX 1 2 3 4 5

MONOTXT 1 2 3 4 5

𝕲𝖔𝖙𝖍𝖎𝖈 𝕰𝖓𝖌𝖑𝖎𝖘𝖍 1 2 3 4 5

𝒮𝒸𝓇𝒾𝓅𝓉 𝒞𝑜𝓂𝓅𝓁𝑒𝓍 1 2 3 4 5

STANDARD 1 2 3 4 5

FIGURE 4.41 Text Fonts (Styles)

4.6.4 Entering Text on a Drawing

The process for entering text on a drawing involves picking the **TEXT** command and then digitizing the location (or giving coordinates) of the required text. You can add multiple positions of the same text by simply digitizing more than one location for the string.

Before the text can be drawn, you may have to determine the desired text height, the rotation angle from the baseline, and the text string itself. AutoCAD prompts you for this information when using the **DTEXT** command. The following **DTEXT** command was used after **STYLE** to insert the text in Figure 4.43:

```
Command: DTEXT
Start point or Align/Center/Fit/Middle/
Right/Style: <PICK LOCATION>
Height <.250>: <RETURN>
Rotation angle <default>: <RETURN>
Text: NOTES: UNLESS OTHERWISE SPECIFIED
1. MATERIAL: ALUMINUM, AA ALLOY 6061-T6
2. ALL FILLETS AND ROUNDS R.25
3. BREAK ALL CORNERS
4. PERMANENT MARK PART NO. 000-000345-001
```

Whether using a CAD system or one of the many different lettering aids described in this chapter, mastering freehand lettering is still essential. Engineering and design sketches and other types of written communication require the mastery of freehand lettering to ensure proper and correct transferring of data. Regardless of future innovations in technology, handwritten communication will always be necessary for the engineer, designer, and drafter in industry.

```
NOTES: UNLESS OTHERWISE SPECIFIED

1. MATERIAL: ALUMINUM, AA ALLOY 6061-T6
2. ALL FILLETS AND ROUNDS R.25
3. BREAK ALL CORNERS
4. PERMANENT MARK PART NO. 000-000345-001
```

FIGURE 4.43 Entering Text with AutoCAD

QUIZ

True or False

1. Inclined lettering, .25 in. high, is preferred on mechanical drawings.
2. When hand lettering a drawing, the distance between lines is equal to the character height used.
3. The distance between words should be a full four units or equal to the letter J.
4. Vertical lettering is preferred over inclined lettering since it reduces better.
5. Vertical and inclined lettering should not be mixed on one drawing.
6. CAD systems eliminate the need to master freehand lettering.
7. There are eight basic strokes for forming letters and numbers.
8. Guidelines need only be used when learning how to letter.

Fill in the Blanks

9. Lettering is divided into three separate methods: _____ , _____ , and _____ .
10. Guidelines must be used when hand lettering except when using _____ paper.
11. The ANSI standard on lettering states that the height of a fraction number should be _____ to the whole number.
12. Notes and dimensions should be at least _____ in height on a "D" size drawing.
13. Inclined lettering should be approximately _____ degrees.
14. Stopline lettering is the same as _____ _____ .
15. ANSI lists and notes are placed in the _____ _____ or _____ _____ side of the drawing.
16. Templates and lettering guides should always be placed against a _____ when lettering.

Answer the Following

17. What ANSI standard covers lettering on engineering drawings?
18. When is lowercase lettering used and on what type of drawings?
19. When are machine lettering devices normally used for a drawing?
20. Define the term *text font*.
21. Explain the difference between manual, mechanical, and machine lettering.
22. What is annotation?
23. Name five variations of lettering characteristics available on most CAD systems.
24. Explain the reasons for mastering manual lettering.

EXERCISES

Exercises may be assigned as freehand, template, or machine lettering projects. Transfer the given information to an "A" size sheet of .25 in. grid paper.

After Reading the Chapter Through Section 4.3.8, You May Complete the Following Exercises

Exercise 4.1   Practice lettering using the standard stroke sequence. You may add vertical or inclined guidelines for this exercise.

Exercise 4.2   Letter the sentence and the notes three times each.

Exercise 4.3   Letter the page as shown using compressed and extended lettering.

Exercise 4.4   Letter the drawing notes as shown using right-justified, left-justified, and center-justified lettering.

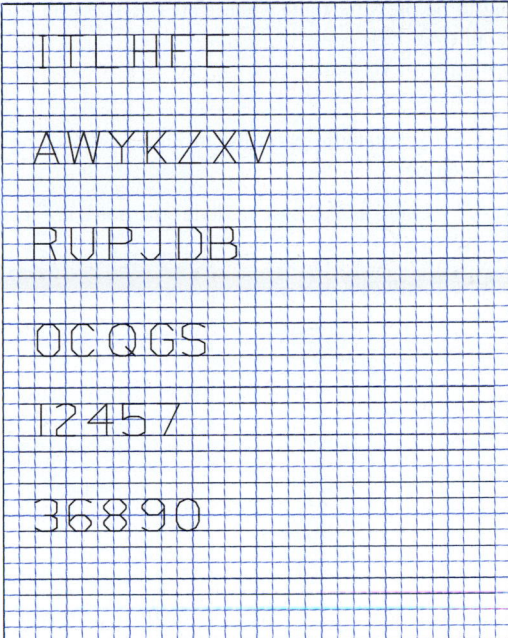

Exercise 4.1

Exercise 4.3

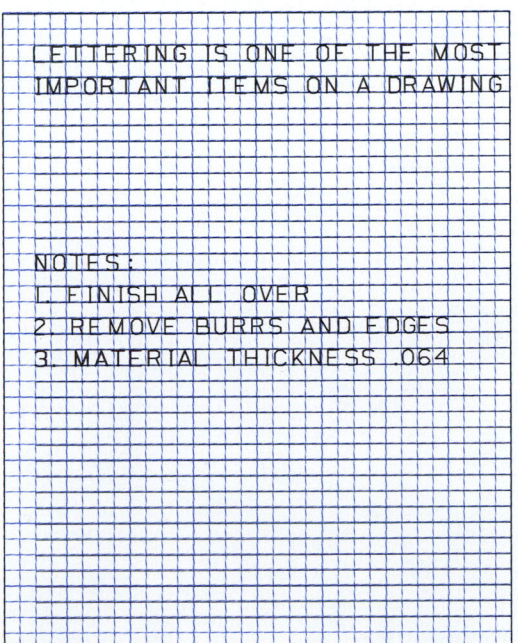

Exercise 4.2

Exercise 4.4

PROBLEMS

Problem 4.1   Using the layout sheet provided in Problem 4.1 complete the lettering assignment as shown. Use this example to lay out the drawing format for the following problems.

Problem 4.2   Letter each of the following twice using compressed and extended, vertical, .5 in. or 15 mm height, uppercase lettering. See Problem 4.1 for the page layout.

ANGLE BRACKET ASSEMBLY
PUMP HOUSING DETAIL
DESIGN ENGINEERING AND DRAFTING, INC.

Problem 4.3   Letter the following note three times at 4 mm height in vertical uppercase lettering.

HEAT TREATMENT:
  MC QUAID-EHN GRAIN SIZE 5-8 HEAT TO 1550
  DEGREES F AND QUENCH IN OIL. DRAW TO BRINELL
  HARDNESS 241-285. 100% BRINELL REQUIRED

Problem 4.4   Letter the following note three times using .25 in. high inclined letters. Instructor may assign project to be inked using a lettering template or a Leroy set.

NOTE:
  1. LOCATING POINTS TO BE CASE FLAT AND SMOOTH
  2. CAST FEATURES ARE DETERMINED BY BASIC DI-
      MENSIONS IN RELATION TO LOCATING SURFACES.

Problem 4.5   Letter the following specifications using vertical mixed uppercase and lowercase characters $\frac{5}{32}$ in. or 4 mm in height.

1. Casting to be pressure tight when tested at 100 P.S.I.
2. Finish all over 125.
3. Do not apply piece mark.
4. Material thickness .125 in.

Problem 4.6   Reletter the parts list in Figure 4.21 using vertical uppercase lettering.

Problem 4.7   Using a CAD system, letter the notes in Figure 4.22.

Problem 4.8   Set up an "A" size drawing as in Figure 4.12 and fill entire page with lettering.

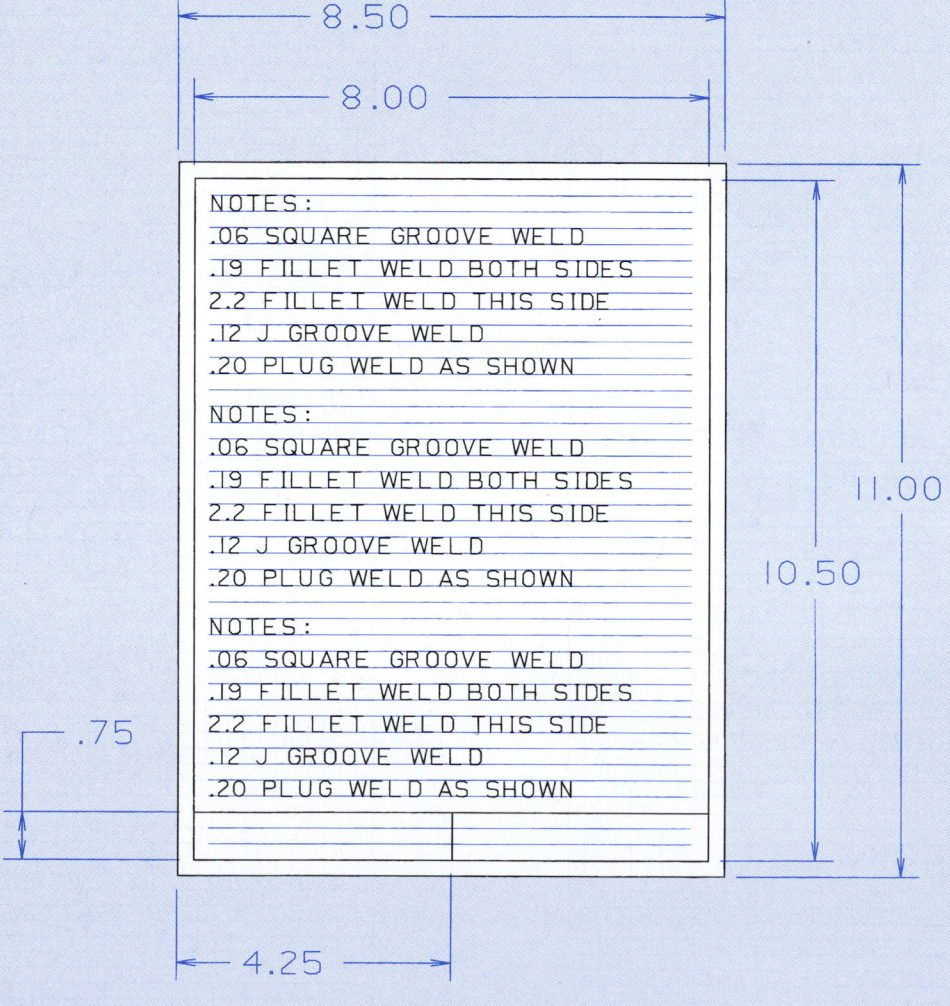

Problem 4.1

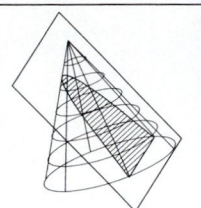

CHAPTER 5

Geometric Constructions

Learning Objectives

Upon completion of this chapter you will be able to accomplish the following:

1. Develop the ability to interpret graphic solutions to common geometrical problems.
2. Define and construct plane geometric shapes: points, lines, curves, polygons, angles, and circles.
3. Define solid geometric shapes: polyhedra, curved surfaces, and warped surfaces.
4. Apply basic construction line drawing techniques.
5. Produce uniformly drawn and scaled examples of commonly used geometric forms and entities.
6. Use geometric construction methods to facilitate feature locations.
7. Develop the ability to generate geometric constructions using a CAD system.

5.1 Introduction

Geometric construction is a system for drawing figures and shapes that does not require a knowledge of mathematical geometry. Instead, it requires an understanding of the shapes of geometric figures and the mechanics of their construction, as well as the ability to solve problems visually. Geometric construction uses a straightforward approach to drawing straight lines, angles, circles, arcs, and curves so that they are consistently accurate in size and shape. It emphasizes scale, uniformity of linework, and the smooth joining of lines and curves. All engineering drawings are constructed using the methods and procedures of geometric construction described in this chapter. Figure 5.1 shows an industrial use of geometric shapes—the stairway is a *cylindrical helix*.

Solving graphical problems involves the use of a variety of standard geometric constructions. You may be familiar with many of these constructions—for example, bisecting an angle or a line, drawing an ellipse, and creating perpendicular and parallel constructions. Until you have mastered the manual geometric construction techniques covered in the first part of this chapter, do not use a template. The second part of the chapter shows how to use CAD to create some of the geometric forms.

5.2 Geometric Forms

Geometric forms include a wide range of shapes and plane figures—such as squares, triangles, arcs, circles, solid shapes, and single-curved, double-curved, and warped surfaces. This section covers geometric concepts and forms that you will use in drafting. The following sections provide you with step-by-step procedures for manually constructing common geometric forms.

FIGURE 5.1 Helical Stairway

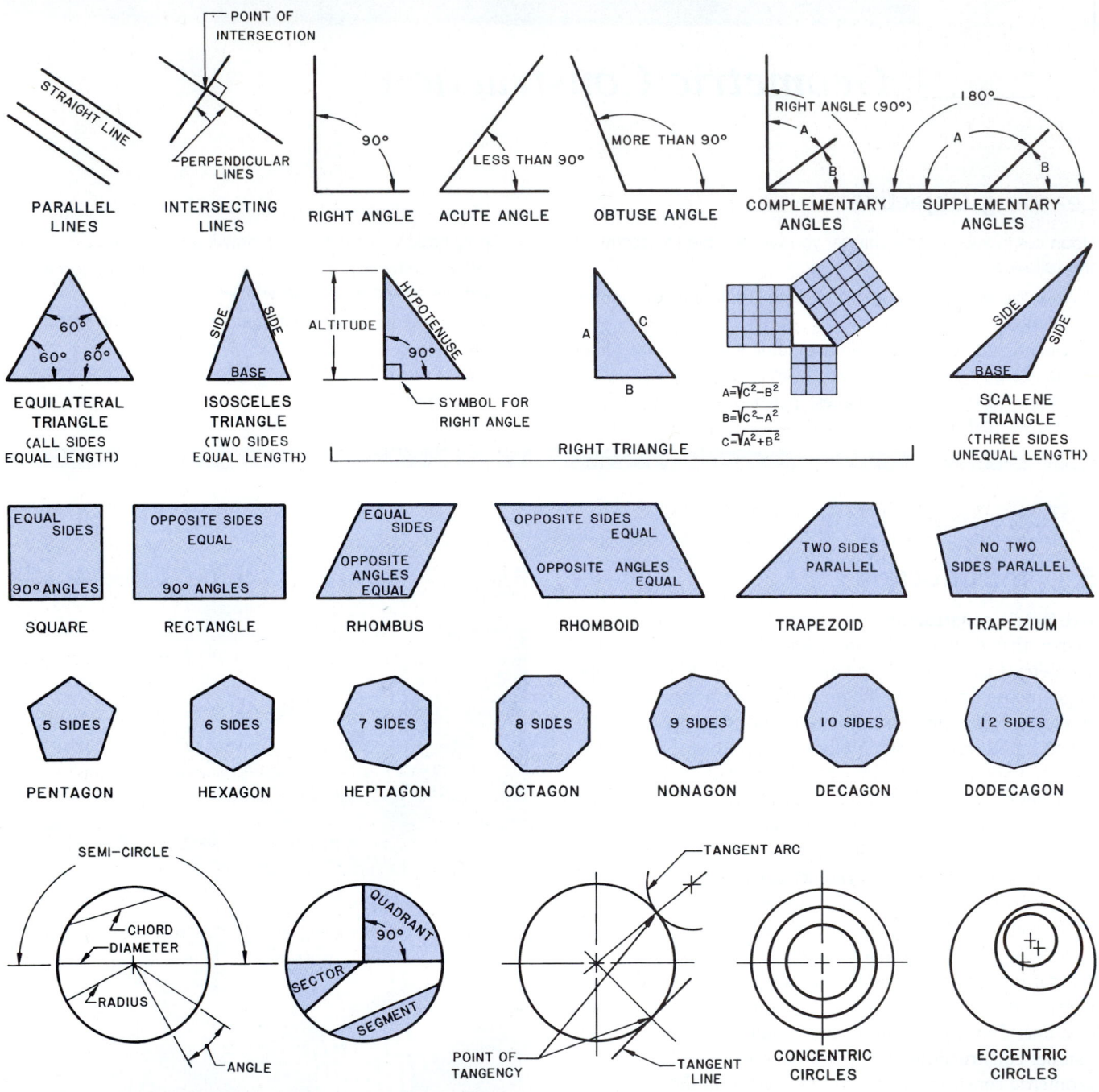

FIGURE 5.2 Geometric Shapes and Items

5.2.1 Points and Lines

Geometric forms and shapes consist of points connected by lines. The **point** is the primary geometric building block in any graphical construction. All projections of lines, planes, surfaces, and solids can be physically located and manipulated by identifying a series of points that represent the figure. These points can locate ends of straight lines or be placed along a curved line to establish the line in space. A point exists at one position in space; therefore, a point can be located in space by establishing it in two or more adjacent projections (views) or as an **X, Y, Z** coordinate position in 3D space using a CAD system.

A **line** can be thought of as a series of points in space, having magnitude (length) but not width. Although a line may be located by establishing any two points and although it may have a specified length, all lines can be extended to solve a problem.

The study and understanding of lines and their relationships are an important part of geometric construction because lines are used to draw plane surfaces and solid shapes. A **straight line** is the shortest distance between two points. The word *line* usually refers to a straight line. A line that bends is a **curve**. When two lines occur in the same plane, they are either parallel or they must intersect. **Parallel lines,** symbolized by //, are the same distance apart along their entire length. Lines that intersect at an angle of 90 degrees are **perpendicular lines,** symbolized by ⊥. Figure 5.2 gives examples of the various types of lines that form geometric shapes.

Geometric constructions require the drawing of arcs, circles, and other *curved lines* that use specific linework techniques. Because the compass lead is fixed in the compass, it cannot be rotated in the same manner as the pencil while drawing. Freeform curves are drawn using an irregular curve, much as a straight line is drawn with a straightedge, but these instruments may fit the curve only for a short distance. Moreover, curves must be drawn equal in width and density to any straight lines to produce a uniform drawing. Circle, ellipse, and other templates for curves are available in many standard shapes and sizes. These tools can be applied to many of the constructions in drafting. Unfortunately, they do not come in every size and shape.

5.2.2   Polygons

A **polygon** is a plane closed figure that has three or more straight sides. A **regular polygon** has all sides of equal length and all angles of equal size. A regular polygon can be *inscribed within a circle* with corners touching the circle, or it can be *circumscribed about a circle* with sides touching the circle.

The **triangle** is a three-sided polygon. The sum of its interior angles always equals 180°. In Figure 5.2, the first type of triangle has equal sides and equal angles (**equilateral triangle**) and is a regular polygon. The second type of triangle is an **isosceles triangle.** It has two equal sides and two equal angles; the unequal side is the base, and the corner opposite the unequal side is the **apex,** or **vertex.** A line drawn through the apex and perpendicular to the base divides an isosceles triangle into two equal perpendicular triangles. **Scalene triangles** have no equal angles or sides.

A **quadrilateral** is a four-sided polygon. The sum of its interior angles is 360°. Figure 5.2 shows the six types of **quadrilaterals.** The first four quadrilaterals have opposite sides that are equal in length and are called **parallelograms.** The first parallelogram is a **square** because all sides and angles are equal. The second parallelogram is a **rectangle** because its opposite sides are equal and its angles are all the same. The third parallelogram is a **rhombus.** It has four equal sides and its opposite angles are equal. The fourth parallelogram is a **rhomboid** and has opposite sides parallel and opposite angles equal. A **trapezoid** has two sides parallel. When a quadrilateral has no equal sides it is called a **trapezium.**

Figure 5.2 also includes seven other regular polygons: **pentagon** (five sides), **hexagon** (six sides), **heptagon** (seven sides), **octagon** (eight sides), **nonagon** (nine sides), **decagon** (ten sides), and **dodecagon** (12 sides).

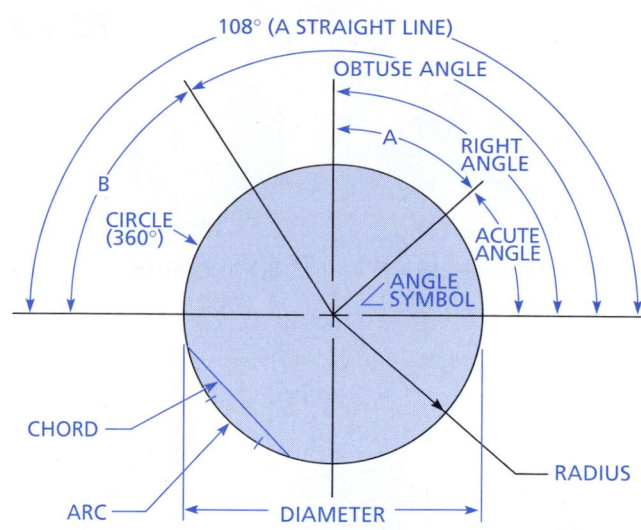

FIGURE 5.3   **Angles and Circles**

5.2.3   Angles and Circles

Angles and **circles** are important building blocks of all drawings. **Angles,** represented by the symbol <, are formed by two intersecting lines (Fig. 5.3). The angle measurement of the distance between lines is typically expressed in **degrees** and sometimes in **radians.** The various types of angles are listed below:

- An **acute angle** is less than 90°.
- A **right angle** is 90° and is formed by two perpendicular lines.
- An **obtuse angle** is more than 90° but less than 180°.
- An angle of 180° is a **straight line.**
- **Complementary angles** are two angles whose sum equals 90°.
- **Supplementary angles** are two angles that total 180°.

Circles are used on drawings to represent holes and solid round shapes. A full circle always has 360°. Geometric construction uses various parts of the circle (Fig. 5.3). The parts of a circle are listed below:

- The **circumference** is the distance around a circle.
- The **diameter** is the distance measured from edge to edge through the center of the circle.
- The **radius** is one-half the diameter measured from the center of the circle to the circumference.
- A **chord** is a straight line that connects two points on the circle's circumference.
- An **arc** is a continuous portion of the circumference from one fixed point to another.
- **Concentric circles** have different radii but have the same center point.
- **Eccentric circles** have different center points and different radii.

5.2.4   Polyhedra

Polyhedra (Fig. 5.4) are solids formed by plane surfaces. Every surface (face) of each form is a polygon. **Prisms** are polyhedra that have two parallel polygon-shaped ends, as

REGULAR SOLIDS

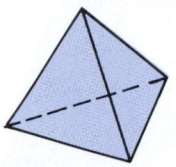 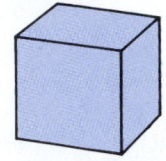 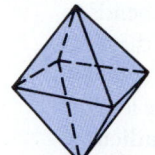 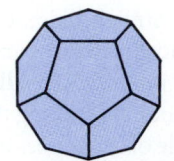 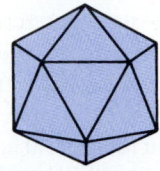

| TETRAHEDRON (4 TRIANGLES) | HEXAHEDRON (CUBE) | OCTAHEDRON (8 TRIANGLES) | DODECAHEDRON (12 PENTAGONS) | ICOSAHEDRON (20 TRIANGLES) |

PRISMS

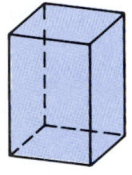 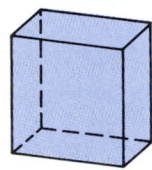 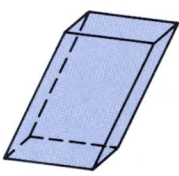  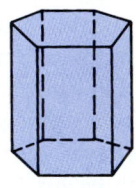 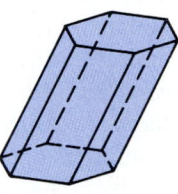

RIGHT SQUARE • RIGHT RECTANGULAR • OBLIQUE RECTANGULAR • RIGHT TRIANGULAR • RIGHT HEXAGONAL • OBLIQUE HEXAGONAL

PYRAMIDS

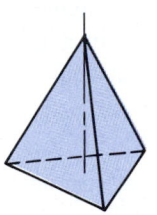 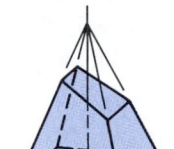 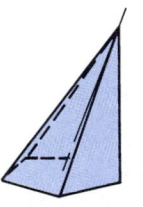

RIGHT TRIANGULAR • RIGHT SQUARE (TRUNCATED) • OBLIQUE PENTAGONAL

CONES

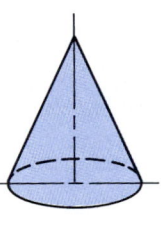 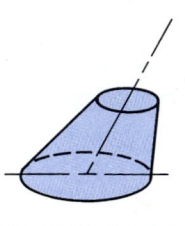 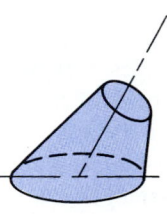

RIGHT CIRCULAR • OBLIQUE CIRCULAR (FRUSTRUM) • OBLIQUE CIRCULAR (TRUNCATED)

CYLINDERS

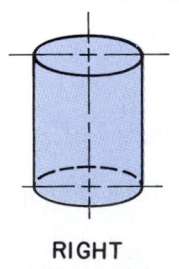 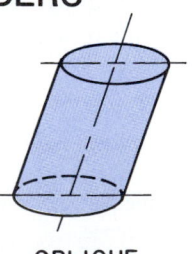 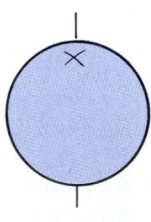 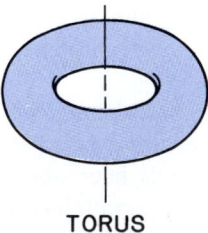 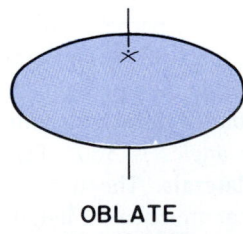

RIGHT CIRCULAR • OBLIQUE CIRCULAR • SPHERE • TORUS • OBLATE ELLIPSOID

FIGURE 5.4   Solids

well as sides that are composed of parallelograms. The cube is a polyhedron that has six equal sides.

A **pyramid** is a polyhedron that has a polygon for a base and triangles with a common vertex for faces. A **tetrahedron** is a pyramid that has four equal sides. Figure 5.4 also illustrates a **right pyramid**, a **truncated pyramid**, and an **oblique pyramid**.

5.2.5 Curved Surfaces

Curved surfaces are divided into two categories: **single-curved** (also called **ruled surfaces**) and **double-curved**. Chapter 20, Intersections, covers these types of forms in detail. Forms that are bounded by single-curved surfaces include **cones** and **cylinders**. Variations of cones include the

right cone, the **frustrum of a cone**, the **oblique cone**, and the **truncated cone**. Figure 5.4 shows a **right cylinder** and an **oblique cylinder**. Double-curved surfaces (Fig. 5.4) are generated by moving a curved line about a straight line axis and include a **sphere**, a **torus**, and an **ellipsoid**.

5.2.6   Warped Surfaces

When a straight line is moved so that it does not lie in the same plane with any of its two closest positions, the generating line will create a **warped surface**. Figure 5.5 shows five types of warped surfaces: **hyperboloid, hyperbolic paraboloid, helicoid, oblique helicoid**, and a **conoid**.

Industry has many uses for specialized geometric forms, including screw threads (oblique helicoid), screw conveyors (right helicoid), and cooling towers (hyperboloid of revolution). The aerospace industry uses single-curved surfaces, double-curved surfaces, and warped surfaces alone and in combination, along with a variety of plane surfaces in the design of spacecraft, airplanes, and missiles.

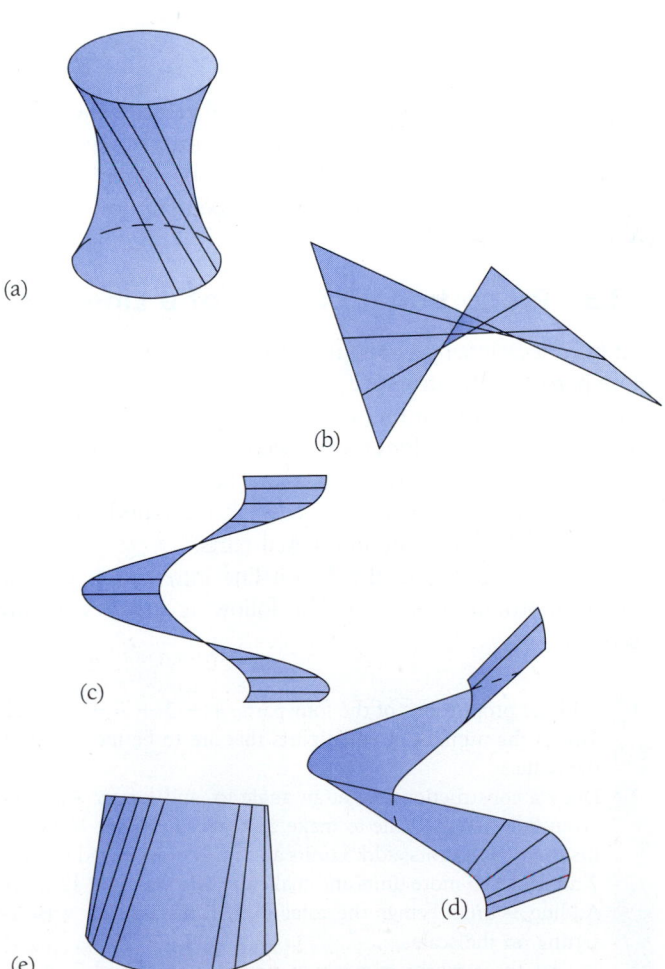

FIGURE 5.5   Warped Surfaces (a) Hyperboloid (b) Hyperbolic paraboloid (c) Helicoid (d) Oblique helicoid (e) Conoid

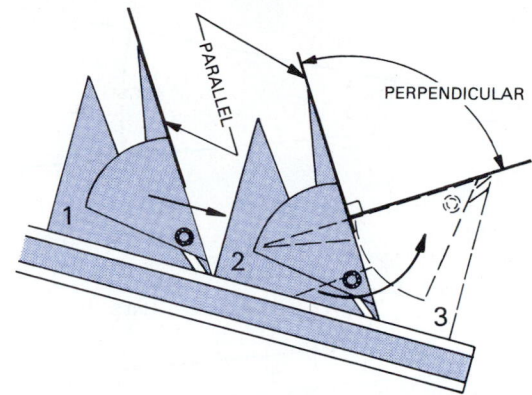

FIGURE 5.6   Drawing Parallel and Perpendicular Lines

5.3   Geometric Constructions

Geometric constructions are used to draw a variety of forms and entities on a drawing. The following section presents step-by-step instructions for drawing geometric constructions including: parallel lines, perpendicular lines, angles, circles, polygons, tangencies, arc tangents, curves, conics, involutes, spirals, and helices.

5.3.1   Drawing Parallel and Perpendicular Lines

Parallel and perpendicular lines are constructed using a straightedge and a triangle. In Figure 5.6 an adjustable triangle is used in the construction, although any triangle could be used as well. *Position 1* is the first line drawn. The following steps describe this process:

1. Move the triangle along the straightedge to *position 2,* and draw a parallel line as shown.
2. Rotate the triangle to *position 3.* A line perpendicular to the first two lines is then drawn. Remember to draw on the same edge of the triangle that you used before it was rotated.

5.3.2   Dividing a Line into Equal or Proportional Parts

One way to divide a line is to calculate its length mathematically, divide the length measurement by the number of required parts, and then use the result to mark the divisions. This method produces an accumulated error. You can prove this by taking a 12 in. scale and marking it in 1 in. increments ten times. The resulting length will not be exactly 10 inches but will be slightly off—for example, 9.985″ or 10.04″. A more accurate way to divide a line equally or proportionally is to use one of the following methods.

Figure 5.7 illustrates the **parallel line method** of equally dividing a line. Any type of scale and unit of measurement can be used in this method. The idea is to simplify the construction and measuring process; therefore, choose the unit type and scale that is the most convenient. In Figure 5.7, line AB

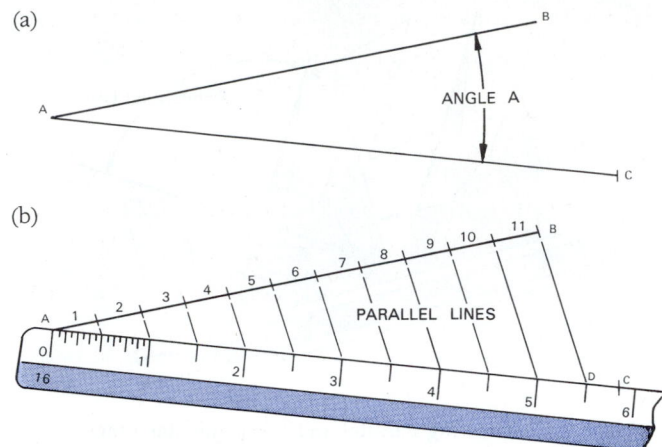

(a)

ANGLE A

(b)

PARALLEL LINES

FIGURE 5.7   **Dividing a Line into Equal Parts**

is given and the line must be divided into eleven equal segments. The following steps describe this process:

1. Draw a construction line AC that starts at either end of line AB. This new line is any convenient length (slightly longer works well). Angle A should not be less that 20° or more than 45°; otherwise, it will be hard to project the divisions from the construction line AC to the original line AB.
2. Find a scale that will approximately divide line AB into the number of parts needed and mark these divisions on line AC. Here, the full-size inch scale was used, with $\frac{1}{2}$ in. marking each division. There are now eleven equal divisions from A to D that lie on line AC.
3. Set the triangle to draw a construction line from point D to point B. Then draw construction lines through each of the remaining ten divisions parallel to the first line BD by moving the triangle along the straightedge.

It is also possible to use dividers for step 2 and divide the construction lines into the required number of equal parts.

In the **vertical line method** (Fig. 5.8), all of the projection lines are vertical lines and are easily drawn using a straightedge and any triangle. Again, any type of scale and unit of measurement can be used. In this example, line AB must be divided into seven equal parts. The following steps were used:

1. Draw a vertical construction line BC through point B of line AB.
2. Using point A as the pivot point, position a scale that gives the required number of divisions and equally divides the distance from point A to some point on line BC. Here full-scale U.S. units were used—a $\frac{1}{2}$ in. unit of the scale corresponds to each division to mark points 1 through 7. Notice that it was necessary to use a scale that gives an overall length of seven units that is longer than the line AB.
3. Using the vertical side of a triangle, draw construction line projections from points 1 through 7 down to line AB. This establishes seven equally spaced segments along line AB.

In the vertical line and parallel line methods we did not need to make measurements that were less than one easily mea-

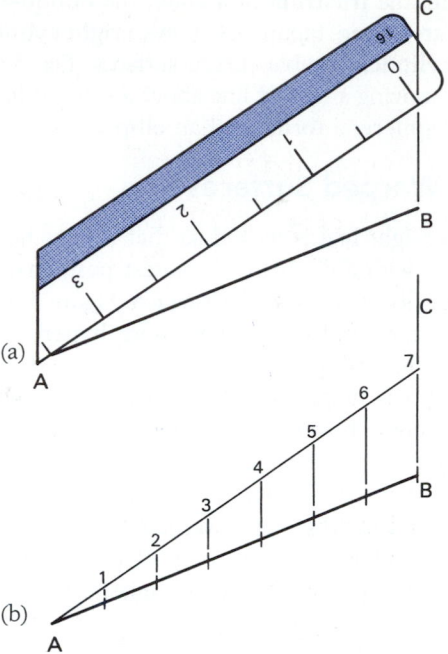

(a)

(b)

FIGURE 5.8   **Dividing a Line into Equal Parts Using the Vertical Method**

sured unit, regardless of the mathematical value of the resulting divisions. The scale is used only to measure equal units without regard to what those units may be. Therefore, any scale that will measure equal units may be used: an architect, engineer, mechanical, or metric scale.

5.3.3   Proportional Division of a Line

You may occasionally be required to divide a line into two or more parts that are in a specified proportion, or *ratio,* to each other. Suppose that a line must be divided so that the first part is three times as long as the second part. This is written as 3:1 and is read as "three parts to one part" or "three to one." To divide a line proportionally, you use a method similar to that used to divide a line into equal parts.

Figure 5.9 illustrates dividing a line into four parts that have proportions of 4:3:5:9. The following instructions are used:

1. Add the proportions of the four parts: 4 + 3 + 5 + 9 = 21. This is the number of equal parts that are to be measured on the scale.
2. Draw a construction line at an angle to, and longer than, the given line. Set the scale to make 21 equal divisions. Make the first mark at 4 units, add 3 units and make the second mark at 7 units, add 5 more units and make the third mark at 12 units. Adding 9 units brings the total to 21 units, which was the setting on the scale.
3. Project these marks to position points 2, 3, 4 and 5 on the given line using the parallel line method. This will create line segments in proportions of 4:3:5:9.

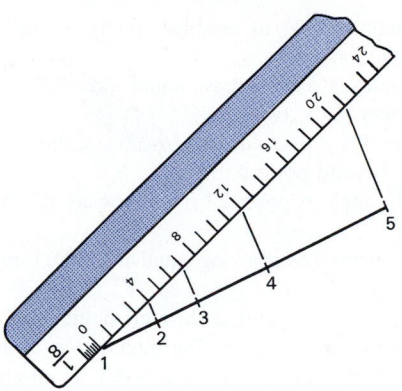

FIGURE 5.9 Proportional Division of a Line

5.3.4 Bisectors for Lines and Angles

A **perpendicular bisector** of a line *divides that line into two equal parts*. A perpendicular bisector can be constructed with only a compass and straightedge (Fig. 5.10) using the following steps:

1. Set the compass at a radius R equal to a distance greater than one-half of AB.
2. Using points A and B as centers, draw intersecting arcs to establish intersection points 1 and 2.
3. Draw construction line 1-2 by connecting the two new points. Line 1-2 intersects line AB at its midpoint and is perpendicular to it.

Figure 5.11 shows how to *divide an angle into two equal parts*. Lines AB and BC intersect and form angle ABC. The following steps were used to bisect the angle:

1. Set the compass to any convenient radius. For small angles and short lines, extend the lines that form the angle. With point B (the vertex) as the center, draw an arc (radius R) that locates points 1 and 2 on their respective lines. The length of B1 is equal to B2.
2. Using the radius R, draw arcs from points 1 and 2. Point 3 is the intersection of these two arcs.
3. Draw line 3B. This is the bisector of the angle.

5.3.5 Locating the Center of a Known Circle

The perpendicular bisector of a chord of a circle passes through the center of the circle. If a significant portion of a circle is known, its center can be located by establishing the perpendicular bisectors of any two chords of the circle. In Figure 5.12, chords 1-2, 2-3, and 3-1 form a triangle inside the circle. Bisectors of two of these chords cross at the center of the circle (point C). The third perpendicular bisector, though not necessary, serves as a check.

5.3.6 Construction of a Circle Through Three Given Points

By using the procedure for constructing a perpendicular bisector of a line, you can construct a circle through three given

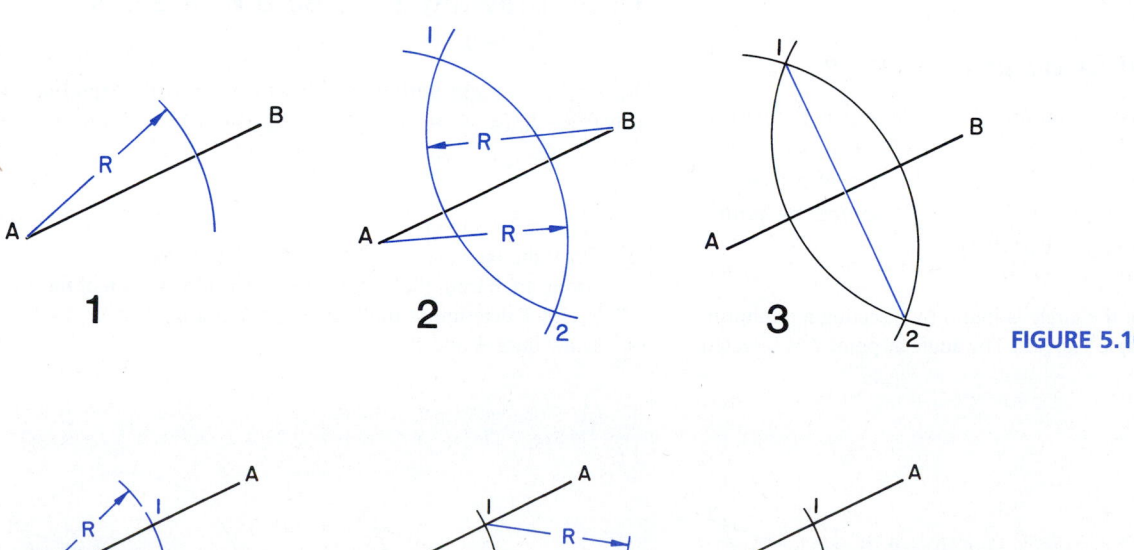

FIGURE 5.10 Bisecting a Line

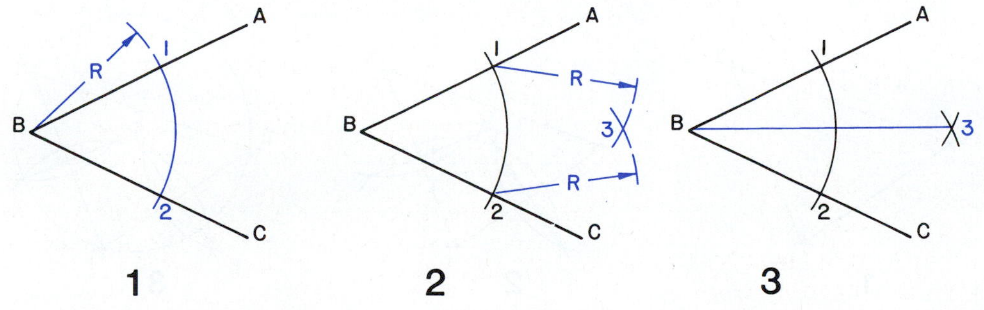

FIGURE 5.11 Bisecting an Angle

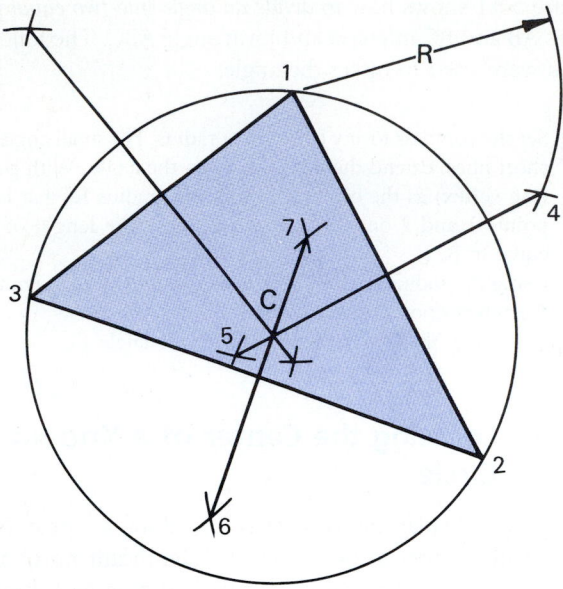

FIGURE 5.12 **Finding the Center of a Circle**

by drawing arc RA to establish points 4 and 5 (RA is any convenient length).

2. From points 4 and 5 draw equal arcs (RB). Point 6 is the intersection of the two arcs.

3. Draw line 1-6 to establish the bisector of the angle and extend this line beyond point 6.

4. Bisect the angle at point 2 by drawing arc RC to locate points 7 and 8.

5. Establish point 9 by drawing equal arcs (RD) from points 7 and 8.

6. Draw a line from point 2 through point 9 and extend it to intersect the first bisector. The intersection of these two lines determines the center of the circle (C). To check the accuracy of this point, construct a third bisector that will also meet at point C.

7. Draw a line from point C perpendicular to one of the triangle's sides (side 1-3 here) to determine radius CR.

8. To complete the solution, draw the inscribed circle using C as the center and distance CR for the radius.

points in space. Figure 5.13 shows points 1, 2, and 3. The following steps were used in the solution:

1. Connect the three points with lines and then construct perpendicular bisectors for any two chords of the circle (lines 1-2 and 1-3 here). The perpendicular bisectors intersect at the center of the required circle (C).

2. Draw the circle using the distance from C to any of the three points as the radius (C1, C2, or C3).

3. Check the solution by drawing a perpendicular bisector through chord 2-3.

5.3.7 Inscribed Circle of a Triangle

An **inscribed circle of a triangle** is a circle that is tangent to (touches) each side of the triangle. Figure 5.14 illustrates the procedure for constructing the inscribed circle of a triangle. In this example, the given triangle is represented by points 1-2-3. The following steps were used:

1. First, the center of the circle is found by bisecting a minimum of two of the triangle's angles. The angle at point 1 is bisected

5.3.8 Circumscribed Circle of a Triangle

A **circumscribed circle of a triangle** touches the three points of a triangle. Constructing a circumscribed circle of a triangle involves the method for constructing a circle through three given points. In Figure 5.12, the perpendicular bisectors of sides 1-2, 2-3, and 1-3 have been drawn. The intersection of the perpendicular bisectors 4-5 and 6-7 establish the center of the circle (C). A third perpendicular bisector (of line 1-3) can be drawn to check for accuracy. The radius of the circle is the distance from C to any of the three points on the triangle (C1, C2, or C3).

5.3.9 Drawing a Triangle with Sides Given

Drawing a triangle with the sides given is called **triangulation**. Use lines A, B, and C in Figure 5.15 to construct a triangle using the following steps:

1. A, B, and C are given.

2. Draw the baseline C and swing arc A as shown.

3. Swing arc B from the end of line C. The intersection of the arcs A and B determines the vertex of the triangle.

4. Draw lines A and B.

FIGURE 5.13 **Drawing a Circle Through Three Given Points**

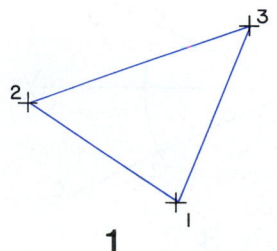

1

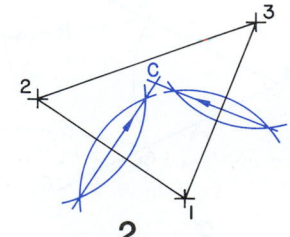

2

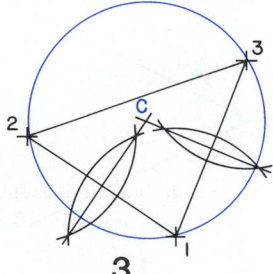

3

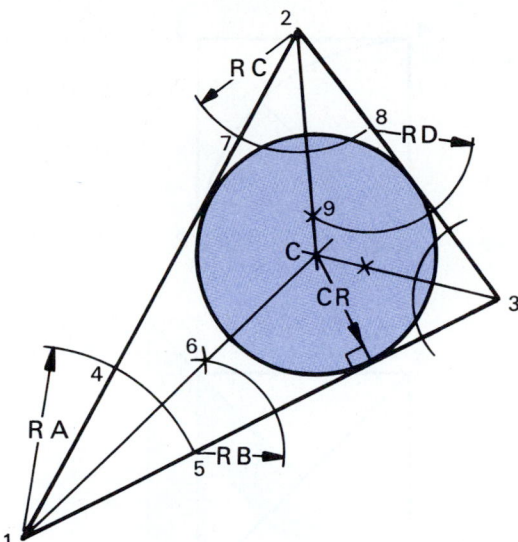

FIGURE 5.14   The Inscribed Circle of a Triangle

5.4   Regular Polygon Construction

Polygons are closed figures having three or more sides. **Regular polygons** have sides of equal length and equal angles at the corners. As we discussed earlier, all regular polygons can be *inscribed* within a circle (corners touching the circle). All regular polygons can also be *circumscribed* about the outside of a circle (sides tangent to the circle at the midpoint of each side). (In this case, the circle drawn tangent to the polygon's sides is inscribed in the polygon.)

To draw a regular polygon, you must have at least one dimension for that figure. The two dimensions that are used for figures with an even number of sides (square, hexagon, octagon, and so on) are *across corners* and *across flats*. Across corners is the maximum measurable straight-line distance across the figure and is equal to the diameter of its circumscribing circle. Across flats is the minimum measurable straight-line distance across the figure and is equal to the diameter of its inscribed circle. The distance across flats is the size of a wrench used on a hexagonal or square-headed bolt or nut. See the appendix for mathematical formulas for polygons.

5.4.1   Construction of an Equilateral Triangle

The simplest type of regular polygon is the **equilateral triangle**, which has three equal sides and three equal angles (60°). Figure 5.16 illustrates the construction of an equilateral triangle. The following steps are used:

1. Given the length of one side of the triangle (line 1-2), draw the baseline.
2. From endpoints 1 and 2, draw arcs using the length of side 1-2 as the radius. The intersection of the arcs establishes the vertex of the triangle.

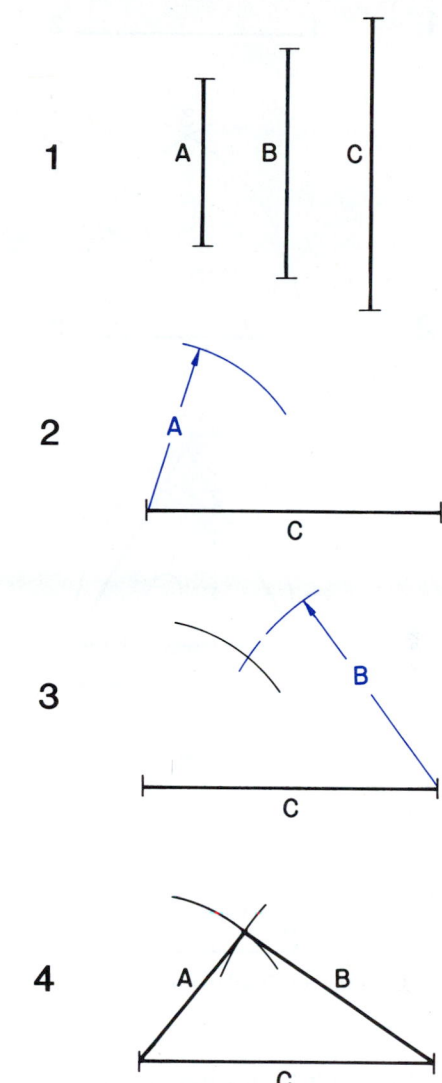

FIGURE 5.15   Drawing a Triangle with Sides Given

Another way to construct an equilateral triangle is to lay out the baseline and then use a 30/60° triangle to draw each side [Fig. 5.16(3)]. The intersection of the sides establishes the vertex. Of course, a drafting machine could also be used.

5.4.2   Construction of a Square

A **square** has four equal sides and four equal angles. Figure 5.17 shows a square inscribed with a circle. The circle will have a diameter equal to the distance across its corners. A circle that is inscribed with a square has a diameter equal to the side of the square. Three methods can be used to construct a square.

In step 1 of Figure 5.17, the base is drawn using the side length. Then an arc R is drawn using point 1 as the center and line 1-2 as the length. The intersection of the arc with a vertical line extended from point 1 establishes the height of the square, after which the square's shape is completed as shown.

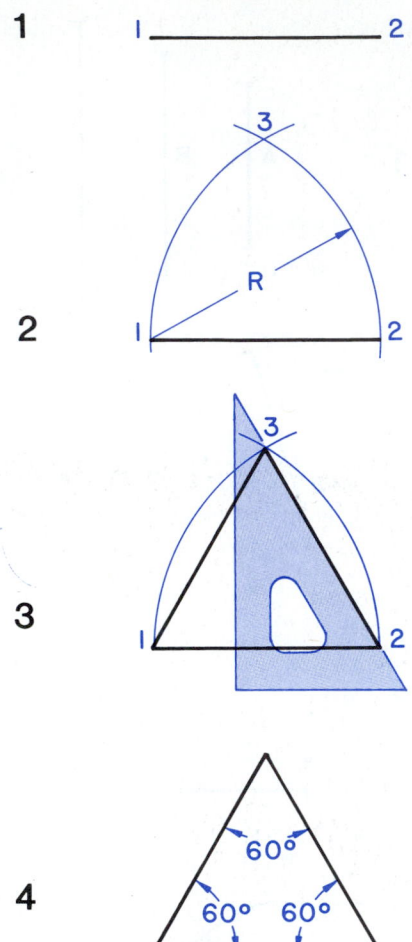

FIGURE 5.16   Drawing an Equilateral Triangle

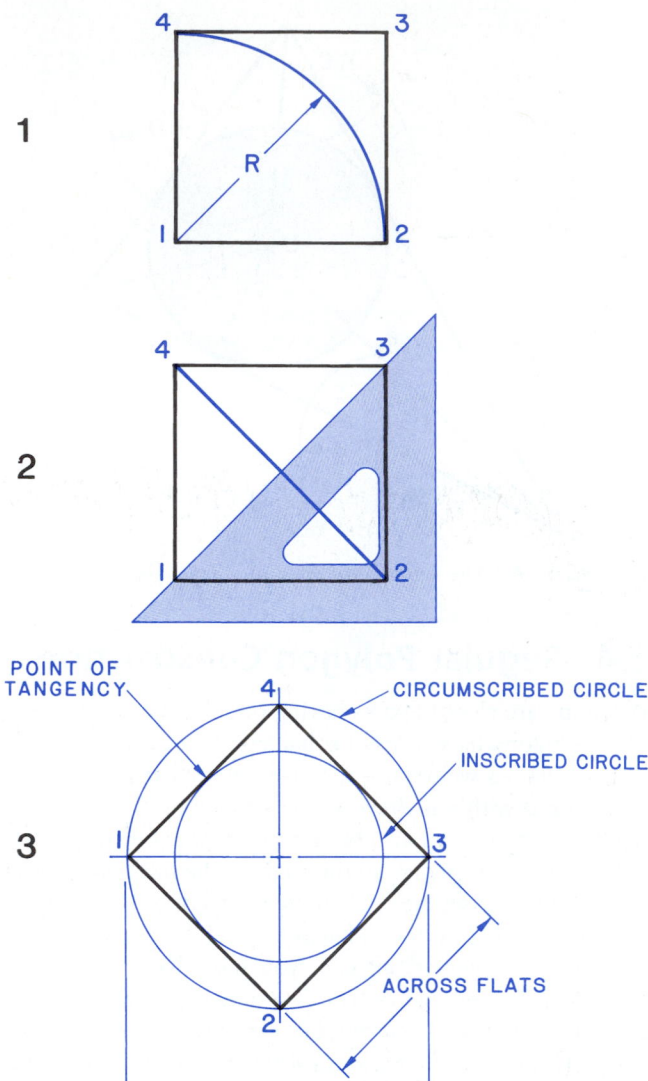

FIGURE 5.17   Drawing a Square

In step 2 of Figure 5.17, the baseline is drawn and a 45° triangle is used to draw lines diagonally through points 1 and 2 to establish points 3 and 4. Points 3 and 4 are at the intersection of the diagonals and lines drawn vertically through points 1 and 2.

Step 3 of Figure 5.17 uses a circle template or a compass to draw inscribed and circumscribed circles to construct a square. The point of tangency is the position where the square's sides touch the circle's circumference.

5.4.3   Construction of a Pentagon

A **regular pentagon** has five equal sides and five equal angles. Figure 5.18 illustrates how to draw a pentagon. The diameter of the circumscribing circle is given. The following steps are used to construct one side:

1. Draw the centerlines of the figure first and then draw the circle. The center of the circle is point 0.
2. Find point 2 by bisecting line 0-1. Radius R (2-3) is used to establish point 4 on the vertical centerline. The distance from point 3 to 4 (radius R2) is then used to locate point 5 on the circumference of the circle.

3. Draw side 3-5. Use radius R2 from point 5 to establish point 6. Then radius R2 is used to establish the remaining sides of the pentagon.

5.4.4   Construction of a Hexagon

A **regular hexagon** has six equal sides and six equal angles. Figure 5.19 shows how to construct a hexagon. In this figure, the distance across the flats was known. The distance across the flats is equal to the diameter of the inscribing circle. The following steps were used in the construction:

1. First, locate the center of the hexagon.
2. Draw a circle equal to the distance across the flats, then use a 30/60° triangle to construct tangents to the circle.

If you know the distance across the corners, then draw the circumscribed circle first and mark off each side length along

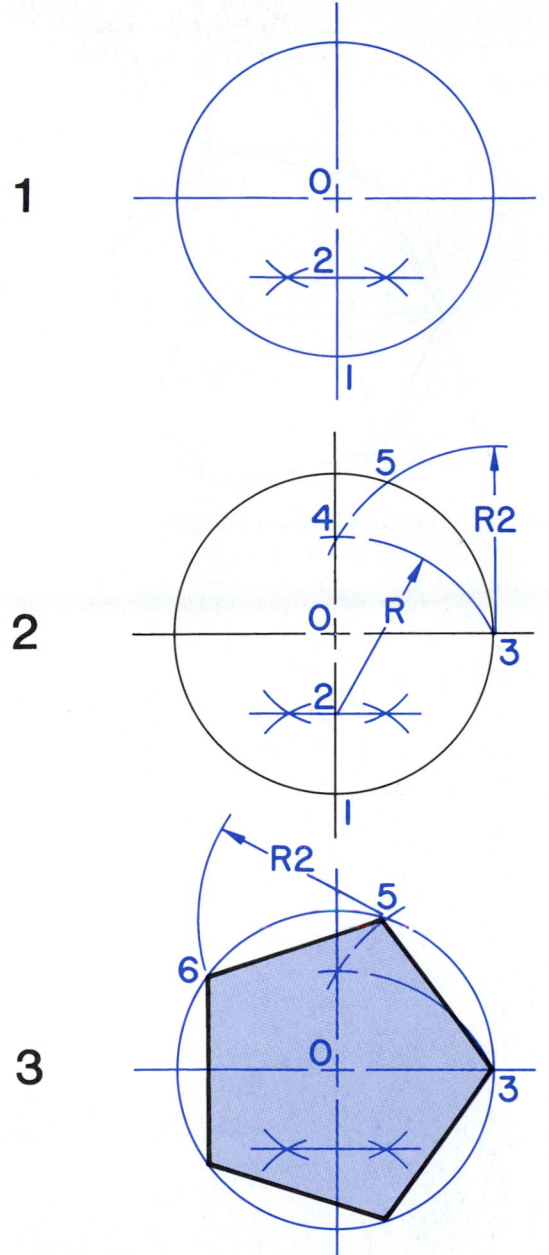

FIGURE 5.18   **Drawing a Pentagon**

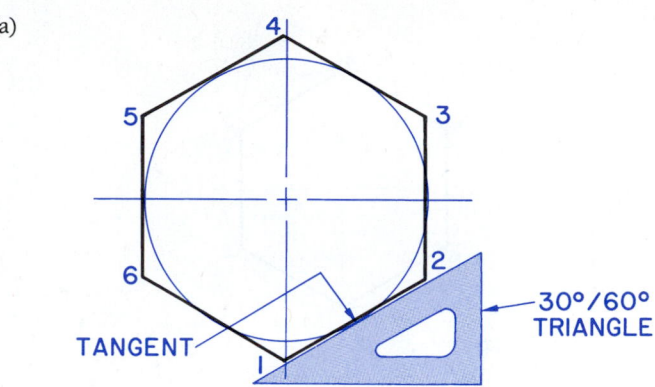

(a)

TANGENT

30°/60° TRIANGLE

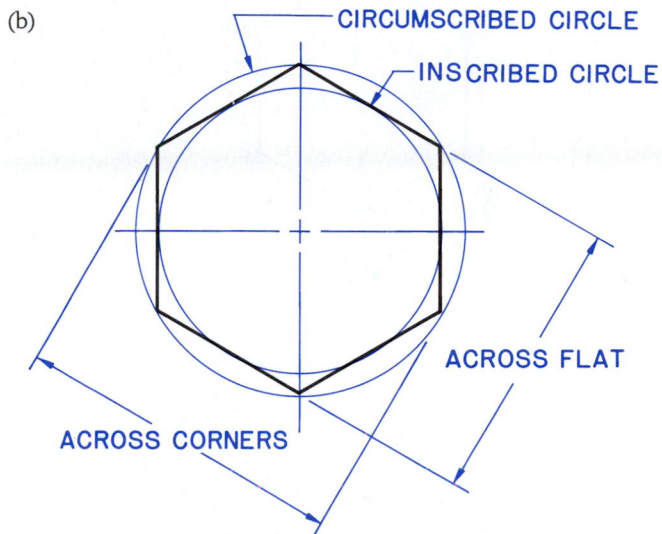

(b)

CIRCUMSCRIBED CIRCLE

INSCRIBED CIRCLE

ACROSS FLAT

ACROSS CORNERS

FIGURE 5.19   **Drawing a Hexagon Using Inscribed and Circumscribed Circles**

the circumference, using a distance equal to the radius of the circle (use dividers) [Fig. 5.20(a)]. Figure 5.20(b) shows an alternate method that also produced an accurate drawing of a hexagon.

5.4.5   Construction of an Octagon

A **regular octagon** has eight equal sides and eight equal angles. To draw an octagon with the distance across the corners known, draw the circumscribing circle first and then mark off the side lengths around the circumference. If you know the distance across the flats, then use a 45° triangle to draw tangent lines to establish the eight sides (Fig. 5.21).

5.4.6   Construction of a Regular Polygon with a Specific Number of Sides

To construct a regular polygon with a specific number of sides, divide the given diameter of the circumscribing circle using the parallel line method described earlier (Fig. 5.22). A polygon with seven sides was required in the example. The following steps were used:

1. First, construct an equilateral triangle (0-7-8) with the diameter (0-7) as one of its sides.
2. Draw a line from the apex (point 8) through the second point on the line (point 2).
3. Extend line 8-2 until it intersects the circle at point 9. Radius 0-9 will be the size of each side of the figure.
4. Using radius R (0-9), mark off the corners of the polygon and connect the points.

5.5   Tangencies

An arc that touches a line at only one point is *tangent* to that line and the line is tangent to the arc. Likewise, two curves

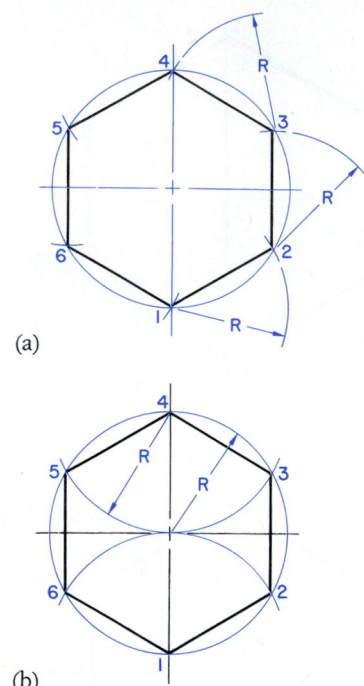

(a)

(b)

FIGURE 5.20   Drawing a Hexagon

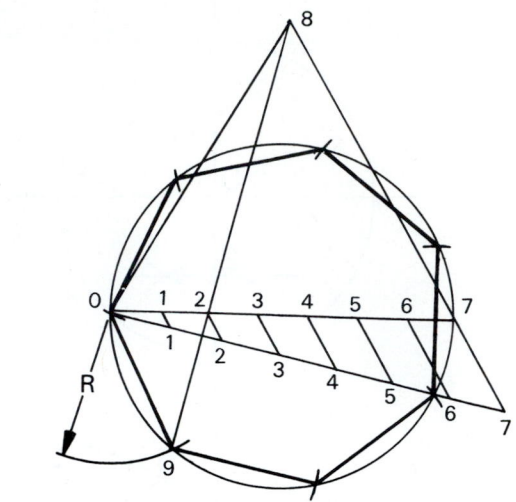

FIGURE 5.22   Drawing a Regular Polygon

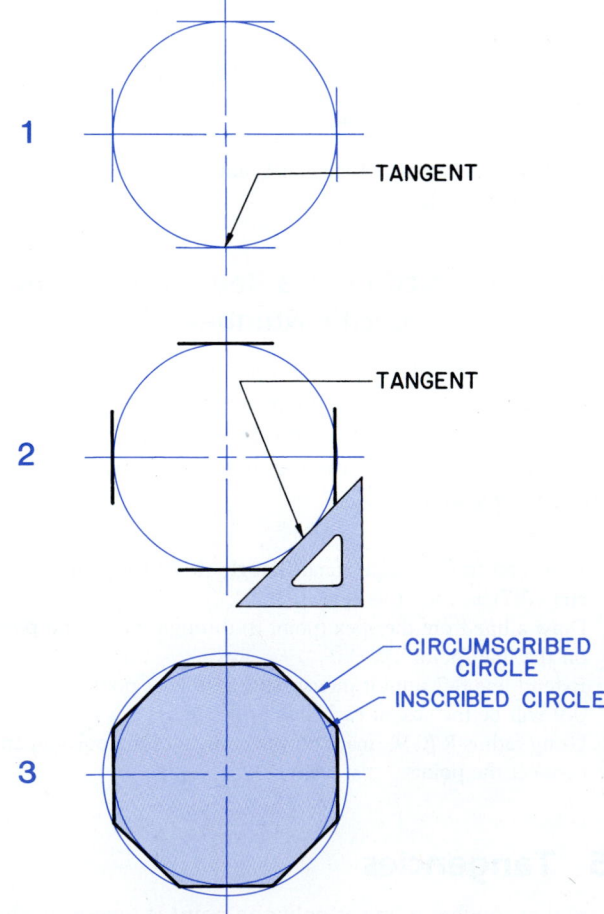

1

TANGENT

2

TANGENT

3

CIRCUMSCRIBED
CIRCLE

INSCRIBED CIRCLE

FIGURE 5.21   Drawing an Octagon

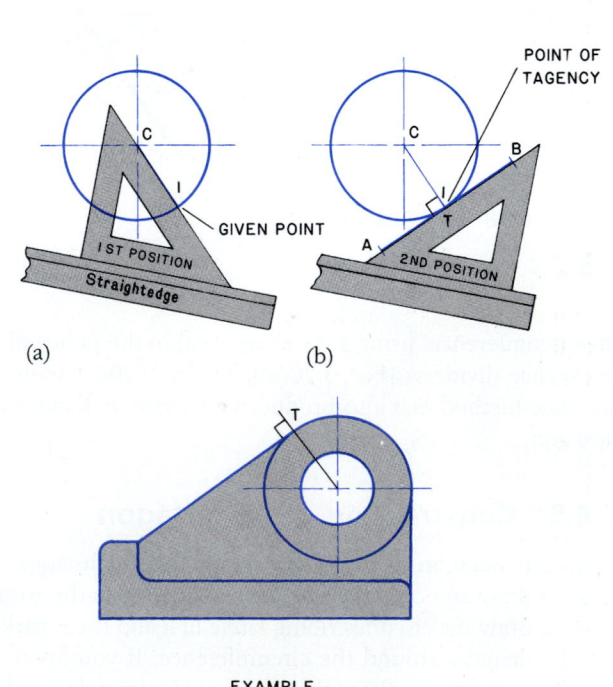

(a)

1ST POSITION

Straightedge

GIVEN POINT

(b)

POINT OF
TAGENCY

2ND POSITION

EXAMPLE

FIGURE 5.23   Drawing a Line Tangent to a Circle

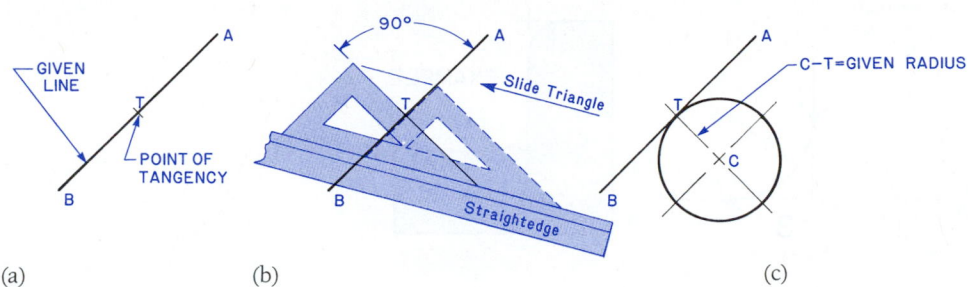

(a)   (b)   (c)

FIGURE 5.24   Drawing a Circle Tangent to a Line

can be tangent. The line and the arc will touch at only one place, even if both are extended. If a line and an arc are tangent, then (1) the tangent line is perpendicular to the radius of the arc at the point of tangency and (2) the center of the arc is on a line that is perpendicular to the tangent line and extends from the point of tangency.

Figure 5.23 illustrates principle 1. To draw a line tangent to the circle at point 1, first draw radius C1. Then construct line AB perpendicular to the radius line C1 passing through point 1. Line AB is tangent to the circle at point 1.

Figure 5.24 illustrates principle 2. To draw a circle tangent to a given line, first project a line perpendicular to the given line AB from point T (tangent point). The center of the circle will lie on this line. Locate the center point by marking off an arc from point T, using the radius of the circle. Using the same radius (line CT), draw the tangent circle.

5.5.1   Line Tangent to Two Circles

Figure 5.25 illustrates the procedure for finding the **points of tangency** between a line and two circles. A line can be tangent to two circles as shown in Figures 5.25(a) and (b). Four tangency positions are possible. In Figure 5.25(a) the lines are tangent to the outside of the circles as shown. This is called an **open-belt tangent**. In Figure 5.25(b) the lines form a **closed-belt tangent**. In both examples the circles are given. The construction is the same as that used for Figure 5.23.

5.5.2   Tangent Arcs

Two methods exist to draw an **arc between two perpendicular lines.** Figure 5.26(a) illustrates the construction of arc 2-3 using only a compass. The following steps are used:

1. Extend the two given perpendicular lines to meet at point 1.
2. From point 1, strike a radius equal to the required radius of the tangent arc. The intersection of this radius and the given lines establishes tangent points 2 and 3.
3. Using the same radius, strike construction arcs from points 2 and 3. The intersection of these two arcs, at point C, establishes the center of the tangent arc.
4. From point C, draw arc 2-3 tangent to both perpendicular lines.
5. Locate points of tangency on both lines.

Figure 5.26(b) illustrates a second method of drawing an arc tangent between two perpendicular lines. Use the following steps:

1. Extend the perpendicular lines so that they meet at point 1.
2. Draw a parallel line distance R from each of the given lines using the required tangent arc radius for dimension R. Point C is at the intersection of these two lines.
3. Locate tangent points 2 and 3 by extending construction lines from C perpendicular to the given lines.
4. From center point C, draw the required tangent arc from point 2 to 3.

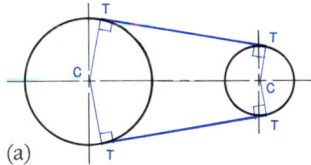

(a)

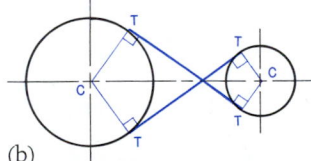

(b)

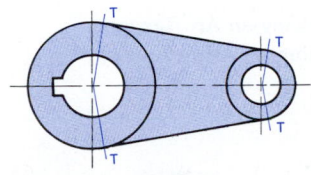

EXAMPLE A

EXAMPLE B

FIGURE 5.25   **Tangencies of a Line and Two Circles**

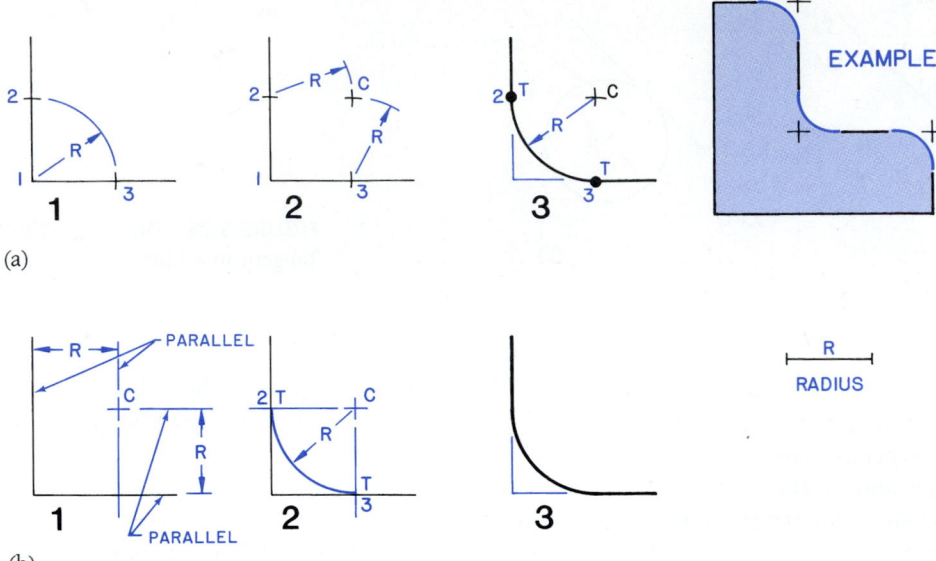

(a)

(b)

FIGURE 5.26   Drawing an Arc Tangent to Two Perpendicular Lines

To draw arcs that are tangent to nonperpendicular lines, use the same procedure as in Figure 5.26(b). This method can be used for lines at acute (Fig. 5.27) or obtuse (Fig. 5.28) angles. In Figures 5.27 and 5.28, the given lines have been extended to meet at point 1. The following steps are used in the construction:

1. Draw construction lines parallel to and at distance R from the given lines using the required tangent arc radius.

2. Where these two lines intersect (point C), draw construction lines perpendicular to the given lines to establish points 2 and 3 as the points of tangency.

3. Draw radius R from point 2 to 3 to establish an arc tangent to both given lines.

4. Darken the lines and the arc to form a continuous smooth figure.

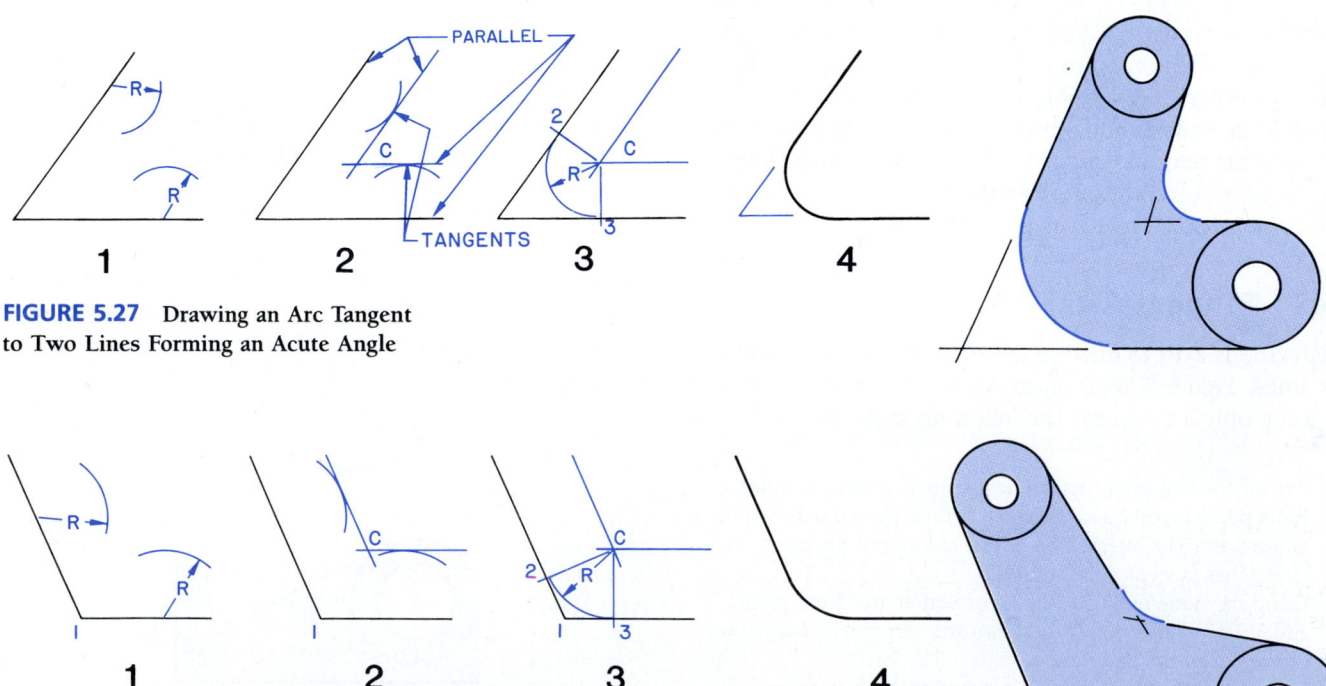

FIGURE 5.27   Drawing an Arc Tangent to Two Lines Forming an Acute Angle

FIGURE 5.28   Drawing an Arc Tangent to Two Lines Forming an Obtuse Angle

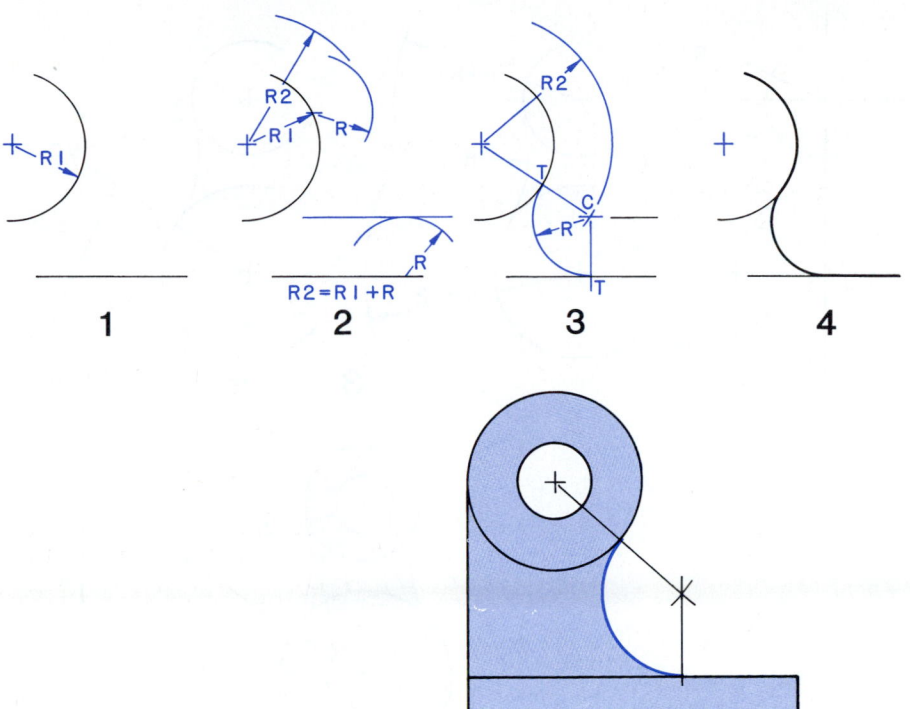

FIGURE 5.29 Drawing an Arc Tangent to a Line and an Arc

5.5.3 Drawing an Arc Tangent to a Line and an Arc

In many cases, it will be necessary to construct an arc tangent to a line on one side and an arc on the other (Fig. 5.29). The line and the arc are given along with the required radius R for the tangent arc. The following steps were used in the construction:

1. Draw the given line and arc.
2. Draw a construction line parallel to and at distance R from the given line. Add R and R1 to establish R2. Use R2 to swing a construction arc until it intersects the construction line at point C.
3. Using R, swing an arc tangent to the line and the given arc. Use C as the center point. Draw construction lines from the center of the given arc to C and from C perpendicular to the given line. These construction lines locate the points of tangency (T).
4. Darken the line and the arcs, forming a smooth, consistent visible line.

5.5.4 Drawing an Arc Tangent to Two Arcs

To construct an **arc tangent to two arcs or circles,** lay out the given arcs as shown in Figure 5.30. Here R1 and R2 are given along with the distance between their centers. The radius length R of the tangent arc is also provided. The following procedure is used:

1. Start the construction by adding the radius length R to R1. Use this length to draw a construction arc.

2. Add R to R2 and draw another construction arc. The two construction arcs intersect at C.
3. Using the given radius length R, draw the tangent arc with C as the center. The point of tangency (T) is located by drawing a line from C to each center of the given arcs. This line is called the *line of centers.*

5.5.5 Drawing an Arc Tangent to Two Arcs with One Arc Enclosed

In Figure 5.31, the problem also requires that a tangent arc joins two arcs. In this example, the tangent arc becomes tangent to the inside of one arc and the outside of the other. The arcs are given along with their centers, A and B. The radius length R of the tangent arc is also provided. The following method is used:

1. Locate centers A and B and construct the two given arcs, R1 and R2.
2. *Add* R and R1 and use this length to draw a construction arc from B. *Subtract* R from R2 and use this length to draw a construction arc from A. The intersection of these two construction arcs locates C. Using the given tangent arc radius R, draw an arc from C tangent to both given arcs.
3. The point of tangency is located by drawing a line (line of centers) from A through C until it intersects the large arc at T. The other point of tangency T can be located by drawing a line from B to C.

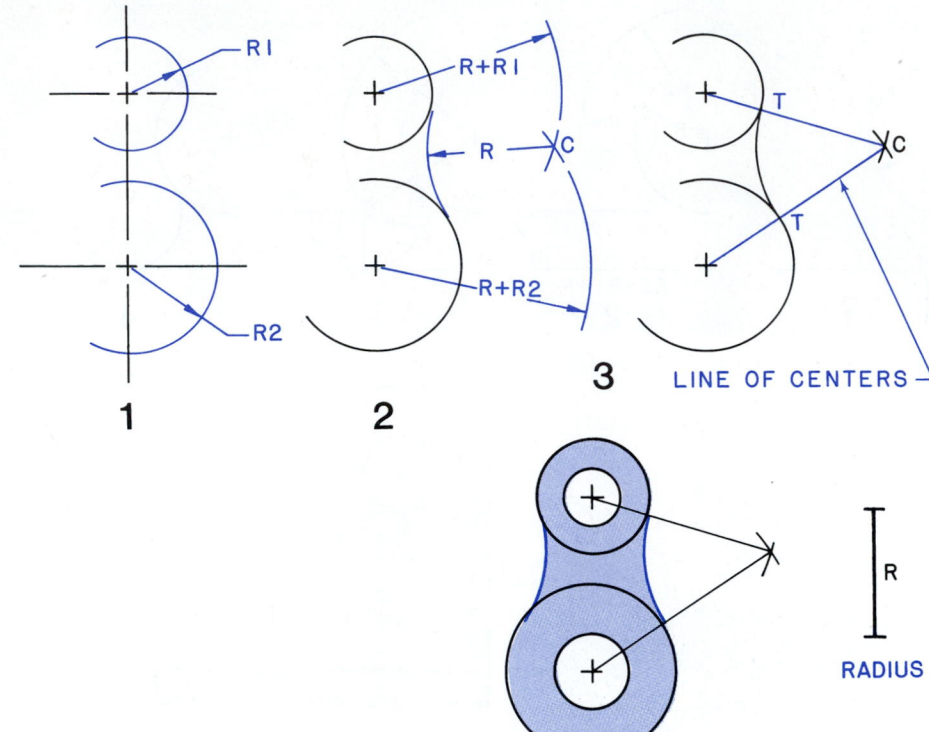

FIGURE 5.30 Drawing an Arc Tangent to Two Arcs

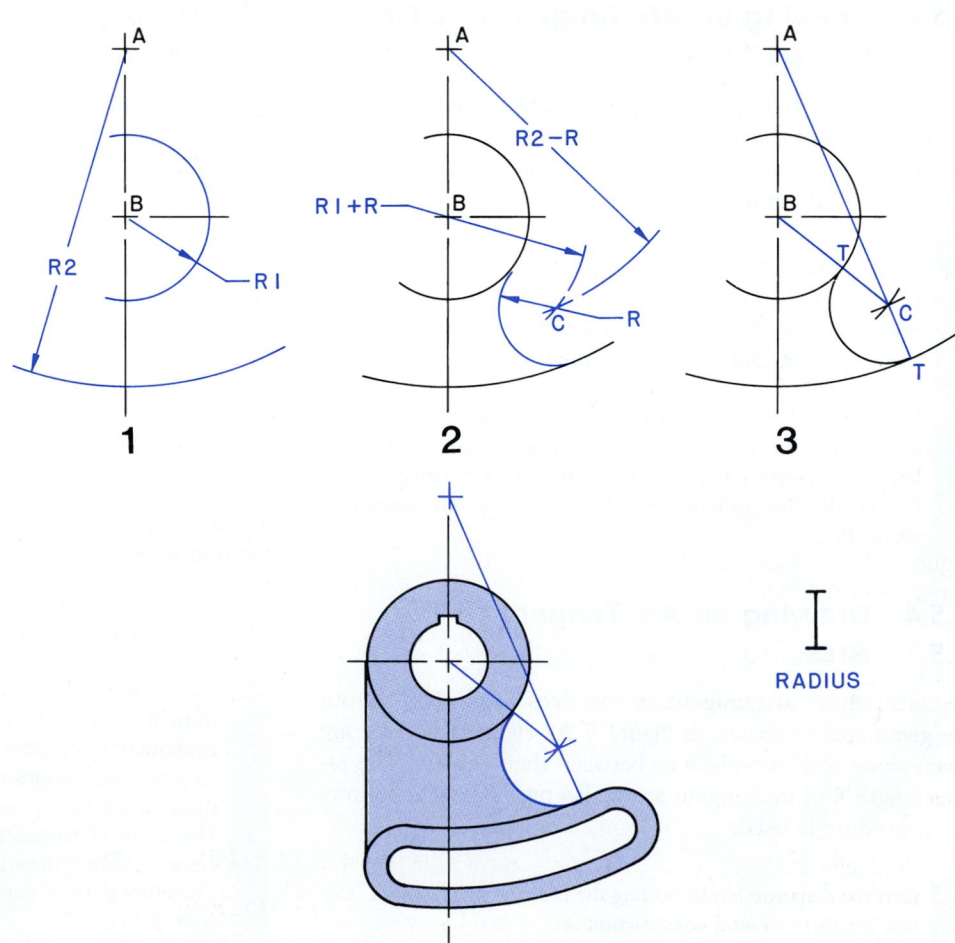

FIGURE 5.31 Constructing a Tangent Arc Between Two Arcs

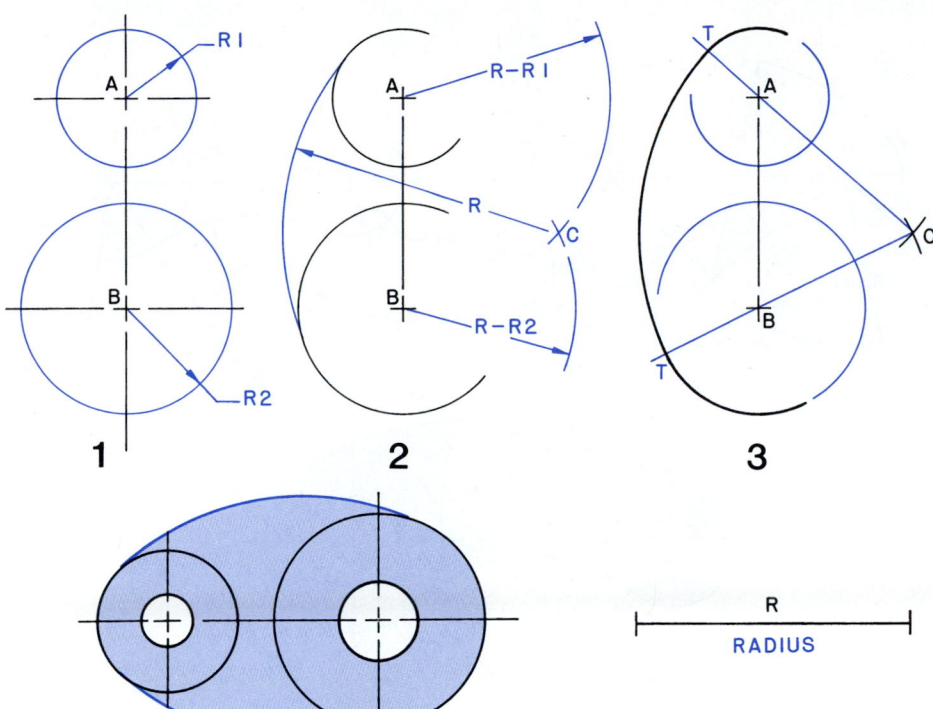

1   2   3

R

RADIUS

FIGURE 5.32 Drawing an Outside (Enclosing) Arc Tangent to Two Arcs

5.5.6   Drawing an Arc Tangent to Two Arcs and Enclosing Both

In Figure 5.32, the tangent arc encloses both given arcs. R1, R2, A, and B are given along with the tangent arc radius R. The tangent arc is drawn by using the following steps:

1. Lay out the two given arcs as shown in the figure (R1 and R2).
2. Subtract the radius length R1 from R to find C. Use this length to draw a construction arc. Subtract R2 from R and draw another construction arc. The intersection of these two arcs locates C. Using R, draw an arc with C as its center and its ends tangent to the two given arcs.
3. The exact point of tangency is determined by drawing construction lines from C to A and from C to B, extending both till they intersect the arc as shown. The intersection of these lines and the two given arcs locates the two tangent points T.

Figure 5.33 provides another example of an arc tangent to two arcs and an enclosing tangent arc.

5.5.7   Drawing Ogee Curves

An **ogee curve** is used to connect two parallel lines with tangent arcs. In Figure 5.34, lines 1-2 and 3-4, their parallel distance, and their location in space are given. The curve is constructed by the following process:

1. Draw lines 1-2 and 3-4. Connect point 2 and 3 and bisect this new line (2-3) to locate point A.
2. Bisect lines 2-A and 3-A. Extend these bisectors until they

intersect perpendiculars drawn from points 2 and 3. This will locate points B and C.
3. Draw arcs (R) using the distance from B to 2 (or C to 3). The points of tangency are 2 and 3 for the arcs and the lines, and A for the two arcs.

You May Complete Exercises 5.1 Through 5.4 at This Time

5.5.8   Rectifying Circles, Arcs, and Curves

Circles and arcs can be laid out (*rectified*) along a straight line. This means that their true length (circumference or arc length) is laid out along a straight line. All rectification is approximate but still graphically acceptable within limits.

To **rectify** the circumference of a circle means to find the circumference graphically. In Figure 5.35, the circumference of the circle has been established by rectification. The following procedure was used:

1. Draw line 2-5 tangent to the bottom of the circle and exactly three times its diameter.
2. Draw line C3 at an angle of 30°.
3. Draw line 3-4 perpendicular to the vertical centerline (line 1-2) of the circle.
4. Connect point 4 to point 5. Line 4-5 will be approximately equal to the circumference of the given circle.

5.5.9   Approximate Rectification of an Arc

To rectify an arc or curved line, start by drawing a line tangent to one end. In Figure 5.36, the line was drawn tangent to the

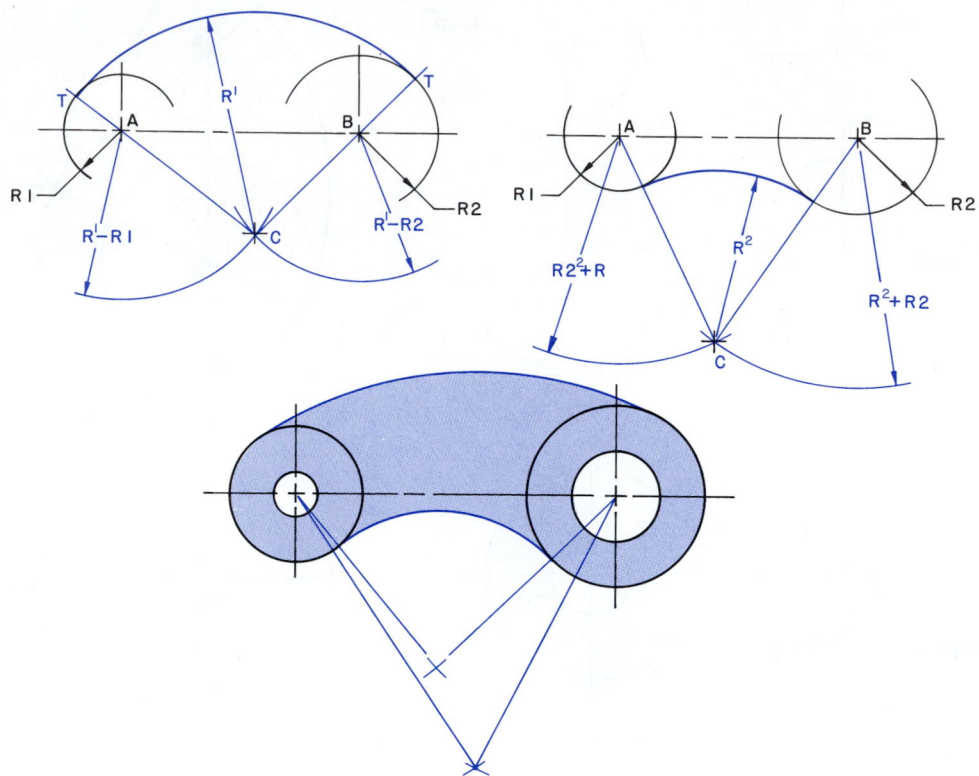

FIGURE 5.33 Drawing an Inside
Arc and an Enclosing Arc
Tangent to Two Arcs

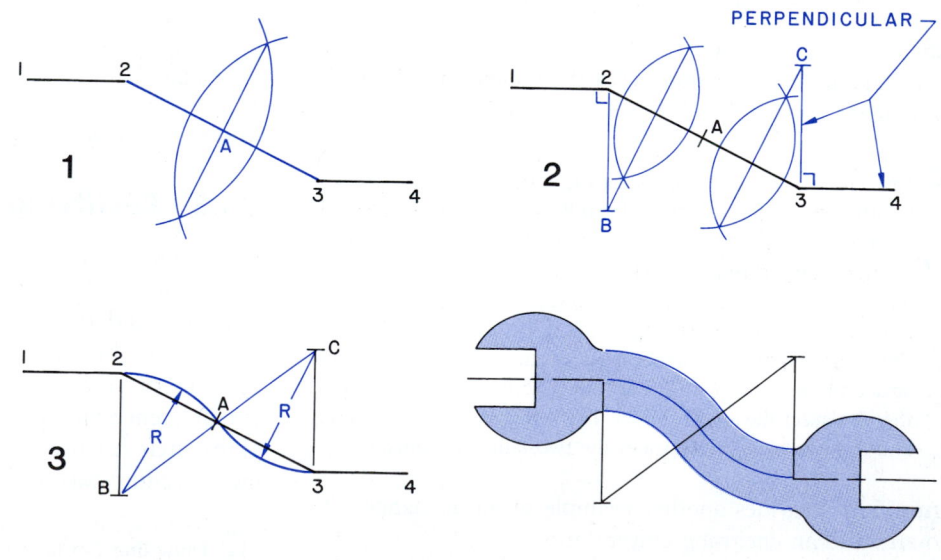

FIGURE 5.34 Drawing an Ogee
Curve

curved line at point 1. (Note that it is not necessary to have
point A, although it does help to establish the exact tangent
points.) The following steps are used:

1. Use dividers to mark off very small equal distances along the
   curve. The smaller the distance, the more accurate the approximation because each distance will be the chord measurement
   of its corresponding arc segment and therefore will be somewhat shorter than the arc's true length.

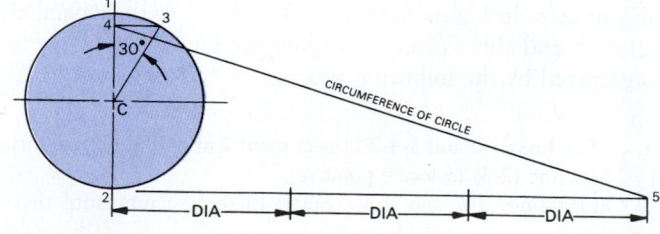

FIGURE 5.35 Rectifying a Circle

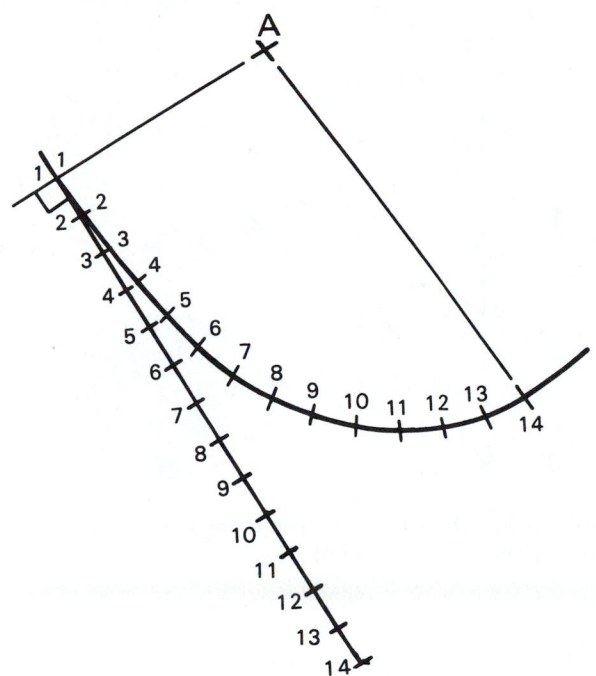

FIGURE 5.36 Rectifying an Arc

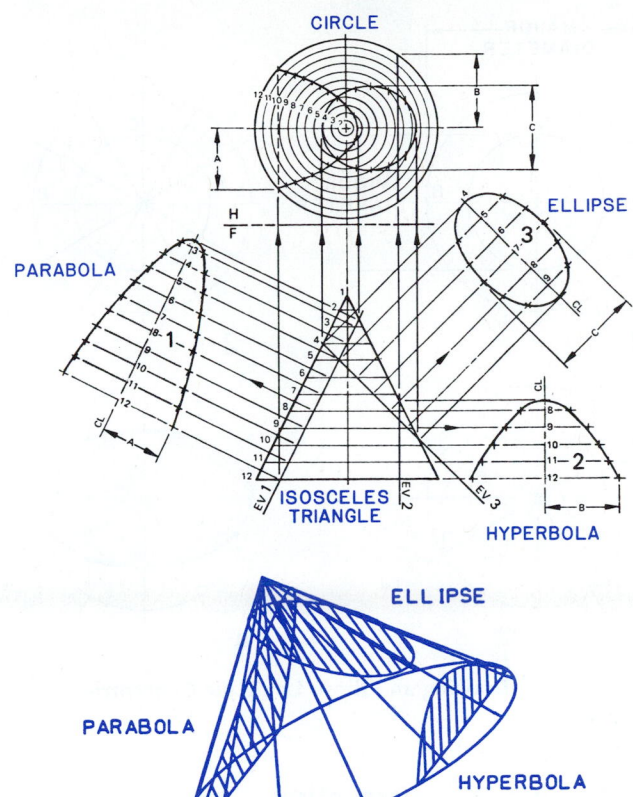

FIGURE 5.37 Conic Sections

2. Starting at the opposite end of the arc, away from the side with the tangent line, mark off equal chords, point 14 to point 13, 13 to 12, 12 to 11, 11 to 10, and so on. Continue marking off each division until less than one full space remains, which is at point 2 in the given example. (Note that in the example it works out perfectly, which will seldom be the case.)

3. Without lifting the dividers, start dividing the tangent line into the same number of segments, 2 to 3, 3 to 4, 4 to 5, and so on. The tangent line 1-14 will approximately equal the length of the given arc.

5.6 Conic Sections

A **right circular cone** is one in which the altitude and the axis coincide (the axis is perpendicular to the base). The intersection of a plane and a right circular cone is called a *conic section*. Five possible sections can result from this intersection (Fig. 5.37). The shapes formed by the sections are:

1. **Parabola** A plane (EV1) passing parallel to a true length element (edge) of the cone, therefore forming the same base angle (angle between the base and the edge), results in a parabola.

2. **Hyperbola** A plane (EV2) passing through a cone, parallel to the altitude and perpendicular to the base, results in a hyperbola.

3. **Ellipse** A plane (EV3) that cuts all the elements of the cone, but is not perpendicular to the axis, forms a true ellipse.

4. **Triangle** A plane that passes through the vertex, and is parallel to the axis, cuts an isosceles (or equilateral) triangle (front view).

5. **Circle** A plane that passes perpendicular to the axis forms a circular intersection. In Figure 5.37, a series of horizontal cutting planes has been introduced in the front view, which project as circles in the top view.

5.6.1 Intersection of a Cone and a Plane

You can establish the **intersection of a cone and a plane** by passing a series of horizontal cutting planes through the cone (perpendicular to its axis). In Figure 5.37, the front and top views of the cone are given along with the edge view of three planes that intersect it. To find the top view and the true shape of each intersection use the following steps:

1. In the front view, pass a series of evenly spaced horizontal cutting planes through the cone, CP1 through CP12.

2. Each cutting plane projects as a circle in the top view.

3. EV1 intersects cutting planes 3 through 12 in the front view. Project intersection points to the top view. The intersection of EV1 and the cone forms a parabola (1).

4. The true shape of the parabola is seen in a view projected parallel to EV1. Draw the centerline of the parabola parallel to EV1, and project the intersection points of the plane (EV1) and each cutting plane from the front view. Distances are transferred from the horizontal view, as in dimension A.

5. Repeat steps 3 and 4 to establish the intersection of EV2 and EV3 with the cone. EV2 projects as a line in the top view and as a hyperbola in a true shape view (2). EV3 forms an ellipse in the top view and projects as a true size ellipse in view (3).

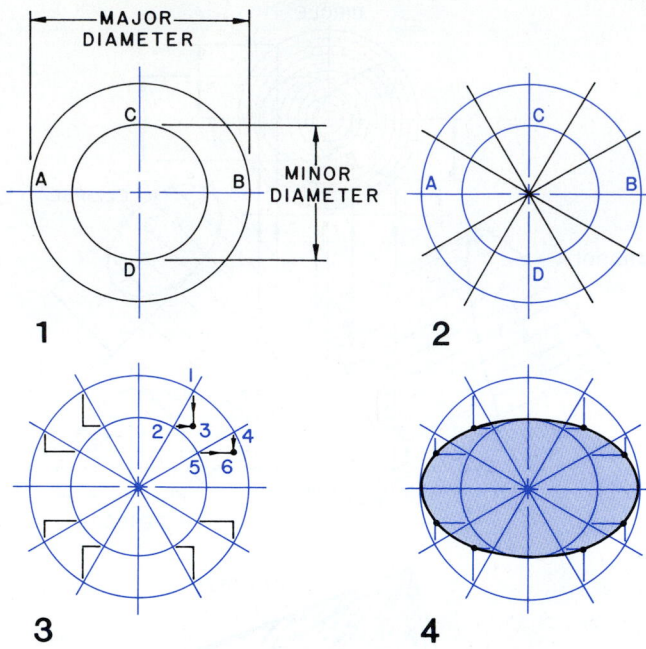

1

2

3   **4**

FIGURE 5.38   Drawing an Ellipse Using the Concentric Circle Method

5.6.2   Ellipse Construction

You can construct an **ellipse** in several ways, two of which we will cover in this section: the **concentric circle method** and the **four-center method**. The two methods are useful for constructing oddly sized or large ellipses. Both methods *approximate* the shape of a true ellipse. Figure 5.38 illustrates the concentric circle method of constructing an ellipse. The following steps were used in this construction:

1. Given the major axis AB and the minor axis CD, draw concentric circles (circles of a different size with the same center point) using the axes as diameters.
2. Divide the circles into an equal number of sections. Figure 5.38 uses 12 equal divisions.
3. Where each line crosses the inner circle (point 2 or 5), draw a line parallel to the major axis; where the same line crosses the outer circle (point 1 or 4), draw a line parallel to the minor axis. The point of intersection of these two lines (point 3 or 6) will be on the ellipse.
4. Repeat this process for each division of the circles. Use an irregular curve to connect the points smoothly. The ellipse is easier to draw and more accurate in direct proportion to the number of divisions used and points located.

Figure 5.39 uses the approximate method, or four-center method, to construct the ellipse. The following steps are used in the construction process:

1. With the major axis AB and minor axis CD given, connect points B and C.
2. Using the distance from the center of the ellipse to point B as the radius, strike arc R1. Point 1 is the intersection of R1 and the extended minor axis.

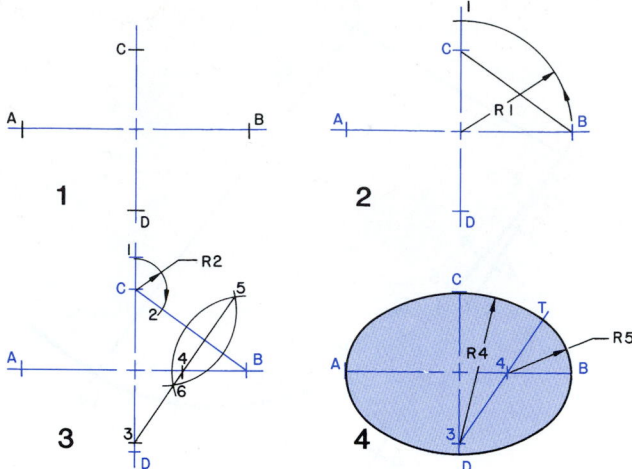

1   **2**

3   **4**

FIGURE 5.39   Drawing an Ellipse Using the Approximate Method (Four-Center Method)

3. The distance from point C to point 1 is used to establish R2. Draw arc R2 so that it intersects line B-C at point 2.
4. Bisect line B-2 and extend bisector 5-6 so that it crosses the minor axis at point 3. Point 3 is the center point for radius R4.
5. Where bisector 5-6 crosses the major axis (point 4), draw radius R5 to establish the sides of the ellipse at point A and point B. R4 is the radius for the upper and lower arc at point C and D of the ellipse.

These two methods work best when the *minor axis is at least 75% of the major axis.* When the minor axis is too small in comparison to the major axis the top and bottom of the ellipse are flattened. The closer the major axis and the minor axis are in length, the more accurate and pleasing looking the ellipse.

5.6.3   Parabola Construction Using a Rectangle or Parallelogram

A **parabola** is the result of an intersection between a cone and a plane passed parallel to one of its elements. It is a plane curve, generated by a point moving so that its distance from a fixed point, known as the *focus,* is always equal to its distance from a fixed line. Parabolas are used in the design of surfaces that need to reflect sound or light in a specific manner. The construction of a parabola using a rectangle in Figure 5.40(a) and a parallelogram in Figure 5.40(b) involves the same steps:

1. Divide side BC into an even number of equal parts and side AB into half as many equal parts.
2. Connect the points along AB and CD to E.
3. Draw parallel lines from the points along BC to where they intersect the lines drawn in step 2. The intersection points are points along the parabola's curve.
4. Connect the intersection points using an irregular curve. The greater the number of divisions, the greater the accuracy of the curve.

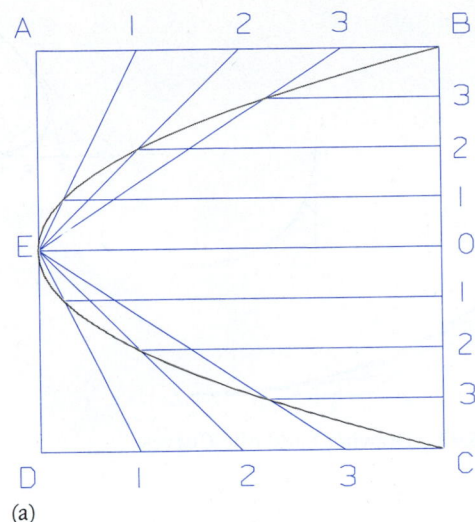

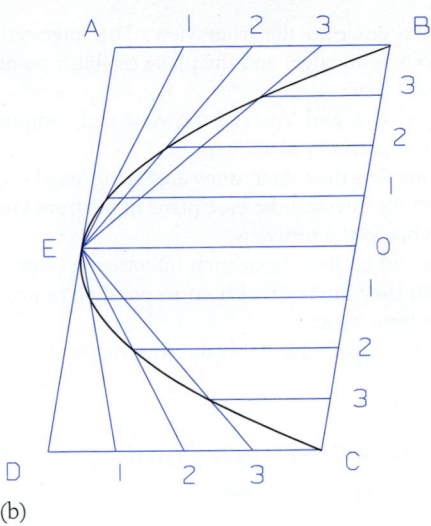

(a)

(b)

FIGURE 5.40   Drawing a Parabola

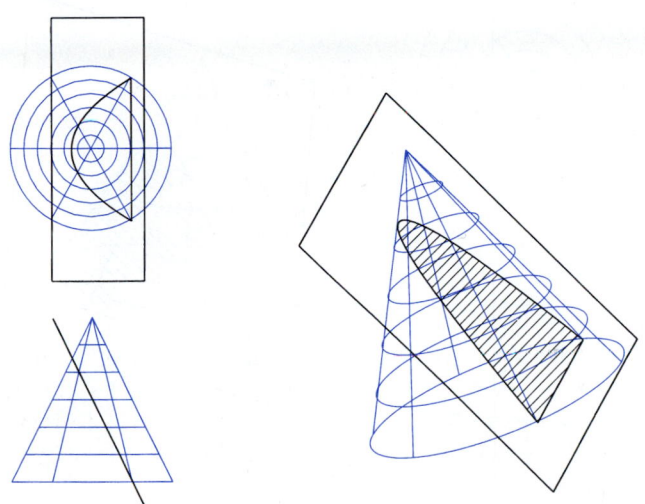

FIGURE 5.41   3D Model of a Conic Section (Parabola)

5.6.4 Parabola Construction by Establishing the Intersection of a Plane and a Cone

Figure 5.41 shows the intersection of a cone and a plane in the top view, the front view, and as a 3D model. Figure 5.42 illustrates the step-by-step procedure for constructing a parabola by establishing the intersection of a plane and a cone. The following steps are used:

1. Draw the given cone and the intersecting plane in the front and top views. A parabola is formed by an intersecting plane that is parallel to one of the cone's elements-edge lines (front view).
2. Draw any number of concentric circles in the top view. The greater the number of circles, the greater the accuracy of the parabola. Figure 5.42(b) uses only two circles to provide a clear picture of the process.

(a)

(b)

(c)

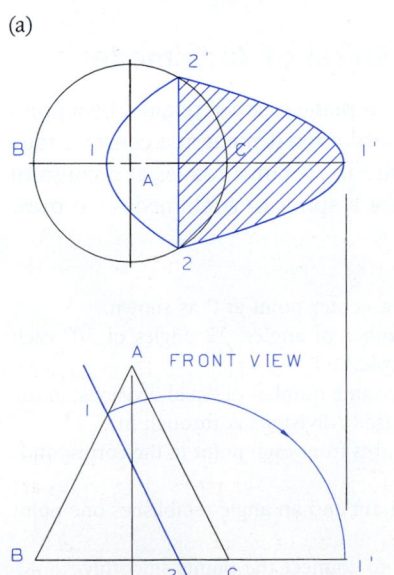

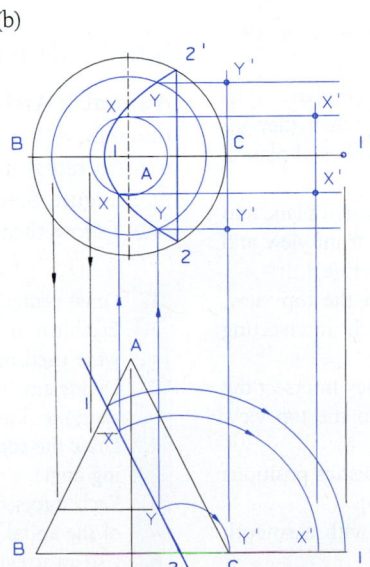

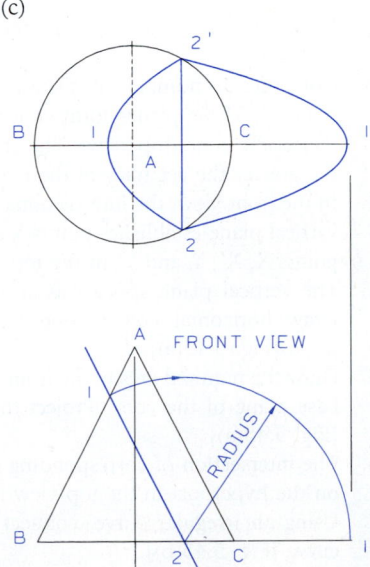

FIGURE 5.42   Construction of a Parabola

3. Project the circle to the front view. The intersection of the circle (seen as an edge) and the plane establish points X and Y in the front view.
4. Project points X and Y to the top view and complete the top view of the parabola as shown.
5. Using point 2 as the center, draw arcs using lengths 2Y, 2X, and 2-1 until they intersect the base plane in the front view. Project these points to the top view.
6. Draw horizontal lines from each intersecting point in the top view until they intersect with corresponding points projected from the front view.
7. Connect these points to form the true shape of the parabola.

5.6.5   Connecting Two Points with a Parabolic Curve

Figure 5.43 shows three parabolic curves. In each case, points X, Y, and 0 are given. The following steps are used for the construction:

1. Draw lines X-0 and Y-0.
2. Divide each line into the same number of equal parts and number the divisions.
3. Connect the corresponding points with construction lines.
4. Sketch a smooth curve that is tangent to each of the elements as shown.
5. Use an irregular curve to draw the curve.

5.6.6   Hyperbola Construction

A **hyperbola** is a plane surface (curve) that is formed by the intersection of a right circular cone and a vertical plane. Figure 5.44 shows the intersection of a plane and cone. The plane is parallel to the cone's axis. Figure 5.45 illustrates the procedure for drawing a hyperbola. The following steps are used:

1. Draw the cone and plane in the top and front view [Fig. 5.45(a)].
2. Construct a number of planes parallel to the base [Fig. 5.45(a)]. These planes form concentric circles when they intersect the cone (top view). The greater the number of planes, the greater the accuracy of the hyperbola.
3. In the front view, the intersection of each horizontal plane and vertical plane establishes points X and Y in the front view and points X, X′, Y, and Y′ in the top view [Fig. 5.45(a)].
4. The vertical plane appears as an edge (EV) in the top view. Draw horizontal construction lines from each intersecting point [Fig. 5.45(a)].
5. Draw the required arcs in the front view until they intersect the base plane of the cone. Project these points to the top view [Fig. 5.45(a)].
6. The intersection of corresponding points establishes positions on the hyperbola in the top view [Fig. 5.45(b)].
7. Using an irregular curve, connect the points with a smooth curve [Fig. 5.45(b)].

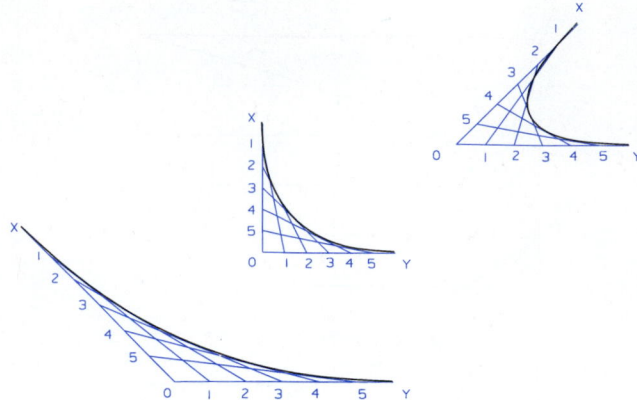

FIGURE 5.43   Drawing Parabolic Curves

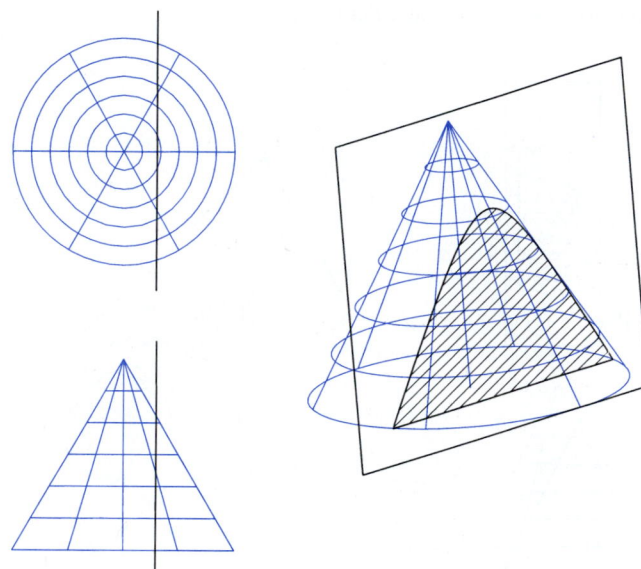

FIGURE 5.44   3D Model of a Conic Section (Hyperbola)

5.6.7   Drawing a Spiral of Archimedes

A **spiral of Archimedes** is a plane curve generated by a point moving away from or toward a fixed point at a constant rate, while a radial line from the fixed point rotates at a constant rate. Figure 5.46 illustrates a spiral of Archimedes. To draw one, follow these steps:

1. Draw centerlines with a center point at 0 as shown.
2. Establish an equal number of angles; 12 angles of 30° each were used in the example.
3. Divide any line into the same number of equal divisions; in the example, line 0-12 is used (divisions A through M).
4. Draw the construction arcs from each point to the corresponding angle.
5. Each intersection of an arc and an angle establishes one point of the spiral.
6. Use an irregular curve to connect the points smoothly.

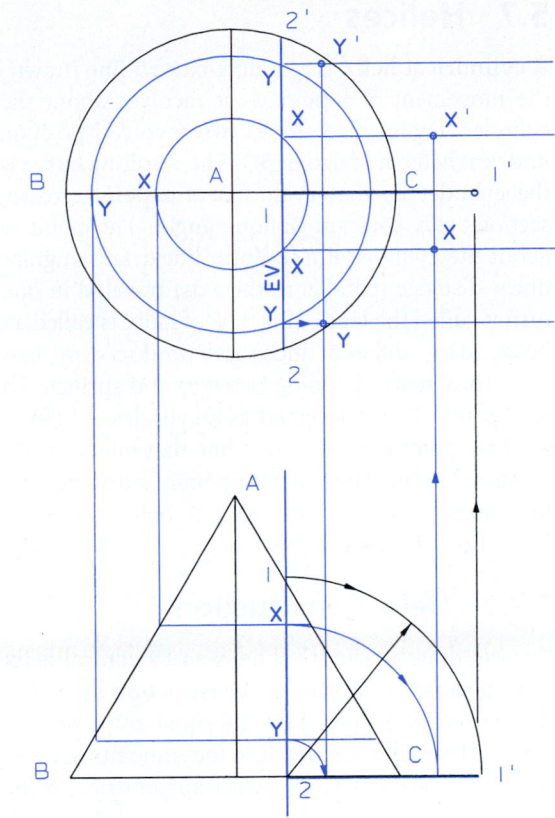

(a)

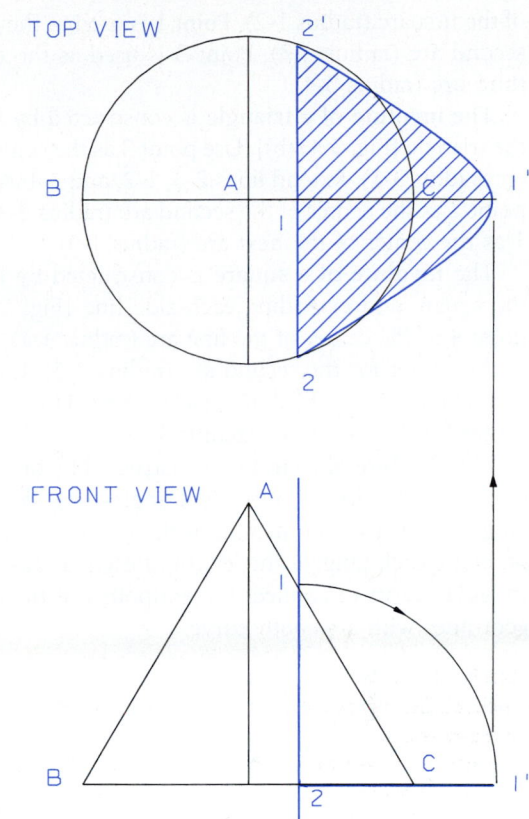

(b)

FIGURE 5.45   Construction of a Hyperbola

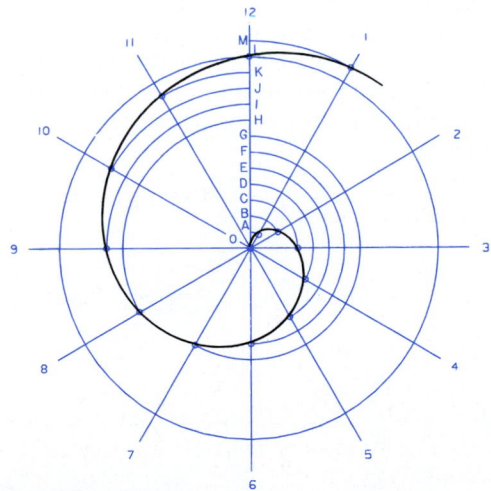

FIGURE 5.46   Drawing a Spiral of Archimedes

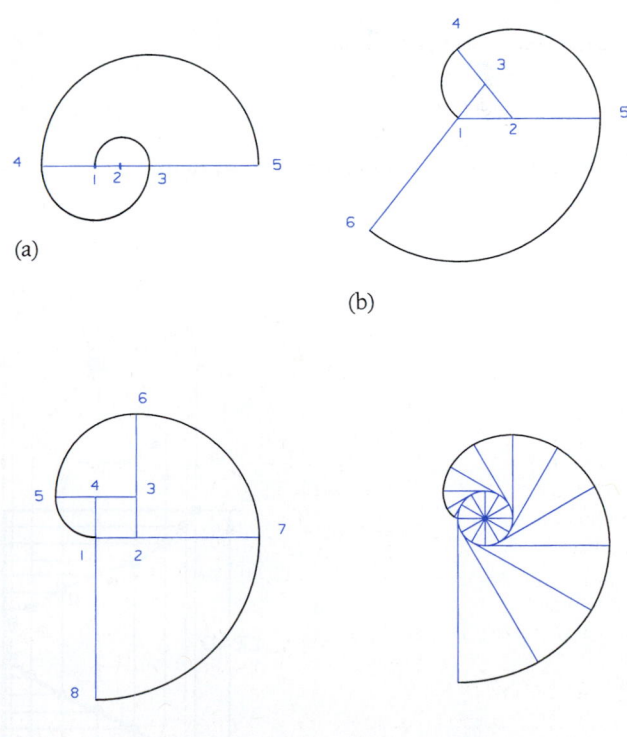

(a)

(b)

(c)   (d)

FIGURE 5.47   Drawing Involutes   (a) Involute of line
(b) Involute of triangle (c) Involute of square (d) Involute of circle

5.6.8 Constructing an Involute of a Line, a Triangle, a Square, or a Circle

An **involute** is a plane curve traced by a point on a thread kept taut as it is unwound from another curve. Figure 5.47 illustrates four kinds of involutes.

In Figure 5.47(a), the **involute of a line** is constructed by first drawing the given line 1-2. Point 2 is used as the center of the first arc (radius 1-2). Point 1 is used as the center of the second arc (radius 1-3). Point 3 is used as the center of the third arc (radius 3-4).

The **involute of a triangle** is constructed by first drawing the triangle [Fig. 5.47(b)]. Use point 3 as the center of the first arc (radius 3-1). Extend lines 2-3, 1-2, and 3-1 as shown. Use point 2 as the center of the second arc (radius 2-4). Use point 1 as the center of the next arc (radius 1-5).

The **involute of a square** is constructed by first drawing the square and extending each side line [Fig. 5.47(c)]. Use point 4 as the center of the first arc (radius 4-1). Use point 3 as the center for the second arc (radius 3-5). Use point 2 as the center for the third arc (radius 2-6). Use point 1 as the center for the fourth arc (radius 1-7).

The **involute of a circle** is constructed by first drawing the circle and dividing it into equal angles [Fig. 5.47(d)]. Draw tangent construction lines from the end of each angle. Mark off along each tangent the length of each circular arc. Use an irregular curve to connect the endpoints of the arc and tangent lines with a smooth curve.

5.7 Helices

A **cylindrical helix** is a double-curved line drawn by tracing the movement of a point as it revolves about the axis of a cylinder. Figure 5.48 shows two revolved positions of a cylindrical helix modeled in 3D. The resulting curve is traced on the cylinder by the revolution of a point crossing its right sections at a constant oblique angle. The point must travel about the cylinder at a uniform linear and angular rate. The linear distance (parallel to the axis) traveled in one complete turn is called the **lead**. This type of helix is called a cylindrical helix. Many different industrial products are based on the cylindrical helix including fasteners and springs. The stairway in Figure 5.1 was designed as a cylindrical helix.

If the point moves about a line that intersects the axis, it is a **conical helix**. The generating point's distance from the axis line changes at a uniform rate. A helix can be either *right-handed* or *left-handed*.

5.7.1 Helix Construction

You can draw a cylindrical helix and a conical helix using the same general steps. Start the construction by radially dividing the end view (curve) into an equal number of parts (Fig. 5.49). The lead is divided into the same number of parts. Use the following steps to construct a cylindrical helix:

1. Draw the right-handed cylindrical helix by first dividing the circular end view into equal divisions. Also divide the lead into equal parts (16 was used in the example).
2. Label the points on both views.
3. Project the end view divisions to the front view as vertical elements on the surface of the cylinder. In the front view, establish a series of points on the surface of the cylinder. Each point represents a position of the generating point as it rotates about the axis.

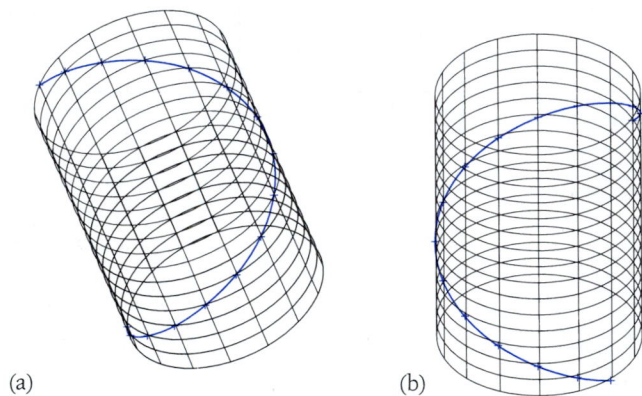

(a)   (b)

FIGURE 5.48   3D Model of a Cylindrical Helix

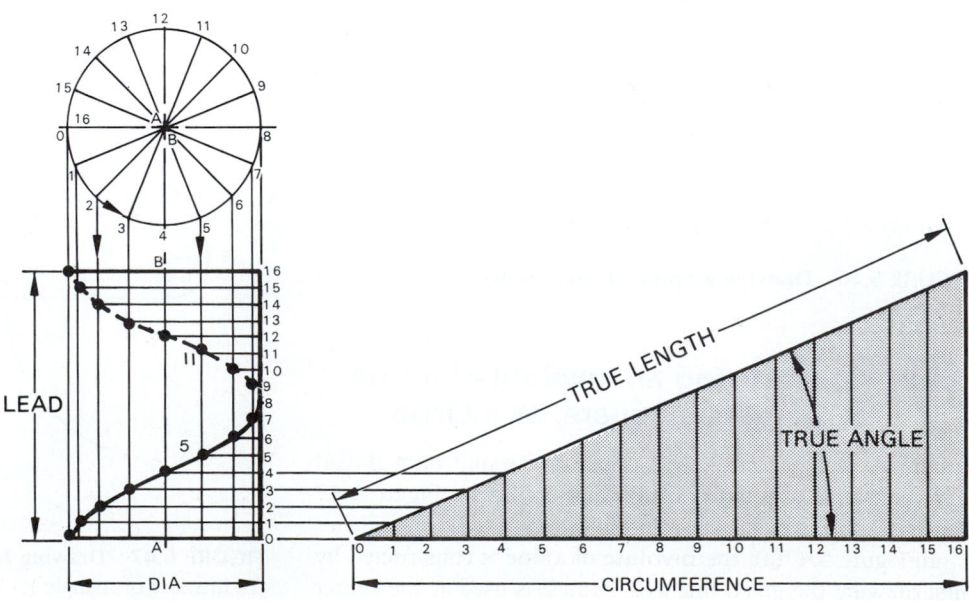

FIGURE 5.49   Drawing a
Cylindrical Helix

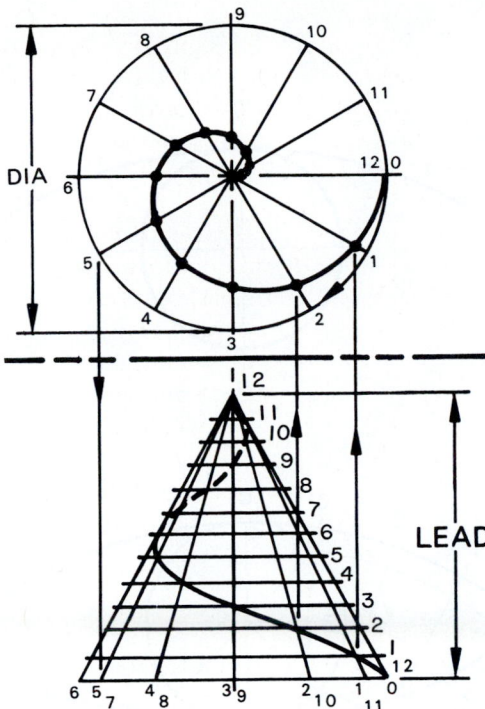

FIGURE 5.50   Drawing a Conical Helix

(a)

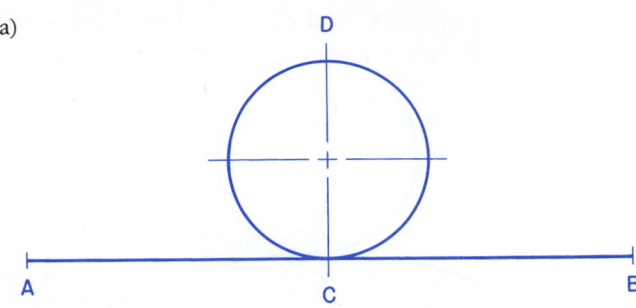

(b)

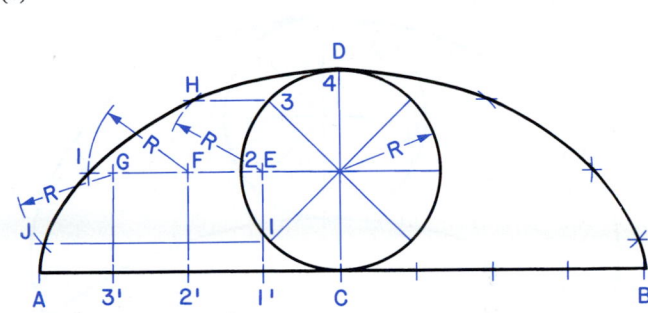

FIGURE 5.51   Drawing a Cycloid

4. You can develop the cylindrical helix by unrolling the cylinder's surface. The helix line is a straight line (true length) on the development. The angle the helix line makes with the baseline is called the **helix angle** (true angle).

To construct a **conical helix**, you must know its taper angle (angle between the cone's axis and an element on the cone's surface) and lead. In Figure 5.50, the lead and the circle divisions are established as for a cylindrical helix. Elements determined in the top (end) view appear in the front view as straight lines, intersecting the vertex of the cone. Lead elements are drawn as horizontal lines. Points on the surface of the cone are located at the intersection of related elements.

You May Complete Exercises 5.5 Through 5.8 at This Time

5.8 Cycloid, Epicycloid, and Hypocycloid Construction

A **cycloid** is a curve that is generated by a point on the circumference of a circle as it rolls along a straight line. The cycloid is used in the design of some gear teeth. The generating circle and the line are given in Figure 5.51. Following are the steps for constructing a cycloid:

1. Draw the generating line tangent to the circle. Locate points A, B, C, and D.
2. Divide line AB and the circle into an equal number of parts (8 here). Locate the points as shown.
3. Draw vertical construction lines from each point on the line and horizontal construction lines from each point on the circle. Locate points E, F, and G.
4. Using the radius R of the circle, draw an arc from point E to where the arc intersects the horizontal line drawn from point 3 on the circle. This will be one point on the cycloid (point H in the figure).
5. Repeat step 4 using the circle's radius and draw an arc from F to establish I.
6. Repeat step 4 using the circle's radius and draw an arc from G to establish point J.
7. Use an irregular curve to draw a smooth curve line through points D, H, I, J and A. You can repeat this process to draw the right side of the cycloid, or you can transfer the curve by tracing.

An **epicycloid** is a curve traced by a point on a fixed circle that rolls on the outside of the circle. Figure 5.52 illustrates the construction of an epicycloid. The curve is drawn in a similar way as the cycloid in Figure 5.51. The epicycloid is used in the design of gear teeth outlines.

A **hypocycloid** is a curve traced by a point on a fixed circle that rolls inside the circle. Figure 5.53 demonstrates the construction of a hypocycloid. This curve can also be constructed like the cycloid in Figure 5.51.

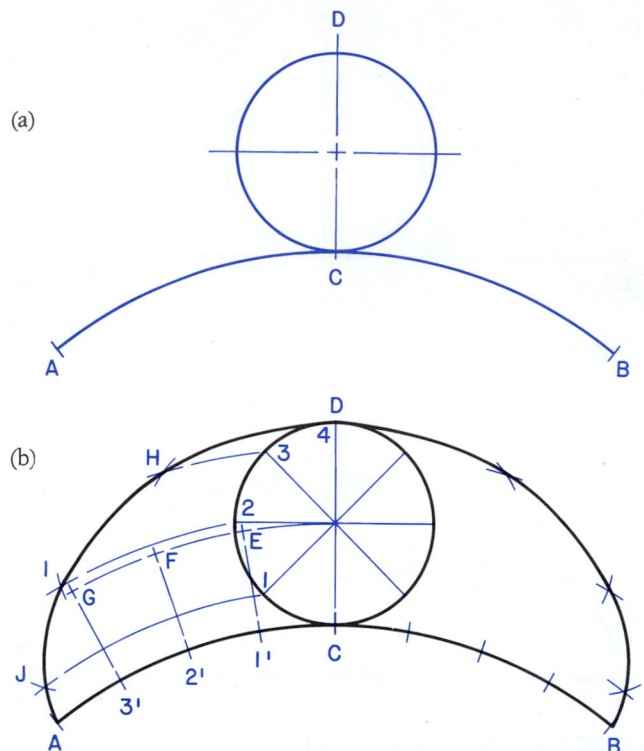

FIGURE 5.52   Drawing an Epicycloid

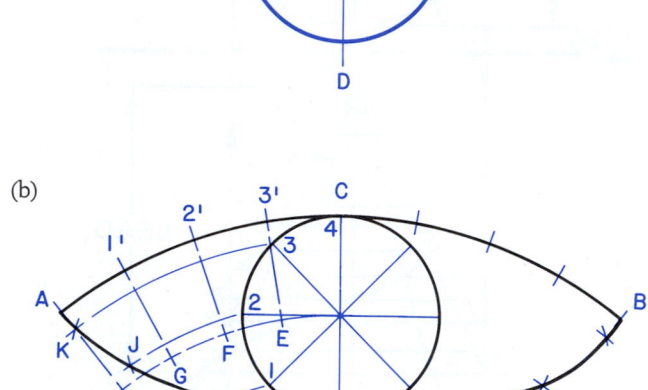

FIGURE 5.53   Drawing a Hypocycloid

5.9   Geometric Construction Using CAD

In CAD, anything placed on a drawing is a geometry **item** or **entity.** Basic geometric entities include points, lines, arcs, and circles (Figs. 5.54 and 5.55). Entities are used to create any type of geometric feature. The CAD capabilities explained in this section can be substituted for many of the geometric constructions introduced in the first portion of this chapter. The techniques described for CAD systems are similar for all systems, but differ in the command names used. The commands presented here are for AutoCAD.

5.9.1   Location of Geometry

There are three ways to indicate a location of geometry on a drawing: (1) by digitizing the location (**free digitizing**), (2) by entering the location's coordinates through the computer keyboard or menu (**explicit entry**), or (3) by snapping to a location on an entity using a **reference**, which AutoCAD calls object snaps (**OSNAPS**). **OSNAPS** are used to specify a location on existing geometry. For example, the endpoint, center, or midpoint of an entity, or the intersection of two entities (Fig. 5.56).

5.9.2   Basic Construction

Regardless of whether a 2D or 3D system is used, creating the geometry is the first step in drawing a *part* with a CAD system. The basic construction instructions are used to create

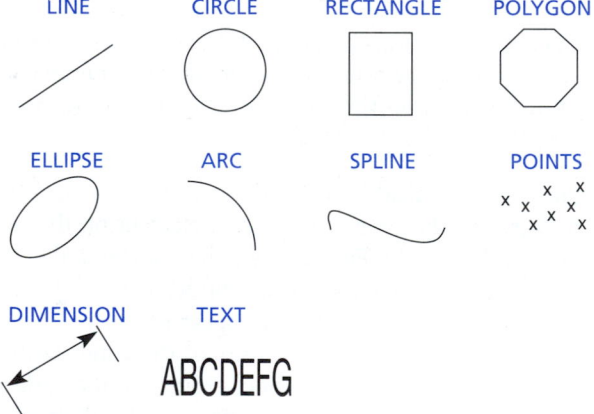

FIGURE 5.54   Geometric Entities

geometry entities such as lines, arcs, and circles. Entities are the building blocks of every part. To construct geometry, the system must know the location, the size, and the appearance of the entity. To specify an entity's size, a value is given and the explicit coordinates are either typed or defined by free-hand digitizing.

OSNAP options (Fig. 5.56) enable the creation of geometry relative to an existing entity; either the **ENDPOINT**, **MIDPOINT**, or **CENTER** of an entity can be referenced depending on its type. The intersection of two entities can also be referenced with an **OSNAP** option (**INT**ersection.) Lines have two

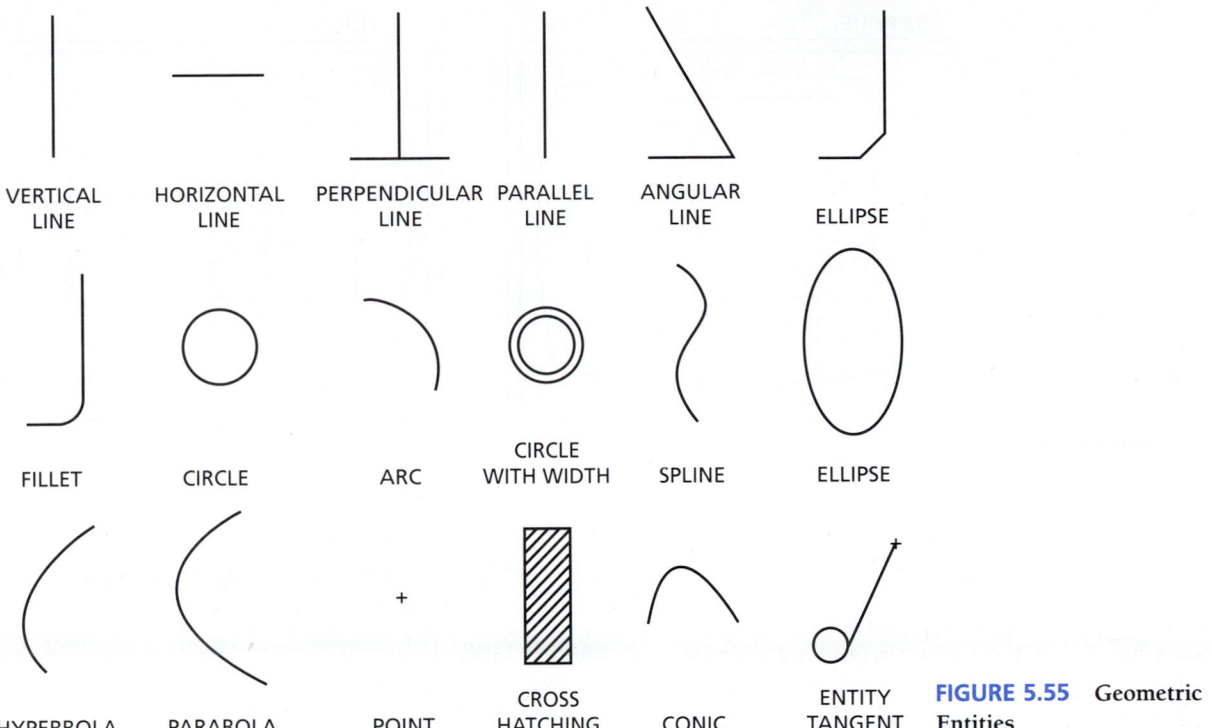

VERTICAL LINE   HORIZONTAL LINE   PERPENDICULAR LINE   PARALLEL LINE   ANGULAR LINE   ELLIPSE

FILLET   CIRCLE   ARC   CIRCLE WITH WIDTH   SPLINE   ELLIPSE

HYPERBOLA   PARABOLA   POINT   CROSS HATCHING   CONIC   ENTITY TANGENT

FIGURE 5.55 Geometric Entities

ENDpoints and a **MID**point. Circles and arcs have at least one **END**point and a **CEN**ter.

The system makes many steps of a geometric construction unnecessary—for instance, a typical problem in manual drafting and geometric construction is to find the center of a circle or an arc. The **POINT** command along with the **CEN**ter **OSNAP** reference will automatically put a point at the center of a circle (when the circle is picked).

For the following discussion, any commands or options to commands enclosed by brackets < > are **defaults** for that command.

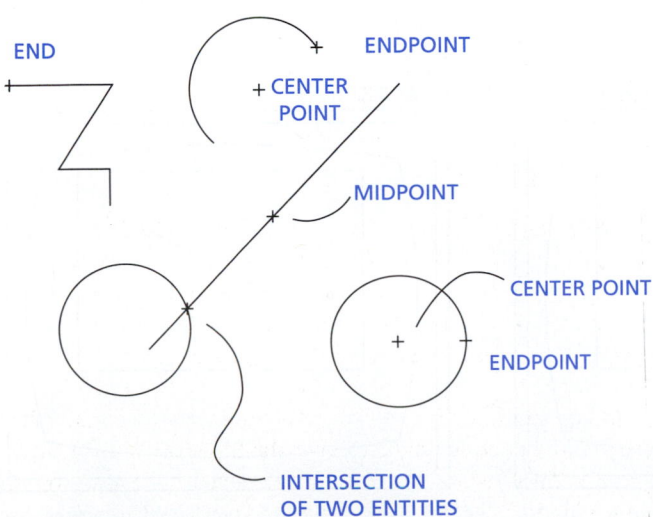

END   ENDPOINT   CENTER POINT   MIDPOINT   CENTER POINT   ENDPOINT   INTERSECTION OF TWO ENTITIES

FIGURE 5.56 Geometry Terminology

5.10 Geometry Entities

In CAD, the term **geometry entity** applies to anything that can be placed on a drawing. This includes geometric forms, groups, figures, text, labels, dimensions, and crosshatching. As a CAD drafter you will specify the shape, size, color, and location of entities. Figures 5.54 and 5.55 show a range of geometry entities available on CAD systems.

5.10.1 Points

As discussed in the first part of this chapter, points are the simplest entities; they serve as references or as placement coordinates for other entities. You can use a digitizer or the keyboard to enter coordinate values and the **POINT** command to place a point at the specified location. Each point has an **X** and a **Y** coordinate (and a **Z** coordinate for 3D).

Figure 5.57 shows three points that have been drawn by free digitizing: D1, D2, and D3. Free digitizing is the same as *picking* a position on the tablet or with a mouse. The "BEFORE" illustration [Fig. 5.57(a)] indicates the digitized locations with an **x** at each location. In the "AFTER" illustration [Figure 5.57(b)], the three points are indicated by crosses (+). A variety of point styles are available, here the cross was previously selected using AutoCAD's **SETVAR** option for **PDMODE** set to 2. The following AutoCAD command was used:

```
Command: POINT (give the POINT command by typing or
from screen menu)
Point: D1, D2, D3 (pick three positions; use <RETURN>
between picks to reenter the POINT command)
Command: REDRAW (repaints the screen and shows the points
as a cross)
```

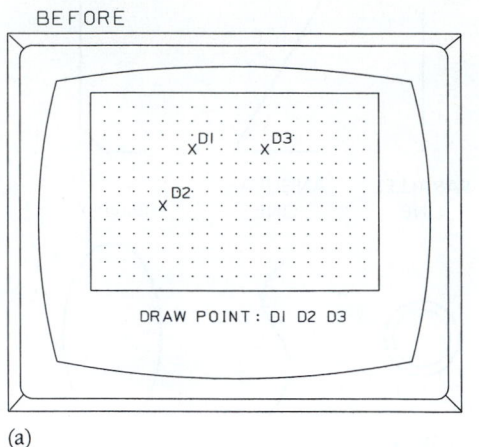

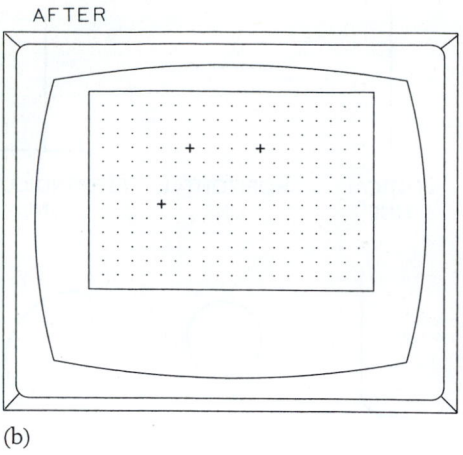

FIGURE 5.57   Drawing Points   (a)   (b)

5.10.2   Lines

Lines are entities that connect two endpoints of a line segment. Each point has **X** and **Y** coordinates (and a **Z** coordinate if you are using a 3D CAD system). Endpoints may be specified explicitly or referenced from existing geometry.

You can use the **LINE** command to create a line, a series of connected lines, or several separate lines. When connected lines are created, the endpoint of one line is also the start point of the next line. Lines that can be created include:

- a series of connected lines
- a closed region with connected lines (using **CLOSE** at end of command)
- a horizontal or a vertical line (using **ORTHO**)
- a line at an angle to an existing line
- a line parallel or perpendicular to an existing line
- a line tangent to a circle, a line, or a point.

In Figure 5.58 a line was created using free digitizing. A series of connected lines was created in Figure 5.59 using the same command, except that D3 and D4 were picked instead of

hitting <RETURN> at the second **To Point** prompt. The following command was used in Figure 5.58:

Command: **LINE**
From Point: **D1** (pick the starting position)
To Point: **D2** (pick the ending position of the line)
To Point: <RETURN> (ends the command)

Drawing a Horizontal or Vertical Line   You can create a horizontal or a vertical line by first turning on the orthogonal (**ORTHO**) option. Orthogonal limits your movement to the **X** and **Y** axis of from your last location. Figure 5.60 shows a horizontal line created using the **LINE** command with **ORTHO** turned on. The first digitize (pick) established the starting point of the line, and the second digitize established the direction and length.

Drawing a vertical line is similar to creating a horizontal line, except that the line is aligned with the **Y** axis instead of the **X** axis. In Figure 5.61, the **LINE** was selected and two points were digitized to create a vertical line. The first point established the line's starting point, and the second point established the line's direction and distance.

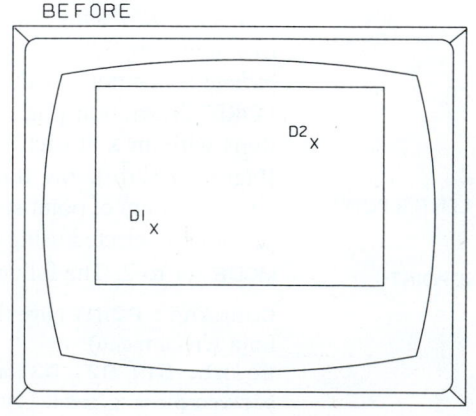

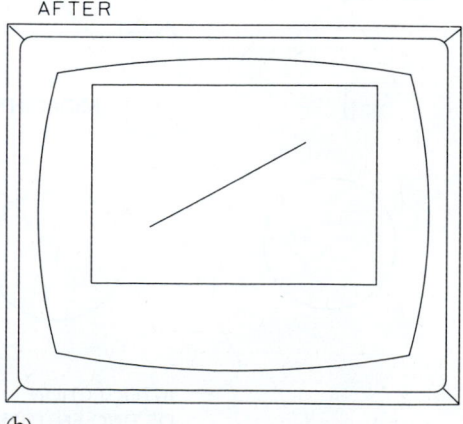

FIGURE 5.58   Drawing a Line   (a)   (b)

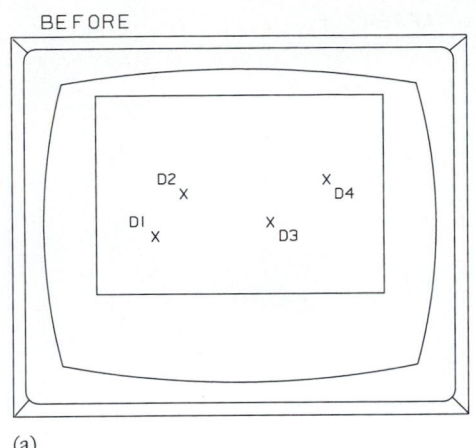
(a)

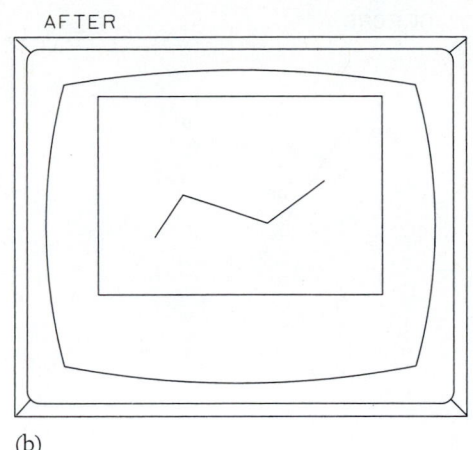
(b)

FIGURE 5.59   Drawing Multiple Lines

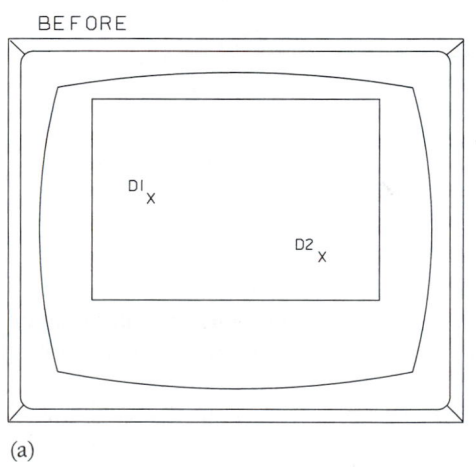
(a)

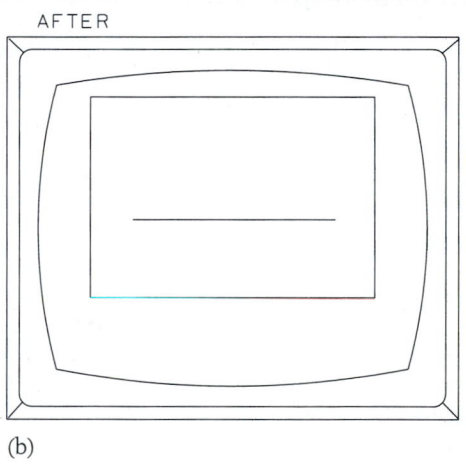
(b)

FIGURE 5.60   Drawing a Horizontal Line

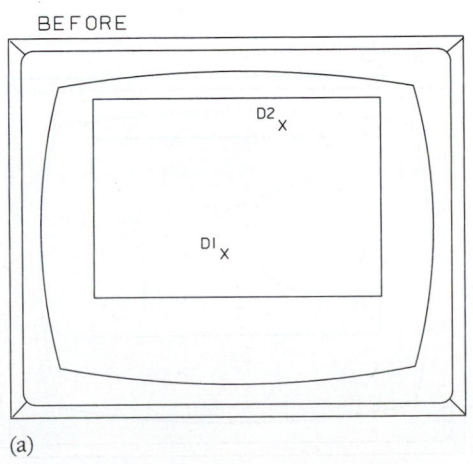
(a)

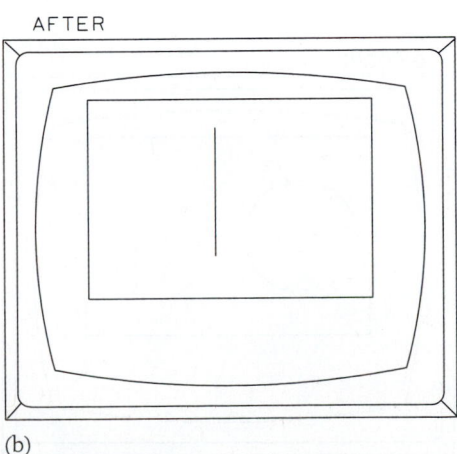
(b)

FIGURE 5.61   Drawing a Vertical Line

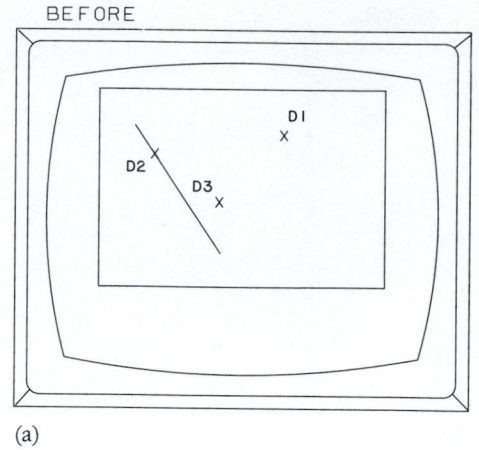
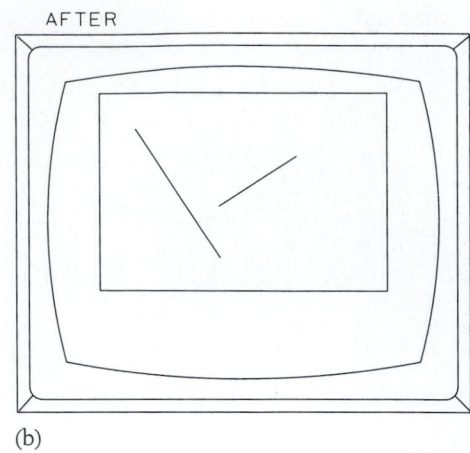

FIGURE 5.62 Drawing a Line
Perpendicular to an Existing Line   (a)   (b)

Drawing a Perpendicular Line   You can draw a line perpendicular to an existing line using the **LINE** command in conjunction with the perpendicular (**PER**) **OSNAP**. Figure 5.62 shows a line that was created perpendicular to an existing line. The **LINE** command was selected as shown below:

```
Command: LINE
From point: D1 (digitize the location of the lines starting
point)
To point: per (pick the OSNAP PER option)
of D2 (pick the line)
To point: D3 (digitize the location of the endpoint of the
line)
```

Drawing a Tangent Line   To create a line tangent to an arc or a circle, use the **OSNAP** tangent option (**TAN**). In Figure 5.63, the **LINE** command was selected. Point D1 was the starting point (at the end of the existing line) and D2 identified the circle to which the line is to be tangent. Because two tangency positions are possible for each circle, the digitized points must be near the point of tangency (the side you wish

the line to connect to the circle). The following command was used:

```
Command: LINE
From point: END (select the OSNAP END)
of D1 (pick near the end of the line)
To point: TAN (select the OSNAP TAN)
of D2 (select the circle on the side of the desired tangency)
```

5.10.3   Circles

In CAD, a circle has its start and endpoint at the 3 o'clock position and its origin at the center. You can create circles in several different ways, depending on the type of information available. You can give three digitized circumference points, the radius or the diameter value, or digitize the radius or diameter.

Drawing Circles by Specifying Three Points on the Circumference   Figure 5.64 shows a circle created by using the **CIRCLE** command and three digitizes (D1, D2, and

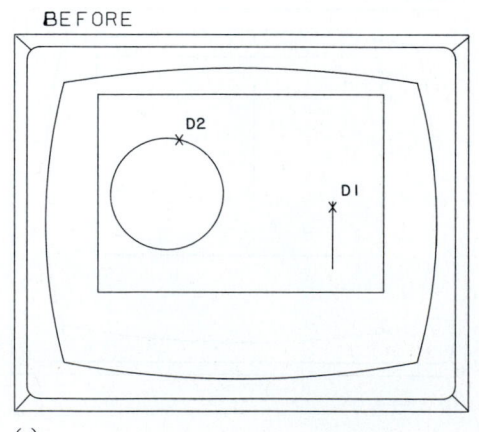
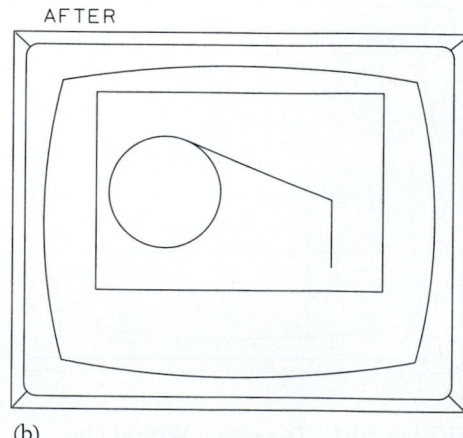

FIGURE 5.63 Drawing a Line
Tangent to a Circle and at the
End of an Existing Line   (a)   (b)

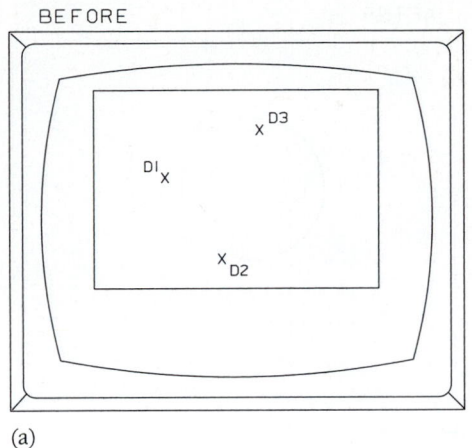

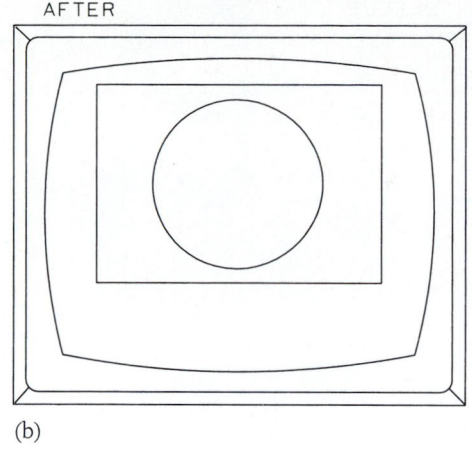

FIGURE 5.64   Drawing a Three-Point Circle

D3), which define three points on the circle's circumference. The following command was used:

```
Command: CIRCLE
3P/2P/TTR/<Center point>: 3P (pick the three-point
option)
First point on circumference: D1
Second point on circumference: D2
Third point on circumference: D3
```

Drawing Circles by Digitizing the Diameter   CAD systems can create a circle by calculating the circle's diameter from the distance between two digitized locations. Figure 5.65 illustrates a circle created by using the **CIRCLE** command and two digitized points (D1 and D2), which established opposite points (the diameter) on the circle's circumference. The following command is used:

```
Command: CIRCLE
3P/2P/TTR/<Center point>: 2P (pick the two-point
option)
First point on diameter: D1
Second point on diameter: D2
```

Drawing Circles by Digitizing the Radius   CAD systems can create a circle by calculating the circle's radius from two digitized locations. In Figure 5.66, the **CIRCLE** command was selected along with two digitized locations. Point D1 established the circle's center, and D2 identified a point on the circumference. The following command is used:

```
Command: CIRCLE
3P/2P/TTR/<Center point>: D1 (pick the center of
the circle)
Diameter/<Radius>: R (pick radius option)
Radius: D2 (digitize location)
```

Specifying a Diameter or a Radius   You can also specify a circle's diameter or radius by entering an explicit value. Only one digitized point is required for creating a circle when the diameter or the radius value is known (Fig. 5.67). The following command is used:

```
Command: CIRCLE
3P/2P/TTR/<Center of circle>: D1 (center of cir-
cle)
Diameter/<Radius>: 3.00 (radius value)
```

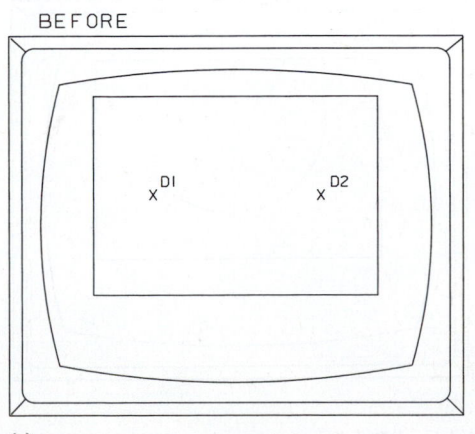

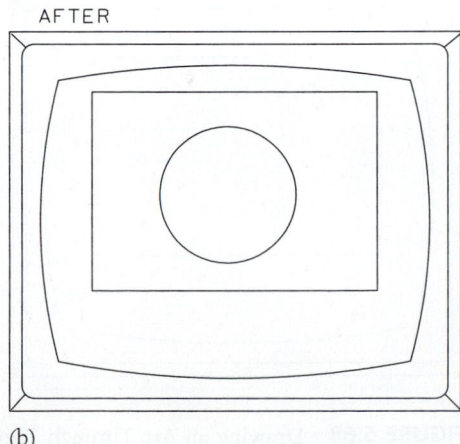

FIGURE 5.65   Drawing a Circle by Digitizing a Diameter

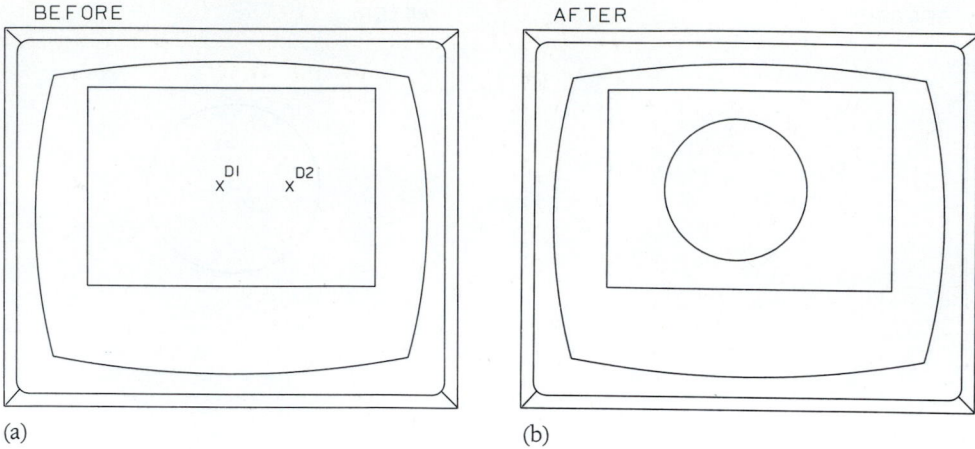

(a)   (b)

FIGURE 5.66   Drawing a Circle by Digitizing a Radius

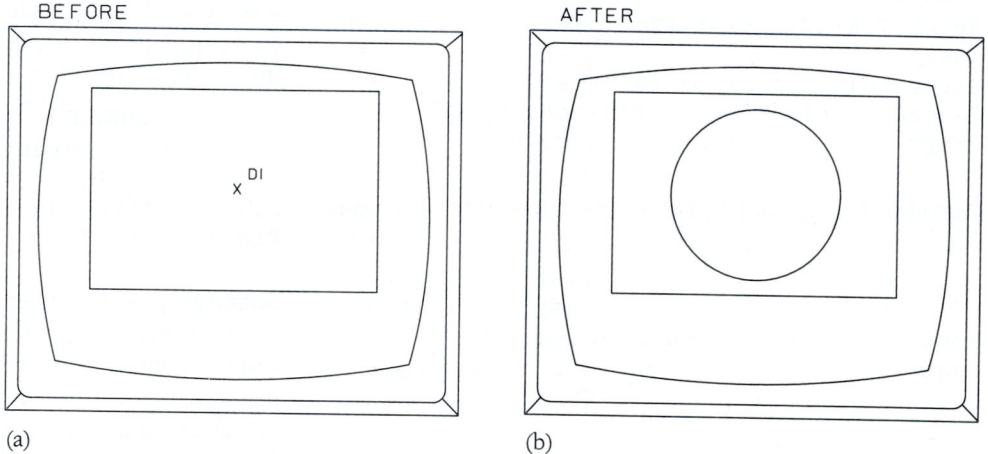

(a)   (b)

FIGURE 5.67   Drawing a Circle by Specifying the Radius Value

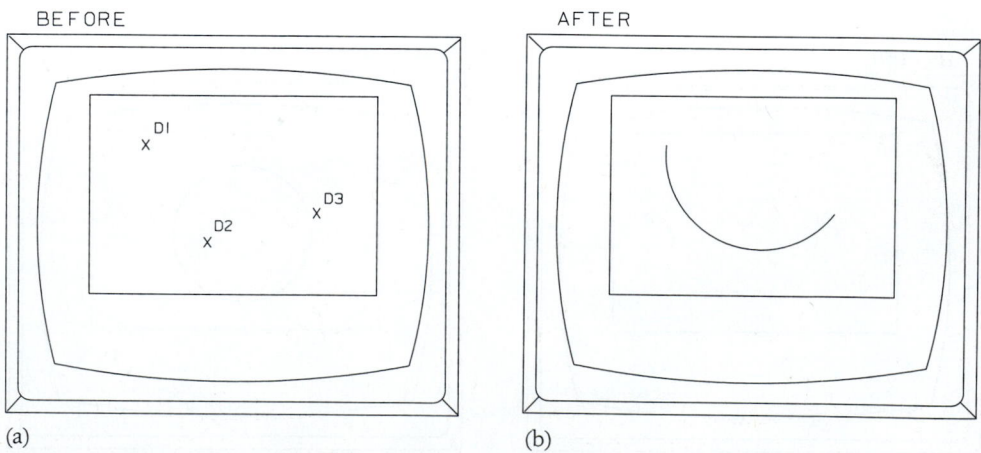

(a)   (b)

FIGURE 5.68   Drawing an Arc Through Three Digitized Points

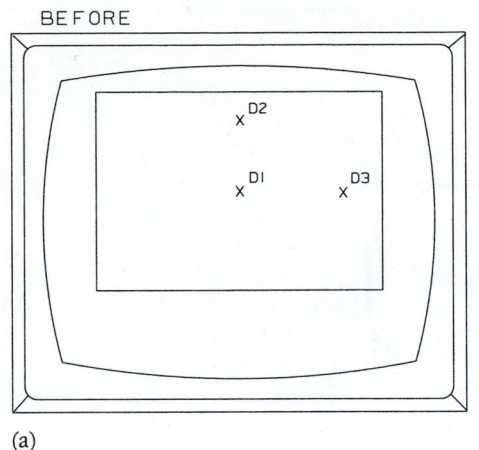

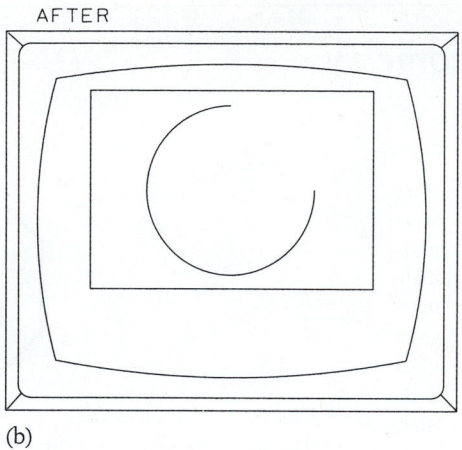

(a)   (b)   **FIGURE 5.69**   **Drawing an Arc**

5.10.4   Arcs

You will recall that an arc is a partial circle. There are many ways to create an arc including specifying the start point, a point on the arc's path, and the endpoint. The system creates the arc in the direction in which the points were digitized. AutoCAD lets you create an arc ten different ways, only two of which we will present here.

Drawing Arcs by Digitizing Three Locations   Figure 5.68 shows an arc that was created using the **ARC** command and three digitizes. Point D1 established the arc's starting point, D2 is a point on the arc, and D3 is the endpoint. The following command was used:

Command: ARC
Center/<Start point>: D1
Center/End/Second point>: D2
End point: D3

Drawing Arcs by Specifying the Center, the Starting Point, and the Endpoint   Figure 5.69 illustrates an arc that was created using the command **ARC** along with specifying the center point, the starting point, and the endpoint.

The following command is used:

Command: ARC
Center/<Start point>: C (pick center option)
of D1 (digitize center of arc)
Start point: D2 (digitize start point)
Angle/Length/<End point>: D3 (digitize the endpoint of the arc)

Drawing Tangent Arcs   A tangent arc is also called a *fillet*. A fillet is an arc created tangent to existing geometry. The **FILLET** command is used to construct tangent arcs. A fillet of a specified size is created by entering the diameter or the radius value. Fillets may be created with respect to points, lines, circles, and arcs. In Figure 5.70, the **FILLET** command was specified and the two lines were picked. In Figure 5.71 (on page 137), the following command was used to create the fillet:

Command: FILLET
Polyline/Radius/<Select first object>: R (select R for radius)
Enter fillet radius: 1.50 (set the radius default)
Command: <RETURN> (reenter the command)
FILLET Polyline/Radius/<Select first object>: D1 (pick first entity)
Select second object: D2 (pick second entity)

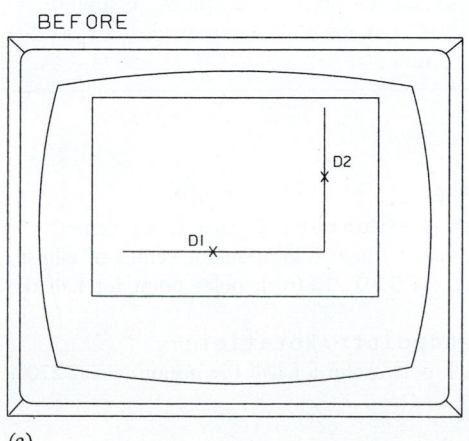

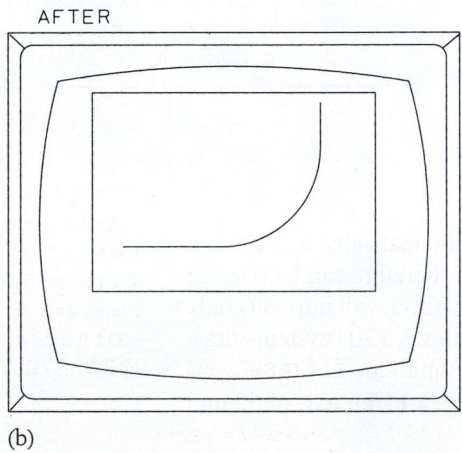

(a)   (b)   **FIGURE 5.70**   **Drawing a Fillet Between Two Lines**

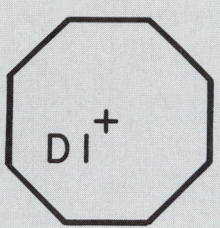

ITEMS OF INTEREST	*Geometry*

If you want to study the properties of figures and the relationships between points, lines, angles, surfaces, and solids, you study *geometry*. Geometry actually means "earth measurement." The name can be traced back to the way in which man first used those concepts. Practical geometry grew out of the needs of the Egyptians to survey their land to reestablish land boundaries after periodic flooding of the Nile. The flooding itself left a rich and sought-after soil. The men who made these measurements became known as "rope stretchers" because they used ropes to do their measuring. The Egyptians also used geometry to help build their temples and pyramids.

Around 600 B.C., the Greeks returned from their travels through Egypt and brought with them their first knowledge of geometry. Thales, the most famous of those men returning from Egypt, was the first to show the truth of a geometric relationship by showing that it followed in a logical and orderly fashion from a set of

```
Command: POLYGON
Number of sides: 8
Edge of/<Center of Polygon>: D1
Inscribed in circle/Circumscribed about circle: C
Radius of circle: .75
```
The **POLYGON** Command of an AutoCAD System

universally accepted statements (axioms or postulates). You may remember axioms and proofs from your geometry class.

Thales's student, Pythagoras, established a society in Italy that was devoted to the study of geometry and arithmetic. His most famous work was the theorem that bears his name. His influence was felt for centuries. Every student of geometry and trigonometry knows the Pythagorean theorem, which relates the lengths of the three sides of a right triangle ($a^2 + b^2 = c^2$). The side opposite the right angle is the longest side or the hypotenuse (c). The other two sides, a and b, are the sides opposite the other two angles in the triangle.

While the early Greeks and others were able to make great contributions, it was not until 1796 that a great advancement was made in geometry. A 19-year-old German, Carl Friedrich Gauss, proved it was possible to construct a regular 17-sided polygon using a compass and a rule. The Greeks had only been able

to construct regular polygons of 3, 4, 5, 6, 8, 10, and 15 sides. The 17-sided polygon was a major breakthrough. In 1799, Gauss was awarded a Ph.D. for developing the first proof of the fundamental theorem of algebra.

It may be difficult to appreciate how each contribution to geometry made engineering graphics possible. Even the most sophisticated CAD system makes use of fundamental geometric principles that were developed long ago. Operators of modern CAD systems can use the **POLYGON** command to create regular polygons of any number of sides (17 sides or 1000 sides, for example).

What started out as a way to measure the earth developed into a discipline that is the key to solving most engineering problems. All the geometric constructions used today in drafting were developed by individuals building on previous developments of others. No doubt, mankind will continue building on the past for the future.

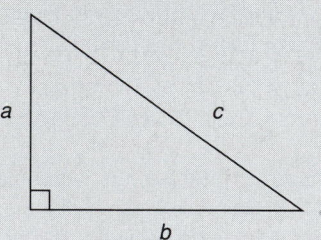

In a right triangle
with sides *a* and *b*, and hypotenuse *c*,
$$a^2 + b^2 = c^2$$
Pythagorean Triangle

5.10.5 Drawing Ellipses

An *ellipse* is an elongated circle. Mathematically, it is defined as a cone intersected by a plane and therefore can be referred to as a conic. Whereas the manual method, will normally only approximate the true shape of an ellipse, CAD systems draw perfect ellipses. In the following example, the **ELLIPSE** command is used to create an ellipse with a major axis of 50 mm and a minor axis of 40 mm:

```
Command: ELLIPSE
<Axis endpoint 1>/Center: C (pick C for center)
Center of ellipse: (digitize location for center of ellipse)
Axis endpoint: @25>0.00 (pick polar point for half the major axis at 0°)
<Other axis endpoint>/Rotation:
@20<270.00 (pick polar point for half the minor axis at 270°)
```

BEFORE

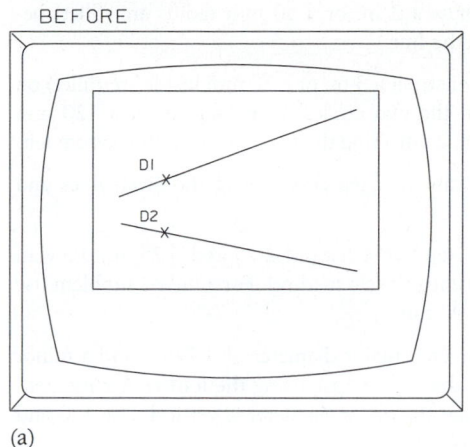

(a)

AFTER

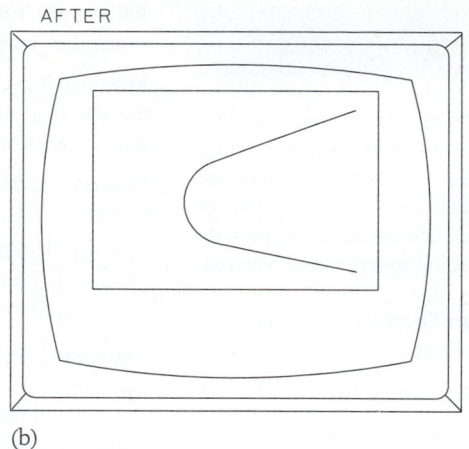

(b)

FIGURE 5.71   **Drawing a Fillet**

5.10.6   Drawing Polygons

Many CAD systems have a command that allows the automatic creation of a polygon. With AutoCAD the **POLYGON** command can be used to draw a polygon with any number of sides and any size. The following command is used to create a hexagon with distance across the flats of 1.00 in.:

Command: POLYGON
Number of sides: 6 (enter number of sides)
Edge of/<Center of Polygon>: (digitize center of polygon)
Inscribed in circle/Circumscribed about circle: C (pick circumscribed)
Radius of circle: 1.00 (distance across flats)

It is important for you, as an aspiring drafter, designer, or engineer, to master the manual procedures and techniques introduced in this chapter. Many of the manual construction techniques are needed when drafting and designing projects in industry, even when a CAD system is available.

QUIZ

True or False

1. Both hyperbolas and cones are generated from conic sections.
2. CAD systems cannot generate ellipses as accurately as templates.
3. In helix construction, the distance traveled by one point for one revolution measured parallel to the axis is called the lead.
4. The concentric method of ellipse construction is more accurate than using a template.
5. Tangent arcs are basically the same thing as fillets.
6. Squares, hexagons, pentagons, and ellipses are regular polygons.
7. A circle can be used to construct all forms of regular polygons.
8. A bisector of a line or an angle divides the line or angle into a number of equal parts.

Fill in the Blanks

9. All geometric forms are composed of _____ and their _____ .
10. _____ are used to divide lines into _____ _____ parts.
11. An _____ circle of a triangle will touch all _____ sides.
12. The distance across the _____ of an octagon will be _____ to the diameter of the _____ circle.
13. To _____ a circle means to _____ out its circumference along a straight line.
14. In CAD an _____ is a basic _____ block.
15. A _____ arc is a curve connecting two entities and is also known as a _____ .
16. _____ _____ are equally spaced along their entire length.

Answer the Following

17. When is it appropriate to use the four-center method of ellipse construction?
18. Describe the method for drawing a circle through three points using a CAD system.
19. Give a simple definition of a line and a curve.
20. What are the five types of figures that result from the intersection of a cone and a plane?
21. Define a cylindrical and a conical helix.
22. Why would the graphical method of dividing a line be more accurate than the mathematical method?
23. Name four solid shapes commonly used in industry.
24. Why is it important to learn the manual method of constructing geometric forms such as ellipses instead of just using templates?

EXERCISES

Exercises may be assigned as sketching, instrument, or CAD projects. Transfer the given information to an "A" size sheet of .25 in. grid paper. Complete all views and solve for proper visibility, including centerlines, object lines, and hidden lines. Exercises that are not assigned by the instructor can be sketched in the text to provide practice and understanding for the preceding instructional material.

After Reading the Chapter Through Section 5.5.7, You May Complete the Following Exercises

Exercise 5.1(A)   Bisect the line, the angle, and the arc.

Exercise 5.1(B)   Divide line one into eleven equal parts using the graphical method. Divide line two into seven equal parts and line three into proportional parts having ratios of 3:2:5.

Exercise 5.1(C)   Construct a hexagon inside and an octagon around the outside of the given circle.

Exercise 5.1(D)   Draw every possible tangency for the three circles.

Exercise 5.2(A)   Draw a 40 mm radius arc (fillet) between the connected lines. Connect the two lines with a tangent arc (fillet) using a 25 mm radius.

Exercise 5.2(B)   Draw a 2 in. or a 50 mm radius arc (fillet) between the circle and the line.

Exercise 5.2(C)   Construct a 3 in. or a 70 mm inside arc (fillet) on the top right side on the two circles. Draw a 5 in. or a 120 mm outside (enclosing) arc connecting the two circles on the bottom left.

Exercise 5.2(D)   Draw an ogee curve using the given lines and points.

Exercise 5.3(A)   Given two circles of 2.25 and 3.75 in., draw an ellipse using the concentric circle method. For a metric problem use diameters of 70 and 90 mm.

Exercise 5.3(B)   Given a major diameter of 4.74 in. and a minor diameter of 2.45 in., draw an ellipse using the four-center method. Draw the ellipse so that the major diameter is vertical. Use 120 and 60 mm for a metric problem.

Exercise 5.3(C)   Given circles of 2.50 and 3.5 in. in diameter, draw an ellipse using the approximate method. Use 60 and 80 mm for a metric problem.

Exercise 5.3(D)   Draw two identical ellipses. Use the concentric circle method for one and the four-center method for the other. For each ellipse, use 4.5 in. for the vertical diameter and 2.75 in. for the minor (horizontal in this case) diameter. Use 110 and 70 mm if metrics are selected as the unit of measurement. Compare the two methods for quality and accuracy.

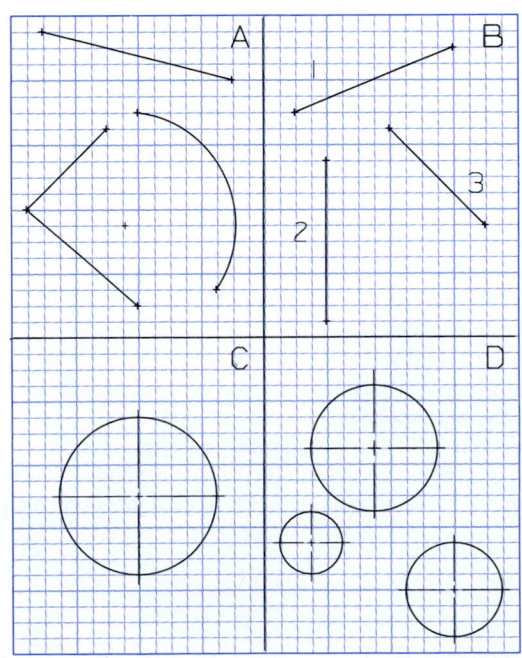

Exercise 5.1

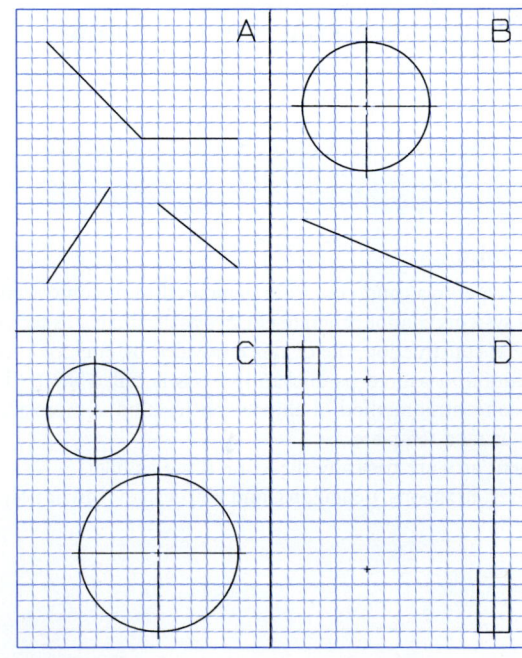

Exercise 5.2

Exercises 5.4(A) and (B)   Draw the two figures using the geometric construction techniques covered in the chapter.

After Reading the Chapter Through Section 5.7.1, You May Complete the Following Exercises

Exercises 5.5(A) and (B)   Given the rectangle, the rise, and the axis, draw a parabola for each of the problems.

Exercises 5.6(A) or (B)   Draw a hyperbola using a 4 in. (or 100 mm) diameter for the cone base and a height of 4 in. (or 100 mm). Pass a cutting plane vertically through the cone 1 in. (or 25 mm) to the right of the cone's vertical axis. For B use 5 in. (or 120 mm) as the base diameter and 4.5 in. (or 110 mm) as the cone's height. Draw the cutting plane vertically through the cone at 1.35 in. (or 35 mm) to the left of the cone's axis. Only one of these two problems can be done on the exercise page since the opposite space will be needed for construction.

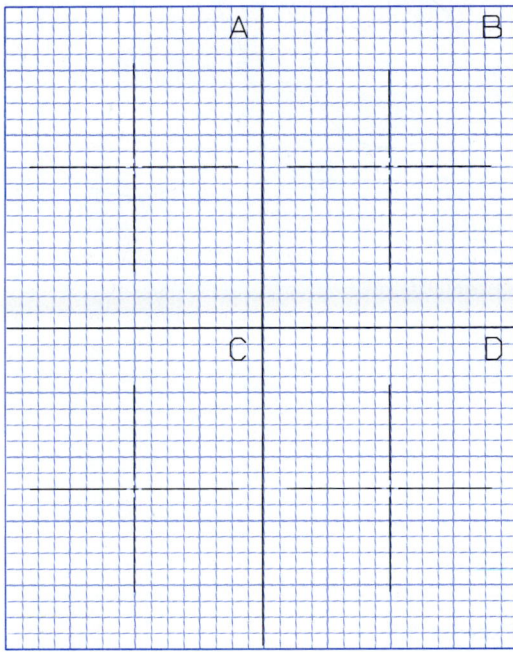

Exercise 5.3

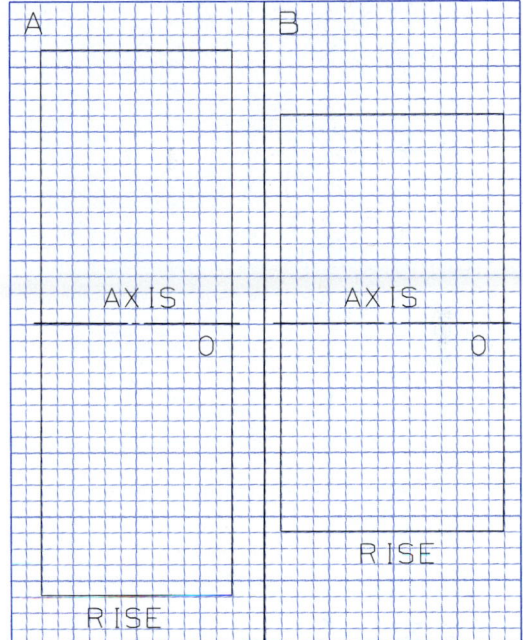

Exercise 5.5

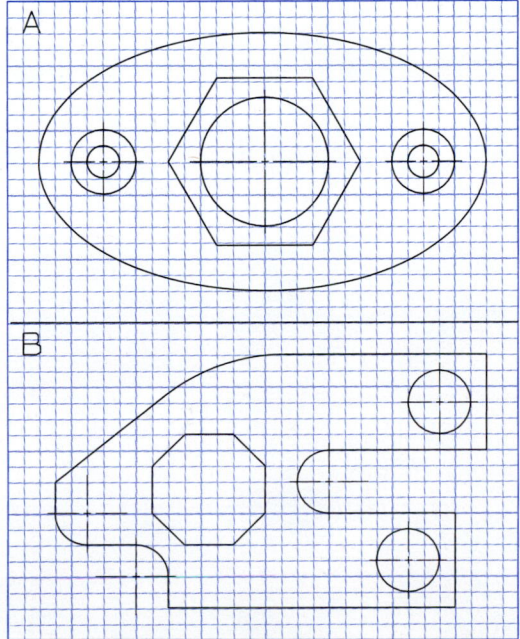

Exercise 5.4

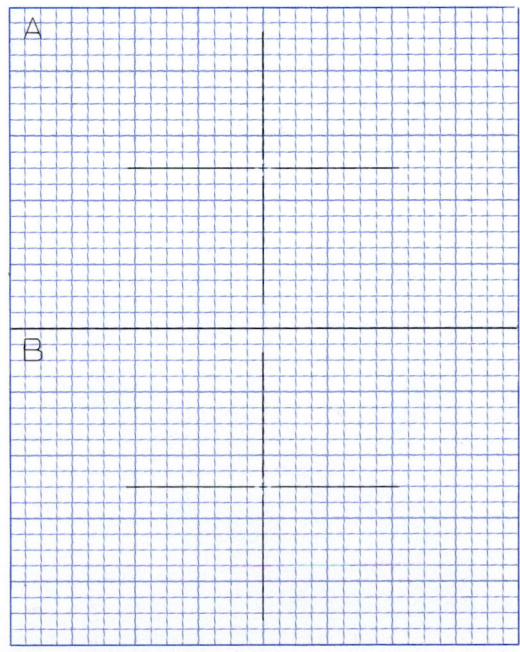

Exercise 5.6

Exercises 5.7(A) and (B) Use the given circle, divisions, and equal angles to construct a spiral of Archimedes. Start at the center and use the division line (vertical in A and horizontal in B) as the beginning line to draw the arcs needed for construction.

Exercise 5.8(A) Using the given cylinder for the diameter and the height, draw a right-handed helix with a lead of 3 in. Start the helix at the middle of the cylinder at the base where the axis line crosses the baseline.

Exercise 5.8(B) Use the given cone diameter and height to construct a left-handed conical helix. Start the helix on the lower left of the baseline. Use a lead of 2.5 in.

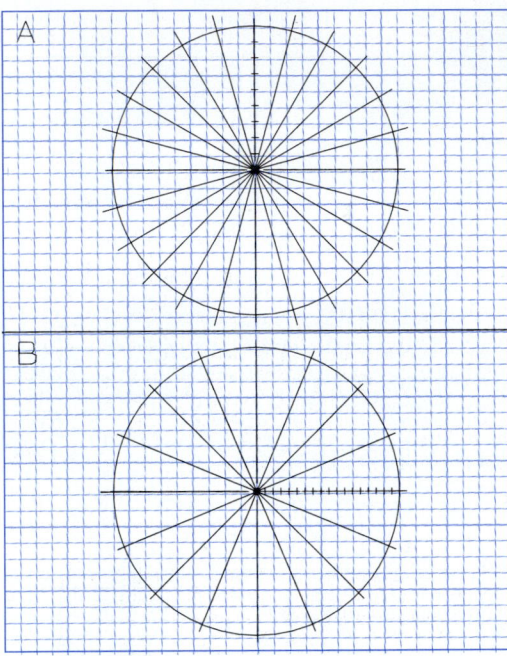

Exercise 5.7

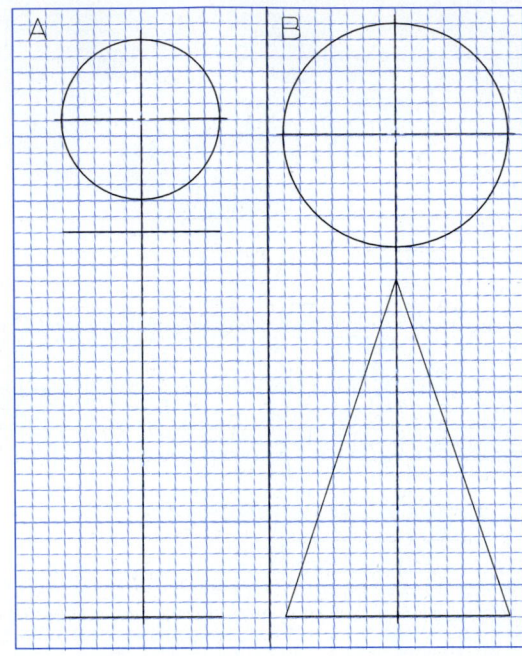

Exercise 5.8

PROBLEMS

Dimensions are provided for construction of each figure. They are not to be considered correct as per ANSI standards described in Chapter 12. Do not dimension without instructor's approval.

Problems 5.1(A) Through (G)   Transfer the problems to an appropriate size drawing format (one per drawing). Use one of the three scales provided.

Problems 5.2 Through 5.13   Draw each of the assigned problems on separate sheets.

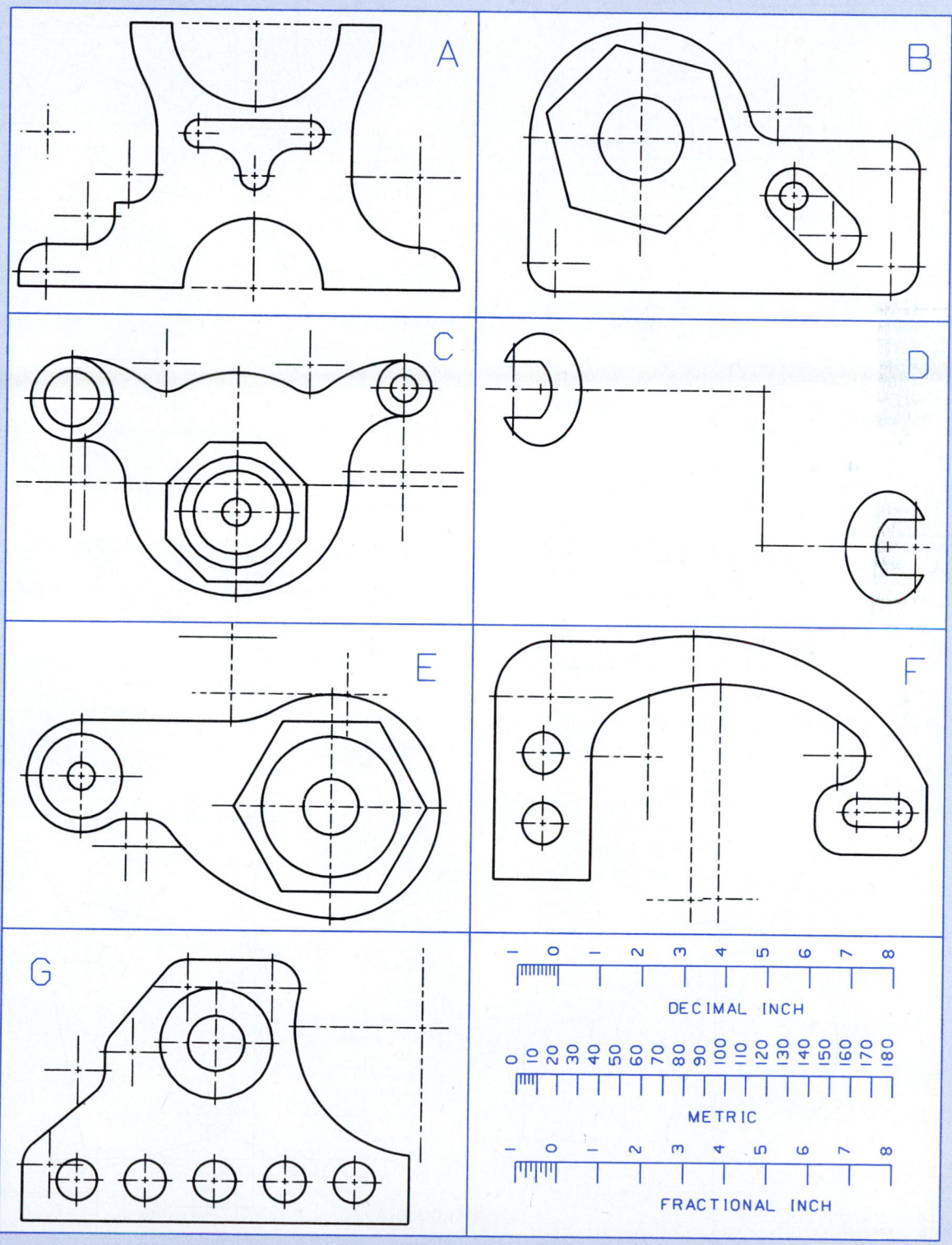

Problem 5.1

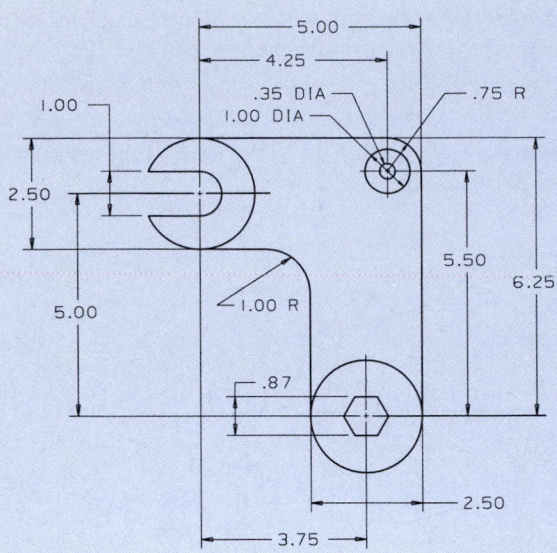

Problem 5.2

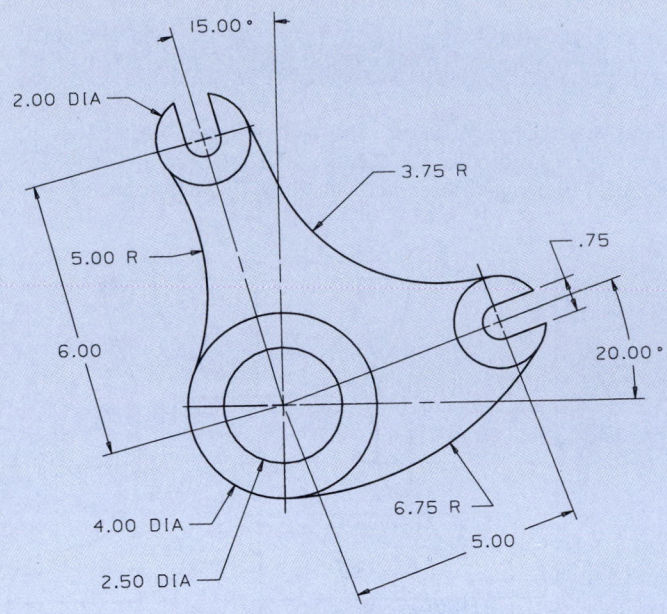

Problem 5.5

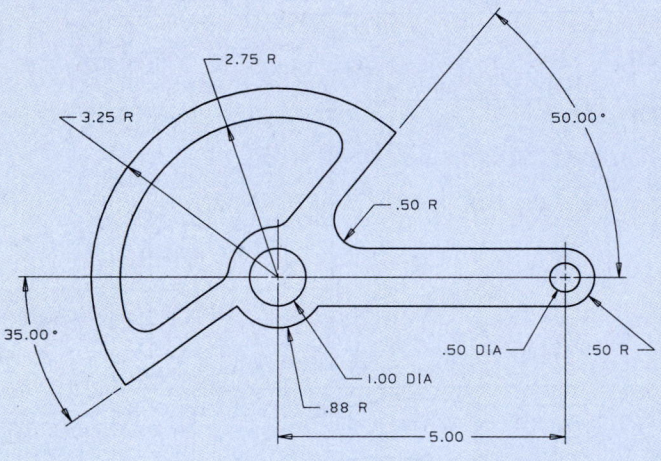

ALL FILLETS .35 R UNLESS
OTHERWISE SPECIFIED

Problem 5.3

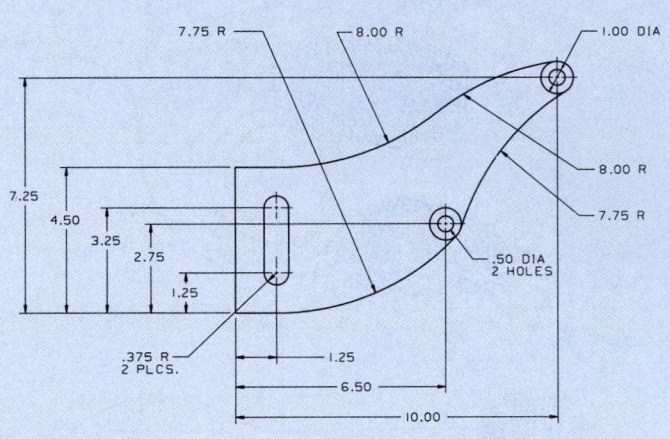

Problem 5.6

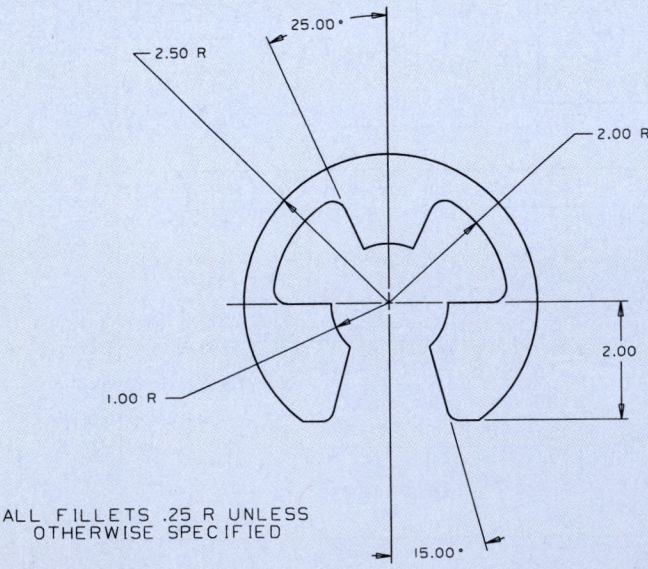

ALL FILLETS .25 R UNLESS
OTHERWISE SPECIFIED

Problem 5.4

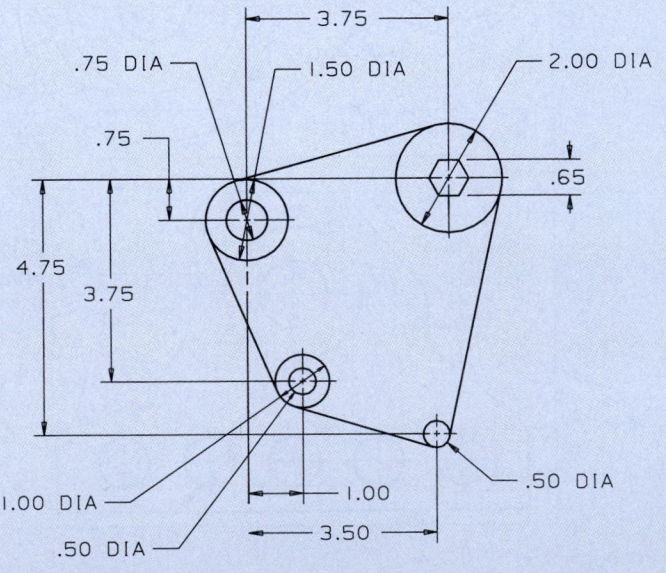

Problem 5.7

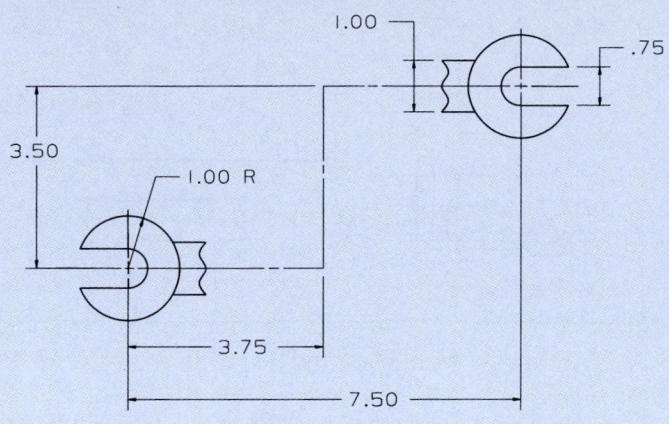

Problem 5.8

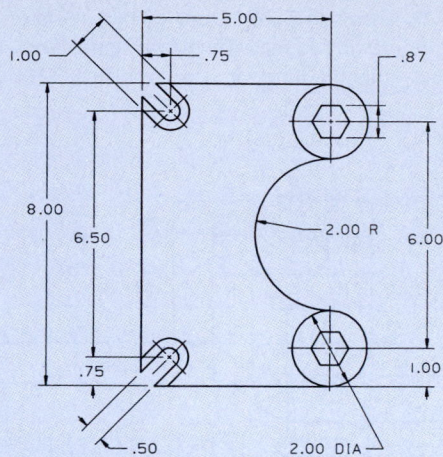

Problem 5.11

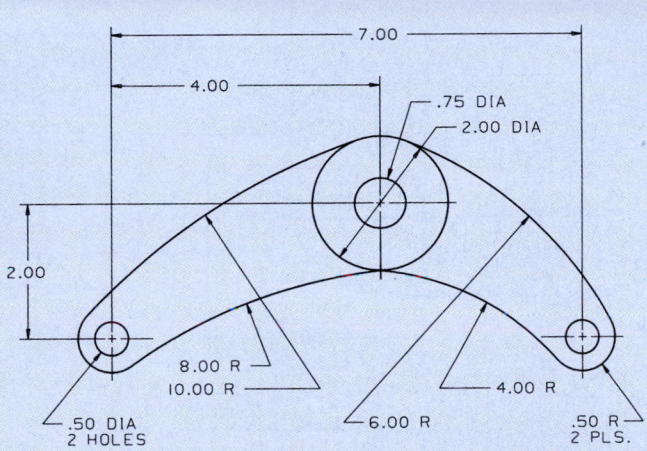

Problem 5.9

ALL FILLETS .25 R UNLESS
OTHERWISE SPECIFIED

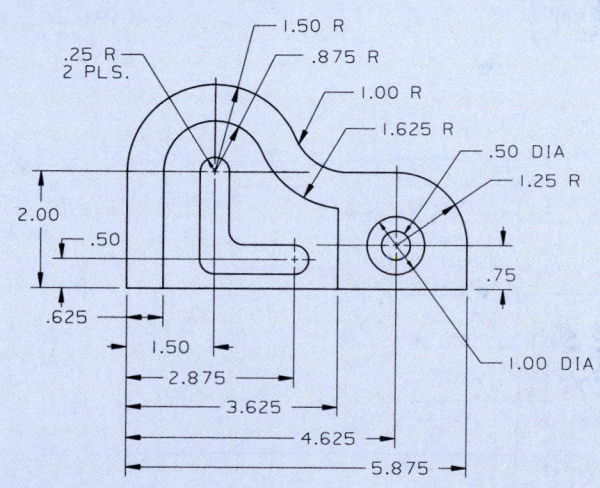

Problem 5.12

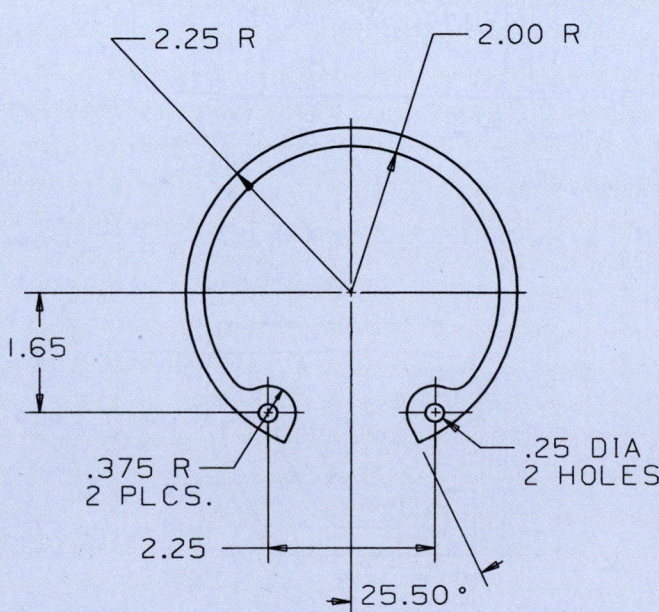

Problem 5.10

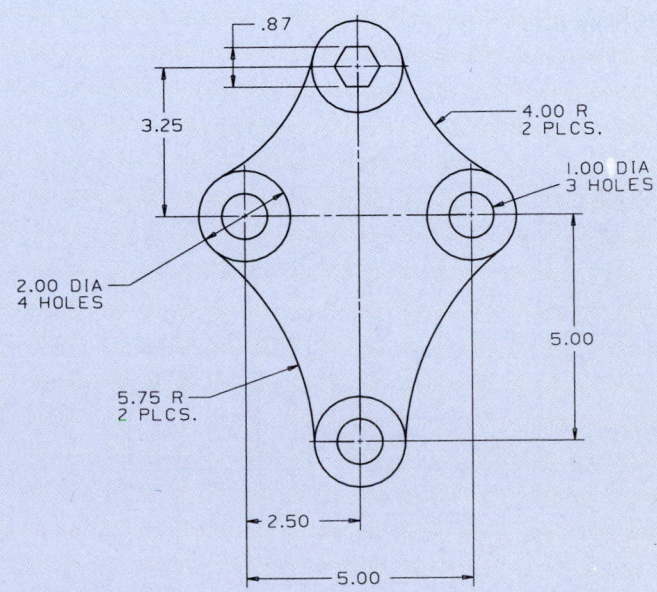

Problem 5.13

Problems 5.14 Through 5.24   Draw each of the projects in an appropriate size drawing format. These problems use metric measurements. Draw only the front view for Problems 5.23 and 5.24.

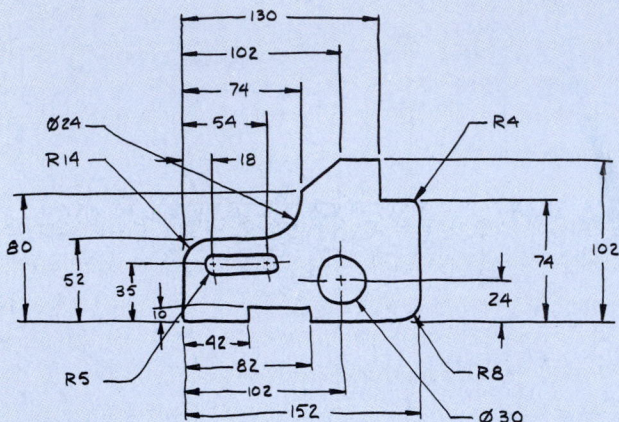

Problem 5.14

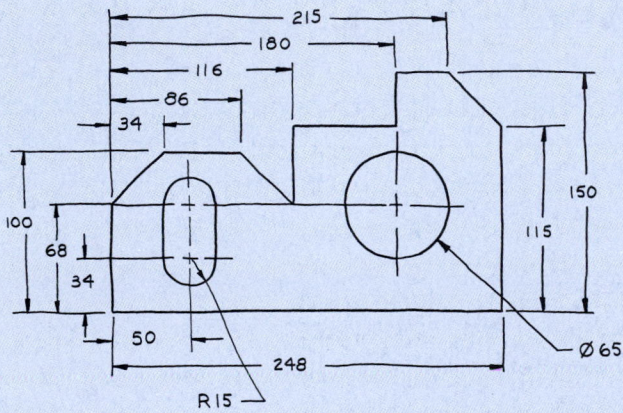

Problem 5.15

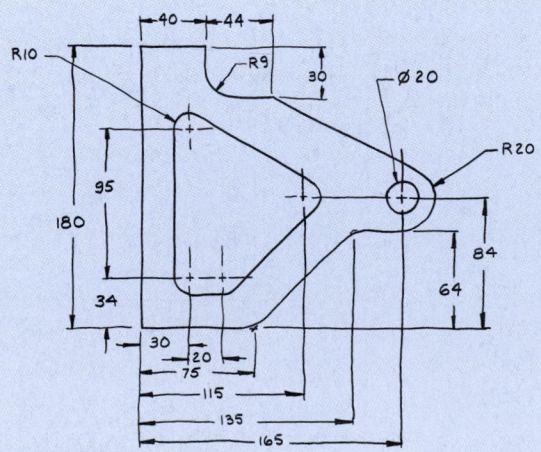

Problem 5.16

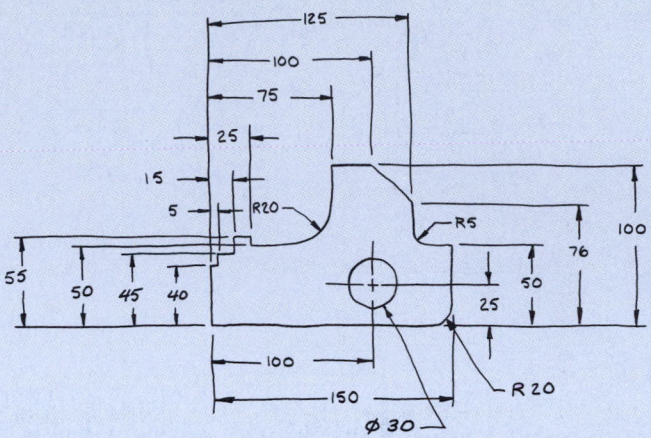

Problem 5.17

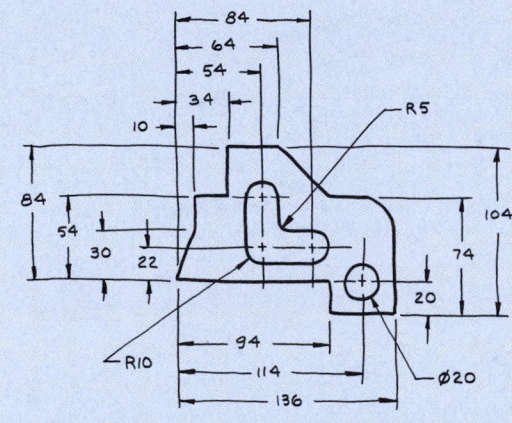

Problem 5.18

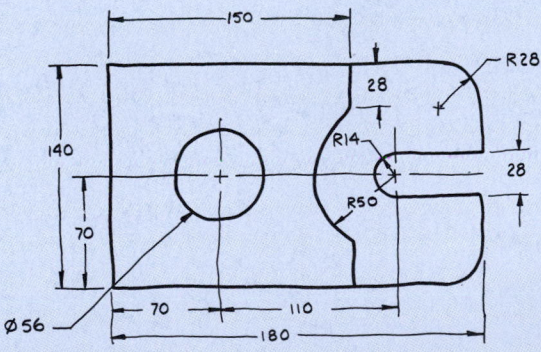

Problem 5.19

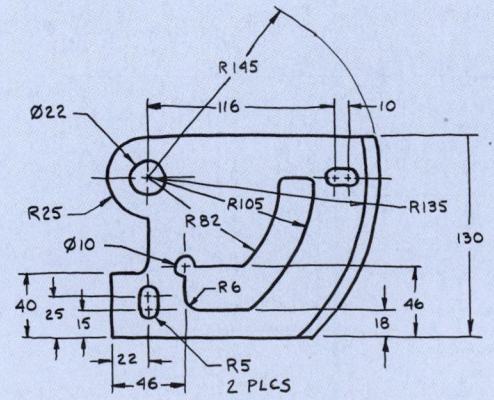

Problem 5.20

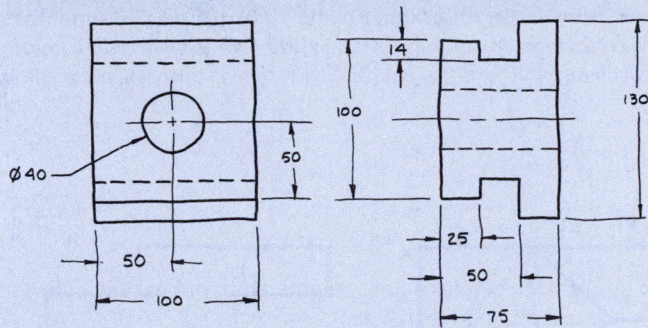

Problem 5.21

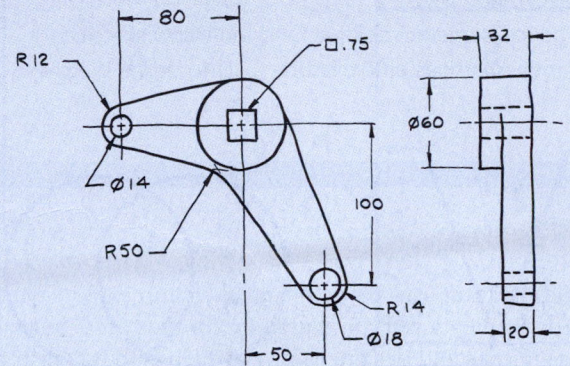

Problem 5.22

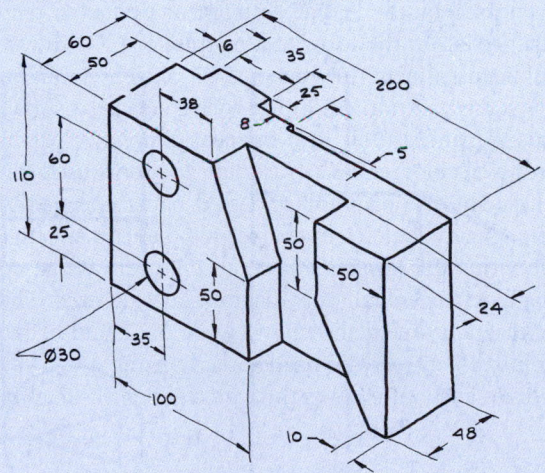

Problem 5.23

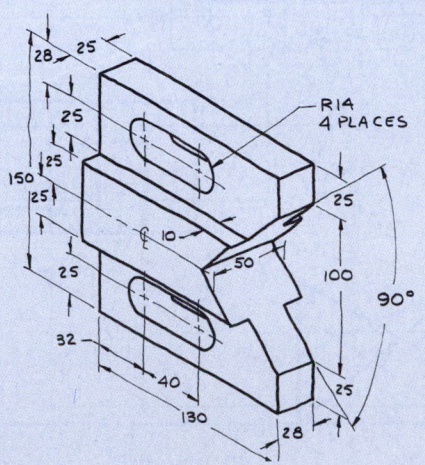

Problem 5.24

Word Problems

Problem 5.25   Divide a 5 in. 120 mm line into five equal parts.

Problem 5.26   Construct bisectors of the angles of a triangle having a ratio of 3:5:6 units for the sides. Use centimeters or inches.

Problem 5.27   Bisect a 55° angle.

Problem 5.28   Draw a triangle having sides with the proportions 3:4:5.

Problem 5.29   Draw a hexagon that is 3 in. (or 70 mm) across the flats.

Problem 5.30   Draw a hexagon that is 75 mm across the corners.

Problem 5.31   Construct a seven-sided regular polygon in a 5 in. or a 120 mm diameter circle.

Problem 5.32   Find the center of a 4 in. or a 100 mm circle.

Problem 5.33   Connect two lines forming a 35° angle with a 1 in. or a 25 mm radius arc.

Problem 5.34   Connect two perpendicular lines with a $1\frac{1}{4}$ in. or a 30 mm radius arc.

Problem 5.35   Draw an ellipse having a major axis of 70 mm and a minor axis of 50 mm.

Problem 5.36   Construct the inscribed circle of a 2 × 3.5 × 4 unit triangle.

Problem 5.37   Draw the circumscribed circle of a 3 × 4 × 5 unit triangle. Use centimeters as units.

Problem 5.38   Find the center of a 4 in. or a 100 mm circle by perpendicular bisectors. Rectify the circle.

Problem 5.39   Draw a cylindrical helix having an 80 mm diameter base and a height of 140 mm and with a lead of 50 mm. Draw as a right-handed helix.

Problem 5.40   Draw a left-handed conical helix with a base diameter of 3 in. or a 70 mm, a height of 4.5 in. or a 110 mm, and a lead of 2.5 in. or a 60 mm.

Problem 5.41   Draw a spiral of Archimedes using a 5 in. or a 120 mm diameter with angles of 30° and .125 in. or 10 mm divisions.

CHAPTER 6

Sketching

Learning Objectives

Upon completion of this chapter you will be able to accomplish the following:

1. Realize how sketches can be used to transform design concepts into visual communication.
2. Differentiate between pictorial, multiview, and diagrammatic sketches.
3. Recognize the importance of proper proportioning and thorough dimensioning.
4. Apply ANSI standard line weights and symbols while developing sketching techniques.
5. Demonstrate an understanding of multiview projection and selection of views.
6. Produce isometric, oblique, and multiview sketches.
7. Identify methods employed by CAD to utilize sketches.

6.1 Introduction

Sketching is one of the primary means of graphic communication among engineering personnel. The ability to sketch is an essential skill for all drafters, designers, engineers, and technicians. *Sketching is used to convey original design ideas from the engineer to the designer and from the designer to the drafter.* There are three types of sketches: pictorial, multiview, and diagrammatic.

Sketches are also used to lay out diagrams so that they can be digitized on a CAD system. Pictorial sketching is popular for clarifying the design of 3D parts and can aid in establishing the proper view orientation for pictorial or multiview drawings.

The rotating cylinder flap shown in Figure 6.1 was one of a number of design concepts investigated at NASA for airplanes. The design stage of this, and any project, brings together the engineer, designer, and possibly the layout drafter.

The design team uses the freehand sketch to explore alternative arrangements and configurations for the part or assembly. The engineer's and designer's primary job is to establish preliminary features and ideas through sketching. These sketches are then used by the layout designer or drafter to refine the original design in the form of a manual or CAD drawing.

Unlike instrument drawing or CAD, sketching can be done at almost any location equipped with a small flat surface and paper and pencils. Soft lead pencils, templates, paper (grid paper if available), and an eraser are the tools used for most sketches. The use of graph and grid paper speeds the construction of any sketch and enables it to be used as a digitizing layout with a CAD system, since all digitizers are based on a grid pattern. In general, only diagrams are digitized. The electronic diagram sketch shown in Figure 6.2 could be redrawn using instruments or digitized directly using a CAD system. Sometimes a layout evolves through a series of sketches as in

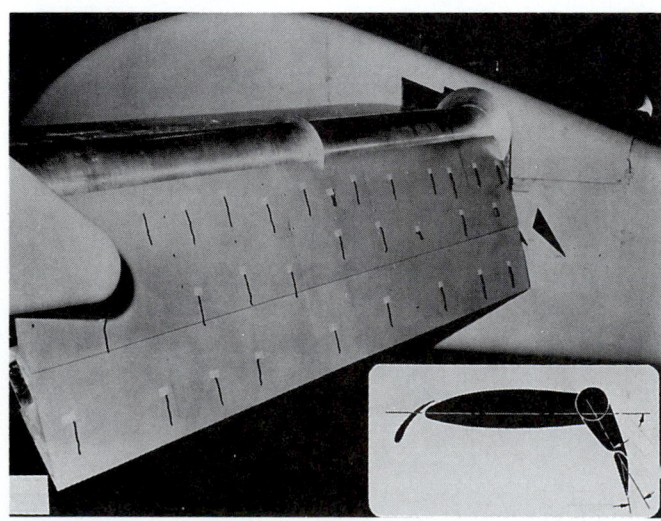

FIGURE 6.1 Rotating Cylinder Flap Design

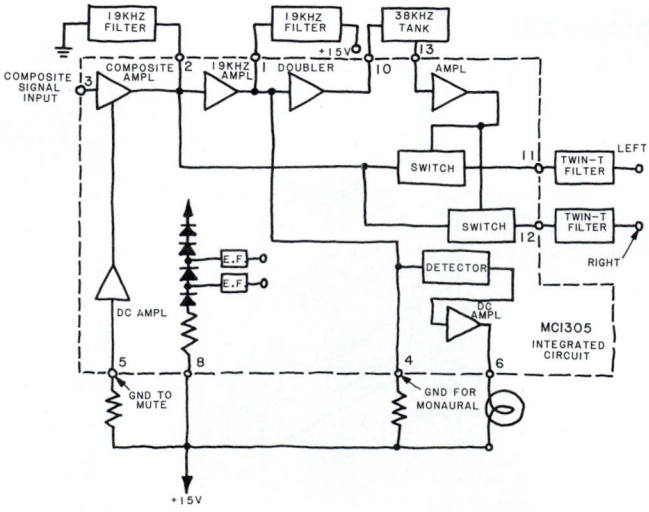

FIGURE 6.2 Electronic Sketch

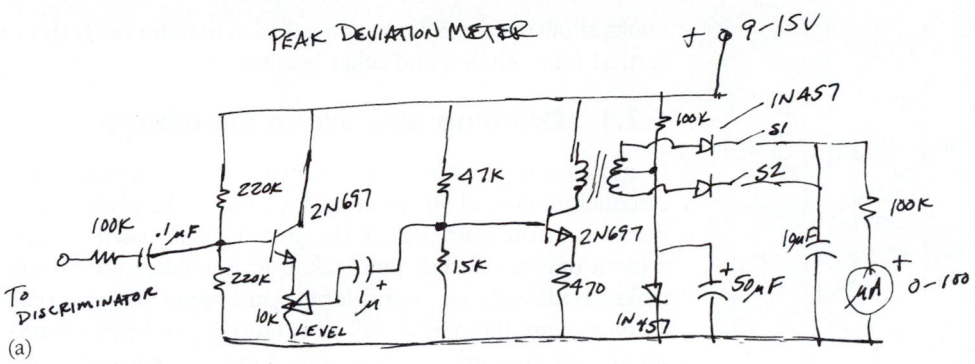

(a)

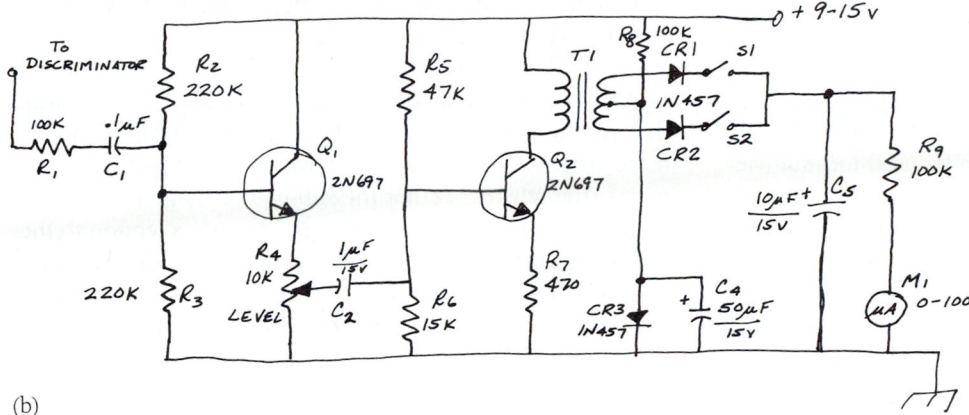

(b)

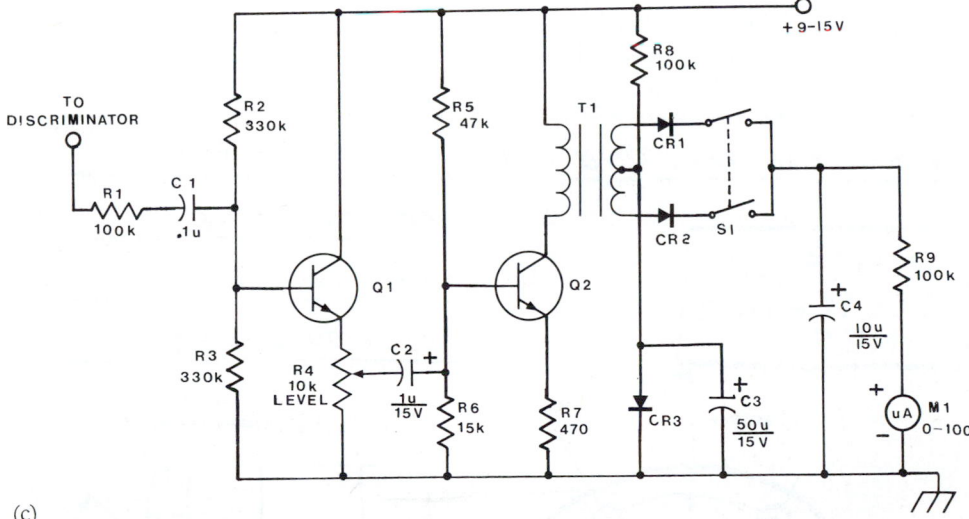

(c)

FIGURE 6.3 Evolution of a **Diagrammatic Drawing** (a) Preliminary sketch (electronic) (b) Refined sketch (c) Finalized drawing

Figure 6.3(a) where the rough sketch of a diagram is provided. Figure 6.3(b) shows a refined stage of this sketch, and the final drawing is shown in Figure 6.3(c).

6.2 Materials and Equipment Used in Sketching

A few simple items and materials are required for sketching. A sketching notebook is ideal for field work, usually attached to a clipboard. The sketch pad should be lined with a grid or

have a crosshatched underlay grid sheet that is placed beneath the transparent sketch paper so the grid shows through. Nonreproducing fade-out grid sheets are also available. *Grid paper* comes in $8\frac{1}{2} \times 11$ in. ("A" size), with an 8×10 in. lined work area. Larger sheets are also available when fade-out paper is used. Isometric grid lined paper is available for pictorial sketching, as are posterboard grid formats with many types of grid arrangements: isometric, oblique, orthographic, and a variety of perspectives. In Figure 6.4, a simple part has been sketched on isometric grid paper. Besides 30° lines receding in both directions, isometric grids have vertical

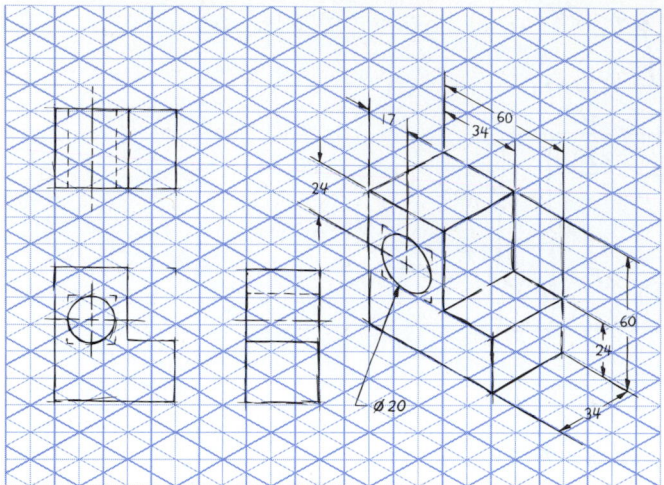

FIGURE 6.4 Grid Paper and Sketching

books allow the sketch to be rotated so as to more easily draw vertical lines, circles, and other features.

6.2.1 Drawing Size When Sketching

In most cases, the size of the sketch is not important. The essential mission of all sketches is to convey the proper proportions of the part. Unless the part is small, sketches are seldom drawn full size. But, whenever possible, you should make an effort to use a grid format and paper size that will accommodate the part as full size. Grid paper helps ensure the proper proportion and in general the size, since the grid sheet is fairly accurate. Very small parts are normally sketched oversize and large parts scaled down.

One of the most important things about all drawings, especially sketches, is that they must be dimensioned. A drawing, regardless of type, should seldom, if ever, be scaled (measured). Drawings and sketches must be "read." This means that you must be able to take the dimensions from it and use these dimensions in the next stage of the project. This remains true whether or not the subsequent stage involves the use of CAD or instrument drawing. The one exception to this rule is when the drawing to be completed is diagrammatic (Fig. 6.3). Diagrams describe a process and are not representing a real-world object. Therefore, a diagram can be measured and even directly digitized. Diagrams are not dimensioned.

and horizontal lines and therefore can be used for multiview drawing as well as isometric sketches.

Sketching involves the mastery of estimating proportions of a part. Grid sheets can help in blocking out the part accurately, because it is a simple matter to count grid squares, thereby maintaining the proper proportion of a part's geometric features. Clipboards used with grid paper or note-

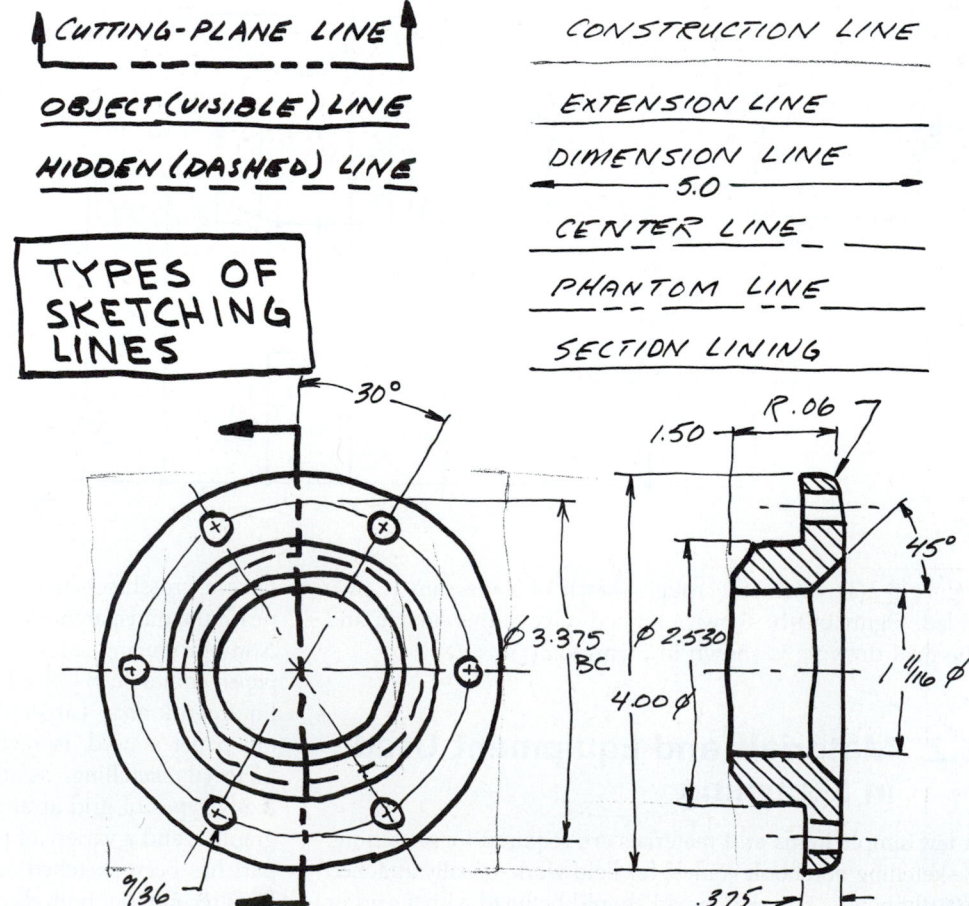

FIGURE 6.5 Line Types for Sketches

6.2.2   Line Types Used in Sketching

Line types and widths are the same as for instrument drawings, CAD drawings, and freehand sketches. The only real difference is that the line quality is not as perfect. ANSI standard line weights, symbols, and dimensioning are used on sketches as well as instrument or CAD drawings. Figure 6.5 shows the typical range of lines encountered in sketching. *Cutting plane lines* are the widest line. *Visible object* and *hidden lines* are medium thickness. *Extension, dimension, centerline, phantom,* and *section lines* are about the same width—thin.

With the exception of construction lines, all others should be black as with instrument lines. The use of construction or layout lines is somewhat different on sketches. They are seldom erased (though sometimes dimmed), although they usually are when doing an instrument drawing. The placement and quality of the lettering used in notes and dimensions also must be clear and easily read.

(a)

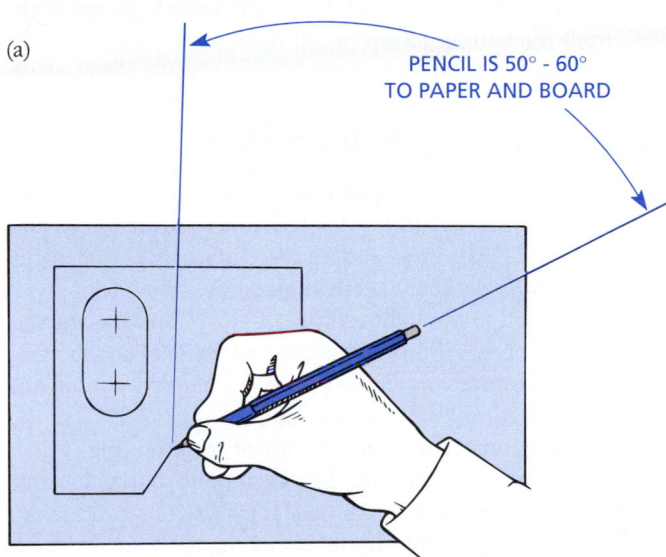

PENCIL IS 50° - 60°
TO PAPER AND BOARD

(b)

PENCIL IS APPROX.
30° TO PAPER AND BOARD

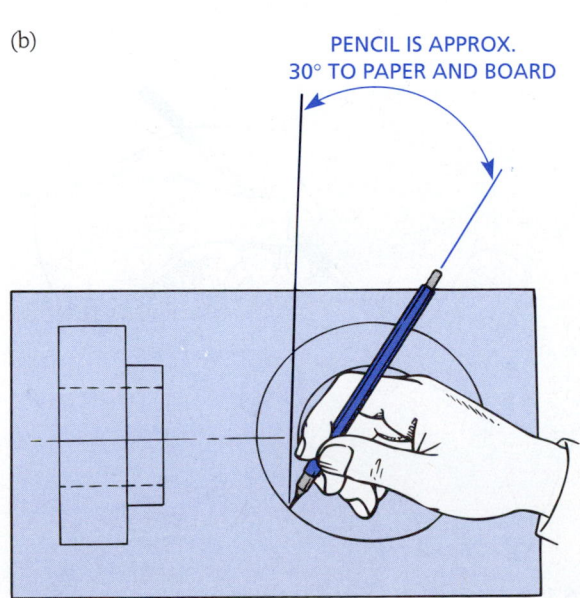

FIGURE 6.6   Angle of Pencil When Sketching

6.3   Sketching Techniques

Good sketching is a skill that must be cultivated throughout your career. Different techniques and methods are useful, including the position of your pencil, the angle it makes with the paper, and rotating the pencil while sketching. Sketching skills are developed over a period of time by practice and effort. Speed in sketching is not important at this stage.

The angle at which you hold your pencil will change for different types of drawing features. When sketching, *your pencil should be held at an angle to the paper* (Fig. 6.6). 50° to 60° is recommended for straight lines and 30° to 45° for circles and arcs.

Rotate your pencil while sketching. This will help maintain a conical point and reduce the amount of time required for sharpening. You may prefer to use fine-line pencils for sketching because they do not require sharpening. For most sketching, a 0.7 to 0.9 mm fine-line pencil with H or HB lead will give good results. Wooden pencils and lead holders will do the job as well. Sharper lines will result from rotating the pencil regardless of type.

Hold the pencil 1.5 to 2 in. (30 to 50 mm) from the tip as shown in Figure 6.7. Some drafters prefer to hold the pencil in the flat position as demonstrated in Figure 6.8. Regardless of pencil position, with practice sketch lines can be made clear and concise even without the aid of grid sheets. Since it helps to maintain scale, size, accuracy, and also increases speed, the use of grid paper is highly recommended.

Remember, it is not the intent of the text to change the way you hold your pencil. The information in this section is provided to help develop sketching skills. Left-handers may hold their pencils at different angles and orientation than right-handers.

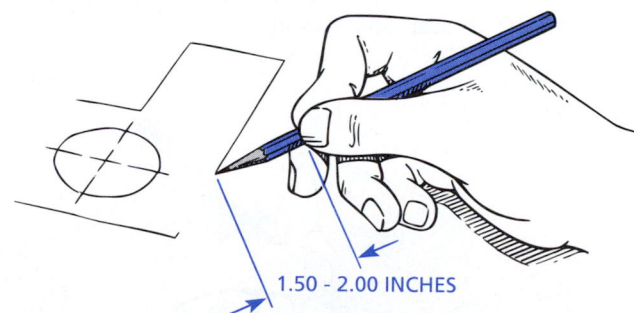

1.50 - 2.00 INCHES

FIGURE 6.7   Holding a Pencil for Sketching

FIGURE 6.8   Flat Pencil Position for Sketching

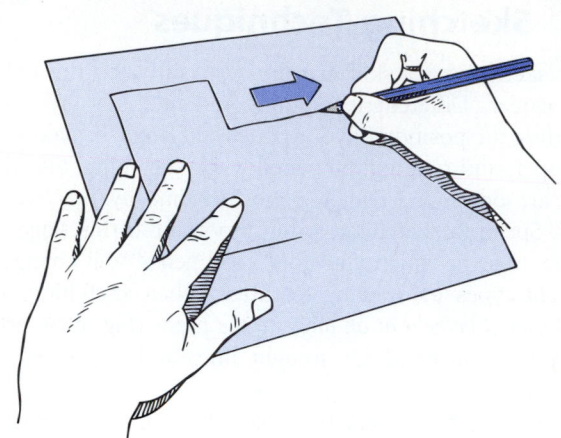

FIGURE 6.9 Sketching Horizontal Lines

6.3.1 Sketching Horizontal Lines and Vertical Lines

Horizontal lines are drawn by locating their endpoints and then connecting them with a line. Draw the lines using construction lines first and later, after the design is close to completion, go back and darken. Normally, the pencil is moved from the left to the right as in Figure 6.9. You should use short strokes and try to avoid "feathering" the lines. Pulling a wooden pencil or a lead holder will avoid the ripping and scarring of the paper surface that results when a pencil is pushed. Since the lead in fine-line pencils tends to break easily, it is suggested that you push rather than pull. Some drafters leave a small space between each line segment. If grid paper is used this is unnecessary.

Vertical lines are drawn with the same general technique as horizontal lines. In this case, move the pencil from the top toward the bottom of the paper (Fig. 6.10). Again, the use of grid sheets is encouraged because it ensures that the lines drawn will be vertical. You also may turn the paper to any

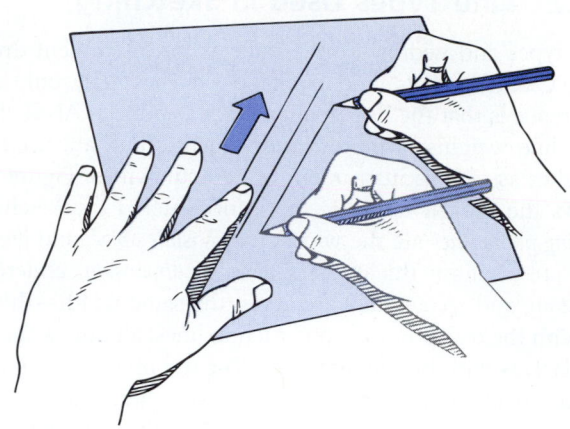

FIGURE 6.11 Sketching Inclined Lines

convenient position to help speed the sketching process. Some drafters prefer to move the pencil away from the body, i.e., from the bottom to top or left to right. Try each method and find one that works for you.

6.3.2 Sketching Inclined Lines

Slanted/angled lines are drawn using the same technique as vertical or horizontal lines. **Angled lines** are drawn as follows: first establish their endpoints, then lightly sketch the line, and finally darken. Sketch angled lines away from you if they are angled to the right as in Figure 6.11 and toward you (or turn the paper) if they are angled to the left (not shown). Use the opposite technique if you are left-handed. This is one line where a grid will be of little use.

Since horizontal lines are the easiest to draw (Fig. 6.12), turning the paper so that the line is close to horizontal (for slanted and vertical lines) will help the sketching process. By turning the paper to the left and sketching each line from left to right, the outline is created by drawing all "horizontal

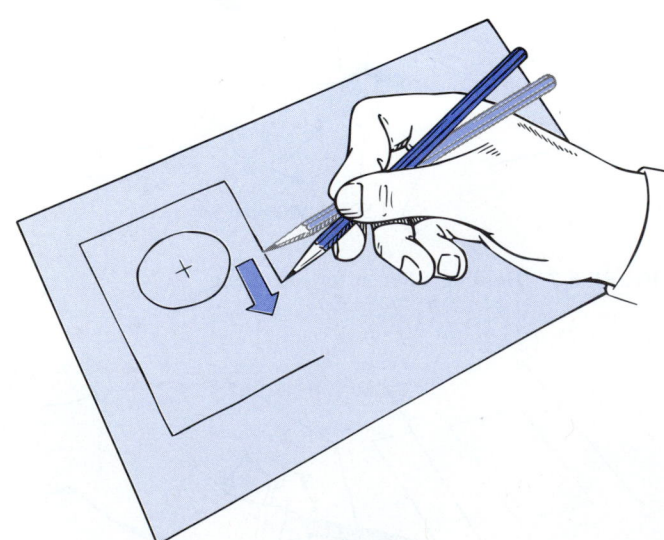

FIGURE 6.10 Sketching Vertical Lines

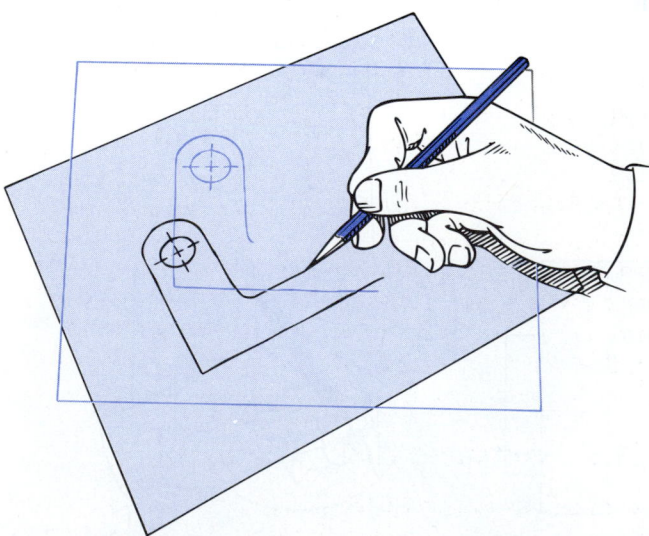

FIGURE 6.12 Turning Paper May Make Sketching Easier

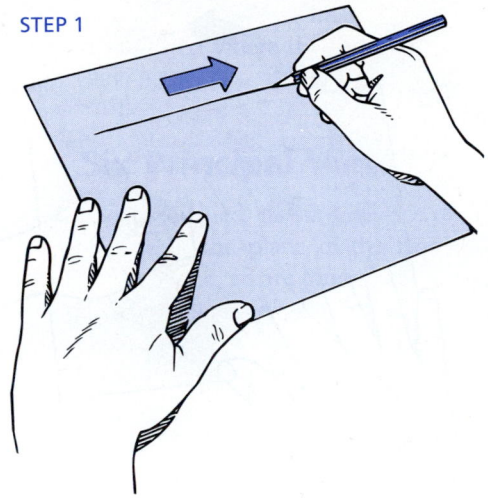

STEP 1

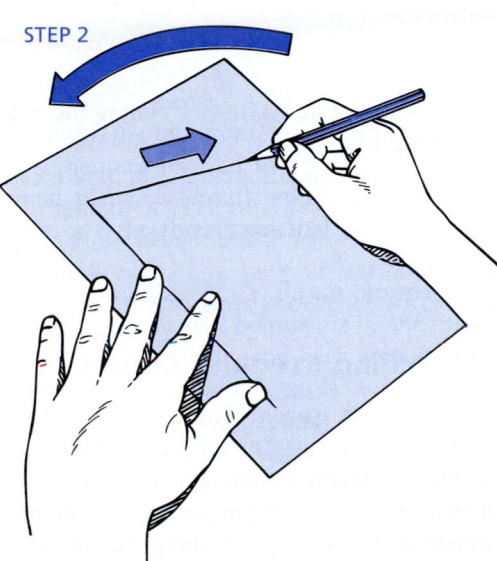

STEP 2

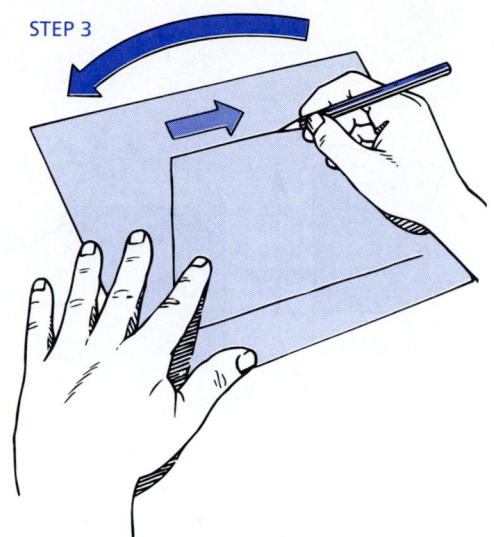

STEP 3

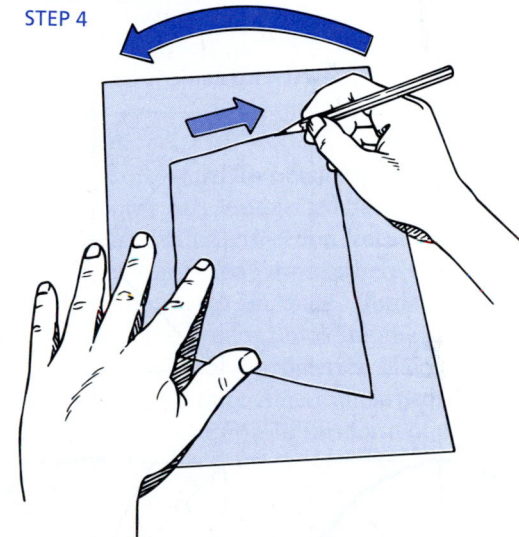

STEP 4

FIGURE 6.13   Sketching by Turning Paper Counterclockwise

lines" in Figure 6.13. When the sketch is large, and the paper is taped to the board, turning the paper is impossible. Therefore, you also should learn to sketch without turning the paper.

The most common angles found on drawings are 15°, 30°, 45°, 60°, and 90°. Estimating angles can be done by drawing two lines perpendicular to one another (90°). Bisecting this angle gives a 45° line. Dividing the 45° into three equal angles provides a 15° and a 30° angle measurement (Fig. 6.14). Regardless of how accurate the angle is drawn, always locate the endpoints by dimensions or by giving an angle dimension.

6.3.3   Sketching Arcs and Circles

Sketching arcs and circles (Fig. 6.15) can be one of the most frustrating aspects of the sketching process. Always start by locating the center point of the circle or arc. Then draw the

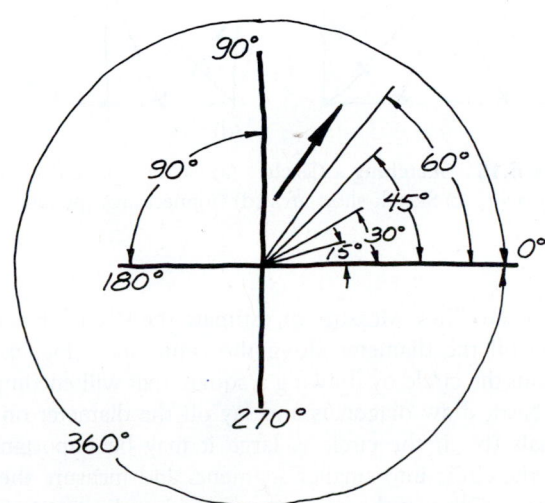

FIGURE 6.14   Typical Angles Used in Sketching

STEP 1

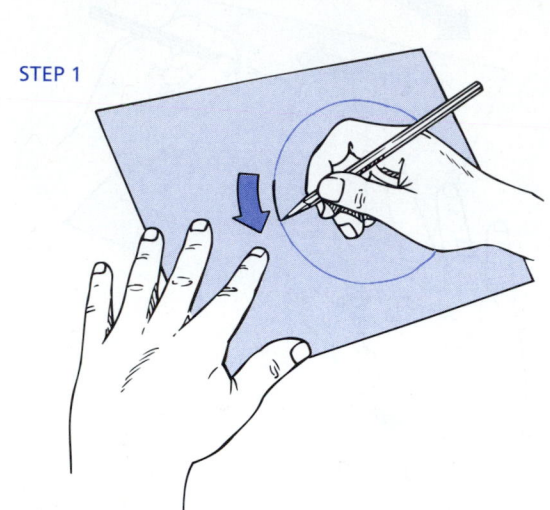

ROTATE PAPER

STEP 2

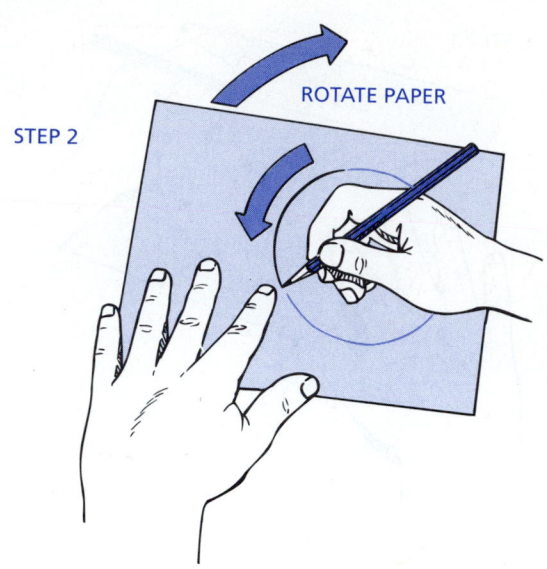

FIGURE 6.15 Sketching Circles by Rotating the Paper

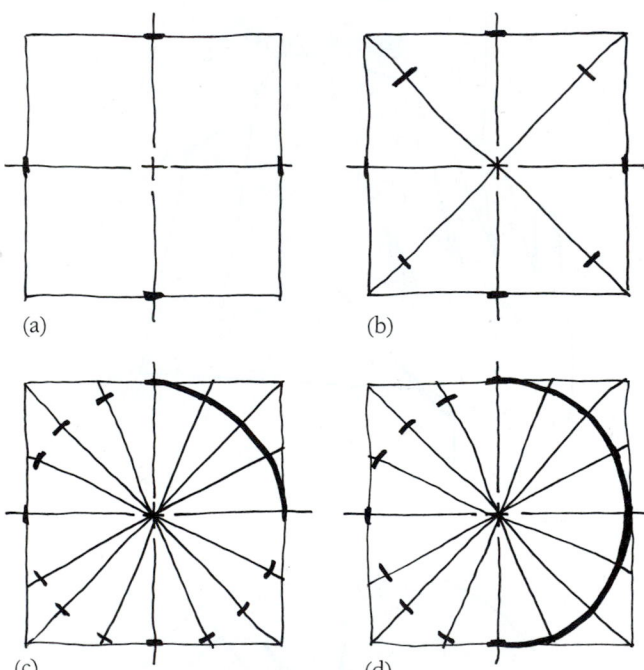

(a)   (b)

(c)   (d)

FIGURE 6.16 **Sketching a Circle** (a) Sketch square (b) Divide into segments (c) Sketch short arcs (d) Connect arcs (points)

circle's centerlines. Measure or estimate the size of the circle and lay off the diameter along the centerlines (Fig. 6.16). Block out the circle by drawing a square that will encompass it (a). Next, draw diagonals and lay off the diameter on the diagonals (b). If the circle is large it may be important to divide the circle into smaller segments and measure the diameter (c). Connect the points by sketching short arcs. Continue to connect the points to complete the circle (d). If the

sketch is small and not taped down, rotating the paper as in Figure 6.15 helps keep the circle fairly "rounded."

Since arcs are portions of circles, sketching arcs involves the same general steps. In Figure 6.17 a number of arcs and circles were required to complete the sketch. Note that centerlines were used for every arc and circle. Both circles and arcs were blocked out before being drawn.

6.3.4 Sketching Irregular Curves

Noncircular curves are drawn with the aid of an irregular curve when doing an instrument drawing and with the **SPLINE** command when a CAD system is used. Freehand sketching of irregular curves involves establishing an adequate number of defining points along the curve and then connecting the points with a smooth curve. A lightly sketched (construction) curve is drawn first and then the irregular curve is darkened. In Figure 6.18 a sketch of an irregular curve is done on grid paper, which makes it easier to establish the controlling points.

6.4 Introduction to Projection Techniques

Engineering and technical work require that a 2D surface (paper) be used to communicate ideas and give the physical description of 3D shapes. This process is the same for sketching, instrument drawings, or 2D CAD. Different types of projection methods are used to accomplish this task. Here, projections have been divided into two basic categories: *pictorial* and *multiview*. Pictorial drawings simulate three dimensions and multiview drawings are basically 2D representations of the part. This simple division separates single-view drawings (oblique, isometric, and perspective) from multiview draw-

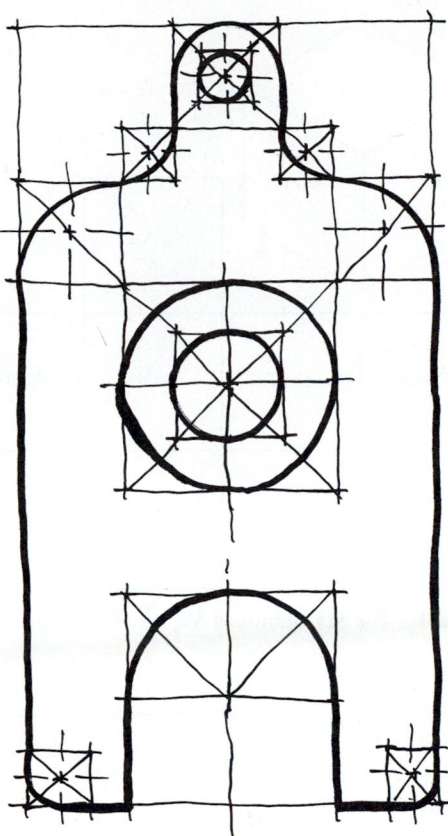

FIGURE 6.17 Blocking-out Circular Shapes When Sketching

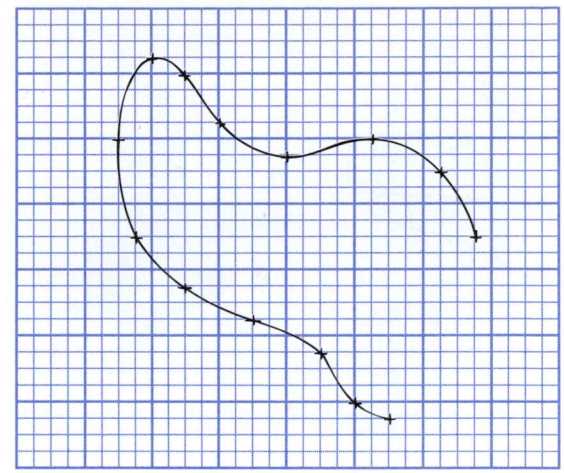

FIGURE 6.18 Sketching Irregular Curves

PICTORIAL

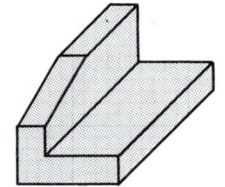

(a) Oblique projection

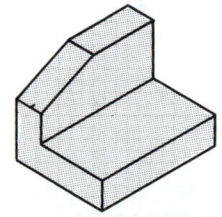

(b) Isometric projection

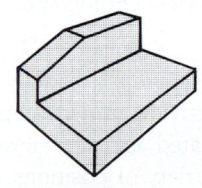

(c) Perspective projection

MULTIVIEW

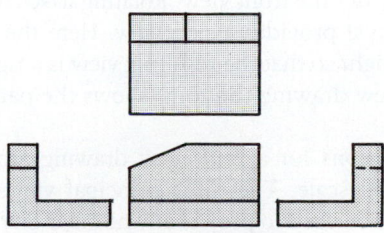

(d) Orthographic projection

FIGURE 6.19 Projection Methods

ings. Multiview drawings are covered in Chapter 7 and pictorial projections in Chapter 8.

Division of types based on whether the drawing is a pictorial or multiview projection separates projection types into those used for engineering working drawings (multiview) and those used for display (technical illustration). In sketching, however, both types are used to refine design concepts. Formal drawings for production, manufacturing, and assembly use multiview projections almost exclusively, except where pictorial projection is needed to explain particular aspects of design.

Figure 6.19 shows each of four projection types with the same scale. This figure illustrates the difference between the types of projections. Pictorial projections are single-view drawings that do not lend themselves to the communication of engineering data except as rough sketches of preliminary ideas. *Perspective* projections are constructed with projecting lines that converge at a point. Though this method provides the most lifelike appearance it does not show the true dimensions of a part. The *oblique* method distorts a part's depth. The *isometric* method uses full-scale dimensions for all lines that are vertical or parallel to the axes. Therefore, it is the most common and useful projection method for engineering sketching.

Multiview drawings, because they show the parts in more than one view, are not lifelike. This, however, is their only

TOP VIEW

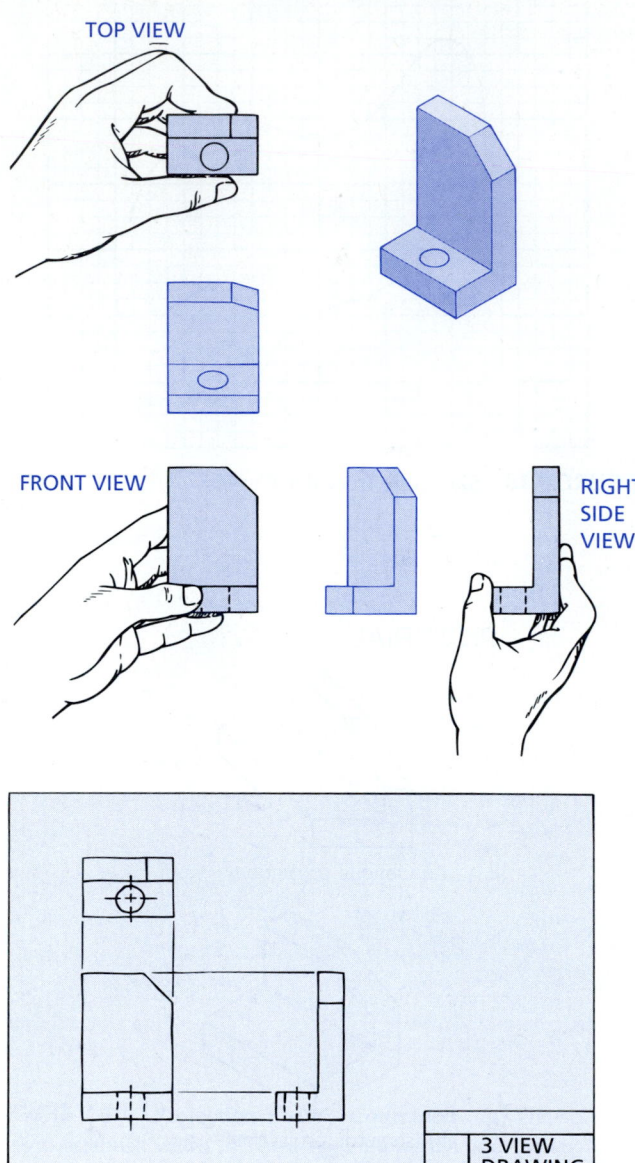

FRONT VIEW

RIGHT SIDE VIEW

3 VIEW DRAWING

FIGURE 6.20 Three-View Orthographic Projection

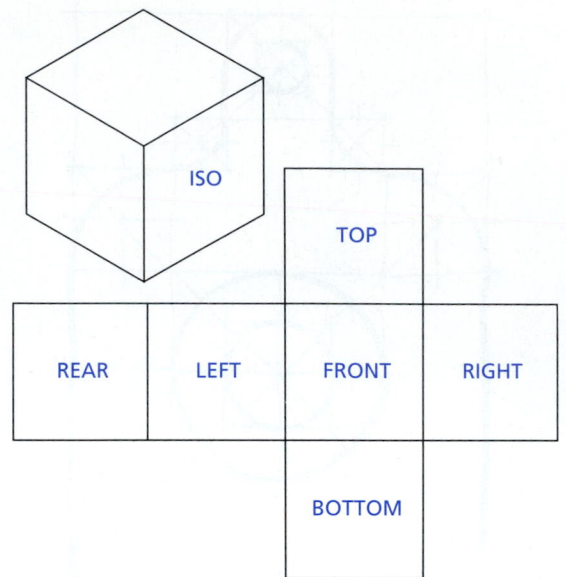

ISO

TOP

REAR LEFT FRONT RIGHT

BOTTOM

FIGURE 6.21 The Six Standard Views of an Object

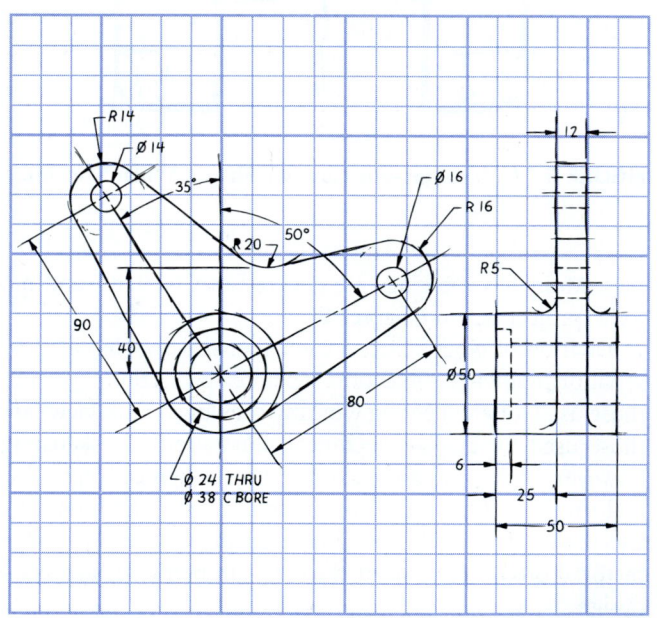

FIGURE 6.22 Two-View Drawing

major drawback. Multiview projection presents the part's top, front, and side in related adjacent views. In Figure 6.20, the part is shown in a variety of positions. Starting with the top view, the theory behind orthographic projection is that the part is rotated by turning it as in this figure. The resulting 90° rotation provides the front view. Rotating it 90° from the front view (sideways) provides a side view. Here the part was rotated to the right so that the resulting view is a right side view. The three-view drawing (bottom) shows the part aligned between views.

All dimensions for a multiview drawing are drawn to a predetermined scale. The three principal views (top, front, and side) can be used to project any number of views in order to solve for or establish engineering data. An *auxiliary* view is

any projection of a part other than one of the six principal views: top, front, right side, left side, back, and bottom (Fig. 6.21).

6.5 Multiview Projection

Multiview projection describes a part's features and dimensions in one or more views that are projected at 90° angles to each other or at specified angles for auxiliary views. Figure 6.22 shows a multiview sketch that conveys ideas, dimen-

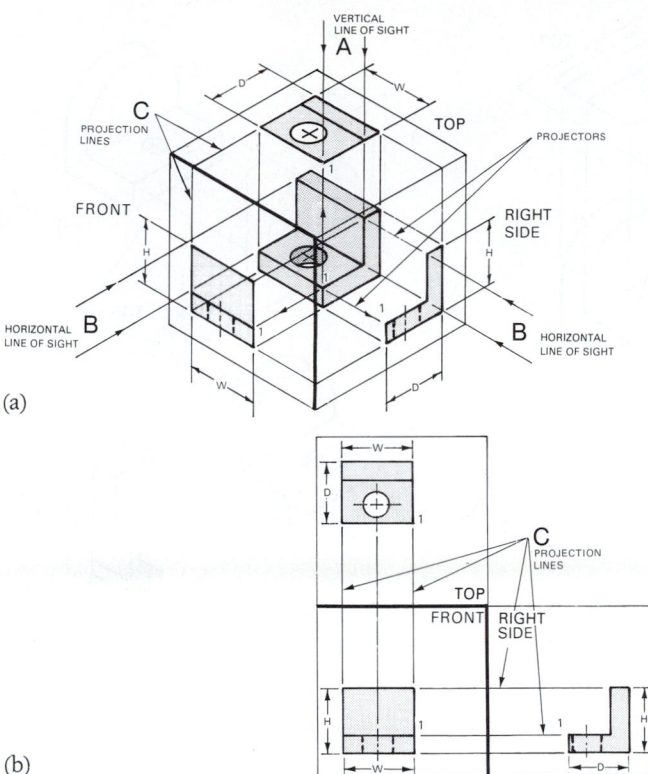

(a)

(b)

FIGURE 6.23   **The Glass Box Method**

sions, and shapes for manufacturing a rocker arm. This is a two-view drawing.

Multiview drawing uses orthographic projection to establish the spatial relationship of points, lines, planes, or solid shapes. There are two primary means of making multiview orthographic projections: the *normal method* and the *glass box method*. In the normal or natural method, the part is viewed perpendicular to each of its three primary surfaces. In the glass box method, you must imagine that the part, with its points, lines, planes, surfaces, and solid shapes, is enclosed in a transparent box. A view of the part is established on its corresponding glass box surface (plane) by perpendicular projectors originating at each point of the part and extending to the box surface [Fig. 6.23(a)].

The glass box is hinged so that it can be unfolded onto one flat plane (the paper). Note that each projection (view) shares a dimension with its adjacent projection (view). The top and the front view share the width dimension, the front and the side share the height dimension, and the side and the top view share the depth dimension. In the glass box method, the sides are revolved outward so that they are in the plane of the paper [Fig. 6.23(b)]. With the exception of the back plane, all are hinged to the front plane (Fig. 6.21). The back plane, though seldom used, is normally revolved from the left side view. Each plane is parallel to the plane opposite, before it is revolved around its hinge line.

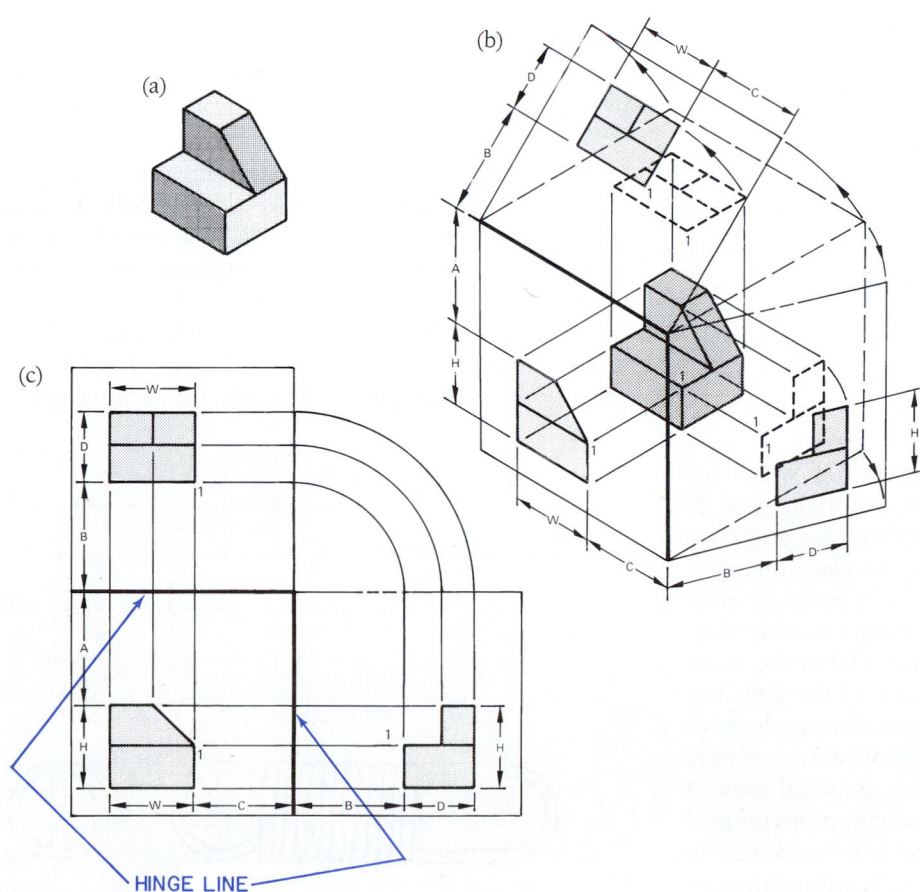

(a)

(b)

(c)

HINGE LINE

FIGURE 6.24   Unfolding the Glass Box

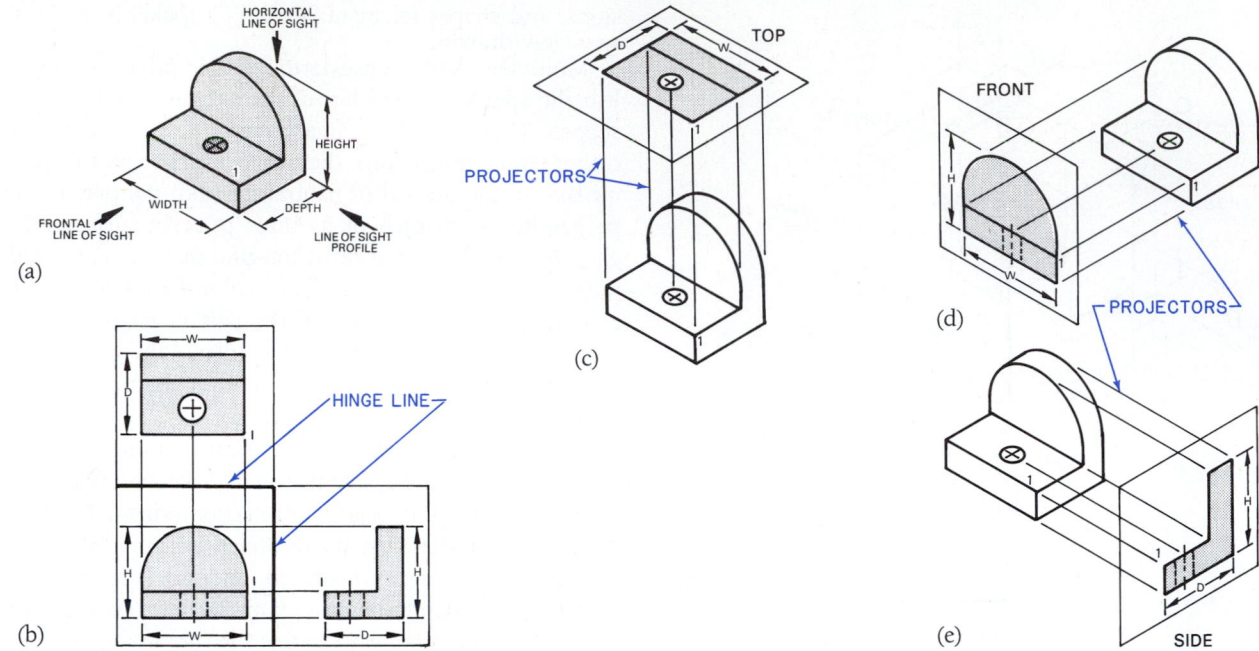

FIGURE 6.25   Line of Sight for Views

A *hinge line* is the line of intersection between any two adjacent image planes, including principal and auxiliary views. The left side, front, right side, and back are all elevation views. In these views the height dimension, elevation, top, and bottom can be seen and dimensioned. The top and bottom surfaces are in the horizontal plane. The depth dimension, width dimension, front, and back are established here.

In the United States and Canada, the six principal views of a part are drawn using *third-angle* projection. In third-angle projection the *line of sight* (direction of viewing) goes through the image plane to the part (Figs. 6.23 and 6.24). To obtain the part you must assume that its features are projected back (along the lines of sight) to the image plane. *Projectors* are used to illustrate this projection from the part to where each point intersects the image plane.

The line of sight represents the direction from which you view the part (Fig. 6.25) and is assumed to originate at infinity. The line of sight is at a right angle to the projection plane. To visualize this properly, you must place the plane between you and the part. Your position will change for every view, so that your line of sight is at a right angle to each image plane; the line of sight is always perpendicular to the image plane which is represented by the surface of the glass box (top, front, and right side). Projection lines connect the same point on the image plane from view to view, always at right angles. Remember, the part could be any graphical form. A point is projected on the image plane where its projector (line of sight) pierces that image plane. Point 1 in Figure 6.25 is located on the part and is projected onto the three primary image planes as shown.

6.5.1   The Glass Box and Hinge Lines

Hinge lines represent the intersection of two perpendicular image planes (Fig. 6.25). Each image plane (surface of the glass box) is connected at right angles to an adjacent view. The top view is hinged to the front view, as is the right side view. Hinge lines are not shown on technical drawings, they are used strictly to help in the visualization process.

In Figure 6.24(a) the part is shown pictorially. In Figure 6.24(b), the part is enclosed in a glass box. Point 1 is located on the corner of the part and is shown projected onto each of the three image planes. The top image plane is shown being rotated about the line of intersection (hinge line), which is between the top image plane (horizontal plane) and the front image plane (frontal plane). The side image plane (profile

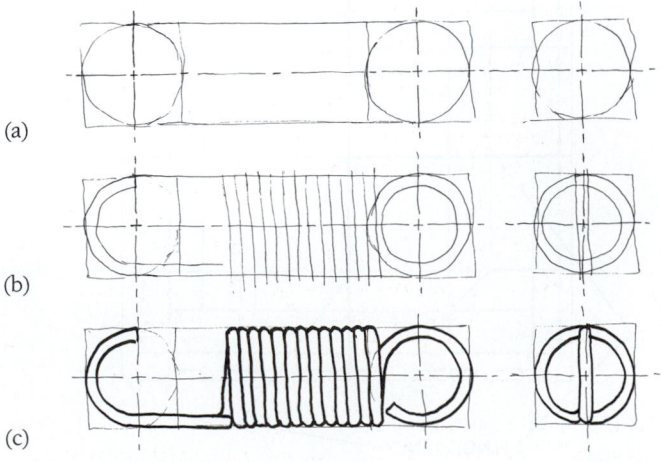

FIGURE 6.26   Blocking-out a Part

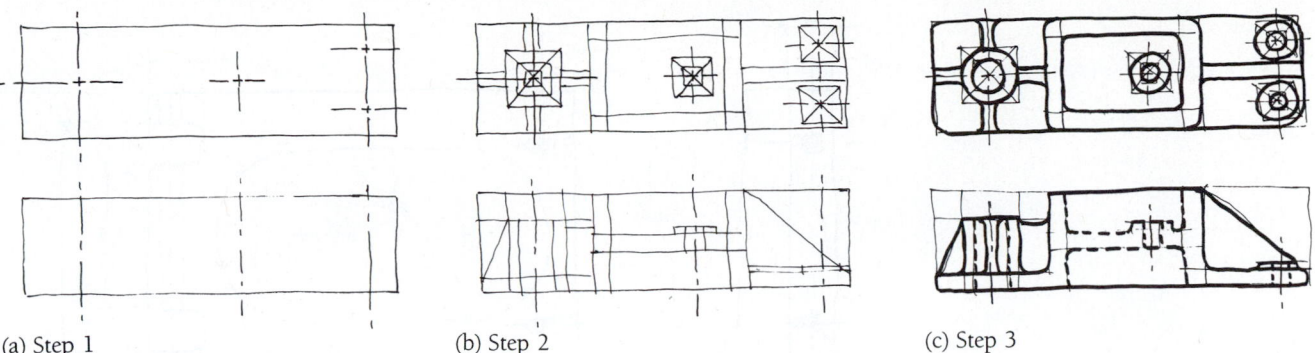

(a) Step 1   (b) Step 2   (c) Step 3

FIGURE 6.27 **Blocking-out a Two-View Sketch** (a) Block-out overall dimensions and centerlines (b) Complete construction of all secondary features (c) Darken features and centerlines

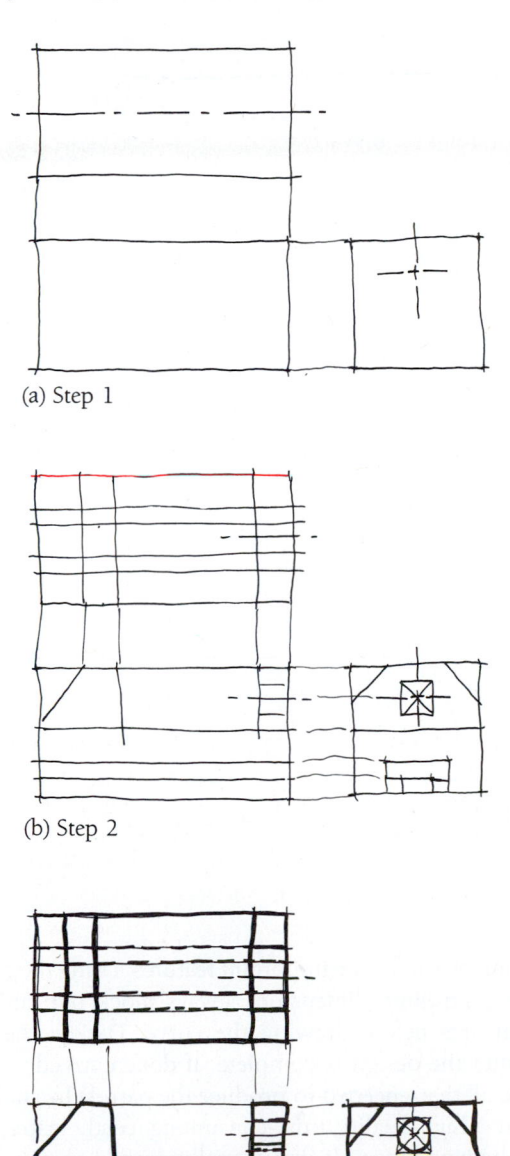

(a) Step 1

(b) Step 2

(c) Step 3

FIGURE 6.28 **Blocking-out a Three-View Sketch** (a) Block-out overall dimensions (b) Complete blocking-out all features (c) Darken all lines

plane) is rotated about the hinge line, between the side and the front image planes. Figure 6.24(c) shows the glass box opened into the plane of the paper. The front view is assumed to be stationary. Each required view is then rotated until it is in the same plane as the front view.

6.5.2 Selection of Views

The proper selection of views and view orientation must take into account the part to be drawn and its natural or assembled position. Normally, the front view shows the primary features of the part in elevation and the top view is obvious in most cases. The choice of views should be determined by the configuration of the part and the minimum number of views necessary to describe it graphically and with dimensions. In general, for cylindrical parts (Fig. 6.26), only one or two views are necessary because the diameter dimensions will describe width and depth while features along the length are dimensioned in the longitudinal view. In most cases, engineering sketches require at least two or more views.

6.5.3 Multiview Sketching

In Figure 6.26, the three stages of a sketch are shown. Two views were needed in the example to describe the part properly. The part's overall dimensions are blocked out first in each view. Centerlines were added to establish the circular or symmetrical aspects of the design. Next, the spring coils were drawn with construction lines and, last, the sketch was darkened. Note that the construction lines may be "dimmed" before the part is darkened.

These three steps are repeated for the part in Figure 6.27, which is also a two-view sketch. In Step 1, the top and front views of the part are blocked out using their overall dimensions (height, width, and depth). The holes are then located by establishing their centerlines in both views. In Step 2, visible and hidden edges of the part are laid out with construction lines, and holes are blocked out with squares equal to their diameters. In Step 3 the part is finalized by darkening in the visible, hidden, and centerlines.

The part in Figure 6.28 is sketched showing three views. The construction steps are the same as for a two-view drawing.

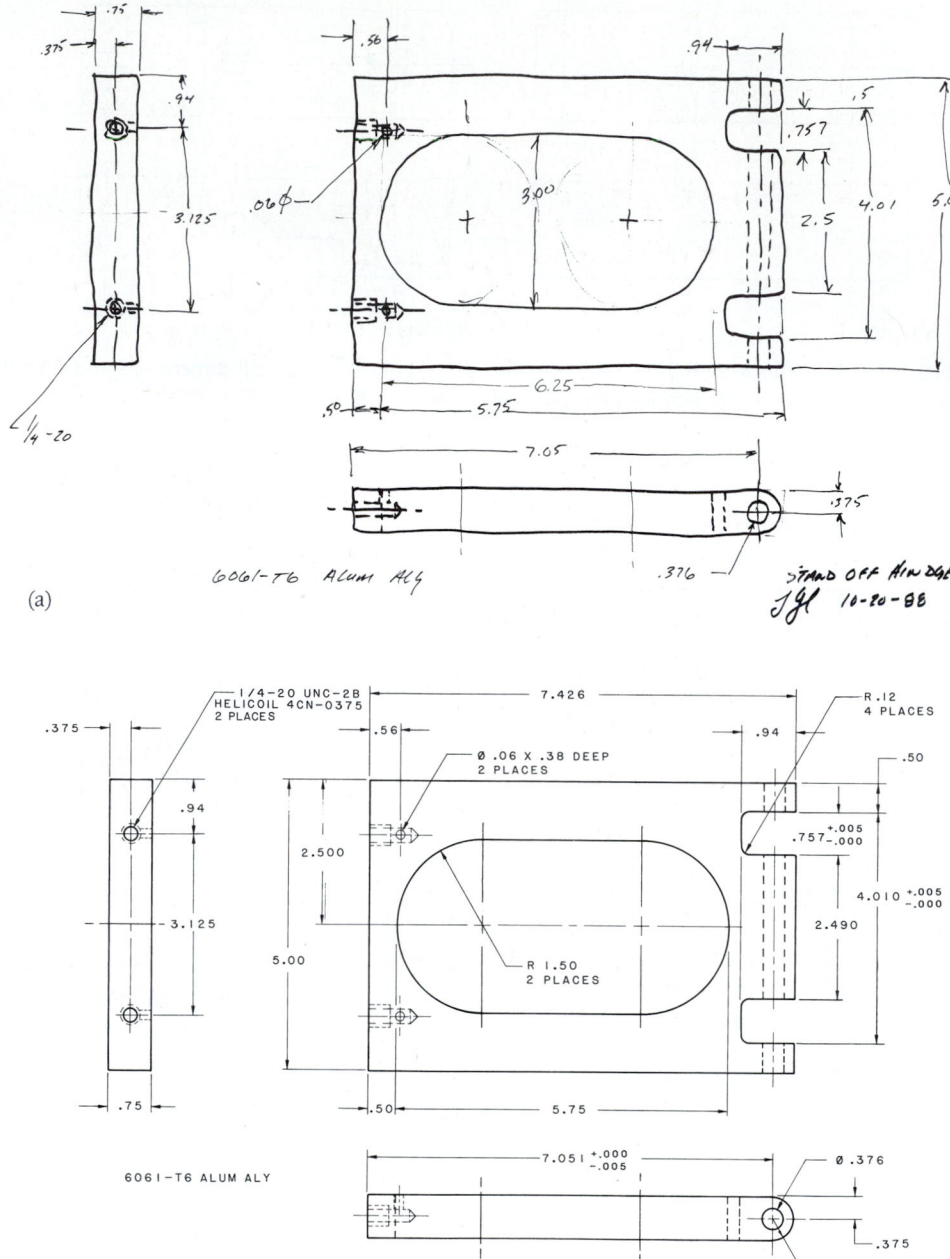

FIGURE 6.29   View Alignment
(a) Three-view sketch of a part
(b) Completed three-view drawing

Note that each view is aligned with its adjacent view, as are all features of the part. Adjacent views of edges, holes, and other shapes are established by projecting the lines between views as shown. Construction lines are extended from view to view. The alignment of the views is the most important factor in a multiview drawing, and it is easily kept correct when grid paper is used. Three views are also required for the sketch of the stand-off hinge in Figure 6.29(a). This sketch was used by the drafter to draw the detail of the part in Figure 6.29(b).

As a designer/drafter, sketching allows you the freedom to try alternative positions of components and trial layouts. Remember to sketch with thin, light construction lines, starting with box shapes. Then, sketch centerlines and lines establish-

ing symmetry to locate important features. Using the diameter as the controlling dimension, always block out circles and circular arcs before drawing the curve. Darken the shapes only after the design is complete. If done correctly, a sketch may be all that's needed to produce the part. Why should you prepare a high-quality, time-consuming, costly instrument or CAD drawing when all that is really needed to manufacture the item is a clear, well drawn, and correctly dimensioned engineering sketch? Many companies use this method to speed the drafting stage of the design-through-manufacturing cycle. This is referred to as *simplified drafting* and has gained wide acceptance in our highly competitive world.

You May Complete Exercises 6.1 Through 6.4 at This Time

Leonardo, "The Sketcher"

Sketches, illustrations, and technical drawings visually represent the designer's ideas so they may be understood by others. The thought required to sketch an idea and the discussion of ideas with others are good ways to refine proposed solutions to engineering problems.

Prehistoric people recorded their experiences by drawing on cave walls. These cave drawings showed hunting scenes and included people, animals, and tools such as spears and arrows. Who knows, they may have even believed these drawings had the power to make events come true.

A freehand sketch has always been a fast and easy way to put on paper ideas formulated in the mind. Leonardo da Vinci sketched hundreds of plans for his inventions. Today, manufactured parts often begin with a freehand sketch.

When you think of Leonardo da Vinci, you probably think about him as one of the greatest painters of the Italian Renaissance. It is true that he was trained to be a painter and he did produce some of the world's greatest paintings, including the *Mona Lisa*. He also designed machines that were far ahead of his time, such as a flying machine and a parachute. He became one of the most versatile geniuses in history because of his achievements, including scientific inventions.

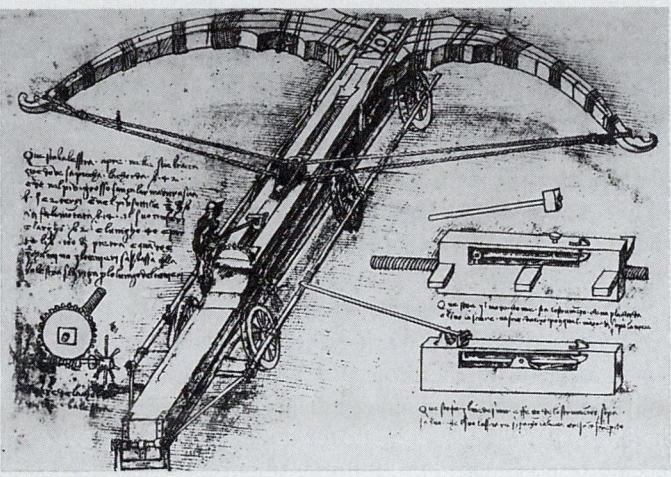

Backward Notes

In approximately 1482, Leonardo went to Milan to be the court artist to the Duke of Milan. One of his duties there was that of a military engineer. He designed artillery and the diversion of rivers. He also designed sets for court pageants. When he was forced to leave that post be-cause of the French invasion, he returned to Florence to serve as a military engineer to that court. During this time, he traveled throughout central Italy preparing sketches for maps that would become important to the history of cartography. Although he never did construct a building, he was held in the highest esteem as an architect. He drew plans ranging from the dome of the Milan cathedral to an enormous bridge over the Bosporus.

During his later years, Leonardo did little painting; instead he produced many sketches of experimental machines and other inventions. These rank among his greatest masterpieces because of their sense of motion and his use of shade and shadows.

Leonardo recorded his ideas in several notebooks, many of which include sketches and drawings that reveal his skill as a drafter and designer. About 4200 pages of his notebooks are still in existence. However, should you decide to read them, be sure to bring a mirror. Leonardo wrote his notes backward!

If all engineers, designers, and drafters recorded their ideas in a similar diligent and elegant fashion, we too might be well known for our graphic communications skills. Leonardo showed us all the value of a sketch or two. His, of course, were also masterpieces.

Leonardo's Mechanical Sketches

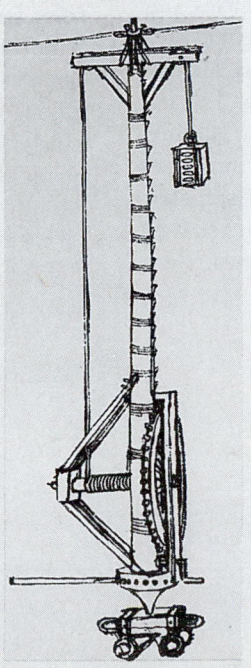

6.6   Isometric Projection

Pictorial drawings are widely used for display illustrations and product literature. The connector in Figure 6.30 is shown as a dimensioned three-view drawing as well as pictorially. Isometric drawing is the most common technique for representing parts pictorially.

Isometric projection is based on the theory that a cube representing the projection axes will be rotated until its front face is 45° to the frontal plane and then tipped forward or downward at an angle of 35° 16′. The resulting rotation displays all three primary surfaces equally. In Figure 6.31 the part has been enclosed in a glass box and projected onto each of its corresponding surfaces. The cube has been rotated 45° and tilted forward to show all three faces equally. The viewing plane 1–2–3 is parallel to the projection plane (image plane). This is an *isometric view*. In true isometric projection, the three axes make equal angles with the projection plane. All three axes are equally foreshortened and make equal angles of 120° among themselves. The three faces of a cube are identical in size and shape. A true isometric projection is about 81% of the size of an isometric drawing. In actual industry practice *isometric drawing*, not isometric projection, is used.

Isometric drawing is commonly used in sketching since it is one of the easiest to construct methods of lifelike projection. The isometric sketch of the pivot in Figure 6.32(a) is shown as a three-view instrument drawing in Figure 6.32(b). Note that the front, right side, and bottom views were used in this detail. The isometric sketch was used to graphically describe the part before the final detail was completed using multiview projection and dimensioning.

Isometric drawings are constructed along three axes, one vertical and the other two at 30° to the horizontal going both right and left. These are called **isometric axes**. The **+Z** axis (height) is vertical, the **+Y** axis recedes to the left at 30°, and the **+X** axis recedes to the right at 30° (Fig. 6.33). All lines in isometric drawings that are on or parallel to the three axes are drawn true length and are considered to be **isometric lines**. Lines not on or parallel to the axes are constructed with offset dimensions and are called **nonisometric lines**. Nonisometric lines are not true length.

6.6.1   Isometric Construction

Isometric construction using the box method is illustrated in Figure 6.34. The procedure for drawing an isometric box is shown in Figure 6.34(a) using 30°/60° triangles. Note that the axes are at 120° to one another. Starting at point A the three axes are drawn: one vertical, one at 30° receding to the right, and one at 30° receding to the left. The edges of the box are constructed from the height, width, and depth dimensions transferred from the multiview drawing [Fig. 6.34(c)]. *Remember, in an isometric drawing the dimensions are not foreshortened.* Each measurement is taken full scale from the multiview projection (or directly from the part), provided that the distance is on or parallel to one of the axes.

After the part is boxed-in, the remainder of the drawing is completed. Dividers (or a scale) are used to transfer the dimensions shown in Figure 6.34(c) to the isometric view of (b). All measurements are taken along lines that are parallel to or on the axes (along isometric lines). Dimension D1 is measured along the vertical axis, while dimensions D2, D3, and D4 are in the horizontal plane and are measured along or parallel to one of the corresponding receding axes. After the centerlines are located, the circles and arcs are drawn.

6.6.2   Isometric Angles

Because of the distortion created by the isometric view of the box, few angles appear as true angles. Angles normally appear larger or smaller than true size on isometric drawings; therefore, they must be established by means of **offset dimensions**. As an example, the plane in Figure 6.35 has angles of 45° and 30°. Both angles are constructed from offset dimensions, measured along isometric lines from the top view of the plane in Figure 6.35(a). The isometric view of the plane, Figure 6.35(b) is boxed in with true length dimensions A and B along the isometric axes. The 30° angle was constructed by transferring dimension C. The 45° angle was drawn by transferring offset dimensions E and F to establish the endpoints.

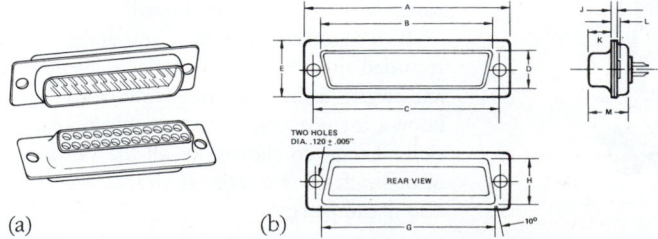

(a)   (b)

FIGURE 6.30 Pictorial and Three-View Drawing of a Connector

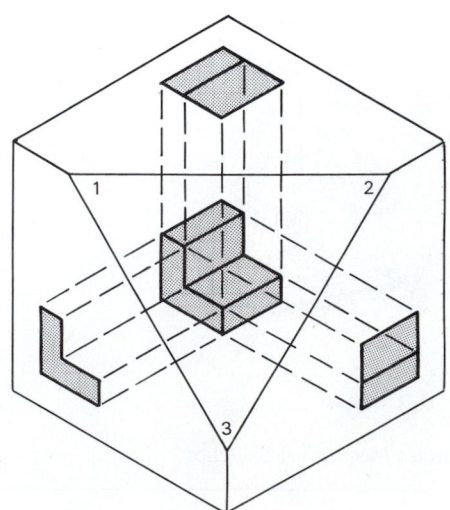

FIGURE 6.31 Isometric Projection

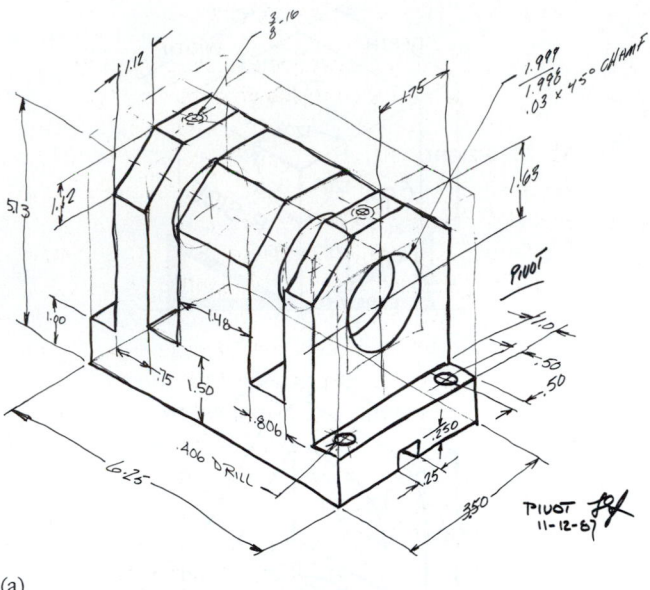

(a)

The points were then connected, completing the figure. Lengths D and H are nonisometric lines (at an angle) and appear distorted (not true length/size), as do both angles.

The part in Figure 6.36 has an angled surface. To draw the part isometrically, it is necessary to use dimensions A, B, and C because they can be taken along true length lines. In Figure 6.37(a), the angled part was sketched in four steps. The finished sketch, Figure 6.37(b), shows the part with dimensions. It is important to block out the part step by step just as it was for multiview sketches. The use of grid isometric paper, as in Figure 6.38, p. 164, increases speed and accuracy and simplifies the sketching process.

6.6.3   Isometric Circles and Arcs

Circles and circular arcs on isometric drawings appear elliptical (Fig. 6.39, p. 164) unless they fall exactly on or parallel to the isometric viewing plane. Various methods are available for *isometric ellipse* construction: template, trammel, four-center, and point plotting, to name a few. In general, a template

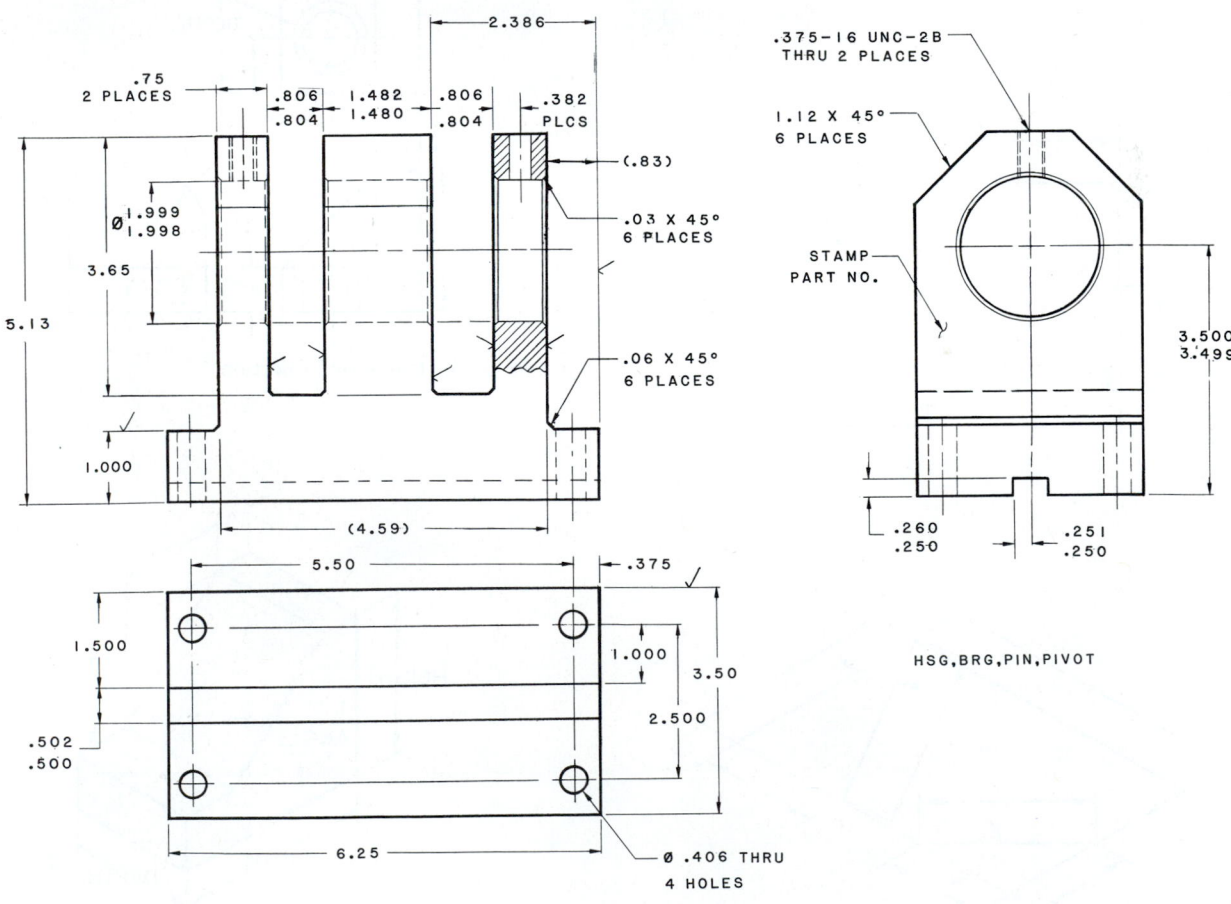

(b)

FIGURE 6.32   Examples of Isometric Drawing   (a) Isometric sketch (b) Instrument drawing

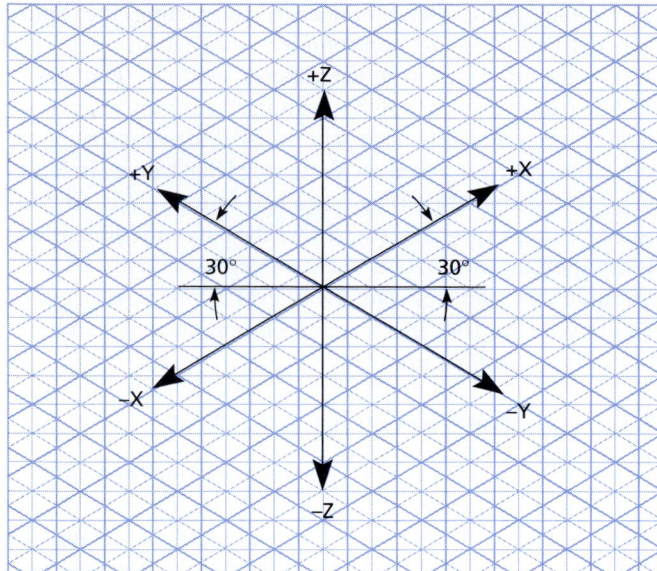

FIGURE 6.33 Isometric Axes

(a)

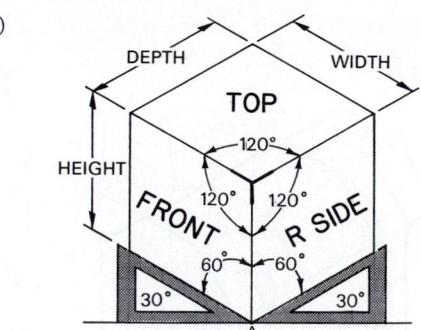

(b)

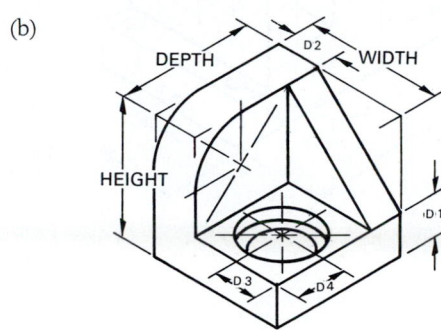

(c)

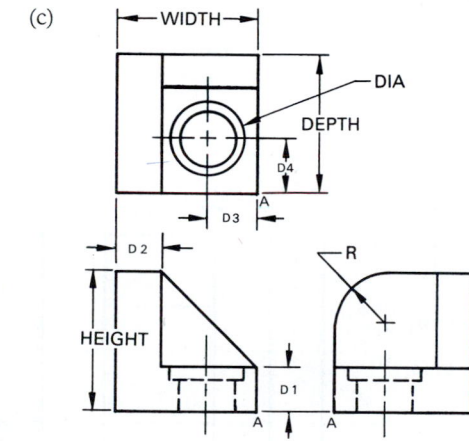

FIGURE 6.34 Isometric Projection

(a)

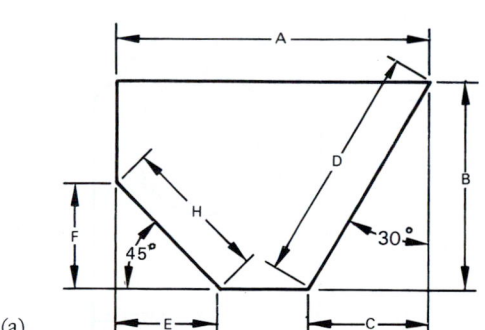

(b)

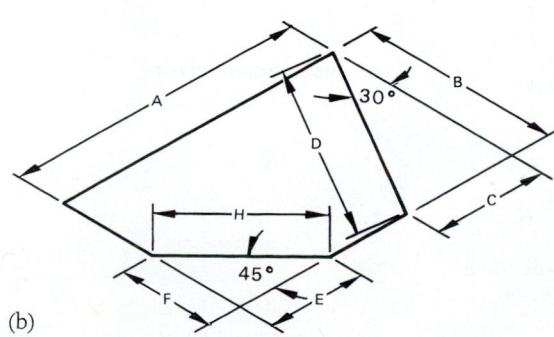

FIGURE 6.35 Isometric Angles (a) Orthographic (b) Isometric

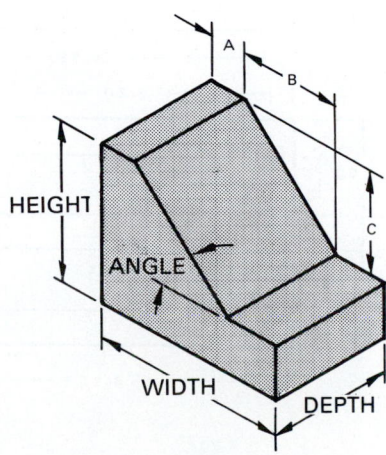

FIGURE 6.36 Offset Dimensions

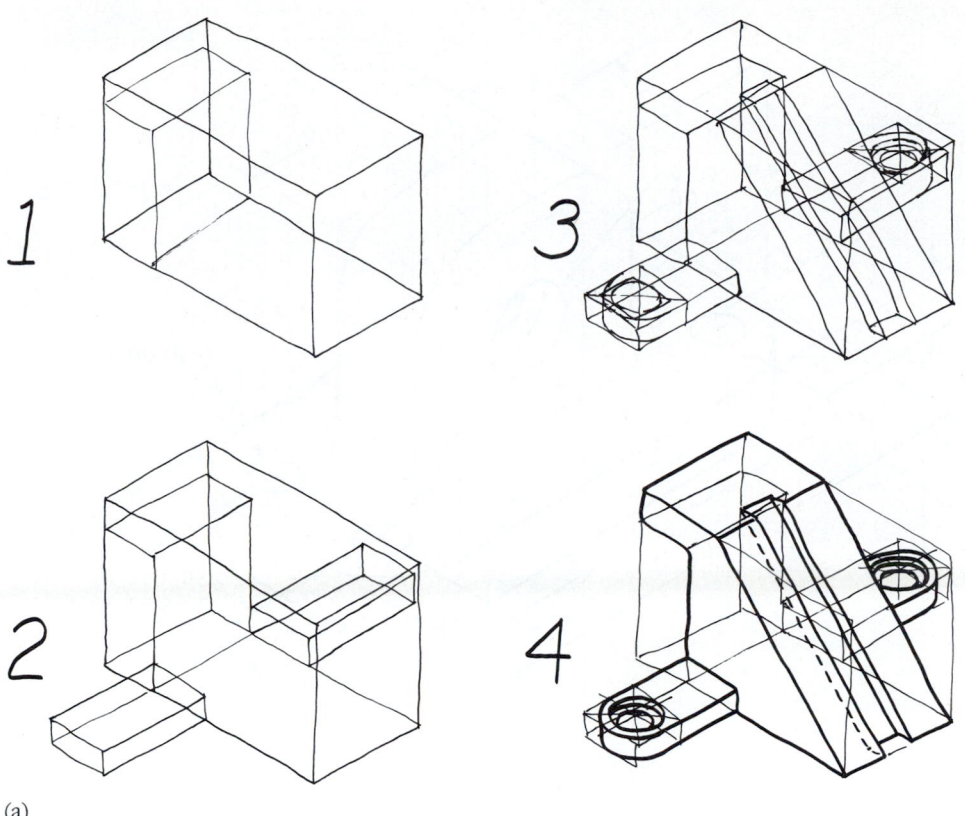

1

2

3

4

(a)

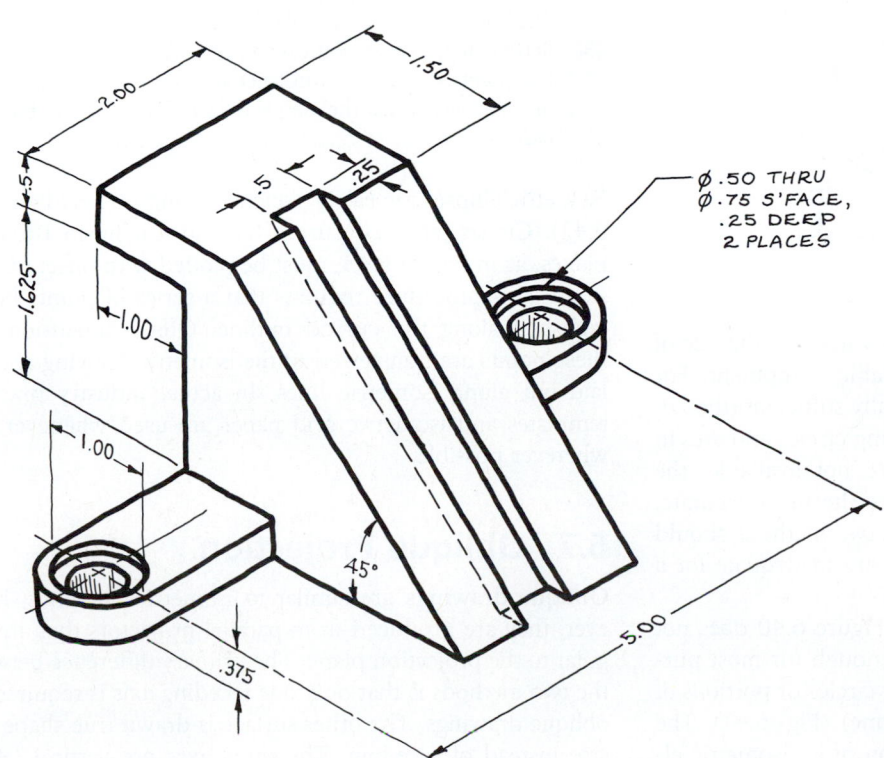

2.00

1.50

.5

.25

1.5

1.625

1.00

1.00

Ø.50 THRU
Ø.75 S'FACE,
.25 DEEP
2 PLACES

45°

.375

5.00

(b)

FIGURE 6.37   Isometric Construction (a) Step-by-step isometric construction (b) Completed sketch with dimensions

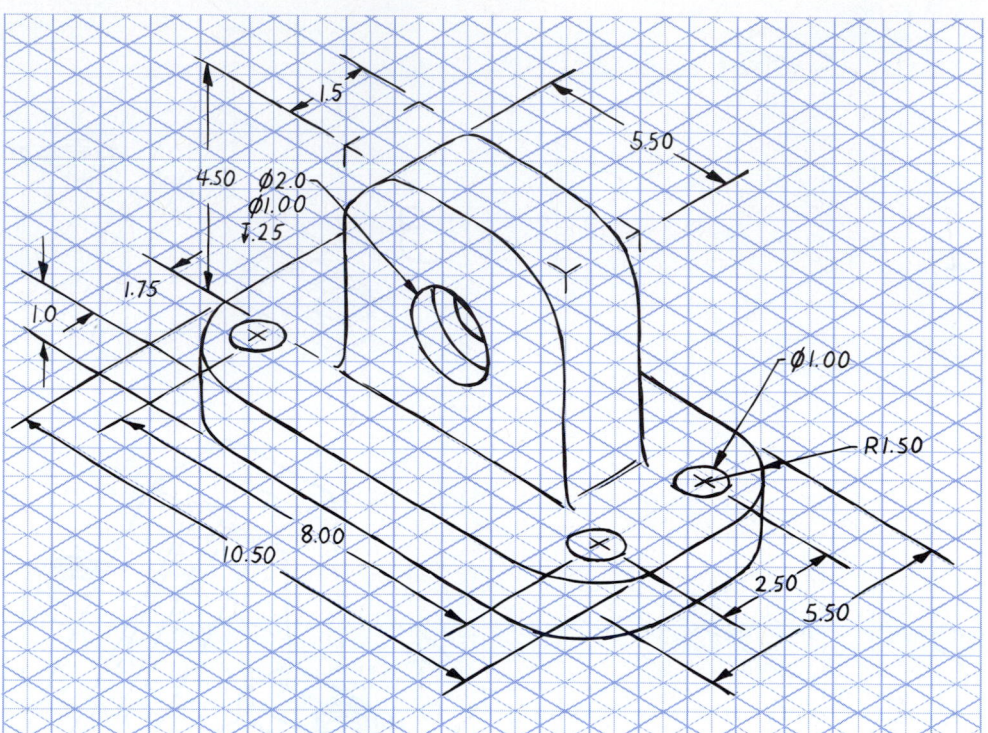

FIGURE 6.38 Isometric Sketch Using Grid Paper

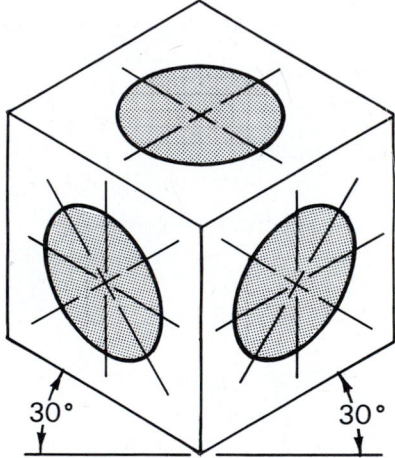

FIGURE 6.39 Isometric Ellipses

should be used for instrument drawings whenever the size of the ellipse can be matched with available equipment. For sketches, freehand techniques are normally sufficient (though templates are still useful). For constructing circles and arcs in isometric drawings when templates are not available, the trammel and point plotting methods are the most accurate, but time-consuming, procedures. These two methods should only be used when the other methods are inadequate for a particular project.

The **four-center method** shown in Figure 6.40 does not create a perfect ellipse but is accurate enough for most purposes. This method can be used to draw circles or portions of circles (arcs) on any isometric face (plane) (Fig. 6.41). The following steps describe the construction of an isometric ellipse (Fig. 6.40):

1. Draw lines DA and DC along the two receding axes (at 30°). Draw line AB parallel to DC, and line CB parallel to AD. *The isometric square has sides equal to the diameter of the circle.*
2. Draw construction lines from point D perpendicular to line AB at its midpoint and perpendicular to line CB at its midpoint. These lines are perpendicular bisectors of each side.
3. Repeat step 2 using point B and lines AD and CD.
4. Use points D and B to construct arcs R1. Arc R2 originates at the intersection of the perpendicular bisectors for both R1 radii.

Isometric ellipses are easily sketched using this method (Fig. 6.42). Circles, arcs, or curves that do not lie in isometric planes, as in Figure 6.43, must be plotted with offset dimensions. This procedure requires that a series of points be established along the curved outline. Offset dimensions for these points are transferred to the isometric drawing and are laid out along isometric lines. In actual industry practice, templates and isometric grid paper are used whenever and wherever possible.

6.7   Oblique Projection

Oblique drawings are similar to isometric drawings; however, they are produced from parallel projectors that are angular to the projection plane. The primary difference between the two methods is that only one receding axis is required for oblique drawings. The other surface is drawn true shape and size instead of receding. The three axes are vertical ($+Z$), horizontal ($+Y$), and receding ($+X$) (Fig. 6.44). In oblique

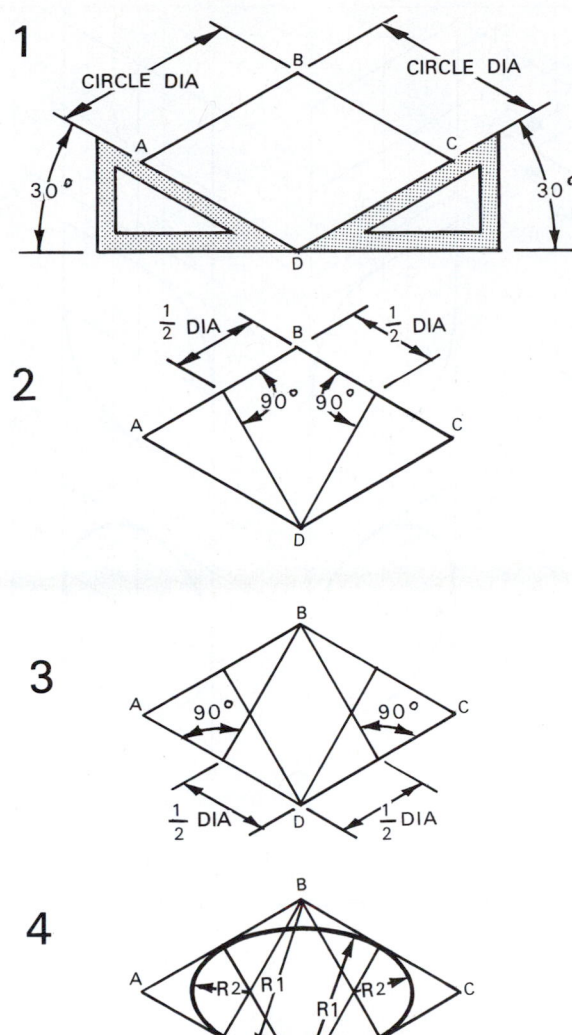

FIGURE 6.40   Ellipse Construction for Isometric Drawings

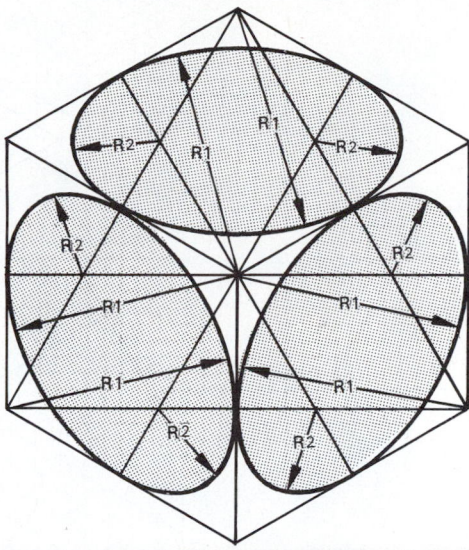

FIGURE 6.41   Isometric Ellipses and the Four-Center Method

Parts that are drawn with oblique projection should be oriented so that the surface with the most curved features lies in the front plane bounded by the axes that are at 90°. This orientation lessens drawing time because all surfaces that lie on the front plane or that are parallel to it are drawn true shape and size (not oblique). Circles and arcs are therefore true projections when placed in this position. Oblique projection is extremely useful for parts with parallel curved or irregular features. The longest or most irregular surface should be the front of the projection wherever possible, as in Figure 6.47. Because cavalier projection was used, all dimensions (parallel to an axis, including the receding faces) are true length and can be transferred from the multiview projection. In this figure the following set of steps is provided for drawing the part:

1. Each dimension from the multiview drawing can be transferred true length to the oblique view.
2. Start by drawing the front face of the part using the height (H) and width (W) dimension. Then determine the receding angle (45° was used here). Transfer the depth (D) dimension along the receding axis and block out the outline of the part. Use dimension A to establish the top of the plane surface.
3. Use dimensions B and C to locate the circular shape. Dimension C is also the diameter of the circle.
4. Complete the part by transferring offset dimensions E and F to establish the angled surface. Using a compass or template, draw a circle (half circle here) using dimension C as the diameter. Note that the circular features are parallel to the front plane and are therefore true shape. For circles and arcs that appear on oblique faces, the oblique four-center method, point plotting, or a template must be used (see Chapter 8).

projection the front face of the part is normally placed parallel to the image plane; therefore, the **Y** and **Z** axes are at 90° and are parallel to the projection (image) plane. The other faces of the part are on receding axes (1 to 89°). In Figure 6.45, the front face of the block and the diameter of the hole are drawn true shape and size. The most commonly used angle for the receding axis is 45°.

The two basic categories of oblique projection are **cavalier** and **cabinet**. In a cavalier projection [Fig. 6.46(a)], receding lines are not foreshortened but are drawn full scale. In a cabinet projection, Figure 6.46(b), the receding lines have been foreshortened to one-half their original length. The receding axis is drawn at any convenient angle, but must be at least 1°, or 89°, or less. The choice of receding angle is determined by the shape of the part and the most descriptive view orientation. The most commonly used angles are 15°, 30°, 45°, 60°, and 75°.

The construction process for slanted, inclined lines and planes is similar to that of isometric drawings. Locate each feature's endpoints along lines that are parallel to one of the axes. For slanted surfaces, locate both ends of the surface and connect the points.

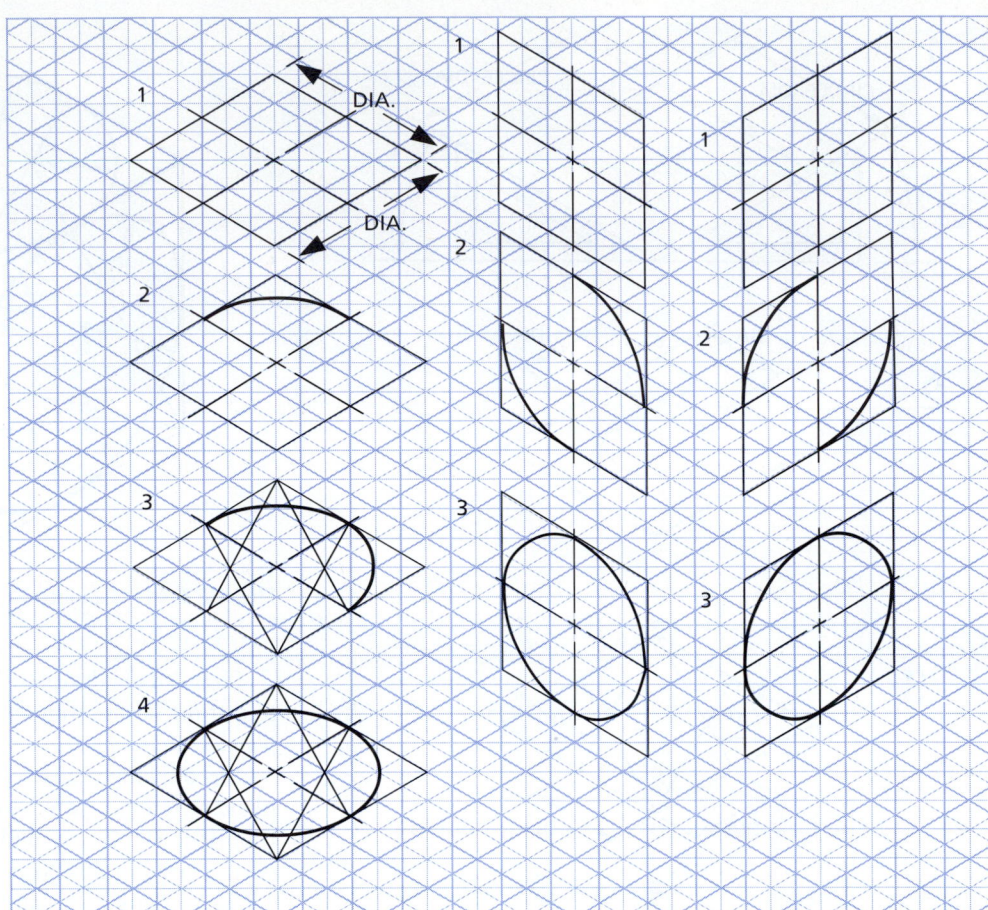

FIGURE 6.42 Sketched
Isometric Arcs and Circles

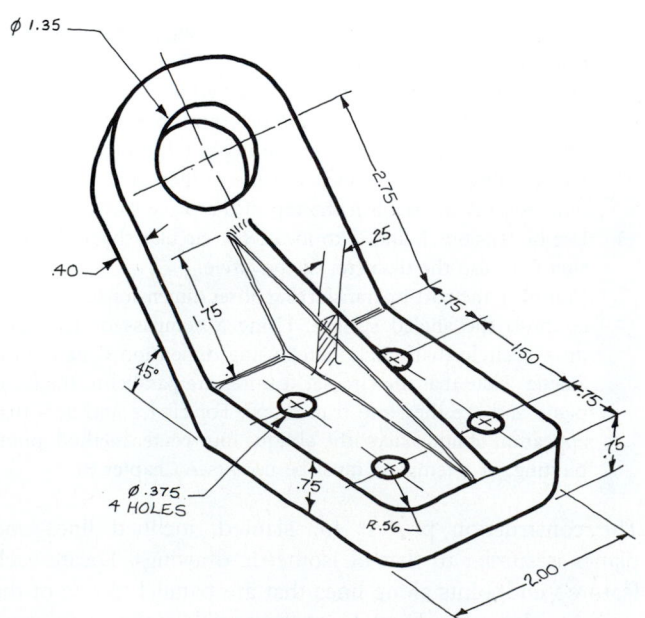

FIGURE 6.43 Isometric Sketch of Part

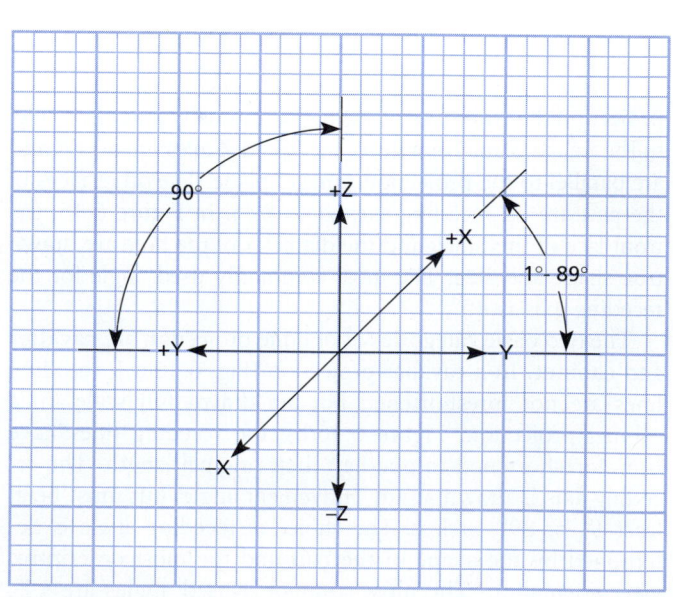

FIGURE 6.44 Oblique Axes

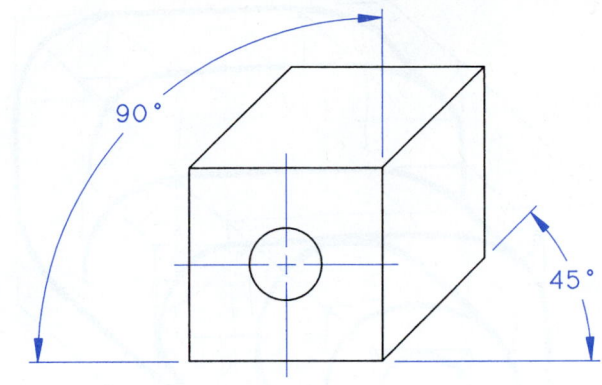

FIGURE 6.45   Oblique Projection

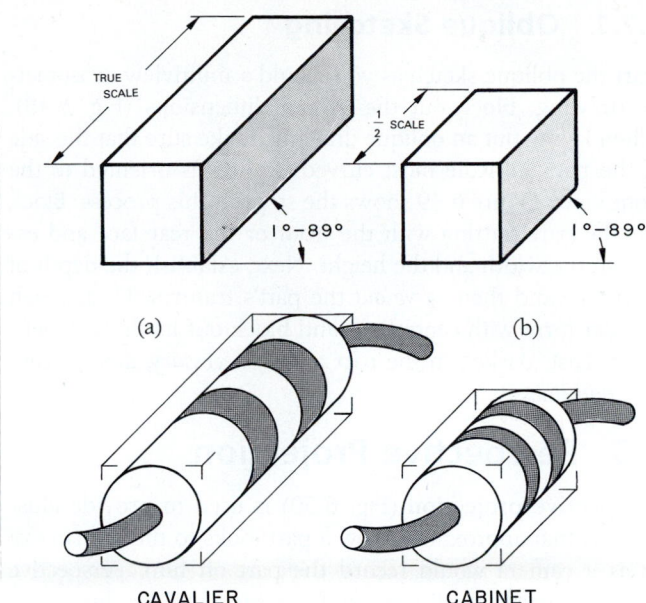

(a)   (b)

CAVALIER   CABINET

FIGURE 6.46   **Oblique Projection**   (a) Cavalier (b) Cabinet

MULTIVIEW

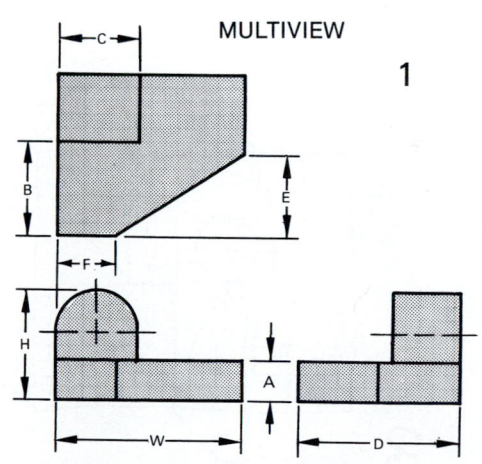

1

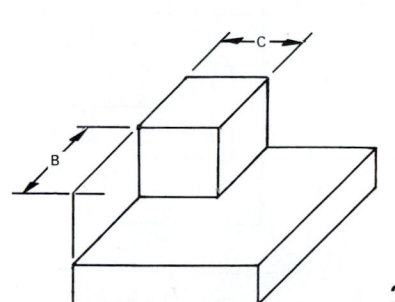

3

OBLIQUE PROJECTION

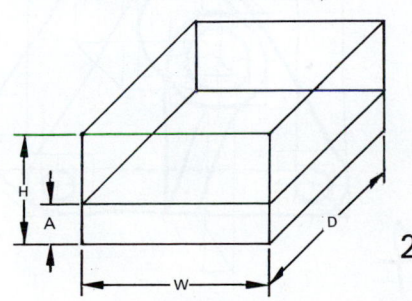

2

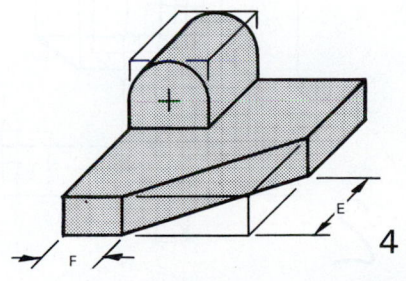

4

FIGURE 6.47   Construction Steps in Oblique Projection

6.7.1   Oblique Sketching

Start the oblique sketch as you would a multiview or isometric drawing; block out the overall dimensions (Fig. 6.48). When laying out an oblique drawing, make sure that the side of the part with the most curved features is oriented to the front view. Figure 6.49 shows the steps in this process. Block out the part starting with the front or the rear face and establish the width and the height. Next, establish the depth of each face and then *carve out* the part's features. Locate each circular form with centerlines and block out its three dimensions. Last, darken in the part and, *if necessary, dim the construction lines.*

6.8   Perspective Projection

Perspective projection (Fig. 6.50) is used to provide illustrations that approximate how a part looks to the human eye or as a camera would record the part on film. Perspective drawings are not dimensionally correct. Many lines and planes on perspective drawings cannot be scaled since they are not drawn true length or true shape. Because of this distortion, perspective drawings are seldom found in engineering or design work. However, technical illustrations for advertisements, sales catalogs, technical manuals, and architectural renderings make extensive use of this form of pictorial projection.

For sketching, perspective projection is more difficult than oblique and isometric projection. For this reason, only a few

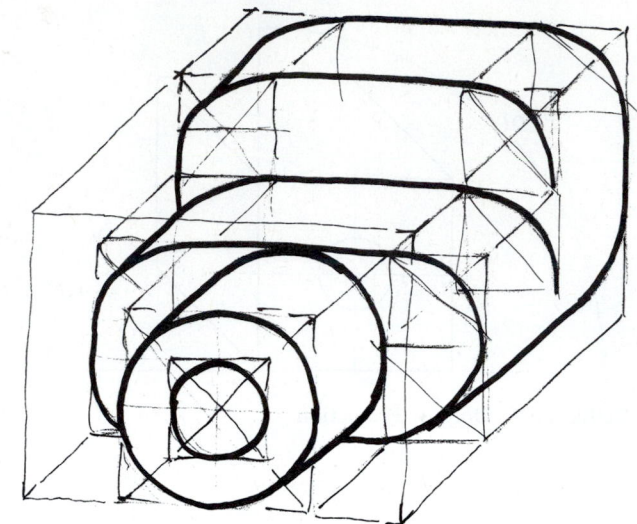

FIGURE 6.48   Oblique Sketch

situations exist for which perspective sketching is employed. Architects use the freehand perspective sketch as do professional technical illustrators. Perspective grid patterns are available for underlays in a variety of perspective orientations and for interior and exterior layouts. For further information regarding perspective drawings, refer to Chapter 8.

You May Complete Exercises 6.5 Through 6.8 at This Time

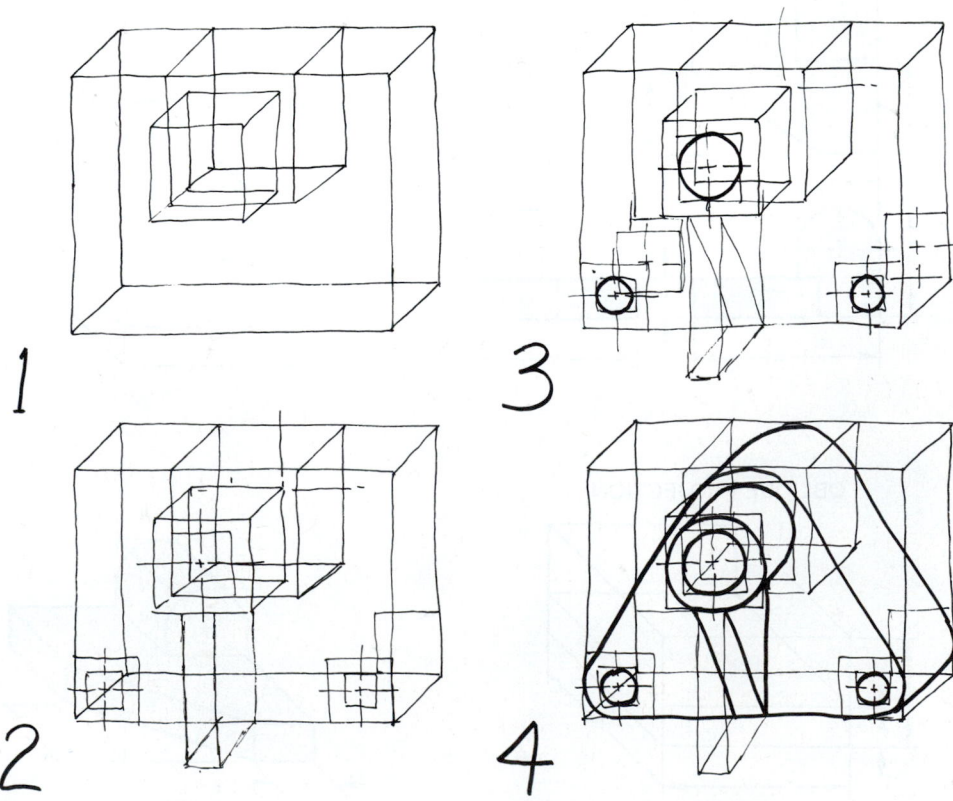

FIGURE 6.49   Step-by-Step Oblique Construction

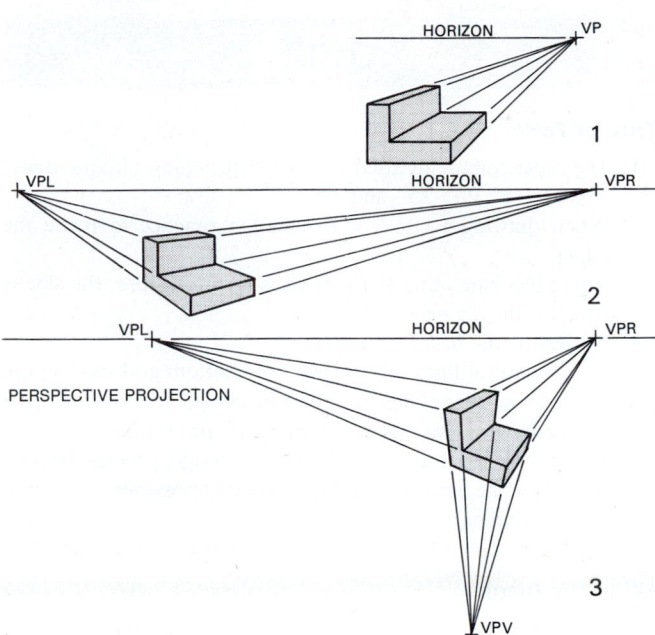

FIGURE 6.50   Perspective Projection

FIGURE 6.51   CAD Designers Sketching at a Reference Table

6.9 CAD and Sketching

Sketches are utilized in three ways when a CAD system is used for drawing and design: directly on the CAD system; to lay out diagrams that will later be digitized; and as a designer's or drafter's tool for graphically exploring a design before using the system. The typical CAD workstation has an area next to it dedicated as a reference surface (Fig. 6.51). Here, the designer or drafter uses the time-proven method of freehand sketching during the initial design stages of a project. Sketches enable you to develop and explore ideas and design alternatives. The sketch is then used as a reference for 3D CAD modeling or 2D CAD drawing and detailing. Freehand sketching directly on the CAD system is also possible with some computer graphics systems. This capability is somewhat limited. By turning on construction lines on one layer, and using a different color, you can sketch directly on the system. The layer with the construction lines is turned off before plotting the sketch.

Digitizing existing drawings and diagrams can be done directly from a freehand sketch with the proper equipment. The digitizing table (Fig. 6.52) is used to input existing instrument drawings or freehand sketches. Freehand sketches are normally completed on grid paper and then taped to the digitizing surface (Fig. 6.53). The drafter can establish any scale for the project. The drawing or sketch is then digitized (Fig. 6.54) using a puck, pen, or other input device to create the 2D drawing.

Besides the digitizing of sketches, some CAD systems have the ability to create sketches using specific commands. The **SKETCH** command on AutoCAD permits freehand drawings to be created as part of a drawing. Freehand drawings are distinguished from normal AutoCAD drawings in that they

are automatically entered as the puck, mouse, or pen is moved, rather than being built from points, lines, arcs, etc. Freehand drawing using a CAD system is best suited for such items as signatures (Fig. 6.55), map contour lines, and other types of irregular material. The **SKETCH** command creates a series of line segments that can be moved, erased (all or part), blocked, and so forth, the same as other entities on a drawing. The **SKETCH** command is entered as shown below:

Command: **SKETCH** Record increment <current>:

You determine the increment distance based on the drawing size and the required resolution. Enter the distance, in drawing units, over which movement of the pen or puck justifies generating a line segment. The smaller the distance, the more accurate (smoother) the sketch, but also the larger

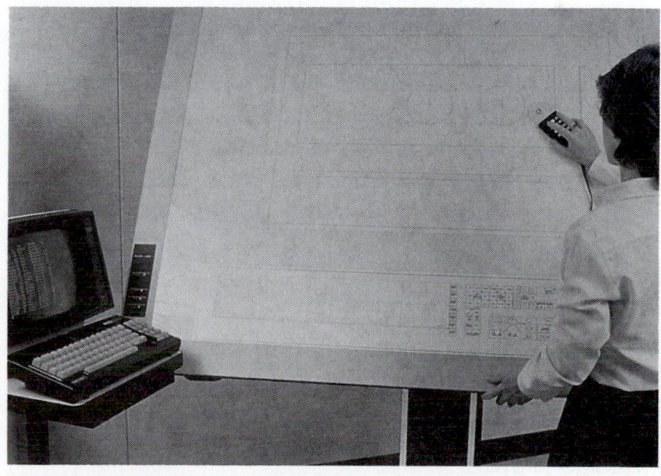

FIGURE 6.52   Drafter Inputting a Sketch

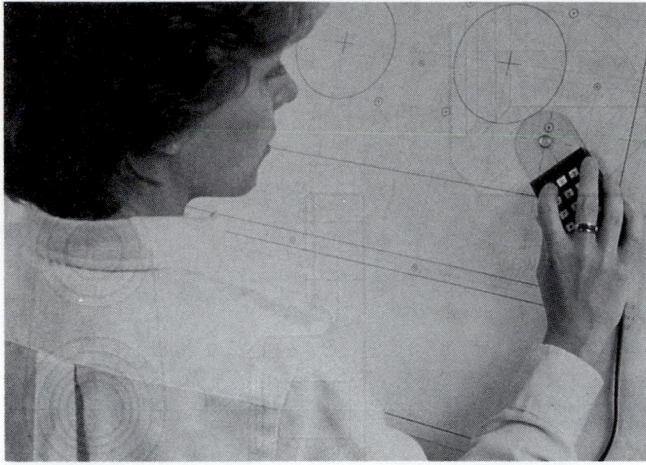

FIGURE 6.53 Using a Puck to Digitize a Sketch Drawn on Grid Paper

FIGURE 6.54 Digitizing a 2D Sketch Command

FIGURE 6.55 Signature Drawn with AutoCAD's SKETCH Command

the required database storage. In general, 0.1 will generate a reasonably high-resolution sketch on AutoCAD. This method of sketching is not as fast or as accurate compared to freehand sketching on grid paper. The final sketch using a CAD system tends to have jagged lines as in Figure 6.55 where the signature is not very smooth, even though an increment of 0.05 was used.

For the foreseeable future, sketching will remain a freehand manual process as it has been since humans "scribbled" on cave walls and flat stones, used sticks to scratch construction ideas in sand, and drew engineering marvels on parchment and papyrus.

QUIZ

True or False

1. The most commonly used angles for sketching oblique drawings are 15°, 20°, 25°, and 40°.
2. When drawing a circle, it is common practice to rotate the paper.
3. When blocking out a circle or an isometric ellipse, the side is equal to the diameter.
4. 6H lead is the best for sketching.
5. Sketch vertical lines starting from the bottom and moving up.
6. Never show centerlines for round or curved portions of a part if it is drawn as an oblique or isometric projection.
7. Pictorial sketches are essential to the design process because they allow the designer to explore different possibilities, shapes, and orientations of the part.
8. Grid paper should be used whenever possible when sketching.

Fill in the Blanks

9. _____ or _____ lead is the best grade for sketching.
10. The pencil is held about _____ from the _____ when sketching.
11. For right-handed drafters, draw horizontal lines by moving the pencil from _____ to _____ .
12. Circles are sketched by first drawing a _____ .
13. _____ lines are used to lay out the outline of the part before darkening the lines.
14. _____ and _____ lines are sketched by moving the pencil from _____ to _____ .
15. _____ , _____ , _____ sketches are used to represent the part pictorially during the _____ design stage of the project.
16. _____ lines are drawn vertical and receding at _____ degrees to the horizontal for isometric drawings.

Answer the Following

17. Explain the steps in sketching a circle.
18. Describe the difference between isometric, oblique, and perspective projection.
19. How is sketching used in conjunction with CAD in the design process?
20. How would you sketch an ellipse that lies in the horizontal plane?
21. What does digitizing a sketch mean?
22. What are the six standard views? Which views are most commonly represented on an orthographic drawing?
23. Why are parts always blocked out before darkening the lines?
24. How does the shape of the part help determine the use of isometric or oblique projection techniques?

EXERCISES

Transfer the given information to an "A" size sheet of .25 in. grid paper. Complete all views and solve for proper visibility, including centerlines, object lines, and hidden lines. Exercises that are not assigned by the instructor can be sketched in the text to provide practice and understanding of the preceding instructional material.

After Reading the Chapter Through Section 6.5.3 You May Complete the Following Exercises

Exercise 6.1   Sketch the one-view drawing.

Exercise 6.2   Sketch the two-view drawing.

Exercise 6.3   Sketch the circular part.

Exercise 6.4   Sketch the two-view section drawing.

These exercises can also be used for isometric and oblique problems after you have completed the chapter.

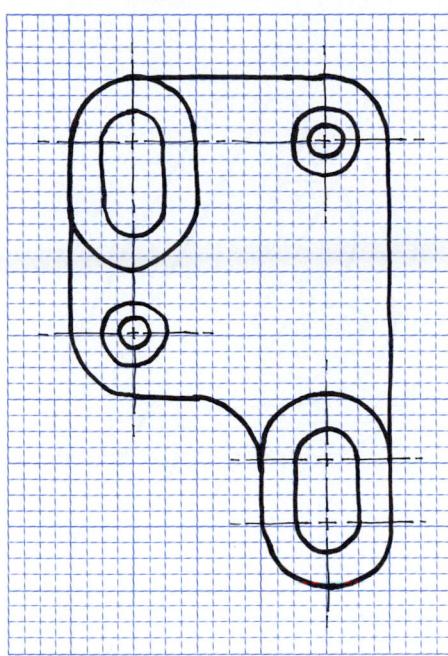

Exercise 6.1

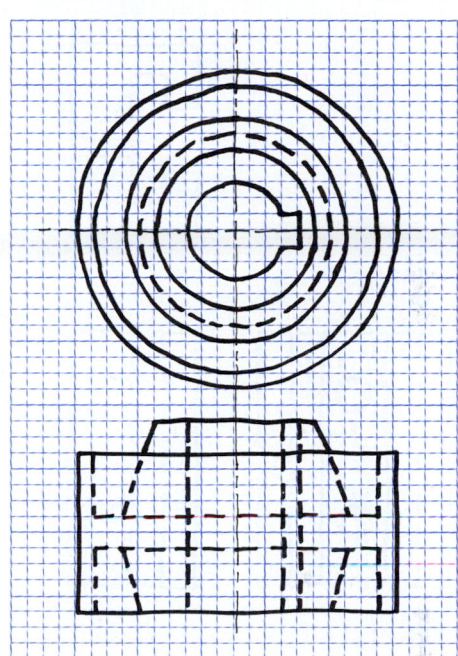

Exercise 6.3

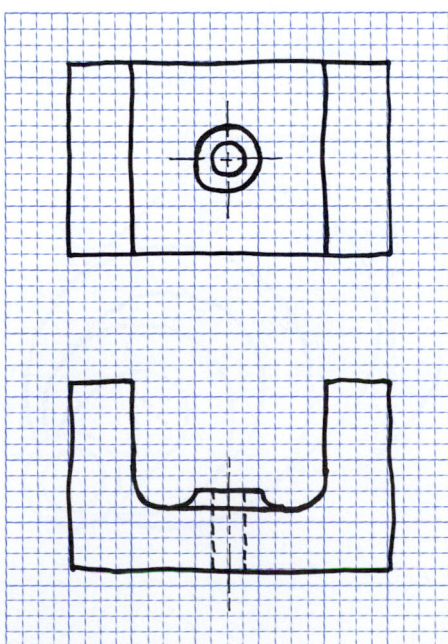

Exercise 6.2

Exercise 6.4

After Reading the Chapter Through Section 6.8 You May Complete the Following Exercises

Exercise 6.5 Sketch the three-view part and complete an isometric sketch of the part on isometric grid paper.

Exercise 6.6 Sketch an isometric view of the part using isometric grid paper and complete a two-view drawing.

Exercise 6.7 Sketch an isometric view of the part on isometric grid paper and complete a three-view drawing.

Exercise 6.8 Sketch an oblique cabinet view of the part (use 45°) and complete a two-view drawing.

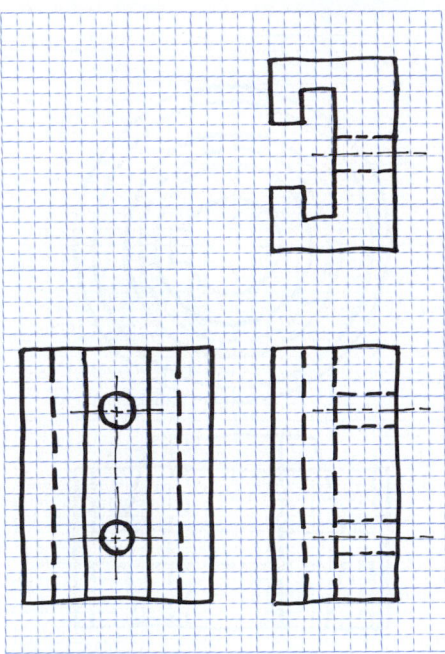

Exercise 6.5

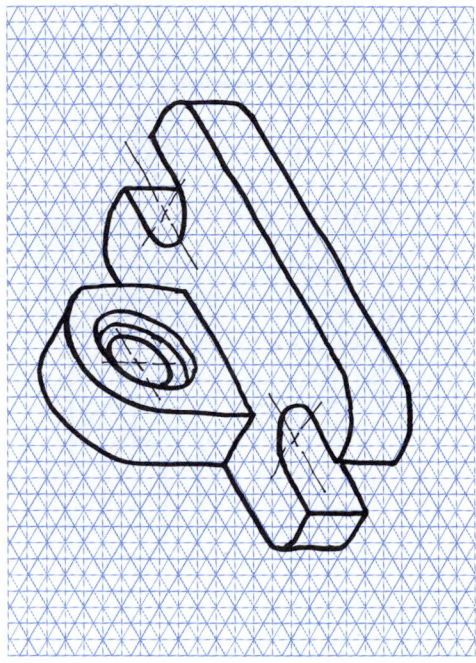

Exercise 6.7

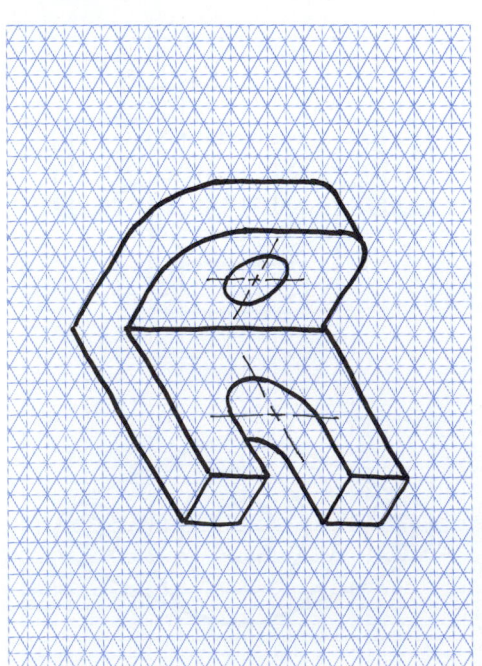

Exercise 6.6

Exercise 6.8

PROBLEMS

projects at two times the book scale. Problems can be either metric, inches, or decimal units. Two or three views may be required for a particular problem.

Problems 6.1(A) Through (H) Freehand sketch the assigned problems in multiview projection using grid paper. Draw the

Problems 6.2(A) Through (I)   Same as Problem 6.1.

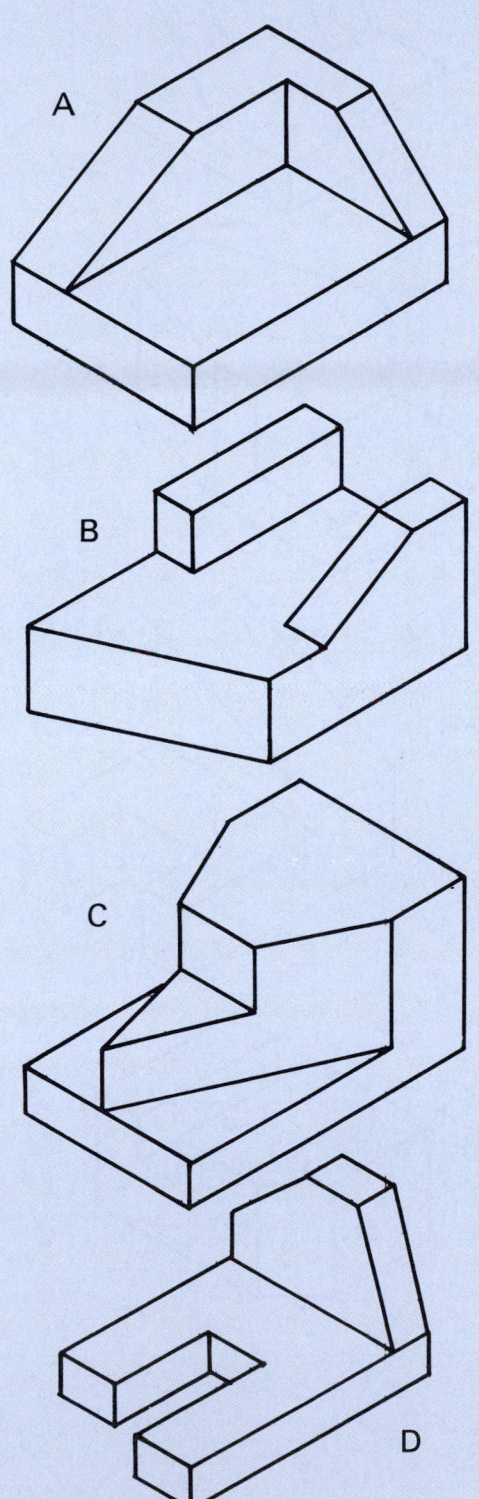

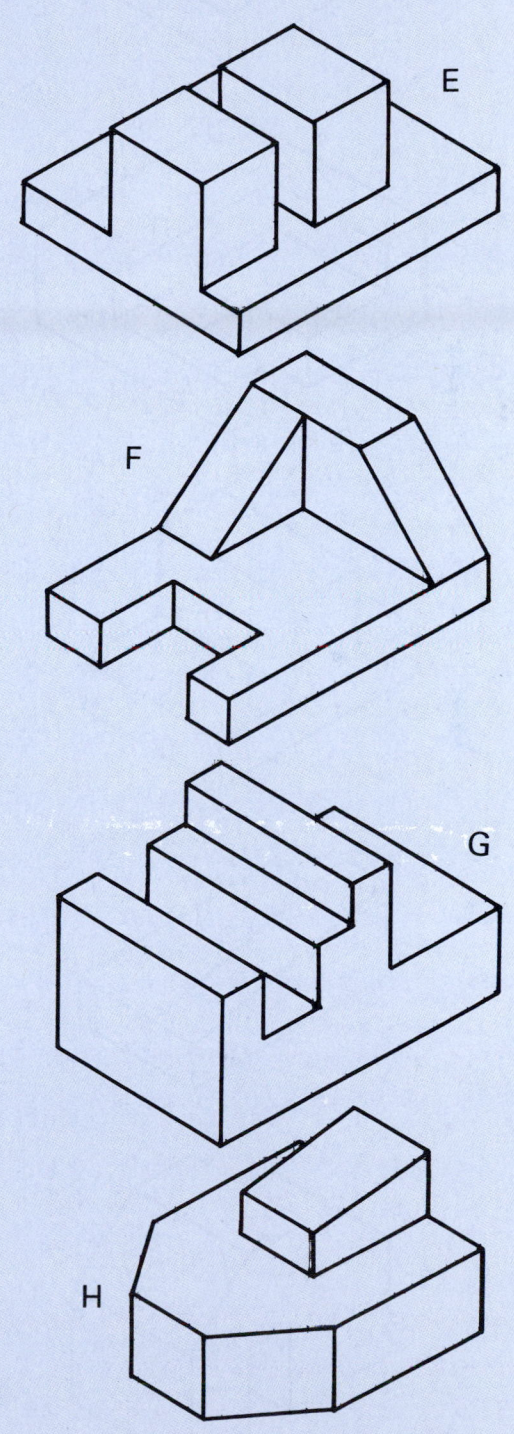

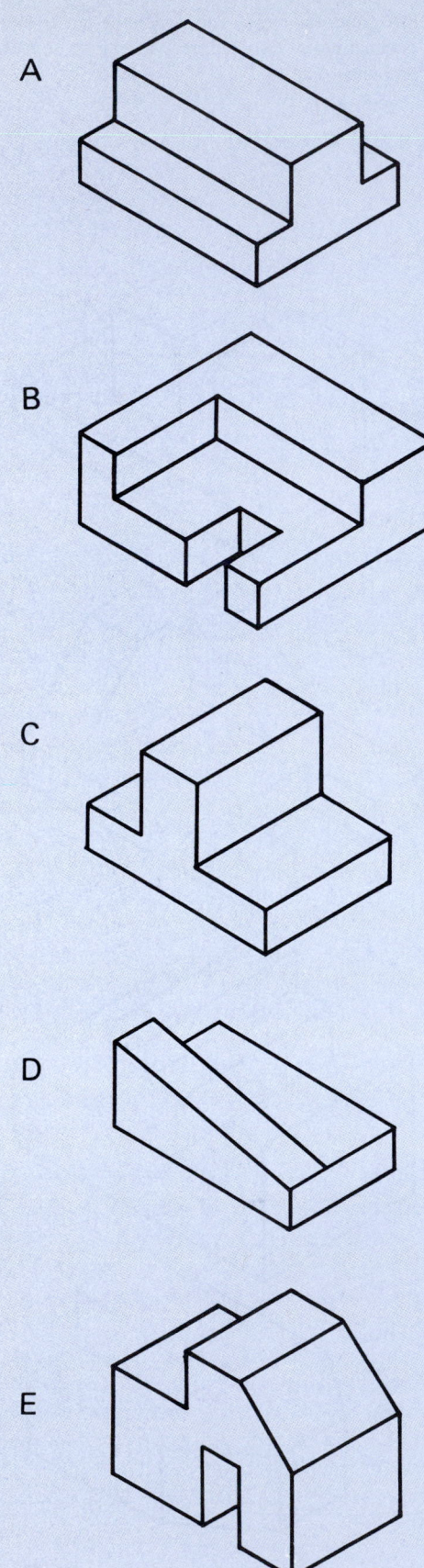

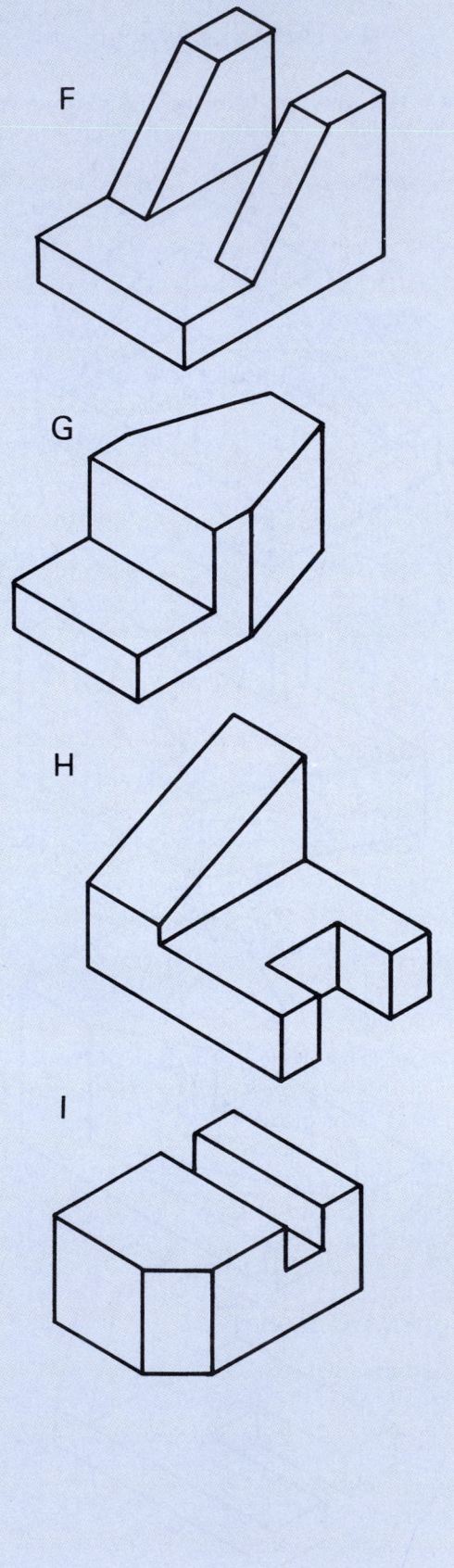

Problems 6.2(A) Through (I)

Problems 6.3(A) Through (G) Using freehand sketching, draw each of the assigned problems. Use oblique projection. Be careful to choose the proper surface for the front face of the part. Draw at two times book scale.

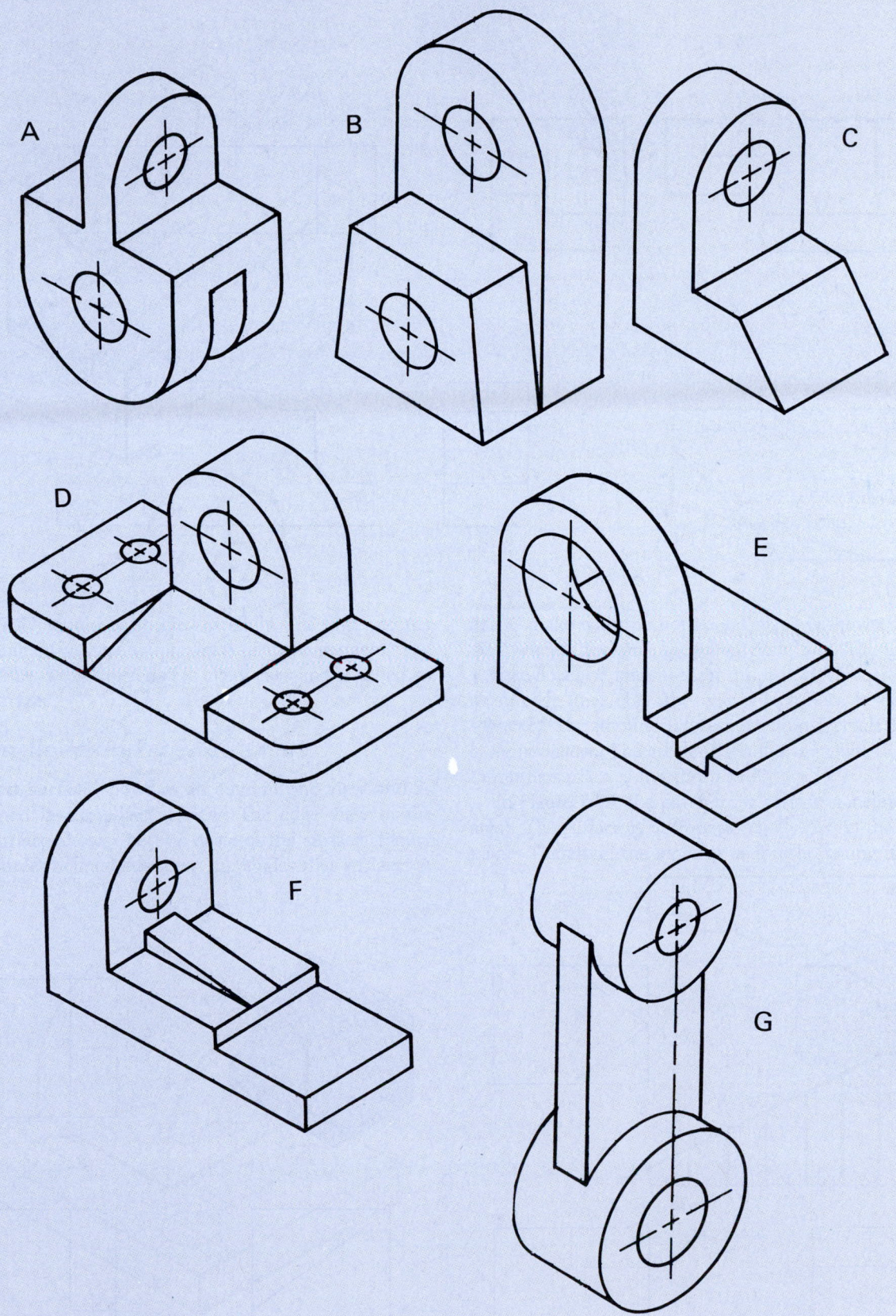

Problems 6.3(A) Through (G)

Problems 6.4(A) Through (C) Complete the three views of each problem. On the same sheet sketch an isometric view. Draw at two times book scale.

Problems 6.4(D) Through (F) Sketch three views of each problem. Draw at two times the book scale.

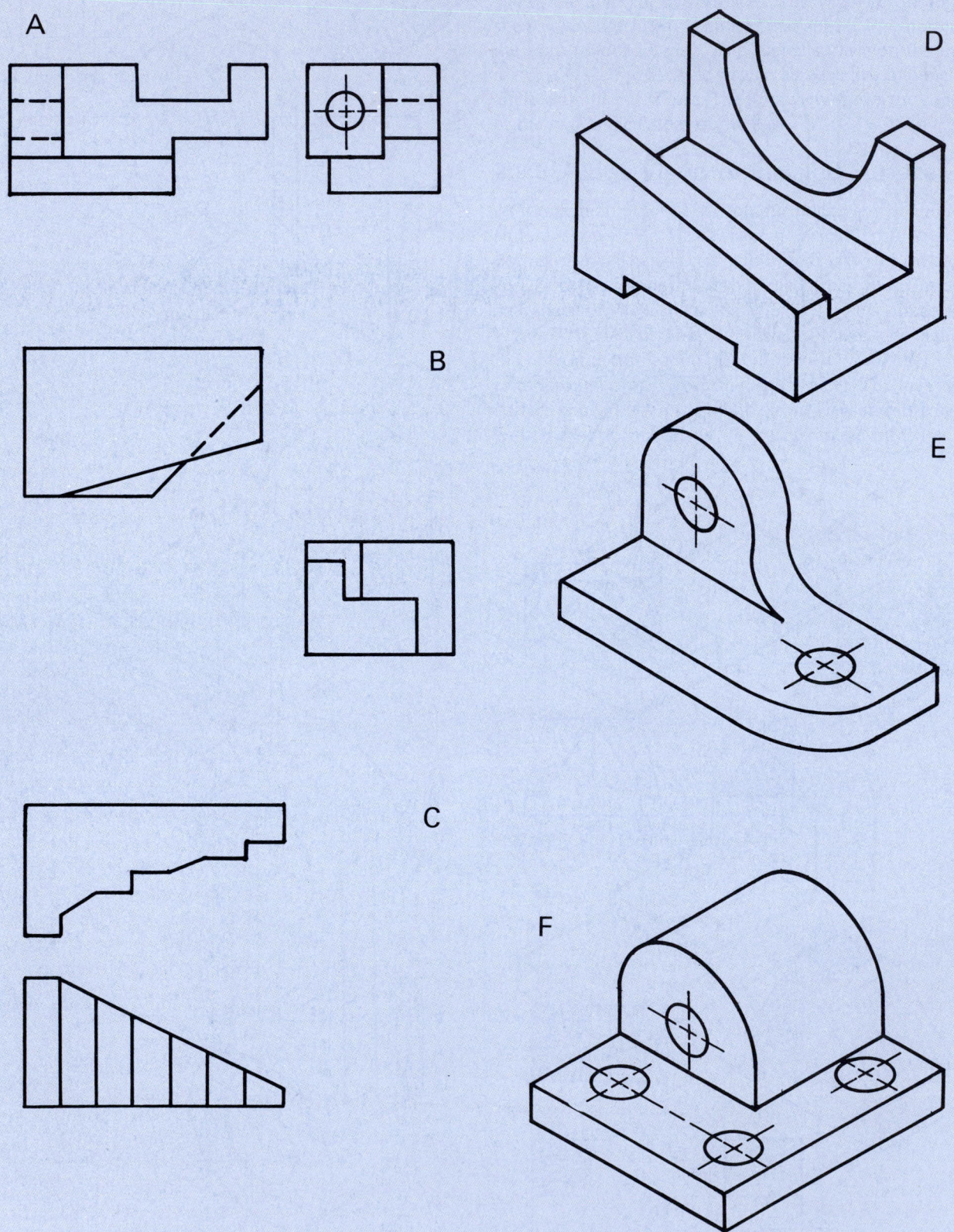

A

B

C

D

E

F

Problems 6.4(A) Through (F)

Problems 6.5(A) Through (J)   Complete the given views and project a third view of each problem. Do an isometric sketch of each problem on a separate sheet of paper. Draw at three times the book scale. Note that the isometric sketch will help solve for the three views of the part.

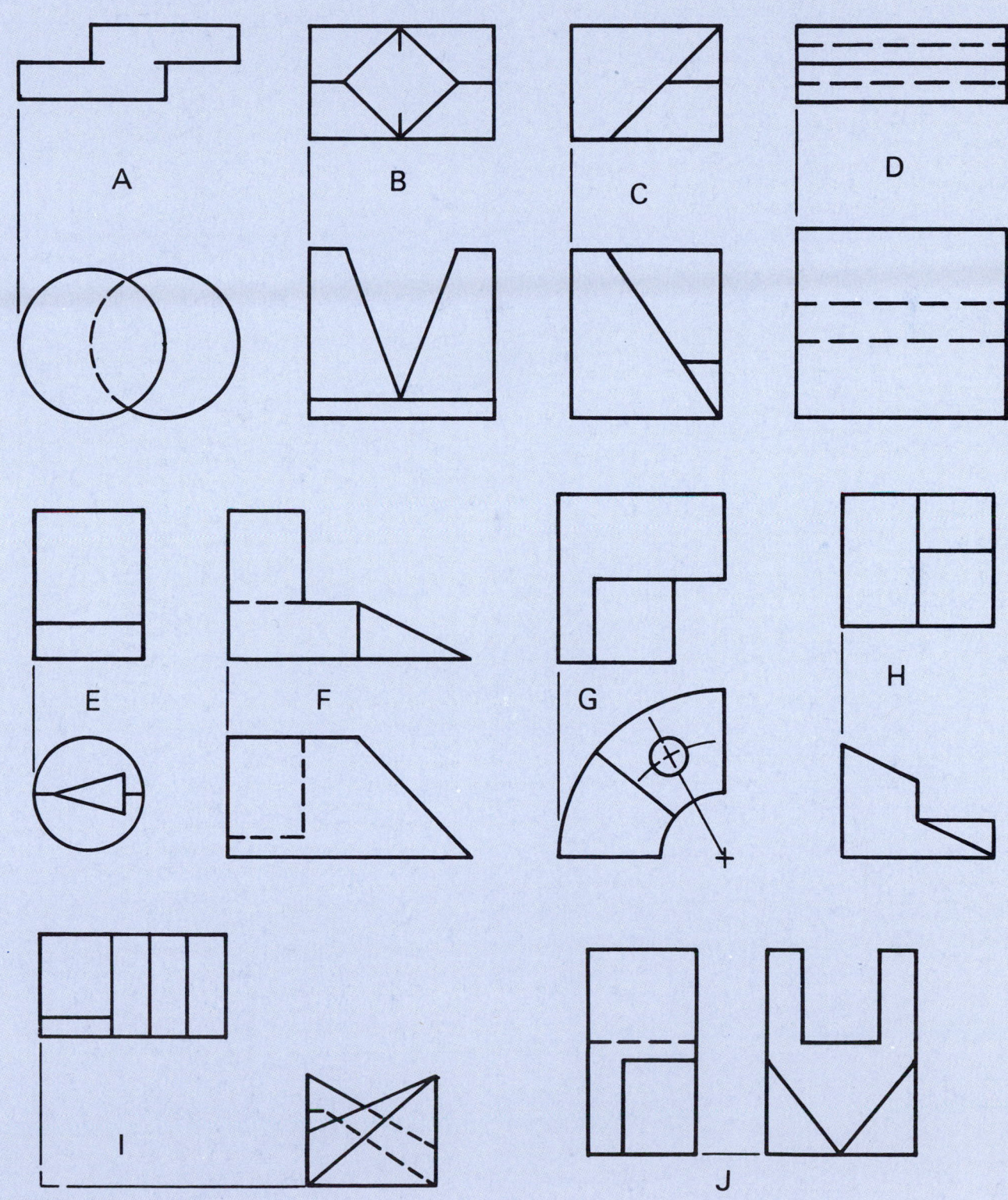

Problems 6.5(A) Through (J)

Problems 6.6(A) and (B)   Sketch three views of each problem. Draw at two times the book scale.

Problems 6.6(C) and (D)   Sketch an isometric and an oblique view of each problem. Draw at two times the book scale.

Problem 6.7   Complete a two-view sketch of the part in Figure 6.43.

Problem 6.8   Draw a three-view sketch of the part in Figure 6.38.

Problem 6.9   Do a multiview sketch of the part in Figure 6.37.

Problem 6.10   Using the part in Figure 6.32, sketch an isometric pictorial.

Problem 6.11   Draw the part in Figure 6.29 as an isometric sketch.

Problem 6.12   Use the part in Figure 6.22 to construct an oblique cavalier sketch.

Problem 6.13   Sketch an oblique pictorial of the part in Figure 6.5.

PART II

Mechanical Drawing Basics

EARTH YAW S
PACKAGE

MASS SPECTROMETER

RADAR ENHANCEMENT
DEVICE

CABLE SEPARATOR

ELECTRICAL POWER
DISTRIBUTION BOX

BATTERY

MAUS 1

S—BAND ANTENNA

ANTENNA REFLECTOR

MAUS 3

TER

TEM

SS SYSTEM

HANDLING SYSTEM

MOMS, MULTISPECTRAL
SCANNER

PRIMARY STRUCTURE

HOUSKEEPING BOX

S—BAND TRANSPONDER

179

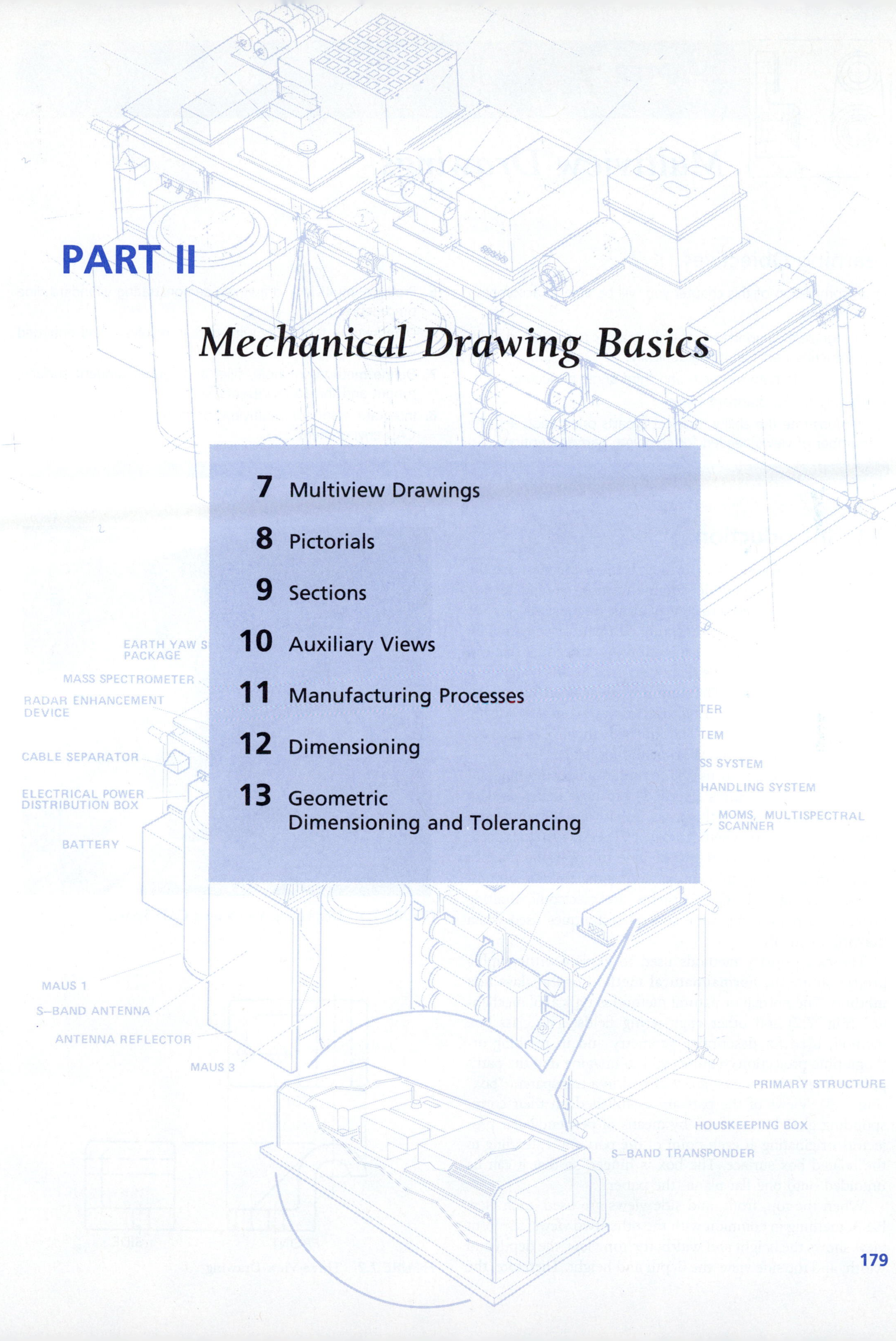

CHAPTER 7

Multiview Drawings

Learning Objectives

Upon completion of this chapter you will be able to accomplish the following:

1. Recognize the importance of orthographic projection in order to describe part features graphically.
2. Differentiate between first- and third-angle projection.
3. Identify the six standard views.
4. Demonstrate the ability to select a parts orientation and the number of views needed for complete part description.
5. Produce multiview drawings demonstrating standard line precedence.
6. Demonstrate familiarity with partial, revolved, and enlarged views.
7. Define methods of hole, fillet and round, tangent surface, runout and thread representation.
8. Integrate standard multiview projection methods into the CAD environment.

7.1 Introduction

Multiview drawings using orthographic projection are the primary means of graphic communication in engineering work. Drawings are used to convey ideas, dimensions, shapes, and procedures for the manufacture of a part or construction of a project. **Orthographic projection** is a procedure that can be used to describe a part's shape and dimensions completely with two or more views. The views are projected at 90° to each other. In general, engineering drawings are completed using this method of projection. The finished drawing is then reproduced and sent to the shop or the job site.

With the widespread use of computer-aided drafting and design (CAD), computers (Fig. 7.1) are now being used to design and draft many of the projects that were formerly hand drawn. Regardless of whether a 3D or 2D CAD system is used, you must still understand and be able to apply the practice and theory of orthographic projection to the creation of multiview drawings. 2D CAD systems are electronic drafting boards and require the same general techniques used when drawing manually.

The two primary methods used to explain orthographic projection are the **normal/natural method** or the **glass box method**. The normal or natural method is typical of mechanical (Fig. 7.2) and other engineering fields. The glass box method, used for descriptive geometry and in teaching orthographic projection, requires you to imagine that the part's points, lines, planes, etc., are enclosed in a transparent "box" (Fig. 7.3). Views of the part are established on their corresponding glass box surfaces by means of perpendicular projectors originating at each point of the part and extending to the related box surface. The box is hinged so that it can be unfolded onto one flat plane (the paper).

When the top, front, and side views are used, each view has something in common with the other two views; the front view shows the height and width; the top view, the depth and width; and the side view, the depth and height. Therefore, the

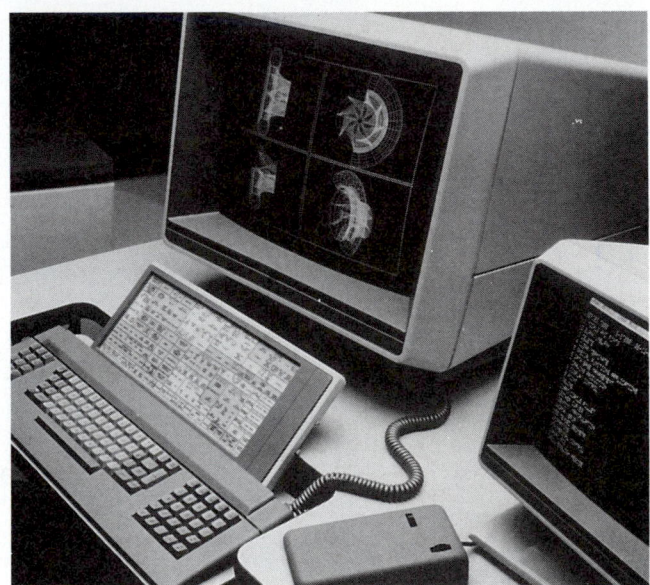

FIGURE 7.1 Displaying Views on a CAD System

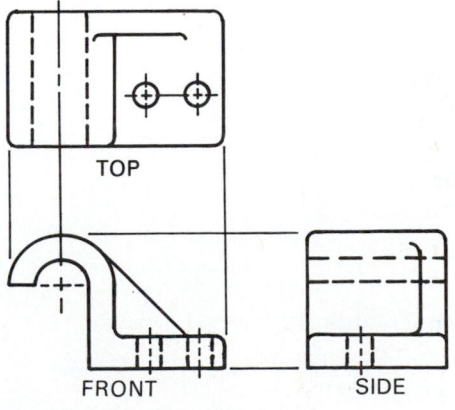

FIGURE 7.2 Three-View Drawing

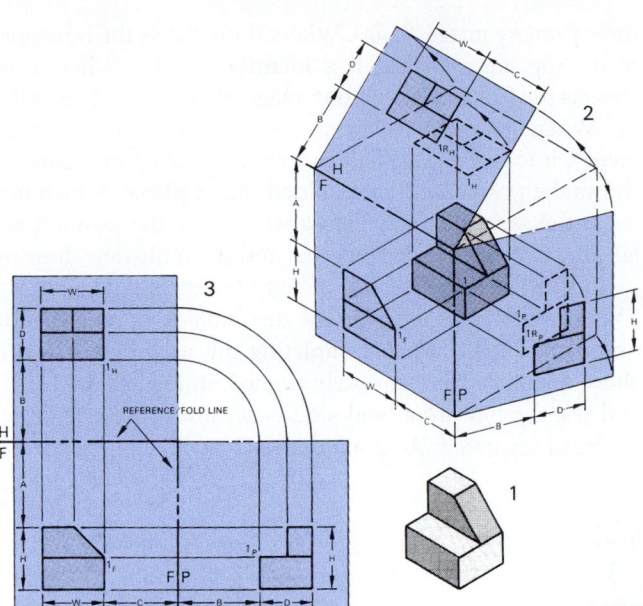

FIGURE 7.3 Multiview Drawing

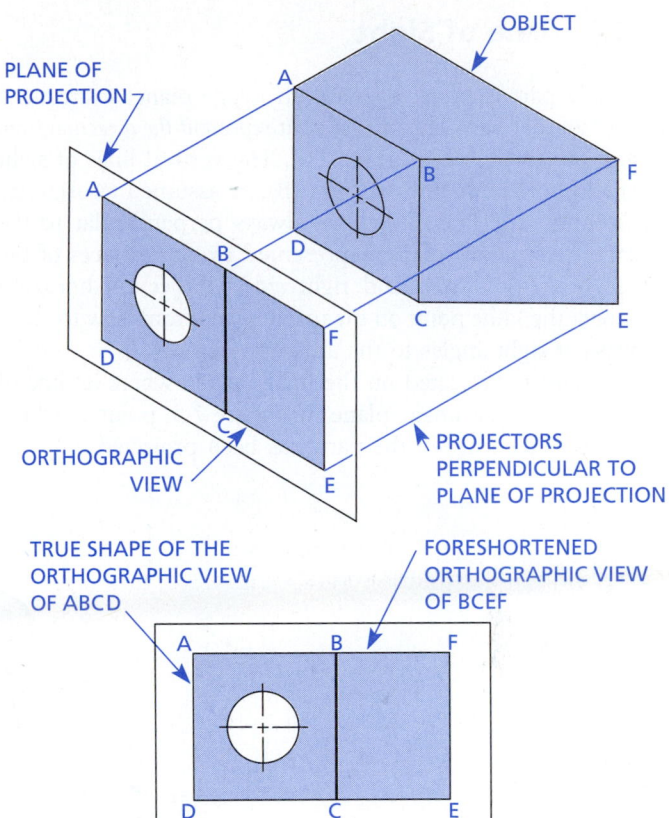

FIGURE 7.4 Third-Angle Orthographic Projection

width dimension will vertically align the top and front views, and the height dimension will horizontally align the front and side views. This method requires that the part be viewed perpendicular to each of its three primary surfaces, changing the position of the observer for each view.

7.2 Orthographic Projection

Orthographic projection may be defined as a system of drawing composed of images formed by projectors extended from a part perpendicular to the desired planes of projection. The figure outlined on one of the projection planes by means of the system of orthographic projection is called an **orthographic view.** Such a view shows the true size and shape of a surface parallel to the projection plane (area ABCD with hole in Fig. 7.4). If an area is not parallel to the plane, the view of the area will be foreshortened (area BCEF in Fig. 7.4).

The glass box method of projection for a part is illustrated in its closed (folded) position and open (unfolded) position in Figure 7.5. The part has been theoretically enclosed in the transparent box. The following concepts are used throughout this chapter and the text:

Lines

    A = Vertical lines of sight

    B = Horizontal lines of sight

    C = Projection lines

Dimensions

    D = Depth

    H = Height

    W = Width

Image Planes (Principal Projection Planes)

    F = Front (frontal plane)

    H = Top (horizontal plane)

    P = Side (profile plane)

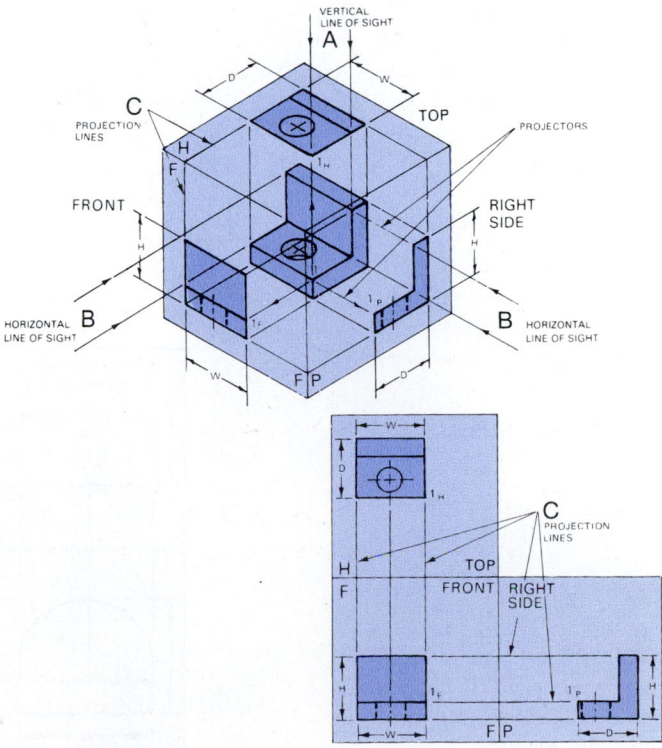

FIGURE 7.5 Orthographic Projection of a Part

7.2.1   Line of Sight

When a part is projected onto an image plane, it creates a *"view"* of that part. The *lines of sight represent the direction from which the part is viewed* (Fig. 7.5). The vertical lines of sight (A) and horizontal lines of sight (B) are assumed to originate at infinity. The line of sight is always perpendicular to the image (projection) plane, represented by the surfaces of the glass box (top, front, and right side). Projection lines (C) connect the same point on the image plane from view to view, always at right angles to the adjacent view.

A point is projected on the image plane where its line of sight pierces that image plane. In Figure 7.5, point 1, which represents a corner of the part, has been projected onto the three primary image planes. Where it intersects the horizontal plane (top image plane), it is identified as 1_H. Where it intersects the frontal plane (front image plane), it is identified as 1_F. Where it intersects the profile plane (right side image plane), it is labeled 1_P. The multiview drawing in Figure 7.5 shows the position of the unfolded image planes, which now lie in the same plane as the paper. Notice the position and labeling of point 1 in the pictorial and the multiview drawing.

In Figure 7.6(a), the line of sight for each view is shown. These lines of sight establish the direction of viewing that the observer will take when completing the view. Figure 7.6(b) shows the three views properly aligned. In Figures 7.6(c), (d), and (e), the top, front, and side views are broken apart and analyzed separately. All points on each surface of the part are

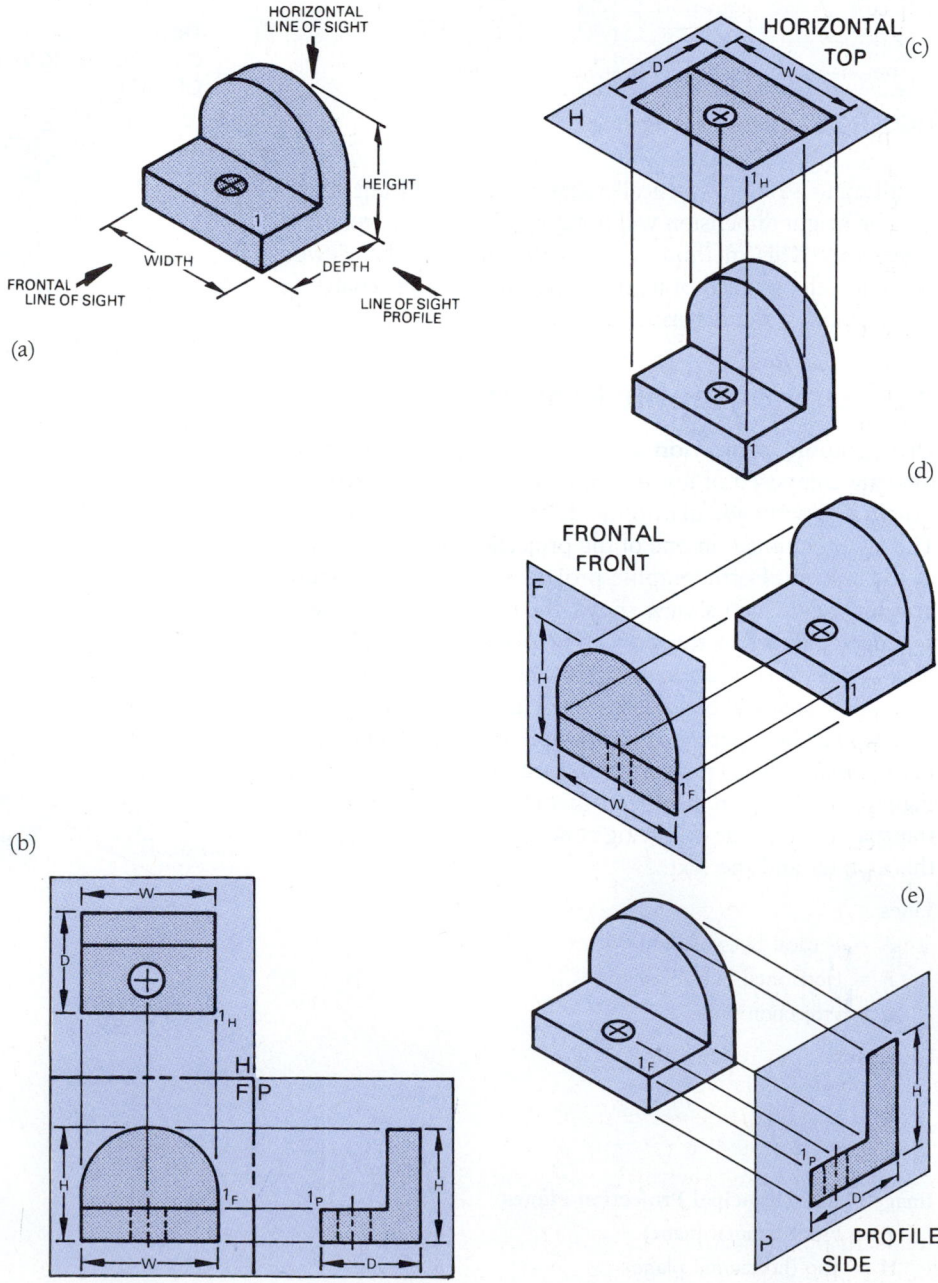

FIGURE 7.6   Line of Sight
(a) Lines of sight (b) Unfolded views (c) Top view (d) Front view (e) Right side view

projected onto their corresponding image plane (view). The view of the part is created where these projectors pierce the image plane.

7.3   The Six Principal Views

When the glass box is opened, its six sides are revolved outward so that they lie in the plane of the paper. With the exception of the back plane, all are hinged to the front plane. The back plane is normally revolved from the left side view, but it can also be hinged to the right side view, as shown in Figure 7.7. Before it is revolved around its hinged fold line (reference line), each image plane is perpendicular to its adjacent image plane and parallel to the image plane across from it. A **fold line** is the line of intersection between any hinged (adjacent) image planes. The left side, front, right side, and back are all **elevation views.** Each is vertical. In these views, the height dimension, elevation, and top and bottom of the view can be determined and dimensioned. The top and bottom planes are in the *horizontal plane.* The depth dimension, width dimension, and front and back can be established in these two horizontal planes.

In most cases, the top, front, and right sides are required. These are sometimes referred to as the horizontal plane, H (top); frontal plane, F (front); and profile plane, P (side). These planes are the three **principal projection planes** or **views.**

In Figure 7.7, the glass box is shown pictorially before it is revolved. The top, front, and bottom are in line vertically, and the left side, front, right side, and back are aligned horizontally. An exception to this alignment is when the glass box is revolved around the top (horizontal) view. This rotation is advantageous when the part has much greater depth than height.

When using directions to establish the location of a point, line, etc., the top and bottom are shown in the frontal plane; the terms *"above"* and *"below"* are also used to describe directions in this plane. The horizontal view can be used to determine if a point is *"in front of"* or *"in back of"* a particular starting point or fold line. To locate a point to the right or left of a fold line or established point, the frontal or horizontal plane can be used. In the profile plane, the top, bottom, front, and back can be determined.

7.4   First- and Third-Angle Projection

Two types of orthographic projection are employed in industry throughout the world: **first-angle** and **third-angle** projections. The six principal views of a part, or the glass box, have been presented in the type of orthographic projection known as **third-angle orthographic projection.** This form of projection is used throughout the United States and Canada and is the primary form of projection found in all of American industry. In third-angle projection, the *line of sight goes through*

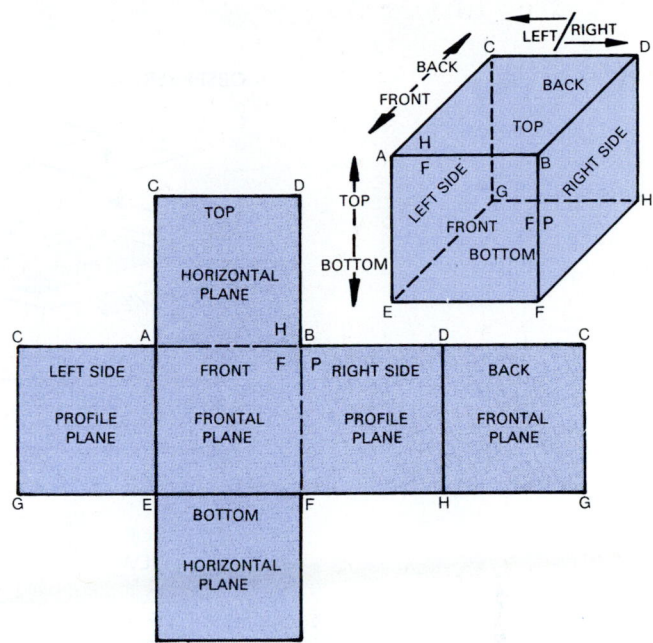

FIGURE 7.7   The Six Standard Views

the image plane to the part. To obtain views of the part, you must assume that the part is projected back (along the lines of sight) to the image plane. Projection lines are used to illustrate this projection from the part to where they intersect the image plane. Figure 7.8(b) illustrates third-angle projection and the normal procedure for unfolding the glass box.

First-angle orthographic projection is used in most foreign countries and on many American structural and architectural drawings [Fig. 7.8(a)]. In this form of projection, the

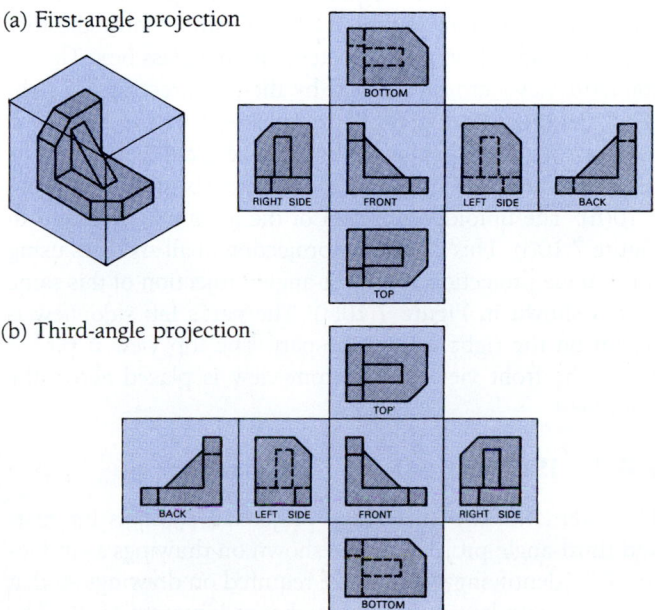

(a) First-angle projection

(b) Third-angle projection

FIGURE 7.8   First- and Third-Angle Projection

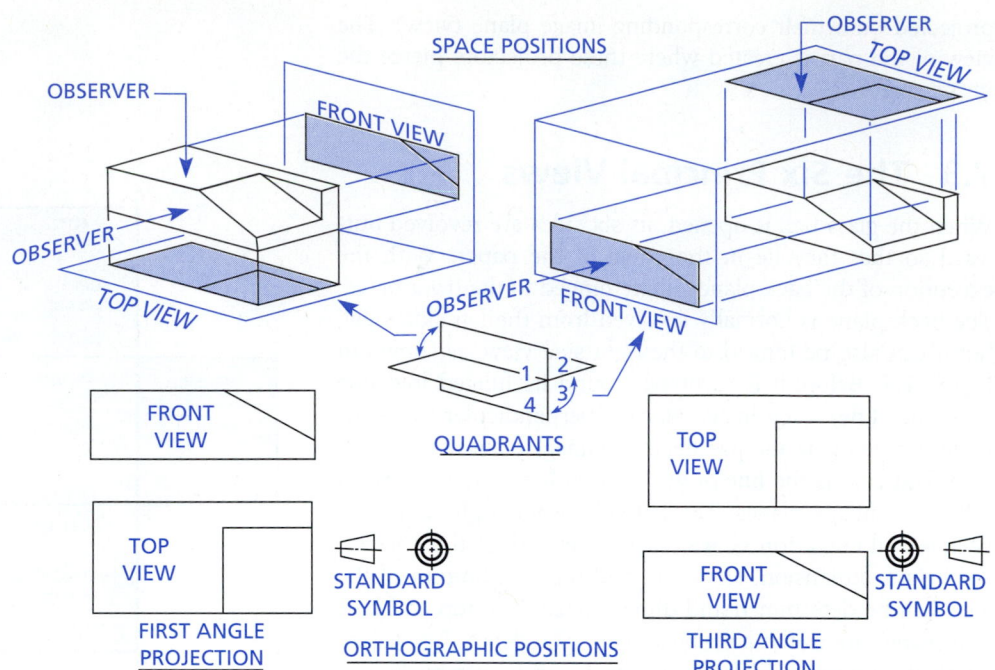

FIGURE 7.9 First- and Third-Angle Projection

part is assumed to be in front of the image plane. Each view is formed by *projecting through the part and onto the image plane*. Figure 7.9 compares first- and third-angle projection.

In Figure 7.10(a), the four quadrants and their corresponding angle of projection are shown. A simple part is placed in the first quadrant in Figure 7.10(b). This is the quadrant used in first-angle projection. In Figure 7.10(c), the same part is placed in the third quadrant, as would be appropriate for third-angle projection. The glass box is added in Figure 7.10(d) and the quadrants are removed in Figure 7.10(e). Here, the part resides inside the glass box and is ready for projection. Figure 7.10(f) illustrates how the top, front, and side views are projected onto the glass box. The six standard views are established by the six directions of sight [Fig. 7.10(g)]: the top, front, right side, left side, rear, and bottom. We have begun to unfold the glass box (with its corresponding projections of each of the six sides) in Figure 7.10(h). The unfolded position of the glass box is shown in Figure 7.10(i). This is the true projection of all six sides using third-angle projection. The first-angle projection of this same part is shown in Figure 7.10(j). The part's left side view is drawn on the right side of the part. The top view is placed below the front view; the bottom view is placed above the front view.

7.4.1   ISO Projection Symbol

The internationally recognized projection symbols for first- and third-angle projections are shown on drawings as in Figure 7.9. Identifying symbols are required on drawings so that they can be understood and interchanged internationally. The symbol is normally placed to the left of the title block as in Figure 7.11. This text uses third-angle projection exclusively.

7.5   Multiview Drawings

Multiview drawings represent the shape of a part using two or more views. These views, together with the necessary notes and dimensions, are sufficient for fabrication of the part without further information concerning its shape. Consideration is given to the choice and number of views so that all surfaces are shown in their true shape and with a minimum of confusion.

Four basic types of drawings are found in engineering work. The choice of which drawing is used is determined by the shape and complexity of the part. One-, two-, three-, and multiple-view drawings are all used in industry. One view can be sufficient to describe many types of parts. The rule to remember is that you must draw as many views as are necessary to describe the part completely. The four types of drawings are:

One-view drawings   (Fig. 7.12, p. 187) Two adjacent views are normally considered the minimum requirement to describe a three-dimensional part. However, the third dimension of some parts (washers, shafts, bushings, spacers, sheet metal parts, etc.) may be specified by a note giving the thickness or dimensions for the diameter.

Two-view drawings   (Fig. 7.13, p. 188) Many parts may be adequately described by showing only two views. These views must be aligned in any standard position that will clearly illustrate the part. In Figure 7.13, the side view was necessary to describe and dimension the part.

Three-view drawings   (Fig. 7.14, p. 188) Most drawings consist of front, top, and side views arranged in their standard positions. Any three adjacent views that best suit the shape of the part may be drawn. In Figure 7.14 each view of the part shows features that could not be graphically described in any of the

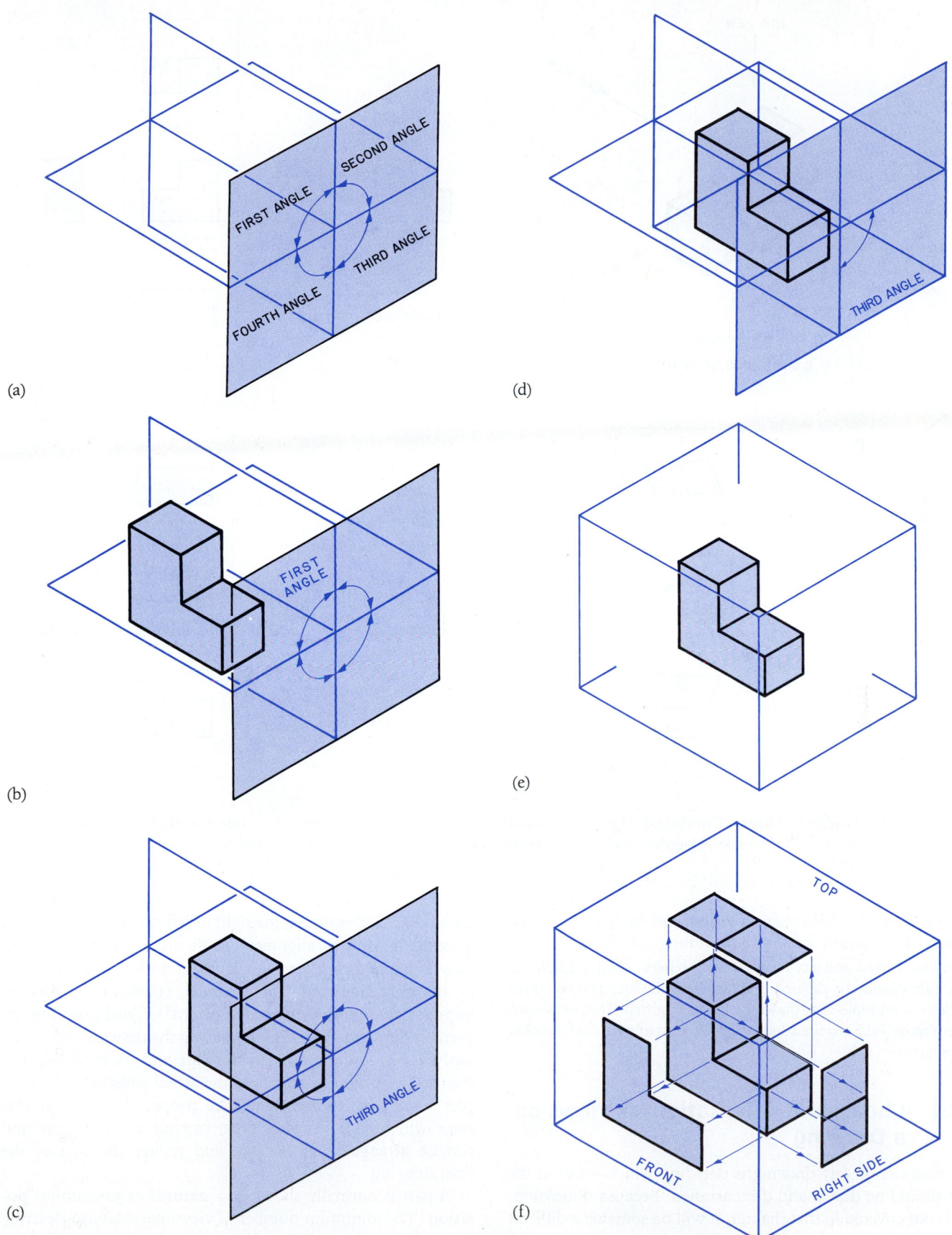

FIGURE 7.10 **Projection Theory** (a) Projection angles (b) Part placed in position for first-angle projection (c) Part placed in third-angle projection (d) Third-angle projection (e) The glass box and orthographic projection (f) Third-angle projection and the glass box

Continues

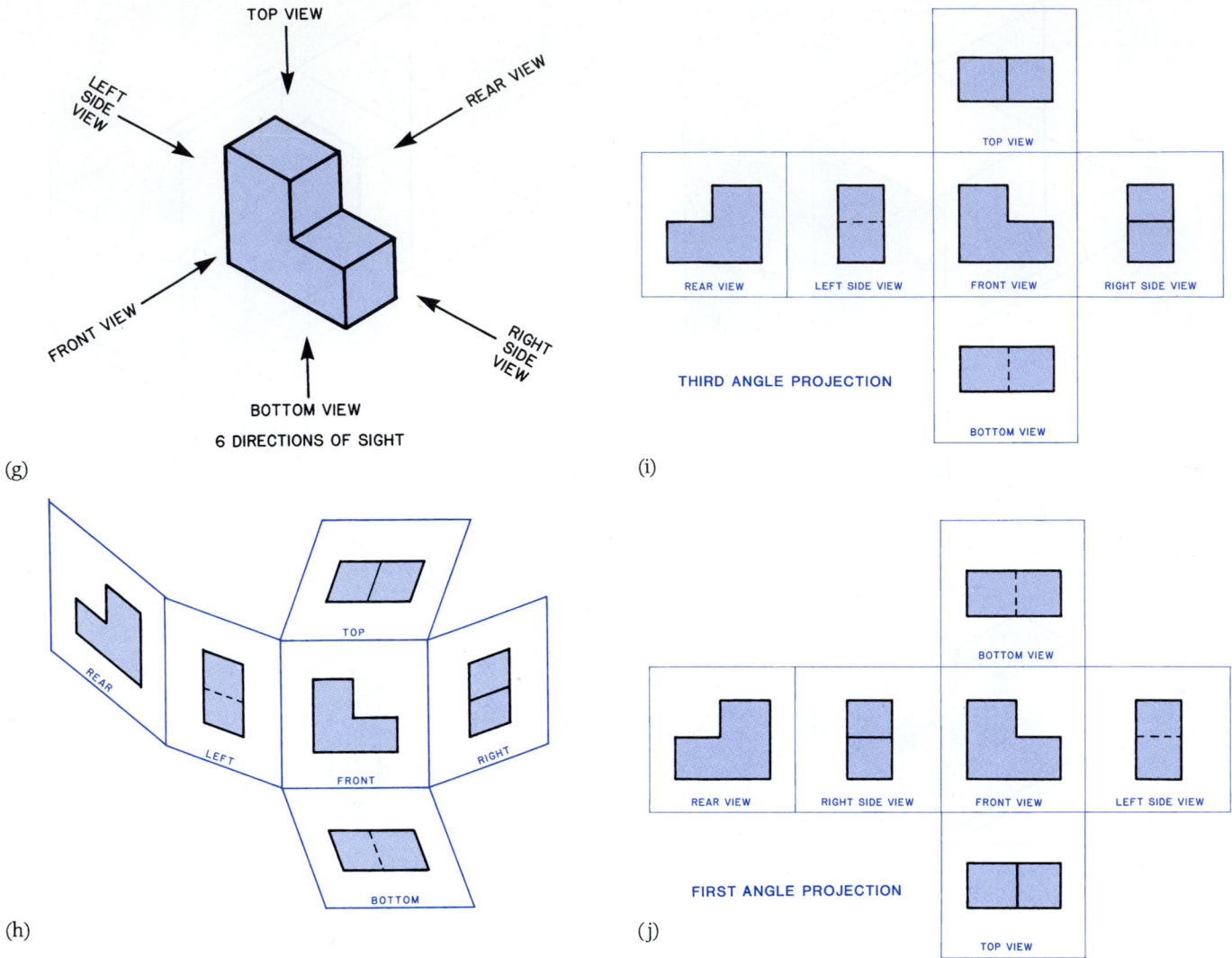

FIGURE 7.10   Projection Theory, Continued   (g) The six standard view directions in orthographic projection (h) Unfolding the glass box to establish views (i) Third-angle projection and the six standard views (j) First-angle projection and the six standard views

other views. The holes show in the top and the front views, and the slot and angled surfaces show in the right side view.

Multiple-view and auxiliary-view drawings   (Fig. 7.15) When a part cannot be defined graphically with one, two, or three views, a multiple-view drawing may be required. The part shown in Figure 7.15 required four views to describe its configuration properly.

7.5.1   Choice and Orientation of Views on a Drawing

The first step in any drawing is deciding which views of the part should be drawn and dimensioned. Because dimensioning is not covered in this chapter, it will be somewhat difficult to estimate the space and view needs of a part to be drawn. Alternate positions of views may be made to conserve space or position dimensions, but they must be properly oriented to

each other. For example, the right or left side might be placed adjacent to, and in alignment, with the top view. The rear view is sometimes placed in alignment with, and to the right of, the right side view. Under certain conditions, it may be impractical to place views in the normal aligned positions, or even on the same sheet. Before starting the drawing, you must analyze the configuration of the part and its view requirements. This preliminary step to the actual construction of the part is extremely important. The proper decisions at this stage will reduce drawing time, provide a more clear and concise arrangement of views, and reduce the cost of the final drawing.

A part is normally shown in a **natural** or **assembled position**. The minimum number of views necessary to describe the part is established first. Views are selected that will show the fewest hidden lines and yet convey maximum clarity. In general, since the part will be mounted or sit on a surface, the

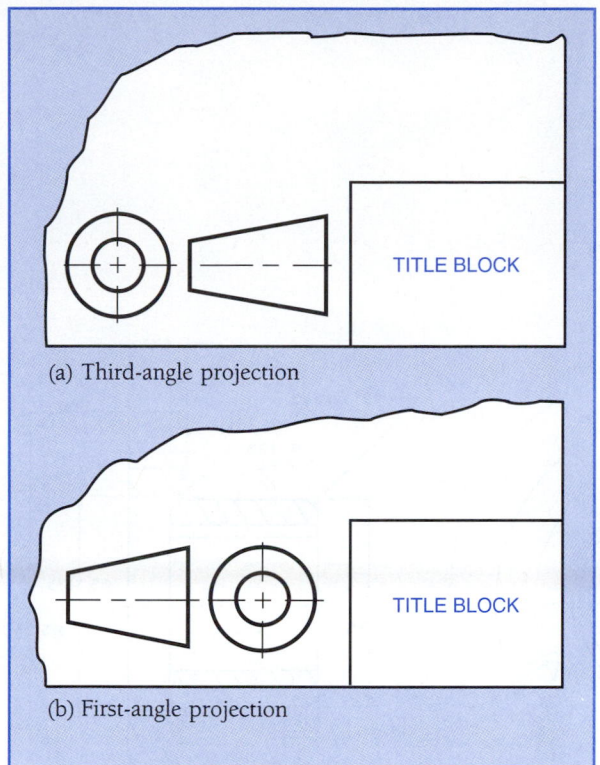

(a) Third-angle projection

(b) First-angle projection

FIGURE 7.11   Projection Symbols (a) Third-angle projection symbols (b) First-angle projection symbols

top view is obvious. The choice of top view may also be determined by the machining process and its complexity.

The front view should normally be the longest orientation of the part. The drawing of the part in Figure 7.16 has three views: the top, front, and right side views. However, two views would have been adequate. The right side view is not needed. *The front was chosen as the longest orientation of the part.* In Figure 7.17 (p. 190), the part requires three views. It could not have been adequately described without all three views. The top view choice was obvious. The front view is the longest orientation and the right side view was required to describe the slot clearly.

7.5.2   Relationship of Views on a Drawing

The **relationship of views** on a drawing is determined by the choice of part orientation. In Figure 7.18(a) (p. 190), the six standard view directions of the part are labeled. In Figure 7.18(b), the views are laid out using third-angle projection. The placement and orientation of the top view determine that the front view will be the longest orientation, or principal shape, of the part. In Figure 7.18(c), the same part is shown slightly differently, but not incorrectly. Here, the part has been turned so that the front view will not show the part's longest orientation. In fact, the side views show the longest orientation [Fig. 7.18(d)]. Although this orientation is not incorrect, it is less acceptable than 7.18(b). The longest orientation should be the front view so that the predominant dimension will be the width.

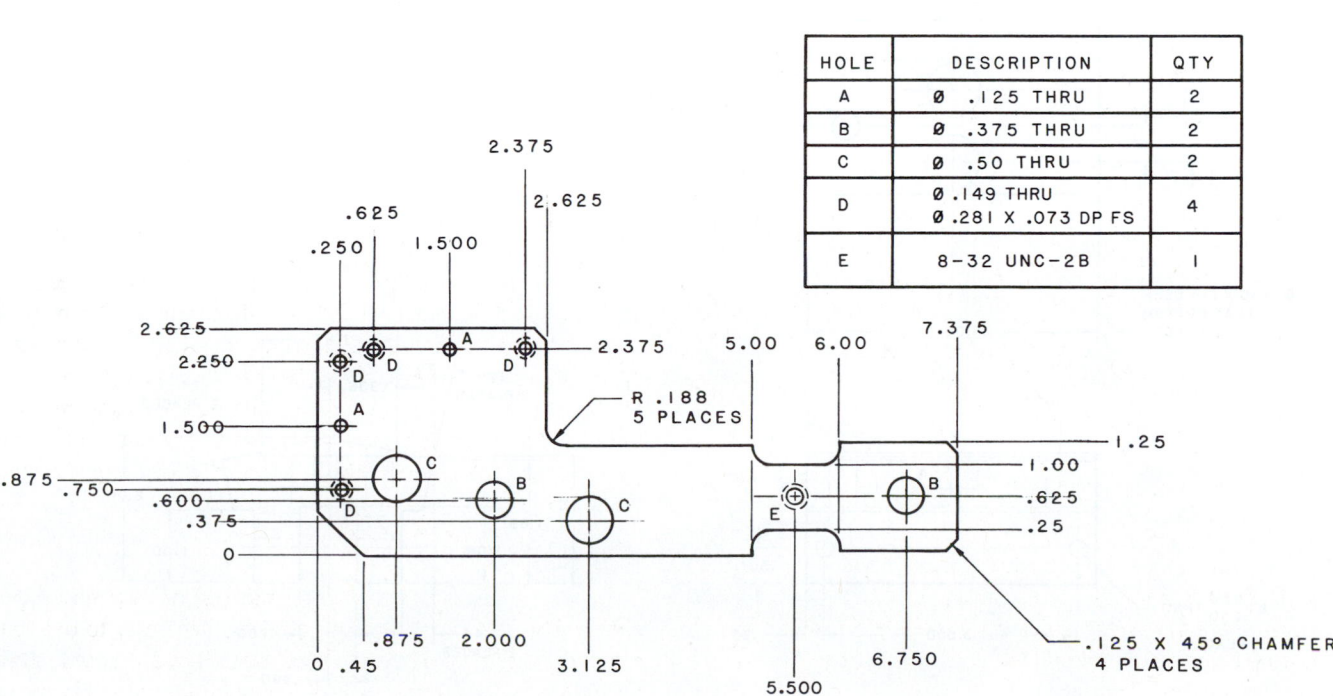

.25 ALY ALUM ANODIZE BLACK

HOLE	DESCRIPTION	QTY
A	Ø .125 THRU	2
B	Ø .375 THRU	2
C	Ø .50 THRU	2
D	Ø .149 THRU Ø .281 X .073 DP FS	4
E	8–32 UNC–2B	1

FIGURE 7.12   One-View Detail of the Connector

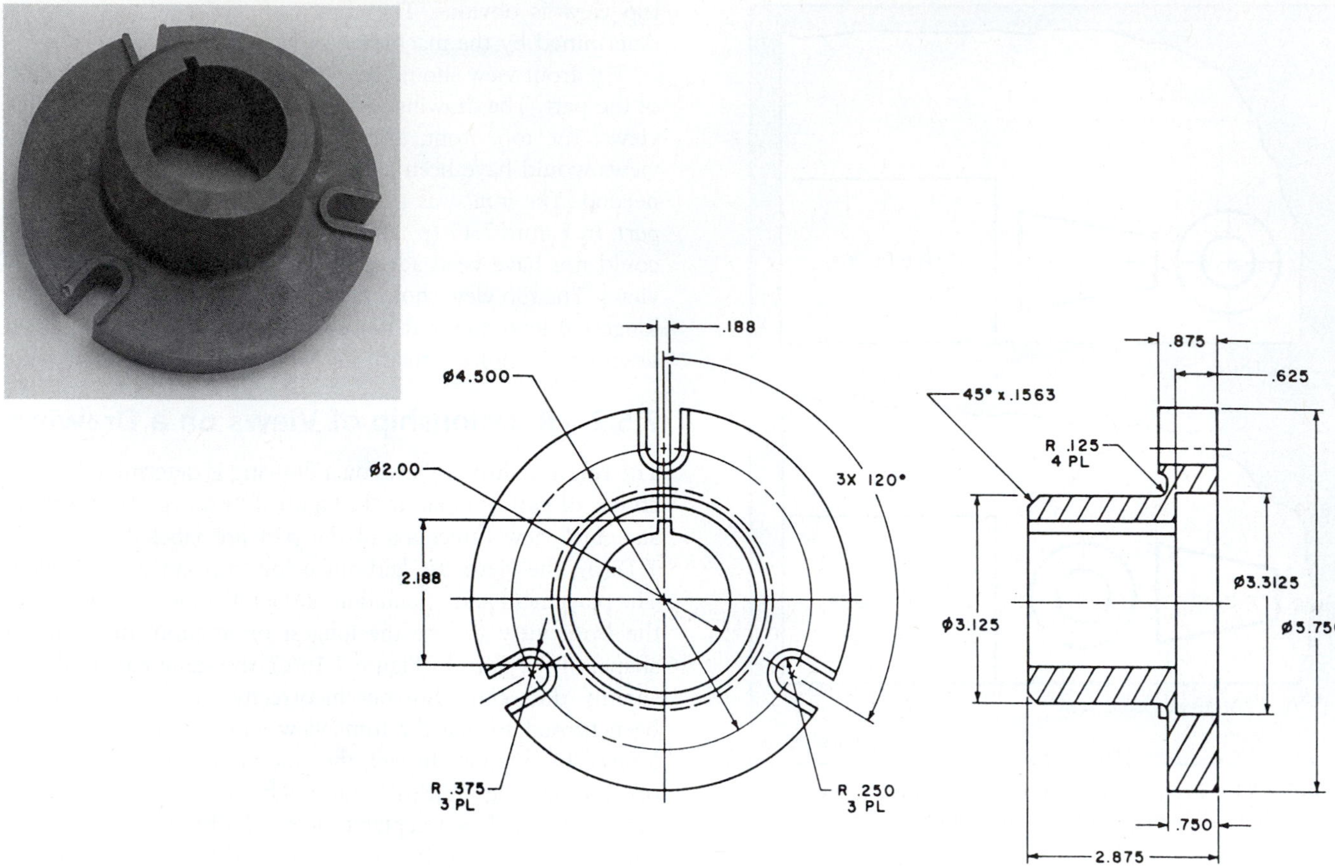

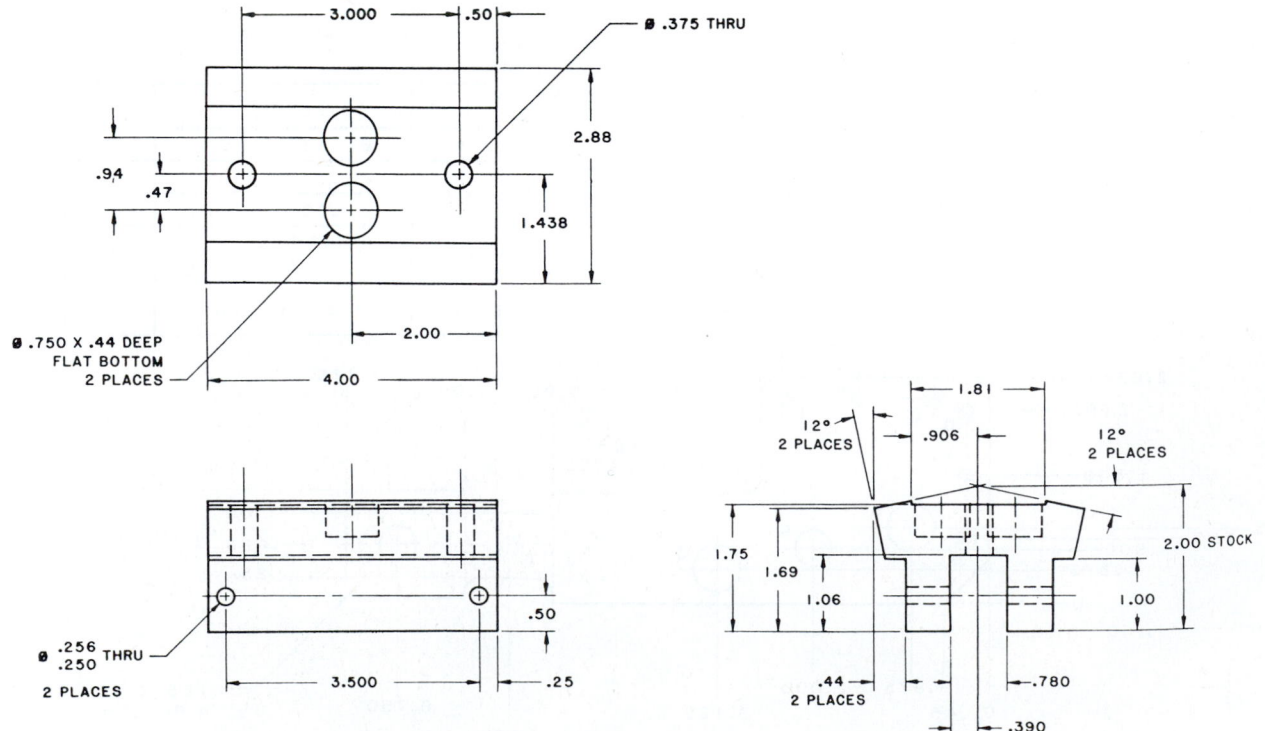

FIGURE 7.13 Two-View Detail of the Reel Post

FIGURE 7.14 Three-View Detail of the Pad Mounting

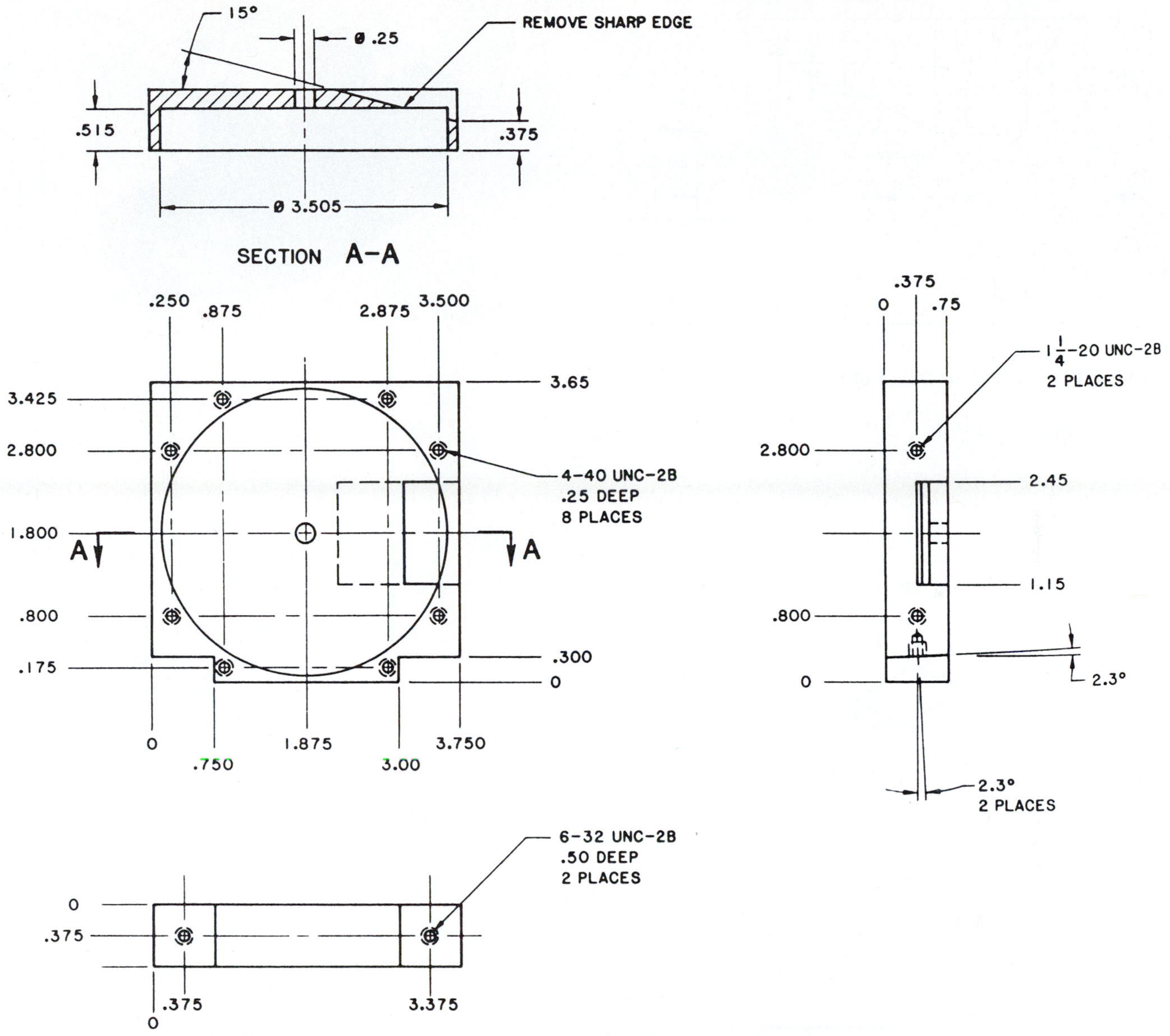

15°
Ø .25
REMOVE SHARP EDGE
.515
.375
Ø 3.505
SECTION A-A
.250
.875
2.875
3.500
3.425
3.65
2.800
4-40 UNC-2B
.25 DEEP
8 PLACES
1.800
A
A
.800
.175
.300
0
0
1.875
3.750
.750
3.00
.375
0
.75
1 1/4-20 UNC-2B
2 PLACES
2.800
2.45
1.15
.800
0
2.3°
2.3°
2 PLACES
6-32 UNC-2B
.50 DEEP
2 PLACES
0
.375
.375
3.375
0

FIGURE 7.15 Top, Front, Back, and Side View of the Interface Bracket

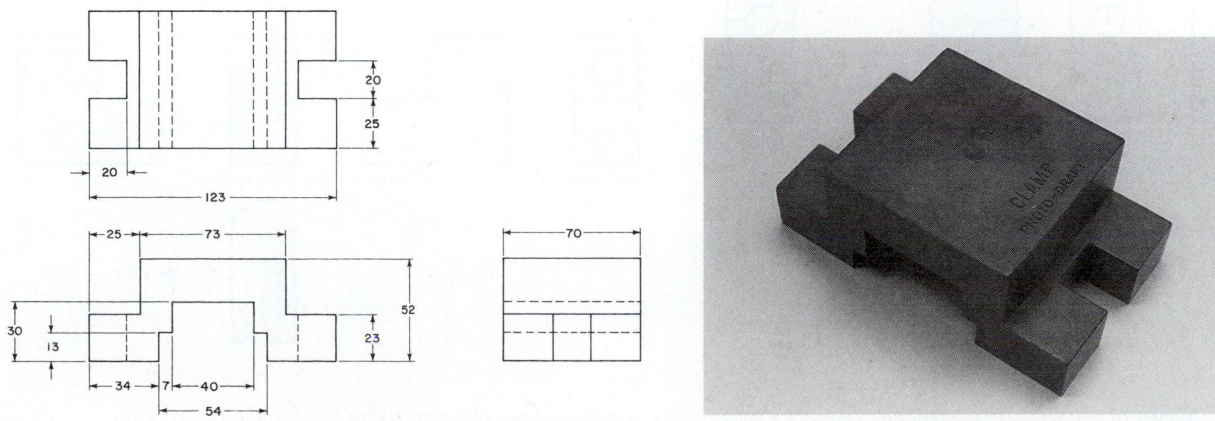

20
25
20
123
25
73
70
52
30
13
23
34
7
40
54
CLAMP
PHOTO-DRAFT

FIGURE 7.16 Three-View Detail of the Clamp

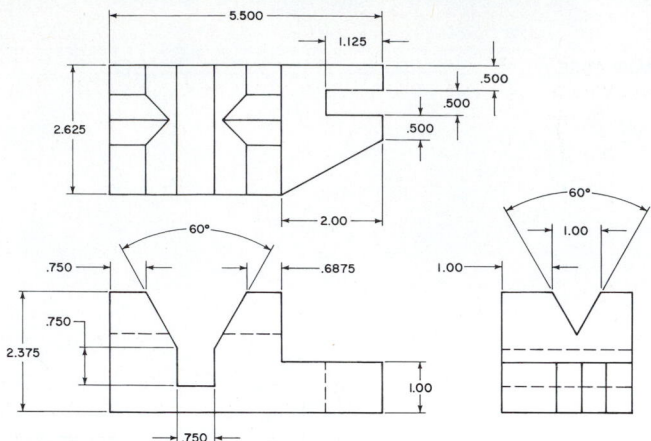

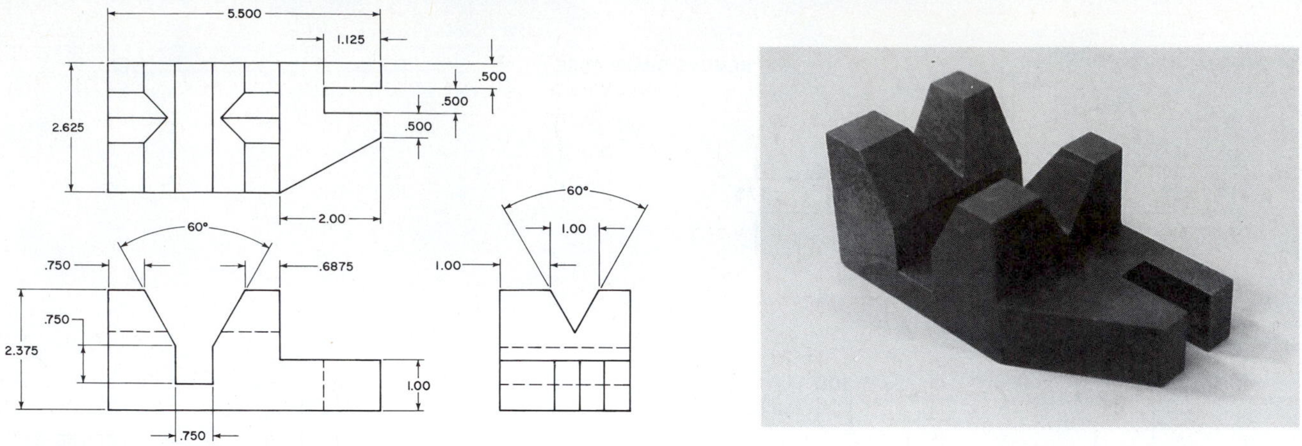

FIGURE 7.17   Three-View Detail of the Base Angle

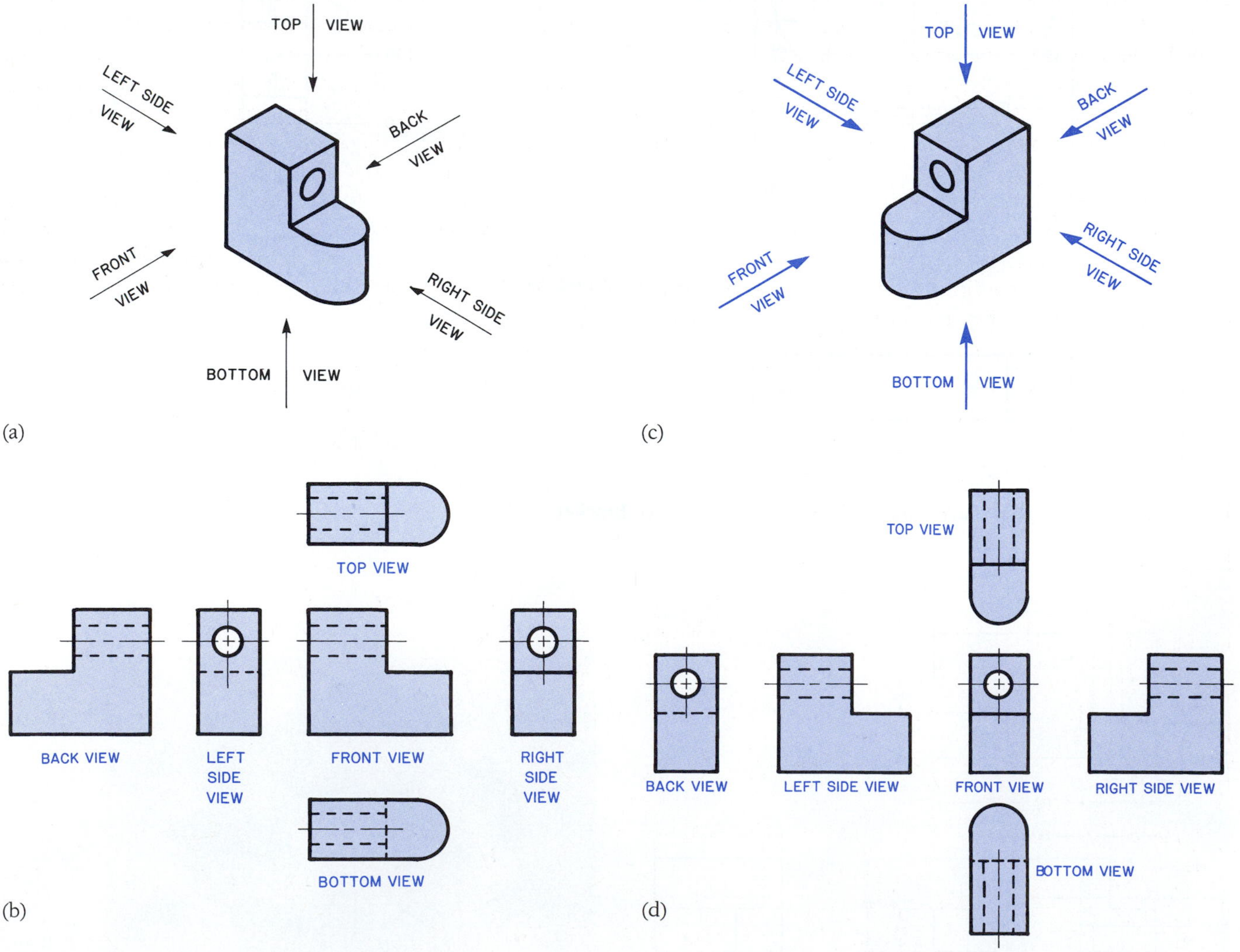

(a)

TOP | VIEW

LEFT SIDE VIEW

BACK VIEW

FRONT VIEW

RIGHT SIDE VIEW

BOTTOM | VIEW

(c)

TOP | VIEW

LEFT SIDE VIEW

BACK VIEW

FRONT VIEW

RIGHT SIDE VIEW

BOTTOM | VIEW

(b)

TOP VIEW

BACK VIEW

LEFT SIDE VIEW

FRONT VIEW

RIGHT SIDE VIEW

BOTTOM VIEW

(d)

TOP VIEW

BACK VIEW

LEFT SIDE VIEW

FRONT VIEW

RIGHT SIDE VIEW

BOTTOM VIEW

FIGURE 7.18   **Views of a Part** (a) Six standard views of a part (b) Six standard views of a part using third-angle projection (c) Alternative arrangement of a part in space (d) Alternative arrangement of views of a part

7.5.3   Spacing Views

After the number of views is established, the next step in preparing a drawing is to establish the paper format size based on the part to be drawn and detailed. Remember, the *drawing must have space for views, dimensions, and notes.* Paper size is determined by the overall size of the part and the views required to display it.

A simple method to determine roughly the sheet size is to add the dimensions of the part—add the width plus the depth (if a side view is required), which gives the total width of the views. Extra space must be added for separation of the views and a margin for each border. The height requirements of the drawing can be determined by adding the height of the part to its depth. Then some space is added for the separation of the views and the necessary margin for the top and bottom borders. The drawing format, A, B, C, D, E, or larger, is determined by these dimensions and company practice.

In Figure 7.19, the part has been laid out on the sheet using the above formula. The height, depth, distance between the lower border and the front view (A), space between the front and top views (B), and the space between the top view and the border (C) were added together to establish the height requirements of the drawing. The width, depth, space between the left border and the front view (D), the space between the front and the right side view (B), and the space between the right side view and the right border (E) were added to establish the width requirements. Remember, dimensions A, B, C, D, and E were determined by the space required for dimensioning.

The spacing requirements between the views are usually determined by the number of dimensions that will be placed in this area. In Figure 7.20, the shaded portion of the drawing shows the space between the top and front views and between the front and side views. Some texts suggest that this area should always be equal. However, this will not always be the case. If a number of dimensions must be placed between the top and front views, this area should be greater than that between the front and side views (unless, of course, a number of dimensions are also needed here).

The drawing is laid out by *blocking in the views with construction lines.* At this stage of the drawing, changes are easily made in the spacing of the views and the general layout. After the construction lines are drawn, the circles and radii are darkened. Each part requires careful individual consideration. There are no hard and fast rules for drawing layouts. In general, you will eventually intuitively understand a part's space requirements and adapt the drawing accordingly.

7.5.4   Related and Adjacent Views

Regardless of whether the drawing to be constructed is to have two, three, or more views, the basics of construction and projection are the same. Two adjoining orthographic views aligned by projection lines are considered **adjacent views.** Two views adjacent to the same intermediate view are called **related views.** Each view shares one dimension with a related view and another dimension with an adjacent view (Fig. 7.21). The top and front view share one common dimension—the width. The front and side view share the height dimension. The top and front views are therefore adjacent views as are the front and side views. The top and the side views share the depth dimension and are considered related views.

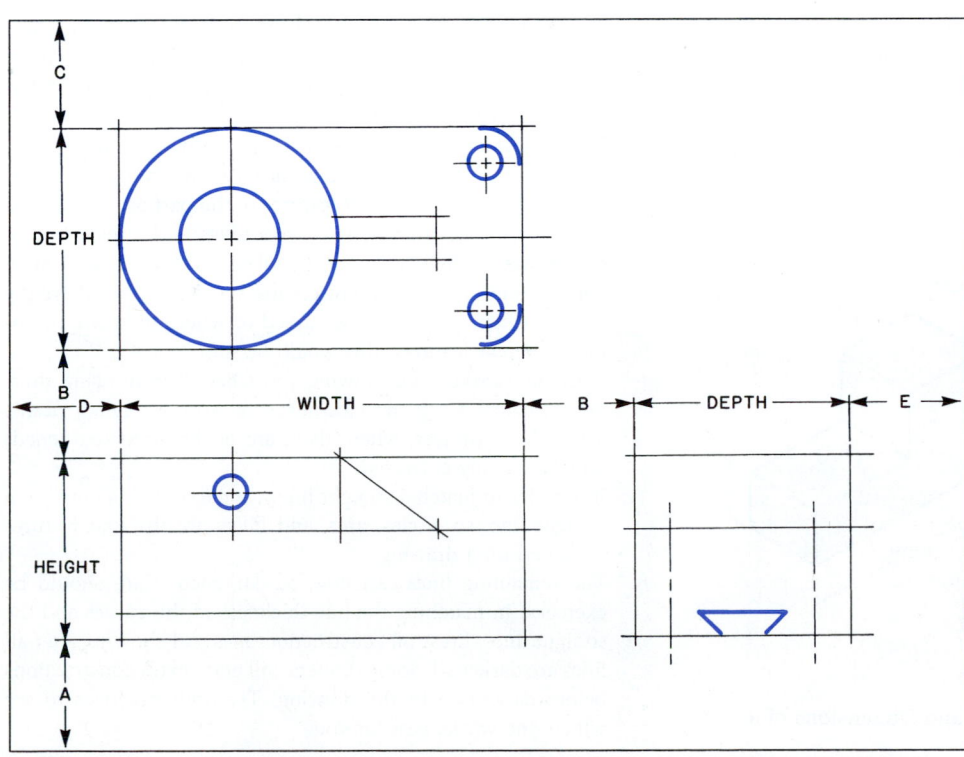

FIGURE 7.19 Laying Out a Drawing

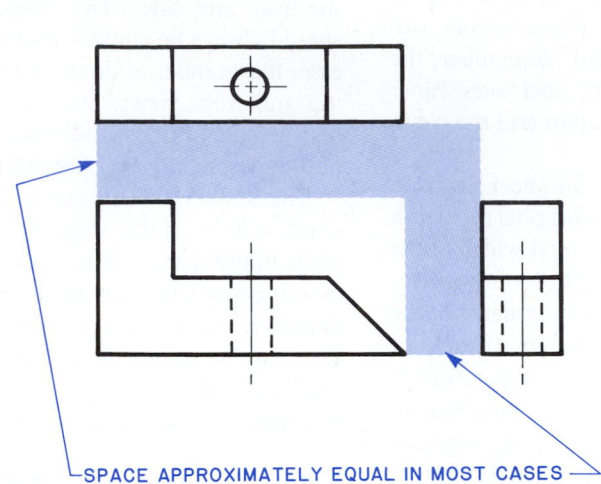
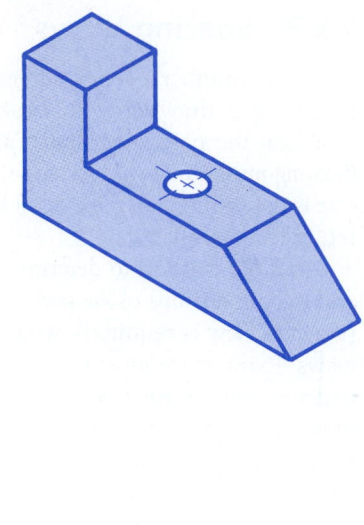

FIGURE 7.20 Spacing Views on a Drawing

SPACE APPROXIMATELY EQUAL IN MOST CASES

7.5.5 Drawing Order

Whether the project is a one-, two-, three-, or multiview project, the same sequence of construction will generally be applied. The order in which you do your work determines the efficiency and quality of the finished drawing. Figure 7.22 provides a series of steps in the construction of a drawing:

1. Figure 7.22(a) shows an isometric view of the part to be drawn. Using the part's overall dimensions, establish the sheet size and format using the technique previously described. The scale and dimensioning requirements also have to be determined at this time. The number of views depends on the part's configuration and complexity and the dimensioning requirements. Sketching the possible view requirements and alternatives helps establish a well-planned drawing that requires fewer alterations at a later stage.
2. Using the part's overall dimensions, lay off the principal dimensions to establish the three views. Use the scale to measure and establish the dimensions with small construction lines as shown in Figure 7.22(b). Since dimensions are shared with adjacent views, it is necessary to scale only once for each of the three major dimensions. The width can be established in the top view and projected to the front view. The height can be established in the front view and projected to the side. Because it can be used for both the adjacent views—side and top—some drafters prefer to draw the front view's outline first.
3. Using construction lines, connect the measured points to establish the outline of the part [Fig. 7.22(c)]. A drafting machine or a straightedge and triangles are used to draw these construction lines. Since unneeded construction lines require erasing before darkening, draw only construction lines that are necessary.
4. At this step [Fig. 7.22(d)], you need to use your scale to measure all secondary details of the part and establish them on the drawing. Measure from the existing principal lines. This step is also done with construction lines.
5. Draw all secondary features of the part. To avoid more measuring, project features to adjacent views where possible.
6. The centerlines and curved features of the part are established using construction lines. The part's fillets and circles require centerlines for their construction. All curved features are drawn with the aid of a template or compass. On projects where the primary shape of the part is curved or where there are prominent circular features, this would be step 3 or 4.

    Do not darken the drawing yet. Check the drawing thoroughly before going on to the next step. Mistakes caught at this stage of the project, where there are no finalized (darkened) lines, are easily corrected.
7. It is easier to match a straight line to a curve than a curve to a straight line, so circles, arcs, and fillets are the first features darkened on a drawing.
8. The remaining lines can now be darkened. Care should be exercised in matching the line thickness of the curves and the straight lines. Erase all construction lines still showing after all lines are darkened. Some drafters will erase extra constructions before darkening in the drawing. Try both practices to see which one works best for you.

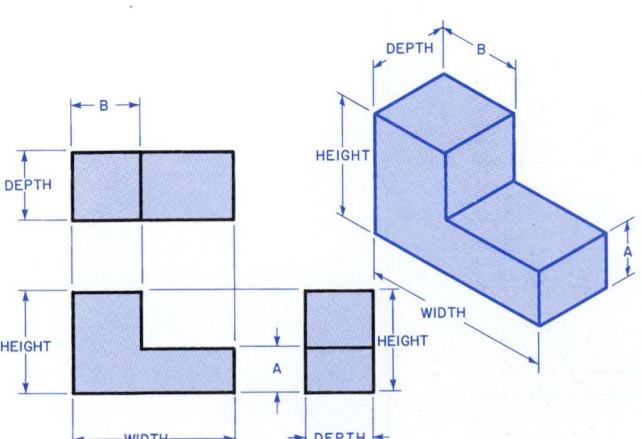

FIGURE 7.21 Height, Width, Depth, and Dimensions of a Part

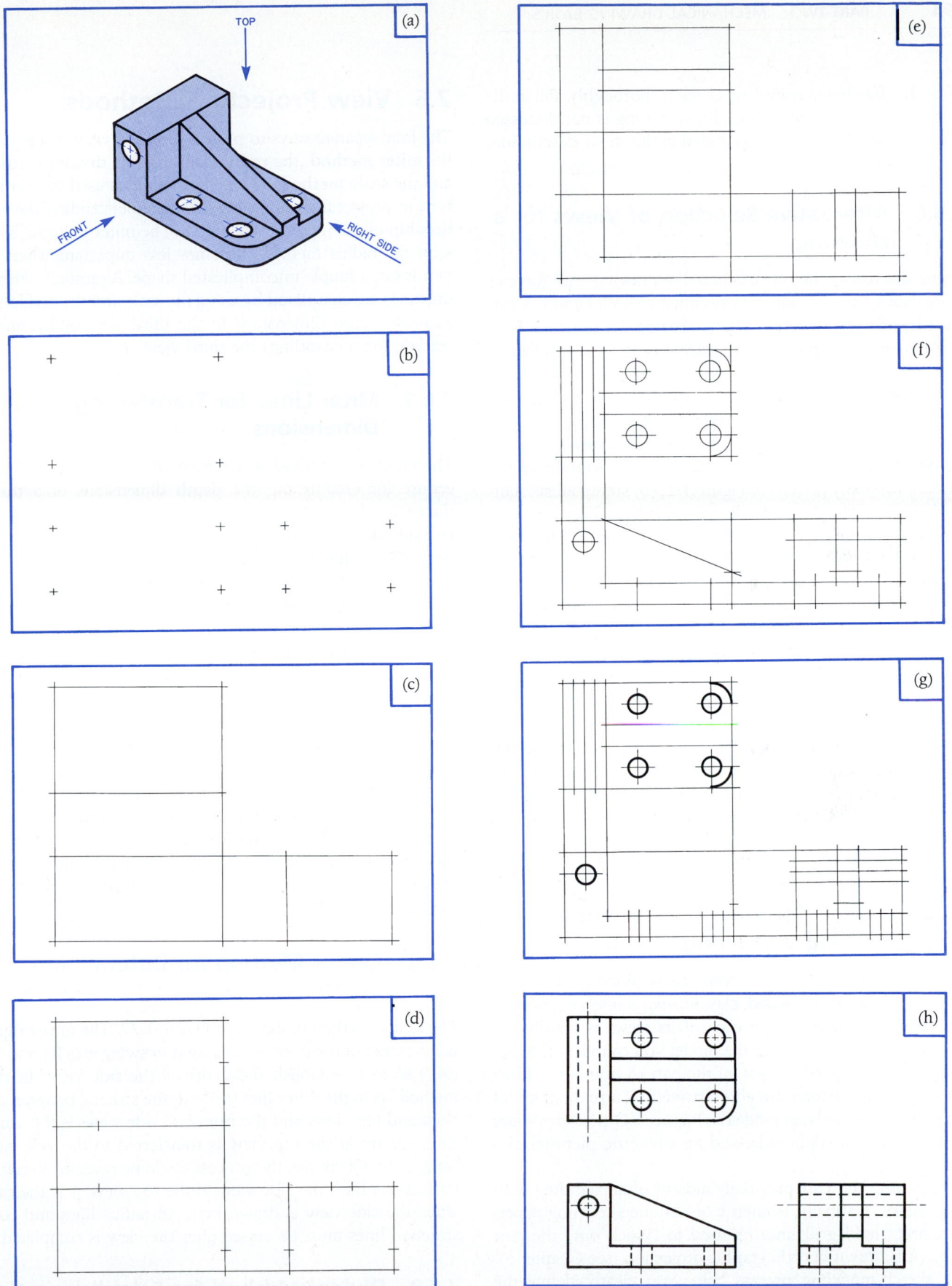

FIGURE 7.22 **Steps in the Construction of a Drawing** (a) Isometric view of a part (b) Establish the overall dimensions of the part using a scale and space appropriately (c) Block-in the part using construction lines (d) Establish all the major features of the part (e) Block-in the secondary features using construction lines (f) Establish all holes and draw circles with construction lines using a compass or template (g) Darken arcs and circles (h) Darken drawing and remove construction lines

After the drawing is complete, check it thoroughly. Fill in the title block as a last step. Since dimensioning is not discussed here, this step has not been included in the above description.

7.5.6   Alternative Selection of Views for a Drawing

Before discussing the construction of a drawing with three or more views, the selection of views must be understood. A part must be analyzed carefully before starting the drawing. During this step, the proper view selection and the number of views must be determined.

In Figure 7.23(a), each side of the part has features that appear clearly in only one view. The choice of views must take into account the part's complexity. The views with the fewest hidden lines that show the principal features of the part are normally preferred. Figure 7.23(b) shows all six standard views of the part, including every hidden line. You must choose from the possible combinations of views. The fewer the number of views, the better. Figure 7.23(c) has the same six views but most have been simplified by the reduction of hidden lines shown. In Figure 7.23(d), the back view has been eliminated since the front view adequately describes that portion of the part. The left side view has been removed in Figure 7.23(e), while the right side view remains, but it is cluttered with hidden lines. Figure 7.23(f) shows the standard three principal views—top, front, and right side. All hidden lines are shown here, but this choice of views does not really describe the part as well as Figure 7.23(g). This last choice of view placement displays the front, left side, and bottom views, and provides a concise uncluttered description of the part.

7.5.7   Models for View Description and Reading a Drawing

Learning to visualize a part's views can be aided by the use of models. Plastic, metal, wood, clay, or soap models enable you to position the part so that each of its views is readily observable. By simply turning the model you can view the top, front, side, or any other view of the part. A number of illustrations in this chapter are accompanied by a photograph of the part which has been modeled. Figure 7.24 provides views of the top, front, right side, and an isometric pictorial of a part.

Sketching the part pictorially aids in understanding each of its views. Normally, isometric or oblique sketching paper, with preprinted grid lines, is used to "block out" the part before it is drawn in orthographic projection (see Chapter 6). The sketch-modeling process helps you clearly define the part. Sometimes hidden edges, surfaces, or other parts of its geometry are discovered or clarified. Even with the advent of automated drafting (CAD), 3D sketching is an important part of the design and drafting process.

7.6   View Projection Methods

The four separate ways to project the third view of a part are the **miter method**, the **radius method**, the **divider method**, and the **scale method.** The miter method is used for learning how to project the third view and in understanding the relationship of the top and side views. The miter method, along with the radius method, becomes less important when the part is not a simple uncomplicated shape. Almost all industry drawings are completed by using the scale and the dividers to establish depth dimensions in the third view or by simply reading (understanding) the third view.

7.6.1   Miter Lines for Transferring Depth Dimensions

The miter line method is a simple and straightforward procedure for establishing the depth dimensions of a three-dimensional part. After the front and top views (or the front and side views) are drawn, construction of the third view can begin. The **miter line** is drawn as a construction line. A 45° line is drawn from the upper right-hand corner of the front view of the part (Fig. 7.25). The upper edge line of the part, in the top view, is then extended until it intersects the miter line. The intersection point is used to establish the outside edge of the side view by drawing a vertical construction line through it. Since it is adjacent to the side view, the height of the part is projected from the front view. Other depth dimensions can now be extended to the miter line from the top view and then to the side view.

The drawing of the part in Figure 7.26 illustrates how each of the depth dimensions has been extended from the top view to the miter line and projected downward to establish the right side view. Height dimensions are projected directly from the front view. Miter lines and projection lines are erased after the view is completed.

7.6.2   Radius Method for Determining Depth

The radius method is shown in Figure 7.27. The upper right-hand corner of the front view is used to swing arcs R1 and R2 (90°) so as to establish the depth of the side view. In this method, as in the miter line method, the spacing between the front and top views and the front and side views is the same. Each feature in the top view is transferred to the side view using radii. Of course, the process could be reversed to transfer features from the side view to the top view as is the case when the side view is drawn first. All radius lines and construction lines must be erased after the view is completed.

7.6.3   Divider Method for Establishing the Depth Dimension

Since the divider method is quick and accurate, it is used for descriptive geometry problems and for engineering drawings.

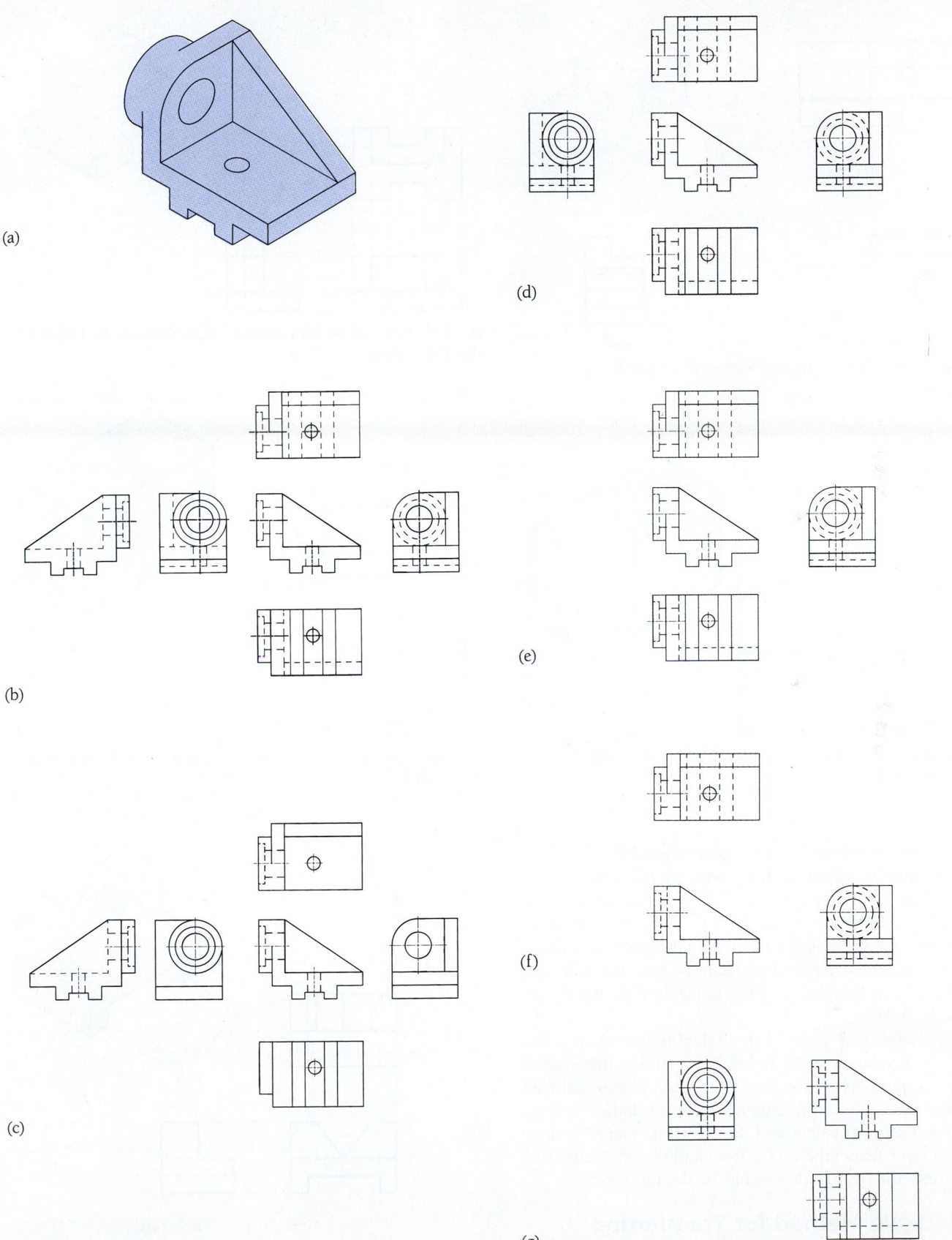

FIGURE 7.23   Selection of Views for a Drawing   (a) Isometric view of a part (b) Six standard views of the part with all hidden lines shown (c) Six standard views of the part with some hidden lines deleted (d) Five views with hidden lines (e) Four drawings with hidden lines (f) Three standard views with hidden lines (g) Front, bottom, and left side views with hidden lines

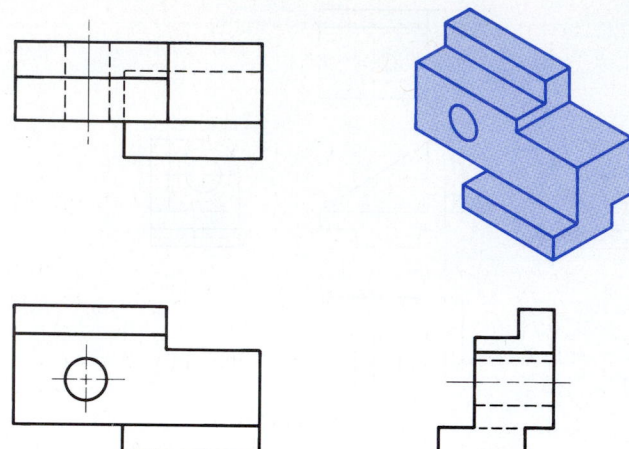

FIGURE 7.24   Three Standard Views of the Block

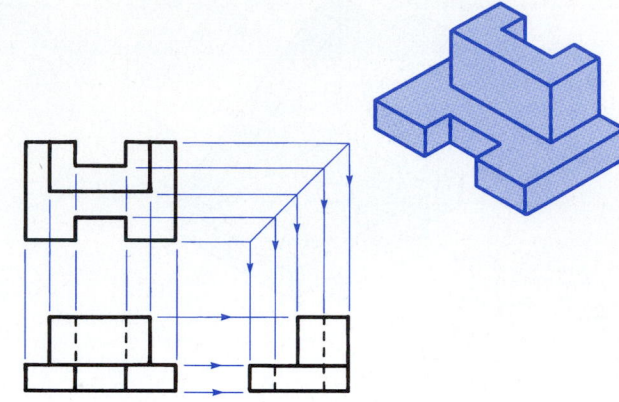

FIGURE 7.26   Miter Line Method of Projecting the Depth of the Third View

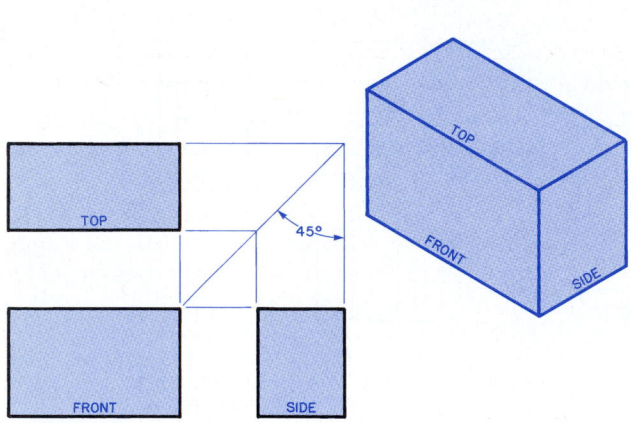

FIGURE 7.25   Establishing the Depth of a Part Using the Miter Line Method

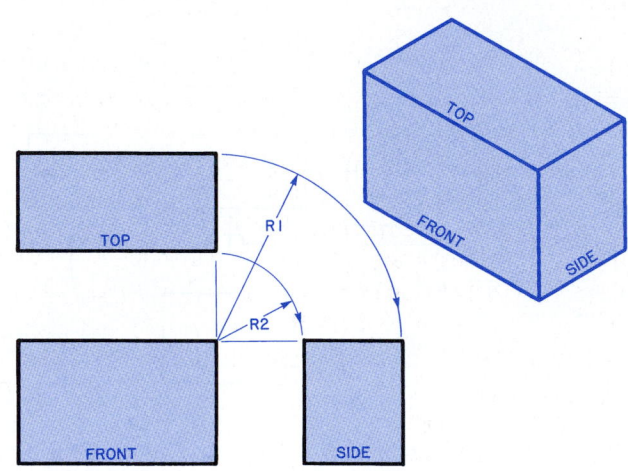

FIGURE 7.27   Radius Method of Projecting the Depth of the Third View

This method allows the drafter to place the third view at any distance from its adjacent projection. In other words, the front and side view spacing need not be the same as the spacing between the front and the top views. Since the spacing between the views is determined by the part's complexity and the dimensions required to detail the part, this will most likely be the case for most projects. In Figure 7.28, the divider method is shown.

Dividers are used to establish all depth dimensions in the third view. Unlike the miter and radius methods, this method does not require that you erase construction lines established after transferring the depth dimensions. Most drafters will use a combination of dividers and scale measurements to draw the third view. Remember, if the front and the side views were drawn first, the "third" view could be the top view.

7.6.4   Scale Method for Transferring Depth Dimensions

The scale method to establish the depth dimension is commonly used in industry. The scale is used to measure the

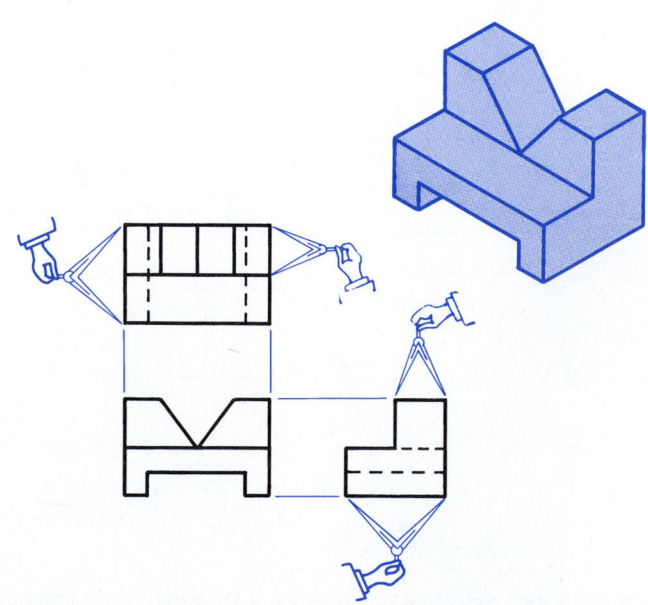

FIGURE 7.28   Transferring the Depth Dimension Using Dividers

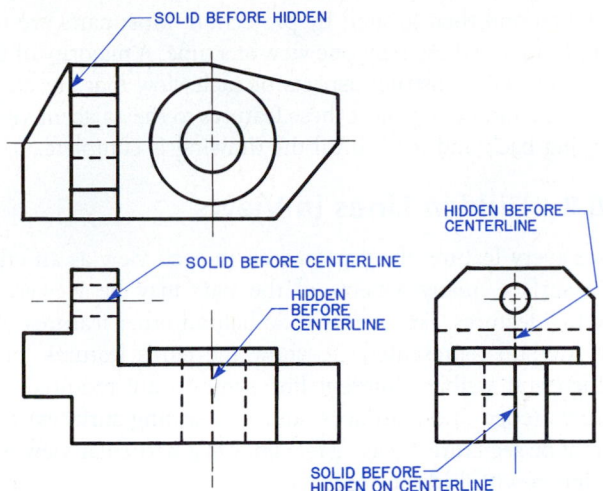

FIGURE 7.29   Precedence of Lines on a Drawing

the miter and radius methods is normally confined to drawing simple parts and learning projection techniques. They are seldom used in industry.

7.6.5   Precedence of Lines on a Drawing

Views of a part will show its edges, surfaces, centerlines, and other features. A surface in one view will show as an edge in its adjacent view and as a surface in its related view. Since each view has so many features, they will at times interfere with one another. In other words, some features will coincide. Because showing all features in every view would only confuse the drawing, an order of importance or **precedence of lines** has been established for engineering drawings. The most important lines are drawn and the less important are left off the drawing. Figure 7.29 shows the proper precedence of lines on a drawing.

All outside edges of a part (boundary lines), in a particular view, will be drawn as **visible lines** and have precedence over all other lines. Visible edges are solid lines and always have precedence over **hidden lines** (dashed). *Dashed lines* represent hidden edge lines of the part and, therefore, have precedence over **centerlines** (which do not really exist as aspects of the part's geometry; they represent the center of curved features, e.g., circles, and arcs). **Dimension** and **extension lines** should always be positioned so as to avoid coinciding with visible and hidden lines. The following shows the order of precedence of lines on a drawing:

1. visible (solid)
2. hidden (dashed)
3. cutting plane or centerline (depending on importance)
4. break (solid)

depth dimension of the part in the top or side views (whichever view was constructed first). Depth dimensions are then used to establish the third view. Many drafters use the dimensions of the part to construct each view (using the scale) without transferring dimensions. Though this method is acceptable, it does require the repetitious use of the scale and takes longer. Measurements established once can normally be projected from adjacent views or transferred by dividers from related views. The efficient use of each of the methods is dependent on the configuration of the part and the required views. A minimum amount of scaling should be used in each view to increase efficiency and speed.

Though a typical drawing can be constructed with a combination of the four methods previously described, the use of

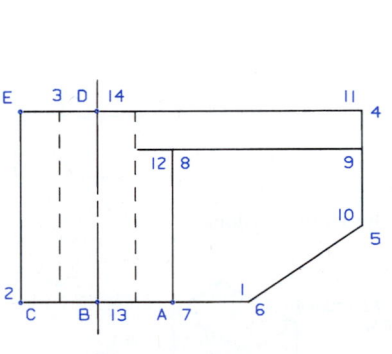

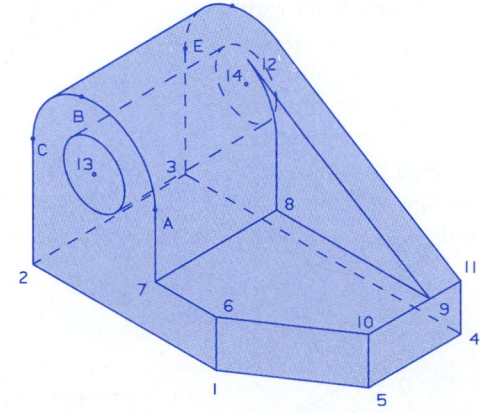

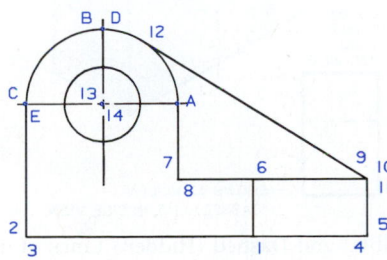

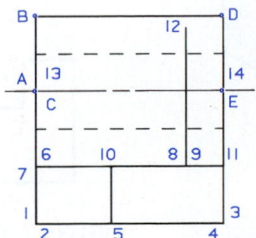

FIGURE 7.30   Labeling Points on a Part to Establish Features in Views

5. extension and dimension (solid-thin)
6. section (crosshatch).

7.6.6 Interpreting Multiview Drawings

The use of numbers or letters to label the part's features may help develop understanding and visualization of three-dimensional parts. This method is also helpful in constructing views of complicated shapes. In Figure 7.30, p. 197, each edge line of the part, where it meets another edge line, has been identified with a number or a letter. This method is also used for completing descriptive geometry problems. Notice that the ends of curved features are identified with letters and straight-line features with numbers. Each line can be seen in every view as *true length, foreshortened,* or as a *point.* Most lines, except for the angled lines 1-5, 6-10, and 9-12 will show as two numbered ends in two views and as a point view (coincident ends) in another view. Line 13-14 is the center-line for the hole and for the curved surface. Projecting views (and individual features) of the part becomes a matter of locating points from view to view.

7.6.7 Projection Lines for Views

Projection lines are thin, lightly drawn construction lines used to "project" features between *adjacent* views. Projection lines are erased after the views are complete and before darkening. Projection lines eliminate the need to measure and scale every aspect of a view. Elements that are already established in one view can be easily extended (projected) to the adjacent view. As an example, in Figure 7.31, the front view has been drawn first. Since the front view is adjacent to both the top and the side view, it can be used to establish those views by projection. The top view is constructed with projectors extended from the front view to establish its width dimensions. The depth dimensions for the top view are constructed with scale measurements. Since it shares all height and elevation dimensions, the side view can be projected from the front view. The depth dimensions must be established by one of the four methods described previously.

Most parts cannot be constructed one view at a time. Edges and features in one view may need to be drawn in the adjacent view first and then located by projection. Most parts are too complicated to draw only one view at a time. A majority of the time, you will construct aspects of each view that are easily identified and then project these features to the adjacent view, working back and forth until the drawing is complete.

7.6.8 Hidden Lines in Views

Since every feature of a part is seen in each view as an edge or a surface, many aspects of the part may be viewed as *"hidden"* features. Features that lie behind other features of a part are still represented. To show the part's features, both hidden and visible, different line symbols are required. All features (edge lines, surfaces, and intersecting surfaces) that cannot be seen directly as visible lines in a particular view will be drawn with **hidden lines.**

The part in Figure 7.32 has two holes drilled through it. The holes must be represented in each view. The top view shows the holes as circular and visible. The front and left side views, on the other hand, only show the outside edges of the holes. Since they pass through the part and cannot be seen by the observer, the edges must be represented by hidden (dashed) lines.

In Figure 7.33, the use of visible (solid) and hidden (dashed) lines is shown. Visible lines in the top view of this

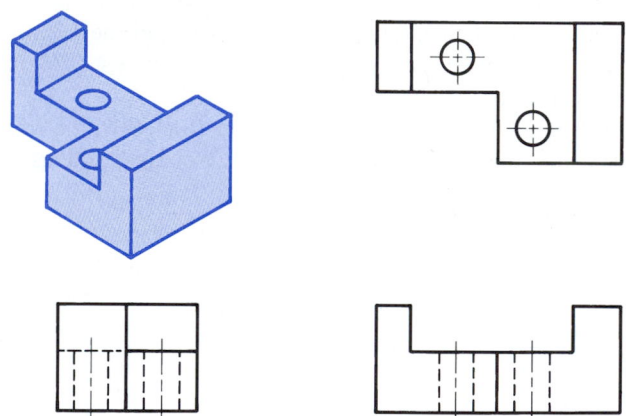

FIGURE 7.32 Views of the Holding Block

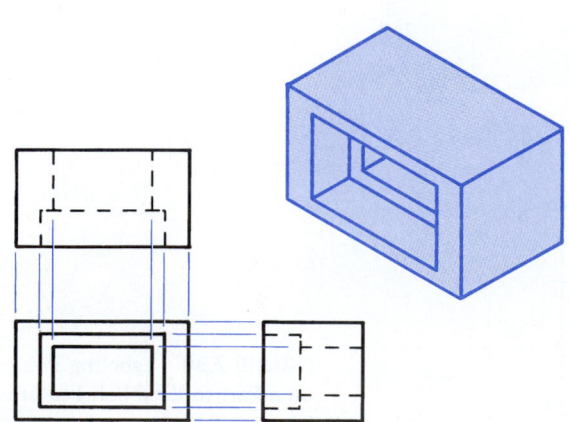

FIGURE 7.31 Projecting Hidden Features of a Part

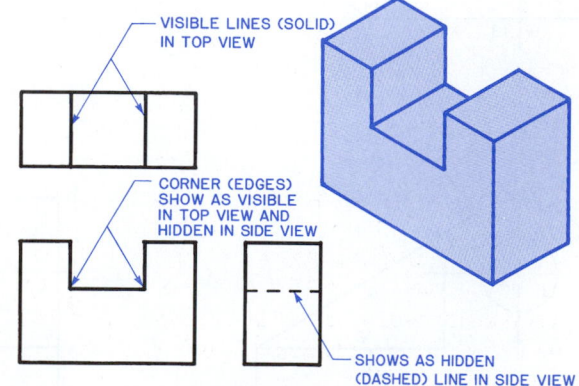

FIGURE 7.33 Solid (Visible) and Dashed (Hidden) Lines of a Part

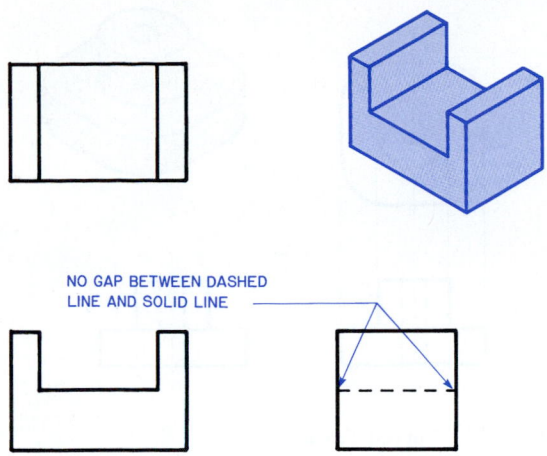

FIGURE 7.34   **Drawing Dashed (Hidden) Lines**

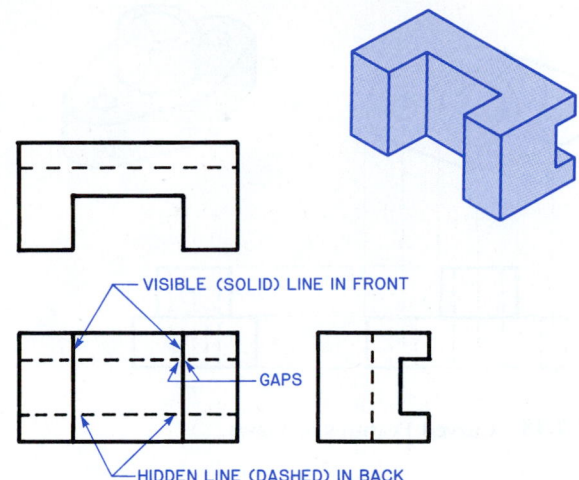

FIGURE 7.35   **Visible and Hidden Lines on a Drawing**

part show as visible edges and corners in the front view and as hidden lines in the side view. When constructing dashed and solid lines, the following drafting conventions for spacing must be maintained:

1. Do not leave a gap between a hidden (dashed) line and a visible (solid) line that meet (Fig. 7.34).
2. When a hidden line crosses a solid line leave a gap (Fig. 7.35).
3. When a hidden line continues as a visible line, after crossing a visible line, leave a gap (Fig. 7.36).
4. Hidden lines that meet other hidden lines should not have gaps between them. In other words, the dashes will touch (Fig. 7.37). Hidden lines that establish corners always touch.
5. When a hidden line (or arc) meets a visible line (or arc) and is tangent to that line, leave a gap.
6. When hidden lines cross, draw the one that lies in front of the other as continuous and through a space (between dashes) in the one behind it.

7.6.9   Curved Lines in Views

All curved features of a part are shown in each view. In most cases, a curved feature shows as a curved line or surface in only one view and as an edge line (straight) in its adjacent projection. The most common type of **curved feature** is the circle. Arcs (and fillets) are also widely used on parts. Circles, arcs, and fillets are really one end of a **curved surface.** Curved surfaces make up much of a typical machined part. A hole is really a cylindrical surface. Connected arcs and fillets are also portions of cylinders. Holes are formed by drills and other rotating tools. Parts that are made up of curved surfaces such as spheres, cylinders, and conical shapes are normally machined on lathes or other turning devices.

Since an internal curved surface (hole) and an external curved surface (normally a cylinder) are both curved surfaces, they are drawn the same way. In Figure 7.38, the part has both internal and external curved surfaces. The holes and the cylinder both show as curves in the top view and as straight edge lines in the front and side views. The hole shows as

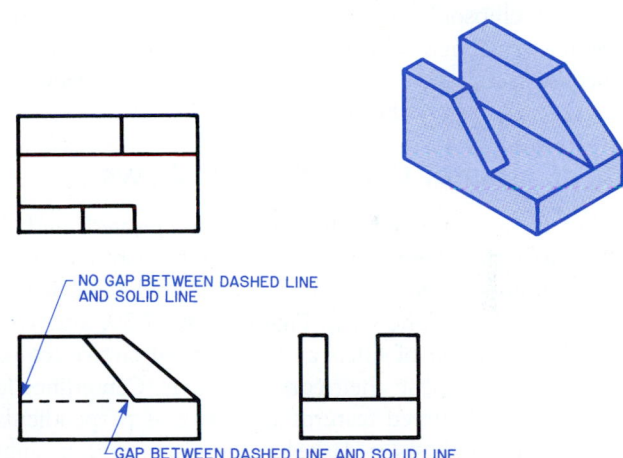

FIGURE 7.36   **Drawing Dashed Lines**

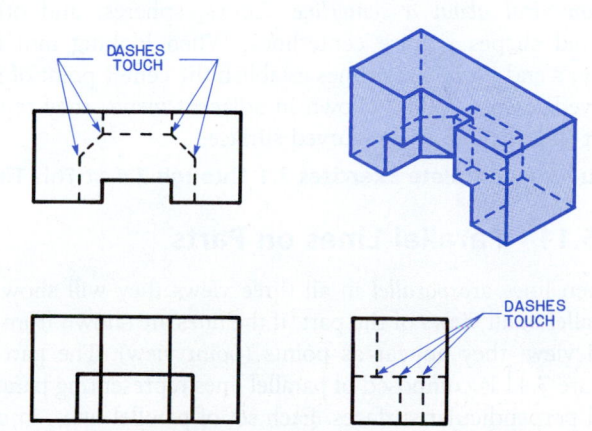

FIGURE 7.37   **Dashed Lines and Drawing Conventions**

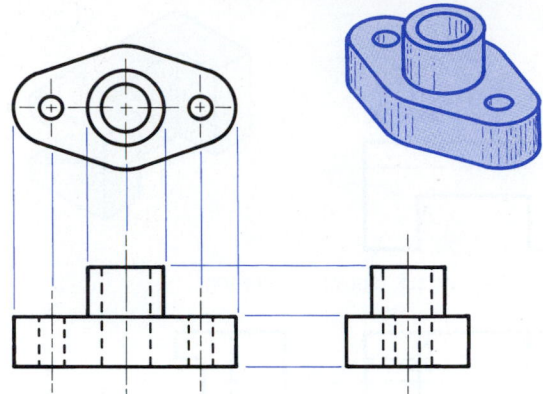

FIGURE 7.38   Curved Features in Views

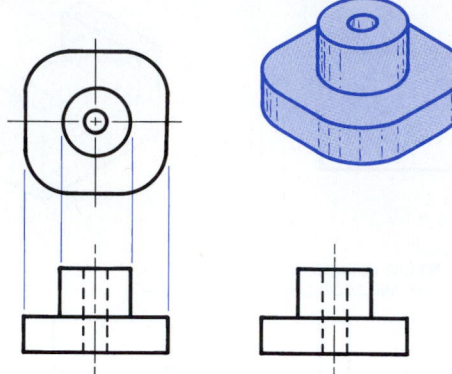

FIGURE 7.39   Curved Features

hidden features in these views and the cylindrical surface as visible lines. The outside arcs of the part also show as visible edge lines in the front and side views. Figures 7.39 and 7.40 also have holes, arcs, and cylindrical surfaces. They should be closely studied. The miter line method is used in Figure 7.40 to project the third view.

Sphere, ellipsoids, or other similar shapes show curved in more than one view. Unless cones and cylinders are part of angled surfaces, they will show as curves in one view and straight lines in the other two views.

7.6.10   Use of Centerlines in Views

Curved features are normally established, located, and dimensioned using a **centerline** to position the feature in space. Except for outside arcs, centerlines are required in all views of curved features, as shown in Figures 7.38, 7.39, and 7.40. With the exception of fillets and rounds, all curves require centerlines to establish their curved features. Centerlines for the end view of curved features are drawn as perpendicular crossing lines with short dashes at the center and as single centerlines (long dash, short dash) in adjacent views. Centerlines do not really exist as a feature of the part. They are not edge or surface lines. Therefore, they are drawn to extend slightly beyond the boundaries of the part or curved feature. They do not take precedence over visible or hidden lines.

Centerlines are also used on drawings where the part is *symmetrical about a centerline.* Cones, spheres, and other curved shapes require centerlines. When looking into the curve's end view, centerlines establish the center point of the curved feature. When shown in adjacent views, they represent the *axis line* of the curved surface.

You May Complete Exercises 7.1 Through 7.4 at This Time

7.6.11   Parallel Lines on Parts

When lines are *parallel* in all three views they will show as parallel in all views of the part. If the lines are shown from an end view, they appear as points (point view). The part in Figure 7.41 is composed of parallel lines representing parallel and perpendicular surfaces. Each set of parallel lines, in one

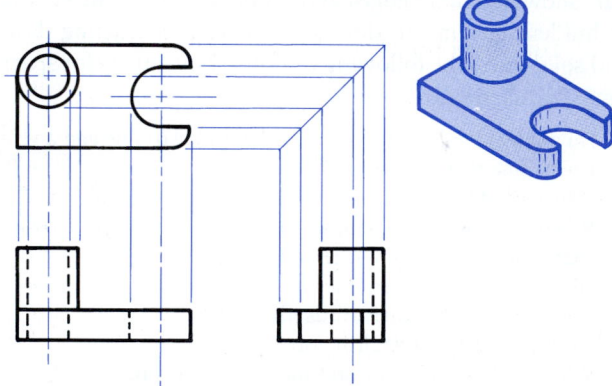

FIGURE 7.40   Miter Line Method for Projecting Curved Features

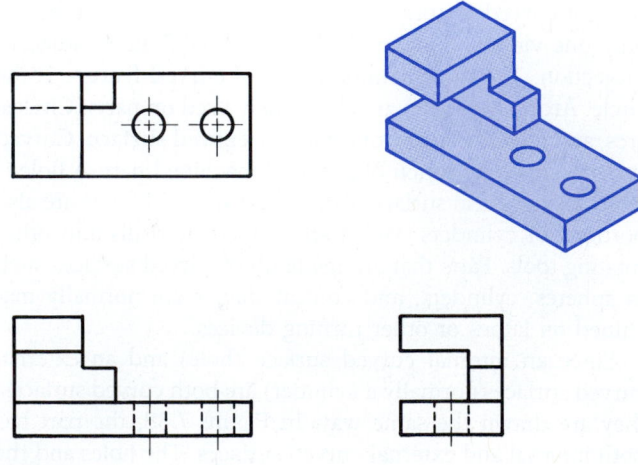

FIGURE 7.41   Parallel Edges

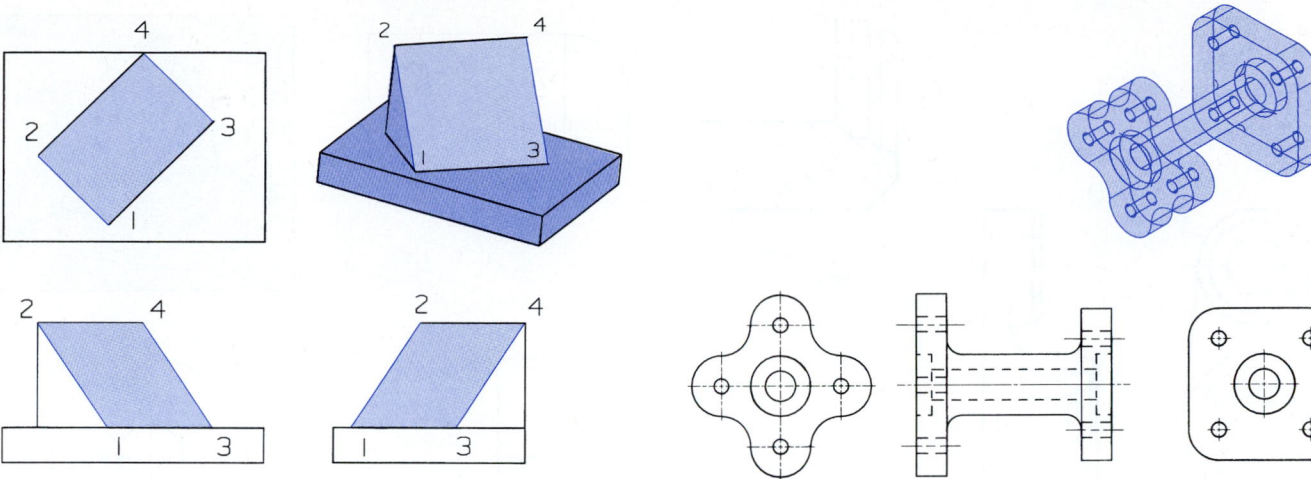

FIGURE 7.42 Parallel Lines on Parts   **FIGURE 7.43** Partial Views

view, will project as point views in the adjacent view and as parallel lines in the related view. *Parallelism* can easily be seen in the pictorial view of the part. In Figure 7.42, the part has an angled surface that does not show as a true shape in any of the three principal views. This *oblique surface* is shown by edge lines 1-2 and 3-4 (or you could say lines 2-4 and 1-3). The top, front, and right side views show that each of these edge lines is parallel to the other in every view (including the pictorial view of the part).

7.7 Drafting Conventions and Special Views

A variety of **drafting conventions** and procedures have been devised to enable the drafter to draw projects concisely, clearly, and quickly. A number of drafting conventions are covered here including partial views, enlarged views, and revolved views.

The need for complete views with all hidden lines shown would take too much costly time and create drawings that were less usable than those with only the necessary lines shown. **Partial views** are one drafting convention procedure used to solve this problem. Complicated, cluttered parts of drawings need to be shown in larger, clearer representations, therefore, the use of **enlarged views** was established. **Rotated** or **revolved views** came into practice to describe parts of a part that were projected as oblique surfaces and actually confused the drawing rather than clarifying the part. Each of these methods was developed and standardized over a number of years. Now, they are considered **drafting conventions**— accepted standardized techniques and practices.

7.7.1 Partial Views

As long as the geometry of a part is adequately described in another view, a **partial view** may be used. A partial view is a view where the dominant features, shape, and outline of the

part are shown without the extra clutter of unneeded hidden lines. In Figure 7.43, the part has different shapes on each end. Since a top view would be very similar to the front view, it has been eliminated. Since they show only the visible lines of the corresponding end, the right and the left side views are *partial views*. These views do not show the hidden features of the opposite end. This would add nothing to the drawing.

Hidden features on a partial view should include only those directly behind the visible shapes. In Figure 7.43, the cylinder's outside diameter (OD) lies directly behind the counterbored hole on each base plate. Therefore, since visible lines take precedence over hidden lines, this feature does not show on the drawing. The two side views do not have any hidden lines. On parts where the hidden feature will not appear on another view, the feature must be included on the partial view.

7.7.2 Enlarged Views

Enlarged views are used to increase the size of a crowded or complicated area of a part. Many times this procedure is necessary to provide sufficient space for dimensions. In Figure 7.44, VIEW A is the enlarged portion of the part. The interior and exterior chamfers are now clearly visible. The area to be enlarged is circled with a phantom line and the **view-letter designation** is positioned as in Figure 7.44. The enlarged view is identified on the drawing with the view-letter designation placed under the view (in the case of Fig. 7.44, VIEW A).

7.7.3 Revolved Views

Rotated or **revolved views** are used where a true projection of the part would only confuse the reader of the drawing. The part in Figure 7.45 is an example of a part that is better described with a rotated view. The detail of this part requires two views to adequately describe its geometry and place dimensions. If a true projection was used, the front view of the part would have been confusing and complicated. The clevis

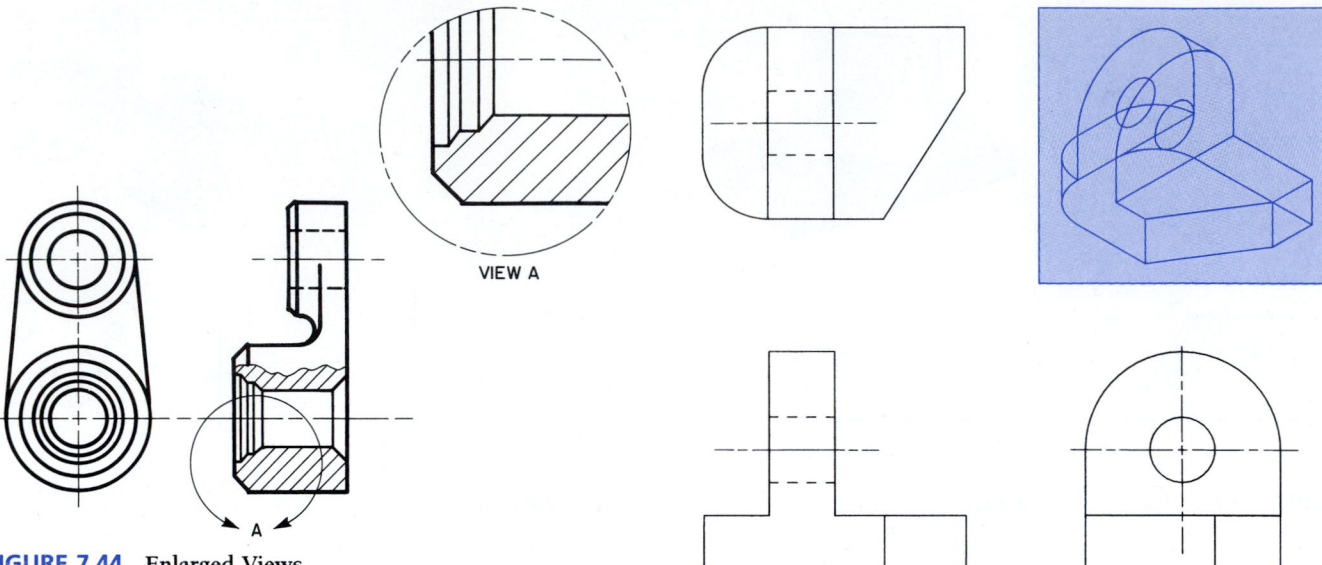

FIGURE 7.44 Enlarged Views

VIEW A

FIGURE 7.46 Surfaces on a Part

portion of the arm was rotated parallel to the front view and projected as a normal (true shape) view. This procedure saved considerable drawing time and is less misleading.

7.7.4 Surfaces and Edges on Multiple-View Drawings

To understand orthographic projection, you must begin to see parts as simple shapes, edges, lines, and points. *Surfaces* are created by combining lines. The surfaces can be combinations of straight lines or straight and curved lines. Surfaces, or *areas* as they are sometimes called, show **true shape/size (TS)** when they are parallel to the plane of projection and as **edges (EV)** when they are perpendicular to the plane of projection. A plane that appears true shape/size in a view is called a **normal surface.** The view is a *normal view of a plane.* The adjacent projection (view) of the plane shows as an edge (edge view).

Curved surfaces show as curved edges in views where they are perpendicular to the viewing plane, and as plane shapes with straight sides in views where they are parallel to the viewing plane. When three surfaces come together, they meet at a corner (point). Most parts can be defined by establishing their corners (points in space). Figure 7.46 provides examples of each condition. The pictorial view in the upper right of the illustration provides a 3D model of the part. The part is composed of planar surfaces and curved surfaces. The hole shows as circular only in the side view. It appears as an edge in the front and top views. Notice that the circular surface of the projected hole shows as a rectangle in the front and top views. The same is true of the vertical curved surface on which the hole appears. All planar surfaces of the part show as true shape or as edges in their adjacent views. Since each of the curved surfaces is perpendicular to this plane of projection, the front view is all straight lines.

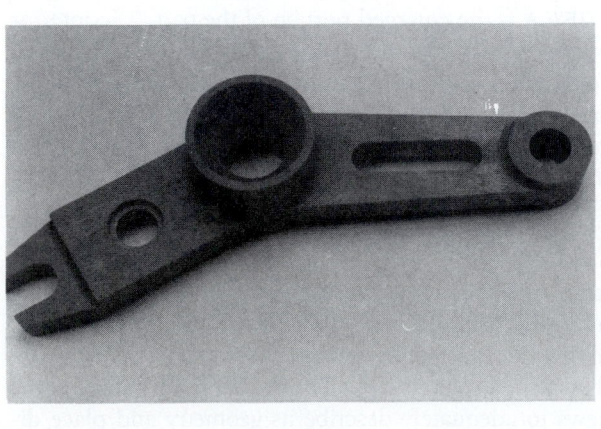

(a)

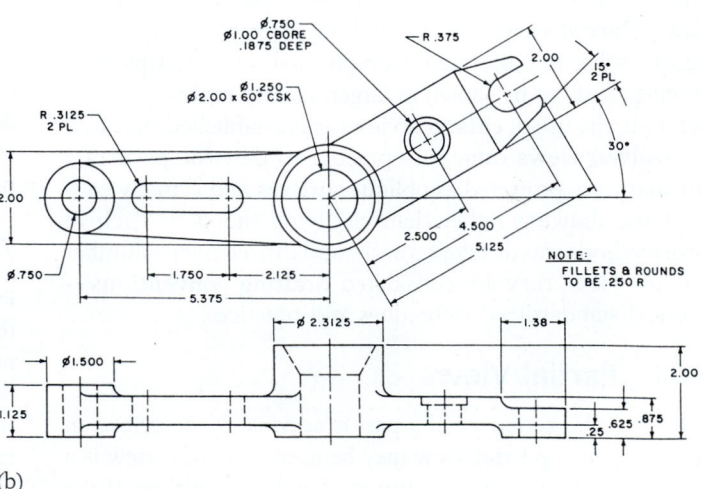

(b)

FIGURE 7.45 Angle Frame (a) Photograph of angle frame (b) Drawing of angle frame

| **ITEMS OF INTEREST** | *Evinrude* |

Who would have imagined that the son of an immigrant farmer, with only a third-grade education, would be responsible for the hours of pleasure experienced by people who fish and boat? Ole Evinrude was born in Norway and came to America with his parents to farm in Wisconsin. He wasn't a very good farmer, preferring to channel his energies into work on mechanical devices. At sixteen, he built his first project, a sailboat. He used this project to secure a job as a machinist in Madison. After several jobs in Chicago and Pittsburgh, he settled in Milwaukee working as a patternmaker. In his spare time, he "tinkered" with his idea of constructing a standard engine for the increasingly popular horseless carriage. The U.S. government became interested in this concept and contracted with him to produce fifty engines. As a result, he opened his own company.

The idea for the outboard motor was the result of being embarrassed during a summer picnic. His future wife asked him to row across the lake to get ice cream. On the return trip, the wind became so gusty that he was unable to row fast enough to keep the ice cream from melting. Ole was a large, strong man and was embarrassed over this inability to control his boat. The following Monday he began work on his outboard motor.

Evinrude introduced his 1.5-hp motor in 1907. It has remained essentially un-

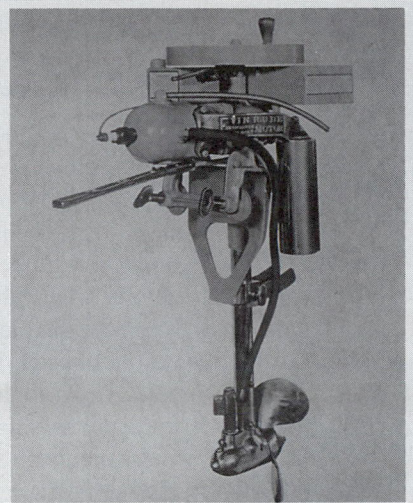

Evinrude's First Motor

changed to this day. It has a horizontal cylinder with a vertical crankshaft, employing power direction changes with gears in a submerged lower unit. Ole was only thirty-two when he formed Evinrude Motor Company to produce the outboard motors.

The company was sold in 1914. Later, another company, Evinrude Light Twin Outboard (ELTO), produced the first practical twin-cylinder outboard. In it, many heavy engine parts were replaced with aluminum. Also, exhaust gases pass through the propeller hub.

Evinrude died in 1934. A few years ago, his original 1909 outboard motor was dedicated as a National Historic Mechanical Engineering Landmark. It was the first consumer product to be so recognized.

No doubt Evinrude spent many hours sketching his ideas. To manufacture those motors, many working and assembly drawings were also produced. Evinrude certainly had the genius to take an idea in his mind and make it into a valuable product. This is not so different from what we try to do today.

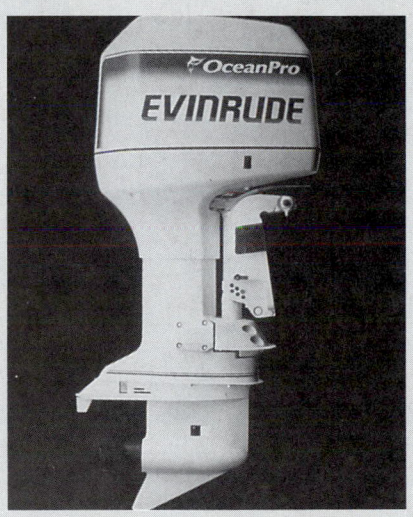

A Modern Outboard Motor

7.7.5 Reading a Drawing

We have already said that a drawing is *"read"*, not scaled. This doesn't mean that you read it aloud. "Reading" is what you as a drafter (designer, engineer, machinist, etc.) do mentally to understand and then interpret the drawing. Here are the mental steps required to read a drawing:

1. Study the total drawing by scanning all views and dimensions.
2. Visualize the shape of the part by orientating oneself as the observer for each view.
3. Reduce the part to simple geometric shapes, e.g., planes, circles, surfaces, and other common features.
4. Study each view and feature as it corresponds to its adjacent and related projection. The depth, for instance, can be studied in the top and related side view. Adjacent views can be studied

to establish the true shape of a surface and its edge view projection.

5. If necessary, sketch a simple 3D pictorial of the part to clarify the general configuration and details.
6. Note each hole, tangent area, curved feature, and other special contour that distinguishes the part.

Assuming that the pictorial view of the part (right side orientation) in Figure 7.47 is not provided, read the part. Notice that three views were required to represent the part's geometry adequately. Most of the part's features can be seen in the front and side views. The top view adds little to the drawing's understanding but does show that the slot extends through the part. The front view shows the angled cut (its edge view). This is the only surface that is not normal and, therefore, does

(a)

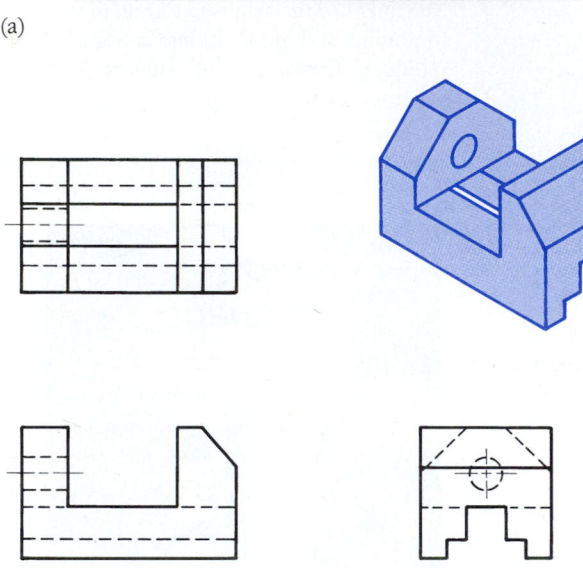

(b)

FIGURE 7.47 **Three Views and Pictorial Illustration of the Guide** (a) Photograph of part from left side orientation (b) Drawing of part

not appear true shape on the drawing in any view. The hole is described in the side view. Since the hole is hidden, only the portion of the part on the far side is penetrated. The side view also shows that the slot extends the entire length of the part. A pictorial sketch would help in reading this project. Note that the photograph of the part was taken from a left side orientation.

7.8 Visualization and Shape Description

The process of reading the drawing assumes that the reader has a certain level of skill at visualization. Visualizing a part is one of the most important skills developed when learning technical drawing. *Visualization is the process of converting a 2D drawing into a 3D image and being able to understand the part as*

it exists in three-dimensional space. This skill is not innate for everyone but can be developed, in most cases, through the study of a variety of drawings, parts, and models.

Upon entering an engineering field that requires the use of drawings, you must be able to understand both the 3D and the 2D illustrations of a part and its representative drawing. Visualizing is a skill that will be necessary for both situations.

7.8.1 Visualizing Views

In Figure 7.48, the part is shown with four views (a pictorial view is also provided). Each of the views provides details of the part. The top view shows the depth and width of the part along with visible lines representing the two removed portions. You cannot tell the actual height of the block or the cutout height in the top view. The front view provides the height of the block and the cutout shapes. The small cutout on the right of the front view is still not completely clear; it could be an angled surface. Only the two side views can clear up the remaining questions about the final shape. Since these views do not show the small cutout with an angled edge line, the block shape of the cutout is understood.

7.8.2 Areas on Adjacent and Related Views of a Drawing

Visualization is used to examine a part by comparing surfaces and edges on adjacent and related views. When studying adjacent areas, it is important to remember that *adjacent areas cannot lie in the same plane.* If they did, they would not exist; they would not have a boundary between them.

Adjacent areas can be studied in Figure 7.49. The three principal views are labeled in each projection and on the pictorial view provided in the top right part of the drawing. In each view, a surface or an edge is labeled. Surface A is shown true shape in the top view and as an edge in the front and side projections. Surface B is also true shape in the top view and, therefore, an edge view in the front and side views of the drawing. Surface C is true shape in the front view. Can you

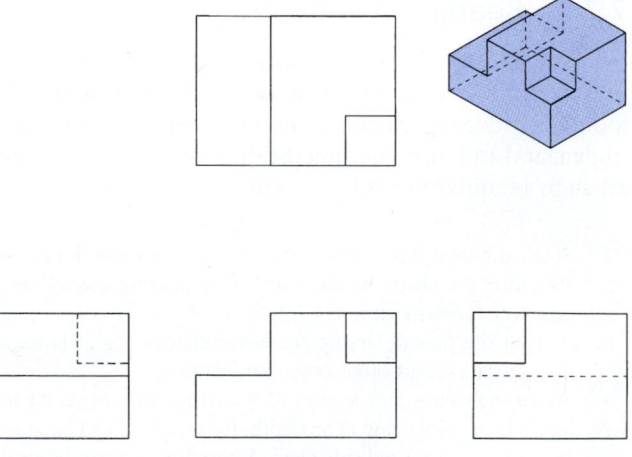

FIGURE 7.48 **Multiple Views of a Part**

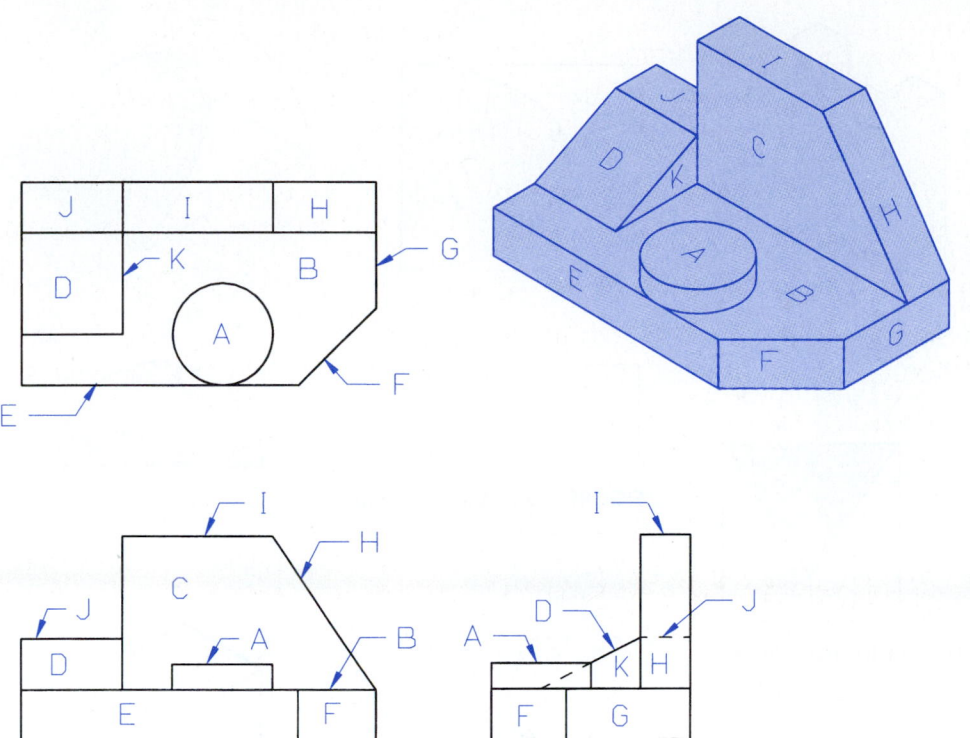

FIGURE 7.49   **Related Surfaces and Edges**

find it in the top and side views? It will show as an edge view in each. If you cannot find it in the top and side projections, the pictorial view will locate surface C. Remember, if a surface is true shape in the top view, it shows as an edge in the other two views (front and side). Surface D is an angled surface. Its slant angle can be seen in the side view where it shows as an edge. The front and top projections of surface D are not true shape. Surface E is along the front of the part and is true shape in the front view. It shows as an edge in the top view and the side view. Surface F is at an angle and does not show in any view as true length. The top view shows this surface as an edge view and its angle to the part can be measured from the edge view of surface E. The side and front views of surface F show as foreshortened (not true shape). Surface G forms the right side of the part and shows as an edge in the top view and as true shape in the front and side views. Surface H is an inclined surface and its slant angle can be measured in the front view as the angle it makes with surface B. Surface H is an edge in this view and is shown foreshortened in the other two projections. Surface I is the top or highest surface on the part and shows as an edge in the front view, true shape in the top view, and as an edge in the side view. If a surface appears as an edge in the front view, it will also be an edge in the side projection. It will be true shape only in the top view. Surface J is parallel to surface I. Therefore, it also is true shape in the top view and an edge in the other two projections. Surface K is true shape in the side view and an edge in the top and front views. Surfaces G and K are the only labeled surfaces that are true shape in the side view.

In addition to seeing the true shape and the edge views of a surface, it is important to develop a sense of how each surface relates to another surface. Surface C, for instance, is parallel to surface E and perpendicular to surfaces I and B. Surface D is at an angle to surface B and surface C. Surface G is parallel to surface K and perpendicular to surfaces B and E. Being aware of *parallelism*, *perpendicularity*, and *angularity* are important aspects of visualizing a 3D part and reading its 2D representation—its drawing.

7.8.3   Visualizing Similar Shapes of Surfaces

A simple rule of projection is that *an area will project as a similar shape or as an edge in an adjacent view.* Adjacent projections of a normal surface project as edges. Related views of a surface project as similar shapes. In Figure 7.50, the drawing

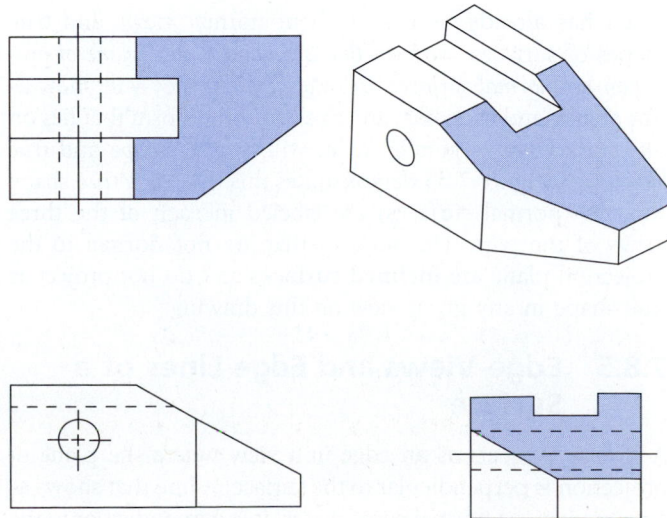

FIGURE 7.50   **Angled Surfaces and Edge Views**

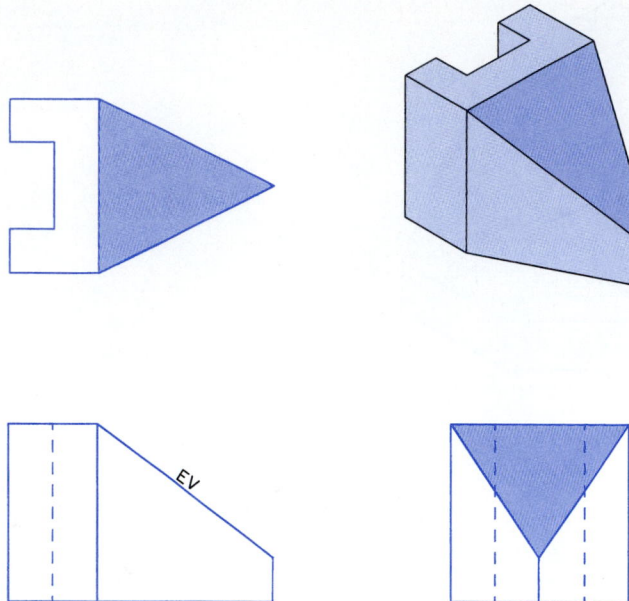

FIGURE 7.51   Similar Shapes of Surfaces in Related Views

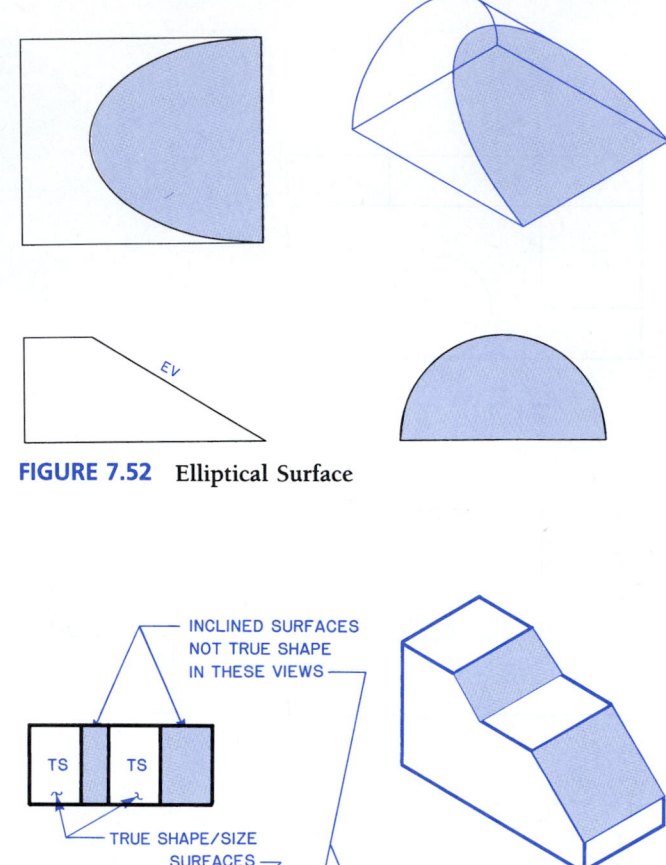

FIGURE 7.52   Elliptical Surface

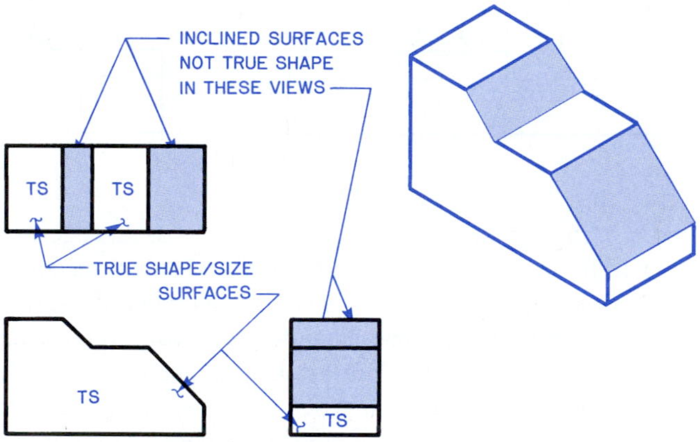

of the part shows that the angled surface is a similar shape in the side and top views. It shows as an edge in the front view. Even though the top and side views show the surface as distorted, their outlines appear as similar shapes.

The triangular-shaped area in Figure 7.51 has the same number of sides in each view where it does not appear as an edge. So, in addition to having a similar shape, the preceding rule has a corollary: *The shapes will have the same number of sides and the sides of the areas are connected in the same sequence.*

Curved shapes may distort in related views, but they maintain similar shapes, as in Figure 7.52. The top and side views show similar shaped views of the angled surface. The front view shows the surface as an edge (EV).

7.8.4   True Shape or Normal Surfaces of a Part

Much has already been said about normal views and true shapes of surfaces. *Surfaces that are parallel to a plane of projection are normal surfaces.* In other words, they will show as true shape, and each line, arc, circle, or other form that lies on this surface, or is parallel to it, will be *true shape* and *true length/size*. Figure 7.53 demonstrates this rule. The true shape surfaces (normal surfaces) are labeled in each of the three views of the part. The surfaces that are not normal to the projection plane are **inclined surfaces** and do not project as true shape in any given view on this drawing.

7.8.5   Edge Views and Edge Lines of a Surface

A surface projects as an edge in a view where the plane of projection is perpendicular to the surface. A line that shows as a point view is a normal edge; that is, it is perpendicular to the projection plane.

FIGURE 7.53   Inclined Surfaces and True Shape Surfaces

Edge lines are always shown on views where the surfaces they represent are perpendicular to the adjacent view. In Figure 7.54, the front view of the part shows two perpendicular surfaces that will project as edge lines in the top view. The surface that is at a slight angle and blends with its mating surfaces is not represented with an edge line in the top view. The same drafting convention is used in the right side view and the left side view.

7.8.6   Angles on Multiview Drawings

In Figure 7.55, the part has two **angled surfaces.** The true angle of these surfaces is shown in the side view of the part where they show as edge lines that lie normal to the view. *Angles can be measured only in views where they are in a normal plane.* The front and top views show the angled surfaces *as if* they were rectangular and true shape; their inclination cannot be read in these views. Without the side view, the part's configuration could not be determined.

The angled surfaces in Figure 7.56 are inclined to the front view (and side view). The angle that each surface makes can be read only in the top view where they appear as edge lines.

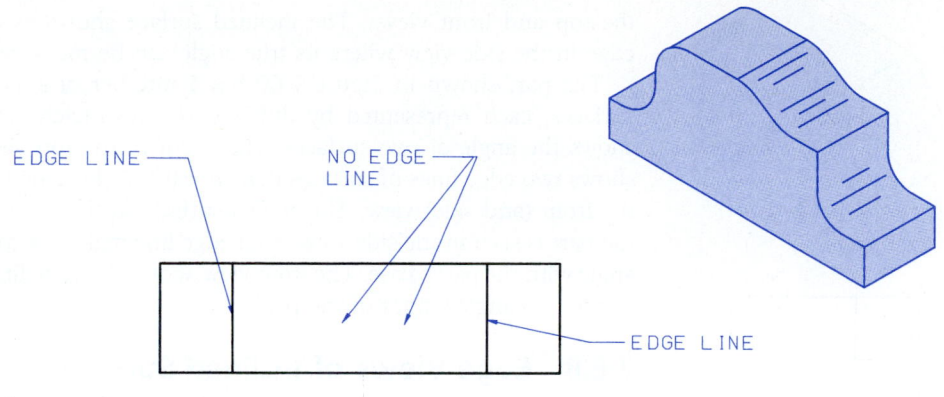

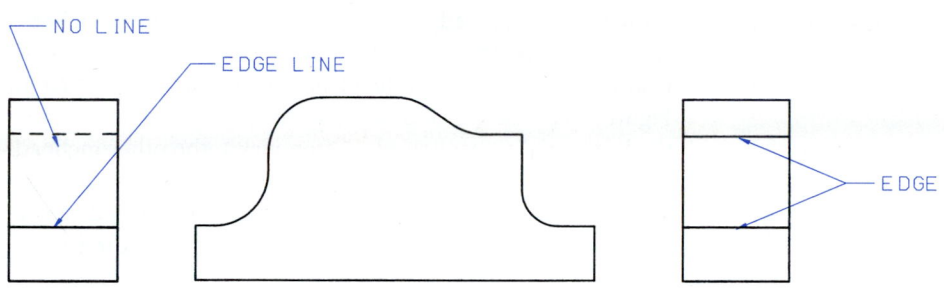

FIGURE 7.54 Curved Surfaces and Edge Lines

Figure 7.57 should be studied carefully. The lower corner has been cut off at an angle to each of three surfaces. The angled surface is foreshortened in every view and is called an **oblique surface.**

7.8.7   Inclined Surfaces of a Part

An **inclined surface** shows as an edge in one view and as foreshortened in the adjacent view. The edge view of the inclined surface shows the *true angle* of the surface. Figure 7.58 has three inclined surfaces. The angles that surfaces A and C make with the horizontal plane is shown in the front view where they each appear as edge lines. The *true angle* of surface B can be measured in the side view where it appears as an edge line. The other views of surface B show as *foreshortened.* The amount of foreshortening depends on the *angle of the inclination.* The greater the angle of incline to a view, the more the surface is foreshortened.

In Figure 7.59, the part's front surface is inclined (shaded area). The surface is at approximately 45° to the horizontal plane. Therefore, the amount of foreshortening is similar in

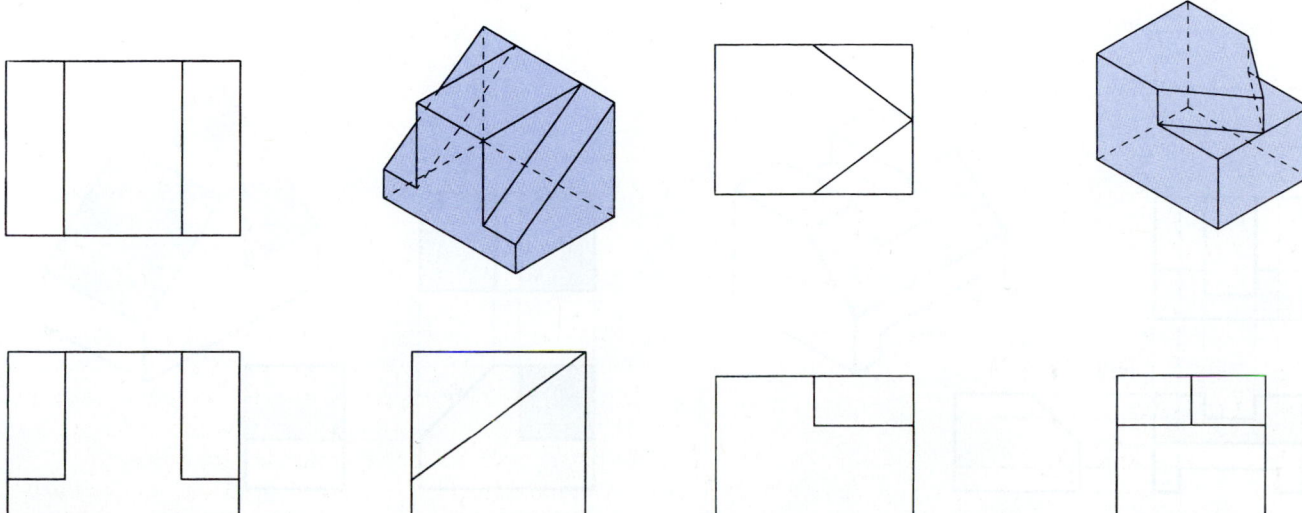

FIGURE 7.55 Inclined Surfaces on Parts

FIGURE 7.56 Angled Surfaces

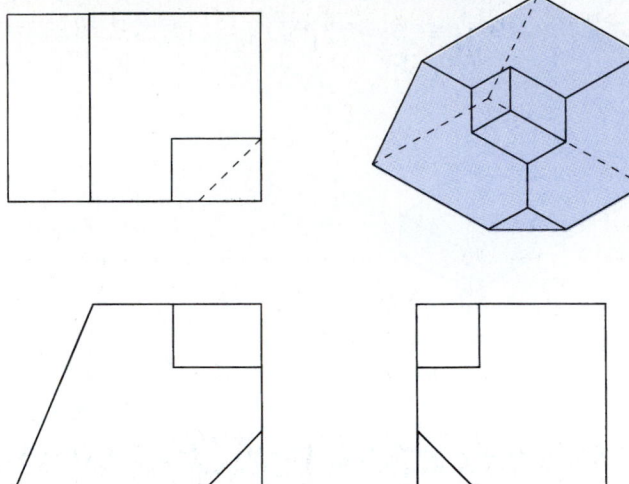

FIGURE 7.57 Inclined and Oblique Surfaces

the top and front views. The inclined surface shows as an edge in the side view where its true angle can be measured.

The part shown in Figure 7.60 has a number of angled surfaces, each represented by different shading. Each view shows the angle of two surfaces. The V cut in the top view shows two edge lines of surfaces that appear foreshortened in the front (and side) view. The angled surface on the front of the part is seen in the side view as an edge line making a true angle with the part's base. The front view shows the edge lines of the two angled sides of the part.

7.8.8 Edge Views of Inclined Surfaces

As was stated in the last section, the **edge view** of an inclined surface shows in a view where it forms a true angle in a normal plane. The adjacent and related views of the inclined surface always appear foreshortened (they never appear as true shape or larger than the plane itself). This can be seen in Figure 7.61. The part has two angled surfaces: one inclined to the horizontal projection plane (top view); the other inclined to the frontal projection plane (front view). The first inclined surface appears as an edge in the front view and its true angle with the horizontal plane (its base) can be measured here.

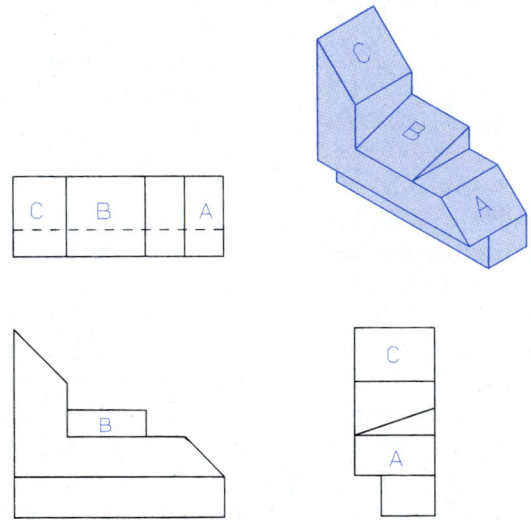

FIGURE 7.58 Inclined Surfaces in Adjacent and Related Views

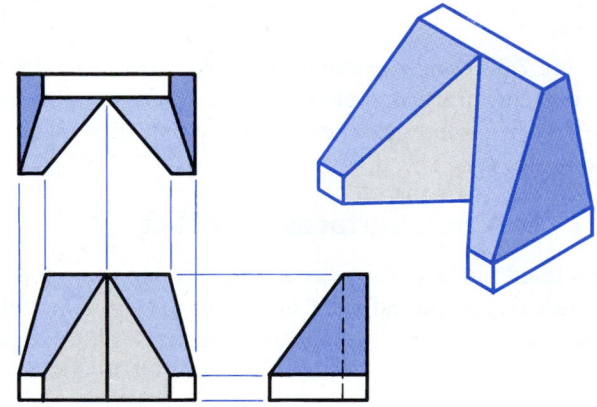

FIGURE 7.60 Inclined Surfaces

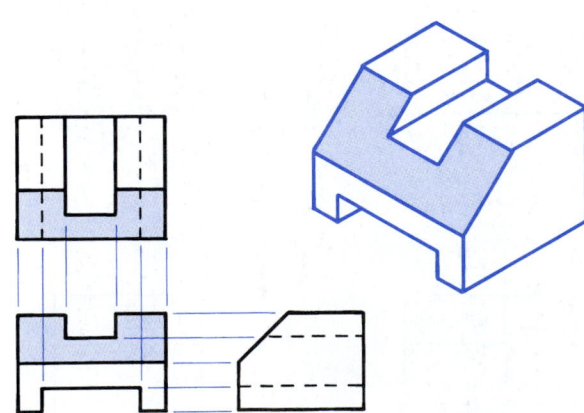

FIGURE 7.59 Surface Inclined in the Side View

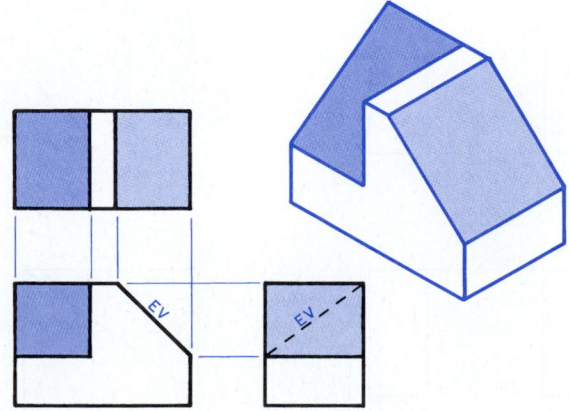

FIGURE 7.61 Edge Views and Inclined Surfaces

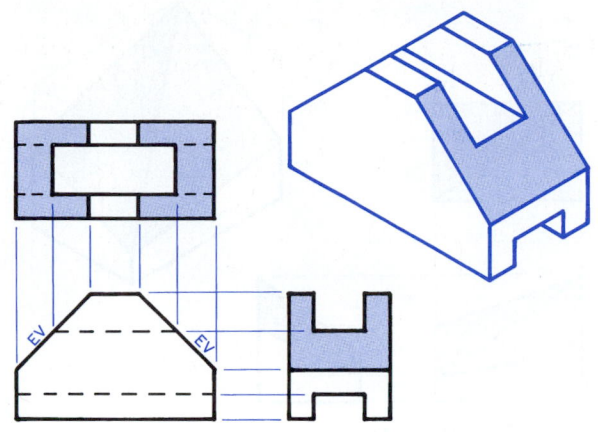

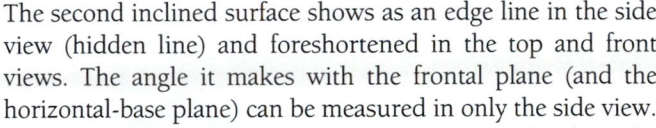

FIGURE 7.62 Angled Surfaces

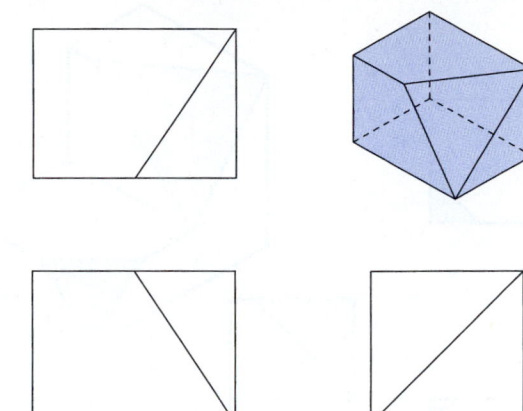

FIGURE 7.64 Oblique Surface

The second inclined surface shows as an edge line in the side view (hidden line) and foreshortened in the top and front views. The angle it makes with the frontal plane (and the horizontal-base plane) can be measured in only the side view.

The angled surfaces in Figure 7.62 are inclined to the horizontal projection plane (top view) and can be measured in the front view only. The foreshortened views of the inclined surfaces are shown shaded.

Since many of its surfaces are at an angle to the standard projection planes, the part in Figure 7.63 is an example of a drawing that does not adequately describe its features. When this happens, an **auxiliary view** showing the angled surface as true shape is necessary. The surfaces are at an angle to the frontal projection plane, front view, and profile projection plane, side view. Nowhere do the vertical surfaces of the part's upper portion show as true shape.

7.8.9 Oblique Surfaces

Oblique surfaces are inclined to all three principal planes of projection, which results in each view of the surface appearing foreshortened (distorted). Since it cannot appear as an

edge line, each view of the oblique plane always displays the same number of sides and has a similar shape. Figure 7.64 is an example of a part with an oblique surface. Since it is three-sided, each view of the surface will have three sides and each view shows the plane distorted.

The true shape of an oblique plane cannot be seen in any of the principal projection planes. To establish a true-shape view of an oblique surface, a secondary auxiliary view must be projected (auxiliary views are discussed in Chapter 10).

In Figure 7.65, the oblique surface is labeled and shaded. The surface is formed by the removal of the front corner of the part. The same type of oblique surface is shown in Figure 7.66 where two corners have been removed from the part. In Figure 7.67, the part has two oblique surfaces. The intersecting line formed by the two oblique surfaces shows as true length in the side view. This line is inclined to the base of the part, but since it shows as true length in one of the three principal planes of projection, it is not an oblique line. *An oblique line is inclined to all three principal planes of projection,* as in Figure 7.68 where the mating (intersection) line between the two oblique planes cannot be measured true length in any of the three principal planes of projection. In other

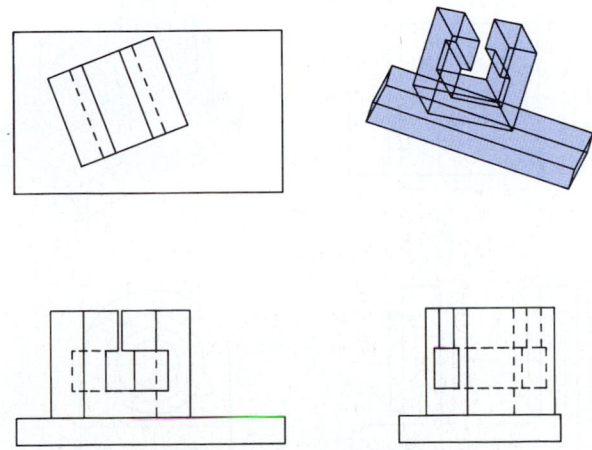

FIGURE 7.63 Distorted View of Surfaces

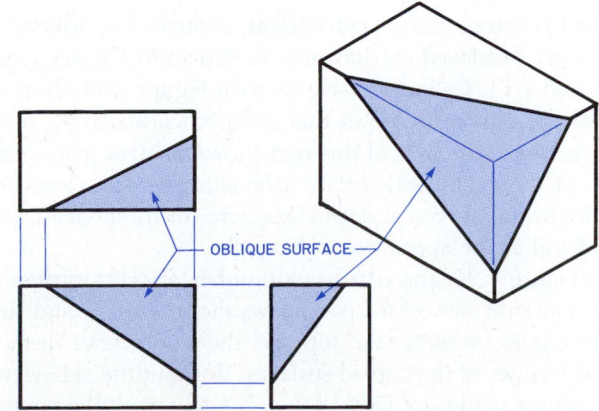

OBLIQUE SURFACE

FIGURE 7.65 Oblique Surfaces in Related and Adjacent Views

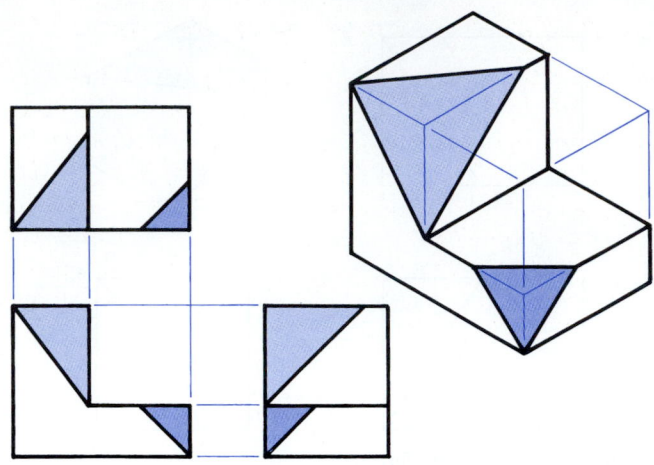

FIGURE 7.66 Oblique Surfaces

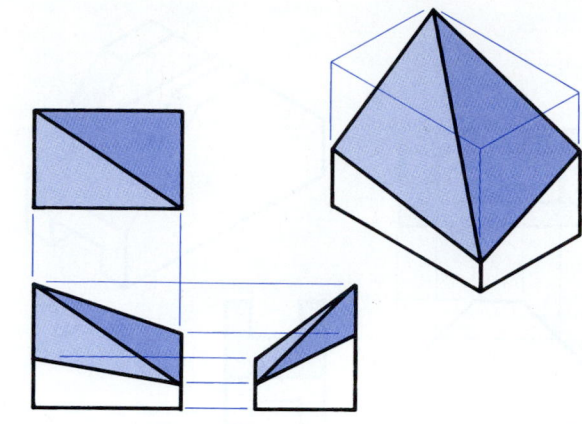

FIGURE 7.68 Oblique Surfaces

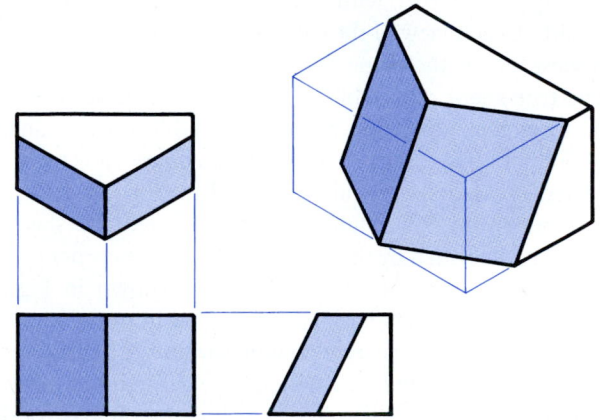

FIGURE 7.67 Oblique Surfaces

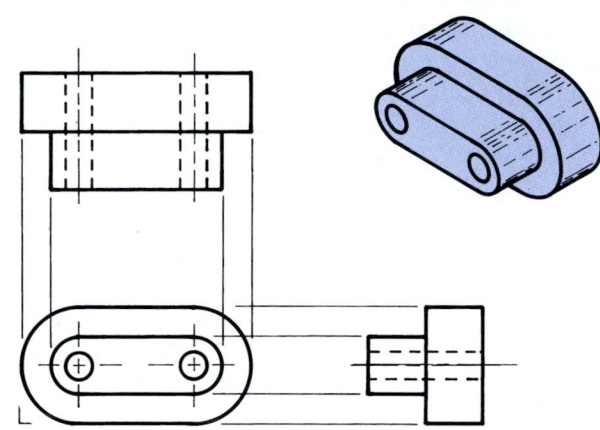

FIGURE 7.69 Cylindrical Features

words, it shows as foreshortened in all three views. This line is also known as an *oblique edge*.

7.8.10 Curved and Cylindrical Surfaces

Curved features such as **cylindrical, conical,** and **spherical** shapes are displayed on drawings, as shown in Figures 7.69, 7.70, and 7.71. Cylindrical shapes, as in Figure 7.69, show as true shape curves in views that are perpendicular to their surface. The front view of this part shows the true shape/size curve of the cylindrical surface. The side and top views are parallel to the curved surface. Therefore, in these views, the cylindrical shape appears as a rectangle.

In Figure 7.70, the part has a number of cylindrical surfaces. The side view of the part shows the true shape and size of the curves, whereas the top and the front views display only the edges of the curved surfaces. Without the side view, the drawing could not have been accurately read; the curved features would not have been apparent. For parts with curved features, *always provide at least one view where the curve appears true shape.*

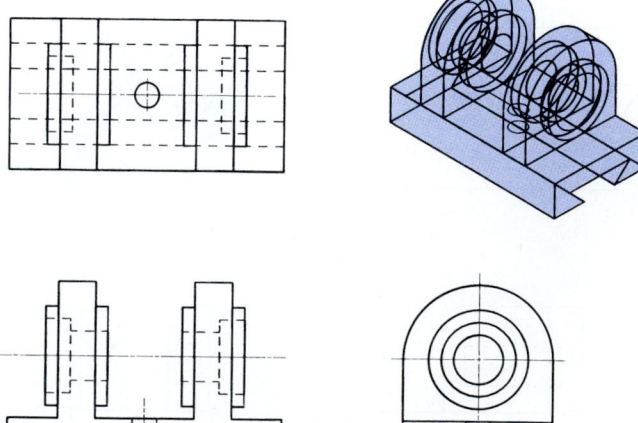

FIGURE 7.70 Curved Surfaces on Drawings

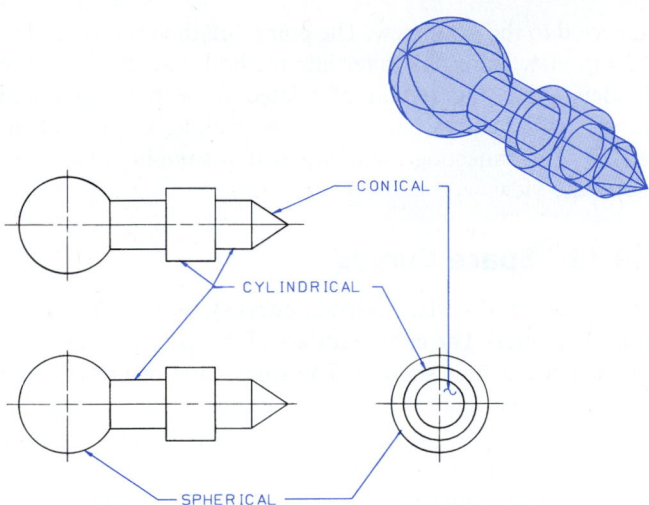

FIGURE 7.71 **Representing Cylindrical, Conical, and Spherical Features**

In Figure 7.71, the three types of curved surfaces are displayed. The **cylindrical surface** shows as a circle in one view and as a rectangle in the other two views. The **conical surface** appears as a circle in one view also, but its other two views show the surface as a triangle. The **spherical surface** shows as a circle in all three views, as would a ball when viewed from any direction.

In both Figures 7.70 and 7.71, the pictorial view of the part provided in the upper right of the illustration is a CAD-modeled true 3D wireframe model of the part, as are many of the examples in the text. Wireframe models are displayed with all edge lines. True visibility is difficult to establish without some experience.

You May Complete Exercises 7.5 Through 7.8 at This Time

7.8.11 Intersection of Curved Surfaces

Where two cylindrical surfaces meet, a *line of intersection* must be determined. When a 3D CAD system is used, the line of intersection is automatically determined by the system by using an intersection of surfaces or union of solids command. The system displays the surfaces and calculates their common line (intersection line).

When the line of intersection is manually derived, it must be plotted or represented according to established drafting conventions. Three conditions are possible:

1. The two curved surfaces have the same diameter.
2. The two curved surfaces have different diameters.
3. One of the two curved surfaces is so small that it would be a waste of time to plot the line of intersection.

In Figure 7.72, the two curved surfaces have the same diameter, therefore the first condition is met. The line of intersection formed between them shows as a straight line in the front view. In Figure 7.73, the other two conditions are exhibited. The small-diameter cylindrical surface, which intersects the vertical cylinder, does not show a distinct enough line of intersection when it intersects the vertical cylinder. Therefore, it is accepted drafting practice to show the intersection as a straight line. Some drafters prefer to use an ellipse template and show a small curved intersection line. The right side of the intersecting cylinders shows a cylindrical surface large enough to be plotted. The *miter line* method can be used or transferring the points with dividers will suffice. Points are established on the curve of the cylinder in the top view, either randomly or evenly spaced as shown here. The points are projected to the side view first. The side and the top views of each point are then projected to the front view as shown. *The*

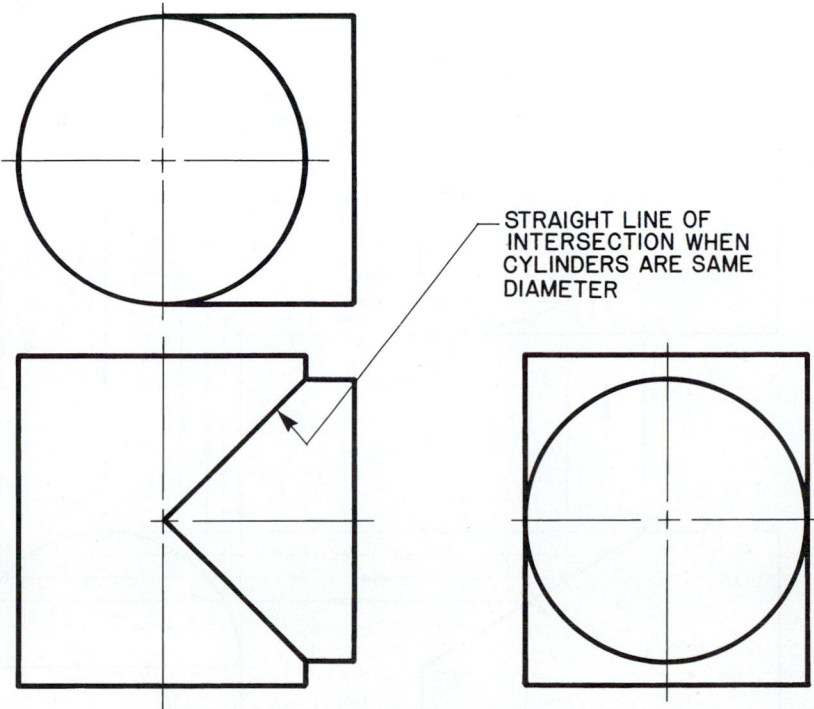

STRAIGHT LINE OF
INTERSECTION WHEN
CYLINDERS ARE SAME
DIAMETER

FIGURE 7.72 **Intersecting Cylinders of the Same Diameter**

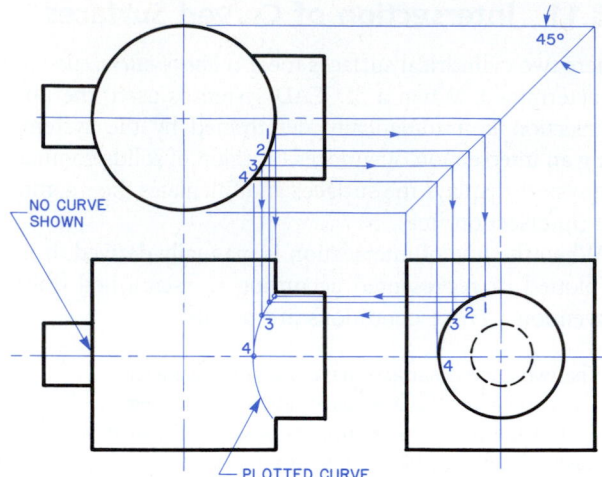

45°

NO CURVE
SHOWN

PLOTTED CURVE

FIGURE 7.73 **Intersection of Dissimilar-size Cylinders**

intersection of related projection lines locates a point on the line of intersection. The points are connected with an irregular curve.

7.8.12 Plotting Elliptical Curves

Elliptical shapes are created by the intersection of planes and curved surfaces. In Figure 7.74, the curve is formed by the intersection of the curved surface and a flat plane surface (not shown). The resulting shape is a surface that is elliptical on one end and a straight line on the other. This inclined surface does not appear as true shape in any of the given three principal planes of projection. To establish the line of intersection in the top view (curved edge), the side view of the cylindrical surface has a series of points located along it, as in Figure 7.73. The greater the number of points used, the greater the accuracy of the plotted curve. Each point on the curve is

projected to the front view. The points are then transferred to the top view using the miter line method or with the aid of dividers. The intersection of related projection lines and transferred distances establishes points along the line of intersection. Connecting the points with a smooth curve completes the view.

7.8.13 Space Curves

Irregular-shaped surfaces (**space curves**), as in Figure 7.75, must be plotted. The curved surface of this part was cut by an inclined plane (not shown). The true shape of the inclined surface does not appear in any of the three views. To plot the resulting intersection, establish a number of points along the curve in the top view where the curve's edge line is shown. The more points that are used, the greater the accuracy of the plotted curve. Each point is projected to the front view. The points are now projected to the side view from the front view. Lastly, the points are transferred to the side view from the top view. The resulting series of points in the side view is connected using an irregular curve to establish a smooth curve.

7.8.14 Hole Representation

The part in Figure 7.76 has a number of curved features, including a through hole and a counterbored hole. The diameter of the hole (.8125) is given for the two holes that are aligned. The counterbored hole has a diameter of .5625 for the through-hole and a counterbore diameter of .875 to a depth of .250. A machinist reading this drawing would be able to choose the proper equipment to accomplish these machined features. In most cases, the type of hole is no longer noted. The machinist determines whether to use a drill, reamer, or boring tool. The decision depends on the hole

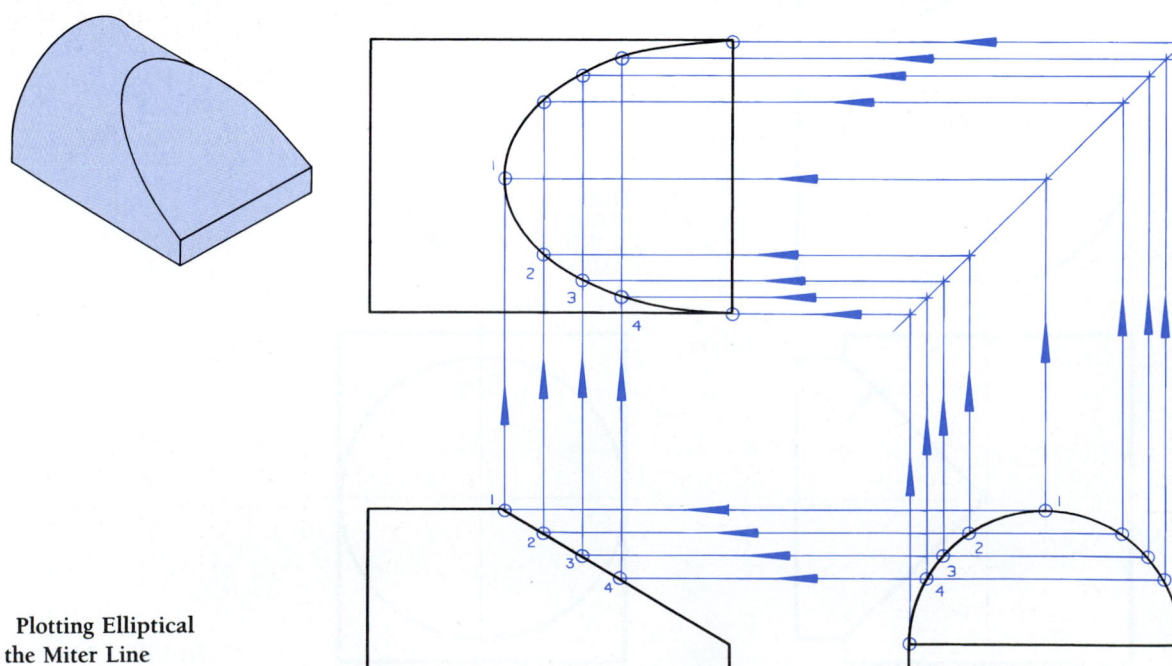

FIGURE 7.74 **Plotting Elliptical Curves Using the Miter Line Method**

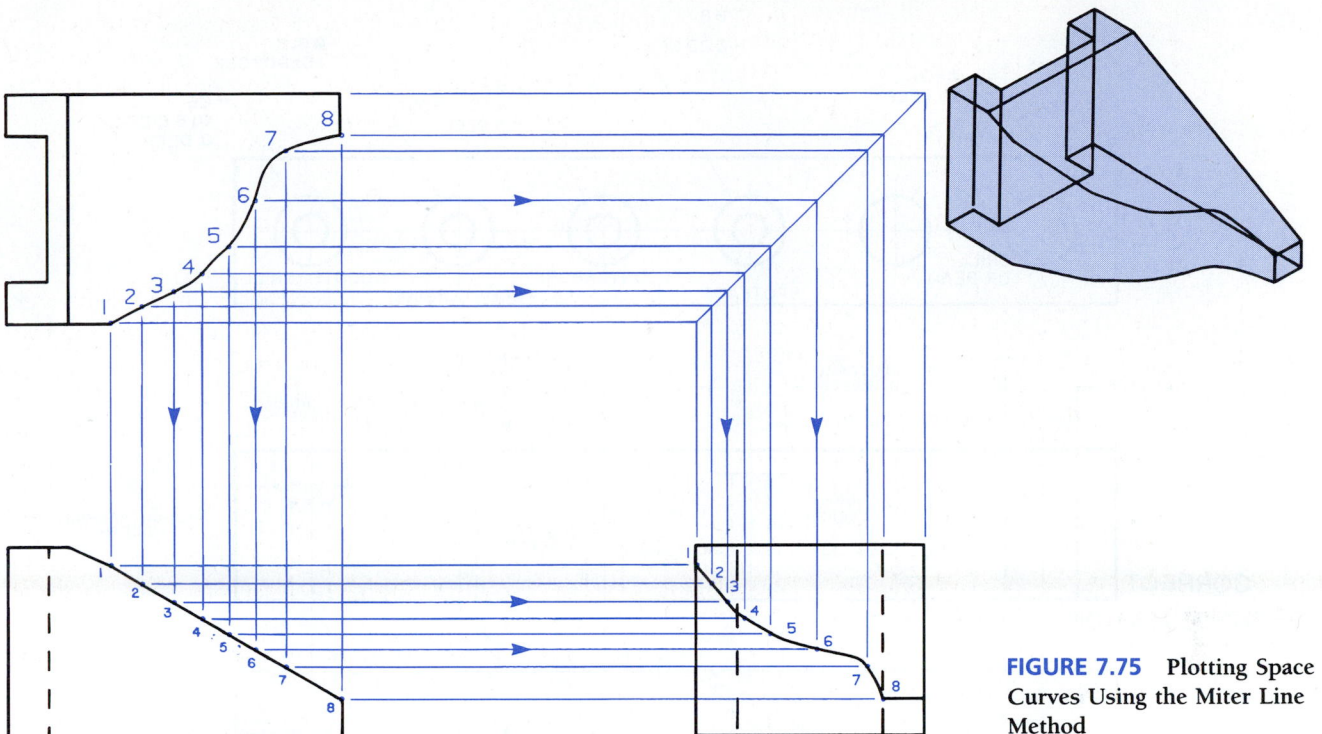

FIGURE 7.75 Plotting Space Curves Using the Miter Line Method

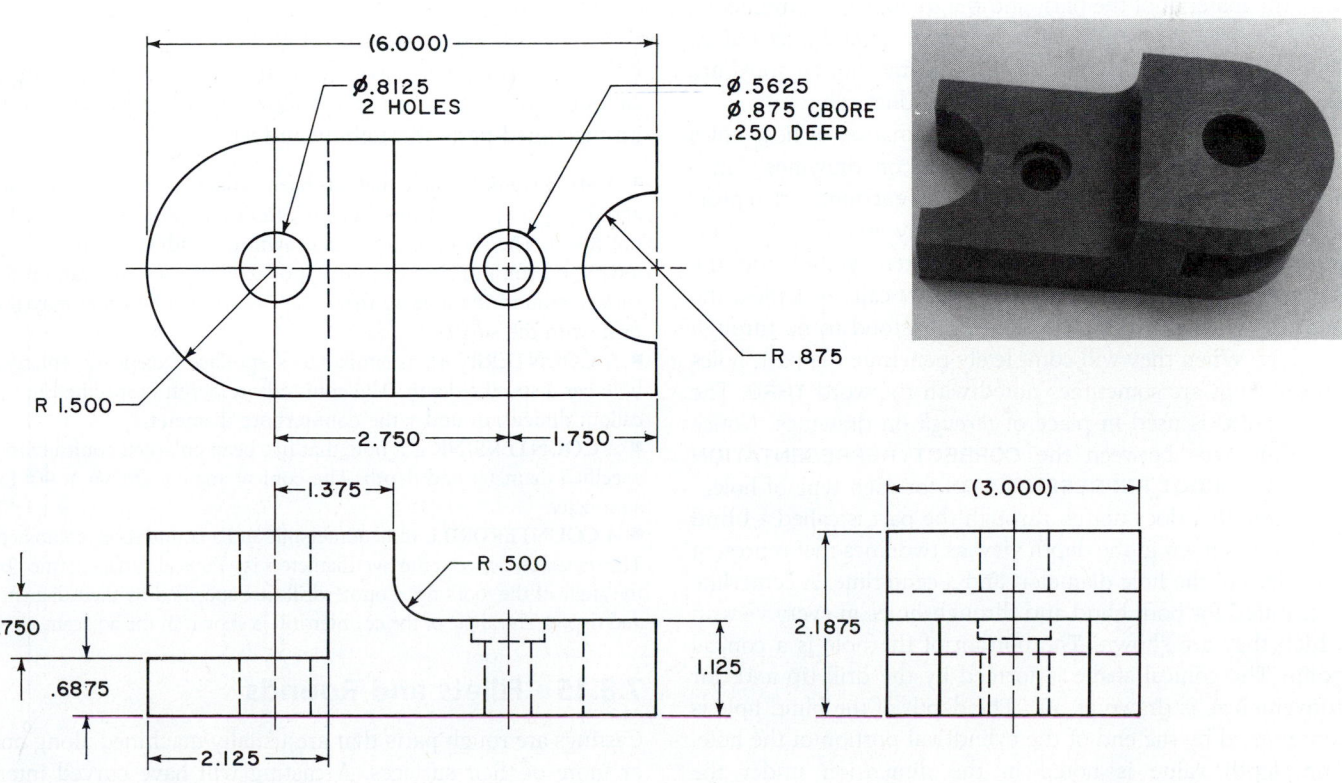

FIGURE 7.76 Detail of Breaker

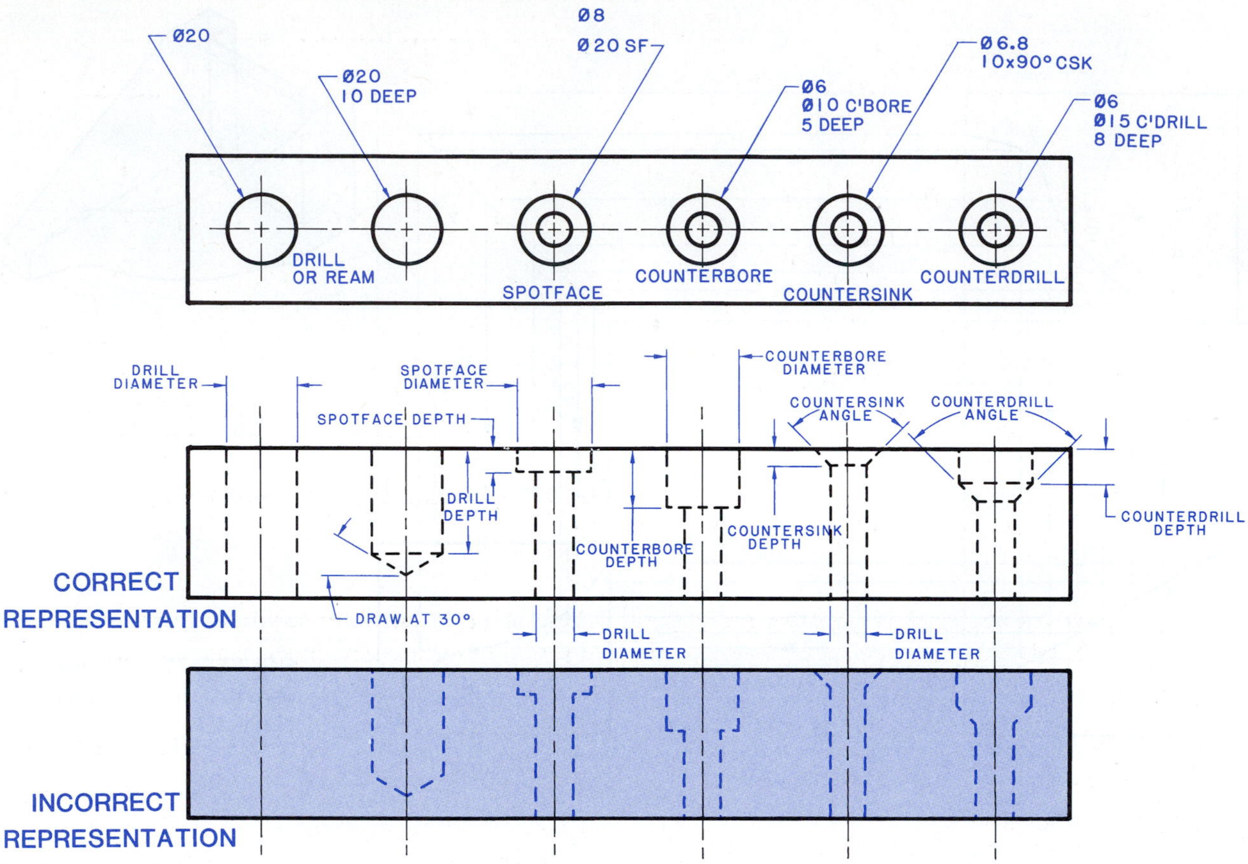

FIGURE 7.77   Types and Representation of Holes on Drawings

size, the material of the part, and the tolerance requirements. *A hole is always defined by its diameter, never by its radius.* Drills, reamers, bores, and other hole machining tools are described by their *diameter,* not their radius value.

Figure 7.77 provides a detailed explanation of how holes should and should not be represented on drawings. Since each situation and type of hole will be encountered repeatedly, this illustration should be carefully studied. The simplest hole callout provides the diameter symbol and the diameter value as in the **DRILL** or **REAM** callout. Unless the depth is given, the hole depth is understood to be through the part. When they will completely penetrate the part, holes on drawings are sometimes noted with the word **THRU**. The word **THRU** is used in place of *through* on drawings. Notice the difference between the **CORRECT REPRESENTATION** and **INCORRECT REPRESENTATION** for each type of hole.

A hole that does not go through the part is called a **blind hole.** It is shown in the depth view as two lines that represent the edges of the hole diameter, and a centerline. A centerline is required for both blind and through-holes in every view in which they are shown. The bottom of the hole is a conical point. The conical shape is formed by the drill tip and, for convenience, is drawn at 30°. The depth of the blind hole is represented by the end of the cylindrical portion of the hole. The depth value is noted in the dimension under the diameter.

Holes are either blind holes or through-holes. In Figure 7.77, five are depicted as through-holes. If they were blind holes, the drill depth would be stated under the diameter callout in the dimension. The following hole types are found on machined parts throughout industry:

■ A **SPOTFACE** is a hole that has been drilled to the required depth and the upper part enlarged. The depth of the spotface is sometimes not noted. The spotface depth is drawn, depending on the part, at .0625 (1.5 mm) to .125 (3 mm). Spotfacing is used to clean up the surface around the hole so that a bolt head or other item may rest flush with the surface.

■ A **COUNTERBORE** is similar to a spotface except the enlarged hole has a specific depth. The counterbore depth is specified in the callout dimension under the counterbore diameter.

■ A **COUNTERSINK** is a hole that has been enlarged conically to a specified diameter and depth. The conical angle is drawn at 90° for simplicity.

■ A **COUNTERDRILL** is a countersink and a counterbore combined. The transition between the two diameters is a conical surface formed by the angle of the tool's tip. Counterdrills are specified by their diameter and depth. The angle of the counterdrill is shown in the adjacent view.

7.8.15   Fillets and Rounds

Castings are rough parts that are usually machined along one or more of their surfaces. A casting will have curved intersections between mating surfaces. Castings cannot be accu-

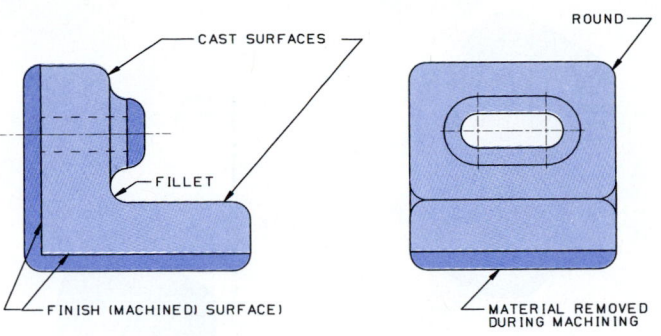

Fillets, Rounds, and Castings

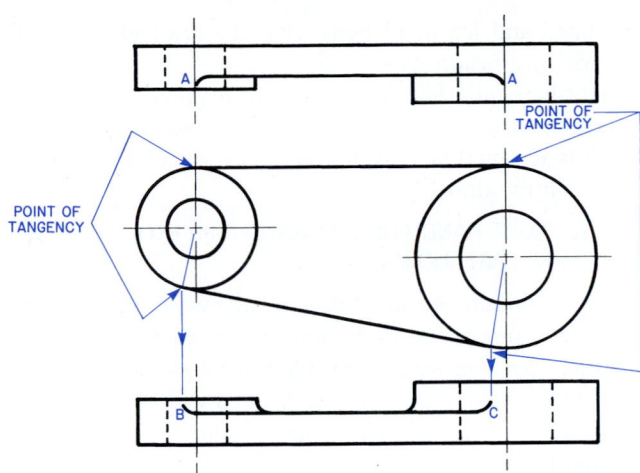

FIGURE 7.79   Runouts and Points of Tangency on Drawings

rately formed without these curved corners. Perfectly sharp corners are not possible with the casting process. Drawings of machined castings require the representation of these surfaces and their intersections. Two rough interior surfaces intersect and form a rounded corner called a **fillet**. Two rough exterior surfaces meet and form a corner called a **round**. The part in Figure 7.78 has a variety of rounds and fillets.

When two intersecting surfaces meet and one is machined, the corner becomes a sharp edge. If both surfaces are machined, the corner is also shown as a sharp edge. Rounds will show only when both mating exterior surfaces are unmachined (rough or cast surfaces). The material removed during machining is determined by the part's casting dimensions and the machining dimensions. Sometimes separate drawings are used. A *casting drawing* is done for the foundry and a *machine drawing* is completed for the machine shop (see Chapter 11).

As a design requirement, fillets and rounds are used to reduce the possibility of failure of a joint. Sharp points are possible points of fracture. Most fillets are determined by the foundry to meet the design requirements, the methods of casting, and the thickness of the part. In many cases, the selection of the fillet diameter is left to the patternmaker.

7.8.16   Tangent Surfaces

When a curved and a plane surface are tangent, a point of tangency may be required. In Figure 7.79, the cylindrical surfaces are connected by plane surfaces along the sides of the part. Since the cylindrical ends are different diameters, the tangent points of the cylinders and the planes will not fall along the centerline in the front view. Since the back surface is flush with the two diameters, tangent points A fall along the centerline. Because the circles are staggered and of different diameters, the front view of the tangent points does not fall along the centerline. Tangent points B and C are determined by drawing construction lines perpendicular to the front edge and through the center of each cylindrical surface in the view

where the diameter shows true shape (top view here). The intersection of this line and the circle's circumference determines the point of tangency (B and C).

7.8.17   Runouts and Edge Representation

After the point of tangency between a plane surface and a cylindrical surface has been determined, the runout can be drawn. **Runouts** are curves at the point of tangency. If the part is a casting, the runout will be a fillet at the tangent point, as in Figure 7.79. Points B and C are the points of tangency of the surface intersections, but they are also the transition points of the cast surfaces. Therefore, the fillet must be drawn as shown. The radius of the fillet is used to establish the runout; it is normally constructed with a template. Only 45° (one-eighth) of the curve need be drawn for most situations.

You May Complete Exercises 7.9 Through 7.12 at This Time

7.9   Opposite-Hand Parts

There are many industrial applications for parts that are the exact opposite of one another. These are called **opposite-hand parts** or **right-hand** and **left-hand parts.** In most cases, only one drawing is needed to describe both parts. To visualize a right-hand and a left-hand part, take an existing drawing (one from the text will do) and hold it up to a mirror. The reflection in the mirror shows the opposite hand of the part. If a right-hand part was used, the mirror shows the left-hand projection. Of course, to see a simple example of right-hand and left-hand, just look at your own hands.

Examples of industrial applications of right-hand and left-hand parts are numerous. A car has many opposite-hand parts, both in the engine and on the body of the automobile. Care must be taken, when viewing parts, so that you do not confuse right-hand and left-hand parts with parts that are the same but just happen to be installed on both sides of an assembly. For instance, a car's fenders and doors are obviously right-hand and left-hand parts. But, the headlights, wheels, hubcaps, and headrests are not.

Right-hand and left-hand parts are required in many circumstances. If a project requires a right-hand and a left-hand part, it is accepted practice to draw only one of the parts and to note on the drawing:

NOTE: RIGHT-HAND AND LEFT-HAND PART REQUIRED.
       RH PART SHOWN.

In general, if there are any differences between the two parts, it is normal practice to draw both. If the differences are minor, such as a hole size or the addition of a hole, then these differences can sometimes be established with a note or with a callout, as in the following example for the diameter dimension for a hole:

.500 DIA THRU
LH PART ONLY

When both LH and RH parts must be drawn, you can save much time and energy by tracing the completed side (or making a copy on an office copier), turning it over, and using it to draw the opposite side. A light table is used to see through the drafting paper to view the reversed drawing that is to be traced.

7.9.1 2D and 3D CAD Mirroring Commands for Opposite-Hand Parts

A CAD system will eliminate the need to draw the opposite-hand part. The **MIRROR** command displays the mirror image view of the part (or selected geometry of a part). Even a 2D system can be used to project the opposite hand of one view of the part. The choice of mirrored views depends on the complexity of the part. The view with the most complex geometry should be mirrored.

A 3D CAD system will have the advantage of projecting a true 3D model of the part's opposite hand as shown in Figure 7.80. In this illustration, the **RIGHT-HAND** and **LEFT-HAND** projections of the part are shown. The part has been mirrored about a plane (shown as a line in the lower illustration and as a plane in the 3D projection). After one hand of the part has been modeled on the system, it is a simple matter to give one command to establish the opposite-hand part.

If using AutoCAD, the mirror command is given as shown below:

```
Command: MIRROR
Select objects: Window
Pick first corner: Pick first corner of window
Pick second corner: Pick second point of window (en-
close the whole part)
Select objects: <RETURN>
First point of mirror line: Pick point on mirror line
Second point: Pick any point above or below—near mirror
line
Delete old objects? <N> <RETURN>
```

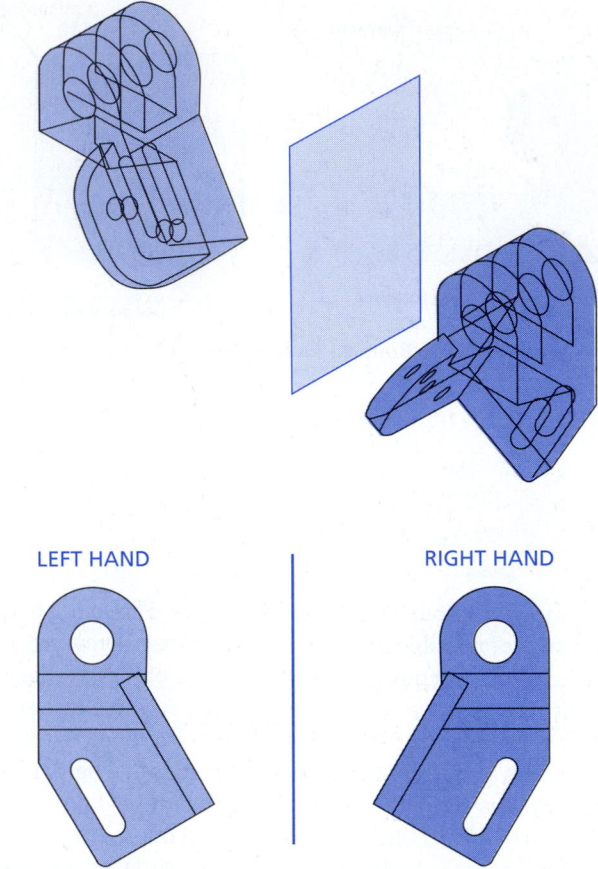

LEFT HAND   RIGHT HAND

FIGURE 7.80 Using the MIRROR Command to Create Opposite-Hand Parts

Because of the speed and simplicity of creating the opposite-hand part, using a CAD system to generate the second drawing of the part is a practical alternative to just noting the need for an opposite-hand part on the drawing.

7.10 View Construction Using CAD

The process used to construct manually drawn projects is the same when using a 2D CAD system. Therefore, all of the preceding descriptions for constructing views are valid. 3D CAD systems, on the other hand, create true three-dimensional models of the part. Because of this, the construction process is very different.

In general, every 3D system requires you to use one or more standard views (or **VIEWPORTS**) when modeling. Since the part can be rotated in 3D space, you need to establish only one "view" (the top normally). As the construction progresses, the model geometry is rotated into other orientations to model the complete part. Afterward, you can request the system to display additional views of the part for dimensioning. In Figure 7.81, the 3D system is displaying the completed model in three standard views and as a true 3D model in a rotated view.

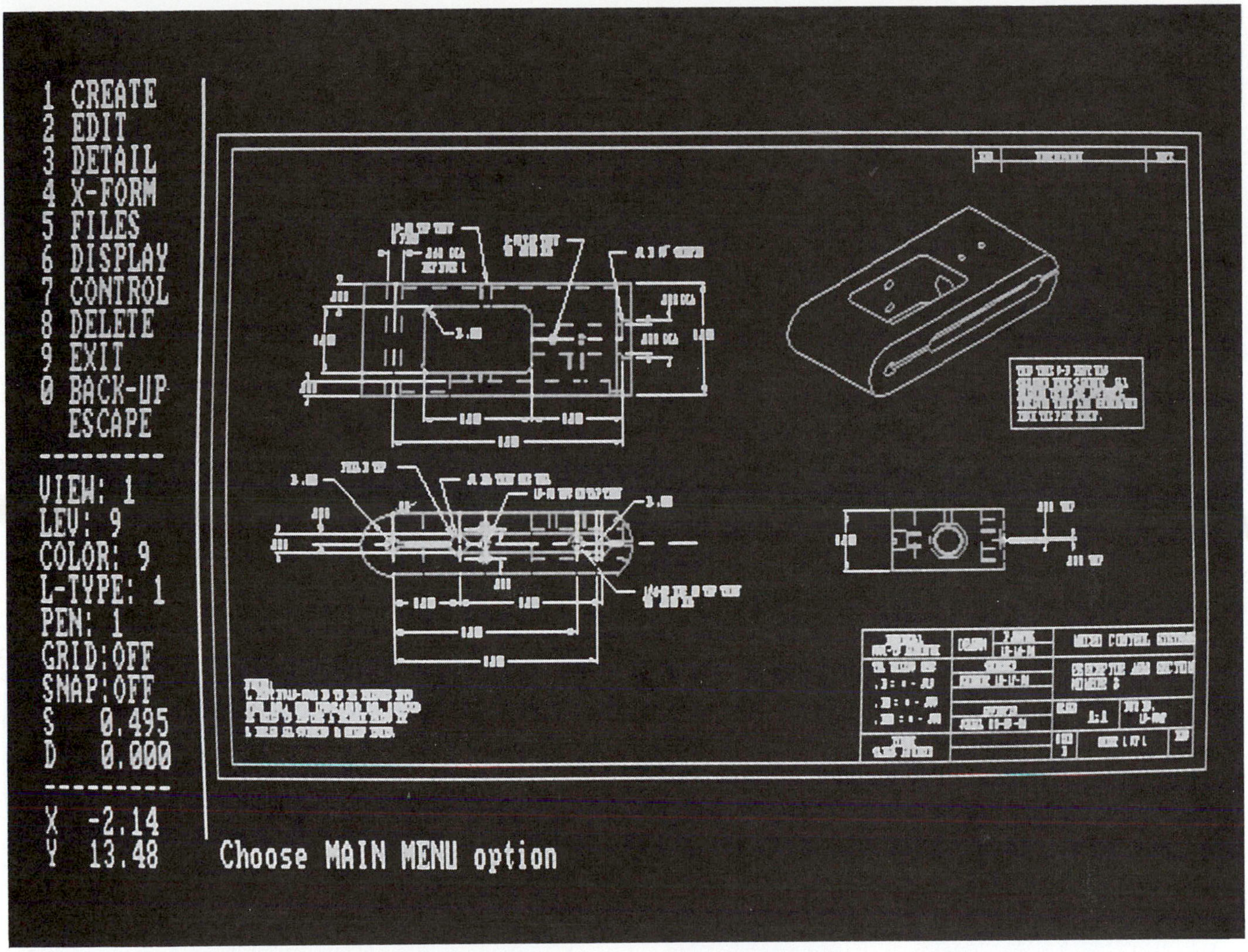

FIGURE 7.81   Views on a CAD System

It is not the purpose of this text to explain in detail the process of 3D modeling, but you should understand the differences in establishing views when using this procedure. Most CAD systems have six or seven standard views along with an infinite number of user-defined views. Six of the predefined views are the same as the six principal views. The seventh (when available) is a standard isometric (or rotated) view. In Figure 7.82, the seven views are shown: (1) top, (2) front, (3) right side, (4) bottom, (5) left side, (6) back/rear, and (7) isometric.

A part was modeled and is shown in a rotated 3D position in Figure 7.83(a). Since you need to show the model in accepted standard orthographic views to place the dimensions, a number of views must be established. The top is displayed in Figure 7.83(b). The front view is then displayed in Figure 7.83(c), and the drawing's right side view is defined in (d).

Regardless of the method used in the drafting and design process (manual, 2D CAD, or 3D CAD), knowledge and understanding of orthographic projection to create multiview drawings is essential for the aspiring drafter, designer, or engineer.

You May Complete Exercises 7.13 through 7.16 at This Time

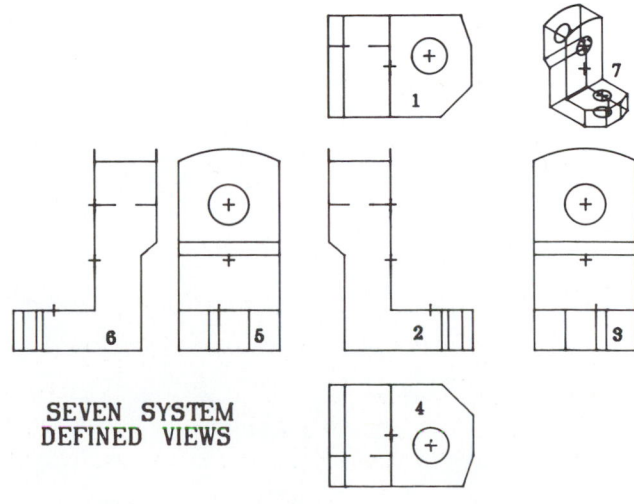

FIGURE 7.82   Seven Predefined Views on a 3D CAD System

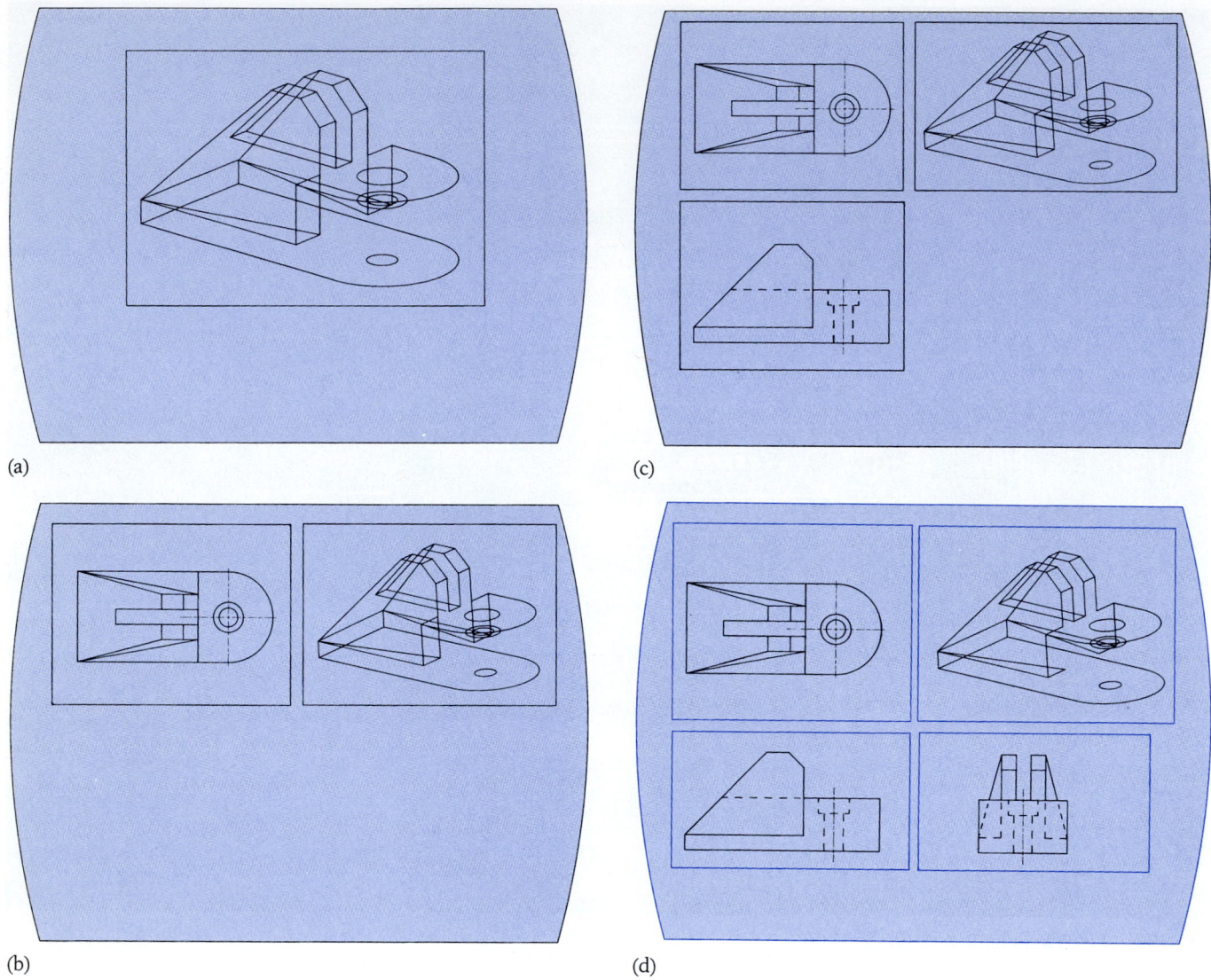

(a)

(b)

(c)

(d)

FIGURE 7.83 **Orthographic Views** (a) 3D model of part (b) Top view of part displayed along with 3D view (c) Front view displayed with top and 3D view (d) Right side view displayed with top, front, and 3D view

QUIZ

True or False

1. Partial projections of views are used to save space and paper.
2. Centerlines, phantom lines, dimension lines, and leader lines are all drawn with the same thickness.
3. Centerlines take precedence over hidden lines.
4. The glass box method of projection is used for most drawings.
5. Adjacent and related views are the same.
6. Parallel lines are parallel in all views.
7. Most foreign countries use third-angle projection for their engineering drawings.
8. All orthographic projection is right-angle projection.

Fill in the Blanks

9. _____ view drawings are normally limited to thin, flat, or _____ round parts.
10. When the object is relatively simple, a _____ line is used to project the third view.
11. Dimensions can be transferred from the top to the side view using _____ lines, the _____ method, or _____ .
12. _____ are considered to be a series of _____ in space having _____ but not _____ .
13. _____ _____ are used to show round features of a part on drawings.
14. **MIRROR** commands are useful in creating _____ _____ and _____ _____ parts.
15. _____ lines always take precedence over hidden lines.
16. A _____ is a specific location in space.

Answer the Following

17. What is a fold line and how is it used?
18. What are the six standard views?
19. What is the difference between the glass box method and the natural method?
20. What is the image plane for projection?
21. Describe adjacent and related views.
22. Explain the difference between first- and third-angle projection.
23. What determines the spacing and choice of views for a drawing?
24. Describe the ISO projection symbol and its use.

EXERCISES

Exercises may be assigned as sketching, instrument, or CAD projects. Transfer the given information to an "A" size sheet of .25 in. grid paper. Complete all views and solve for proper visibility, including centerlines, object lines, and hidden lines. Exercises that are not assigned by the instructor can be sketched in the text to provide practice and understanding of the preceding instructional material.

After Reading the Chapter Through Section 7.6.10, You May Complete the Following Exercises

Exercise 7.1   Complete each of the given views and the third view, if required.

Exercise 7.2   Complete each of the given views and the third view, if required.

Exercise 7.3   Complete each of the given views and the third view, if required.

Exercise 7.4   Complete each of the given views and the third view, if required.

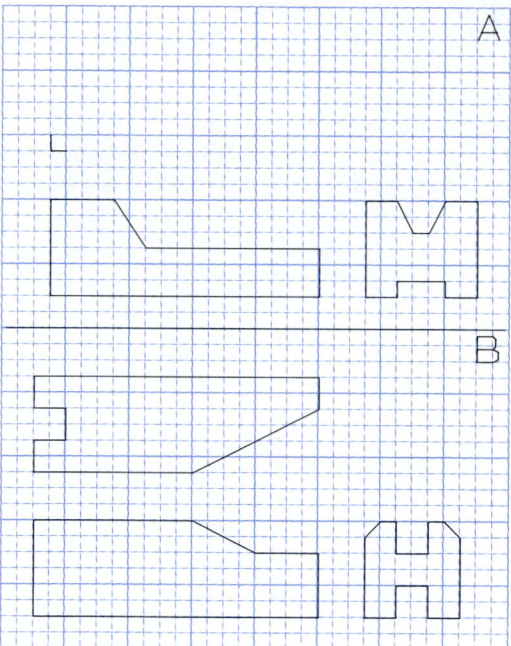

Exercise 7.1

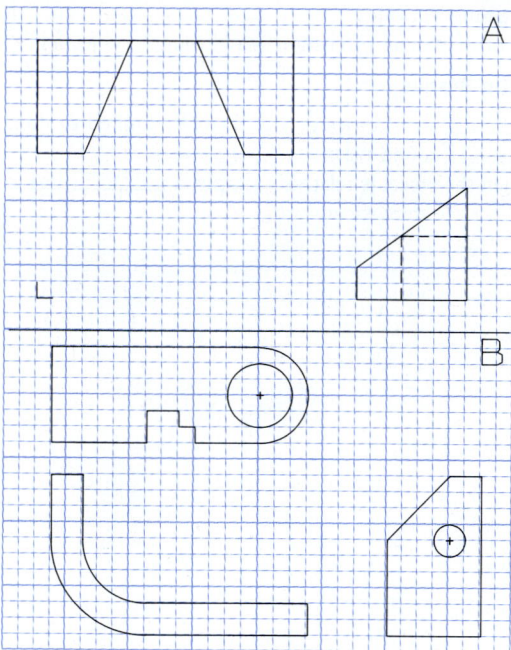

Exercise 7.3

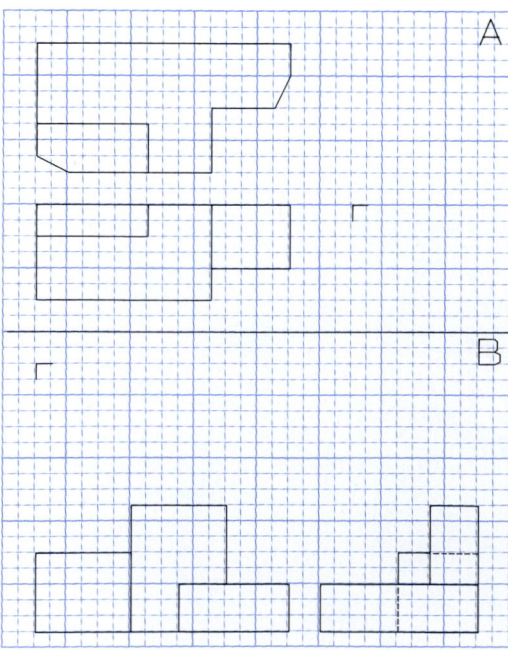

Exercise 7.2

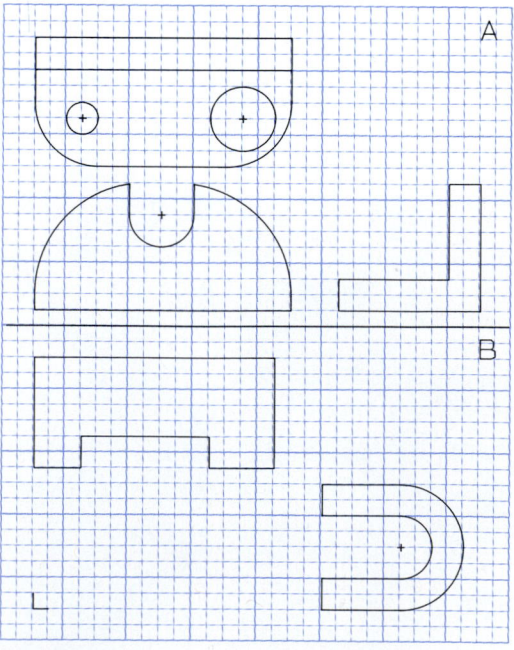

Exercise 7.4

After Reading the Chapter Through Section 7.8.10, You May Complete the Following Exercises

Exercise 7.5   Complete each of the given views and the third view, if required.

Exercise 7.6   Complete each of the given views and the third view, if required.

Exercise 7.7   Complete each of the given views and the third view, if required.

Exercise 7.8   Complete each of the given views and the third view, if required.

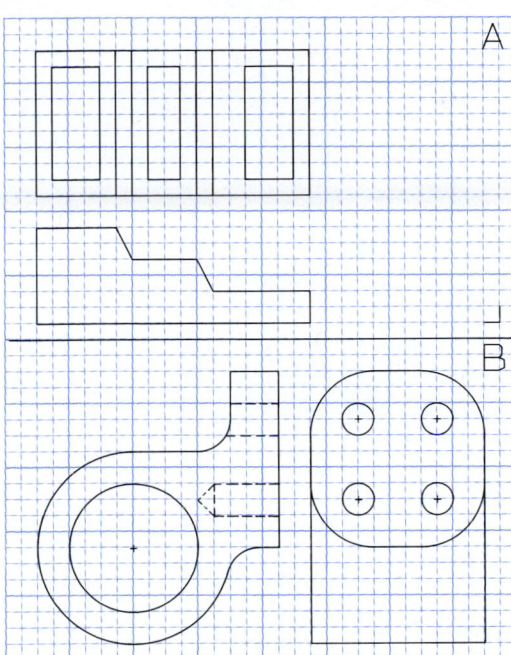

Exercise 7.5

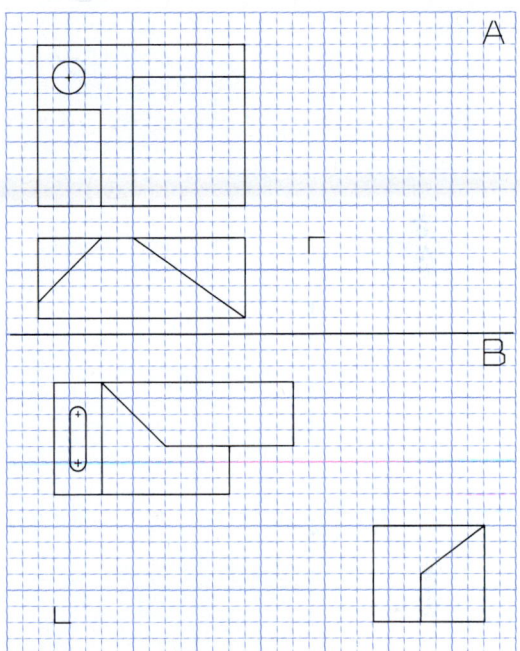

Exercise 7.7

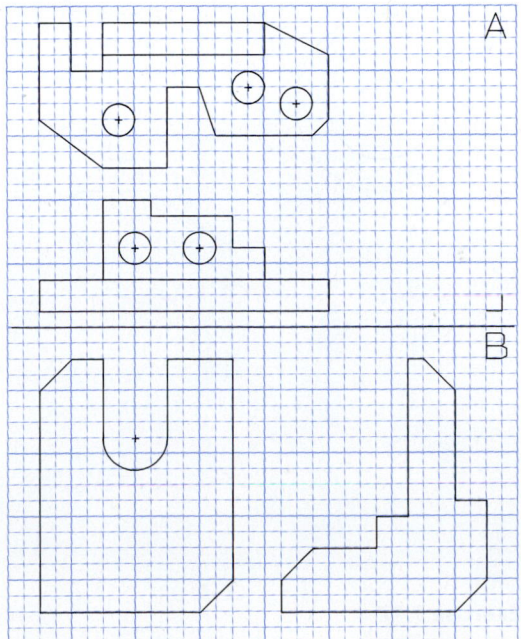

Exercise 7.6

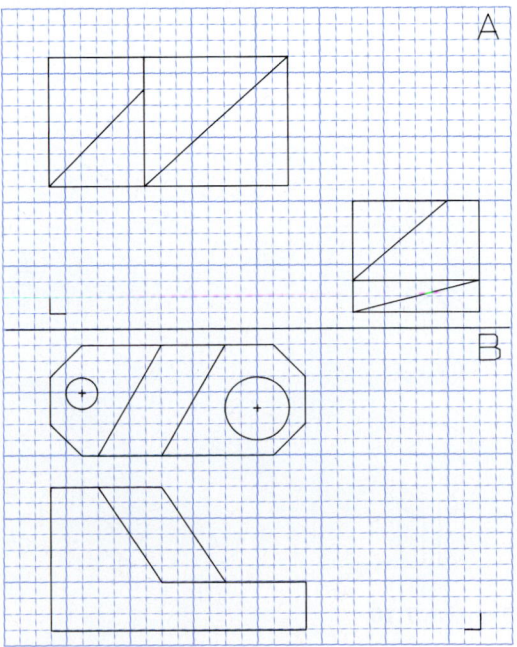

Exercise 7.8

After Reading the Chapter Through Section 7.8.17, You May Complete the Following Exercises

Exercise 7.9 Complete each of the given views and the third view, if required.

Exercise 7.10 Complete each of the given views and the third view, if required.

Exercise 7.11 Complete each of the given views and the third view, if required.

Exercise 7.12 Complete each of the given views and the third view, if required.

Exercise 7.9

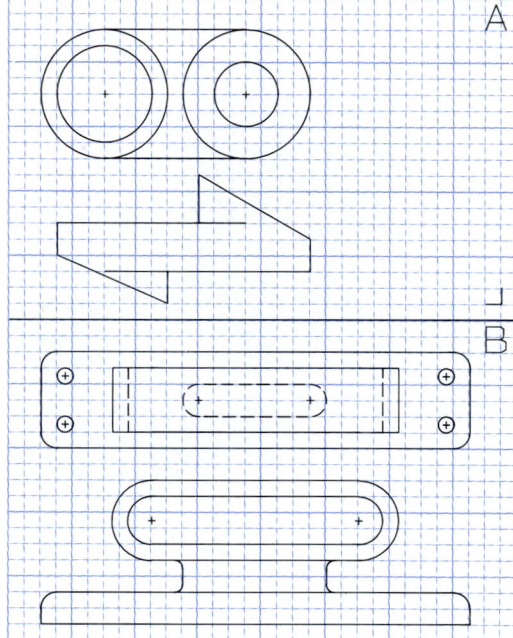

Exercise 7.11

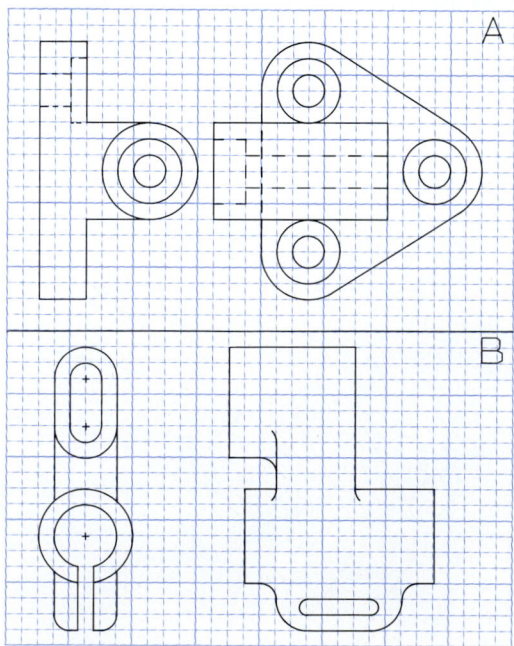

Exercise 7.10

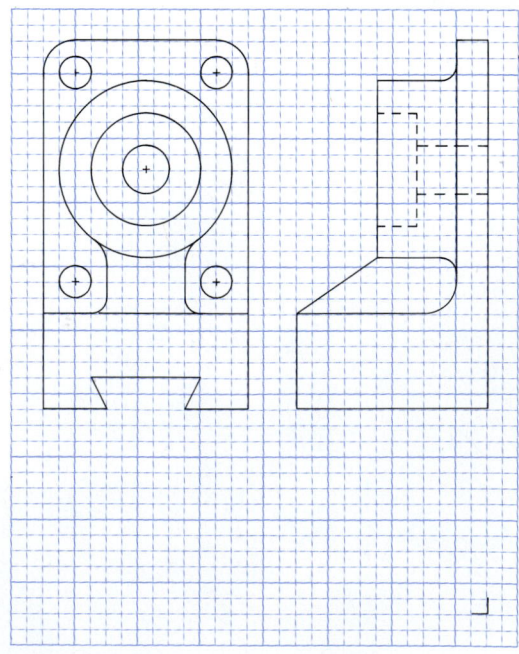

Exercise 7.12

After Reading the Chapter Through Section 7.10, You May Complete the Following Exercises

Exercise 7.13 Complete each of the given views and the third view, if required.

Exercise 7.14 Complete each of the given views and the third view, if required.

Exercise 7.15 Complete each of the given views and the third view, if required.

Exercise 7.16 Complete each of the given views and the third view, if required.

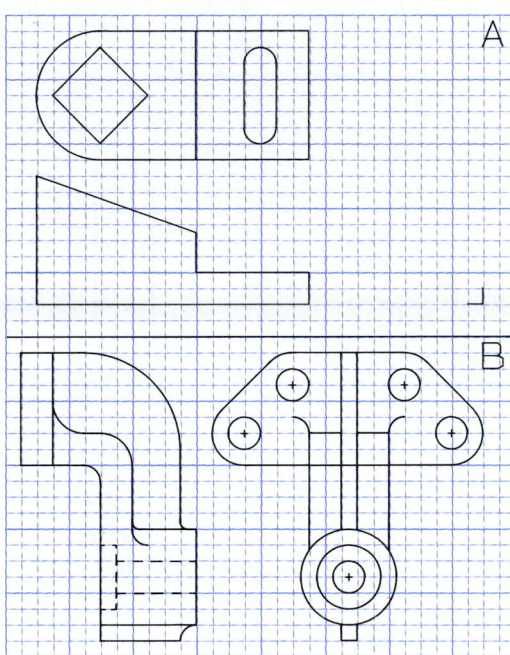

Exercise 7.13

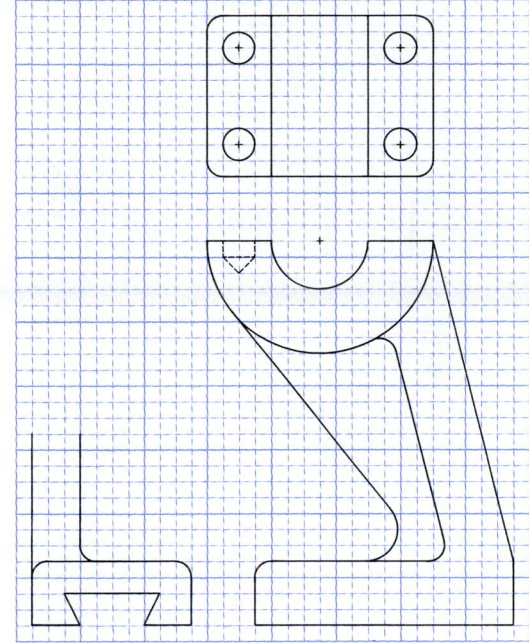

Exercise 7.15

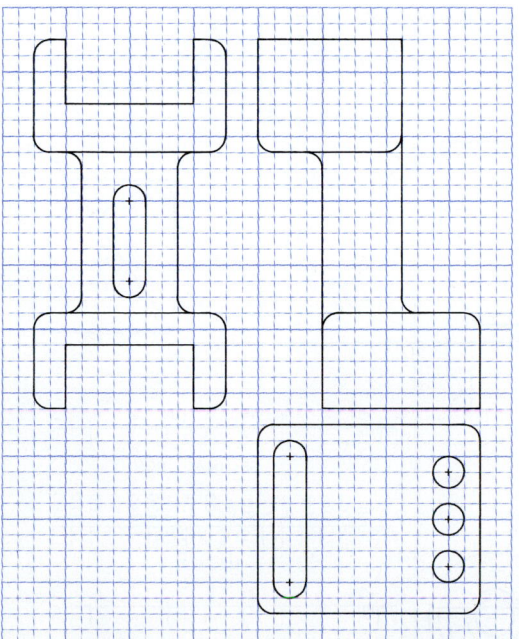

Exercise 7.14

Exercise 7.16

PROBLEMS

Problems 7.1(A) Through (K) Complete each of the problems on an "A" or "B" size sheet as required. Use one of the three scales provided in the lower left corner of the page. Use dividers to take measurements from the drawing and set off on one of the scales to establish the parts dimensions. Round off dimensions where necessary. Solve for the missing view in each problem. All projects will have three views.

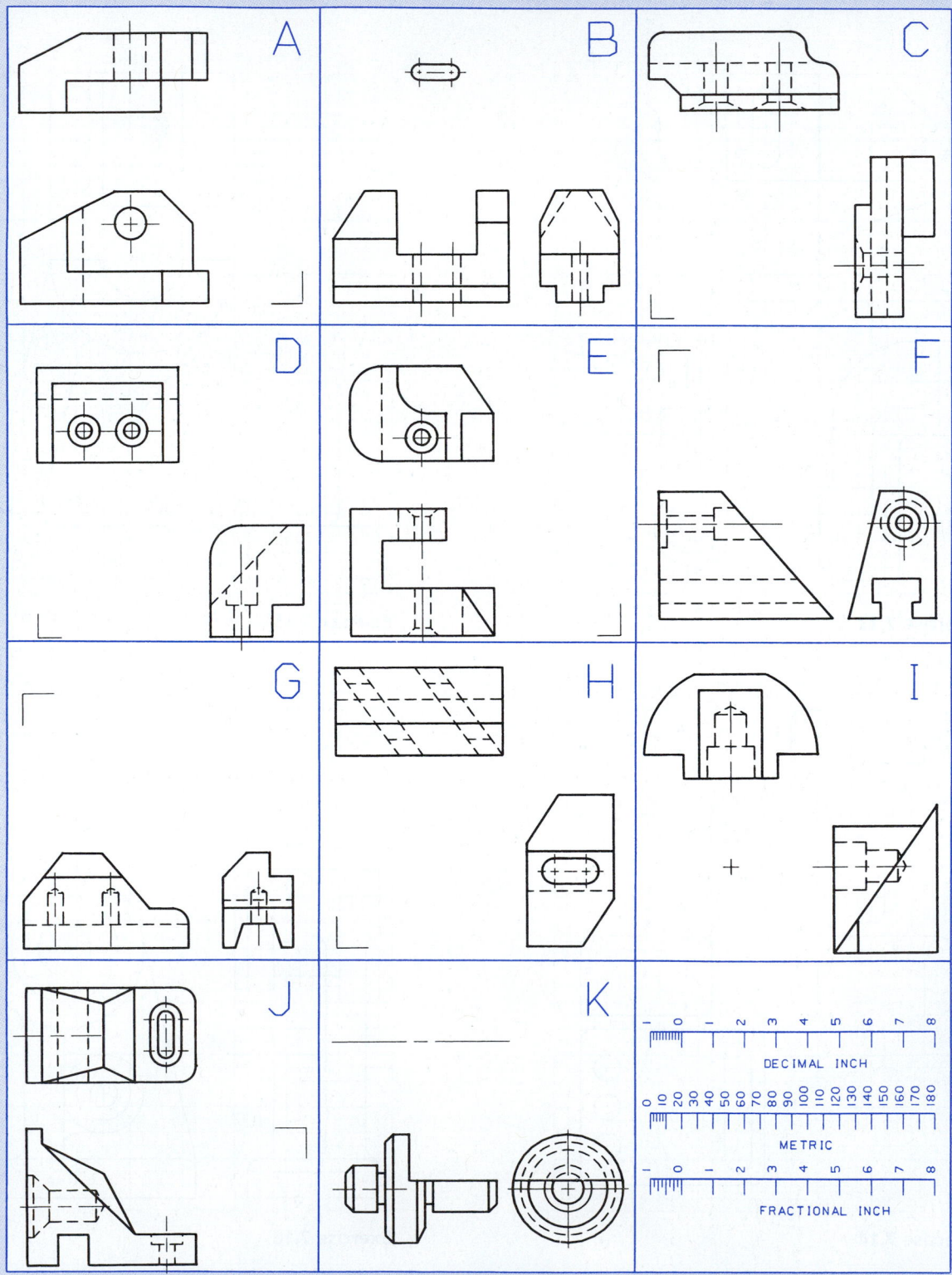

Problems 7.2(A) Through (G)   Use the same directions as for Problem 7.1. In these problems, some of the given views are incomplete though the outline of each of the three views is given. Complete the views as needed.

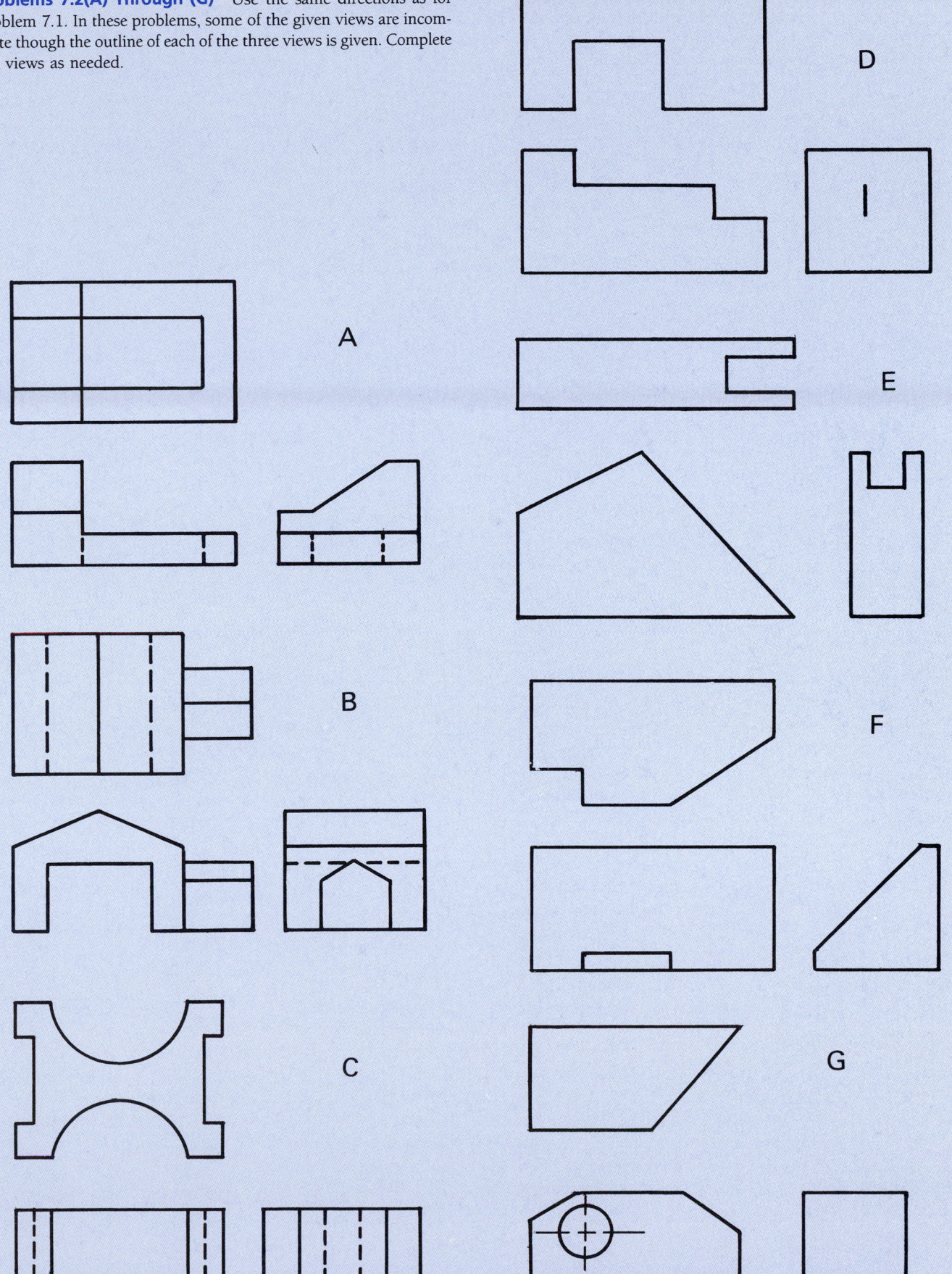

Problems 7.3 Through 7.10   Draw enough views to describe the part graphically. These projects can be used later for dimensioning projects after completing Chapter 12. Because of this, leave sufficient spacing between views to accommodate dimensions and notes.

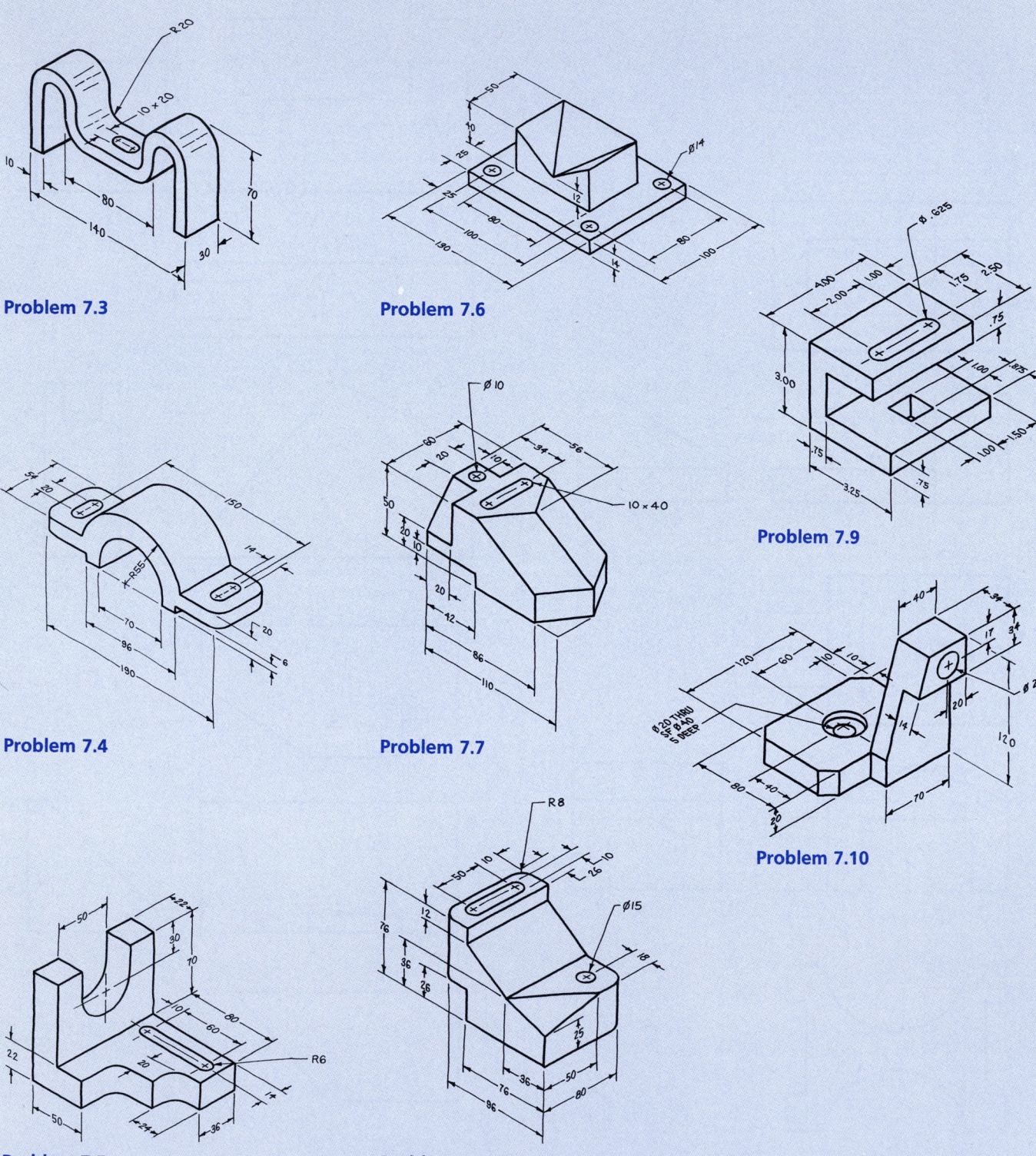

Problem 7.3

Problem 7.6

Problem 7.9

Problem 7.4

Problem 7.7

Problem 7.10

Problem 7.5

Problem 7.8

Problems 7.11 Through 7.30   Draw three views for each of the given problems. Use an "A" size sheet for each project. Establish all dimensions by grid squares equaling 1″ or 20 mm as assigned by the instructor.

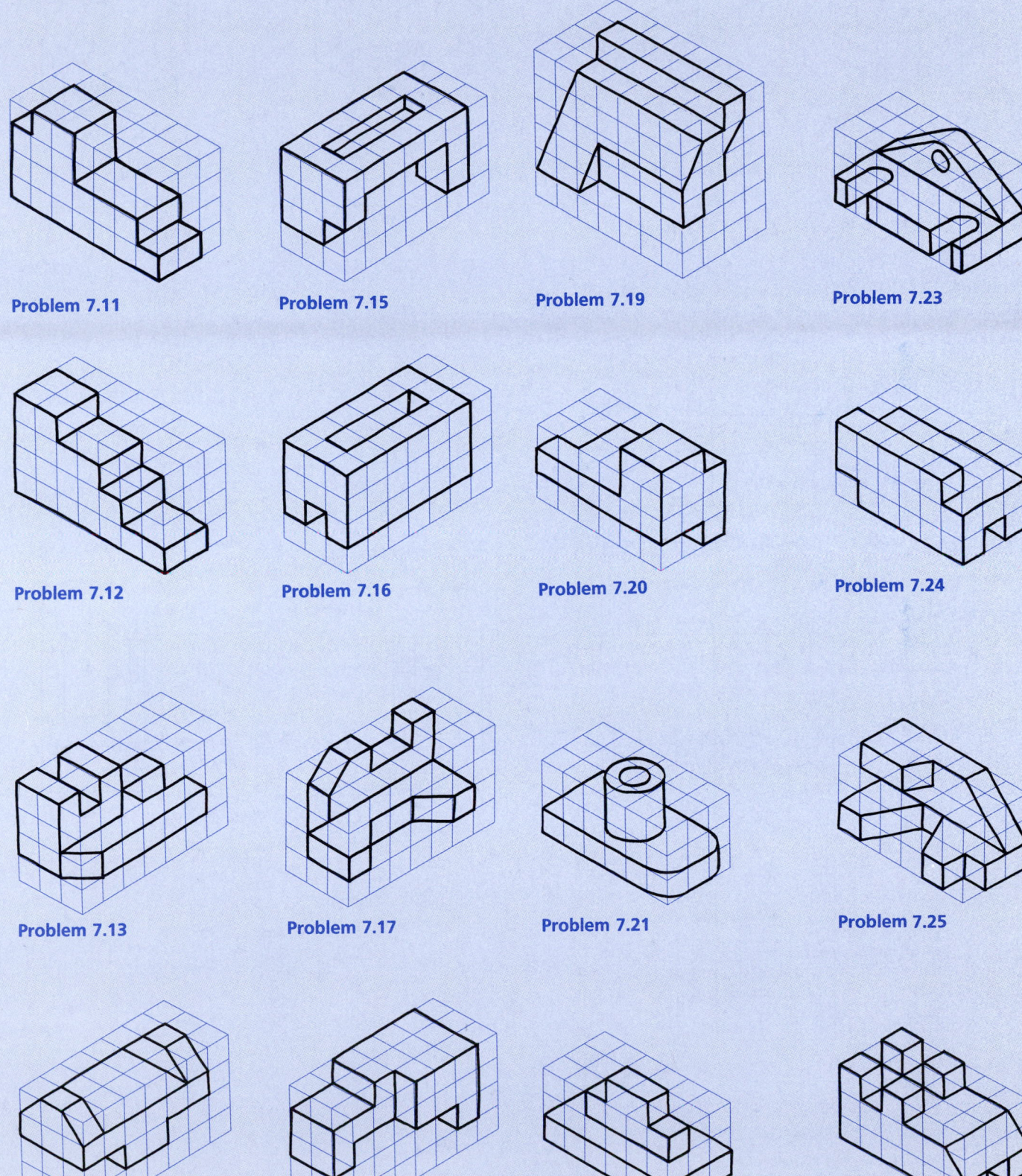

Problem 7.11

Problem 7.15

Problem 7.19

Problem 7.23

Problem 7.12

Problem 7.16

Problem 7.20

Problem 7.24

Problem 7.13

Problem 7.17

Problem 7.21

Problem 7.25

Problem 7.14

Problem 7.18

Problem 7.22

Problem 7.26

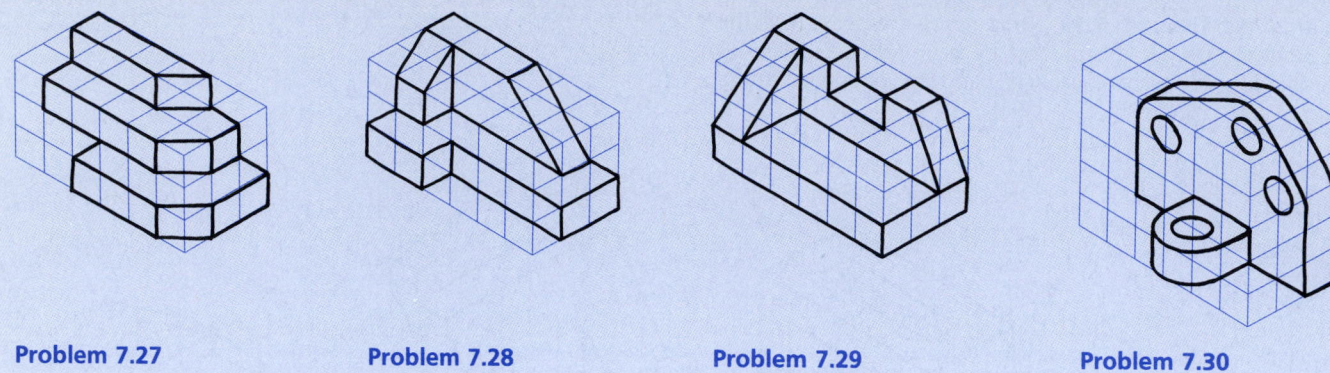

Problem 7.27　　　　**Problem 7.28**　　　　**Problem 7.29**　　　　**Problem 7.30**

Problems 7.31 Through 7.43　Draw, but do not dimension, each problem assigned by the instructor. Do not section any of the parts.

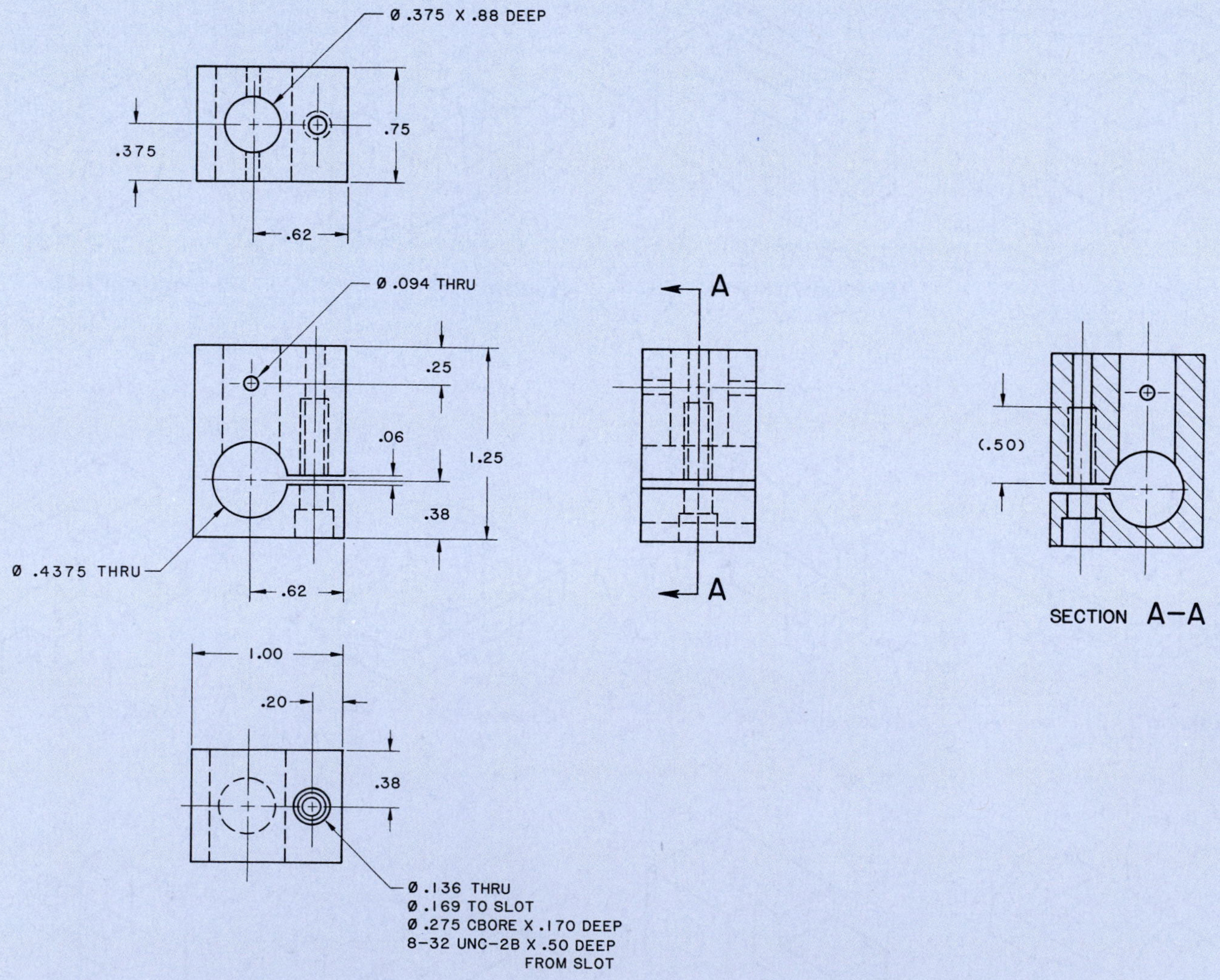

Ø .375 X .88 DEEP

.375

.75

.62

Ø .094 THRU

.25

.06

1.25

.38

Ø .4375 THRU

.62

A

A

SECTION A–A

(.50)

1.00

.20

.38

Ø .136 THRU
Ø .169 TO SLOT
Ø .275 CBORE X .170 DEEP
8–32 UNC–2B X .50 DEEP
FROM SLOT

NOTE: 1. USED ON Q.A. TEST FIXTURE–CASTLE

Problem 7.31

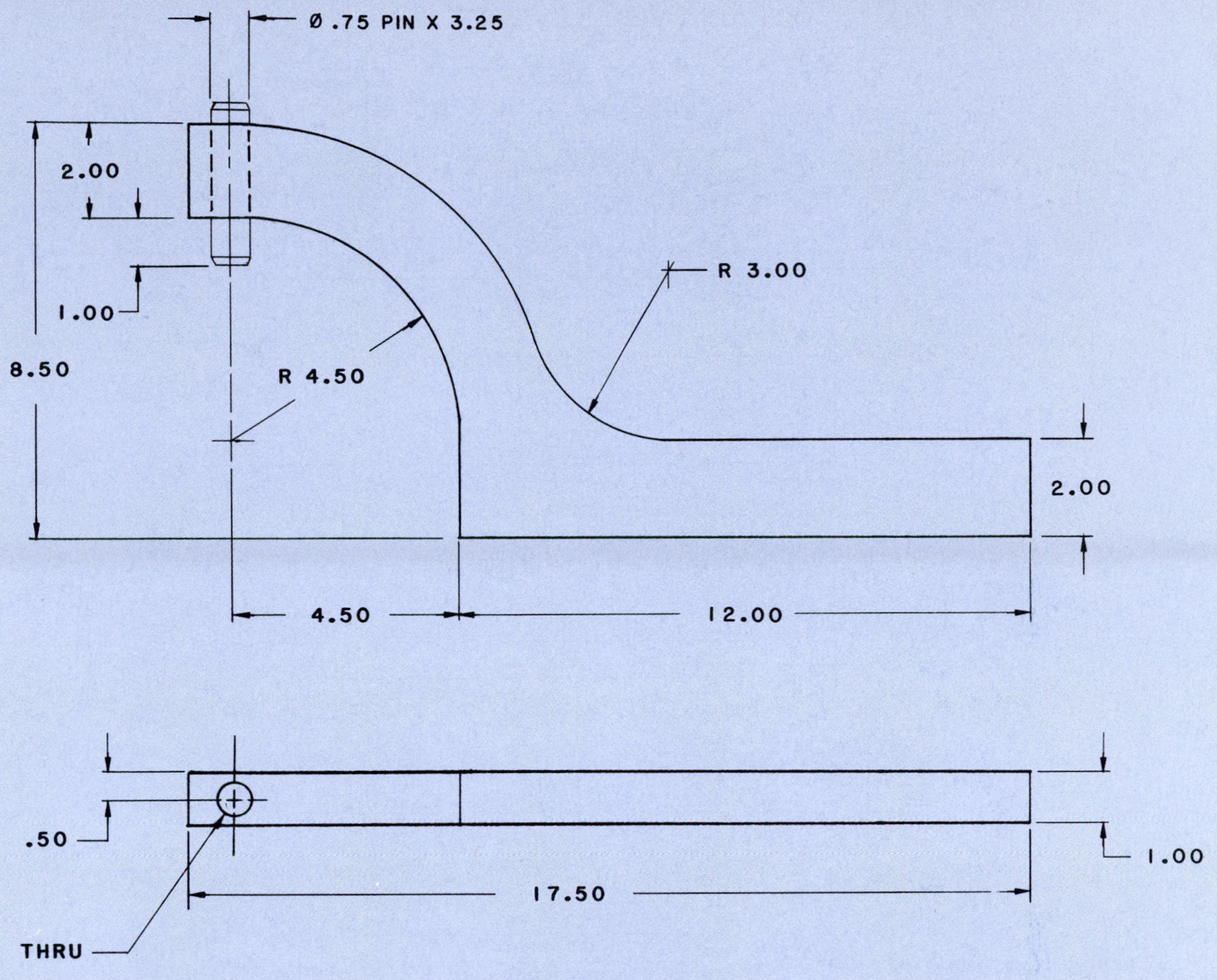

Ø .75 PIN X 3.25

2.00

1.00

8.50

R 4.50

R 3.00

2.00

4.50

12.00

.50

17.50

1.00

Ø .7505 / .7500   THRU

Problem 7.32

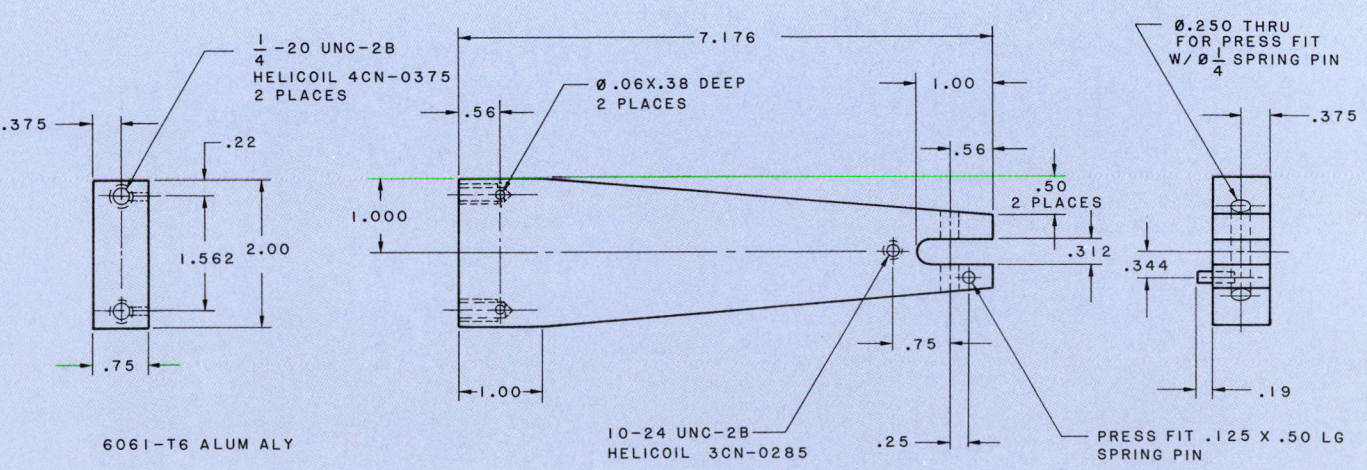

6061-T6 ALUM ALY

Problem 7.33

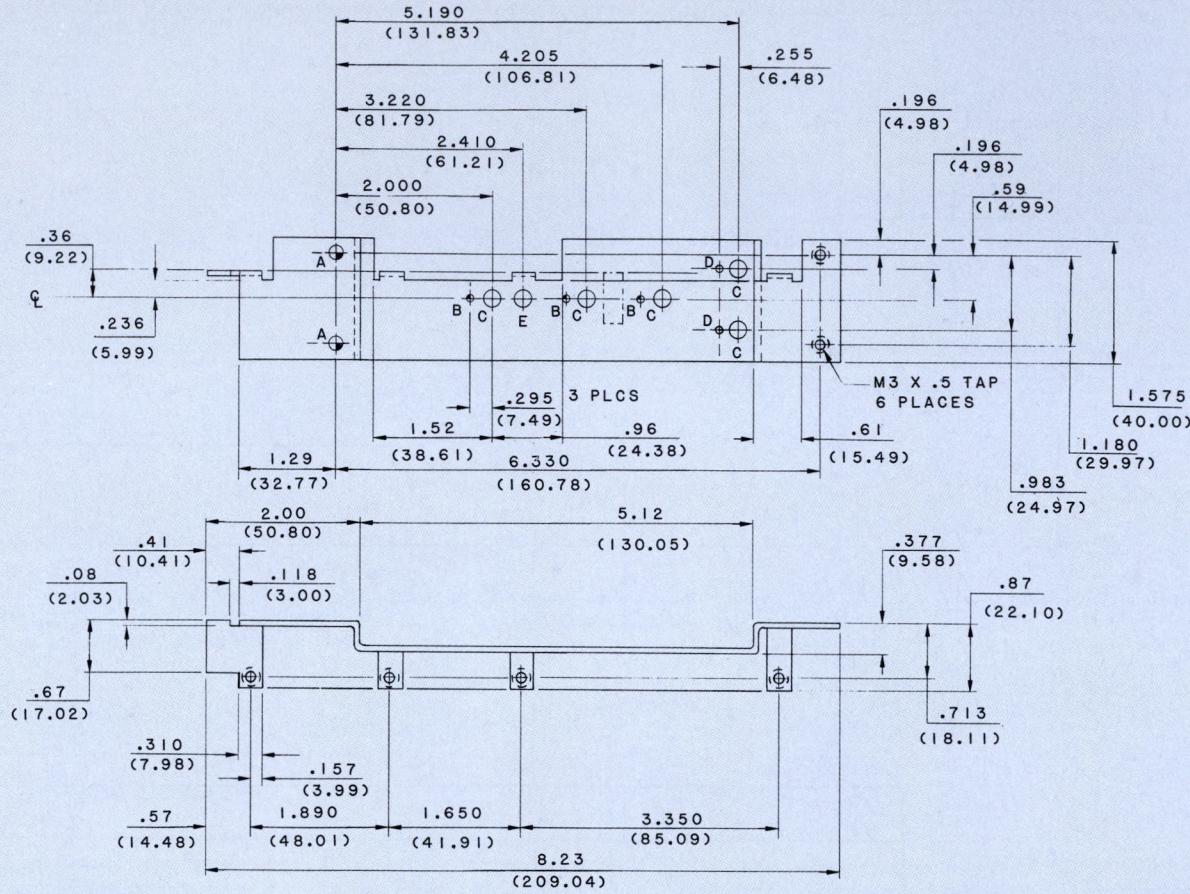

NOTES:

1. REMOVE ALL BURRS AND SHARP EDGES

2. BEND RADII .06 MAX

3. MARK PART NO. NEARSIDE

HOLE CHART		
CODE	DESCRIPTION±.005	QTY
A	.140 (3.56)	2
B	1.109 (2.78)	3
C	.219 (5.56)	5
D	.094 (2.38)	2
E	.188 (4.76)	1

SUBPANEL,PREV-2 BD

Problem 7.34

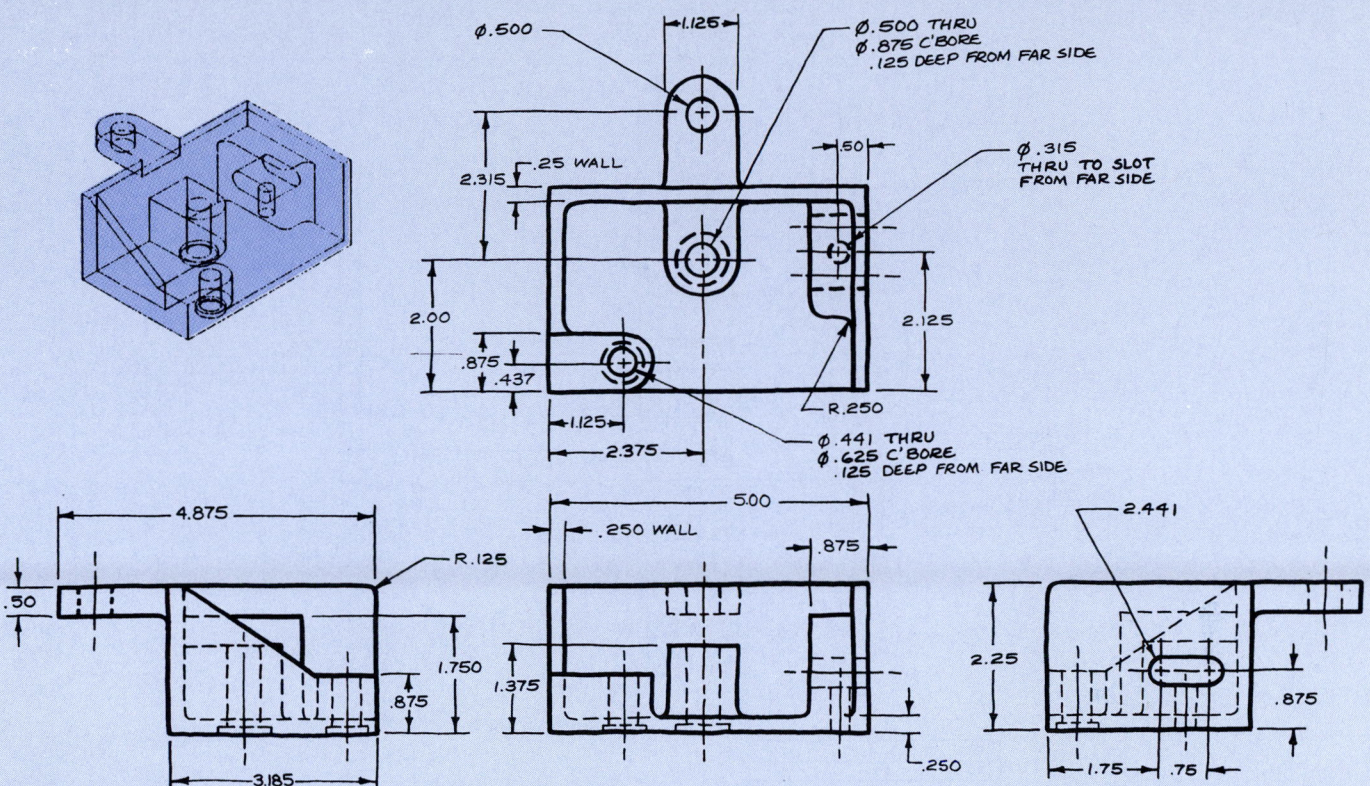

Problem 7.35

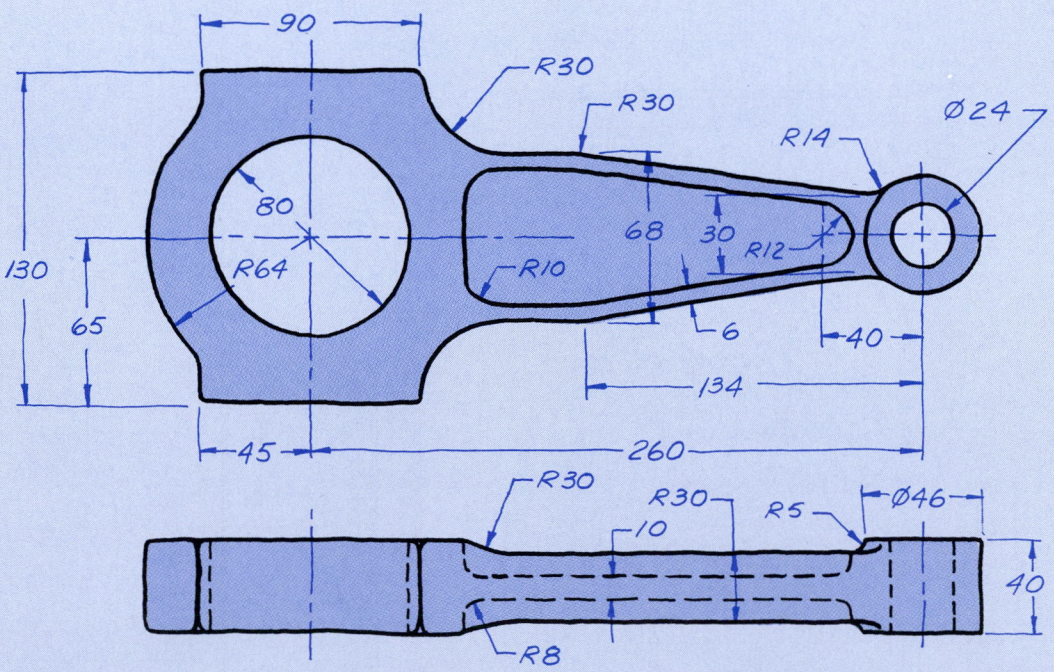

Problem 7.36

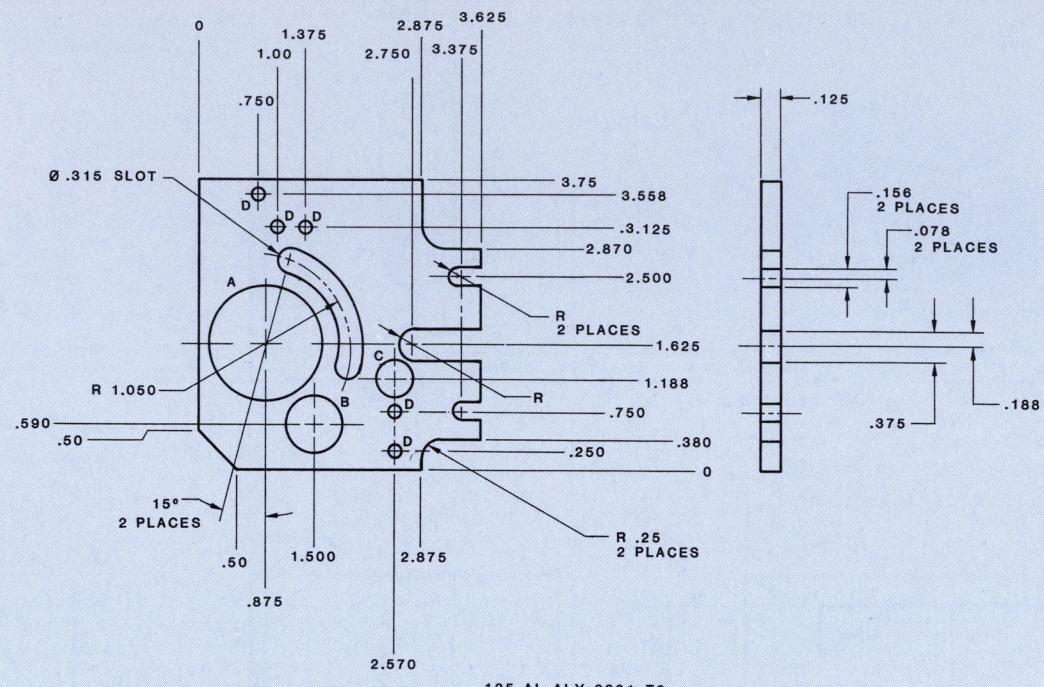

.125 AL ALY 6061-T6

ANODIZE, BLACK

HOLE	DESCRIPTION	QTY
A	Ø 1.552	1
B	Ø .688	1
C	Ø .500	1
D	Ø .149	5

Problem 7.37

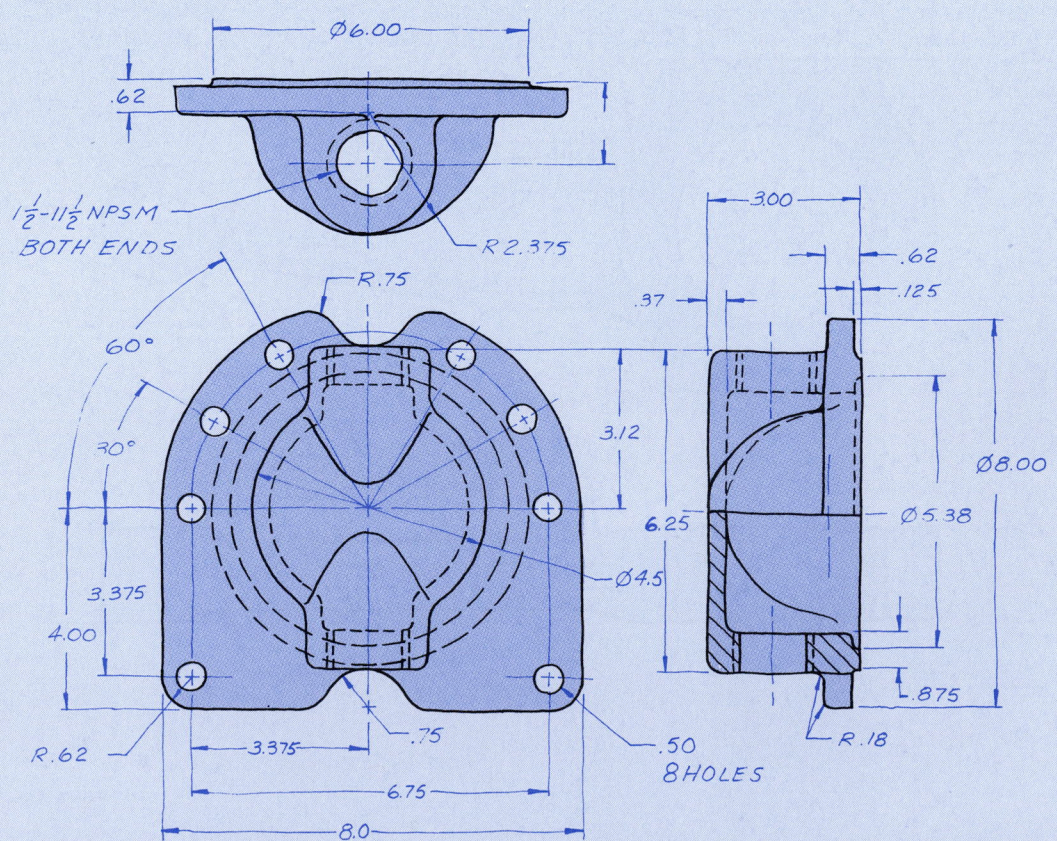

Problem 7.38

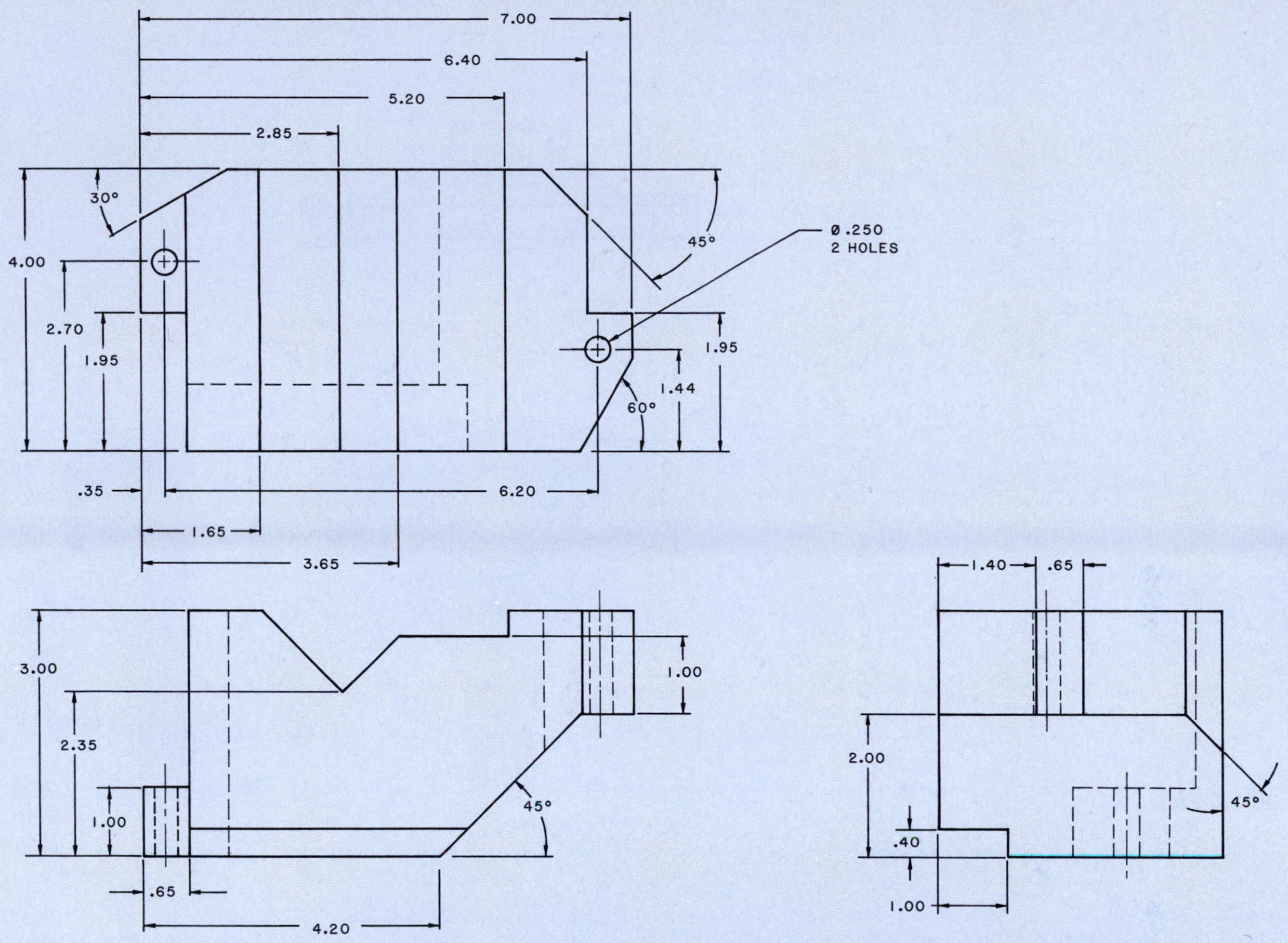

Problem 7.39

7.00
6.40
5.20
2.85
30°
45°
Ø .250
2 HOLES
4.00
2.70
1.95
1.95
1.44
60°
.35
6.20
1.65
3.65

3.00
2.35
1.00
1.00
45°
.65
4.20

1.40   .65
2.00
.40
1.00
45°

Problem 7.40

R .133
TYP
.750   .510
.620
1.800
-A-
1.450
.266
4 PLCS
⊕ .008 A
.470
.240
10.00°
SEE NOTE

.266
2 SLOTS
R .133
TYP
.900
⊕ .008 A
.15

NOTE: 10° REF AND 10° REF ON PART
NO. B-2FL-21-002 ARE TO
BE WITHIN 0 5' OF EACH OTHER
(MACHINE AT SAME SET-UP)

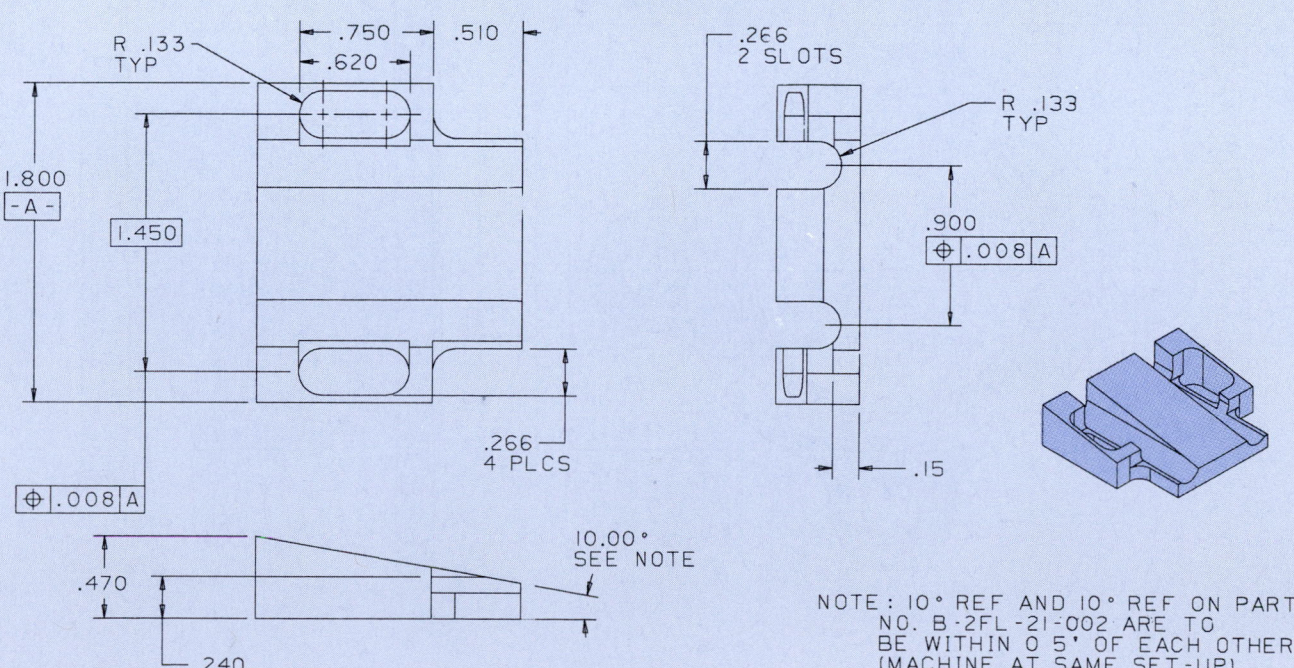

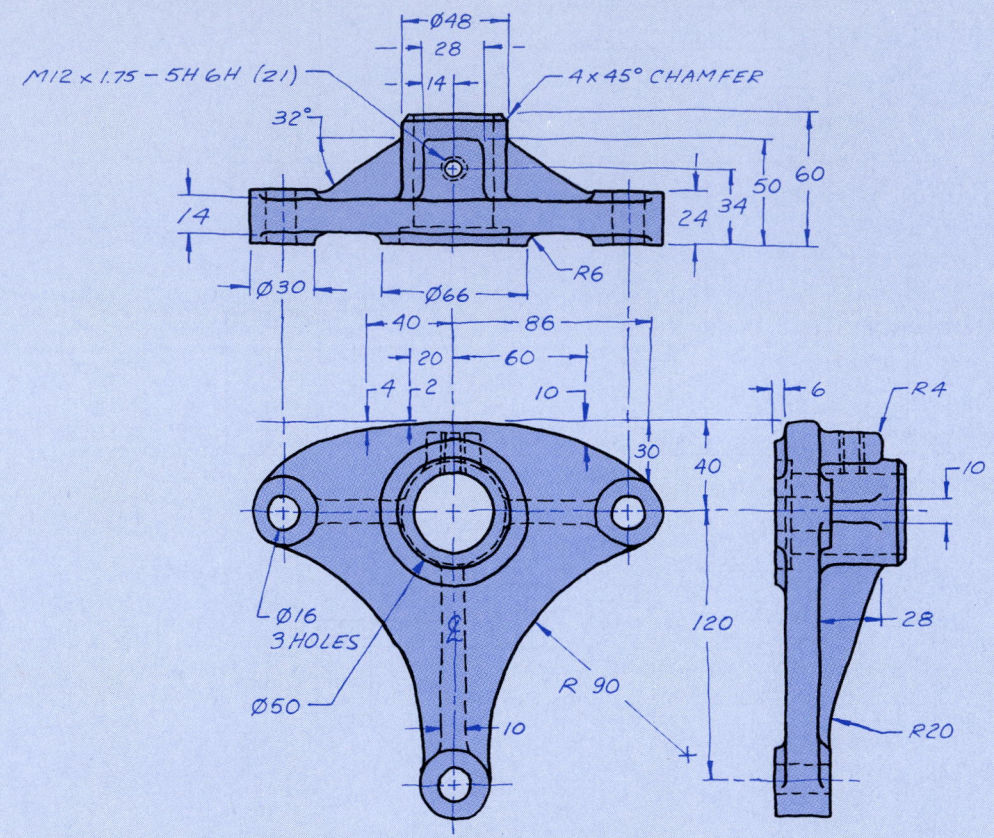

Problem 7.41

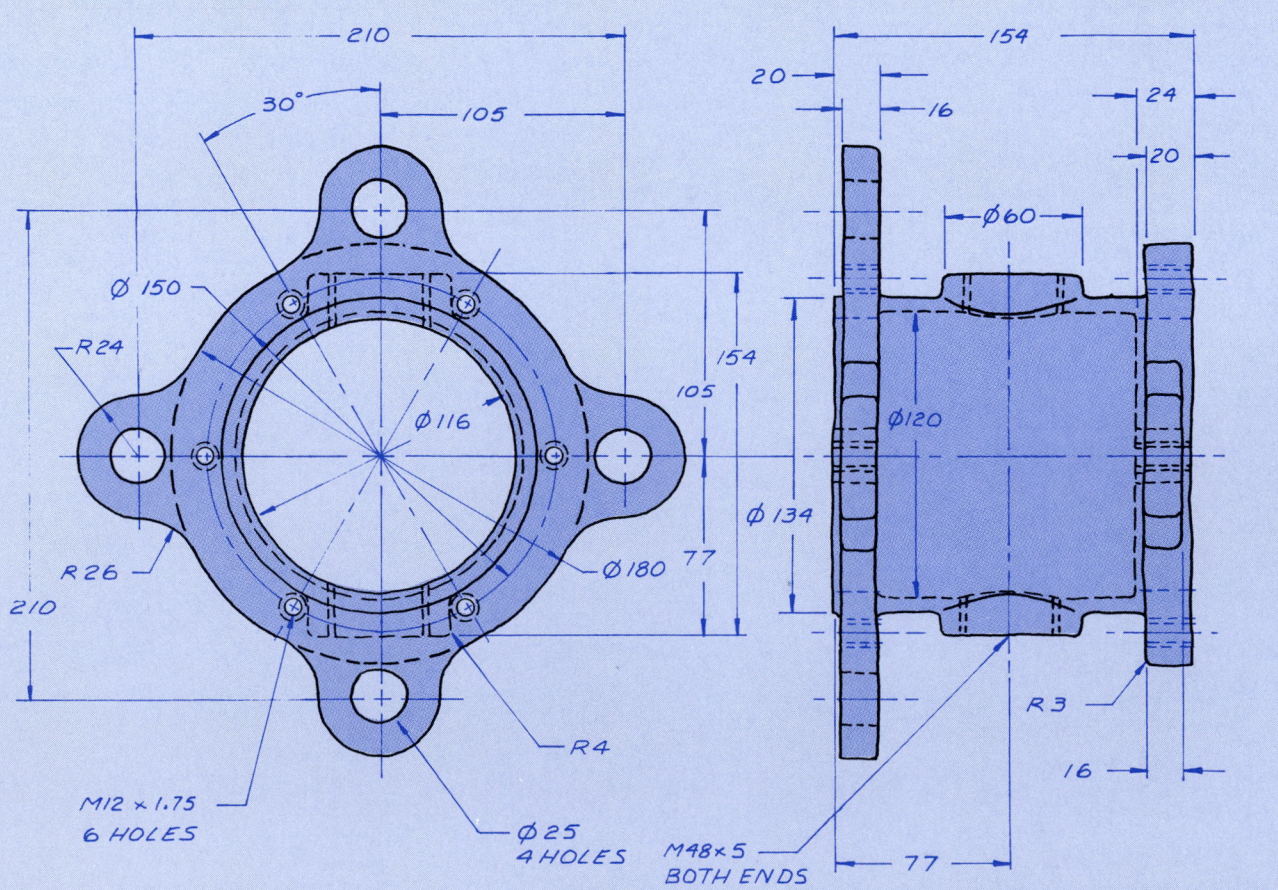

Problem 7.42

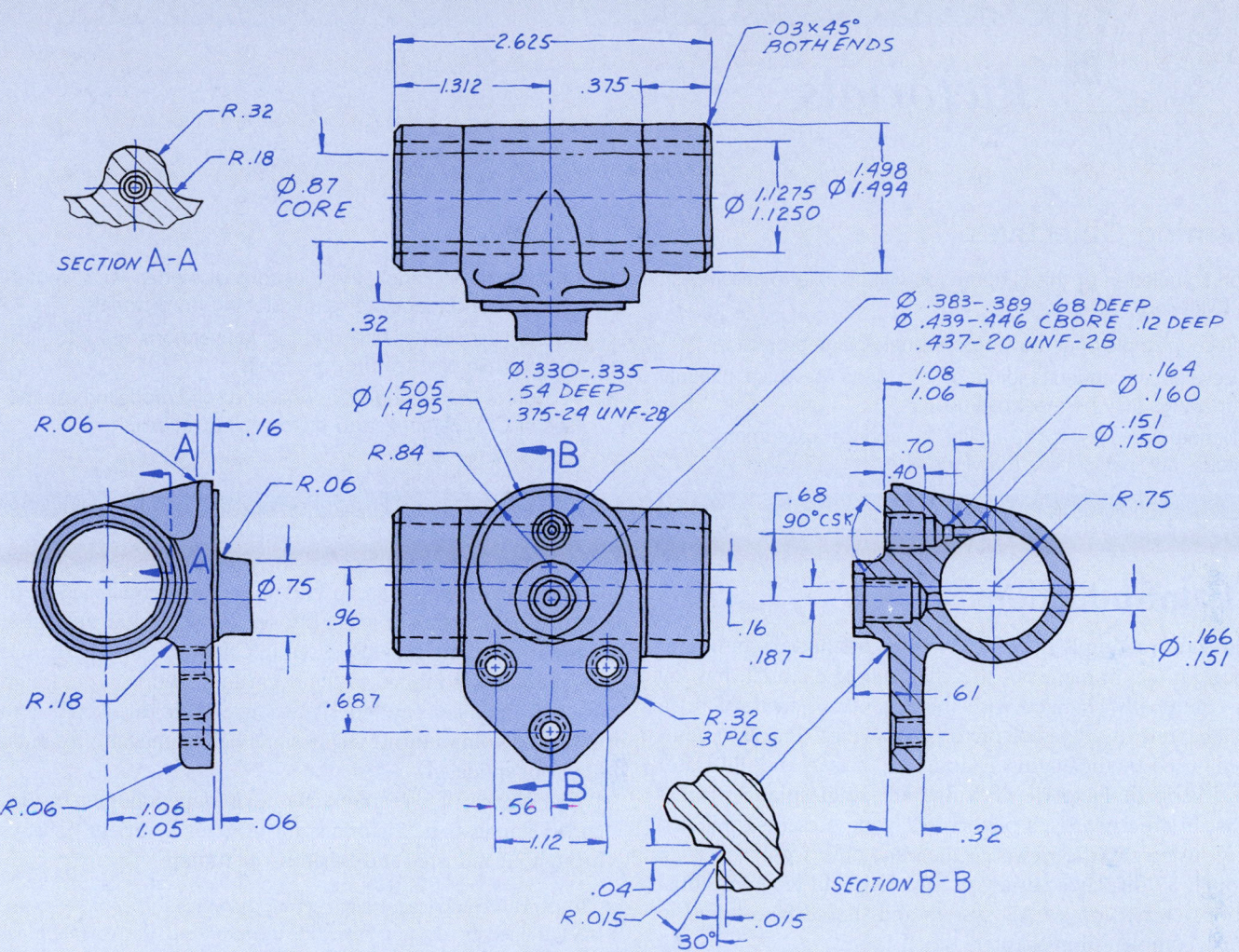

Problem 7.43

Problem 7.44   Redraw Figure 7.12; show a side view and make the part 1.00 inches thick. Do not dimension.

Problem 7.45   Draw Figure 7.13. Do not section or dimension.

Problem 7.46   Draw Figure 7.14. Do not dimension.

Problem 7.47   Draw Figure 7.15. Do not dimension.

Problem 7.48   Draw Figure 7.16. Do not dimension.

Problem 7.49   Draw Figure 7.17. Do not dimension.

Problem 7.50   Draw Figure 7.45. Do not dimension.

Problem 7.51   Draw Figure 7.76. Do not dimension. Show only the required views.

CHAPTER 8

Pictorials

Learning Objectives

Upon completion of this chapter you will be able to accomplish the following:

1. Recognize pictorial drawings as single-plane projections.

2. Develop an understanding of the ways in which pictorial drawings may be most useful.

3. Define and possess the ability to produce axonometric, oblique, and perspective drawings.

4. Understand and apply the functions of hidden lines, centerlines, and techniques for dimensioning on pictorials.

5. Develop familiarity with drafting conventions used to illustrate certain part features pictorially.

6. Recognize the three-dimensional and solid modeling capabilities of CAD as applied to pictorial illustrations.

8.1 Introduction

Pictorial drawing is the oldest written method of communication known to man, but the character of pictorial drawing has continually changed with the advance of civilization. In this chapter, the types of pictorial drawings (Fig. 8.1) commonly used by the engineer, designer, drafter, and illustrator are described. Pictorial drawings are **single-plane projections.** In other words, a pictorial drawing presents three primary surfaces to the viewer at the same time. Color Plates 23 through 27 display a variety of pictorials and technical illustrations created on a CAD system and should be referred to as you complete this chapter.

Pictorial drawings are useful in design, construction or production, erection or assembly, service or repairs, and sales. Pictorial sketching was discussed in Chapter 6, where the use of pictorials was limited to the beginning stages of the design process. Engineers and designers use pictorial sketches to refine and communicate 3D designs before they are formally drawn or modeled.

The choice of pictorial drawing is dependent on its intended application. Pictorials are used in a variety of ways throughout industry and business including:

- To explain complicated engineering drawings to people who are not trained or do not have the time to read the conventional multiview drawings.
- To help the designer or drafter work out problems in 3D space, such as clearances and interferences.
- To train new employees in the shop with illustrated training manuals.
- To speed up and clarify the assembly of a machine.
- For ordering new parts as in parts catalogs and service manuals.
- To transmit ideas from person to person, from shop to shop, or from sales to purchasing.
- As an educational aid in developing visualization.

8.2 Types of Pictorial Drawing

The three general groups into which pictorial projections may be divided are: **axonometric, oblique,** and **perspective.** These three differ from each other in the fundamental scheme of projection (Fig. 8.2). Axonometric projection is a form of orthographic projection. Each of the three groups is subdivided by varying some of the relationships between point of sight, plane of projection, and the object. In Figures 8.3, 8.4, and 8.5, the same assembly has been displayed using each of the projection types and their accompanying versions. The four versions of axonometric projection are illustrated in Figure 8.3: **isometric projection, isometric drawing, dimetric projection,** and **trimetric projection.** The three versions of

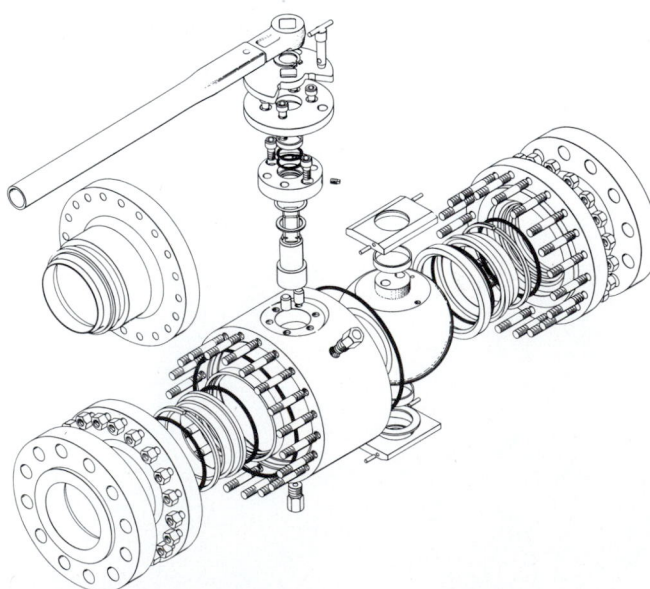

FIGURE 8.1 Technical Illustration of a Ball Valve from a Sales Catalog

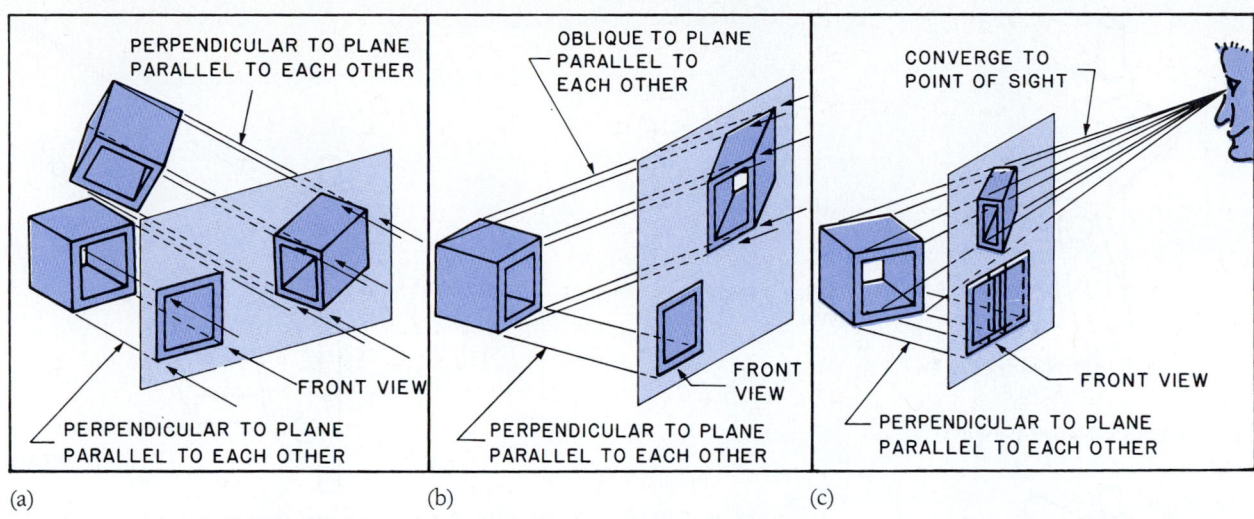

FIGURE 8.2   Types of Pictorial Projection   (a) Axonometric (b) Oblique (c) Perspective

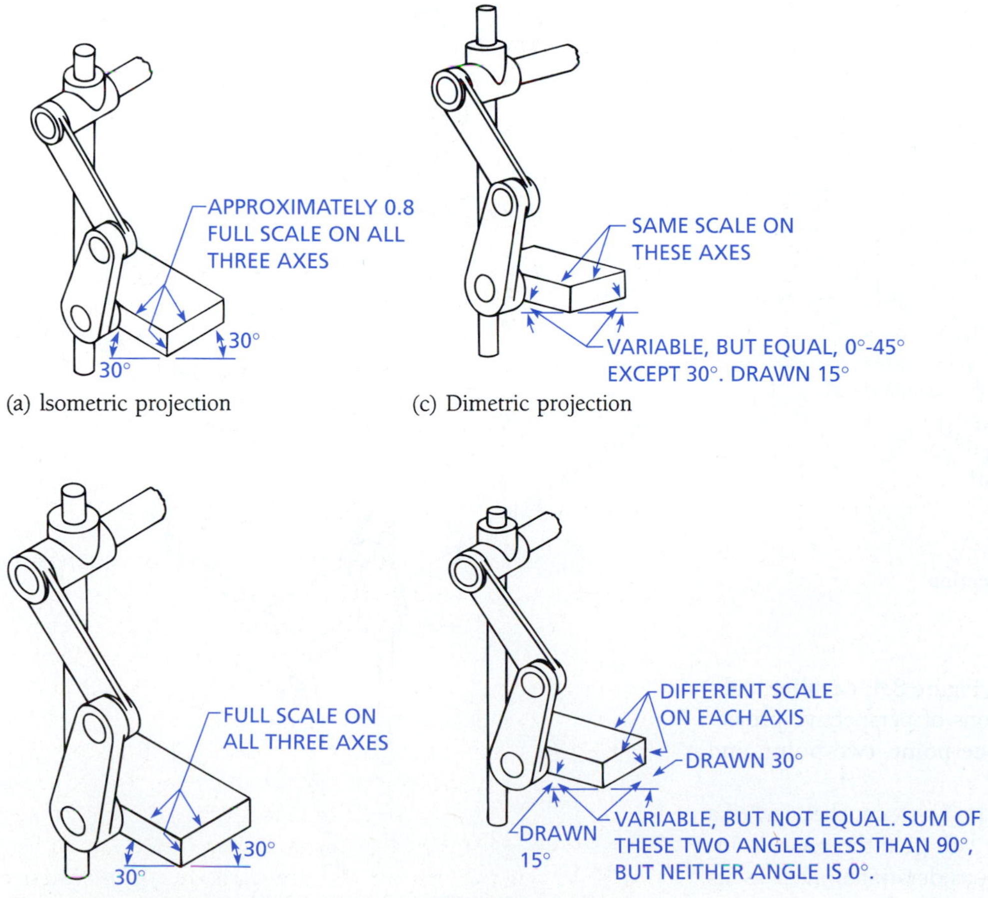

(a) Isometric projection

APPROXIMATELY 0.8 FULL SCALE ON ALL THREE AXES

30°
30°

(c) Dimetric projection

SAME SCALE ON THESE AXES

VARIABLE, BUT EQUAL, 0°-45° EXCEPT 30°. DRAWN 15°

(b) Isometric projection

FULL SCALE ON ALL THREE AXES

30°
30°

(d) Trimetric projection

DIFFERENT SCALE ON EACH AXIS

DRAWN 30°

DRAWN 15°

VARIABLE, BUT NOT EQUAL. SUM OF THESE TWO ANGLES LESS THAN 90°, BUT NEITHER ANGLE IS 0°.

FIGURE 8.3   Types of Axonometric Projection

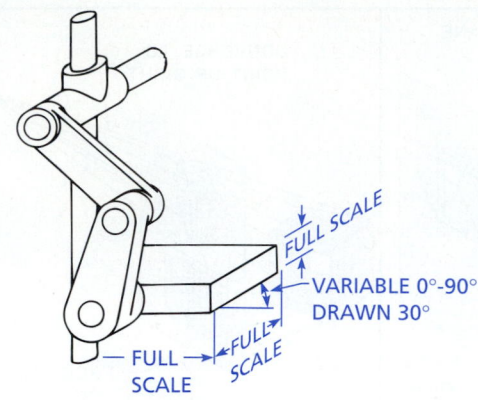

(a) Oblique projection (cavalier)

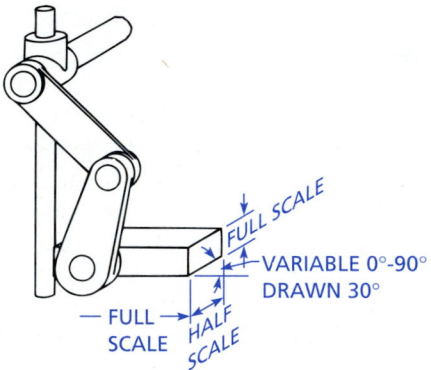

(b) Oblique projection (cabinet)

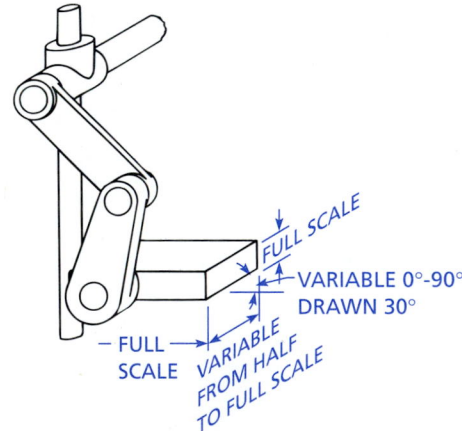

(c) Oblique projection (general)

FIGURE 8.4   Types of Oblique Projection

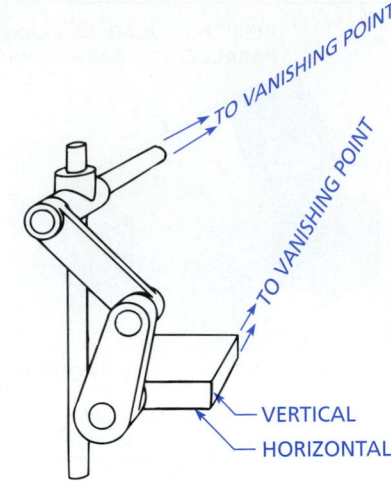

(a) Perspective (one-point)

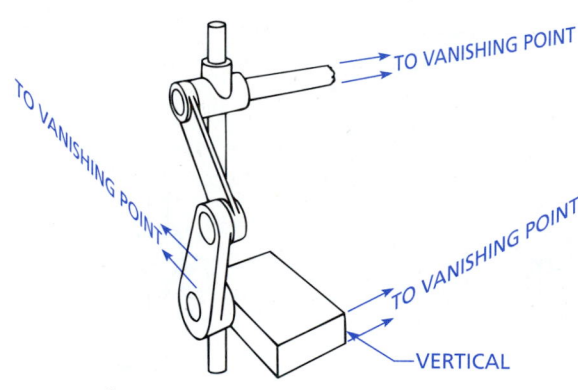

(b) Perspective (two-point)

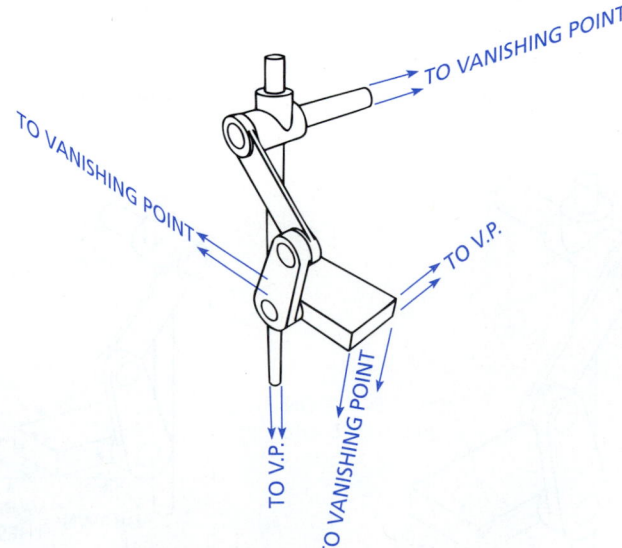

(c) Perspective (three-point)

FIGURE 8.5   Types of Perspective Projection

oblique projection are illustrated in Figure 8.4: **cavalier, cabinet,** and **general.** The three versions of perspective projection are illustrated in Figure 8.5: **one-point, two-point,** and **three-point** projections.

Regardless of the projection method chosen, the view of a part is normally selected so that it will give the greatest information possible, unless other considerations, such as its natural position or its relationship to other parts, must take precedence.

8.3   Axonometric Projection

A projected view in which the lines of sight are perpendicular to the plane of projection, but in which the three faces of a rectangular object are all inclined to the plane of projection, is called an **axonometric projection.** The projections of the three principal axes may make any angle with each other except 90°. Three types of axonometric projections are used: isometric, dimetric, and trimetric. Isometric is the most common.

An **isometric projection** is a pictorial drawing in which the three principal faces and the three principal axes of the object are inclined equally to the plane of projection. The plane of projection is called the *isometric plane.* The three axes on the drawing also make equal angles with each other [Fig. 8.6(a)], but may be placed in a variety of positions. A true orthographic projection of an object on the isometric plane is an isometric projection. The scales on all three axes are equal and foreshortened in the ratio of approximately 0.8 to 1.0. The term *axes* refers to the projections of the principal axes, unless otherwise stated.

A **dimetric projection** [Fig. 8.6(b)] is drawn with two axes making equal angles and the third axis at any selected angle. A **trimetric projection** uses three different scales (one for each axis), and has three different angles for the axes [Fig. 8.6(c)]. Trimetric projection is the most lifelike method, but it is also the most time-consuming and difficult to draw.

Since most pictorials are drawn with isometric projection methods, the following discussion will concentrate on this type. Dimetric projection and trimetric projection are com-pleted with the same general layout procedures as isometric projection. Therefore, the following techniques will apply for all three types.

8.3.1   Isometric Drawings

For **isometric drawing,** the distances on each axis are measured *true length,* with any standard scale, thus making a drawing larger than isometric projection (which is normally 81% of the original in size). This is the form in which the isometric technique is most commonly used.

Isometric projection and isometric drawing are both based on the theory that a cube representing the projection axes will be rotated until its front face is 45° to the horizontal plane and then tipped forward or downward at an angle of 35° 16′. The axes make equal angles of 120° between themselves [Fig. 8.7(a) and (b)]. The resulting rotation displays all three primary surfaces equally. Figure 8.7(d), (e), and (f) show the isometric cube in three different orientations. All three axes make equal angles with the projection plane and can be drawn easily using 30/60° triangles [Fig. 8.7(c)]. The three faces of the cube are identical in size and shape. The projected lengths of each edge are not foreshortened.

Because isometric drawings are constructed along the three axes (one vertical, and the other two at 30° to the horizontal to the right and left), *each dimension is measured true length* (not foreshortened) along an axis. All lines in isometric drawings that are on or parallel to the three axes are drawn true length. Lines not on or parallel to the axes are constructed with offset dimensions.

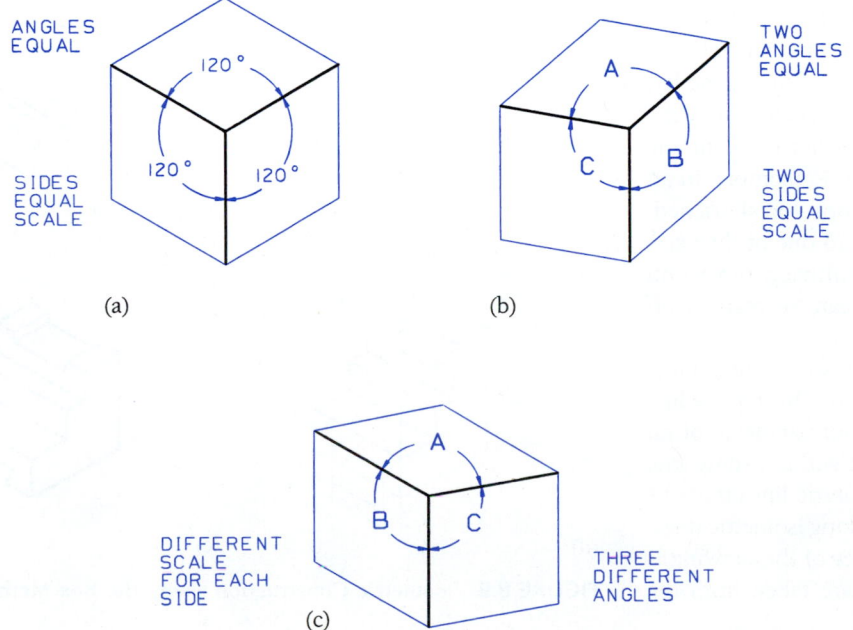

(a)

(b)

(c)

FIGURE 8.6   **Axonometric Axes**
(a) Isometric (b) Dimetric
(c) Trimetric

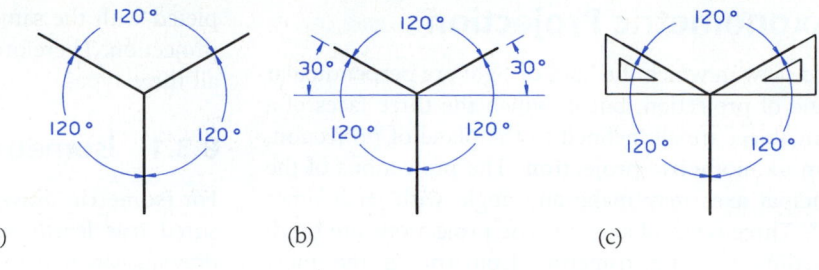

FIGURE 8.7   Isometric Axes
(a) Isometric axes
(b) 30° receding axes
(c) Using 30/60° triangles
(d) Isometric drawing (from top)
(e) Isometric drawing
     (turned on side)
(f) Isometric drawing
     (from bottom)

The orientation of the axis determines what faces of the part are visible. Figure 8.7 shows three of many alternatives for placing the axes. The most typical orientation is Figure 8.7(d), where the cube is viewed so that the top, front, and side of the object is visible. In Figure 8.7(e), the axes have been turned on their side, and in (f), the bottom, front, and side are visible because the axes are shown from under the isometric cube. A variety of arrangements are possible for the isometric axes as long as they remain at 120° to one another.

8.3.2   Isometric Construction

Isometric construction using the **box method** is illustrated in Figure 8.8. The three axes are drawn first: one vertical, one 30° receding to the right, and one at 30° receding to the left [Fig. 8.8(b)]. The edges of the box are constructed from the height, width, and depth dimensions transferred from the multiview drawing of the part [Fig. 8.8(a)]. Remember, in an isometric drawing the dimensions are not foreshortened. Therefore, if the distance is on or parallel to one of the axes, each measurement is full scale from the multiview projection (or directly from the part). Dimensions can be marked off with a scale or transferred with dividers.

As stated, all lines on isometric drawings that are parallel to or on one of the three axes are true length. This type of line is called an **isometric line.** Lines that are not parallel to or on an axes are called **nonisometric lines** and will not show true length on the isometric drawing. Nonisometric lines must be established from their endpoints, located along isometric lines.

After the part is boxed-in, the remainder of the drawing is completed. Dimensions A, B, C, and D are taken from the

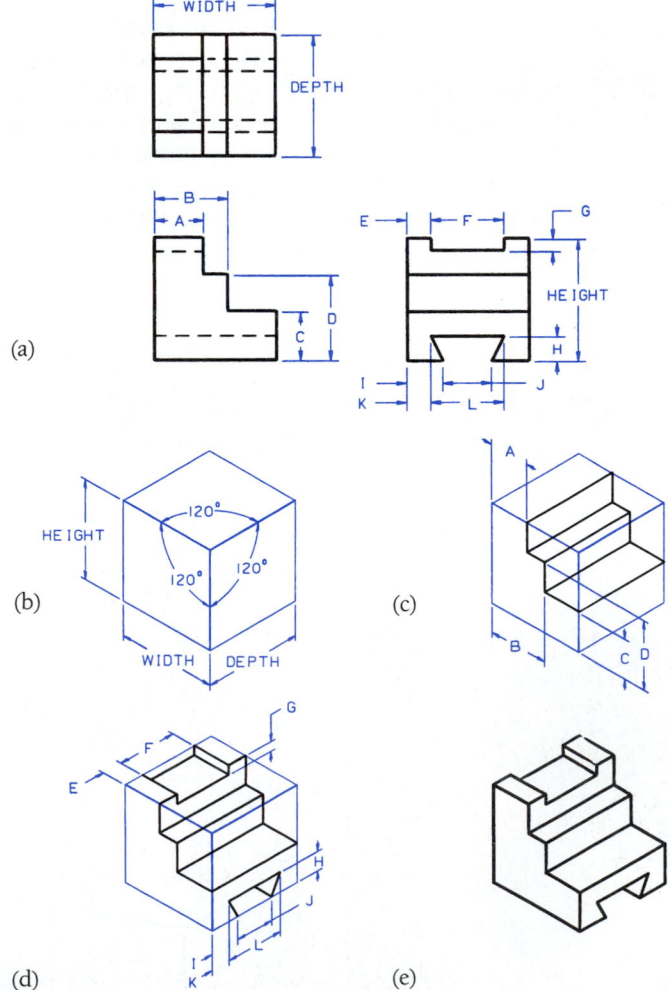

FIGURE 8.8   Isometric Construction Using the Box Method

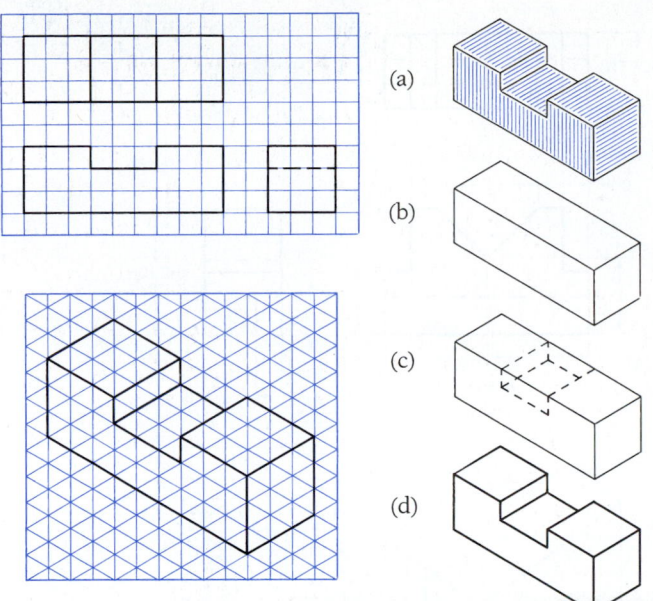

multiview drawing of the part in Figure 8.8(a) and transferred to the isometric box shown in Figure 8.8(c) to establish the step-like features of the part. The remaining features of the part are established in the same manner [Fig. 8.8(d)]. After the part is complete, all axes and construction lines are erased and the part is darkened [Fig. 8.8(e)].

The procedure of "blocking-in" a part is similar to carving a model out of some soft material with a knife. One aid in this process is the use of isometric grids (Fig. 8.9). Here, the part has been drawn in three views on grid paper and then transferred to the isometric grid. Since the part's features all fall on grid lines, no measurements are necessary to complete the project. Transferring the part from the three-view drawing to the isometric drawing simply involves counting grid lines.

Figure 8.10 is a three-view drawing of an integrated circuit complete with dimensions. Figure 8.11 shows the steps used

FIGURE 8.9   Box Construction and Grids for Isometric Drawings

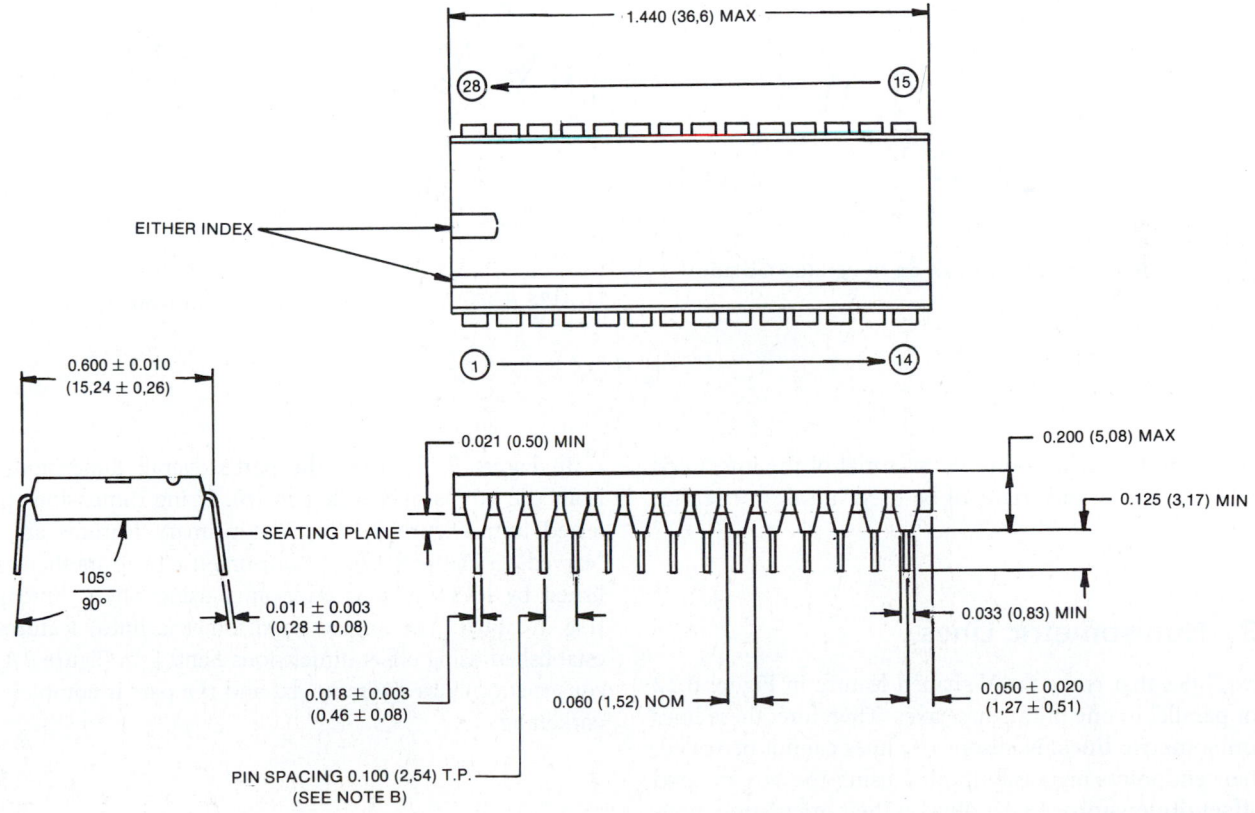

FIGURE 8.10   Three-View Drawing of an Integrated Circuit   See Figure 8.11 on the following page for an isometric drawing of this integrated circuit.

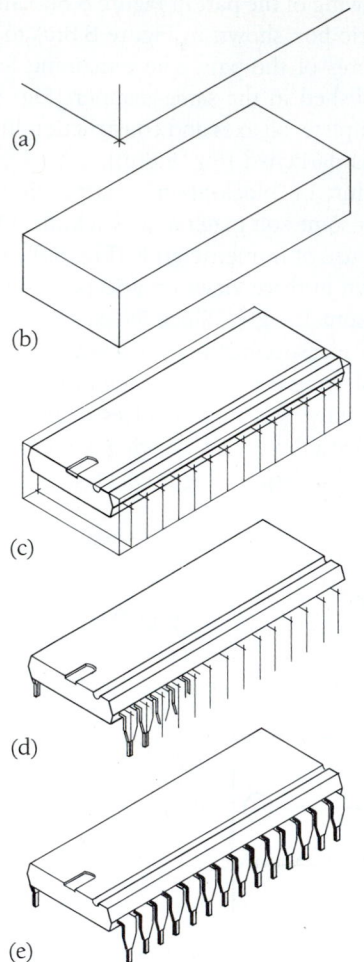

FIGURE 8.11   Isometric Drawing of an Integrated Circuit

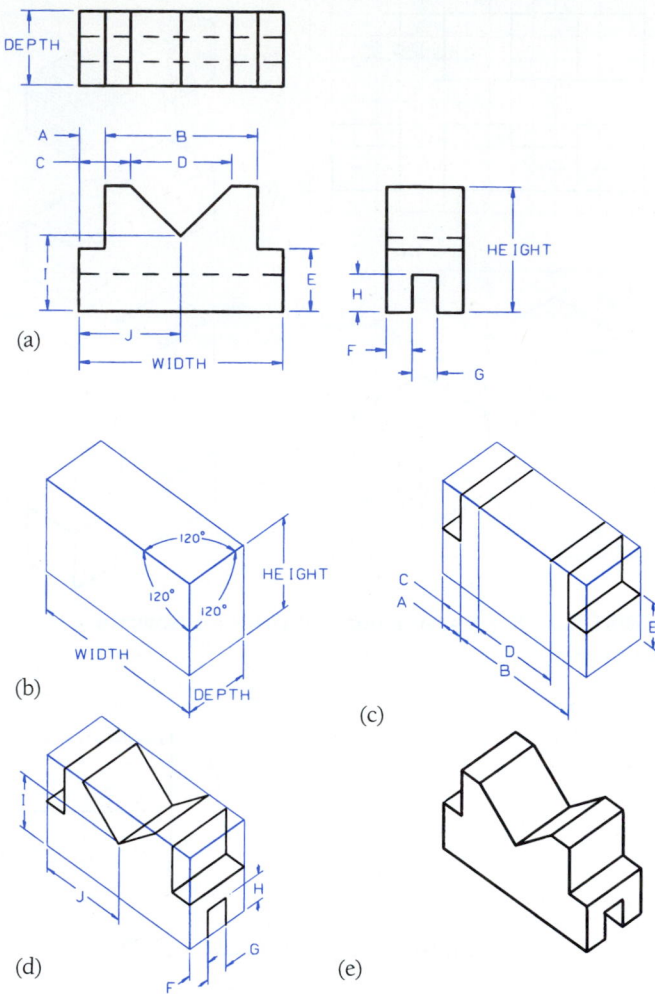

FIGURE 8.12   Nonisometric Lines in an Isometric Drawing

to block-in and draw an isometric pictorial of the integrated circuit. This type of pictorial will be used in sales or service manuals.

8.3.3   Nonisometric Lines

The two lines that make the V-shaped feature in Figure 8.12 are not parallel to one of the three axes. Therefore, these lines are **nonisometric lines**. Nonisometric lines cannot be scaled, but their endpoints are easily located using the box method and **offset dimensions**. Depending on their orientation, nonisometric lines may become longer or shorter on the isometric drawing. In this figure, the nonisometric lines are at the same angle, but slanting from different directions. In the isometric view of Figure 8.12(d), the two lines now make different angles. One is longer than the original line and the other is shorter. This distortion is typical of nonisometric lines.

In Figure 8.12, using the part's overall dimensions, the isometric box is drawn first in (b). Using dimensions transferred from Figure 8.12(a), the primary features are then "carved" in Figure 8.12(c). Nonisometric lines are then established by locating their endpoints using offset dimensions [Fig. 8.12(d)]. The angled (nonisometric lines) features are established using offset dimensions I and J. In Figure 8.12(e), construction lines are removed and the part is completed by darkening.

8.3.4   Isometric Angles

The three major axes along an isometric box (or cube) are at 120° angles to one another. In reality, all lines of a cube are at 90° or are parallel to each other. *Because of the distortion created by the isometric view of the box, few angles appear as true*

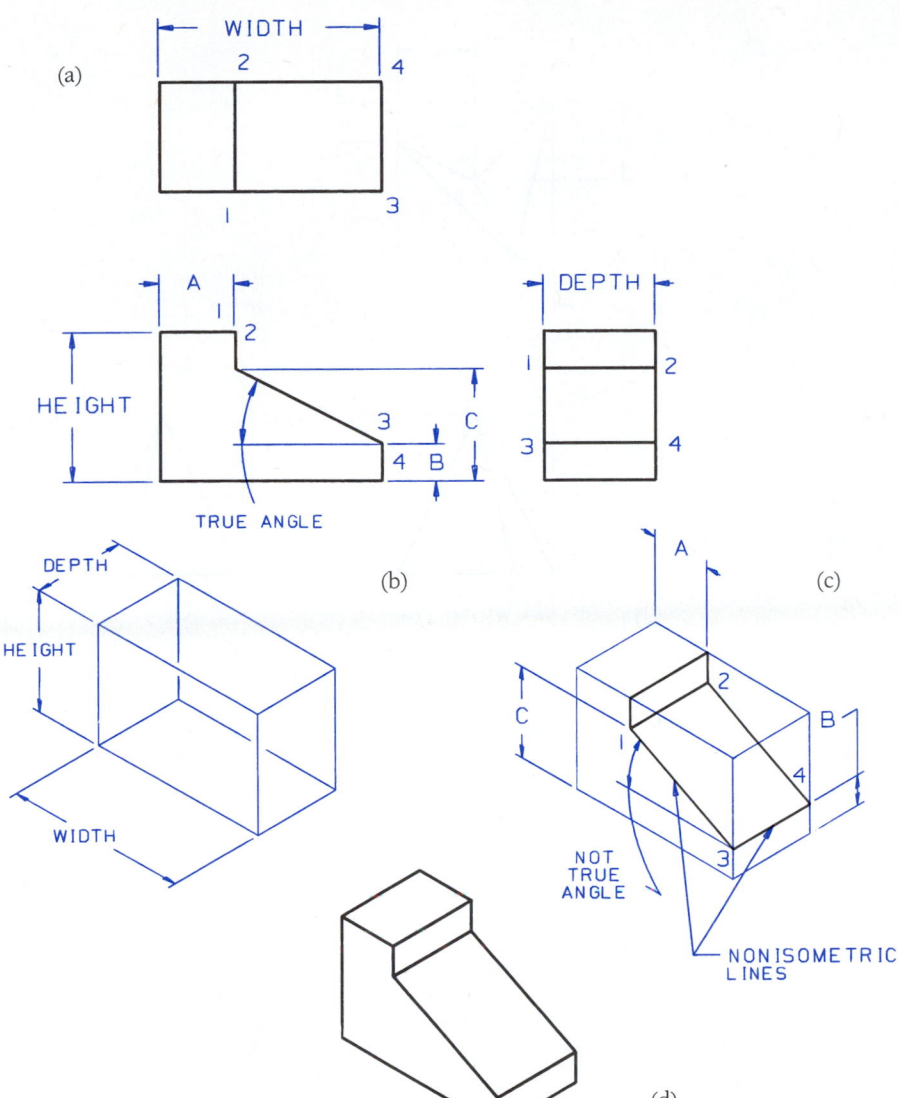

FIGURE 8.13 Offset Dimensions for Isometric Construction
(a) Three-view drawing
(b) Block-out overall dimensions
(c) Establish secondary features
(d) Completed isometric

angles. Angles, as with nonisometric lines, must be established by means of offset dimensions. Angles appear larger or smaller than true size on isometric drawings in relation to their position in the view. The lines that make an angle are nonisometric lines. Angles cannot be measured from the multiview drawing and transferred directly to the isometric view. They must be drawn by locating their endpoints along isometric lines using offset dimensions, as when drawing nonisometric lines.

The block in Figure 8.13 has an angled surface. To draw the part in isometric, it was necessary to use dimensions A, B, and C. These dimensions can be taken along true length lines. Points 1, 2, 3, and 4 are established in the isometric view using these dimensions. The angle is not true size (it is smaller than the original) in the isometric view. The steps used in this figure were the same ones used to draw a part containing

nonisometric lines with the box method and offset dimensions. Remember, offset dimensions are always taken parallel to one of the three axes or along isometric lines.

8.3.5   Irregular Objects on Isometric Drawings

Any shape can be drawn isometrically with the box method and offset dimensions. In Figure 8.14, the pyramid has been drawn using this method. Given the three-view drawing of the part in Figure 8.14(a), the isometric drawing is started as in the previous examples. The isometric box is drawn with the part's three primary dimensions [Fig. 8.14(b)]. Using offset dimensions A and B, the base is established first (points 1, 2, and 3). Point 0 is located with offset dimensions C and D, as shown in Figure 8.14(c).

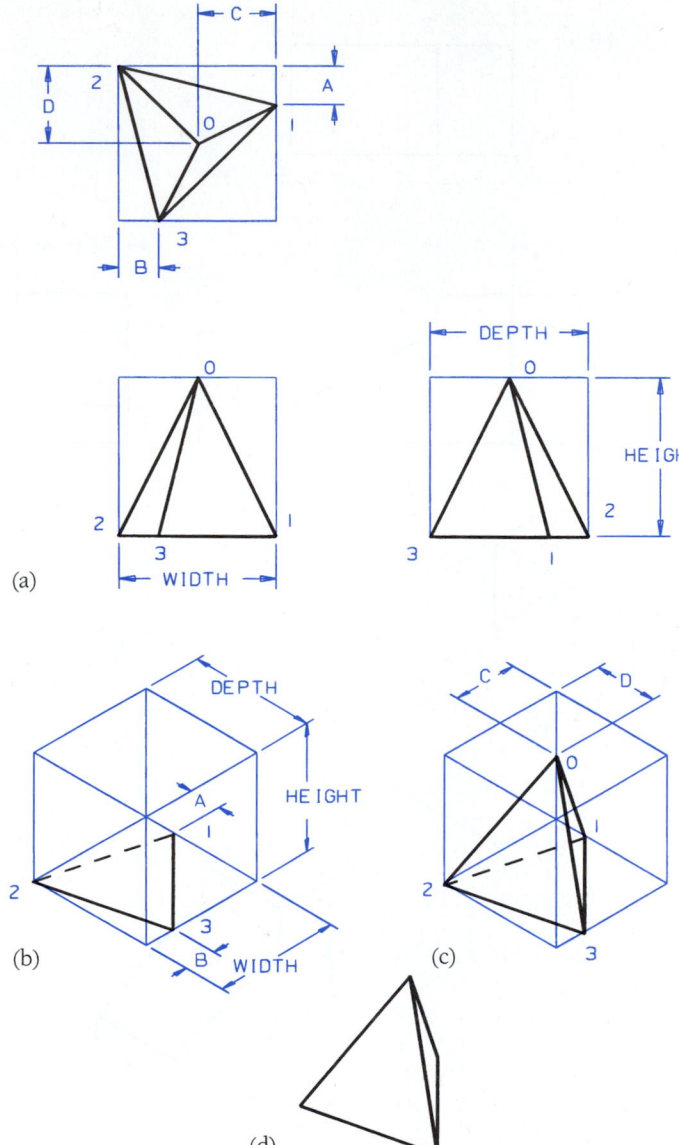

FIGURE 8.14   Construction of Irregular Objects in an Isometric Drawing   (a) Three-view drawing (b) Block-out height, width, depth, and base features (c) Locate apex (d) Darken in isometric

8.3.6   Circles and Arcs on Isometric Drawings

All circles and circular arcs on isometric drawings appear elliptical. A variety of methods is available for isometric ellipse construction: *template, trammel, four-center,* and *point plotting,* to name a few. In general, a template should be used for instrument drawings whenever the size of the ellipse can be matched with available equipment. For sketches, freehand techniques are normally sufficient. Chapter 6 covers freehand methods and Chapter 5 covers a variety of ellipse construction techniques.

If templates are not available, the trammel and point plotting methods are the most accurate, but they are time-consuming procedures for constructing circles and arcs in isometric drawings. These two methods should be used only when the other methods are inadequate.

The four-center method shown in Figure 8.15 does not create a perfect ellipse, but is accurate enough for most purposes and for constructions that are unable to be made with an ellipse template. This method can be used to draw circles or portions of circles (arcs) on any isometric face/plane (Fig. 8.16). The following steps describe the construction of an isometric ellipse (Fig. 8.15):

1. Lines DA and DC are drawn along the two receding axes (at 30°). Line AB is parallel to DC, and line CB is parallel to AD. Each of the lines will be the same length as the diameter of the circle [Fig. 8.15(a)].
2. Construction lines are drawn from point D perpendicular to line AB at its midpoint and perpendicular to line CB at its midpoint [Fig. 8.15(b)].
3. Step 2 is repeated using point B and lines DA and DC [Fig. 8.15(c)].

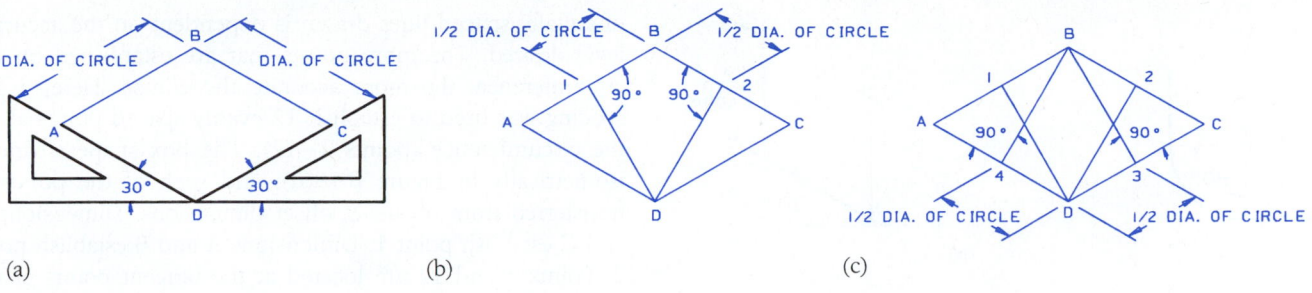

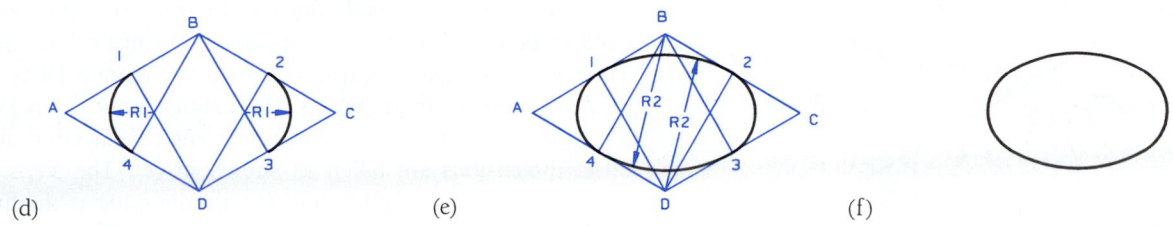

FIGURE 8.15   **Drawing a Four-Center Ellipse**   (a) Block-out overall size of ellipse (b) Find midpoint of lines A-B and B-C (c) Find midpoint of lines A-D and D-C (d) Swing R1 arcs (e) Swing R2 arcs (f) Erase construction lines and darken ellipse

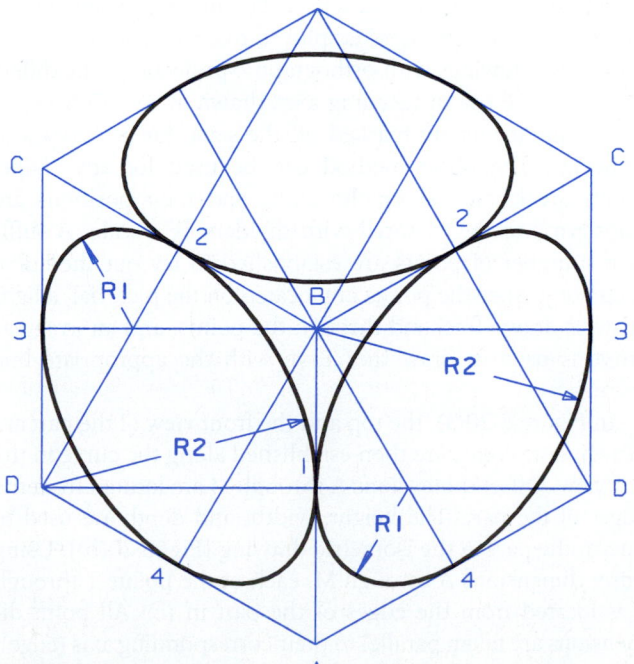

FIGURE 8.16   **Four-Center Ellipses on the Surfaces of an Isometric Cube**

4. The intersection of the construction lines is used to draw R1. The radius is equal to the distance from the intersection of the construction lines to one of the numbered points (1, 2, 3, or 4). The radius will thus be tangent to two edge lines (AB and AD or CB and CD) [Fig. 8.15(d)].
5. Points D and B are used to draw arc R2. Arc R2 originates at the intersection of the construction lines for both sides of the ellipse (B or D). Radius R2 will be tangent to two sides each (BA and BC or DA and DC) [Fig. 8.15(e)].
6. All construction lines are erased and the ellipse is darkened [Fig. 8.15(f)].

Portions of circles (arcs) are sometimes required for parts that have fillets and rounds. The same procedure for construction is used for these cases. In Figure 8.17, the **round** has been constructed as a portion of an isometric ellipse. In Figure 8.17(a) the round is shown as a true shape. The ellipse is boxed-in using two times the radius as each side for construction lines in Figure 8.17(b), and the radius of the bend is located to establish the tangent points in (c). Since just one-quarter of the circle (one-quarter ellipse) is being drawn, only one radius is necessary [Fig. 8.17(d)]. Unless the ellipse is an odd size or very large, a template is normally used for

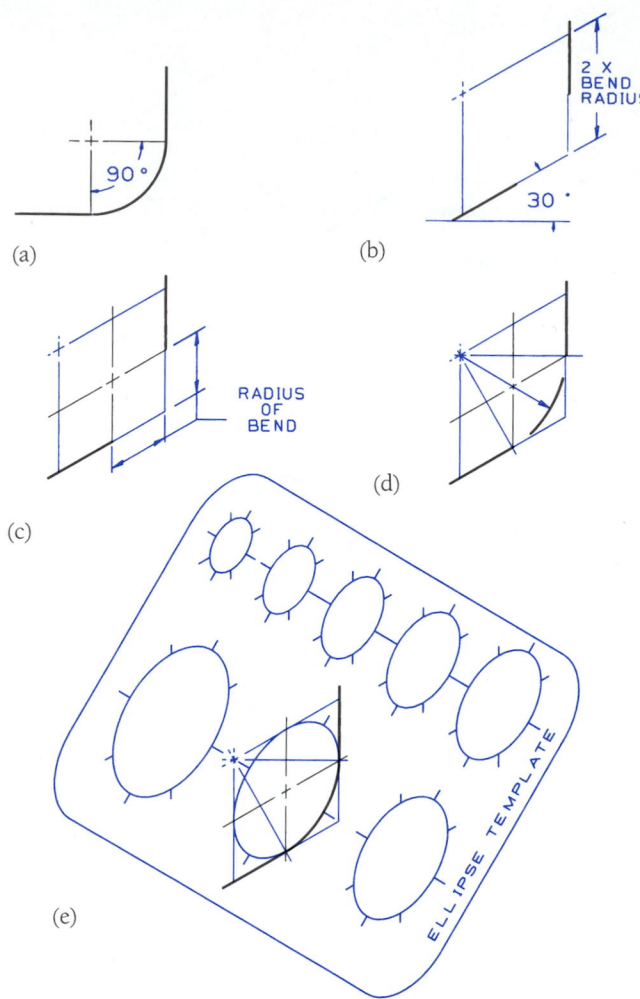

FIGURE 8.17 Construction of Arcs in an Isometric Drawing

of equally spaced lines drawn is dependent on the accuracy level desired. The more points that are established on the circumference, the more accurate the ellipse. Here, a 30° spacing was used to establish 12 evenly spaced points along the circumference (points 1–12). The box shape is drawn isometrically in Figure 8.18(d), and each of the points is transferred from (c) using offset dimensions. Dimensions D and C establish point 1. Dimensions A and B establish point 2. Points 3 and 12 are located at the tangent points of the circle and the box and are established on the isometric view at the intersection of the box and the centerline. To complete the ellipse, each of the four quadrants can be drawn using the same method [Fig. 8.18(e)]. Actually, since quadrants 1 and 3 are the same as are quadrants 2 and 4, only two quadrants need to be established. The opposite side can be mirrored. The darkened finished ellipse is shown in Figure 8.18(f).

The second method (Fig. 8.19) is similar, but the points are arbitrarily fixed along the circumference of the circle and offset dimensions are taken as shown in (c). The steps of Figure 8.19(a), (b), (d), (e), and (f) are the same as the first method. The points should be located and of sufficient number on the circumference such that a smooth curve can be established.

Circles, arcs, or curves that do not lie in isometric planes must be plotted with offset dimensions. This procedure requires that a series of points be established along the curved outline. Offset dimensions for each point are transferred to the isometric drawing and marked off along isometric lines.

8.3.8 Curves on Isometric Drawings

A **space curve** can be constructed isometrically using offset dimensions and box construction. The methods used are not much different from those employed to draw space curves on multiview drawings with orthographic projection. The difference is in the use of receding axes drawn at 30°. Otherwise, all measurements are marked off the same for both types of drawings. The offset method can be used for any shape. Points are located along the curve and their positions are transferred to the pictorial with dividers or a scale. A sufficient number of points are established to lay out the curve accurately. After the points are located on the pictorial, a light curve is drawn freehand through the points, and an irregular curve is used to draw the curve with the appropriate line thickness.

In Figure 8.20(a), the top and the front view of the part are drawn first. Points are then established along the curve in the top view. Offset dimensions A through M are located from the edges of the part. The height, width, and depth are used to box-in the part in the isometric drawing [Fig. 8.20(b)]. Using offset dimensions A through M, each of the points 1 through 7 is located from the edges of the part in (c). All point dimensions are taken parallel to their corresponding axis (edge). Point 1 is located by dimensions A and G; point 2 by dimensions B and H; point 3 by dimensions C and I. Vertical lines

this construction as shown in Figure 8.17(e). When using a template to construct the ellipse, care must be taken. The major axis of the ellipse will be at 30° unless the curve falls in the top or bottom face of the part.

8.3.7 Using Offset Dimensions for Ellipse Construction

The **offset dimension** method locates a series of points along the curve of an ellipse. This method is more accurate than the four-center method, but is time-consuming and the quality of the finished curve is dependent on the drafter's skill with an irregular curve. Two versions of this method are given here. The first method (Fig. 8.18) divides the circle evenly by drawing equally spaced construction lines emanating from the center of the circle to where they intersect the circle's circumference. The circle is drawn first along with its centerline in Figure 8.18(a); then, the circle is boxed-in in (b). Equally spaced construction lines are drawn from the center of the circle to the circle's circumference [Fig. 8.18(c)]. The number

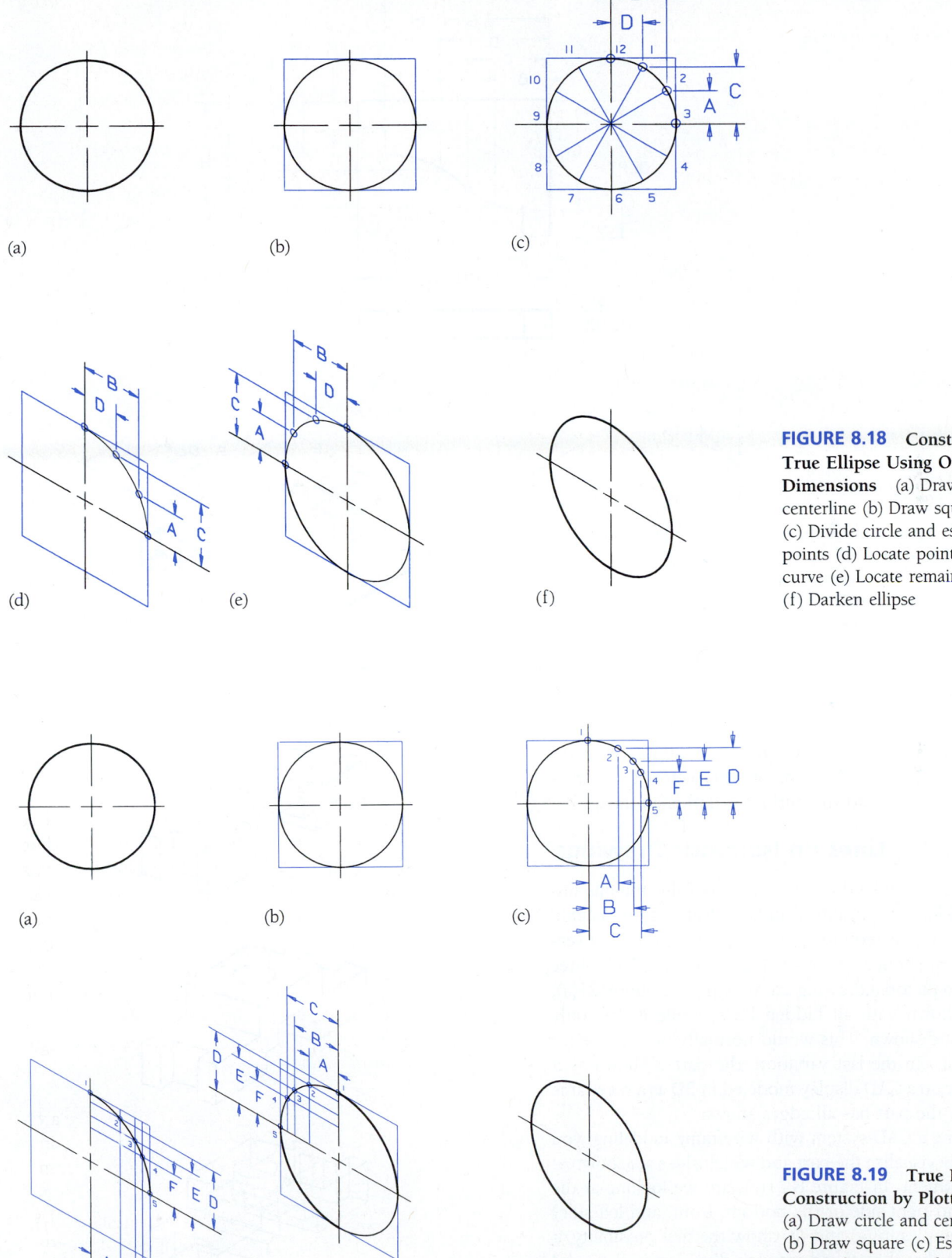

FIGURE 8.18 **Construction of True Ellipse Using Offset Dimensions** (a) Draw circle and centerline (b) Draw square (c) Divide circle and establish points (d) Locate points along curve (e) Locate remaining points (f) Darken ellipse

FIGURE 8.19 **True Ellipse Construction by Plotting Points** (a) Draw circle and centerline (b) Draw square (c) Establish points along circumference of circle (d) Locate points along curve (e) Locate remaining points (f) Darken ellipse

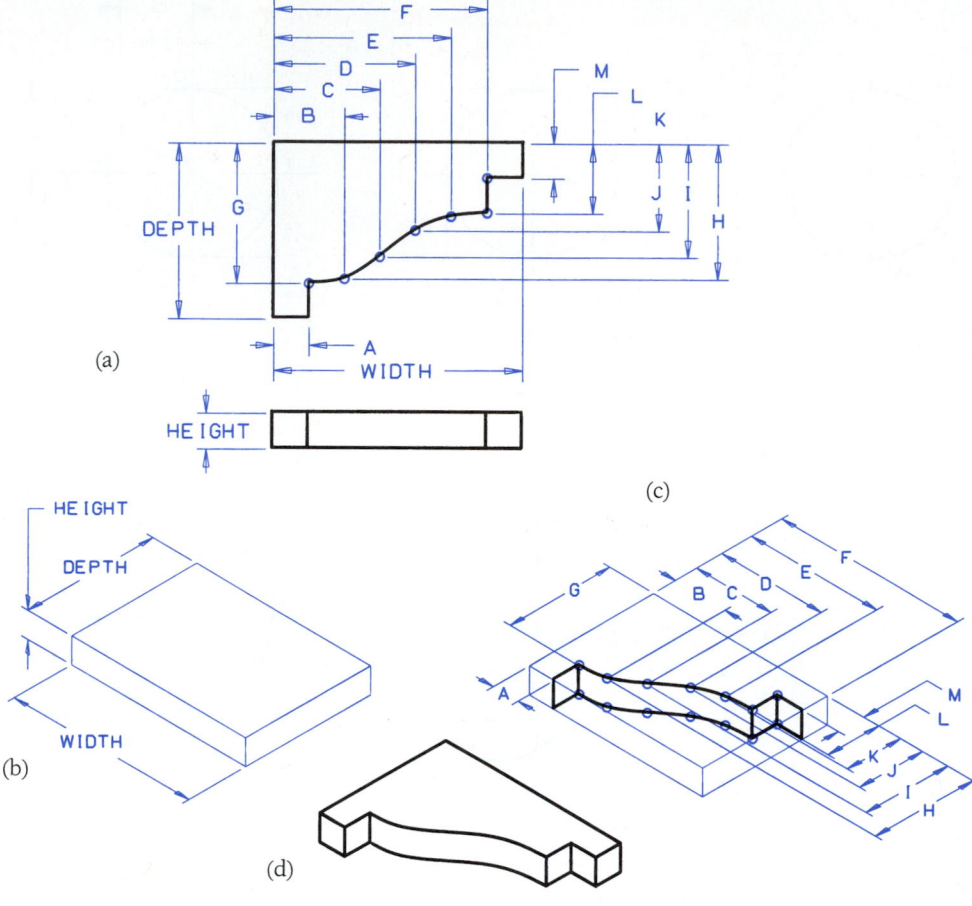

(a)

(c)

FIGURE 8.20 **Space Curves in an Isometric Drawing** (a) Locate points along curve in two-view drawing (b) Block-out overall dimensions (c) Locate points (d) Erase construction lines and darken lines

(b)

(d)

were drawn from points 1 through 7 to establish the part's thickness [Fig. 8.20(c)]. To complete the pictorial construction, lines are erased and the outline is darkened in (d).

8.3.9 Hidden Lines on Isometric Drawings

Hidden lines are omitted on most pictorial illustrations unless required for clarification of interior features. In general, when an illustration requires the use of hidden lines, a sectioned pictorial should be considered. In Figure 8.21, three variations of a pictorial drawing are shown. In Figure 8.21(a), the part is shown with all hidden lines, while in (b), only visible lines are shown. This would normally be the case for most pictorials. In the last variation, the part is shown as it would appear on a CAD display modeled in 3D as a wireframe model. Here, the part has all edges shown.

When using a CAD system with wireframe modeling, you must correctly visualize the part and which sides are shown at any given moment. In Figure 8.21(c), are we looking at the top, front, and right side or the bottom, front, and left side? Since the examples in (a) and (b) show the first possibility, it is hard to see that the second viewing direction is also valid when viewing (c). A hidden line removal capability (**HIDE** command) is available on many CAD systems that eliminates the problem of determining the correct viewing direction of a wireframe model.

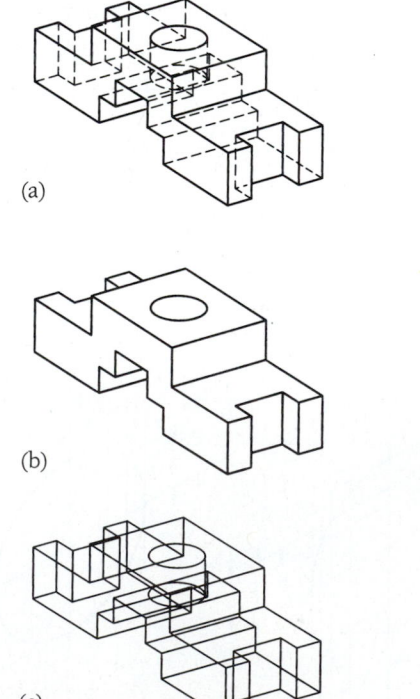

(a)

(b)

(c)

FIGURE 8.21 **Hidden Lines in an Isometric Drawing** (a) Part with hidden lines (b) Part with hidden lines removed (c) Wireframe model of part on 3D CAD system

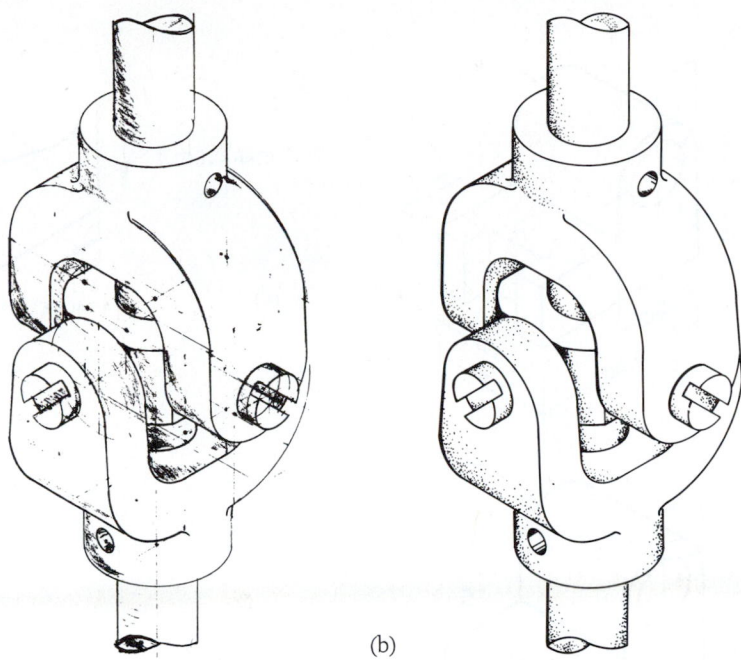

(a)   (b)

FIGURE 8.22 Pictorial
Illustration Construction
(a) Construction of universal joint
in an isometric drawing
(b) Pictorial illustration of universal
joint

8.3.10   Centerlines on Isometric Drawings

Centerlines that are needed to locate and identify circular or symmetrical aspects of a part are found on isometric drawings. Many pictorials do not show centerlines so that the part looks more realistic. If dimensions are required on the drawing, centerlines are usually included.

During the construction of a pictorial, centerlines identifying the origin of a part's symmetrical or curved features are as necessary as any other construction line [Fig. 8.22(a)]. In most cases, they may be erased after the pictorial is constructed and before it is darkened in with pencil or inked [Fig. 8.22(b)].

8.3.11   Dimensioning Isometric Pictorials

Dimensions on isometric drawings can be either aligned or unidirectional. **Aligned dimensions** look pictorially correct but are harder to draw. **Unidirectional dimensions** and notes are easier to add to the illustration and are often either typeset or labeled mechanically.

In Figure 8.23, the part's dimensions are shown by both methods. Figure 8.23(a) was drawn with aligned dimensions. Guidelines for the lettering must be drawn parallel to the item being dimensioned and in the isometric plane of the face being dimensioned. The arrowheads for aligned dimensions are drawn with their backs parallel to the extension line as shown in Figure 8.23(a) in the upper right enlargement. With a 3D CAD system, you can automatically insert dimensions isometrically.

Unidirectional dimensions are positioned horizontally and are therefore easiest to construct [Fig. 8.23(b)]. Guidelines are drawn horizontally and dimensions are added with ver-

tical lettering. Inclined lettering is seldom used for pictorial drawings.

8.3.12   Dimensioning Pictorials

Although the scaling ability varies with the kind of projection used, any type of pictorial can be dimensioned. The rules of dimensioning used in conventional multiview drawings should be applied whenever possible.

For all pictorials, the dimension line, extension lines, and the dimension text (unless unidirectional lettering is used) should lie in the same plane as the line or feature being dimensioned [Fig. 8.23(a)]. Arrowheads should be long and narrow, with a ratio of 3:1, and should lie in the plane of the dimension and extension lines [Fig. 8.23(a)]. For unidirectional dimensioning, the lettering should be made with vertical letters and should read from the bottom of the sheet [Fig. 8.23(b)].

8.3.13   Dimetric Projection

An axonometric projection in which two sides and two of the axes of a rectangular object make equal angles with the plane of the projection, while the third face and the third axes make a different angle is called **dimetric projection** [Fig. 8.3(c)]. Two of the angles on the drawing between the axes are equal but the third is different. A variety of positions of the axes may be used. Under certain conditions, a dimetric projection may be constructed conveniently by scaling along the axes using two different scales. These scales change whenever the angles of the axes change. Most methods and rules for isometric drawings can also be applied to the dimetric projection.

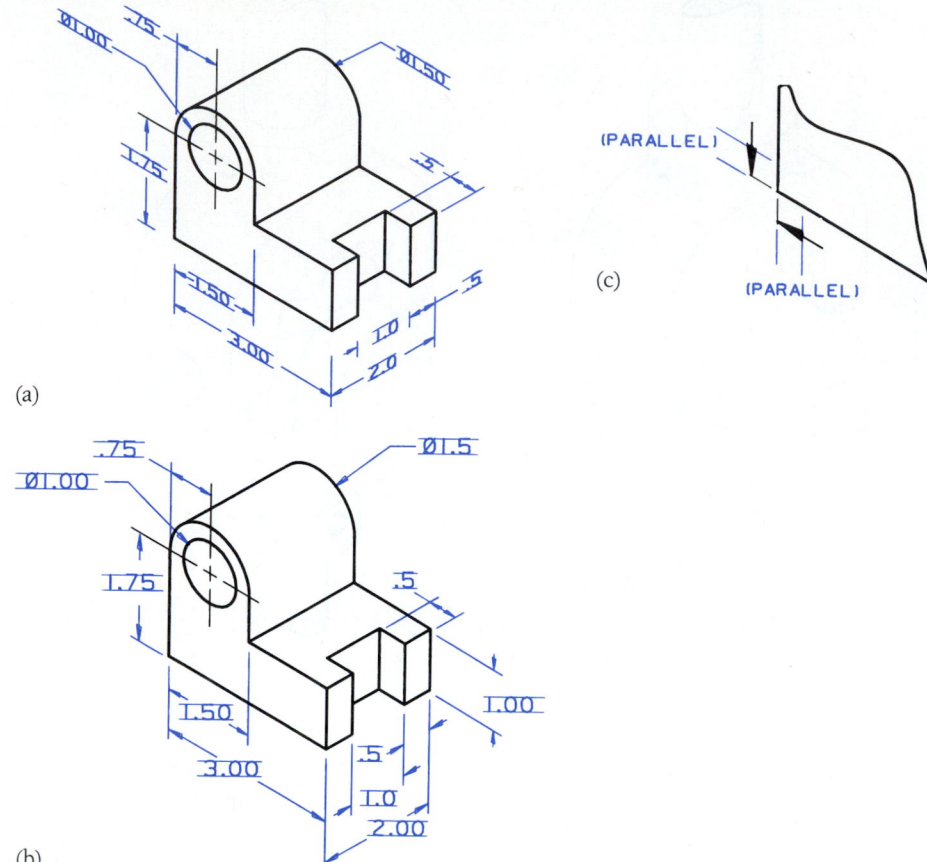

FIGURE 8.23   Dimensioning
Isometric Drawings
(a) Aligned (b) Unidirectional
(c) Arrowhead construction

8.3.14   Trimetric Projection

An axonometric projection in which all three faces and three axes of a rectangular object make different angles with the plane of the projection is called **trimetric projection** [Fig. 8.3(d)]. Figure 8.24 shows a **patent drawing** that employs the use of trimetric projection. The angles on a trimetric drawing between the axes are all different, and may be placed in a variety of positions. Under certain conditions, a trimetric drawing may be constructed by scaling along the three axes using three different scales. Each scale changes whenever the angle of the axis changes.

The choice of axes in axonometric projection is dependent on the part. To avoid the appearance of distortion on large flat areas, the angle which that face makes with the picture plane should be increased. For more important faces where details must be shown more clearly, the angle between that face and the picture plane should be decreased. Since the horizontal plane is less distorted, and more detail can be seen in the vertical face, Figure 8.25(b) is clearer than (a).

You May Complete Exercises 8.1 Through 8.4 at This Time

8.4   Oblique Projection

A projected view in which the lines of sight are parallel to each other but inclined to the plane of projection is called an **oblique projection** (Fig. 8.4). For practical purposes, the principal face is placed parallel to the plane of projection, thus making it and parallel faces show in true shape. In all forms of oblique projection, the receding axis may be drawn in any direction (Fig. 8.26). By changing the axis angle and choice of front face, any orientation required to exhibit the part properly and clearly can be attained.

Oblique projection was introduced in Chapter 6. Techniques for using oblique projection on sketches are covered in that chapter as are a number of other techniques that will be helpful here. *You should reread Chapter 6 before completing this chapter.*

Oblique drawings are similar to isometric drawings. However, they are produced from *parallel projectors* that are not perpendicular to the projection plane. The primary difference lies in the use of only one receding axis and the ability to draw one surface as true shape and size in the front plane.

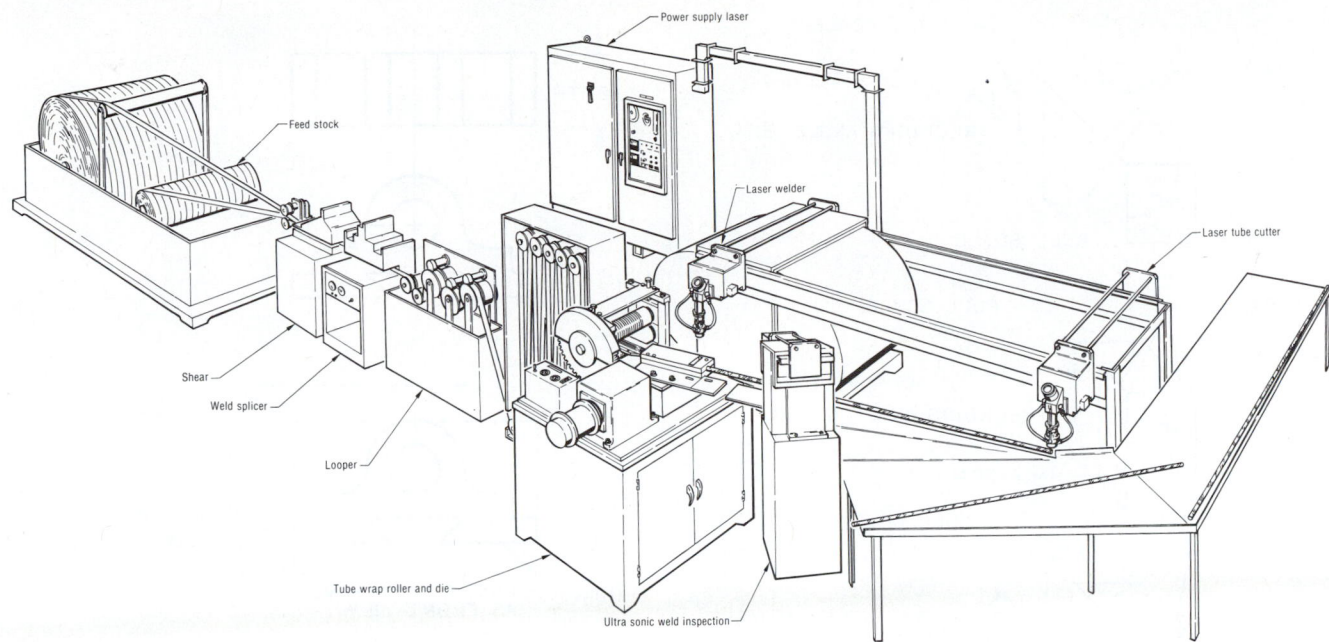

FIGURE 8.24   Trimetric Illustration of Welding Station (Patent Drawing)

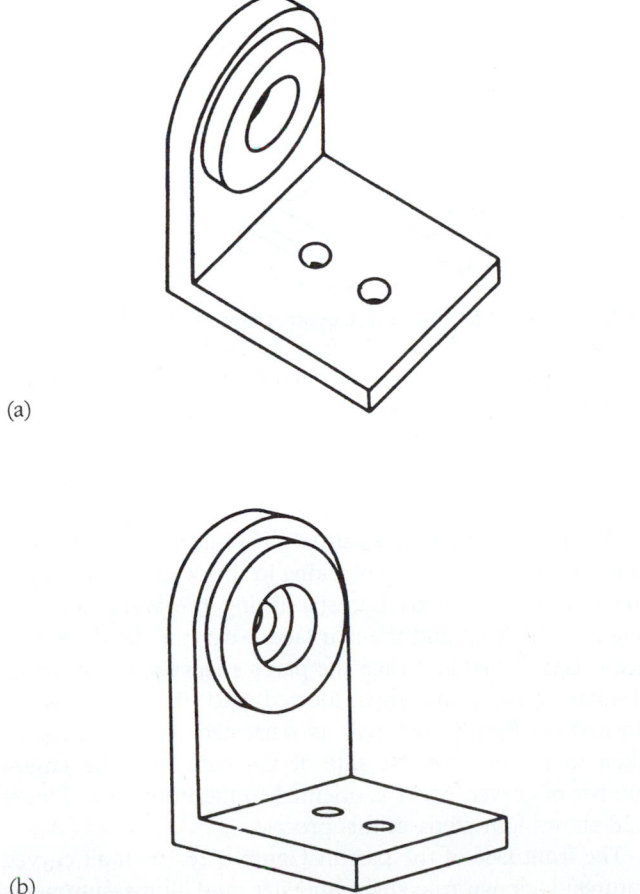

(a)

(b)

FIGURE 8.25   **Choice of Axonometric View Based on Part Distortion**

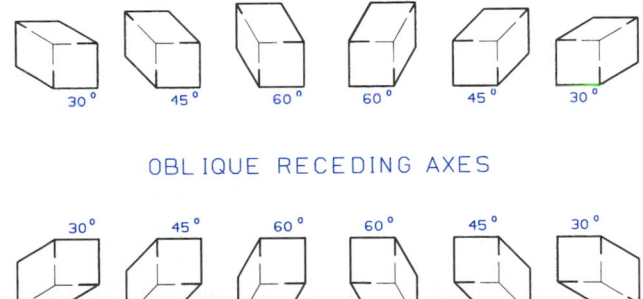

OBLIQUE RECEDING AXES

FIGURE 8.26   Axis Choice for Oblique Projection

There are three versions of oblique projection, differing only in the comparative scales used along the receding axis and the angle of the receding axis (Fig. 8.27). An oblique projection on which the lines of sight make an angle of 45° with the plane of projection is called a **cavalier projection** [Fig. 8.27(a)]. The front is drawn full scale and true shape as with all forms of oblique projection. The same scale is used on all axes. Therefore, the receding faces are drawn *full scale* (but not true shape). An oblique projection in which the lines of sight make an angle of between 63 to 26° with the plane of projection is called a **cabinet projection** [Fig. 8.27(b)]. The scale on the receding axis is *one-half* of the scale on the other axes. An oblique projection in which the lines of sight make any angle other than 45° or 63 to 26° is called a **general oblique**. The scale on the receding axis should be something between full scale and one-half scale of the horizontal and

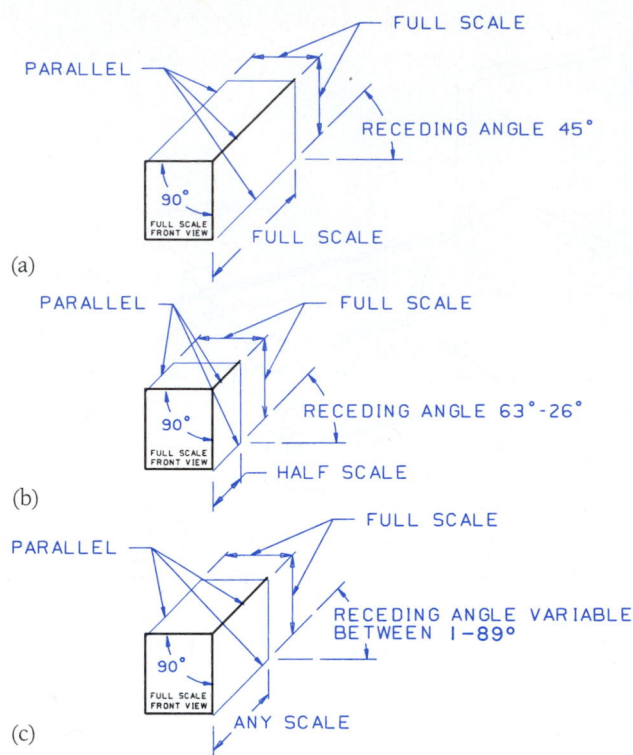

FIGURE 8.27   **Types of Oblique Projection**
(a) Cavalier projection (b) Cabinet projection (c) General oblique

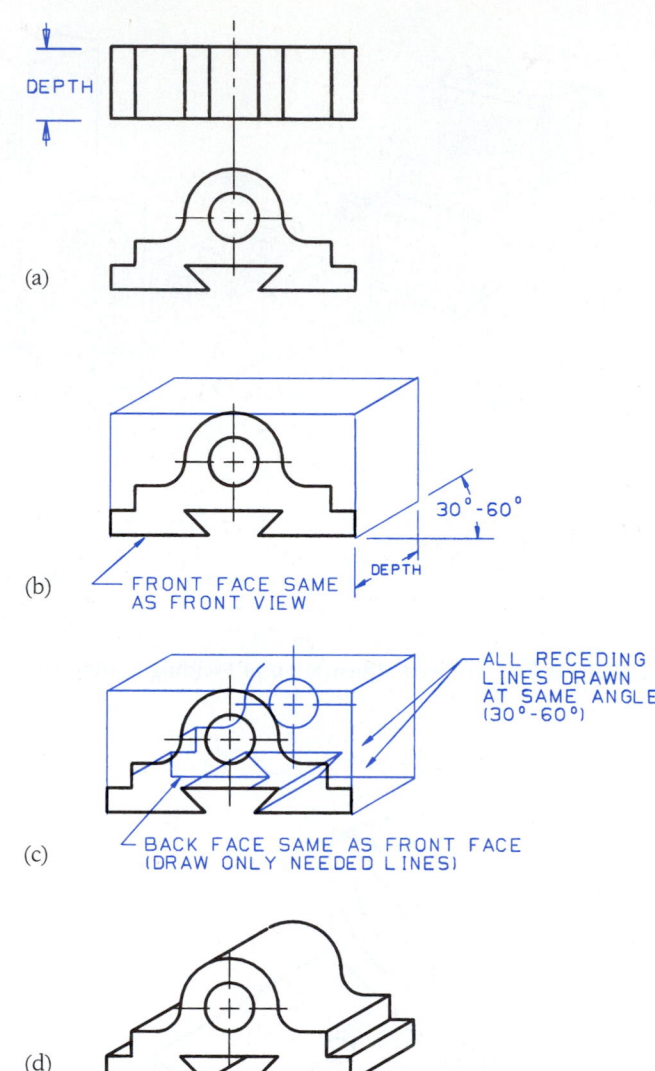

FIGURE 8.28   **Step-by-Step Construction of Oblique Drawing**
(a) Two-view drawing (b) Draw front face and establish receding angle (c) Establish rear (back) face and receding lines (d) Erase construction lines and darken

vertical axes, as shown in Figure 8.27(c). The choice of the receding angle (1 to 89°) is determined by the shape of the object and the most descriptive view orientation.

The distortion often noticeable in oblique projection may be decreased by reducing the scale on the receding axis. Cylinders and cones should have their axes on the receding axis to reduce distortion and to make it possible to draw circles with a compass or template.

Oblique projection is most commonly used for objects that have a series of circles, curves, or irregular outlines in the same or parallel planes (Fig. 8.28). By placing curved outlines in the front face, they can be drawn true shape and full scale without distortion. A standard circle template or a compass can be used in the construction. In other words, the front face of an oblique projection is exactly the same as the front view of a part drawn in a multiview projection.

8.4.1   Oblique Construction

Objects that are drawn with oblique projection should be oriented so that the surface with curved lines lies in the front plane bounded by the axes that are at 90°. Since all surfaces that lie on the front plane or that are parallel to it are drawn true shape and size, this orientation lessens drawing time. Circles and arcs are, therefore, true projections.

Oblique construction is started the same as a multiview or an isometric drawing—by blocking in the overall dimensions. The drawing is started by establishing the width and the height of the front and the rear face. Next, the depth of each face is established and then the part's edges are constructed. Circular features are then located and their dimensions blocked-in. Finally, the part is darkened. Care should be taken to ensure that the side of the part with the largest number of curved edges is oriented to the front view. Figure 8.28 shows four steps in this process.

The front face of the part in Figure 8.28 (with all curved features) is drawn true shape and size, and all measurements on this front face are true length. The measurements are taken from the front view in (a) and transferred to (b). The angle for

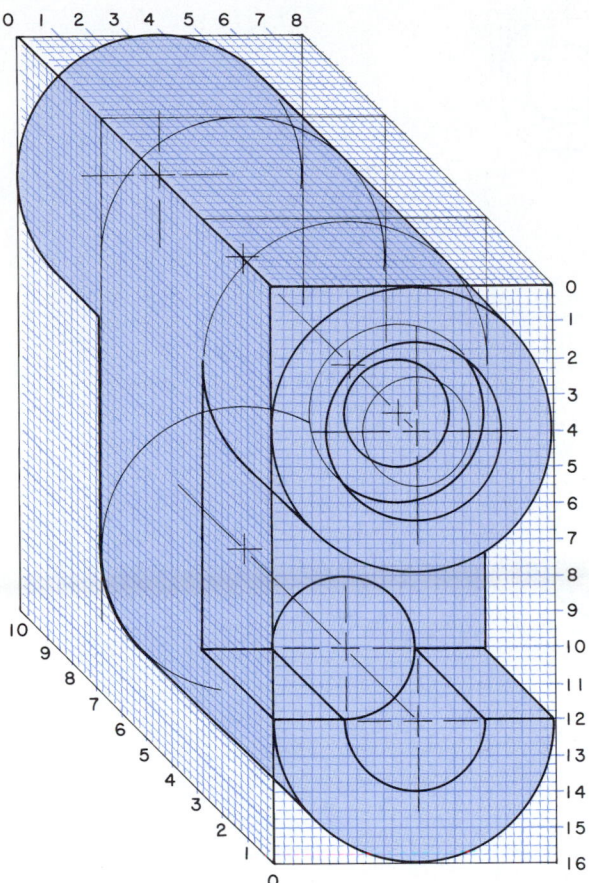

FIGURE 8.29 **Using an Oblique Grid**

curved features, offset measurements must be used to establish the curves. After the feature's points are plotted, an irregular curve is used to draw the curve.

In Figure 8.30, the angle bracket is shown in three views. The curved features are divided vertically and horizontally with construction lines in (a). The intersection of vertical construction lines with related horizontal construction lines establishes points on the curved feature.

The oblique projection is started by establishing a front face. The choice of front face in this example was made solely on the need to demonstrate this procedure. The construction lines are transferred to the oblique view and the points are plotted in Figure 8.30(b). A smooth curve is drawn through the points using an irregular curve. Since the opposite portion can be mirrored, only half of each hole needs to be plotted. The projection is completed by drawing the end lines parallel to the axes and tangent to the curves in Figure 8.30(c), and darkening in the lines in (d). If a cabinet drawing is used, the depth dimensions are halved and the same procedure used in its construction.

The construction process for oblique projection with slanted, inclined lines and inclined planes is similar to that for isometric drawings. Their endpoints are located along lines that are parallel to one of the axes.

8.5 Perspective Projection

A pictorial drawing made by the intersection of the picture plane with lines of sight converging from points on the object to the point of sight that is located at a finite distance from the picture plane is called a **perspective.** Perspective drawings are pictorials that appear similar to photographs. Figure 8.31 shows a perspective rendering of an array of radiotelescope antennas. The use of perspective projection gives the illustration a "photo-like" realism. The observer is stationed at a fixed position relative to the object being drawn as with a photograph.

Perspective projection is used to provide illustrations that approximate how a particular object looks to the human eye or as a camera would record the object on film. Since a perspective drawing approximates how an object really looks, it is not dimensionally correct and cannot be scaled. The only lines that can be scaled are those lines on the object that actually lie in the picture plane. Because of this distortion, perspective drawings are seldom found in engineering or design work. Technical illustrations for advertisements, sales catalogs, technical manuals, and architectural renderings make extensive use of this form of pictorial projection. All lines in perspective drawings converge at one, two, or three points on the horizon (vanishing points) and, therefore, are not parallel, as in oblique and axonometric projection.

the receding axis is then determined. The most commonly used angle for the receding axis is 45°. After the angle is determined, the rear face of the part is blocked-in. The features of the rear face can then be drawn as in Figure 8.28(c). The front and the rear faces are parallel and therefore identical. Only the portions of it that show along the receding face need to be drawn. The receding edge lines are drawn parallel to the receding axis between the part's corners and tangent to the curved feature on the top edge [Fig. 8.28(c)]; the part is completed by darkening in the visible edges in (d).

In Figure 8.29, all curved features are parallel to the front plane, and successive circular outlines and surfaces are not distorted. Depth dimensions are established along the receding axis, which, in this case, is the centerline of the part. The use of an oblique grid underlay will speed the construction process.

8.4.2 Using Offset Measurements for Oblique Drawings

When the object to be drawn is placed so that the curved features do not fall in the front face or two or more faces have

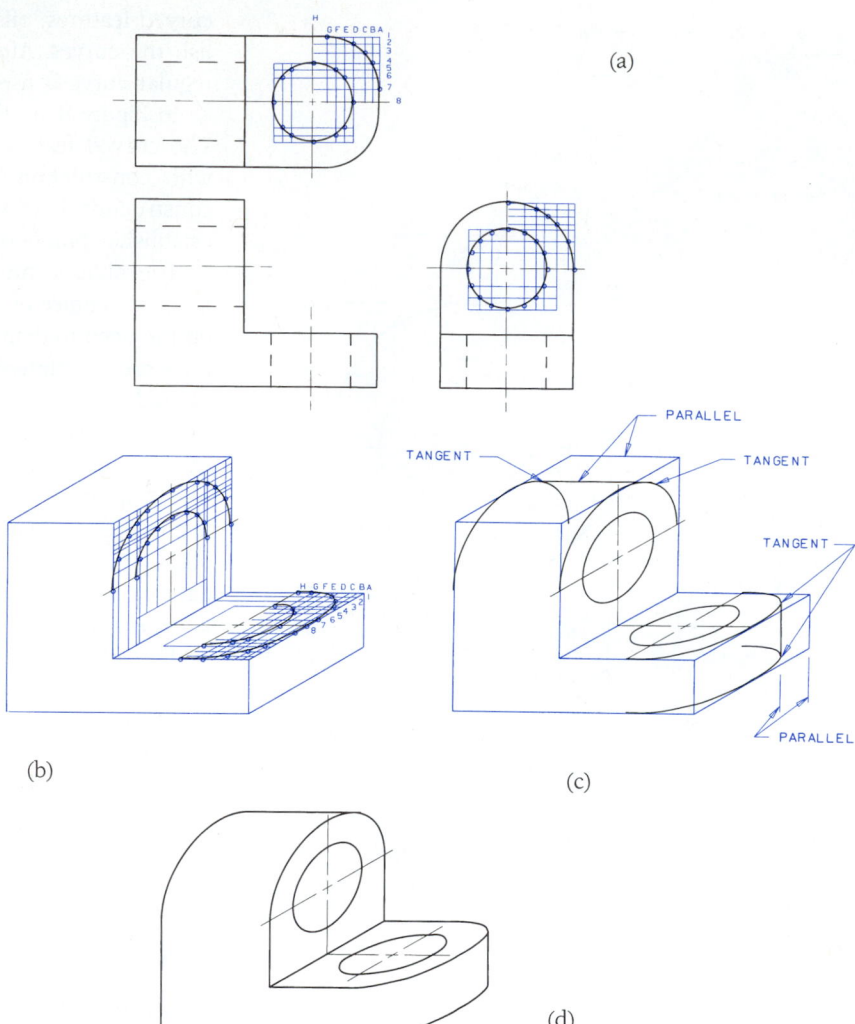

(a)

(b)

(c)

FIGURE 8.30   Offset Dimensions for Curves Not in or Parallel to the Front Face of the Part (a) Locate points on three-view drawing (b) Locate points on curves (c) Establish tangent points (d) Erase construction lines and darken lines

(d)

FIGURE 8.31   Perspective Rendering of Radiotelescope Antennas

There are three basic categories in perspective projection: **parallel, angular,** and **oblique** (Fig. 8.32). A perspective in which two of the principal axes of the object are parallel to the picture plane and the third is perpendicular to the plane is called **parallel perspective** or **one-point perspective** [Fig. 8.32(a)]. A perspective in which one axis of the object (usually the vertical axis) is parallel to the picture plane and the other two axes are inclined to it is called an **angular** or **two-point perspective** [Fig. 8.32(b)]. A perspective in which all three principal axes of the object are oblique to the plane or projection is called an **oblique** or **three-point perspective** [Fig. 8.32(c)].

8.5.1   Perspective Pictorial Drawing Terminology

The following terms are used with perspective drawings (Fig. 8.33):

Station point (SP)   The assumed position of the observer.

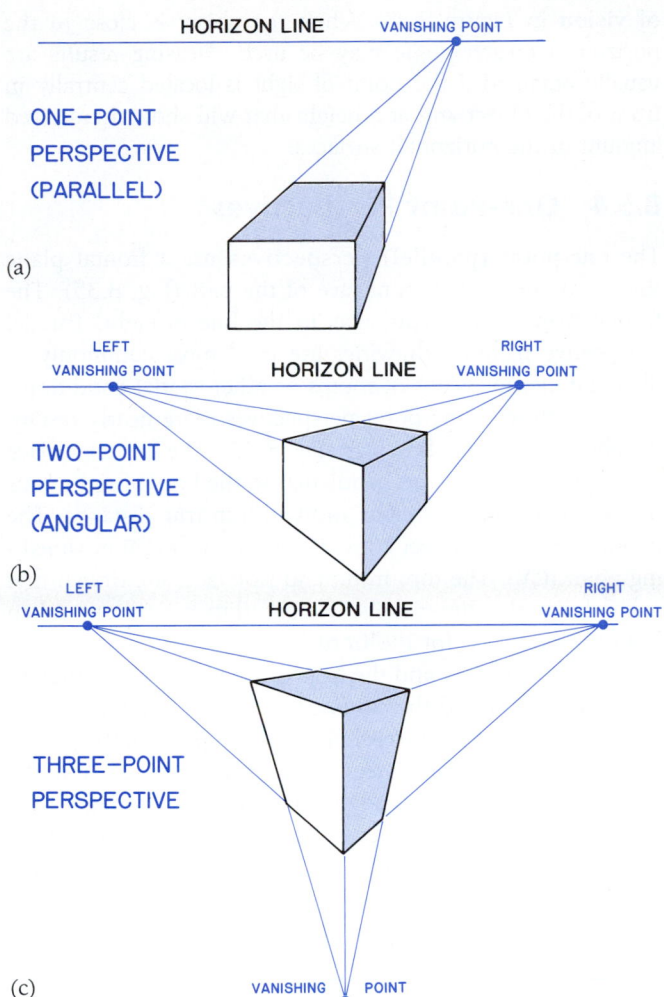

ONE–POINT
PERSPECTIVE
(PARALLEL)

(a)

TWO–POINT
PERSPECTIVE
(ANGULAR)

(b)

THREE–POINT
PERSPECTIVE

(c)

FIGURE 8.32 Types of Perspectives
(a) Parallel or one-point perspective (b) Angular or two-point perspective (c) Oblique or three-point perspective

Picture plane A vertical plane that is 90° to the line of sight from the station point (SP). The picture plane is usually placed between the object and the station point.

Horizon line (HL) The line of intersection made by a horizontal plane located at eye level and the picture plane. The horizon line is raised or lowered as the observer is raised or lowered. The horizon line remains in a horizontal position.

Ground line (GL) The intersection of the ground surface plane and the object or structure contacting the ground surface.

Vanishing point (VP) A point located in space where the ground line appears to intersect with the horizon line. The number of vanishing points is dependent on the type of perspective. There will be either one, two, or three vanishing points (in this figure there are two; VPL and VPR).

Height line (HL) A vertical line in the plane of sight that falls on the line of sight on which measurements of height correspond to the height in the elevation (distance 1-2 in Fig. 8.33). It is drawn perpendicular to the edge view of the picture plane.

8.5.2 Locating the Horizon Line

The **horizon line** is usually located on eye level with the observer in the horizontal plane. The use of a higher horizon line will change the perspective appearance. Figure 8.34 shows three possible positions of the horizon line. The **ground line** remained the same for each projection, but the horizon line (VP1H, VP2H, VP3H) was adjusted to see the part from the bottom, the front, and the top.

8.5.3 Location of Station Point in Perspective

To avoid undue distortion in perspective, the **station point** should be located so that the **cone of rays** has its apex at the point of sight and includes the entire object. This should have an angle at the apex not greater than 30°, shown as the **angle**

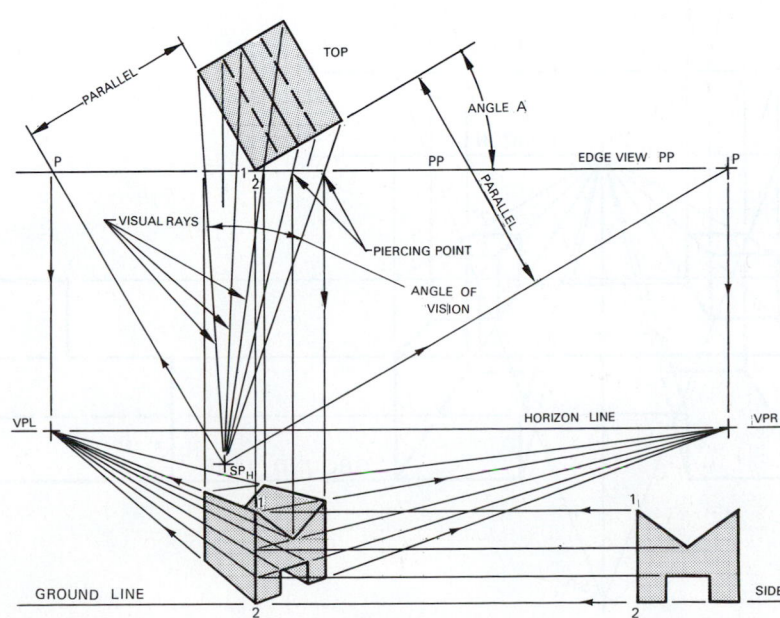

FIGURE 8.33 Angular Perspective Projection

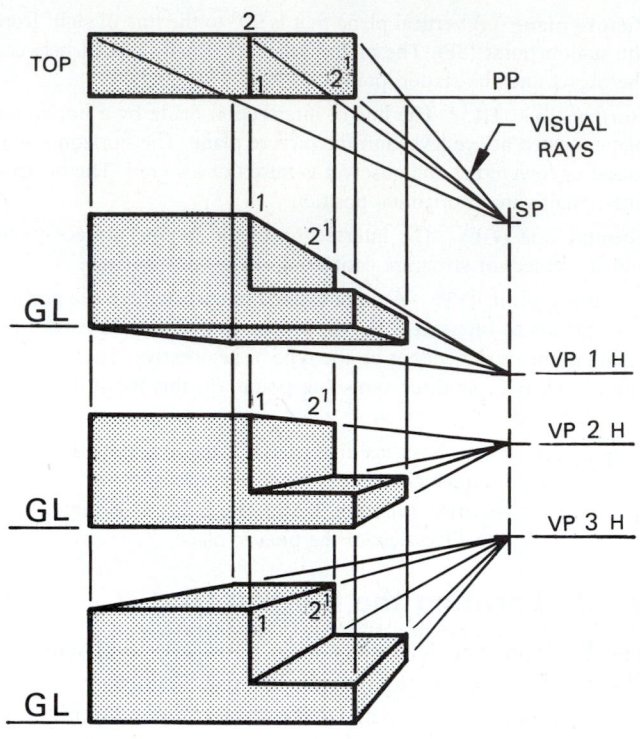

FIGURE 8.34 Variations in the Placement of the Horizon Line

of vision in Figure 8.33. When the object is close to the horizon, a greater angle may be used. Pleasing results are usually obtained if the point of sight is located centrally in front of the object and at a height that will show the desired amount of the horizontal surfaces.

8.5.4 One-Point Perspectives

The **one-point (parallel) perspectives** use a frontal plane that is parallel to the front face of the part (Fig. 8.35). The frontal plane is perpendicular to the line of sight. Parallel perspective pictorial drawings are used most commonly to illustrate interior views of rooms or other spatial conditions. On solid objects, one-point perspectives more nearly resemble oblique pictorial drawings (Fig. 8.35). The frontal surface of the pictorial box is perpendicular to the lines of sight (axis of vision) and shows height and width in true distance. The depth lines of the object converge toward a common vanishing point (CV). The top, front, and side faces are drawn first using full-scale dimensions. Height dimensions are taken from the side view for the front face.

After the top view and the front face of the part are drawn, the station point and the common vanishing point are established. Visual rays are projected from each point of the part to the station point. The intersection of a visual ray and the picture plane establishes points along the picture plane that are then projected to the front view. The intersection of these points and rays extending from the front view to the CV

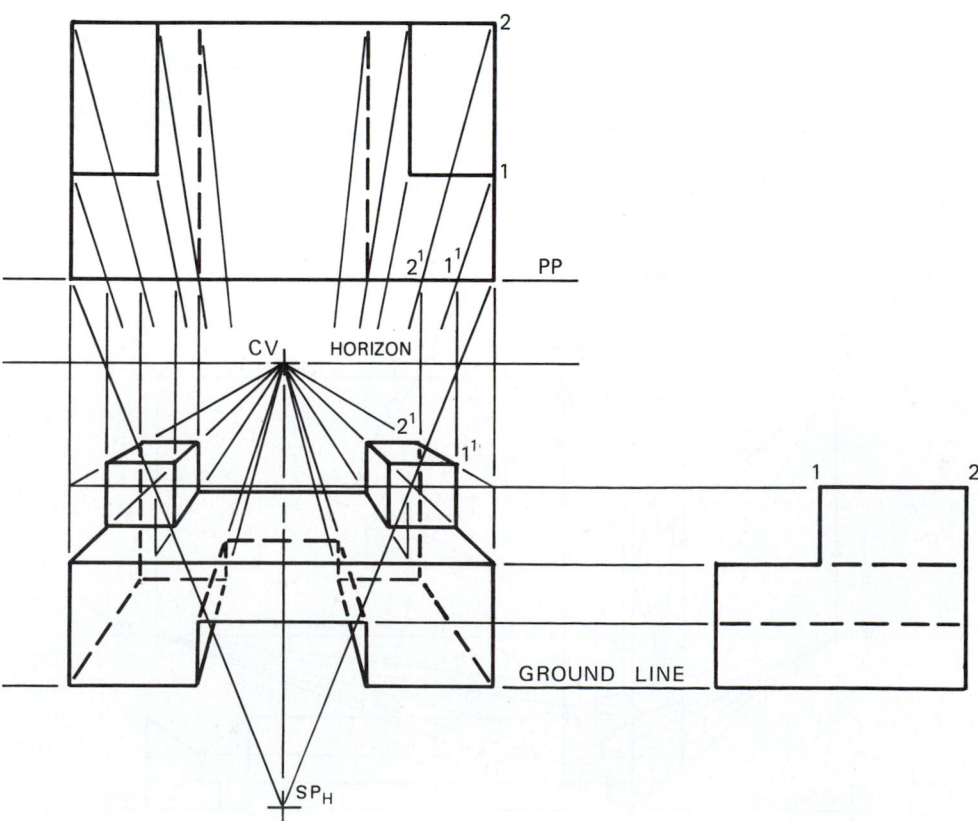

FIGURE 8.35 One-Point Perspective Projection

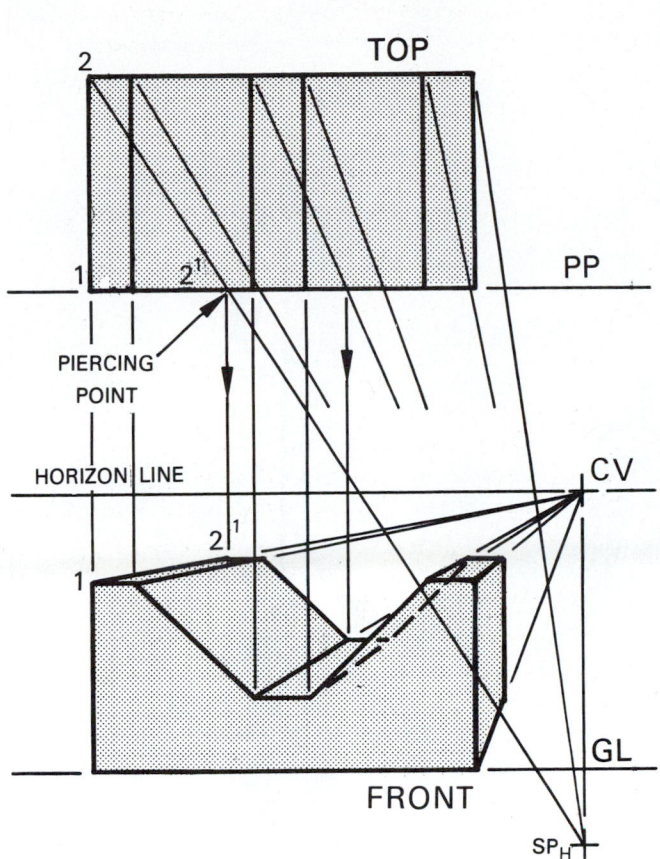

FIGURE 8.36 Parallel Perspective Projection

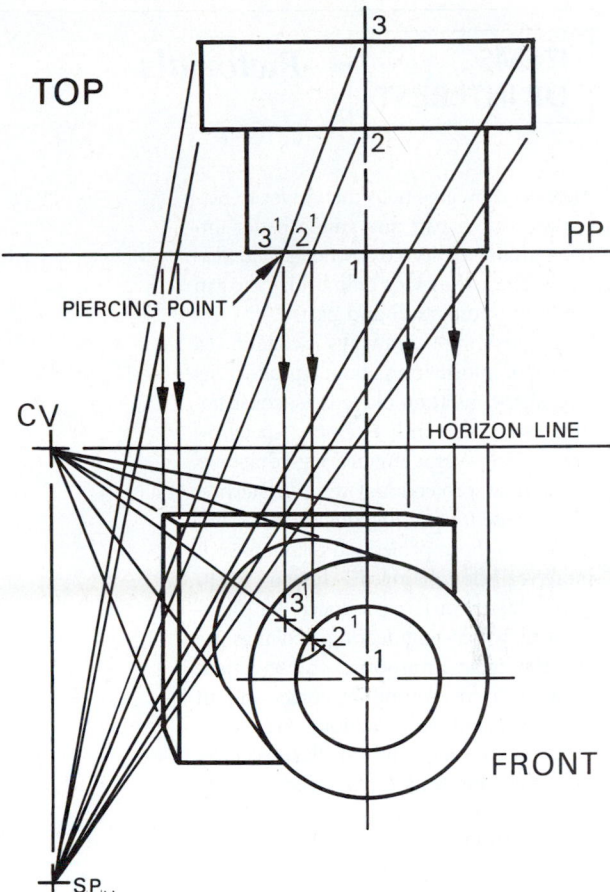

FIGURE 8.37 Circles in Parallel Perspective Projection

establishes the depth features of the part. This same procedure was used in drawing Figure 8.36. Here, the CV was placed to the right of the part, not centered as in the previous example.

Since the curves are drawn without distortion in the front plane, parts with curved features on one surface are easily drawn using this form of perspective (Fig. 8.37). Receding curves are located in the perspective view (front) by establishing the intersection of each curve's center point with the picture plane, point 1′, 2′, and 3′.

8.5.5 Two-Point Perspectives

The **two-point perspective** is also identified as an **angular perspective.** In Figure 8.38, the top view shows the width and depth of the part. The height is either projected to the height line (common to the line of sight) or is measured directly (to scale) on this line. There are two height lines on this example because *two mating parts* are drawn. Each has the same top view (with the exception of visibility). The height line for the top piece goes from the TOP LINE to point 1. The bottom piece has a height line from the GROUND LINE to point 1. The side views of each piece are reversed (and have different visibility).

The part is angled in the top view so that it makes 30° with the picture plane (PP). Lines are drawn from the SP parallel to the part's edge in this view. The angle formed by the SP and the two vanishing points in the top view will be 90° (angle A-SP-B). The intersection of each line and the PP determines the right and left vanishing points, which are then projected to the front view on the horizon line.

All lines on the drawing are determined by projection from location points on the height lines with lines extended to the proper vanishing points. Lines to the left of the plan view go toward the left vanishing point (VPL). Lines to the right on the plan view are drawn toward the right vanishing point (VPR). Projection from these points must follow the direction of the planes in the plan view of the part. If these lines change planes in following the contour or details of the part, the direction must also change from that point toward the vanishing point for that plane.

A line from the station point toward the outer points, both left and right, should make an angle with the height line (line of sight) of 15° or less. In other words, the angle made by the visual rays should not exceed 30° in most cases. In Figure 8.38 a slightly larger angle was used. A larger angle is likely to create excessive distortion. The horizon line should be

ITEMS OF INTEREST

Pictorials

Pictorial drawings help the viewer to better visualize a part and gain a better understanding of its components and features. These drawings help bridge the gap between photograph and part.

Engineering drawings contain a wealth of information about a product: its size, shape, location of features, construction materials, and assembly specifications. However, engineering drawings (multiview projections) are not always easy to read for a nontechnical person untrained in those projection techniques. A more realistic looking 3D drawing (technical illustration) is produced for situations in which engineering drawings are not the most appropriate presentation, such as in marketing meetings and in maintenance documentation.

Early tries at technical illustration by the Egyptians and Greeks didn't really show all three dimensions in one view. Around 1500 A.D., pictorial drawings that showed all three dimensions in one view evolved. Leonardo da Vinci was the most famous of this group of inventors/illustrators. His artistic ability and scientific foresight provided the means for true technical illustration. Techniques were further refined during the Industrial Revolution. After 1940, technical illustrations became popular design and development tools.

Today, technical illustrators produce pictorial drawings that aid in product development, assembly, marketing, illustration, repair, and maintenance. It is a fact that technical illustrations accelerate production, improve communications during development, and reduce product

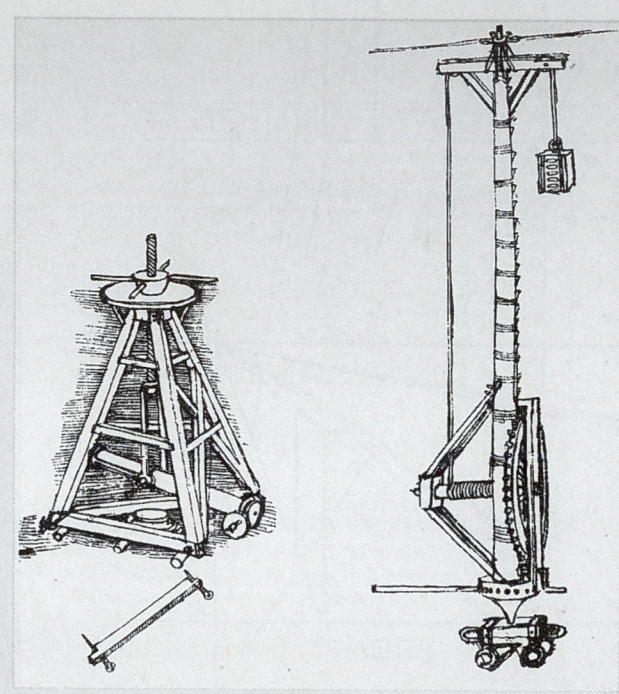

Leonardo's Mechanical Sketches

cost. Even people with limited technical knowledge can understand complex assemblies and interrelationships of parts and features. Indeed, pictorials prove to us "a picture is worth a thousand words."

The solid models on advanced CAD stations today are an extension of this same principle. Not only do these parts look three dimensional, they are 3D mathematically. The advanced renderings of parts on these sophisticated systems make the parts look very real on the computer screen—in

fact, they look almost as good as photographs. The 3D database can be used to make renderings and illustrations and can be used to generate a toolpath to machine the part. Improved visualization is one of the key factors driving the increasing popularity of these systems.

However, the lesson learned by mankind long ago is that we really need to be able to "see" a part to understand it. Leonardo da Vinci was a master of this long before the computer age.

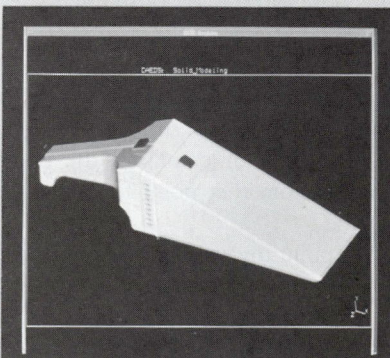
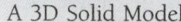
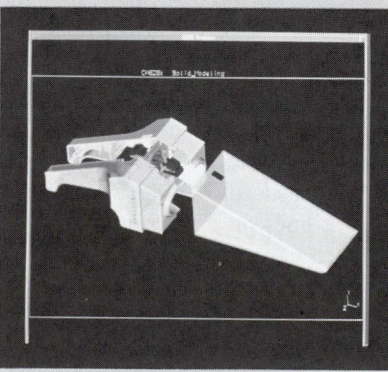
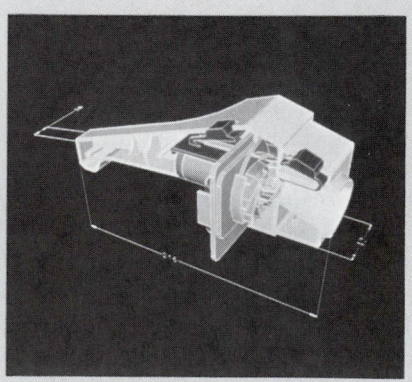

A 3D Solid Model

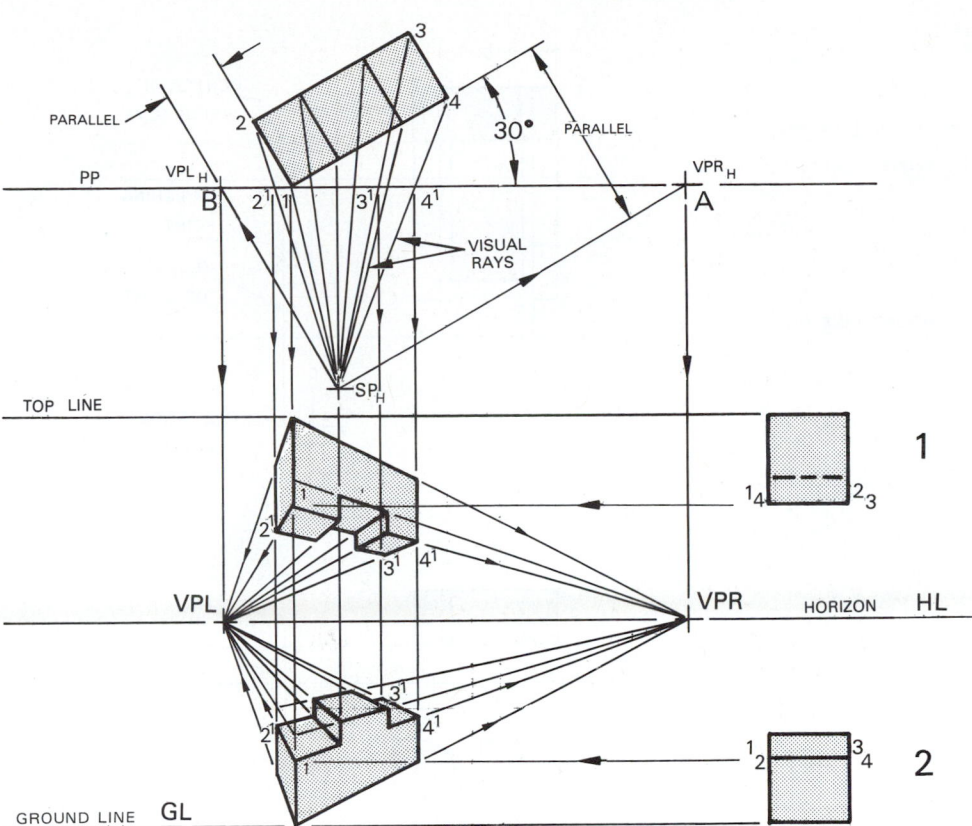

FIGURE 8.38 Two-Point Perspective Projection

located at some distance from the picture plane to avoid overlapping of the plan view and the perspective pictorial drawing. This was not done in Figure 8.33 and, therefore, the construction overlaps. Figure 8.38 is easier to read because the construction lines of the two views do not overlap.

The vertical dimensions of the part are measured to scale or projected from the side view directly. The scale of the plan view and the elevation should be the same to avoid distortion on the pictorial drawing.

Increasing the distance between the plan view of the part and the edge view of the picture plane decreases the size of the perspective and gives an appearance of distance from the part. However, increasing this distance does not compensate for a change in height and can cause distortion. The plan view should touch the edge view of the picture plane (Fig. 8.38).

8.5.6   Three-Point Perspectives

Three-point perspectives are called **oblique perspectives** [Figure 8.32(c)]. They are used in situations where the object would not appear excessively distorted, as for very tall buildings. The use of oblique perspective pictorial drawings lends very little to the aid of perception. A three-point perspective requires that all three axes of the object be oblique to the plane of projection. Height cannot be measured directly on the height line, as with the two-point perspective. When creating a three-point perspective, grid underlays are helpful.

8.6   Construction of Perspectives

The three examples presented in this section use the same basic object as the part to be drawn in perspective. Figure 8.39 is a one-point perspective of the part, Figure 8.40 is a two-point perspective of the same part, and Figure 8.41 is a two-point perspective of the same basic shape but with curved features.

8.6.1   One-Point Construction

The construction of a one-point perspective starts with the determination of the part's scale and position in space. In general, the top surface and the right side of the part should be viewed. The top view is drawn first [Fig. 8.39(a)]. The picture plane is passed through the front face of the part. In other words, the edge view of the picture plane and the edge view of the front face are along the same line. The horizon line is drawn according to the desired position of eye level and whether the part is to be viewed from eye level, below eye level, or above eye level. The ground line is drawn last. The distance between the ground line and the horizon line determines how far above or below eye level the part will be observed by the viewer.

The front view is drawn second [Fig. 8.39(b)]. The distance between the picture plane line in the top view and the station point is drawn two times (or more) the width of the part (dimension D in this figure). The location of the vertical

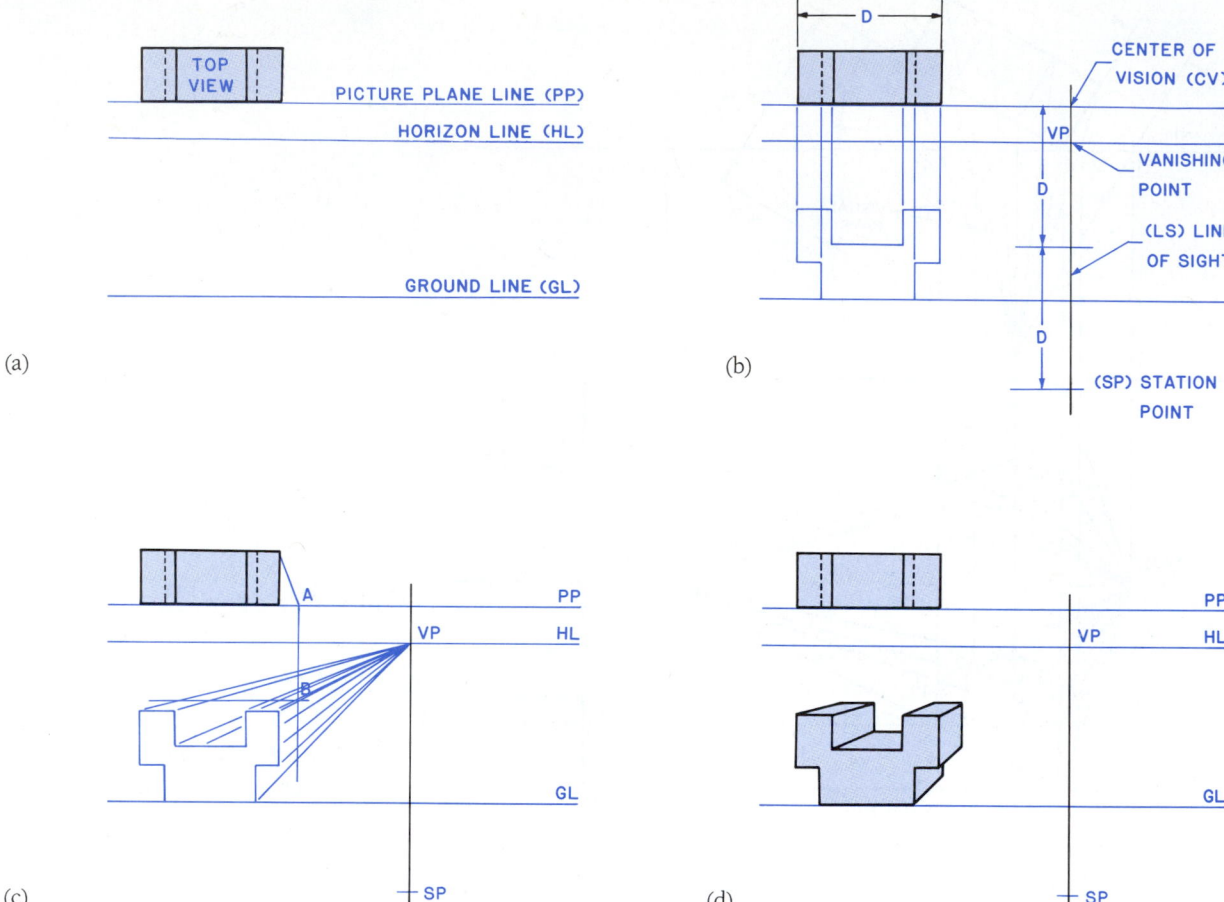

FIGURE 8.39 Constructing a One-Point Perspective

line (line of sight) will be determined by what side the part is to recede to and how much of the part's side needs to be shown. Here, the vertical line was drawn on the right of the part, therefore the perspective recedes to the right. Dimension D is used to establish this distance. The line of sight is to the right of the part at a distance equal to dimension D. The farther to the side this line is drawn, the more the right side will show. The front view is then drawn using the width dimensions projected from the top view and completing the front face's features. The vanishing point is at the intersection of the line of sight (vertical line) and the horizon line.

Lines are now drawn from every point on the front view to the vanishing point (VP) in Figure 8.39(c). Draw a line from the station point to the back corner of the part in the top view. This line intersects the picture plane (PP) to establish point A. A line is then drawn vertically from point A to the receding lines, which extend from the front view toward the VP. This will establish point B and the back vertical edge of the part. A horizontal line is then drawn from point B to the left to establish the back edge. All other features are now drawn using the same procedure to establish points along the picture plane and project to the front view [Fig. 8.39(d)].

8.6.2 Two-Point Construction

In Figure 8.40 a two-point perspective of the same part shown in Figure 8.39 is provided. Note the differences and similarities of the procedure and the finished illustration. Two-point perspectives require more work and the end result is more realistic.

Start by drawing the picture plane line (PP) as shown. The top view is then drawn with one of its corners touching the picture plane line. This will also establish the center of vision (CV). The front face is drawn at an angle of 30° to the PP as shown. Other angles can be used. To show enough detail, the side with the most features should be at the smaller angle to the PP. The line of sight is drawn as a vertical line extending from the intersection of the part's front corner (the one touching the PP) in Figure 8.40(a). The horizon line, ground line, and the station point are established as in Figure 8.39. Draw lines (SPA and SPB) from the station point parallel to the edges of the part to where they intersect the PP and establish points A and B. Vanishing point left (VPL) and vanishing point right (VPR) are drawn by dropping vertical lines from points A and B to the horizon line [Fig. 8.40(b)].

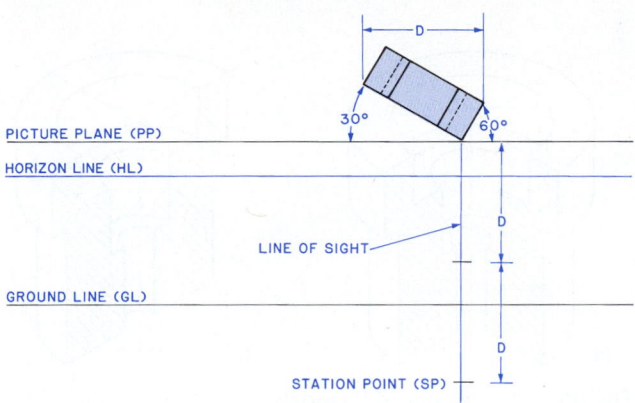

(a)

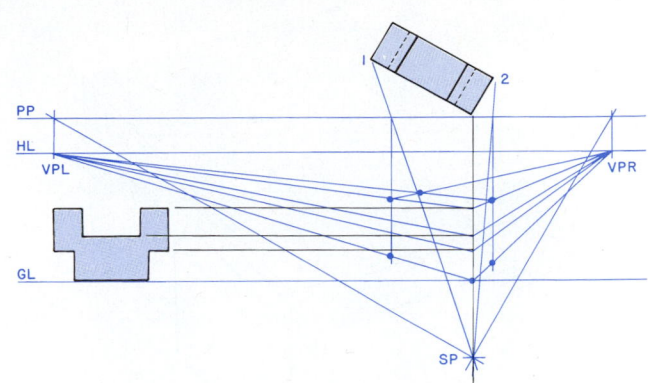

(c)

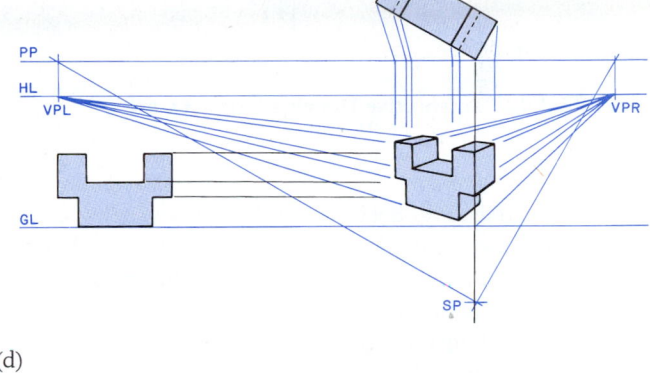

(b)

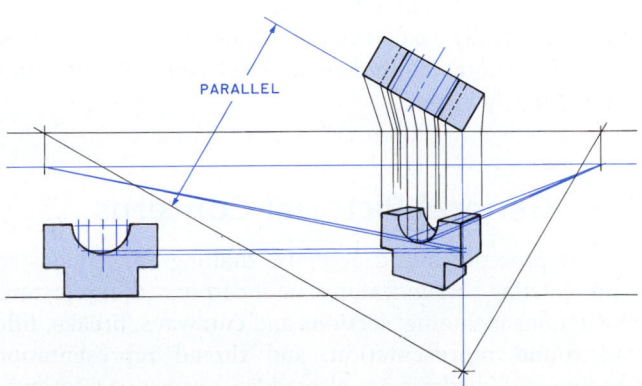

(d)

FIGURE 8.40 Constructing a Two-Point Perspective

The right or left side view is then drawn with its base on the ground line, as shown in Figure 8.40(c). Height lines are established in the perspective view by projecting each vertical dimension from the side view to the line of sight. The intersection of each line projected from the side view to the line of sight establishes points. Draw a line from each point to the VPL and the VPR. Draw lines from the SP to the corners of the top view at points 1 and 2. The intersection of these projectors and the PP establishes the outside limits of the perspective view when they are drawn vertically until they intersect their corresponding receding projectors. The part's outside dimensions have now been determined. Using the previous two steps every feature of the part is established by projection. The perspective is then darkened as in Figure 8.40(d).

8.6.3 Two-Point Construction of Curved Features

In Figure 8.41 the part has been constructed using the same procedure as in Figure 8.40. The parts are identical except that the cutout is now curved instead of rectangular. To draw a perspective of a part with curved features, points are established

FIGURE 8.41 Constructing a Two-Point Perspective with Curved Features

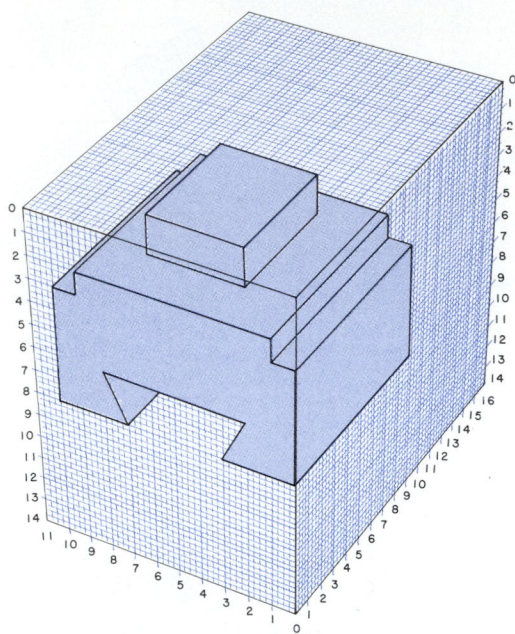

FIGURE 8.42   Perspective Drawing Using a Grid

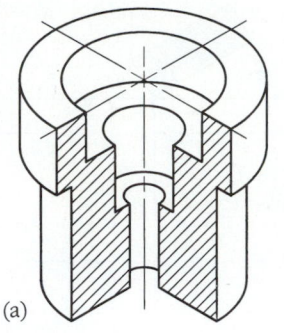 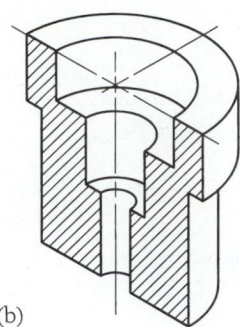

(a)   (b)

FIGURE 8.43   Sectioned Pictorials
(a) Half section (b) Full section

along the curve (Fig. 8.41). After the part's general shape is established, the points along each curve are projected and located with the same procedure used to locate an endpoint of a line or any straight feature. After a sufficient number of points is established along the curve in the perspective view, the curve can be drawn with the aid of an irregular curve.

8.6.4   Perspective Drawing Grids

Perspective grids (Fig. 8.42) and perspective circle templates are used to speed the illustration process. The use of a common grid standardizes the size and scale of the pictorial. It also permits several drafters to work together on the same set of illustration drawings. When all parts are drawn in their relative position in the total grid, and the same perspective scale is used, the drawings of mating parts can be placed, one over the other, for minute inspection of the design before parts are actually made from the drawings. These drawings should have both vanishing points and station points plainly and accurately located.

8.7   General Pictorial Concerns

Various procedures and accepted drafting conventions for representating certain features are incorporated into pictorial illustrations including: **sections** and **cutaways**, **breaks**, **fillet** and **round representation**, and **thread representation**. Shading and shadows are also added to pictorials to give a more lifelike representation of the part. Pictorial **assemblies** incorporate **exploded views** when it is necessary to show how a device fits together.

8.7.1   Sectional and Cutaway Views

Sectioned pictorials allow the viewing of the interior of a part or assembly. When possible, section cutting planes are passed through centerlines and parallel to one of the principal faces of the part. Figure 8.43 shows a half section (a) and a full section (b) of a part. Section lines in a half section should be drawn so that they would appear to coincide if the planes were folded together [Fig. 8.43(a)]. When a full section is used, the crosshatching should all be drawn in the same direction [Fig. 8.43(b)].

In assemblies, individual pieces are differentiated by using appropriate symbols and by changing the direction of the section lining. When a section plane passes through shafts, bolts, keys, pins, and solid round items, it is desirable to run the section around that item and show the entire bolt or shaft in the pictorial. Except for such cases, the section lines should show exactly what material has been cut. Figure 8.44(a) shows the first step in the creation of a section of a pictorial assembly. Each of the parts is blocked out. The assembly is then completed [Fig. 8.44(b)].

Any of the types of sections presented in Chapter 9 may be used in pictorial drawing. The standard weights for lines and spacing, as well as standard symbols, should be used for section lining.

8.7.2   Break Lines

For long parts, **break lines** may be used to shorten the length of the drawing. When the length of the part is beyond the size of the drawing format, and there are no features that require displaying and dimensioning, you may shorten the drawing by using break lines. Position the break at a place on the part that does not interfere with the part features and the required dimensions. **Freehand breaks** are preferred as shown in Figure 8.45. Here, the preferred and acceptable methods for showing breaks are given.

8.7.3   Fillets and Rounds

Fillets and **rounds** usually can be highlighted or can be shown as straight or curved lines representing the filleted and

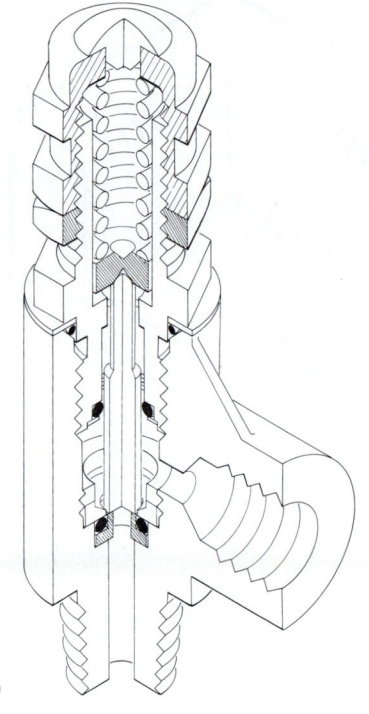

(a)   (b)

FIGURE 8.44 **Pictorial Construction**
(a) Construction of needle valve in an isometric drawing using a half section (b) Completed pictorial of needle valve

rounded edges of a part, as in Figure 8.46. Highlighting is drawn freehand. Fillets and rounds are covered in depth in Chapter 11.

8.7.4   Thread Representation

Threads may be represented by a series of ellipses or circles uniformly spaced along the centerline of the thread. Shading increases the effectiveness of the thread appearance, as in Figures 8.47, 8.48, and 8.49. In Figure 8.47, the exploded assembly has internal and external threads. Threads should be evenly spaced, but it is not necessary to reproduce the actual pitch (distance between crests of the threads) or the exact number of threads.

8.7.5   Shading and Shadows

Many types of **shading** are used on pictorials. The type of shading used depends on the purpose of the drawing and the type of pictorial. Smudge shading, as shown in Figure 8.48, is sometimes used on pictorial drawings. For catalog illustrations, some form of overall shading is generally preferred. Excellent results can usually be obtained by use of the airbrush. This is illustrated in the pictorial of the valve shown in Figure 8.49. For more artistic results, the pictorial may be completely shaded with shadows added to the illustration. When **shadows** are added to an illustration, they add depth and realism to the drawing. Choosing a proper light source will make the illustration look as if it is a photograph.

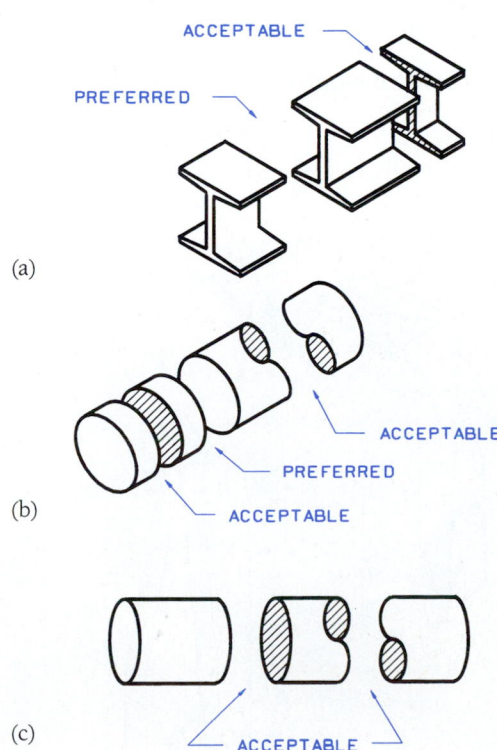

FIGURE 8.45 **Break Lines for Pictorials**

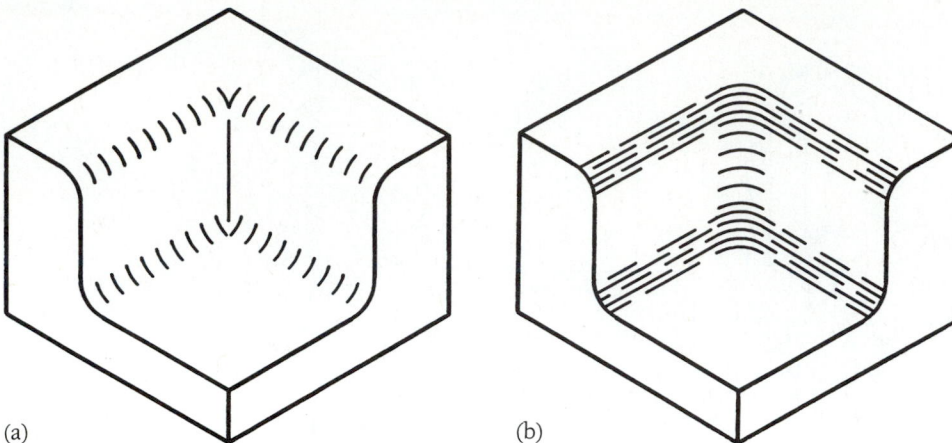

FIGURE 8.46   Fillets and Rounds in Pictorials (a) Curved highlighting (b) Straight highlighting   (a)   (b)

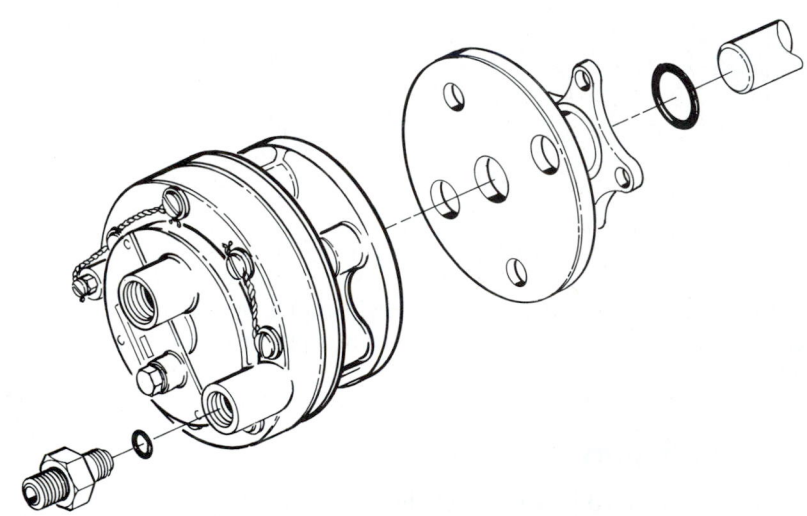

FIGURE 8.47   Exploded Pictorials

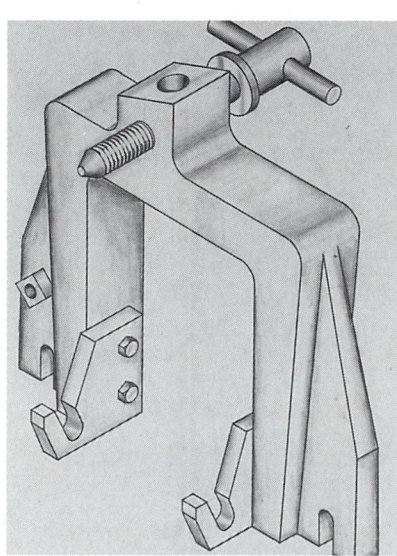

FIGURE 8.48   Shading Pictorials

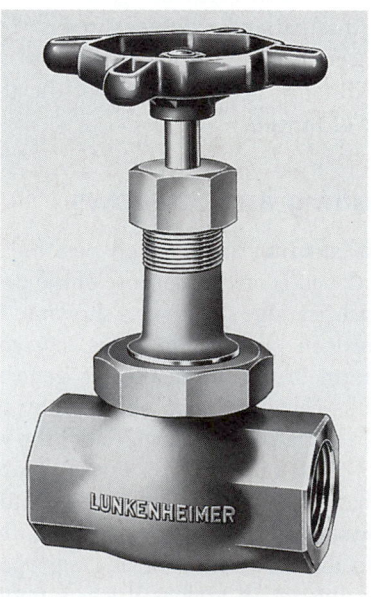

FIGURE 8.49   Airbrushed Shading in Pictorials

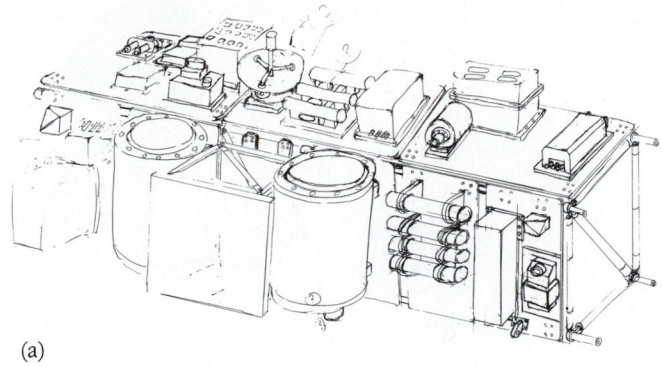

(a)

8.7.6   Assembly Pictorials

Assembly pictorials require a number of preliminary sketches and drawings. In Figure 8.50(a), a rough sketch of an assembly is shown. This layout is essential to establish the proper positions of each piece of the assembly and the proper angle of viewing. A number of trials may be required. Each of the pieces is then drawn correctly, as shown in Figure 8.50(b). The separate piece shown as a **cutaway** in Figure 8.50(c) will be added to the assembly as an **enlarged view** of one of the pieces. The completed project is shown in Figure 8.50(d) where the labels have been added to identify each piece. Cutaway assemblies are also used to show portions of a project that would not be clear without the removal of some part of the assembly.

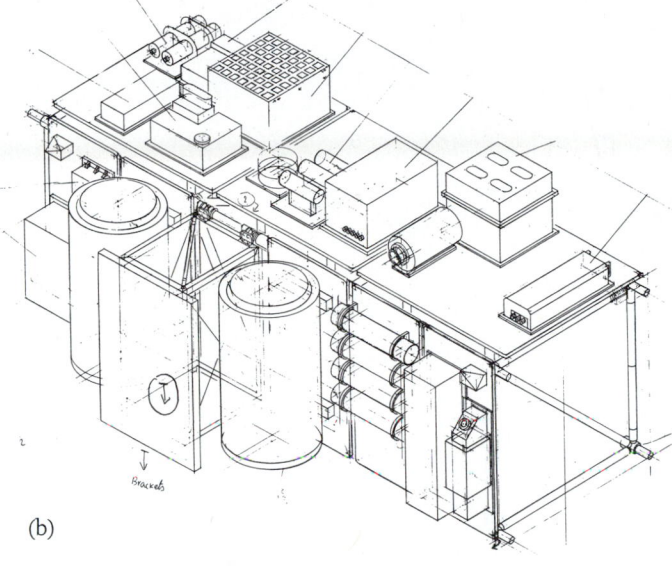

(b)

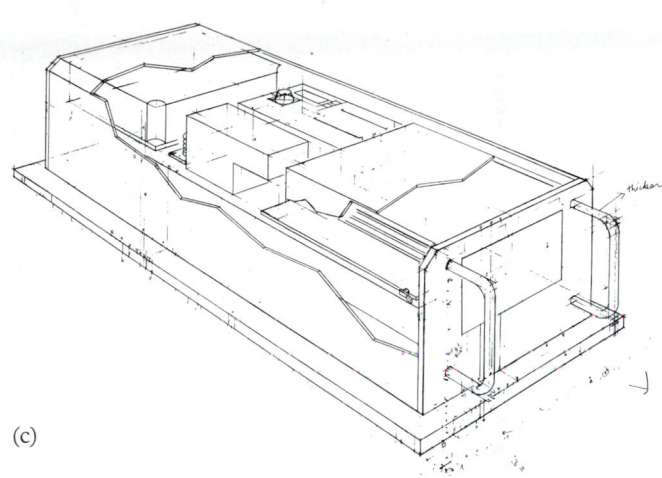

(c)

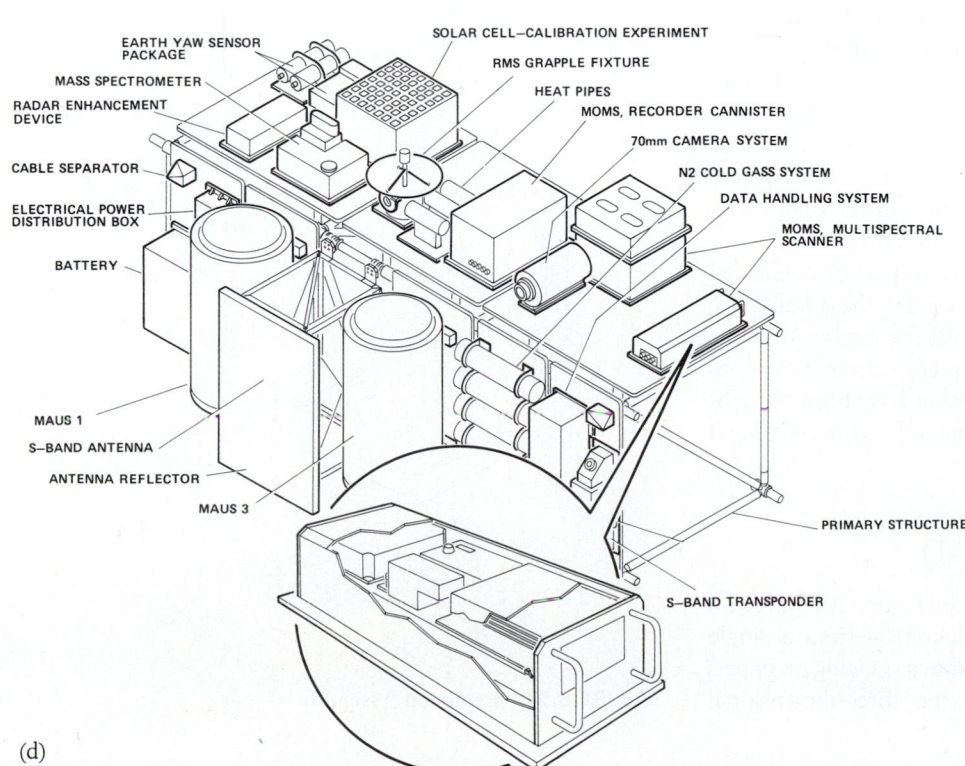

(d)

FIGURE 8.50   Assembly Pictorial Construction
(a) Laying-out an assembly pictorial
(b) Blocking-in an assembly pictorial (c) Construction of subcomponent for pictorial assembly (d) Completed pictorial assembly

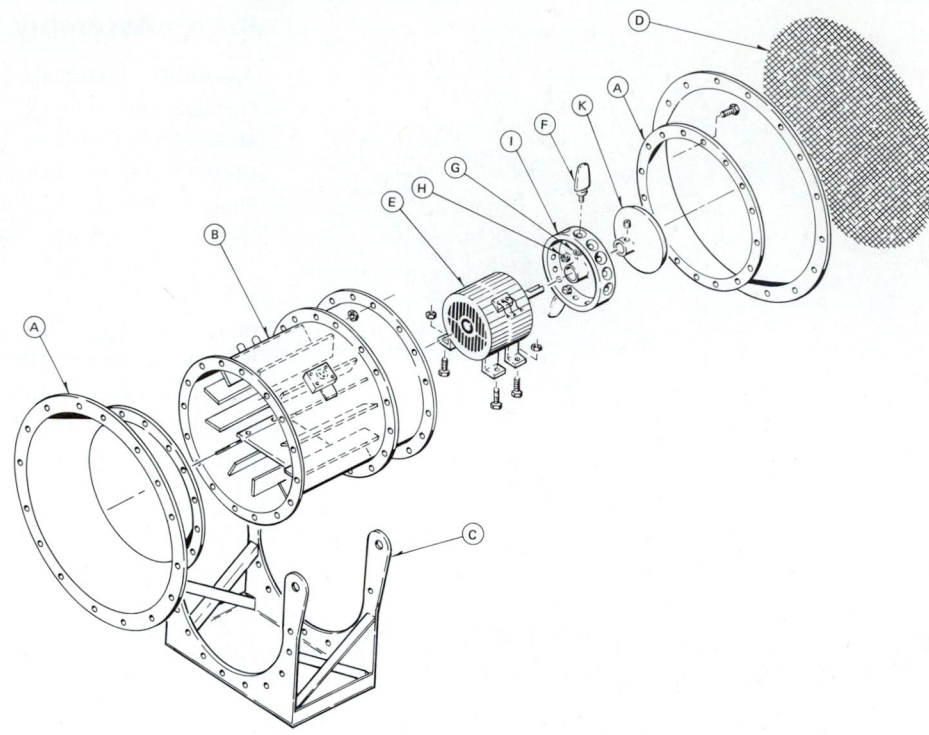

FIGURE 8.51 Exploded Pictorial

8.7.7 Exploded Pictorials

A pictorial drawing showing the various parts of an assembly, separated, but in proper position and alignment for reassembly, is called an **exploded assembly** (Fig. 8.51). Exploded pictorials are used extensively in service manuals and as an aid in assembling or erecting a machine or structure. Any type of pictorial drawing may be used for this purpose and the shading may be as simple or as complete as desired. In Figures 8.51 and 8.52, exploded assemblies were drawn isometrically. Simple highlighting and shading has been added to provide a realistic illustration of the pieces. The round pieces in Figure 8.51 have dot shading on their lower right sides. This establishes the fact that they are curved features.

Each piece in an exploded assembly should be connected to its mating part by a centerline, as shown in these examples. If there is not sufficient room to extend the exploded pieces out from each other in one line, the piece can be moved, as in Figure 8.52, where the bolt and washer have been brought forward and up. The jogged centerline still connects related pieces.

8.8 Pictorials Using CAD

A drafter seated at the CAD station in Figure 8.53 gets no more feeling of three-dimensional definition from a single view on the display than they would from a drawing on paper. However, you can better visualize the three-dimensional

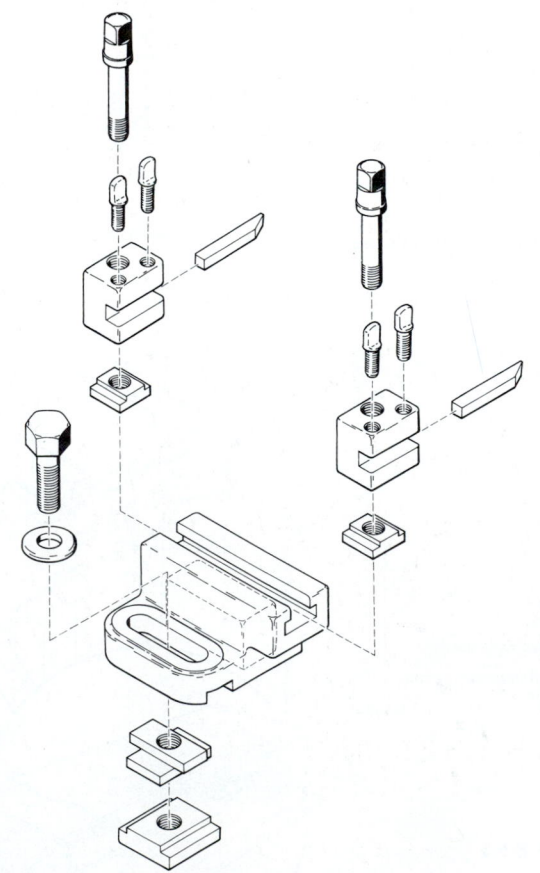

FIGURE 8.52 Exploded Assembly

FIGURE 8.53   Designer Creating 3D Part

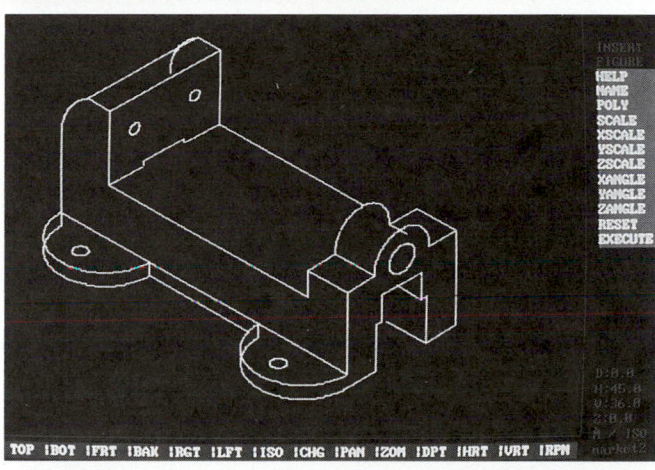

(a)

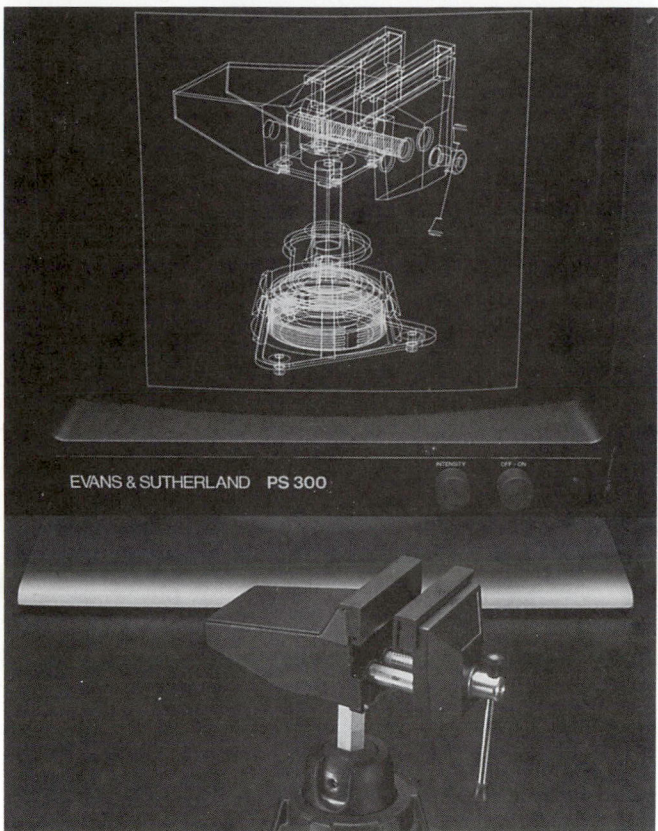

(a)

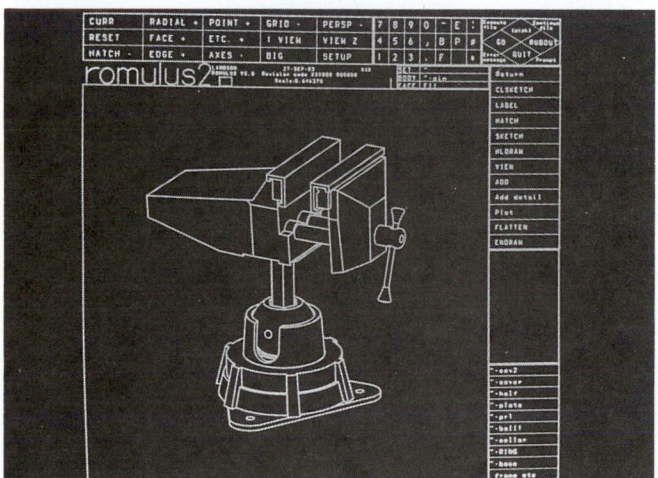

(b)

FIGURE 8.55   **Vise Model**   (a) 3D model of a vise (b) Vise model with hidden lines removed

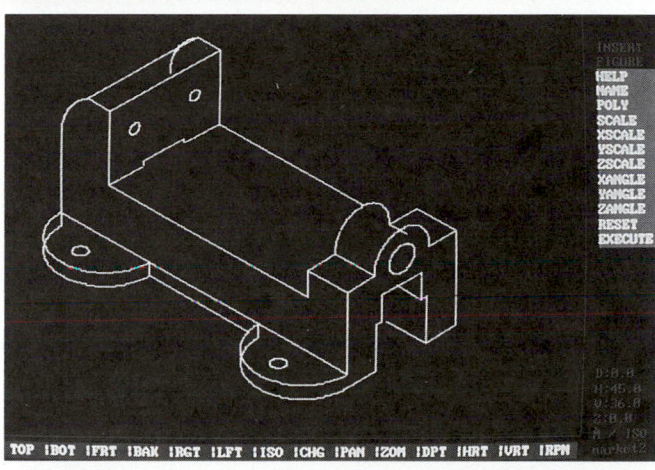

(b)

FIGURE 8.54   **3D Part Design**   (a) 3D Part displayed in an isometric view (b) Part displayed in isometric and a right side view

part when features are displayed in the view that indicates depth. A 3D CAD system allows you to work in any of the standard six views and at the same time see a pictorial (rotated) view. Figure 8.54(a) shows the part pictorially with hidden lines removed. In Figure 8.54(b), the same part is shown with a right side view displayed on the upper right portion of the screen. The drafter uses this view to aid in the modeling of the part. Pictorial views of a part are extremely useful in visualizing part features during the design stage (see Color Plates 23 through 27).

After a part is modeled [Fig. 8.55(a)], it can be rotated, enlarged, and zoomed into a desired pictorial position. This capability eliminates the need to redraw the part as an isometric, oblique, or perspective drawing. In Figure 8.55(b), the model of the vice has had all hidden lines removed using a **HIDE** command. The model is now visibly correct. After the illustrator displays the desired pictorial views, they can embellish the 3D model as required: adding shading, color, or other artistic qualities to prepare the final output to be used as an illustration for technical manuals, advertisements, training manuals, or sales literature.

While perspective, isometric, and rotated views are useful in depicting 3D objects more realistically, many CAD systems offer the capability to use solid models. Here, the illusion of depth can be added through the use of color and shading. This technique is shown in the color section insert where a number of plates are full four-color slides taken from the screen on a solid modeling CAD system.

You May Complete Exercises 8.5 Through 8.8 at This Time

QUIZ

True or False

1. Curves that do not lie in isometric planes must be constructed with offset measurements.
2. A general oblique drawing is constructed using 45° for the receding axis.
3. An isometric drawing is constructed using true-length measurements along all three axis lines.
4. A cavalier drawing is always foreshortened.
5. Centerlines are included on all pictorials.
6. Cabinet and cavalier drawings are types of perspective projections.
7. The point of sight for a perspective should be located so that the angle the cone of rays makes does not exceed 45°.
8. A trimetric projection uses different angles for all three axes.

Fill in the Blanks

9. A _____ view shows the interior of the part or assembly.
10. _____ dimensioning is found on most pictorial drawings.
11. _____ projection approximates how a part will look to the human eye.
12. In true isometric projection all _____ _____ make equal _____ with the projection plane.
13. _____ lines are not parallel to or on one of the isometric axes.
14. A _____ oblique projection uses a half-scale for all receding measurements.
15. The _____ _____ method of ellipse construction does not create a _____ ellipse.
16. _____ features should be orientated so that they lie in the _____ face of the object when _____ projection is used on a drawing.

Answer the Following

17. What is the difference between an isometric drawing and an isometric projection?
18. In what situation would an oblique drawing be used instead of an isometric drawing?
19. What are the three types of oblique projection? Describe each and how they differ.
20. How does 3D CAD eliminate the need to construct traditional 2D pictorial drawings?
21. Give four uses of pictorial drawings.
22. Describe the three types of perspective projection and explain their differences.
23. What are offset measurements and when are they used in the construction of a pictorial drawing?
24. What are the various types of axonometric projection?

EXERCISES

Exercises may be assigned as sketching, instrument, or CAD projects. Transfer the given information to an "A" size sheet of .25 in. grid paper. Exercises that are not assigned by the instructor can be sketched in the text to provide practice and understanding for the preceding instructional material.

After Reading the Chapter Through Section 8.3.14 You May Complete the Following Exercises

Exercise 8.1   Using the part provided in Exercise 7.5B draw an isometric pictorial.

Exercise 8.2   Using the part provided in Exercise 7.9A draw an isometric pictorial.

Exercise 8.3   Using the part given in Exercise 7.10B draw an isometric pictorial.

Exercise 8.4   Using the part provided in Exercise 7.3A draw an isometric pictorial.

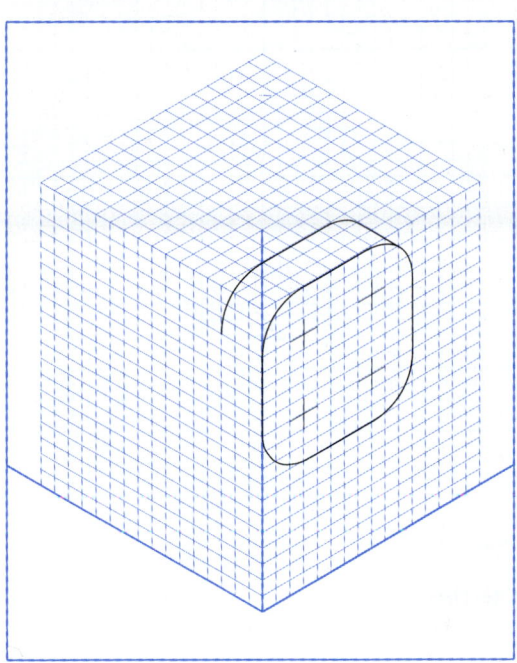

Exercise 8.1

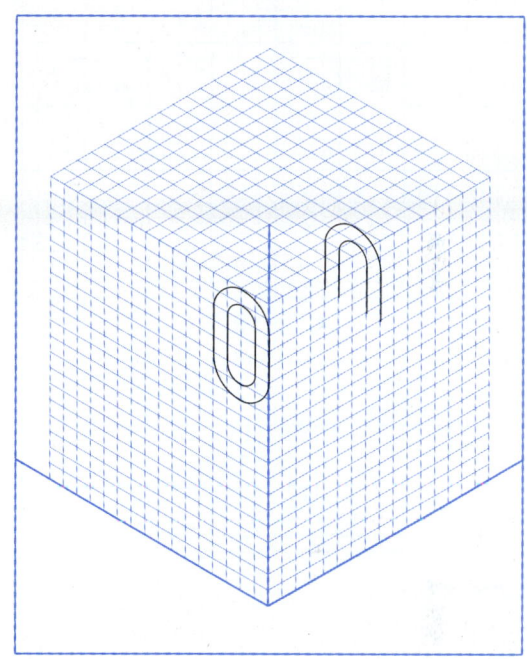

Exercise 8.3

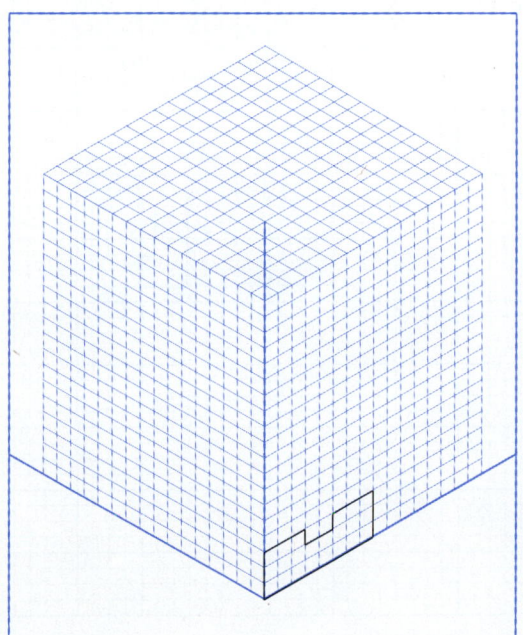

Exercise 8.2

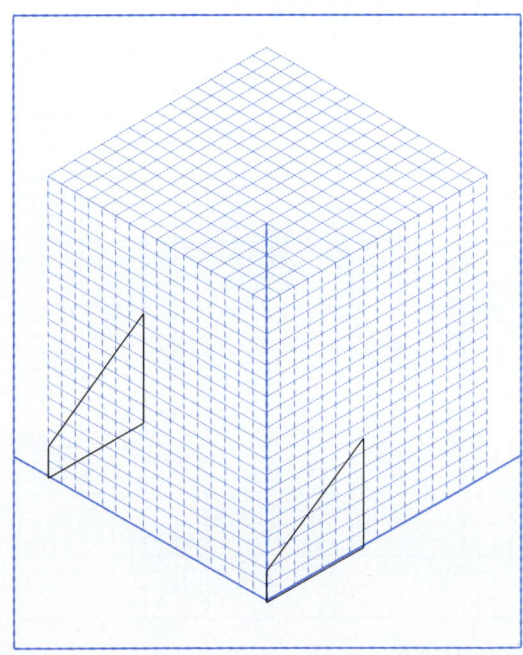

Exercise 8.4

After Reading the Chapter Through Section 8.8 You May Complete the Following Exercises

Exercise 8.5 Using the part given in Exercise 7.13B complete an oblique pictorial.

Exercise 8.6 Using the part given in Exercise 7.11B draw an oblique pictorial.

Exercise 8.7 Using the part provided in Exercise 7.4B draw an oblique pictorial.

Exercise 8.8 Using the part provided in Exercise 7.1A draw a one-point perspective pictorial.

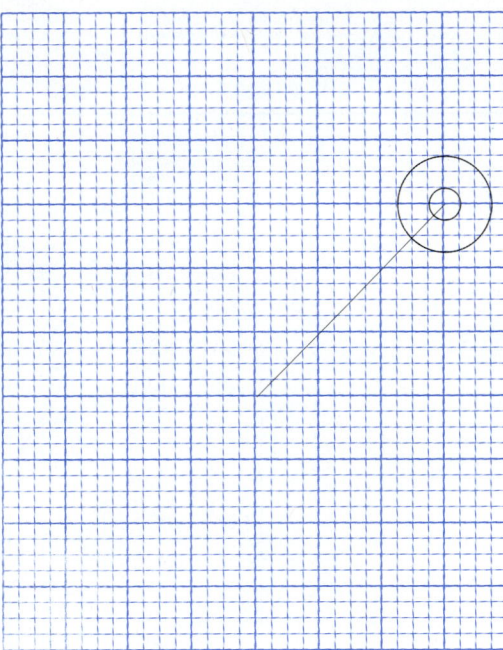

Exercise 8.5

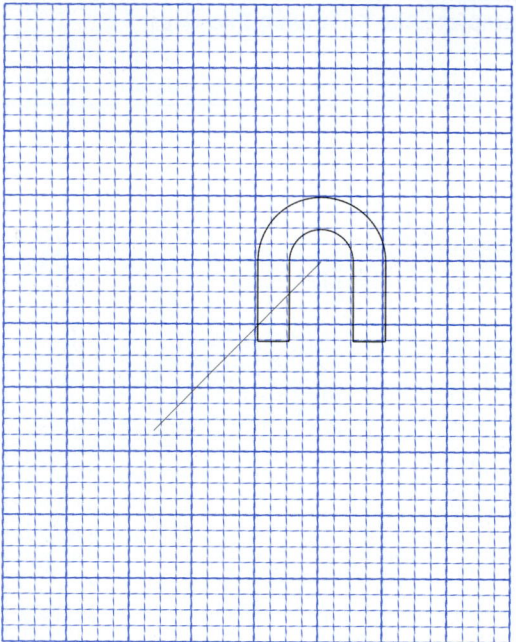

Exercise 8.7

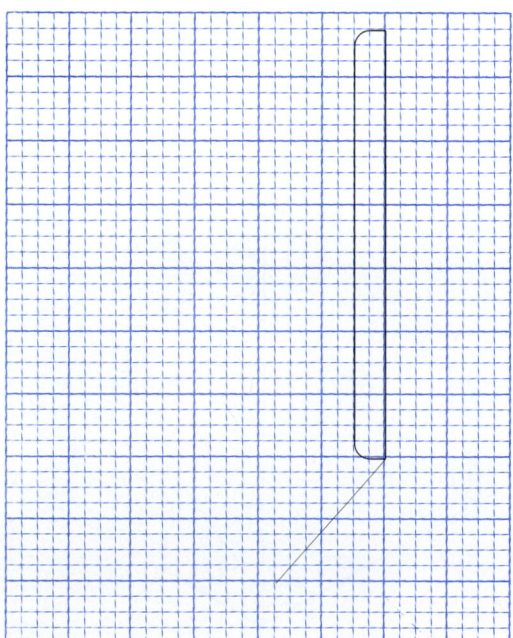

Exercise 8.6

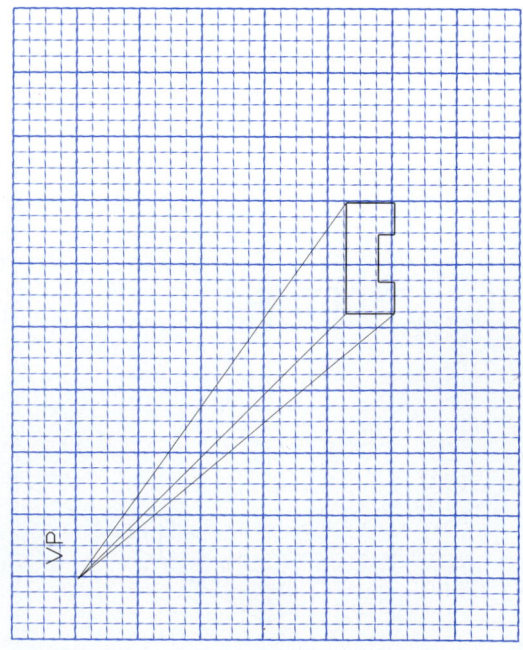

Exercise 8.8

PROBLEMS

Problems 8.1(A) Through (K)   These problems can be assigned as any of the three major types of pictorial projection. Unless assigned as a specific type of projection, the following problems could be used to test the students' understanding of the suitability of projection types for a particular problem. The instructor can allow the student to determine the projection method based on the part's features and pictorial requirements as described by the instructor.

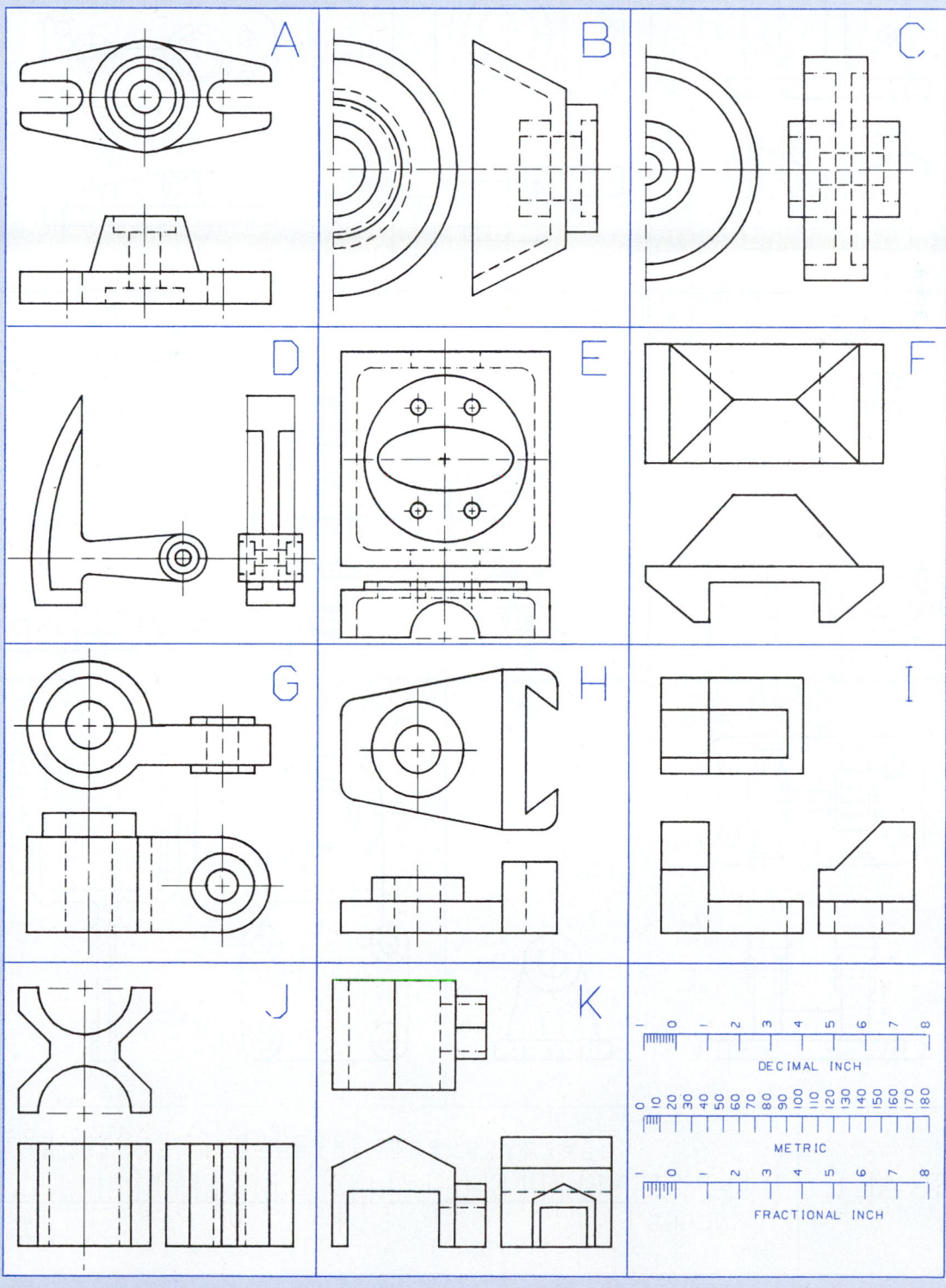

Problems 8.2 Through 8.4 These problems were created in metric units and the scale provided is to be used when taking the part from the text and transferring it to the drawing board (or computer). The decimal scale can also be used if the problem as assigned will be done in decimal inch units.

Problems 8.2(A) Through (H) These problems are meant for isometric projection but can be drawn as any type of pictorial projection as assigned.

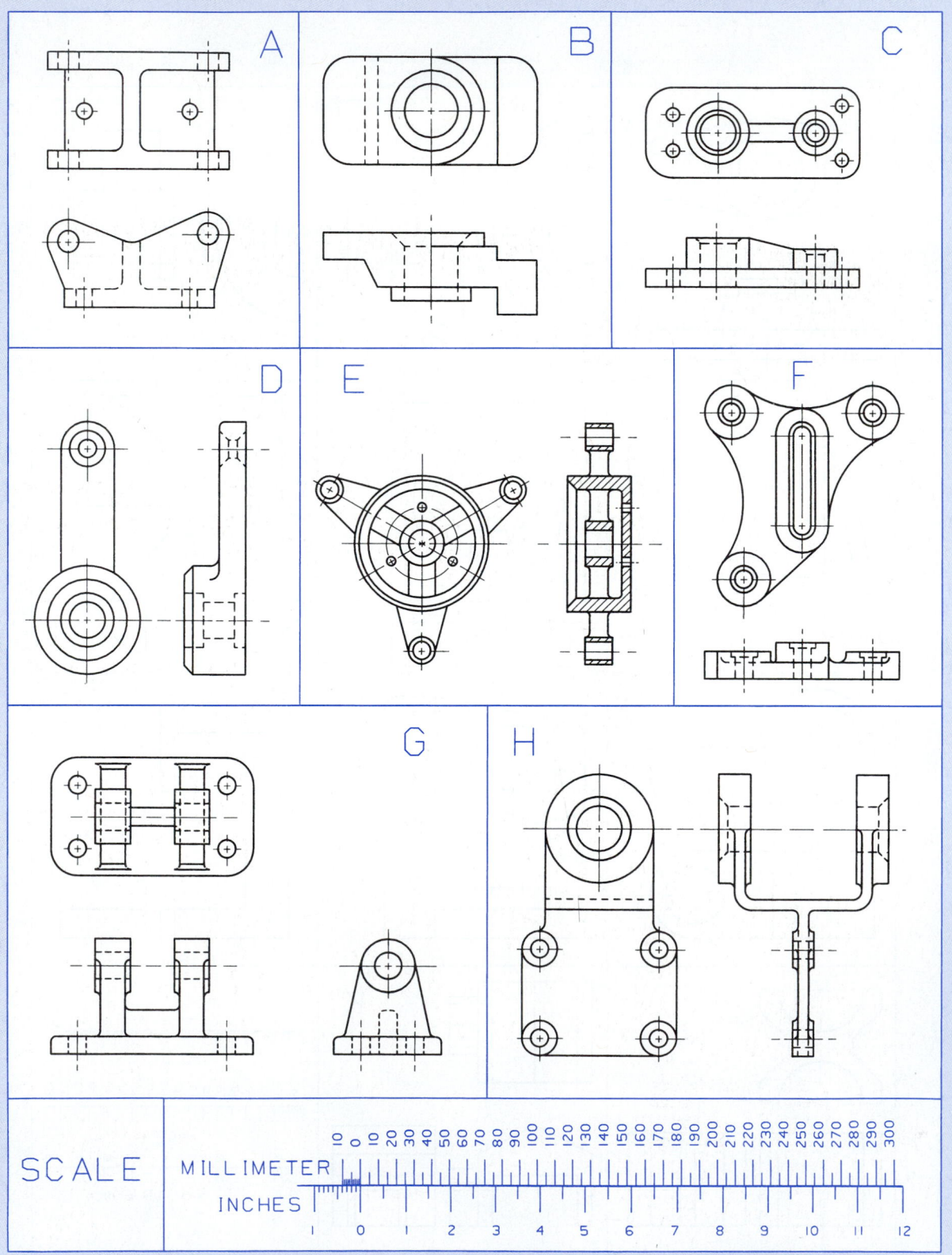

Problems 8.3(A) Through (F) These problems are designed as oblique projects although the instructor can assign other methods of projection.

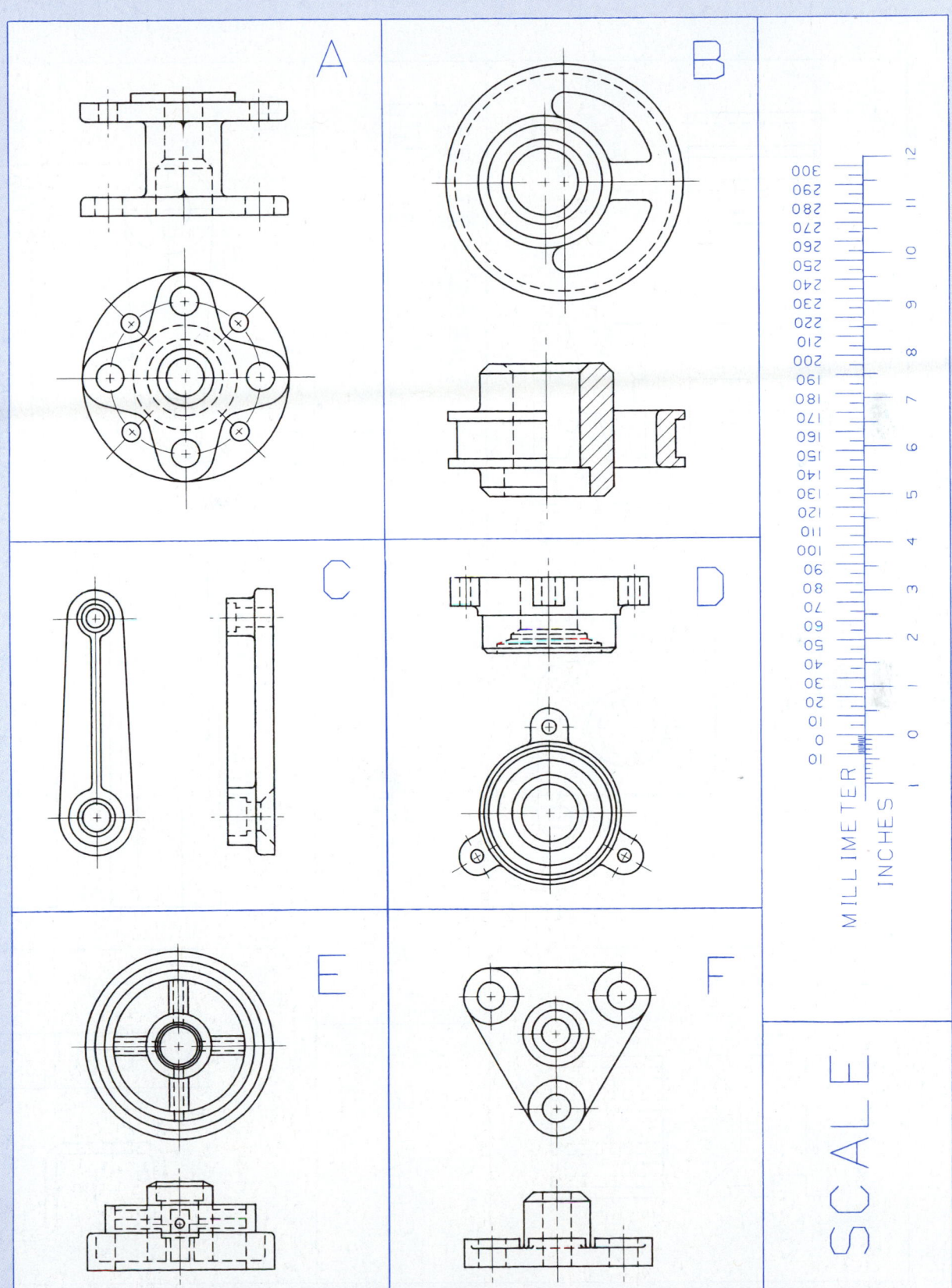

Problems 8.4(A) Through (F) These problems can be used for any method of pictorial projection but were intended as perspective projection projects.

Instructor may assign any appropriate problems or figures found in Chapters 7, 9, 10, or 18 as pictorial drawing projects, either manual or CAD.

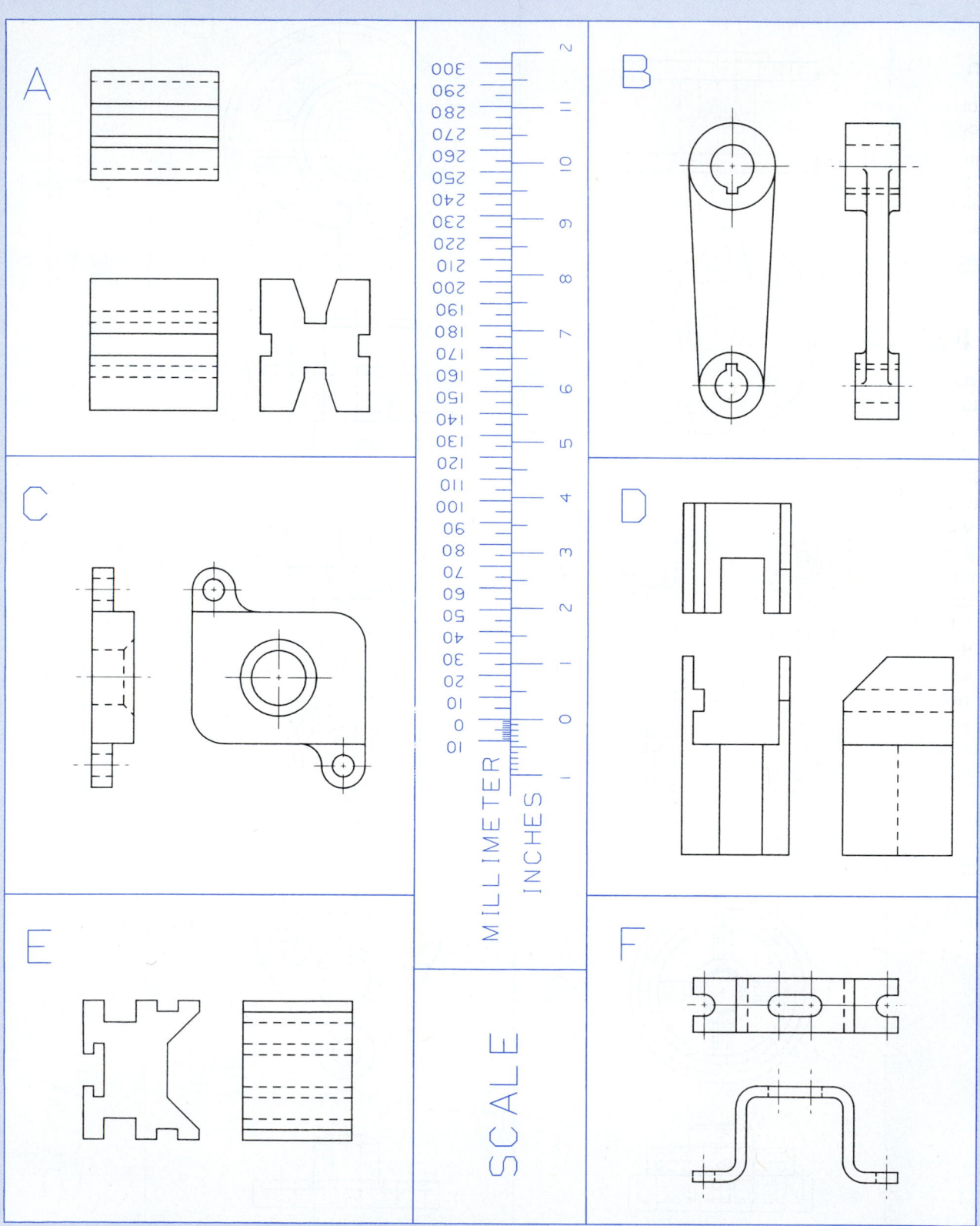

CHAPTER 9

Sections

Learning Objectives

Upon completion of this chapter you will be able to accomplish the following:

1. Identify the need for sectional views in order to clarify interior part features.
2. Apply standard drafting conventions and line types to illustrate interior features.
3. Identify cutting planes and resulting views.
4. Differentiate between and produce full, half, offset, aligned, removed, revolved, broken-out, and assembly sections.
5. Integrate standard sectioning methods into the CAD environment.

9.1 Introduction

Designers and drafters use **sectional views**, also called **sections**, to clarify and dimension the internal construction of a part. Sections are needed for interior features that cannot be clearly described by hidden lines in conventional views. For example, the valve in Figure 9.1 has a portion of its exterior body removed to allow a view of the disk, seating, and stem. Figure 9.2 shows the same valve with its front removed (full section), allowing a view of all the interior parts. Without removing portions of the valve body it is impossible to describe accurately the internal features of the valve.

This chapter presents different types of sections and discusses their variations when used on mechanical parts and assemblies. Sections make use of a number of **drafting conventions**—standard, accepted ways of showing part features on a drawing.

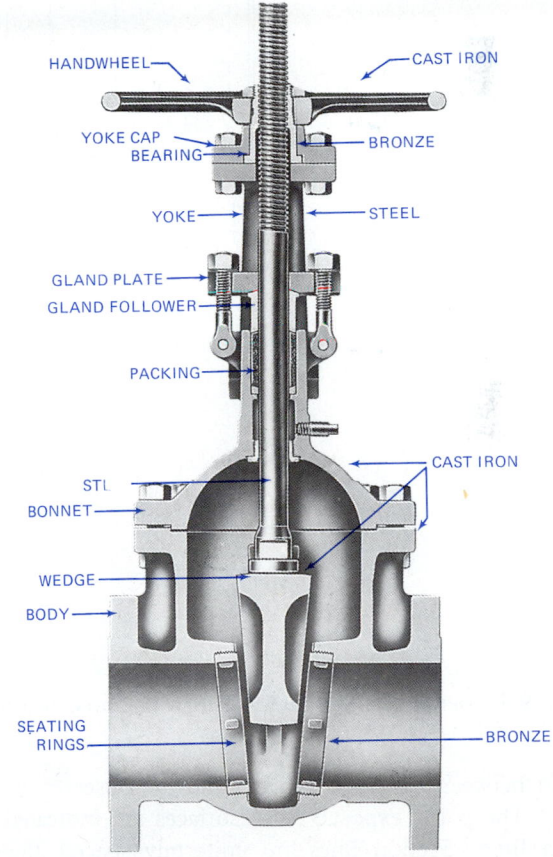

FIGURE 9.2 Front Section of a Gate Valve Showing the Stem and Disk

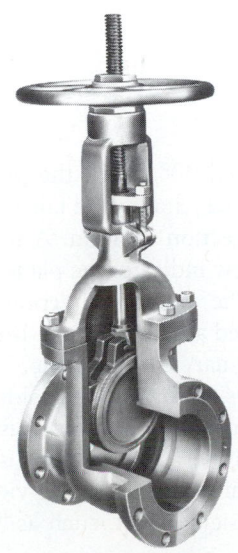

FIGURE 9.1 Sectioned Gate Valve

9.2 Sections

A sectional view is obtained by passing an imaginary **cutting plane** through the part, perpendicular to the **line of sight**, as in Figure 9.3 (**SECTION A–A**). The line of sight is the direction in which the part is viewed (Fig. 9.4, p. 278). The portion

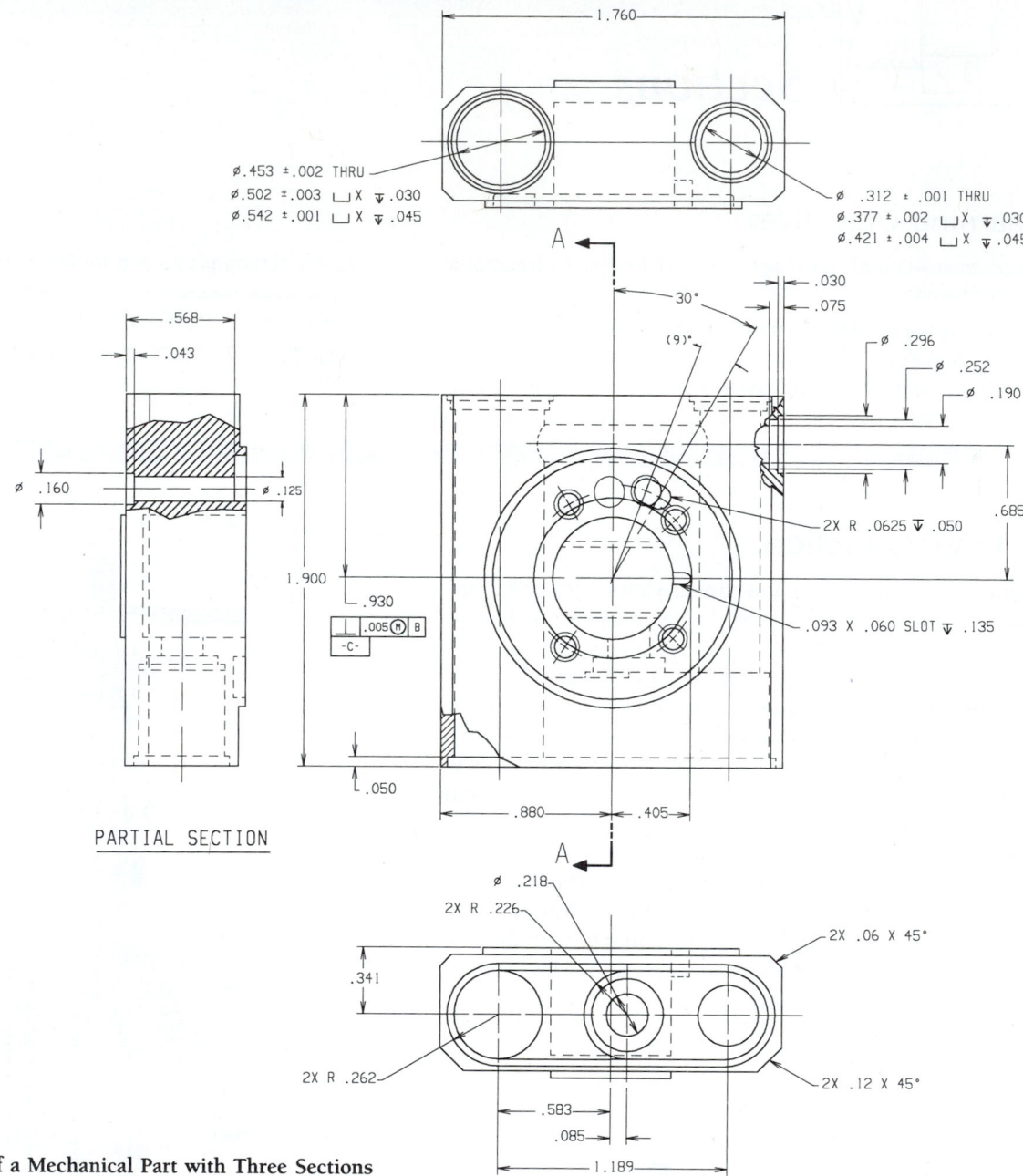

FIGURE 9.3 Detail of a Mechanical Part with Three Sections

the part between the cutting plane and the observer is "removed." The part's exposed solid surfaces are indicated by **section lines**. Section lines are uniformly spaced angular lines drawn in proportion to the size of the drawing.

In all section views on a drawing, section lines for the same part are identical in angle, spacing, and uniformity (Fig. 9.4). Spacing of section lines should be as generous as possible and yet preserve the unity of the sectioned area. In other words, construct section lines so that they are spaced clearly, are pleasing to look at, and will reduce and enlarge without distorting.

There are many different types of section views. Figure 9.3 shows a drawing of a complex part containing a full section (**SECTION A–A**), a partial section (left side), and a broken-out section (left corner of front view). These types of sections are covered in detail later in the chapter.

Sections are rotated 90° out of the plane of principal or auxiliary views from which they are taken, following the customary rules of projection rotation. A heavy line across or near the principal view indicates the plane of projection, with arrows to indicate the viewing direction-line of sight (Fig. 9.4). This line is called a **cutting plane line** and it represents the edge of the imaginary cutting plane. The sections in Figure 9.4 are also views (front and right side). When the plane of projection passes through the view, it is called the **cutting plane** and the resulting adjacent view is called a **section**. Each cutting plane, and corresponding view, has **view identification letters**, assigned to it, such as "**SECTION A–A**" in Figure 9.4.

When cutting planes pass through solid portions of the part, these areas are shown by section lines in the adjacent

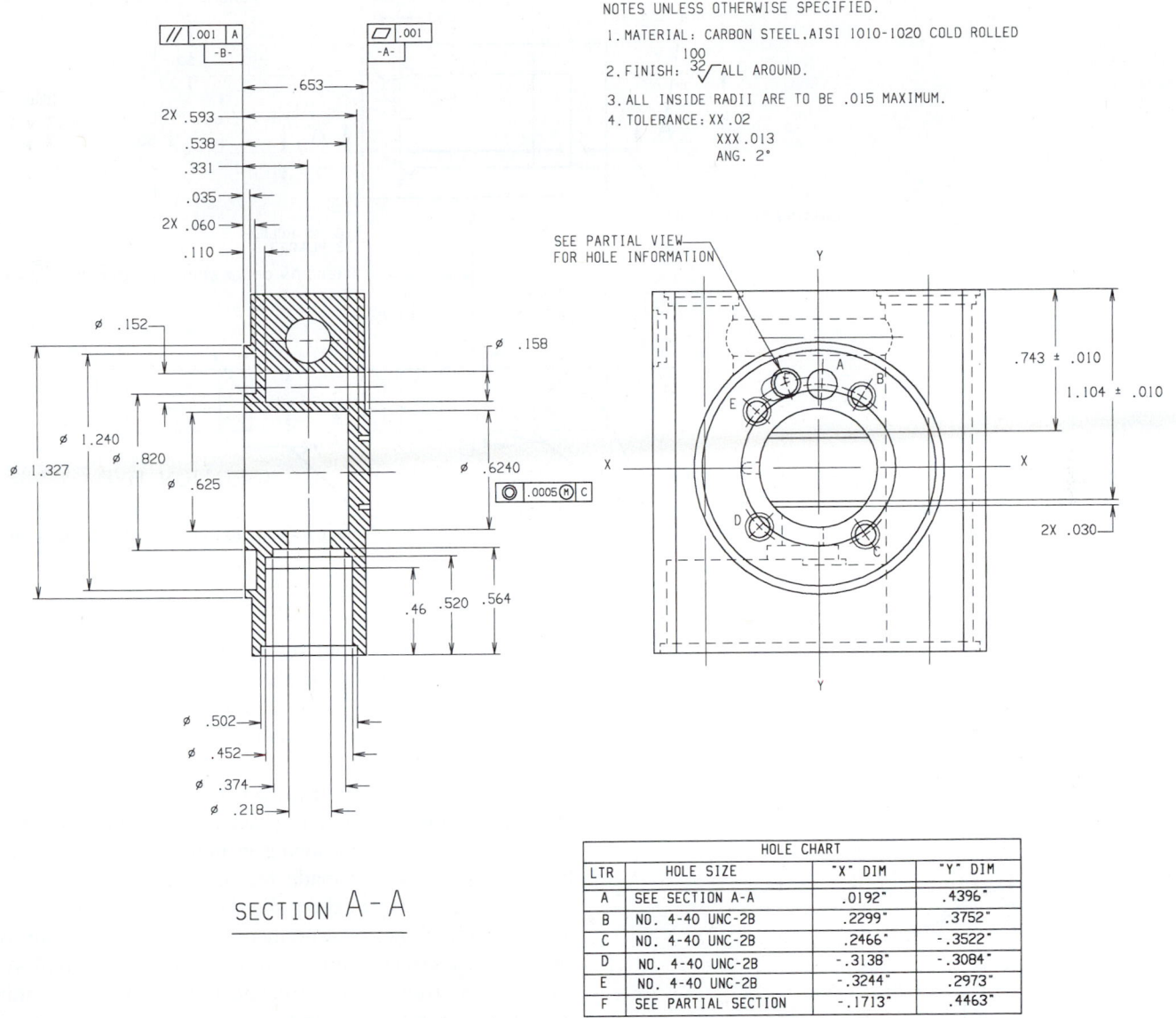

FIGURE 9.3   Detail of a Mechanical Part with Three Sections—*Continued*

section view. When the cutting plane passes through void areas (open spaces) such as a slot, hole, or other cutouts, the area is left blank (without section lines) in the adjacent section view (Fig. 9.4).

Since cutting planes are positioned to reveal interior details most effectively, selecting the proper location for the cutting plane is important. In Figure 9.5, the pictorial illustration of the section shows the cutting plane passing through the middle of the part in order to reveal its interior. This is typically the most common location for the cutting plane.

9.2.1   Section Material Specification

Sometimes you must distinguish between materials of a part by the use of symbolic section lining. **Symbolic section lining** is sometimes used on assembly drawings such as illus-

trations for parts catalogs, display assemblies, promotional illustrations, and when it is desirable to distinguish between different materials.

Since it may not reduce and enlarge well, symbolic section lining is not recommended for drawings that will be microfilmed or put onto microfiche. Thus, the most common practice is to use the general-purpose symbol for all materials.

9.2.2   General-Purpose Section Lines

The first type of lining in Figure 9.6(a) is the symbol for cast iron, which is also considered the **general-purpose symbol**. General-purpose section lines—which do not distinguish between different materials—are normally drawn at an angle of 45°. These lines identify the cut solid surfaces of the section view. Most drawings use general-purpose section lines (single

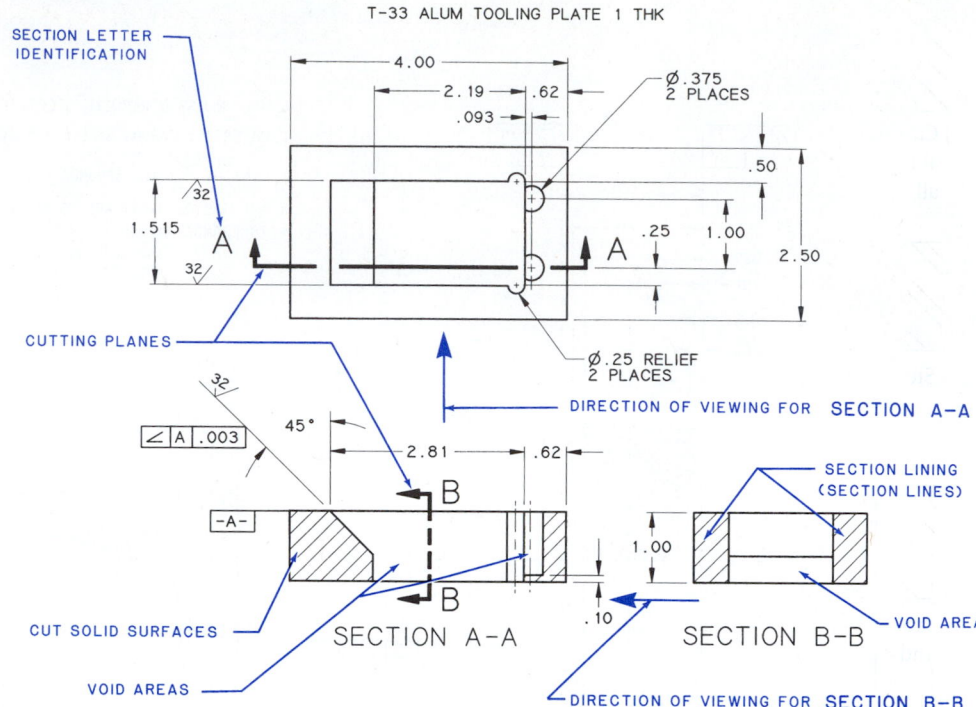

FIGURE 9.4 Three-View Drawing Using Sections as the Front and Side View

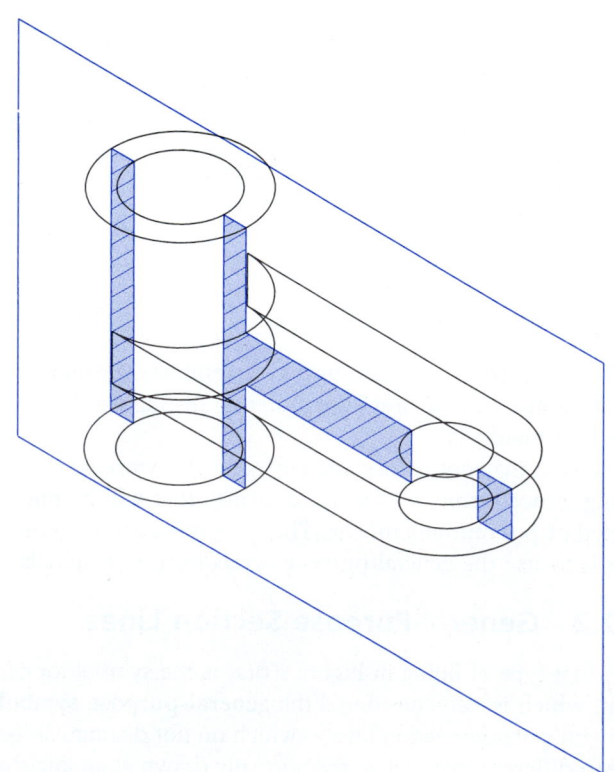

FIGURE 9.5 Sectioned 3D Part

lines at 45°, slanting from the lower left toward the upper right, and spaced evenly at about .10 in. (2.5 mm). Some drafters prefer to use $\frac{1}{8}$ in. (.125 in.) spacing when using decimal-inch measurements and 2.5 to 3 mm spacing on drawings that use SI units.

Since they are easy to draw, general-purpose section lines are quickly constructed. The exact material specification is given elsewhere on the drawing in note form or in the title block. An exception is made for parts made of wood, for which it is necessary to show the direction of the grain.

Figure 9.7 shows measurements for the construction of general-purpose section lines. This figure includes examples of incorrect construction. The thickness of section lines is thin (0.25 to 0.30 mm), sharp, and black. Section lines should not be too close [Fig. 9.7(d)] or they may merge and blot during reduction and reproduction. Section lines must be consistently spaced [Fig. 9.7(b) and (e)] and must end at visible object lines [Fig. 9.7(f)]. When the shape or position of a section area is such that the section lines would be parallel or perpendicular to a prominent visible line bounding the sectioned area, a different angle should be chosen [Fig. 9.7(g)]. To avoid drawing section lines perpendicular or parallel to object lines, the angle of the section lines should change (Fig. 9.8). Remember, 45° is preferred, but not mandatory.

9.2.3   Lines Behind the Cutting Plane

Sections describe the interior space of a part. *Hidden features that are behind the cutting planes are almost always omitted.* In half sections, however, hidden lines are occasionally shown on the unsectioned half when needed for dimensioning or for

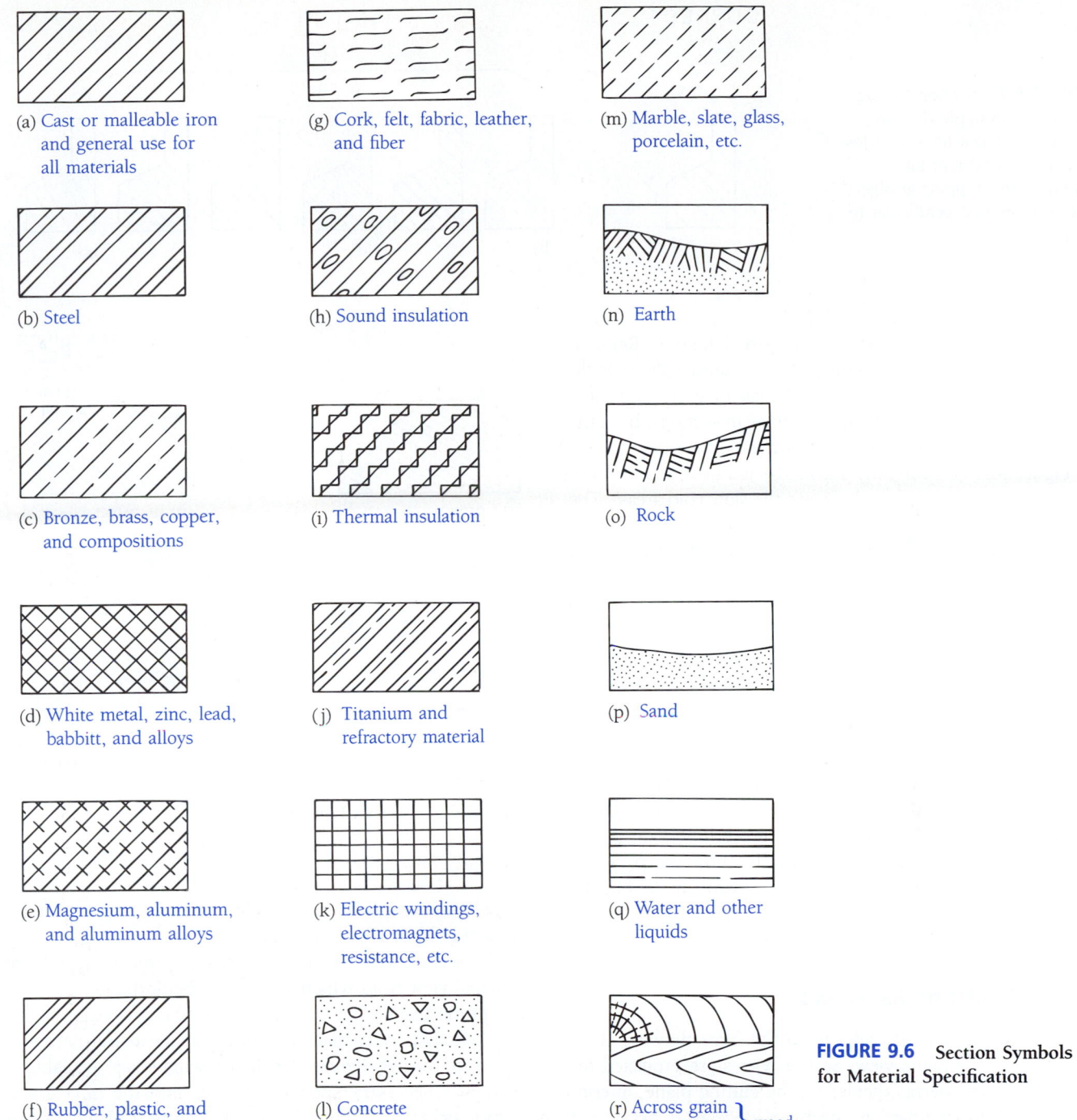

(a) Cast or malleable iron and general use for all materials

(b) Steel

(c) Bronze, brass, copper, and compositions

(d) White metal, zinc, lead, babbitt, and alloys

(e) Magnesium, aluminum, and aluminum alloys

(f) Rubber, plastic, and electrical insulation

(g) Cork, felt, fabric, leather, and fiber

(h) Sound insulation

(i) Thermal insulation

(j) Titanium and refractory material

(k) Electric windings, electromagnets, resistance, etc.

(l) Concrete

(m) Marble, slate, glass, porcelain, etc.

(n) Earth

(o) Rock

(p) Sand

(q) Water and other liquids

(r) Across grain / with grain } wood

FIGURE 9.6 Section Symbols for Material Specification

clarity (see Section 9.3.2). The following rules apply when determining the precedence of lines on a section:

1. **Visible object lines** take precedence over hidden lines and centerlines.
2. **Hidden lines** take precedence over centerlines.
3. **Cutting plane lines** take precedence over centerlines when locating a cutting plane. However, the cutting plane line can be omitted entirely if it falls along a centerline of symmetry for the part. This will be discussed in Section 9.2.5.

Figure 9.9 illustrates a few examples of line representation in sections. The correct procedure shows all visible lines as solid [Fig. 9.9(a)]. Remember, even though the section "removes" a portion of the part in front of the cutting plane, the object lines on and behind the plane are still visible. Figure 9.9(b) does not show the back portion of the hole's edges (void area), which should be shown with solid lines. Figure 9.9(c) shows a hidden line running through the section. This practice should be avoided because it complicates the drawing

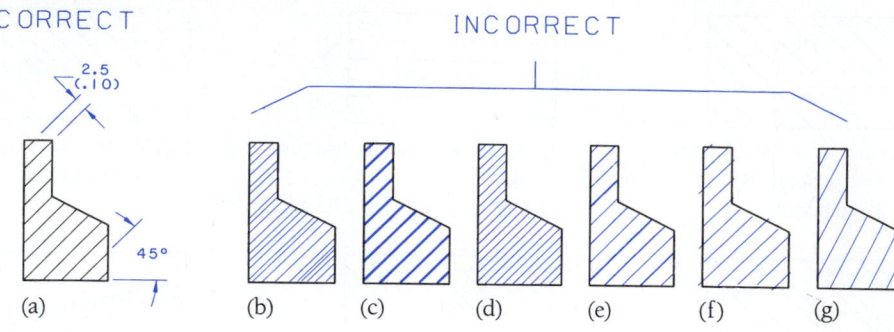

FIGURE 9.7 **Section Lining**
(a) Correct example (b) Poor
spacing (c) Thick lines (d) Close
lines (e) Inconsistent lines
(f) Lines not stopping at object
lines (g) Lines perpendicular to
object lines

and does not add any clarity to the part definition. Remember, *visible lines behind the cutting plane are always shown in the sectional view whereas hidden lines are not.* In some cases, it is acceptable practice to show hidden lines in sections, but only if the part could not be properly defined otherwise.

Figure 9.9(d) incorrectly shows dashed interior lines representing the outline of the hole and the slot (void areas). The outline of a part should never be described using dashed lines. This type of line symbol is used for hidden lines, not visible lines.

Section lines on the same part must run in the same direction, not opposing directions (on assemblies, mating parts that are sectioned have section lines with differing angles). Figure 9.9(e) shows the incorrect procedure for section lines on the same part that are separated by a void area.

Dimensions or other labeling should not be placed within sectioned areas of the drawing. When this is unavoidable, the section lines are omitted behind the label (see Chapter 12).

Some features on a part are shown with double-spaced section lines as in Figure 9.10. Here, the cutting plane passes through distinct features of the part. To show the part correctly, the section lining is drawn at the same angle, but the *spacing is doubled.*

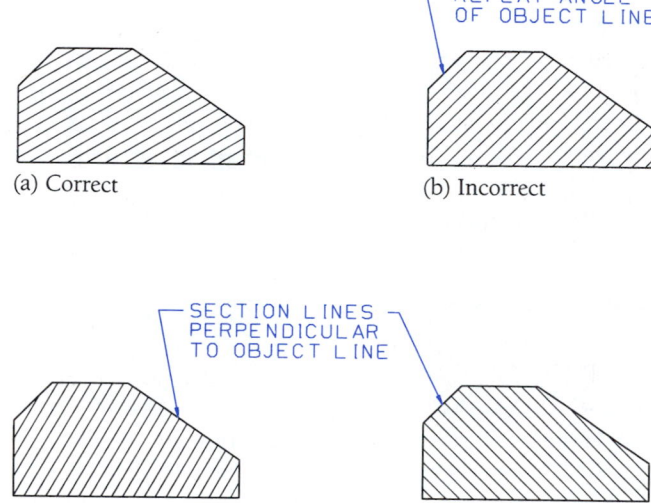

FIGURE 9.8 **Section Line Direction**

9.2.4 Sections as Views

The section view should appear on the same drawing sheet with the cutting plane view. Section views are projected directly from, and perpendicular to, the cutting plane, in conformity with the standard arrangement of views. If, because of space limitations, this arrangement of views is impractical, the views should be clearly labeled.

The section view is placed in direct projection with the principal view from which it is taken, behind and normal to the cutting plane. The view should not be rotated or shown on a different sheet than the cutting plane *unless* necessary due to the size of the view or the drawing space available. If rotation is necessary, specify the angle and the direction of rotation below the section label as in Figure 9.11 where only

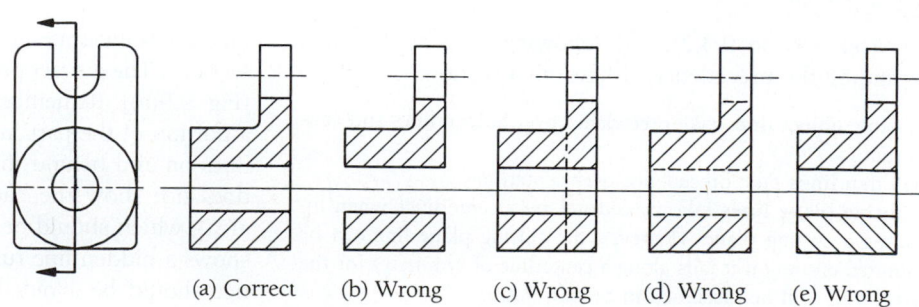

FIGURE 9.9 **Hidden Lines in Sections** (a) Correct example
(b) through (e) Incorrect examples

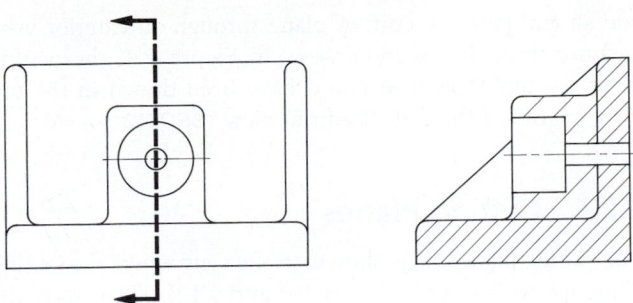

FIGURE 9.10   Double-spaced Section Lines

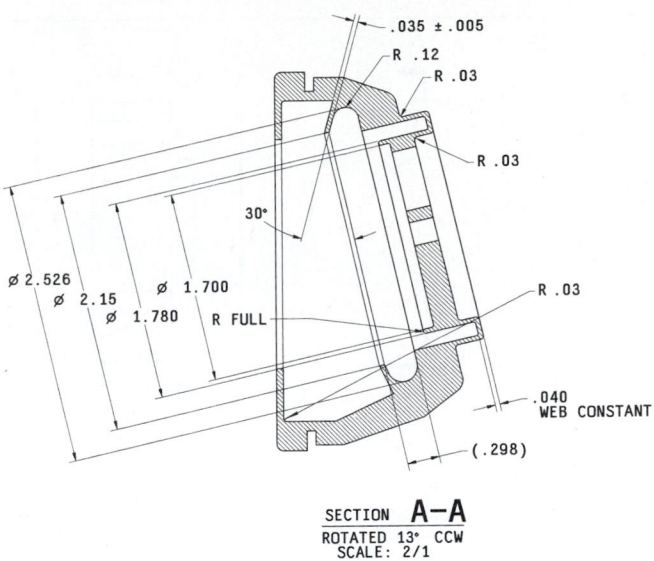

SECTION **A–A**
ROTATED 13° CCW
SCALE: 2/1

FIGURE 9.11   Rotated Sections

the section view is shown. Here, **SECTION A–A** has been rotated counterclockwise (**CCW**) out of its normal position 13°. In some cases, the section will be enlarged as in this figure. In Figure 9.11, the section identification gives the following information:

SECTION A–A
ROTATED 13° CCW
SCALE: 2/1

Figure 9.4 illustrated the practice of using a section as a principal view. **SECTION A–A** is the front view and **SECTION B–B** is the right side view of the part. In Figure 9.4, a cutting plane is passed through the front view—which is also

a section. In general, *avoid constructing a section through a section view.* This can lead to confusion and misinterpretation because it sometimes involves multiple plane rotations. As a rule, drawing a section through a section view should only be used when it is necessary to clarify the intent of the drawing or to make an assembly sequence understandable. Instead,

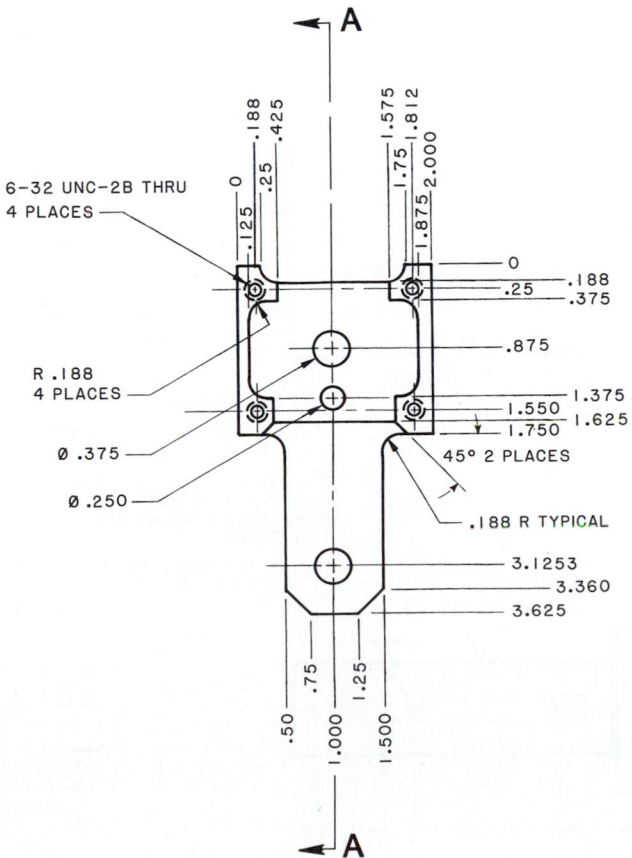

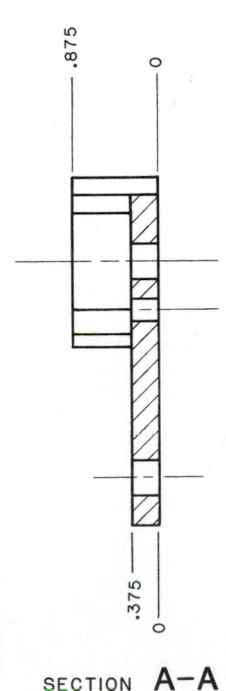

SECTION **A–A**

FIGURE 9.12   Section with Correct Cutting Plane Arrow Direction

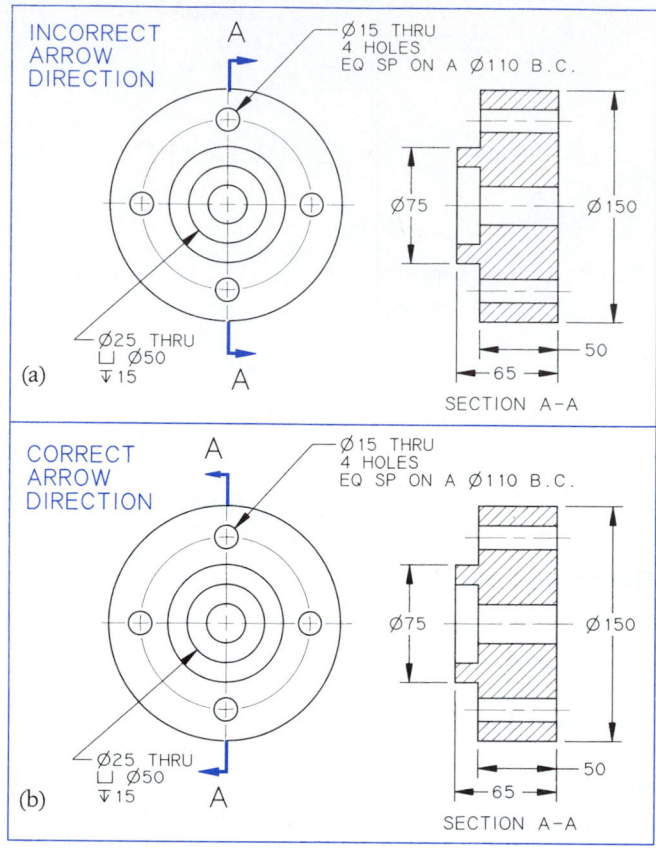

FIGURE 9.13 Arrow Direction on Sections

you should pass the cutting plane through an exterior view and not through a section view. In Figure 9.4, the cutting plane for **SECTION B–B** could have been drawn in the top view instead of through the front view (**SECTION A–A**).

9.2.5 Cutting Planes

The cutting plane line is shown on the view where the cutting plane appears as an edge (Figs. 9.4 and 9.12). The ends of the cutting plane line are turned 90° and terminated with large arrowheads to show the direction of sight, as was shown in Figure 9.4. *The cutting plane arrows point away from the viewer and away from the section view.* Figure 9.12 shows the proper direction of the cutting plane arrows. Figure 9.13(a) shows the incorrect direction for arrows and in (b) the correct direction.

In simple sections, or when the location of the section is obvious, the cutting plane line is omitted. The cutting plane line and all identifying letters may be omitted *only* when the location of the cutting plane coincides with a centerline of symmetry (Fig. 9.14) or, as mentioned, when the location is obvious. Figure 9.14 is an industry example of a welded pipe fabrication. The pipe and flange are separate pieces that are to be joined by welding. The front view is a full section assembly. The pieces have section lines drawn at different angles so as to differentiate between the pipe and the flange.

Figure 9.15 shows the accepted sizes and line types to be used when constructing cutting plane lines. The first two

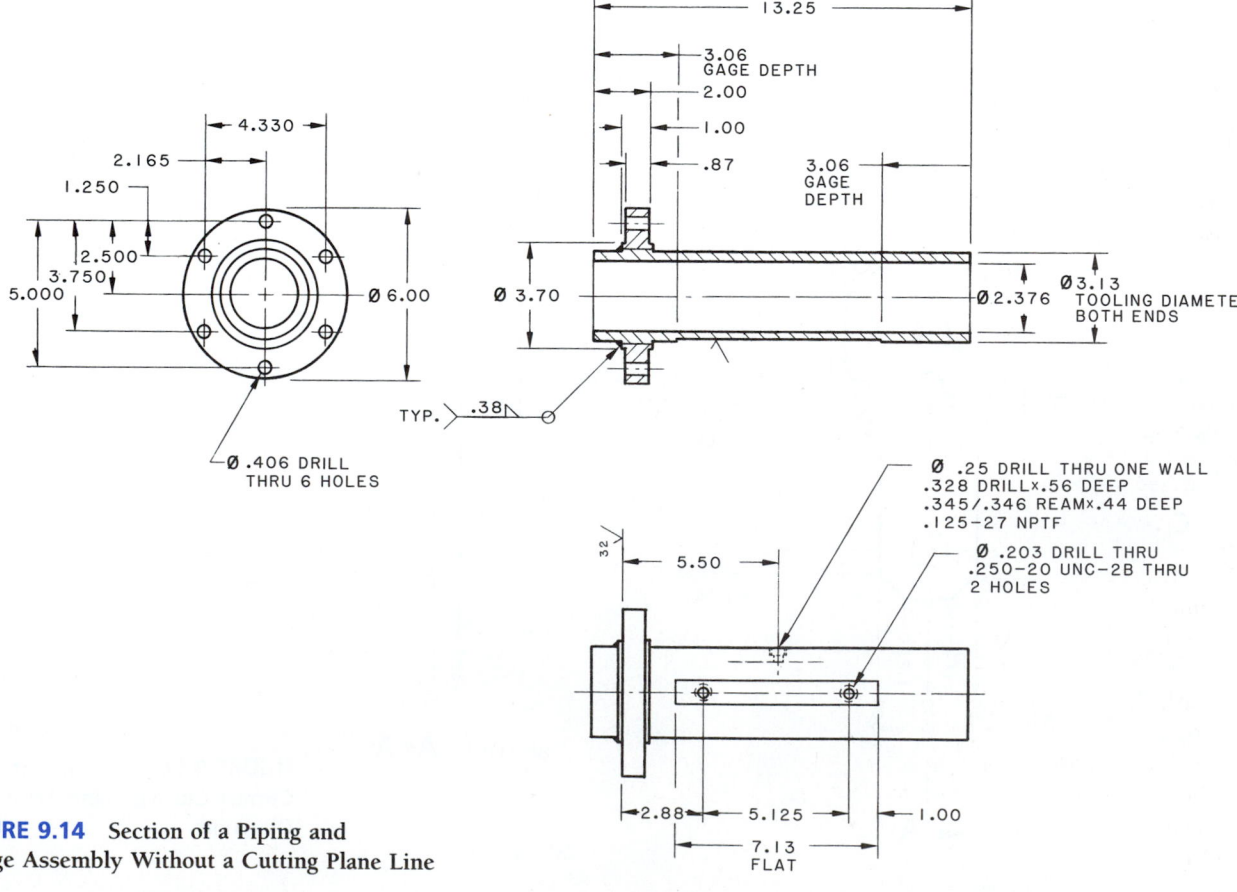

FIGURE 9.14 Section of a Piping and Flange Assembly Without a Cutting Plane Line

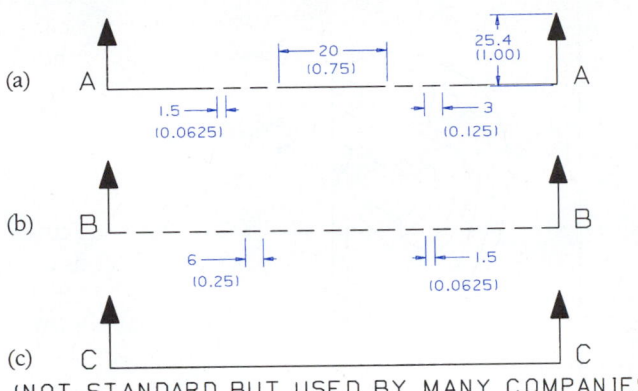

(NOT STANDARD BUT USED BY MANY COMPANIES)

FIGURE 9.15 Dimensions for Drawing Cutting Plane Lines and Arrows (a) Traditional method (b) Dashed method (c) Solid line method

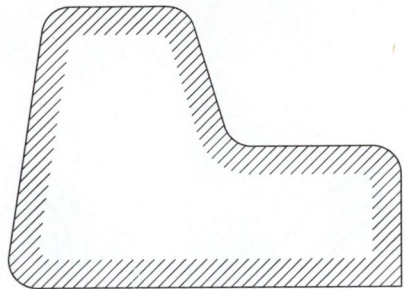

FIGURE 9.16 Outline Section Lining

examples in this figure follow the accepted ANSI standard. However, some companies use a solid line (third example) or just a portion of the cutting plane line—the bent ends and the arrows (Fig. 9.12). The cutting plane line is always shown when the cutting plane is bent or offset or when the resulting section is nonsymmetrical. Cutting plane lines are drawn 0.7 to 0.9 mm thick. Border lines and cutting plane lines will be the thickest lines on your drawing.

9.2.6 Section Identification and Multiple Sections

To identify the cutting plane with its sectioned view, capital letters (A, B, C, etc.) are placed adjacent to or behind the arrowheads. These letters are called **section identification letters.** The corresponding section views are identified by the same letters; for example, **SECTION A–A, SECTION B–B,** and **SECTION C–C.** If two or more sections appear on the same sheet, they are arranged in alphabetical order from left to right and/or top to bottom (Fig. 9.4, p. 278). This applies to the cutting plane as well as the sectional view.

Section letters are used in alphabetical order, excluding I, O, and Q. If all alphabet letters have been used, use double letters for additional sections; for example, **AA–AA, AB–AB, AC–AC,** etc., in alphabetical order.

9.2.7 Conventional Representation

Conventional representation or accepted practice is any recognized practice of description or representation of a part that has been established in industry over time. Ordinarily, conventional representations involve simplifications to speed the drawing task. This is done in the interest of drawing economy and clarity.

For **outline sections,** limited section lines drawn adjacent only to the boundaries of the sectioned area are the preferred conventional representation for large sectioned areas. **Outline section lining** is used only where clarity is not sacrificed (Fig.

9.16). This eliminates the need to cover large areas with section lines.

Thin sections such as sheet metal, packing, and gaskets are drawn solid (filled). When drawing two or more thicknesses or layers, leave a narrow space between them to maintain their separate identities. Figure 9.17 illustrates the use of the solid sectioning symbol on thin materials such as gaskets.

9.3 Types of Sections

Many types of sections are used on technical drawings including the following:

1. full sections
2. half sections
3. offset sections
4. aligned sections
5. removed sections
6. revolved sections
7. broken-out sections
8. assembly sections
9. auxiliary sections (covered in Chapter 10)

A drawing may contain one or more of these types of sections, as in Figure 9.3 (p. 276). Each of the section variations is covered in the following material, except auxiliary views, which, as noted, are covered in Chapter 10.

9.3.1 Full Sections

When the cutting plane extends through the entire part, in a straight line, usually on the centerline of symmetry, a **full**

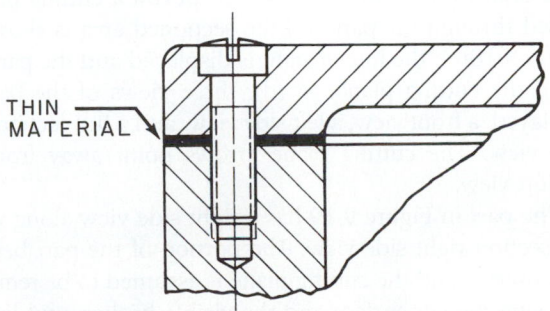

FIGURE 9.17 Thin Materials in Sections

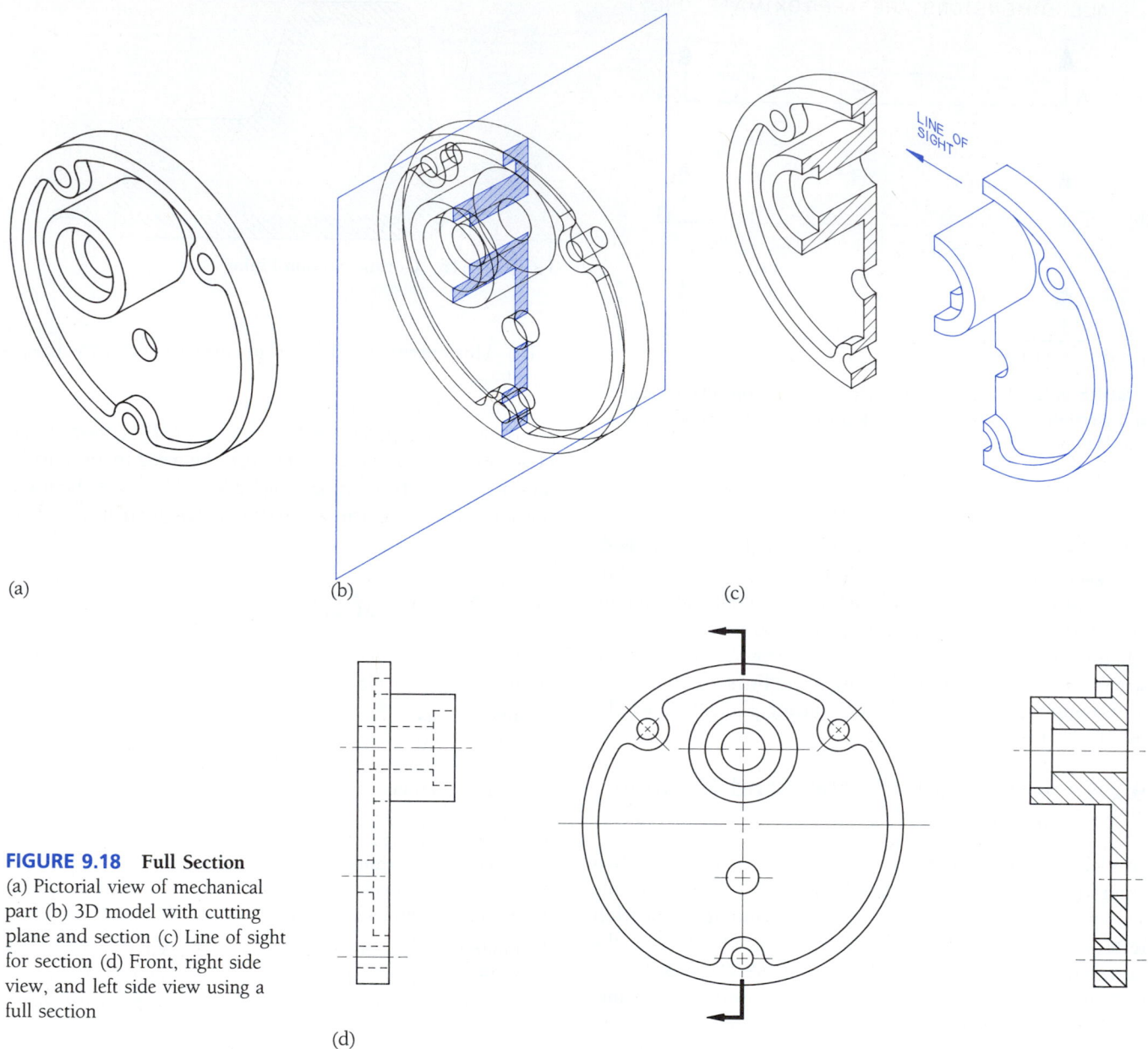

(a)   (b)   (c)

FIGURE 9.18   Full Section
(a) Pictorial view of mechanical
part (b) 3D model with cutting
plane and section (c) Line of sight
for section (d) Front, right side
view, and left side view using a
full section

(d)

section results (Fig. 9.18). Full sections are the most common type of section view. The part in Figure 9.18 shows four different aspects of the sectioning process. In Figure 9.18(a), a pictorial view of the part is given. In (b), a cutting plane is passed through the part and the sectioned area is shown. In Figure 9.18(c), the line of sight is displayed and the part split along the cutting plane. In (d), three views of the part are displayed: a front view, a left side view, and a full section right side view. The cutting plane arrows point away from the section view.

The part in Figure 9.19 has a right side view along with a full section right side view. The portion of the part between the observer and the cutting plane is assumed to be removed, exposing the cut surface and the visible background lines of the remaining portion. (This is an actual industry drawing.)

Figure 9.20 contrasts a full section view and a half section view. The front view is a normal external view. Note that the outline of each is the same.

9.3.2   Half Sections

The view of a symmetrical or cylindrical part that represents both the interior and the exterior features by showing one-fourth in section and the other three-fourths as an external view is known as a **half section** (Fig. 9.21). Figure 9.22 is a half section that was obtained by passing two cutting planes at right angles to each other. The intersection line of the two cutting planes is coincidental with each axis of symmetry of the part. One-fourth of the ⸏⸏t is "removed," and the interior is exposed. Figure 9.22(b)   ⸏vs the part placed in the front

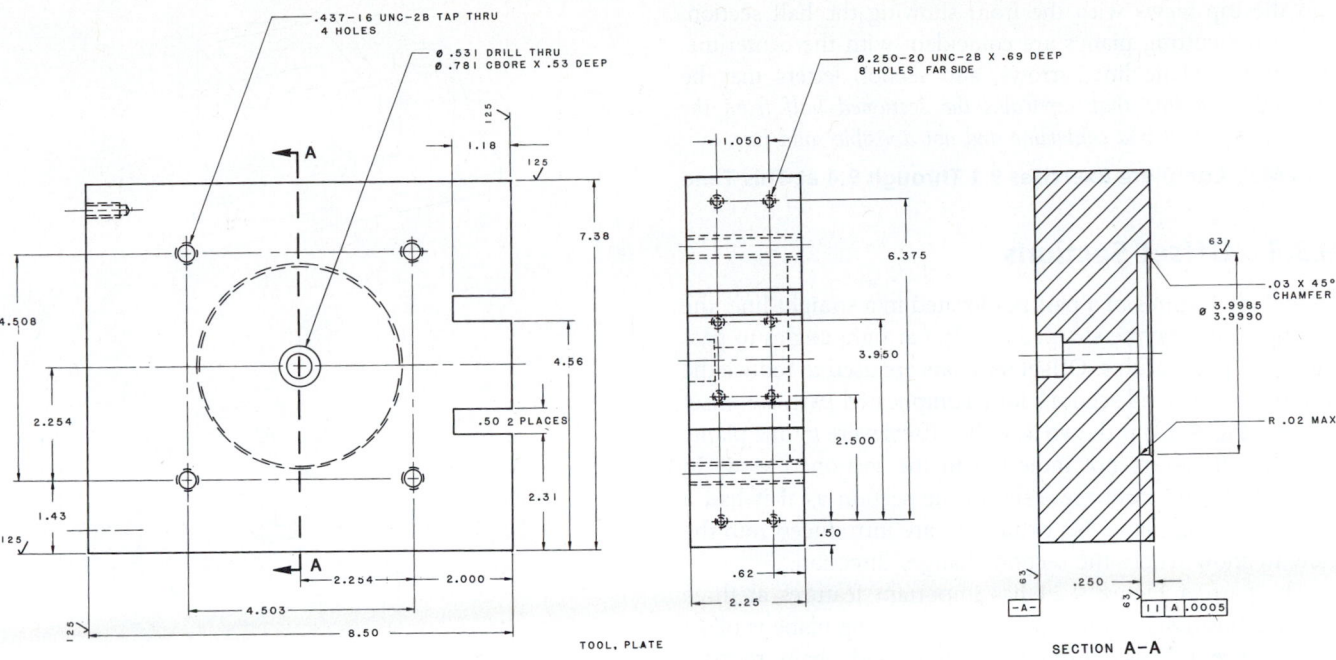

FIGURE 9.19 Detail with Both an External Right Side View and a Full Right Side Section

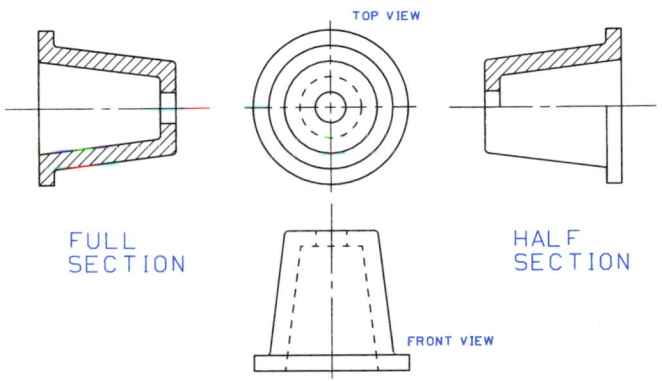

FIGURE 9.20 Full Section, Half Section, and External Views

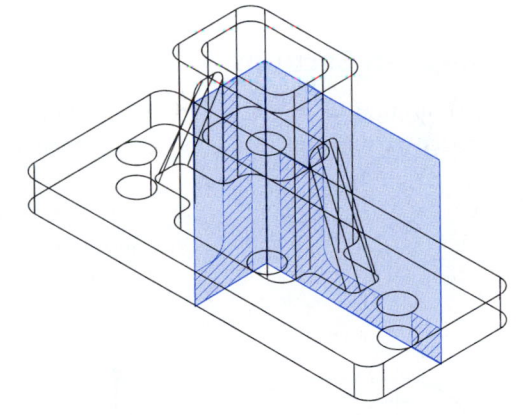

(a)

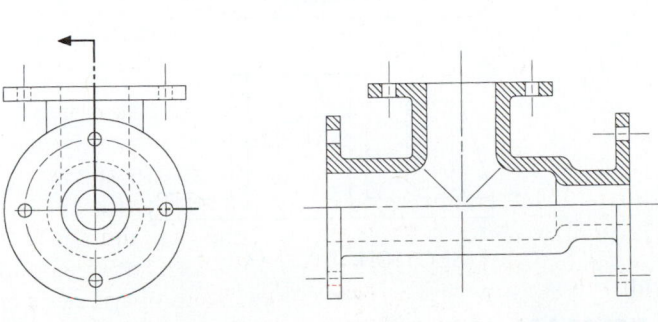

FIGURE 9.21 Half Section

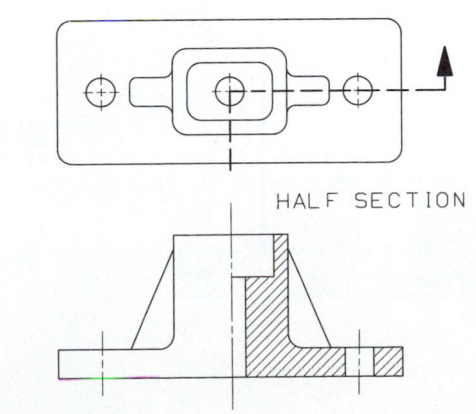

(b)

FIGURE 9.22 Half Sections (a) Pictorial illustration of a half section (b) Top view and front half section of a part

and the top views with the front showing the half section. When the cutting planes are coincident with the centerline, the cutting plane line, arrows, and section letters may be omitted. *The line that separates the sectioned half from the nonsectioned half is a centerline and not a visible solid line.*

You May Complete Exercises 9.1 Through 9.4 at This Time

9.3.3   Offset Sections

To include features of a part not located in a straight line, the cutting plane may be stepped or offset at right angles to pass through these features. **Offset sections** are used to reduce the number of required sections for a complicated part. An offset section (Fig. 9.23) is drawn as if the offsets were in one plane, and the offsets are not indicated in the sectioned view. In Figure 9.23 the front view shows the section as if it had a straight cutting plane. No extra lines are introduced into the view to show where the section changes direction.

The part in Figure 9.24 has important features at three separate positions in the top view. The cutting plane is offset twice, once to pass through the hole and again to pass through the counterbored hole near the back of the part. Observe that no line is shown at the offset in the cutting plane line in the section view [Fig. 9.24(d)]. When changes in viewing direction are not obvious, you can place reference letters at each turning point of the cutting plane.

9.3.4   Aligned Sections

If the true projection of a part results in foreshortening, or requires unnecessary drafting time, inclined elements such as

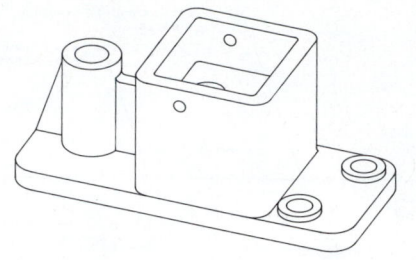

(a)

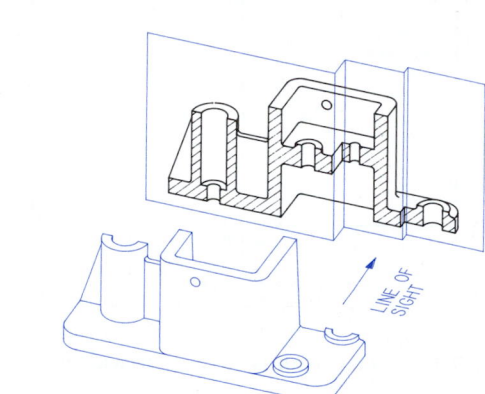

(b)

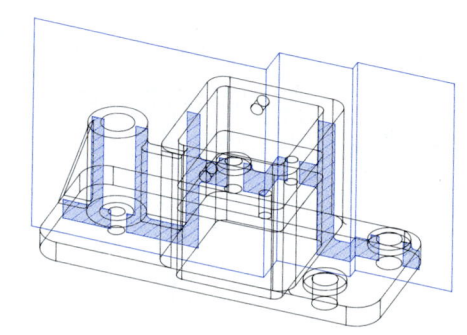

(c)

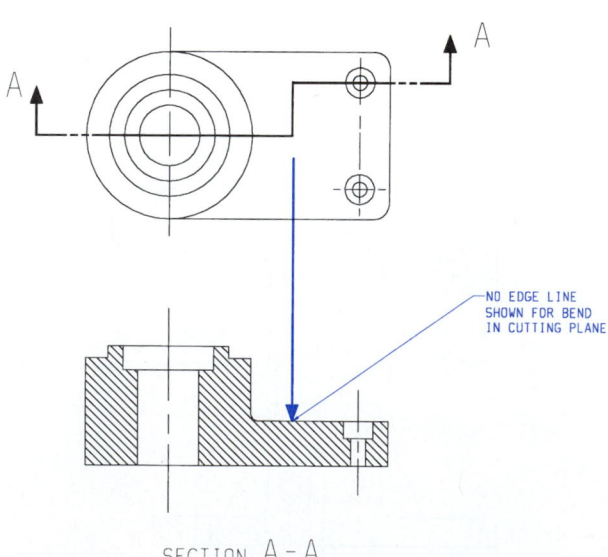

SECTION A-A

FIGURE 9.23   Offset Section

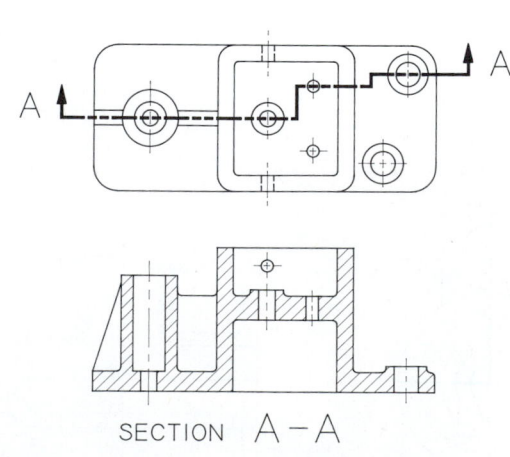

SECTION A-A

(d)

FIGURE 9.24   Multiple Bends in an Offset Section

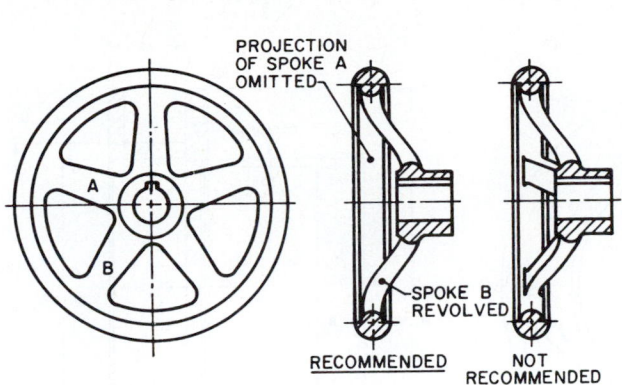

FIGURE 9.25 Spokes in Section

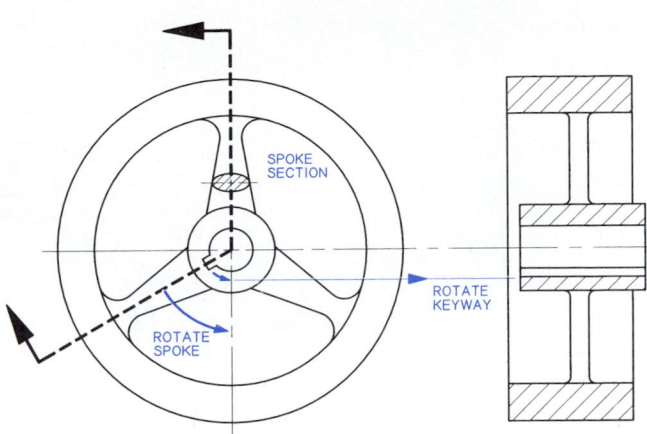

FIGURE 9.26 Conventional Layout for Aligned and Rotated Sections

lugs, ribs, spokes, and arms are rotated into a plane perpendicular to the line of sight of the section. Cutting plane lines are normally omitted for rotated features. This type of section is called an **aligned section** (Fig. 9.25).

Aligned sections are the recommended conventional practice in industry. This convention speeds the construction of the view, even though it is not a *true projection*. The true projection is completed only if it is important to establish clearance between features of a part or in an assembly of parts. Holes, slots, and similar features spaced around a bolt circle or a cylindrical flange may also be rotated to their true distance from the center axis and then projected to the section view.

In aligned sections, features of a symmetrical part that would be foreshortened in a strict interpretation are rotated into the plane of the paper. This preserves the feeling of symmetry, is easier to draw, and is more easily interpreted by

the machinist. In Figure 9.25, the nonrecommended, foreshortened, true projected view of the part is provided to contrast the two methods. The true projected view of the spokes is hard to construct and does not add to the drawing's clarity. In this figure, the spokes of the wheel have been rotated to project as true shape in the right side view. In Figure 9.26, the right side view is an aligned section. Both spokes and the keyseat are drawn as if they were cut by the cutting plane.

Another example of an aligned section is provided in Figure 9.27. Here, Figure 9.27(a) shows the true front view projection of a part and in Figure 9.27(b) the rib has been rotated. Note that it is now easier to complete a full section of the part. Compare the two views for clarity and simplicity. You will see that Figure 9.27(a) is a less clear and more complex projection than (b).

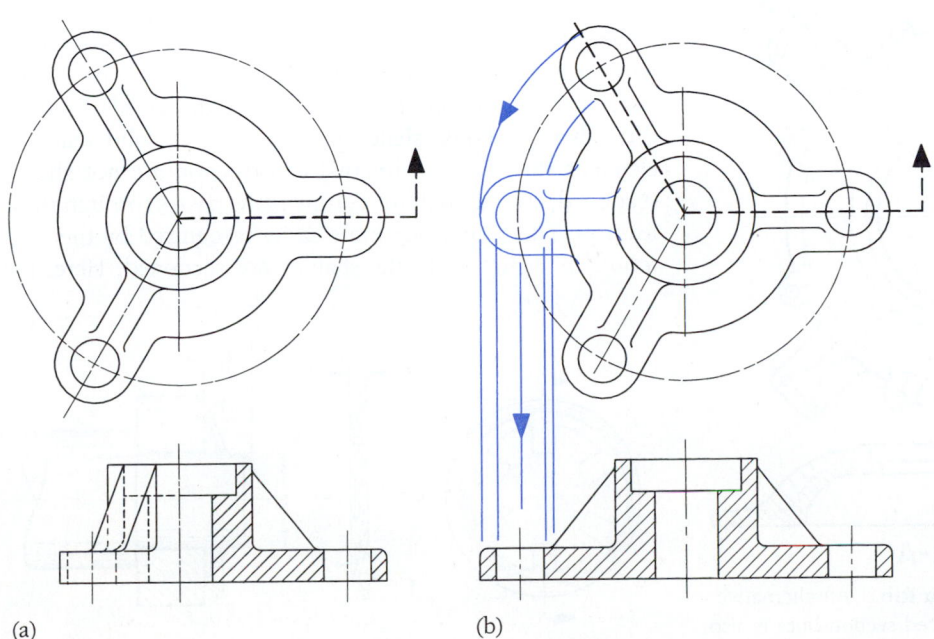

(a)

(b)

FIGURE 9.27 Full and Half Sections (a) Half Section with True Front Projection of the Part (b) Full Section with Aligned (Rotated) Frontal Projection

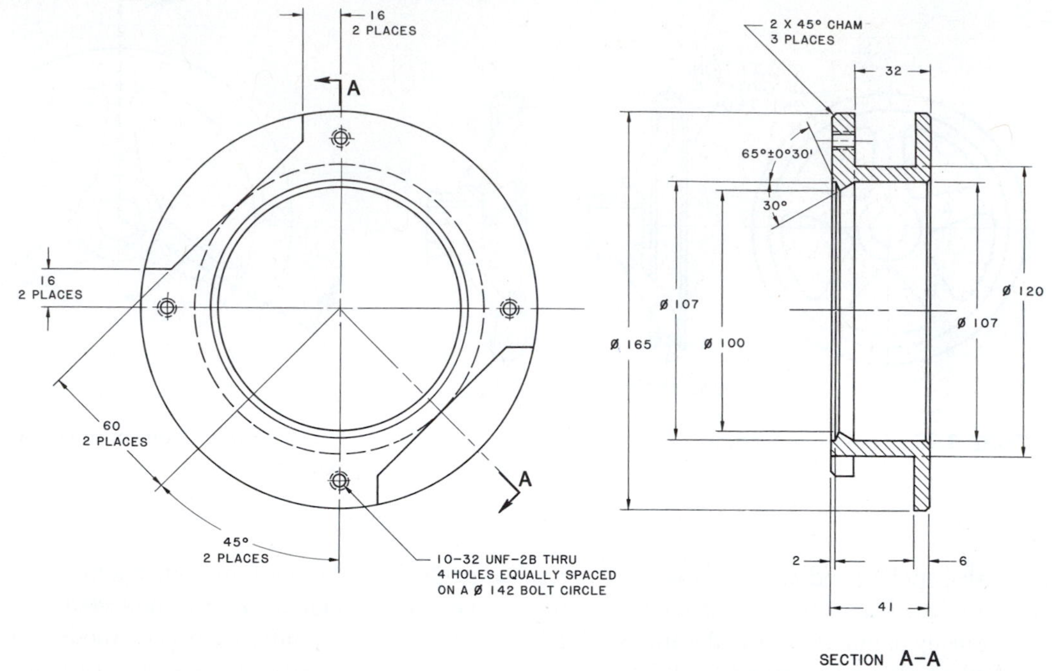

FIGURE 9.28 Mechanical Detail of a Part Using an Aligned Section

SECTION A-A

When the features of a part lend themselves to an angular change of less than 90° in the direction of the cutting plane, the section view is drawn as if the cutting plane and feature were rotated into the plane of the paper. In some cases, the cutting plane is bent to pass through a desired feature as in the industry drawing in Figure 9.28. In Figure 9.29, the cutting plane is drawn through the portion to be rotated.

Figure 9.29 also shows an *alternative way of sectioning a rib* (also see Section 9.3.5). Here, the cutting plane passes through the rib. Instead of leaving the rib area without section lines as is common practice, the area was **double sectioned**

by extending every other section line from the surrounding area. This method was also used in Figure 9.10 (p. 281).

9.3.5 Nonsectioned Items in a Section View

When the cutting plane lies along the longitudinal axis of shafts, bolts, nuts, rods, rivets, keys, pins, screws, ball or roller bearings, gear teeth, ribs, and spokes, sectioning is not required except where internal construction must be shown. This convention is required mainly on assembly sections where more than one part is sectioned and a number of standard hardware items such at bolts, screws, and dowels are found.

For shafts and other machine parts detailed as separate parts, it is normal practice to use broken-out sections for any internal construction that needs to be displayed. Sections through nuts, bolts, shafts, pins, and other solid machine elements that have no internal construction are not shown sectioned, even though the cutting plane passes through these features. These items are more easily recognized by their exterior. In Figure 9.30, the shaft is not sectioned. Here, the

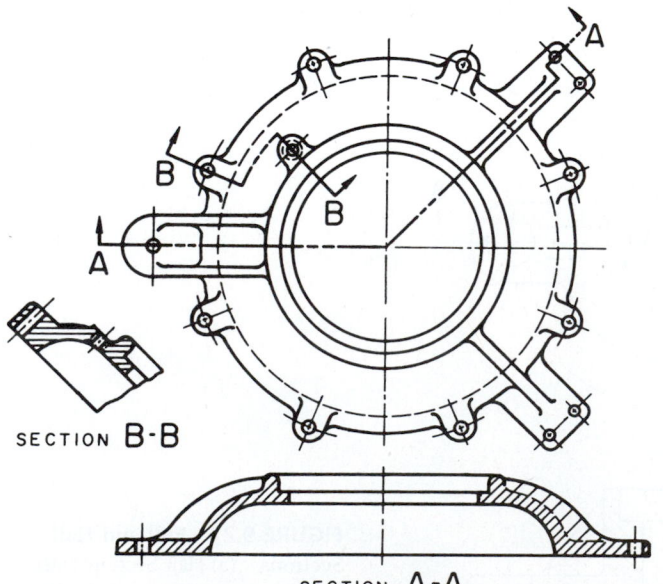

FIGURE 9.29 **Aligned Section Through a Rib.** An alternative method of sectioning a rib with double-spaced section lines is also shown.

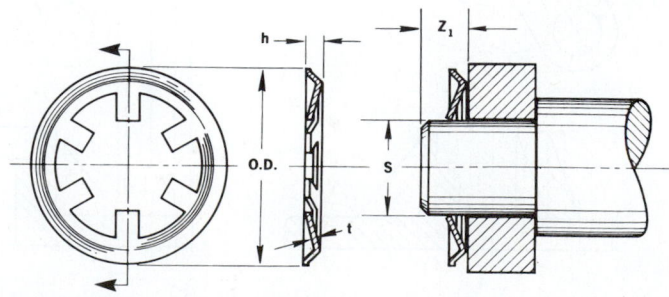

FIGURE 9.30 Shafts and Solids in Section

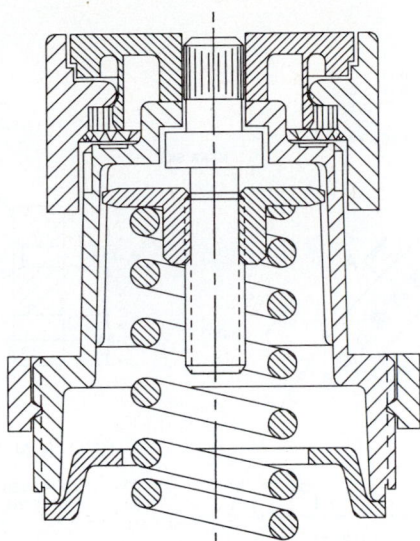

FIGURE 9.31 **Assembly and Solid Threaded Parts in Sections**

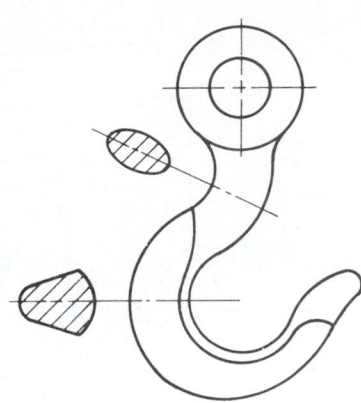

FIGURE 9.33 Removed Sections

shaft has been shaded. This illustration is used for a parts manual. Normally, shading is not used on sections of solid items unless the drawing is used for sales literature. Figure 9.31 shows another example of a sectioned assembly. The shaft in this figure is also unsectioned.

When a cutting plane passes through a rib (Fig. 9.32), leave the rib portion of the section without section lining. Because ribs fall into the category of a *thin solid shape,* they are usually represented without section lining or are sometimes double sectioned as in Figure 9.29.

Sectioning ribs gives the appearance of more mass than actually exists as in the incorrect example of Figure 9.32. Ribs are not sectioned when the cutting plane passes through them "flatwise," but are shown as visible edges. However, ribs are sectioned when the cutting plane passes perpendicular to them.

9.3.6 Removed Sections

Removed sections are used to show the special or transitional details of a part. They are like revolved sections, except that they are placed outside the principal view. In some cases, removed sections are drawn to a larger scale.

Removed sections that are symmetrical may be placed on centerlines extended from the imaginary cutting planes (Fig. 9.33). A removed section is usually not a direct projection from the view containing the cutting plane line; it is displaced from its normal projection position. In this case, formal identification is used; Figure 9.34 shows a detailed mechanical part from industry. **SECTION A–A** is a removed section drawn at **2 : 1** scale.

If it is impractical to place a removed section on the same sheet with the regular views, you must clearly identify the sheet number and the drawing zone location of the cutting plane line. On the drawing where the cutting plane is shown, place a note that refers to the sheet and the zone where the removed section or section title is, along with a leader pointing to the cutting plane. Figure 9.35 is an example of a casting that employs a removed section (**SECTION A–A**) to display interior features that would be difficult to dimension using only an exterior view.

9.3.7 Revolved Sections

A **revolved section** is constructed by passing a cutting plane perpendicular to the axis of an elongated symmetrical feature such as a spoke, a beam, or an arm, and then revolving it in place through 90° into the plane of the drawing (Fig. 9.36). Visible lines extending on each side of the revolved section may be left in, or they may be removed and break lines used.

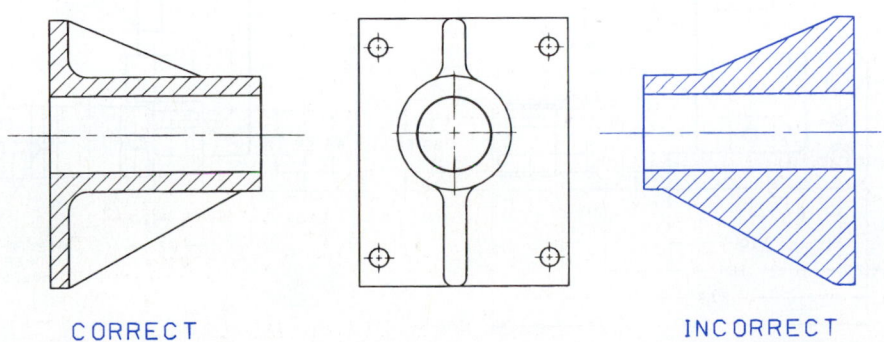

CORRECT   INCORRECT

FIGURE 9.32 Ribs in Sectional Views

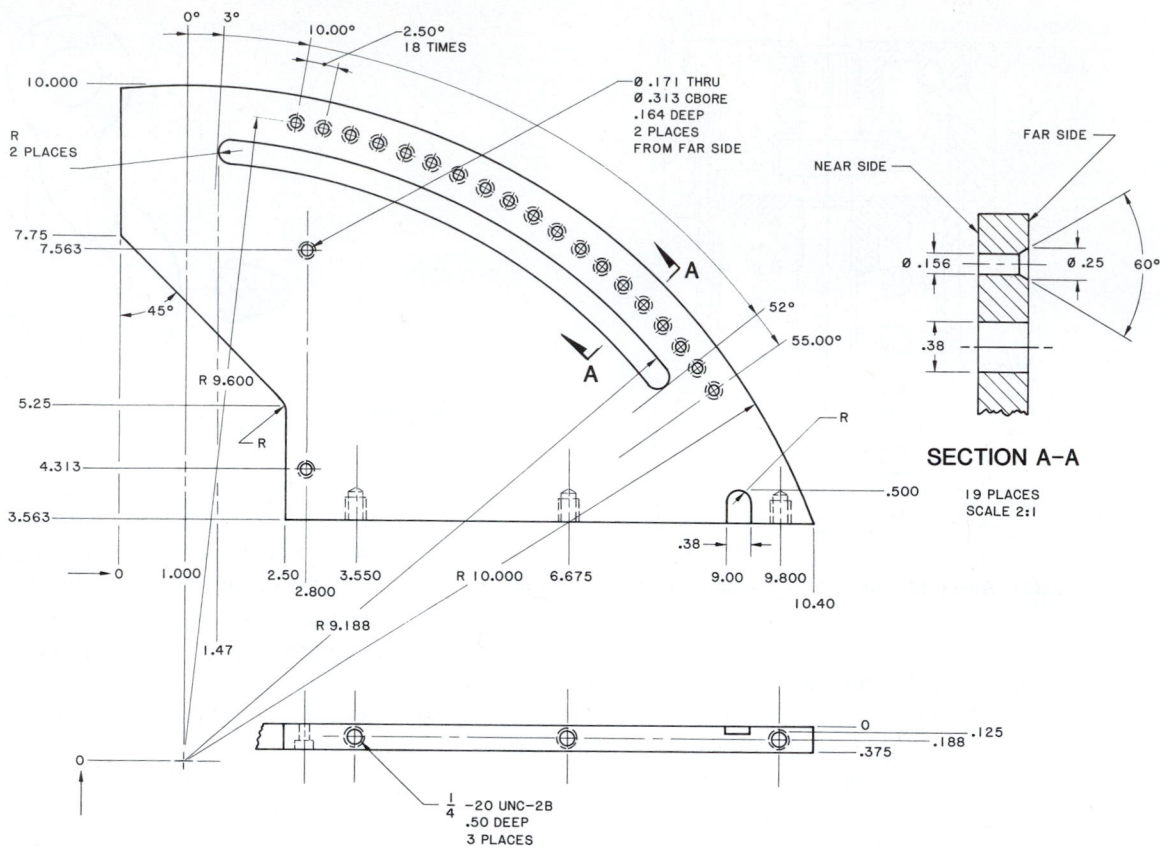

FIGURE 9.34 Detail of a Mechanical Part with a Removed Section

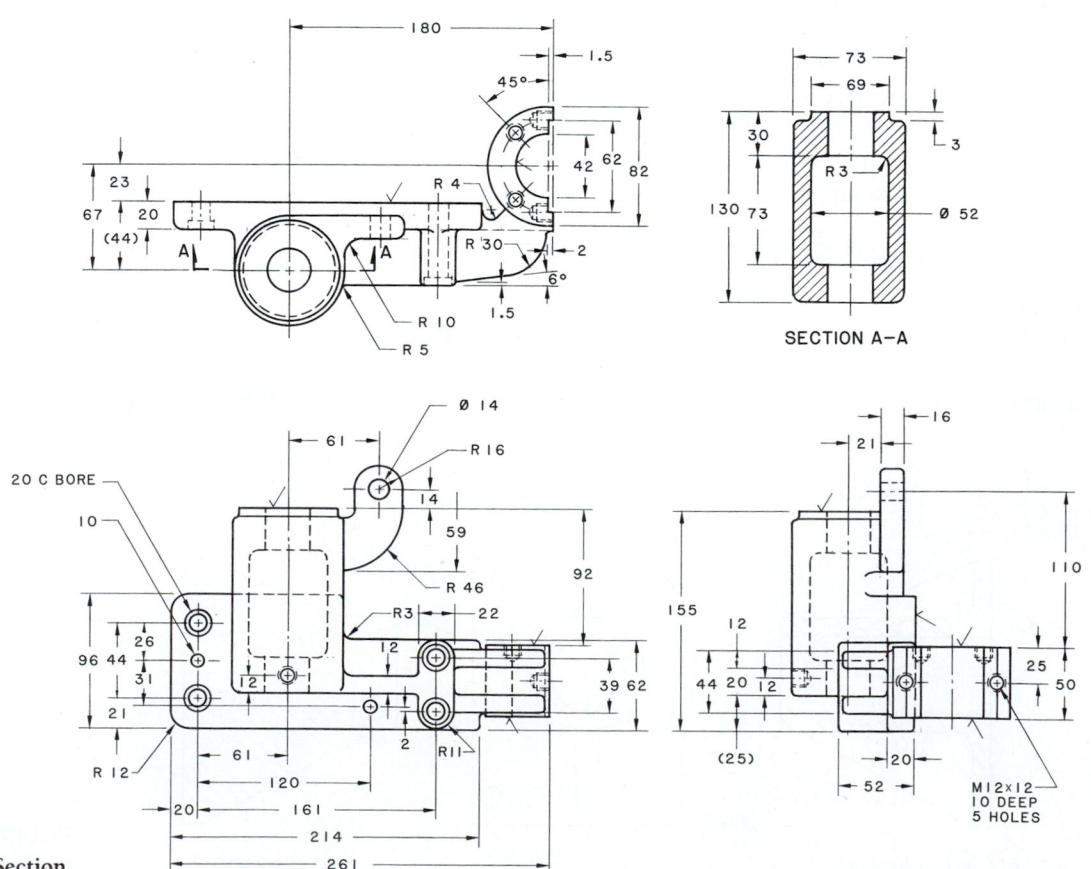

FIGURE 9.35 Removed Section

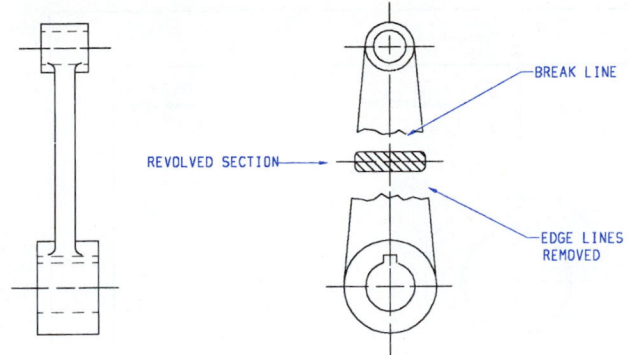

FIGURE 9.36 Revolved Section of an Arm

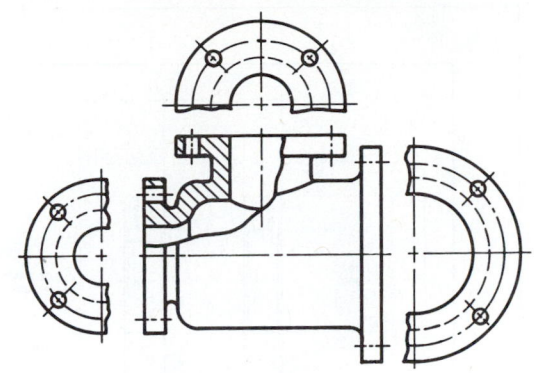

FIGURE 9.38 Broken-out Section of a Pipe Fitting

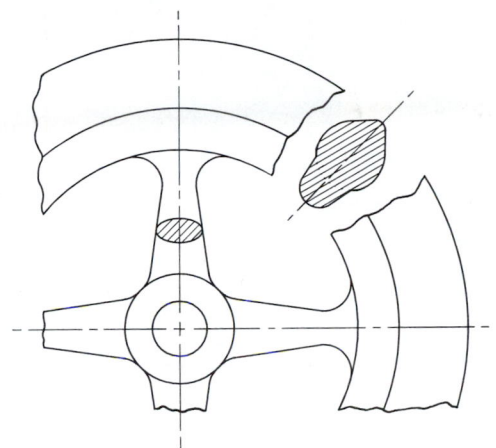

FIGURE 9.37 Revolved Section of a Spoke and Wheel

Figure 9.37 uses both methods. The spoke section does not have the visible lines removed and broken, as does the wheel section. Cutting planes are not indicated on this type of section.

9.3.8 Broken-out Sections

When it is necessary to show only a portion of the part in section, the sectioned area is limited by a freehand *break line* and the section is called a **broken-out section** (Fig. 9.38). A cutting plane line is not indicated for this type of section. Broken-out sections are sometimes referred to as **partial sections** (see Fig. 9.3, p. 276).

One of the most important reasons for using sections on a drawing involves the ability to display complicated interior features that require dimensioning. Figures 9.39 and 9.40 show industry drawings that make use of broken-out sections to display and dimension normally hidden features.

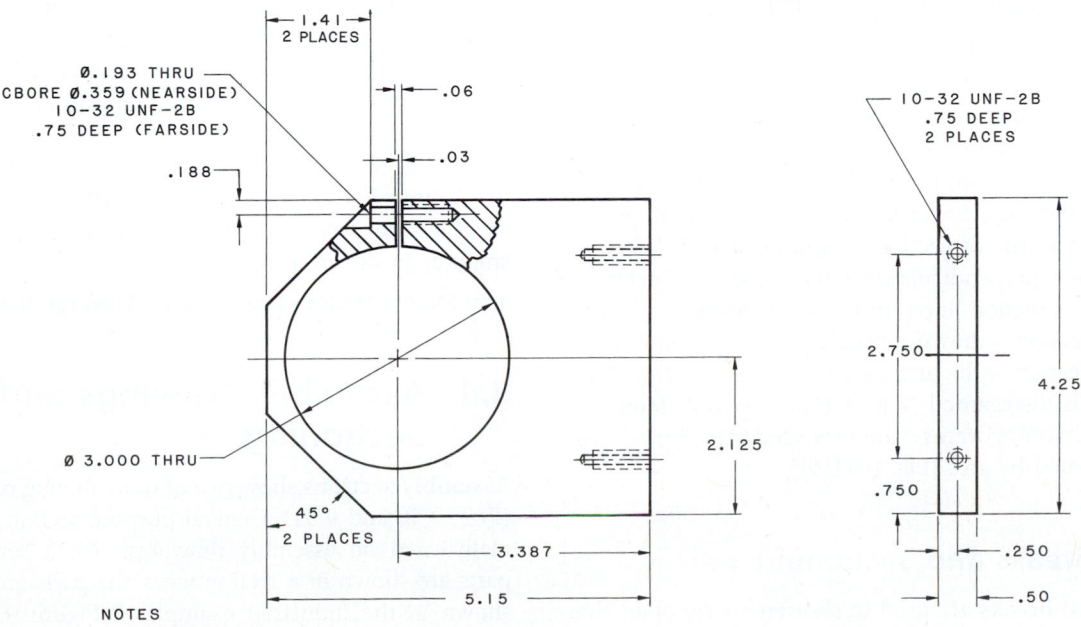

NOTES
1. REMOVE ALL BURRS AND EDGES.

FIGURE 9.39 Broken-out Section

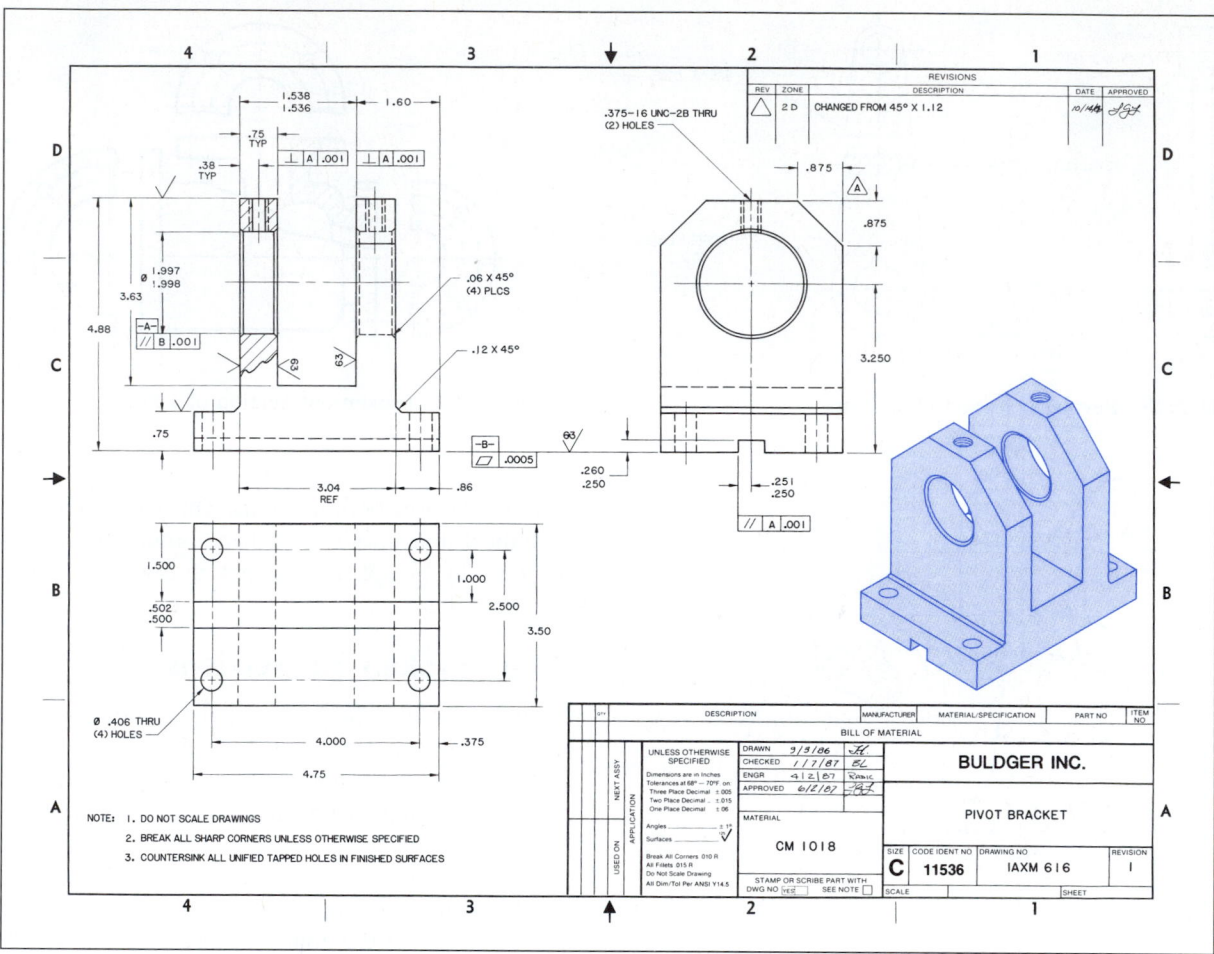

FIGURE 9.40 Mechanical Part with a Broken-out Section

9.3.9 Intersections in Section

If the exact shape or the curve of the intersection is slight or of no consequence, you may simplify sections through intersections by ignoring the true projection. Conventional practice ignores the true projection when the true lines of intersection are time-consuming to draw or are of no value in reading the drawing. However, when a difference in proportions exists, the true projection should be shown. When the cutting plane is perpendicular or cuts across these items, the section view is section lined in the usual manner.

When a section is drawn through an intersection in which the true projection of the intersection is small, the true line of intersection is disregarded [Fig. 9.41(a) and (c)]. More pronounced intersecting features are projected true [Fig. 9.41(b)] or approximated by arcs [Fig. 9.41(d)].

9.3.10 Breaks and Sectioning

Conventional breaks are used to shorten a view of an elongated part (Fig. 9.42) and in broken-out sections. The type of break representation is determined by the material and the shape of the part. Solid and tubular rounds are shown in Figure 9.42(a) and (b). The break can be drawn with the aid of an ellipse template or constructed manually. In industry, because they are time-consuming and therefore costly, such representations are never constructed using precise methods.

Tubular shapes are sectioned as shown in Figure 9.42(c). Break lines for Figure 9.42(c) and (d) are drawn freehand. The break for wood is also drawn freehand but is jagged, not smooth, as shown in (e).

You May Complete Exercises 9.5 Through 9.8 at This Time

9.4 Assembly Drawings and Sectioning

Assembly sections show two or more mating parts in section (Figs. 9.30 and 9.31). General-purpose section lines are normally used on assembly drawings. When several adjacent parts are shown in a section view, the parts are sectioned as shown in the industrial example in Figure 9.43. Here the fixture has its two major parts sectioned using the general-purpose sectioning symbol. Because the piece to be machined

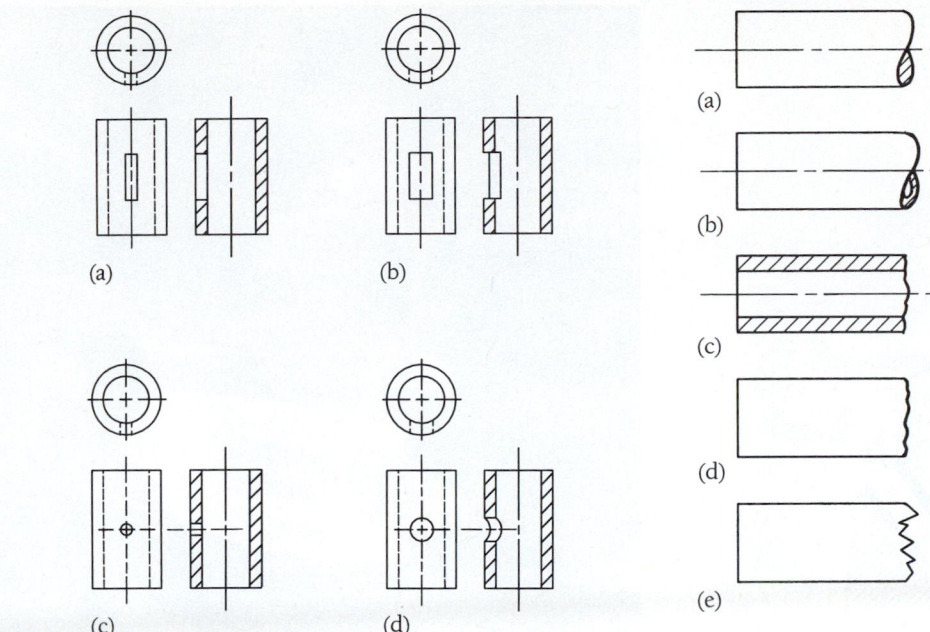

FIGURE 9.41 **Intersections in Section**   (a) and (c) Small intersection therefore the line of intersection is disregarded. (b) and (d) More pronounced intersecting features are projected true.

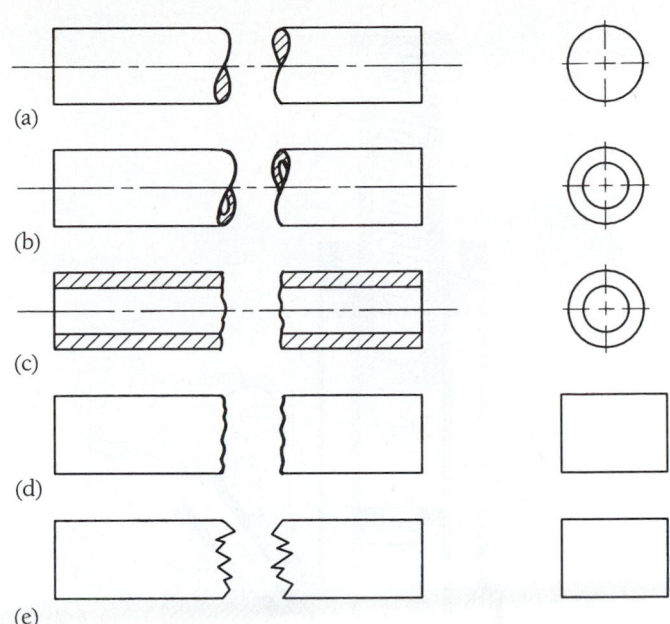

FIGURE 9.42 **Conventional Representation of Breaks in Elongated Parts**   (a) Solid rod (b) Round tube (c) Sectioned tube (d) Rectangular bar (e) Wood

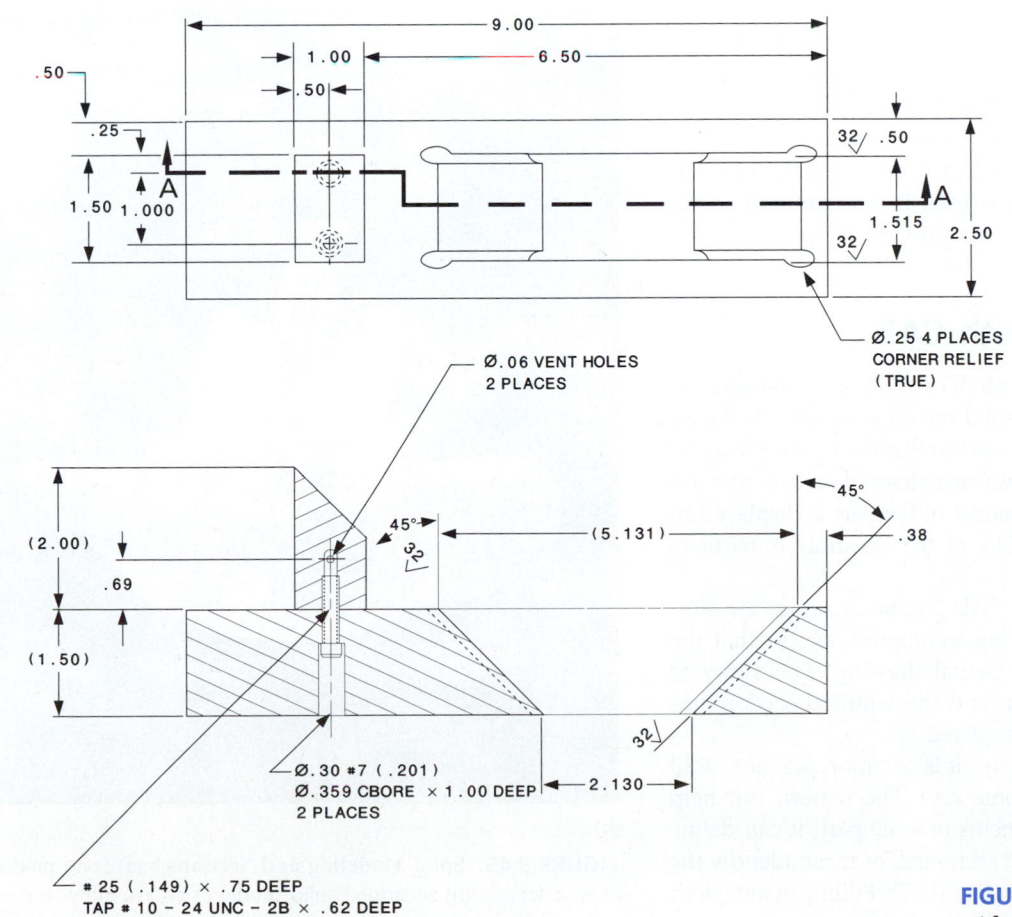

FIGURE 9.43 **Assembly of Fixture with a Full Front Section View**

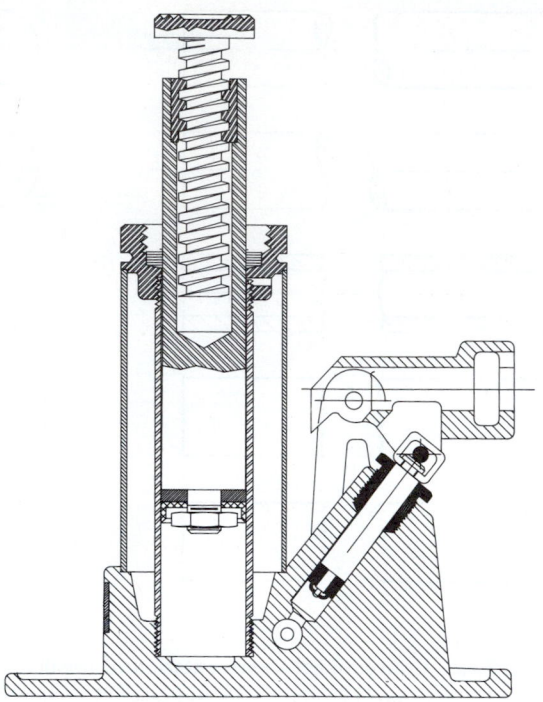

FIGURE 9.44 Assembly Section

is not really a portion of this fixture, it is shown in *phantom lines* and is not sectioned.

Figure 9.44 shows the jack assembly as a front section. Each individual piece of the assembly has section lines running in different directions than the adjoining piece. The threaded pieces and other solid items are not sectioned per the sectioning conventions explained earlier in the chapter. Symbolic section lines are also used in this example. (Sectioned assemblies are also covered in Chapter 18.)

9.5 Sectioning with CAD

Sectioning can be done on both 3D and 2D CAD systems. In Figure 9.45(a) we see a 3D solid model assembly. In Figure 9.45(b), the assembly is sectioned so that the interior features can be seen. Figure 9.46 shows two views of an assembly on the screen. A 3D wireframe model of the part is displayed in two views. The right side view of the assembly is partially sectioned.

The methods used for 2D CAD section drawings are similar to those of manual drafting techniques, except that the computer is used to do the actual drawing. The views to describe the part are laid out and the required sections including dimensioning are completed.

In many drafting applications, it is common practice to fill an area with a pattern of some sort. The pattern can help differentiate between components of a 3D part, it can define an area of a part that has been sectioned, or it can identify the material that composes a part (Fig. 9.47). Filling an area with

(a)

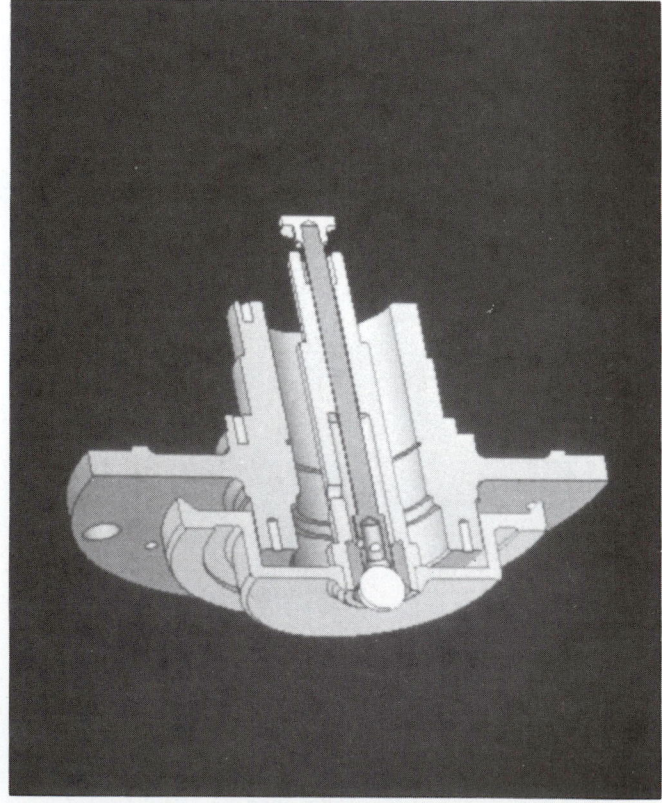

(b)

FIGURE 9.45 Solid Modeling and Sections (a) Solid model of an assembly (b) Sectioned solid model of an assembly

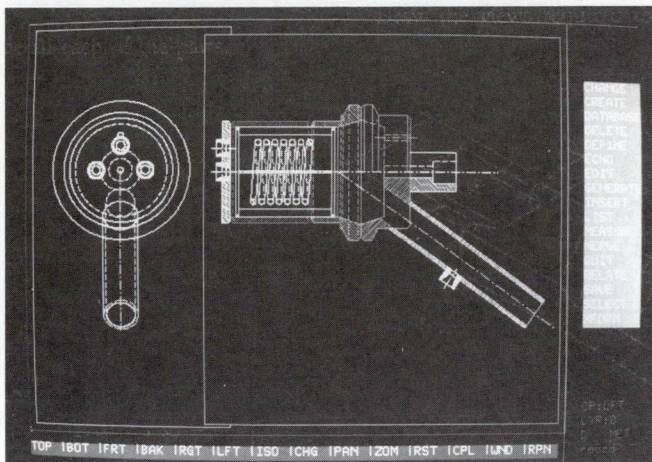

FIGURE 9.46 Section of an Assembly Shown on a CAD System

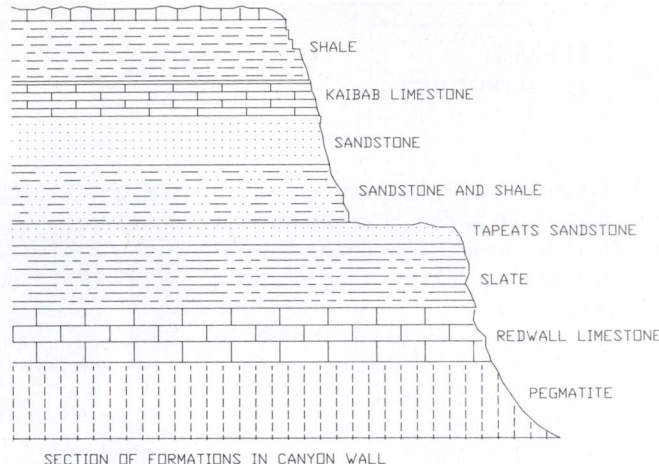

FIGURE 9.47 Section Formations in Canyon Wall Using Hatch Patterns to Represent the Types of Rock and Mineral Layers of Stratification

a pattern is called crosshatching, hatching, or pattern filling, and it can be accomplished using a **HATCH** command.

CAD systems provide a library of standard ANSI hatch patterns. You can hatch with one of these standard patterns, with a custom pattern from your own library, or with a simple pattern defined during the command. Normally the screen or tablet menu on most systems has a variety of hatch patterns available for immediate insertion (Fig. 9.48).

As an example, AutoCAD has more than 40 predefined patterns that can be identified using the **HATCH** command and then giving a ? response. This procedure will list the pattern names with descriptions. AutoCAD also has pull-down menus and dialogue boxes that will graphically display the hatch patterns and allow you to select visually the hatch pattern for your application. Hatch patterns can be modified before insertion by specifying a different scale and angle.

9.5.1 Hatch Patterns on CAD Systems

Each hatch pattern is composed of one or more hatch lines or figures at specified angles and spacing. The pattern you insert is repeated or clipped, as necessary, to fill the area being hatched exactly.

Hatching generates line entities for the chosen pattern and adds them to the drawing. Hatched areas are *blocks* or *groups*. This means that the CAD system treats the group of section lines as a unit. Therefore, if you have hatched an area but then decide you don't like the hatching, you can select any one line of the pattern with the **DELETE** or the **ERASE** command and the hatching will be removed.

9.5.2 Defining the Boundary Using CAD

Hatching fills in an area of the drawing enclosed by a boundary made from lines, arcs, circles, splines, polylines, or other geometric entities. When hatching an area, the entities that define the boundary must be selected (normally in sequence). The entities forming the hatching boundary should intersect.

FIGURE 9.48 Typical Hatch Patterns Available on a CAD System

If your system requires that the endpoints of the entities meet, overhanging entities will produce incorrect hatching and hatching may spill out of the selected boundary area. Some systems allow for entities to cross, and some even hatch areas not completely enclosed by boundaries, although on most systems you must define a *closed nonintersecting envelope of geometry*.

Figure 9.49 illustrates the hatching of a section of a part using AutoCAD. After the hatching command is given, the boundaries of the area to be hatched are successively indicated by picking each entity; in this case, D1 through D5. The following command illustrates the procedure. Enter the

ITEMS OF INTEREST

Ultrasound

What do submarines, bats, whales, fish finders, and modern hospital technology have in common? They all depend on information gained by using ultrasonic waves.

Ultrasonic waves are vibrations similar to the sound waves that are audible to humans. They are measured by intensity, length, velocity, wave period, and frequency. The number of vibrations per unit time is the frequency of that wave. Waves with a frequency greater than 20,000 Hz are ultrasonic waves.

Ultrasonic waves are generated by passing an electric current through quartz or certain other materials. As an echo strikes the quartz, an electric current is produced, which in turn is used to produce a picture. This property of quartz is called *piezoelectricity*. The generating and receiving device is a *transducer*. In medical equipment, the transducer passes over the part of the body that is being examined.

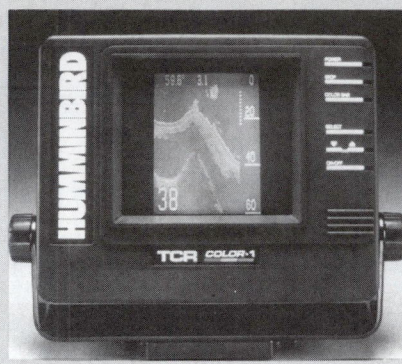

A Fish Finder

Since each tissue varies in density, these waves are reflected differently, producing different images. These images are displayed on a screen or recorded. Internal organs such as the heart and heart valves can be viewed in a static image or, by moving the transducer to different views, can be viewed in sequences in real time.

Recently, tiny ultrasonic transducers have been developed that can produce images from inside blood vessels and ducts. The transducer is rotated 360° to create a series of 2D cross sections. Computers are used to combine these 2D section images into a 3D image.

The sections produced with ultrasound equipment for medical applications are not unlike the sectional drawings used in mechanical drawing. Both types of sections show internal details. It doesn't really matter whether they are the internal features of a part or of an organ. The concepts are the same. Mechanical engineers also use ultrasound waves to check for internal defects, such as cracks and small holes (voids). Sectional views in medicine and in graphics are intended to show internal features that would not otherwise be visible. Sectional views are valuable for visualization regardless of the application involved.

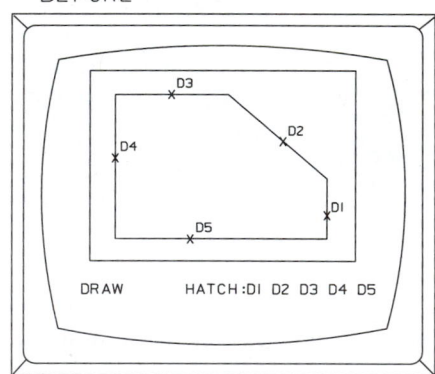

FIGURE 9.49 **Defining Areas of a Part to Be Hatched**

HATCH command from the **DRAW** pull-down menu and use the following steps:

Command: HATCH
Pattern (? or name/U,style): Pick the desired hatch pattern, ANSI31 was used here.
Scale for Pattern: Press the *Enter* key to accept full scale
Angle for Pattern <0>: Select angle
  or use default by pressing the *Enter* key, ANSI31 uses 45°
Select Objects: D1 D2 D3 D4 D5 (select the outline border)

Hatching patterns are varied by specifying the angle of the hatching and the spacing as in Figure 9.50. Figure 9.51 shows two concentric circles. The outer circle is picked first and then the inner circle is picked. The resulting hatch filled a doughnut-shaped area on the part. Because *default values* were used, the pattern was a series of lines with a predetermined angle and spacing. The system inserted hatching inward, starting at the boundary, the first circle. When an internal entity is encountered, the hatching turns off until another entity is encountered (each item must be picked in the command). AutoCAD has an option called **OUTERMOST**, which hatches from an outside boundary to the first interior boundary it encounters.

Some systems (though not AutoCAD) provide you with a **CHAIN** capability. **CHAIN** is normally used with a command to

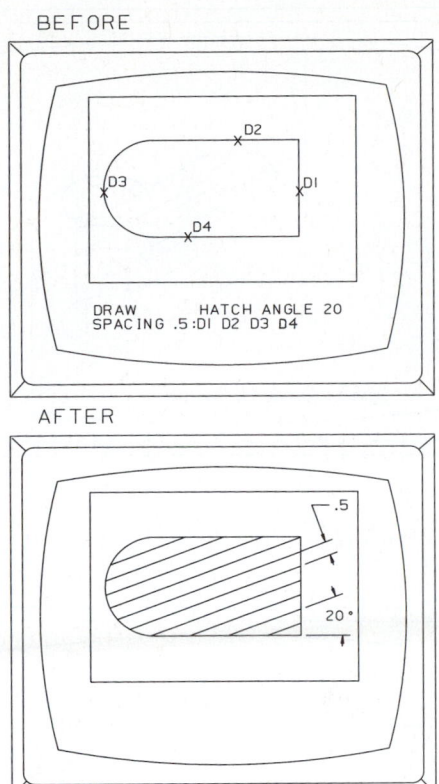

FIGURE 9.50   **Altering the Default Angle and Spacing for a Crosshatch Pattern**

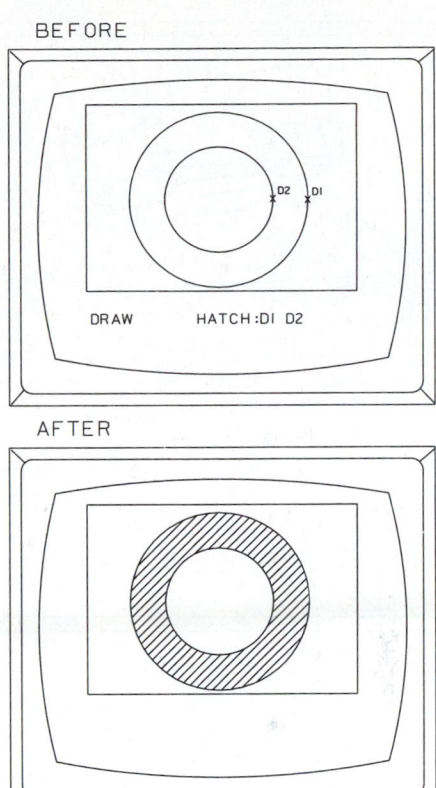

FIGURE 9.51   **Hatching an Area with an Exterior and Interior Boundary**

select a series of connected entities quickly. The **CHAIN** modifier ties all entities that touch into a single, temporary unit. The area to be hatched is identified by entering the **CHAIN** modifier and then simply selecting one entity on the boundary. The area enclosed (linked) by the chain is then quickly hatched (Fig. 9.52).

By creating a boundary with a *string* or a *polyline* you can hatch an area by simply picking the entity. The system uses the polyline or string as the outer boundary for the hatch pattern.

9.5.3   Sectioning with 3D CAD

Because the section can be an actual 3D slice through the part at a selected level or along a defined plane, the 3D process is different. In Figure 9.53(a), a 3D model of the part is shown in two orientations. Unlike a 2D section, which is confined to its views on the drawing, the 3D model can be displayed in multiple viewports, rotated, and viewed from any angle.

In Figure 9.53(b), a rotated view of the 3D part is shown as a wireframe model. Figure 9.53(c) shows the part in a front view; a plane has been established lengthwise along its center. A **CUT PLANE** (or **INTERSECT SURFACE**) command is used to section the model by selecting the plane (D1, D2, and D3) and then identifying the surfaces to be intersected. The rotated model is shown in Figure 9.53(d). Here, the cut lines are

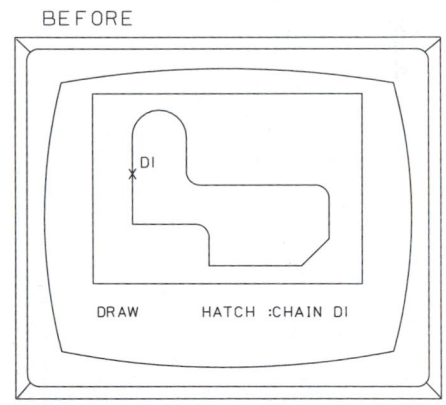

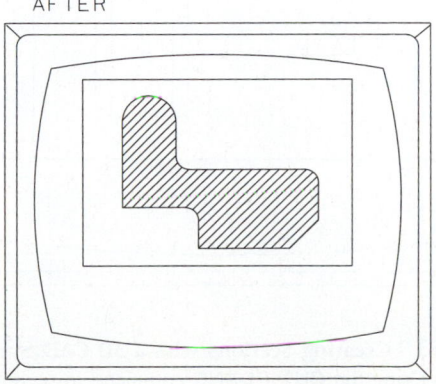

FIGURE 9.52   **Hatching Using the CHAIN Modifier**

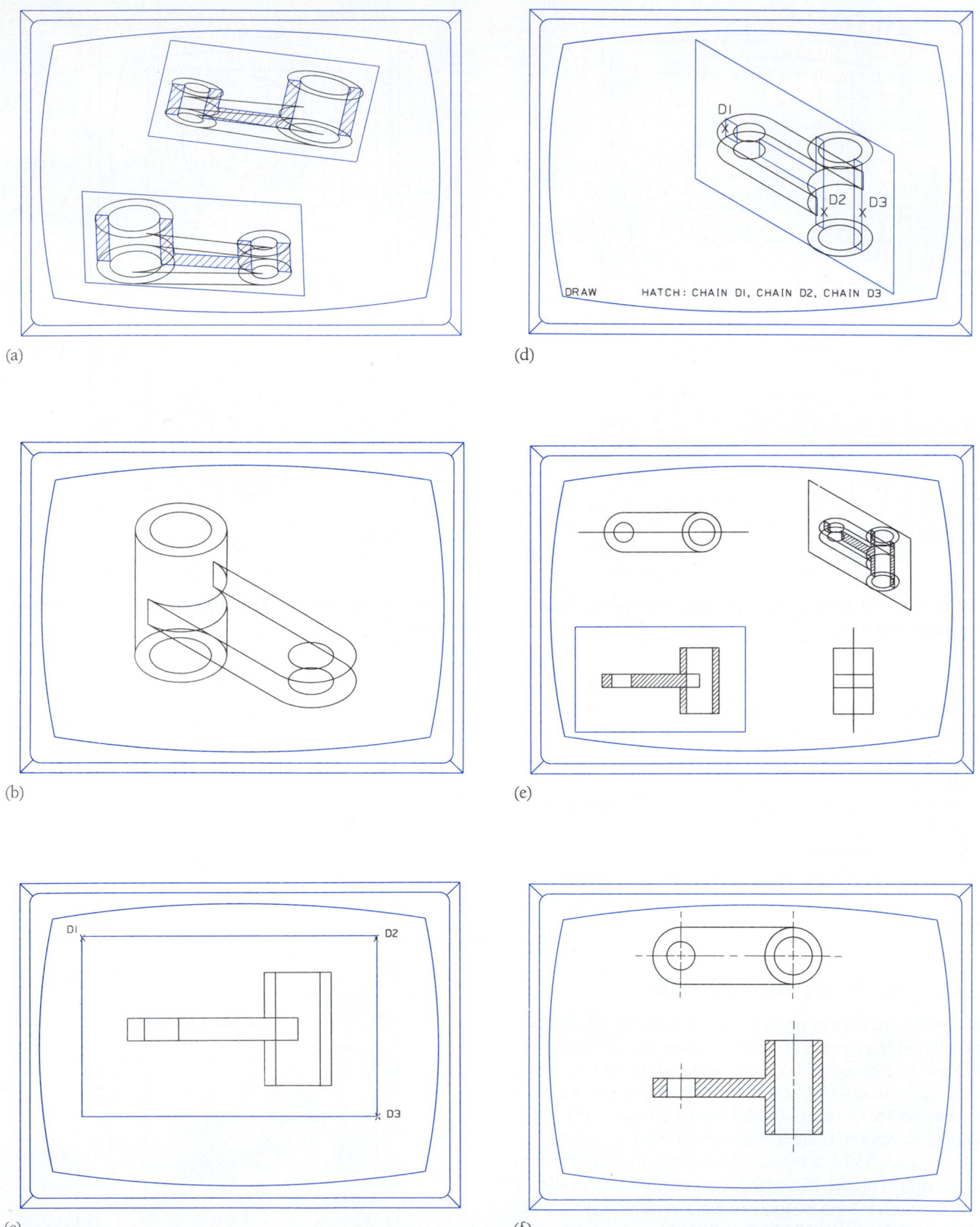

FIGURE 9.53 **Creating Sections with a 3D CAD System** (a) 3D model of a part showing two separate orientations (b) 3D model of a part (c) Using the **CUT PLANE** command to section a part (d) Inserting the hatch pattern in the model mode (e) Four views of the sectioned part (f) Top and front sectional view of part with proper visibility established

shown along with the plane used in the command. Figure 9.53(e) shows the section and the hatch pattern in the three standard views and in a rotated pictorial view. In Figure 9.53(f), the part is placed in the standard top, front view orientation, the cutting plane is removed, and the drawing displayed according to ANSI projection standards. Center-lines are also added. The result looks basically the same when using 2D or 3D CAD or if drawn manually. However, with 3D CAD the section and model can be rotated to other positions. (The part in Figure 9.53 was designed and sectioned using Computervision's Personal Designer CAD system.)

You May Complete Exercises 9.9 Through 9.12 at This Time

QUIZ

True or False

1. Sections are used to describe the exterior of a part so that fewer views are required.
2. Sections and views are always rotated 90° as projections from existing views.
3. It is common conventional practice to show all hidden lines that fall behind the cutting plane.
4. The cutting plane arrows are always pointing in the direction of sight.
5. Section lines should be drawn thick, black, and close together so as to be readily seen and identified.
6. Material-specific hatching symbols are used on all drawings.

7. The placement of dimensions within sectioned areas is a common and accepted practice.
8. Intersections in sections always show the true projection of the elements.

Fill in the Blanks

9. A section is an _____ cut taken through an _____ .
10. Section lining on assembly drawings should be drawn at _____ angles for each _____ .
11. A _____ taken through an existing _____ view should be avoided.
12. Section lettering for identification of sections and views should be used in _____ _____ .
13. Thin sections are always shown _____ .
14. _____ , _____ , _____ , _____ , and _____ are usually not shown sectioned.
15. The _____-_____ symbol is used on most sectional drawings.
16. On simple drawings or where the section location is obvious, it is common practice to _____ the _____ _____ _____ .

Answer the Following

17. What is the difference between a removed section and a revolved section?
18. When is a broken-out section likely to be used?
19. What are hatch patterns and how are they used with a CAD system?
20. Describe the difference between a full section, a half section, and an external view.
21. What is an offset section and when is it used?
22. What type of part features are rotated in aligned sections?
23. Define a cutting plane.
24. Name and describe three conventional practices used on sections.

EXERCISES

Exercises may be assigned as sketching, instrument, or CAD projects. Transfer the given information to an "A" size sheet of .25 in. grid paper. Complete all views and solve for proper visibility, including centerlines, object lines, and hidden lines. Exercises that are not assigned by the instructor can be sketched in the text to provide practice and understanding for the preceding instructional material.

After Reading the Chapter Through Section 9.3.2 You May Complete the Following Exercises

Exercises 9.1(A) and (B) Draw the two views of the part and do a full section for the front view.

Exercises 9.2(A) and (B) Draw three views of the part. Construct a full front section.

Exercises 9.3(A) and (B) Section the appropriate views for each problem.

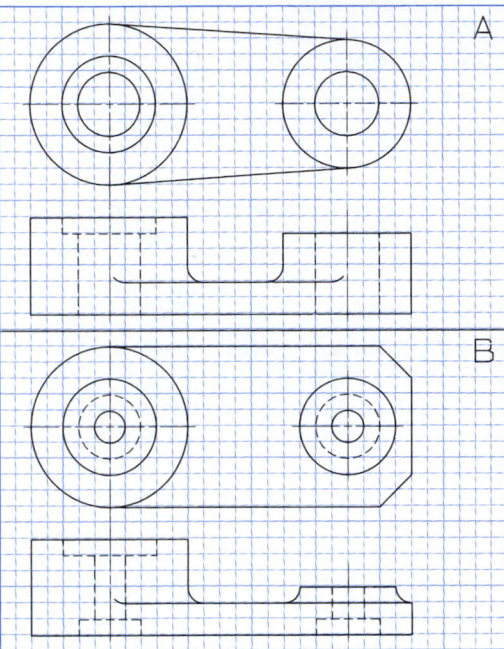

Exercise 9.1

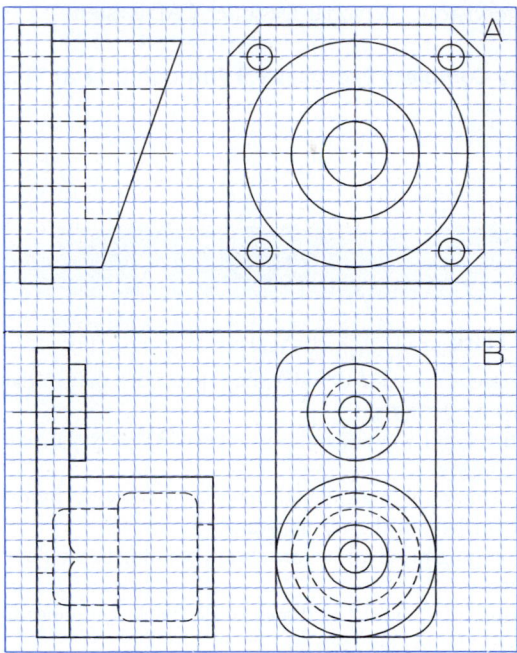

Exercise 9.3

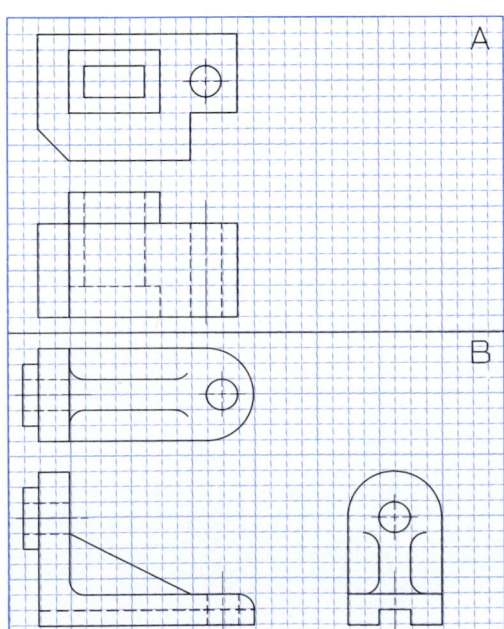

Exercise 9.2

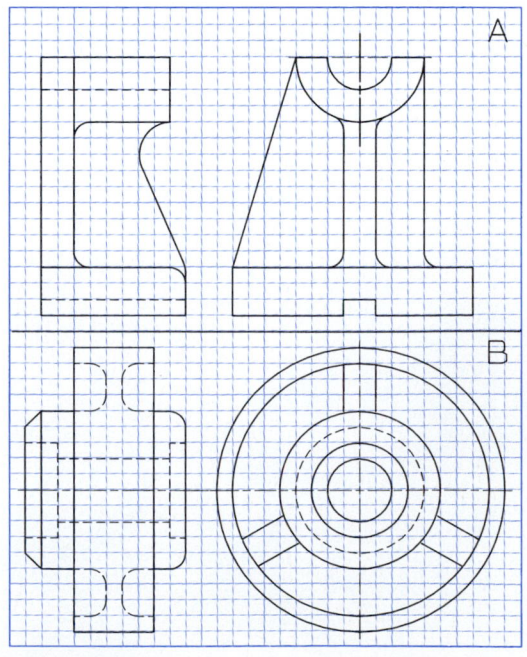

Exercise 9.4

Exercise 9.4(A) Draw a full left side section.

Exercise 9.4(B) Draw the two views. Construct a half section for the left side view.

After Reading the Chapter Through Section 9.3.10 You May Complete the Following Exercises

Exercises 9.5(A) and (B) Construct a full left side view section for each part.

Exercises 9.6(A) and (B) Draw half sections of the parts.

Exercises 9.7(A) and (B) Draw full sections of the parts.

Exercises 9.8(A) and (B) Draw half sections of the parts.

After Reading the Chapter Through Section 9.5.3 You May Complete the Following Exercises

Exercise 9.9 Section the right side view of the part.

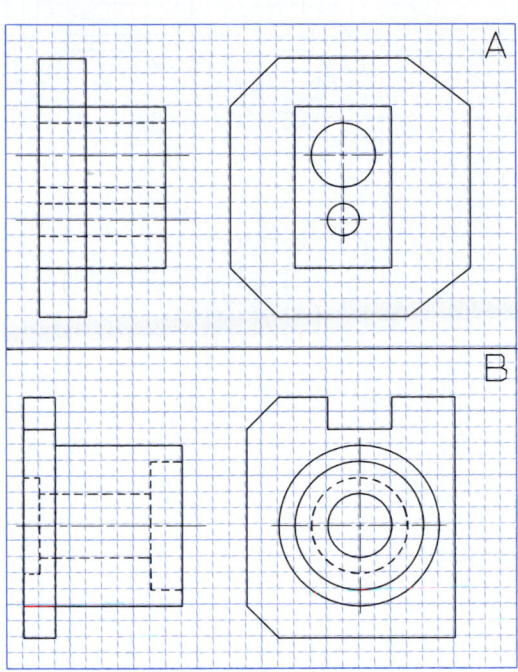

Exercise 9.5

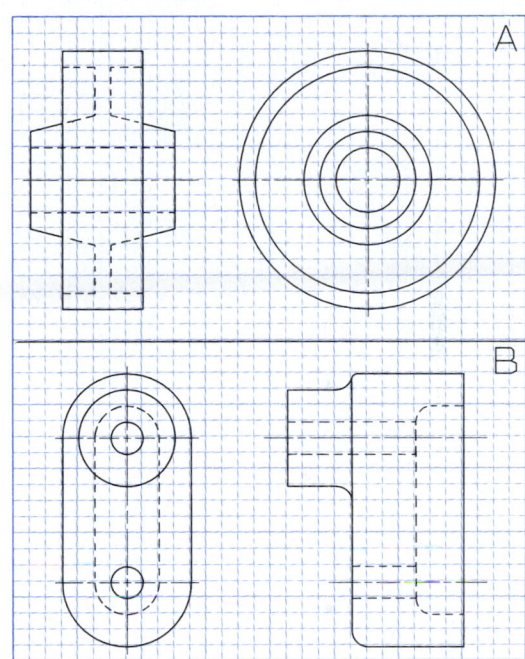

Exercise 9.7

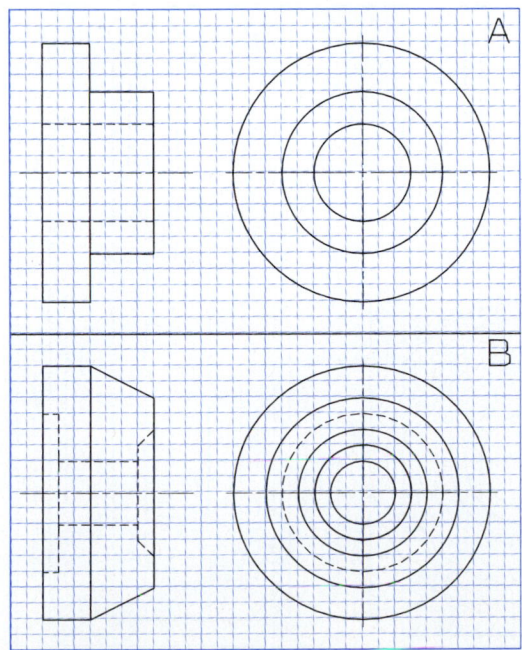

Exercise 9.6

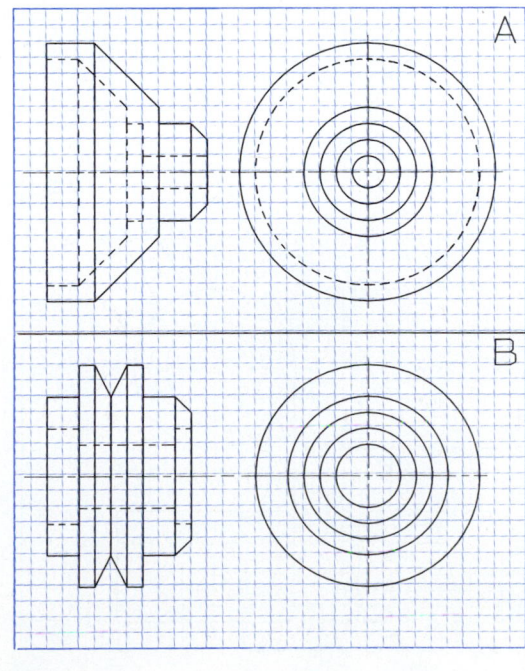

Exercise 9.8

Exercise 9.10   Section the whole part in the right side view and construct a partial (broken-out) section as required for the hub in the front view (left). The right side view is an aligned view.

Exercise 9.11   Draw an offset section of the part. Pass the cutting plane through the two holes and the slot.

Exercise 9.12   Draw a complete full section of the assembly.

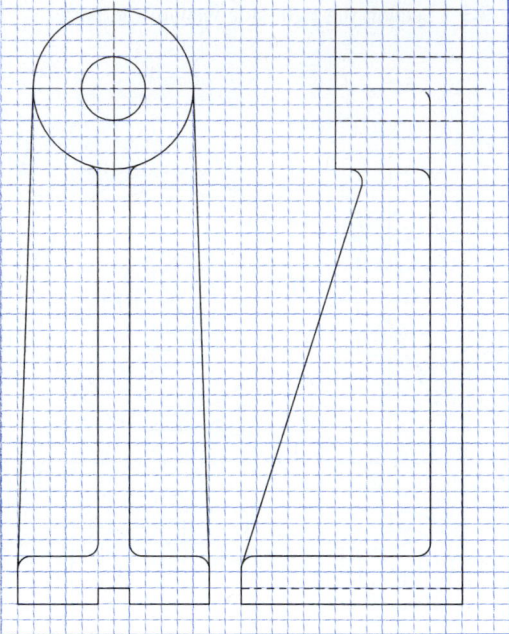

Exercise 9.9

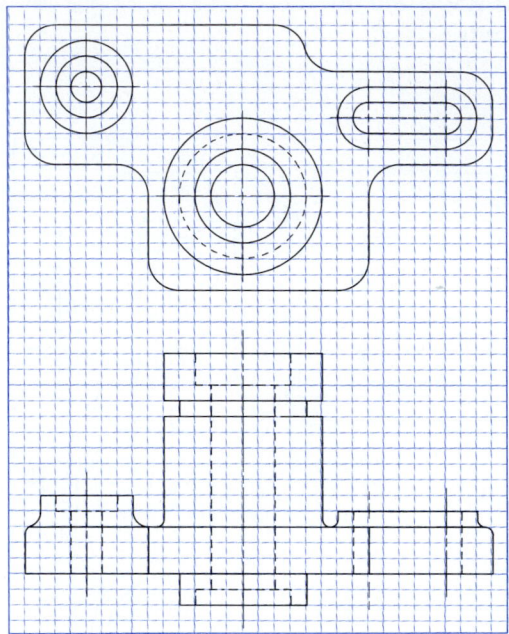

Exercise 9.11

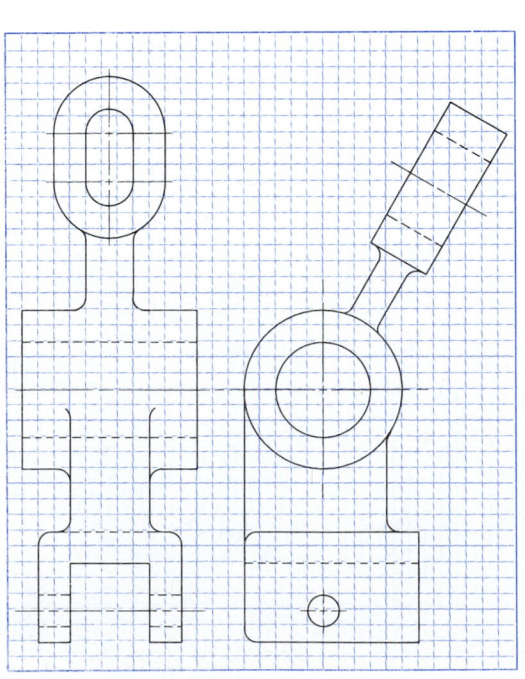

Exercise 9.10

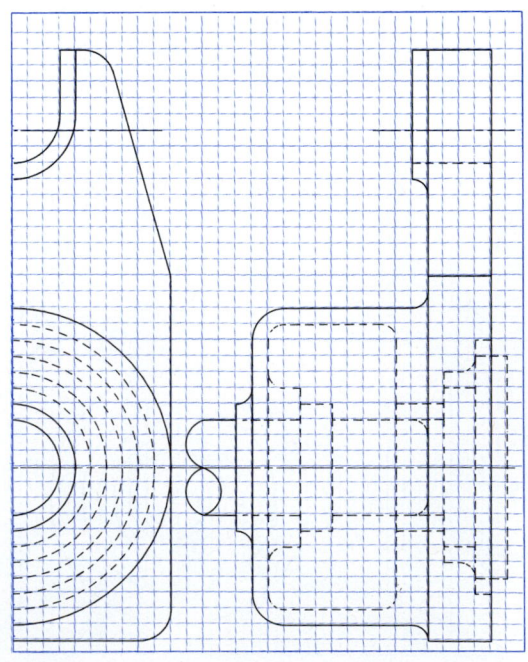

Exercise 9.12

PROBLEMS

To use these same projects for dimensioning after covering Chapter 12, allow enough space between views and use an appropriate size sheet of paper when completing these problems. Complete all views and solve for proper visibility, including centerlines, object lines, and hidden lines. Do not dimension any of the following problems until you complete Chapter 12 or are requested to do so by your instructor.

Problems 9.1(A) Through (K)   Using the scales provided, draw and section the appropiate views. Problems can be either metric, fraction-inches, or decimal-inch units. One, two, or three views may be required for a particular problem.

Problems 9.2(A) Through (H)   Same as Problem 9.1.

Problems 9.3 Through 9.12   Establish the views and sections required to describe the part properly. Do not dimension the parts. Use half sections, broken-out sections, aligned sections, and revolved sections where useful to describe the part.

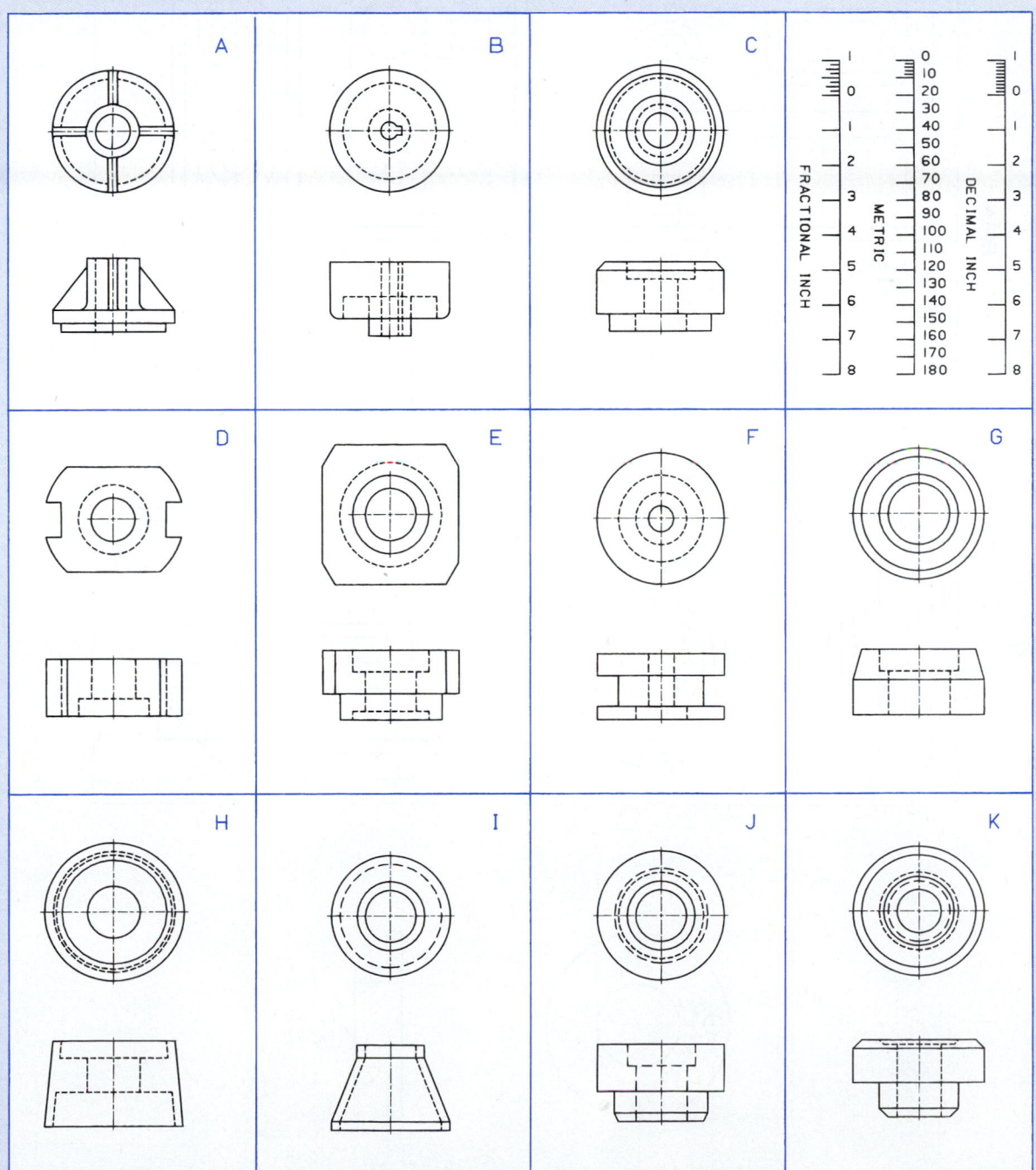

Problems 9.1(A) Through (K)

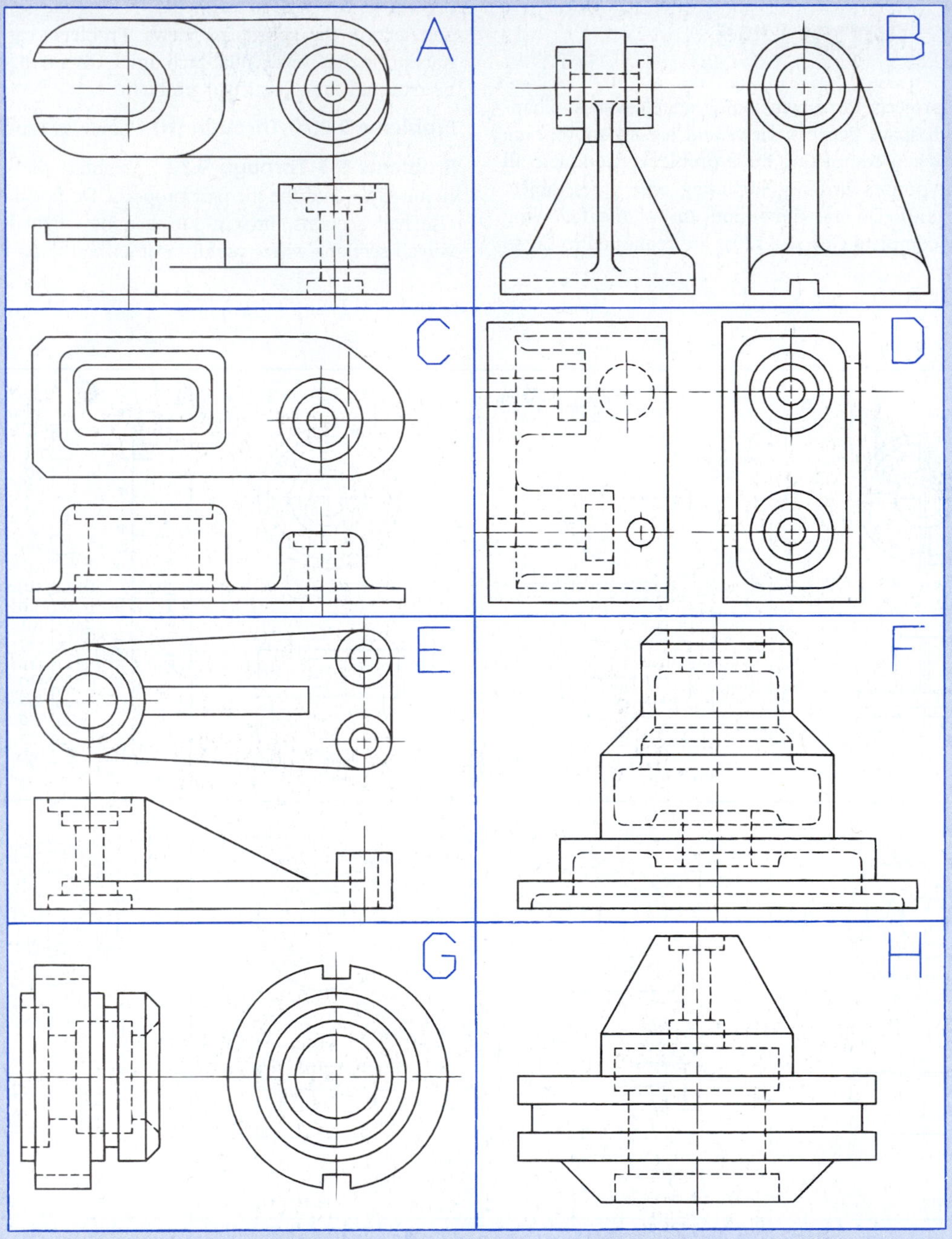

A

B

C

D

E

F

G

H

Problem 9.2

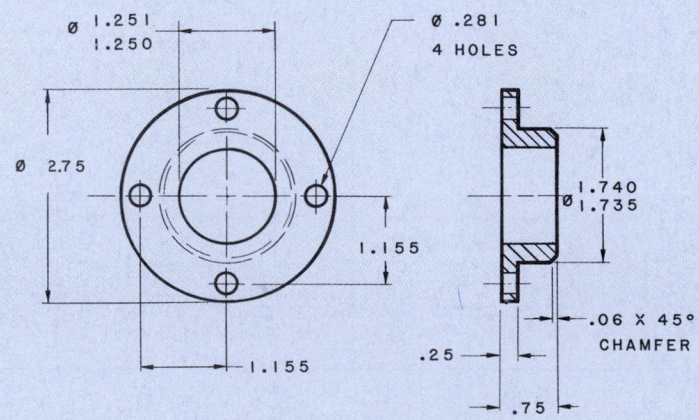

Ø 1.251
1.250

Ø .281
4 HOLES

Ø 2.75

1.155

1.155

1.740
Ø 1.735

.06 X 45°
CHAMFER

.25

.75

Problem 9.3

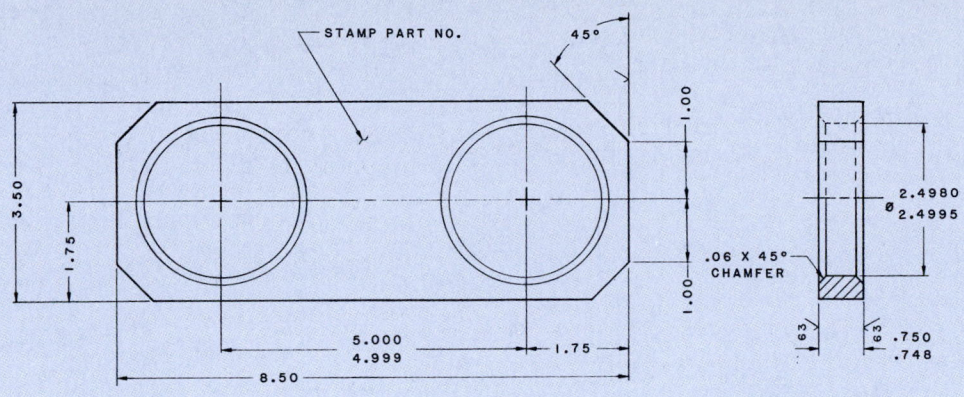

Problem 9.4

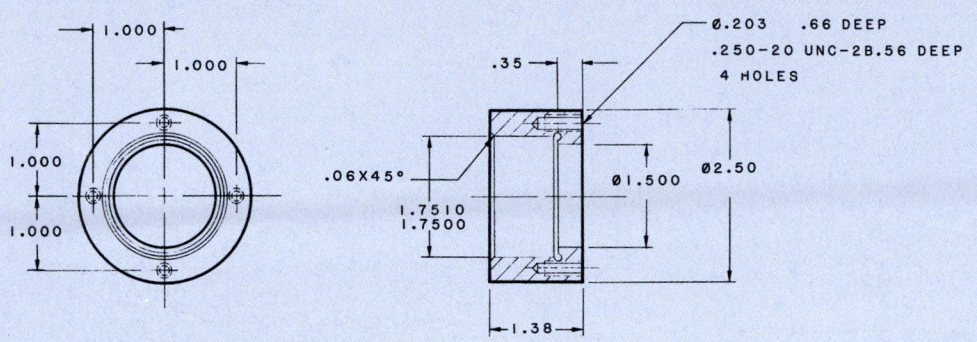

HOUSING BEARING
GUIDE ROD

Problem 9.5

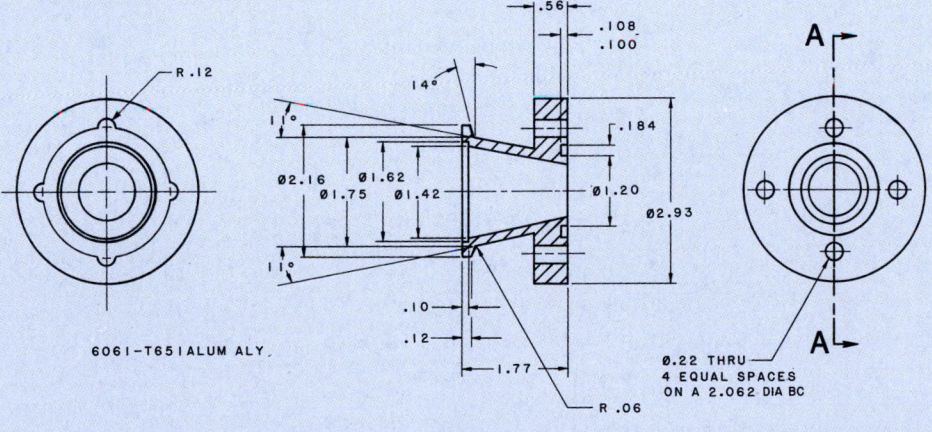

SECTION **A–A**

Problem 9.6

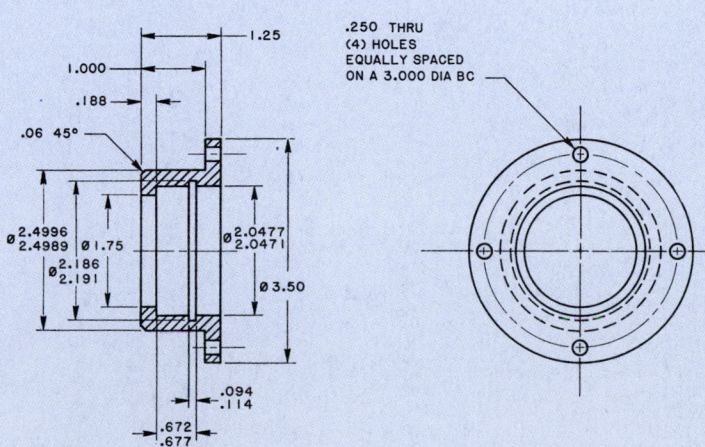

Problem 9.7

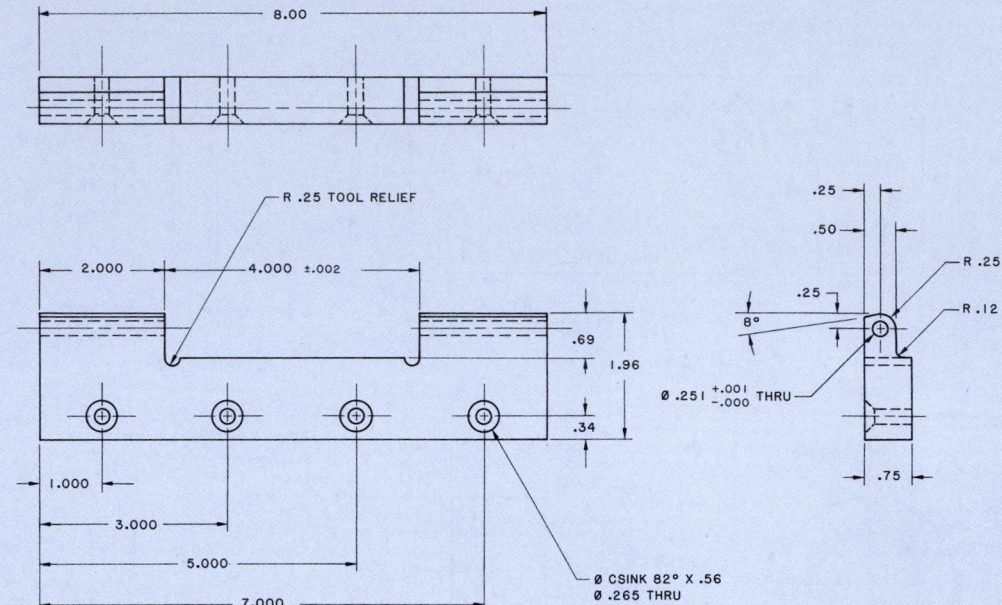

Problem 9.8

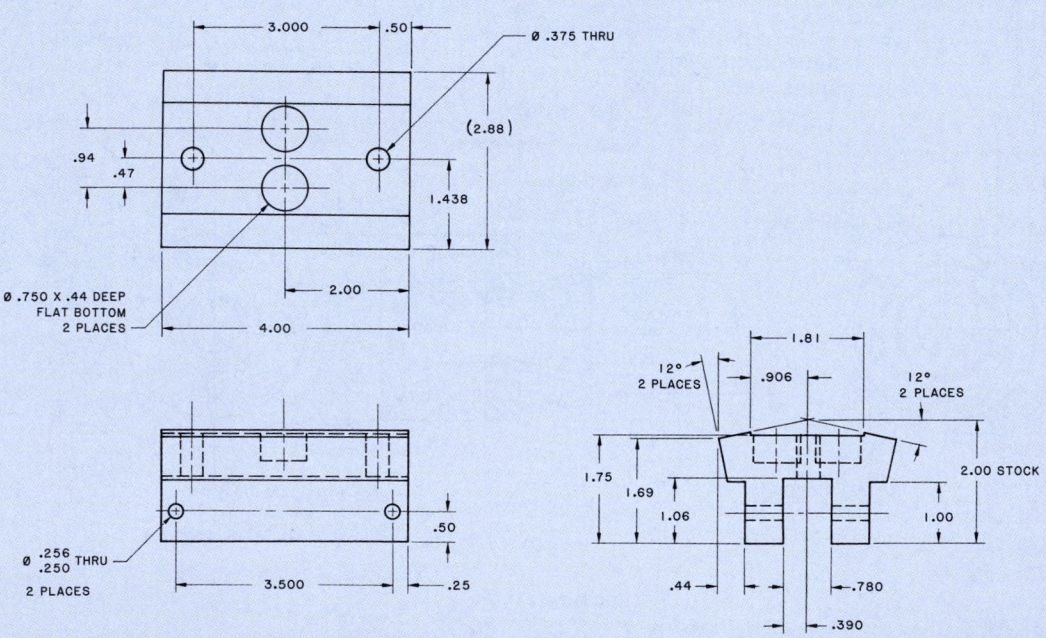

Problem 9.9

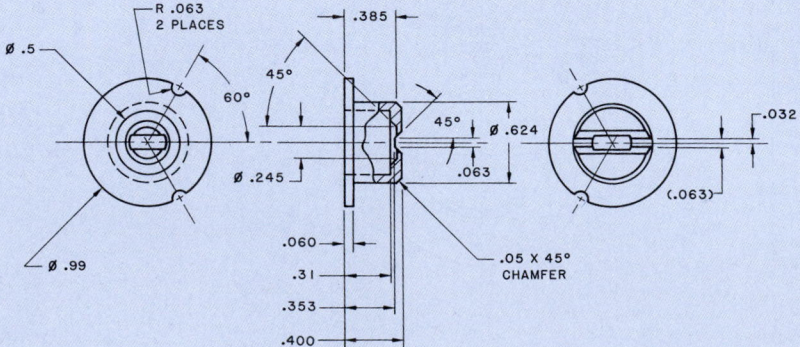

Problem 9.10

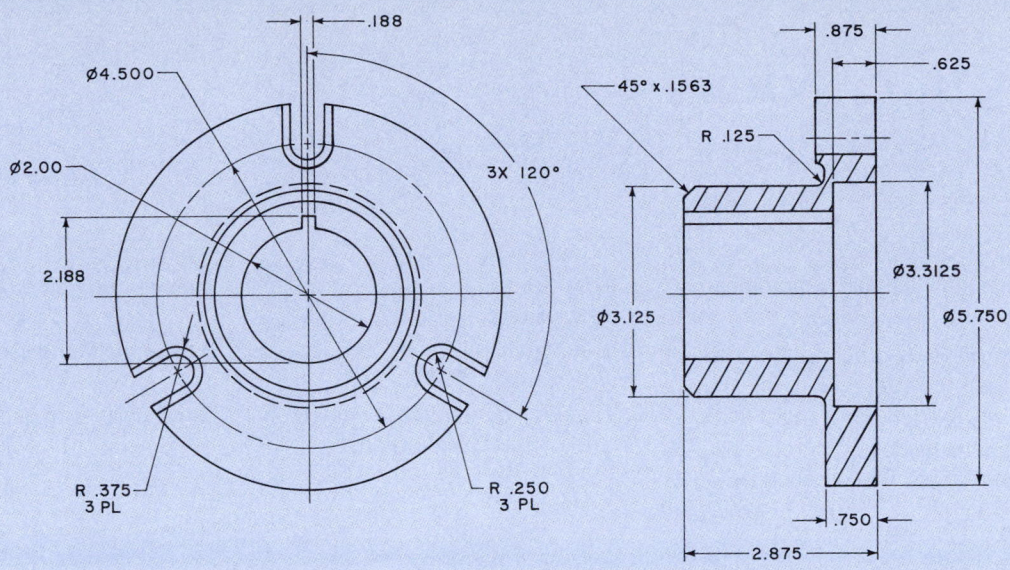

Problem 9.11

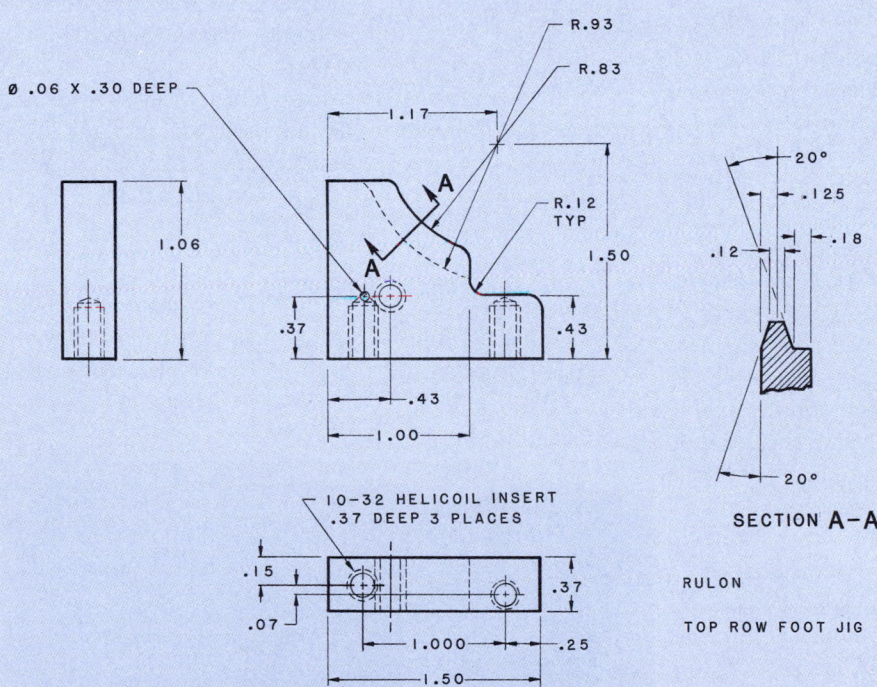

SECTION **A–A**

RULON

TOP ROW FOOT JIG

Problem 9.12

Problem 9.13   Redraw the part in Figure 9.3. (*Note:* This is an advanced problem.)

Problem 9.14   Redraw the part in Figure 9.4. Construct a top view, sectioned front view, and a left side view section.

Problem 9.15   Using Figure 9.12, construct a three-view drawing of the part. Provide a left side view section.

Problem 9.16   Draw Figure 9.13.

Problem 9.17   Redraw the weldment shown in Figure 9.14.

Problem 9.18   Draw a front view and a right side full section of the part shown in Figure 9.19.

Problem 9.19   Draw and section the part in Figure 9.28.

Problem 9.20   Using a full right side view offset section, redraw the part shown in Figure 9.34.

Problem 9.21   Redraw the part shown in Figure 9.35. Use broken-out sections where needed.

Problem 9.22   Redraw the part in Figure 9.39.

Problem 9.23   Using a full front section, redraw Figure 9.40.

Problem 9.24   Draw three views of the assembly shown in Figure 9.43. Section as needed.

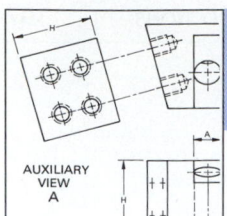

CHAPTER 10

Auxiliary Views

Learning Objectives

Upon completion of this chapter you will be able to accomplish the following:

1. Identify the need for auxiliary views in order to show the actual shape, size, and relationship of a part feature that may not be parallel to any of the principal planes of projection.

2. Differentiate between and demonstrate ability to produce primary and secondary auxiliary views using the fold line method as well as the reference plane method.

3. Solve for the true shape of an angled surface using an auxiliary view.

4. Develop the ability to produce partial, broken, half, and sectional auxiliary views.

5. Discern two- and three-dimensional CAD capabilities to generate auxiliary projections.

10.1 Introduction

Auxiliary views are used to show the true shape/size of a feature, or the relationship of part features that are not parallel to any of the principal planes of projection. The basic method of multiview drawing, described in Chapter 7, has been adequate to draw parts having horizontal and vertical surfaces and for parts that have simple inclined features. However, many parts have inclined surfaces and features that cannot be adequately shown and described by drawings using principal views alone. To provide a clear description of these features, it is necessary to draw a view that will show them true shape/size.

In Figure 10.1, the anchor has an inclined surface that cannot be seen in its true shape in a principal view. The detail of the part (Fig. 10.2) used a front, left side, and an auxiliary view. The auxiliary view shows the inclined surface and the hole's true shape/size.

Besides showing features true size, auxiliary views are used to dimension features that are distorted in principal views and to solve graphically a variety of engineering problems. Auxiliary views can be used to check the interference between two parts or clearances between pieces of an assembly. In these cases, the view may or may not display the true shape of an inclined surface, depending on the part's features and the selection of the view direction.

10.1.1 Selection and Alignment of Views

The proper selection of views, view orientation, and view alignment are determined by a part's features and its natural or assembled position. Normally, the front view is the primary view and the top view is obvious based on the position of the part in space or when assembled. The choice of additional views is determined by the configuration of the part and the minimum number of views necessary to describe the part and

show its dimensions. The detail of the anchor in Figure 10.2 required three views; front, left side, and auxiliary. The top view was not needed for this part.

As with all multiview drawings, auxiliary views are aligned with the views from which they are projected. In many cases, a centerline or a projection line continues between adjacent views to indicate the proper alignment (Fig. 10.3).

10.2 Auxiliary Views

Any view that lies in a projection plane other than the horizontal (top), frontal (front), or profile (side) plane (or a plane

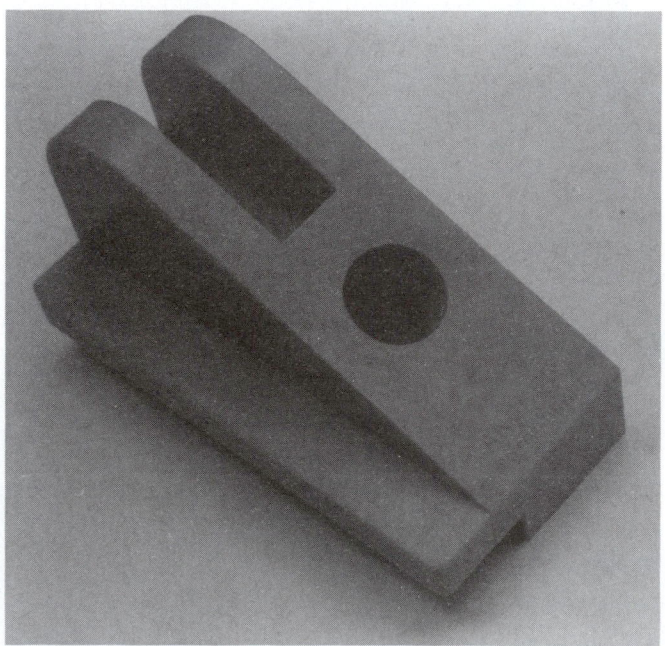

FIGURE 10.1 Anchor

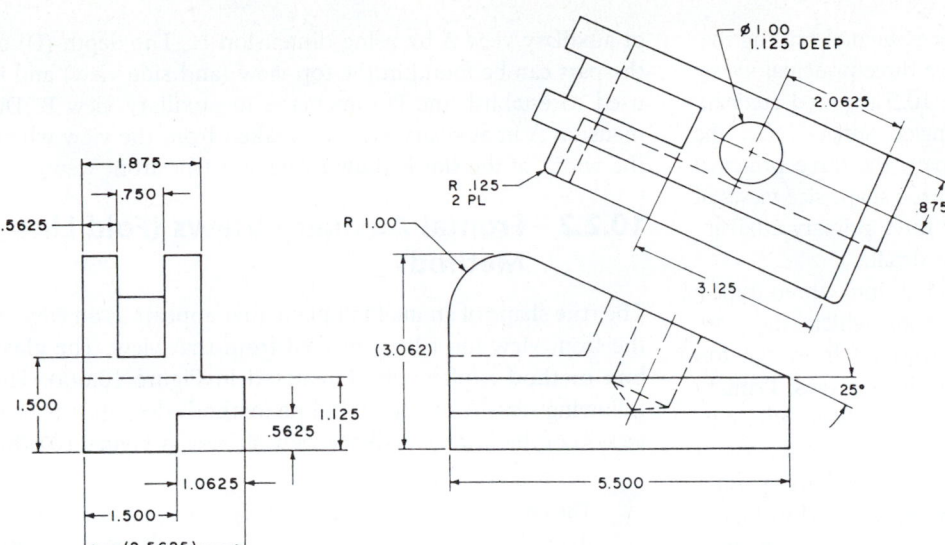

FIGURE 10.2 Detail of Anchor Showing Auxiliary View

parallel to one of these three—bottom, back, opposite side) is an **auxiliary view.** This type of projection is essential if the part to be drawn is complex and has a variety of lines or planes that are not parallel to one of the three principal planes.

Auxiliary views are classified by the view from which they are projected. **Primary auxiliary views** are projected from one of the principal views. A primary auxiliary view is perpendicular to one of the three principal planes and inclined to the other two. **Secondary auxiliary views** are projected from a primary auxiliary view and are inclined to all three principal planes of projection. **Successive auxiliary views** are projected from secondary auxiliary views.

In industry, auxiliary views are used to describe graphically the true configuration of a part and to dimension features where they appear true shape/size. In most cases, only **partial auxiliary views** are constructed, as in Figure 10.4, where only the features that appear true shape are drawn. Features that appear distorted are left off the view or partially shown and cut off using break lines. In Figure 10.4, the top view is also a partial view.

10.2.1   Primary Auxiliary Views

A **primary auxiliary view** is one that is adjacent to and aligned with one of the principal views. Primary auxiliary views are identified as **front-adjacent, top-adjacent,** or **side-adjacent** to indicate the principal view with which it is aligned (and projected from). In industry, auxiliary views are used to show aspects of a mechanical part or portions of a

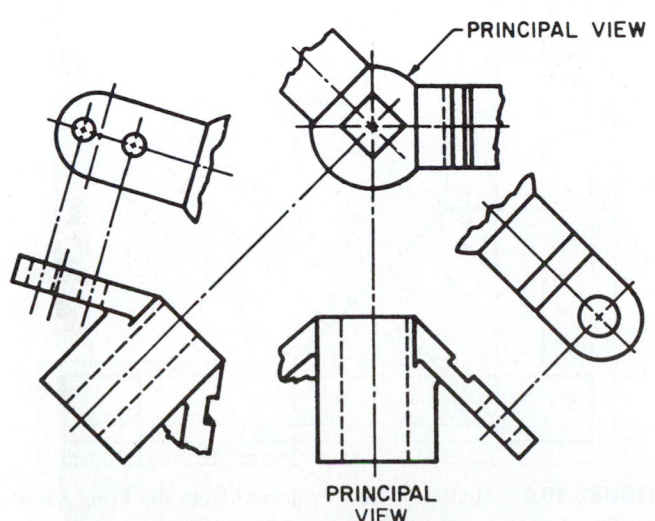

FIGURE 10.3 Principal and Auxiliary Views of a Part

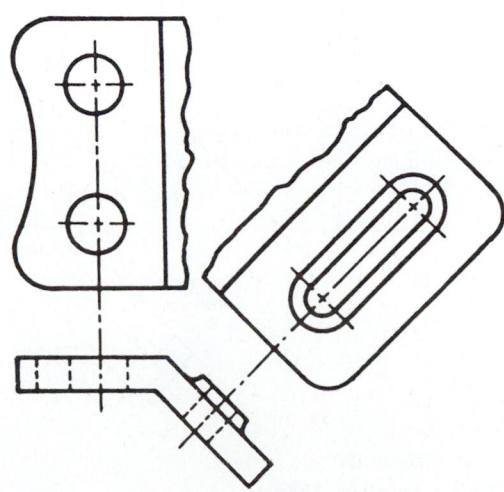

FIGURE 10.4 Primary Auxiliary View of a Part

system such as piping configurations or structural bracing that cannot be adequately represented in the three principal views. The machined block shown in Figure 10.5 required auxiliary views to clarify the shape of the angled surfaces and the position of holes and slots. For this part, the three principal views (top, front, side) do not provide true shape/size views of each surface. It is necessary to project three primary auxiliary views to describe the angled surfaces in detail.

Primary auxiliary views are divided into three types, depending on the principal view from which they are projected. Primary auxiliary views projected from the top (top-adjacent) view are **horizontal auxiliary views.** Primary auxiliary views projected from the front (front-adjacent) view are **frontal auxiliary views.** Primary auxiliary views projected from the side (side-adjacent) view are **profile auxiliary views.** These three types are represented in Figure 10.5 where auxiliary view A is projected from the top (horizontal) view, auxiliary view B is projected from the front (frontal) view, and auxiliary view C is projected from the side (profile) view. The auxiliary projections in this figure are partial views, showing only the inclined surfaces as true shape. This is normal industry practice, since the projection of the total part would not only add little to the understanding of the part's configuration, but may actually confuse the view. *Hidden lines that fall behind the true shape surface in an auxiliary view can normally be eliminated for the same reason.*

Each primary auxiliary view, besides being projected from one of the three principal views, will have one common dimension with at least one other principal view. The height (H) dimension in the front view is used to establish the limits

of auxiliary view A by using dimension H. The depth (D) of the part can be found in the top view (and side view) and is used to establish the D dimension in auxiliary view B. Dimension A in auxiliary view C is taken from the view where the width of the slot is drawn true size (the front view).

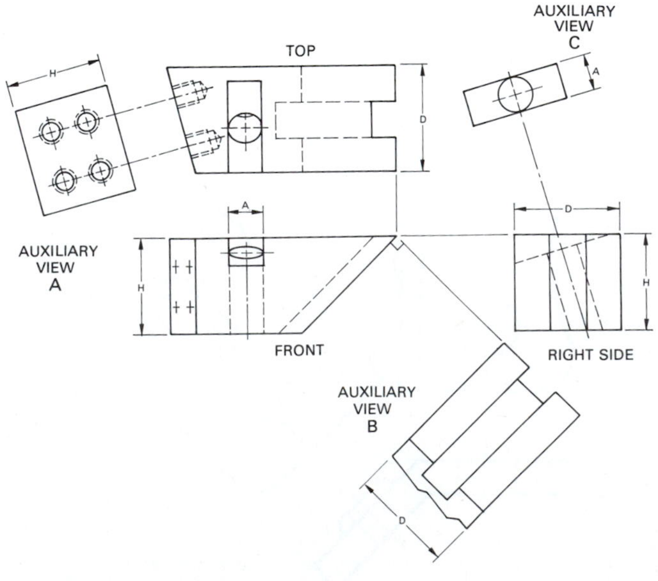

10.2.2 Frontal Auxiliary Views (Fold Line Method)

The true shape of an inclined plane that appears as an edge in the front view must be projected from that view. The **glass box method** is pictorially illustrated in Figure 10.6(a). The following steps (using the fold line method) describe the projection of the frontal auxiliary view shown in Figure 10.6(b):

1. The line of sight for a frontal auxiliary view is perpendicular to the inclined surface, which appears as an edge in the frontal view.

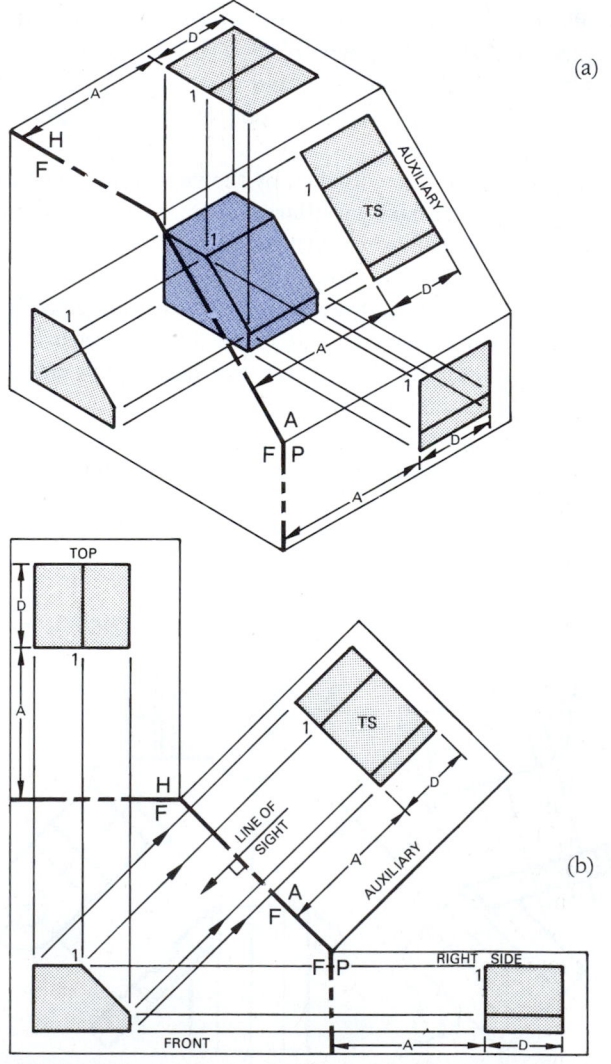

(a)

(b)

FIGURE 10.6 Auxiliary View Projected from the Front View
(a) The glass box method (b) The fold line method

FIGURE 10.5 Auxiliary Views

Hand Tools and Devices

There is evidence that hand tools and other devices were used by primates nearly a million years ago. It could be assumed that hand tools, after evolving with mankind for a million years or so, would now be specifically adapted for human use. In fact, this is not the case. Until recently, human biomechanical factors have been mostly ignored in the design of hand tools.

The human hand and wrist are complex structures of bones, nerves, ligaments, tendons, and arteries. Movement of the wrist occurs in two planes. The hand is flexed up and down in the first plane. Side to side movement or ulnar deviation occurs in the second plane. Continued use of tools that call for motions along these planes can injure the hand and wrist.

Recent studies have shown us how to design tools to avoid these types of motion. Using x rays of the wrist and computer-generated wire frame auxiliary models, de-

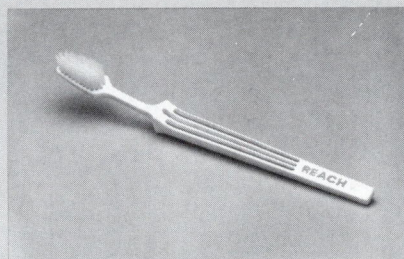

Ergonomically Designed Toothbrush

signers are able to design tool configurations that use a relatively straight wrist motion. For example, by bending or rotating the handle of a pair of pliers or a hammer about 19°, grip strength is increased while fatigue is reduced. This bent handle design is now being used in softball bats and is approved for regulation play. Golf clubs and fishing rods also incorporate this technology into their designs.

The most common hand-held device

is probably the toothbrush. The only major development since it was introduced in 1780 was the use of nylon bristles. Nylon replaced hog hair in the 1930s.

Johnson and Johnson, Inc. designed a new toothbrush using human factor and time-motion research data. Prototypes were developed with different handle shapes and bristle head rotations. These prototypes were tested and the optimal features found from the testing were used in the final design. The result was the Reach toothbrush. The Reach incorporates a small bilevel bristle head into an angled, countered handle for easier handling, better gum stimulation, and better plaque removal.

The new toothbrush is one example of design with human factors. Future tool designs will require these research studies to produce hand tools specifically adapted for human use. Without using auxiliary views, projections, and models, none of this would have been possible.

---

2. Fold line F/A is established perpendicular to the line of sight and parallel to the inclined surface (edge view).
3. Projectors are drawn from all points in the front view perpendicular to the fold line. Hidden lines were omitted in this example.
4. Measurements are taken (using dividers for speed and accuracy) from fold line H/F or P/F to establish the front face of the part in the auxiliary view. Dimension A is transferred from the top or side view to establish the distance from the F/A fold line to the front face of the part in the auxiliary view. The depth dimension (D) of the part is then transferred.

10.2.3   Horizontal Auxiliary Views (Fold Line Method)

The second type of primary auxiliary view is the **horizontal auxiliary view.** In this case, the auxiliary view is taken perpendicular to the horizontal plane and is inclined to the other two principal planes. The glass box method is shown pictorially in Figure 10.7(a). In this example, the auxiliary view is projected at a required viewing angle, and is *not* being used to solve for the true shape of an inclined surface, as was the case in Figure 10.6. Because of this, the view does not show the true shape of a surface but instead provides a different viewing angle. The following steps describe the process of projecting a horizontal auxiliary view using the fold line method shown in Figure 10.7(b):

1. Establish a line of sight at a required angle of viewing; 45° was used here.
2. Fold line H/A is drawn perpendicular to the line of sight.
3. From each point in the top (horizontal) view, extend a projector parallel to the line of sight and perpendicular to the fold line. In this example, hidden lines are shown.
4. Dimension D is transferred from the side or front view to establish the distance from the H/A fold line to the top of the part. The height (H) dimension is then transferred to locate the bottom of the part. Visibility is determined and the view is completed.

10.2.4   Profile Auxiliary Views (Fold Line Method)

The third type of primary auxiliary view is the **profile auxiliary view.** In Figure 10.8 one of the surfaces of the part is inclined to the front and top view, and appears as an edge in the side view. By projecting an auxiliary view with a line of sight perpendicular to the edge view of the inclined surface, the true shape of the surface will be seen in the profile auxiliary view. The same basic steps are used to draw profile auxiliary views, as in Sections 10.3.1 and 10.3.2. Notice the need for a top view projected from the right side view. This is the alternate position for a top view.

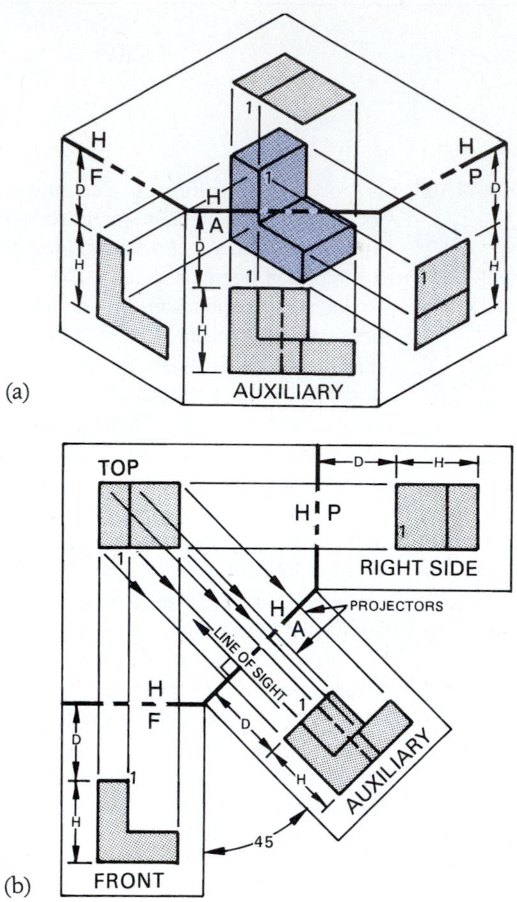

FIGURE 10.7 Auxiliary View Projected from the Top View
(a) The glass box method (b) The fold line method

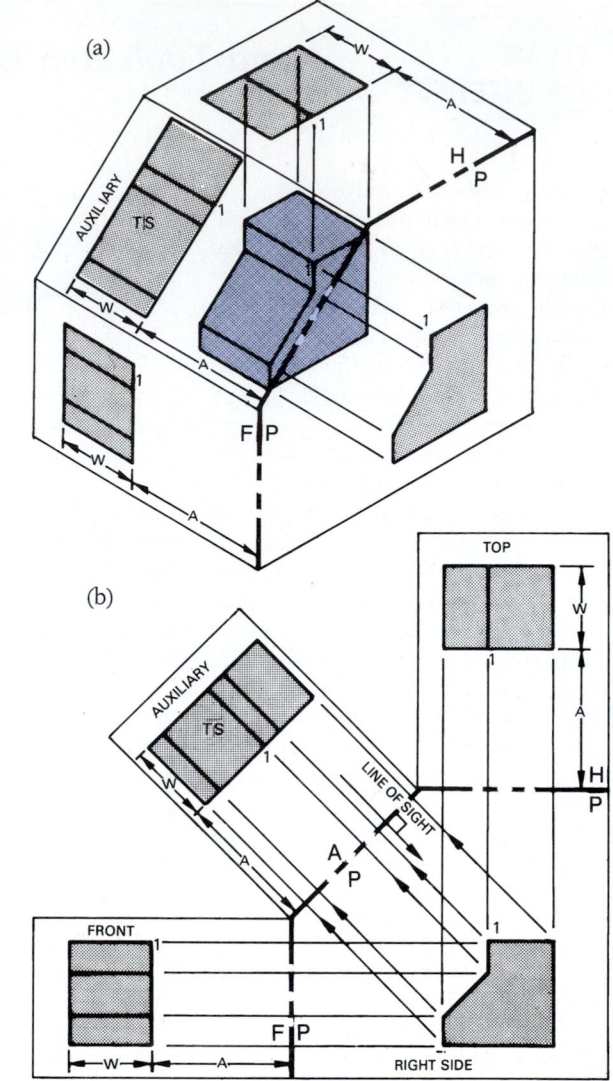

FIGURE 10.8 Auxiliary View Projected from the Side View
(a) The glass box method (b) The fold line method

10.2.5 Secondary Auxiliary Views Using Fold Lines

A **secondary auxiliary view** is one that is adjacent to and aligned with (projected from) a primary auxiliary view. In Figure 10.9, the part has *one surface that is inclined to all three principal planes of projection.* Therefore, it is not possible to solve for the true shape of the surface in a primary auxiliary view. This type of surface is normally referred to as an **oblique surface** (not to be confused with oblique projection). Since all consecutive views of a part are at right angles, secondary auxiliary views are perpendicular to primary auxiliary views. Views projected from a secondary auxiliary view are called **successive auxiliary views.** The following steps were used to draw the part in Figure 10.9.

1. Establish the line of sight parallel to true length (TL) line 1-2 in the front view.
2. Draw fold line F/A perpendicular to the line of sight and a convenient distance from the front view.
3. Complete the primary auxiliary view by transferring dimensions A, C, and D from the front view and draw the part.

4. Establish a line of sight perpendicular to the edge view (EV) of surface 1A-2A-3A in the primary auxiliary view.
5. Draw fold line A/B perpendicular to the line of sight and at a convenient distance from auxiliary view A.
6. Complete the secondary auxiliary view by transferring dimensions from the front view. Draw only plane 1-2-3, which will show true shape. Dimensions D and E establish points 3 and 2.

10.2.6 Adjacent Views

Each view and its preceding and following view are considered adjacent views. An **adjacent view** is any view that is aligned with another view by means of a direct projection. Each of the primary auxiliary views (A, C, D, and G) of the pyramid in Figure 10.10 is projected from its adjacent principal views. Secondary auxiliary views (B, E, and I) are taken from their adjacent primary auxiliary view. Notice that view H

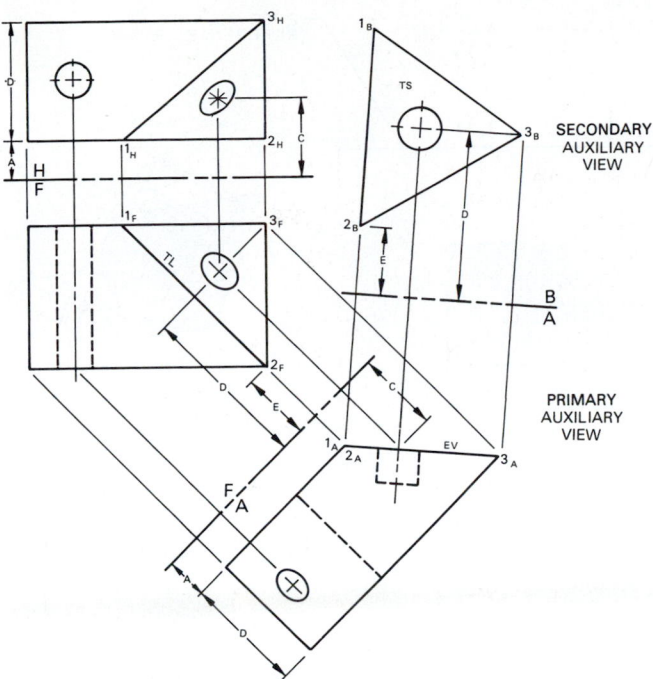

FIGURE 10.9 Secondary Auxiliary Views

has two auxiliary views projected from it, view A and view C.

It is important to understand that principal views can also be adjacent views. The top (H) view is adjacent to the front (F), the front (F) to both side (P) and top (H), and the side (P) to the front (F). Principal views are also adjacent to their primary auxiliary views (see Section 7.5.4).

In Figure 10.10 dimensions are used to establish apex point 0 from view to view. These dimensions are used on alternate (related) views, not consecutive (adjacent) views. Therefore, dimension 1 is the distance from fold line H/F to point 0 in the front view, and is used to locate point 0 in primary auxiliary views A and C. Dimension 3 locates the apex (point 0) in auxiliary view D. Dimension 4 locates the apex in view G, and dimension 5 locates it in view E, and dimension 6 in view I.

10.3 Auxiliary Views Using the Reference Plane Method

In drawing the auxiliary view, dimensions in one direction are projected into the auxiliary view from the adjacent view. The dimensions in the other direction are transferred to the

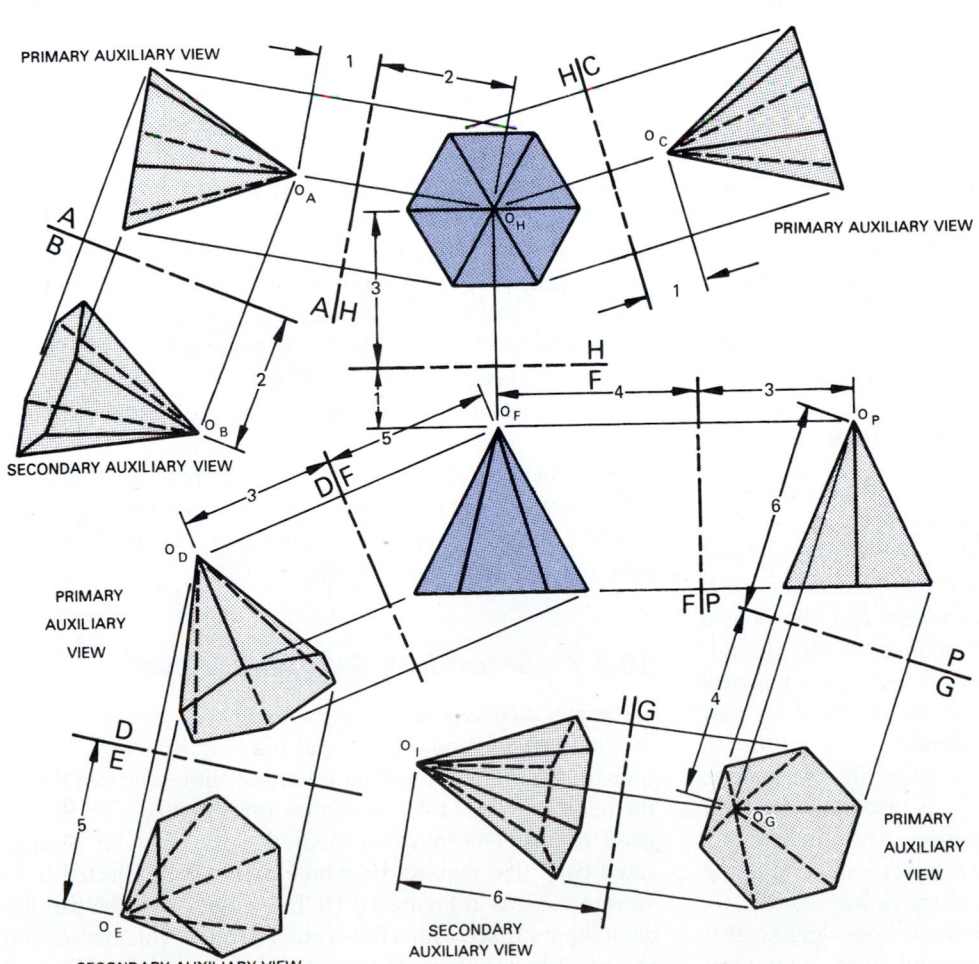

FIGURE 10.10 Multiple Auxiliary Views

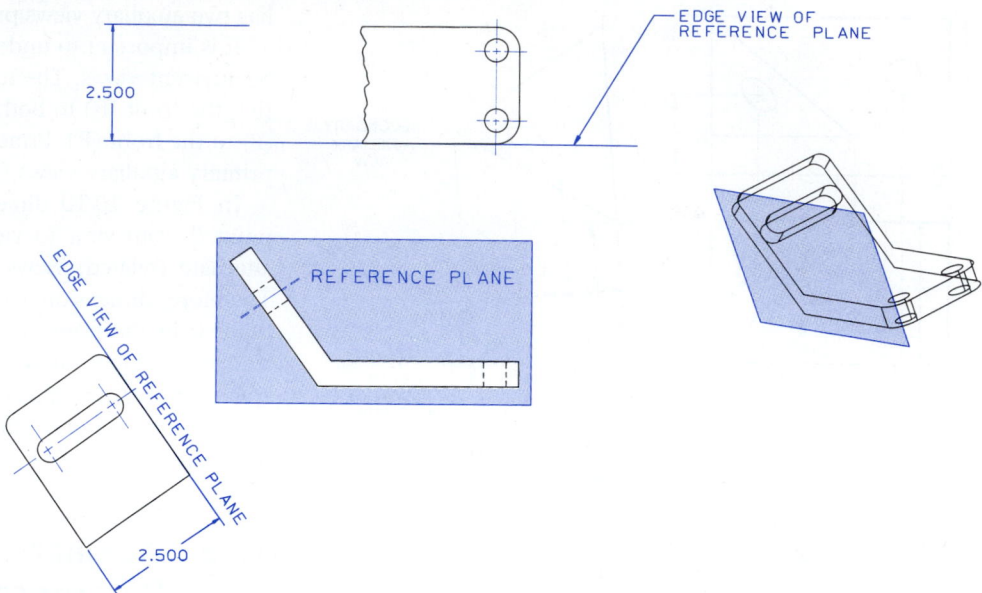

FIGURE 10.11 Auxiliary View Projection Using Reference Plane Method.

auxiliary view by measurement. To aid in the transfer of these measurements, a **reference plane** can be used instead of a fold line. The reference plane is placed perpendicular to the inclined surface that is being drawn and represented in this view by its edge, which shows as a line. All measurements are transferred from the edge view of the reference plane.

The reference line (edge) appears in the view where the inclined surface is shown as foreshortened. It will not appear in the view where the surface to be drawn is seen as an edge. In Figure 10.11, the reference plane shows as a plane surface in the front view and as an edge in the top view and the auxiliary view. Any convenient parallel position can be used to establish the reference plane. It could have been passed through the center of the part (as seen from the top) or the back plane instead of the front plane as is the case.

10.3.1 Drawing an Auxiliary View

To draw the auxiliary view in Figure 10.11 using the reference plane method, first locate the reference plane for the auxiliary view so that it is parallel to the edge view of the inclined surface being drawn. Here, the plane was passed so that it coincided with the front surface of the part and shows as a reference line (edge) in the top and auxiliary views. The reference line is positioned a distance away from the edge view of the inclined surface that is equal to the depth of the part plus the space desired between the views.

Spacing of the views can also be accomplished as is done when drawing standard normal views, as discussed in Chapter 7. The thickness (depth dimension **2.500** in. in Fig. 10.11) plus the space required between views determine the amount of space needed for the auxiliary view.

Place the auxiliary view (the reference line-edge) so that there is sufficient space for dimensions and notes. Do not put the auxiliary view too close to the view from which it is

projected. Since each part will have a different shape and dimensioning requirements, it is impossible to give a specific distance that could be applied to each part. You will learn through practice and experience the amount of room necessary for the view to be properly positioned.

After the extents of the view are projected (perpendicularly) from the adjacent view (the front view in Fig. 10.11), measurements for establishing the thickness of the auxiliary view are then taken from the existing view (here **2.500**). Measurements that can be taken perpendicular to the reference line are then transferred to the auxiliary view. At the same time, all dimensions that are parallel to the reference line are projected to the auxiliary view. This procedure (projection lines and transfer distances) is exactly the same as that for the fold line method. The line of projection for each point is always perpendicular to the reference line. All features can be established in the auxiliary view by projecting one point at a time.

Note that the fold line or the reference line, depending on which method was employed, is always erased after the projection of the auxiliary view is completed. Finished drawings have only views of the part (Fig. 10.12).

10.3.2 Secondary Auxiliary Views

Secondary auxiliary views have already been presented using the fold line method. For typical industry drawings that require the detailing of an oblique surface, either the fold line or the reference plane method can be implemented with equally good results. The fold line method works best for complicated parts that require the whole part to be projected from view to view, as in Figure 10.10. In Figure 10.13, the part has an oblique surface with a hole centered on it. This surface and the hole do not show as true shape in any of the principal views. This is an example of a part where a primary and

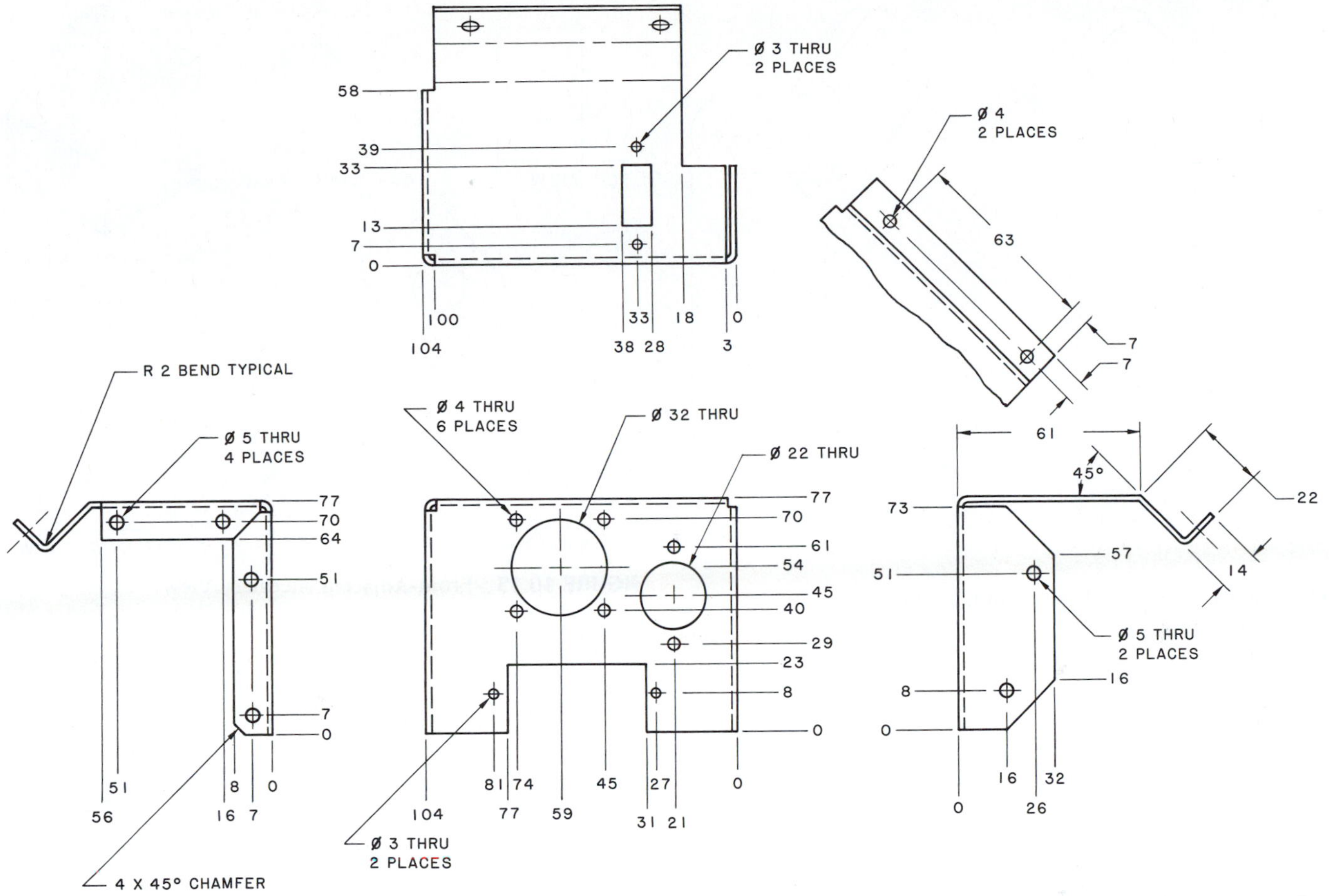

Ø 3 THRU
2 PLACES

58

39
33

13
7
0

Ø 3 THRU
2 PLACES

100   33   18   0
104   38 28   3

Ø 4
2 PLACES

63

7
7

61
45°   22

73
51   57
                                      14
8   16

Ø 5 THRU
2 PLACES

8   16

0   26
   16   32

R 2 BEND TYPICAL

Ø 5 THRU
4 PLACES

Ø 4 THRU
6 PLACES   Ø 32 THRU

Ø 22 THRU

77
70
64

51

7
0

51   8   0
56   16 7

77
70

61
54
45
40

29
23
8

0

104   77   59   31 21
   81 74   45   27

Ø 3 THRU
2 PLACES

4 X 45° CHAMFER

FIGURE 10.12 Electronic Bracket
Mount Detail

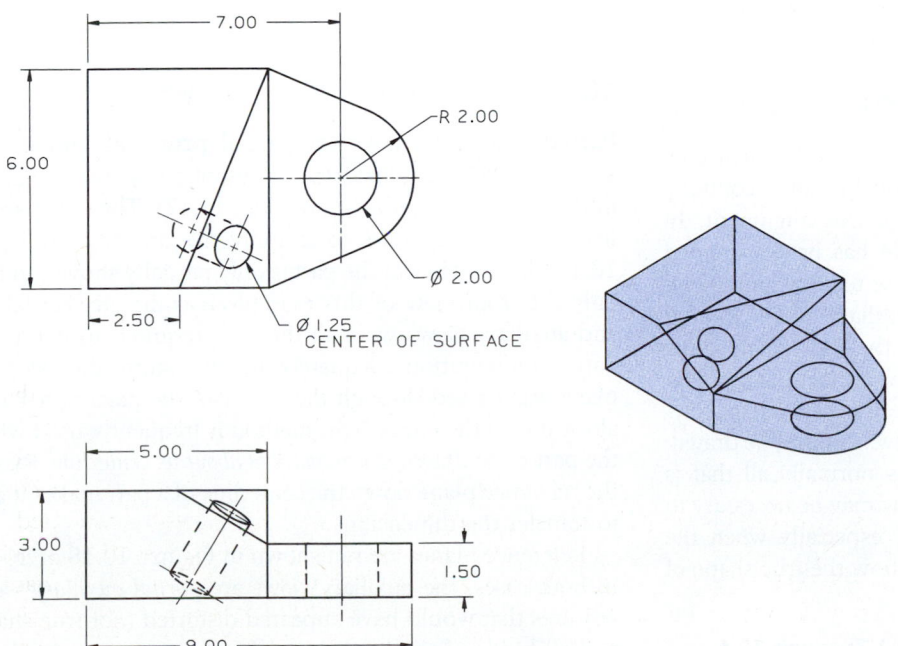

7.00

6.00

R 2.00

Ø 2.00

2.50

Ø 1.25
CENTER OF SURFACE

5.00

3.00

1.50

9.00

FIGURE 10.13 Oblique Surface
on a Part

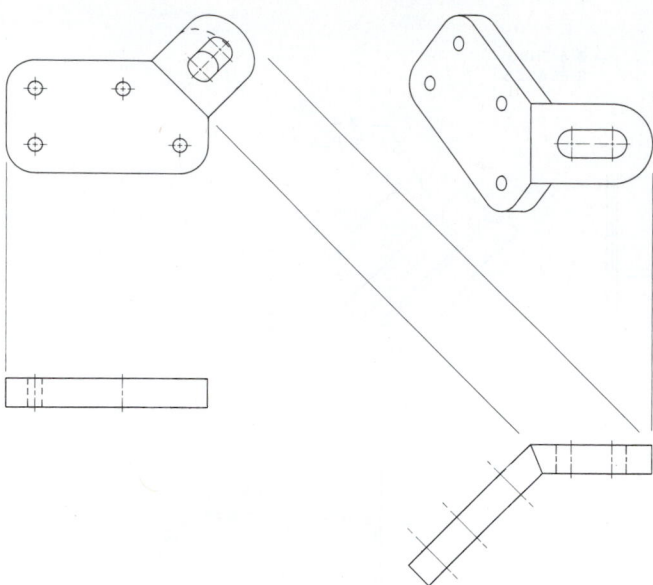

FIGURE 10.14   True Shape of an Oblique Surface by Auxiliary View

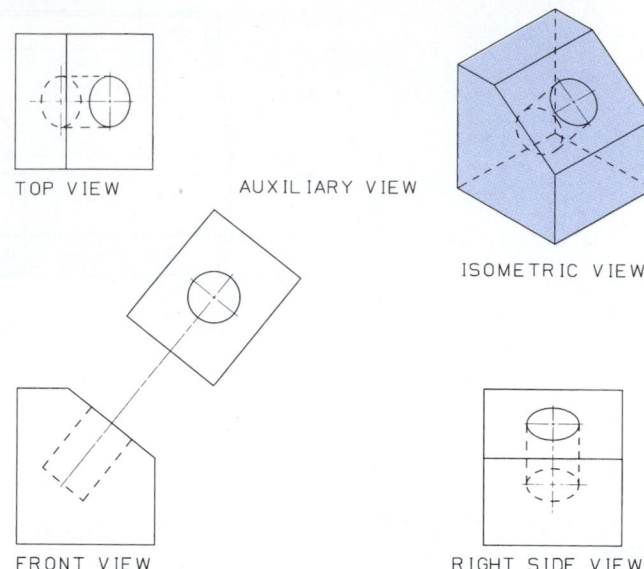

FIGURE 10.15   Front-Adjacent Auxiliary View

secondary auxiliary view will be required in order to display and detail the part properly.

The part in Figure 10.14 has a surface that is oblique. This surface also has a slot positioned on it. To solve for the true-shape view of the surface, a primary auxiliary view showing the surface as an edge was projected first. By projecting a view perpendicular to the edge view, a true-shape secondary auxiliary view was then established. Note that fold lines and reference planes are not shown. The primary auxiliary view shows the *true angle* that the inclined surface makes with the base of the part.

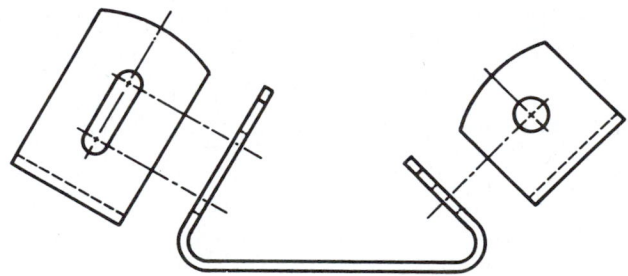

FIGURE 10.16   Front View and Two Auxiliary Views

10.4   Auxiliary View Conventions

Auxiliary views are aligned with the views from which they are projected. A centerline or projection line may continue between the adjacent views to indicate this alignment. In Figure 10.15 the centerline of the hole has been extended from the front view to the auxiliary view to show *alignment*.

In many cases, hidden lines in auxiliary views are not shown, unless they would help clarify the view. Only show hidden lines when they do not complicate the auxiliary view or where they are necessary to describe the part adequately.

In general, the complete auxiliary view need not be drawn. Showing only the true-shape surface is normally all that is required (Fig. 10.16). The complete view may be necessary to show clearances or other information, especially when the auxiliary projection was not drawn to show the true shape of a surface.

You May Now Complete Exercises 10.1 Through 10.4

10.4.1   Partial Auxiliary Views

Partial auxiliary views (or **partial principal views**) may show only pertinent features not described by true projection in the principal or other views (Fig. 10.12). They are used in lieu of complete views to simplify the drawing. In Figure 10.17, the top view of the part is only partially shown; in fact, only the front view of this example is complete. Partial top and auxiliary views were all that was required to define the part's configuration adequately. In this figure, the reference plane was passed through the center of the part, rather than along one of the edges. This method is frequently used where the part to be drawn is *symmetrical about its centerline*. Passing the reference plane down the centerline of a part makes it easy to transfer the dimensions.

Reference planes are not shown in Figures 10.18 or 10.19. In both cases, the auxiliary views are *partial auxiliary views*. Features that would have appeared distorted (not true shape) and all hidden lines have been left off.

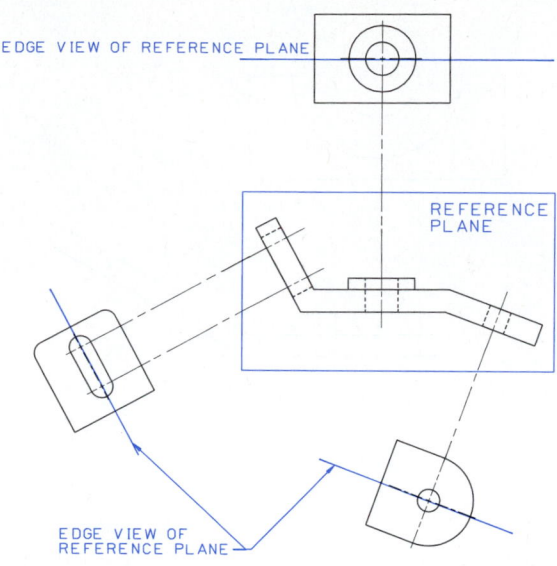

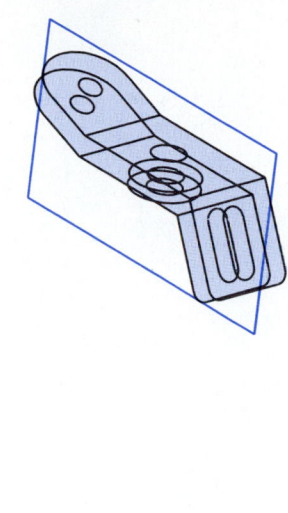

FIGURE 10.17   Reference Plane Method of Auxiliary View Projection

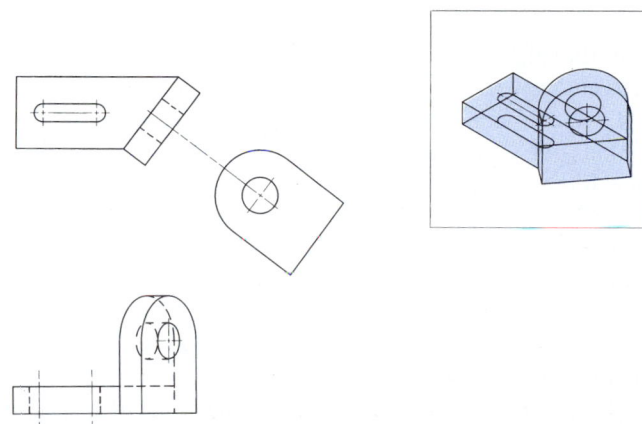

FIGURE 10.18   Partial Auxiliary View

10.4.2   Broken and Half Auxiliary Views

In some situations, a portion of the auxiliary view must be shown as in Figure 10.20. Here, the base is partially shown (broken) in the auxiliary view. This is a form of partial auxiliary view. In Figure 10.21, a **half top view** and a **half auxiliary view** are shown. The part is symmetrical about its centerline; therefore, little is gained by drawing a complete top view. The same can be said of the auxiliary views. In this example, one of the auxiliary views is shown as a full view to show the difference between the types. The only complete view in this example is the front view. The centerline dividing the part is always shown on half views.

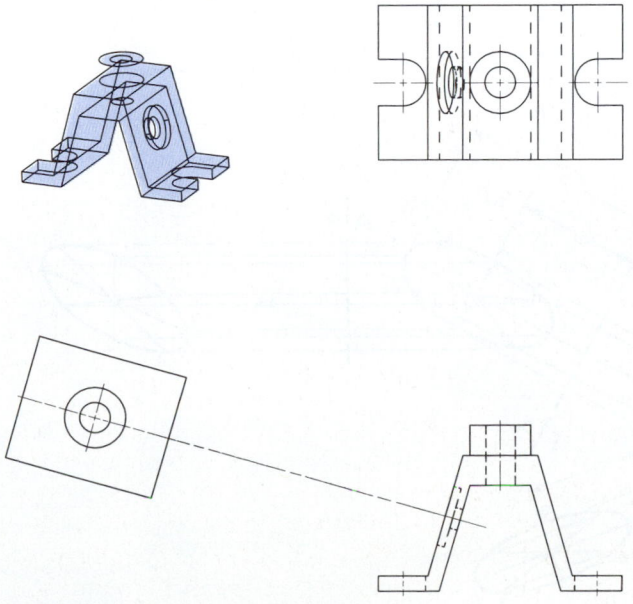

FIGURE 10.19   Partial Auxiliary View

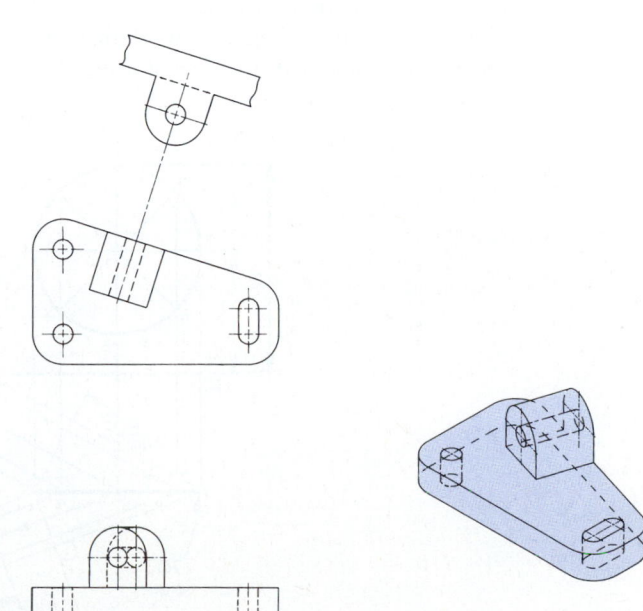

FIGURE 10.20   Broken Partial Auxiliary View

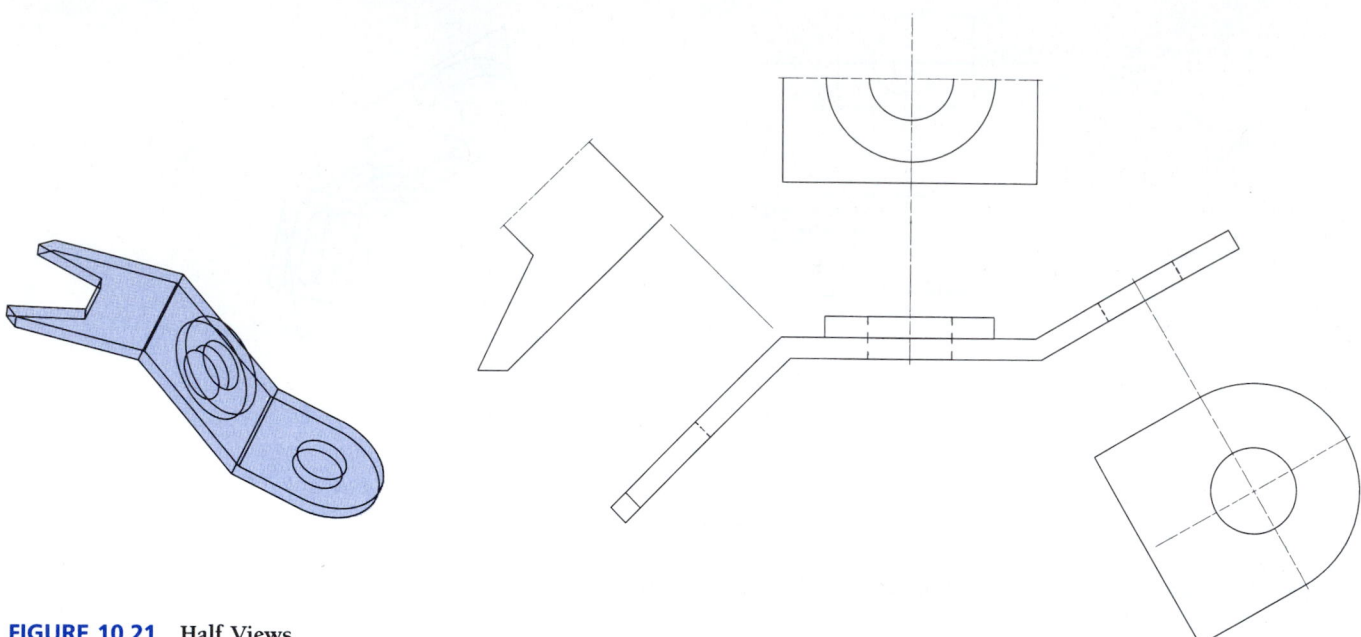

FIGURE 10.21 Half Views

10.4.3 Auxiliary Views of Curved Features

Circular and curved features are true size/shape in views where the line of sight is perpendicular to the edge view of the surface on which they lie. In the adjacent projection the plane appears as an edge and parallel to the fold line. The length of the edge view line is equal to the circle's diameter.

When a circular plane is oblique, it appears as an ellipse. An elliptical view of a circular plane along with each adjacent auxiliary view is plotted by locating a series of points along the outline of the circle in a true size view. These points are located in each adjacent view by projection and by transferring distances to establish each individual point. The series of points is connected with a template or an irregular curve.

In Figure 10.22, a normal view (true size) of the circular plane is given along with its frontal edge view. Primary auxiliary view A forms a 30° angle with the line of sight; there-

fore, the edge view of the plane forms a 60° angle with the adjacent view (and fold line F/A). Auxiliary A shows the plane as a 30° ellipse. Secondary auxiliary view B is drawn by projection and transferring distances for each point. Auxiliary view B is a secondary auxiliary view. Auxiliary C is projected at a 70° angle to the edge view and shows as a 20° ellipse. Note that dimension D1 establishes points 3 and 7 and dimension D2 locates point 1 in auxiliary view A and C.

To locate a given circle on a plane, a true-shape view of the plane must be found. A typical problem found in industry is the location of a hole centered on a given surface. In Figure 10.23, plane 1-2-3-4 is given and a hole/circle of a specific size is to be drilled/drawn so that it is located in the exact center of an oblique plane. Primary and secondary auxiliary views will be required. The following steps were used to complete the problem:

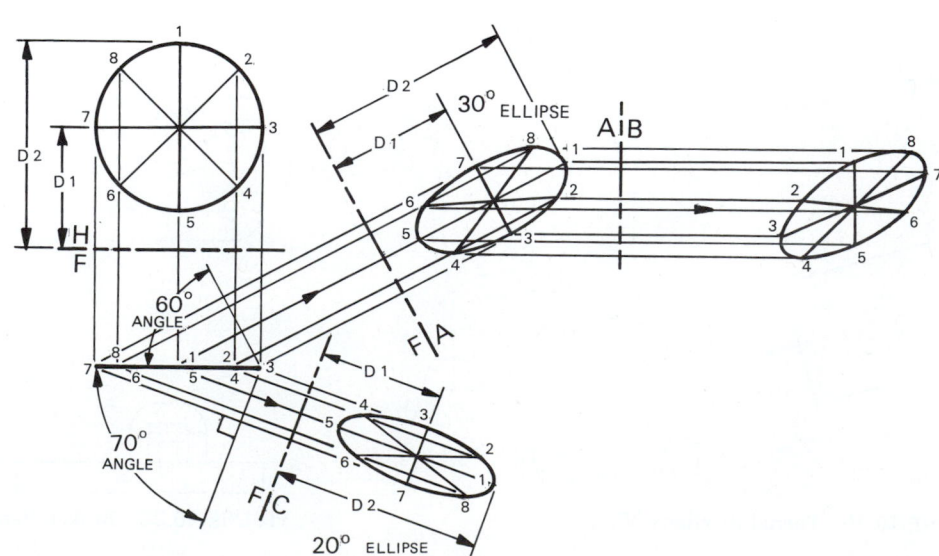

FIGURE 10.22 Plotting Points on Circular Planes

1. Line 1H-3H and line 2H-4H are horizontal lines (true length in the horizontal view). Therefore, a true-length line need not be constructed to find the edge view. Draw H/A perpendicular to the horizontal lines and project auxiliary view A. Plane 1A-2A-3A-4A is an edge in this view [Fig. 10.23(a)].
2. Draw A/B parallel to the edge view of plane 1A-2A-3A-4A and project auxiliary view B. This view shows the true size of the plane [Fig. 10.23(a)].
3. Locate the exact center of plane 1B-2B-3B-4B and draw the given circle [Fig. 10.23(a)].
4. To project the centered circle back to all previous views, a series of points needs to be located along its circumference. A simple method to locate points on the circle is to divide the circle evenly by drawing lines from the corners of the plane [Fig. 10.23(b)].
5. Locate each point in auxiliary view A by projection where they fall on the edge of plane 1A-2A-3A-4A. Dimensions D1, D2, and D3 are used to locate each point in the horizontal view by transferring them along their respective projection lines. Axes A (major diameter) and B (minor diameter) could also be used to locate and draw each view of the circle [Fig. 10.23(b)].
6. The frontal view of the circle is obtained by projection and by transferring distances from auxiliary view A (from H/A to each point on the edge view).
7. The points are then connected with a smooth curve using an irregular curve.

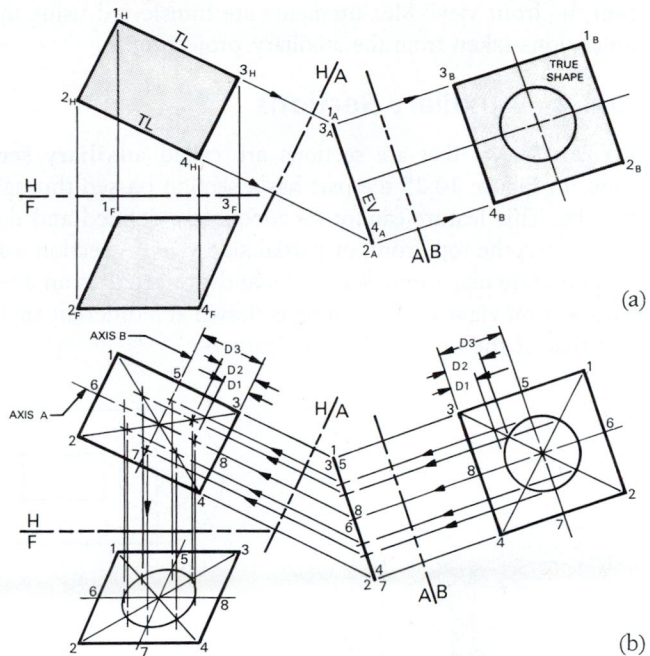

(a)

(b)

FIGURE 10.23   Reverse Construction for Plotting Curves on Views

In Figure 10.24, the part has curved features that appear oblique in the top view, show as an edge in the front view, and are true shape in the auxiliary projection. In this situation, *reverse construction* of the curved features is required if the features are to be projected back to the top view (where they appear distorted—*not true shape*). After the front view and the true-shape features of the top view are drawn, the auxiliary view is constructed as shown. Since the curved features show true shape in the auxiliary projection, a series of points is established along the curved outline. The points are then projected to the front view where they fall along the edge view of the curved surface. The points are projected to the top view

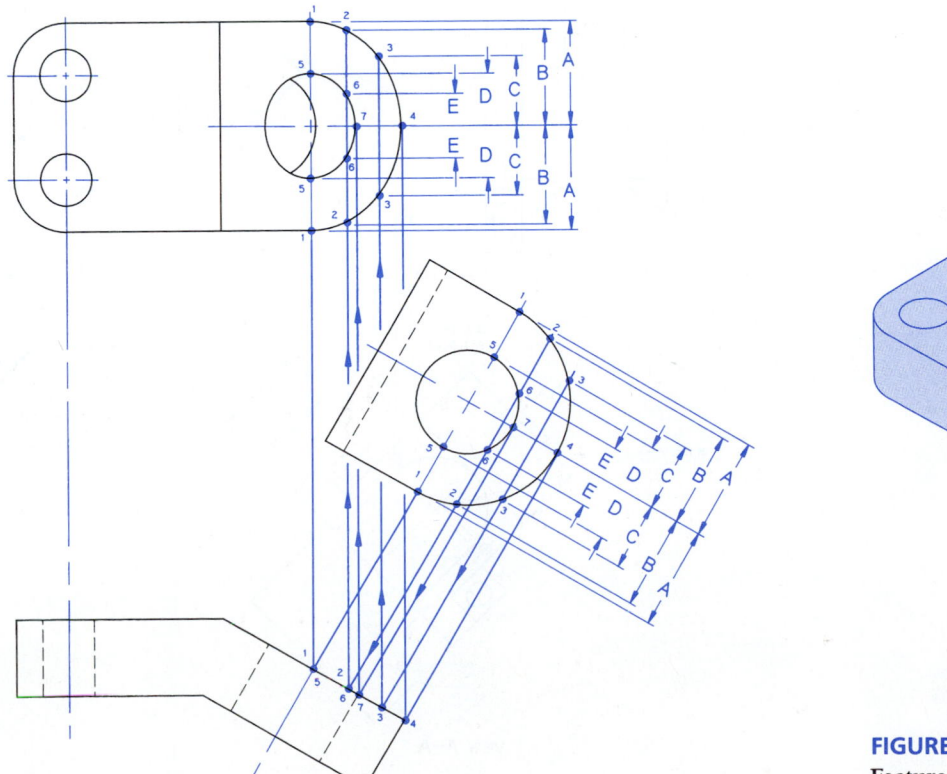

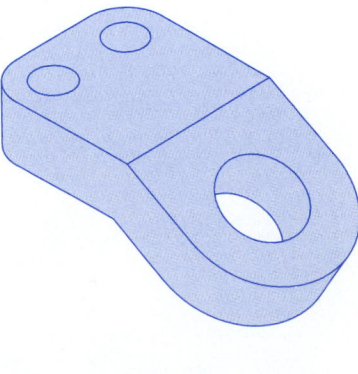

FIGURE 10.24   Projecting Curved Features into Principal Views

from the front view. Measurements are transferred using the dimensions taken from the auxiliary projection.

10.4.4   Auxiliary Sections

Auxiliary views that are sections are called **auxiliary sections.** In Figure 10.25 the part has a section passed through the ribs. This feature cannot be adequately defined and detailed using the top, front, or partial side view. A section was cut perpendicular through the ribs and projected as an auxiliary section view. Section lining is drawn at a different angle than that of the lines of the part features.

10.4.5   Auxiliary Views and Dimensioning

The primary reason for projecting auxiliary views is to show and dimension the shape of a part that cannot be defined in one of the principal views. In Figure 10.26 the part has a surface that is inclined. This surface needs to be shown as true shape in order for it to be dimensioned. The front and right side views along with the auxiliary views were used to detail the part. Dimensions were placed on each view where the part's features are shown true shape. The auxiliary view is used to dimension the slot and the holes (see Chapter 12).

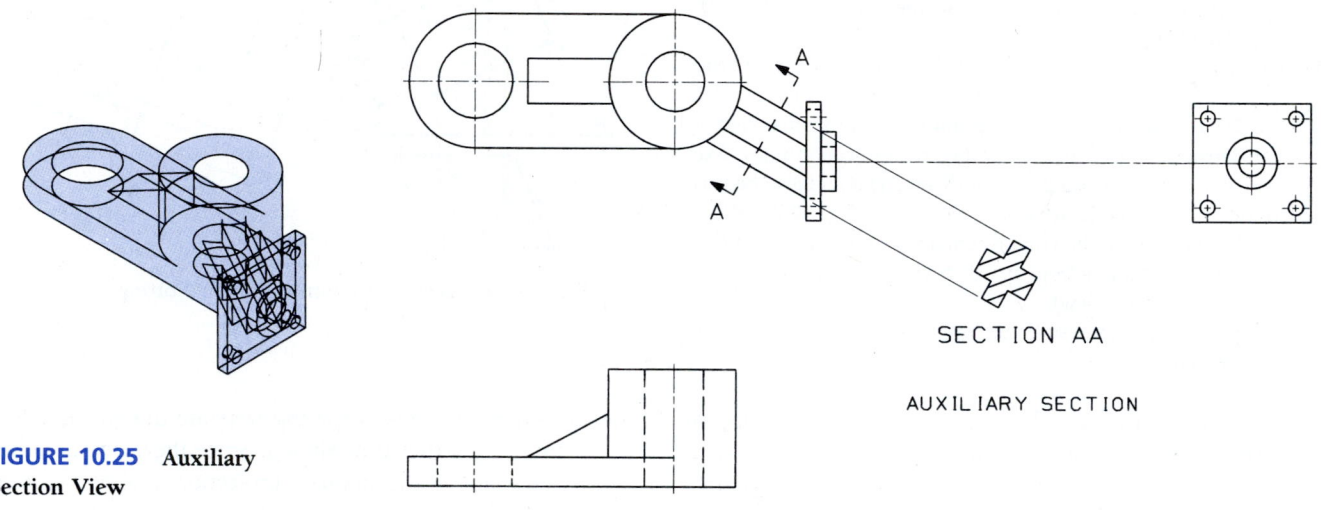

FIGURE 10.25 Auxiliary
Section View

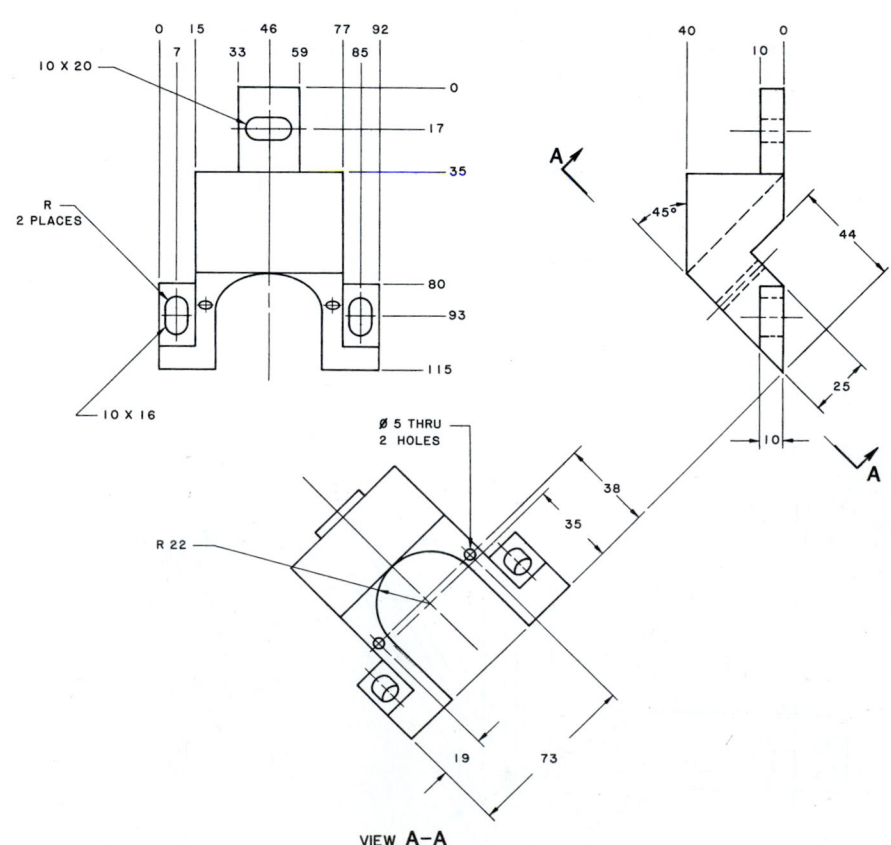

FIGURE 10.26 Auxiliary Views
and Dimensioning

VIEW **A–A**

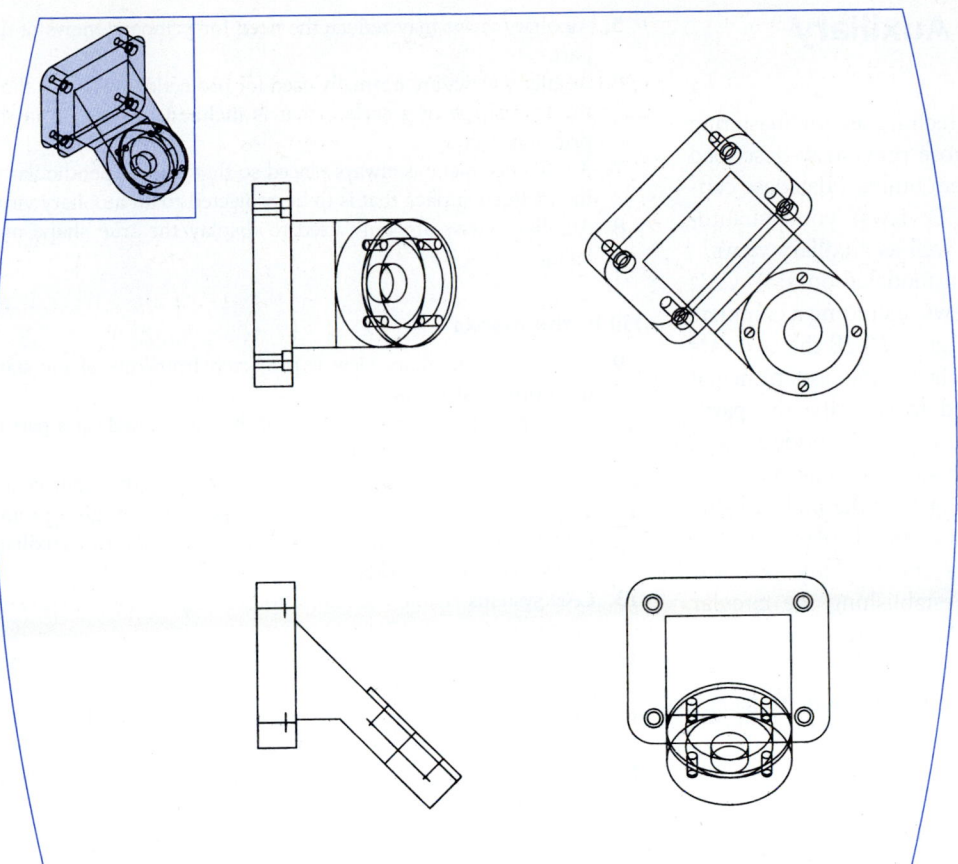

FIGURE 10.27   Auxiliary View Projection Using 3D CAD

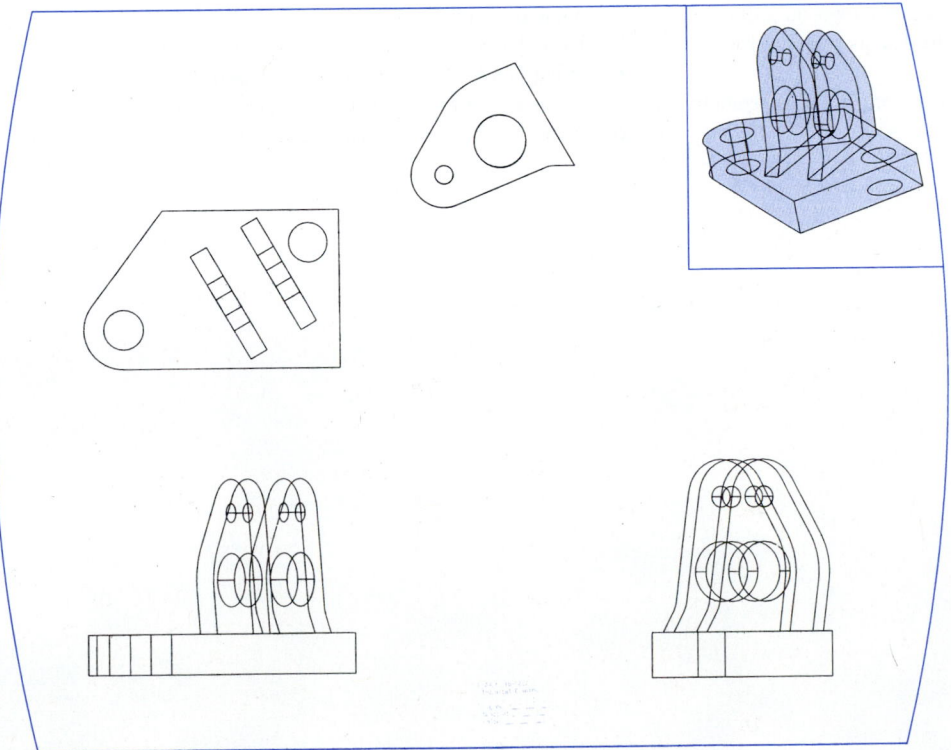

FIGURE 10.28   Partial Auxiliary View Projection Using 3D CAD

10.5 CAD-Generated Auxiliary Views

2D CAD systems require the same techniques for mastering and projecting auxiliary views as those previously described for manual drafting. Since a 3D system builds a database containing the complete part (not just 2D views), you can automatically display standard views as well as auxiliary views.

In Figure 10.27 the part has been modeled on a 3D CAD system. After modeling, the part's views, including a complete auxiliary view, were displayed. In Figure 10.28 the two ears of the part are at an angle to the front and top principal planes. An auxiliary view is needed to describe the part's features properly. The part had already been modeled and displayed in the top, front, and right side views as shown. A partial view was established by folding only the inclined surfaces. All other edges of the part are not displayed in the auxiliary view. In each of these cases, the auxiliary view was generated for the sole purpose of establishing the circular features of the part that did not show as true shape in a principal view.

You May Now Complete Exercises 10.5 Through 10.8

QUIZ

True or False

1. Most auxiliary views are only partial projections.
2. Oblique, inclined, and otherwise distorted geometry is always shown on a view.
3. The top, front, and side views are always shown on a drawing when an auxiliary view is required to display inclined features for a part.
4. Views can be automatically generated from existing geometry on a 2D CAD system.
5. Auxiliary views may reduce the need for principal views of the part.
6. Auxiliary views are normally used for projecting a view to show the true shape of a surface that is inclined or oblique in the principal views.
7. A reference plane is always placed so that it is perpendicular to the inclined surface that is to be projected to an auxiliary view.
8. Auxiliary views are only used to display the true shape of a feature.

Fill in the Blanks

9. A _____ auxiliary view is projected from one of the standard principal views.
10. A reference plane or a fold line can be established on a part to aid in the _____ of an _____ view.
11. _____ _____ views are projected from the front views.
12. The _____ _____ is normally passed through a prominent feature of the part so as to make projection of auxiliary views easier and quicker.
13. CAD systems enable the drafter to _____ views from existing projections of a 3D part.
14. An auxiliary view can be _____ from an adjacent view when using a 3D CAD system.
15. Half auxiliary views are normally used where the part is _____ about a _____ .
16. A _____ _____ view is adjacent and aligned with a secondary view.

Answer the Following

17. What is the edge view of a plane, and how is it used in the projection of a true-shape view?
18. What is the primary purpose for an auxiliary view?
19. Compare the fold line method with the reference plane method.
20. Why are partial auxiliary views more common than complete auxiliary projections?
21. How does 3D CAD affect auxiliary view projection?
22. What is a fold line and how is it used?
23. What are half sections and why are they used?
24. What is a broken auxiliary view?

EXERCISES

Exercises may be assigned as sketching, instrument, or CAD projects. Transfer the given information to an "A" size sheet of .25 in. grid paper. Complete all views and solve for proper visibility, including centerlines, object lines, and hidden lines. Exercises that are not assigned by the instructor can be sketched in the text to provide practice and understanding for the preceding instructional material.

After Reading the Chapter Through Section 10.5 You May Complete the Following Exercises

Exercise 10.1   Draw the required views.

Exercise 10.2   Draw the required views as shown.

Exercise 10.3   Draw the required views. Complete a full top view.

Exercise 10.4   Draw the three views as shown.

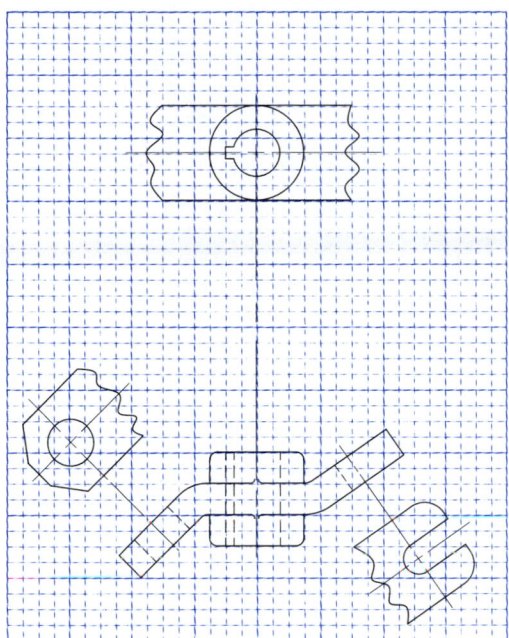

Exercise 10.1

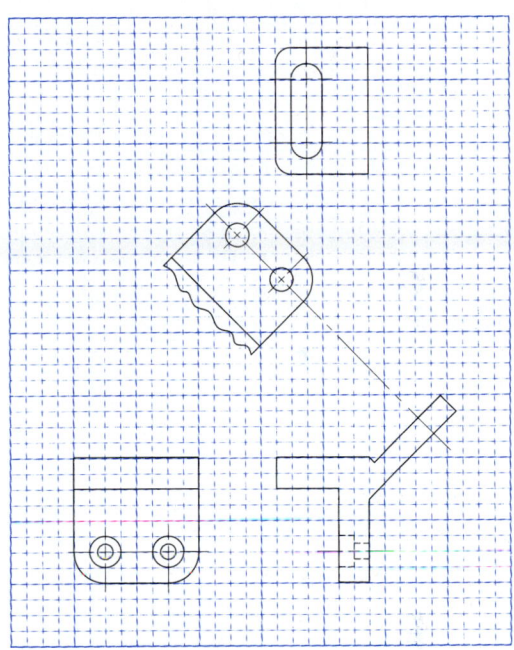

Exercise 10.3

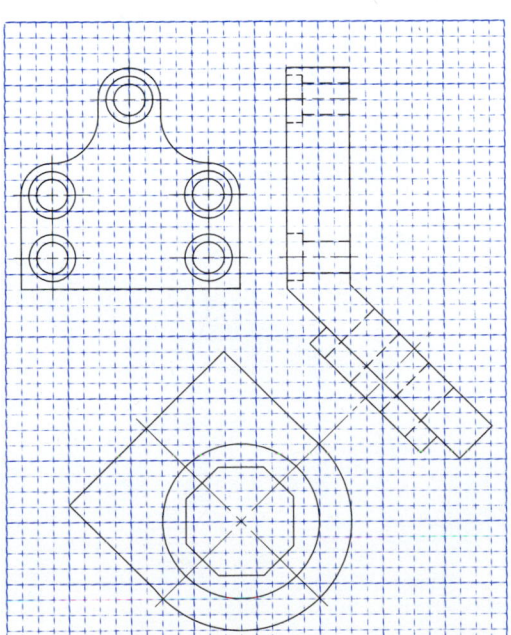

Exercise 10.2

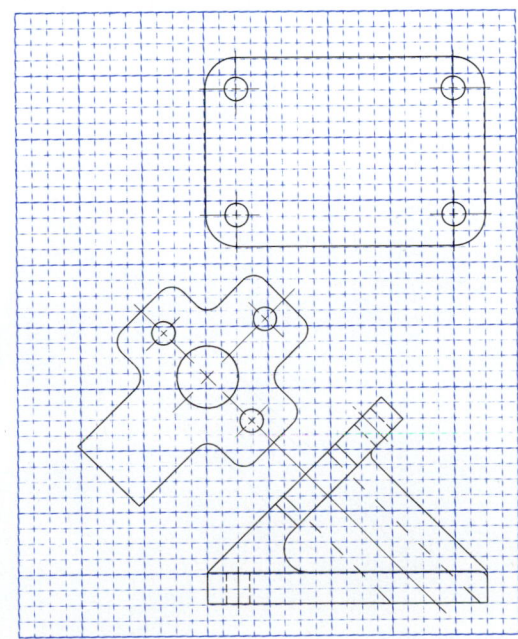

Exercise 10.4

After Reading the Chapter Through Section 10.5 You May Complete the Following Exercises

Exercise 10.5 Complete the required views and the auxiliary section.

Exercise 10.6 Draw the required views.

Exercise 10.7 Complete the required views and draw a full front view.

Exercise 10.8 Draw the required views. Project a secondary auxiliary view showing surface A or B as true shape/size.

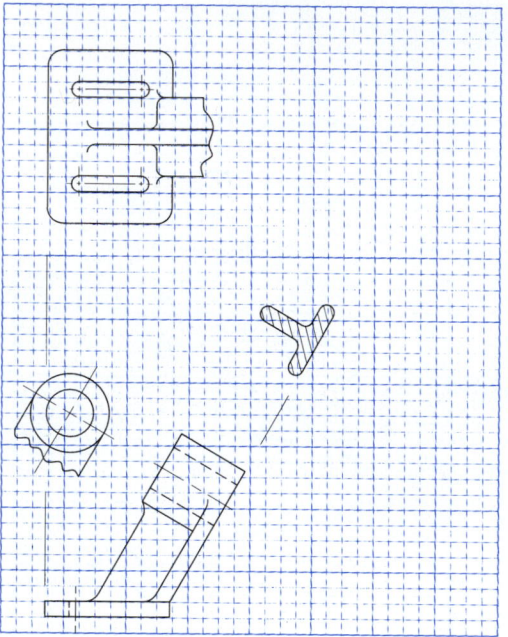

Exercise 10.5

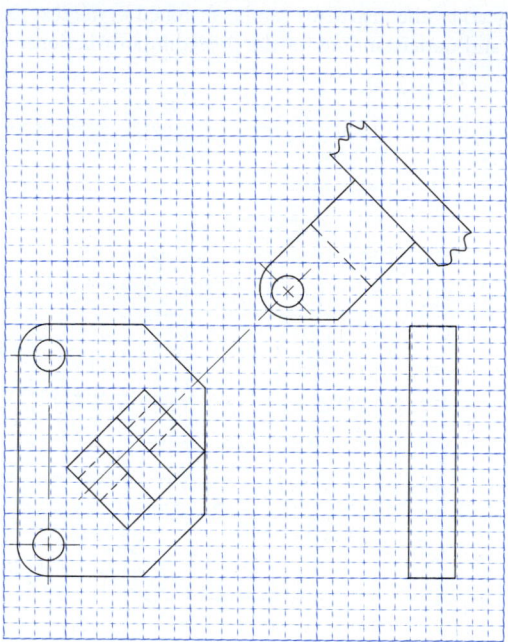

Exercise 10.7

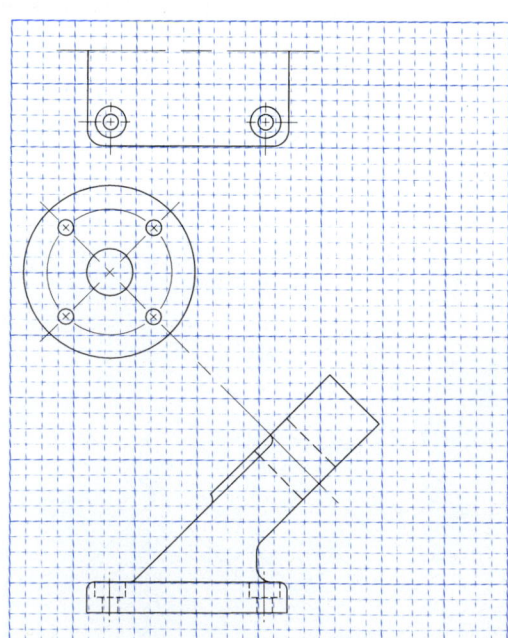

Exercise 10.6

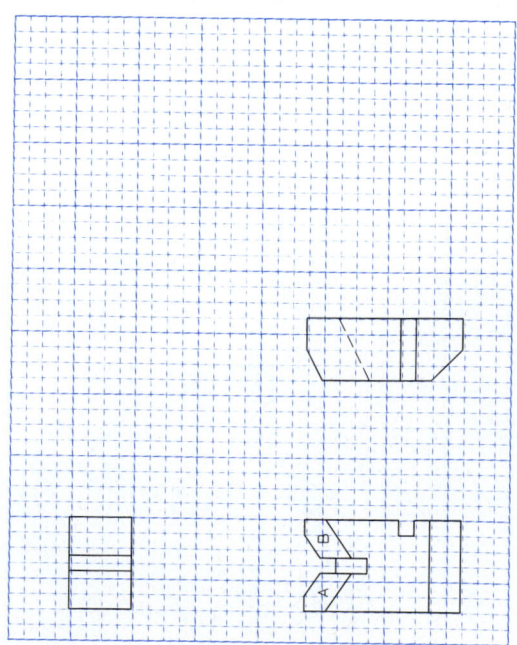

Exercise 10.8

PROBLEMS

Problems may be assigned as sketching, instrument, or CAD projects. Use these projects for problems when completing the dimensioning chapter. Complete all views and solve for proper visibility, including centerlines, object lines, and hidden lines. When laying out these projects leave sufficient room to allow dimensioning. Instructor may assign projects to be dimensioned as problems for Chapter 12.

Problem 10.1   Draw the appropriate views of the part in order to describe each of its surfaces completely.

Problem 10.2   Draw the top, front, and auxiliary views of the part.

Problem 10.3   Draw the right side, top, and auxiliary views of the part in order to show each surface as true shape.

Problem 10.4   Draw the top, front, and auxiliary projections of the part.

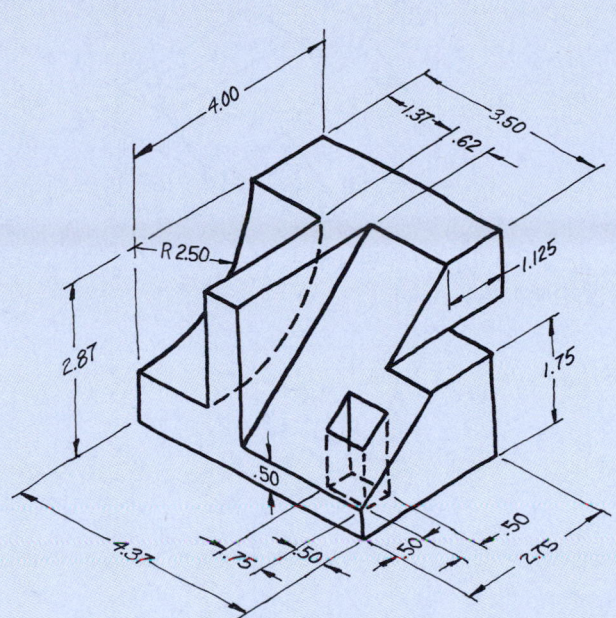

Problem 10.1

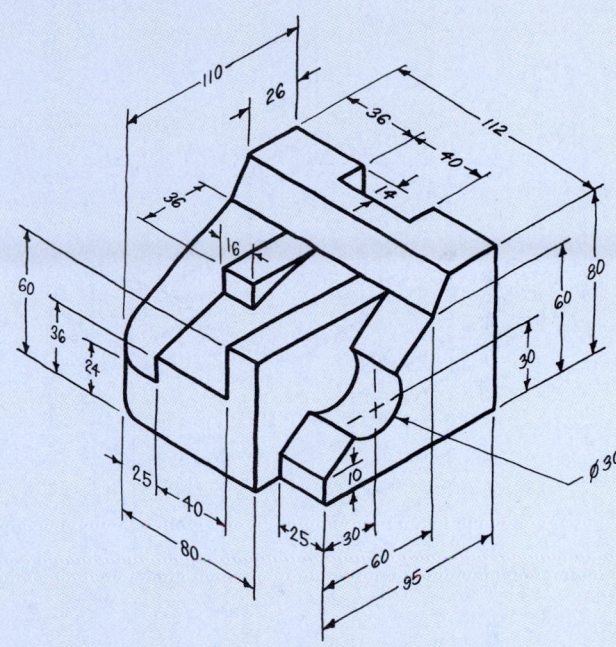

Problem 10.3

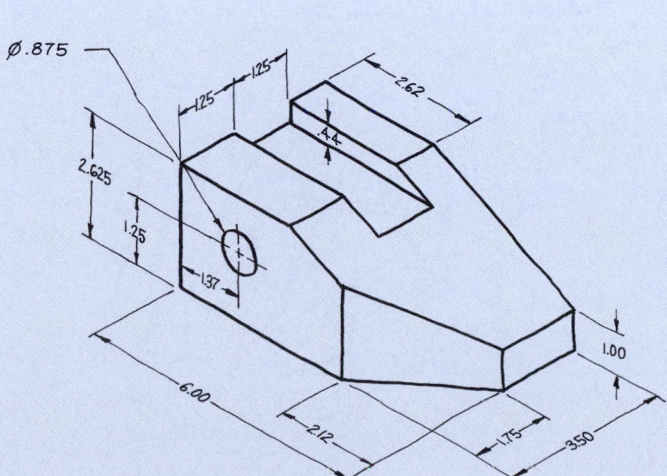

Problem 10.2

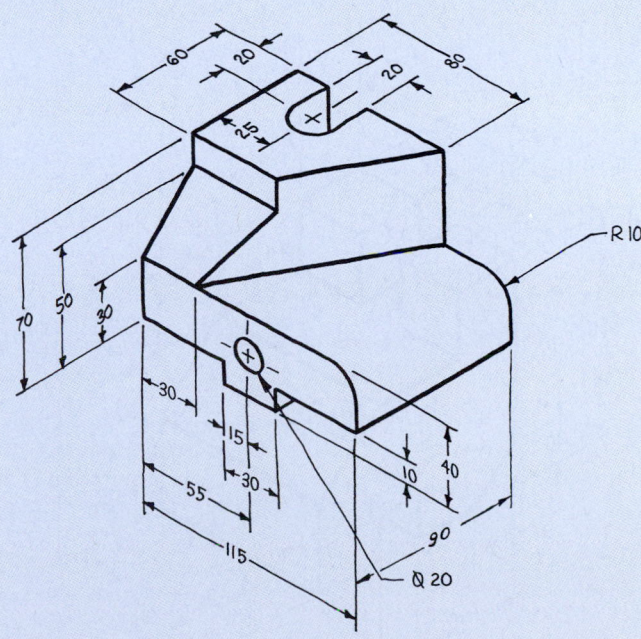

Problem 10.4

Problem 10.5 Draw the front and right side view of the part. Project a true-shape view of the inclined surface. Position a 1.00 in. diameter hole near the middle of the surface and show in all views. The hole is to be .25 inches deep with a flat bottom.

Problem 10.6 Draw the top, front, side, and an auxiliary view projected from the top of the part. Center a 20 mm hole on the auxiliary surface. The hole is 15 mm deep with a flat bottom.

Problem 10.7 Draw the appropriate views needed to describe the part completely.

Problem 10.8 Draw the top and front views and any auxiliary views needed to display the triangular surface's true shape.

Problem 10.9 Draw the views necessary to describe the part completely. The auxiliary projection should be a complete view.

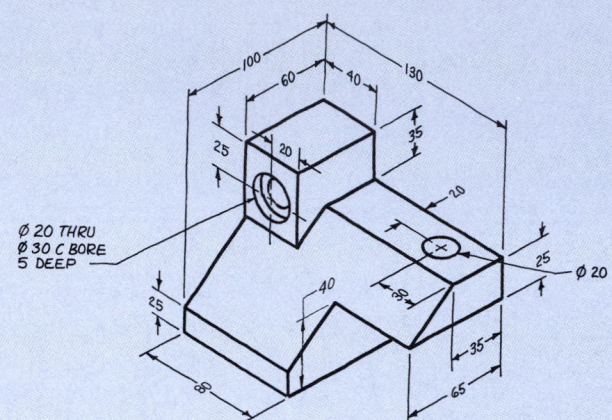

Problem 10.7

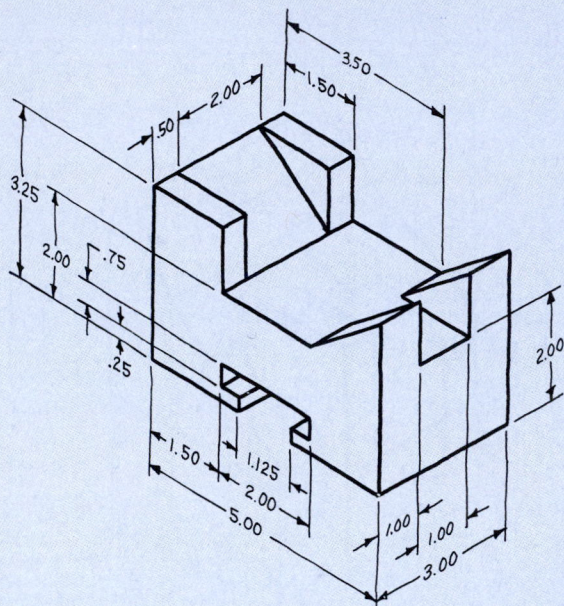

Problem 10.5

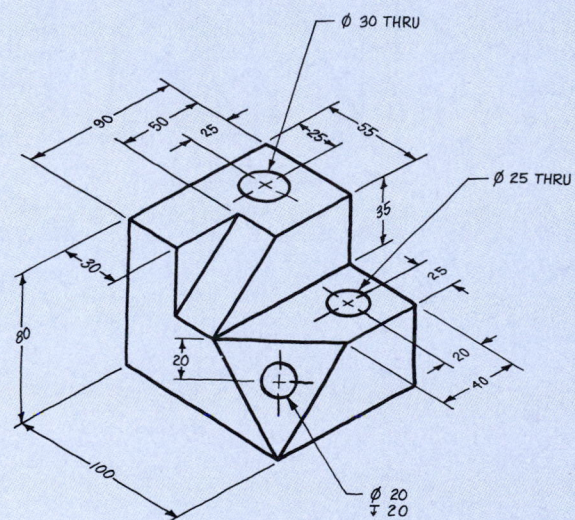

Problem 10.8

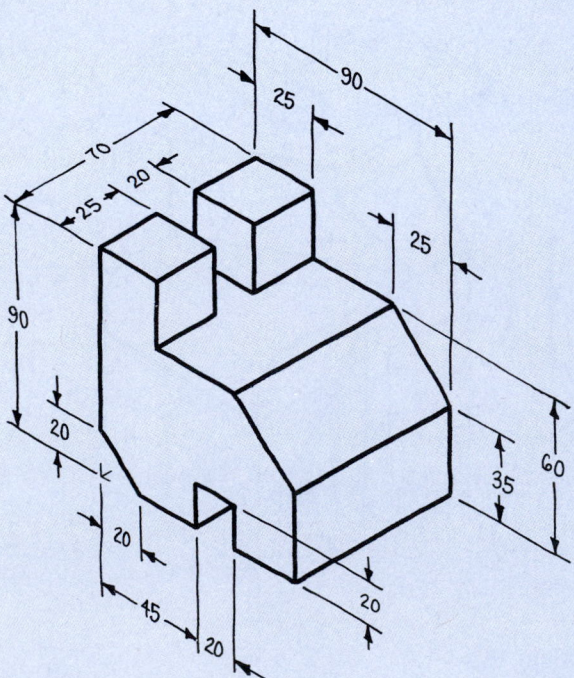

Problem 10.6

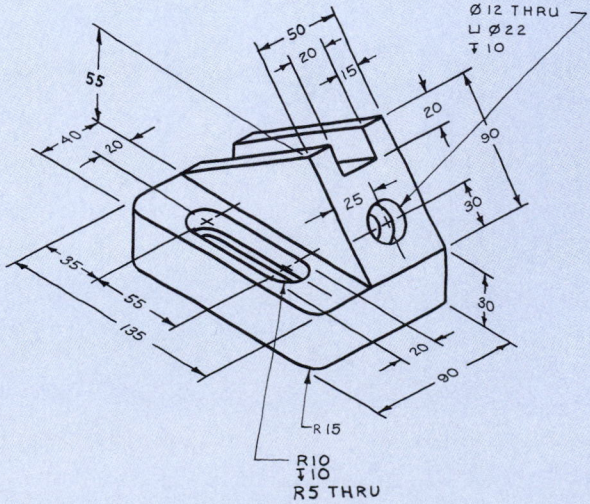

Problem 10.9

Problems 10.10 Through 10.15 Draw the views required to detail each of the parts.

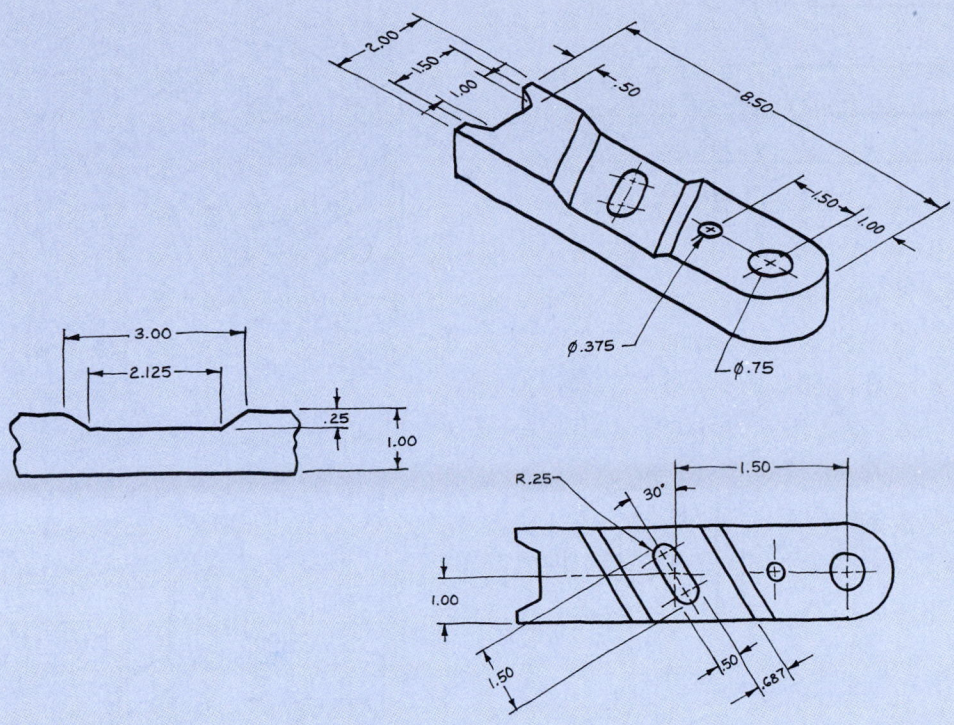

Problem 10.10

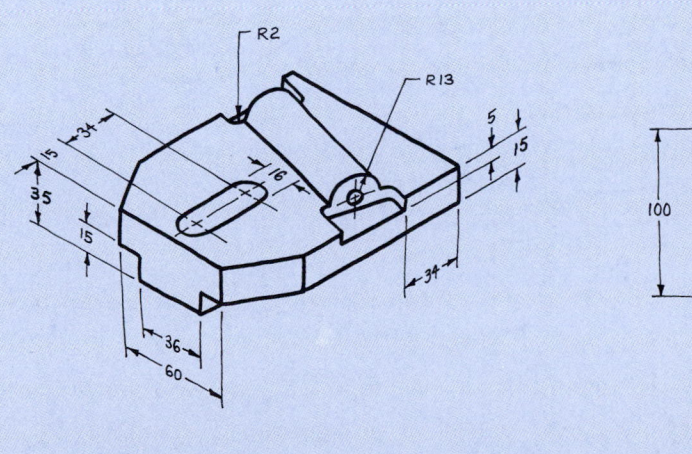

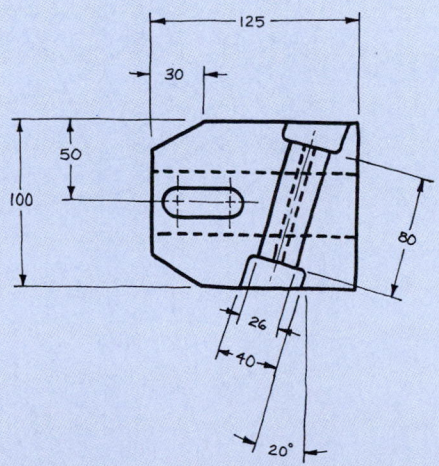

Problem 10.11

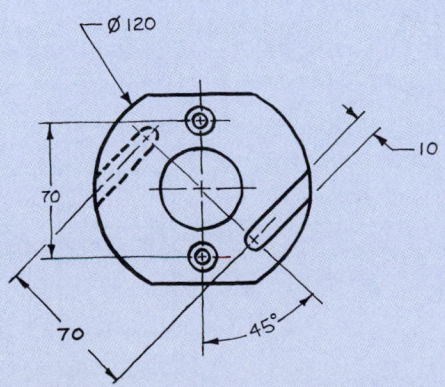

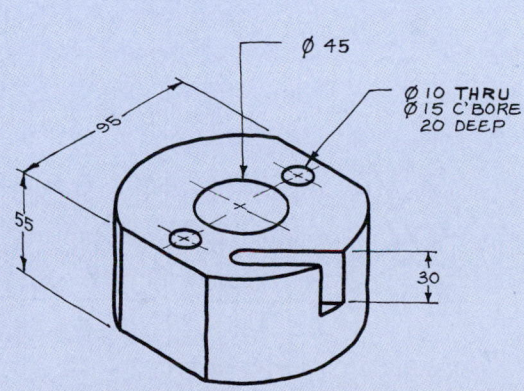

Problem 10.12

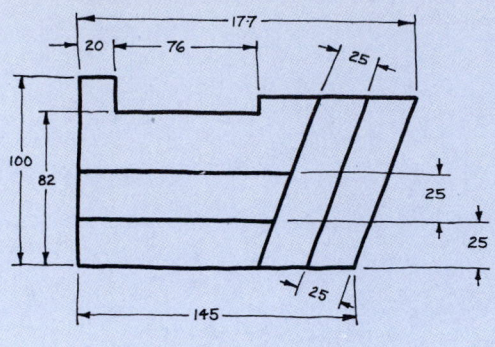

Problem 10.13

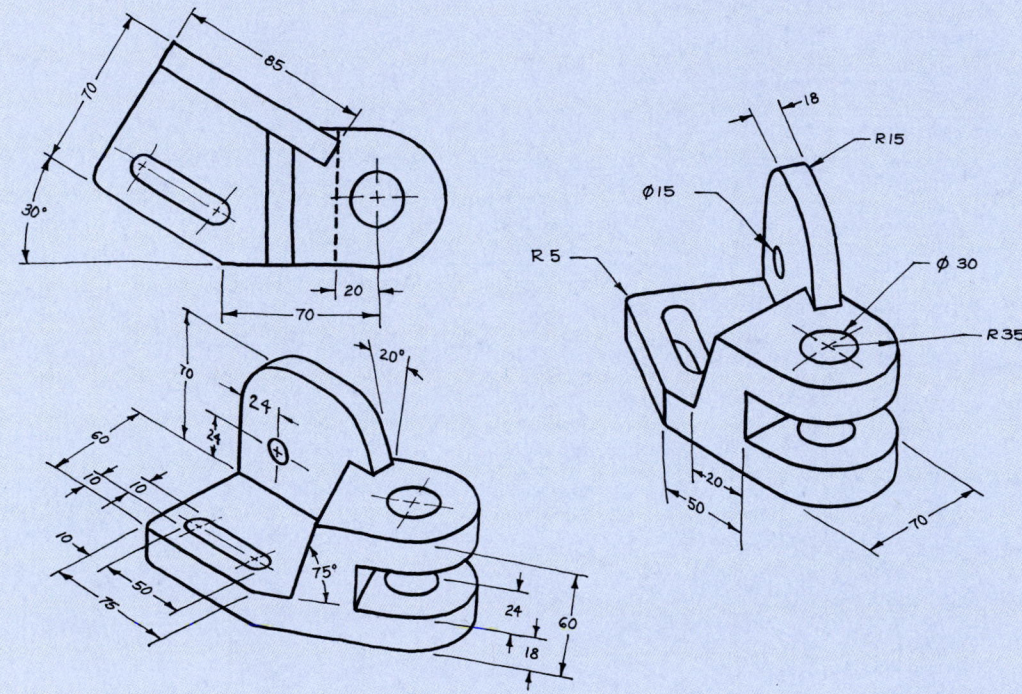

Problem 10.14

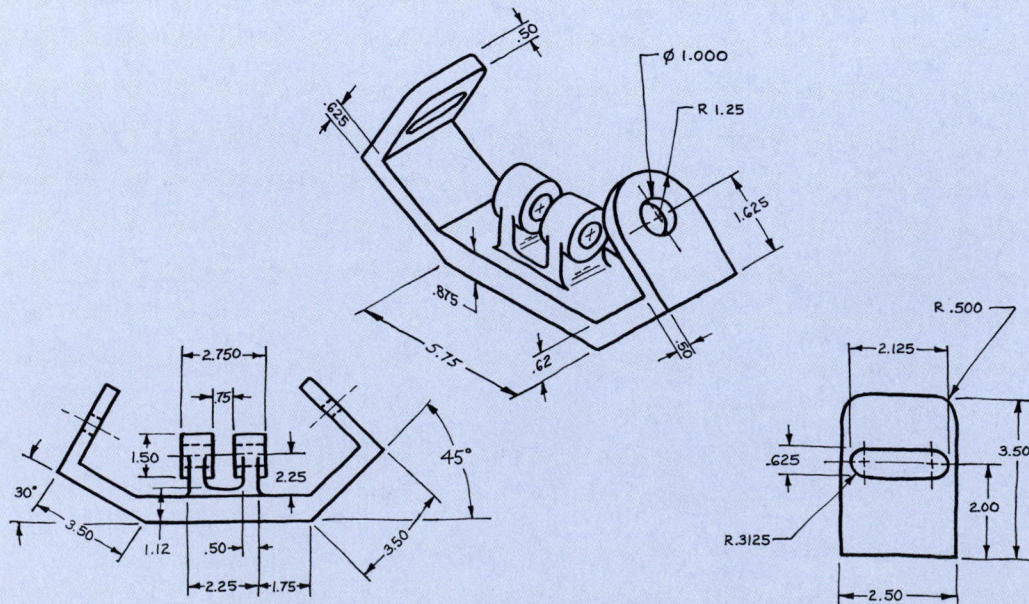

Problem 10.15

Problem 10.16   Model the bracket on a 3D CAD system and then display the proper views.

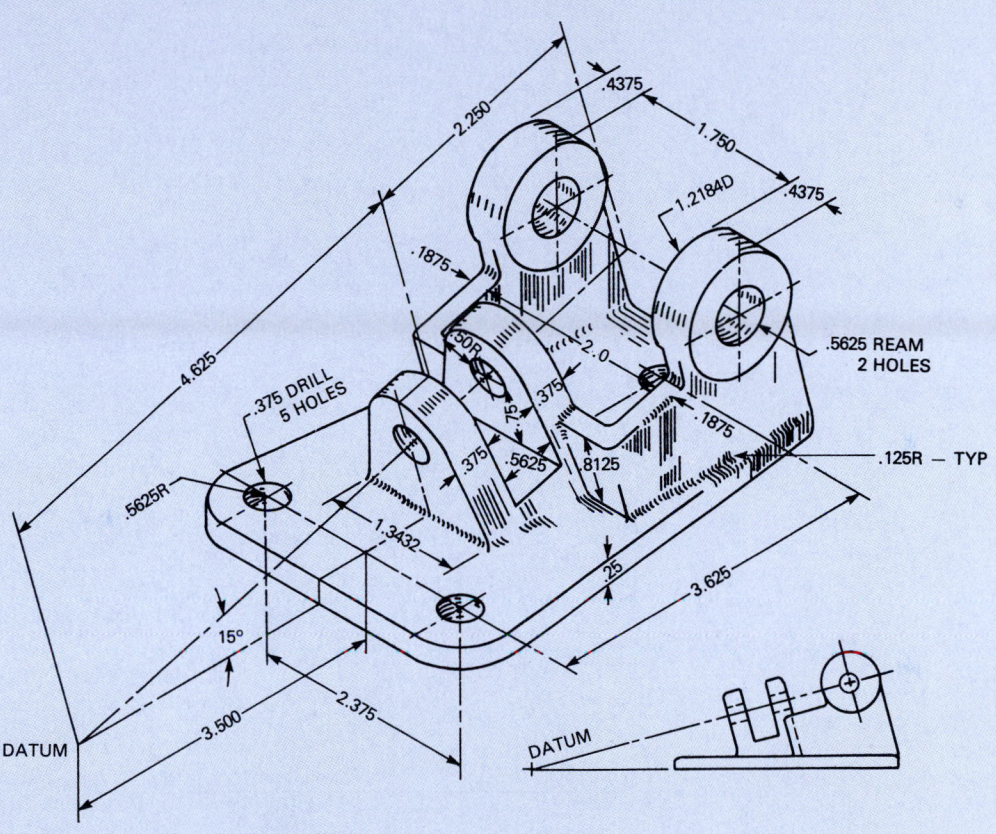

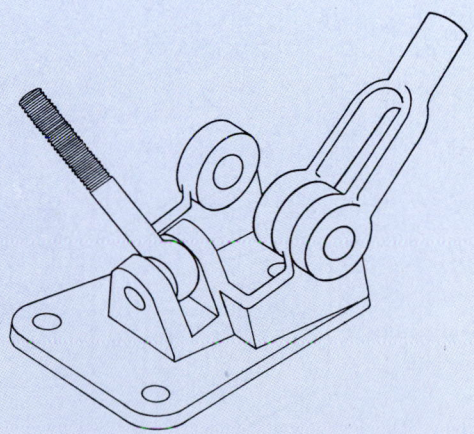

Problem 10.16

Problem 10.17   Model the housing cover and display the proper views.

Problem 10.18   Model the part and show all required views.

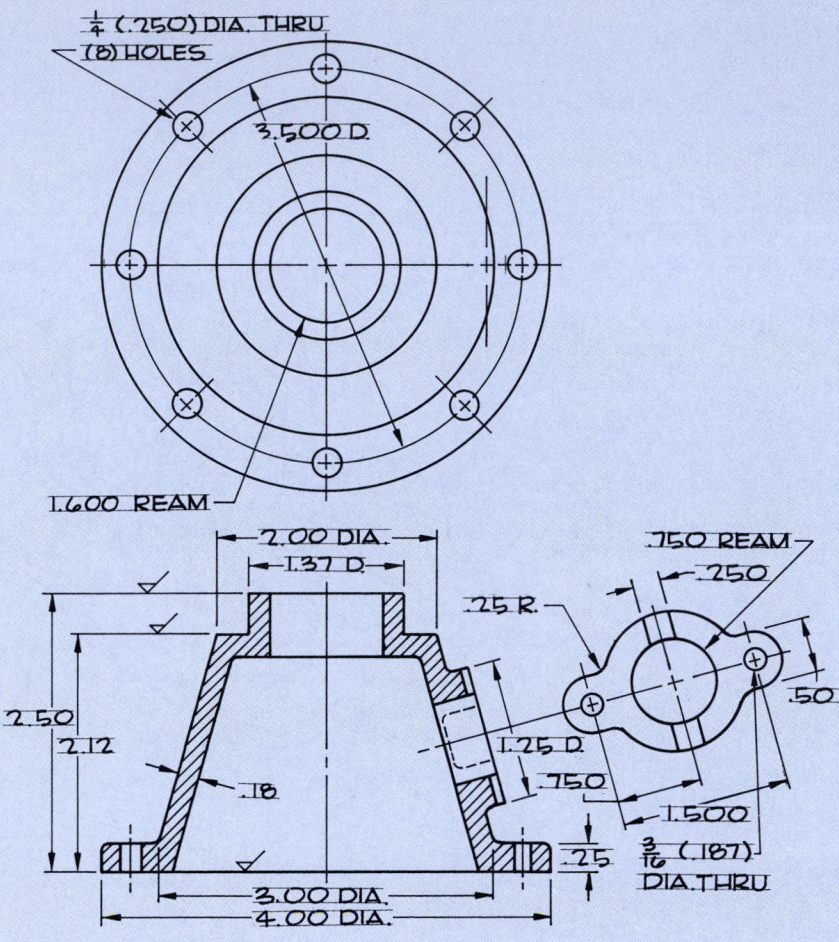

Problem 10.17

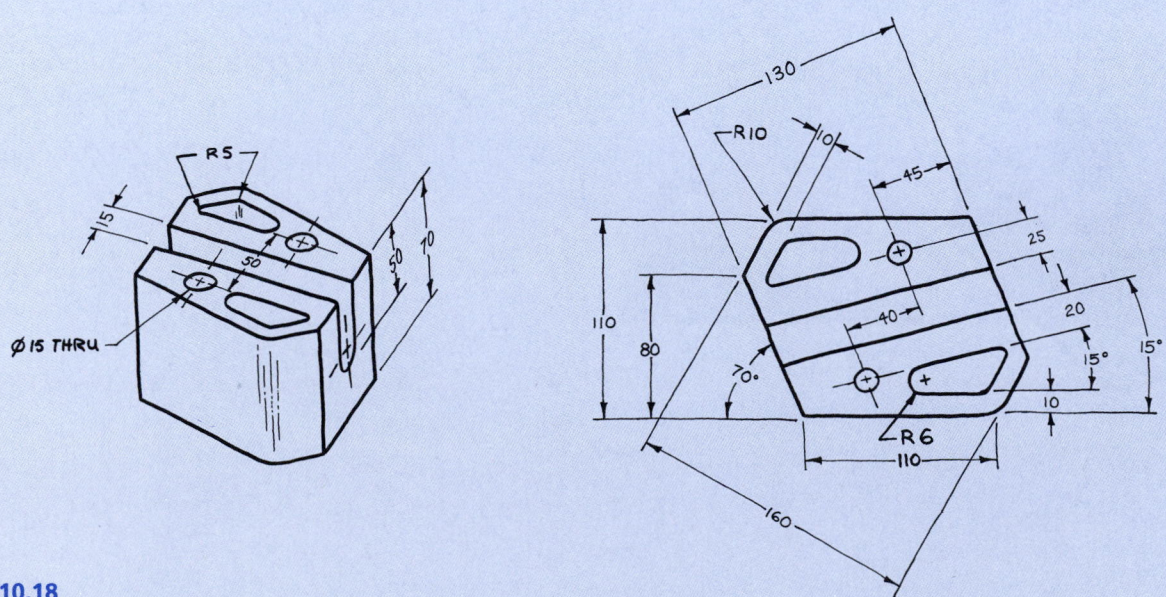

Problem 10.18

Problem 10.19   Create a 3D model and display a minimum amount of views to detail the part.

Problem 10.20   Draw or model the part. Lay out the views required to describe the part completely. Do not use partial views.

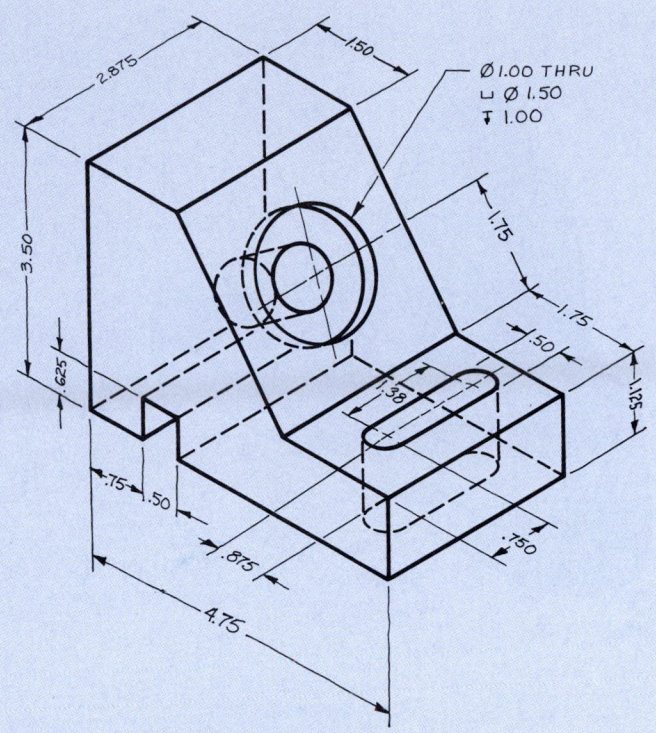

Problem 10.19

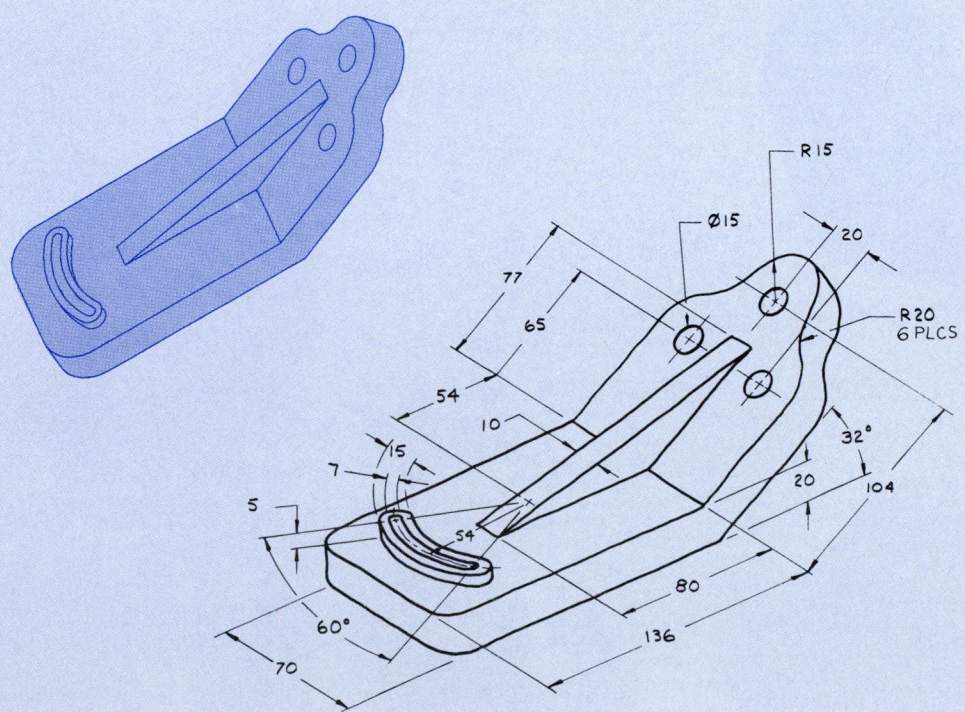

Problem 10.20

Problem 10.21   Draw or model the part and display the required views in full.

Problem 10.22   Draw the required views necessary to describe the part. A secondary auxiliary view will be required.

Problem 10.23   Draw the three views of the part shown in Figure 10.2.

Problem 10.24   Draw the detail of the electronic unit bracket shown in Figure 10.12.

Problem 10.25   Draw the part shown in Figure 10.26.

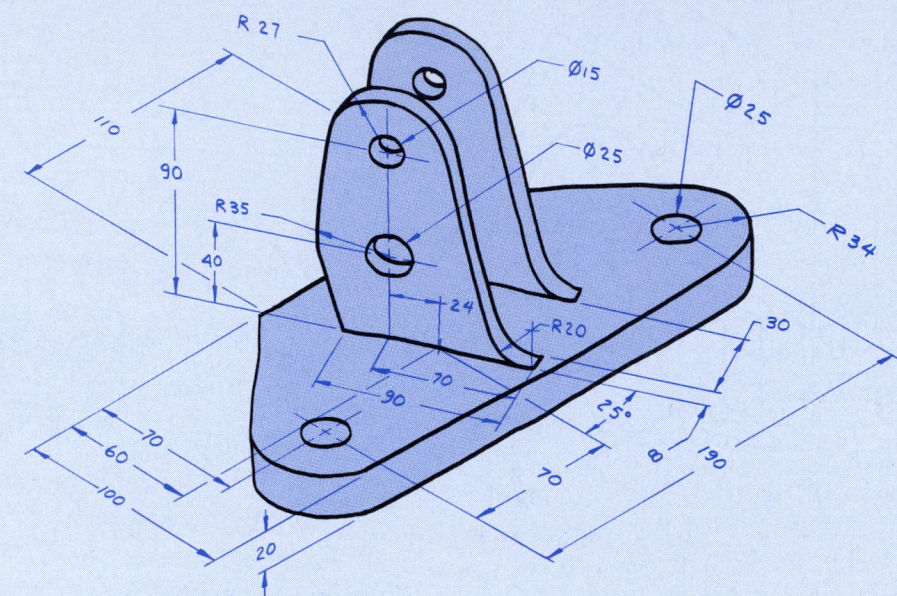

Problem 10.21

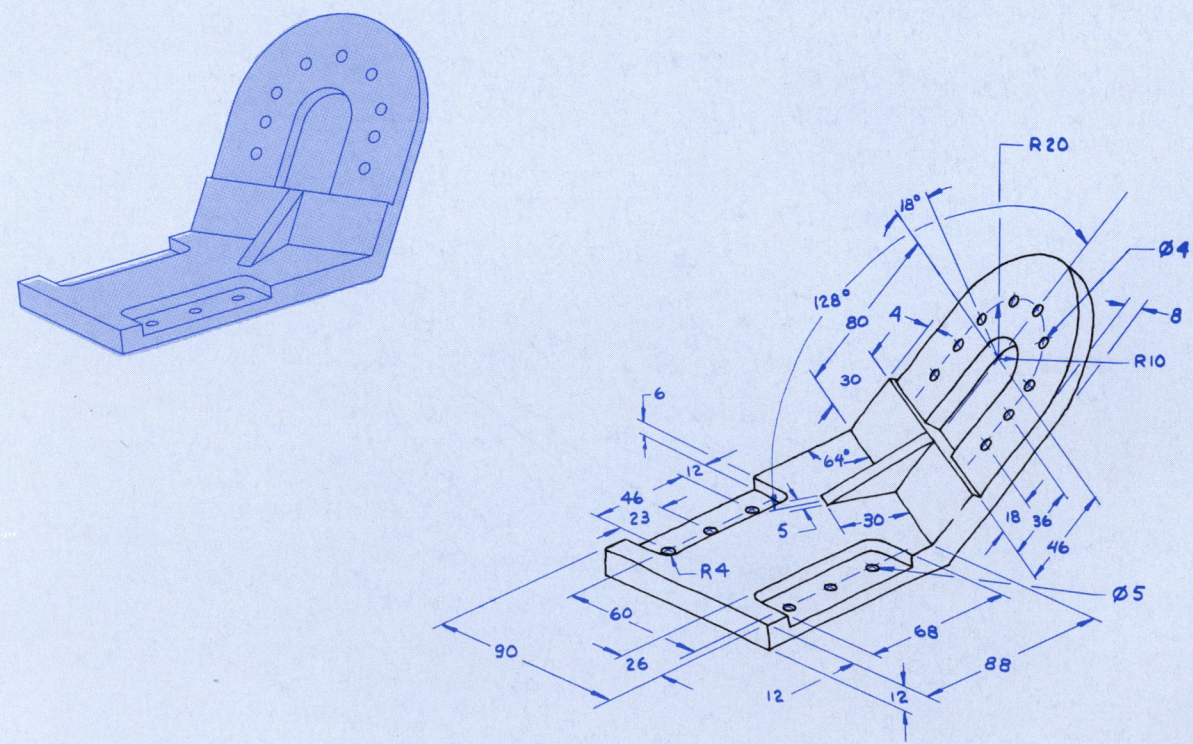

Problem 10.22

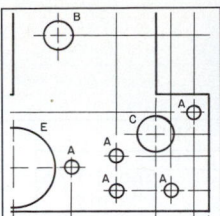

CHAPTER 11

Manufacturing Processes

Learning Objectives

Upon completion of this chapter you will be able to accomplish the following:

1. Identify the specific stages in the manufacturing process.
2. Demonstrate an understanding of materials used in the manufacturing process.
3. Develop an understanding of design-for-manufacturability (DFM) concepts.
4. Identify the basic types of machine tool operations.
5. Define the processes involved in the technology of materials forming.
6. Discern the difference between finishing techniques.
7. Demonstrate familiarity with the process of automated and computer-aided manufacturing.
8. Define robotics and its role in the manufacturing process.

11.1 Introduction

The purpose of any engineering drawing (or design database when using 3D CAD) is to provide the information necessary to allow construction or manufacture of a part or a system. To achieve this purpose, engineering drawings must fully and completely describe and detail the desired part or system. This chapter overviews manufacturing and production processes associated with individual mechanical parts.

When using a high-level 3D CAD/CAM system, the part design might be completely described in the database. When this is the case, as with the part being machined in Figure 11.1, the need for an engineering drawing may be lessened or entirely eliminated. In Figure 11.1, CADAM was used to design and manufacture the part without generating drawings. However, whether you are using traditional drawings or creating a part in 3D on a CAD/CAM system, the part must be completely defined. Regardless of the method of manufacture, the part must be produced from the information provided the manufacturing facility by the engineering/design/drafting department.

FIGURE 11.1 Main Bulkhead of an Antisubmarine Airplane

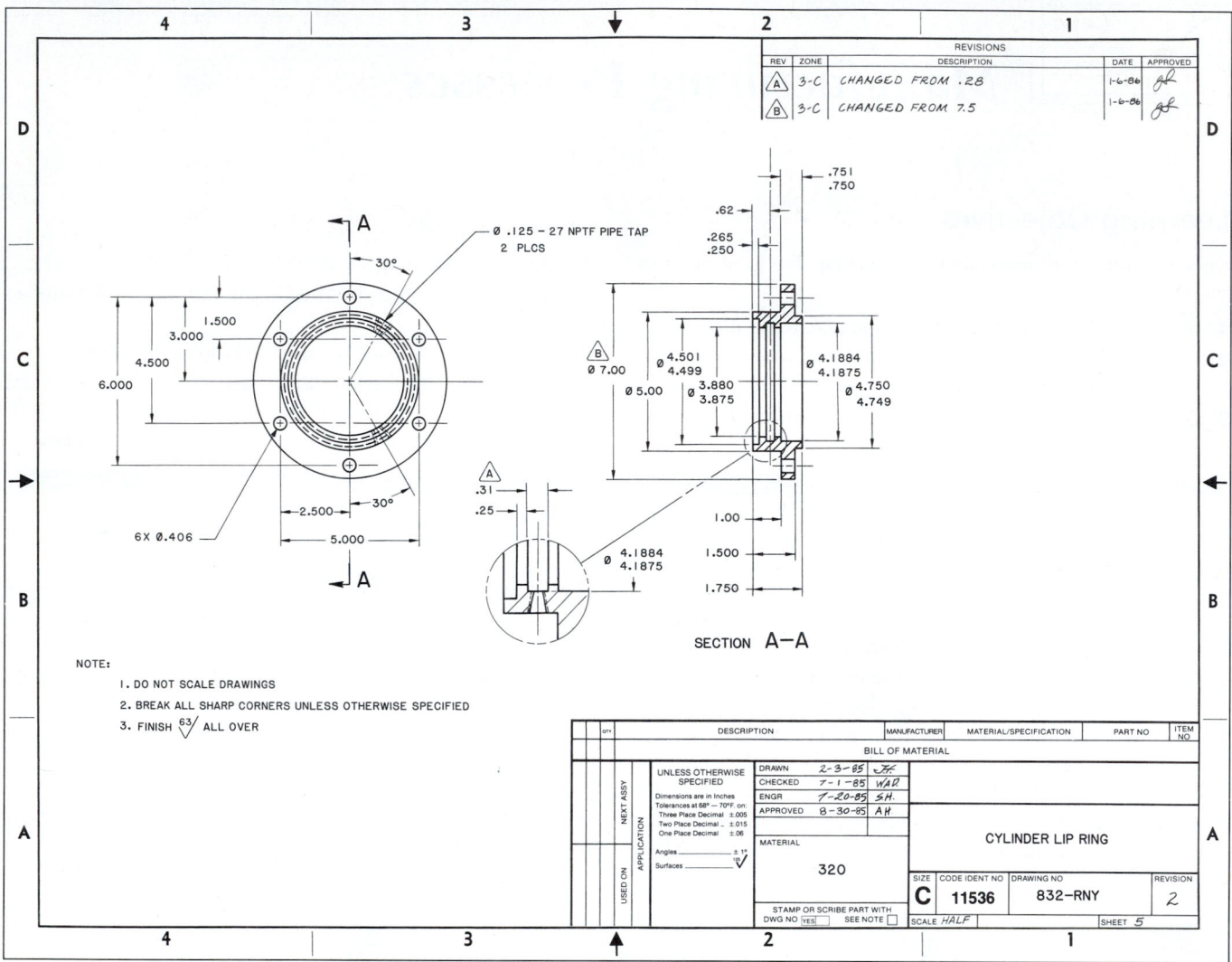

FIGURE 11.2 Cylinder Lip Ring Detail Drawing

The engineering drawing shows the specific size and geometric shape of the part (Fig. 11.2). It also furnishes the related information about the material specifications, finish requirements, and required treatments, along with the revisions and releases made to the document. In the upper right-hand portion of the drawing shown in Figure 11.2 the revisions are noted. The notes, in the lower left-hand corner, provide manufacturing with information about the part. Here, the corners are to be ground to "**BREAK ALL SHARP CORNERS**" and the finish (surface texture) is established for the part.

11.2 Manufacturing

To design and manufacture a part properly, the designer and drafter should thoroughly understand the methods used in manufacturing. *Manufacturing is the process of coordinating workers, machines, tools, and materials to create a product.* Therefore, the primary purpose of the manufacturing area is to produce quality parts from raw materials and assemble

related parts to create assemblies. This conversion process includes the following:

1. materials and manufacturing methods
2. determining assembly requirements
3. production control
4. planning and tooling requirements for the production department
5. production and manufacturing of the product
6. inspection and quality control

Many companies have separate design and drafting areas for product development, tooling and manufacturing, and for facilities. **Product development** refers to the conceptual work done in the research and development of a product. Production and manufacturing of a product normally requires a number of new machines, tools, dies, jigs, and fixtures (all of which need to be designed and detailed); therefore, **tool design** is very important to the success of the product. *Facility* designers and drafters do building and plant upgrades, maintenance design, and new additions using structural, electrical, mechanical, and architectural design.

By understanding the cost, mechanical capabilities, and limitations of the basic processes used in manufacturing, you can design the part with the manufacturing processes in mind. This increases **manufacturability** and reduces the cost of the item. The "product" of the engineering, design, and drafting division of a company is not a drawing. The final product is what is manufactured and produced for sale or use in the real world. The drawing or CAD database is the starting point for the design-through-manufacture sequence.

11.2.1 Manufacturing Processes and Manufacturability

Machine or shop processes refer to the basic methods used by the manufacturing facility of a company to make a part described by an engineering drawing. The primary goal of all manufacturing is the production of a product that is produced cost-effectively, quickly, and at the required level of accuracy. Manufacturing engineers decide the method used to produce the part, but designers provide major input.

When manufacturing receives the engineering drawing, as a print or directly on the computer, it is reviewed to ensure that all information needed to make the part is provided. During this review, manufacturing personnel decide on tooling, machines, inspection, and the time involved to produce the part. New concepts, including the integration of manufacturing decisions into the beginning stages of design, are being implemented throughout industry. **Design for manufacturability** (DFM) is covered in detail in Chapter 17. DFM is a company design philosophy. Because the design of a product determines 70 to 90% of the total ongoing cost of the product, it makes sense to design in quality by designing for manufacturability. **Concurrent engineering** is the effort to get design teams such as engineering, manufacturing, and production to work in parallel rather than in sequence. Concurrent engineering attempts to help designers control and understand the growing complexity of a typical modern product design, while DFM attempts to establish ways to simplify the design and therefore reduce manufacturing costs. The following considerations are important for the successful manufacture of a product. They must be considered during design when changes can be implemented most readily:

1. material specification
2. size and configuration
3. production run (how many parts are needed), which greatly influences the production method chosen
4. tolerance specified for the part, which determines the manufacturing process
5. machine and tooling operations, and the required types and number of machines needed to produce the part

The drawing must contain all specifications and dimensions so that the part can be manufactured from a **stock piece** or other raw material. Various standard **stock forms** are available for the manufacturing and machining of mechanical parts. **Bar stock** comes in square, round, and hexagonal shapes (Fig. 11.3). Figure 11.4 shows the available types of

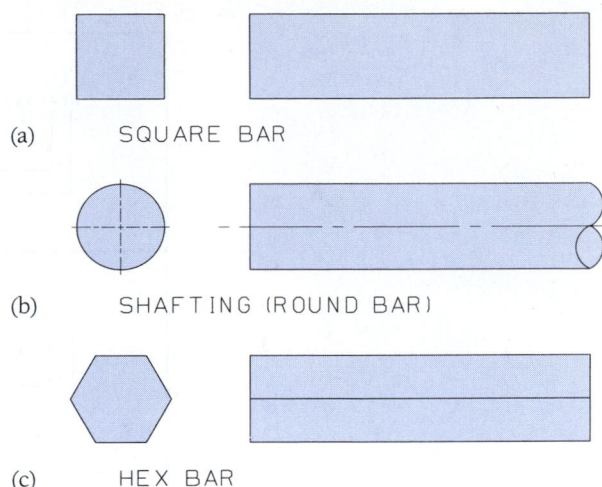

(a) SQUARE BAR

(b) SHAFTING (ROUND BAR)

(c) HEX BAR

FIGURE 11.3 **Stock Forms** (a) Square bar (b) Shafting or round bar (c) Hex bar

structural shapes. Round or rectangular tubing, standard pipe sizes, plate stock, tees, angles, channels, and beams can be ordered directly from the manufacturer by providing the shape, size, material, and length. If a stock form is not used, then the part must be cast, extruded, or formed using other processes. There are five basic families of processes:

1. **Molding** or **casting** into the proper configuration.
2. Forcing by **bending** into the required shape.
3. **Cutting** or **sawing** into the proper size and shape.
4. **Pounding** or **forging** into shape.
5. **Fabricating** using a fastening method: *welding, riveting, bolting, screwing, adhering,* or *nailing* parts formed by the above processes.

11.3 Machine Tool Operations

Machine tools are machines that cut metal or form new material. Some machines are dedicated to a single type of operation, while others can be altered to perform many types of cutting or drilling operations. Five basic processes are performed on machine tools:

1. **drilling** (drilling, reaming, counterboring, countersinking, spotfacing)
2. **turning** (lathe work)
3. **planing** and **shaping**
4. **milling**
5. **grinding**

11.3.1 Drilling

Drilling is one of the most common basic machine tool operations. Included in this process is the drilling of holes from under $\frac{1}{64}$ inch (0.4 mm) to more than 2 inches (50 mm). Besides drilling, types of machined holes include counterboring, countersinking, spotfacing, spot or center drilling, and reaming (Fig. 11.5). Drilling is the most familiar of the machine tool processes and one that most people have employed in their homes using simple hand tools. For industrial drilling,

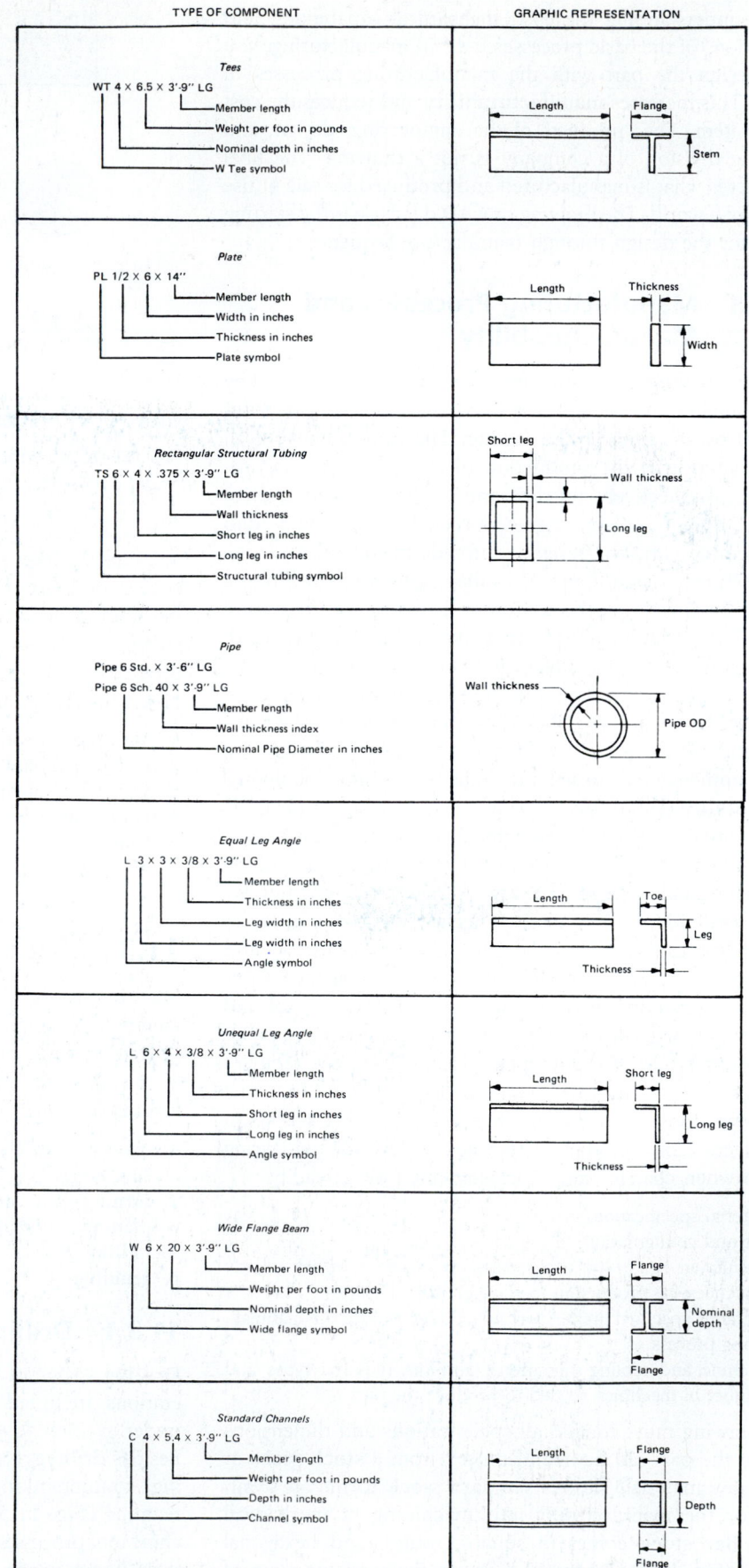

FIGURE 11.4 Structural Stock Forms

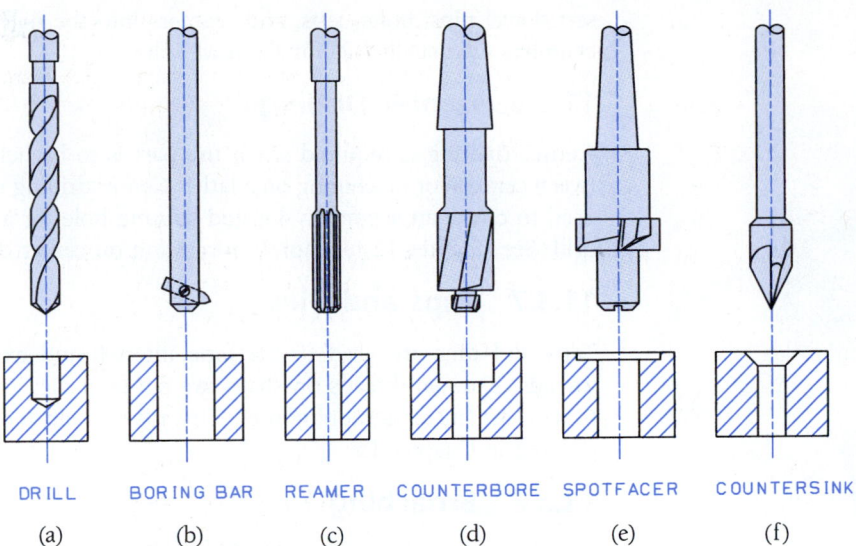

| DRILL | BORING BAR | REAMER | COUNTERBORE | SPOTFACER | COUNTERSINK |
| (a) | (b) | (c) | (d) | (e) | (f) |

FIGURE 11.5   **Machined Holes**

the **drill bit** [Fig. 11.6(a)] is a cutting tool that is held by a chuck and rotated by a large motor. The rotating tool is fed into the part at a controlled rate. The **turning speed** and **feed rate** of the drill are important factors and are influenced by the size of the hole and the material to be drilled.

Almost every machined part has a number of drilled holes. On most drawings, the type of process required is determined by the tolerance of the hole. Drilling is also used to create rough holes before the boring, reaming, counterboring, countersinking, or tapping operations are performed. Reamers [Fig. 11.6(b)] and center drills and countersinks [Fig. 11.6(c)] are used after a hole has been drilled.

A drill (sometimes called a tap drill) is also used when the hole to be created will eventually have a **thread** applied to it using a tapping tool. The tap drill must be the proper size to produce the minor diameter of the internal thread.

The drilling process requires that the part being machined be held firmly in place. A **drill jig** was required for the precise drilling of the small part shown in Figure 11.7(a) (front). The drill jig has a hinged cover plate with integral drill bushings to guide and position the drill accurately [Fig. 11.7(b)].

11.3.2   Reamers

In situations where a hole must be extremely precise, a **reamer** [Figs. 11.5(c) and 11.6(b)] is used. Reamers are required because twist drills [Fig. 11.6(a)] make holes that are not accurately sized, precisely round, or have poor finishes. Reamers are not used to make the entire hole. An undersized drill is used to remove most of the material, and the reamer finishes the hole. Reamers are usually made of tungsten carbide or tool steel. Many different types of reamers are available.

11.3.3   Counterboring

Counterboring requires that a drilled hole be made first [Fig. 11.5(d)]. A counterbored hole is deeper than a spotfaced hole and has a specific dimension to its recessed depth. Counterboring is used primarily to allow socket head and fillister screws to be seated with their heads flush or below the surface of the part.

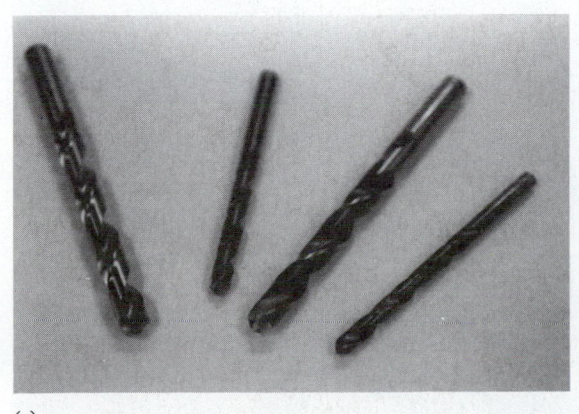

(a)

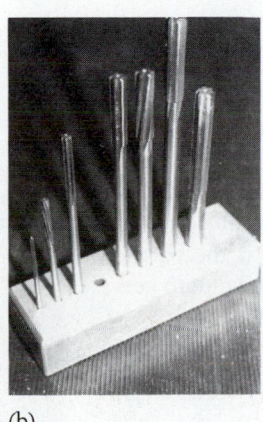

(b)

(c)

FIGURE 11.6   **Machine Tools**   (a) Drills (b) Reamers (c) Center drills and countersinks

(a)

(b)

FIGURE 11.7   **Drill Jig**   (a) Drill jig with part (b) Drill jig with hinged top open

11.3.4   Spotfacing

Spotfacing [Fig. 11.5(e)] is basically the same process as counterboring, but is normally no more than $\frac{1}{8}$ inch (3 mm) deep. In other words, the depth of the hole below the surface of the part is very shallow. This process is typically used to clean up the area around the hole, especially if the part is made of a cast material. The spotface provides a smooth surface for **fasteners** (nuts, bolts, screws, rivets) to seat.

11.3.5   Countersinking

Countersinking creates a small **chamfer** or bevel at the edge of a hole [Fig. 11.5(f) and Fig. 11.6(c)]. The hole is drilled before countersinking. Countersinking makes it easier to in-

sert dowel pins, bolts, taps, and reamers into the hole. The chamfers are usually 82° for flathead bolts.

11.3.6   Center Drilling

Center drilling is required when the part is to be held between centers for machining on a lathe. Center drilling is also used to create an accurately located starting hole for a twist drill. See Chapter 12 for more information on center drills.

11.3.7   Taps and Dies

Taps and **dies** are used to machine internal and external threads. External threads on shafts are cut by a die; internal threads are cut by a tapping tool. Threads and tap tools are covered in Chapter 15.

11.3.8   Broaching

All of the tools mentioned in the previous section create round holes or portions of holes. The common drill, the reamer, the counterbore, and the countersink are all tools that require the use of a drill press, lathe, or milling machine. The creation of odd-shaped holes or openings requires the use of a **broach** (Fig. 11.8). A broaching machine is used to cut special features like keyseats and for forming square, hexagonal, or odd-shaped holes after a drilled hole has been made. A broach is a long tool with a series of teeth or cutting edges that increase in size progressively so that each of the teeth removes only a small portion of the material as it is pulled or pushed through the part.

11.3.9   Boring

Boring requires the use of a milling machine, lathe, or special boring machine. Some drill presses provide shallow boring, but, in general, boring is done on a different type of machine tool where accuracy can be more closely controlled. Boring is a machining process used for a wide range of hole diameters that require precise tolerances or geometry.

The part in Figure 11.9 shows an example of an industrial part that required multiple holes and slots. Study each of the "callouts" provided on the drawing. Each hole is dimensioned

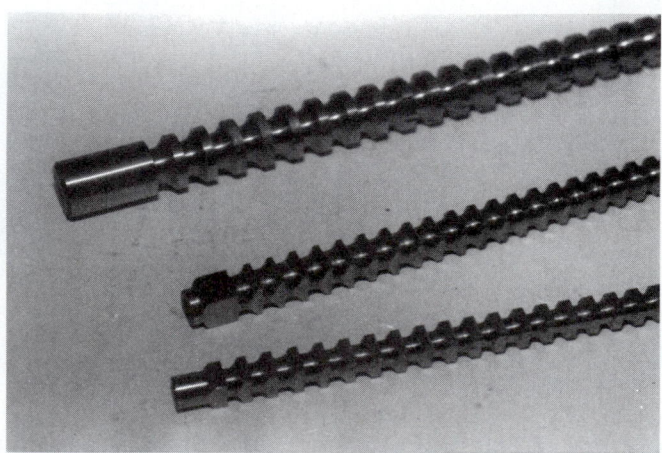

FIGURE 11.8   **Broaches**

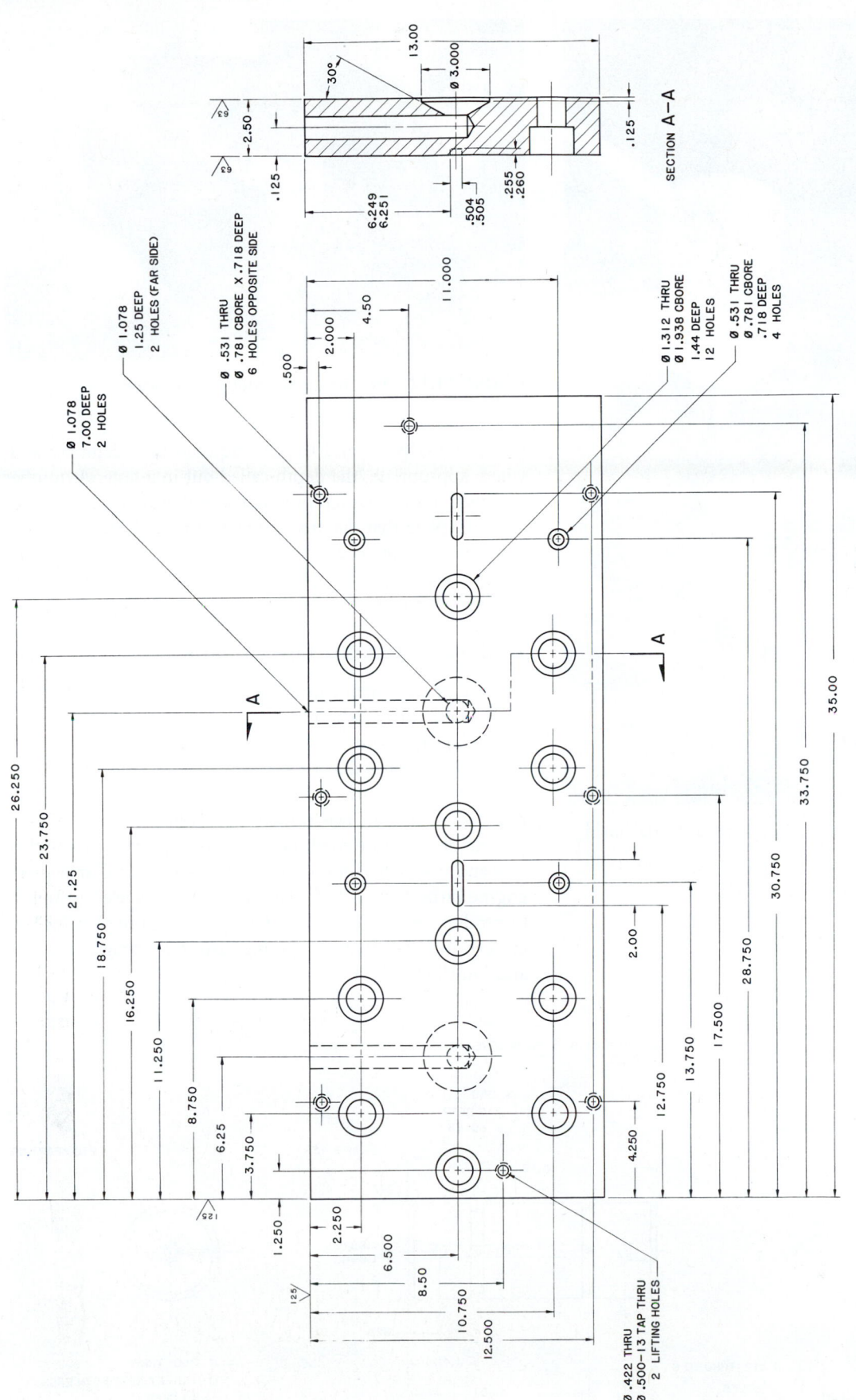

FIGURE 11.9   Detail Drawing

FIGURE 11.10   Machinist Setting Up a Part to Be Machined on a Lathe

FIGURE 11.12   Part Being Machined on a Lathe

to the center point and has the required hole diameter and, where appropriate, the depth called out in a note. A number of drilled holes, counterbored holes, and taps are required for the part. Note that *the process required for a particular hole is not specified in the note, only the size and type.* Manufacturing determines the proper tool and machine to use in order to machine and manufacture the part economically.

11.3.10   Turning Operations

Turning operations include the use of the engine lathe (Fig. 11.10), the turret lathe in its many variations, and a variety of **boring machines.** The **vertical boring** mill is used for turning large parts that need round cuts, and for facing and contouring. In Figure 11.11, an industrial detail of a pin pivot is shown. This part was turned on a lathe.

One of the most common and versatile types of machine tool and one that is found in every machine tool area is the **engine lathe** (Fig. 11.12). The engine lathe is used primarily to produce cylindrical parts utilizing operations that include cutting threads, facing, tapering, parting, straight turning, and knurling (Fig. 11.13).

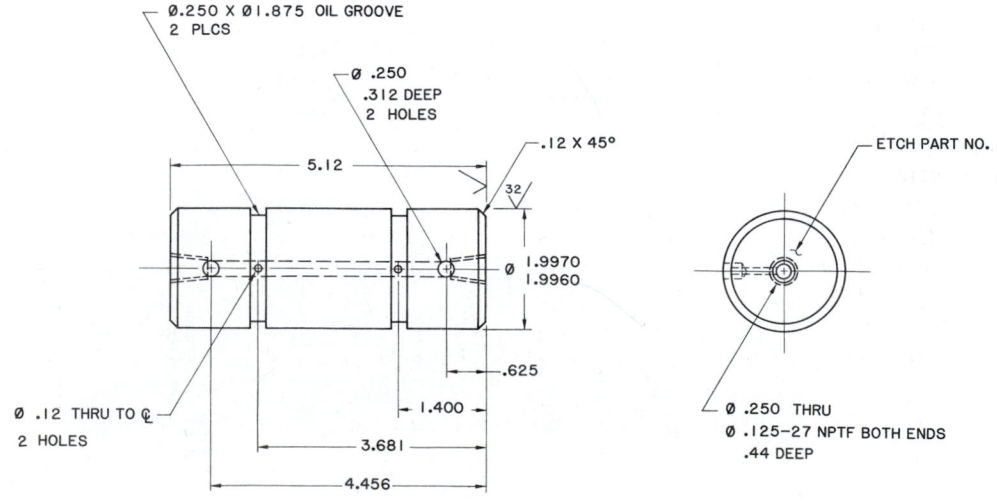

FIGURE 11.11   Pivot Pin Detail Drawing

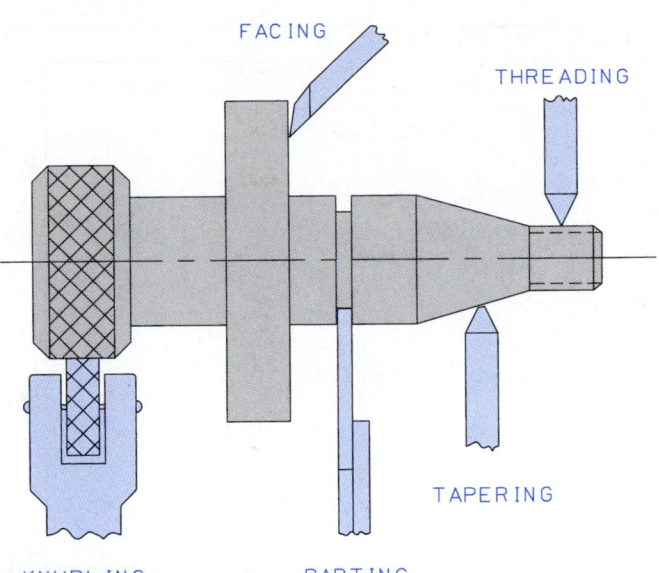

FACING

THREADING

TAPERING

KNURLING   PARTING

FIGURE 11.13   Lathe Processes

(a)

(b)

FIGURE 11.14   Lathe Chuck   (a) Lathe chucks (b) Part held by a chuck on a lathe

In general, a lathe is a machine that rotates the part rapidly while a stationary cutting tool is used to perform the operation. In Figure 11.10, the machinist is setting up the part. The most typical method of holding a part in a lathe is with the use of a **chuck** [Fig. 11.14(a)]. The chuck is connected to the powered end of the machine [Fig. 11.14(b)]. Collets, faceplates, driveplates, and other devices are also used to hold and drive the work piece in the lathe.

A lathe is also used for drilling, reaming, boring, counterboring, facing, threading, knurling, and polishing. Drilling, reaming, boring, and counterboring are done on the face of the part as it turns. In other words, boring and reaming on a lathe can only be accomplished in the **Z** axis, in line with the center of the tail stock. The **tail stock** is used to support the part at one end, and the **tool post** is used to fasten the tool holder securely. The tool post can be moved to the right or the left and rotated at an angle.

Computer numerical control (CNC) engine lathes are also available. All of the functions are controlled by the computer program. Therefore, manual controls are limited on this type of machine. The **turret lathe** has a rotating multisided turret where a variety of cutting tools can be mounted. This allows the tools to be changed rapidly for small to large volume production.

Turning is the process of using a lathe to reduce the outside diameter of a part. In this situation, the tool bit will travel parallel to the **Z** axis. **Facing** decreases the length of the part or a flange and creates a flat surface (Fig. 11.13). **Threading** is done on an engine lathe with a single point tool, although this a slow process. Drilling and reaming can be done on a lathe but the hole location is limited to the center of the lathe's **Z** axis, in line with the tail stock center. **Knurling** (Fig. 11.13) is a pattern that is formed into the surface of a part, either for appearance or to provide easy gripping. The pattern may be either straight or diamond-shaped.

The cylinder rod in Figure 11.15 is an example of a part that would be produced on a lathe. Dimensions A, B, and C are given in three different sizes. This part is made out of 1020 cold rolled steel (CRS) and requires a tapped hole in the large end. Chamfering, facing, parting, drilling, and threading were processes required to complete the part.

11.3.11 Milling Machines and Milling Cutters

A **milling machine** is one of the most important machines found in the manufacturing area. Milling machines are also one of the most accurate machines used. The typical milling machine has a table where the part is securely fastened. Cutting is accomplished with a rotary milling cutter with single or multiple cutting edges. One or more rotary milling cutters are on each machine. Drilling, boring, reaming, slotting, facing, pocketing, and other types of cuts can be made with this machine.

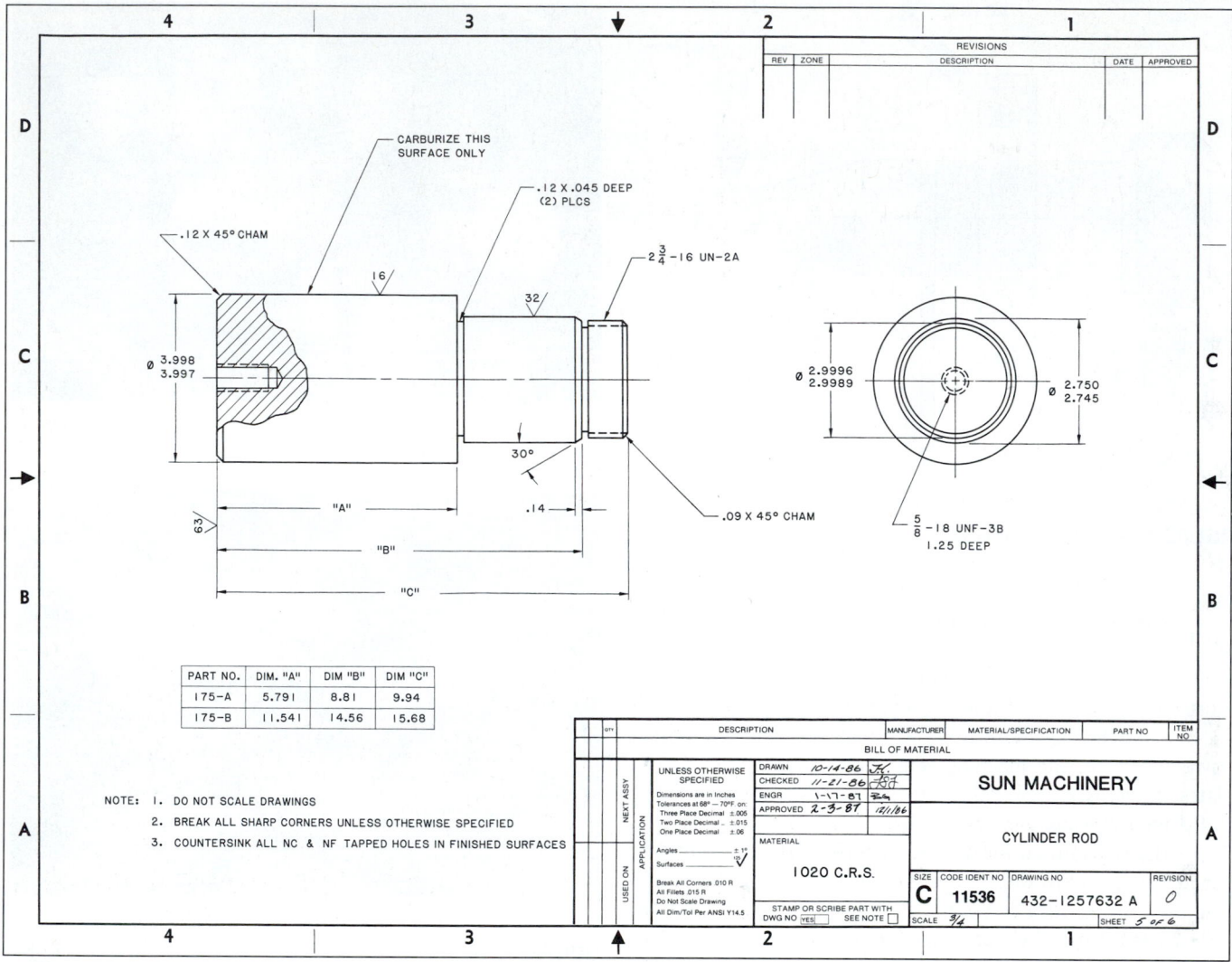

FIGURE 11.15 Cylinder Rod

Milling machines are divided into two categories: vertical and horizontal. The classification depends on the orientation of the **spindle.** In Figure 11.16, a vertical milling machine is shown. As on most milling machines, the table is a flat surface with a variety of tee slots to insert clamping mechanisms that hold the part in place. Milling machines are also used to cut irregular surfaces, gears, slots, and keyways. Figure 11.17 shows the horizontal spindle milling machine using a side cutting mill to cut a keyway in a part. This could also be referred to as a **slitting saw.** Cutters are held in place by **collet adapters, arbors,** and quick-change **holders.** Cutters fall into four basic catagories:

1. end mills [Fig. 11.18(a)]
2. shell mills [Fig. 11.18(b)]
3. face mills [Fig. 11.18(c)]
4. plane milling cutters, including side mills

End mills are probably the most versatile cutters and are used for more types of machining work; especially where close tolerances must be maintained. The end mill in Figure

11.18(a) is held by a tool holder. An end mill is being used to mill the parts in Figure 11.19(a) and (b). End mills are also used for **pocketing** parts. **Shell mills** [Fig. 11.18(b)] are used for simple facing or cutting steps that cannot be done by a face mill. **Face mills** are used for facing flat surfaces and are used primarily on horizontal milling machines. Face mills come with inserted teeth or are slab types. The face mill in Figure 11.18(c) is a **slab mill.**

11.3.12 Grinding

Grinding is also a cutting process except that the cutters used are grinding wheels made of irregular-shaped abrasive grit. This abrasive grit is used to cut or grind a part. Grinding can be applied to both external and internal requirements. The basic purpose of a grinding wheel is to provide a fine-finished surface and maintain very accurate size control.

Removing edges and corners from a part is done with stones and sandpaper or hand grinders. As an example, the notes on the link pull detail in Figure 11.20 require that the machinist

FIGURE 11.16   **Bridgeport Mill**

(a)

(b)

FIGURE 11.17   **Milling Machine**   (a) Horizontal mill
(b) Horizontal mill machining a keyseat

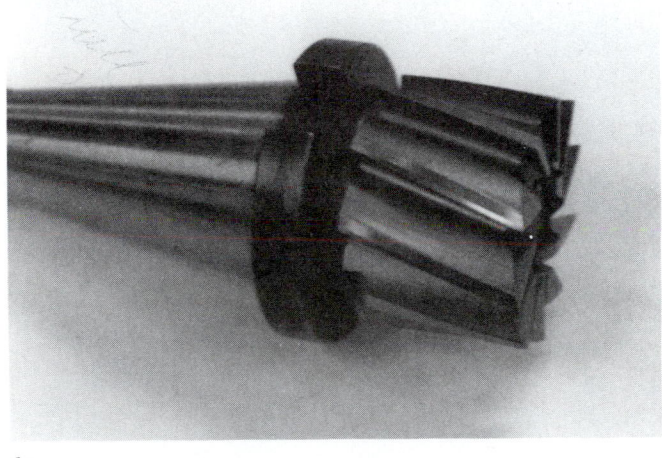

(a)

(b)

(c)

FIGURE 11.18   **Mills**   (a) End mill and tool holder (b) Shell
mill and holder (c) Face mill (slab type)

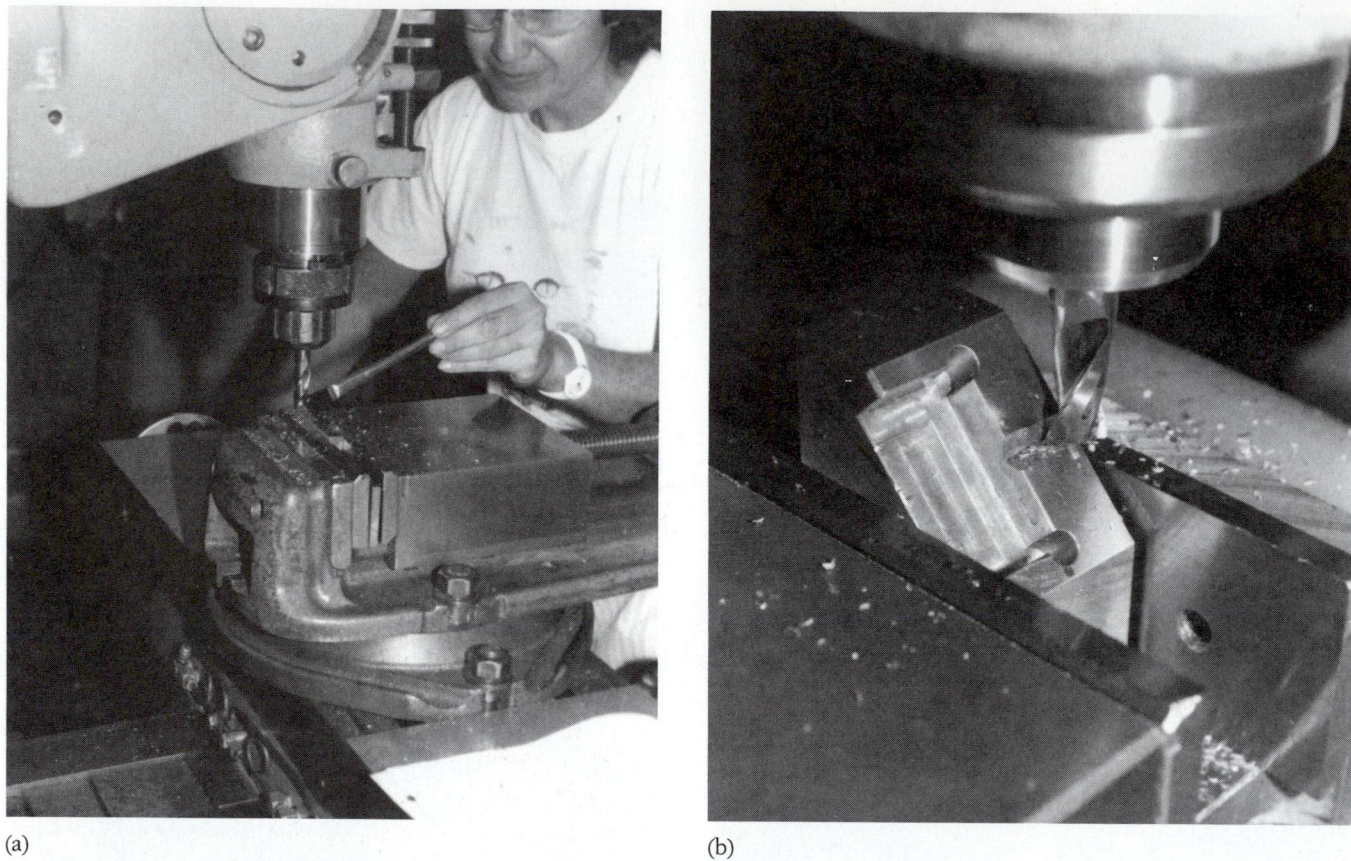

(a)   (b)

FIGURE 11.19 **Machining a Part** (a) Machinist adding lubricant to a part before milling (b) Part being machined on a vertical mill

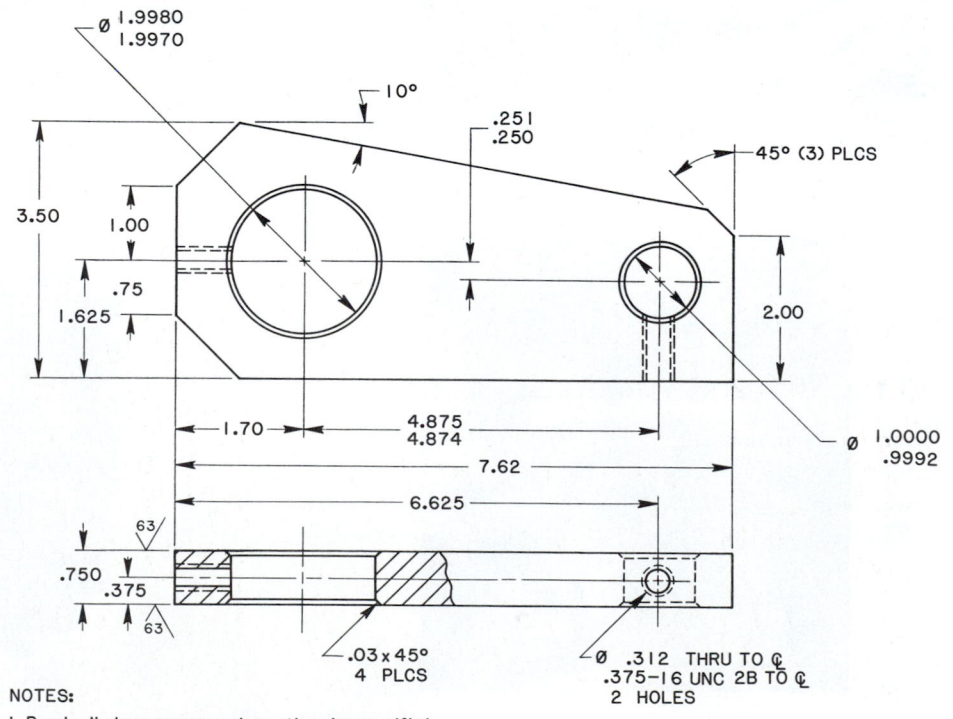

NOTES:

1. Break all sharp corners unless otherwise specified

FIGURE 11.20 **Pull Link Detail**

2. Countersink all tapped holes in finished surfaces

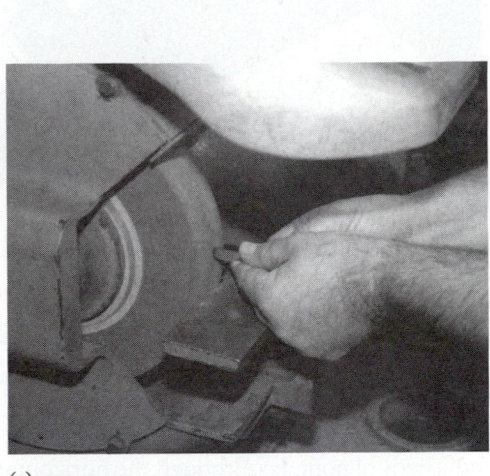

(a)   (b)   (c)

FIGURE 11.21   **Grinders**   (a) Surface grinder (b) OD grinder (c) Pedestal grinder

"BREAK ALL SHARP CORNERS UNLESS OTHERWISE SPECIFIED."

Figure 11.21(a) shows a surface grinder that has a movable table. Grinding machines are divided into surface types: cylindrical grinders, internal grinders, and centerless grinders that finish cylindrical shapes. Vertical spindle surface grinders and surface grinders machine flat surfaces. A number of single-purpose abrasive machines such as abrasive cutoff machines and snagging grinders are commonly used. Figure 11.21(b) shows an outside diameter grinder (OD grinder), and 11.21(c) provides an example of a pedestal grinder.

11.3.13   Saws

Many different types of **sawing machines** are also found on the machine shop floor. The power saw, such as that shown in Figure 11.22, is a band-saw cutoff machine, which uses a continuous band-saw blade. This type of saw is used to cut bar stock to length. These machines are used on thin material to cut irregular shapes, to make beveled cuts on tubing or solid stock, or to make slots or slits.

11.3.14   Shapers and Planers

Shapers and **planers** are limited to straight-line cuts. The difference between the two is that a shaper can only handle relatively small parts, whereas a planer can be used on parts weighing up to several thousand pounds. Planers and shapers make facing cuts (both top and side), slotting, step cuts, and dove tails (both male and female). Both machines are used to create finished surfaces. Larger flat surfaces that require finishing are machined on the planer rather than the shaper. Multiple pieces can be machined at the same time because of the size of this machine. The planer is normally used to machine large iron castings or steel weldments that weigh

FIGURE 11.22   **Metal Band Saw**

FIGURE 11.23 Hand-Held Measuring Instruments

FIGURE 11.24 Vernier Calipers

hundreds of pounds. Although the horizontal type is the most common, shapers come in both horizontal and vertical types. Vertical shapers are sometimes called **slotters.**

11.3.15 Hand-Held Measuring Devices

In addition to the large machine tools previously described, various measuring tools (Fig. 11.23) are used by manufacturing. The **pocket steel ruler** is a common instrument found in the machine tool area. Inside and outside **calipers**, micrometers, and vernier or **dial calipers** are used. **Vernier calipers** (Fig. 11.24) can measure both the inside and the outside of the part. The scale on the vernier calipers is similar to that of the micrometer and is read in very much the same way. The vernier calipers have a beam or bar marked in inches and hundredths or in centimeters and millimeters.

The **micrometer**, also referred to as the micrometer caliper, comes in inside and outside versions (Fig. 11.25). The micrometer (Fig. 11.26) is the most accurate of the precision hand-held measuring instruments. Digital versions of vernier calipers and micrometers are available in a variety of sizes.

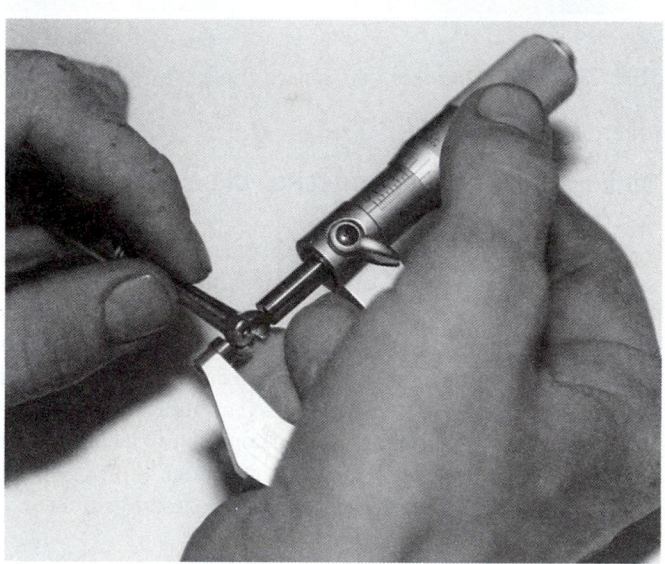

FIGURE 11.25 Measuring a Part with a Micrometer

11.4 Surface Texture Specification

A variety of standards have been developed by the American National Standards Institute (ANSI) and American Society of Mechanical Engineers (ASME) for specifying **surface textures.** The **surface roughness measurement** is an important factor in machining. Normally, the finer the finish, the more expensive the machine process required. Certain machine processes such as milling, shaping, and turning can produce precise surface textures ranging from 125 to 32 μin. Only a lathe can get to 8 μin. on a production basis. Grinding operations produce surface textures ranging from 64 to 4 μin. The Greek letter μ (microinch, μin.; micrometer, μm) is used on drawings.

Surface texture is specified on a drawing as part of the design specifications. The surface texture value is used along

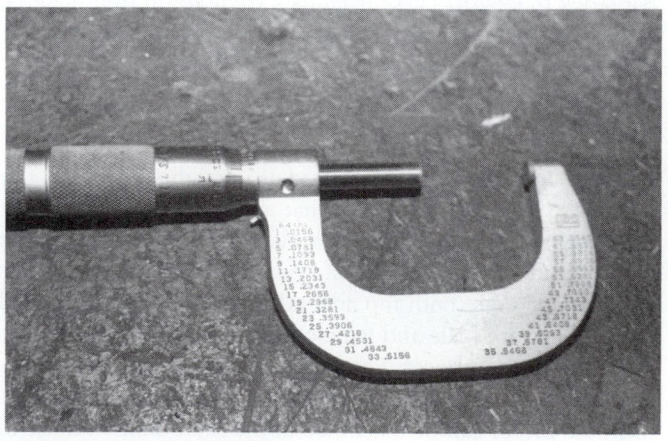

FIGURE 11.26 Micrometer

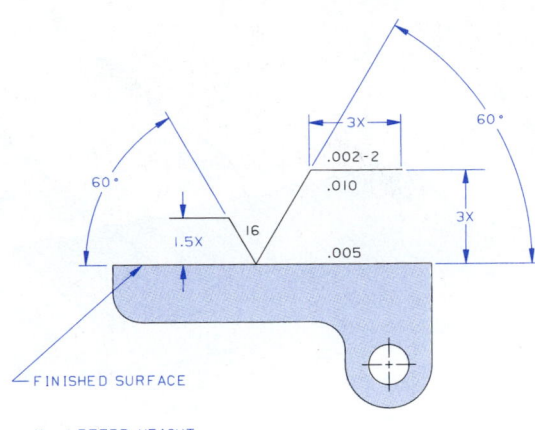

FIGURE 11.27   Surface Texture Symbol Specifications

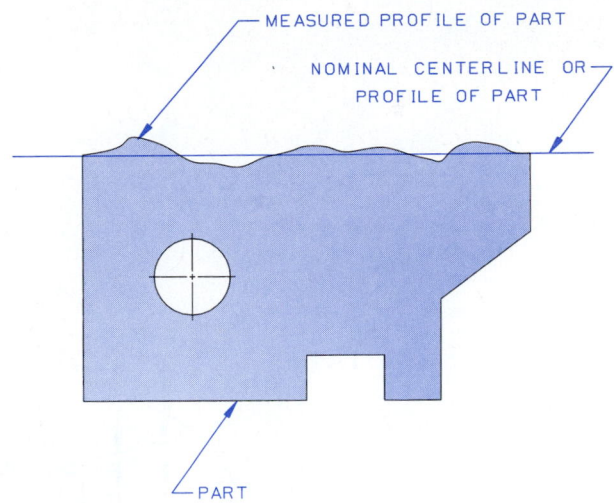

FIGURE 11.29   Nominal Center and Measured Profile of a Part's Surface

with the **surface texture symbol** (Fig. 11.27). The surface texture symbol designates the waviness, lay, and classification of roughness. **Roughness** is the irregularity on the surface of the part; it is not the distance between the peaks and valleys of the roughness, but the average amount of irregularity above and below an assumed centerline. **Waviness** is the irregularity from the centerline. The **waviness height** is the peak-to-valley height of the roughness.

Roughness is caused by the action of the machining during the production process. The roughness height is designated above the V portion of the surface texture symbol (Fig. 11.27). The symbol is constructed with the measurements provided. Figure 11.28 defines each of the portions of this symbol and what they mean. *The surface texture symbol provides information on the waviness height, the waviness width, roughness height, and width.* In Figure 11.29 a part is shown with an exaggerated measured profile. The **nominal centerline** or **profile of the part** is used to establish the surface roughness deviation.

The measurement of **smoothness** of a surface texture or a specific finish produced by a machine tool is accomplished with a profilometer, which measures the roughness in microinches or micrometers. Surface texture is the deviation from

the nominal centerline or nominal surface that forms the pattern of the surface and includes flaws, lay, waviness, and roughness. The direction of lay, roughness width cutoff, waviness width, waviness height, and roughness height, are shown in Figure 11.30.

The centerline or nominal surface line (Fig. 11.29) is a line about which the roughness is measured and is parallel to the direction of the profile within the limits of the roughness width cutoff. The roughness consists of the finer irregularities in the surface texture, including those that result from action in the production process. These include transverse feedmarks and other irregularities. **Roughness height** (Fig. 11.30) is an average deviation expressed in microinches or micrometers and is measured normal to the centerline. **Roughness width** is the distance parallel to the nominal surface between successive peaks or ridges on the part. Nominal surface is the surface contour shape that is usually shown and dimensioned by the drafter. The **roughness width cutoff** is the distance over the surface in which the roughness measurement is made. One hundred thousandths of an inch is commonly used.

Waviness is caused by vibration of the machine during the machining process, heat treatment, or other processes applied to the part. The **waviness width** is rated as a measurement of spacing of successive wave peaks or wave valleys. The **lay** is the direction of the surface pattern. **Flaws** are the irregularities, which include different types of defects including cracks, blowholes, checks, ridges, and scratches.

As a drafter you will be required to draw the surface texture symbol and provide the information for surface standards for a particular part. Figure 11.31 shows the removal of material by machining that will be specified by variations in this symbol; optional, required, prohibited, and removal allowance are shown here. The preferred series of roughness height values is shown in Figure 11.32.

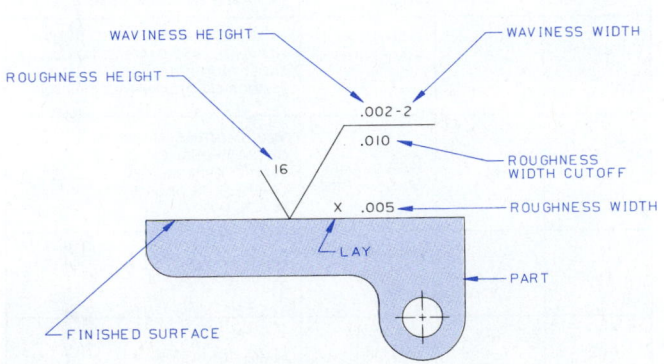

FIGURE 11.28   Surface Texture Symbol Description

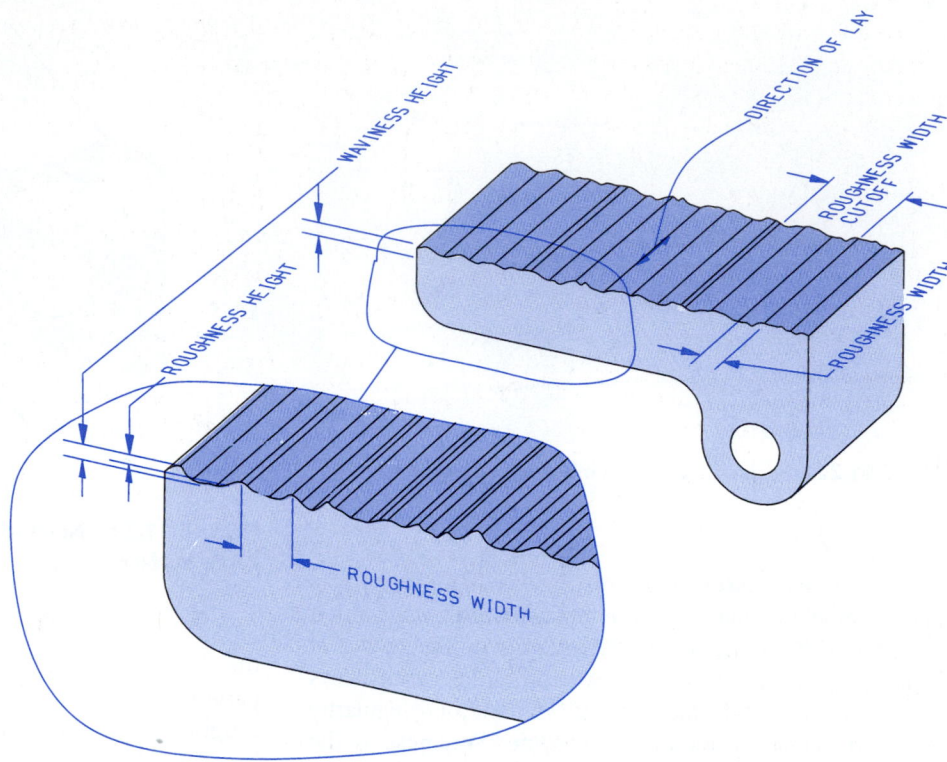

FIGURE 11.30 Surface Texture Terminology

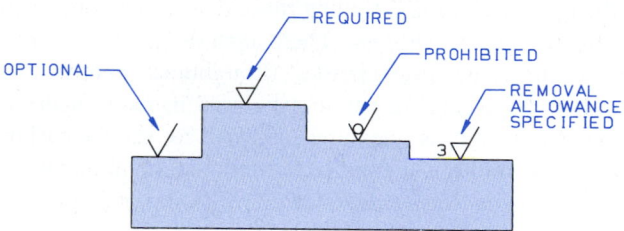

FIGURE 11.31 Surface Texture Symbols

11.5 Production Processes

Production processes include casting, forging, bending, rolling, press work, injection molding, dies, EDM, ECM, blow molding, and variations of other hot and cold processes. Understanding the types of processes and knowing their limitations will ensure a better designed and manufactured part. In other words, *design for manufacturability.*

Designing for automated production helps ensure a more efficient and cost-effective production process. Production processes must be integrated into the design and drafting stage so as to remove problems with the design during manufacturing. Designers and drafters should know the processes that will be used to build their designs. This method ensures that the right process is chosen, existing factory processes are understood, setup times are minimized, and tolerances are

ROUGHNESS HEIGHT RATING		SURFACE DESCRIPTION	PROCESS
MICROMETERS	MICROINCHES		
25.2	1000	VERY ROUGH	SAW AND TORCH CUTTING, FORGING OR SAND CASTING.
12.5	500	ROUGH MACHINING	HEAVY CUTS AND COARSE FEEDS IN TURNING, MILLING AND BORING.
6.3	250	COARSE	VERY COARSE SURFACE GRIND, RAPID FEEDS IN TURNING, PLANNING, MILLING, BORING AND FILING.
3.2	125	MEDIUM	MACHINE OPERATIONS WITH SHARP TOOLS, HIGH SPEEDS, FINE FEEDS AND LIGHT CUTS.
1.6	63	GOOD MACHINE FINISH	SHARP TOOLS, HIGH SPEEDS, EXTRA FINE FEEDS AND CUTS.
0.8	32	HIGH GRADE MACHINE FINISH	EXTREMELY FINE FEEDS AND CUTS ON LATHE, MILL AND SHAPERS REQUIRED. EASILY PRODUCED BY CENTERLESS, CYLINDRICAL AND SURFACE GRINDING.
0.4	16	HIGH QUALITY MACHINE FINISH	VERY SMOOTH REAMING OR FINE CYLINDRICAL OR SURFACE GRINDING, OR COARSE HONE OR LAPPING OF SURFACE.
0.2	8	VERY FINE MACHINE FINISH	FINE HONING AND LAPPING OF SURFACE.
0.05 0.1	2–4	EXTREMELY SMOOTH MACHINE FINISH	EXTRA FINE HONING AND LAPPING OF SURFACE.

FIGURE 11.32 Description of Roughness Height Values

specified correctly. These procedures will reduce labor costs and break down barriers between different areas (islands) of information in the company (engineering, design-drafting, manufacturing, and quality control).

11.5.1   Casting

Casting can be defined as the process of forming parts to approximate rough sizes by introducing liquid material into a formed cavity called a **mold** and allowing the material to solidify by cooling. The mold is then removed, leaving the solid part. Various casting methods are available including sand casting, mold casting, die casting, and investment casting. **Molding** and **die casting** are similar to casting except that the material used in the process is not liquid, but is softened to a plastic state and is forced into the mold under high pressure.

Many everyday items are created using casting and molding, from toys to electronic components. One common type of casting is **sand casting**. Figure 11.33 is a sand cast part shown before machining. Figure 11.34 shows a sand casting after machining. Casting is divided into two basic processes, **gravity** or **pressure.** Sand casting molds are formed by patterns. **Patterns** look like the cast part and are used to create a shape in the mold cavity. The wood pattern in Figure 11.35(a) is inserted into sand to create the proper configuration of the part (front). Figure 11.35(b) provides another example of a wood pattern. Here, the pattern is designed to shape six identical parts.

In most cases, you will be asked to prepare a combination casting and machining drawing. Some companies require separate drawings. The **casting detail** is used by the pattern-maker and the **machining drawing** by the machinist. Figure 11.36 is an example of a casting detail. In this case, it is an aluminum alloy sand casting. The notes establish the heat treatment requirements and the size of the fillets and rounds. The **draft angle** is the angle of the **taper** on the part that makes it easier to withdraw the pattern from the mold. After the material hardens, the sand is removed from the casting, thereby destroying the mold. In Figure 11.36 the draft angle is specified as 3° maximum per side.

FIGURE 11.34   Machined Sand Cast Part

(a)

(b)

FIGURE 11.35   Casting Patterns   (a) Wood pattern and cast part (b) Wood pattern designed for casting multiple parts

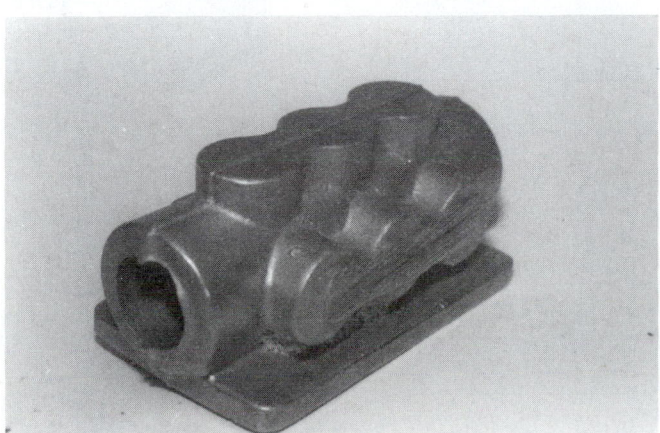

FIGURE 11.33   Sand Cast Part Before Machining

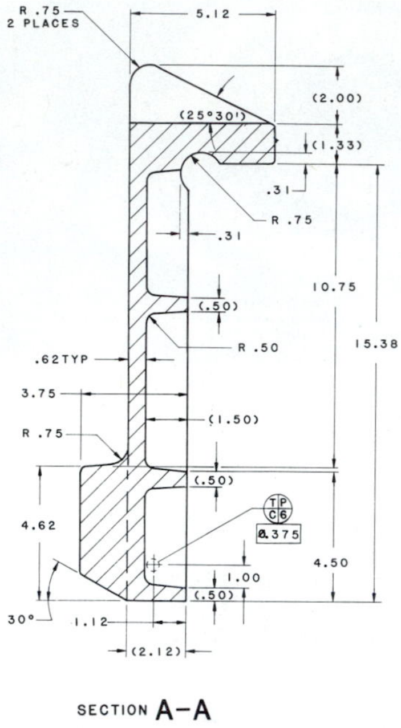

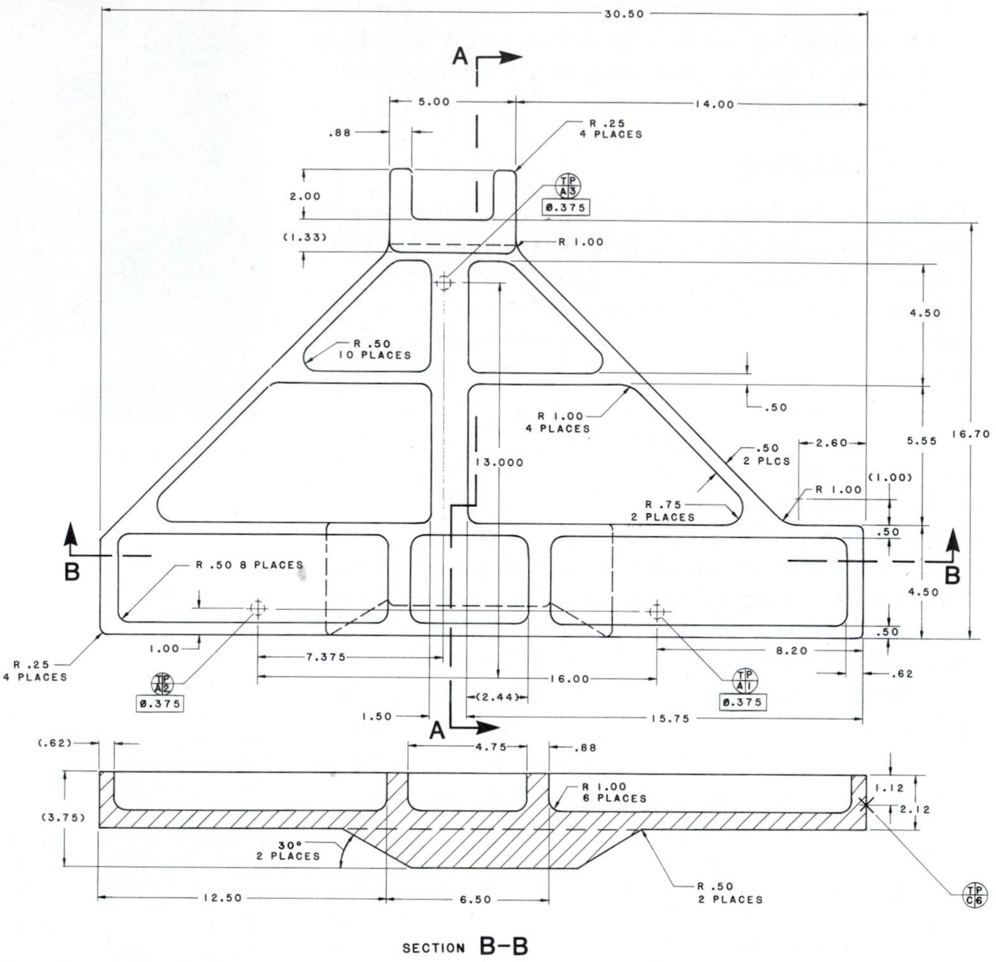

SECTION **A–A**

NOTES:

1. WORKMANSHIP PER MIL-STD-454, REQ T 21
2. AL ALY SAND CASTING PER QQ-A-601, ALY 771-T6
3. STRESS RELIEVE AND HEAT TREAT TO T6 CONDITION
4. FILLETS TO BE R.25 MAX
5. ROUNDS TO BE R.12 MAX
6. DRAFT ANGLE TO BE 3° MAX PER SIDE
7. ◆ INDICATES Ø.375 TOOLING POINT TO BE FREE OF
   SURFACE IRREGULARITIES EXCEEDING .005 1INCH POSITION
   TOLERANCE ON TOOLING POINT LOCATION IS±.060

FIGURE 11.36   Casting Detail for Adaptor

SECTION **B–B**

Tooling points are also provided on the drawing. Tooling points on three **datum planes** that are perpendicular are used to locate dimensions on the casting. The planes are established by the tooling points on the casting and are used during the measuring or machining processes.

Since it is not possible to cast sharp corners and angles very accurately, the internal angles on a casting are normally filled with a material to eliminate sharp corners. Contoured surfaces that fill the sharp inside corners produced by two faces on a pattern are known as **fillets** (Fig. 11.37). **Rounds** are the exterior corners that have been smoothed to remove their sharp edges. In Figure 11.36, the notes state that fillets are to be R .25 maximum and rounds are a R .12 maximum.

The type of material to be used for a particular part is called out on a drawing. It is the responsibility of the engineer or designer to specify the material. Aluminum, magnesium, zinc, copper, bronze, and brass as well as iron and steel are used to make castings. The design of castings includes

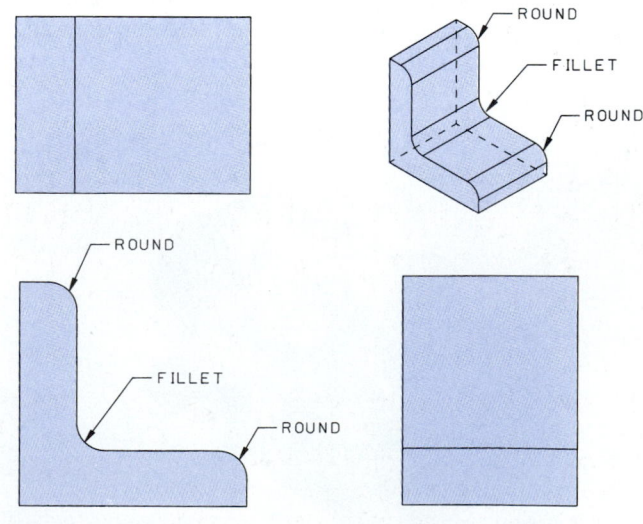

FIGURE 11.37   Fillets and Rounds

Computers in Manufacturing

Computer numerically controlled (CNC) machines have transformed manufacturing methods and techniques during the past twenty years. Today, they are integral parts of flexible manufacturing systems (FMS) that can machine one part, a thousand parts, or several different kinds of parts. Changes to the computer program controlling the system modify what part the system machines by redefining the sequence of events needed to complete the machining steps.

Numerical control (NC) began in 1947 with John Parsons's experiments on producing aircraft components with three-axis curvature data to control machine tools. The U.S. Air Force awarded Parsons a contract in 1949 to build the first NC machine. The Massachusetts Institute of Technology took over the development contract in 1951 and produced the first machine in 1952. Refined industrial machines followed in 1955.

Early NC machines used either punched tape or punched cards to send commands to the machine. Most machines used punched tape and tape readers. The tape was fragile and broke easily in industrial settings and, if 1,000 parts were to be made, the reader read the tape 1,000 times. Because of the need to make NC more efficient, computer control was developed. The part programmer uses English-like commands to write the program and the computer does the work of translating the commands into machine code.

Distributed numerical control (DNC) allows control of a system of CNC machines by using a networked computer. By planning a network of computer control effectively, it is possible to control an entire factory. FMS systems are networked into the computer control scheme.

Numerical control was developed to increase productivity, increase quality, increase accuracy, reduce labor costs, and do jobs that were considered impossible or impractical. CNC machines require a large initial investment and have higher per hour operating costs than traditional machines tools, but the other advantages outweigh these disadvantages.

NC, CNC, and DNC machines will play increasingly important roles in automated and flexible manufacturing in the future. Today stand-alone or networked CNC machines are widely used in both large and small production shops. Because of the great advances in and great advantages of this technology, the "factory of the future" will rely on these machines to be the backbone of the machining processes.

Coordinate Measuring Machine (CMM)

Flexible Manufacturing System (FSM)

---

understanding how much the material will actually shrink during the cooling process. The dimensions shown on the casting drawing must reflect the **shrinking factor** of the part. This is called the **shrinkage allowance.**

In addition to sand castings there are **centrifugal castings,** in which the molten material is fed into a rotating mold. The rotation forces the molten material to fill the cavity or mold. Permanent molds are normally used for this process, not sand molds. **Die casting** is a permanent mold process that involves the use of pressure to force the molten material into a metal die. **Injection molding** is also a type of permanent mold casting. Fig. 11.38 shows an injection-molded part before and

FIGURE 11.38   Injection Mold and Part

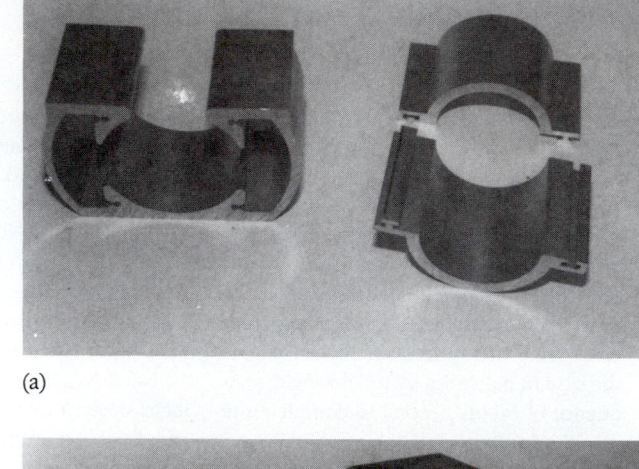

(a)

FIGURE 11.39   Extrusions

(b)

FIGURE 11.40   **Extrusions**   (a) Three extruded parts
(b) Assembled extrusions

after machining. Injection molds are very similar to die casting molds. The only difference is the manner in which the materials are loaded into the mold cavity. Many other types of molding processes exist, including blow molding, compression molding, transfer molding, layup molding, pressure molding, and vacuum molding.

11.5.2   Extruding

Materials forming processes include a wide range of processes that use pressure to change the shape or the size of the material. This category of processes includes extruding, forging, stamping, punching, rolling, bending, and shearing.

Extrusion is a metalworking process that is used to produce long, straight, semifinished products having constant cross sections (Fig. 11.39) such as bars, tubes, solid and hollow sections, wire, and strips. Extrusion is accomplished by squeezing a solid slug of metal from a closed container through a die. Extrusion can be either a hot or cold process. **Cold extrusion** is also called **impact** or **cold forming** and is

similar to cold forging. In cold extrusion, a piece of metal that has not been heated is used. This process displaces the material at stresses above the material's elastic limit and the form is created by using one or more punch and die sets.

Hot extrusion is used to make long and irregular-shaped parts. During this process, the desired alloy metal is rolled into bars, which are cut into billets or slugs of the required length. The billets and slugs are then induction heated above their critical temperature, placed on a press, and squeezed through a die into the required shape. Figure 11.40(a) shows three aluminum extrusions that were designed to fit together in the interlocking assembly of (b).

11.5.3   Forging

Forging is the use of impact and pressure to form parts. It includes smith forging, upset forging, and drop forging. A forging is a metal part shaped to its desired form by hammering, pressing, or upsetting. Forging is normally done after

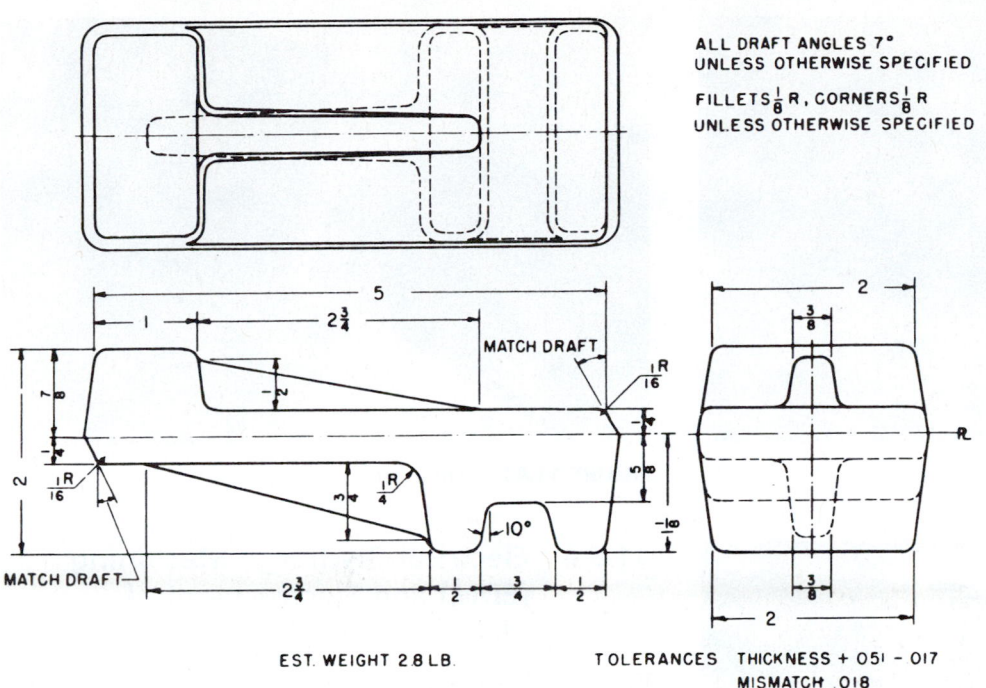

ALL DRAFT ANGLES 7°
UNLESS OTHERWISE SPECIFIED

FILLETS $\frac{1}{8}$R, CORNERS $\frac{1}{8}$R
UNLESS OTHERWISE SPECIFIED

EST. WEIGHT 2.8 LB.   TOLERANCES THICKNESS + 05I – 0I7
                                       MISMATCH .018
                                       DIE WEAR .035

FIGURE 11.41 Forging Drawing

the metal has been heated to an elevated temperature. Forging without heating the material is known as **cold forging.**

In Figure 11.41, a forging drawing is shown. A drop forging of a wrench before the part is cleaned is shown in Figure 11.42(a). The finished wrench is shown cleaned, with the excess material removed, in Figure 11.42(b). In **drop forging,** the hot metal is forced into dies by means of drop hammers. The material itself is very hot, but not molten, and is forced into the die by pounding. This pounding force pushes the metal into the shape of the cavity of the die. Pounding does not create a very accurate part and is limited to only certain types of shapes. Tolerances are quite large for this process and the dies are normally expensive; however, forging produces stronger parts than many other manufacturing processes. Since the material needs to be heated, furnaces are required. Hammers and presses are also used in the forging process. Most metals can be forged, though low-carbon and low-alloy steels and aluminum alloys are the most common.

11.5.4 Stamping

In **stamping,** a punch and die are used to cut or form sheet material. The assembled tool is called a **die** as is the cutting part of the tool itself. **Progressive dies** require that several operations take place in a sequential order. Stamping includes cutting, parting, blanking, punching, piercing, perforation, trimming, slitting, shaving, forming, bending, coining, embossing, and drawing operations.

In Figure 11.43(a) and (b) a stamped part is shown. This part was made by a progressive stamp that uses dies to cut or form the metal sheets into the desired or required form. Dies are assemblies that include a housing and the cutter. A

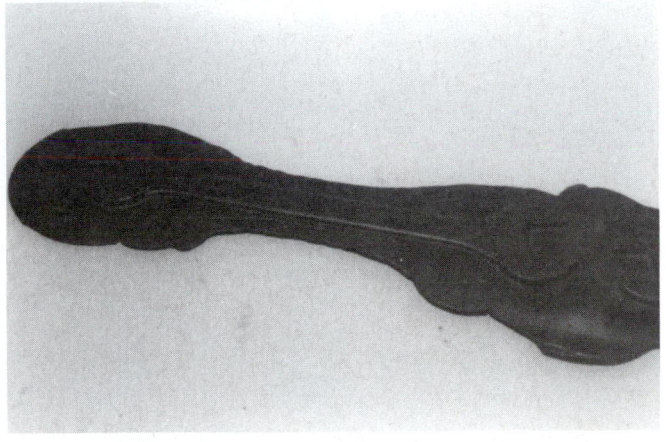

(a)

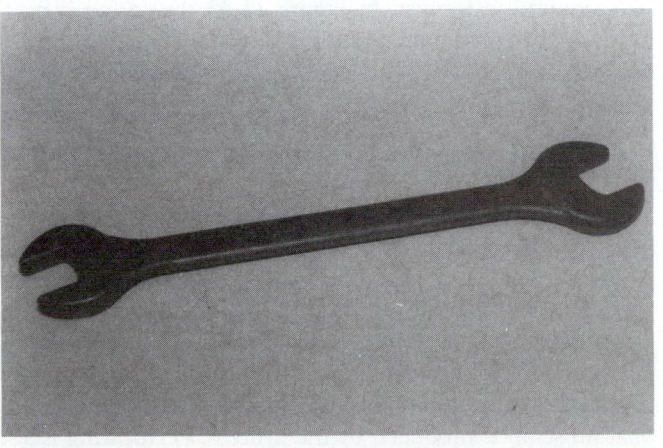

(b)

FIGURE 11.42 **Forging** (a) Forging of wrench (b) Wrench

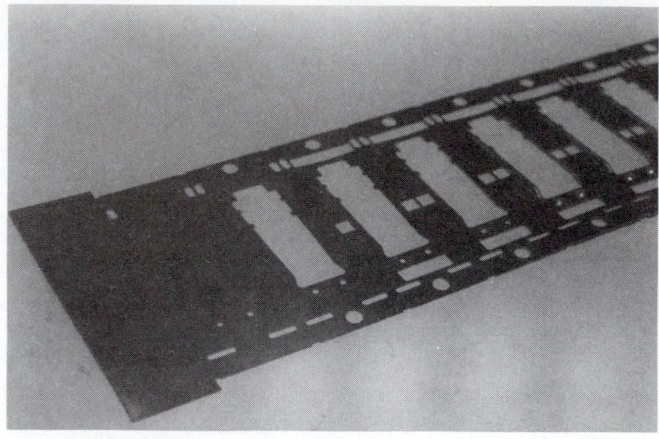

(a)

FIGURE 11.44 Stamp Die

11.5.6 Electrical Discharge Machining (EDM) and Electrochemical Machining (ECM)

Electrical discharge machining (EDM) is the process of machining by removing small particles of metal with an electrical spark. Vaporization of the material is accomplished by exposing the metal to sparks from a shaped electrode. The electrical discharge machine is a vertical spindle milling machine with a rectangular tank on the work table. The table can be moved along the **X** and **Y** axes or it can be numerically controlled. Originally, EDM was used as a rough method for removing metal. EDM has been refined to do the precision work required in the electronics, aerospace, and toolmaking industries. EDM is also used to remove objects such as taps or other tools that are broken and lodged in holes.

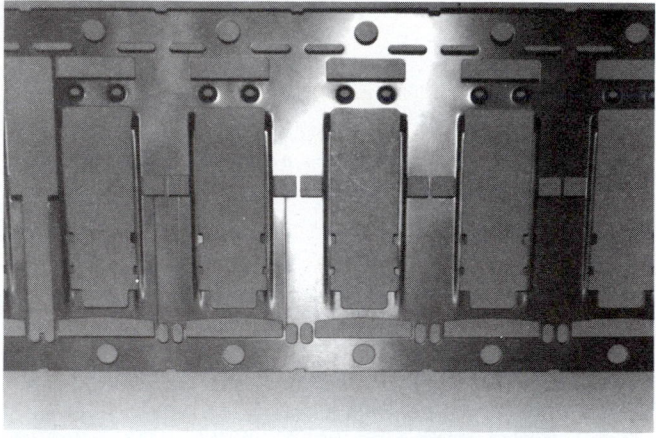

(b)

FIGURE 11.43 **Stamps** (a) Stamped part (b) Progressive stamping

stamped part is shown in Figure 11.44 along with the tool and die required to form it. In Figure 11.45 the spring is made from stainless steel and was formed by bending after the part was stamped. The material used in this part is .025 inches thick. Stamping operations are limited to thin metal parts.

11.5.5 Punching

Punching operations include shearing, cutting off, and blanking. **Shearing** is done along a straight line on a part. **Cutting** is performed on a part producing an edge other than a straight edge. **Blanking** produces parts with a punch and a die; then the part falls through the die after the process. Holes are also produced by punching, but this is limited to thin sheets of material. **Piercing** is also similar to punching, except that no scrap is produced by the process. **Perforating** is also a stamping operation performed on sheets to produce a hole pattern or decoration.

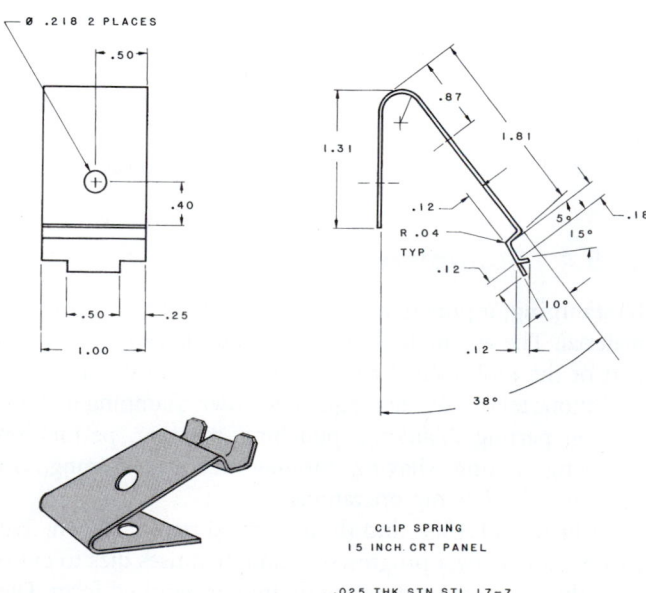

FIGURE 11.45 Clip Spring

Electrochemical machining (ECM) provides many of the same machining capabilities as EDM, but will machine a part much faster. ECM requires more electricity and is more expensive. This process uses electrolyte fluid and electric current to ionize and remove metal from the part.

11.6   Heat Treatment

Heat treatment is the process of applying heat to a material to change the *properties* of the metal but not the shape or size. Some of the typical heat treating terms a drafter and designer will need to know are *annealing, punching, tempering, hardening,* and *normalizing.* Heat treatment can increase the strength and hardness, improve ductility, change the grain size and chemical composition, and improve the machinability of the part. Heat treatment relieves stresses, hardens the part, and modifies the electrical and magnetic properties of the material.

The selection of the appropriate material and heat treatment process is done by the engineer. Heat treating is done in a furnace that generates heat by burning gas or oil or using electricity. Heat treatment covers a wide range of applications and processes.

Heating metal just above its upper critical temperature for a specified period of time and controlled slow cooling in the furnace is called **annealing**. This results in a fully softened, stress-free part. **Quenching** the material in a solution of lime or sand during the cooling period softens the metal and relieves the internal stresses and strains. Heating the metal just below the lower critical temperature and cooling by a predetermined method is called **process annealing**. Process annealing is often used on metals that have been work hardened. Process annealing softens the metal for further cold work.

The heating of metal above its lower critical temperature and quenching in water, oil, or air is called **hardening**. Hardness can be tested by the Rockwell Hardness Test. The **Rockwell Hardness Number** is a value ranging from 15 to 64 and refers to the hardness of the steel. The higher the number, the harder the steel. This numbering system is commonly found on engineering drawings.

Tempering is also called **drawing**. In this process, hardened steel is reheated to a predetermined temperature below its lower critical temperature and then cooled at a specified rate. Drawing or tempering removes the brittleness and toughens the steel. Steel in this condition is called **tempered martensite.**

Heating the steel just below the upper critical temperature and then cooling the material in still air is called **normalizing**. This process is done to improve the grain structure and remove the stresses and strains. The **lower critical temperature** is the lowest temperature at which steel may be quenched in order to harden it. The **upper critical temperature** is the highest temperature at which steel can be quenched in order to attain the finest grain structure and the maximum hardness (martensite).

In Figure 11.36 the notes established the stress relief level at T6. Typically, heat treatment requirements are listed in the notes of a drawing or in the title block. Heat treatment is normally applied after the part has been machined, welded, or forged. Heat treatment can be defined as the heating and controlled cooling of materials to produce a desired mechanical property.

Since the configuration of the part affects the heat treatment itself, the drafter and designer must understand the heat treatment process. To avoid problems during machining and heat treatment, the following considerations must be taken into account during the design stage: balancing the areas of mass, avoiding sharp corners and internal recesses, and keeping hubs of gears, pulleys, and cutters a consistent thickness.

11.7   Automated Manufacturing Processes

Automated manufacturing techniques are used throughout industry. The role of CAM in a CAD/CAM environment includes helping firms achieve the benefits of **computer-integrated manufacturing (CIM)**. (See Color Plates 1–15, 35–43, 61–65, and 68–76.) The CIM concept encompasses manufacturing and computer-based automation applications. CIM can be thought of as a system whose primary *inputs* are product requirements, and whose *outputs* are finished products. CIM comprises a combination of software and hardware for product design, for production planning/control, and for production processes.

CAD/CAM is the CIM integrator for computer-based applications in manufacturing especially computer numerical control programming and robotics. CAD/CAM's integration ability depends on a common engineering and manufacturing database. This database allows engineering to define a product model (part design) and the manufacturing department to use that same model definition to produce the product (Fig. 11.46).

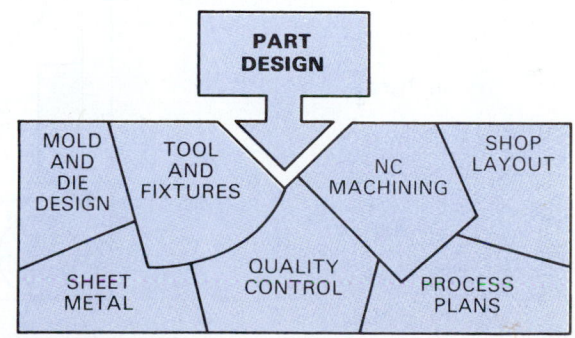

FIGURE 11.46   Part Design   The part database created during the design phase is used by all groups associated with the manufacturing process.

11.7.1 Computer-Aided Manufacturing

CAD is the process that uses a computer to help create or modify a design. *CAM is the process that uses a computer to manage and control the operations of a manufacturing facility.* CAM includes computer numerical control (CNC) for machining operations, tool and fixture design and setup, and integration of industrial robots in the manufacturing process. The integration of computer-aided design and computer-aided manufacturing eliminates duplication of effort by the engineering/design and manufacturing or production departments. An engineering drawing created on a graphics terminal defines the product geometry, which otherwise must be manually derived from the drawing by the manufacturing department before the product is produced.

The production process is computerized from the original graphics input through to the manufacture of the part on a numerically controlled machine. Shop production drawings have been entirely eliminated with this process. By obtaining the product geometry directly from the engineering data, the programmer can extract accurate geometric data replicating the engineer's definition of the part to be manufactured.

As mentioned, CAM speeds the manufacturing process since it uses the same common database initially created in the design and drafting cycle. This database, representing the part (model) design, is used by the manufacturing group. The system serves all applications, promotes standardization to enhance management control, accumulates (rather than randomly collects) manufacturing information, and reduces redundancy and errors.

Many **design-through-manufacture** processes require skilled labor, which is, and probably will continue to be, in short supply. One of the major goals of the CAD/CAM system is to transfer the experience and skills of a few individuals to the database. This provides less experienced personnel with access to technical information. DFM usually simplifies the part design and the manufacturing requirements for the production of the part, therefore reducing the level of skilled labor required to produce the product.

Using a CAD/CAM system, the engineer or designer applies the CAD features to create a model of the part. Then, using the information stored in the database, the manufacturing engineer applies the CAM capabilities. A CAD system may have a variety of specialized CAM capabilities including the following:

- group technology
- process planning
- shop layout
- programming of machining operations
- CNC postprocessing
- sheet metal applications
- tool and fixture design
- mold design and testing
- technical publications and manufacturing documentation
- quality control

To use computer-aided manufacturing, the following steps must be accomplished:

1. *Process planning:* The engineering drawing of the part to be tooled must be interpreted in terms of the manufacturing processes to be used. This step is referred to as process planning, and it should be given thought and consideration before part programming is begun.
2. *Part programming:* A part programmer plans the process for the portions of the job to be accomplished by computer numerical control. Part programmers are knowledgeable about the machining process and they have been trained to program for computer numerical control. They are responsible for planning the sequence of machining steps to be performed by CNC and to document these in a special format. There are two ways to program for CNC: manual part programming and computer-assisted part programming

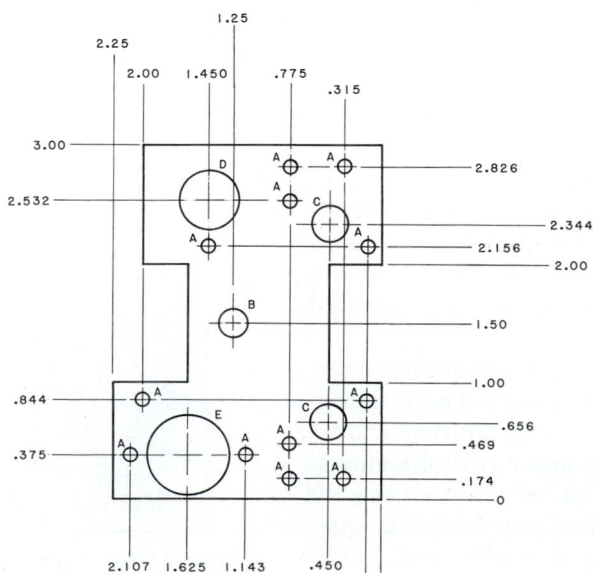

HOLE	DESCRIPTION	QTY
A	.125 DIA	12
B	.250 DIA	1
C	.312 DIA	2
D	.500 DIA	1
E	.688 DIA	1

.063 ALY ALUM 6061-T6 ANODIZE BLACK

FIGURE 11.47   Connector Plate

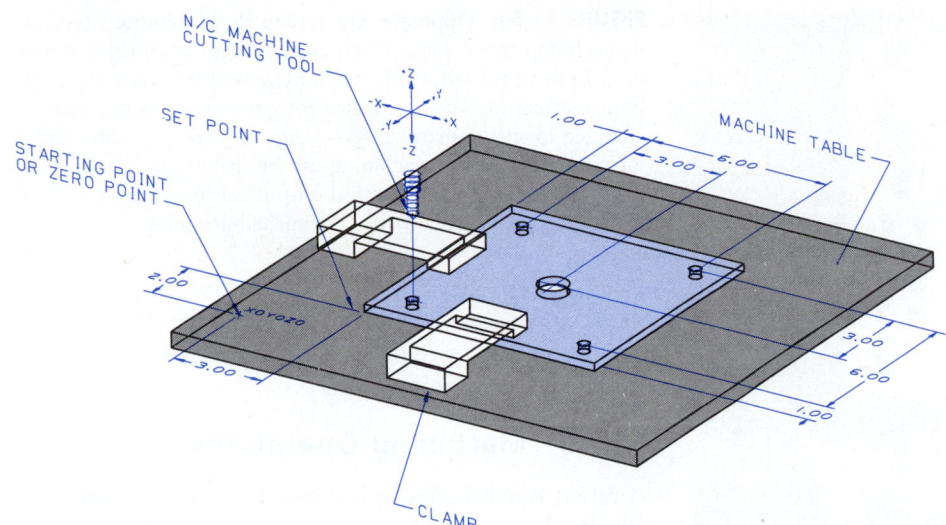

FIGURE 11.48   CNC Part Setup

In **manual part programming**, the machining instructions are prepared on a form called a part program manuscript. The manuscript is a listing of the relative cutter positions that must be followed to machine the part. In **computer-assisted part programming**, much of the computational work required in manual part programming is transferred to the computer. This is especially advantageous for complex part geometries and jobs with many machining steps. In computer-assisted part programming, the computer interprets the list of part programming instructions, performs the necessary calculations to convert this into a detailed set of machine tool motion commands, and develops a chosen transfer medium containing the CNC data for the specific CNC machine.

3. *Verification:* The program is checked by plotting the tool movements on paper. In this way, errors in the program can be discovered. The test of the part program is making a trial part on the machine tool. A foam or plastic material is sometimes used for this test. CAD systems with CAD/CAM capabilities allow verification of toolpaths and cutter motion on the display.

4. *Transfer media preparation:* Punched tape was originally used to transfer a part program from the computer to an NC machine. Floppy and mini disks and direct computer networks are now used as a transfer medium.

5. *Production:* Production involves ordering the rough parts, specifying and preparing the tooling and any special fixturing that may be required, and setting up the CNC machine. The machine tool operator's function during production is to load the data in the machine and establish the starting position of the cutting tool relative to the rough part. The CNC system then machines the part according to the instructions. When the part is completed, the operator removes it from the machine and loads the next part. In more automated operations, a programmable robot performs these tasks in conjunction with computer control instead of an operator.

11.7.2   Numerical Control

Numerical control (NC) can be defined as a form of programmable automation, in which the process is controlled by numbers, letters, and symbols. In NC, the numbers form a program of instructions designed for a particular part or job. When the job changes, the program of instructions is changed. This capability to change the program for each new

job is what gives NC its flexibility. It is much easier to write new programs than to make major changes in the production equipment.

Programming a NC machine requires a good working knowledge of machine tools, tool design, print reading, and manufacturing processes. Figure 11.47 shows a part dimensioned for ease of NC programming. Each hole and edge has a dimension taken from the **X0,Y0,Z0** position of the piece, which in this case is in the lower right-hand corner. The **X0,Y0,Z0** position is established according to the machine and the part configuration and machining requirements. In Figure 11.48 the machining table, the part, and the clamps holding the part are shown. The starting point is **X0,Y0,Z0**. Note the 3D coordinate system shown at the top of the cutting tool.

The two major types of NC machines in use today are point-to-point and continuous path machines. The movement of the tool in reference to the work piece establishes the difference between the two. **Point-to-point** machines operate on a series of programmed coordinates to locate the position of the tool. When the tool finishes at one point, it continues to the next point (position). This type of control is used for drilling and punching machines. Milling machines require continuous control of tool position and therefore they use a **continuous path**. Complicated operations including contouring, angle surfaces, fillets, and radii can be programmed using the continuous path method. The toolpath can be displayed on the CAD/CAM system, thereby providing verification of the cutter's movement without running an actual part on the machine. The **toolpath** is the trace of the movement of the tip of a cutting tool that is used to guide or control machining equipment.

Computer numerical control (CNC) is eliminating the older form of programming. When the program is complete, repetitive productions are done by controls having memory of the part in the computer system. Figure 11.49 shows a CNC mill. In CNC, the design database is passed directly form the CAD/CAM system to the machine's computer. The description

FIGURE 11.49 CNC Mill

FIGURE 11.50 Opposite, On-screen Programming (a) Task menu from control data's ICEM engineering library (b) The solid model can be rotated, exploded, and viewed from any angle. (c) A finite element model is generated for common geometry and analyzed to ensure that it meets design criteria. (d) Cutter paths for numerical control machining can be defined and modified at the CAD terminal. (e) Numerical output can be used for CNC machining of the actual part. (f) Finished assembly review

Plates 13, 14, and 15). Output from the postprocessor can then be used for machining of the actual part [Fig. 11.50(e)], and the finished assembly can, as a last step, be displayed and reviewed, as shown in (f).

11.7.3 Machining Operations

A variety of machining operations, ranging from simple two-axis point-to-point functions to complex multiaxis machining, are possible. These operations may include drilling, punching, milling, turning, profiling, pocketing, surface machining, and flame cutting. The types of parts that may be produced on CNC equipment from output generated by CAD/CAM systems include:

- irregular or uniquely machined parts
- 2D parts created by point-to-point operations
- lathe parts produced by turning operations
- $2\frac{1}{2}$D parts, which may require pocketing and profiling operations
- 3D parts produced by using all of the CNC operations provided on the CAD/CAM system

Pocketing is the process of completely removing material within a bounded area (Fig. 11.51). Machine pocket programs provide automatic pocketing on a CAD system by generating a toolpath to remove the material contained within a closed boundary. Capabilities include multiple-base **rough cutting**, **multiple-side cutting**, a designer-specified final **finishing pass**, and **islands** defined within a pocket (Fig. 11.52).

Profiling is the automatic generation of a continuously contoured toolpath around a boundary (Figs. 11.51 and 11.52). The cutting tool moves outside or inside a profile. Capabilities include multiple-base rough cutting, multiple side rough cutting, and a designer-specified final finishing pass.

11.7.4 Toolpath Simulation and Verification

CAD/CAM systems provide accurate and realistic verification of both 2D and 3D toolpaths without cutting metal. The programmer can simulate and visually verify the toolpath on the display. The toolpath seen on the display may show the tool and holder actually moving along the part from any viewing angle. This permits the designer to check for toolpath correctness and clearance of tools, parts, and fixtures. Once toolpaths are created, they may be edited and assembled into sets, machining statements may be added, and then toolpaths may be output to a specific machine. Toolpaths may also be transformed into programming languages such as APT or COMPACT.

of the part developed with the computer-aided design system is the input to the computer-aided manufacturing system, which, in turn, commands the machine tool postprocessor to develop the machine instructions (see Color Plates 13–15 and 41–43).

The programmer defines cutting tools, creates a tool library, and retrieves these tools later to create toolpath information. CAM packages support most types of cutting tools; therefore, the programmer can describe many types of generally used cutting tools (flat, ball, tapered). The CAM system allows for definition of machining characteristics such as retract and clearance plane, cutting depth, feed rate (rate of travel), and spindle speed (rate of spindle rotation).

Figure 11.50(a) through (f) show a sequence of design, analysis, simulation, and manufacturing for a spindle. The menu shown in (a) is used to manage the engineering data needed to model and test the part. The **solid model** of Figure 11.50(b) is used to assist the designer in creating, analyzing, and visually displaying the part. In (c), finite element analysis packages are used for part analysis and generating a mesh of the part from the geometry (see Color Plates 1–15 and 35–43). **Cutter paths** for CNC machining are defined and modified by the part programmer in Figure 11.50(d) (see Color

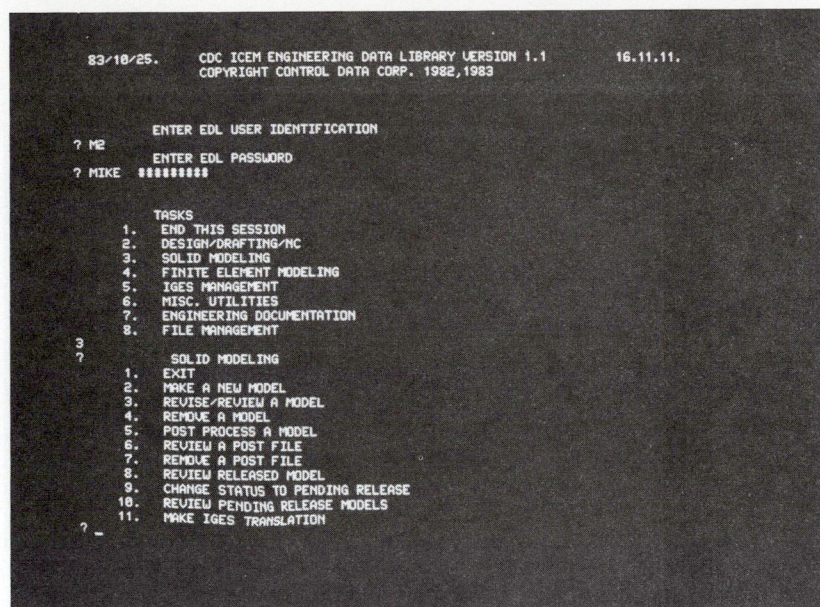

(a)

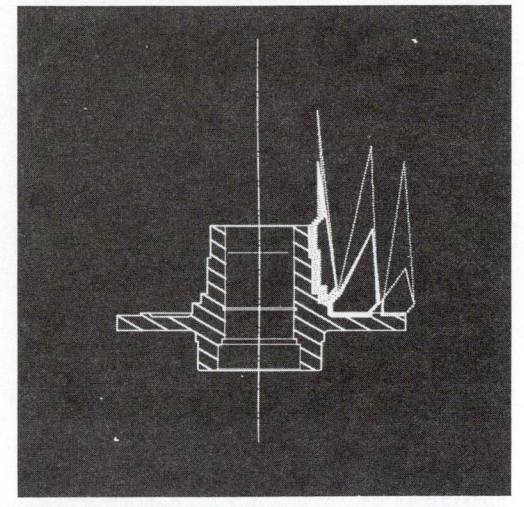

(d)

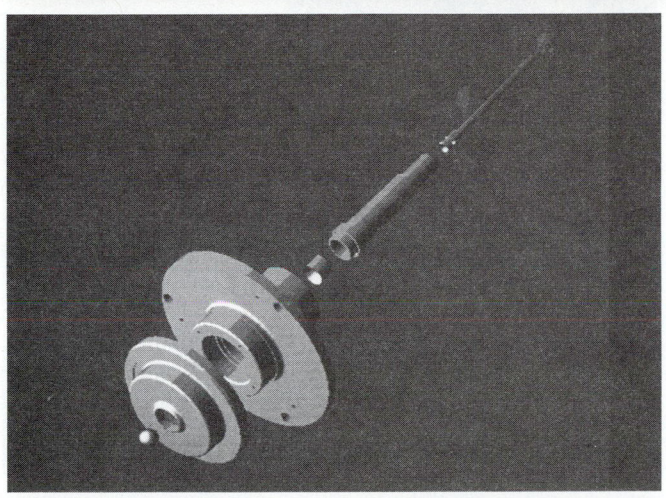

(b)

(e)

(c)

(f)

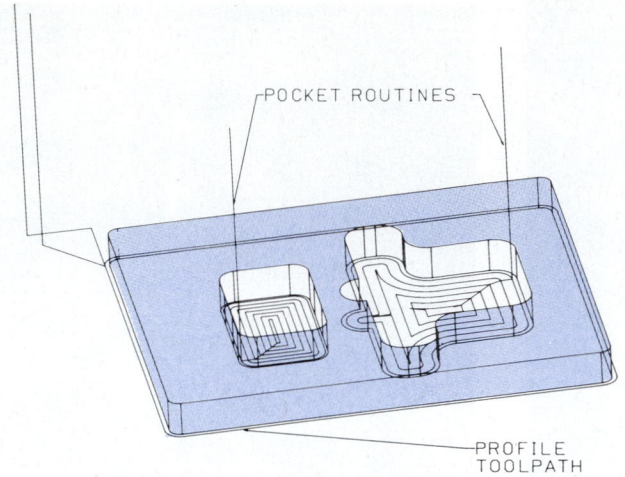

FIGURE 11.51 **Toolpath Generation** A variety of toolpaths can be created including profiling and pocketing.

(a)

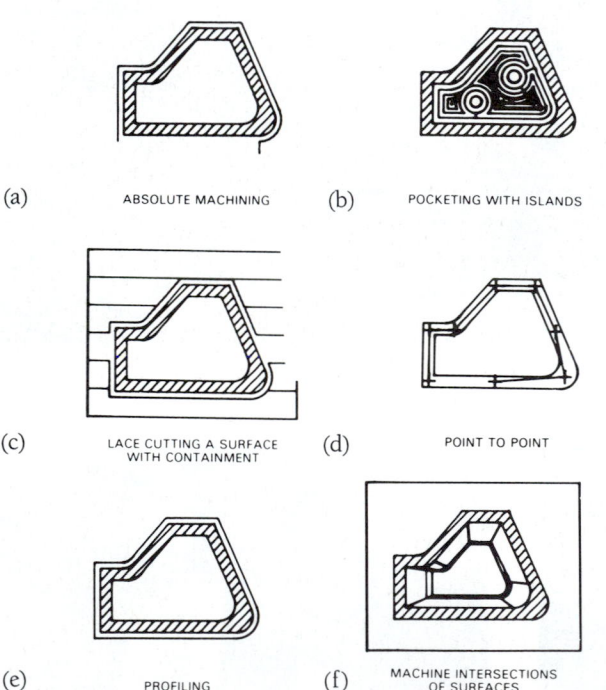

(a) ABSOLUTE MACHINING

(b) POCKETING WITH ISLANDS

(c) LACE CUTTING A SURFACE WITH CONTAINMENT

(d) POINT TO POINT

(e) PROFILING

(f) MACHINE INTERSECTIONS OF SURFACES

FIGURE 11.52 **NC Toolpaths** Six examples of toolpath generation are shown: (a) Absolute machining is a totally operator-controlled toolpath definition process for milling, drilling, and lathe operations. (b) Pocketing with islands is an operation where the user defines the part's boundaries and other machining parameters. (c) Lace cutting is a surface machining operation creating a laced toolpath for pocketing and milling. (d) Point-to-point machining automatically generates a toolpath for specified drilling locations. (e) Profiling automatically generates toolpaths for contour milling inside or outside of a part. (f) Machining intersections automatically generates multiple-surface machining toolpaths.

(b)

(c)

FIGURE 11.53 **Mold Design** (a) Computer design of part (b) Mold being machined (c) Finished part and mold

11.7.5   Tools, Fixtures, and Mold Design

In general, a **tool** is a piece of equipment that helps create a finished part. It may be anything that must be designed and/or made in order to manufacture the part. CAD systems may support the design and manufacture of the following tools:

- **Molds** are used to form a variety of parts for consumer, industrial, and medical applications.
- **Dies** are used to forge, cast, extrude, and stamp materials while in various physical states (solid through fluid).
- **Tooling** is the individual component of mold or die; tooling might include a cavity, nest, core, punch, bushing, slide, or sleeve.

Figure 11.53(a) shows an example of mold design using a CAD system. The mold for the part being machined in (b) is shown complete in (c). In Figure 11.54(a) through (c) a shoe was designed and displayed on a CRT using a mesh model. The mold was also designed on the system in (b) and is shown being machined in (c).

Fixtures are used to hold and locate parts of assemblies during machining or other manufacturing operations [Fig. 11.55(a) and (b)]. See Chapters 17 and 18 for more information on fixtures. The accuracy of the product being produced determines the precision with which a fixture is designed. To design and manufacture a finished part efficiently, product design engineers must work with tool and fixture designers as well as manufacturing engineers. CAD promotes this interaction by providing one common database for the product design and the associated tool/fixture design, manufacture, and production. When designing a tool or fixture, the manufacturing engineer retrieves the part design from the database to determine how the tool or fixture should be built to produce the finished product.

To determine the materials needed to produce a tool/fixture designed on the system, CAD can automatically output a bill of materials for the purchasing department. A bill of materials lists quantities and associated information needed to manufacture the product(s). Process planners can then use the database to create process instructions and plans.

11.8   Robotics

Robotics is the integration of computer-controlled robots in the manufacturing process. Industrial robots (Fig. 11.56) are used to move, manipulate, position, weld, machine, and do a variety of other manufacturing processes. A **robot** is a reprogrammable, multifunction manipulator designed to move material, parts (including the workpiece), tools, or specialized devices through variable, programmed motions for the performance of a variety of tasks. Robotics includes the control and synchronization of the equipment that the robot works with, a capability that can eliminate the need for humans to work in hazardous environments. Robots are controlled by a microprocessor and are composed of a separate stand-alone computer station, the robot mechanism itself, and an electrical-hydraulic power unit.

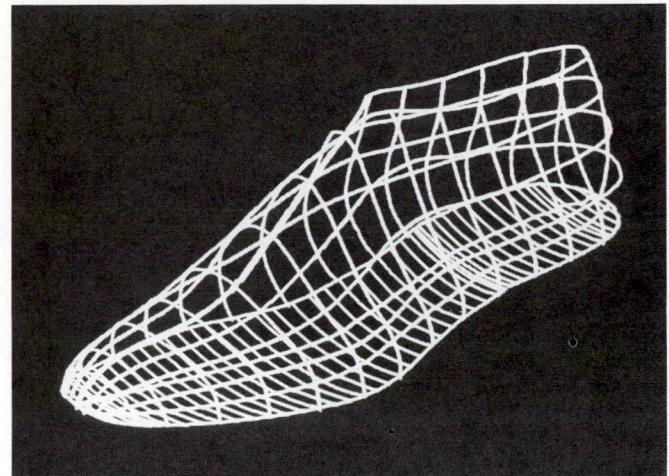

(a)

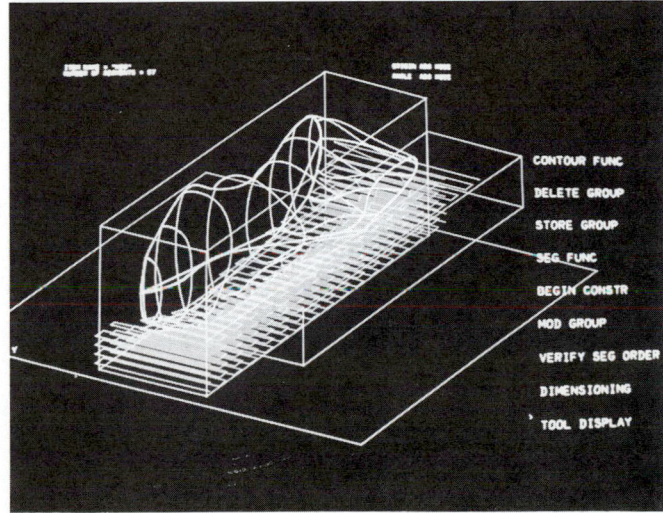

(b)

(c)

FIGURE 11.54   Shoe Mold   (a) Mesh model of a shoe design (b) Shoe mold design (c) CNC machining of a shoe mold

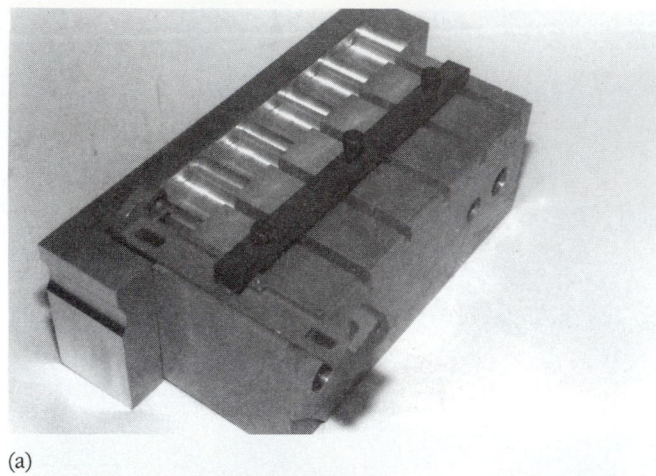

(a)

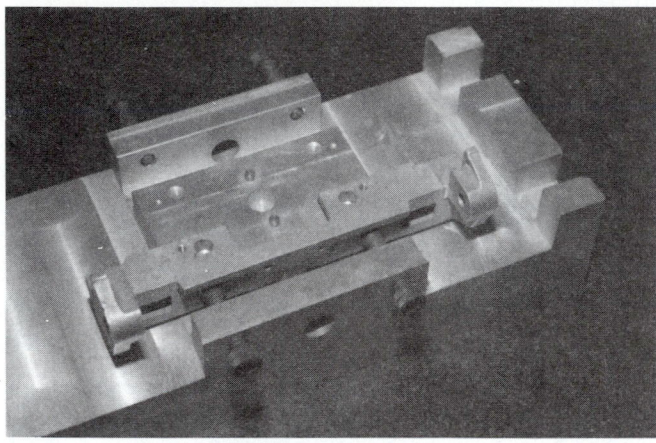

(b)

FIGURE 11.55   **Fixtures**   (a) Fixture for machining multiple parts (b) Fixture for machining two parts

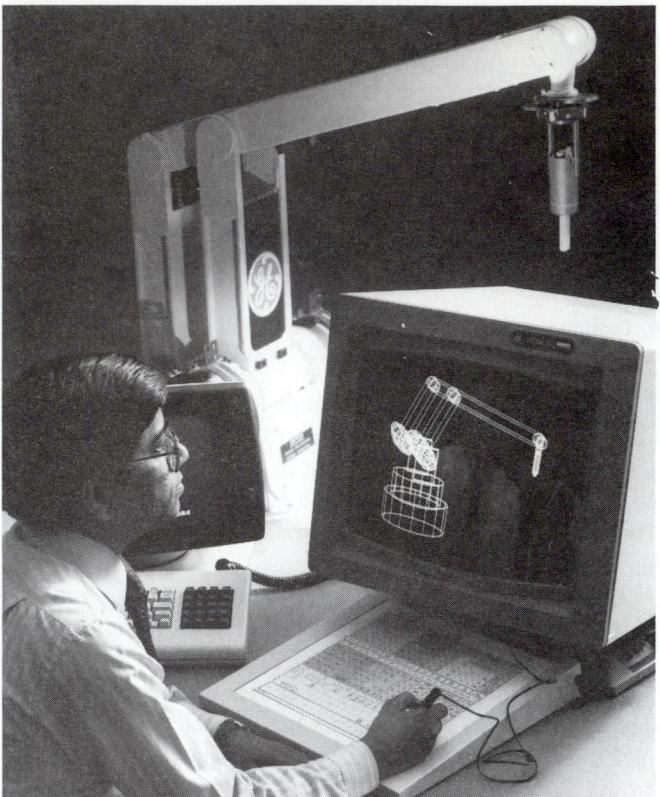

FIGURE 11.56   **Robot Simulation**   Robotics simulation program enables automation engineers to put a robot through its paces on the computer screen—rather than through trial-and-error on the factory floor. You can design a factory workcell, simulate a robot's movements and performance in it, and then modify both the robot's movements and the surrounding machinery for optimal efficiency. This can be accomplished at the computer terminal without employing any robotic hardware.

The part workpiece can be visually placed on the screen by the robot using simulation (Fig. 11.56). To take fullest advantage of robotic control and movement of the workpiece during manufacturing, the designer needs to design the part with robotic manufacturing methods in mind—not after the fact. Using a 3D CAD database for the part allows this type of robotic programming before manufacturing begins. DFM includes part design with robotic manufacturing techniques designed into the part at the earliest stages of the project.

11.8.1   CAD/CAM Robotic Applications

The integration of CAD/CAM and robotics results in increased productivity for robotic implementation activities. CAD/CAM robotic applications include: robotic workcell design, robotic workcell programming, and robotic workcell simulation.

The **robotic workcell** contains all the physical equipment needed to create a functioning robot application [Fig. 11.57(a)]. Besides the robot, a workcell can have special fixturing, automated machines (CNC machines, coordinate measuring machines, or visual-inspection equipment),

material-handling devices, part-presentation equipment, and robot grippers.

The equipment in the workcell must be arranged so that the **robot work envelope** includes all required device areas. The work envelope is controlled by the size of the robot. Libraries [Fig. 11.57(b)] of workcell components can be stored on the CAD/CAM system and recalled when needed. For example, a **robot library** could contain commercial robots along with their work envelopes.

CAD/CAM workcell design results in many benefits. First, the design activity is more productive, plus design time and costs are reduced. Second, CAD/CAM for workcell layout allows more alternatives to be considered, resulting in an optimal layout. Third, the lead time to design and lay out the cell is reduced. Fourth, quality of the designed components and the overall cell quality is increased.

With **graphic robotic simulation** CAD systems are used to simulate the programmed robot path. Simulation checks whether or not the robot can position its end effector to the specified positions and orientations. It is possible that the robot's end effector cannot assume the desired position and

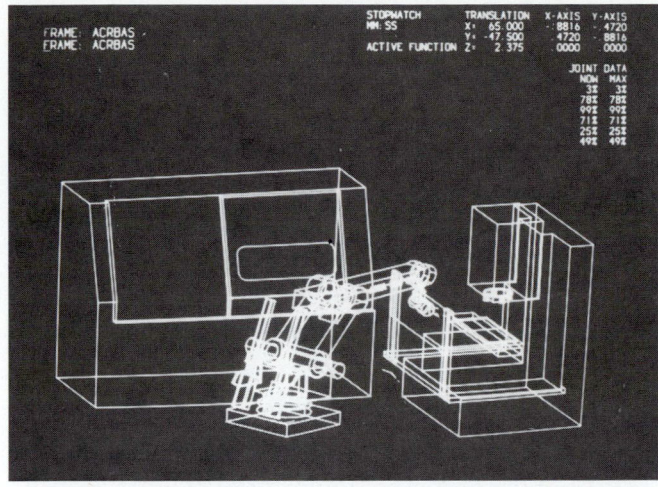

(a)

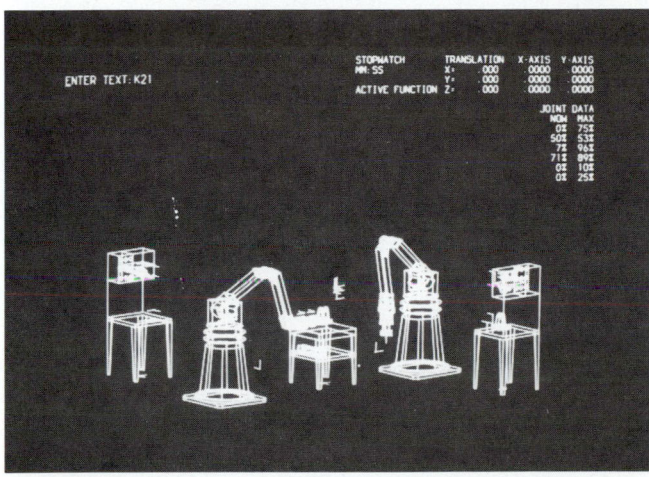

(b)

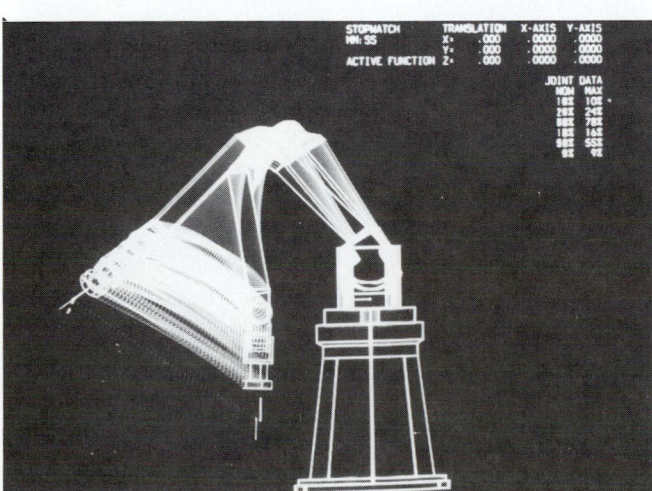

(c)

FIGURE 11.57   **Robotics**   (a) Robot and related machinery workcell evaluation simulation shown on a display (b) Robotic workcell library (c) Robot simulation of arm movement

orientation required, so revision of the path or workcell may be required. Also, the robot's **degrees of freedom** [Fig. 11.57(c)] may not be sufficient to accomplish a given task. The degrees of freedom are the total area and movement capability of the robot. Simulation creates the actual robot trajectory using end-effector positions available from graphic robotic programming.

QUIZ

True or False

1. Patterns are made smaller than the real size of the part to allow for expansion of the metal (expansion allowance).
2. The surface texture symbol is used for designating the classification of roughness, waviness, and lay.
3. Roughness is the distance between ridges or peaks on a surface.
4. Robots can be programmed and their movements verified without touching the actual robot hardware.
5. NC is a form of programmable automation controlled by numbers, letters, or symbols.
6. Pocketing is the process of removing material from the outer boundaries of a part.
7. A true CAD/CAM system can create a common database, which is then used to derive part geometry for all areas of manufacturing and design.
8. Toolpaths can be simulated on 2D and 3D CAD systems.

Fill in the Blanks

9. _____ , _____ , and _____ are done on a drill press.
10. _____ , _____ , _____ , _____ , and _____ are the five basic types of machining processes.
11. A _____ _____ is used to allow the cast part to be removed from the form more easily.
12. _____ is the process of pouring molten metal into a mold.
13. Machining a continuous toolpath about a part is called _____ .
14. The creation of a common _____ enables the part geometry to be used by many departments.
15. Robot _____ _____ simulation helps ensure accurate movement of the robot and its relation to the operation and surrounding equipment.
16. Toolpaths can be _____ and _____ on the display.

Answer the Following

17. Describe the difference and uses of drilling, reaming, and boring.
18. From your own experience name five metal parts that have been cast.
19. Drilling is used before what types of basic tooling operations?
20. What are robots and how are they being used in industry? What type of tasks are they doing and why?
21. What part does CAD play in the total process of CAM? How does the use of a common database affect the design-through-manufacturing process?
22. How can a CAD system be used in verification? Discuss its uses and effects on CAM in general. Mention CNC, tooling design, and robotics in your evaluation.
23. What is a robotic workcell and how can a CAD system help in its overall efficiency?
24. What is profiling and pocketing?

PROBLEMS

For each of the following problems, draw the part using the minimum number of views necessary to display the design graphically. Leave sufficient space for dimensioning. After completing Chapter 12, dimension each of these projects as assigned by your instructor.

On a separate sheet of paper, list the operations required for manufacturing each of the parts—drilling, reaming, boring, threading; milling machine operations including profiling, pocketing, etc.; lathe operations including facing and parting, etc. List the material and whether the part is to be made from a stock piece or cast, forged, stamped, or some other process.

Problem 11.1   Draw the detail of the cylinder lip ring shown in Figure 11.2.

Problem 11.2   Redraw the part in Figure 11.9.

Problem 11.3   Draw the part in Figure 11.11.

Problem 11.4   Draw the cylinder rod shown in Figure 11.15.

Problem 11.5   Draw the link shown in Figure 11.20.

Problem 11.6   Draw the aircraft part provided in Figure 11.36.

Problem 11.7   Redraw the detail of the part in Figure 11.41.

Problem 11.8   Draw the spring in Figure 11.45. Show a view of the part before it was bent (unfolded).

Problem 11.9   Draw the part in Figure 11.47.

CHAPTER 12

Dimensioning

Learning Objectives

Upon completion of this chapter you will be able to accomplish the following:

1. Analyze part features in terms of integral geometric shapes to facilitate concise dimensioning within prescribed tolerances.
2. Apply ANSI standards for dimensions and tolerances.
3. Apply angular, callout, overall, limited length, and area dimensions.
4. Develop ability to dimension and recognize standard symbols for curved features.
5. Define and dimension chamfers, threads, centerdrills, tapers, knurling and keyways.
6. Recognize finish marks, general symbols and notes, and ANSI basic surface texture symbols.
7. Apply rectangular continuous coordinate dimensioning and polar coordinate dimensioning.
8. Develop familiarity with the associative dimensioning capabilities of CAD.

12.1 Introduction

Almost all engineering design relies on common geometrical shapes. Complete or portions of prisms, cylinders, cones, and spheres, alone or in combination, will be predominant in all designs of mechanical parts. Partly for ease of manufacture and partly due to design requirements, these shapes are used throughout engineering work. Being able to analyze a part by breaking it into simple geometric shapes enables you to understand what dimensions are required. The sole purpose of an engineering drawing is not the drawing or illustration itself, but the part manufactured from the information on the drawing.

Engineering drawings require dimensions and notes to convey the proper information for manufacturing or construction. Regardless of whether the part is drawn and dimensioned manually or with a CAD system (Fig. 12.1), knowledge of the methods and practices of dimensioning and tolerancing is essential. The multiview projections of a part provide a graphic representation of its shape, called its *shape description*. However, for the drawing to describe the part completely so it can be correctly fabricated, it must contain information that specifies the size and other requirements, such as manufacturing requirements.

Drawings for a part are *annotated* with dimensions and notes. Dimensions must be provided between points, lines, or surfaces that are functionally related to each other or to control relationships with other parts. A drafter must provide sufficient and correct dimensions so that manufacturing personnel will not have to compute dimensions or guess intent. Each dimension on a drawing has a **tolerance**, either implied or specified. The general tolerance given in the title block is called a **general** or **sheet tolerance** (see Fig. 12.77, p. 395). Specific tolerances are provided with each appropriate dimension. Together, the views, dimensions, and notes give the

FIGURE 12.1 **Dimensioning with a CAD System**

complete shape and size description of the part (Fig. 12.2). If any of these is incorrect, the part will be fabricated incorrectly—assuming that the shop follows the drawing. Therefore, accuracy of views and dimensions is of utmost importance. Tolerances are discussed in greater detail in Chapter 13.

12.2 Dimensioning Standards

Uniform practices for stating and interpreting dimensioning and tolerancing requirements were established in **ANSI Y14.5M**. An aspiring drafter or designer should have a copy of the standards. The International System of Units (SI) (i.e., metric) is used along with U.S. customary units in this chapter and in Chapter 13 because SI units are eventually expected to replace U.S. customary units on engineering drawings.

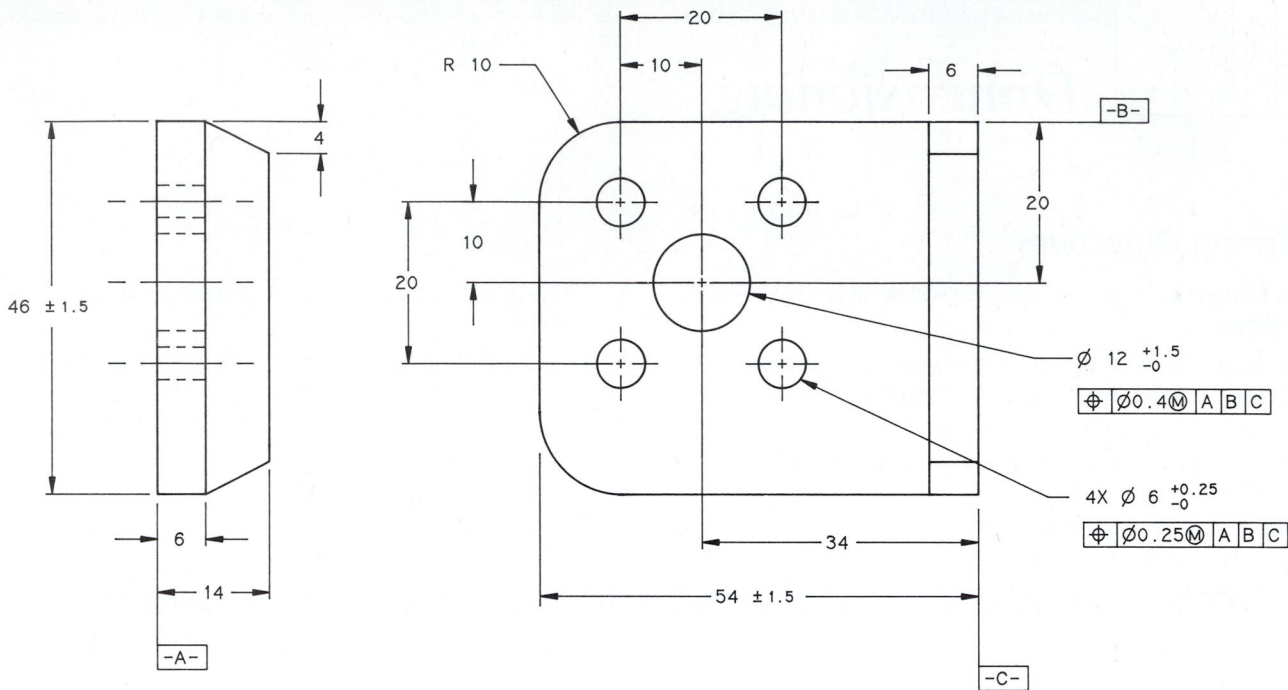

FIGURE 12.2 Mechanical Drawing Using SI Units of Measurement

Figure 12.2 shows a simple part dimensioned in SI units (millimeters) and Figure 12.3 shows a part dimensioned in U.S. decimal-inch units. Either type of unit could have been used in each of the examples and illustrations throughout the text with equal results.

Some of the industry example drawings and problems in the text conform to earlier standards. Because you will come in contact with drawings that do not reflect the newest standards, study all the examples carefully. In fact, a few companies continue to use the older practices rather than face the expense and trouble of converting to new standards. *However, when completing any project or exercise from the text, follow the practices of the most recent standards.*

All drawings must be clear, well laid out, and contain the required dimensions, text, notes, finishes, etc. The advantage of a CAD database over a manual drawing is that checker changes and corrections are easily incorporated into the drawing and a new "original" drawing plotted. The manual method requires the original drawing to be erased and corrected, a time-consuming process. Another advantage of creating a CAD database for a part is that manufacturing can call up the part and *read the database*: verify (**LIST** on AutoCAD) the geometry, ask the system for clarification of a feature, and request measurements not provided on the plotted drawing.

12.2.1 Dimensioning Terms

The following terms are used throughout this chapter:

Dimension A numeric value expressed in appropriate units of measure and indicated on a drawing and in other documents along with lines, symbols, and notes to define the size or geometric characteristic, or both, of a part or part feature. Example: 12.875 (in.), 25 (mm), etc.

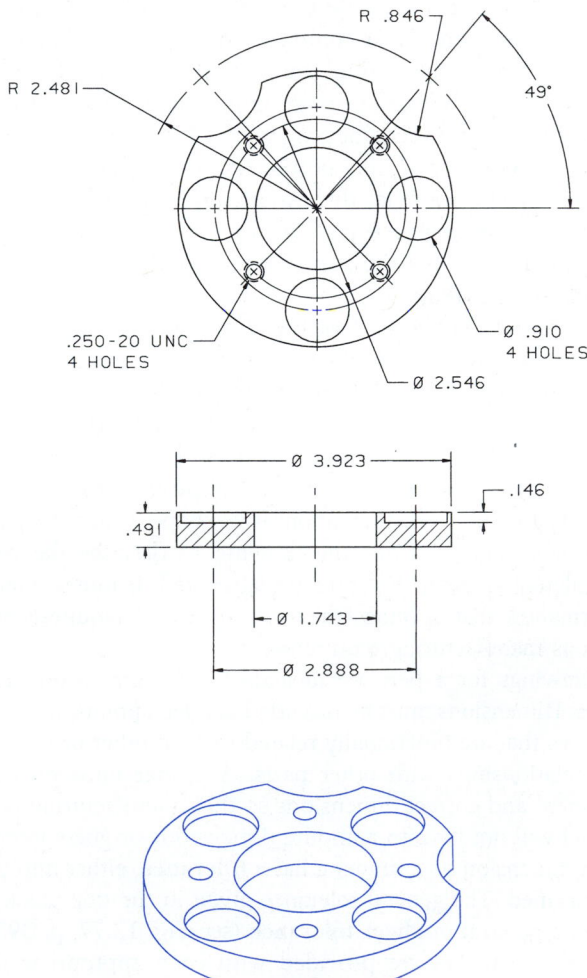

FIGURE 12.3 Mechanical Drawing Using U.S. Decimal Units

ITEMS OF INTEREST

The History of the Metric Standard

The metric system is a "standard" system of weights and measures based on the meter, a unit of length, and the kilogram, a unit of mass. But what does "standard" mean?

Noah was told to build his ark 300 cubits long. A cubit was the measured distance from the elbow to the extended finger. Some people have longer arms and fingers than others, so this is an interesting standard unit of length. On average, a cubit is about 18 inches, which means that Noah built an ark about 450 feet in length (as big as an ocean liner)!

If you study the history of measurement, you will discover that standards were loosely defined and crudely measured. Many variations were found within a country. Charlemagne, emperor of the Holy Roman Empire from 800–814, used his foot as the standard length measurement. In Europe, the measure used was shorter than the English foot. The Chinese used a measure that was longer. King Henry stated that a yard was the distance from his nose to his outstretched middle finger of his right hand. An inch was the width of three barley corns laying side by side.

It was obvious to many that a "standard" system of measurement was desperately needed. In the 1790s Thomas Jefferson proposed a plan for the adoption of a standard system to Congress. Louis XVI of France tried to persuade the United States and Great Britain to cooperate in setting a standard. Although Great Britain and the United States did not join his effort, many other countries did. The end result of that project was the metric system. The standard was organized when a committee from the French Academy made its report to the National

The Cubit, An Ancient Unit of Measure

Assembly. It was adopted into French law and even though other countries adopted it, use of the system spread slowly.

Originally, the meter was one ten-millionth part of the distance from the North Pole to the Equator, passing through Paris. Later, they discovered the measurement was slightly short, so they defined it again. This time it was the distance between two marks on a platinum/iridium bar. The bar became known as the International Prototype Meter and was placed in the Bureau of Archives in Paris. A meter was later redefined as 1,650,763.73 wavelengths of the orange-red line of krypton 86. The International Bureau of Weights and Measures was formed in 1875 (Paris). The copies of the standards owned by the United States are housed in the National Institute of Standards and Technology, NIST, in Washington D.C. (formerly the National Bureau of Standards).

The metric system has been universally accepted—except in the United

States and some of the British Commonwealth. Its use was legalized in the United States in 1866. In 1975, the U.S. Congress passed a bill allowing for voluntary conversion to the metric system. A special board, the U.S. Metric Board, was formed to implement this program.

The use of the metric system in the United States has increased consistently over the years. The automobile industry has been one proponent of this conversion. With cars assembled from parts manufactured all over the world, it seems very reasonable to agree on one standard measurement. However, there is an investment in the "English" system in the United States. The "English" system is now called the U.S. Customary System. New computer numerically controlled (CNC) machines can be used to cut a millimeter or an inch because of the way their motors are controlled. It seems reasonable to expect metric units to replace U.S. customary units in the United States and become the universal "standard." When is another question.

Reference dimension   A dimension, usually without tolerance, used for information only. It is considered auxiliary information and does not govern production or inspection operations. A reference dimension repeats a dimension or size already given or is derived from other values shown on the drawing or related drawings. Reference dimensions are enclosed in parentheses. Example: (23.50), (50), etc.

Datum   The origin from which the location or geometric characteristics of features of a part are established.

Feature   The general term applied to a physical portion of a part, e.g., a surface, hole, or slot.

Datum feature   A geometric feature of a part that is used to establish a datum. Example: a point, line, surface, hole, etc.

Actual size   The measured size of the feature.

Limits of size   The specified maximum and minimum limits of a feature.

Tolerance   The total amount by which a specific dimension is permitted to vary. The tolerance is the difference between the maximum and minimum limits.

12.2.2   Units of Measurement

The SI linear unit commonly shown on engineering drawings is the millimeter. The U.S. customary linear unit used on engineering drawings is the decimal-inch. On drawings where all dimensions are either in millimeters or inches, individual identification of linear units is not required. However, the drawing must contain a note stating:

> UNLESS OTHERWISE SPECIFIED, ALL DIMENSIONS ARE IN MILLIMETERS (or INCHES).

Dimensions are shown to only as many decimal places as accuracy requires. The inch or millimeter symbol is omitted unless the dimension may be misunderstood or where feet and inches are used on construction drawings. When U.S. customary units are used, fractions and decimals are not mixed on the same drawing. (See Appendix for U.S. customary and SI equivalent measurements.) If inch dimensions are shown on a millimeter-dimensioned drawing, the abbreviation "in." must follow the inch values. If millimeter dimensions are shown on an inch-dimensioned drawing, the symbol "mm" must follow the millimeter values.

Angular dimensions are expressed in either decimal parts of a degree or in degrees, minutes, and seconds. These latter dimensions are expressed by symbols: for degrees, °; for minutes, ′; and for seconds, ″. If degrees are indicated alone, the numerical value is followed by the symbol ° .

12.3   Types of Dimensioning

Decimal dimensioning is used on drawings except where certain commercial commodities are identified by standardized nominal designations such as pipe, steel, and lumber sizes. The following rules apply to all drawings:

Metric Dimensioning (Figs. 12.2 and 12.4):

1. If the dimension is less than 1 mm, a zero precedes the decimal point.
2. If the dimension is a whole number, neither the decimal point nor a zero is shown.
3. If the dimension exceeds a whole number by a decimal fraction of 1 mm, the last digit to the right of the decimal point is not followed by a zero.
4. Neither commas nor spaces are used to separate digits into groups in specifying millimeter dimensions on drawings.

Decimal-Inch Dimensioning (Figs. 12.3 and 12.5):

1. A zero is not used before the decimal point for values of less than 1 in.
2. A tolerance is expressed to the same number of decimal places as its dimension. Zeros are added to the right of the decimal point where necessary for both the dimension and the tolerance.

Decimal Points (SI and U.S. units):

1. Decimal points must be uniform, dense, and large enough to be clearly visible and to meet the reproduction requirements of ANSI Y14.2M. Decimal points are placed in line with the bottom of the associated digits.
2. When a dimension is 1 unit, always add a decimal and a zero (1.0).

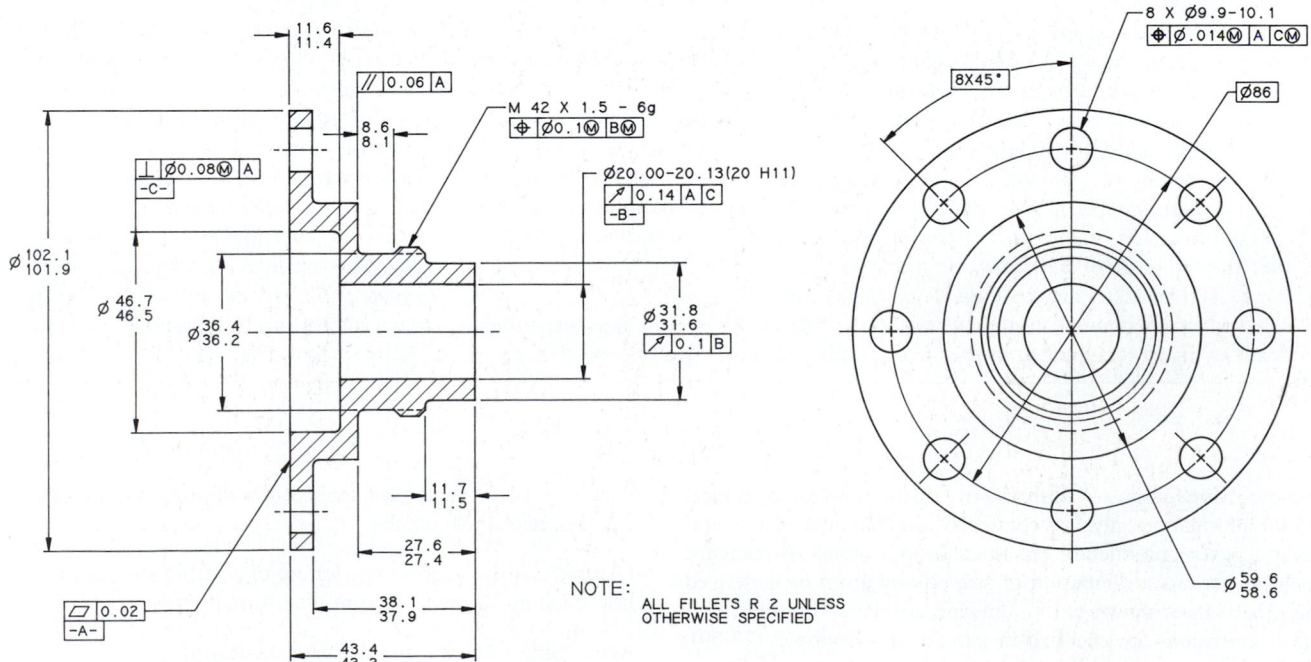

FIGURE 12.4   Geometric Tolerancing and Dimensioning Employed to Dimension a Mechanical Part

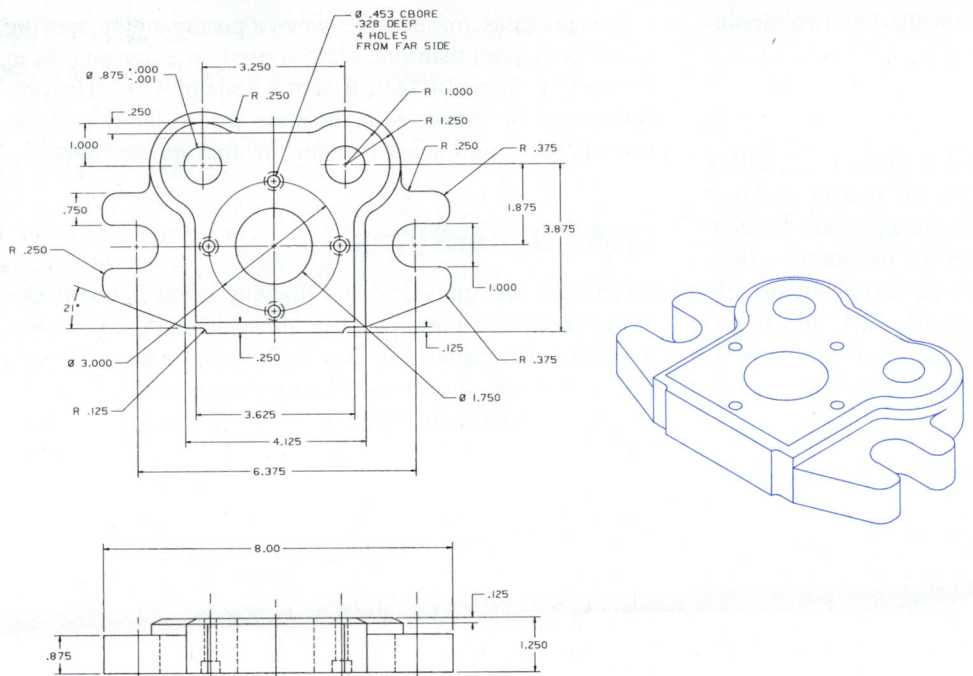

FIGURE 12.5 Mechanical Part Designed and Dimensioned in U.S. Standard Decimal Units

12.3.1 Dual Dimensioning

Many parts designed in the United States are manufactured overseas. Therefore, some drawings use **dual dimensioning,** which includes U.S. customary units *and* metric units. The top measurement, or first measurement when placed on the same line, in dual dimensioning is always the unit of measurement used to design the part. Example: $\frac{1.00}{25.4}$

12.3.2 Dimensioning Numerals

Whole numbers in the inch system are normally shown to at least one decimal place (e.g., 1.0, 2.0, 3.0). This practice prevents dimensions from being "lost" on the drawing, which is a common occurrence when the number 1 is not accompanied by a decimal point and a zero (1.0).

Common fraction dimensions are seldom used, except on construction drawings. Before the adoption of the decimal-inch, common fractions were used for subdivisions of the inch to specify nominal sizes and dimensions. Some firms still use this system, especially where the tolerance factor is relatively unimportant. Older company and sheet metal drawings also show this type of dimensioning.

The use of decimals has many advantages over the use of fractions. Decimals simplify arithmetic computations and greatly reduce the computing time and effort. For example, it can take as much as five times longer to add a series of fractions than a series of decimals. On the other hand, fractions need to be converted into the equivalent decimals, which may vary from two to six places, and the total still has to be converted back to a fraction. Many decimal measurements must be rounded before using.

12.3.3 Rounding Off Decimal-Inch Measurements

A method of rounding off numbers has been adopted by the American National Standards Institute. A decimal-inch value may be rounded off to a lesser number of places by the following procedure:

1. If the last digit to be dropped is less than 5, there is no change in the preceding digits.
   Examples:
   .47244 rounds to .4724
   .1562 rounds to .156
   .20312 rounds to .2031
   .35433 rounds to .3543

2. If the last digit to be dropped is greater than 5, the preceding digit is increased by 1.
   Examples:
   .23437 rounds to .2344
   .55118 rounds to .5512
   .03937 rounds to .0394
   .6406 rounds to .641

3. If the last digit to be dropped is 5 and followed by a zero, round off the preceding digit to the nearest even number.
   Examples:
   .98425 rounds to .9842
   .59055 rounds to .5906
   .19685 rounds to .1968
   .4375 rounds to .438

If precise calculation is required, values should be calculated to two places beyond the desired number of places and the rounding should be based on the last two significant digits.

12.3.4 Drawing Scale

Drawings should be drawn to a scale that allows easy reading and accurate interpretation. Scales should remain constant within a given project where multiple drawings are needed. The choice of scale takes into account the maximum reduction required for the drawing. Scales are stated in the title block: 1:1 (full scale), 1:2 (half scale), 5:1, 10:1, and so on. CAD-generated drawings are normally modeled at *full scale*. If the drawing does not fit full size on the paper it may be plotted at any convenient reduction.

In some cases, for instance, when a portion of the drawing is enlarged, more than one scale is used on a drawing, as in Figure 12.6. Here, **DETAIL B** is at a scale of **4/1**. The predominant scale is shown in the scale area in the title block; any other scales are placed under the appropriate views.

12.4 Dimensions

Dimensions are applied to the drawing using standard elements: dimension lines, extension lines, leaders, arrowheads, and dimension values. The types of dimensions include vertical, horizontal, and aligned linear dimensions, angular dimensions, and callout dimensions using leaders for notes

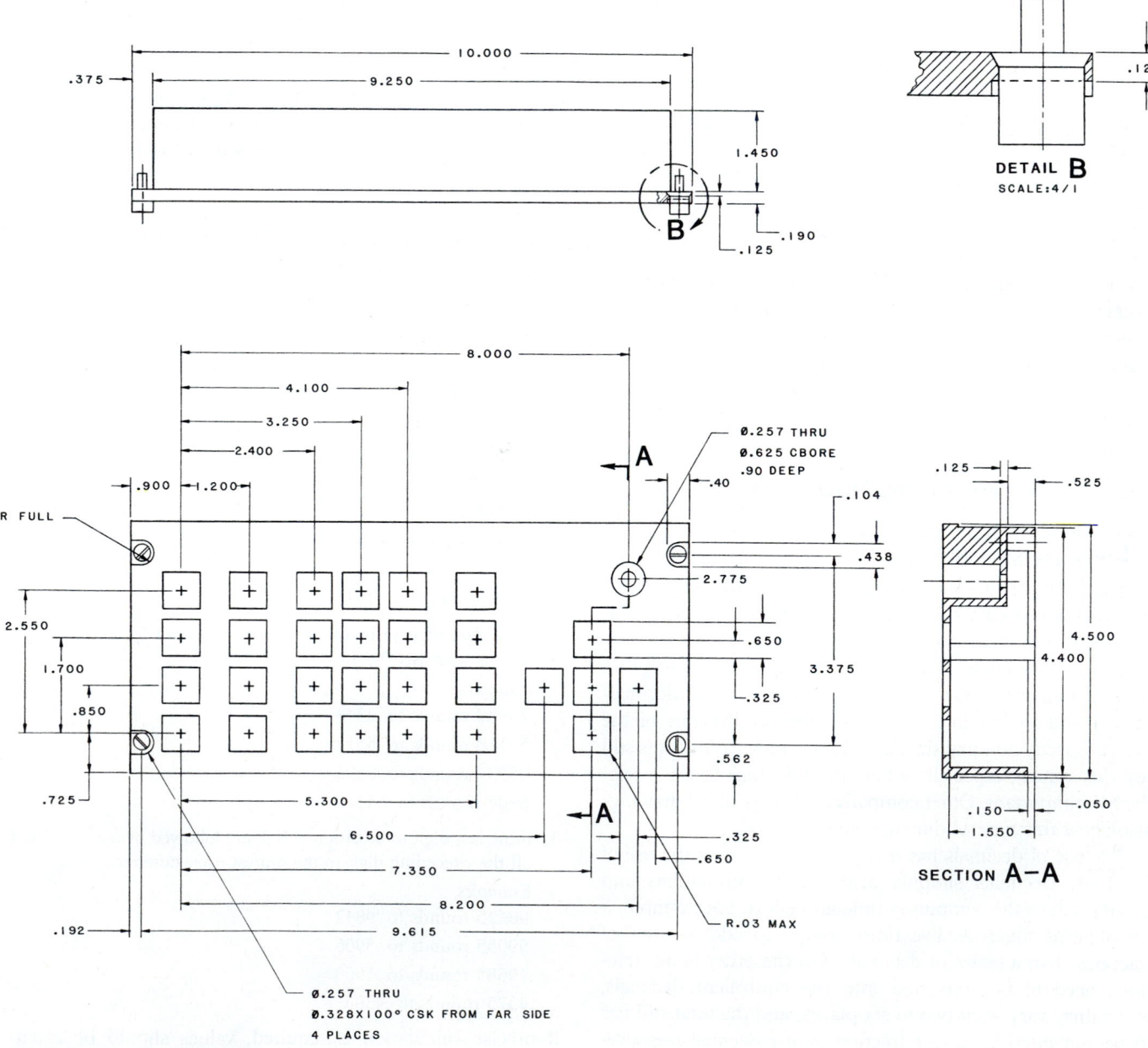

FIGURE 12.6 **Panel Detail**

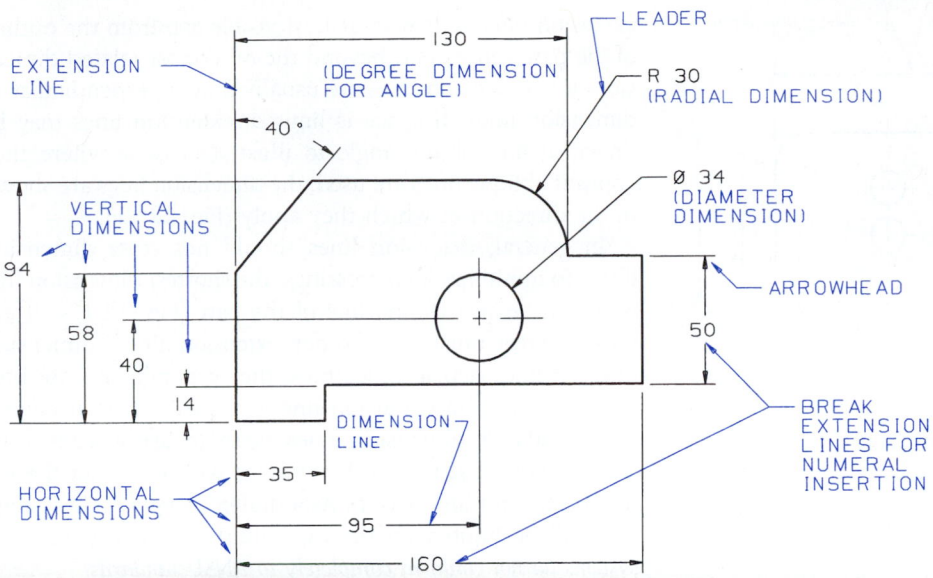

FIGURE 12.7 Dimension Elements

(Fig. 12.7). Figure 12.8 shows typical dimensions with examples in both decimal-inches and millimeter measurements. Note the placement options for each dimension. When a dimension is small, the arrowheads and dimension line can go on the outside of the extension lines with the value inside. Another method allows the dimension value to be placed outside of the extension lines. Study this figure carefully.

Any part, manual or CAD drawn, is only as good as its dimensioning. Therefore, great care must be put into the dimensioning stage of every project. Accurate drawing and correct placement of all dimensioning elements is essential for the engineering drawing to transfer geometric and manufacturing data to the machine tool area or the construction site. In other words, *dimension such that the part will be made correctly.*

12.4.1 Dimension Lines

A **dimension line**, with its arrowheads, shows the direction and extent of a dimension. Numerals indicate the number of units of a measurement. Preferably, dimension lines are broken to insert these numerals, as shown in Figure 12.7. If horizontal dimension lines are not broken, the numerals are placed above and parallel to the dimension lines. The following should not be used as a dimension line:

- a centerline
- a phantom line
- an object line that represents the outline of the part
- a continuation of any of these lines

A dimension line is used as an extension line only where a simplified method of coordinate dimensioning is used to define curved outlines (see Fig. 12.47).

Crossing dimension lines should be avoided. Where unavoidable, the dimension lines should remain unbroken at the crossing point. In general, if this situation is unavoidable, it is acceptable to cross a dimension line with an extension

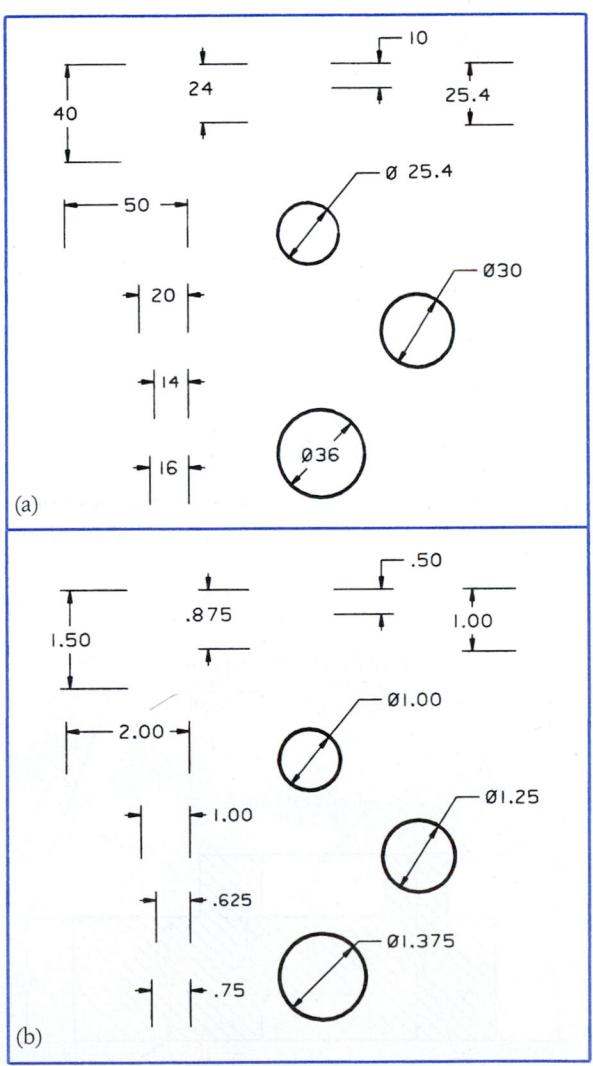

FIGURE 12.8 **Dimensions** (a) Millimeter dimensions (b) Decimal inch dimensions

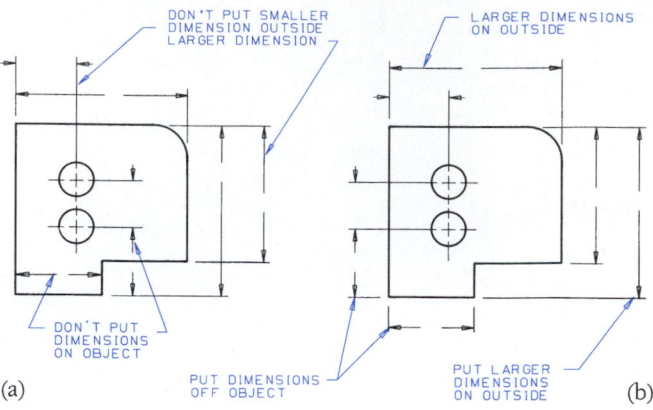

FIGURE 12.9 Dimension and Extension Lines (a) Incorrect (b) Correct

line once for each dimension. The largest dimension always goes on the outside—farthest from the part's outline. From Figure 12.9, a number of rules can be stated:

1. Cross a dimension line only if it is unavoidable.
2. Do not place dimensions within the part outline unless there is no other place to show the dimension properly.
3. Place larger dimensions farthest from the part's outline.

Dimensions are usually placed outside the outline of the part. If directness of application makes it desirable or if extension lines or leader lines would be excessively long, dimensions may be placed within the outline of a view. On large, complex drawings, dimensions are sometimes placed within the outline of the part, even when this contradicts the dimensioning rules. If it becomes necessary to place a dimension inside a part's outline that is sectioned, then break the section lines around the dimension (Fig. 12.10).

12.4.2 Extension Lines

Extension lines are used to indicate the extension of a surface or point to a location outside the part outline. Normally,

extension lines start with a short visible gap from the outline of the part and extend beyond the outermost related dimension line. Extension lines are usually drawn perpendicular to dimension lines. If space is limited, extension lines may be drawn at an oblique angle to illustrate clearly where they apply. If oblique lines are used, the dimension lines are shown in the direction in which they apply (Fig. 12.11).

In general, extension lines should not cross dimension lines. To minimize such crossings, the shortest dimension line is shown nearest the outline of the part (Fig. 12.12). If extension lines must cross other extension lines, dimension lines, or lines depicting features, they generally are not broken. However, an extension line is broken where it crosses arrowheads or dimension lines close to arrowheads (Fig. 12.12). Note that most CAD systems will not break the extension line for any reason. As a drafter using a CAD system, you will be limited by the capabilities of the system. *Most systems do not conform completely to ANSI standards!*

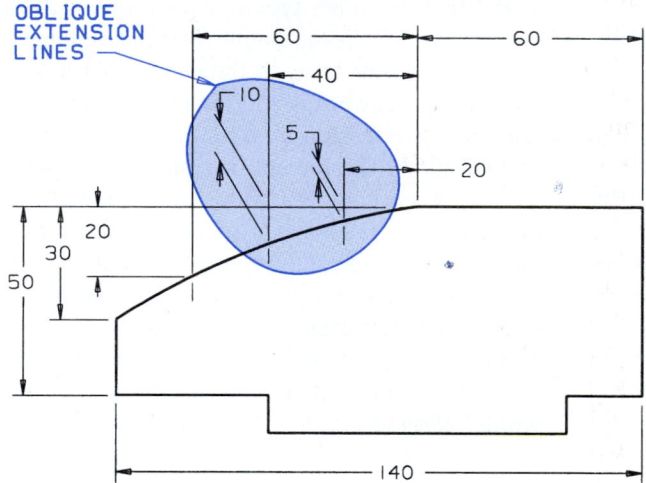

FIGURE 12.11 Oblique Dimensions

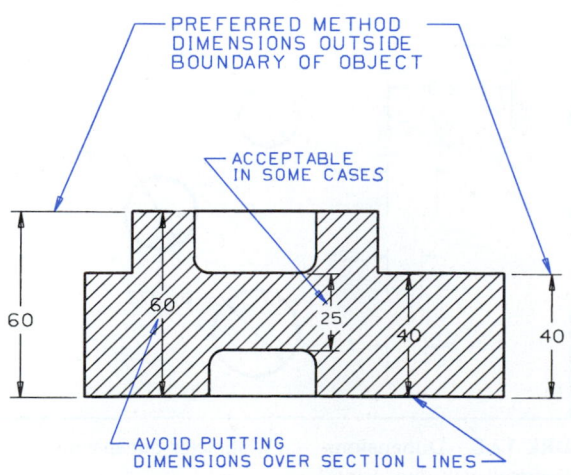

FIGURE 12.10 Dimensions on Section Lining

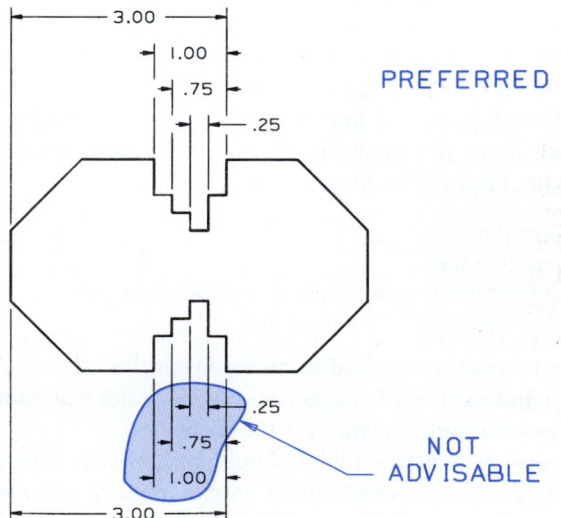

FIGURE 12.12 Breaks in Extension Lines

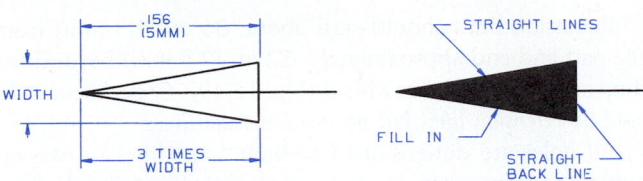

FIGURE 12.13 Arrowheads

12.4.3 Drawing Dimension Arrowheads

The thickness of a dimension, leader, or extension line is normally 0.3 to 0.35 mm, which makes it, except for section lining, the thinnest line on the drawing. As with all lines, it must still be drawn crisp and black. For all lines except construction lines, the thickness may change but the darkness remains constant. The actual numeric value is approximately as thick as a hidden or visible object line (0.45 to 0.6 mm).

The arrowhead used for dimensions is shown in Figure 12.13. The sides and back of the arrowhead are straight, not curved. An arrowhead is about three times as long as it is wide, with a length approximately equal to the height of the lettering used on the drawing. Arrowheads are normally drawn completely filled. Other types of line terminators used throughout industry include open arrowheads, dots, and slashes. Keep arrowheads consistent and uniform throughout a project. Avoid large arrowheads that stick out when reading the drawing. Arrowheads are usually not constructed using templates or with measurements. With time and practice, your freehand arrowheads will become well formed and easily constructed.

CAD systems provide arrowheads in a variety of sizes, shapes, and types, all of which can be inserted automatically. With a CAD system you do not actually construct dimensions and arrowheads, but the proper selection of dimensions and their placement is still the responsibility of the drafter.

12.4.4 Drawing Dimension and Extension Lines

Whenever feasible, dimension lines are aligned and grouped for uniform appearance (Fig. 12.14). If there are several parallel dimension lines, the numerals should be staggered for easier reading (Fig. 12.15). Figure 12.16 shows staggered spacing for horizontal dimensions, while Figure 12.17 shows staggered vertical dimensions.

The minimum distance from the first dimension line to the part outline should be .375 in. (10 mm). The minimum spacing between parallel dimension lines should be .25 in. (6 mm) (Fig. 12.18). In general, .50 in. (12 mm) from the part and .375 to .50 in. (10 to 12 mm) between dimensions is suggested for large drawings and those that need to be greatly reduced. The larger sizes are used whenever there is enough room. These spacings are intended as a guide when dimensioning, not as a rule. If the drawing meets the reproduction requirements of the accepted industry or military reproduction specification, these spacing requirements are not mandatory.

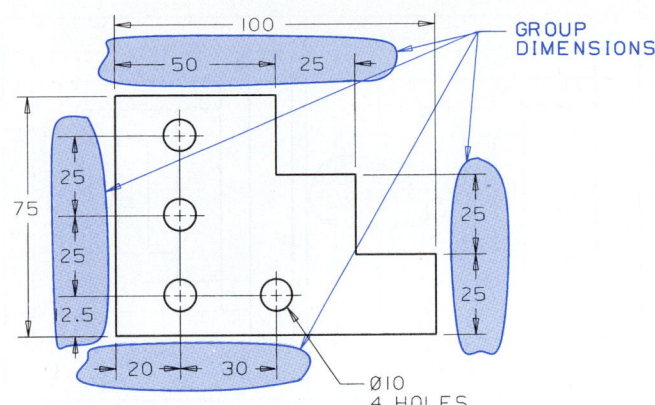

FIGURE 12.14 Grouping Dimensions

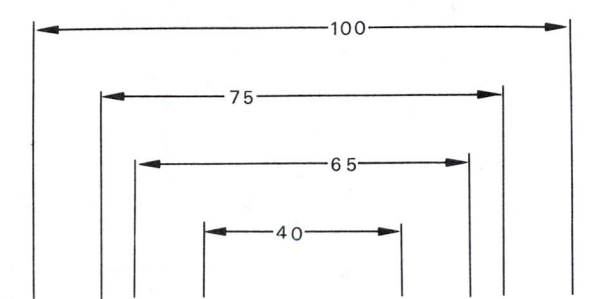

FIGURE 12.15 Staggered Dimensions

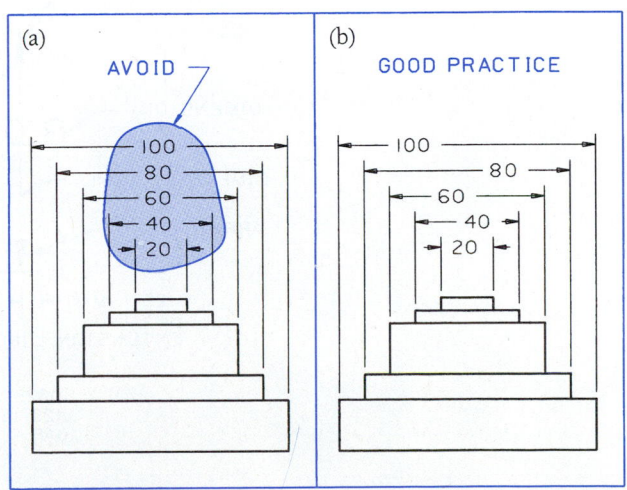

FIGURE 12.16 Horizontal Dimensions   (a) Not staggered (b) Staggered

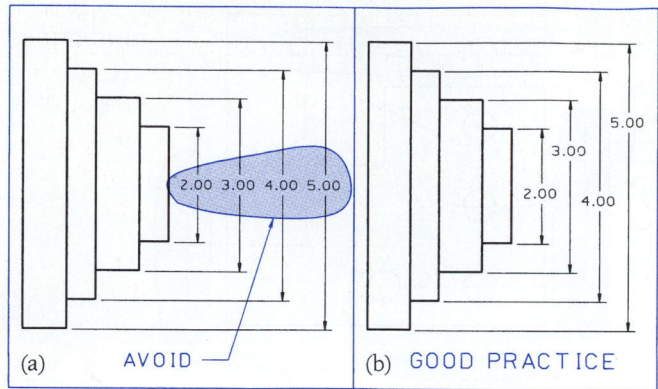

FIGURE 12.17   **Vertical Dimensions**   (a) Not staggered
(b) Staggered

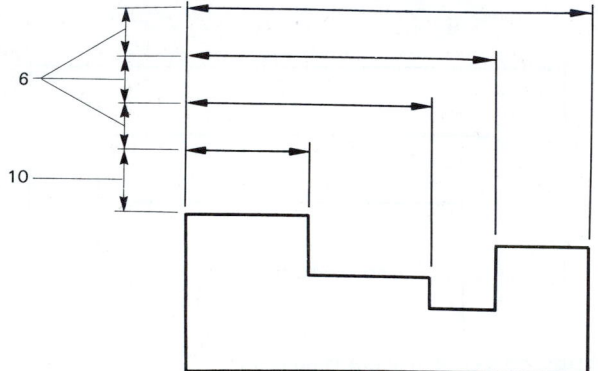

FIGURE 12.18   **Setup and Spacing of Dimensions**

Extension lines should start about .06 in. (1.3 mm) from the part and end approximately .12 in. (2.5 mm) beyond the dimension line and arrowhead (Fig. 12.19). *Centerlines can be used as extension lines but not as dimension lines.*

All holes are dimensioned to their centerlines in two directions, except when the holes are arrayed in a circular pattern about the same center, as with a bolt circle. This exception is covered later in the chapter. If a point is to be located only by extension lines, the extension lines (from the surfaces) pass through the point (Fig. 12.20).

In general, extension lines are not drawn to hidden lines or hidden features of the part. However, dimensioning to hidden features is acceptable in some circumstances, for instance, when a feature cannot be seen in another view. Another way to avoid dimensioning to hidden lines is to make use of a broken-out section for the hidden features. *Whenever possible, dimension to a visible feature.*

As you may already recognize, for almost every dimensioning rule, there is an exception. However, the rules apply in 90% of the situations that you will encounter.

12.4.5   Lettering Dimensions

Lettering for dimensions should conform to Figure 12.21. The preferred heights are shown in this figure and should be adhered to whenever possible. See Chapter 4 for a more in-depth discussion of lettering heights on different size drawings. Dimension heights are standardized for each drawing size and reduction requirement. If reduction is not required, .125 in. (3 mm) height for lettering is acceptable. When completing projects from the text, follow the spacing of lettering in dimensions as shown in Figure 12.21. The space between lines of numerals is also important.

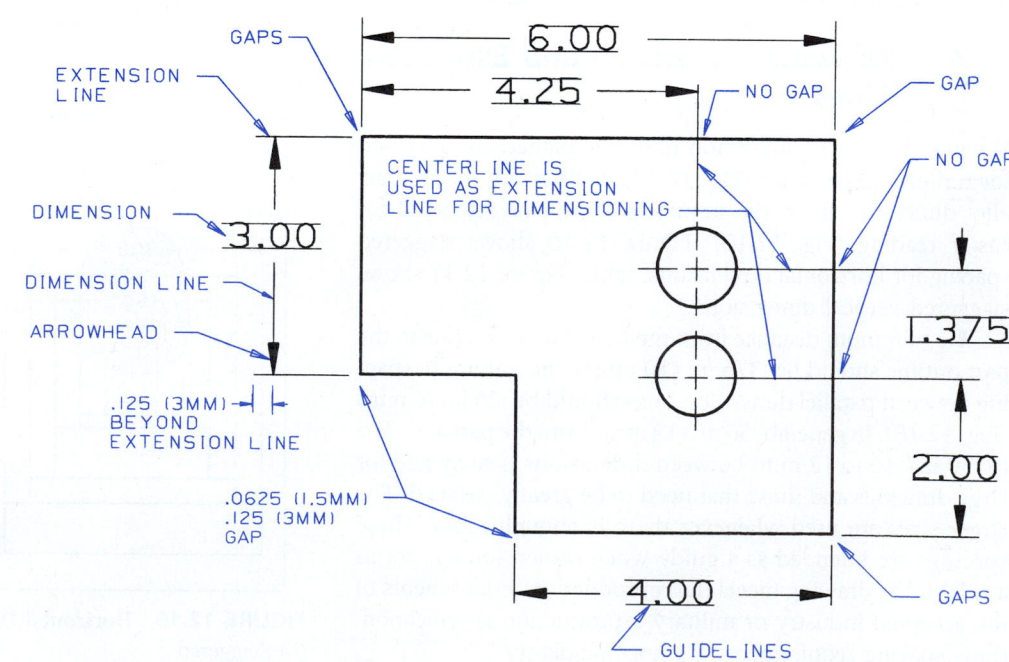

FIGURE 12.19   **Gaps and Placement of Extension Lines**

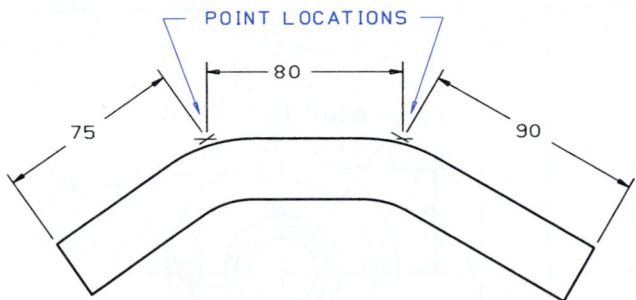

FIGURE 12.20   **Point Locations Using Extension Lines**

Numerals that are placed parallel to dimension lines are called **aligned dimensions** (Fig. 12.22). Horizontal dimensions are readable from the bottom; vertical dimensions, from the right side of the drawing. Point-to-point dimensions of angled edges have the dimensions aligned (parallel) to the edge itself. Aligned dimensions are not accepted ANSI standard practice, though some companies still follow this practice.

Unidirectional dimensioning (Fig. 12.22) places the dimension text parallel to the bottom of the drawing and, therefore, is readable from the bottom of the drawing (Fig. 12.23). This system is preferred since the drawing may be read and lettered without being turned.

For mechanical drawings, the dimension line should be broken to insert the measurement numerals. In piping, archi-

tecture, civil, structural, and other construction drawings, numerals normally do not break the dimension line, but instead are placed above the dimension line.

Regardless of the type, unit, or alignment of the dimension value, use thin, lightly drawn guidelines or a lettering guide. The lettering itself must be crisp, black, and as thick as a hidden or visible object line.

12.4.6   Angular Dimensions

Size and location dimensions may be given as either linear distances or angles. **Angular dimensions** are expressed in degrees, minutes, and seconds or as decimal equivalents of degrees, as in Figure 12.24 (20.10°). If angles are less than 1°, precede the minute by 0°. For both unidirectional and aligned dimensioning, angular dimensions are placed to read horizontally between guidelines, with no dash between degrees and minutes.

Whenever possible, angular dimensions should be avoided by locating the endpoints of inclined lines and planes. Because it is easier, quicker, and more reliable, coordinate dimensioning of angled features increases the accuracy during the manufacturing stage.

The dimension line for an angle is drawn as an arc from a center at the intersection of the sides of the angle. A variety of methods are used to dimension angles, depending on the available space (Fig. 12.24). The arrowheads terminate at the

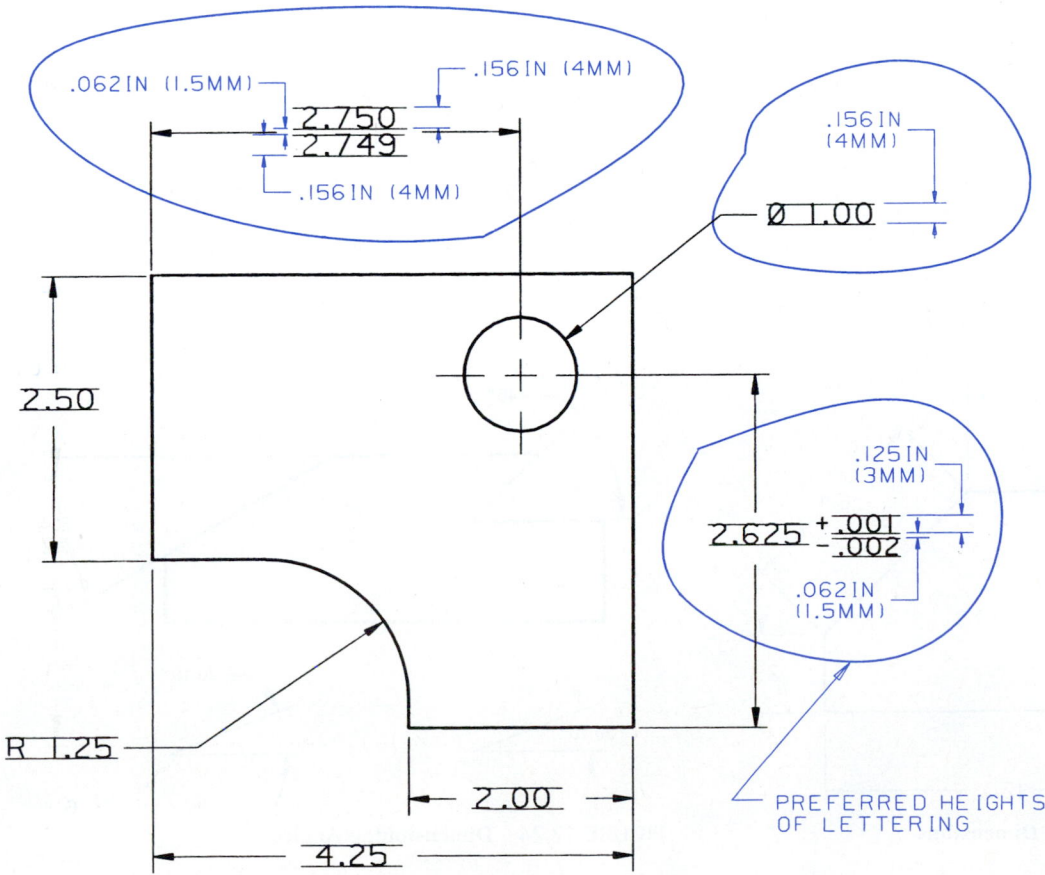

FIGURE 12.21   **Preferred Lettering Height for Dimensions**

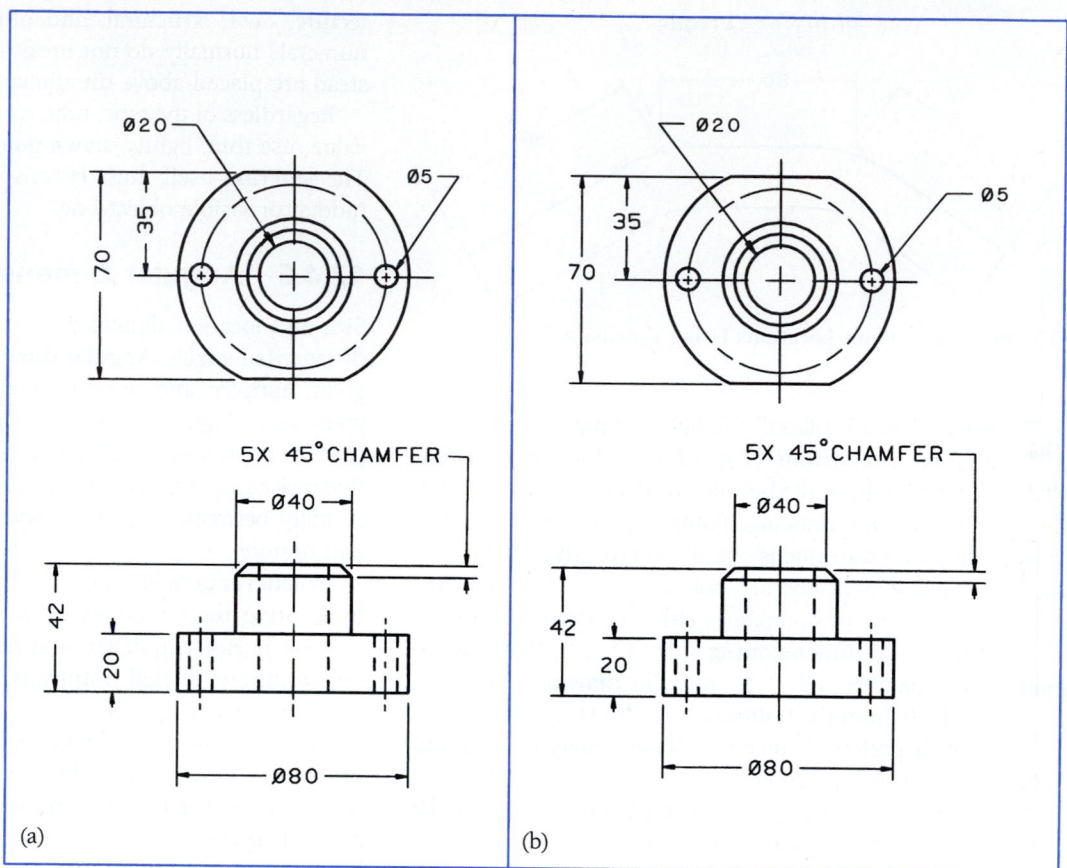

FIGURE 12.22
Dimensioning Methods
(a) Aligned dimensioning
(b) Unidirectional
dimensioning

(a)

(b)

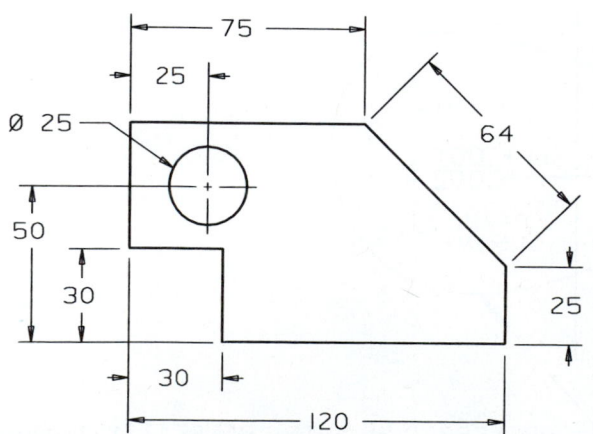

FIGURE 12.23   Unidirectional Dimensions

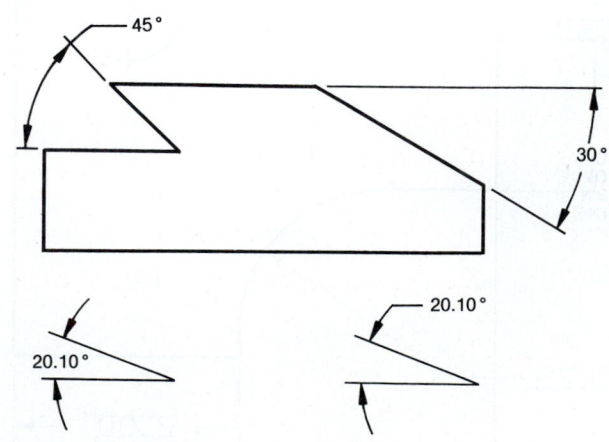

FIGURE 12.24   Dimensioning Angles

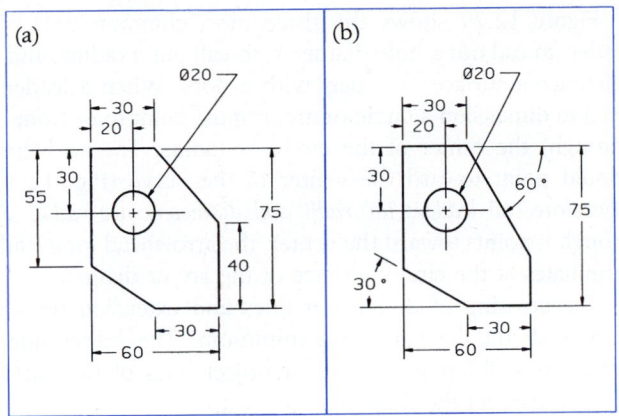

FIGURE 12.25 **Dimensioning** (a) Offset (square) dimensioning (b) Angular dimensioning

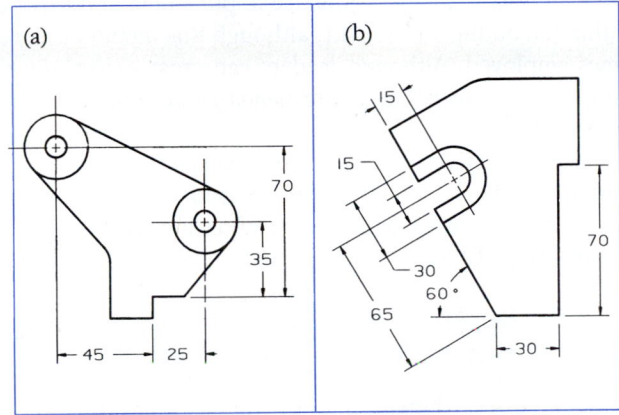

FIGURE 12.26 **Dimensioning** (a) Offset dimensioning (b) Angular dimensioning

extensions of the two sides, inside or outside the extension lines. The dimension line is an arc with its center at the vertex of the angle being measured, and the angular dimension is placed inside or outside the two controlling extension lines.

Angles are used only where other forms of linear dimensions are unsuitable. In Figure 12.25, two methods of dimensioning a part are shown. One method uses angle dimensions and the other uses the offset (or square) method. Because it is easier for the machinist to locate the features of the part with linear measurements, the offset method is preferred. Angles are less accurate and harder to set up. Figure 12.26 shows another example of these methods. Here the parts are different and lend themselves to different dimensioning styles: (a) uses the offset method to locate the holes; (b) has a slot angled to the base. Because the features in Figure 12.26(b) would be difficult to locate with offset dimensions, an angle dimension works best. The features of this part (b) are related to the angled surface and, therefore, are located in relation to them when establishing dimensions.

12.4.7   Callout Dimensions and Notes Using Leaders

A **leader** is used to direct a dimension, note, or symbol to the intended feature on the drawing (Fig. 12.27). Leaders are normally used to point to a curved feature of a part or to reference a portion or surface. Most leaders are drawn at 45 to 60° to the horizontal (30° to the vertical) (Fig. 12.28). The end of a leader terminates in an arrowhead. The dimension figure for a callout is placed at the end or the head of a short 6 mm (.25 in.) horizontal line.

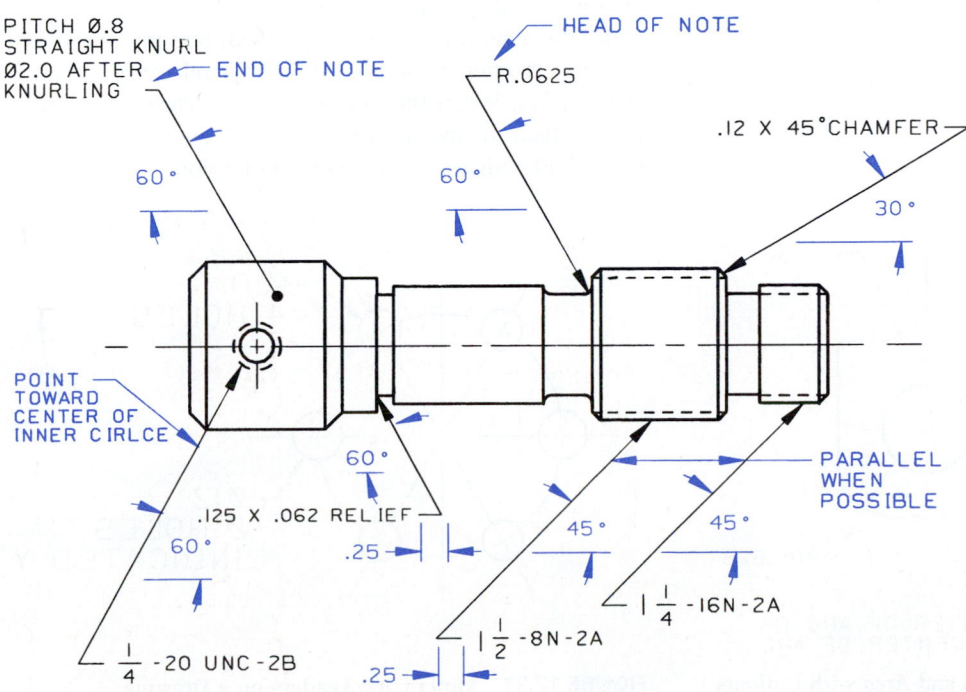

FIGURE 12.27 **Leaders on Drawings**

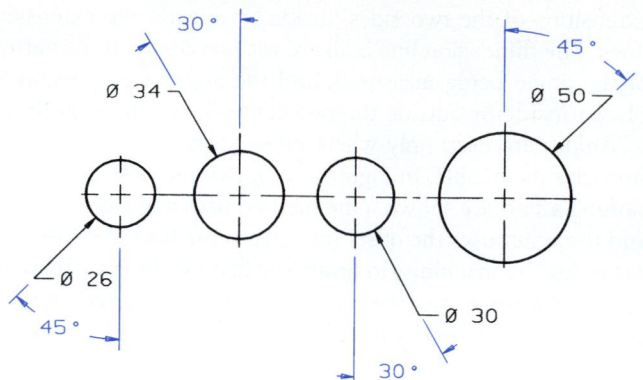

FIGURE 12.28   Leaders for Hole Callouts

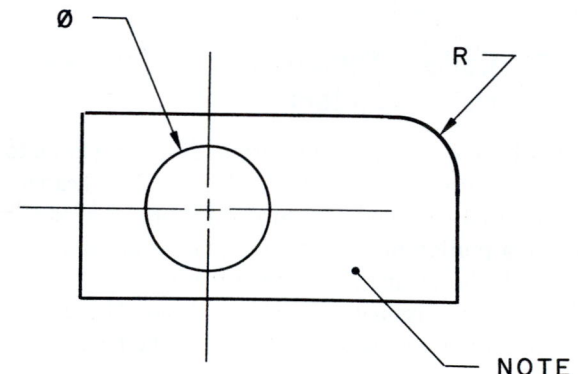

FIGURE 12.29   Three Common Uses of Leaders

Figure 12.29 shows the three most common uses of a leader: to call out a hole diameter, to call out a radius, and to reference a surface or a part with a note. When a leader is used to dimension a circle or arc, it must point to or from (or through) the center of the circle or radius. The arrowhead should point toward the center of the curve (Fig. 12.30). Therefore, *all leaders for radii and diameters are radial.* Although it points toward the center, the arrowhead for a leader terminates at the circumference of the arc or diameter.

The crossing of dimension lines and extension lines by leaders should be kept to a minimum. The leader line is drawn at a different angle than object lines of the part or section lines on the drawing.

Leaders and their accompanying notes and callouts are kept outside dimension lines and away from the part being dimensioned. Leaders are placed on the drawing after the part is dimensioned. It is poor practice to put a note or dimension within the outline of the part, although this method is sometimes employed. Although leaders can cross object, dimension, and extension lines, *care should be taken never to cross other leader lines.*

Leader-directed dimensions are specified individually for simplicity (Fig. 12.30). If too many leaders impair the legibility of the drawing, letters or symbols are used to identify features (Fig. 12.31).

12.4.8   Reference, Overall, and Not-to-Scale Dimensions

In some cases, dimensions for reference information or checking purposes are given. **Reference dimensions** are not used for manufacturing or for inspection. To identify a reference dimension or reference data on drawings, *enclose the dimension or data in parentheses.*

If an overall dimension is specified, one intermediate dimension is omitted or identified as a reference dimension (Fig. 12.32). When the intermediate dimension is more important than the overall dimension, the overall dimension, if used, is identified as a reference dimension.

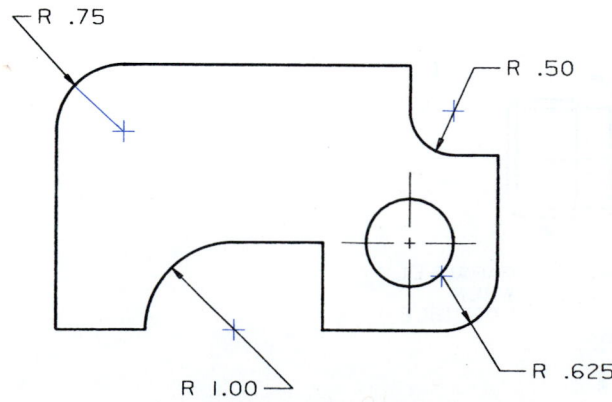

POINT TOWARDS CENTER OF ARC OR
PASS LEADER THRU CENTER OF ARC

FIGURE 12.30   Dimensioning Fillets and Arcs with Callouts

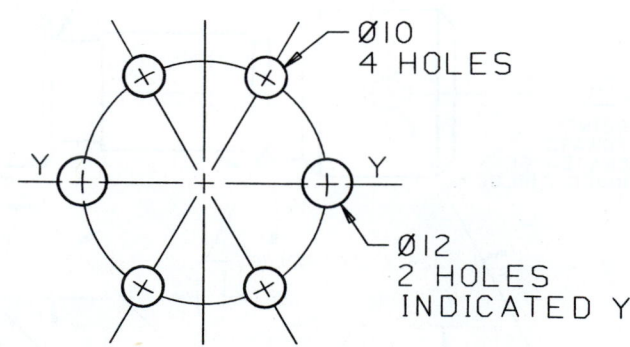

FIGURE 12.31   Minimizing Leaders on a Drawing

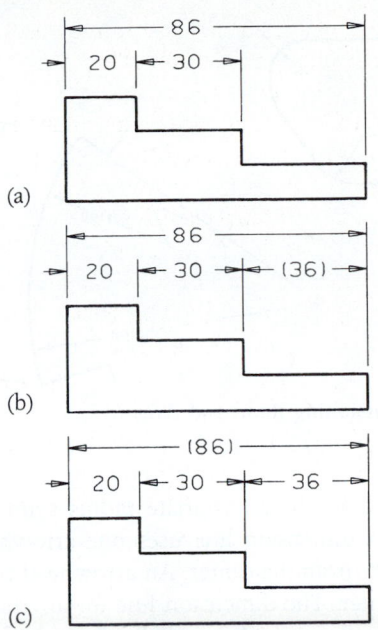

( ) = REFERENCE DIMENSION SYMBOL

FIGURE 12.32 **Overall and Reference Dimensions**
(a) No reference dimension (b) Intermediate reference dimension
(c) Overall reference dimension

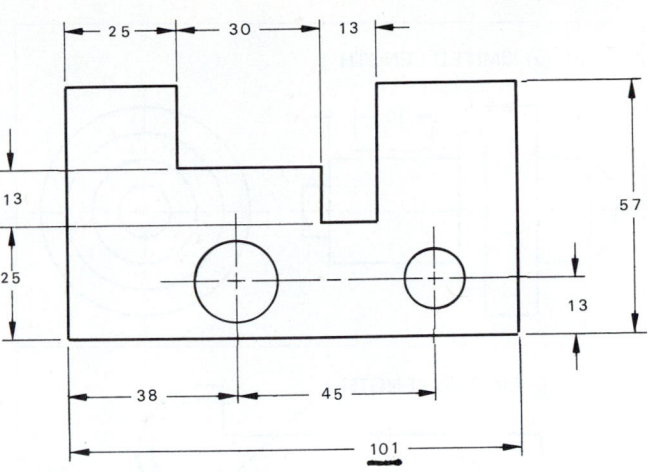

FIGURE 12.33 Not-to-Scale (NTS) Dimensions

When you want to indicate that a particular feature is **not to scale**, the dimension should be underlined with a straight thick line or **NTS** (not to scale) should be added to the dimension, as in Figure 12.33, dimension **101**.

Only the dimensions required for manufacturing the part should be given on the drawing. In Figure 12.34, the overdimensioned part is shown on the top of the figure and the correctly dimensioned part below it. Note that the correctly dimensioned example has fewer dimensions and an uncluttered look. The placement of ₵ on the part's centerline means it is *symmetrical about the centerline*.

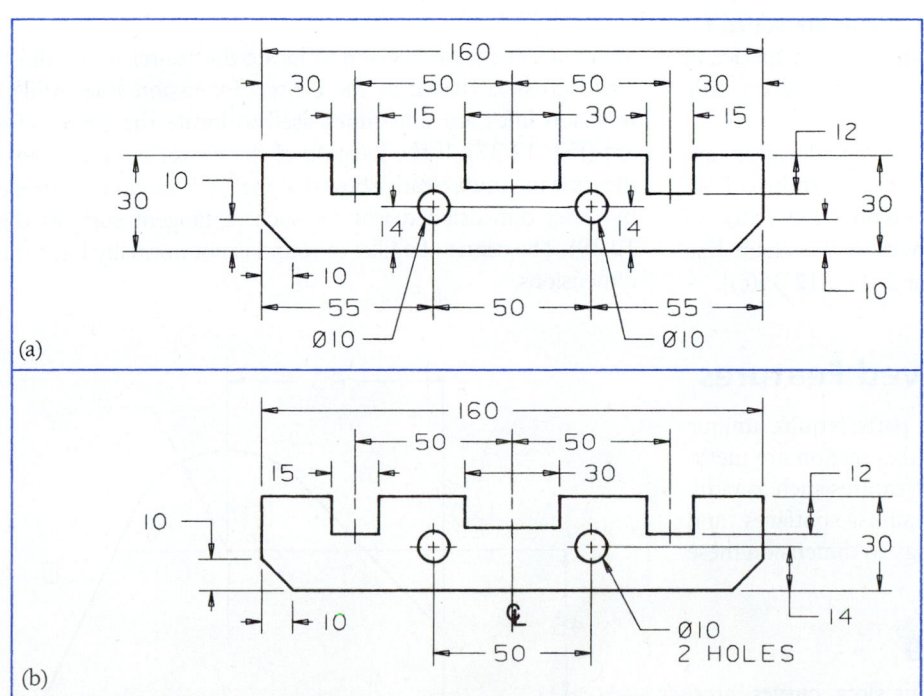

FIGURE 12.34
Overdimensioning a Part
(a) Over dimensioned (b) Correctly dimensioned

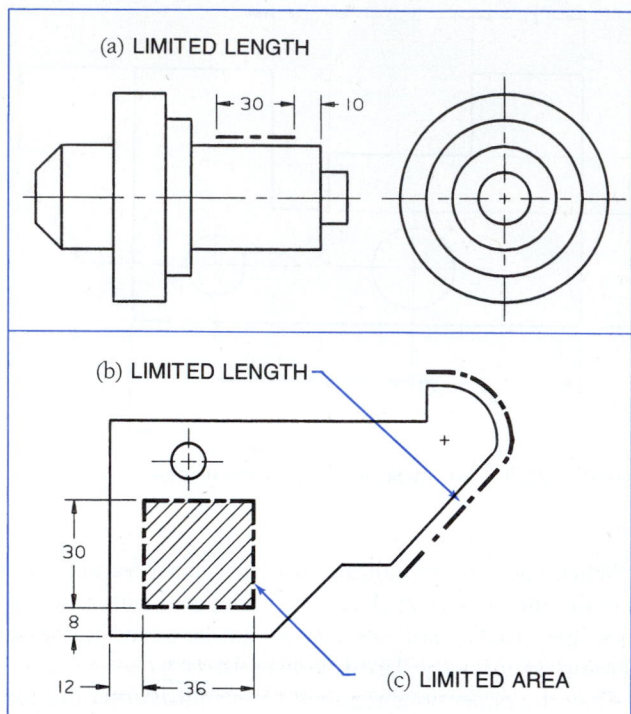

FIGURE 12.35   Limited Length and Limited Area Indicators
(a) and (b) Limited length (c) Limited area

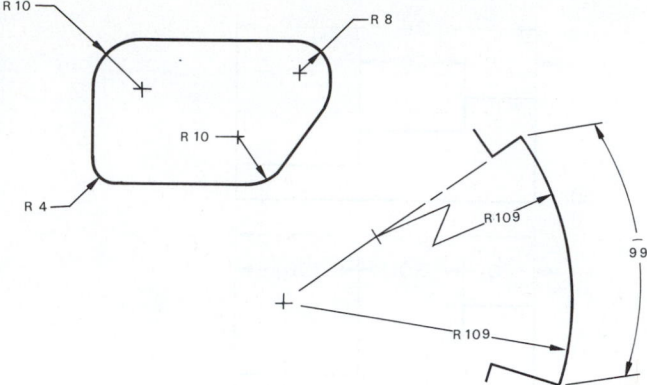

FIGURE 12.36   Dimensioning Radii and Arcs

12.4.9   Limited Length or Area Indicated

To indicate that a limited length or area of a surface is to receive additional treatment or consideration within limits specified on the drawing, the extent of these limits is indicated by use of a **chain line** (Fig. 12.35). In an appropriate view or section, a chain line is drawn parallel to the surface profile at a short distance from it. Dimensions are added for length and location [Fig. 12.35(a)]. If applied to a surface of revolution such as a shaft, the indication is shown on one side only [Fig. 12.35(a)].

As long as the chain line clearly indicates the location and extent of the *limited length,* dimensions may be omitted [Fig. 12.35(b)]. When the *limited area* is shown on a direct view of the surface, the area is section-lined within the chain line boundary and appropriately dimensioned [Fig. 12.35(c)].

12.5   Dimensioning Curved Features

Various characteristics and features of parts require unique methods of dimensioning. Included in this section are methods of noting and dimensioning curved features such as radii, diameters, slots, counterdrills, countersinks, spotfaces, and counterbores. The use of ANSI symbology to dimension these features is also covered.

12.5.1   Radius Dimensioning

Radius dimensions are used to call out slots, curves, arcs, rounds, and fillets on drawings. Each radius value on a radius

dimension is preceded by the appropriate radius symbol **R** (Fig. 12.36). A radius dimension line uses one arrowhead, which points to the arc from the center. An arrowhead is not used at the radius center. The dimension line for any radius is drawn as an angular line *extending radially* through, from, or toward the feature's center. Do not use horizontal or vertical lines when dimensioning arcs. Each of the following situations is illustrated in Figure 12.36:

1. If the location of the center is important and space permits, a dimension line is drawn from the radius center with the arrowhead touching the arc. The dimension is placed between the arrowhead and the center.
2. When space is limited, the dimension line is extended through the radius center.
3. When it is inconvenient to place the arrowhead between the radius center and the arc, it can be placed outside the arc with a leader.
4. If the center of a radius is not located dimensionally, the center is not indicated.

When a dimension is given to locate the center of a radius, a small cross is drawn at the center. Extension lines and dimension lines are sometimes used to locate the center of an arc (Fig. 12.37). If the location of the center is unimportant, the drawing must clearly show that the arc location is controlled by other dimensioned features such as tangent surfaces (Fig. 12.38). The center of a fillet or round is not normally located by dimensions.

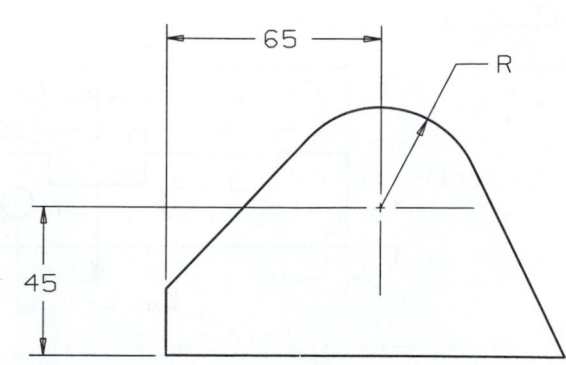

FIGURE 12.37   Radius with a Located Center

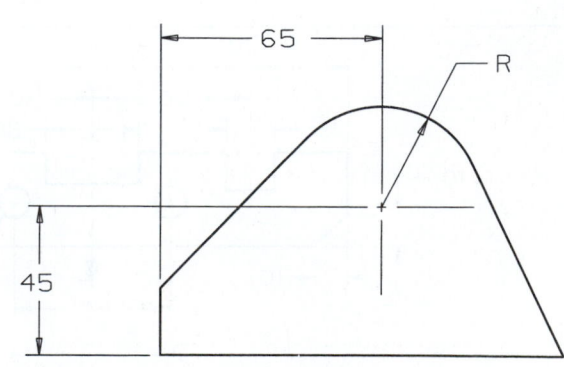

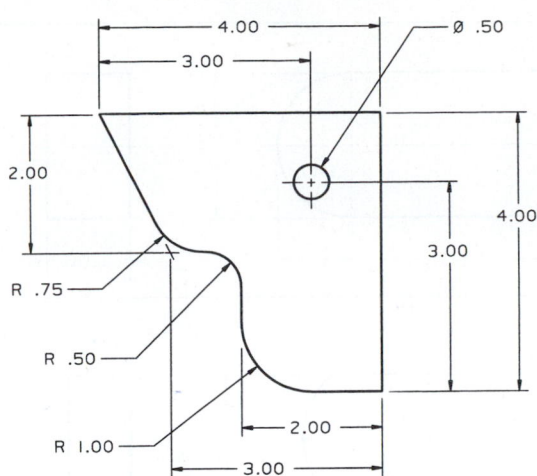

FIGURE 12.38   Radii with Unlocated Centers

Sometimes the center of an arc is moved on a drawing because either there is a break or the center lies outside the drawing paper (Figs. 12.36 and 12.39). In such a case, the new position is on a centerline of the arc, and the newly located "false" center leads to a *staggered dimension*. The portion of the dimension line touching the arc is a radial line drawn from the true center, whereas the staggered dimension is drawn parallel to the first radial line. In other words, when the center of an arc lies outside the limits of the drawing, the center is moved closer along a centerline of the arc, and the dimension line is jogged. When the radius dimension line is foreshortened and the center located by coordinate dimensions, the dimension line locating the center is foreshortened as well.

When a radius is dimensioned in a view that does not show the true shape of the radius, **TRUE R** is added before the radius dimension. A true-shape view of the radius is shown and dimensioned whenever possible.

When a part has a number of radii of the same dimension, a note such as

ALL RADII .75 UNLESS OTHERWISE NOTED

may be used instead of dimensioning each radius separately.

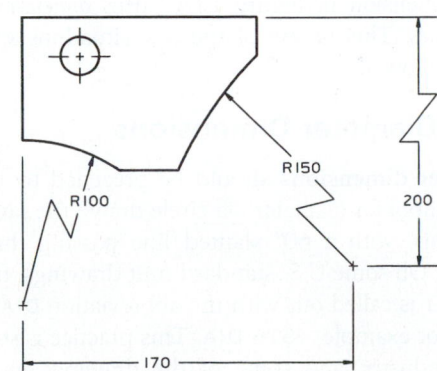

FIGURE 12.39   Foreshortened Radii Dimensions

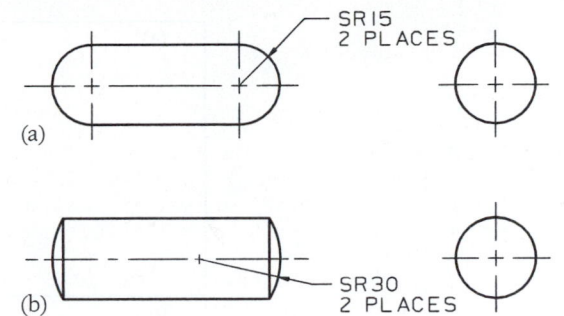

FIGURE 12.40   Spherical Radius Dimensions   (a) Half sphere
(b) Partial sphere

A **spherical surface** for a solid part is dimensioned by a radius dimension preceded by the symbol **SR** (Fig. 12.40).

12.5.2   Detailing Chords, Arcs, and Rounded Ends

Arcs and *chords* are dimensioned using radius dimensions as shown in Figure 12.41. This figure shows three situations. The use of an angle measurement is the most common. The arc dimension with the arc symbol and the chord dimension are used in applications such as nipple placement on large pressure vessels in piping design.

Overall dimensions are required for parts having rounded ends. For the fully rounded ends of Figure 12.42(a), the radii are indicated but not dimensioned. For parts with partially rounded ends, the radii are dimensioned [Fig. 12.42(b)]. If corners are rounded, dimensions define the edges, and the arcs are tangent to the edge lines (Fig. 12.43). Note that the radii dimensions use leaders to point to the arc. *The leader "aims" at the arc's center point.* If it cannot be avoided, it is acceptable practice to cross one extension or one dimension line.

A curved outline composed of two or more arcs is dimensioned by giving the radii of all arcs and locating the necessary centers with coordinate dimensions (Fig. 12.44). Other radii are located on the basis of their points of tangency.

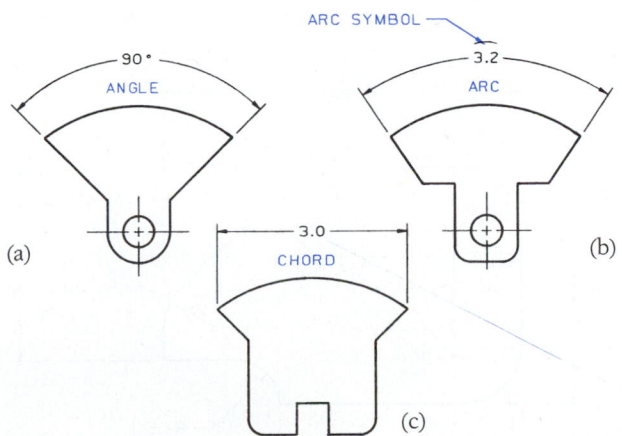

FIGURE 12.41   Dimensioning Angles, Arcs, and Chords
(a) Angle (b) Arc (c) Chord

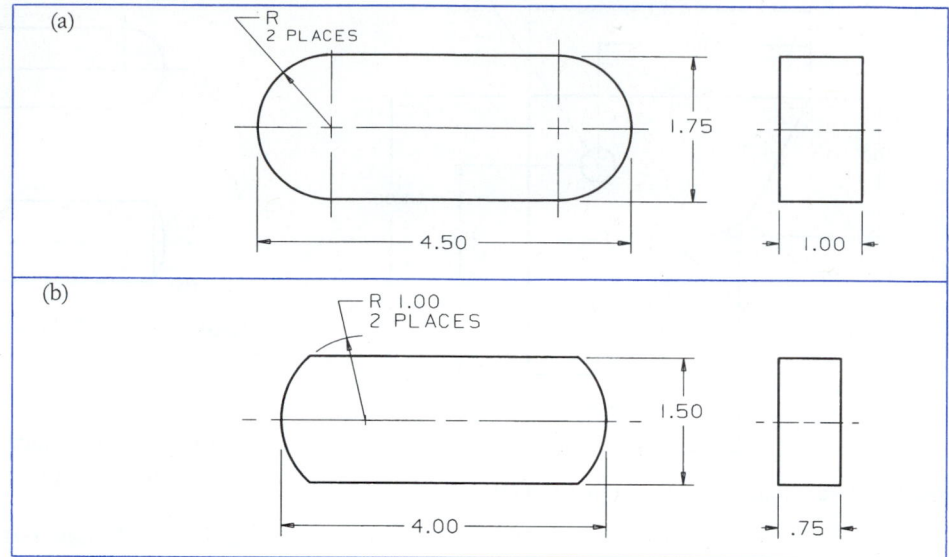

FIGURE 12.42 Dimensioning Rounded Ends (a) Fully rounded ends (b) Partially rounded ends

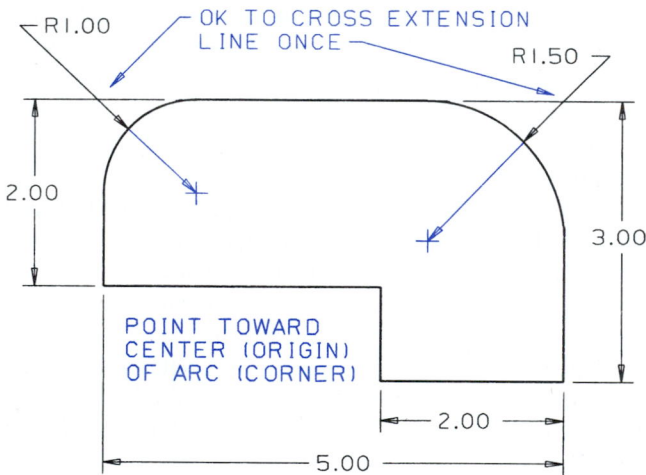

FIGURE 12.43 Dimensioning Rounded Corners

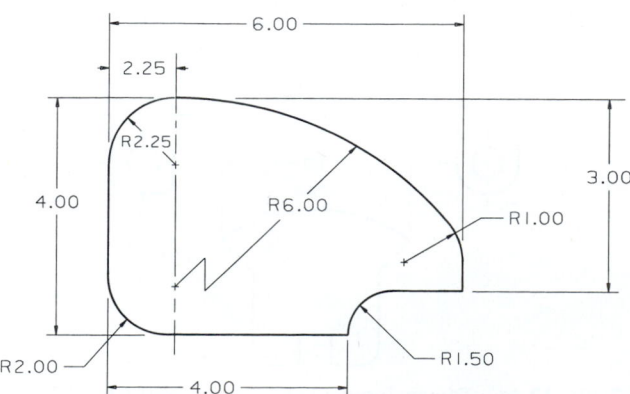

FIGURE 12.44 Dimensioning Circular Arc Outlines

Regardless of the arc requirements, the dimensions for a part are shown in a view that best displays the features. In Figure 12.45, the dimensions for the part's angles and radii are dimensioned in the only view that shows them accurately; the true shape is seen in the front view.

12.5.3   Irregular Outlines

Irregular outlines are dimensioned as shown in Figures 12.46 and 12.47. Circular or noncircular outlines can be dimensioned by the rectangular coordinate or offset method shown in these figures. Coordinates are dimensioned from base or datum lines. If many coordinates are required to define an outline, the vertical and horizontal coordinate dimensions can be given in a table.

12.5.4   Symmetrical Outlines

Symmetrical outlines can be dimensioned on one side of their *centerline of symmetry* when, due to the size of the part or space limitations, only part of the outline can be conveniently shown (Fig. 12.47). One-half of the outline of the symmetrical shape is shown and symmetry is indicated by applying symbols for part symmetry to the centerline. Notice that the dimension in Figure 12.47 uses *dimension lines as extension lines*. This is one of the few situations where this practice is allowed.

12.5.5   Diameter Dimensions

All **diameter dimensions** should be preceded by the international symbol for diameter—a circle drawn the same size as the numerals, with a 60° slanted line passing through its center ($\emptyset$). On some U.S. standard unit drawings, the size of the diameter is called out with the abbreviation **DIA** after the numerals; for example, **.375 DIA**. This practice is still widely found in industry, and some of the drawings in this text reflect the older practice.

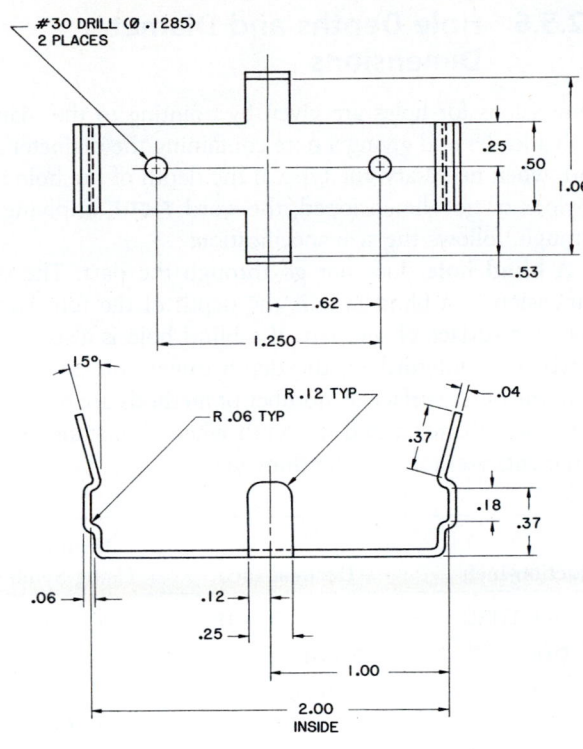

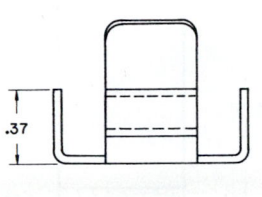

NOTES:
1. HEAT TREAT TO CONDITION R.H. 950
   (REF. JORGENSEN STEEL BOOK)
   HEAT CONDITION "A" MATERIAL
   TO 1750° F FOR 10 MIN. COOL TO 100° F AND HOLD FOR 8 HOURS
   HEAT TO 950° F AND HOLD FOR 1 HOUR. COOL IN AIR TO ROOM TEMP.

FIGURE 12.45   Detail of CRT Holder

The diameter symbol precedes all diametral values as shown in Figure 12.48. When the diameters of a number of concentric cylindrical features are specified, the diameter can be dimensioned in a longitudinal view (a view where the hole or round feature shows rectangular) (Fig. 12.48). The edge view of the part can also be a section showing the interior of the piece and the required holes.

Holes in side views or section views are dimensioned when the hole cannot be adequately called out where it shows as a circle. If it is not included in the note, the depth of the hole is dimensioned in the longitudinal view. A drafter can show

the dimensions of a very large hole by drawing the dimension line at an angle through the diameter (lower left of Fig. 12.48). For aligned dimensions placed inside the circular form, the area within the shaded 45° section should be avoided when the dimension runs through the diameter.

A number of different methods can be used to dimension diameters, depending on the size of the diameter and whether the diameter represents a hole or a solid shape. In general,

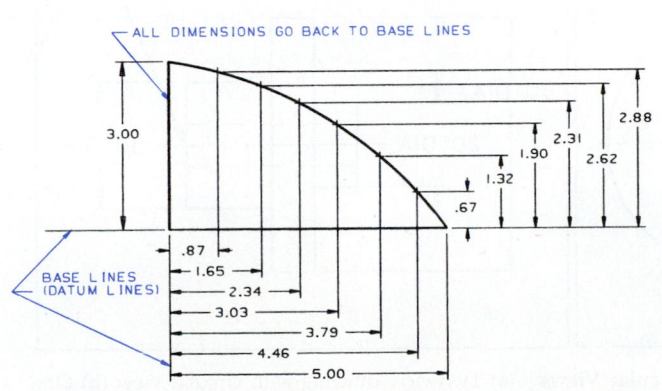

FIGURE 12.46   Coordinate Dimensioning of Curved Outlines

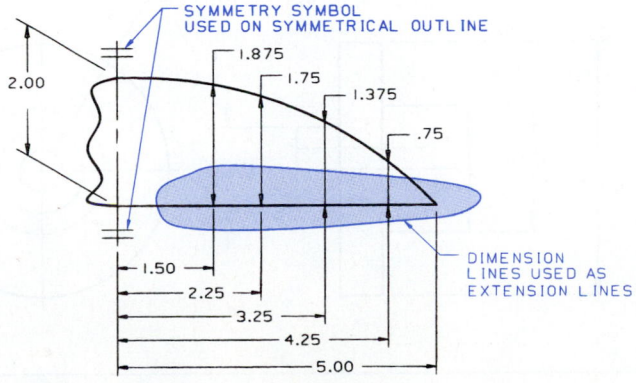

FIGURE 12.47   Dimensioning Symmetrical Outlines Using Dimension Lines as Extension Lines

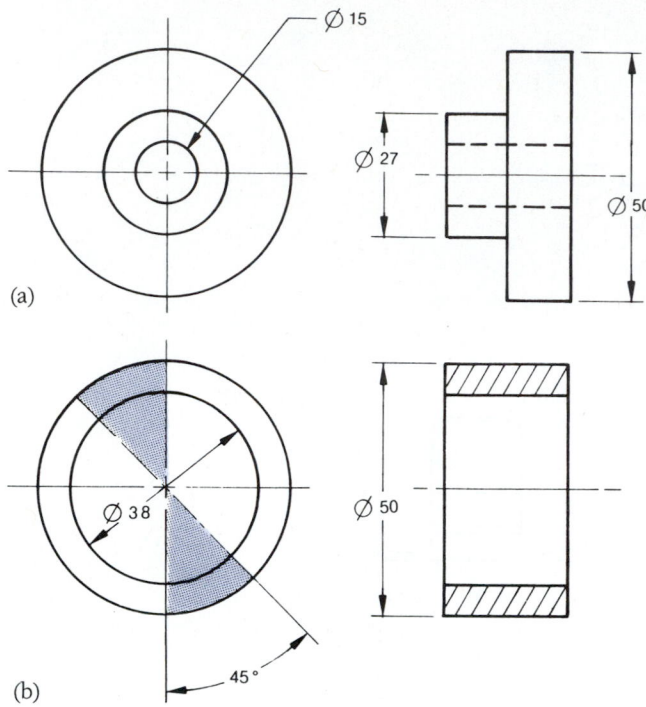

FIGURE 12.48 Dimensioning Diameters (a) Diameter callouts (b) Diameter dimensions and area to avoid

holes should be called out with a leader and note. The leader must point toward the center of the circle. *Solid round* shapes are dimensioned on the noncircular view.

Figure 12.49 shows an alternative way to dimension a cylindrical part. The first method [Fig. 12.49(a)] shows two views of the part with standard dimensioning callouts for the hole diameters. The second method (b) gives only the longitudinal edge view of the part and uses the **DIA** callout for all diameter dimensions.

You May Complete Exercises 12.1 Through 12.4 at This Time

12.5.6 Hole Depths and Diameter Dimensions

Dimensions for holes are given by pointing to the diameter with a leader and giving a note containing the diameter's size and, when necessary, the type. If the depth of the hole is not obvious or not dimensioned, the word **THRU**, implying drill through, follows the size specification.

A **blind hole** does not go through the part. The depth dimension of a blind hole is the depth of the full diameter from the surface of the part. If a blind hole is also counterbored or counterdrilled, the depth dimension is still taken from the outer surface. A number of methods are used to call out a hole diameter and its depth when U.S. standard measurements are used for the drawing:

Fraction-Inch		Decimal-Inch		Decimal-Inch Using Symbology
$\frac{1}{2}$ DIA THRU	or	.50 DIA THRU	or	Ø .50 THRU
$\frac{1}{2}$ DIA		.50 DIA		
$\frac{3}{4}$ DEEP	or	.750 DEEP	or	Ø .50 ↧.750

12.5.7 Dimensioning Slotted Holes

Slotted holes are found on a variety of mechanical parts. Slots may be dimensioned many ways; Figure 12.50 shows three variations. In Figure 12.50(a), the slot's centerlines are located between centers. A dimension from the edge of the part or other controlling feature is given as well. The slot width is given as an **R** (radius) pointing to the end of the slot arc. The **R** normally is accompanied by the note "**2 PLACES**." ANSI standards call for the use of **R** for a radius; however, many companies use **RAD** for U.S. standard drawings. The method of Figure 12.50(b) uses a leader and a note stating the

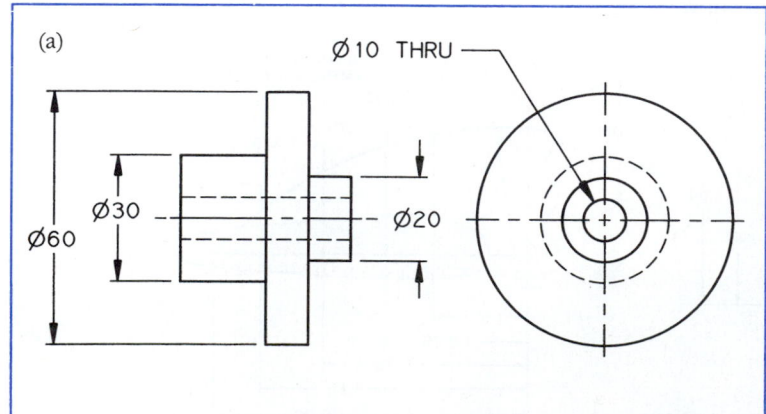

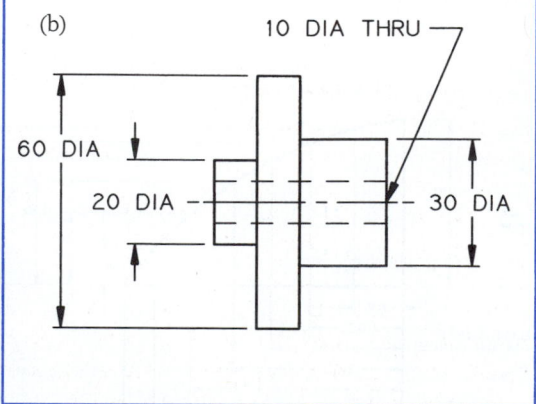

FIGURE 12.49 Dimensioning Diameters on Drawings Without Circular Views (a) Two view drawing with circular view (b) One view drawing without circular view

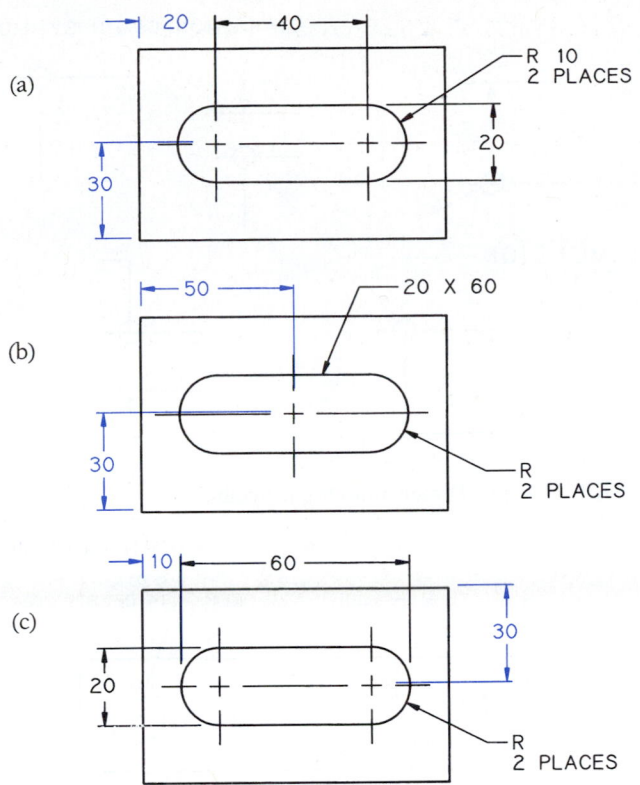

FIGURE 12.50   **Dimensioning Slots**   (a) Locating centerlines of slot (b) Leader and note callout (c) Overall slot dimensions

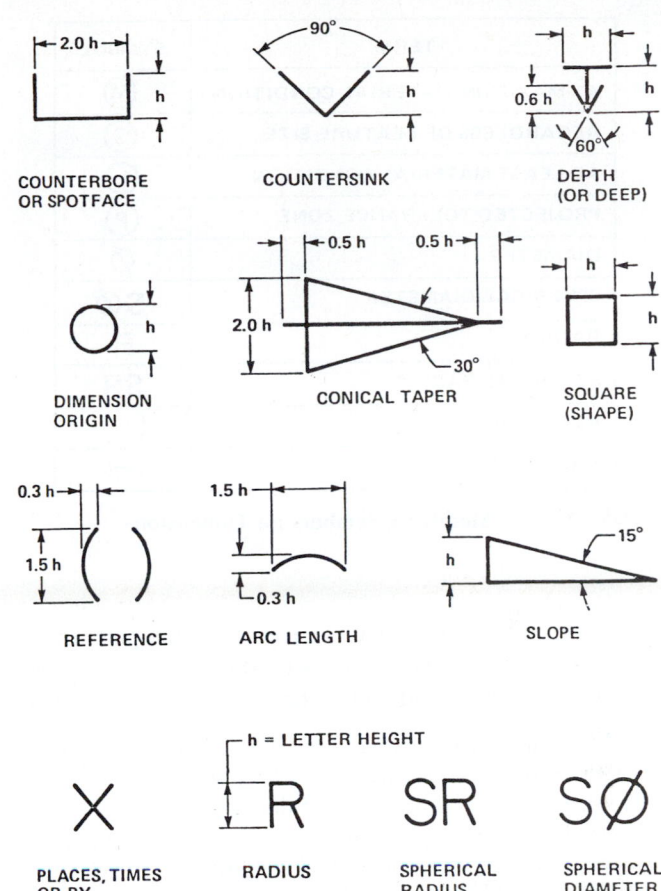

FIGURE 12.51   **Form and Proportion of Dimensioning Symbols**

outside dimensions of the slot, **20 × 60**). An **R** callout is also included. The slot also can be located from the part's edges [as in Fig. 12.50(c)], or its centerlines can be located from two controlling edges. Figure 12.50(c) shows the dimensions of the slot on the view, giving the overall length and width along with its location dimensions. An **R** callout is provided, as in the other methods.

The choice of methods for dimensioning slots is determined by design factors and the required slot tolerance. If something fits into the slot, accurate tolerance and dimensions must be given for the slot shape and location on the part. The methods of Figure 12.50(a) and (c) are recommended when accuracy is important. If the slot position and size need not be accurate, the method of (b) can be applied, such as for air vent slots or loose control-handle travel-guides. The method of Figure 12.50(a) is used for milled slots and (c) is used for punched forms.

12.6   Dimensioning Features with Symbols

Geometric characteristics and other dimensional requirements can be established on engineering drawings using standard **symbols** instead of traditional terms and abbreviations. These symbols must conform to ANSI Y14.2M, including the following: the symbols denoting geometric characteristics (Fig. 12.51) and the symbols used to identify a basic dimen-

sion (Fig. 12.52). *A basic dimension is a numerical value used to describe the theoretically exact size, profile, orientation, or location of a feature or datum target.* Basic dimensions are the basis from which permissible variations are established by tolerances on other dimensions or in notes.

The symbols used to indicate diameter, spherical diameter, radius, and spherical radius are shown in (Fig. 12.53). Symbols precede the value of a dimension or tolerance given as a diameter or radius, as applicable. Once again, a reference

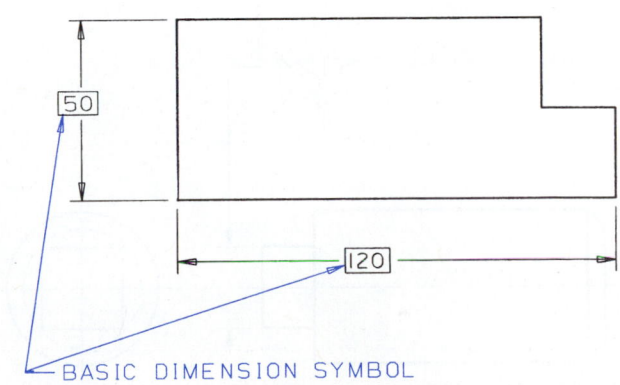

FIGURE 12.52   **Basic Dimensioning Symbol**

TERM	SYMBOL
AT MAXIMUM MATERIAL CONDITION	Ⓜ
REGARDLESS OF FEATURE SIZE	Ⓢ
AT LEAST MATERIAL CONDITION	Ⓛ
PROJECTED TOLERANCE ZONE	Ⓟ
DIAMETER	Ø
SPHERICAL DIAMETER	SØ
RADIUS	R
SPHERICAL RADIUS	SR
REFERENCE	( )
ARC LENGTH	⌒

FIGURE 12.53 Modifying Symbols for Dimensions

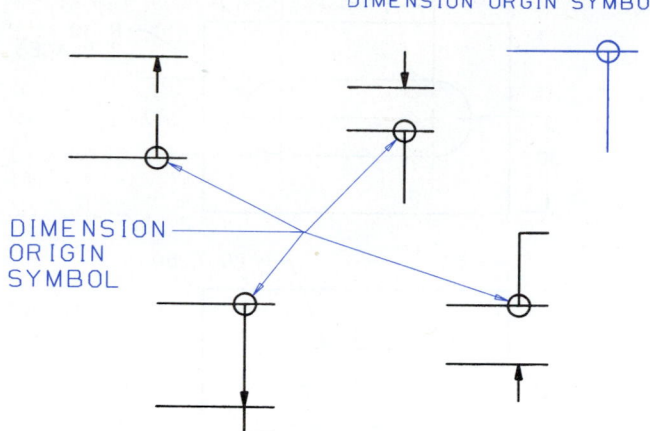

FIGURE 12.55 Dimension Origin Symbol

dimension (or reference data) is enclosed within parentheses; for example, (3.56). Symbology is used to designate a variety of geometric features and dimensions including the following:

- The symbol used to indicate that a linear dimension is an arc length measured on a curved outline is also shown in Figure 12.53. The symbol is placed above the dimension (Fig. 12.41).
- The symbol used to indicate that a single dimension applies to a square shape precedes that dimension with the symbol for a square (Fig. 12.54).
- The symbol used to indicate that a toleranced dimension between two features originates from one of these features is shown in Figure 12.55.
- The depth of a hole (Fig. 12.56), countersink (Fig. 12.57) or counterdrill (Fig. 12.57), spotface (Fig. 12.58), or counterbore (Fig. 12.59) can be given symbolically. The symbol to indicate where a dimension applies to the depth of a feature precedes the dimension with the depth symbol, as shown in these figures.

Symbols speed the drafting and detailing process. You must take care to construct the symbol according to the proper standards, with the correct line weights, with clarity for legibility and reproducibility. Other symbols are described in Chapter 13.

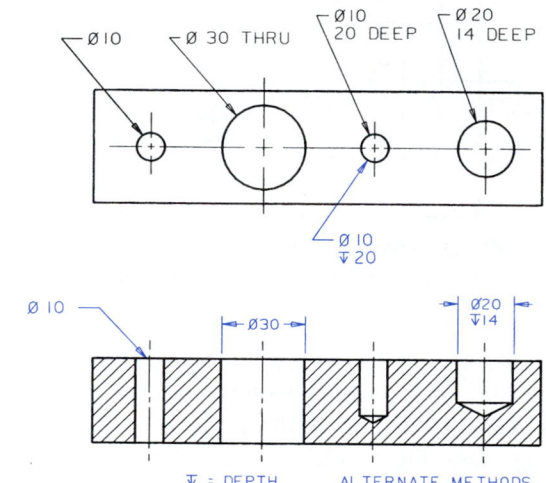

FIGURE 12.56 Using Symbols to Dimension Holes

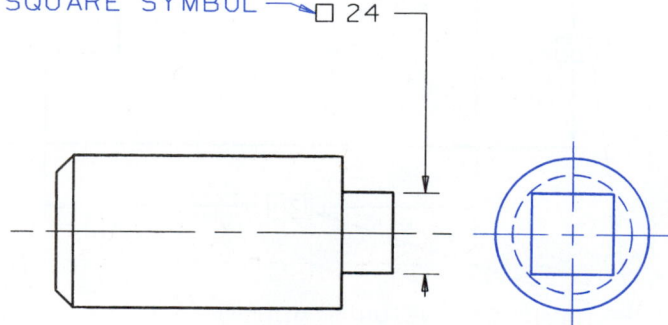

FIGURE 12.54 Square Dimensioning Symbol

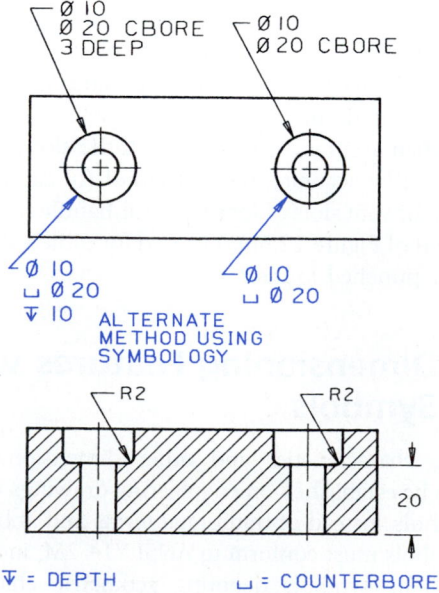

FIGURE 12.57 Dimensioning Counterbores

12.6.1 Countersunk and Counterdrilled Holes

Countersinking (CSK) is used on holes so that flathead screws will be flush with the surface of the part (Fig. 12.59). The flathead screw requires a conical seat usually specified by the included angle and the diameter at the large end. For countersunk holes, the diameter and included angle of the countersink are specified.

For **counterdrilled holes (CDRILL)**, the diameter and depth of the counterdrill are given. Specifying the included angle of the counterdrill is optional (Fig. 12.57, lower right). The depth dimension is the depth of the full diameter of the counterdrill from the outer surface of the part. Symbology can be used on these features, as shown in the alternate examples in Figure 12.57. A counterdrilled hole differs from a counterbored hole in that the bottom of the counterdrilled hole is conical—similar to a countersink. Counterdrilled holes are created with a step drill or two drills of different diameters.

12.6.2 Spotfaced Holes

A **spotface (SF)**, shown in Figure 12.58, is a method of cleaning up and squaring a rough surface such as on a cast metal part. Material is removed so a screw head will seat flush against the surface. Its depth is usually not dimensioned, but if necessary can be dimensioned like a CBORE.

The diameter of the spotfaced area is specified by using the diameter symbol and a value. When a depth is required, either the depth or the remaining thickness of material may be specified. A spotface is sometimes specified by a note and is not delineated on the drawing. If no depth or remaining thickness of material is specified, the spotfacing is the mini-

mum depth necessary to clean up the surface to the specified diameter. Figure 12.58 shows both methods, notes and symbols, for calling out the spotface.

12.6.3 Counterbored Holes

Counterbored holes are used extensively for socket head screws so the head of the screw will be flush with or below the surface of the part. A **counterbore (CBORE)** is an enlarged hole, piloted from a smaller hole to maintain concentricity. Counterbored holes are machined to a square seat at a specified depth (Fig. 12.59). The depth can be called out within the hole note as the distance from the upper surface (beginning surface) to the bottom of the counterbore. Either the symbol for the counterbore or the note **CBORE** is used. In Figure 12.59, the counterbore is called out using the traditional note method at the top and the alternate method of using a symbol is provided at the bottom. Note that the symbol precedes the dimension of the counterbore. The depth symbol or the note **DEEP** can also be used alternatively. When the thickness of the remaining material has significance, it, rather than the depth, is normally dimensioned as shown in Figures 12.58 and 12.59 (right lower side of figures). Figure 12.60 shows a simple mechanical part dimensioned with symbols.

You May Complete Exercises 12.5 Through 12.8 at This Time

12.7 Dimensioning Special Features

Numerous special geometric features are found on industrial parts. Chamfers, threads, center drills, tapers, knurling, keyways,

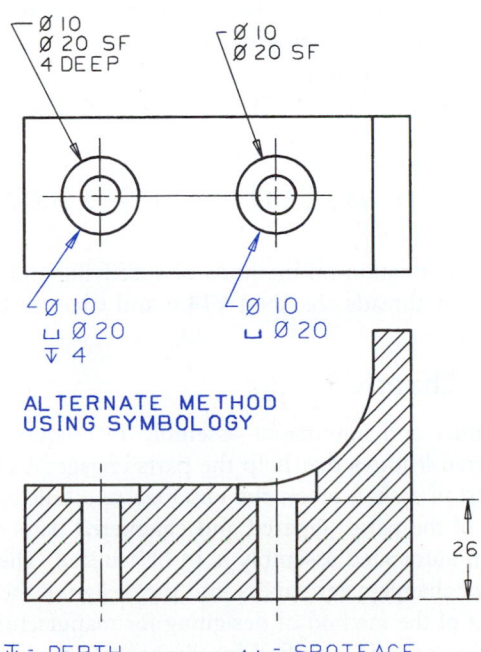

FIGURE 12.58 Dimensioning Spotfaces

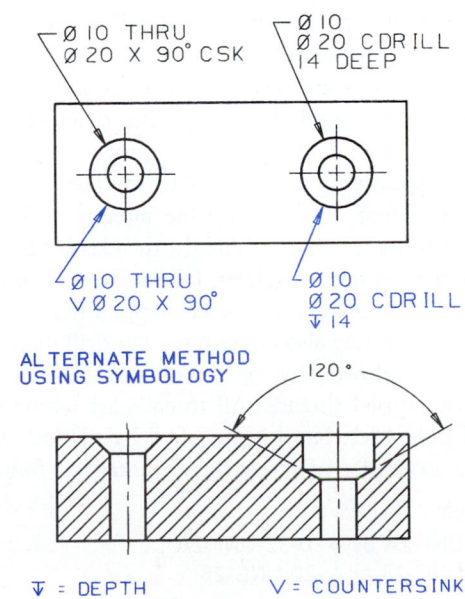

FIGURE 12.59 Dimensioning Counterdrills

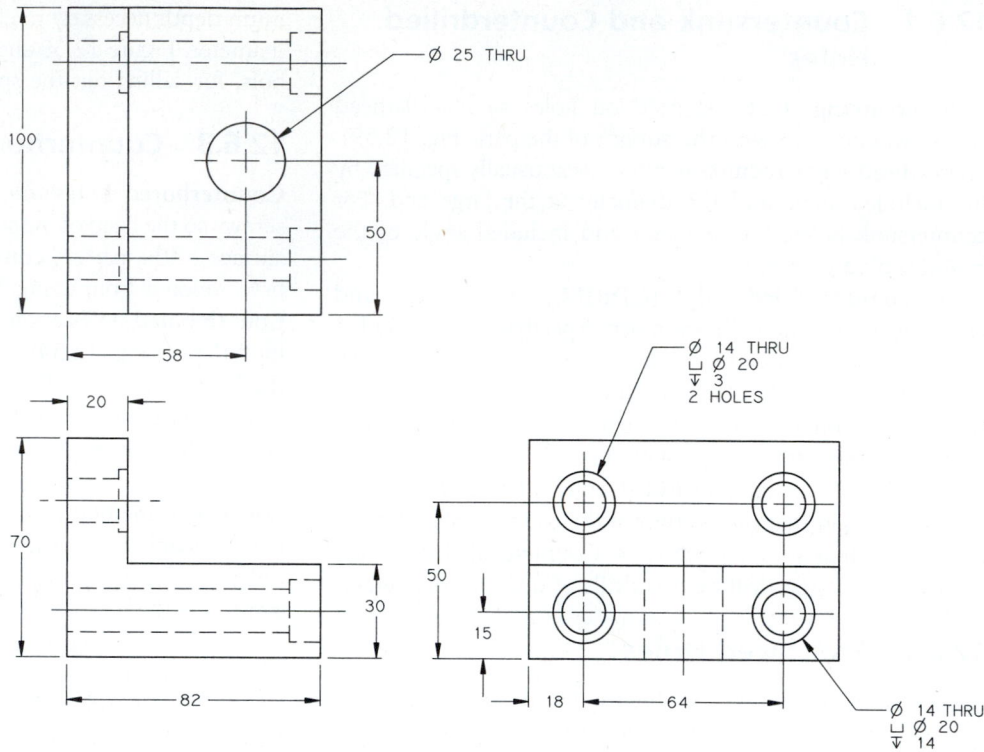

FIGURE 12.60 Part Dimensioned Using Dimensioning Symbols

and other *geometric features* require specific, standardized dimensions. These dimensions are usually based on the method used to machine them or on a standard purchased part inserted into or mated with the feature.

12.7.1 Threads

Thread callouts are found an almost every mechanical drawing. Figure 12.4 shows a part designed with metric units. The callout **M42 × 1.5–6G** specifies a metric thread. Figure 12.3 shows an example of a unified thread callout on a decimal-inch drawing (**.250–20 UNC**).

Nonmetric threads are classified in series according to the number of threads applied to a specific diameter. Unified (UN) thread is the standard type of thread for the United States. When specifying screw threads, the *nominal major diameter* is given first, followed by the *number of threads per inch,* and the *series designation.* Finally, the class of fit between male and female threads is given, followed by an **A** for male threads or a **B** for female threads. For tapped holes, however, the complete note may also contain the tap drill diameter and depth of hole, followed by the thread specification and the length of the tapped threads. All threads are assumed to be right hand unless left hand is specified by **LH** following the class. A few examples of screw thread notations follow:

Decimal-Inch:

- .190-32 UNF-2A or #10-32 UNF-2A
- .250-20 UNC-2B or $\frac{1}{4}$-20 UNC-2B
- 2.000-16 UN-2A
- 2.500-10 UNS-2B

Metric:

- M6 × 1 – 4h6h
- M16 × L4-P2-4h6h

In most cases, the thread type and size are given on a drawing and the machinist chooses the correct drill diameter and tool. Specifying the drill and tapping requirements of a hole sometimes requires that the diameter and depth be given. In this case, the tap drill size, its depth, the thread specification, and the depth of threads are provided, as in the examples that follow:

- Ø .312, 1.25 DEEP
  .375-16 UNC-2B, .88 DEEP   or $\frac{3}{8}$-16 UNC-2B
  3 HOLES
- Ø .422 1.25 DEEP
  .500-13 UNC-2B LH, 1.12 DEEP   or $\frac{1}{2}$-13 UNC-2B LH
  2 HOLES

For more information on methods of specifying and dimensioning screw threads see ANSI Y14.6 and Chapter 15.

12.7.2 Chamfers

Both manual and automated assembly techniques benefit from tapered features that help the parts engage. A **chamfer** on the end of a shaft or on the entrance to a hole also aids assembly of the parts. Tapered and chamfered parts may be required if automated assembly is to be realized. The incorporation of chamfers and tapers into the design of the part is one aspect of the method of designing for manufacturability.

Chamfers may be specified by dimensions or notes. It is not necessary to use the word **CHAMFER** when the meaning

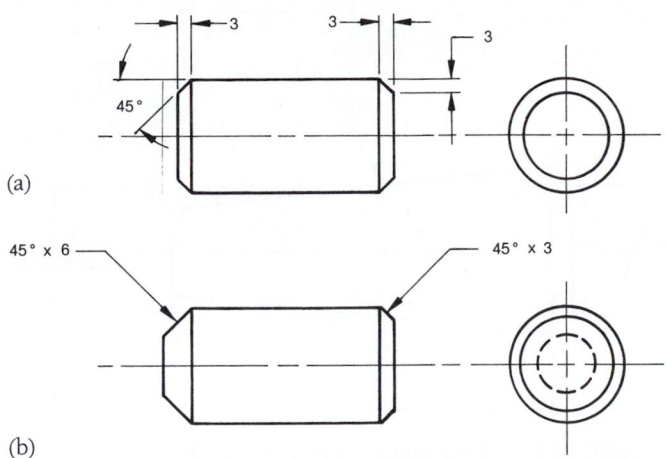

(a)

(b)

FIGURE 12.61   **Dimensioning Chamfers**   (a) Dimensioning chamfer angle and one leg (b) Angle and one leg given in callout

is obvious. If the chamfer is other than 45°, dimensions are used to show the direction of the slope. Figure 12.61 provides methods for dimensioning external chamfers. You can show chamfer dimensions by giving the chamfer angle and one leg, dimensioning both legs, or pointing to the chamfer and giving the angle and one leg as a callout. Internal dimensions for chamfers (Fig. 12.62) are dimensioned by giving the included angle (here 90°) and the largest diameter. An alternate method gives the chamfer angle (here 45°) and the largest diameter. The metric method of dimensioning chamfers is shown on this figure. For inch-unit drawings, the angle is sometimes given second and the leg first, for example,

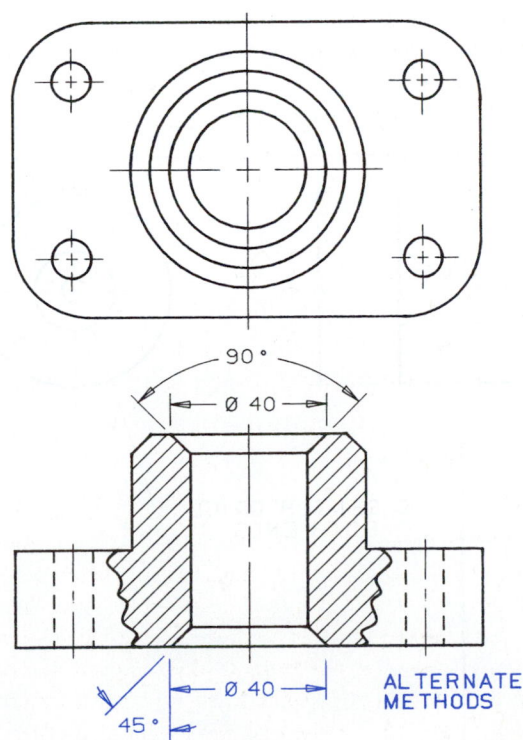

FIGURE 12.62   **Internal Chamfers**

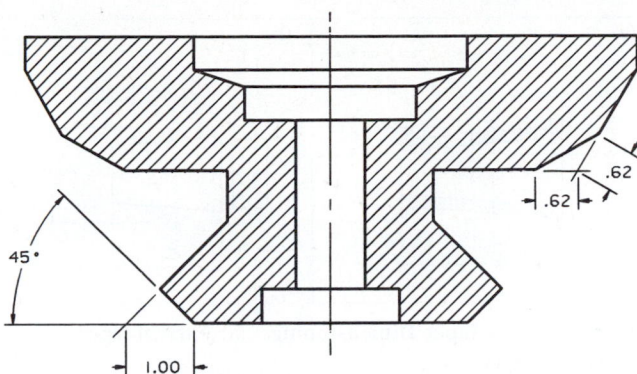

FIGURE 12.63   Dimensioning Chamfers Between Surfaces Not at 90°

.25 × 45°. This method, however, is being replaced by the international method, as in ANSI Y14.5M. If chamfers are required for surfaces intersecting at other than right angles, the methods shown in Figure 12.63 are used.

12.7.3   Taper Dimensioning

Tapers are used on machines to align and hold machine parts such as taper shanks for drills and arbor presses that require simple and speedy repeated assembly and disassembly. A round taper is a uniform increase in the diameter on a round part for a given length measured parallel to the axis of the work piece; round tapers therefore are conical. Internal or external tapers are noted by taper per foot (TPF), taper per inch (TPI), or by degrees. TPF or TPI refer to the difference in diameters within 1 foot or 1 inch [Fig. 12.64(a)]. The difference is measured in inches. The *angles of taper* refer to the inclined angles with the part's centerline (axis) [Fig. 12.64(b)].

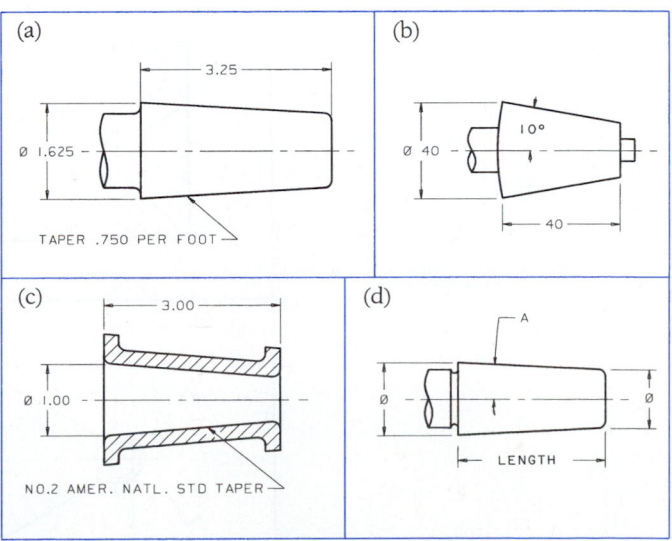

FIGURE 12.64   **Dimensioning Tapers**   (a) Taper per foot (b) Taper angle, diameter, and length (c) National Standard Taper (d) Angle of taper, length, and diameter at both ends

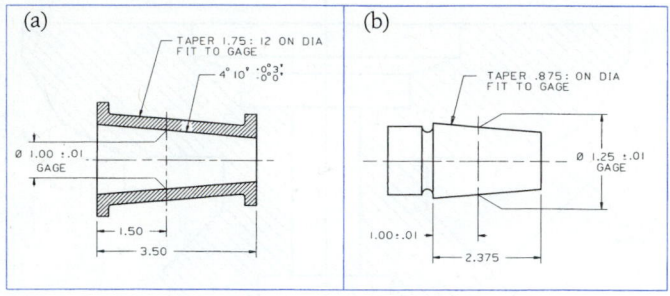

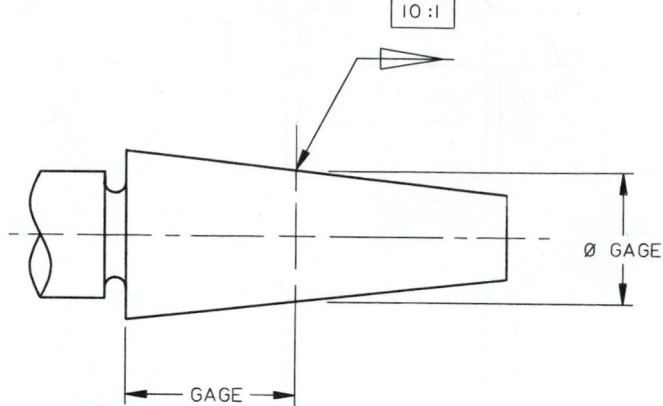

FIGURE 12.65   Taper Dimensioning   (a) Internal taper
(b) External taper

FIGURE 12.66   Dimensioning Tapers with a Ratio

Tapers can be designated in a number of different ways. In Figure 12.64(a), the taper per foot, the length of the part, and the large diameter are given. In Figure 12.64(b), the diameter, length, and the angle are given. Still another method used to note a taper is shown in Figure 12.64(c), where the length, diameter, and the note **NO.2 AMER. NATL. STD TAPER** are given. In the last example [Fig. 12.64(d)], the two diameters, the length, and the angle are given where one of the three is a reference dimension.

In Figure 12.65(a) the internal taper is designated by giving a note (**TAPER 1.75:12 ON DIA FIT TO GAGE**), the gage diameter (**1.00 GAGE**), locating dimension (**1.50**), angle (**4°10′**), and the part length (**3.50**). Figure 12.65(b) uses this same method for an external taper. Figure 12.66 expresses the taper as a ratio (**10:1**) and gives the gage location and gage diameter.

12.7.4   Center Drill Dimensioning

When a part is held and turned between the centers of a lathe, a *center hole* is required on each end of the cylindrical work piece. The center hole has a 60° angle that conforms to the lathe center and a smaller drilled hole to clear the center's point. The center hole is made with a combination drill and countersink called a **center drill** (Fig. 12.67). In this figure, the A dimension is the work piece diameter. The B dimension is the body diameter of the center drill. The C dimension is for the diameter of the drilled center hole and the D dimension is the depth. The drill tip is drawn at 120° as shown. Center drills come in standard sizes from $\frac{1}{8}$ to $\frac{3}{4}$ inches and a complete listing can be found in the *Machinery's Handbook*. Center drills are classified by numbers from 00 to 8. A number 3 center drill has a $\frac{1}{4}$ in. body diameter and a $\frac{7}{64}$ in. drill diameter (see Appendix C).

12.7.5   Keys and Keyseats

A **key** is a demountable machinery part. When assembled into *keyseats*, a key provides a positive means for transmitting torque between a shaft and a hub. A **keyseat** is an axially

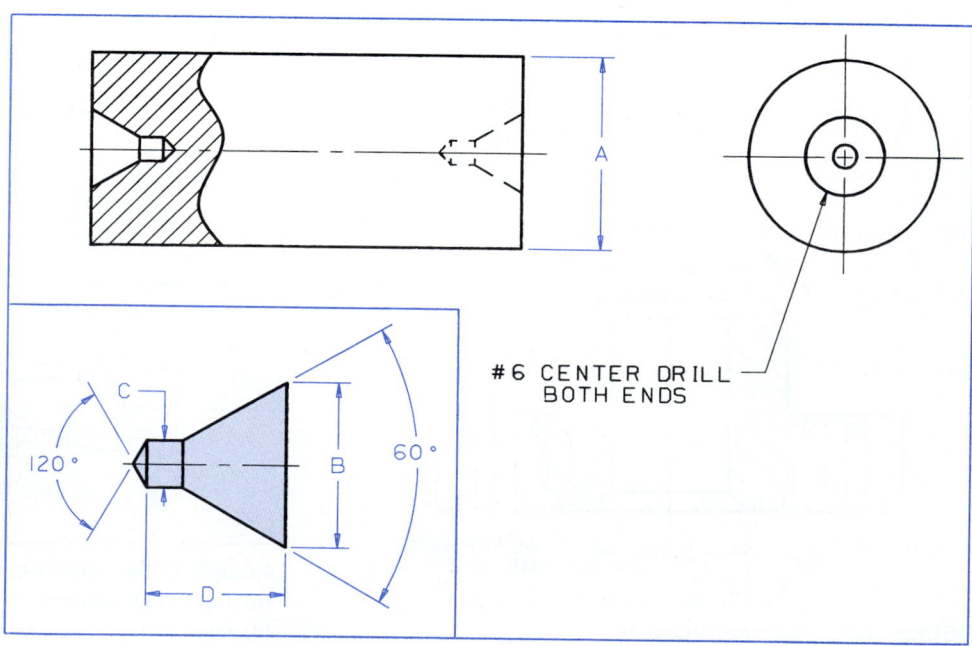

FIGURE 12.67   Center Holes and
Center Drills

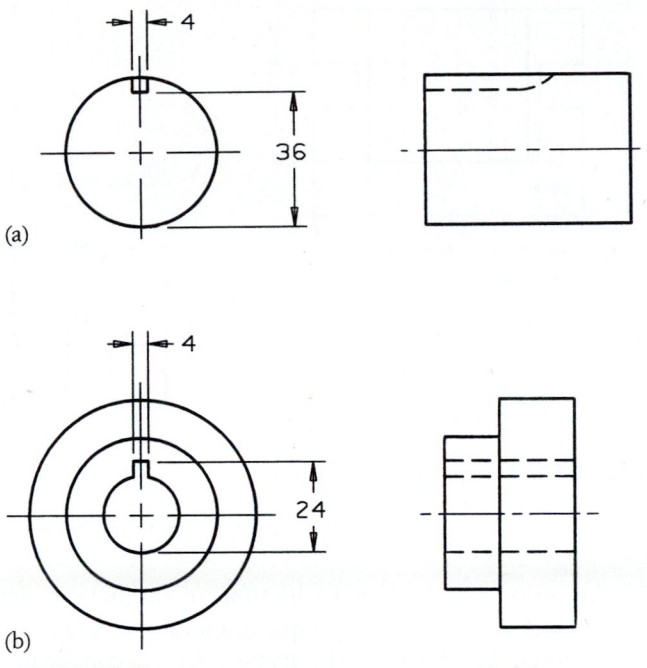

FIGURE 12.68   **Dimensioning Keyseats**   (a) Shaft keyseat
(b) Hub keyseat

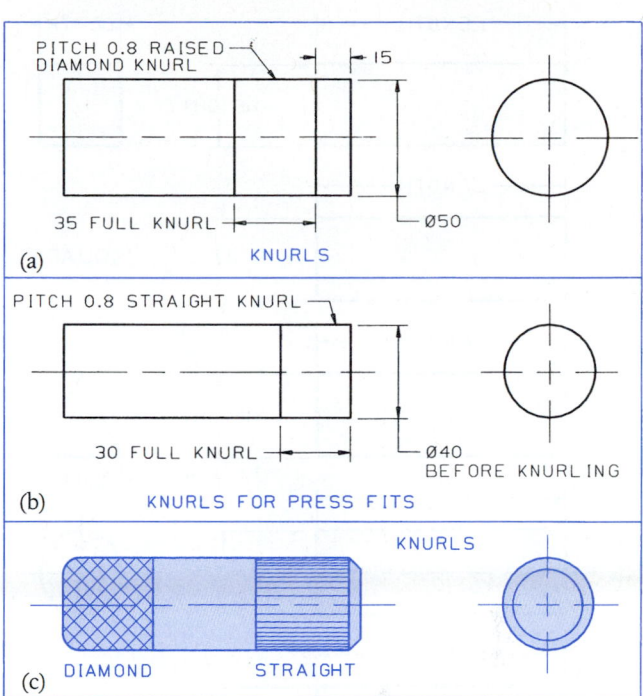

FIGURE 12.69   **Dimensioning Knurling**   (a) Diamond knurl
(b) Straight knurl (c) Knurling representation

located rectangular groove in a shaft or hub. Keyseats are dimensioned by width, depth, location, and, if required, length (Fig. 12.68). The depth is dimensioned from the opposite side of the shaft or hole. Keys and keyseats are covered in greater detail in Chapters 15 and 16.

12.7.6   Knurling

A **knurl** is a machined rough geometrical surface on a round metal part. Knurling is used to improve the grip or for press-fitting the knurled part into a hole in a mating part. Sometimes knurling is done for appearance.

Knurling is specified in terms of type, pitch, and diameter before and after knurling. When diameter control is not required, the diameter after knurling is omitted. If only a portion of a feature requires knurling, axial dimensioning must be provided. Knurling can be either diamond patterned or straight patterned and fine, medium, or coarse. Knurling is specified by a note that includes the type of knurl required, its pitch, the toleranced diameter of the feature prior to knurling, and the minimum acceptable diameter after knurling if required to provide a press fit between parts (Fig. 12.69).

12.8   Locating Features on a Drawing

The location of holes, slots, and machined features on a part is one of the most important aspects of dimensioning. Each designed part is composed of geometric shapes and surfaces with a variety of cylindrical holes. Locating these features is the job of the drafter. When dimensioning, *you must consider how the part is to be machined.*

If a CAD system was used for the design of the part, the drafter need only call up the 3D design and place it in the views necessary to describe the part with dimensions and notes. If the traditional manual method of design was used, the detailer will get a print of the project assembly and "pick off" each part that requires *detailing.* A separate sheet of paper normally is used for each individual part. Understanding the detailing and dimensioning process begins with analyzing the part geometrically.

12.8.1   Geometric Analysis of a Part

The simple shapes found in Figure 12.70 show the geometric shape and the dimensions required to describe the shape. The machinist should have all necessary dimensions; nothing should be taken for granted. *The drawing must never be "scaled" to find a location or size that should have been described by a dimension.*

In Figure 12.71 a simple clamp is shown in three views with appropriate dimensioning. Note that it is composed entirely of rectangular prisms. Each of these prisms must be provided with sufficient dimensions to allow the machinist to make the part. *The three most important dimensions are also required: height, width, and depth.*

The negative areas (portions removed from the part) are as important as the shapes and areas remaining. During the machining of the part, the removed areas are not available to measure so the positive areas normally need dimensions. The 20 × 20 cutout seen in the top view of Figure 12.71 is an example of a negative area. When a mating part must fit into the area, the negative area needs to be dimensioned.

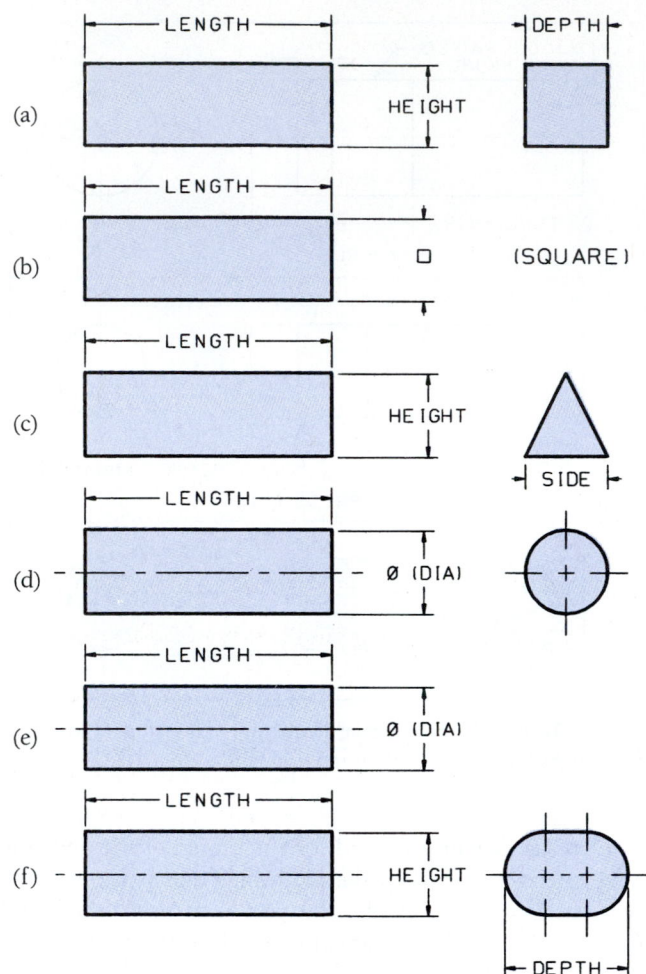

FIGURE 12.70   Dimensions for Common Geometric Shapes

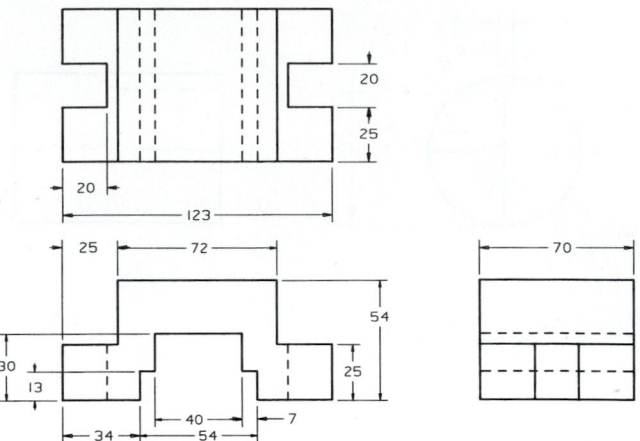

FIGURE 12.71   Dimensioned Clamp

The part in Figure 12.72 is composed entirely of cylindrical shapes. In fact, only the ends are flat planar surfaces. Note that the holes are removed negative cylinders.

Size dimensions for a part are given to establish the shape itself. The diameter of the cylinder is a size dimension. **Location dimensions** position a geometric shape in space. The

.34 dimension establishing the location of the hole in the front view (Fig. 12.73) is an example of a location dimension. The location of a shape and the shape's size are equally important. A sufficient number of dimensions must be given to describe the part's geometry completely. *Nothing must be left for the machinist to interpret.* Size and location dimensions must be complete to avoid misunderstandings. On the other hand, it is important not to overdimension or to give two dimensions that locate the same feature of the part.

12.8.2   Mating Parts and Dimensions

In Figure 12.74, the part has features that obviously relate to a mating piece. The base of the part attaches to a mating part using the .187 clearance holes. A .750 diameter chamfered hole runs through the part. A shaft or other cylindrical item will be inserted here during assembly and will be held in place by one or more screws entering the side of the part. It is impossible to analyze the true use and final assembly of the part, but, from what can be seen by the detail, certain things can be understood. In most cases, the part to be detailed will be accompanied by a description and or illustration of the

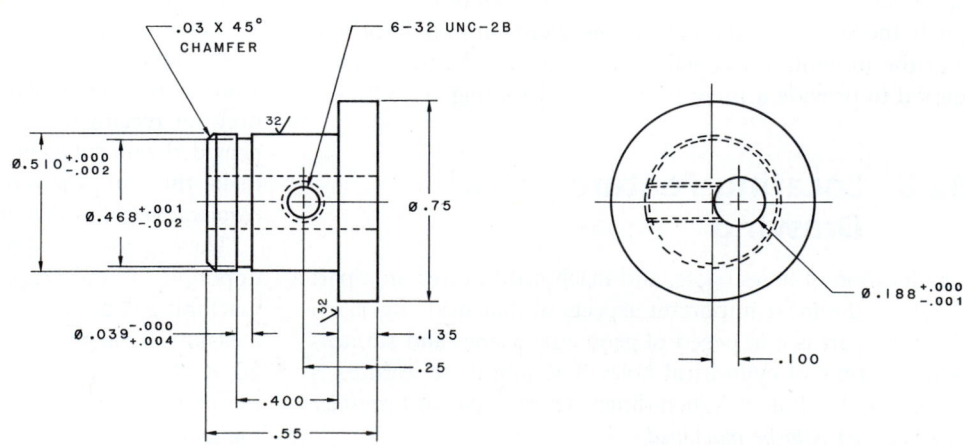

FIGURE 12.72   Cap Detail

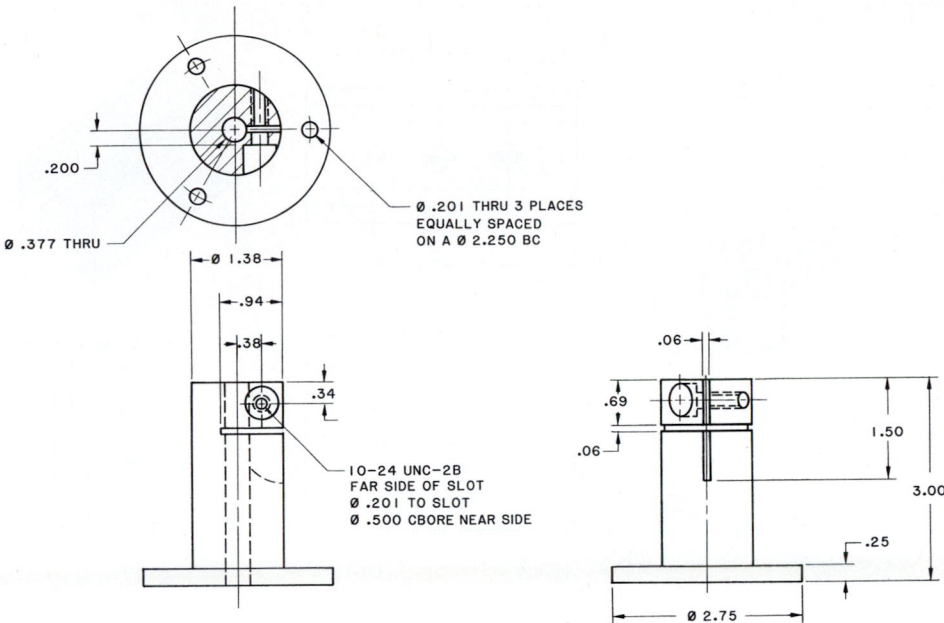

Ø .201 THRU 3 PLACES
EQUALLY SPACED
ON A Ø 2.250 BC

.200

Ø .377 THRU

Ø 1.38

.94

.38

.34

10-24 UNC-2B
FAR SIDE OF SLOT
Ø .201 TO SLOT
Ø .500 CBORE NEAR SIDE

.06

.69

.06

1.50

3.00

.25

Ø 2.75

FIGURE 12.73 Pedestal Detail

assembly. *From the assembly drawing, the use, location, orientation in space, and mating pieces are readily identified.*

The assembly of the slide plate in Figure 12.75(a) was designed on a 3D CAD system. Each piece is shown separately in Figure 12.75(b), (c), and (d). An assembly is also provided in Figure 12.75(e). Because the slide must fit into the slot in the base, the slide and the base have **related dimensions**. The slide's bottom portion is mated with the top of the base. The mating dimension for the slide is slightly smaller than that for the base because it must fit inside the slot. The designer establishes the *clearance fit*. Clearances and fits are discussed in detail in Chapter 13.

When dimensioning parts that must mate with other parts in an assembly, the related surfaces on each part should be dimensioned. Mating dimensions are also necessary when establishing hole patterns used to secure one part to another. In Figure 12.75 the parts are secured by three screws. The clearance hole in the slide must match the dimensions of the tapped holes in the base to align the pieces and allow the screws to be inserted and tightened. The hole pattern dimensioning on the slide has to be the same as it was on the base or the screws will not align the two parts.

12.8.3 Finish Marks and Machined Surfaces

Rough stock shapes, castings, and forgings have *rough unmachined* surface textures. **Machined surfaces** are established on

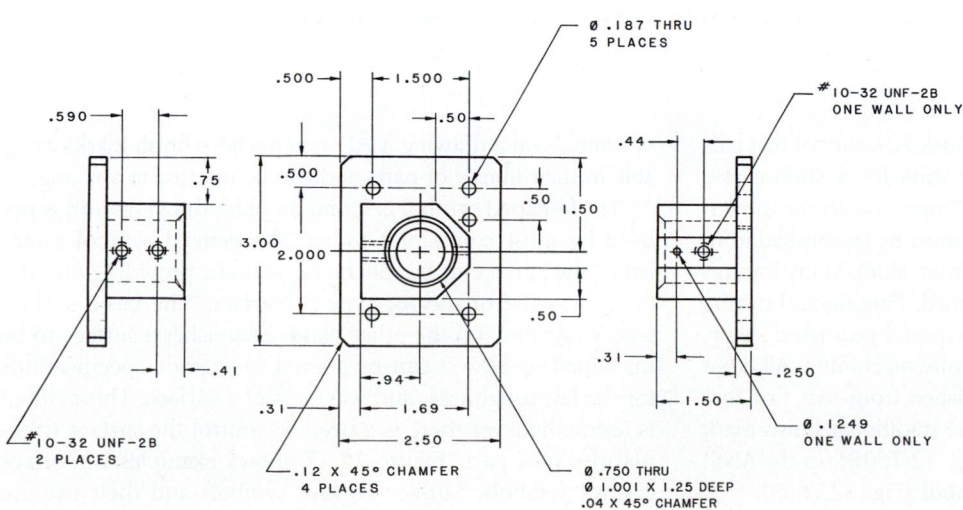

Ø .187 THRU
5 PLACES

#10-32 UNF-2B
ONE WALL ONLY

.590

.500

1.500

.75

.50

.500

.44

.500

.50

1.50

3.00

2.000

.41

.94

.31

1.69

.31

.250

2.50

.12 X 45° CHAMFER
4 PLACES

1.50

Ø .750 THRU
Ø 1.001 X 1.25 DEEP
.04 X 45° CHAMFER

Ø .1249
ONE WALL ONLY

#10-32 UNF-2B
2 PLACES

6061-T6 ALUM ALY BLACK ANODIZE

FIGURE 12.74 Base Mounting
Detail

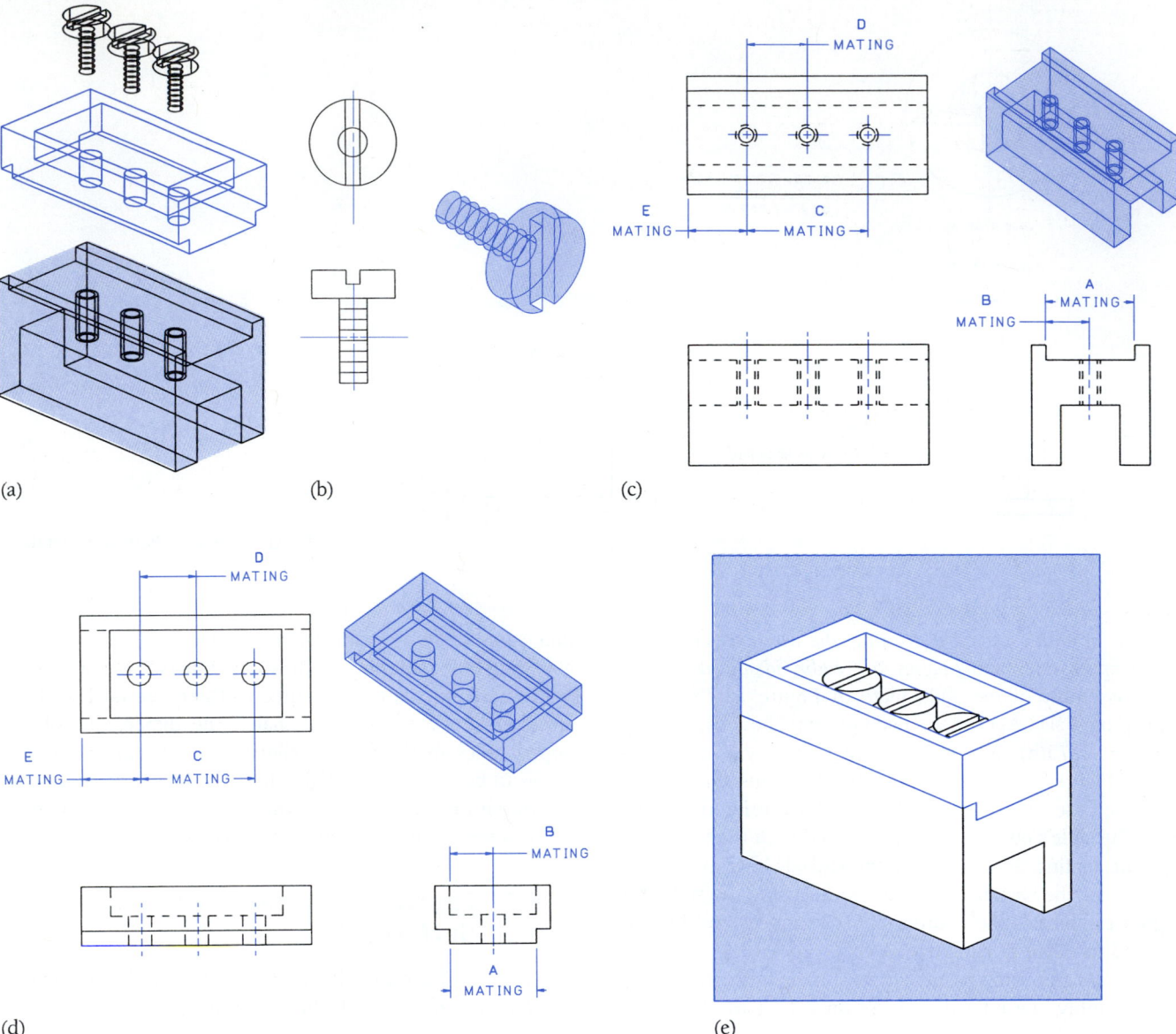

FIGURE 12.75 **Mechanical Assembly** (a) Exploded view of assembly (b) Bolt for assembly (c) Base detail of assembly showing mating dimensions (d) Slide plate of assembly showing mating dimensions (e) Assembly created by inserting parts together

the part using finish marks. A **finish mark** is a symbol that tells the machinist the machining requirements for a surface (see Chapter 11). *Surface finish symbols* are important to the dimensioning procedure. Machined surfaces must be established from a rough surface, in any direction (top, front, side). Many features on a casting or forging must be machined. Forging and casting processes produce a part with every required geometric shape, but some of the part's surfaces will require machining. All other machined surfaces or holes are established from that first machined surface. The symbol can be the traditional finish mark [Fig. 12.76(a)]; the general symbol [Fig. 12.76(b)]; or the ANSI recognized **basic surface texture symbol** [Fig. 12.76(c)].

The placement and measurements for construction of the three types of symbols are shown in Figure 12.76. Symbol templates are available for quick, easy, and accurate insertion

of symbols on a drawing. CAD systems have finish marks available in their library of parts and can be inserted at any angle.

The **f**-shaped symbol is found on older drawings and is not used by most companies today. The general symbol establishes the surface to be machined without providing any details as to the quality or type of surface. The basic surface texture symbol, on the other hand, establishes a surface to be machined or how it can be altered to provide specifications for the lay, roughness, and waviness of a surface. This symbol is used whenever there is a need to control the surface irregularities of a part. Figure 12.77 shows examples of surface control symbols. Surface control symbols and their use are described in detail in Chapter 11.

You May Complete Exercises 12.9 Through 12.12 at This Time

(a)

(b)

(c)

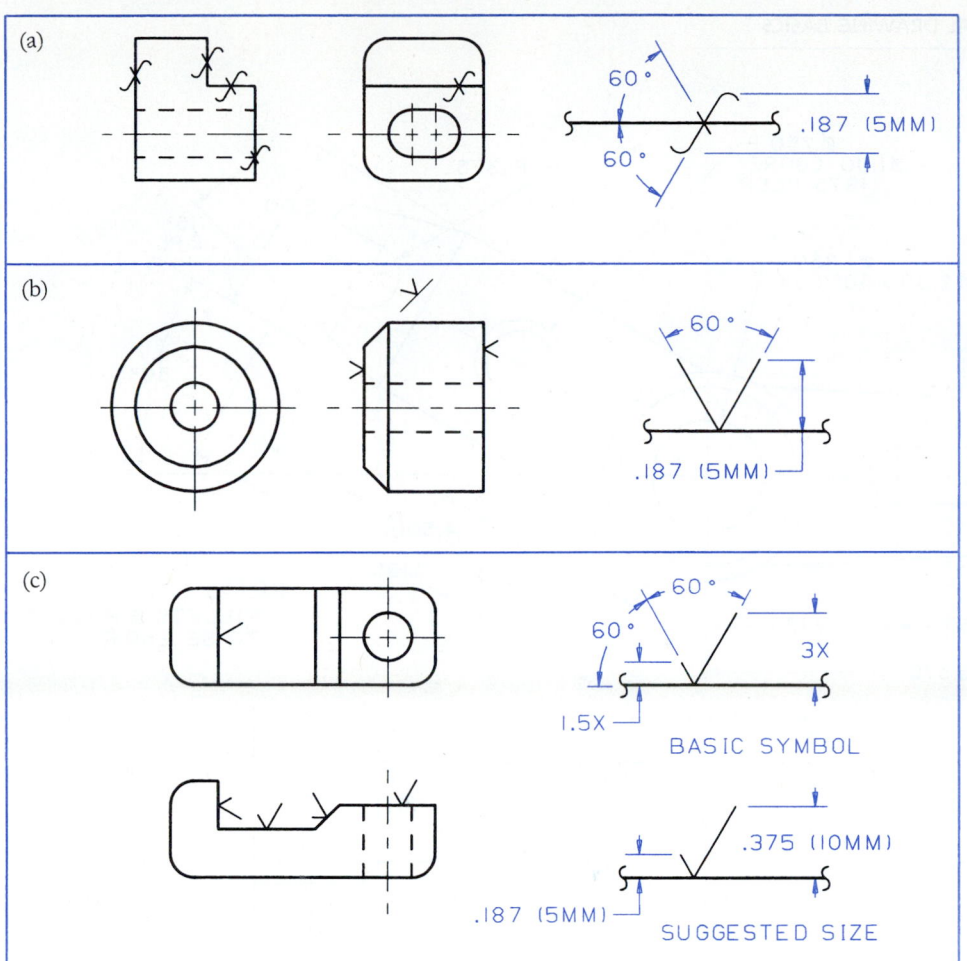

BASIC SYMBOL

SUGGESTED SIZE

FIGURE 12.76 Finish Marks
(a) Traditional finish symbol
(b) Old general finish symbol
(c) New basic finish symbol

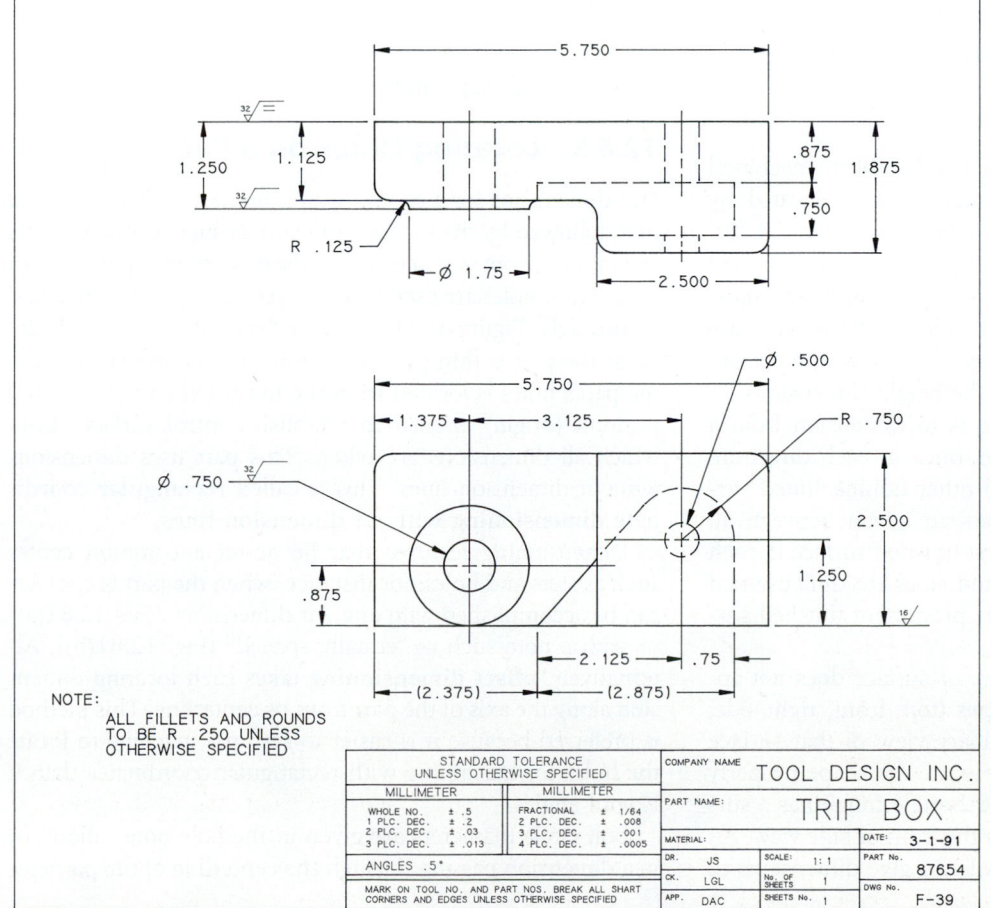

NOTE:
ALL FILLETS AND ROUNDS
TO BE R .250 UNLESS
OTHERWISE SPECIFIED

STANDARD TOLERANCE UNLESS OTHERWISE SPECIFIED		COMPANY NAME	TOOL DESIGN INC.	
MILLIMETER	MILLIMETER	PART NAME:	TRIP BOX	

WHOLE NO.	± .5	FRACTIONAL	± 1/64
1 PLC. DEC.	± .2	2 PLC. DEC.	± .008
2 PLC. DEC.	± .03	3 PLC. DEC.	± .001
3 PLC. DEC.	± .013	4 PLC. DEC.	± .0005

ANGLES .5°

MARK ON TOOL NO. AND PART NOS. BREAK ALL SHART
CORNERS AND EDGES UNLESS OTHERWISE SPECIFIED

MATERIAL:		DATE: 3-1-91
DR. JS	SCALE: 1:1	PART No. 87654
CK. LGL	No. OF SHEETS 1	DWG No. F-39
APP. DAC	SHEETS No. 1	

FIGURE 12.77 Finish Marks
Used on Mechanical Detail

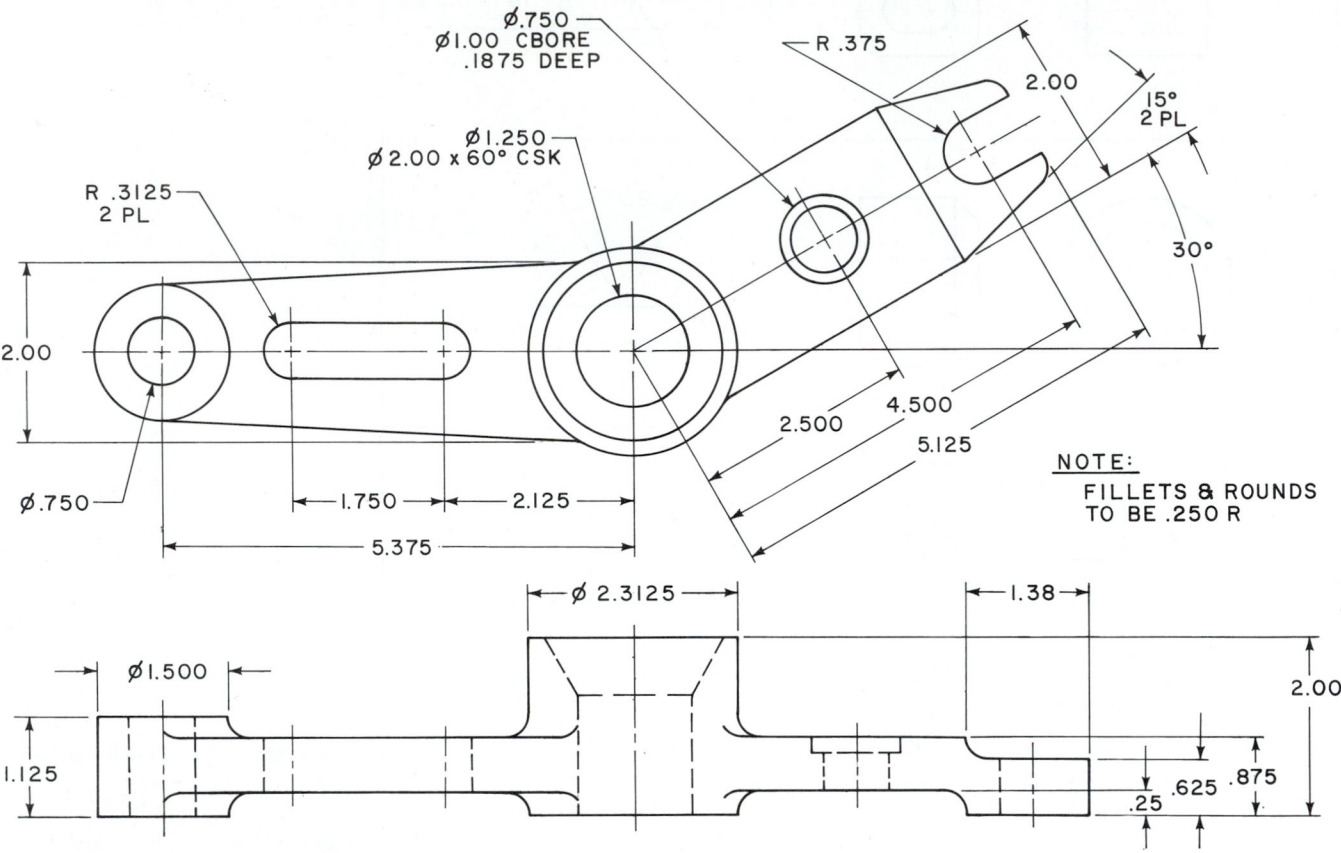

FIGURE 12.78   Dimensioning Machined Features

12.8.4   Locating Holes and Features on a View

Because machined surfaces are used to establish machined features such as holes and slots, they must be located by dimensions from a prominent feature or surface (Fig. 12.78). The bracket arm is a cast part and has a number of machined surfaces and holes. The central hole is obviously the most important; therefore, all machined holes and the slots are located from it in the top view. In the front view, the bottom surface was used to locate each of the height dimensions.

A general rule for dimensioning is to dimension from a rough surface to a finished surface, once in each direction, and between rough surfaces for all other nonmachined surfaces in each direction. Dimensions are given between all other machined surfaces and the first finished surface in each direction. Features such as holes and slots are dimensioned between each other and back to the prominent finished surface in each direction.

When the true shape of a feature or surface does not appear in one of the six standard views (top, front, right side, left side, rear, or bottom), an auxiliary view of that surface and feature should be projected to locate the shape properly with dimensions. In Figure 12.79 the angle frame has a surface whose true shape is not seen in the front or side view. An auxiliary projection allows the detailer to give dimensions to the hole and provide a note pointing to the feature where it shows its true shape and size.

12.8.5   Locating Holes on a Part

Size dimensions for a part's features are normally established first, followed by the location of features such as holes. Holes are located from a machined surface whenever possible. In most cases, holes are established in patterns and dimensioned accordingly. Figure 12.80 shows a detail of a connector. Because the part is thin (.25), only one view is needed. Each of the part's holes is located from the lower left corner. The 0,0 position (origin) is used to establish control surfaces from which all dimensions are taken. This part uses dimensions without dimension lines. This is called **rectangular coordinate dimensioning without dimension lines.**

Dimensioning features that lie about a common center such as slots and holes, for instance, when the part is circular, can be accomplished with angular dimensions [Fig. 12.81(a)] or with a note such as "equally spaced" [Fig. 12.81(b)]. Alternatively, **offset dimensioning** takes each locating dimension along the axis of the part from its centerline. This method is preferred because it is easier to set up a machine to locate the holes for machining with rectangular coordinates than it is with angles.

Bolt circle diameters are given in the hole note callout, or in a dimension passing through the centerline of the part (see

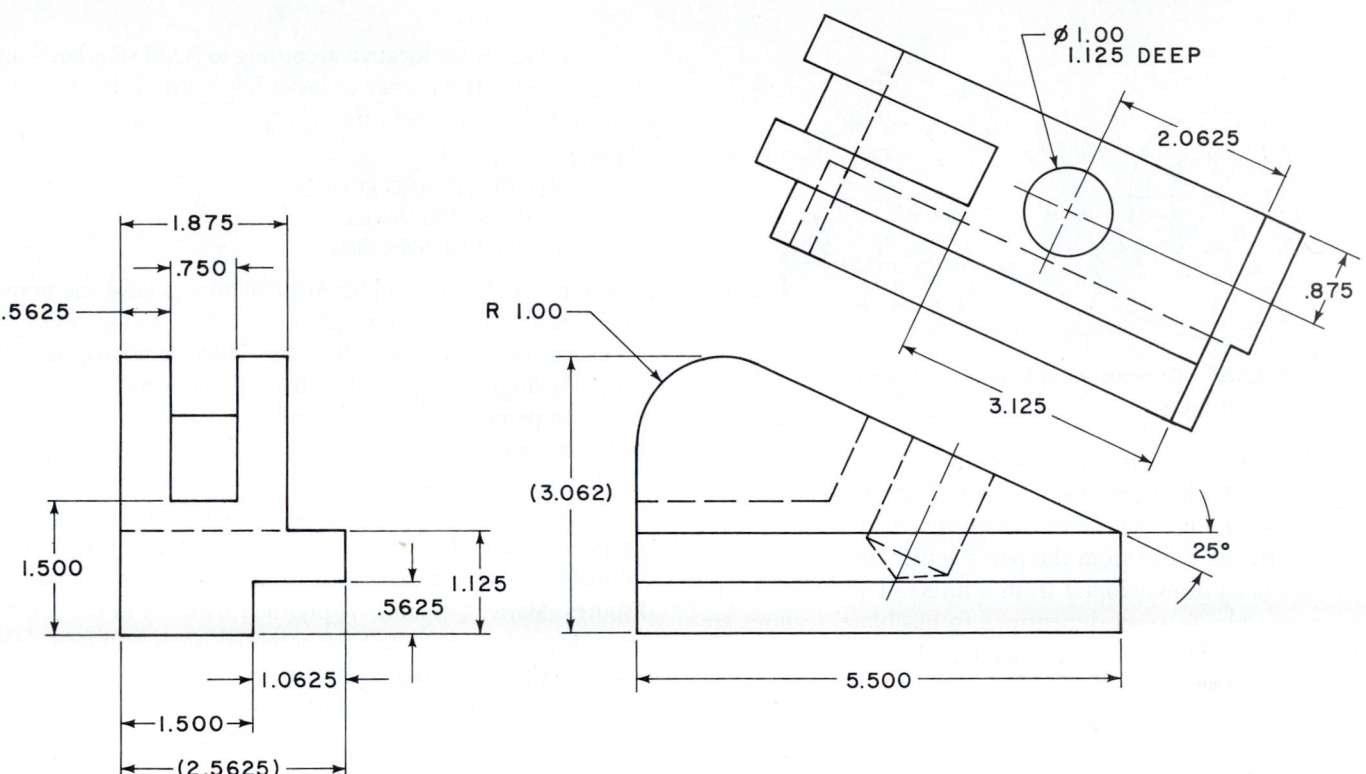

FIGURE 12.79   Anchor Detail

.25 ALY ALUM ANODIZE BLACK

HOLE	DESCRIPTION	QTY
A	Ø .125 THRU	2
B	Ø .375 THRU	2
C	Ø .50 THRU	2
D	Ø .149 THRU Ø .281 X .073 DP FS	4
E	8–32 UNC–2B	1

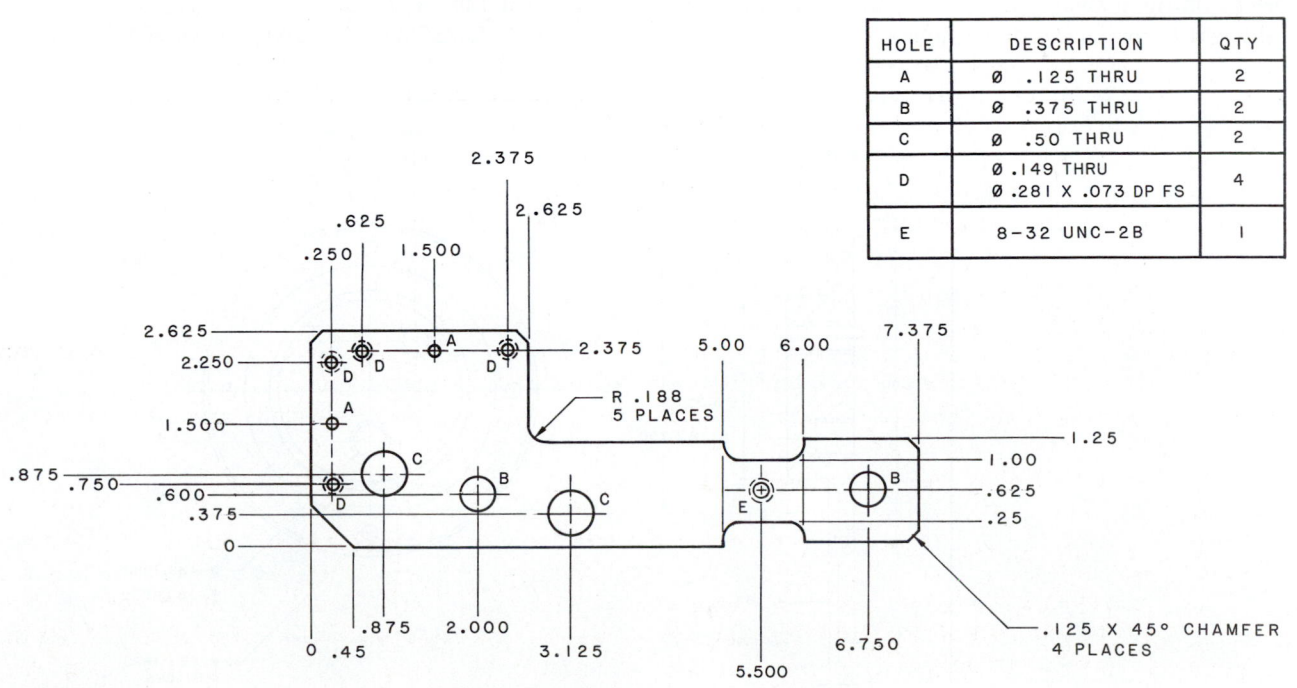

FIGURE 12.80   Dimensioned Part

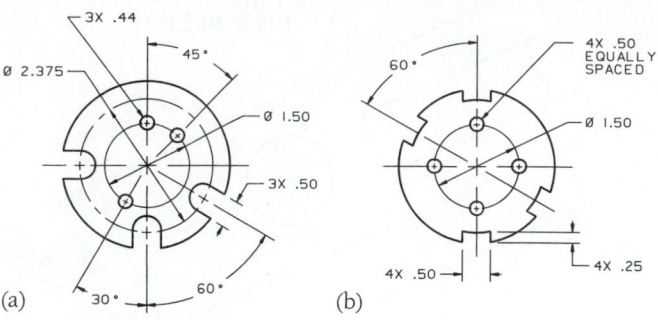

FIGURE 12.81   **Dimensioning Repetitive Features**   (a) Three holes (b) Four holes

Figs. 12.4 and 12.5, pp. 368–369). The first method is easier and does not clutter the view with a dimension.

Because each of the holes dimensioned in Figures 12.81 and 12.82 are taken from the part's center, they can be said to have been **dimensioned from a finished surface.** Whenever possible, location dimensions to machined features are taken from a finished surface (see Fig. 12.2, p. 366).

Hole patterns, a set of holes related to another mating part, are established by locating their center hole, if they have one, or to the same hole in both directions. Dimensions between the holes are then given.

12.9 Notes on Drawings

In addition to dimensions, every drawing has notes. **Notes** can be either **local notes,** as in the callout of a hole, or **general notes** (Fig. 12.45, p. 383) that apply to the total drawing. General notes are placed outside the part's geometry and beyond the dimensions. Notes are one of the last items to be placed on the drawing, usually after the views are drawn and the part is completely dimensioned.

General notes are located, according to ANSI standards, in the upper left-hand corner or lower left-hand of the drawing as in Figure 12.77 where the following note appears:

NOTE:

ALL FILLETS AND ROUNDS
TO BE R .250 UNLESS
OTHERWISE SPECIFIED

Drawings completed to older ANSI standards have the notes above the title block on the right side of the drawing. Some of the examples in the text reflect this older standard, as will many drawings encountered on the job. As previously noted, some companies find that the old standards work well for their situation and are hesitant to convert because conversion to different standards requires extensive retraining of all users: engineers, designers, drafters, checkers, and manufacturing personnel such as line supervisors and machinists. Retraining is costly and may cause labor problems and contract disputes. Many companies apply their own "in-house" standards, which may deviate from accepted ANSI standards. All new employees are responsible for learning the old and new ANSI standards and specific company practices. Each of these three possibilities may appear on drawings within the same company! Older drawings may conform to older standards and, in some cases, may need to be updated or used on projects that are only slightly different from a former design.

The following is an example of a typical general note as it would appear on the drawing:

NOTES:

1. MATL: .093 THK. ALUMINUM-5052.
2. FINISH: CLEAR ANODIZE- FRONT & REAR PANELS BRUSHED.
3. OPTIONAL RELIEF FOR BREAK.
4. MIN. BEND RAD. TYP. (4) PLACES.
5. SILKSCREEN PER DWG. 18014-201

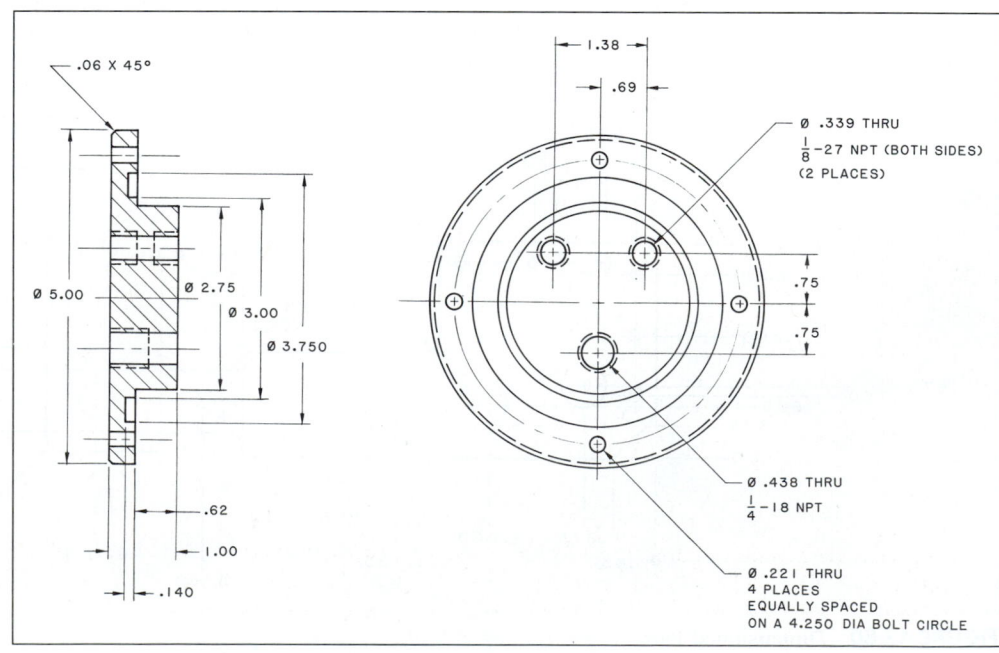

FIGURE 12.82   **Square Dimensioning Holes**

Why Change ANSI Standards?

Ever since you began your study of technical or engineering drawing, you have been learning how to produce drawings according to standards that have been established by the American National Standards Institute (ANSI). You may not have realized that these established standards change and evolve to match the needs of the ever-changing technology involved in manufacturing and production. At first thought it might seem odd to you that an established standard could or should change. After all, the very purpose of a standard seems to oppose the idea of changing it. However, standards exist to assist manufacturers and to make the production of parts and assemblies more efficient. If you think carefully about the quick evolution of modern technology and the new worldwide marketing and manufacturing environment, it seems reasonable to expect standards to change.

In 1935 the American Standards Association (the predecessor to ANSI) published the first recognized standard for engineering drawings in the United States—"American Drawing and Drafting Room Practices." The document was 18 pages long and the entire subject of tolerancing was covered in two paragraphs. It was clear in that era that the assembly line manufacturing process created largely by Henry Ford and his Model T replaced the old "fit and file to size" craftsman type manufacturing process forever. This mass assembly process created a pressing need for different shops to be able to produce the same parts. The exchange of drawings for those parts became critical and a group was formed to create a standard way to communicate manufacturing and engineering details graphically. It took years for the group to publish the standards document. Whose standard is best is, and will continue to be, a difficult question for any group of individuals charged with creating a standard.

World War II provided the motivation to continue to improve engineering drawings and mass production techniques. Scrap rates were too high and assemblies were hampered by the limitations of the plus/minus tolerance system. It became apparent that geometry and not just variation in size controlled many assemblies. How many times have you drilled a hole with a hand drill and realized that the

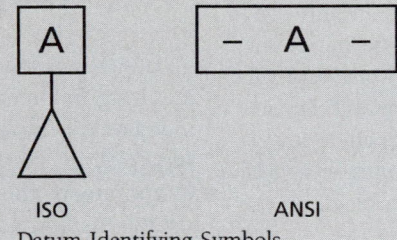

ISO   ANSI
Datum-Identifying Symbols

hole was the correct size but it was of no use to the assembly because the axis of the hole wasn't perpendicular to the right plane? The U.S. Army published an Ordinance Manual on Dimensioning and Tolerancing in 1945 that used symbols to specify form and position tolerances. Unfortunately, the American Standard Association's "American Standard Drawing and Drafting Room Practice," second edition published in 1946, lacked a comprehensive section on tolerancing. To make matters worse, the Society of Automotive Engineers published its own standards in 1946 and in 1952. After the war, there were *three different standards* for tolerancing engineering drawings. It wasn't until 1966 after years of debate that ANSI published the first unified standard on tolerancing and dimensioning—ANSI Y14.5. The standard was updated in 1973 to replace notes with symbols for all tolerancing, and the current version was published in 1982. As you may have guessed, a new version is expected soon—in 1993 or 1994. If that all seems a bit complicated, remember that the rest of the world has been developing their own standards and formed the International Organization for Standardization (ISO).

Evolving technology and the need to compete in world class manufacturing seem to be the drivers for the next rounds of ANSI standards revisions. CAD and CAM have become key components in manufacturing since the last ANSI Y14.5 revision. Producing a part with a CNC machine becomes easier when the part is dimensioned with that production technique in mind. The use of decimals has replaced fractions for that same reason. Unfortunately, anyone who has used a CAD system will tell you that keeping to ANSI standards has never seemed to worry the makers of CAD systems very much. The outcome of that dilemma has not been resolved. However, competing in world class manufacturing is very important to all American manufacturers. Parts for any one assembly will more than likely be produced in a variety of shops across the world. To be part of that network, it seems that ANSI standards and ISO standards must be compatible so that engineering drawings convey the same information worldwide. Conveying information quickly and correctly is a must to effectively compete in today's world class manufacturing environment.

The men and women charged with making ANSI and ISO standards have a difficult and complex job. Each document they produce must contain compromises. As technology and the world environment changes, standards must evolve with them. As the world economy becomes more unified, more world unified standards will certainly follow. The ability to change and adapt seems more important to our continued success than ever.

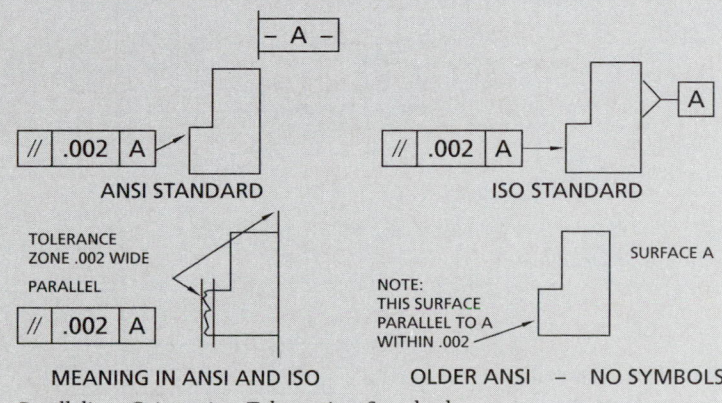

Parallelism Orientation Tolerancing Standards

Notice that a variety of abbreviations are used in this and other notes. Abbreviations should conform to ANSI Y1.1. See the Appendix for commonly used abbreviations on drawings. In general, keep the usage of abbreviations to the minimum.

Notes are usually uppercase except when long and detailed, in which case lowercase lettering is acceptable. In fact, this is the only place on a mechanical drawing where lowercase lettering is permitted. The width of your notes should be limited to the width of the parts list or revision block on the drawing.

Some notes that apply to a view can be placed under the view as needed. All notes should be free and clear of any geometry and placed to be clearly seen and read. **Local notes** are placed away from the view outline, as in Figure 12.83, where the following notes appear:

6-32 UNC-2B	4-40 UNC-2B	$\frac{1}{4}$ -20 UNC-2B
.50 DEEP	.25 DEEP	2 PLACES
2 PLACES	8 PLACES	

If a drawing is large and complicated, local notes are sometimes allowed within the view. Whenever possible, avoid this practice. If the notes are placed on the view, it is important to position them away from the part outline or dimension lines for clarity.

12.10   Location of Features and Dimensioning Methods

To design a part you need to know the method of its manufacturing beforehand so proper dimensioning can be provided on the drawing. If the part to be manufactured does not require close tolerancing, simple dimensioning methods such as continuous dimensioning can be applied. If the manufacturing method is automated, coordinate dimensioning is needed. Design for manufacturability (DFM) is also an important factor in creating clear, precise, manufacturable, and successful parts and products.

Rectangular coordinate dimensions accurately locate features with respect to one another and, as a group or individually, from a datum or origin (Fig. 12.82). The features that establish the datum or origin must be clearly identified on the drawing. Coordinate dimensioning is the most frequently used method of dimensioning because of automation in the machine tool and manufacturing area. Automated manufacturing and machining uses the database of the CAD-generated model and detail drawings when required. If CNC machines are to be used in manufacturing the part and drawings are required, coordinate dimensioning is employed. Regardless of

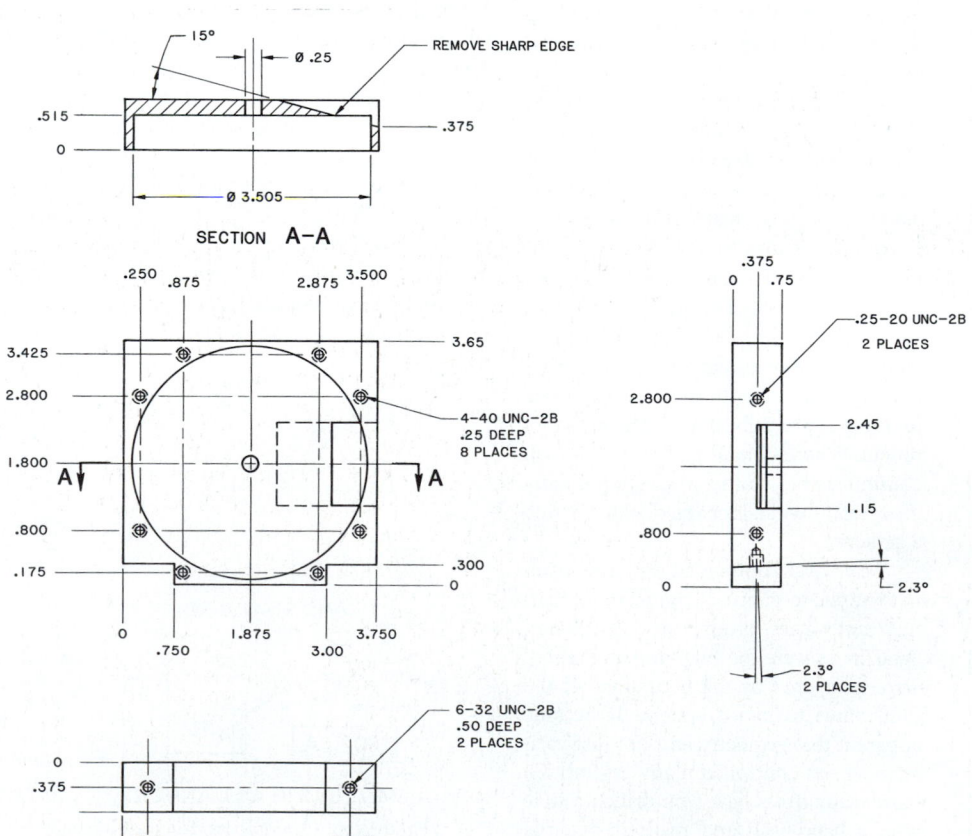

FIGURE 12.83   Part Detailed Using Dimensions Without Dimension Lines

the units of measurement or method of dimensioning, all dimensions are given in decimal units.

12.10.1 Rectangular Coordinate Dimensioning

Rectangular coordinate dimensioning locates the features of a part by providing dimensions from two or three *mutually perpendicular planes*. The cylindrical part in Figure 12.84 is dimensioned using geometric tolerancing. Here, the three mutually perpendicular planes are established. In general, this type of dimensioning either establishes **datum lines** (**X**, **Y**, and **Z** coordinate lines from which all dimensions are taken), or uses the centerlines of a symmetrical or circular shape, as in Figure 12.84. In Figure 12.85(a), the **X** and **Y** coordinates are used as datum lines. Here, all dimensions are positioned rectangularly from the datum/baselines. The part is located in Quadrant I so that all values for dimensions are

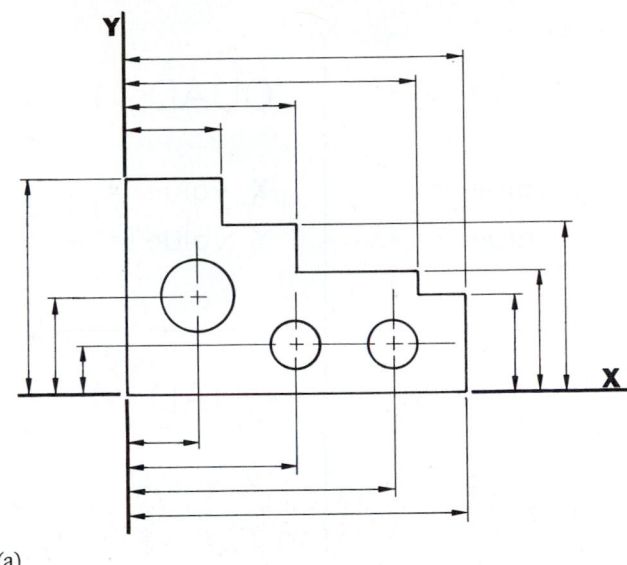

(a)

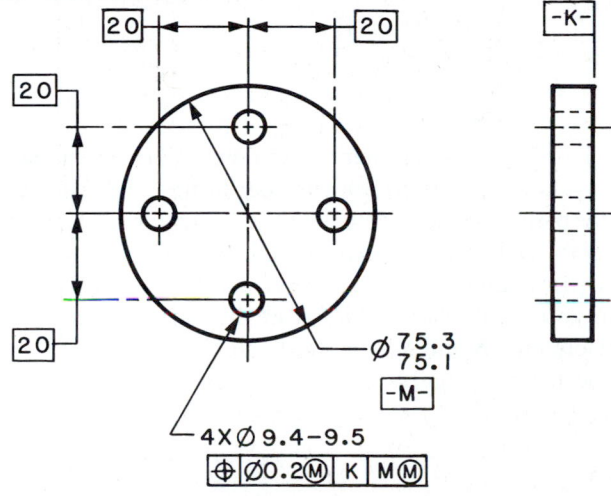

(a)

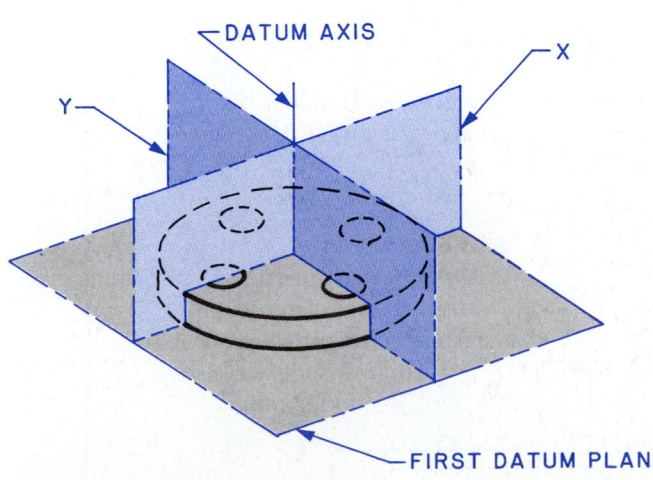

(b)

FIGURE 12.84 **Part with Cylindrical Datum Feature** (a) X and Y coordinates used as datums (b) Datum planes

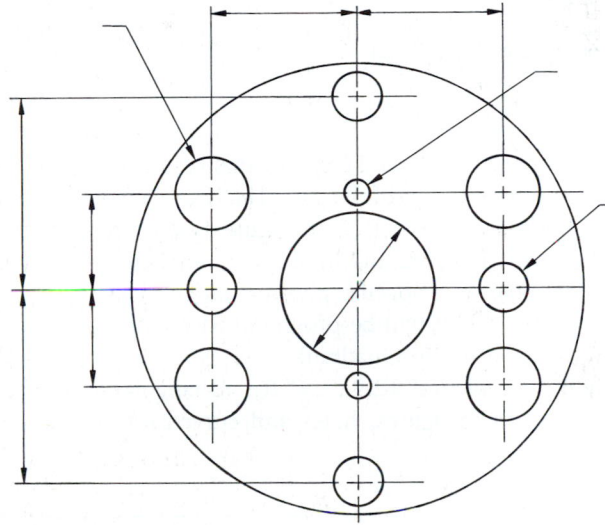

(b)

FIGURE 12.85 **Dimensioning Methods** (a) Datum line dimensioning (b) Rectangular coordinate dimensioning

positive. In Figure 12.85(b), the circular part and its hole pattern are dimensioned from the center of the piece. All dimensions are drawn perpendicular to the part's center.

The four quadrants of the rectangular coordinate system are shown in Figure 12.86. The rectangular coordinate system consists of perpendicular axes **X** and **Y**. The plane formed by the **X** and **Y** axes establishes the origin of the **Z** axis, which is perpendicular to the **X-Y** plane (Fig. 12.87). The intersection of the three axes is called the **origin** and has a numeric value of zero (**X0,Y0,Z0**). The **Z** axis is normally located along the height of the part when using a CAD system. For CNC machines, the **Z** axis is the spindle axis. This is true regardless of whether the machine has a vertical or horizontal spindle. In most cases, the three reference planes are used to locate the

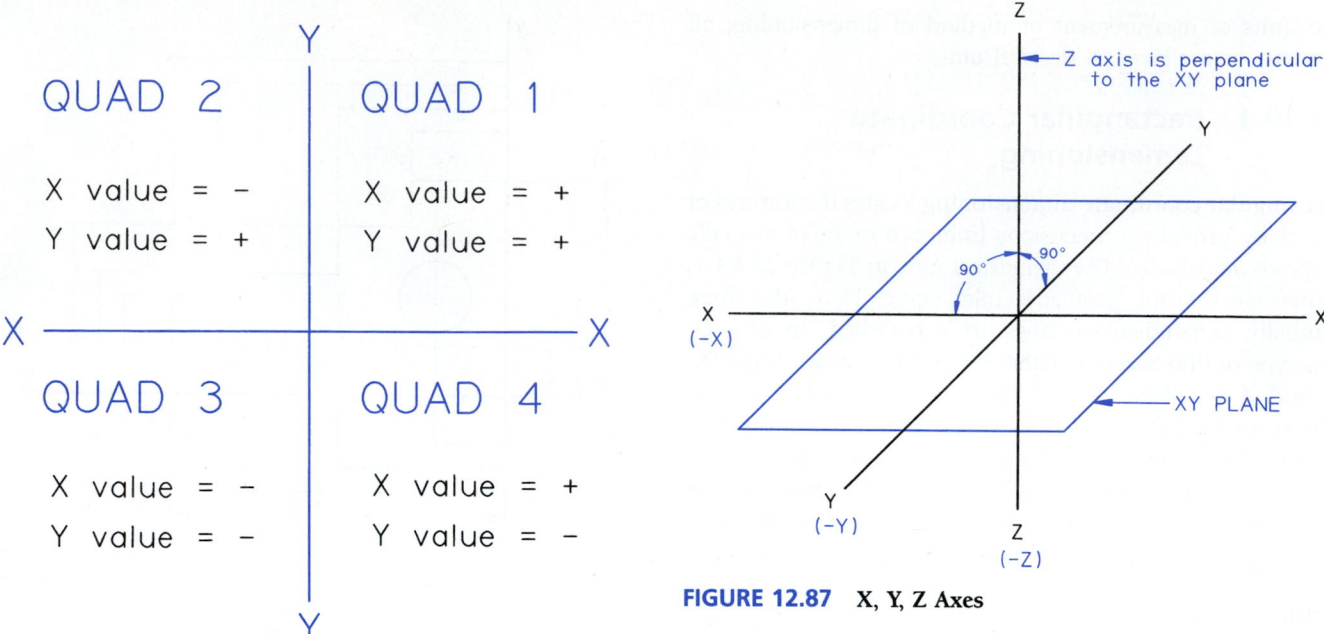

FIGURE 12.86   Quadrants

FIGURE 12.87   X, Y, Z Axes

part as shown in Figure 12.88. In this case, the planes are touching three surfaces of the part. The **X** and **Y** axes may also be established off the part as in Figure 12.89. This situation occurs when the CNC machine has a **setpoint** established from the edge or a specific position on the work table. In either case, the part will be programmed with positive coordinates since it lies in Quadrant I.

Figures 12.90 and 12.91 use the rectangular coordinate method. In these figures, holes and curved features are di-

mensioned by locating their center points from datum/base-lines, which are indicated by zero coordinates. Both examples use the part's lower left corner for the 0,0 position. Dimensions are established so as to have values that can be easily entered when programming the part for CNC machining. Both of these figures use a hole chart. All holes are through the work piece, therefore only **X** and **Y** dimensions are required.

The parts in Figures 12.90 and 12.91 are dimensioned using datum lines. The dimension lines have been eliminated,

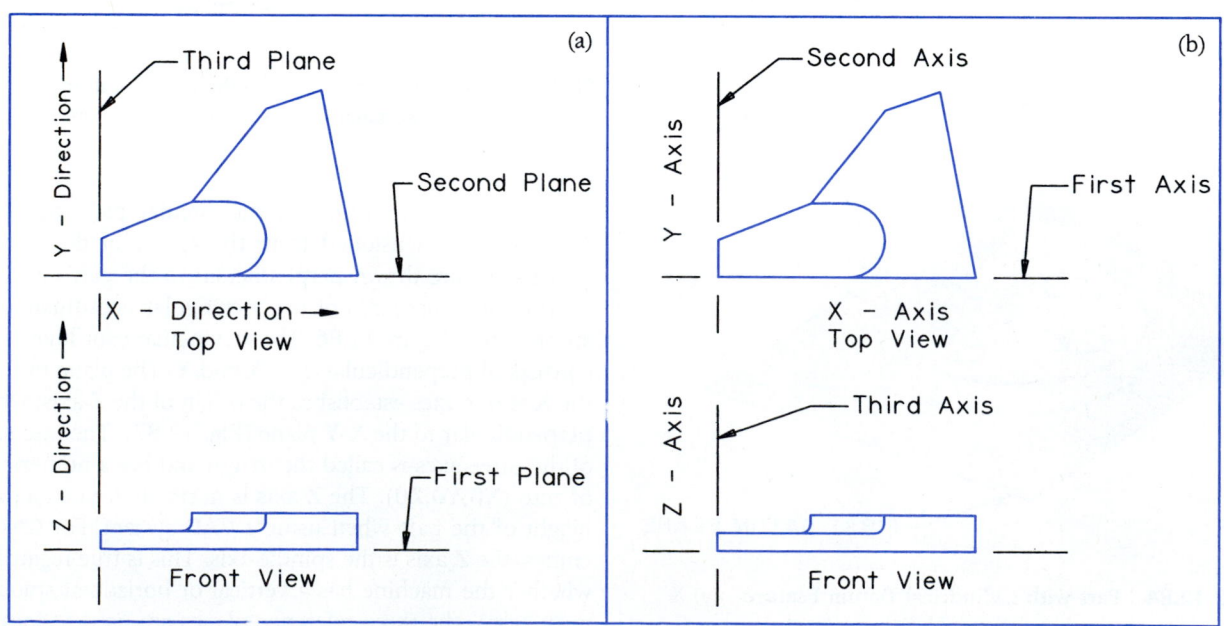

FIGURE 12.88   Reference Surfaces   (a) Reference planes (b) Reference axes

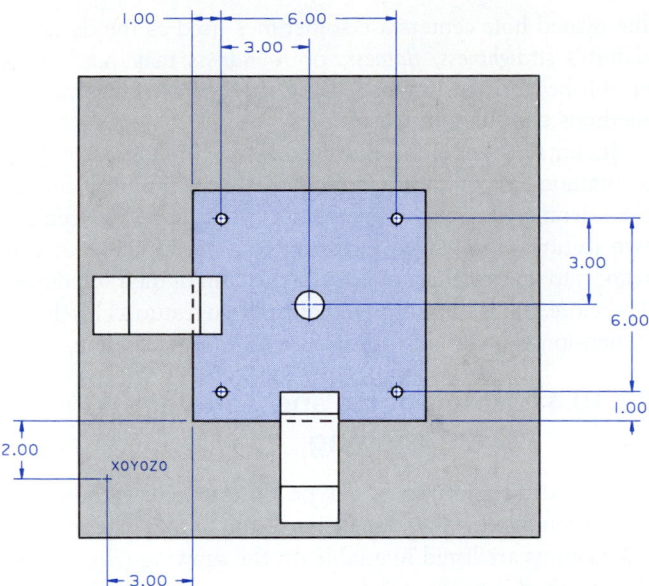

FIGURE 12.89   0,0,0 Position Established Off the Workpiece
Work table and clamps shown with part

with only measurements and extension lines shown. This is called **rectangular coordinate dimensioning without dimension lines** (ordinate method). **Ordinate dimensioning** is one of the easiest and clearest ways to dimension a part. Dimensions may be shown on extension lines without the use of dimension lines or arrowheads. The base (datum) lines are indicated as zero coordinates, or they may be labeled as **X, Y,** and **Z.**

12.10.2   Polar Coordinate Dimensioning

When **polar coordinate dimensioning** is used to locate features, a linear and an angular dimension specify a distance

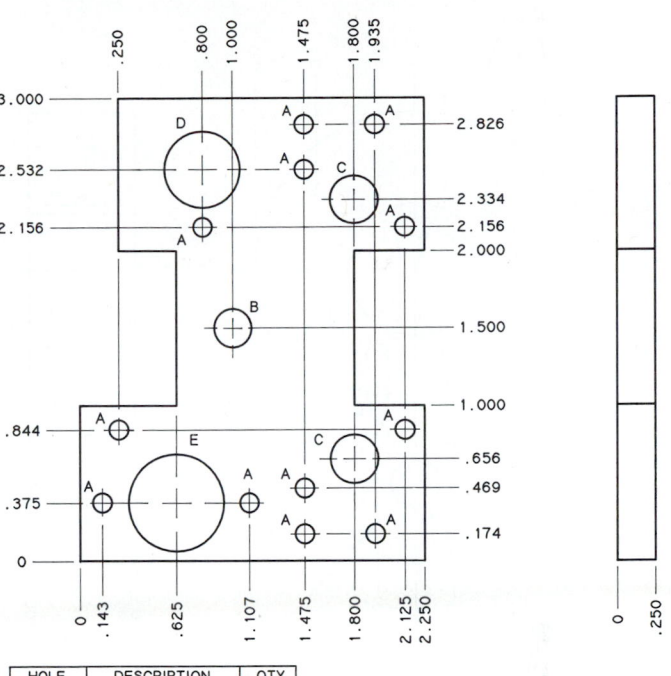

HOLE	DESCRIPTION	QTY
A	.125 DIA	12
B	.250 DIA	1
C	.312 DIA	2
D	.500 DIA	1
E	.625 DIA	1

NOTE: ALL HOLES THRU
.25 ALY ALUM 6061-T6 ANODIZE BLACK

FIGURE 12.91   Hole Charts and Coordinate Dimensioning

from a fixed point at an angular direction from two or three mutually perpendicular planes. The fixed point is the intersection of these planes. Figure 12.92 shows how polar dimensioning is used. The holes are established with a radial value (R2.62) and angles for each hole. In this figure, the 0,0 position is in the lower left of the part; the radial value and the angles are established from a location hole.

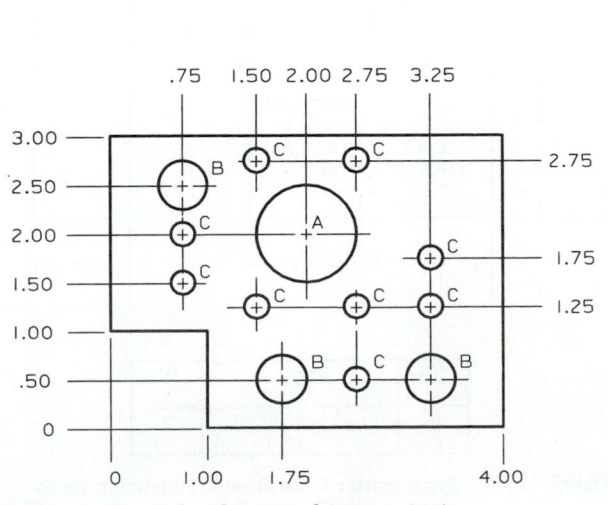

FIGURE 12.90   Hole Charts and Dimensioning

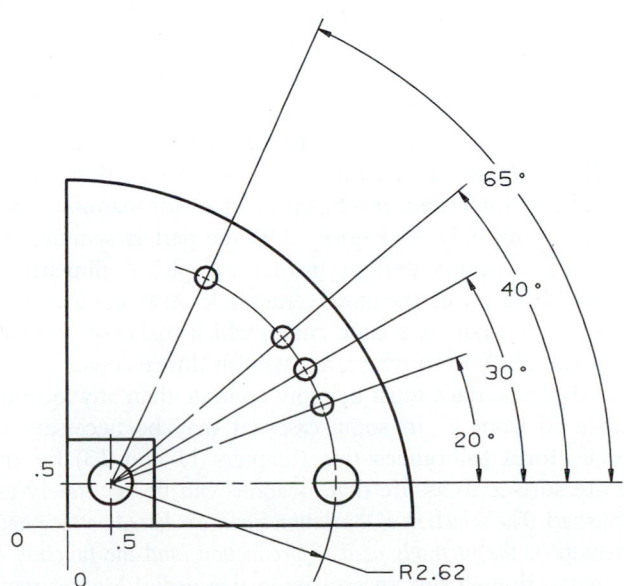

FIGURE 12.92   Polar Coordinate Dimensioning

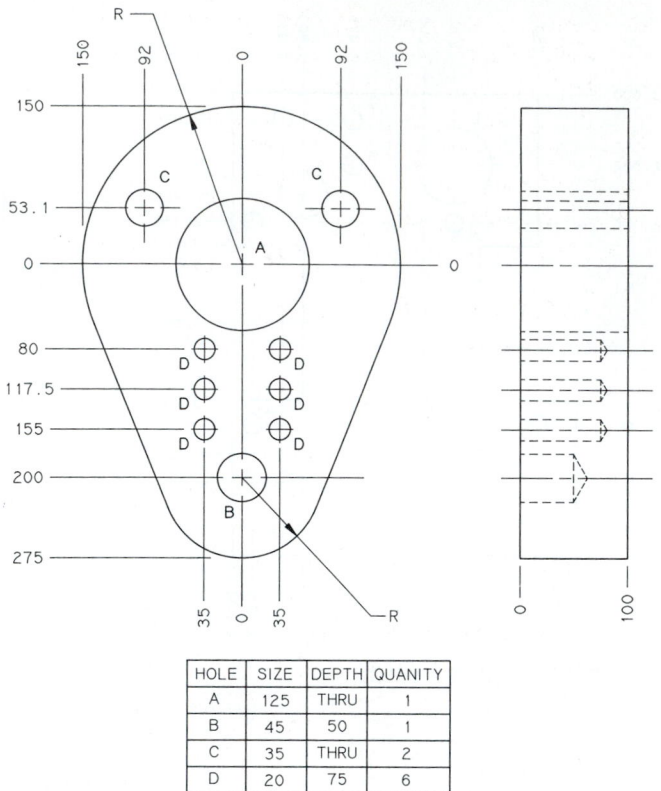

HOLE	SIZE	DEPTH	QUANITY
A	125	THRU	1
B	45	50	1
C	35	THRU	2
D	20	75	6

FIGURE 12.93 0,0 Position Established at Center of Part

If a CAD system is used to detail the part, polar coordinates should be given in decimal units and in decimal degrees; hence $45\frac{1}{2}°$ would be given as $45.50°$ instead of $45° 30'$.

12.10.3 Datums and Tolerances

Datum points, **lines**, or **surfaces** are features of a part that are assumed to be exact. They act as a baseline or reference for locating other features of the part. A feature selected as a datum must be easily accessible and clearly identified. In many cases, datums are established as the far left surface and bottom surface in a view (Figs. 12.90 and 12.91). The vertical datum is designated as the **Y** axis and the horizontal datum as the **X** axis. An artificial datum such as a construction hole or line edge is sometimes machined in a part for manufacturing and checking only. In Figure 12.93 the part is symmetrical about its vertical centerline. In this example, all dimensions are established from the part's center hole. Also, the lower left corner of the part is a large curve, which makes it an inappropriate place from which to establish dimensions.

A datum surface must be more accurate than any location measured from it. In some cases, it may be necessary to specify **form tolerances** (see Chapters 11 and 13) for the datum surface to assure that locations can be accurately established. *The selection of the datum surface is based on the part's orientation, the methods used in production, and the function of the part—*though not necessarily in this order. Mating parts use the same feature surface. When parts must match or mate,

the related hole centers are sometimes used as the datum. A datum's *straightness, flatness,* or *roundness* may need to be established on the drawing using the geometric tolerancing methods described in Chapter 13.

If cumulative tolerances are excessive, dimensioning from a common base or datum reduces the overall accumulation of the tolerance. But the tolerance on the distance between any two features, located with respect to a datum and not with respect to one another, is equal to the sum of their tolerances. Therefore, if it is important to control two features closely, the dimension is given directly from a datum or baseline.

12.10.4 Hole Charts and Tabular Dimensioning

Tabular dimensioning is a type of rectangular coordinate dimensioning in which dimensions from mutually perpendicular datums are listed in a table on the drawing (Fig. 12.94). This method is used on drawings that require the location of a large number of similarly shaped features, such as multiple holes, slots, or hole patterns. Tables are prepared in any suitable manner that adequately locates the features. For automated tooling and programming CNC machines, providing

HOLE	FROM	X	Y	−Z
A1	X,Y	90	44	10
B1	"	26	150	30
B2	"		150	30
B3	"	26	26	30
C1	"	64	100	40
C2	"	40	76	40

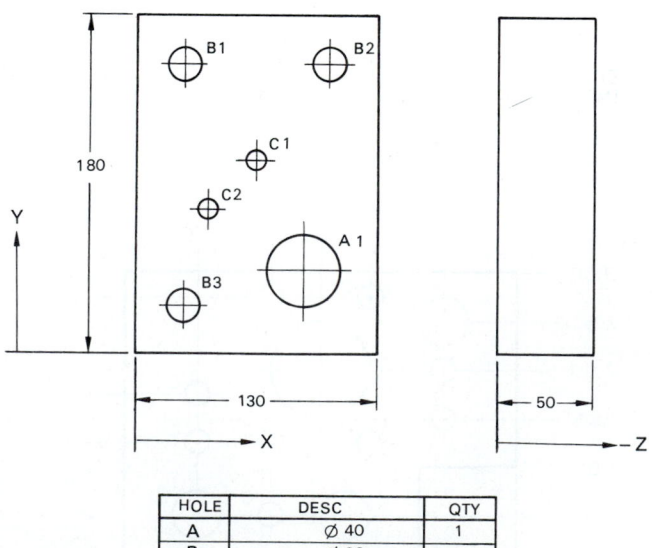

HOLE	DESC	QTY
A	Ø 40	1
B	Ø 20	3
C	Ø 10	2

FIGURE 12.94 Rectangular Coordinate Dimensioning in Tabular Form

X,Y dimensions and Z depths is the best method. Hole sizes are also given on a hole chart.

For complicated parts or a part with a multitude of holes in one or more surfaces, **hole charts** may be used to simplify the drawing. In hole charts, the surface of hole entry and each hole must be identified on the drawing. In Figure 12.94, the part has holes of differing depth. The hole chart establishes the **X** and **Y** position of each hole along with the depth (**Z**). The top of the part is used as the **X-Y** plane; therefore, the depth dimensions have −**Z** values.

The surfaces of hole entry are identified with the names of the principal views. The order of these views for charting purposes is as follows:

1. top
2. front
3. right
4. left
5. bottom
6. rear
7. auxiliary view (if used)

A hole chart shows the surface of entry of each hole, the symbol number that identifies each hole, and the number of times each hole is used in this surface. The chart also gives the complete specification for each hole. Identical holes in a surface are shown by a single symbol number or letter. Hole charts are commonly used for sheet metal details and drilling drawings for printed circuit boards. On parts with very complex hole patterns, the locating dimensions for the holes are shown in the chart as the **X** and **Y** positions in each view; this is called **rectangular dimensioning in tabular form** (Fig. 12.94).

In **X** and **Y** coordinate dimensioning, each hole has a separate identifying symbol. You can group holes by giving diameters the same size and the same letter symbols or by numbering them consecutively. The bottom left or bottom

right corner of the view is usually selected as the zero point for labeling the **X** and **Y** axes. The **Z** axis is also provided for the depth dimension when only one view has holes in it. The direction of dimension measurement is always from a datum/base/coordinate line in the direction of the arrow. All holes are listed in the hole chart. Holes are normally listed alphabetically starting from the largest with the letter A.

In another method of labeling holes for tabular dimensioning each hole is numbered consecutively beginning with 1 without regard for size. If a numerical controlled machine is to do the machining operation, holes of the same size are normally grouped for easy programming, although this may be determined by the software for the machine.

When the hole is to be completely through the part, THRU should be used as the **Z** dimension. If more than one surface needs to have holes called out, **X** and **Y** axes can be established for each surface or view. The depth must be specified for each hole, and the view is noted in the hole chart.

Tabular dimensioning is also found in many catalogs where a standard part has varying size and length dimensions. Instead of providing a separate drawing for each part, a table is given that lists each dimension as a letter on the drawing and a value for the particular detail in the table. Many standard parts are provided in Appendix C. Bolts, screws, keys, pipe fittings, valves, and other standard items are provided with dimensions in tabular form (see Appendix C).

12.10.5   Repetitive Features or Dimensions

Repetitive features (Fig. 12.95) or dimensions may be specified by the use of an "X" following a numeral to indicate the "number of times" or "places" that a feature is required. Features such as holes and slots, which are repeated in a series or pattern, may

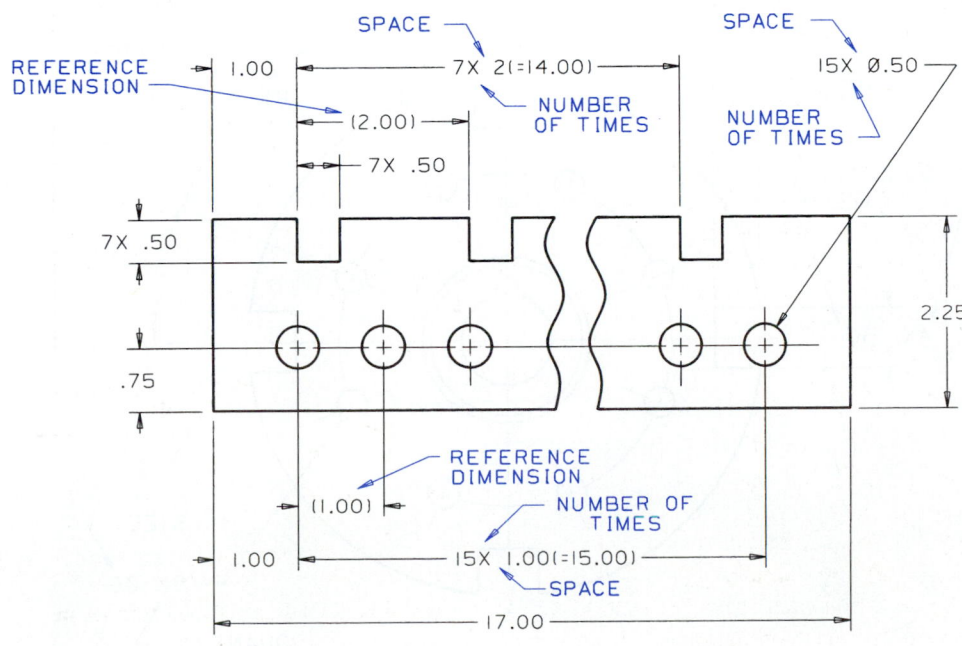

FIGURE 12.95 Repetitive Feature Dimensioning

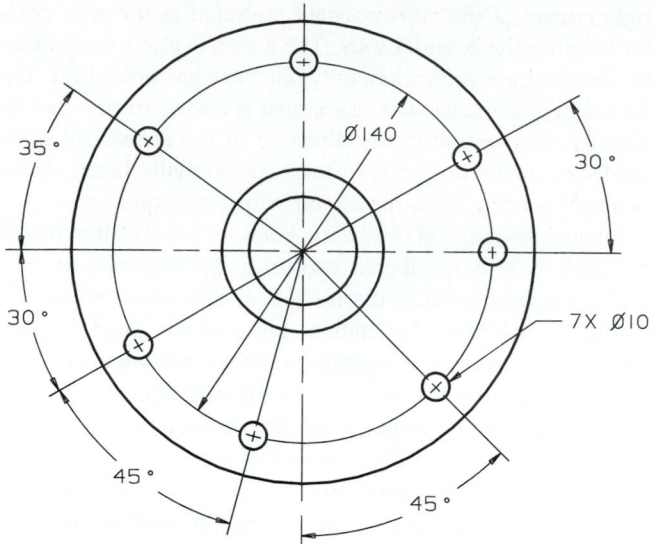

FIGURE 12.96 Dimensioning Repetitive Holes on a Common Center

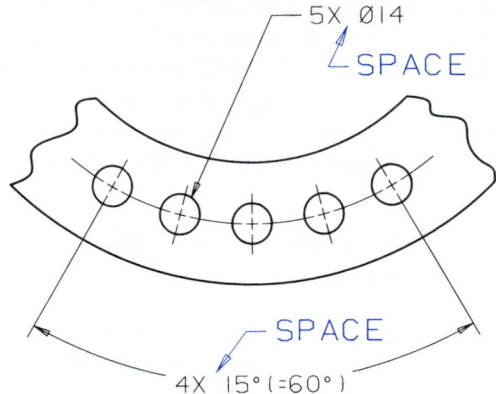

FIGURE 12.97 Repetitive Dimensions

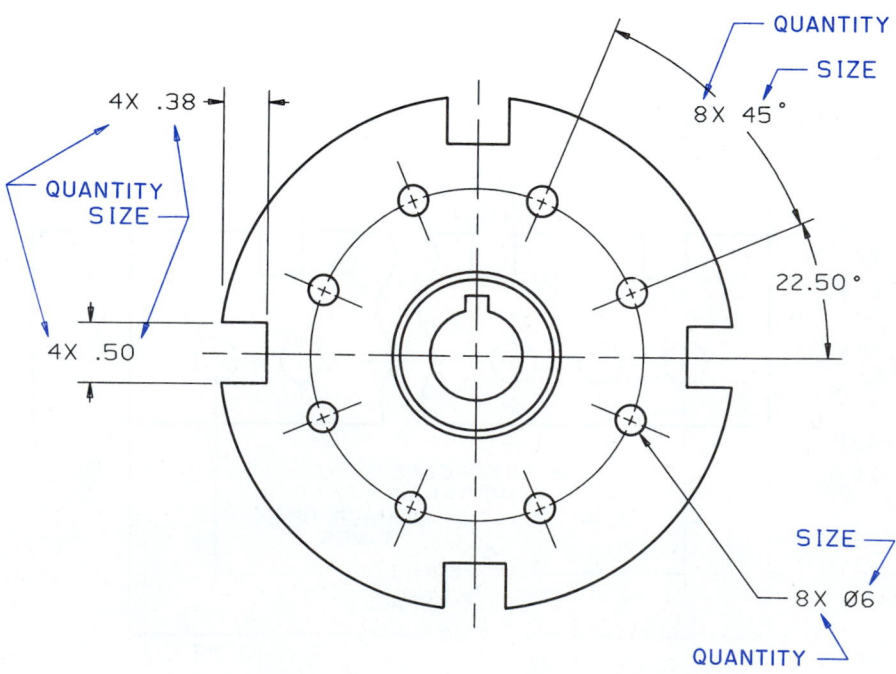

FIGURE 12.98 Repetitive Features and Dimensioning

be specified by giving the required number of features and an X, followed by the size dimension of the feature. A space is used between the X and the dimension. In Figure 12.95 the part requires fifteen equally spaced .50 diameter holes. A 1.00 dimension is given between the edge of the part and the first hole. The dimension **15X 1.00** (=**15.00**) is then provided.

If it is difficult to distinguish between the dimension and the number of spaces, one space is dimensioned and identified as a reference (1.00 in Fig. 12.95). *Reference dimensions are enclosed in parentheses and are used for information only. They are not used by the machinist to create the part.* Reference dimensions are provided only as a guide during production. Reference dimensions do not affect manufacturing methods or operations, establish sizes, or locate features.

In Figure 12.96 the part has repetitive features (holes) that are not equally spaced. Angle dimensions, in degrees, are given to each hole from the vertical or horizontal centerline and a note giving the size and number of holes is provided.

Equal spacing of features in a series or pattern may be specified by giving the required number of spaces and an X, followed by the applicable dimension (Figs. 12.97 and 12.98). A space is used between the X and the dimension. In Figure 12.97 the part has five holes with a diameter of 14 mm equally spaced at 15°. The dimension for spacing the holes gives the number of spaces (4), the degrees between each hole (15), and the total degrees (60).

The notation X also may be used to indicate BY between coordinate dimensions. An example of this practice is when dimensioning chamfer, e.g., **50° X 45, 30° X .250**. *In such cases, the X is preceded and followed by a space.* If these two practices (use of BY and "number of features") are used on the same drawing, care must be taken to ensure that each usage is clear. When both cases are used on the same drawing, the proper spacing is very important. When automated tooling machines are programmed using increments, repetitive feature dimensioning methods can be used in conjunction with coordinate dimensioning.

You May Complete Exercises 12.13 Through 12.16 at This Time

12.11 Dimensioning with a CAD System

One of the most important aspects of the introduction of the computer into the design process is that the modeled 3D part is **associative** to the dimensions, which means that the drafter inserts the dimensions with regard to placement, but the system puts the proper dimension value on the drawing based on the size and location when the geometry was created.

The elements that make up the geometry of the part are established mathematically. Therefore, it is impossible to put the wrong size dimension value on the drawing. Others using the same database can verify (**LIST**) each feature as to size and location. This is impossible when a manual drawing is produced. If a CAD-generated part is dimensioned insufficiently, manufacturing can activate the part and request the information from the system using an **ID**, **LIST**, or **MEASURE** command (AutoCAD).

In most engineering applications, a precise drawing plotted to scale is not sufficient to convey all of the desired information. *Annotations* must be added to show the lengths of features, the distances between features, or angles between features. Until all CAD databases can be transmitted to the machine tool area for postprocessing and used to drive a numerical control machine, dimensioning will be required. The machine tool area and the manufacturing department will be able to use the graphically created database directly to machine and manufacture the part. Many companies already use this method, and a fully integrated CAD/CAM system is the goal of most manufacturers. Until this technology is in place throughout industry, the designer or drafter will need to define the drawing with dimensions using the most recent ANSI standards. All CAD systems provide ANSI standards for geometric tolerancing and dimensioning, though the quality of dimensioning packages differs widely between systems. The drafter must still determine the proper dimensioning requirements and decide on their placement on the drawing.

Dimensioning in CAD is the process of adding annotations to a drawing. Dimensioning also refers to the annotations themselves. CAD systems provide a variety of dimensioning. The commands and procedures for dimensioning differ among systems. All systems provide quick and easy insertion of dimensions, but you still need to know why certain things are dimensioned and where to place the dimensions. CAD systems automate the process, but the knowledge of ANSI or other standard dimensioning and tolerancing specifications must be mastered along with how to enter the commands for a specific system.

The detailer selects dimension options that include decimal or fractional representation, U.S. or SI units of measure, bilateral or unilateral tolerances, feature control symbols, and datums. Dimensions are easily inserted on a drawing by identifying the two locations to be measured and dimensioned. A third location places the dimensioning text and associated values. The system automatically inserts extension lines, dimension lines, leader lines, dimension arrowheads, and dimensioning text at the location indicated. Linear, rotated, diameter, radial, angular, and ordinate dimensioning are available. A variety of arrowhead lengths and types can also be selected (Fig. 12.99). Dimension text, notes, and labels are easily inserted on detail drawings.

You can determine what type of text font (**STYLE**) to use and its height, width, slant, spacing, case, and justification. **Labels** offer the same variety of characteristics, include a leader line that is automatically inserted and attached to the associated label. The angle of the leader line can be defined by the drafter.

Dimensioning is a *drawing* activity rather than a *modeling* activity when creating the part geometry; in other words, it is 2D not 3D. The geometry of the part can be 3D or 2D depending on the system's capabilities. Dimensions, like text, are for information only. They do not exist as actual part entities or features. Therefore, all dimensions are 2D. The same procedure is used to detail a part on a 2D system as on a 3D system.

Before proceeding with the details of dimensioning with CAD, a few terms, system capabilities, and options must be explained. Each system has certain differences that determine exactly where dimensions can be placed. Sometimes it is necessary to work around these limitations. *Remember, you can do only what the system will allow.*

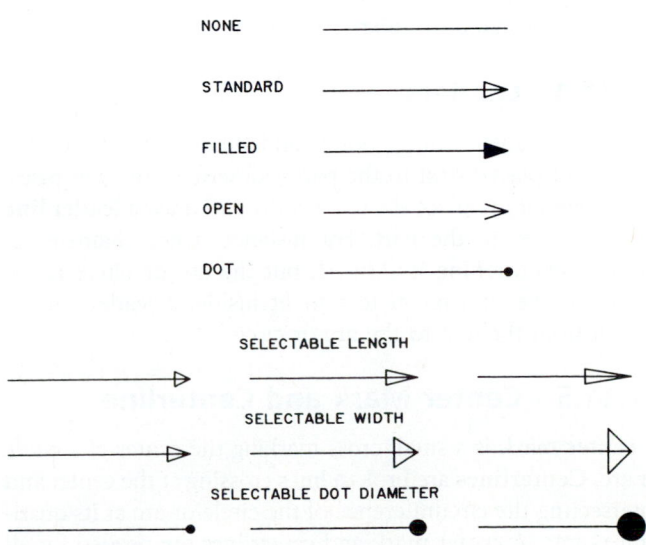

FIGURE 12.99 Arrowhead Variations

12.11.1   Dimension Line

A **dimension line** is a line with arrows at each end, drawn at the angle at which the dimension has been measured. The dimension text is situated along this line, usually dividing it into two lines. Normally, the dimension line is inside the measured area; sometimes, however, it does not fit. In such cases, two short lines are drawn outside the measured area, with the arrows pointing inward. The option for arrows inside or arrows outside is available on most CAD systems. The dimension line is established on the drawing by selecting the distance away from the part, normally the third selection in the command. The first two selections locate the feature ends or two positions to be dimensioned. For angular dimensioning, the dimension line is actually an arc.

12.11.2   Extension Lines

If the dimension line is drawn outside the part being measured, straight **extension lines**, sometimes called *witness lines,* are drawn from a feature of the part, perpendicular to the dimension line. Extension lines are used only in linear and angular dimensioning. When not needed, one or both of them can be left off using a suppression capability available on most systems.

12.11.3   Dimension Text

Dimension text is a **text string** that specifies the actual measurement. Most CAD systems provide methods to use the measurement computed automatically by the system, supply different text, or suppress the text entirely. If you use the default text, the system can be instructed to append plus or minus tolerances to it automatically.

The dimension text is drawn using the currently selected text font (style). When using the default text, its format is governed by the default units. Defaults are embedded in the software when it is installed. Defaults can be changed before or during part creation on most systems. See Chapter 4 for a detailed explanation of text characteristics and commands.

12.11.4   Leaders

For some dimensioning, notes, and other annotations, the text is not placed next to the part it describes. In such cases, it is customary to place the text nearby and draw a **leader line** from the text to the part. For instance, when diameter or radius dimensioning is desired, but the arc or circle is too small for the dimension text to fit inside, a leader can be drawn from the text to the arc or circle.

12.11.5   Center Mark and Centerline

A **center mark** is a small cross marking the center of a circle or arc. **Centerlines** are broken lines crossing at the center and intersecting the circumference of the circle or arc at its quadrant points. A center mark and centerlines are needed for all circular dimensions. CAD systems know where the center of

each circle or arc is located. Inserting a point or center mark at the origin of an arc or circle involves telling the system to put it at the center of the selected arc, fillet, or circle. For many systems, drawing a centerline involves one command that inserts two perpendicular centerlines with their short dashes crossing at the center of the curved entity.

12.11.6   Dimensions and Scaling

A drafter can change the display size of the part on the CRT for dimensioning purposes. For example, if the part is increased in size for some reason (e.g., for visual clarification), dimensions inserted by the drafter will reflect the true size of the part and not the new CRT display scale. In other words, the display size may be set at 2 to 1, but the dimensions will always be 1 to 1. By zooming in on a portion of a drawing, it is easier to place dimensions, especially in complicated or cluttered portions of a complex part.

12.11.7   Layer Separation of Dimensions on CAD Systems

A **layering scheme** is a means to separate logical groups or types of entities. Each part created on the CAD system has multiple layers associated with it. Direct access is available to any of these layers and the specific entity or information contained on it. These layers should be thought of as transparent sheets on which the drafter places specific types of information. Any number of these layers can be displayed at one time. For example, text can be placed on one layer, all bolt holes on another layer, and all the centerlines on the third layer. Any combination of these layers can be displayed. Some systems have the ability to assign automatically specific types of items to be placed on selected layers determined by the drafter. *Dimensions should always be assigned a layer of their own.* Figure 12.100 shows an example of placing dimensions on a separate layer from the geometry of the part. The dimensions or the geometry can be viewed separately [(a) and (b)] or together (c).

12.11.8   Color and Linetype

CAD systems with color capabilities provide a palette of multiple colors. *Colors* make it easy to identify and distinguish different kinds of information on the drawing. Many drafters associate a certain color with a specific layer. Layers, entities, or information such as dimensions or notes can all be color coded.

With layers, components of a drawing are easily grouped. A layer or a set of layers holds the items related to a particular aspect of the drawing. Visibility, color, and line type are easily controlled. Most companies develop a *standard layering scheme,* with assigned layers for construction lines, dimensions, and the part itself, each with its own associated color and *linetype* (font). The following examples show possible layering schemes:

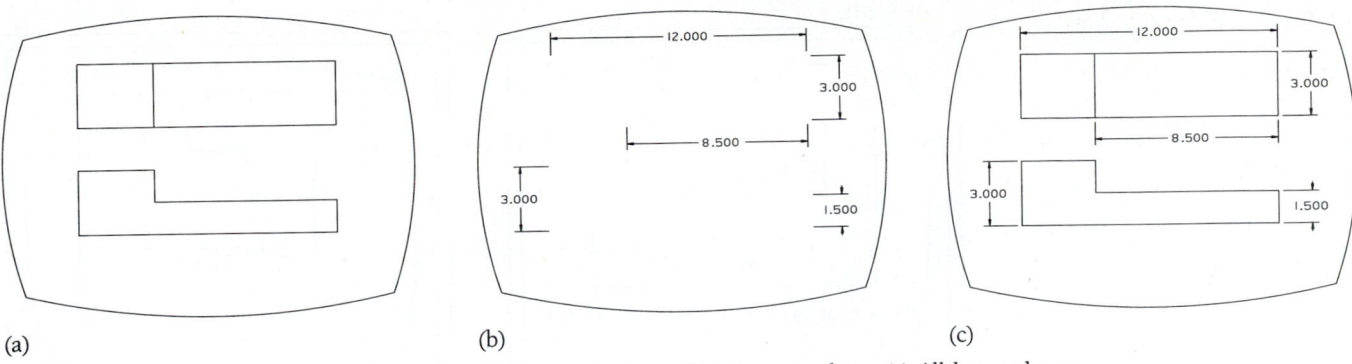

(a)   (b)   (c)

FIGURE 12.100 **Dimensioning and Layers** (a) Part feature layer (b) Dimension layer (c) All layers shown

Font, Color, Pen Size, and Layer Scheme

Layer	Color Number	Use	Linetype (Font)	Pen Size (mm)
1	4 (Yellow)	Part geometry	Continuous	0.7
5	7 (Magenta)	Hidden geometry	Dashed	0.5
10	6 (Gray)	Dimensions	Continuous	0.35
15	3 (Cyan)	Centerlines	Centerline	0.35
20	8 (Red)	Labels	Continuous	0.5
30	12 (Blue)	Border and title block	Continuous	0.9

Industry Layering Scheme

Layer Number	Contents
0	Layer Index/Table of Contents
1–50	Construction Geometry and Drawing Formats [contains all construction items used in the design of your part(s), e.g., lines, points, arcs, and the different types of drawing formats you may use]
51–120	Manufacturing (contains manufacturing information, e.g., NC and tool path information, jigs, fixtures, and tooling)
121–145	Dimensions, Text, Labels (contains all dimension information, text, and labels)
146–175	Illustrations [contains technical illustrations using the part(s) as its source—may be presented in 3D view with hidden lines removed)
176–200	Analysis (Engineering), FEM, Physical Properties (contains different kinds of analytical information concerning the part's structure, content, and properties)
201–254	Construction Aids, Miscellaneous Information (contains construction items that help design and dimension a part, as well as any miscellaneous information connected with the part design)

A layering scheme makes it easy to keep track of where different information resides. Layering can also be used to sort graphic information temporarily. For example, layers can be used to separate geometry in a congested area of the part. By turning off the display of unnecessary information, such as text and dimensions, computer processing takes less time. Placing geometry on one layer and dimensions on another allows for viewing of the model (part) with or without dimensions.

12.12   Dimensioning Commands

When dimensioning a drawing, the **DIMENSION** command is entered from the keyboard or picked from a screen or tablet menu. All systems provide screen or tablet menus for quick and efficient dimensioning. Figure 12.101 shows a tablet menu with areas for selecting dimension parameters, changing existing dimensions, adding text, suppressing extension lines, altering the arrows and leader style or location, and specifying the type of dimension and its tolerance. Most systems also have *screen menus* devoted entirely to dimensioning commands. Selecting standards as defaults, inserting dimensions, and changing existing dimensions can be accomplished with pull-down menus, dialogue boxes, and other dynamic

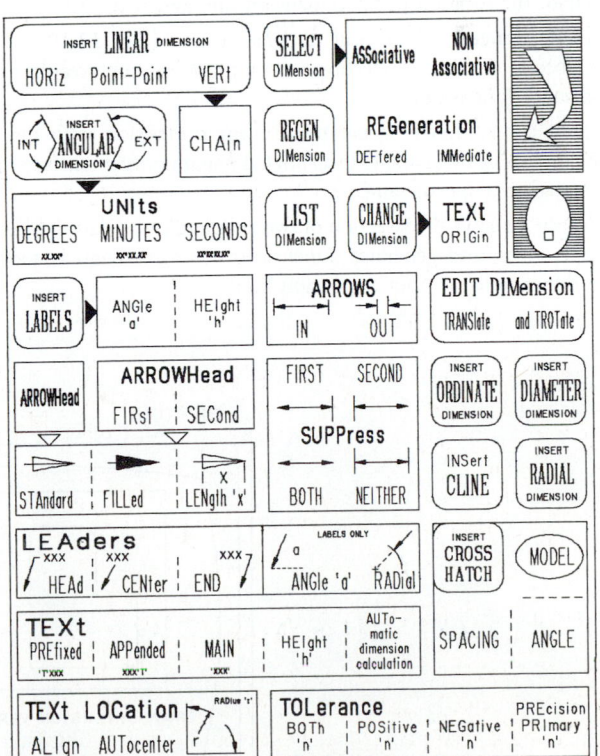

FIGURE 12.101 **Dimensioning Menu**

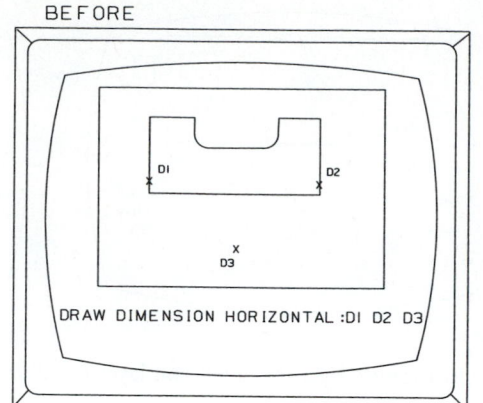
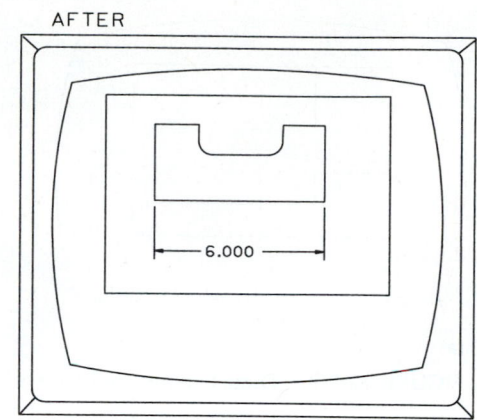

FIGURE 12.102   Placing a Horizontal Dimension

menu capabilities. Dimensioning commands can be grouped into four general categories:

1. linear dimensioning (vertical, horizontal, point-to-point, ordinate)
2. angular dimensioning
3. diameter dimensioning
4. radius dimensioning

12.12.1   Linear Dimensioning Commands

The following gives a general overview of linear dimension capabilities:

Horizontal   generates a horizontal dimension line (Fig. 12.102). After the dimension command is entered, the drafter selects the endpoints of the horizontal distance to be dimensioned (**D1** and **D2**) and then the location of the dimension line and text (**D3**).

Vertical   generates a vertical dimension line (Fig. 12.103). The first, second, and third selections accomplish the same results as in horizontal dimensioning.

Aligned (or rotated)   generates a linear dimension with the dimension line drawn parallel to an angled linear entity or surface edge or rotated to a specific angle.

Ordinate   allows the selection of two perpendicular datum lines or surface edges, and generates dimensions using rectangular coordinate dimensions without dimension lines.

12.12.2   Angular Dimensioning

Angular dimensioning generates an arc to show the angle between two nonparallel lines. The angle can be either inside or outside; Figure 12.104 shows examples of both inside (60°) and outside (300°) angular dimensioning. In both cases, the drafter enters the command, identifies the two lines to be measured, and places the dimension with the third selected location.

12.12.3   Diameter and Radius Dimensioning

When dimensioning the diameter of a circle, only two selections are required. After the command is entered, the drafter identifies the circle to be dimensioned then locates the dimension and the end of leader with the second selection (Fig. 12.105).

Radius dimensioning is the same as **diameter dimensioning**, except the system measures and then dimensions the radius of an arc (Fig. 12.105). Remember, circles are dimensioned by giving a diameter dimension, not a radius dimension. Radius dimensions are to be provided for fillets, arcs, and slots.

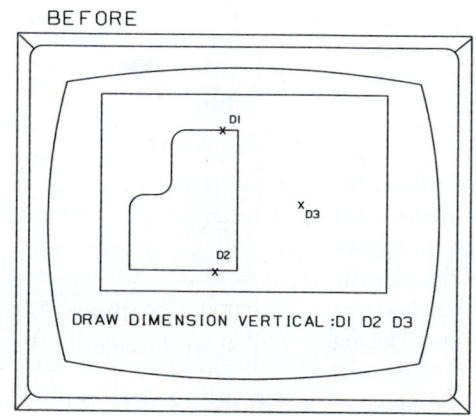
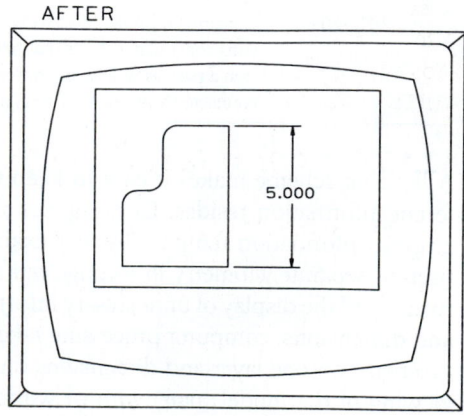

FIGURE 12.103   Placing a Vertical Dimension

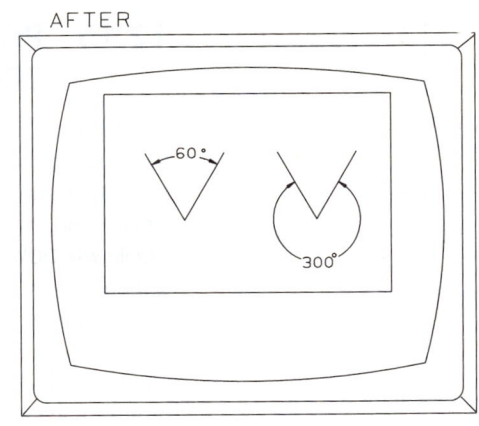

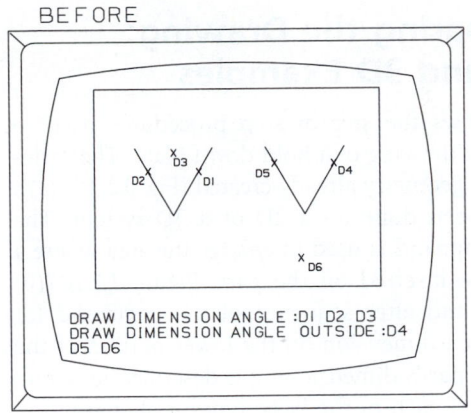

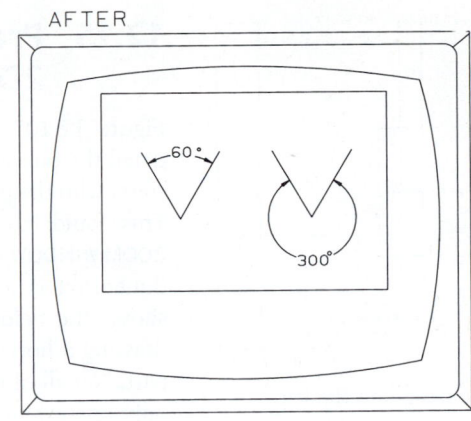

FIGURE 12.104   Placing Angle Dimensions

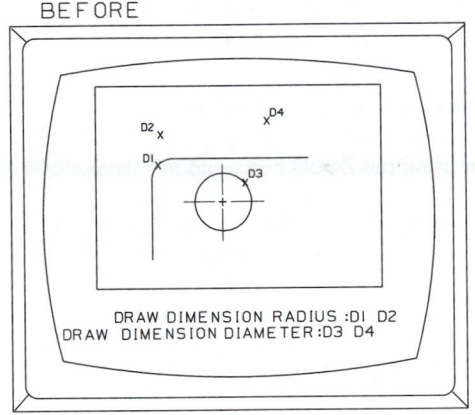

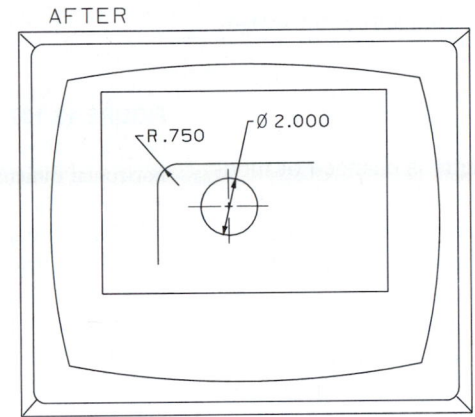

FIGURE 12.105   Placing Radius and Diameter Dimensions

12.13   CAD and Dimension Standards

Some CAD systems are designed to use dimensions that adhere to American National Standards Institute (ANSI) standards. Some systems provide the option to choose Japanese Industrial Standards (JIS) and the International Organization for Standardization (ISO) standards, which differ somewhat from the ANSI conventions. The selection of a drafting standard and unit of measurement should be made before the project is started, though many CAD systems allow you to reset standards, units, tolerances, etc., and automatically update the entire project. These become the defaults for that project. AutoCAD uses the **SETTINGS**, **SETVAR**, and the **UNITS** command to establish defaults for a project.

12.13.1   U.S. or Metric Units

You can choose either SI or U.S. customary units of measurement for your design. Both of these standards can have particular units specified for dimensions: inches, feet, yards, or miles for U.S. standard units of measurements, or centimeters, millimeters, or kilometers for SI (metric) units.

Some systems allow the automatic placement of U.S. units on one layer and SI units on another. In addition, the option for dual dimensioning may be available. The drafter dimensions the part once and the system automatically places the specified primary unit together with the secondary unit in one dimension.

Designs created in one unit of measurement can be converted to other units by changing the setup units (**UNITS** command) and then updating the file with the **UPDATE** command when using an AutoCAD system. **UPDATE** is reached through the **DIMENSION** command. This capability makes dual dimensioning obsolete.

12.14   Mechanical Design and Dimensioning with CAD

Mechanical drafting CAD programs can add dimensional information, notes, and labels to your drawings. You also can manipulate drawings of the model for aesthetic reasons or for visual clarification. These manipulation features include choosing a variety of line patterns, hidden line removal, defining any type or number of views, inserting dual dimensions, defining standards, sectioning, and crosshatching. Dimensional information is associative.

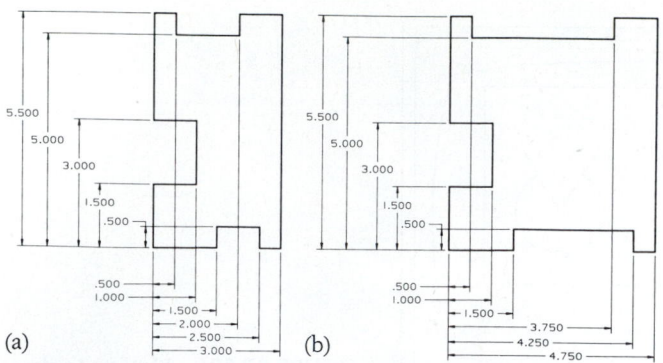

(a)   (b)

FIGURE 12.106   Associativity (a) The design on the left shows the original part geometry that was created and later dimensioned. (b) The design on the right is the original part with design modifications made to it. The dimensions on the right were automatically updated when the modifications to the design were made.

12.14.1 Associativity

Associativity means that if the geometry is changed or modified in the model, its dimensions will automatically be updated to reflect those changes on detail drawings. Associativity also refers to the ability to carry out design change specifications all the way to the manufacturing of the product, e.g., changes to the database could automatically update CNC files and quality control features as well as inventory and other items attached to the database. Both 2D and 3D systems can be associative, but a 3D system is associative in all of its 3D views. A 2D system is associative in one view at a time. In other words, the system just recognizes views, not the complete part.

It is not unusual for design changes to occur after a part is dimensioned. If the model has modifications, existing dimensions are automatically updated by the system to reflect those changes. In Figure 12.106 the design on the left is the original dimensioned part. After design modifications to the part, the dimensions were automatically updated by the system (right).

12.15 Preparing the Drawing: 2D and 3D Examples

Figure 12.107 shows the step-by-step procedures used to detail the one-view drawing of a hold down plate. The series starts with the part geometry already created [Fig. 12.107(a)]. This could have been done on a 2D or a 3D system. The **ZOOM WINDOW** command is used to enlarge the area where a dimension is to be inserted on the part. Figure 12.107(b) shows the before and after sequence of the command for drawing a horizontal dimension on the lower portion of the part. Not all of the part's dimensioning is described in detail; only one example of each of the basic types is shown.

A vertical dimension is inserted between the center of the hole and the bottom of the plate [Fig. 12.107(c)]. Normally, you would have had to tell the system to lock onto the

FIGURE 12.107   Dimensioning a One-View Drawing
(a) Single-view drawing of a hold down plate (b) Placing a horizontal dimension using the **ZOOM** command to enlarge the area to be dimensioned and then placing the dimension (c) Dimensioning the vertical distance between the hole and the hold down plate's lower edge (d) Dimensioning the angled cut with the point-to-point linear dimensioning command (e) Dimensioning the angled cut using the dimension angle command (f) Dimensioning the small holes (g) Dimensioning the large radius (h) Inserting notes (i) The completed detail of the hold down plate

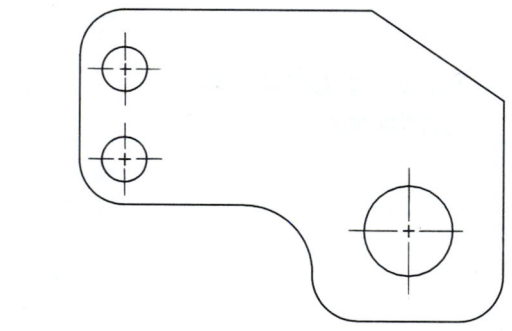

(a)

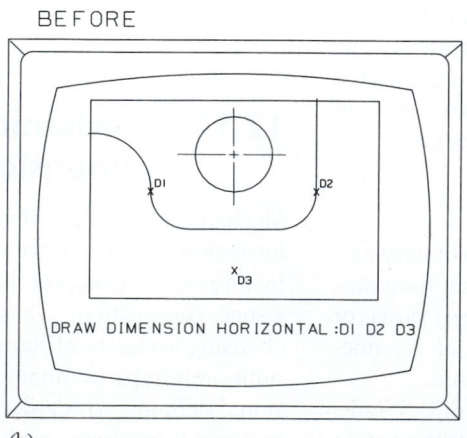

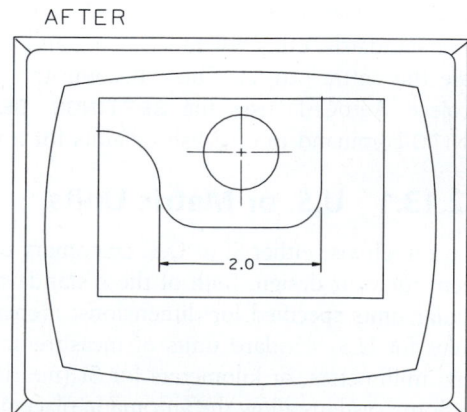

(b)

BEFORE

AFTER

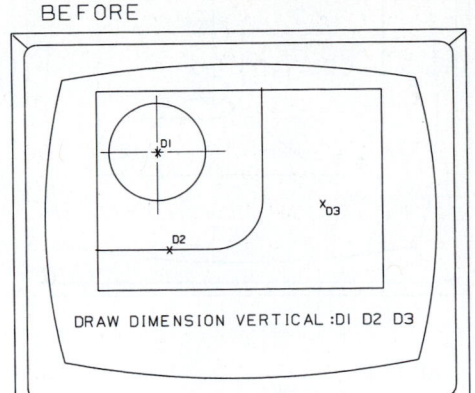

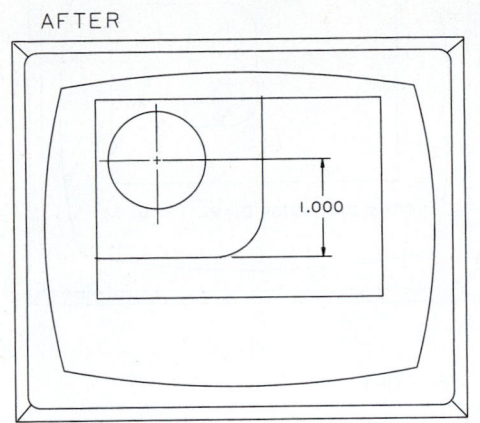

DRAW DIMENSION VERTICAL :DI D2 D3

(c)

BEFORE

AFTER

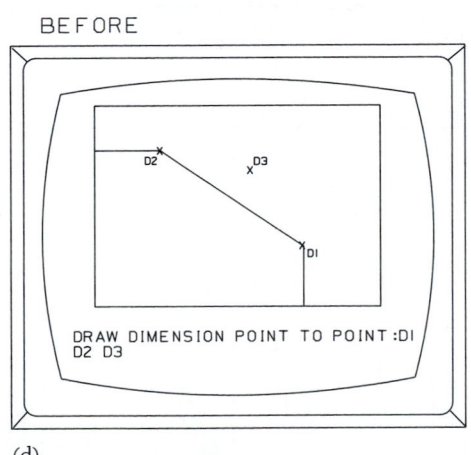

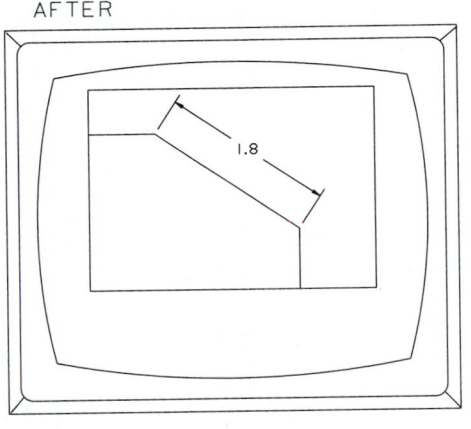

DRAW DIMENSION POINT TO POINT :DI
D2 D3

(d)

BEFORE

AFTER

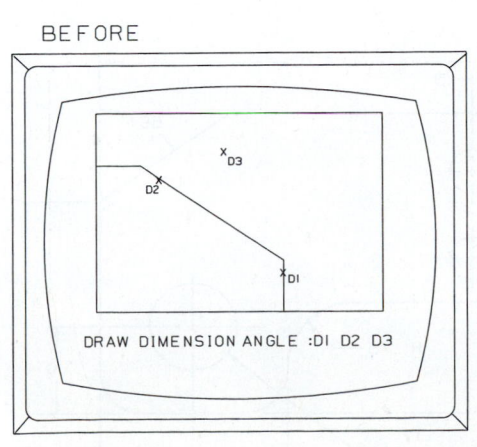

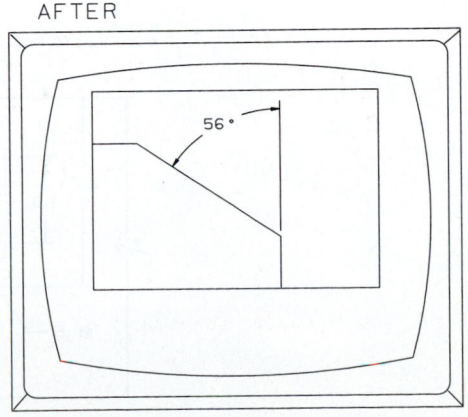

DRAW DIMENSION ANGLE :DI D2 D3

(e)

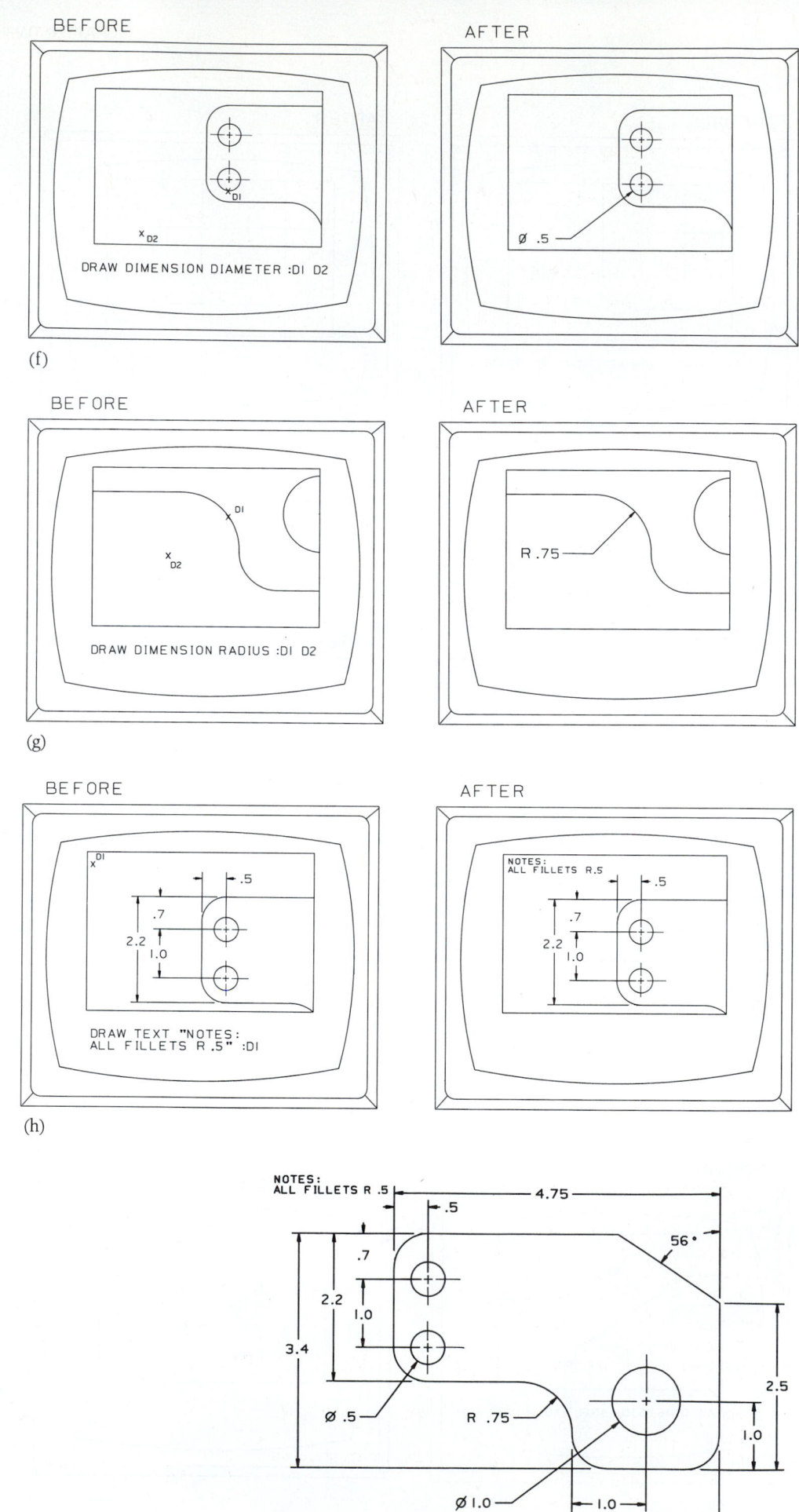

FIGURE 12.107 **Dimensioning a One-View Drawing—Continued** (f) Dimensioning the small holes (g) Dimensioning the large radius (h) Inserting notes (i) The completed detail of the hold down plate

endpoint of the line and the center of the circle. Figure 12.107(d) shows an alternative to an angle dimension. Here, a **rotated** or **aligned** linear dimension is inserted to measure the distance of the angled cut. The **DIMENSION ANGLE** command is used [Fig. 12.107(e)] to show the angle of the cut instead of using an aligned measurement. The diameter of the two small holes is dimensioned next [Fig. 12.107(f)]. The large fillet is then dimensioned with a radius [Fig. 12.107(g)]. Last, the notes are added using a text insertion command [Fig. 12.107(h)]. Figure 12.107(i) shows the completed part with all dimensions placed on the drawing. Figure 12.107 was created with Personal Designer.

Computer vision was used to create the breaker shown as a 3D model in Figure 12.108(a). The drafter activates the part file, and places it in appropriate views [Fig. 12.108(b)]. The drafter then changes the appearance of the model to conform to standard drafting conventions. For example, the hidden lines are changed to dashed lines and the centerlines are added. Last, the part is dimensioned [Fig. 12.108(c)].

Remember, regardless of the method used to draw the part, manual or CAD, the standards and rules of dimensioning apply to every drawing.

12.16 Basic Dimensioning Rules and Drawing Checklist

The following list is provided as a guide to dimensioning the drawing and to check a drawing after it is dimensioned. This list is by no means exhaustive:

1. Give the dimensions that will be used to fabricate the part in the shop or in CNC programming.

2. Make all figures totally legible—a misread dimension can result in an error in fabrication.

3. To help legibility, do not crowd dimensions around the part. Allow space for the dimensions in their proper location by planning for dimensions at the layout stage of the project.

4. Do not dimension on the part unless it is absolutely unavoidable. Use extension lines and whenever possible keep figures off the views. Place dimensions outside a view.

5. Use proper lettering technique (with guidelines) for all lettering.

6. Dimension the views that show the characteristic shape and prominent features of each part of the part.

7. Place numbers for dimension values so that they can be read from the bottom of the drawing (aligned) unless the drawing is for one of the construction engineering fields.

8. Do not use a part line as a dimension line. Object lines are used as extension lines only if unavoidable.

9. Dimension lines are located so they do not cross extension lines by placing the largest dimensions outside of smaller dimensions.

10. Never cross two dimension lines.

11. Place parallel dimensions equally spaced and the numerals staggered to avoid confusion on the drawing.

12. Give locating dimensions to the centers of circles that represent holes, cylindrical features, bosses, and slots.

13. Group related dimensions on the view where the contour of a feature is prominent.

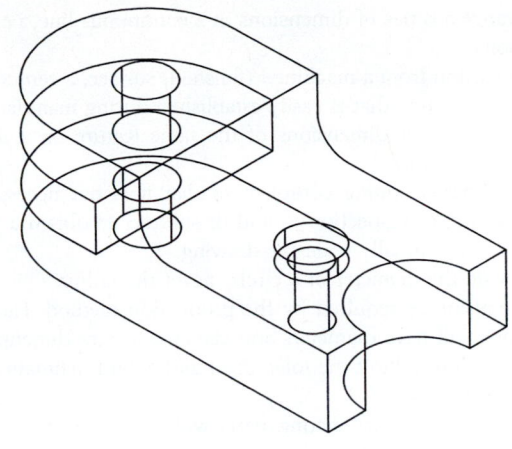

(a)

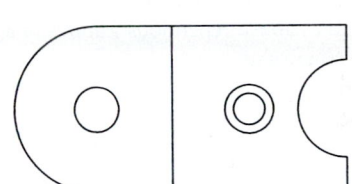

(b)

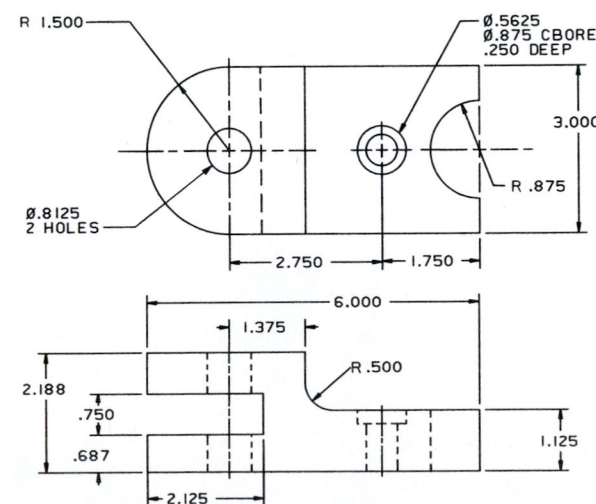

(c)

FIGURE 12.108   Dimensioning a 3D Part   (a) 3D finite element model of the breaker (b) Front and top views with border and title block added (c) Completed detail

14. Arrange a series of dimensions in a continuous line, i.e., chain dimensions.

15. Dimension from a machined (finished) surface, a centerline, or a datum (base) line that is easily established during manufacturing.

16. Do not repeat dimensions of the same feature on a drawing (double dimension).

17. Make dimensioning complete so that it is not necessary for manufacturing or inspection to add or subtract to obtain a needed dimension or manually scale the drawing.

18. Provide the diameter of a circle, never the radius.

19. Dimension as required by the production method. Parts with radial ends will have diameters and center-to-center dimensions.

20. Dimension to limit the tolerance buildup and maintain ease of manufacture.

21. Dimension so that mating parts will fit in the worst case of tolerance buildup on the part.

22. When all dimensions are in inches, the inch symbol is generally omitted, except for construction drawings.

23. The radius of an arc should be provided and the abbreviation R placed before the dimension.

24. If possible, avoid dimensioning to a hidden line.

25. Avoid dimensioning on sectioned areas of the part.

26. Use a note to establish repetitious features of a part, e.g., fillets with the same radius value.

QUIZ

True or False

1. Dimensioning is not as important as a graphically correct drawing.
2. Holes should be called out with a note giving the radius of the hole and its depth.
3. Center drills are used to hold a workpiece between centers on a lathe.
4. Dual dimensioning is used on most drawings in the United States.
5. Simplified methods for showing threads should be used on metric drawings only.
6. The diameter symbol always follows the size dimension.
7. Symbols can be used when calling out counterbores, spotfaces, and counterdrills.
8. Leaders are always drawn radially from a curved feature when placing a local note.

Fill in the Blanks

9. Fractions are used on _____ , _____ , and _____ drawings in the United States.

10. The ability of the system to update dimensions automatically by the system after design changes have been made is called _____ .

11. Angles can be called out as _____ angles, or _____ , _____ , and _____ .

12. SR is used to define and _____ _____ .

13. Counterbores can be specified by the symbol or _____ .

14. _____ dimensions are enclosed with parentheses.

15. Chamfers can be specified by _____ or _____ .

16. There are two types of knurling: _____ and _____ patterned.

Answer the Following

17. Describe the difference between the dimensioning process of a 3D CAD system and a 2D CAD system.
18. What are the four types of linear dimensions? Describe the process of placing each on a part.
19. Describe four methods of calling out a taper.
20. Describe the process of geometric breakdown of a part.
21. Why are mating parts and mating dimensions important when dimensioning a part?
22. What is the difference between a radial and a diameter dimension and when should each be used?
23. What is a finish mark and why is it important when dimensioning a part?
24. Explain what notes are used for on a drawing. What is a local note and what is a general note?

EXERCISES

Exercises may be assigned as sketching, instrument, or digitizing projects. Transfer the given information to an "A"-size sheet of .25 in. grid paper. Complete all views and solve for proper visibility, including centerlines, object lines, and hidden lines. Exercises that are not assigned by the instructor can be sketched in the text to provide practice and understanding of the preceding instructional material. Complete the views and add hidden lines where required.

After Reading the Chapter Through Section 12.5.5 You May Complete the Following Exercises

Exercise 12.1 Completely dimension the .25 in.-thick one-view part.

Exercise 12.2 Dimension the .125 in.-thick aluminum plate completely.

Exercise 12.3 Dimension the two-view part as needed.

Exercise 12.4 Show the proper placement of all dimensions on appropriate views.

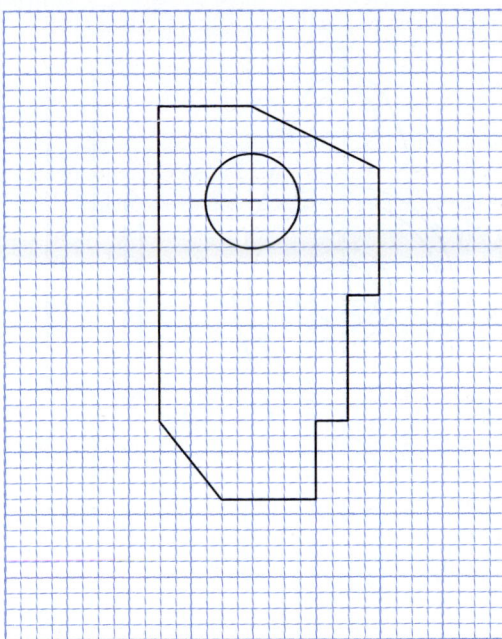

Exercise 12.1

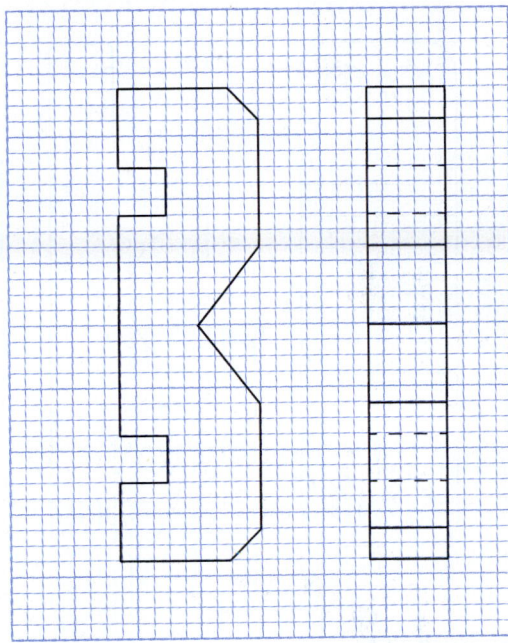

Exercise 12.3

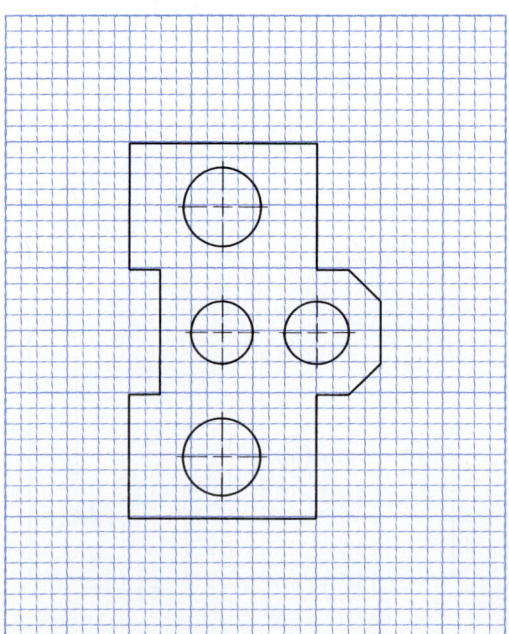

Exercise 12.2

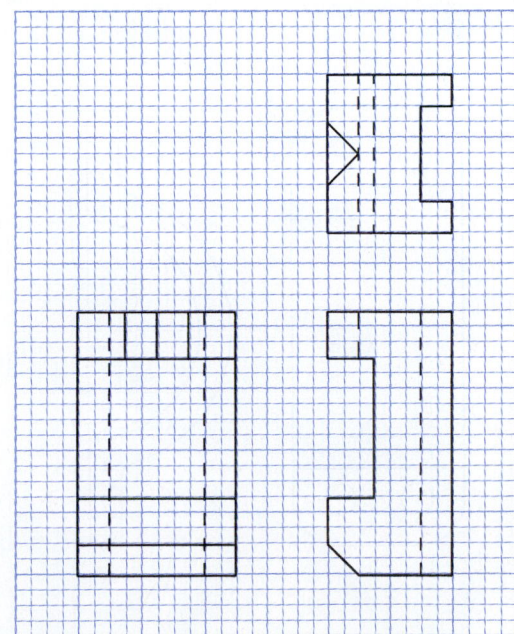

Exercise 12.4

After Reading the Chapter Through Section 12.6.3 You May Complete the Following Exercises

Exercise 12.5 Completely dimension the part as required. Use symbology to call out the spotfaced holes. Place finish marks on the machined faces and dimension accordingly.

Exercise 12.6 Completely dimension the part. The bottom surface is machined.

Exercise 12.7 Dimension the two-view part.

Exercise 12.8 Dimension the three views of the part. The bottom surface, the left side surface, and the boss are the only finished surfaces. Add appropriate fillets and rounds for the cast surfaces (top and around the boss). Place basic finish marks on machined surfaces.

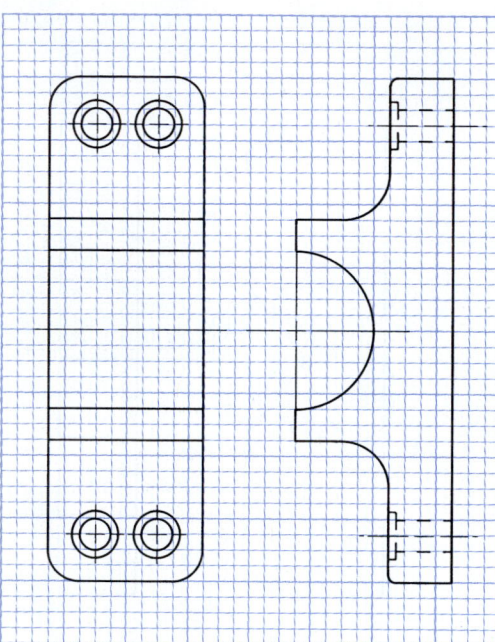

Exercise 12.5

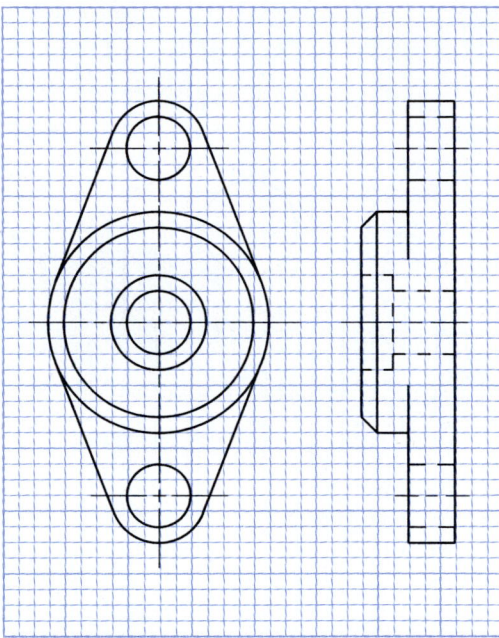

Exercise 12.7

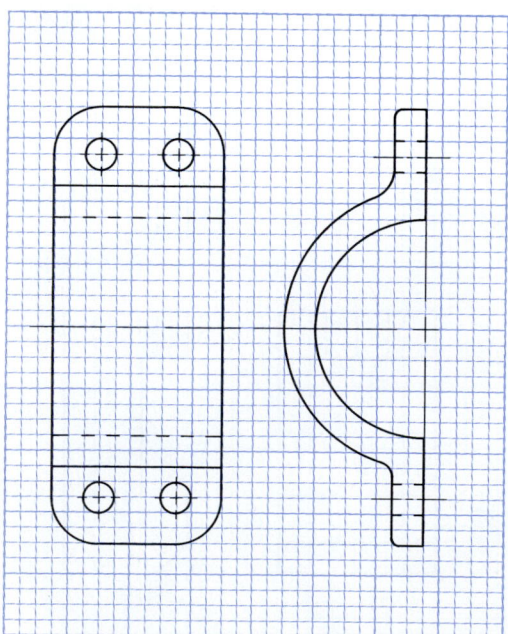

Exercise 12.6

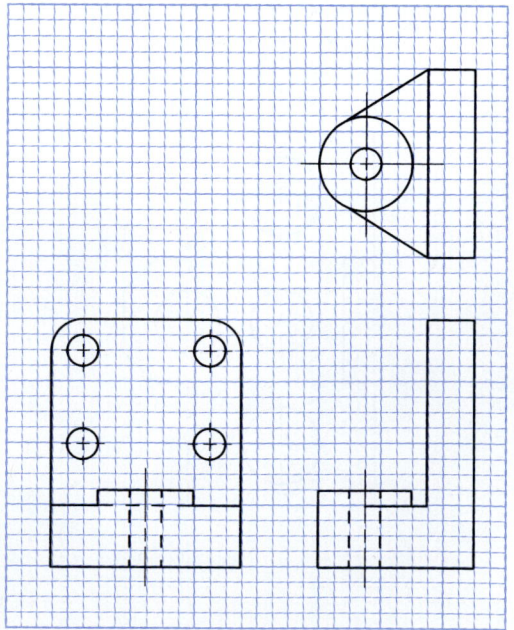

Exercise 12.8

After Reading the Chapter Through Section 12.8.3 You May Complete the Following Exercises

Exercise 12.9   Completely dimension the cast part. Add appropriate fillets and rounds to cast surfaces. Place finish marks on machine surfaces. The left surface and bottom surface are machined along with the upper U-shaped surface. All other surfaces are cast.

Exercise 12.10   Because of space limitations, dimension only the hole pattern and holes (call out the bolt circle), the slots, and the chamfer. Make sure all views are visually correct.

Exercise 12.11   Completely dimension the part. Complete the views for proper visibility. Call out the knurling with a note. The small hole goes through to the center hole only.

Exercise 12.12   Because of limited space, dimension only the hole pattern, slot, and the counterdrilled holes. Use symbology to call out the holes.

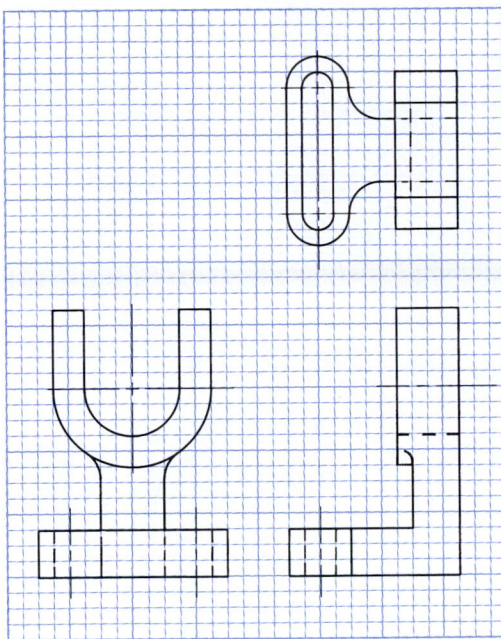

Exercise 12.9

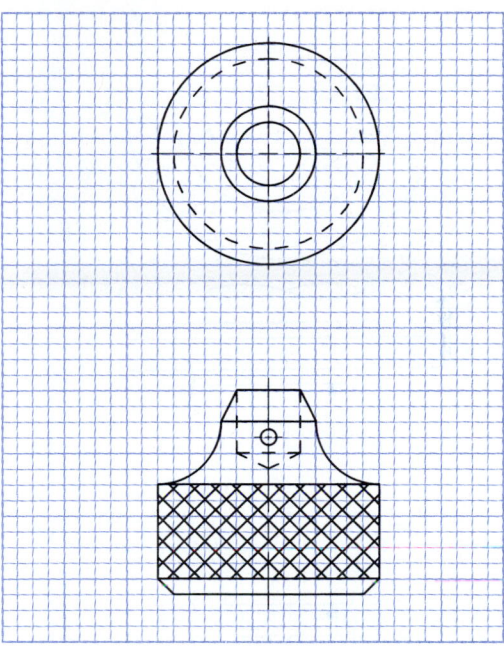

Exercise 12.11

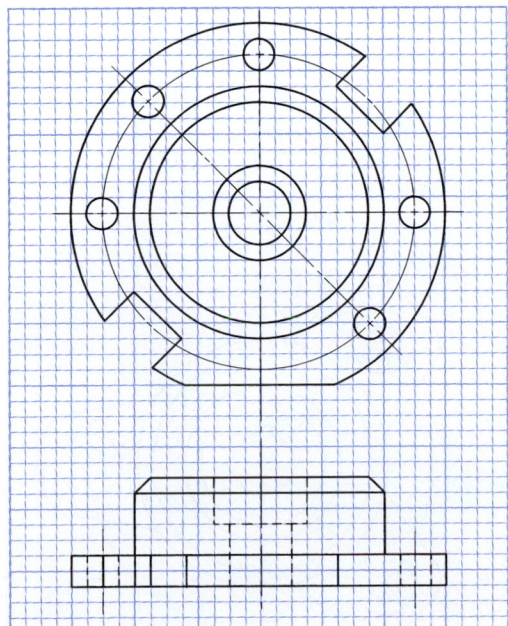

Exercise 12.10

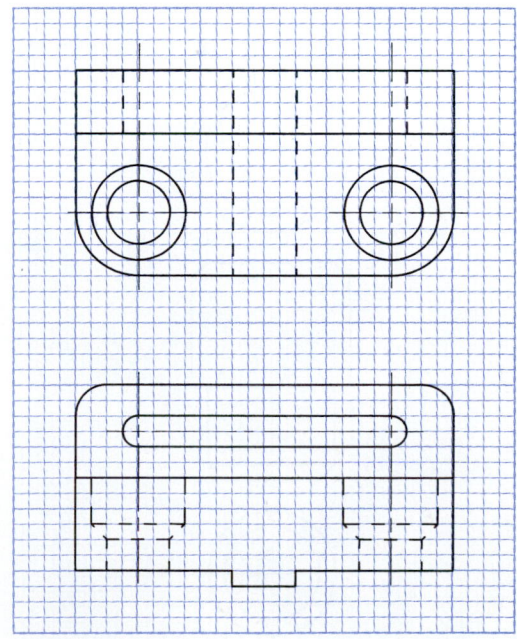

Exercise 12.12

After Reading the Chapter Through Section 12.10.5 You May Complete the Following Exercises

Exercise 12.13   Dimension the taper with a callout. Because of space limitations, dimension only the lateral length dimensions, not the diameter dimensions of the rest of the part.

Exercise 12.14   Place a #4 center hole for a center drill on both ends of the workpiece. Dimension the whole part and call out the center drill with a note. Complete the views.

Exercise 12.15   Complete the side view. Dimension the hole pattern, the hole sizes, and the keyway. Look up the proper keyway size and type for the given shaft diameter in Chapter 15 and Appendix C.

Exercise 12.16   Complete the side view of the part. Dimension the holes with a callout using symbology. Call out the keyway based on the shaft diameter. Dimension only one "ear" of the part.

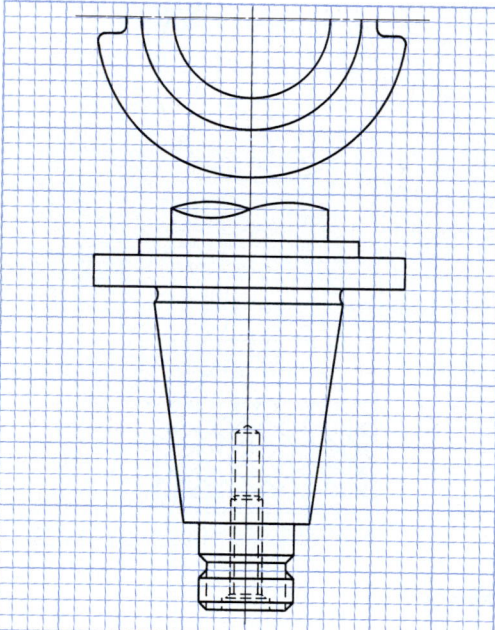

Exercise 12.13

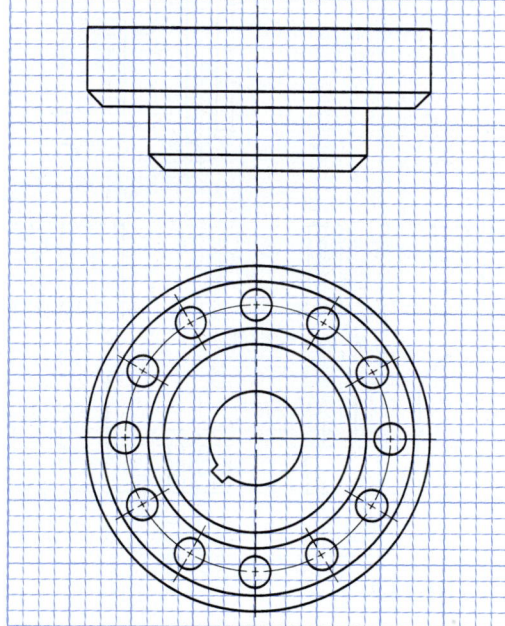

Exercise 12.15

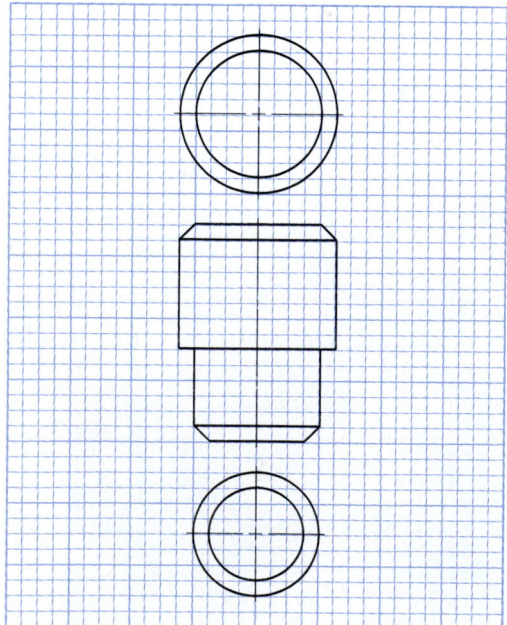

Exercise 12.14

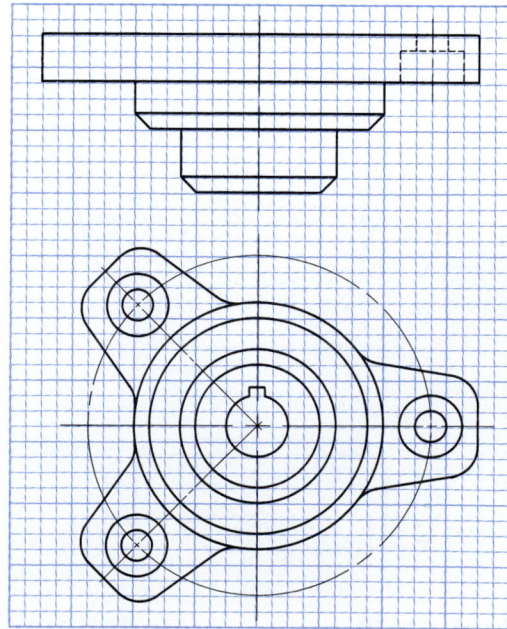

Exercise 12.16

PROBLEMS

Your instructor can assign any of the figures presented in this chapter as problems. For every problem, redraw the part and dimension using the most recent ANSI Y14.5M standards. Other industry drawings and problems at the end of each chapter throughout the text can also be assigned by the instructor. The projects completed for Chapter 11 can now be dimensioned.

CHAPTER 13

Geometric Dimensioning and Tolerancing

Learning Objectives

Upon completion of this chapter you will be able to accomplish the following:

1. Differentiate between precision and accuracy while acquiring knowledge of tolerancing terms and techniques.
2. Recognize ISO and ANSI interpretations of angle of projection and limits of size.
3. Become familiar with general and geometric tolerancing rules, symbology, and modifiers.
4. Identify feature control frames.
5. Develop an understanding of datums and datum systems.
6. Demonstrate skill in interpreting form, profile, orientation, location, and runout tolerances.
7. Apply fixed, floating fastener, and system tolerance formulas.
8. Employ recommended guidelines for dimensioning and tolerancing using a CAD system.
9. Develop an understanding of standardized limits, and fits.

13.1 Introduction

In our physical world, all parts are imperfect and vary in size; no feature of a part is exact in size, form, orientation, or location. Therefore, **tolerances** must be applied to all features of a part. Cost-effective designs provide the largest allowable tolerances consistent with the function and interchangeability requirements of the design.

The technical drawing has been a means of communicating engineering information for more than 6,000 years, but it's been less than 100 years since the introduction of tolerancing or holding variations within limits. This elementary concept, taken for granted today, gradually evolved in association with improvements in the science of weights and measures or measurements (metrology). The skilled craftsman of old did not have measuring instruments of sufficient accuracy to determine variations in size, location, and geometry from the exact dimensions. Surely, items always varied in size, location, and geometry, but these variations were restricted, rather than avoided. Part variations were controlled by the worker rather than by engineering. It was not until the evolution of interchangeable manufacture that the *exact* size gave way to holding parts within *limits*.

The *Taylor concept*, introduced in 1905 and still used today, revealed methods of limit gaging for holes and shafts. But large mass-produced items of that period were produced with precision rather than accuracy. **Precision** is exact duplication using matched or common fixtures and tools similar to master (or matched) tooling techniques. It was used extensively by Germany during World War II and is used for selected items today. **Accuracy**, on the other hand, means producing parts relative to standard measures and forms. This is the prevalent method used today.

As production rates increased to meet demands, and technologies in engineering, manufacturing, and quality control advanced to meet more demanding specifications for products, the precise control of tolerance variations became compelling. Figure 13.1 is an example in which **geometric dimensioning and tolerancing** (GD&T) is used on a drawing. GD&T is a symbolic system of tolerancing to control size, form, profile, orientation, location, and runout of a part according to geometry.

The increased production rates of World War II led to more sophisticated designs, and engineering became further removed from the manufacturing and inspection operation. With the frequent use of larger factories and suppliers, the inadequacy of the technical drawing as a communication medium became more apparent. In 1945, the *Gladman papers* of Great Britain, which advanced the issues of drawing inade-

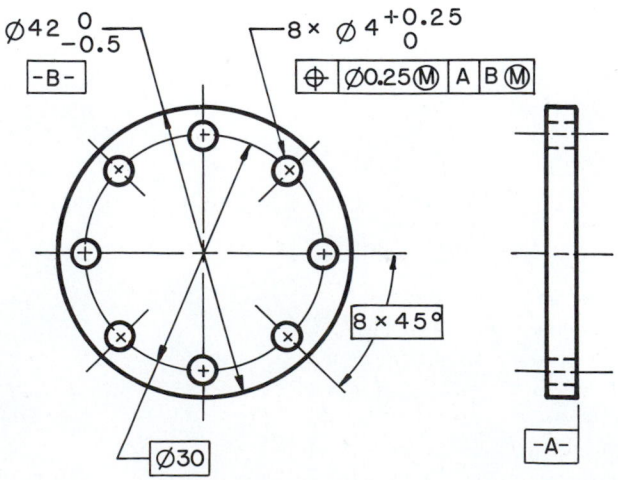

FIGURE 13.1 Drawing with Geometric Tolerancing

| ITEMS OF INTEREST | *Tolerancing and Its Role in Industry* |

Mass production of interchangeable parts played an important role in the Industrial Revolution. Much of the technology that we enjoy today also relies on interchangeable components. Automobiles and computer circuits are good examples of mass production and the importance of size control.

While it is impossible to make any part exactly the same size as another part, it is possible to keep component dimensions to a specific range of sizes. Geometrical relationships can also be specified. These dimension restrictions are specified with *tolerances*. Component function determines the degree of tolerance. This process assures that parts made in one location are interchangeable with parts made in another location.

For example, Eagle Engine Manufacturing produces V-8 engines for top fuel dragsters. The Eagle engine can produce 3,000 hp and is designed to allow for different configurations. Cylinders are interchangeable and the head accommodates one to three spark plugs per cylinder. This means the engine can be configured for a dragster or a tractor. Specific parts for the engine were designed on a CAD system with tolerance capabilities to sixteen decimal places. The design was easily modified to fit another configuration with its tolerance specifications.

Producing components to specific tolerances makes it possible to mass produce goods and modify existing components to fit different needs. This system adds flexibility to the manufacturer, allowing the part to change quickly with market trends and technological advances. This kind of flexibility is essential to compete in the competitive world of today and tomorrow.

quacy, were published and discussed at the first American, British, Canadian Conference on the Unification of Engineering Standards.

Advanced tolerancing techniques started in the late 1930s. Stanley Parker of the Royal Torpedo Factory in Alexandria, Scotland, originated the theory of **positional tolerancing**, and in 1940, Chevrolet's *Draftsman's Handbook* introduced the **maximum material condition** (MMC) concept. In the 1940s Rolls Royce introduced **tolerancing symbols.**

Geometric tolerancing was used only partially in the 1950s and 1960s. In 1972, however, the International Organization for Standardization (ISO), recognizing the need, established a subcommittee to develop dimensioning and tolerancing standards. Mil Std 8C was released in 1963 and because of the perceived economic effect of the new requirements, the work was taken over by the ASA which is now ANSI, the American National Standards Institute. In 1966, the first ANSI Y14.5 was released. During the 1970s and 1980s, geometric tolerancing was being used extensively by the military and industry in the United States as well as other countries.

13.1.2 Terms Used in Geometric Tolerancing and Dimensioning

The following terms will be used throughout the chapter:

Actual size   The measured size.

Basic dimension   A numerical value used to describe the theoretically exact size, profile, orientation, or location of a feature or datum target. It is the basis from which permissible variations are established by tolerances on other dimensions, in notes, or in feature control frames.

Basic size   The size to which limits or deviations are assigned. The basic size is the same for both members of a fit.

Clearance fit   The relationship between assembled parts when clearance occurs under all tolerance conditions.

Datum   A datum is the origin from which the location or geometric characteristics of features of a part are established.

Datum feature   An actual geometric feature of a part that is used to establish a datum.

Datum target   A specified point, line, or area on a part used to establish a datum.

Deviation   The difference between the actual size and the corresponding basic size.

Feature   The general term applied to a physical portion of a part, such as a surface, hole, or slot.

Feature of size   A cylindrical or spherical surface, or a set of two parallel surfaces, each of which is associated with a size dimension.

Interference fit   The relationship between assembled parts when interference occurs under all tolerance conditions.

Least material condition (LMC)   The condition in which a feature of size contains the least amount of material within stated limits of size, for example, maximum hole diameter, minimum shaft diameter.

Limits of size   The specified maximum and minimum sizes.

Lower deviation   The difference between the minimum limit of size and the corresponding basic size.

Maximum material condition (MMC)   The condition in which a feature of size contains the maximum amount of material within the stated limits of size, for example, minimum hole diameter, maximum shaft diameter.

Regardless of feature size (RFS)   The term use to indicate that a geometric tolerance or datum reference applies at any increment of size of the feature within its size tolerance.

Tolerance   The total amount by which a specific dimension is permitted to vary. The tolerance is the difference between the maximum and minimum limits.

Tolerance, bilateral   A tolerance in which variation is permitted in both directions from the specified dimension.

Tolerance, geometric   The general term applied to the category of tolerances used to control form, profile, orientation, location, and runout.

Tolerance, unilateral   A tolerance in which variation is permitted in one direction from the specified dimension.

Tolerance zone   An area representing the tolerance and its position in relation to the basic size, not just size.

Transition fit   The relationship between assembled parts when either a clearance or interference fit results, depending on the tolerance conditions of the mating parts.

True position   The theoretically exact location of a feature established by basic dimensions.

Upper deviation   The difference between the maximum limit of size and the corresponding basic size.

Virtual condition   The boundary generated by the collective effects of the specified MMC limit of size of a feature and any applicable geometric tolerances.

13.2   Standards and Specifications

Standards were developed because of the need for a communication medium that could be developed to ensure universal interpretation of tolerance requirements. ANSI and ISO currently satisfy this need.

Although most companies use the standards "as is," many corporations prefer to use a company drafting manual that tailors these standards to their particular product requirements. The notes and title block of a technical drawing must be read carefully to ensure interpretation in accordance with the correct specification. To avoid misinterpretation, a note such as "Interpret drawing in accordance with ANSI Y14.5M-1982" should be referenced directly on the drawing, indicating not only the applicable standard but also the date and revision.

Additionally, some companies and government agencies include reference to a manufacturing standard that includes many types of geometric tolerances, generally based on feature size, to be applied where the drawing fails to specify a standard directly. It is preferable to show the geometric tolerances directly on the technical drawing to avoid misuse of this practice.

Our age of multinational companies, where parts are made both here and in other countries, requires accurate communication between those using ISO standards and Americans using ANSI standards. However, such accuracy is hampered by two major differences between the ISO and ANSI standards: *angle of projection* and *limits of size*.

This chapter provides tolerancing techniques in accordance with the ANSI standard. In some instances the ANSI and ISO standard are not in strict accord. If the ISO standard is to be used, it should be specified on the drawing.

13.2.1   Third-Angle Versus First-Angle Projection

In third-angle orthographic projection, the view to the right of the front view of a part depicts the right side of the part

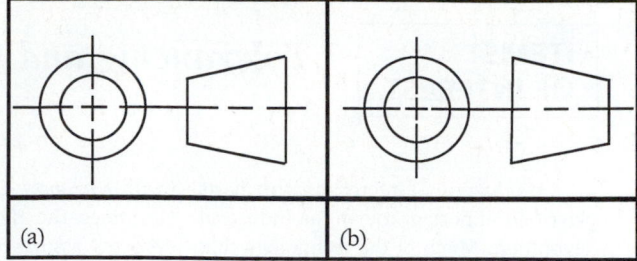

FIGURE 13.2   **ISO Versus ANSI Orthographic Projection** (a) Third-angle projection (b) First-angle projection

(Fig. 13.2). In first-angle projection, the left side view would be shown. Similarly, the view of the top of a part is placed above the front, the bottom view below, and so on, in third-angle projection. The bottom view is placed above the front and the top view below the front view in first-angle projection.

From a tolerancing standpoint, the difference between the standards in the interpretation of limits of size has a much greater significance than the angle of projection. Despite a difference between the two methods of projection, the resulting views are the same. This is not the case for limits of size.

13.3   Limits of Size

Unless otherwise specified, the **limits of size** of a feature prescribe the extent within which variations of geometric form are allowed. Where only a size tolerance is specified, the limits of size of an individual feature prescribe the extent to which variations in its geometric form, as well as size, are allowed.

The **actual size** of an individual feature at any cross section must be within the specified tolerance of size. The form of an individual feature is controlled by its limits of size.

The surface or surfaces of a feature must not extend beyond a boundary of perfect form at MMC (maximum material condition). This boundary is the true geometric form represented by the drawing. No variation in form is permitted if the feature is produced at its MMC limit of size. Where the actual size of a feature has departed from MMC toward LMC (least material condition), a variation in form is allowed equal to the amount of such departure. There is no requirement for a boundary of perfect form at LMC. Thus, a feature produced at its LCM limit of size is permitted to vary from true form to the maximum variation allowed by the boundary of perfect form at MMC. The control of geometric form prescribed by limits of size does not apply to the following:

1. stock such as bars, sheets, tubing, structural shapes, and other items produced to established industry or government standards that prescribe limits for straightness, flatness, and other geometric characteristics (Unless geometric tolerances are specified on the drawing of a part made from these items, standards for these items govern the surfaces that remain in the "as furnished" condition on the finished part.)

2. parts subject to free state variation in the unrestrained condition

The limits of size do not control the orientation or location relationship between individual features. Features shown perpendicular, coaxial, or symmetrical to each other must be controlled for location or orientation to avoid incomplete drawing requirements. If it is necessary to establish a boundary of perfect form at MMC to control the relationship between features, the following methods are used:

1. Specify a zero tolerance of orientation at MMC, including a datum reference (at MMC, if applicable), to control the angularity, perpendicularity, or parallelism of the feature.
2. Specify a zero positional tolerance at MMC, including a datum reference at MMC, to control coaxial or symmetrical features.
3. Indicate this control for the features involved with a note such as

   PERFECT ORIENTATION (or COAXIALITY or SYMMETRY) AT MMC REQUIRED FOR RELATED FEATURES.

4. Relate dimensions to a datum reference frame.

13.3.1   ISO Interpretation of Limits of Size

In the ISO system, where datums are specified, measurements are made both from the datums and relative to them. Where datums are not specified, linear dimensions are intended to apply on a point-to-point basis or directly between the points indicated on the drawing. This criterion is faulty in that caliper measurements *float* relative to one another; therefore, the exact shape is not known (Fig. 13.3). This requires generally that, if the configuration is to be controlled, a form tolerance such as straightness or flatness must be given.

Additionally, the direction of measurement can be a problem for a geometry that is not ideal. In Figure 13.4 the vertical measurements are not perpendicular to the horizontal ones. If the sides of a part are not parallel, finding the center plane to orient measurements is another problem associated with the ISO interpretation of "limits of size."

For thin parts, the rule changes to measuring parallel to the base (Fig. 13.5). Further, to make this system work, a rule of independence was devised:

> Every requirement on a drawing is intended to be applied independently, without reference to other dimensions, conditions or characteristics, unless a particular relationship is specified.

This rule is voided, however, where "limits and fits" are specified. In that case the Taylor principle, which is the basis for the American version of limits of size, is used. Rule 1 of the ANSI standard regarding limits of size follows:

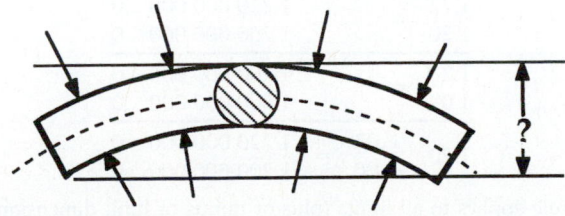

FIGURE 13.3   Caliper Measurements Do Not Measure Form Illustration shows a cylindrical part.

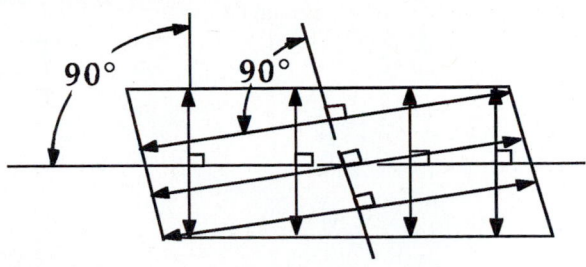

FIGURE 13.4   Measuring Orientation for Caliper Measurements   Illustration shows a rectangular part.

Rule 1: The surface(s) of a feature shall not extend beyond a boundary (envelope) of perfect form at MMC. This boundary is the true geometric form represented by the drawing. There is no requirement for a boundary of perfect form at the other limit (LMC) (Fig. 13.6).

This rule does not apply to stock materials that use established industry or government standards; to parts specified in the "free state" (nonrigid); and to those specifically excluded, such as straightness of the axis or where the note **PERFECT FORM AT MMC NOT REQUIRED** is specified.

This rule applies to individual features and, although they control the form of an individual feature of size, they do not control the orientation, location, or runout of features to each other. These relationships are defined by tolerances, notes, or other specifications called out directly on the drawing.

Furthermore, in the ANSI version, the Taylor principle is supported as is the "limits and fits" series for cylindrical parts (ANSI B4.1 and ISO 286). Inspection with small measuring instruments such as the micrometer, digital caliper, or dial indicator cannot determine conformance to the "envelope of perfect form" requirement. Note, however, that advances in metrology, especially where computerized mathematical models and algorithms are used such as on coordinate measuring machines (CMM), lend themselves to the ANSI version of limits of size.

According to the Taylor principle, a ring gage made to the MMC size of a shaft, and as long as the shaft, may be used to verify a shaft for Rule 1 compliance. A micrometer or caliper would be used to verify the LMC limit. A plug gage, made to the MMC size of a hole, and as long as the hole, may be used to verify a hole for Rule 1 compliance. An inside micrometer or caliper would be used to verify the LMC limit.

13.3.2   U.S. Interpretation of Limits of Size

In the United States, unless otherwise specified, the **limits of size** of a feature prescribe the extent within which variations of geometric form, as well as size, are allowed. This control

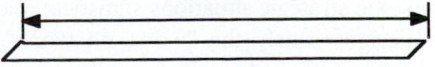

FIGURE 13.5   Measuring Thin Parts

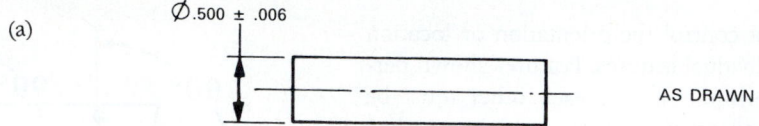

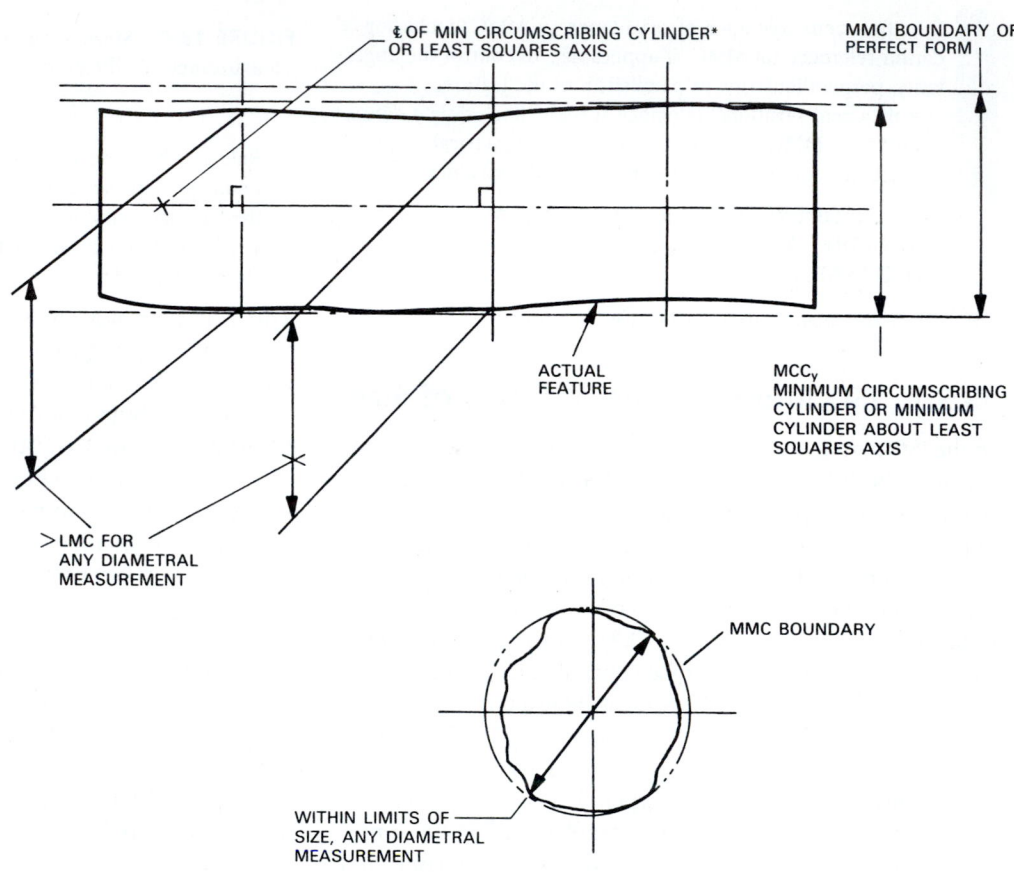

FIGURE 13.6 Limits of Size Interpretation for Individual Features

*WHERE A PREFERENCE FOR A LEAST SQUARES OR ₵ OF ENVELOPE AXIS EXISTS IT MUST BE SPECIFIED ON THE DRAWING.

applies solely to individual features of size. **Feature of size** refers to one cylindrical or spherical surface, or a set of two plane parallel surfaces, each of which is associated with a size dimension. It goes on to state that, where only a **tolerance of size** is specified, the limits of size of an individual feature prescribe the extent to which variations in its geometric form, as well as size, are allowed (Fig. 13.7). The **actual size** of an individual feature at any cross section is to be within the specified tolerance of size.

13.4 General Tolerancing Rules

Although in some strategic situations statistical tolerancing is used, most designs satisfy the "worst on worst" situation. Rules have been established to ensure uniform interpretation

and avoid costly errors and misunderstandings. The following six rules should be closely studied:

1. The system of indicating tolerances (whether size, location, or geometry) does not necessarily require the use of any particular method of production or quality.

2. Regardless of the number of places involved, all toleranced limits are considered to be absolute. Each limit is considered to be continued with trailing zeros. For example:

$$\frac{1.22}{1.20} = \frac{1.220\ 000\ 000\ ...0}{1.200\ 000\ 000\ ...0}$$

$$\frac{1.2}{1.0} = \frac{1.200\ 000\ 000\ ...0}{1.000\ 000\ 000\ ...0}$$

$$1.20\ \begin{matrix} +.02 \\ -.00 \end{matrix} = \frac{1.220\ 000\ 000\ ...0}{1.200\ 000\ 000\ ...0}$$

This rule applies to all limits (plus or minus or limit dimensioned) including those where title block tolerances are applied.

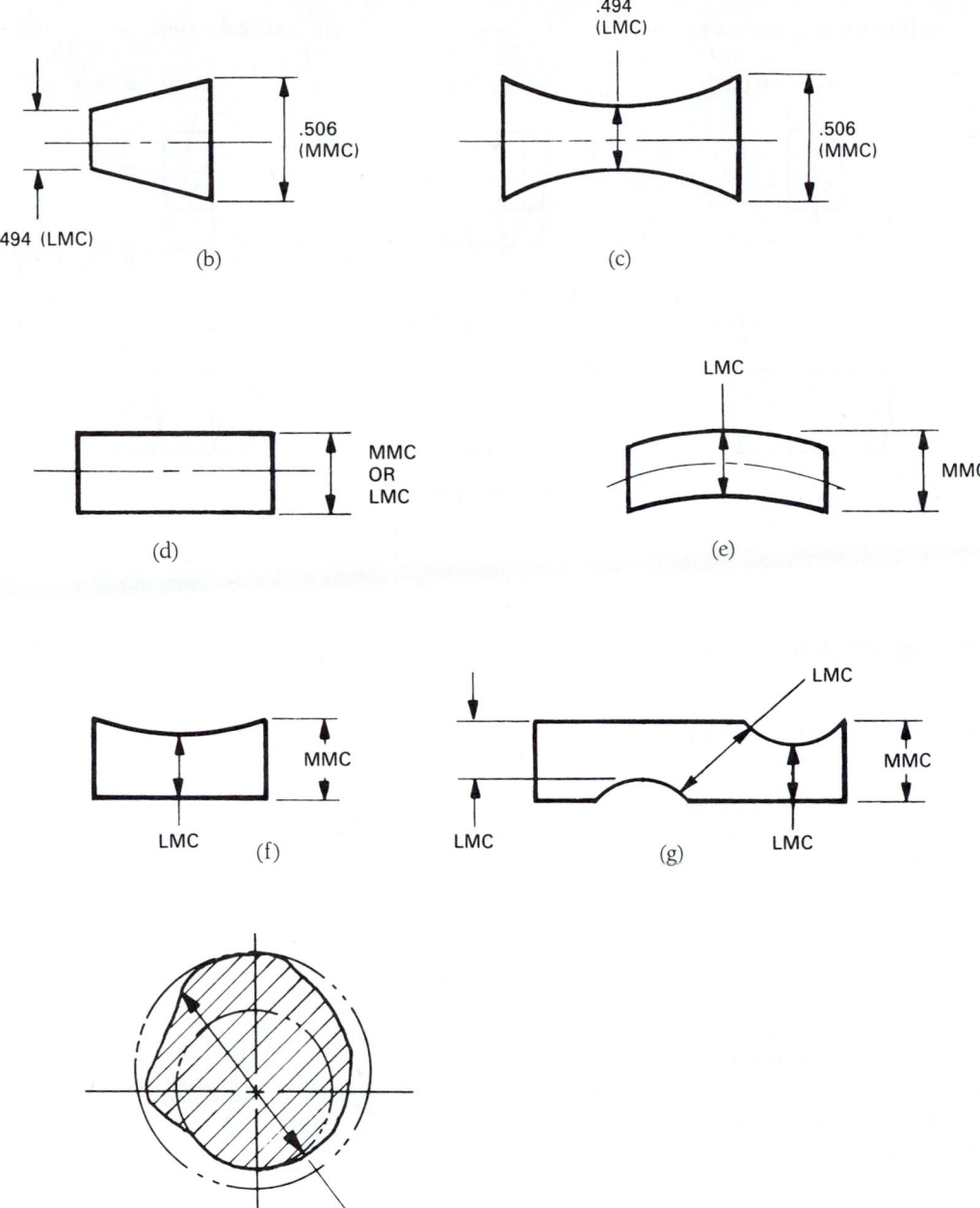

FIGURE 13.6 Limits of Size Interpretation for Individual Features—Continued

3. All dimensions and tolerances are understood to apply at 68°F (20°C) unless otherwise specified.

4. Surfaces drawn at 90° are subject to the title block tolerance specified for angles or by a note, such as

PERFECT ORIENTATION REQUIRED AT MMC.

If the drawing and associated specifications fail to specify a tolerance, it is *not an inspection attribute* and, except for obviously poor workmanship, the considered attribute would be accepted. This rule also applies to features that have a common centerline or axis of revolution. Where function or interchangeability is affected, the tolerances are to be specified.

5. Theoretical constructions such as centerlines or planes, shown at right angles, and from which features such as holes or pins are dimensioned, are considered to be at 90° BASIC. Variations in the inspection setup are subtracted from the allowable tolerances during the verification process.

6. The tolerance specified on the drawing is the total amount allowable, including manufacturing, inspection, and gaging variations. To assure rapid part acceptance, manufacturing does not generally use more than 90% of the available tolerance.

THIS ON THE DRAWING   (a)   ALLOWS THIS   (b)

FIGURE 13.7 Tolerance Variations Allowed for Individual Features

13.4.1 General Rules of Geometric Tolerancing

The following rules can be used to apply geometric tolerancing to a part:

1. The surface(s) of a feature must not extend beyond a boundary (envelope) of perfect form at MMC. This boundary is the true geometric form represented by the drawing. There is no requirement for a boundary of perfect form at LMC.

2. Position tolerance requirements for modifiers are specified in the feature control frame. A modifier M, S, or L is to be specified after the feature tolerance and after each datum for features and datums of size. No modifier is to be specified for a single-plane surface.

3. Requirements for modifiers of tolerances other than position are specified in the feature control frame. RFS applies, unless another modifier is specified, for all features and datums. The RFS modifier is usually not shown in the feature control frame. MMC is specified for features and datums of size where the design allows it.

13.4.2 Setting Tolerances

The **nominal size** is often referred to as the **basic size** or **design size**. The nominal and the associated tolerances have the same number of decimal places except in the metric system. The "plus" value is shown above the "minus" value. European drawings also use +, + and −, and − tolerances. This indicates positive or negative deviations from the basic.

In **unilateral tolerancing** [Fig. 13.8(a)], the tolerance is applied in one direction, the other value being zero:

$$1.200 \begin{array}{l} +.002 \\ -.000 \end{array} \qquad 1.200 \begin{array}{l} +.000 \\ -.006 \end{array}$$

In **bilateral tolerancing** [Fig. 13.8(b)], the tolerance is applied in both directions from the nominal:

$$.500 \pm .005 \quad \text{or} \quad 1.200 \begin{array}{l} +.002 \\ -.005 \end{array}$$

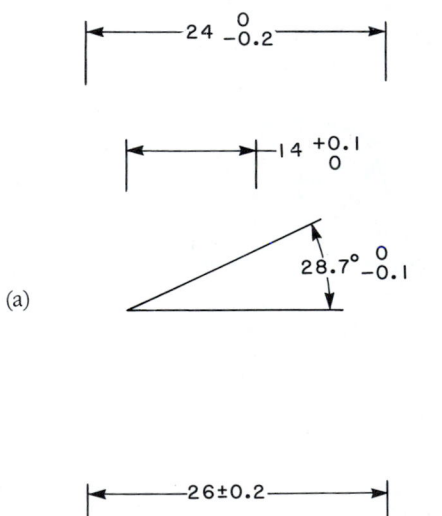

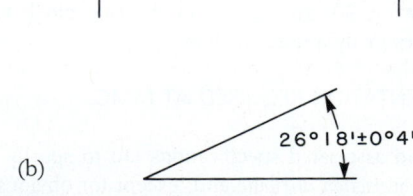

FIGURE 13.8 Plus and Minus Tolerancing on Dimensions (a) Unilateral tolerancing (b) Bilateral tolerancing

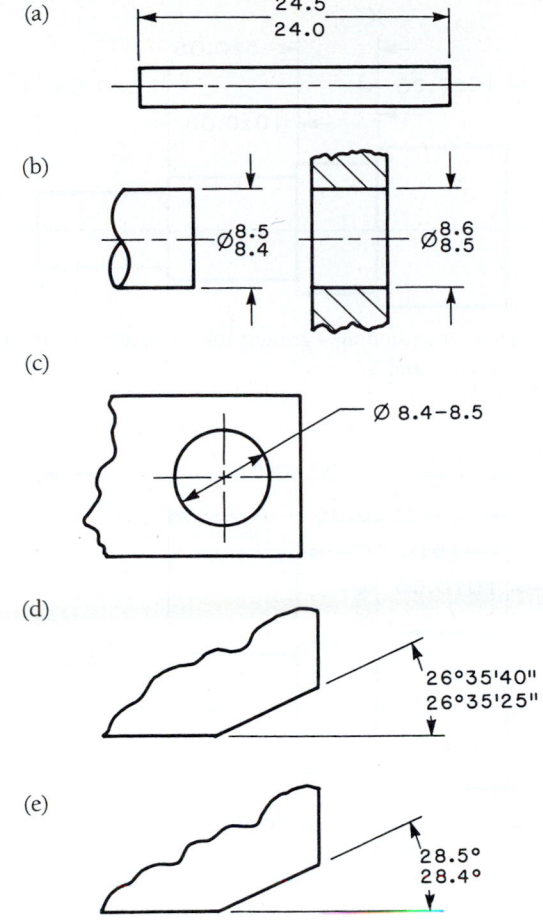

FIGURE 13.9 Limit Dimensioning on Drawings

13.4.3 Limit Dimensioning

In **limit dimensioning**, the larger (maximum) value is placed above the lesser (minimum) value (Fig. 13.9). In note form, the larger value is placed to the right of the lesser value separated by a dash. Both limits have the same number of decimal places

$$\begin{array}{c} .750 \\ .748 \end{array} \quad \text{or} \quad .748-.750$$

In practice, even values are preferred. Although there is generally at least one trailing zero, the number of decimal places is minimized. Plus or minus and limit dimensions may appear on the same drawing. Generally, limit dimensions are used to specify the size of features; plus or minus dimensions are used to specify the location of the features. Plus or minus dimensions, in bilateral form, are preferred for numerical control production, where the mean is used, and for probability studies.

13.4.4 Title Block Tolerances

Title block tolerances may be used where there is a uniformity in tolerances (Fig. 13.10). In Figure 13.11 the nominal dimension alone is given on the face of the drawing and a bilateral tolerance is shown in the title block. If larger tolerances are allowed for a feature, they should be specified. In Europe, title block tolerances are based on feature size. In the American system, however, they are based on the number of decimal places specified (Fig. 13.11). For example, a two-place dimension on the drawing may be associated with a $\pm .03$ tolerance in the title block.

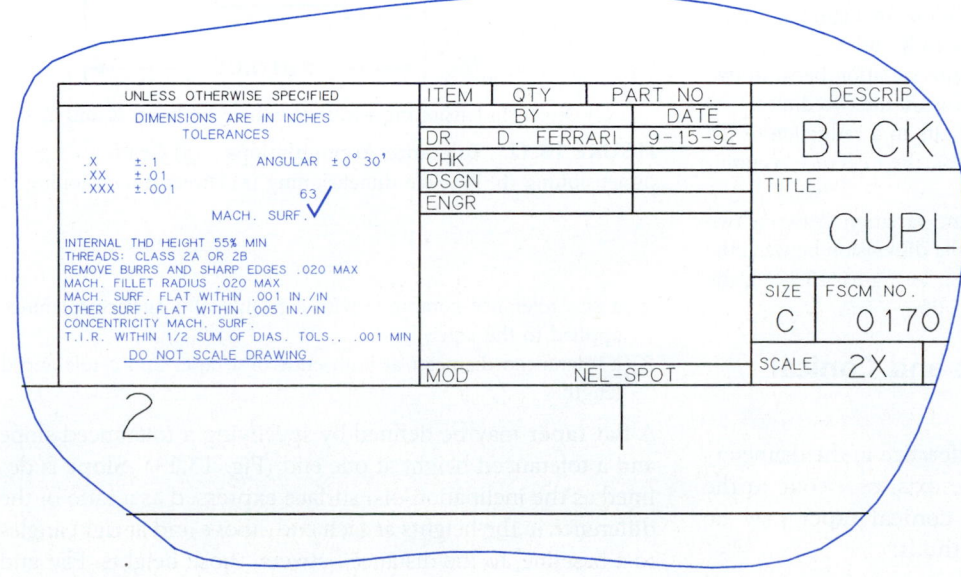

FIGURE 13.10 Title Block Tolerances

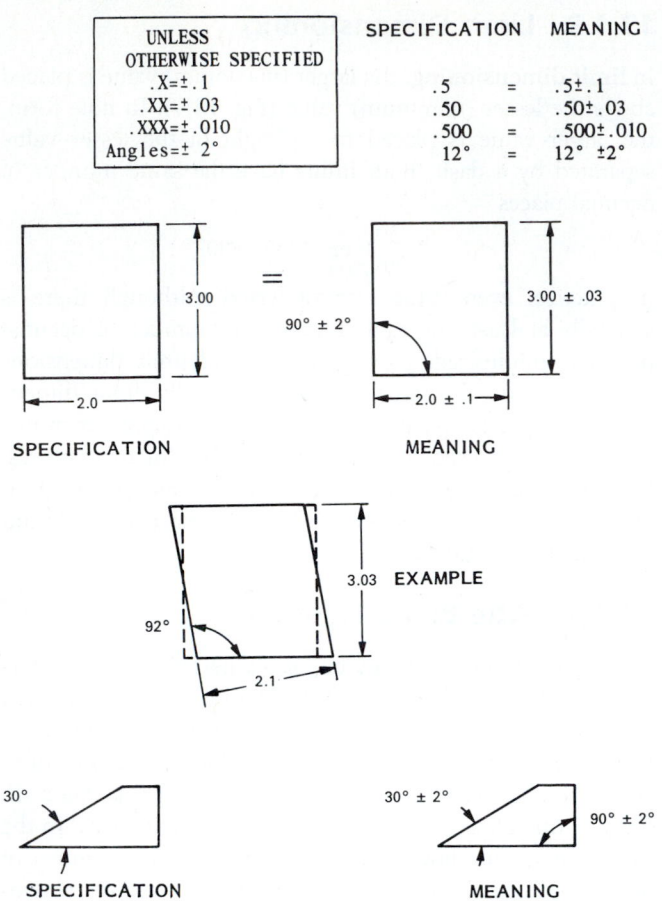

FIGURE 13.11   Title Block Tolerance Application

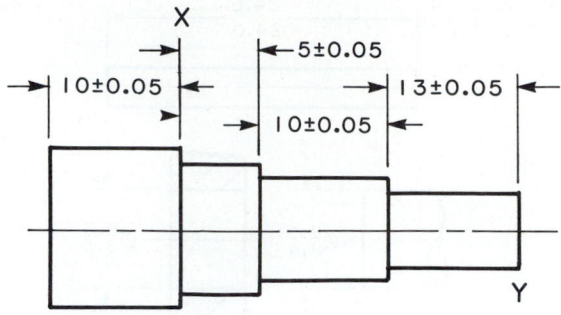

(a) Chain dimensioning—greatest tolerance accumulation between X and Y

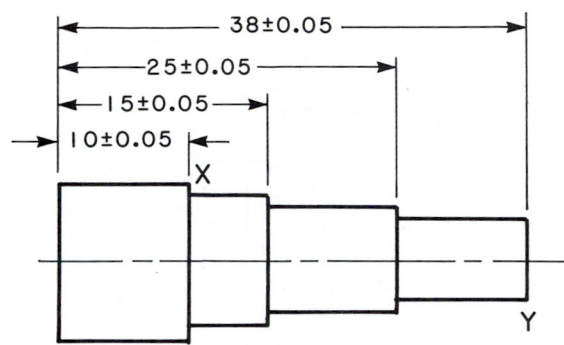

(b) Base line dimensioning—lesser tolerance accumulation between X and Y

13.4.5   Tolerance Accumulation

Figure 13.12 compares the tolerance values resulting from three methods of dimensioning:

1. Chain dimensioning   The maximum variation between two features is equal to the tolerances on the intermediate distances. This results in the greatest tolerance accumulation. In Figure 13.12(a), the tolerance accumulation between surfaces **X** and **Y** is $\pm .15$.

2. Baseline dimensioning   The maximum variation between two features is equal to the sum of the tolerances on the two dimensions from their origin to the features. This results in a reduction of the tolerance accumulation. In Figure 13.12(b), the tolerance accumulation between surfaces **X** and **Y** is $\pm .1$.

3. Direct dimensioning   The maximum variation between two features is controlled by the tolerance on the dimension between the features. This results in the least tolerance. In Figure 13.12(c), the tolerance between surfaces **X** and **Y** is $\pm .05$.

13.4.6   Tolerances for Flat and Conical Tapers

Taper is defined as the ratio of the difference in the diameters of two sections, perpendicular to the axis, of a cone to the distance between these sections. A **conical taper** may be specified by one of the following methods:

1. a basic taper and a basic diameter (Fig. 13.13)

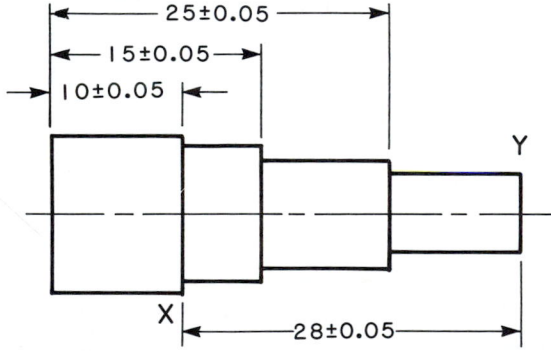

(c) Direct dimensioning—least tolerance between X and Y

FIGURE 13.12   **Tolerance Accumulations**   (a) Chain dimensioning (b) Baseline dimensioning (c) Direct dimensioning

2. a size tolerance combined with a profile of a surface tolerance applied to the taper

3. a toleranced diameter at both ends of a taper and a toleranced length

A **flat taper** may be defined by specifying a toleranced slope and a toleranced height at one end (Fig. 13.14). **Slope** is defined as the inclination of a surface expressed as a ratio of the difference in the heights at each end, above and at right angles to a baseline, to the distance between those heights. Flat and conical tapers are toleranced as shown in Figure 13.15.

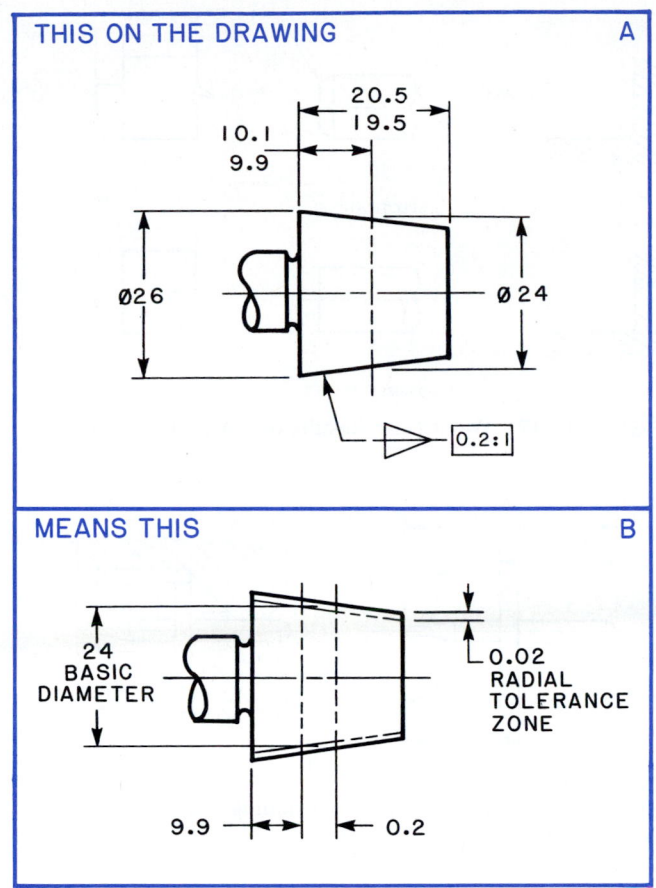

FIGURE 13.13   Specifying a Basic Taper and a Basic Diameter

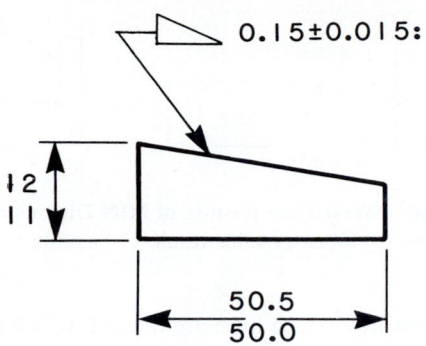

FIGURE 13.14   Slope Designation on a Drawing

13.4.7   Single Limits—Min and Max

The unspecified limit in minimum dimensions (the maximum limit) approaches infinity. Therefore, as a practical matter, overall lengths are not specified as minimum (Fig. 13.16). The unspecified value in maximum dimensions (the minimum limit) approaches zero (Fig. 13.17).

13.4.8   Reference Dimensions

Reference dimensions, as discussed in Chapter 12, are specified by enclosing the dimension in parenthesis, e.g., (.500). No tolerance is given. Reference dimensions are not intended to govern production or inspection; they are informational, not controlling. Therefore, they should be used sparingly on the drawing. Caution should be exercised when using reference dimensions. They are frequently left unchanged when

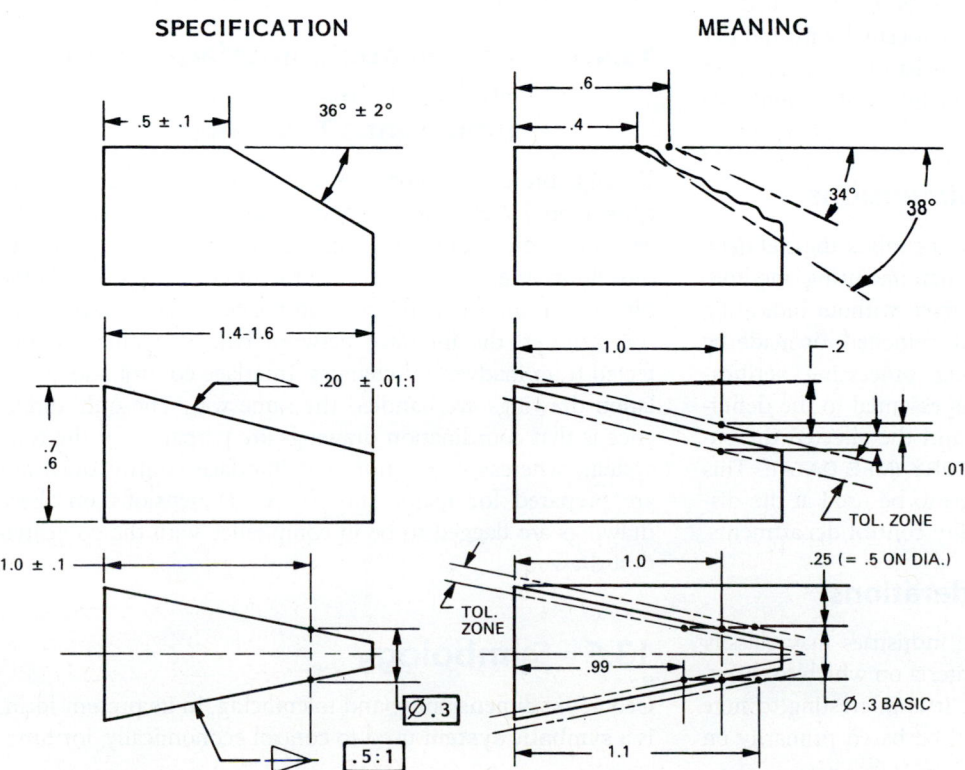

FIGURE 13.15   Flat and Conical Taper Tolerance Zones

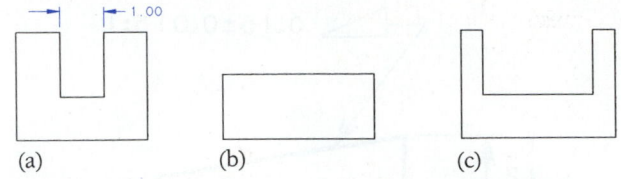

FIGURE 13.16   Worst Case Results of MIN Dimensioning
(a) Specification (b) Worst possible result (c) Possible result

the values they are derived from are revised, which can cause confusion and result in serious errors.

13.4.9   Functional Dimensions

Tolerances can have a cumulative effect (Fig. 13.12). An example of how to control this stituation is shown in Figure 13.18. The most important function of the firing pin is to project far enough to detonate the primer, but not far enough to pierce the primer. Additionally, the point must be fully below the bolt face, in the retracted position, to ensure against premature detonation in the cartridge. This function is controlled by dimension A, a *direct dimension* from the point face to the interface with the bolt in the full forward position. Dimension B is established the same way. Dimensions that affect function should be dimensioned directly to avoid tolerance buildup. Conversely, dimension C1 was replaced by (C) during a producibility team review. This dimension must be long enough to ensure that the hammer will drive the pin to its full forward position, but the length is not critical since the pin has plenty of overtravel. Dimension (C), for ease of manufacture, was taken to the end of the spherical surface that is contacted by the hammer. The tapered section need not be particularly accurate, but it must be located. This is accomplished by dimension D. *Producibility teams* are associated with the design review function and generally consist of members from the design, manufacturing, gaging, quality control, and systems engineering departments.

13.4.10   Nonmandatory Dimensions

If practical, the finished part, sometimes called the *end item,* is defined without specifying the manufacturing method. Thus, only the diameter of a hole is given without indicating whether it should be drilled, reamed, punched, or made by any other operation. If manufacturing, processing, verification, or environmental information is essential to the definition, it is specified on the drawing and the affected dimensions are identified as "**NONMANDATORY (MFG DATA)**." This allows improved or superior methods to be used at the discretion of the manufacturing or quality control departments.

13.4.11   Inspection Considerations

In the inspection instructions, some industries may classify characteristics to better determine criteria on which to reject, use as is, rework, or scrap the part. It is interesting to note that the frequency of inspection may be based primarily on

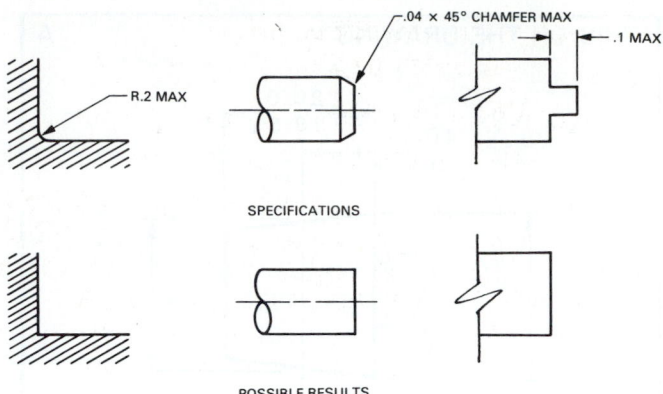

SPECIFICATIONS

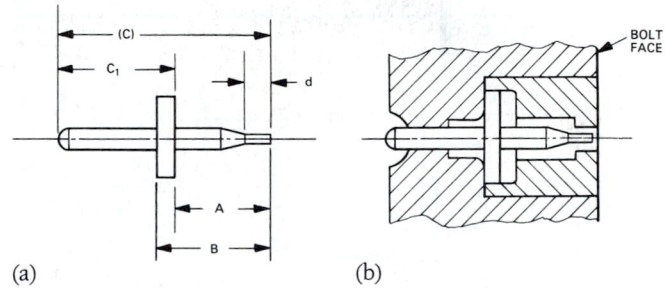

POSSIBLE RESULTS

FIGURE 13.17   Worst Case Results of MAX. Dimensioning

FIGURE 13.18   Functional Dimensioning   (a) Firing pin
(b) Firing pin assembly

purely functional requirements, difficulty of manufacture, or a combination of the two criteria. A producibility team should review each drawing and submit comments to the designer for consideration. This will ensure economical processing of the item and application of the company's collective wisdom.

13.4.12   Coordination, Interface Control, and Correlation Dimensions/Tolerances

On large projects or programs, dimensions and tolerances are agreed on by all parties. A coordination drawing secures agreement on a functional, mating, shipping, equipment removal, or other interface among the interested parties. These dimensions are then "flagged" on the hardware drawings. In this manner, the interface between two companies is protected from inadvertent changes. Interface control and correlation drawings are handled the same way. The only difference is that coordination drawings are prepared for the total system, whereas correlation and interface control drawings are prepared for major subsystems. Dimensions on these drawings are flagged to be in compliance with the coordination drawings.

13.5   Symbology

Geometric dimensioning and tolerancing, in its present form, is a **symbolic system** used to control economically, for func-

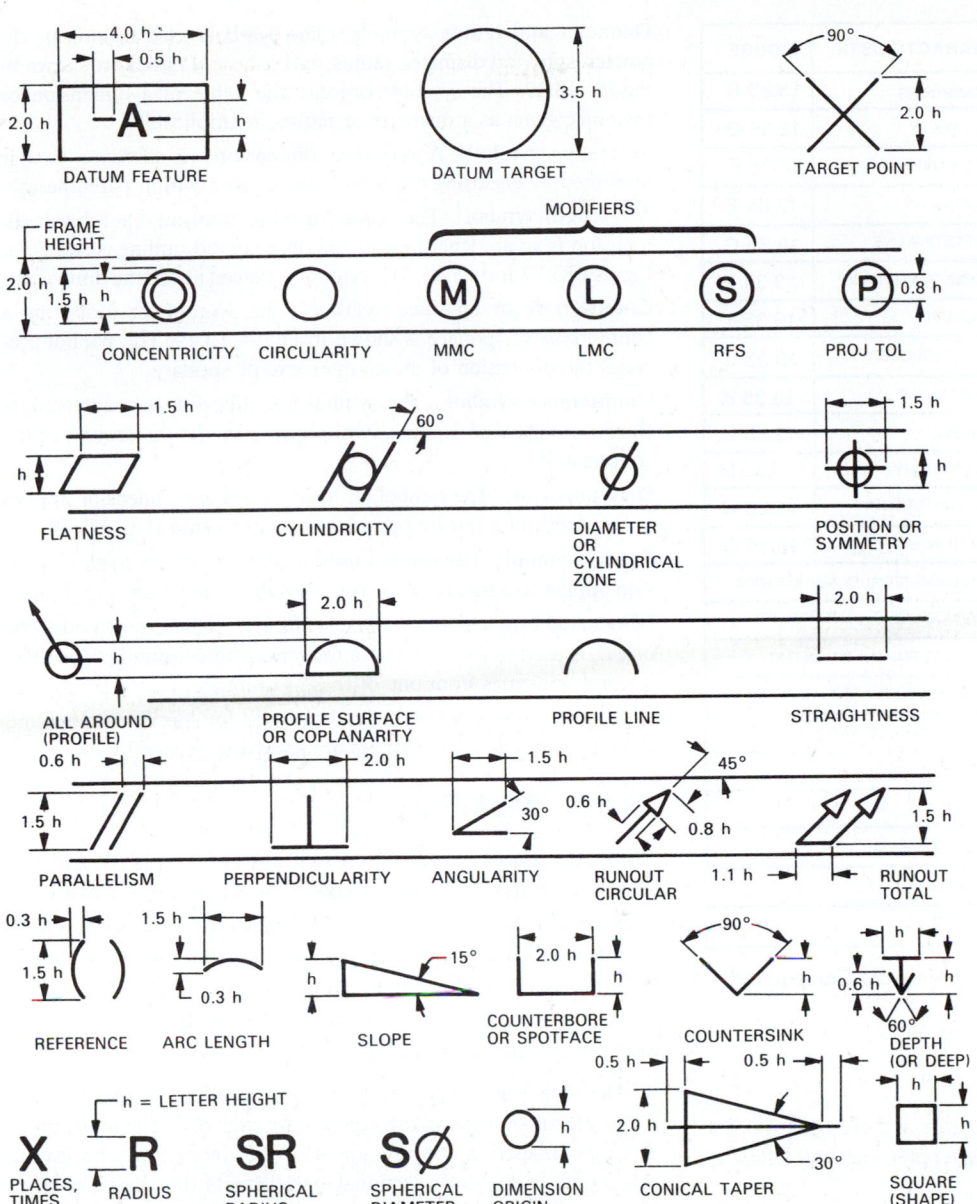

FIGURE 13.19   Geometric Tolerancing Symbols

tion and interchangeability, the size, form, profile, orientation, position, and runout of features or parts and to establish datums and other necessary tolerancing concepts and practices. This section establishes the symbols for specifying geometric characteristics and other dimensional requirements on engineering drawings. Symbols should be of sufficient clarity to meet the legibility and reproducibility requirements of ANSI Y14.2M.

Symbols are preferred to notes because they use less space, transcend language barriers, and are less subject to interpretation. Symbology is used in a unique way in geometric tolerancing because most individual symbols not only represent an entire standardized engineering concept, but are combined in a **feature control frame** in various combinations that form complete engineering, production, and inspection/quality specifications. The form and proportion of geometric toler-

ancing symbols are shown in Figure 13.19. Note that there are only thirteen types of actual geometric tolerances. The geometric characteristic symbols and the modifying symbols are further categorized in Figure 13.20.

Situations may arise where the desired geometric requirement cannot be completely conveyed by symbology. In such cases, a note may be used to describe the requirement, either separately or supplementing a geometric tolerance.

13.5.1   Geometric Characteristic Symbols

The symbols denoting geometric characteristics are described below:

Basic dimension symbols   A basic dimension is identified by enclosing the dimension in a rectangle. The symbols used to identify a basic dimension are shown in Figures 13.19 and 13.20.

FEATURE	TOLERANCE TYPE	SYMBOL	CHARACTERISTIC	FIGURE
INDIVIDUAL (SINGLE)	FORM (SHAPE)	—	STRAIGHTNESS	13.35 B
		▱	FLATNESS	13.35 D
		○	CIRCULARITY	13.35 E
		⌭	CYLINDRICITY	13.35 F
INDIVIDUAL OR RELATED	PROFILE (CONTOUR)	⌒	PROFILE OF A LINE	13.35 G
		⌓	PROFILE OF A SURFACE	13.35 H
RELATED	ORIENTATION (ATTITUDE)	∠	ANGULARITY	13.35 I
		⊥	PERPENDICULARITY	13.35 J
		∥	PARALLELISM	13.35 K
	LOCATION	⊕	POSITION	13.35 L
		◎	CONCENTRICITY	13.35 M
	RUNOUT	↗	CIRCULAR RUNOUT	13.35 N
		↗↗	TOTAL RUNOUT	13.35 O
MODIFYING SYMBOLS		Ⓜ	MAXIMUM MATERIAL CONDITION-MMC	
		Ⓢ	REGARDLESS OF FEATURE SIZE-RFS	
		Ⓛ	LEAST MATERIAL CONDITION-LMC	
ADDITIONAL SYMBOLS		Ⓟ	PROJECTED TOLERANCE ZONE	
		∅	DIAMETER (FACE OF DWG.)	
		S∅	SPHERICAL DIAMETER	
		R	RADIUS	
		SR	SPHERICAL RADIUS	
		( )	REFERENCE	
		—	ARC LENGTH	

FIGURE 13.20   Geometric Tolerancing Symbols Categorized

Datum feature symbol   The datum feature symbol consists of a frame containing the datum identifying letter preceded and followed by a dash.

Letters of the alphabet   Letters of the alphabet (except I, O, and Q) are used as *datum identifying letters*. Each datum feature requiring identification is assigned a different letter. When datum features requiring identification on a drawing are so numerous as to exhaust the single alpha series, the double alpha series is used—AA through AZ, BA through BZ, etc.

Datum target symbol   The datum target symbol is a circle divided horizontally into two halves. The lower half contains a letter identifying the associated datum, followed by the target number, assigned sequentially starting with 1, for each datum. If the datum target is an area, the area size may be entered in the upper half of the symbol. Otherwise, the upper half is left blank. A radial line attached to the symbol is directed to a target point (indicated by an "X"), target line, or target area, as applicable.

Material condition symbol   The symbols used to indicate "at maximum material condition," "regardless of feature size," and "at least material condition" are shown in Figures 13.19 and 13.20. The use of these symbols in local and general notes is prohibited.

Projected tolerance zone symbol   The symbol used to indicate a projected tolerance zone is shown in Figures 13.19 and 13.20. The use of this symbol in local and general notes is prohibited.

Diameter and radius symbols   The symbols used to indicate diameter, spherical diameter, radius, and spherical radius are shown in Figure 13.19. The symbols precede the value of a dimension or tolerance given as a diameter or radius, as applicable.

Reference symbol   A reference dimension or reference data is identified by enclosing the dimension or data within parentheses.

Arc length symbol   The symbol used to indicate that a linear dimension is an arc length measured on a curved outline is shown in Figures 13.19 and 13.20. The symbol is placed above the dimension.

Counterbore or spotface symbol   The symbol for indicating a counterbore or spotface is shown in Figure 13.19. The symbol precedes the dimension of the counterbore or spotface.

Countersink symbol   The symbol for indicating a countersink is shown in Figure 13.19. The symbol precedes the dimensions of the countersink.

Depth symbol   The symbol for indicating that a dimension applies to the depth of a feature precedes that dimension (Fig. 13.19).

Square symbol   The symbol used to indicate that a single dimension applies to a square shape precedes that dimension (Fig. 13.19).

Dimension origin symbol   The symbol, a small circle placed at the origin, is used to indicate that a toleranced dimension between two features originates from one of these features.

Taper and slope symbols   Symbols used for specifying taper and slope for conical and flat tapers are shown in Figure 13.19.

13.5.2   Modifiers

Modifiers stipulate whether a tolerance is to apply regardless of size or only at a specific size. Concentricity, for example, controls the axis of the entire feature to the axis of the entire datum and, because an axis has no size, this tolerance cannot be modified. The modifiers are shown in Figure 13.21. The following rules for modifiers are based on the size of features and the geometry involved:

1. Modifiers may be used only for features and/or datums that have a size tolerance; single-plane surfaces are excluded. The MMC modifier may be used in conjunction with the straightness of a feature axis based on the cross-sectional size, flatness (by special note on features of size), datums of size used with profile tolerances, and all datums and features of size for orientation and position tolerances.
2. RFS and LMC are limited to use in conjunction with position tolerances. The RFS symbol is used exclusively in the United States. In other countries, unless otherwise specified, all tolerances automatically apply RFS.
3. Position, except in the case of a single-plane surface, requires a modifier for all features and datums (Fig. 13.22).
4. Circularity, cylindricity, runout, concentricity, straightness of element lines, and profile of a feature may not use the MMC modifier.

MODIFYING SYMBOLS		
symbol	abbreviation	meaning
Ⓜ	MMC	Maximum Material Condition
Ⓢ	RFS	Regardless of Feature Size
Ⓛ	LMC	Least Material Condition

FIGURE 13.21   Modifying Symbols

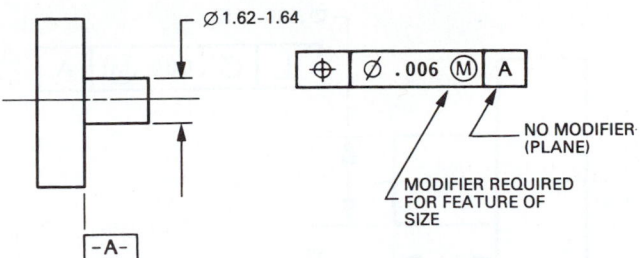

FIGURE 13.22   Single-Plane Surface—No Modifier

The exception is for datums of size used in conjunction with profile. A special note is required

PERFECT FORM AT MMC NOT REQUIRED

to use the MMC modifier in conjunction with flatness.

13.6   Feature Control Frame

Geometric tolerances are placed in a **feature control frame**, which contains a geometric characteristic symbol, the tolerance, modifiers, and datums, as applicable (Fig. 13.23). Other notations, such as **zone shape symbols**, may also be included, but only when the diameter symbol ( ) applies. The feature control frame consists of at least the first two compartments shown in Figure 13.24, but may contain three or more compartments. The *first compartment* contains the geometric characteristic symbol (one of the thirteen from Fig. 13.19). The *second compartment* may contain a zone shape symbol such as the diameter symbol indicating the diameter of a cylindrical zone; the tolerance, in inches or millimeters; and a modifier, if applicable. The *third compartment* generally contains datums. This third compartment may have **separators** to order the datums.

Other forms of feature control frames are used, the most common of which are shown in Figure 13.25. If *composite feature control frames* are used, the tolerance in the upper block controls the location of the pattern of features as a group. The tolerance in the lower block controls the location of the features, within the pattern, to each other. In terms of tooling, the upper block specifies the locating tolerance for the drill jig relative to the part. The lower block specifies the accuracy of the drill bushing locations to each other. If composite tolerancing is used for straightness, the upper block restricts the overall tolerance for a feature, over its entire length. The lower block specifies the allowable tolerance variation per unit-length, e.g., .001/1.00 or one-thousandth of an inch per inch. Feature control frames are not repeated or referenced on a technical drawing. **Datum identification symbols,** -A- , may be repeated where it is essential to ensure correct meaning.

13.6.1   Maximum Material Condition (MMC)

In the **maximum material condition (MMC)**, a feature or datum feature is at the tolerance limit, resulting in the part

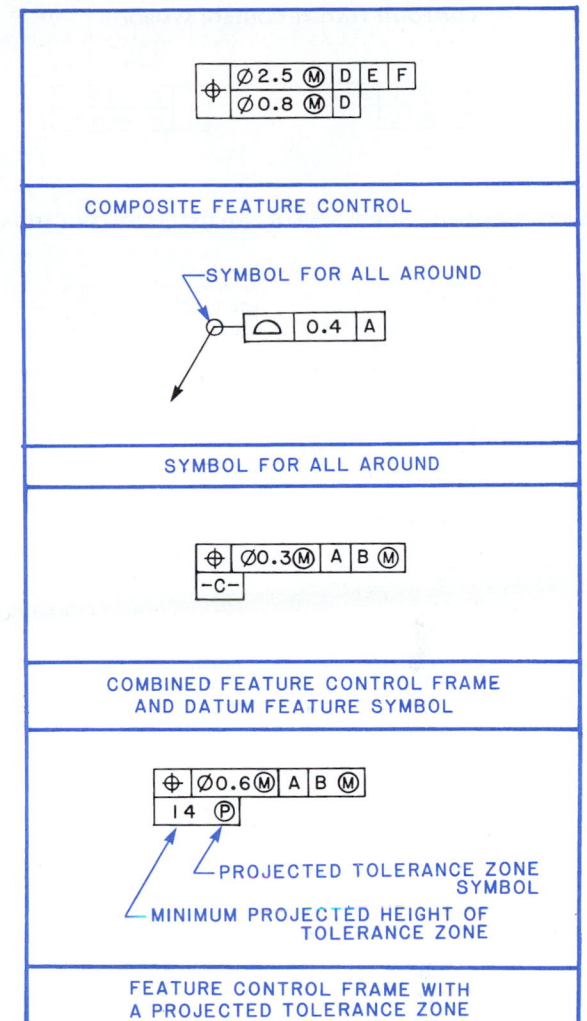

FIGURE 13.23   Feature Control Frames

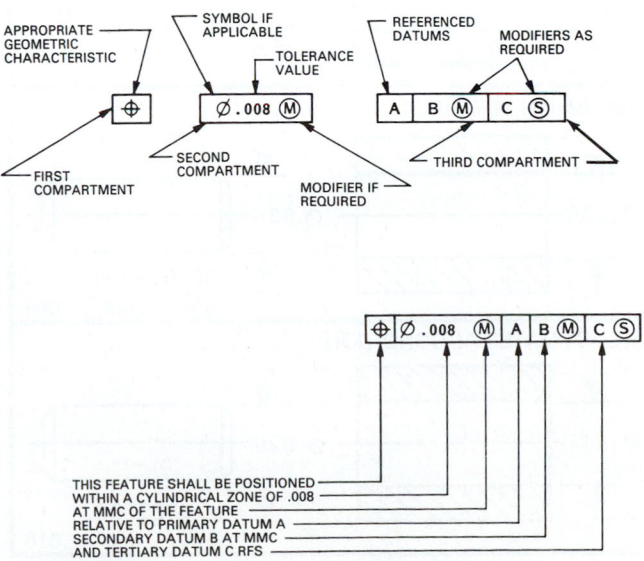

FIGURE 13.24   Feature Control Frame—Typical Configurations

COMPOSITE FEATURE CONTROL SYMBOL

COMBINED FEATURE CONTROL SYMBOL AND DATUM IDENTIFICATION

FEATURE CONTROL SYMBOL COMBINED WITH PROJECTED TOLERANCE ZONE CALLOUT

FEATURE CONTROL SYMBOL WITH MODIFIER WORD

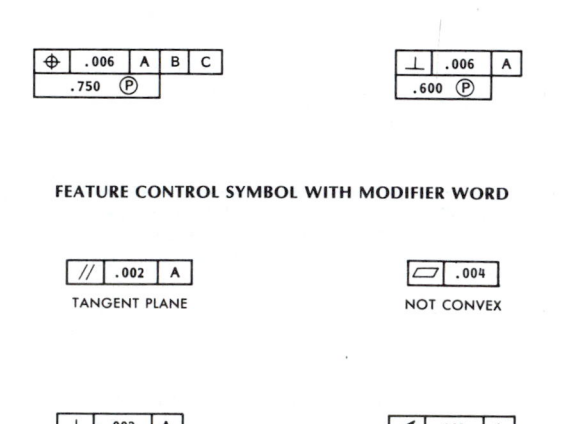

TANGENT PLANE

NOT CONVEX

ELEMENT LINES

OVER AREA SHOWN

FIGURE 13.25 Feature Control Frames

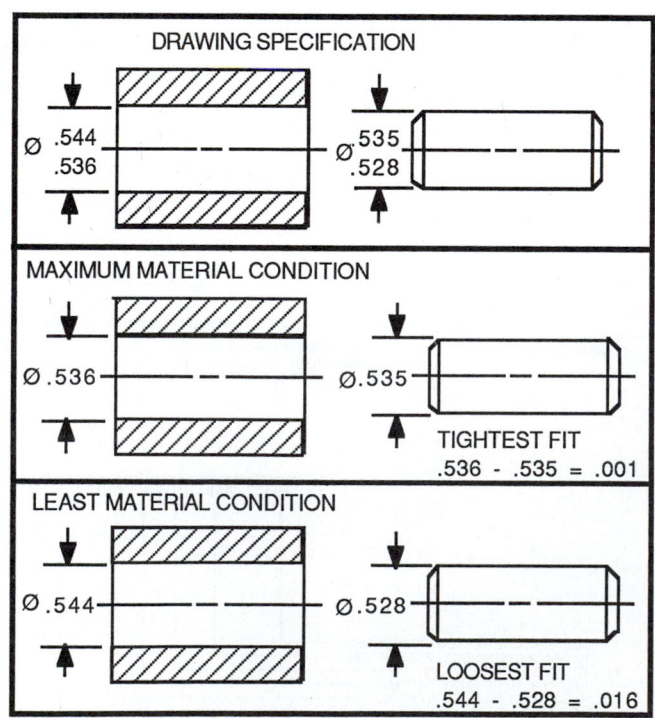

FIGURE 13.26 MMC and LMC Limits

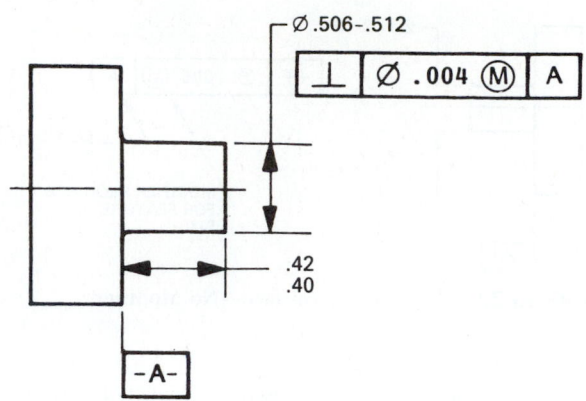

FIGURE 13.27 Orientation of a Feature at MMC

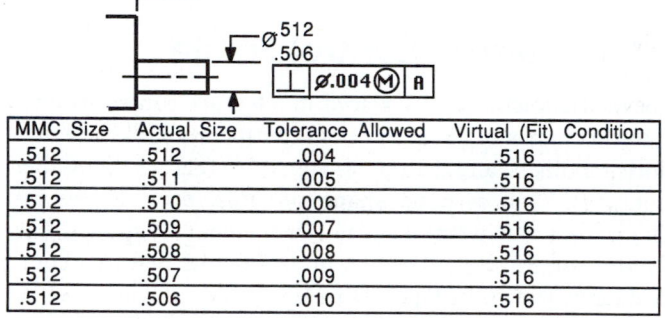

MMC Size	Actual Size	Tolerance Allowed	Virtual (Fit) Condition
.512	.512	.004	.516
.512	.511	.005	.516
.512	.510	.006	.516
.512	.509	.007	.516
.512	.508	.008	.516
.512	.507	.009	.516
.512	.506	.010	.516

FIGURE 13.28 Bonus Tolerance Addition to Geometric Tolerance at MMC

containing the most material (weighing the most). For an external feature, such as a pin, MMC is the maximum limit. For an internal feature, such as a hole, MMC is the minimum limit (Fig. 13.26).

If the MMC modifying symbol is used in a feature control frame (Fig. 13.27), the specified tolerance applies only at MMC. In Figure 13.27, the perpendicularity tolerance is .004 when the feature is at MMC (.512). As the feature deviates from MMC, additional perpendicularity tolerance equal to the deviation is allowed. This is called the *bonus tolerance* (Fig. 13.28). In other words, as the male diameter decreases in size, the increase in perpendicularity results in the same fit to the mating part. The modifying symbol for MMC, specified in the feature control frame for the feature, datum, or both, works the same way for all geometric tolerances. A *double bonus* is allowed where MMC is applied to both the feature and the datum; both must be features of size.

When the datum deviates from MMC, an additional bonus tolerance, equal to the datum's deviation from MMC, is allowed. This is in addition to the increase in geometric tolerance due to the feature's deviation from MMC. The additional tolerance from a datum does not necessarily apply to individual features.

MMC controls the *envelope of a feature* and is generally used where fit is the main concern. In this case, we assume

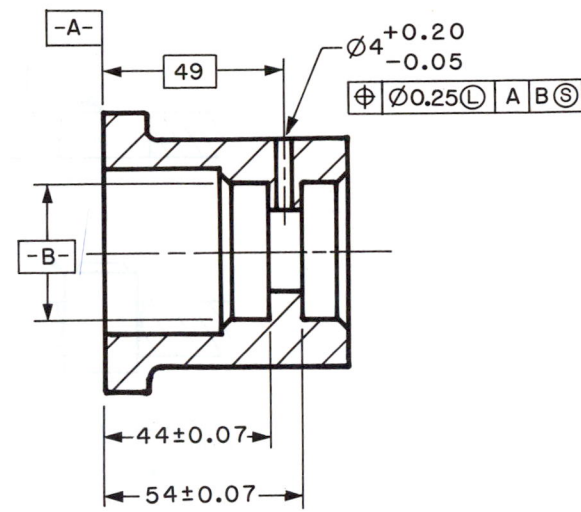

MIN WIDTH IS
MAX FEATURE
LENGTH
.42

RELIEF OR CORNER R

Ø.516 (MINUS GAGE TOL. AND
WEAR ALLOWANCES)

FLAT FOR SEATING
WITH DATUM PLANE -A-

FIGURE 13.29 Go Ring Gage—Verification of Perpendicularity at MMC

FIGURE 13.30 LMC Applied to a Single Feature

the mating part would have a hole fitting over the shaft and look like the gage from an interface standpoint (Fig. 13.29). Several general observations can be made from the above example:

1. If the feature or datum is not at MMC, applying MMC to features and datums of size results in larger tolerances.
2. If MMC is specified, manufacturing may target a size to realize a corresponding geometric tolerance.
3. If a geometric tolerance was violated within the size range, the feature can be resized away from MMC.
4. A gage made to the virtual condition of the feature may be used to verify the geometric tolerance in production.

13.6.2 Least Material Condition (LMC)

In the **least material condition (LMC)**, a feature or datum feature is at the tolerance limit, resulting in the part containing the least material (weighing the least). Figure 13.30 shows LMC applied to a single feature. For an external feature, such as a pin, LMC is the minimum limit. For an internal feature, such as a hole, LMC is the maximum limit (Fig. 13.26). The modifying symbol for LMC, specified in the feature control frame for the feature, datum, or both, works the same way for all geometric tolerances. A double bonus is allowed where LMC is applied to both the feature and the datum; both must be features of size. In this case, as the datum deviates from LMC, an additional bonus tolerance, equal to the datum's deviation from LMC, is allowed. This is in addition to the increase in geometric tolerance due to the feature's deviation from LMC. Table 13.1 shows the result of using Figure 13.26 as though LMC were specified in the feature control frame in lieu of MMC. LMC is generally used where minimum bearing areas, minimum wall thickness, or alignment of parts is the main concern, not fit.

13.6.3 Regardless of Feature Size (RFS)

The **RFS** modifier is used only for features and datums of size and only in conjunction with the **positional tolerance.** The Europeans have no modifier for RFS. In the ISO standard,

RFS applies to every geometric tolerance unless MMC or LMC is specified. In American standards, RFS automatically applies to all geometric tolerances except position. MMC, RFS, or LMC must be specified for all features and datums of size for positional tolerance.

If the RFS modifier is placed after the feature tolerance in the second compartment, the tolerance must be met unconditionally. If MMC is specified after a datum, the datum must be "picked up" by the tooling and or gaging by an interface that matches the MMC size of the datum (Fig. 13.31).

13.6.4 Virtual Condition

The **virtual condition** (Fig. 13.32) is the condition resulting from the worst case effect of the size and geometric tolerance applied to the feature. The free assembly of components is dependent on the combined effect of the actual sizes of the part features and the attendant errors of form, orientation, location, or runout. If, for example, the axis is out of straight, the size of a shaft is virtually increased or a hole virtually decreased. In addition to using the virtual condition of mating features to assess interchangeability, it is used to determine gage element sizes. *Functional gages* are built to the virtual

TABLE 13.1 Bonus Tolerance Addition to Geometric Tolerance at LMC

LMC Size	Actual Size	Tolerance Allowed	Minimum Bearing Area
.506	.506	.004	.502
.506	.507	.005	.502
.506	.508	.006	.502
.506	.509	.007	.502
.506	.510	.008	.502
.506	.511	.009	.502
.506	.512	.010	.502

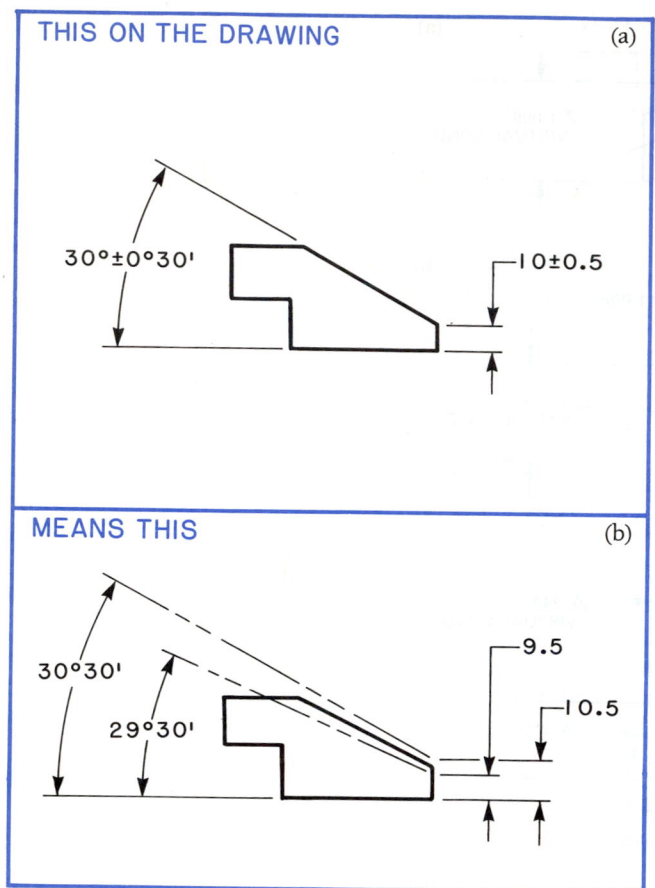

FIGURE 13.33   Tolerancing an Angular Surface Using Linear and Angular Dimensions

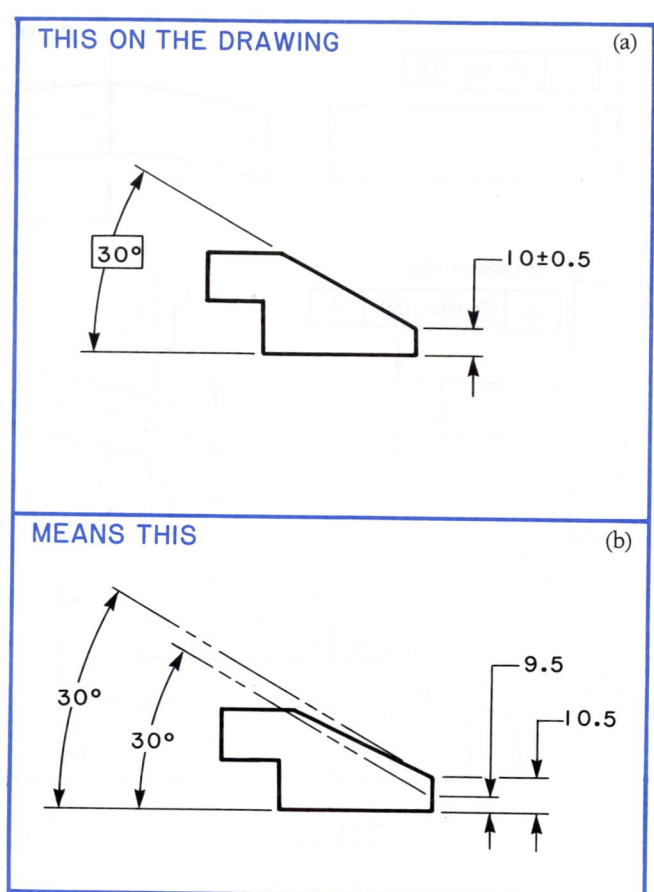

FIGURE 13.34   Tolerancing an Angular Surface with Basic Dimensions

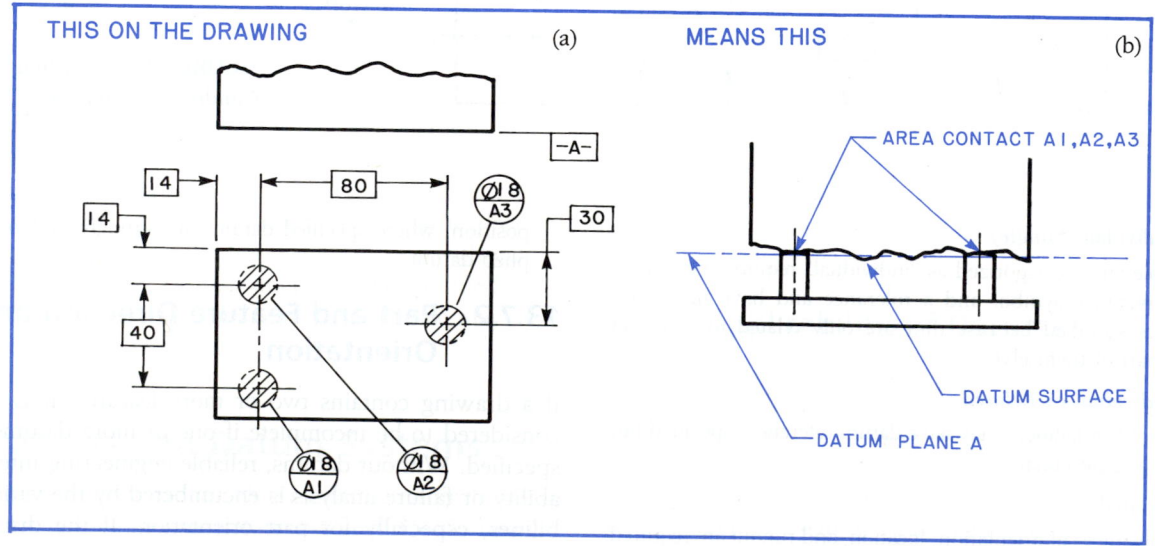

FIGURE 13.35   Primary Datum Plane

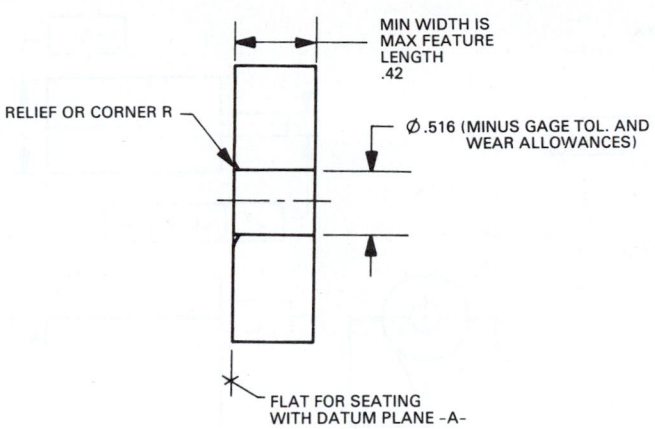

FIGURE 13.29 Go Ring Gage—Verification of Perpendicularity at MMC

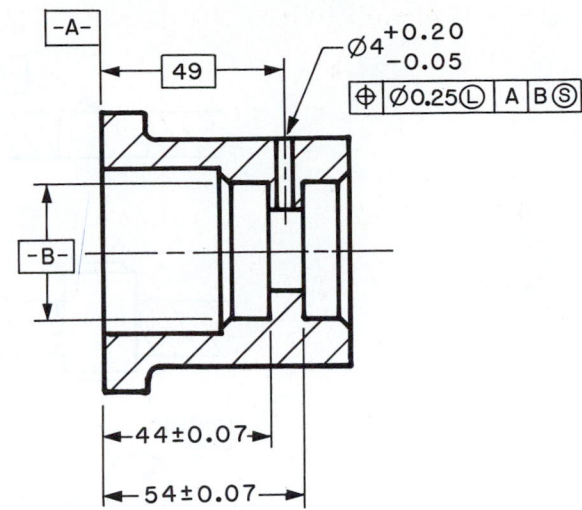

FIGURE 13.30 LMC Applied to a Single Feature

the mating part would have a hole fitting over the shaft and look like the gage from an interface standpoint (Fig. 13.29). Several general observations can be made from the above example:

1. If the feature or datum is not at MMC, applying MMC to features and datums of size results in larger tolerances.
2. If MMC is specified, manufacturing may target a size to realize a corresponding geometric tolerance.
3. If a geometric tolerance was violated within the size range, the feature can be resized away from MMC.
4. A gage made to the virtual condition of the feature may be used to verify the geometric tolerance in production.

13.6.2   Least Material Condition (LMC)

In the **least material condition (LMC)**, a feature or datum feature is at the tolerance limit, resulting in the part containing the least material (weighing the least). Figure 13.30 shows LMC applied to a single feature. For an external feature, such as a pin, LMC is the minimum limit. For an internal feature, such as a hole, LMC is the maximum limit (Fig. 13.26). The modifying symbol for LMC, specified in the feature control frame for the feature, datum, or both, works the same way for all geometric tolerances. A double bonus is allowed where LMC is applied to both the feature and the datum; both must be features of size. In this case, as the datum deviates from LMC, an additional bonus tolerance, equal to the datum's deviation from LMC, is allowed. This is in addition to the increase in geometric tolerance due to the feature's deviation from LMC. Table 13.1 shows the result of using Figure 13.26 as though LMC were specified in the feature control frame in lieu of MMC. LMC is generally used where minimum bearing areas, minimum wall thickness, or alignment of parts is the main concern, not fit.

13.6.3   Regardless of Feature Size (RFS)

The **RFS** modifier is used only for features and datums of size and only in conjunction with the **positional tolerance**. The Europeans have no modifier for RFS. In the ISO standard,

RFS applies to every geometric tolerance unless MMC or LMC is specified. In American standards, RFS automatically applies to all geometric tolerances except position. MMC, RFS, or LMC must be specified for all features and datums of size for positional tolerance.

If the RFS modifier is placed after the feature tolerance in the second compartment, the tolerance must be met unconditionally. If MMC is specified after a datum, the datum must be "picked up" by the tooling and or gaging by an interface that matches the MMC size of the datum (Fig. 13.31).

13.6.4   Virtual Condition

The **virtual condition** (Fig. 13.32) is the condition resulting from the worst case effect of the size and geometric tolerance applied to the feature. The free assembly of components is dependent on the combined effect of the actual sizes of the part features and the attendant errors of form, orientation, location, or runout. If, for example, the axis is out of straight, the size of a shaft is virtually increased or a hole virtually decreased. In addition to using the virtual condition of mating features to assess interchangeability, it is used to determine gage element sizes. *Functional gages* are built to the virtual

TABLE 13.1 Bonus Tolerance Addition to Geometric Tolerance at LMC

LMC Size	Actual Size	Tolerance Allowed	Minimum Bearing Area
.506	.506	.004	.502
.506	.507	.005	.502
.506	.508	.006	.502
.506	.509	.007	.502
.506	.510	.008	.502
.506	.511	.009	.502
.506	.512	.010	.502

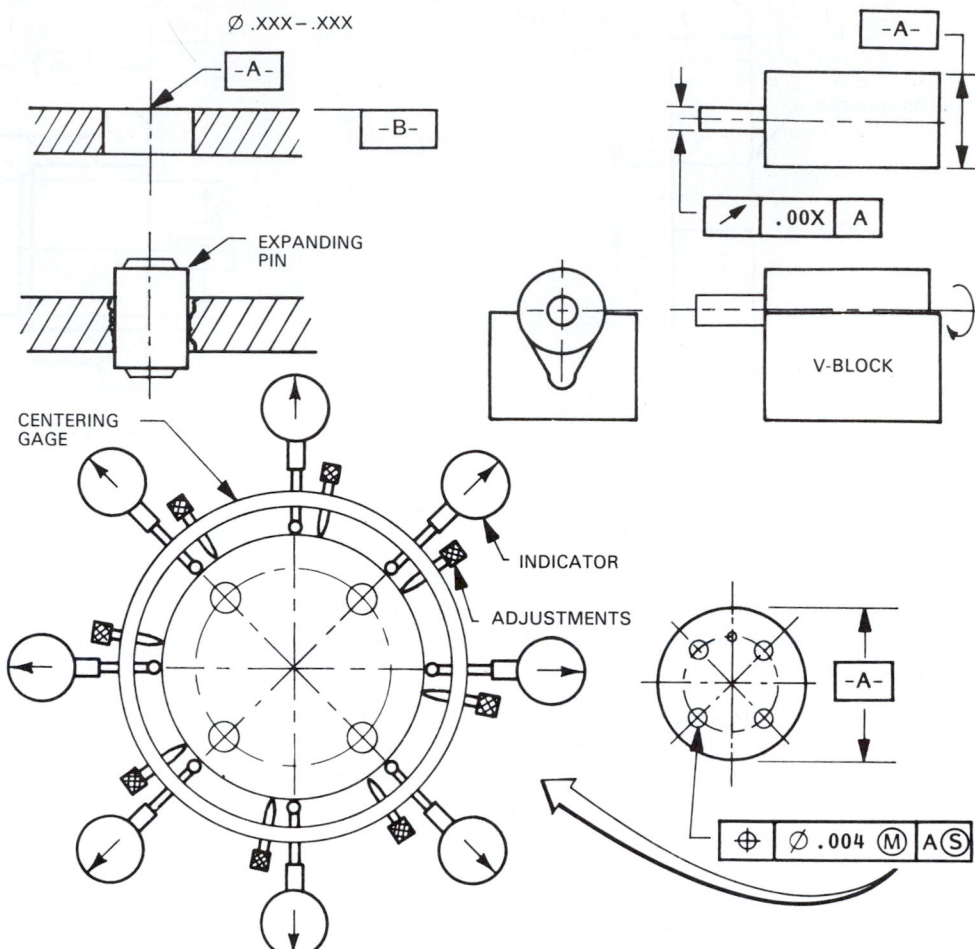

FIGURE 13.31 RFS Datum—Tooling and Gaging Interfaces

condition of the part. The formulas for determining the virtual condition are as follows:

External Feature
Virtual Condition = MMC size + Geometric Tolerance

Internal Feature
Virtual Condition = MMC size − Geometric Tolerance

13.6.5 Angular Surfaces

If an **angular surface** is defined by the combination of a linear dimension and an angle, the surface must lie within a tolerance zone represented by two nonparallel planes (Fig. 13.33). The tolerance zone will be wider as the distance from the apex of the angle increases. If a tolerance zone with parallel boundaries is desired, a basic angle may be specified, as in Figure 13.34. Additionally, an angularity tolerance may be specified within these boundaries.

13.7 Datums and Datum Systems

As has been stated, *datums are theoretically exact geometric references derived from the datum feature.* Figure 13.35 shows the primary datum plane established on a surface by three

area contact positions. Datums are not assumed to exist on the part itself, but are simulated by the more precisely made manufacturing or inspection equipment or a computerized mathematical model. A datum plane, for example, could be *simulated* from the datum feature by a surface plate (Fig. 13.36).

Datums are points, lines, and planes. Datums provide repeatable part and feature orientation for manufacturing and inspection consistent with the expected mating characteristics or orientation at assembly. Datums should be established from "hard" features on the part, such as one or two specific diameter(s) on a shaft (Fig. 13.37). The theoretical centerline, for example, would be ambiguous and not be identified as a datum (Fig. 13.38).

13.7.1 Applicability of Datums

A **datum** is a theoretically exact point, axis, or plane derived from the true geometric counterpart of a specified datum feature. A datum is the origin from which the location or geometric characteristics of features of a part are established. A **datum target** is a specified point, line, or area on a part used to establish a datum. Tolerances, as they relate to datums, are described according to the feature they locate:

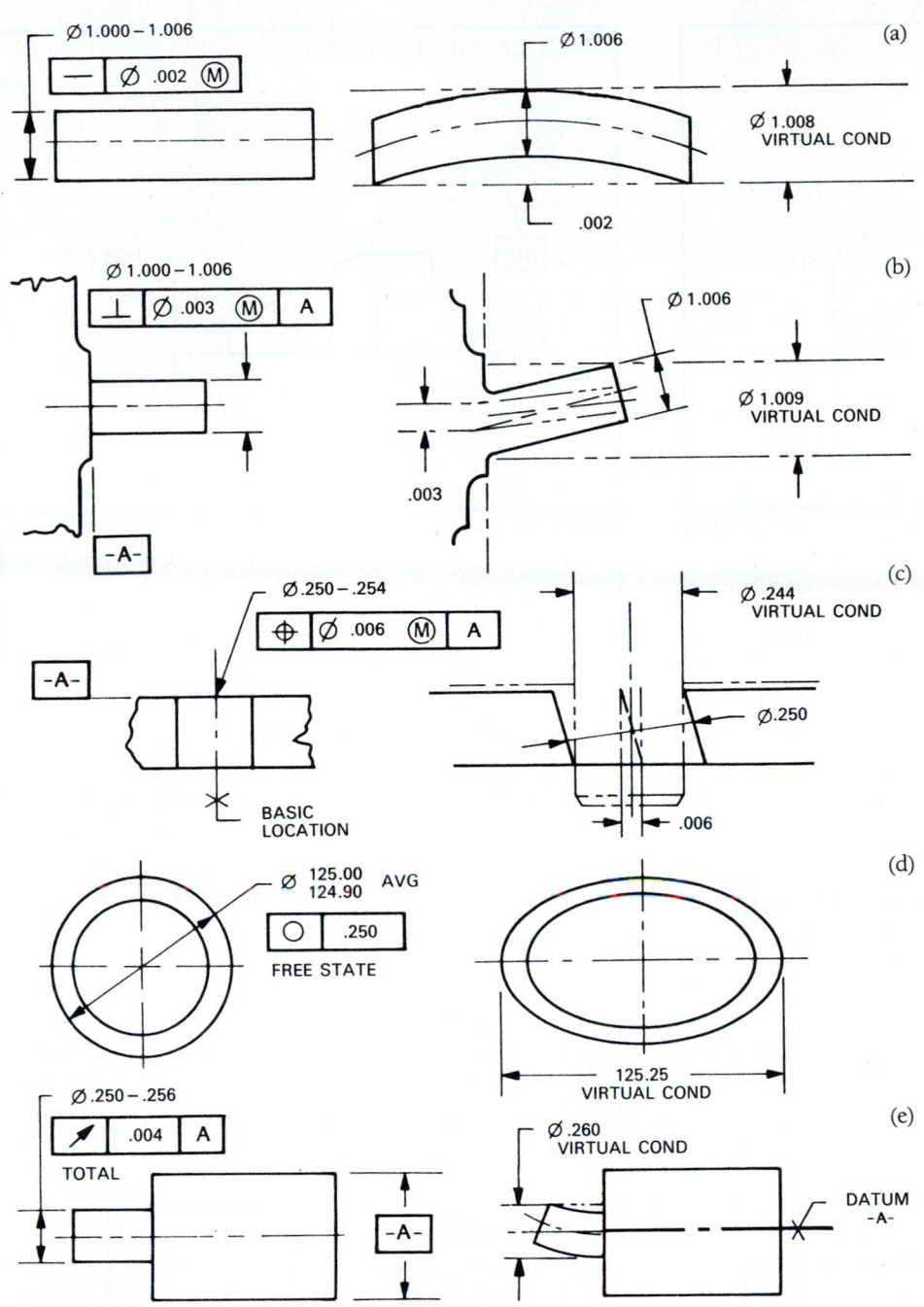

FIGURE 13.32 Virtual
Condition Examples

Feature: *Individual (Single)*

Those tolerances categorized as "individual" require only a geometric tolerance symbol and a tolerance and have no datum references specified because they are only related to a perfect counterpart of themselves.

Feature: *Individual or Related*

These profile tolerances may have datum references specified but it is not a requirement.

Feature: *Related*

These tolerances of orientation, location, and runout are required to have a datum reference(s) specified in every case, except for

position, where specified datums are strongly preferred to implied datums.

13.7.2   Part and Feature Direction and Orientation

If a drawing contains two or more features, it is generally considered to be incomplete if one or more datums are not specified. Without datums, reliable engineering interchangeability or failure analysis is encumbered by the varied possibilities, especially for part orientation. If the discipline of datums were not employed, setup criteria for manufacturing

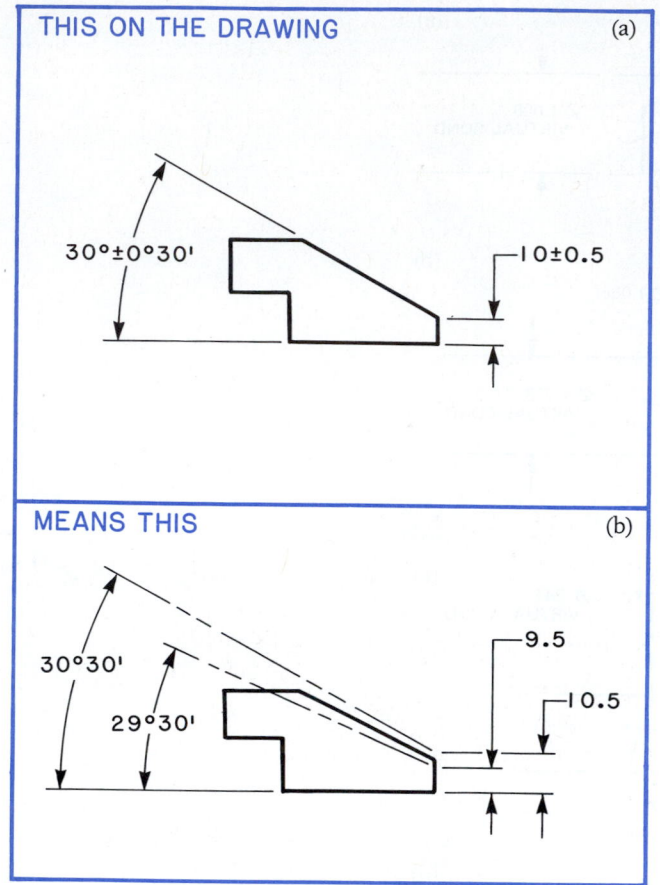

FIGURE 13.33 Tolerancing an Angular Surface Using Linear and Angular Dimensions

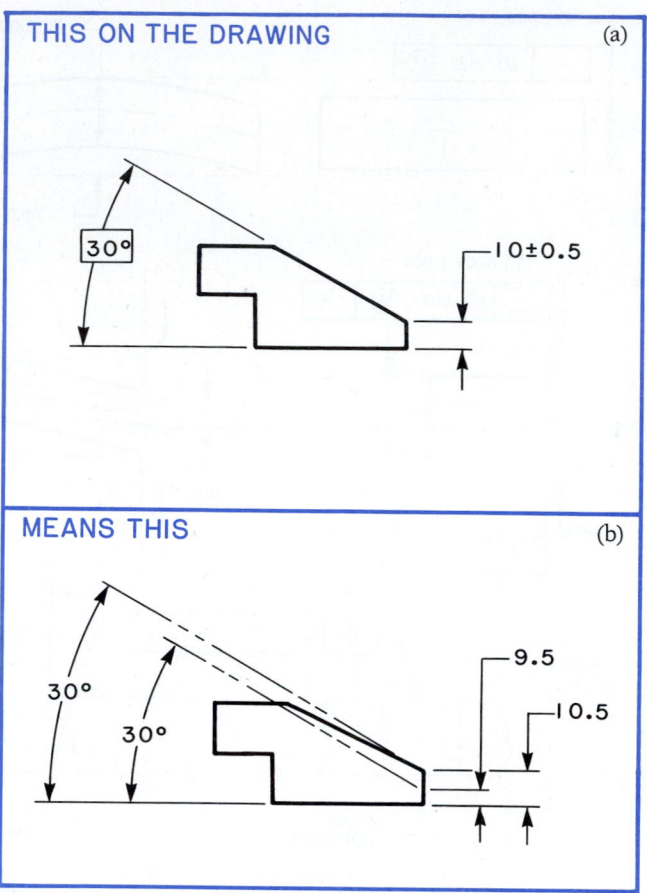

FIGURE 13.34 Tolerancing an Angular Surface with Basic Dimensions

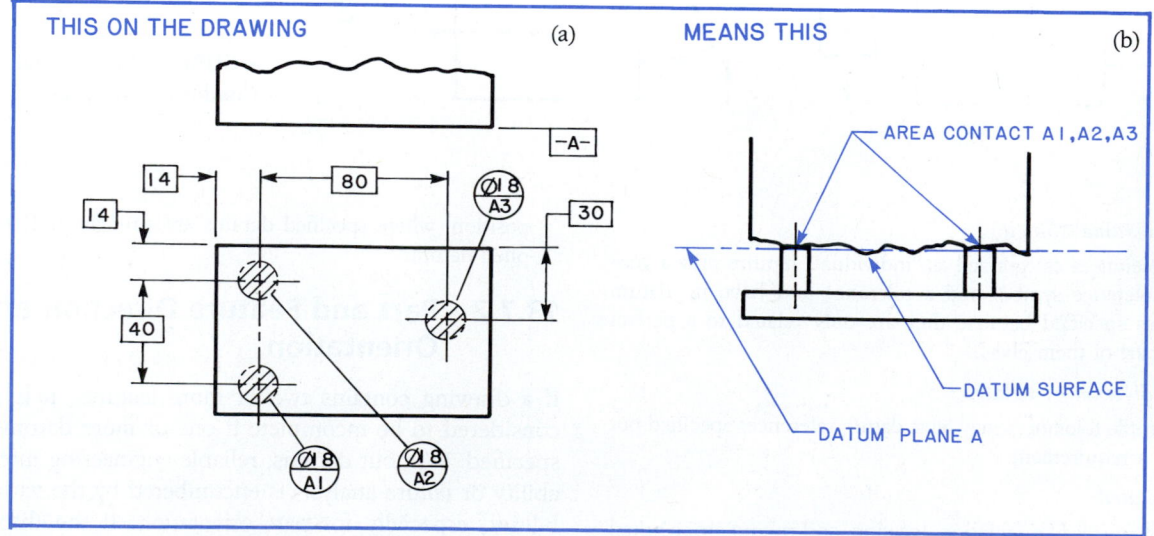

FIGURE 13.35 Primary Datum Plane

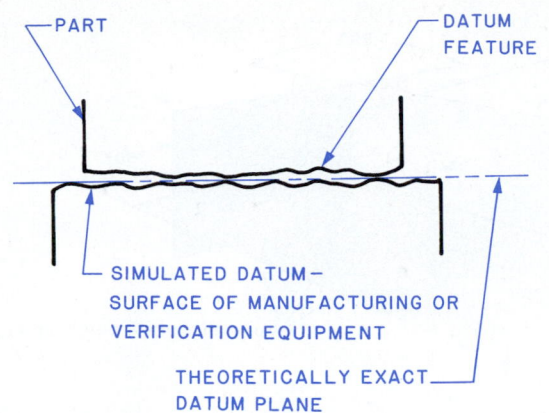

FIGURE 13.36   **Theoretical and Simulated Datum and Datum Plane**

and inspection, to a large degree, would be arbitrary. Without datums, the design could be compromised and the resulting end items may not function as intended. Practical dimensions, intended for manufacture, must have at least three attributes: **magnitude** or **length**, **allowable variation**, and **direction**. The last must be satisfied by datums.

13.7.3   Datum Reference Frame

In our 3D world, locations and measurements are taken relative to three mutually perpendicular planes (Fig. 13.39). This is called a **datum reference frame** and, although this frame is theoretical, it is simulated by manufacturing and

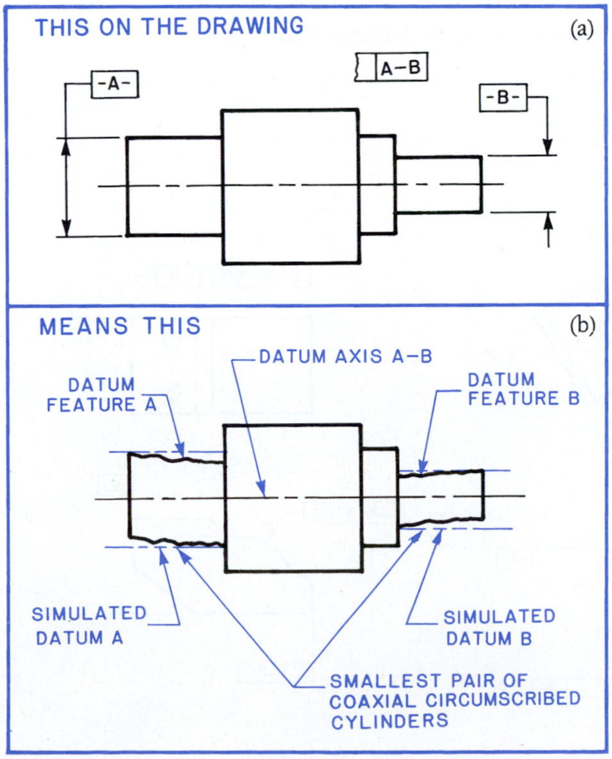

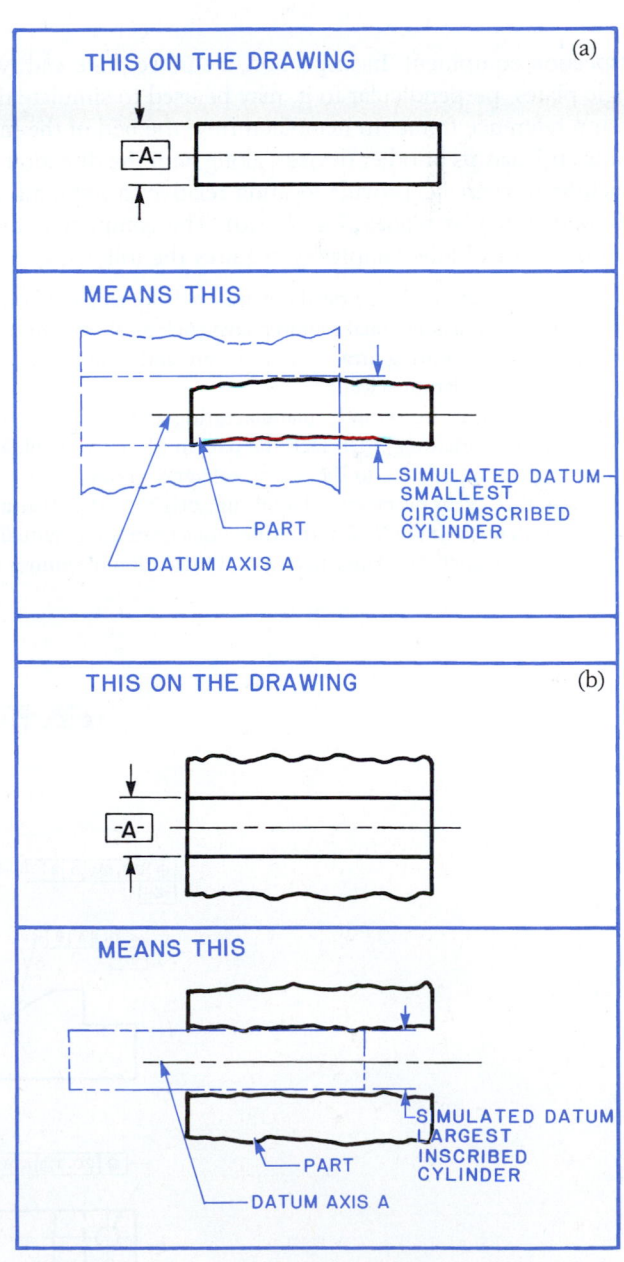

FIGURE 13.38   **Primary Datums**   (a) Primary external datum diameter—RFS (b) Primary internal datum diameter—RFS

FIGURE 13.37   **Coaxial Datum Features**

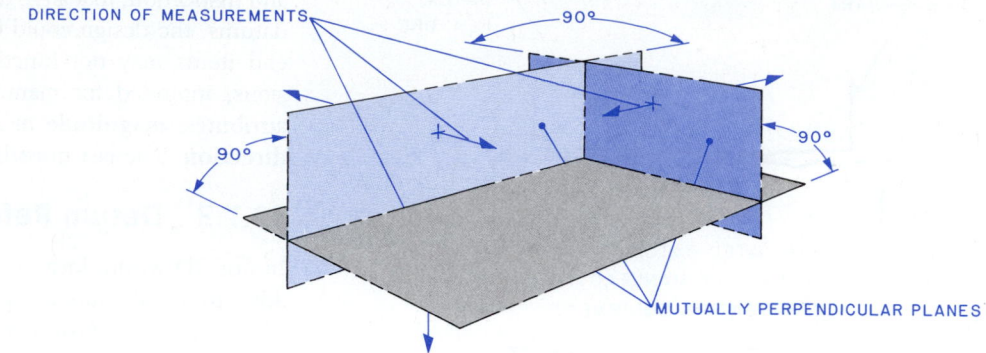

FIGURE 13.39 Datum Reference Frame

inspection equipment. In inspection, a surface plate and two angle plates, perpendicular to it, may be used to simulate the datum reference frame. In manufacturing, the bed of the machine and clamps or other devices, along with the direction of machine movement, provide location relative to three mutually perpendicular planes (Fig. 13.40). The complete definition of a part of any complexity requires the following:

1. Specify the datums based on the mating relationships of corresponding parts and functional requirements such as alignment, relative motion, and bearing area. Manufacturing and quality are also considerations in datum selection.
2. Use the datums, for setup in manufacturing and inspection, on positioning and orienting, then lock the part in place for manufacture or inspection, relative to the datum reference frame.
3. Ensure that every necessary relationship, origin, and measuring direction is defined in the **X**, **Y**, and **Z** directions from three mutually perpendicular planes, or relative to an axis. Orientation of features to

a datum reference frame or axis is generally advisable, even if no functional or mating relationship exists.

13.7.4 Datum Features

Datum features are selected to ensure the orientation of the part and its associated features for interchangeability and to ensure functional relationships. If a functional datum feature is undesirable from a manufacturing or inspection standpoint, such as the major diameter of a gear or thread, a nonfunctional feature with a precise toleranced relationship to the functional feature may be used, provided all design requirements are met. To be practical, datums should be related to corresponding mating features; accessible, functional, and more accurate in form than measurements taken from them; of sufficient size for manufacture and gaging; unambiguous; and should facilitate fixtures and gages.

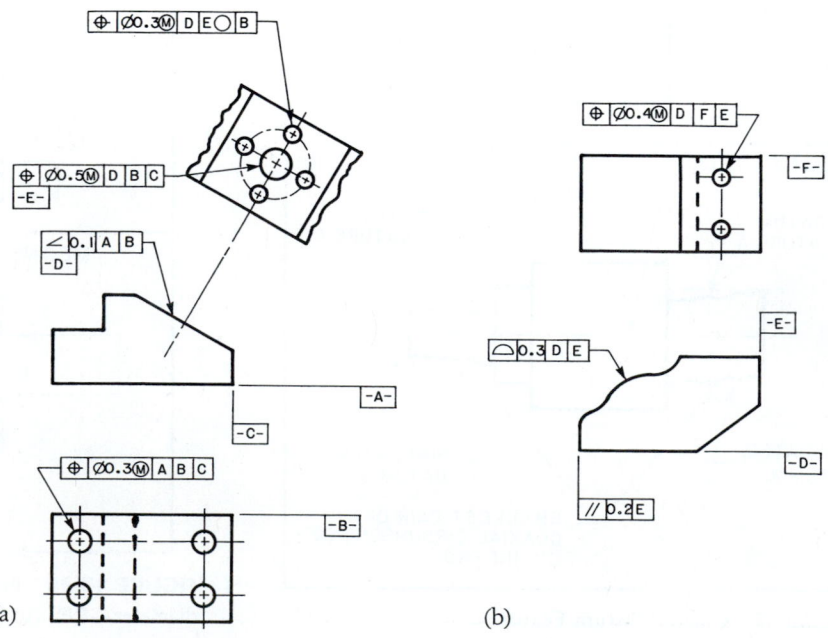

FIGURE 13.40 Multiple Datum Plane Reference Frames

(a)   (b)

Implied datums are not recommended. **Convenience datums**, such as tooling holes for azimuth locating, may be added but, are nonmandatory (MFG. DATA).

13.7.5 Datum Precedence

The sequence of datums specified in the feature control frame determines the order in which the datum features contact the datum reference frame. In datum reference frame sequencing (Fig. 13.41):

1. The part primary datum feature is aligned with the primary datum (a).
2. While in full contact with the primary datum, the part's secondary datum feature is aligned with the secondary datum (b).
3. While in full contact with the primary datum and aligned to the secondary datum, the part's tertiary datum feature is pushed into contact with the tertiary datum (c).

The datums are three precise, mutually perpendicular planes. The **primary datum** is established by full contact with a minimum of three noncollinear points on the part. In Figure 13.42, the primary datum is established by two point contacts and one line contact. The **secondary datum** is perpendicular to the primary datum and is established by contacting a minimum of two points on the part. The **tertiary datum** is perpendicular to the primary and the secondary and, therefore, needs only one point of contact on the part to establish it. The part is locked into position now that it has an exact orientation. The datum features are considered inaccurate, nonperpendicular, part surfaces. In Figure 13.41, notice that the three directions of measurement, **X**, **Y**, and **Z**, are established on the part, as are their origin datums. Precise and repeatable measurements may now be made as the part is oriented and locked in position. If not for this procedure, a rectangular part with six nonperpendicular sides could be positioned many ways. Figure 13.43 shows one possibility. Notice that measurements from the two frames are different! To ensure the intended datum reference frame, datums are specified on the drawing.

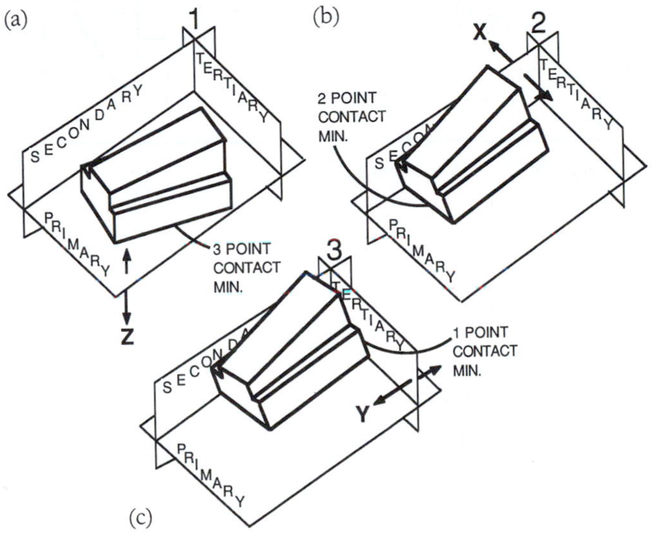

FIGURE 13.41 Datum Reference Frame—Datum Precedence/Sequencing

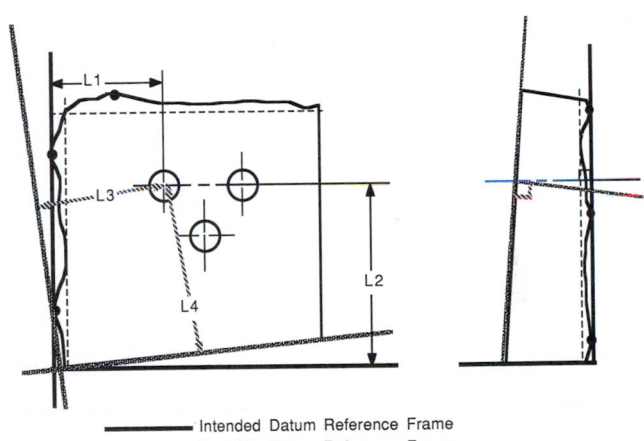

FIGURE 13.43 Intended vs. Potential Datum Reference Frame

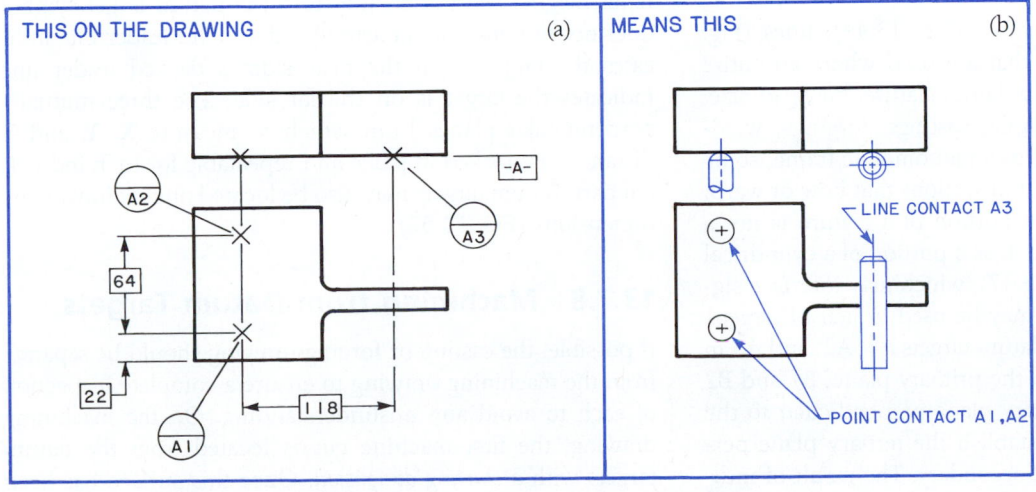

FIGURE 13.42 Primary Datum Plane Established by a Line and Two Point Contacts

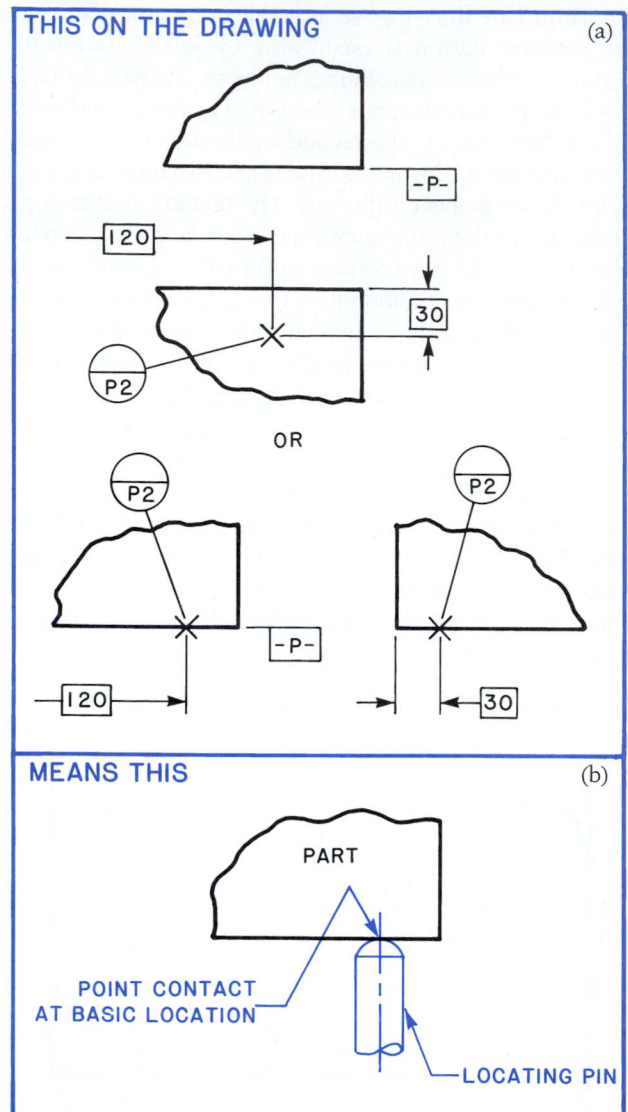

FIGURE 13.44 Datum Target Point

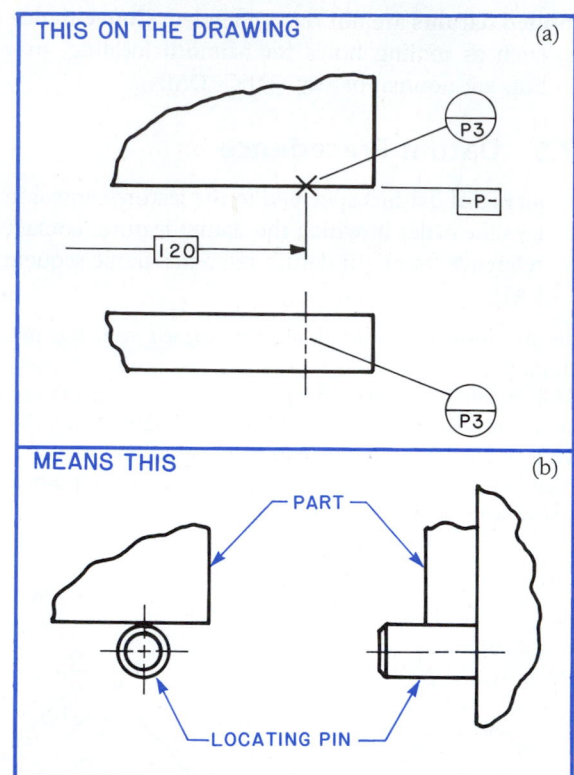

FIGURE 13.45 Datum Target Line

13.7.6 Datum Targets

Datum targets are specific points (Fig. 13.44), lines (Fig. 13.45), or areas (Fig. 13.46) that are used where an entire surface may not be suitable as a datum feature due to its size, inaccuracy, or form, for example, castings, forgings, weldments, large fabrications, such as an automobile frame, some sheet metal and formed parts, thin sections that bow or warp, and molded parts. If a limited portion of a feature is not a point, line, or local flat area, such as a portion of a cylindrical surface, partial datums (Fig. 13.47), which may interface significant parts of an assembly, may be used in lieu of targets.

In Figure 13.48, although datum targets A1, A2, and A3 in a triangle are used to establish the primary plane, B1 and B2 are used to establish a secondary plane perpendicular to the primary; and C1 is used to establish the tertiary plane perpendicular to the primary and secondary. The result of indi-

cating datum target point, line, or areas is shown in Figure 13.49. The datum target identification symbol is shown in Figure 13.50.

13.7.7 Datum Target Depiction

Datum target points are depicted by a dense 90° "cross" at 45° ("**x**") to the centerline (Figs. 13.49 and 13.51), at two times letter height. The leader line from the datum target symbol does not terminate in an arrowhead. A solid leader line indicates the target is on the near side; a dashed leader line indicates the target is on the far side. The three mutually perpendicular planes from which to measure **X**, **Y**, and **Z** distances are locked in place and repeatable for each individual part. Datum targets may also be located on the drawing by dimensions (Fig. 13.52).

13.7.8 Machining from Datum Targets

If possible, the casting or forging drawing should be separate from the machining drawing to ensure a complete inspection of each to avoid any misunderstanding. On the machining drawing, the first machine cut is located from the datum targets with a *starting dimension*. Once this surface has been

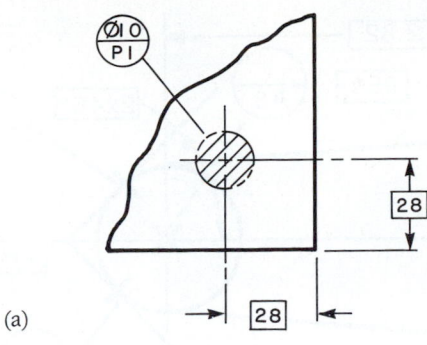

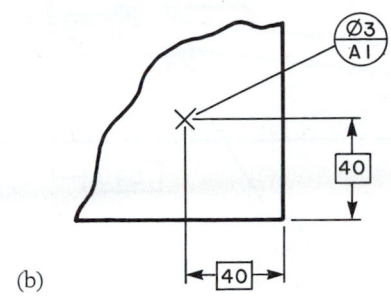

FIGURE 13.46   Datum Target Area

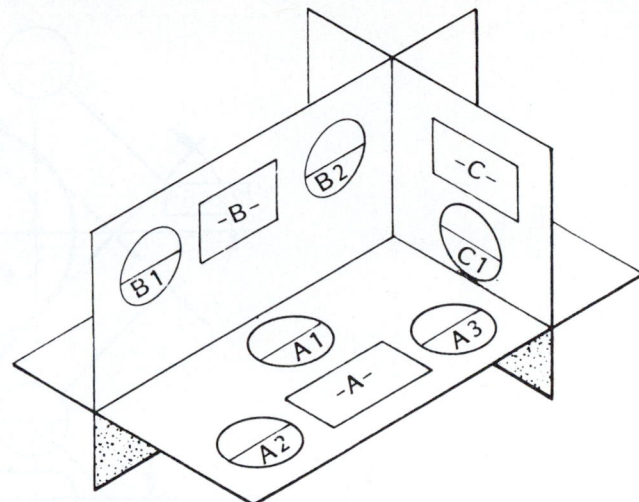

FIGURE 13.48   Datum Targets Used to Establish a Datum Reference Frame

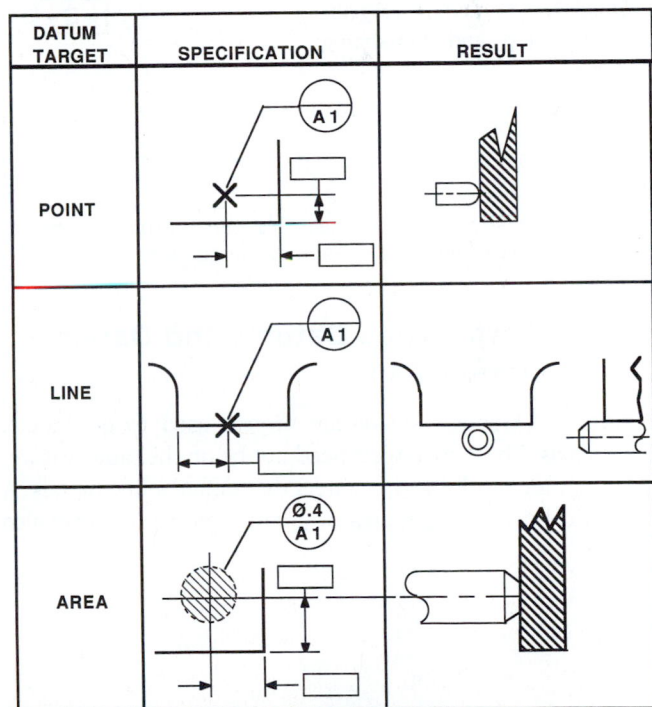

FIGURE 13.49   Datum Target Point, Line, and Area Depiction

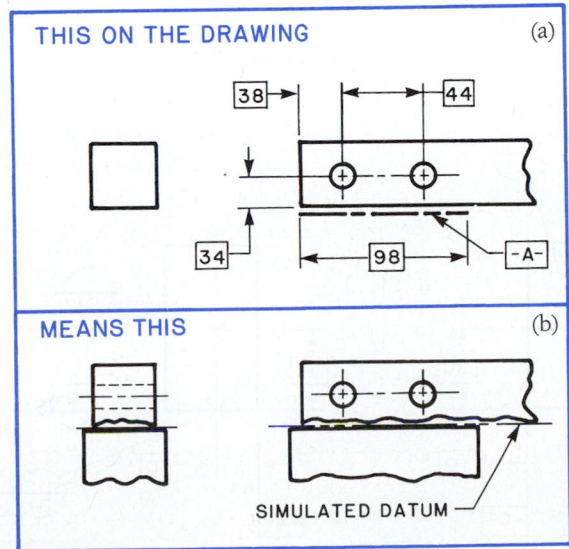

FIGURE 13.47   Partial Datum

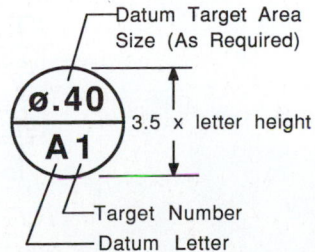

FIGURE 13.50   Datum Target Identification Symbol

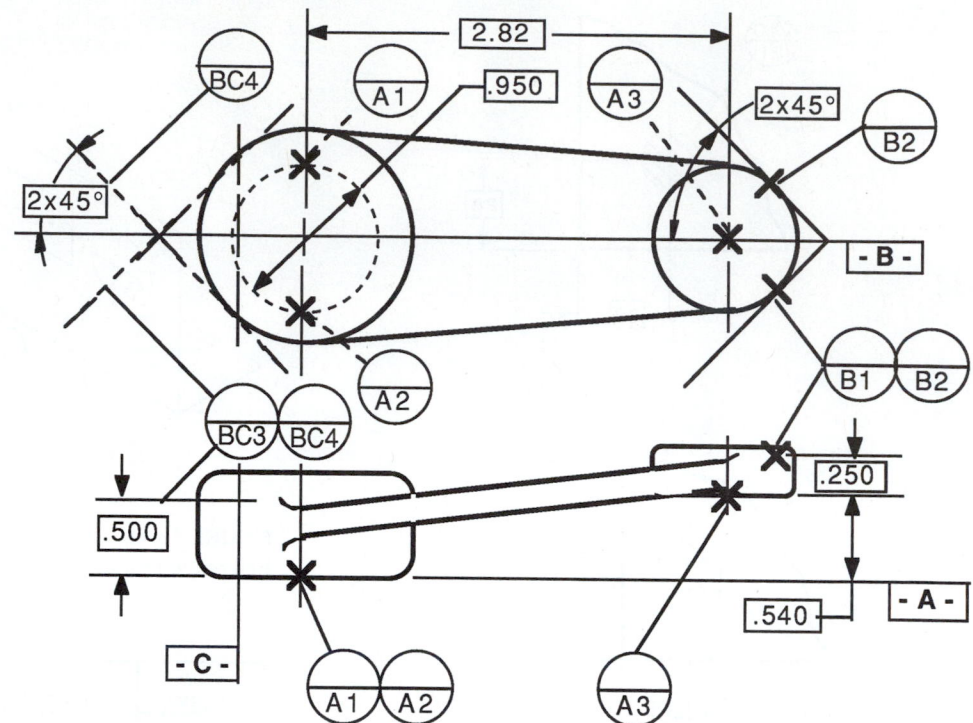

FIGURE 13.51 Datum Targets Showing "Step" and "Equalizing Datums"

produced, it serves as the basis for the datum system for machining the remainder of the machined part.

13.7.9 Partial Area Datums and Datum Target Axis

Figure 13.53 shows six datum targets used to generate a datum axis. These six targets need not be on the same feature, because they result in two centers that define a line or axis. A cylindrical datum target area or a datum target line may also

be used. Figure 13.54 shows a cylindrical datum used for a secondary datum axis.

13.8 Geometric Tolerances of Form, Profile, Orientation, Location, and Runout

Geometric tolerances of form, profile, orientation, location, and runout are presented here, for the most part, in the form

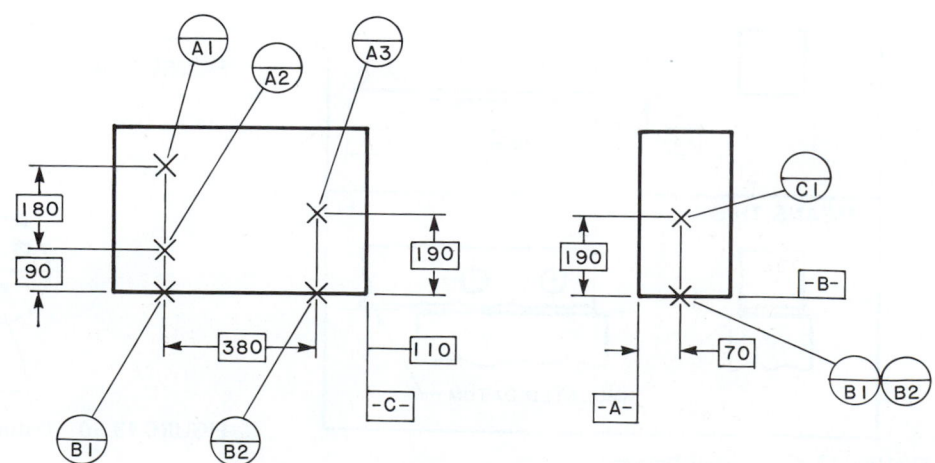

FIGURE 13.52 Dimensioning Datum Targets

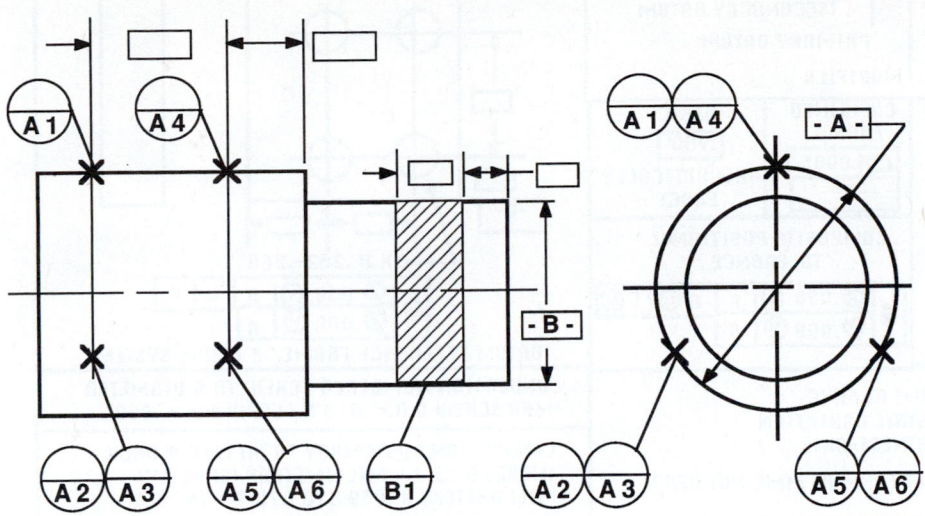

FIGURE 13.53 Datum Target Axis and Areas

of a set of **Summary Fact Data Sheets** (SFDS), illustrated in Figures 13.55(a) through (p). There is an individual SFDS for each geometric tolerance and two generalized ones [Fig. 13.55(a)]. Each SFDS contains the following information:

- geometric characteristic symbol
- control of geometry
- tolerance zone information
- explanation of tolerance zone
- size rule
- datum/modifier
- typical drawing specifications
- interpretations
- inspection diagrams
- additional examples and supplementary notes

13.8.1   Form Tolerances

Form tolerances are applicable to individual features or elements of single features. These tolerances do not use datums because they are related to a perfect counterpart of themselves [Fig. 13.55(b)]. The pure form tolerances are straightness, flatness, circularity, and cylindricity.

13.8.2   Straightness

Only **straightness** on the axis may use the MMC modifier where an element of the surface or an axis is a straight line. For **element control** [Fig. 13.55(b)], if straightness of an element is specified, the leader from the feature control frame

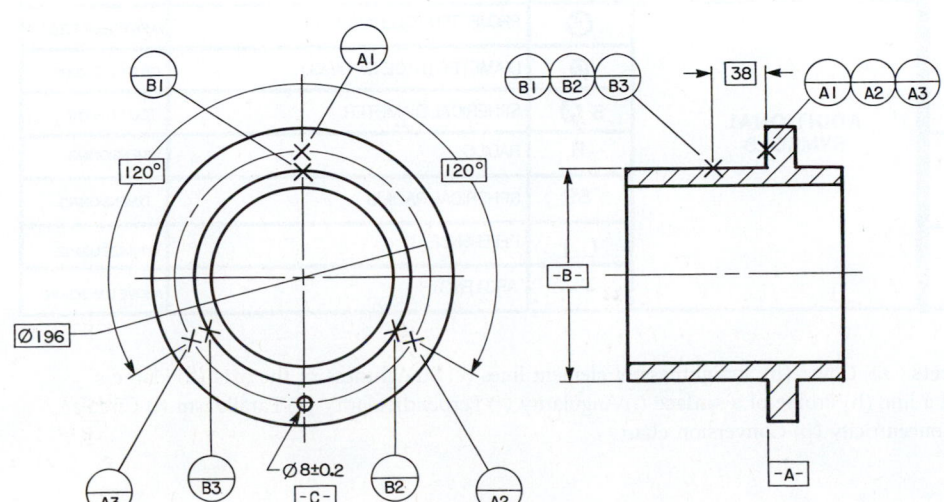

FIGURE 13.54 Secondary Datum Axis

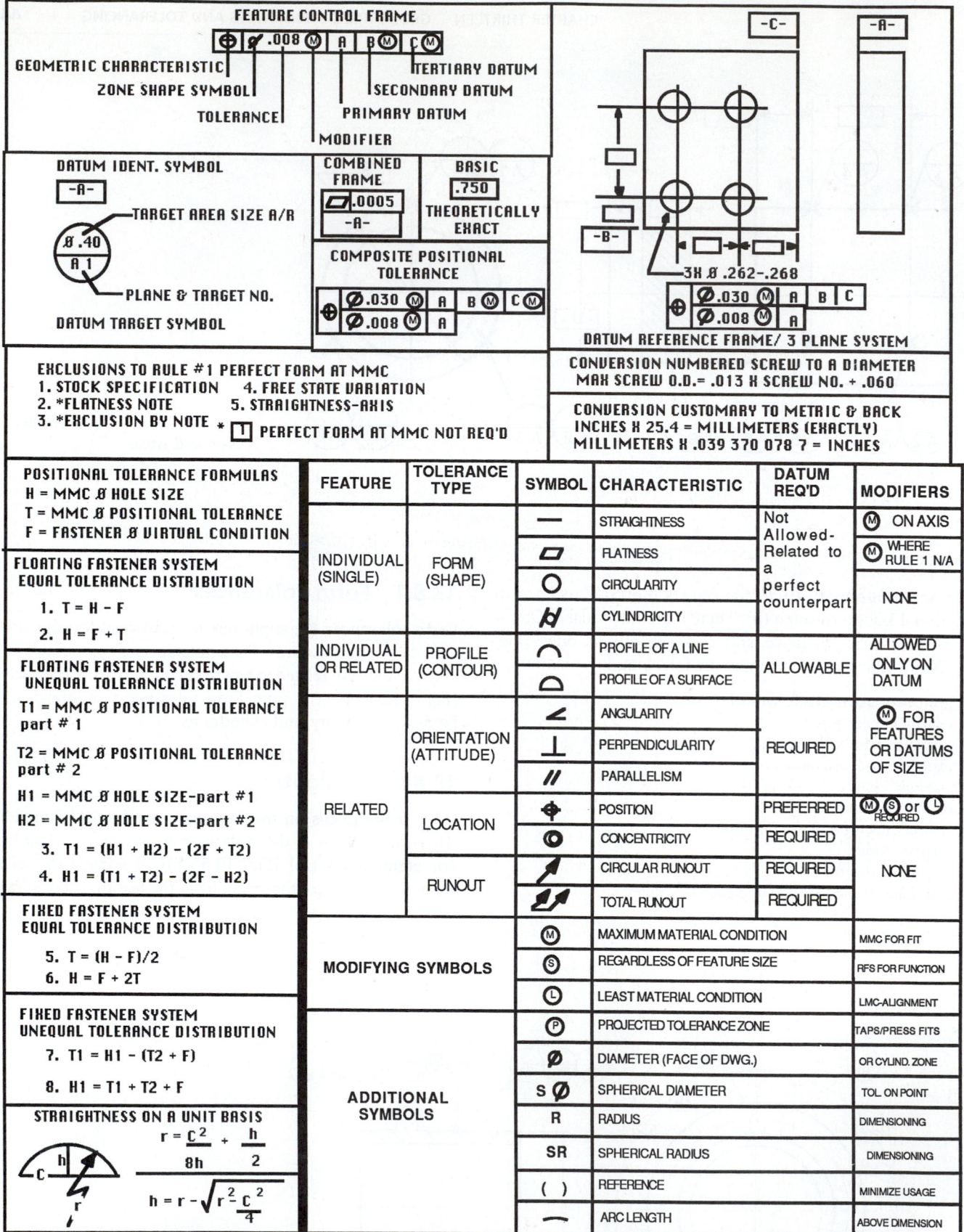

(a)

FIGURE 13.55 Summary Fact Data Sheets (a) Cover (b) Straightness of element lines (c) Straightness of the axis (d) Flatness (e) Circularity (f) Cylindricity (g) Profile of a line (h) Profile of a surface (i) Angularity (j) Perpendicularity (k) Parallelism (l) Circular Runout (m) Total runout (n) Position (o) Concentricity (p) Conversion chart

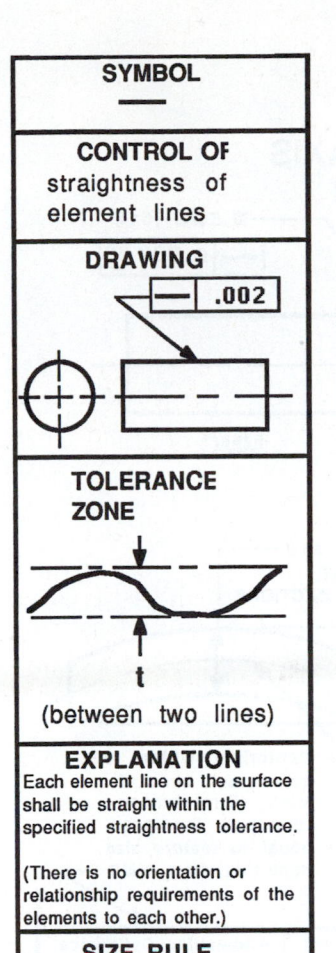

SYMBOL
—

CONTROL OF
straightness of
element lines

DRAWING

.002

TOLERANCE ZONE

t

(between two lines)

EXPLANATION

Each element line on the surface shall be straight within the specified straightness tolerance.

(There is no orientation or relationship requirements of the elements to each other.)

SIZE RULE

Entire feature shall lie within size tolerance envelope/boundary. (Rule 1 applies)

DATUM/MODIFIER

Applies RFS only for elements

Ⓜ *NOTE: may only be applied to straightness of the axis, elements must be RFS.*

A datum may not be specified in conjunction with straightness.

FORM TOLERANCE
STRAIGHTNESS OF ELEMENT LINES
DRAWING SPECIFICATION

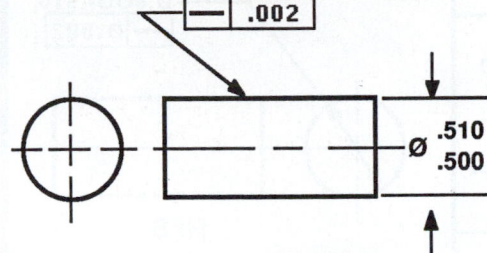

.002

Ø .510
.500

DRAWING MEANING

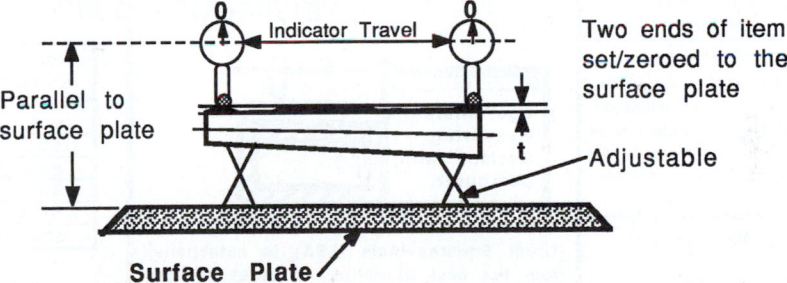

≥ LMC (.500)

> LMC (.500)

All elements on all features straight within t (.002)

≤ MMC (.510)

≤ MMC (.510)

INSPECTION DIAGRAM

0   Indicator Travel   0

Parallel to surface plate

Two ends of item set/zeroed to the surface plate

t

Adjustable

Surface Plate

Inspection Notes:
1. Several elements are to be verified independently
2. Vee Block and Dial Indicator combination is considered inconclusive for rejection as parallelism of the elements contacting the Vee are included.

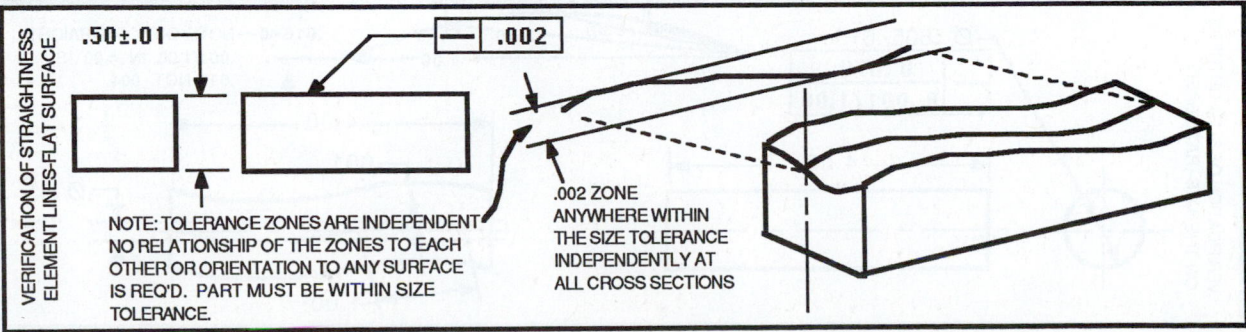

VERIFICATION OF STRAIGHTNESS ELEMENT LINES-FLAT SURFACE

.50±.01

.002

.002 ZONE ANYWHERE WITHIN THE SIZE TOLERANCE INDEPENDENTLY AT ALL CROSS SECTIONS

NOTE: TOLERANCE ZONES ARE INDEPENDENT NO RELATIONSHIP OF THE ZONES TO EACH OTHER OR ORIENTATION TO ANY SURFACE IS REQ'D. PART MUST BE WITHIN SIZE TOLERANCE.

(b)

FIGURE 13.55   Summary Fact Data Sheets—Continued   (b) Straightness of element lines

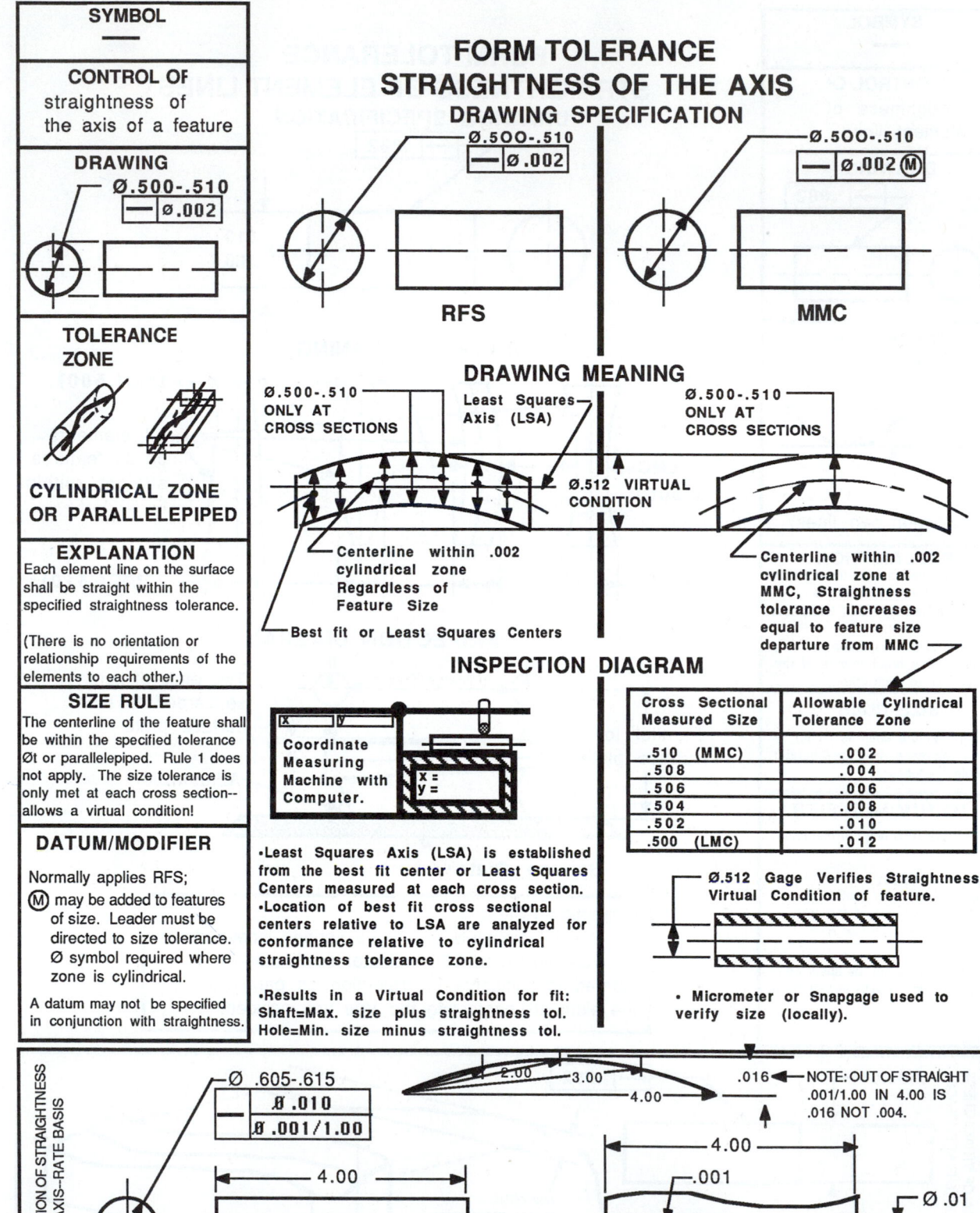

SYMBOL
—

CONTROL OF straightness of the axis of a feature

DRAWING

Ø.500-.510
— | Ø.002

TOLERANCE ZONE

CYLINDRICAL ZONE OR PARALLELEPIPED

EXPLANATION
Each element line on the surface shall be straight within the specified straightness tolerance.

(There is no orientation or relationship requirements of the elements to each other.)

SIZE RULE
The centerline of the feature shall be within the specified tolerance Øt or parallelepiped. Rule 1 does not apply. The size tolerance is only met at each cross section-- allows a virtual condition!

DATUM/MODIFIER

Normally applies RFS;
Ⓜ may be added to features of size. Leader must be directed to size tolerance. Ø symbol required where zone is cylindrical.

A datum may not be specified in conjunction with straightness.

FORM TOLERANCE
STRAIGHTNESS OF THE AXIS
DRAWING SPECIFICATION

Ø.500-.510
— | Ø.002

RFS

Ø.500-.510
— | Ø.002 Ⓜ

MMC

DRAWING MEANING

Ø.500-.510 ONLY AT CROSS SECTIONS

Least Squares Axis (LSA)

Ø.512 VIRTUAL CONDITION

Centerline within .002 cylindrical zone Regardless of Feature Size

Best fit or Least Squares Centers

Ø.500-.510 ONLY AT CROSS SECTIONS

Centerline within .002 cylindrical zone at MMC, Straightness tolerance increases equal to feature size departure from MMC

INSPECTION DIAGRAM

Coordinate Measuring Machine with Computer.

x =
y =

•Least Squares Axis (LSA) is established from the best fit center or Least Squares Centers measured at each cross section.
•Location of best fit cross sectional centers relative to LSA are analyzed for conformance relative to cylindrical straightness tolerance zone.

•Results in a Virtual Condition for fit: Shaft=Max. size plus straightness tol. Hole=Min. size minus straightness tol.

Cross Sectional Measured Size	Allowable Cylindrical Tolerance Zone
.510 (MMC)	.002
.508	.004
.506	.006
.504	.008
.502	.010
.500 (LMC)	.012

Ø.512 Gage Verifies Straightness, Virtual Condition of feature.

• Micrometer or Snapgage used to verify size (locally).

VERIFICATION OF STRAIGHTNESS ON THE AXIS-RATE BASIS

Ø .605-.615
Ø .010
Ø .001/1.00

4.00

2.00
3.00
4.00
.016 ◄ NOTE: OUT OF STRAIGHT .001/1.00 IN 4.00 IS .016 NOT .004.

4.00
.001
1.00
Ø .01

(c)

FIGURE 13.55   Summary Fact Data Sheets—Continued   (c) Straightness of the axis

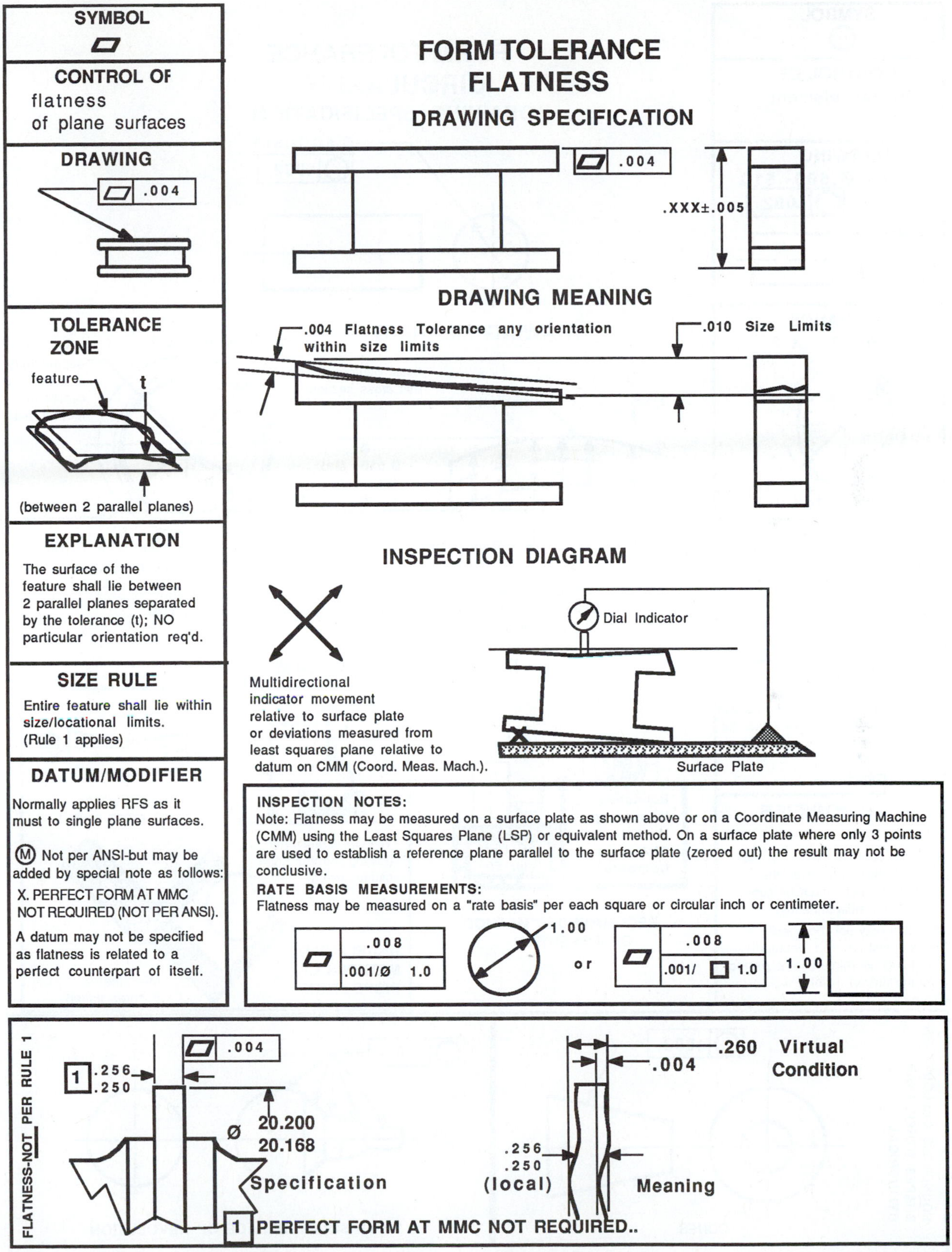

SYMBOL
▱

CONTROL OF
flatness
of plane surfaces

DRAWING

▱ .004

TOLERANCE ZONE

feature   t

(between 2 parallel planes)

EXPLANATION

The surface of the feature shall lie between 2 parallel planes separated by the tolerance (t); NO particular orientation req'd.

SIZE RULE

Entire feature shall lie within size/locational limits. (Rule 1 applies)

DATUM/MODIFIER

Normally applies RFS as it must to single plane surfaces.

Ⓜ Not per ANSI-but may be added by special note as follows:

X. PERFECT FORM AT MMC NOT REQUIRED (NOT PER ANSI).

A datum may not be specified as flatness is related to a perfect counterpart of itself.

FORM TOLERANCE
FLATNESS
DRAWING SPECIFICATION

▱ .004

.XXX±.005

DRAWING MEANING

.004 Flatness Tolerance any orientation within size limits

.010 Size Limits

INSPECTION DIAGRAM

Multidirectional indicator movement relative to surface plate or deviations measured from least squares plane relative to datum on CMM (Coord. Meas. Mach.).

Dial Indicator

Surface Plate

INSPECTION NOTES:
Note: Flatness may be measured on a surface plate as shown above or on a Coordinate Measuring Machine (CMM) using the Least Squares Plane (LSP) or equivalent method. On a surface plate where only 3 points are used to establish a reference plane parallel to the surface plate (zeroed out) the result may not be conclusive.

RATE BASIS MEASUREMENTS:
Flatness may be measured on a "rate basis" per each square or circular inch or centimeter.

▱	.008
	.001/Ø 1.0

1.00

or

▱	.008
	.001/ ▢ 1.0

1.00

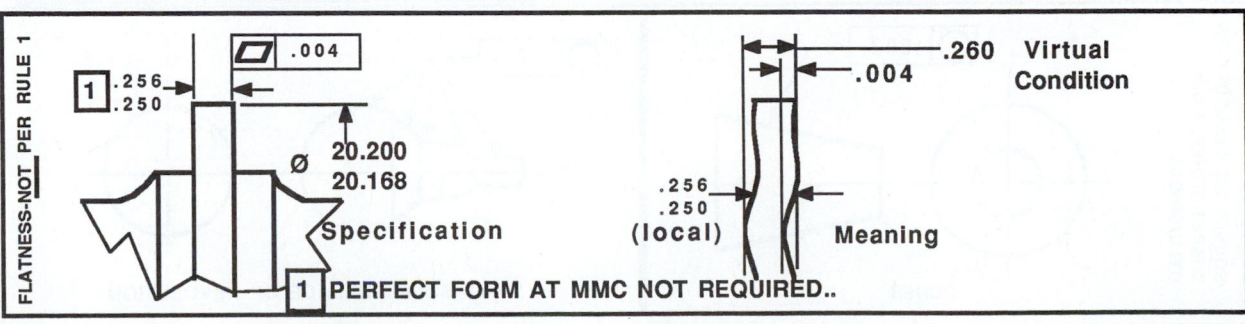

FLATNESS-NOT PER RULE 1

1 .256
.250

▱ .004

Ø 20.200
20.168

Specification

1 PERFECT FORM AT MMC NOT REQUIRED..

.260 **Virtual Condition**
.004

.256
.250

(local)   **Meaning**

(d)

FIGURE 13.55 **Summary Fact Data Sheets—Continued**   (d) Flatness

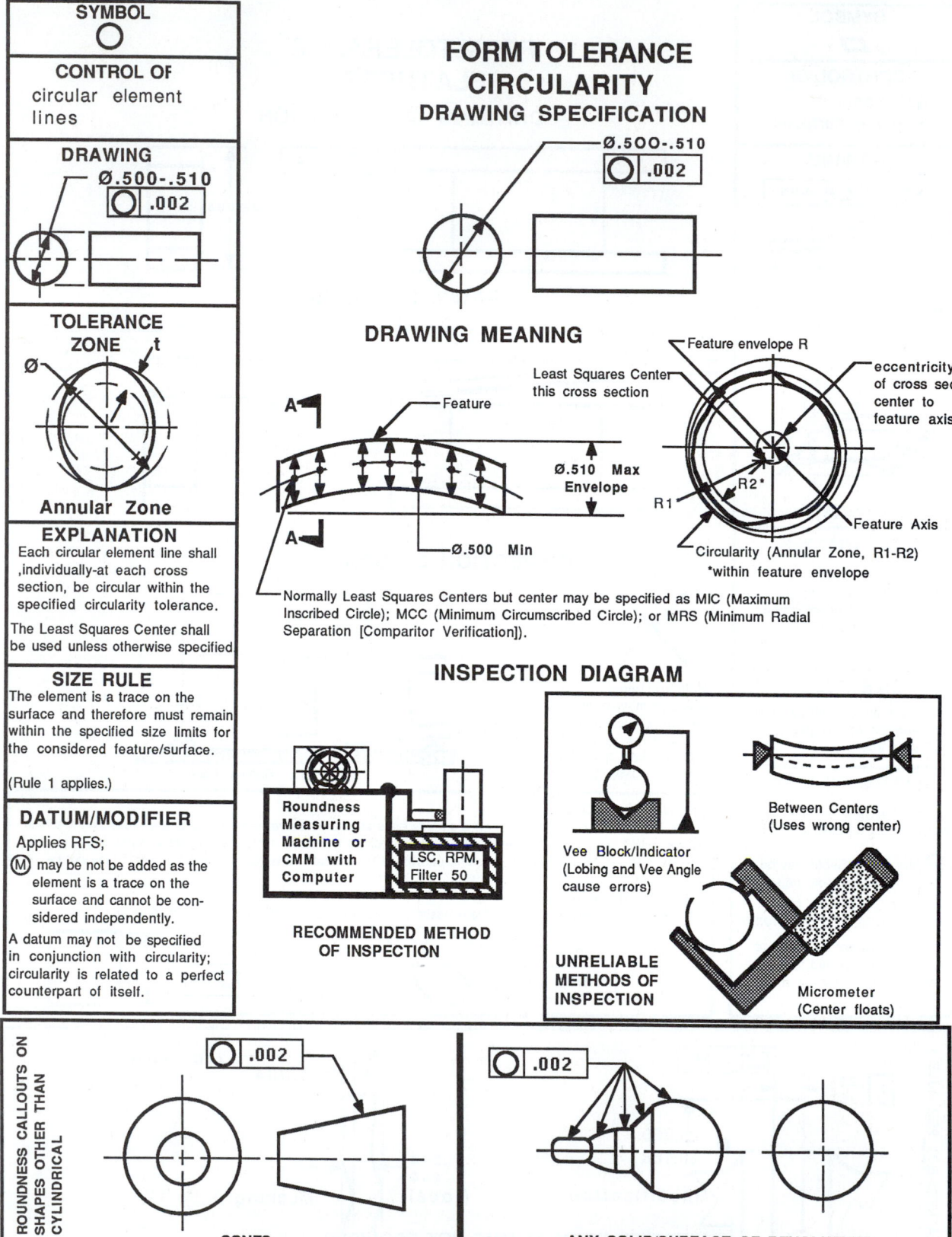

SYMBOL

CONTROL OF
circular element
lines

DRAWING

Ø.500-.510

.002

**TOLERANCE
ZONE   t**

Ø

Annular Zone

EXPLANATION
Each circular element line shall
,individually-at each cross
section, be circular within the
specified circularity tolerance.

The Least Squares Center shall
be used unless otherwise specified.

SIZE RULE
The element is a trace on the
surface and therefore must remain
within the specified size limits for
the considered feature/surface.

(Rule 1 applies.)

DATUM/MODIFIER

Applies RFS;

Ⓜ may be not be added as the
element is a trace on the
surface and cannot be considered independently.

A datum may not be specified
in conjunction with circularity;
circularity is related to a perfect
counterpart of itself.

**FORM TOLERANCE
CIRCULARITY**
DRAWING SPECIFICATION

Ø.500-.510

.002

DRAWING MEANING

Feature envelope R

Least Squares Center
this cross section

eccentricity
of cross sect.
center to
feature axis

Feature

Ø.510 Max
Envelope

R2*

Ø.500 Min

R1

Feature Axis

Circularity (Annular Zone, R1-R2)
*within feature envelope

Normally Least Squares Centers but center may be specified as MIC (Maximum
Inscribed Circle); MCC (Minimum Circumscribed Circle); or MRS (Minimum Radial
Separation [Comparitor Verification]).

INSPECTION DIAGRAM

Roundness
Measuring
Machine or
CMM with
Computer

LSC, RPM,
Filter 50

**RECOMMENDED METHOD
OF INSPECTION**

Vee Block/Indicator
(Lobing and Vee Angle
cause errors)

Between Centers
(Uses wrong center)

**UNRELIABLE
METHODS OF
INSPECTION**

Micrometer
(Center floats)

ROUNDNESS CALLOUTS ON
SHAPES OTHER THAN
CYLINDRICAL

.002

CONES

.002

ANY SOLID/SURFACE OF REVOLUTION

(e)

FIGURE 13.55 Summary Fact Data Sheets—Continued (e) Circularity

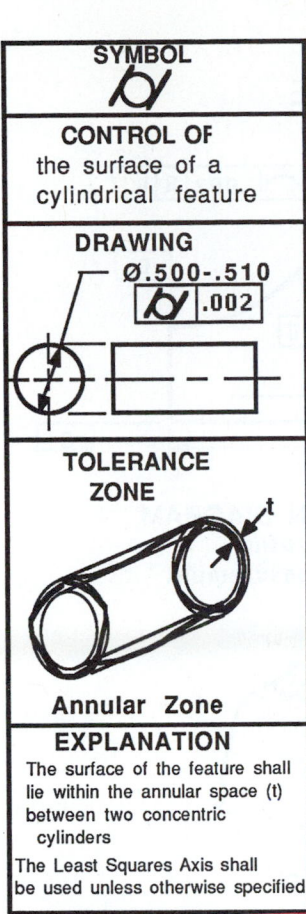

SYMBOL

CONTROL OF
the surface of a
cylindrical feature

DRAWING

Ø.500-.510

.002

**TOLERANCE
ZONE**

t

Annular Zone

EXPLANATION

The surface of the feature shall
lie within the annular space (t)
between two concentric
cylinders

The Least Squares Axis shall
be used unless otherwise specified

SIZE RULE

The cylindricity tolerance for
*rigid parts must be within the
specified size limits for the
considered feature/surface.
(Rule 1 applies.)
*Parts in the free state excepted.

DATUM/MODIFIER

Applies RFS;

Ⓜ may be not be added as this
tolerance is a refinement of
the surface shape and cannot
be considered independently.

A datum may not be specified
in conjunction with cylindricity;
cylindricity is related to a perfect
counterpart of itself.

FORM TOLERANCE
CYLINDRICITY
DRAWING SPECIFICATION

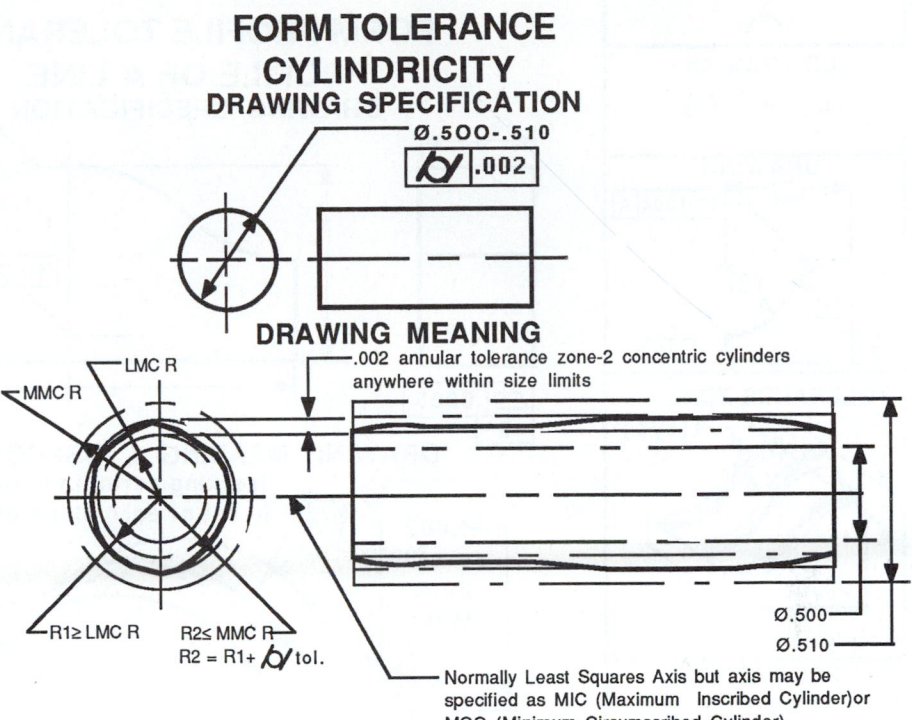

Ø.500-.510

.002

DRAWING MEANING

.002 annular tolerance zone-2 concentric cylinders
anywhere within size limits

LMC R

MMC R

R1≥ LMC R   R2≤ MMC R
R2 = R1+ tol.

Ø.500
Ø.510

Normally Least Squares Axis but axis may be
specified as MIC (Maximum Inscribed Cylinder)or
MCC (Minimum Circumscribed Cylinder).

INSPECTION DIAGRAM

Roundness
Measuring
Machine or
CMM with
Computer

LSC, RPM,
Filter 50

**RECOMMENDED METHOD
OF INSPECTION**

Vee Block/Indicator
(Lobing and Vee Angle
cause errors.)

Between Centers
(uses wrong center)

Micrometer
(Floating center)

**UNRELIABLE
METHODS OF
INSPECTION**

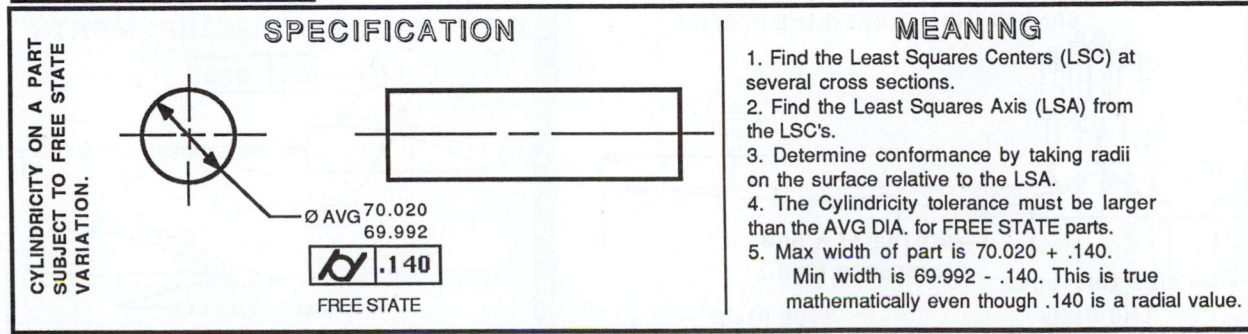

CYLINDRICITY ON A PART
SUBJECT TO FREE STATE
VARIATION.

SPECIFICATION

Ø AVG 70.020
69.992

.140

FREE STATE

MEANING

1. Find the Least Squares Centers (LSC) at
several cross sections.
2. Find the Least Squares Axis (LSA) from
the LSC's.
3. Determine conformance by taking radii
on the surface relative to the LSA.
4. The Cylindricity tolerance must be larger
than the AVG DIA. for FREE STATE parts.
5. Max width of part is 70.020 + .140.
   Min width is 69.992 - .140. This is true
   mathematically even though .140 is a radial value.

(f)

FIGURE 13.55   Summary Fact Data Sheets—Continued   (f) Cylindricity

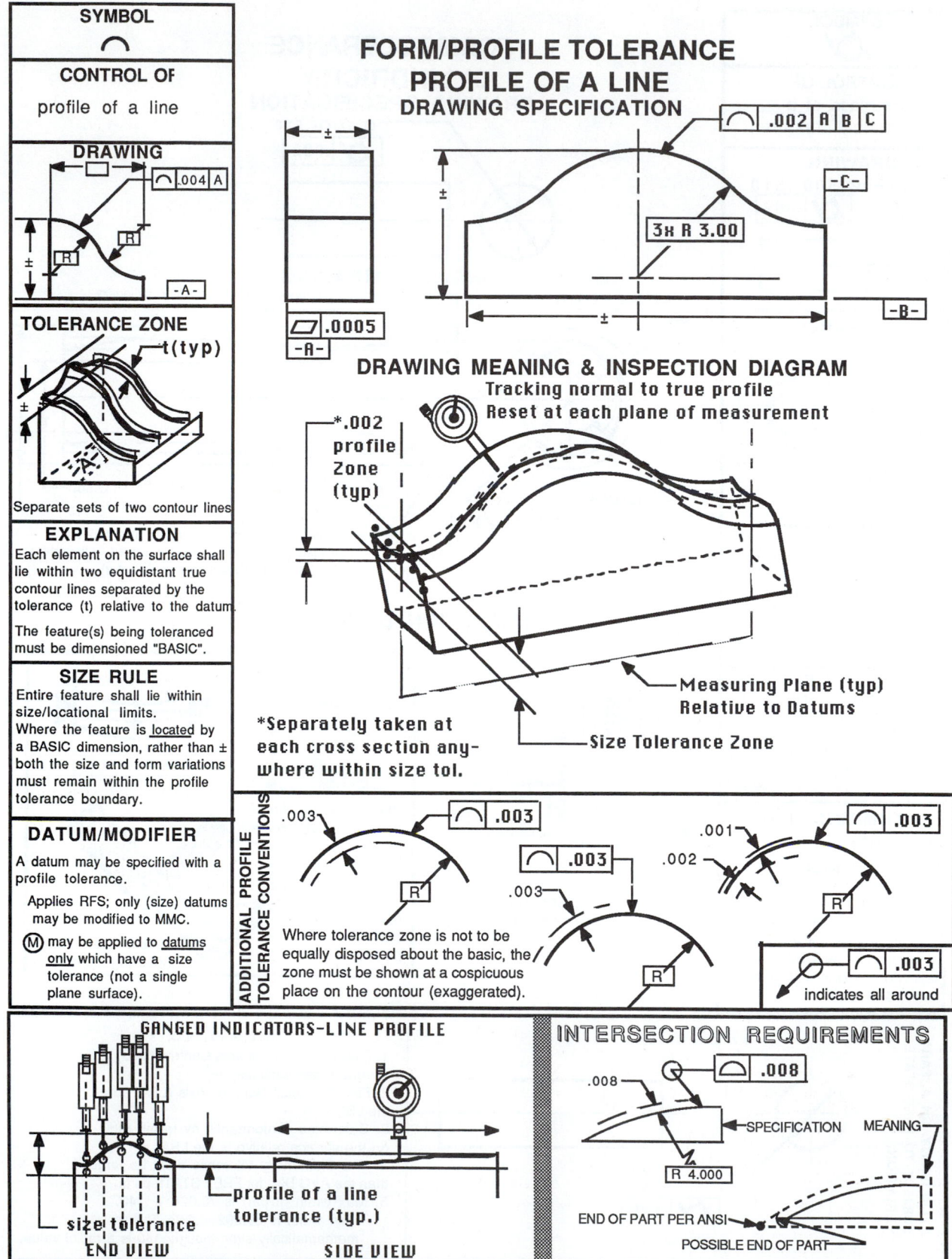

FIGURE 13.55   Summary Fact Data Sheets—Continued   (g) Profile of a line

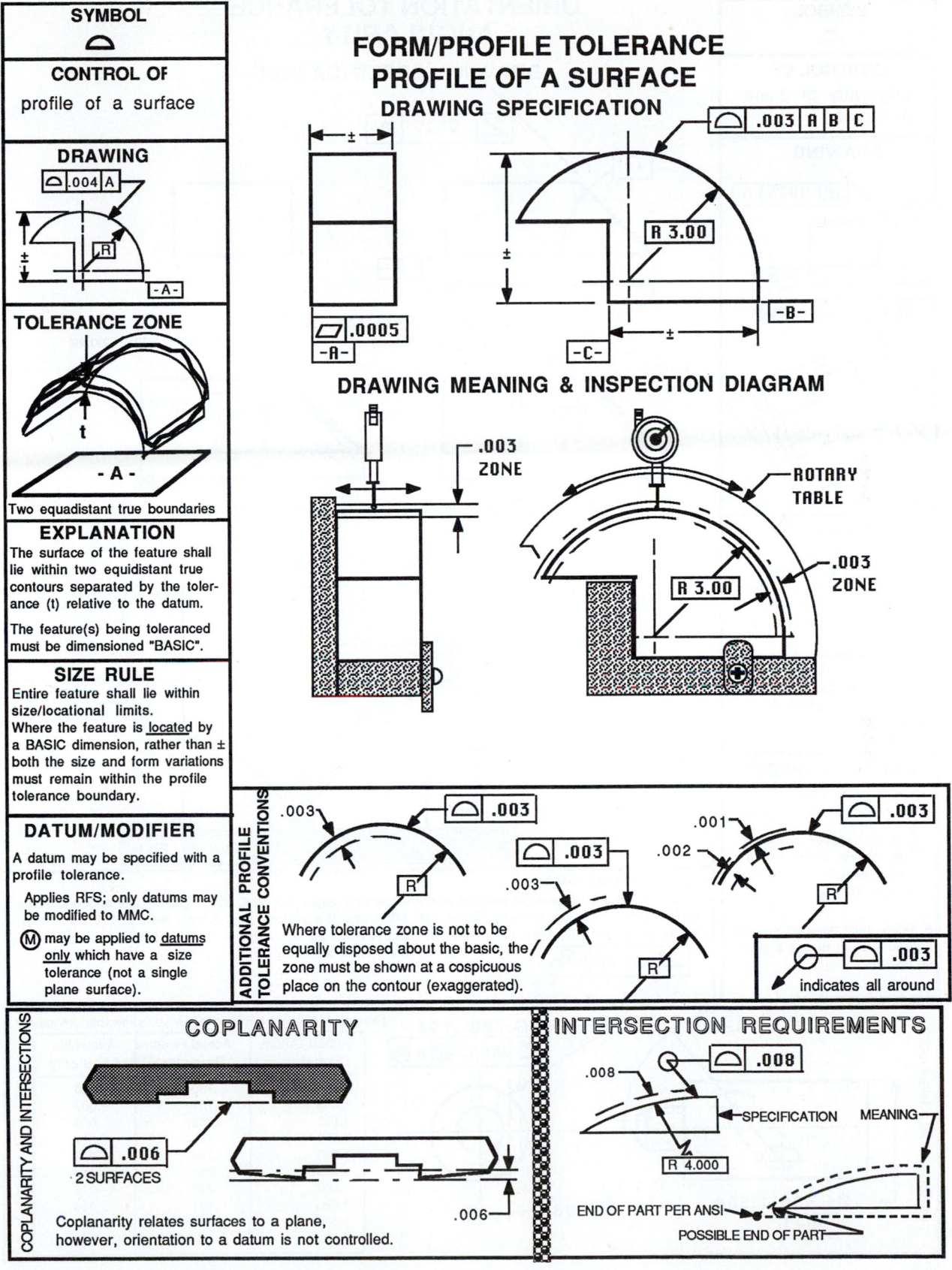

SYMBOL

CONTROL OF
profile of a surface

DRAWING

TOLERANCE ZONE
Two equidistant true boundaries

EXPLANATION
The surface of the feature shall lie within two equidistant true contours separated by the tolerance (t) relative to the datum.

The feature(s) being toleranced must be dimensioned "BASIC".

SIZE RULE
Entire feature shall lie within size/locational limits.
Where the feature is located by a BASIC dimension, rather than ± both the size and form variations must remain within the profile tolerance boundary.

DATUM/MODIFIER
A datum may be specified with a profile tolerance.

Applies RFS; only datums may be modified to MMC.

(M) may be applied to datums only which have a size tolerance (not a single plane surface).

FORM/PROFILE TOLERANCE
PROFILE OF A SURFACE
DRAWING SPECIFICATION

DRAWING MEANING & INSPECTION DIAGRAM

ROTARY TABLE

.003 ZONE

R 3.00

ADDITIONAL PROFILE TOLERANCE CONVENTIONS

Where tolerance zone is not to be equally disposed about the basic, the zone must be shown at a cospicuous place on the contour (exaggerated).

indicates all around

COPLANARITY AND INTERSECTIONS

COPLANARITY

2 SURFACES

Coplanarity relates surfaces to a plane, however, orientation to a datum is not controlled.

INTERSECTION REQUIREMENTS

SPECIFICATION   MEANING

R 4.000

END OF PART PER ANSI

POSSIBLE END OF PART

(h)

FIGURE 13.55 **Summary Fact Data Sheets—Continued**   (h) Profile of a surface

SYMBOL
∠

CONTROL OF
angularity of plane surfaces

DRAWING

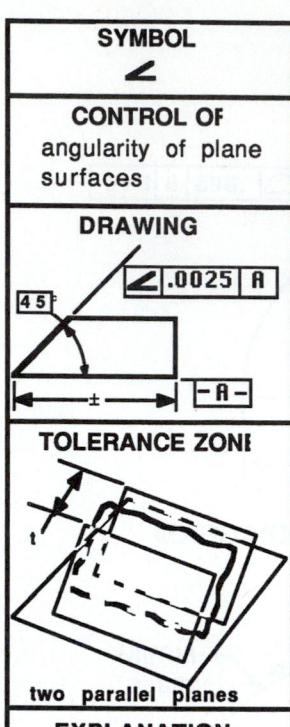

TOLERANCE ZONE

two parallel planes

EXPLANATION

The surface of the feature shall lie between 2 parallel planes separated by the tolerance (t) which are at the basic angle to the datum.

SIZE RULE

The end of the part is measured to the end of the physical feature; not the zone intersection.

DATUM/MODIFIER

Normally applies RFS as it must to single plane surfaces.

Ⓜ may be applied to datums or features which have a size tolerance (not a single plane surface).

A datum must be specified with angularity even though it may be obvious.

ORIENTATION TOLERANCE
ANGULARITY
DRAWING SPECIFICATION

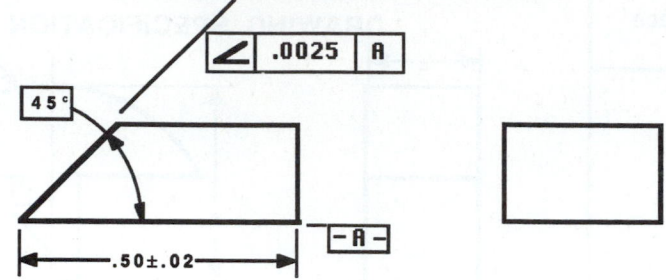

DRAWING MEANING

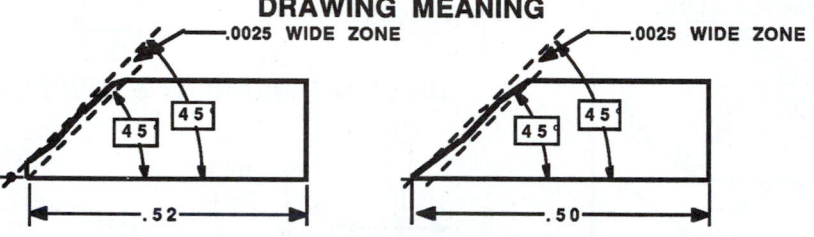

NOTE: LENGTH IS MEASURED INDEPENDENT OF THE ANGLE.

INSPECTION DIAGRAM

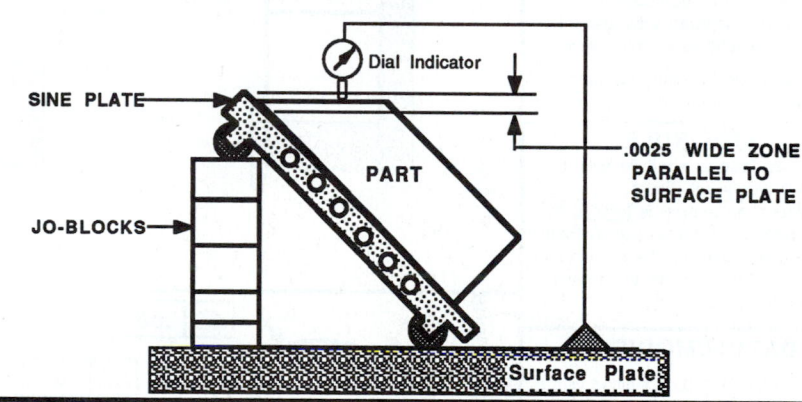

INSPECTION AT MMC

Where features or datums (or both) of size are specified angular at MMC the angularity tolerance increases as the feature or datum (or both) depart from MMC by a like amount. (e.g. A male feature .502 ±.002 with an actual size of .502; and a male datum of .754±.004 with an actual size of .754 which are may be .002+.004+.005 out of angularity (.011).

| ∠ | .005 Ⓜ | A Ⓜ |

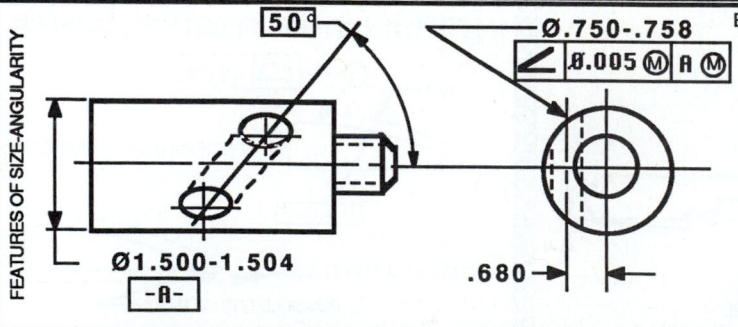

Examples of feature/datum sizes vs. allowable Angularity

Actual Datum Diameter	Actual Feature Diameter	Allowable Angularity
1.504 (MMC)	.750 (MMC)	.005
1.503	.751	.007
1.502	.752	.009
1.501	.753	.011
1.500	.754	.013
1.500	.755	.014
1.500	.756	.015
1.500	.757	.016
1.500	.758	.017
1.502	.750 (MMC)	.007

(i)

FIGURE 13.55 Summary Fact Data Sheets—Continued   (i) Angularity

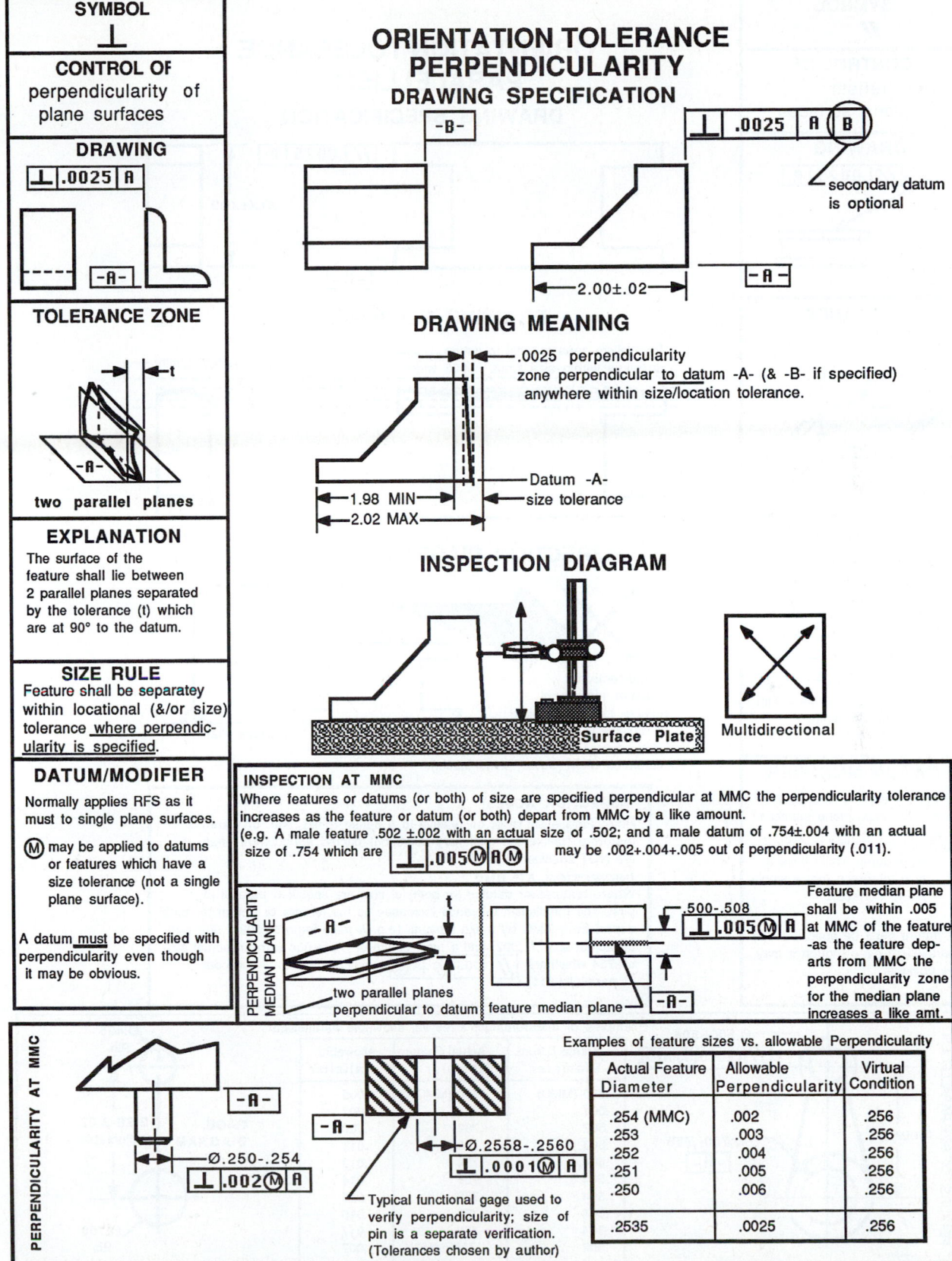

FIGURE 13.55   Summary Fact Data Sheets—Continued   (j) Perpendicularity

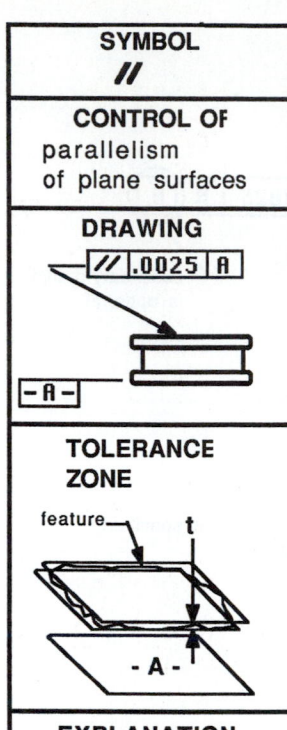

SYMBOL
//

CONTROL OF
parallelism
of plane surfaces

DRAWING

TOLERANCE ZONE

feature   t

- A -

EXPLANATION

The surface of the feature shall lie between 2 parallel planes separated by the tolerance (t) which are parallel to the datum.

SIZE RULE

Entire feature shall lie within size/locational limits. (Rule 1 applies)

DATUM/MODIFIER

Normally applies RFS as it must to single plane surfaces.

Ⓜ may be applied to datums or features which have a size tolerance (not a single plane surface).

A datum _must_ be specified with parallelism even though it may be obvious.

ORIENTATION TOLERANCE PARALLELISM
DRAWING SPECIFICATION

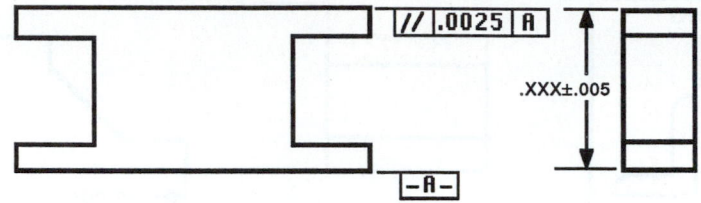

DRAWING MEANING

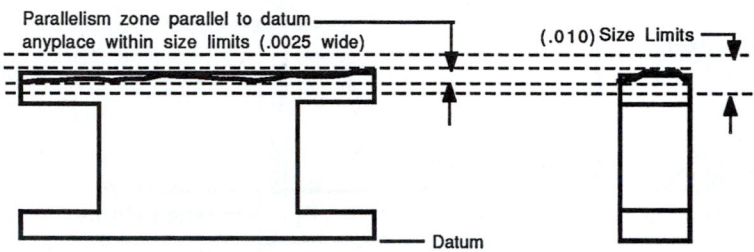

Parallelism zone parallel to datum anyplace within size limits (.0025 wide)

(.010) Size Limits

Datum

INSPECTION DIAGRAM

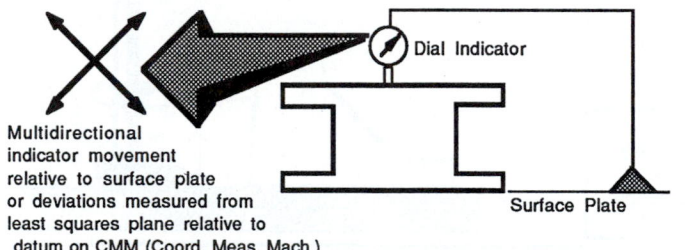

Dial Indicator

Surface Plate

Multidirectional indicator movement relative to surface plate or deviations measured from least squares plane relative to datum on CMM (Coord. Meas. Mach.).

INSPECTION NOTES:

Note: Parallelism must be relative to a datum (point, line, or plane) therefore (unlike the dictionary definition) curved equadistant lines are NOT considered parallel.

INSPECTION AT MMC

Where features or datums (or both) of size are specified parallel at MMC the parallelism tolerance increases as the feature or datum (or both) depart from MMC by a like amount. (e.g. A male feature .502 ±.002 with an actual size of .502; and a male datum of .754±.004 with an actual size of .754 which are ┃// ┃.005 Ⓜ┃A Ⓜ┃ may be .002+.004+.005 out of parallel (.011).

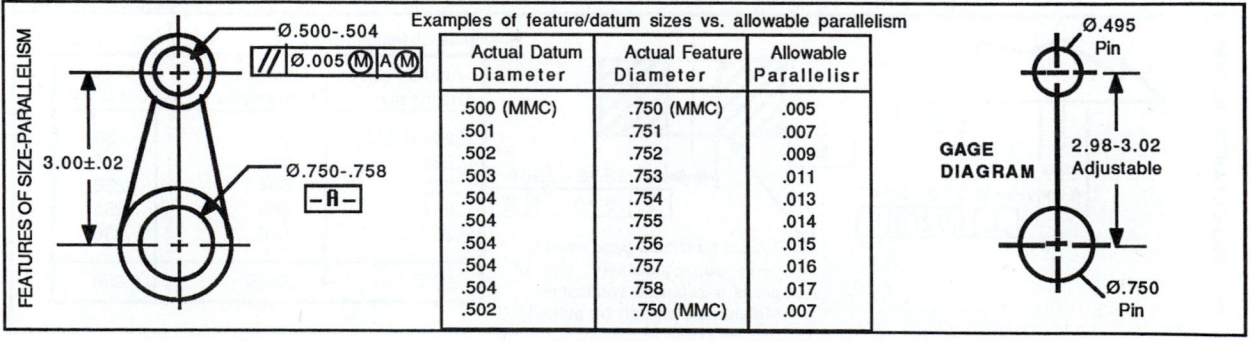

Examples of feature/datum sizes vs. allowable parallelism

Actual Datum Diameter	Actual Feature Diameter	Allowable Parallelisr
.500 (MMC)	.750 (MMC)	.005
.501	.751	.007
.502	.752	.009
.503	.753	.011
.504	.754	.013
.504	.755	.014
.504	.756	.015
.504	.757	.016
.504	.758	.017
.502	.750 (MMC)	.007

FEATURES OF SIZE-PARALLELISM

Ø.500-.504
┃// ┃Ø.005 Ⓜ┃A Ⓜ┃

3.00±.02

Ø.750-.758
┃-A-┃

GAGE DIAGRAM

Ø.495 Pin

2.98-3.02 Adjustable

Ø.750 Pin

(k)

FIGURE 13.55   Summary Fact Data Sheets—Continued   (k) Parallelism

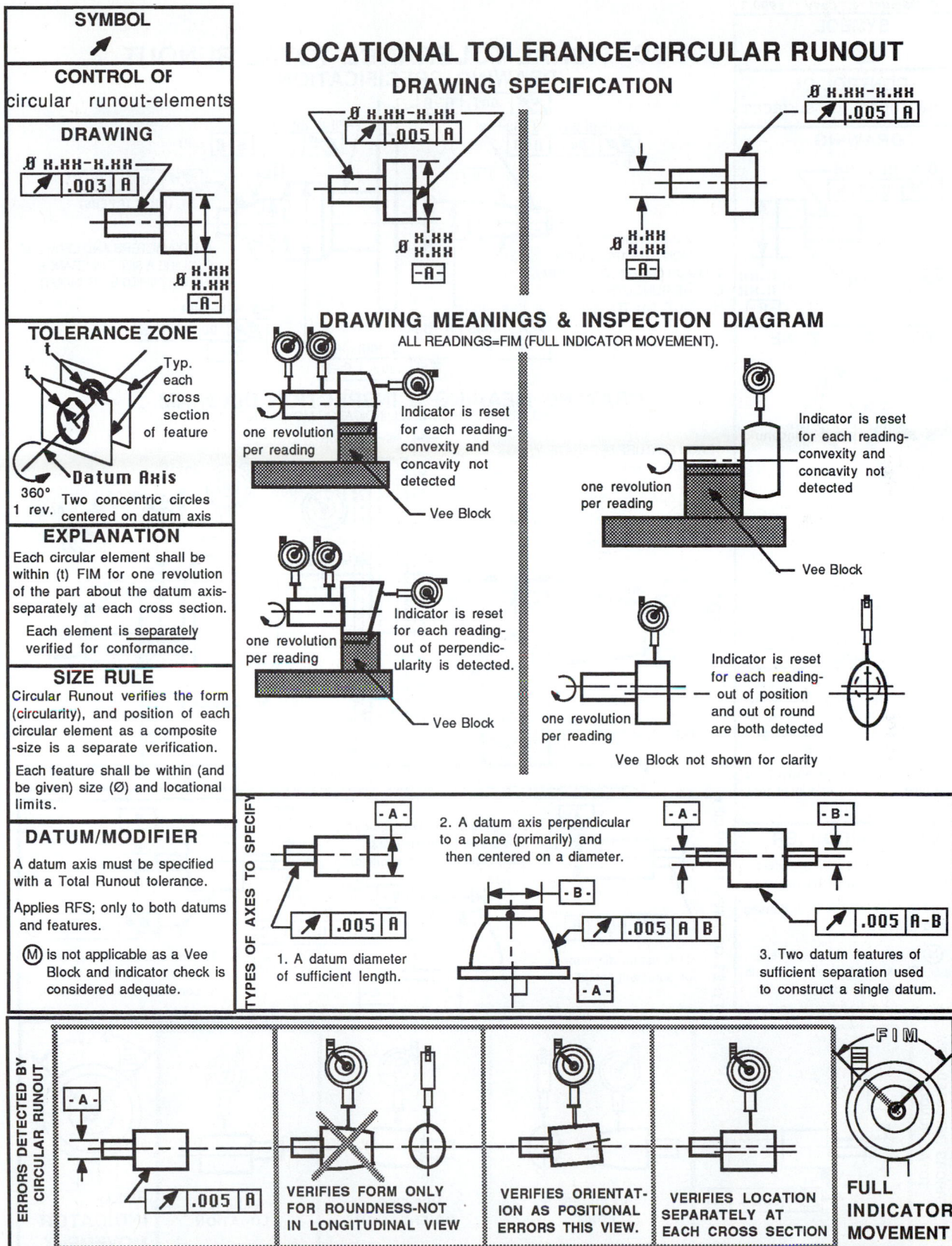

FIGURE 13.55   **Summary Fact Data Sheets—Continued**   (l) Circular runout

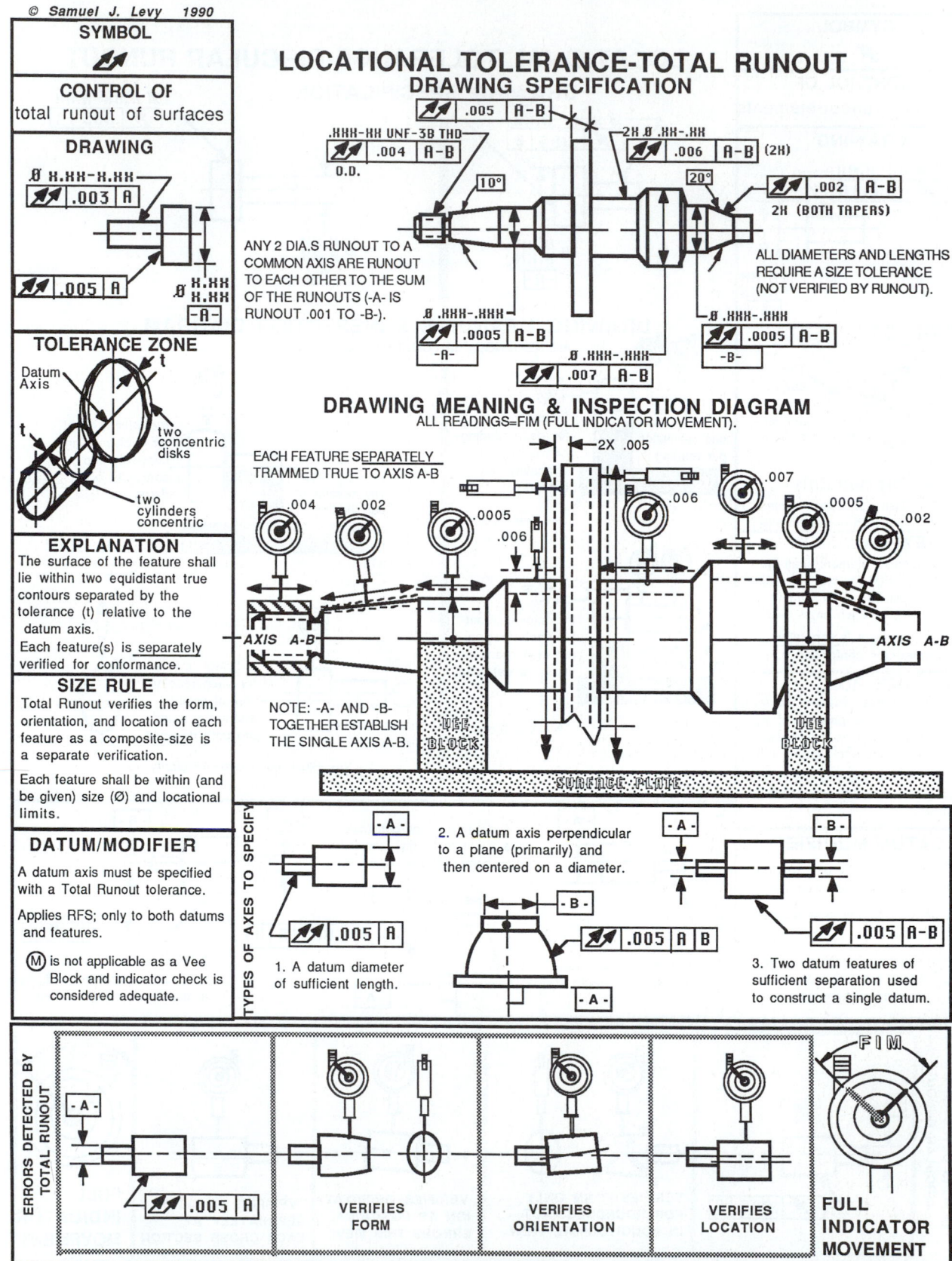

© Samuel J. Levy 1990

SYMBOL

CONTROL OF
total runout of surfaces

DRAWING

Ø X.XX-X.XX
.003 A

.005 A   Ø X.XX X.XX
-A-

TOLERANCE ZONE

Datum Axis   t
two concentric disks
t
two cylinders concentric

EXPLANATION
The surface of the feature shall lie within two equidistant true contours separated by the tolerance (t) relative to the datum axis.
Each feature(s) is separately verified for conformance.

SIZE RULE
Total Runout verifies the form, orientation, and location of each feature as a composite-size is a separate verification.

Each feature shall be within (and be given) size (Ø) and locational limits.

DATUM/MODIFIER
A datum axis must be specified with a Total Runout tolerance.

Applies RFS; only to both datums and features.

Ⓜ is not applicable as a Vee Block and indicator check is considered adequate.

LOCATIONAL TOLERANCE-TOTAL RUNOUT
DRAWING SPECIFICATION

.005 A-B

.XXX-XX UNF-3B THD
.004 A-B
O.D.

2X Ø .XX-.XX
.006 A-B (2X)

10°   20°

.002 A-B
2X (BOTH TAPERS)

ANY 2 DIA.S RUNOUT TO A COMMON AXIS ARE RUNOUT TO EACH OTHER TO THE SUM OF THE RUNOUTS (-A- IS RUNOUT .001 TO -B-).

ALL DIAMETERS AND LENGTHS REQUIRE A SIZE TOLERANCE (NOT VERIFIED BY RUNOUT).

Ø .XXX-.XXX
.0005 A-B
-A-

Ø .XXX-.XXX
.0005 A-B
-B-

Ø .XXX-.XXX
.007 A-B

DRAWING MEANING & INSPECTION DIAGRAM
ALL READINGS=FIM (FULL INDICATOR MOVEMENT).

2X .005

EACH FEATURE SEPARATELY TRAMMED TRUE TO AXIS A-B

.004   .002   .0005   .006   .007   .0005   .002
.006

AXIS A-B   AXIS A-B

NOTE: -A- AND -B- TOGETHER ESTABLISH THE SINGLE AXIS A-B.

VEE BLOCK   VEE BLOCK
SURFACE PLATE

TYPES OF AXES TO SPECIFY

-A-
.005 A
1. A datum diameter of sufficient length.

2. A datum axis perpendicular to a plane (primarily) and then centered on a diameter.
-B-
.005 A B
-A-

-A-   -B-
.005 A-B
3. Two datum features of sufficient separation used to construct a single datum.

ERRORS DETECTED BY TOTAL RUNOUT

-A-
.005 A

VERIFIES FORM

VERIFIES ORIENTATION

VERIFIES LOCATION

FIM

FULL INDICATOR MOVEMENT

(m)

FIGURE 13.55   Summary Fact Data Sheets—Continued   (m) Total runout

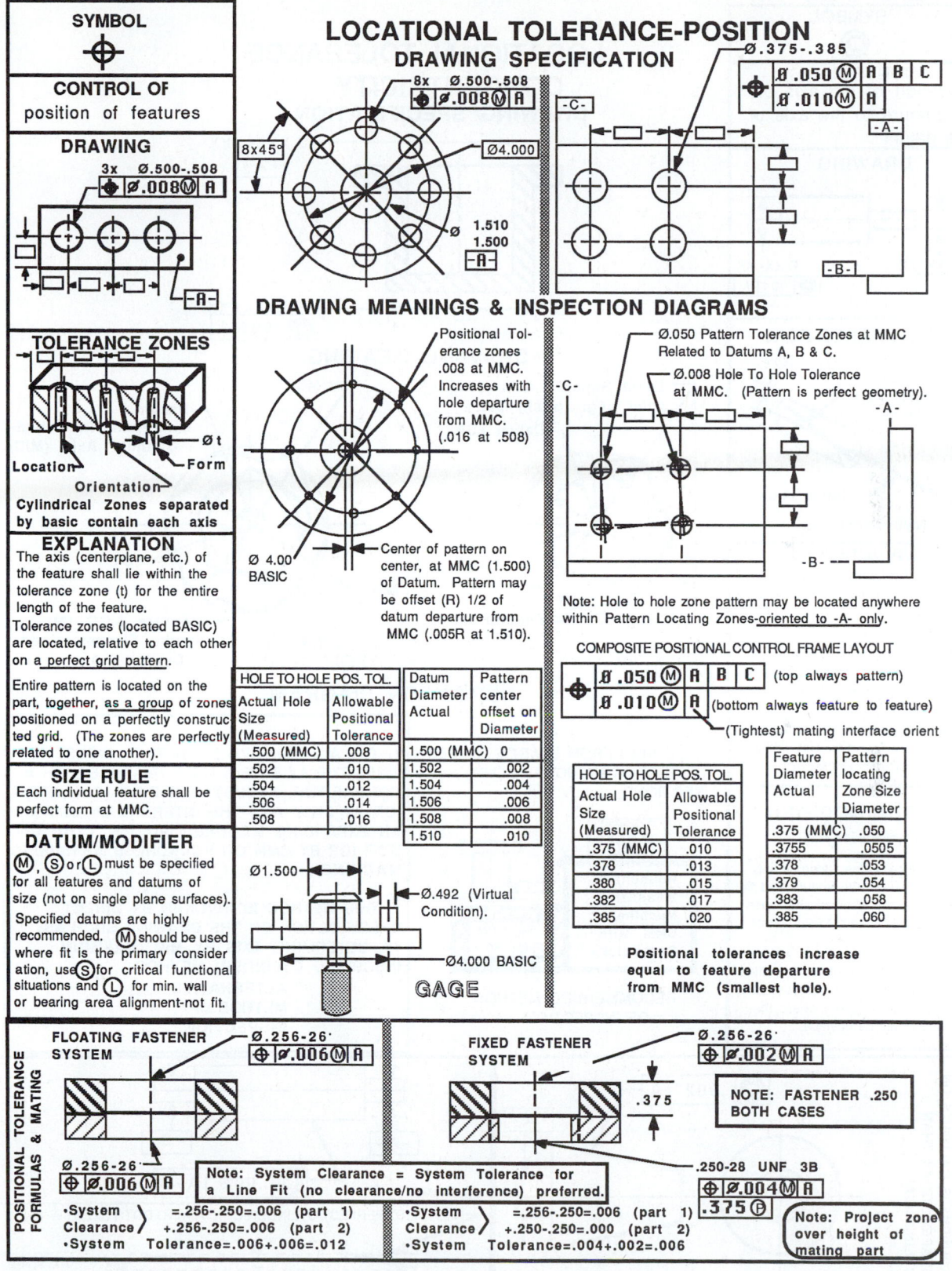

FIGURE 13.55   Summary Fact Data Sheets—Continued   (n) Position

SYMBOL

◎

CONTROL OF
location of the axis of
a feature to the axis of
a datum

DRAWING

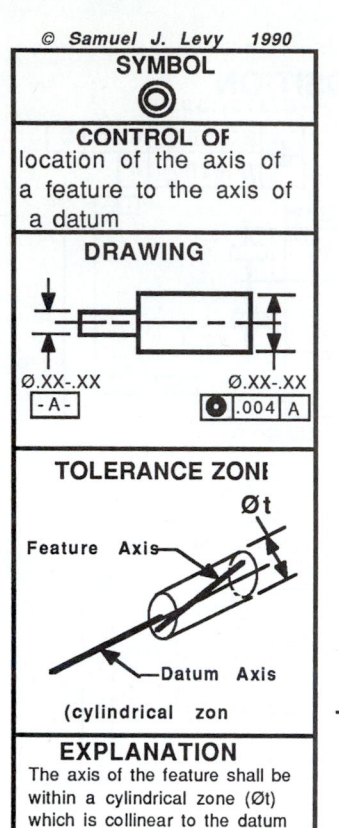

Ø.XX-.XX
- A -

◉ .004 A

TOLERANCE ZONE

Øt

Feature Axis

Datum Axis

(cylindrical zone)

EXPLANATION

The axis of the feature shall be
within a cylindrical zone (Øt)
which is collinear to the datum
axis.

The Least Squares Axes shall
be used unless otherwise specified.

SIZE RULE

The feature (and datum) must be
within the specified size limits.
(Rule 1 applies to each.)

DATUM/MODIFIER

Always applies RFS;

Ⓜ may be not be added as only
the axis of the feature and the
datum are involved and these
are not subject to variations
of size.

A datum (axis) must be specified
in conjunction with concentricity;
this is required even where the
datum would be obvious.

LOCATIONAL TOLERANCE
CONCENTRICITY
DRAWING SPECIFICATION

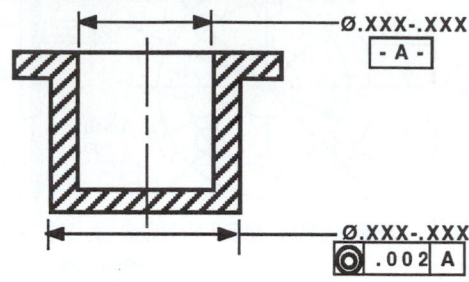

Ø.XXX-.XXX
- A -

Ø.XXX-.XXX

◎ .002 A

DRAWING MEANING

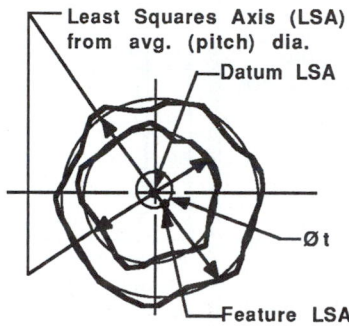

Least Squares Axis (LSA)
from avg. (pitch) dia.

Datum LSA

Øt

Feature LSA

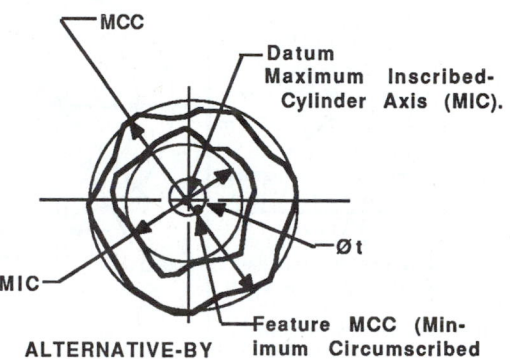

MCC

Datum
Maximum Inscribed-
Cylinder Axis (MIC).

Øt

MIC

Feature MCC (Min-
imum Circumscribed
Cylinder). Axis.

**ALTERNATIVE-BY
SPECIFICATION**

INSPECTION DIAGRAM

LSA FOUND FROM LEAST SQUARES
CENTERS AT VARIOUS CROSS
SECTIONS.

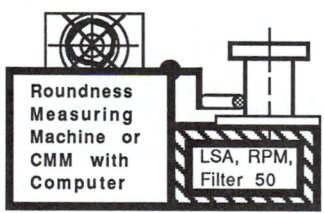

Roundness
Measuring
Machine or
CMM with
Computer

LSA, RPM,
Filter 50

**RECOMMENDED METHOD
OF INSPECTION**

1. THE ALTERNATIVE METHOD OF INSPECTION
FINDS THE AXIS OF A MALE FEATURE WITH A
COMPARITOR, ADJUSTABLE RING (COLLETT)
(OR BY CMM) AND THE INTERNAL BY USING
AN EXPANDING MANDREL, FIT PIN, COMPAR-
ITOR (OR BY CMM OR ROUNDNESS MEASURING
MACHINE).

2. THIS METHOD IS INVOKED BY DIRECT
SPECIFICATION ON THE DRAWING SUCH AS:
"X. DETERMINE AXIS BY MIC (MAXIMUM
INSCRIBED CYLINDER) METHOD.
        **ALTERNATIVE
        METHOD OF
        INSPECTION**

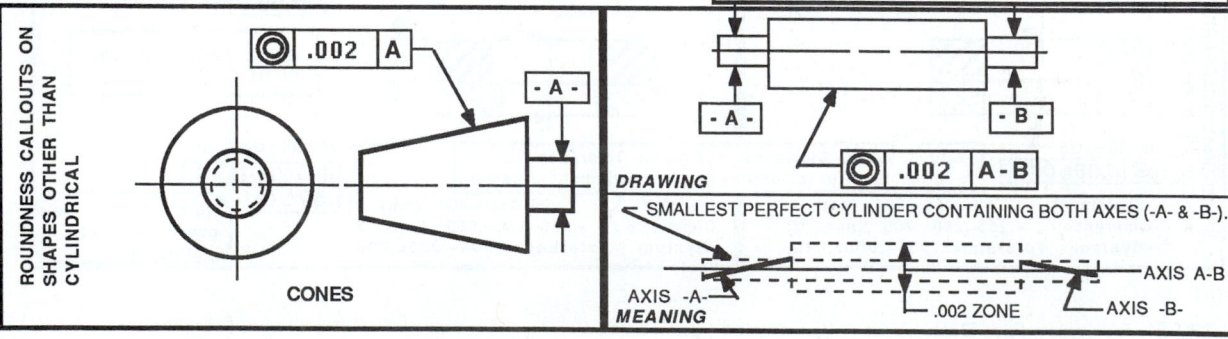

ROUNDNESS CALLOUTS ON
SHAPES OTHER THAN
CYLINDRICAL

◎ .002 A

- A -

CONES

- A -   - B -

DRAWING

◎ .002 A - B

SMALLEST PERFECT CYLINDER CONTAINING BOTH AXES (-A- & -B-).

AXIS A-B

AXIS -A-
MEANING

.002 ZONE   AXIS -B-

(o)

FIGURE 13.55   Summary Fact Data Sheets—Continued   (o) Concentricity

Coordinate (CMM) to Positional Zone Conversion (Chart Above).

	.002	.003	.004	.005	.006	.007	.008	.009	.010	.011	.012	.013	.014	.015	.016	.017	.018	.019	.020
.020	.040200	.040450	.040790	.041230	.041760	.042380	.043080	.043860	.044720	.045650	.046650	.047710	.048830	.050000	.051220	.052500	.053810	.055170	.056570
.019	.038210	.038470	.038830	.039290	.039850	.040500	.041230	.042050	.042940	.043910	.044940	.046040	.047200	.048410	.049680	.050990	.052350	.053740	.055170
.018	.036220	.036500	.036880	.037360	.037950	.038630	.039400	.040250	.041180	.042190	.043270	.044410	.045610	.046860	.048170	.049520	.050910	.052350	.053810
.017	.034230	.034530	.034930	.035440	.036060	.036770	.037580	.038470	.039450	.040500	.041620	.042800	.044050	.045340	.046690	.048080	.049520	.050990	.052500
.016	.032250	.032560	.032980	.033530	.034180	.034930	.035780	.036720	.037740	.038830	.040000	.041230	.042520	.043860	.045250	.046690	.048170	.049680	.051220
.015	.030270	.030590	.031050	.031620	.032310	.033110	.034000	.034990	.036060	.037200	.038420	.039700	.041040	.042430	.043860	.045340	.046860	.048410	.050000
.014	.028280	.028640	.029120	.029730	.030460	.031300	.032250	.033290	.034410	.035610	.036880	.038210	.039600	.041040	.042520	.044050	.045610	.047200	.048830
.013	.026310	.026680	.027200	.027860	.028640	.029530	.030530	.031620	.032800	.034060	.035380	.036770	.038210	.039700	.041230	.042800	.044410	.046040	.047710
.012	.024330	.024740	.025300	.026000	.026830	.027780	.028840	.030000	.031240	.032560	.033940	.035380	.036880	.038420	.040000	.041620	.043270	.044940	.046650
.011	.022360	.022800	.023410	.024170	.025060	.026080	.027200	.028430	.029730	.031110	.032560	.034060	.035610	.037200	.038830	.040500	.042190	.043910	.045650
.010	.020400	.020880	.021540	.022360	.023320	.024410	.025610	.026910	.028280	.029730	.031240	.032800	.034410	.036060	.037740	.039450	.041180	.042940	.044720
.009	.018440	.018970	.019700	.020590	.021630	.022800	.024080	.025460	.026910	.028430	.030000	.031620	.033290	.034990	.036720	.038470	.040250	.042050	.043860
.008	.016490	.017090	.017890	.018870	.020000	.021260	.022630	.024080	.025610	.027200	.028840	.030530	.032250	.034000	.035780	.037580	.039400	.041230	.043080
.007	.014560	.015230	.016120	.017200	.018440	.019800	.021260	.022800	.024410	.026080	.027780	.029530	.031300	.033110	.034930	.036770	.038630	.040500	.042380
.006	.012650	.013420	.014420	.015620	.016970	.018440	.020000	.021630	.023320	.025060	.026830	.028640	.030460	.032310	.034180	.036060	.037950	.039850	.041760
.005	.010770	.011660	.012810	.014140	.015620	.017200	.018870	.020590	.022360	.024170	.026000	.027860	.029730	.031620	.033530	.035440	.037360	.039290	.041230
.004	.008940	.010000	.011310	.012810	.014420	.016120	.017890	.019700	.021540	.023410	.025300	.027200	.029120	.031050	.032980	.034930	.036880	.038830	.040790
.003	.007210	.008490	.010000	.011660	.013420	.015230	.017090	.018970	.020880	.022800	.024740	.026680	.028640	.030590	.032560	.034530	.036500	.038470	.040450
.002	.005660	.007210	.008940	.010770	.012650	.014560	.016490	.018440	.020400	.022360	.024330	.026310	.028280	.030270	.032250	.034230	.036220	.038210	.040200

THE RULES IN PLAIN ENGLISH

Rule 1: For individual features of size the MMC boundary of perfect form is respected over the entire feature length, the other (LMC) limit is verified locally by 2 point (caliper) measurement. (Not totally reliable in practice-form tolerance may be req'd).

RULE 2: Position Tolerance Only- Modifier for MMC, RFS or LMC must be specified for features and datums of size in the feature control frame. Not for single plane surfaces.

Rule 3: All Geometric Tolerances Except Position-RFS understood w/o specification MMC specified where allowed by design for economy/producibility.

Tolerances of Orientation or Position or Datum References are understood to apply to the Pitch Diameter of a thread unless otherwise specified (e.g. Ø MAJOR or Ø MINOR)

Tolerances apply at 68°F (20°C) unless otherwise specified.

Datum features establishing a Datum Reference Frame without orientation tolerances are considered oriented to 0 at MMC for Virtual Conditions used in Gagemaking.

VIRTUAL CONDITION
EXTERNAL FEATURE:
MMC Size + Geometric Tolerance
INTERNAL FEATURE:
MMC Size - Geometric Tolerance

Counterbore and Spotface — Countersink — Depth/Deep — All Around — Spherical Dia — Square — Conical Taper — Arc Length — Origin Dimension — Radius

Datum Target — Slope — s Ø Spherical Dia — R Radius

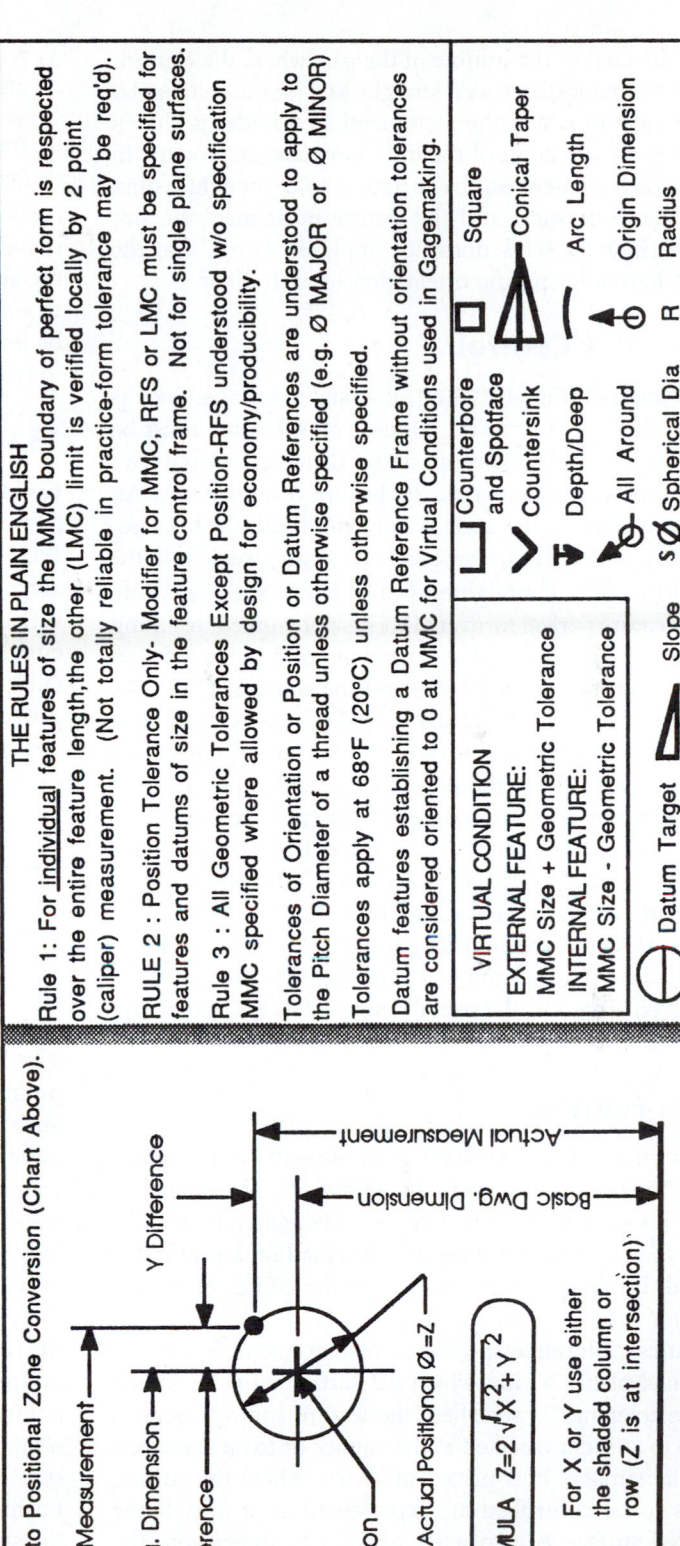

Actual Measurement — Basic Dwg. Dimension — Y Difference — X Difference — True Position — Actual Positional Ø =Z — Origin

FORMULA $Z = 2\sqrt{X^2 + Y^2}$

For X or Y use either the shaded column or row (Z is at intersection)

(p)

FIGURE 13.55 Summary Fact Data Sheets—Continued (p) Conversion Chart

must be directed to the outline of the part where the element to be controlled appears as a straight line. For a rectangular part, the view in which the aforementioned leader is shown determines the direction of the indicator movement zone. In this case, each element on the surface is to be straight within the specified tolerance, and the feature must meet the size tolerance (Rule 1). This does not imply, however, that the elements have any specific orientation to each other.

13.8.3 Axis Control

For **axis control** [Fig. 13.55(c)], if straightness of an axis is specified, the leader from the feature control frame must be directed to the size dimension, and a diameter symbol ($\emptyset$) must precede the tolerance in the feature control frame. An exception is made if the zone is not cylindrical. In this case, explanatory notes may be necessary for clarity, such as **THIS DIRECTION ONLY**. If straightness of an axis is specified, Rule 1 (single feature perfect form at MMC) is not implied, resulting in a virtual size condition that is the sum (or difference for an internal feature) of the local size and the straightness.

Caution should be exercised if straightness is used on a per-unit basis, such as ($\emptyset$) .001/1.00. The resulting virtual condition is more than the per-unit tolerance multiplied by the length because we are dealing with a curve not a slope— .001/1.00 over a 4.00 length is .016, not .004. The formulas on the SFDS of Fig. 13.55(a) under **STRAIGHTNESS ON A UNIT BASIS** are used. First compute the radius, knowing the height of .001 and the unit length of .001 (125.005 in this case). Then solve for h, the height of the zone, knowing the radius of 125.005 and the overall length of 4.00. The answer is .016!

13.8.4 Flatness

Flatness means that a surface has all elements in one plane [Fig. 13.55(d)]. Flatness must be within the size tolerance, but has no orientation requirement. Therefore, it may be tilted in the size zone. If flatness is specified on a unit basis, it should be specified as shown in the SFDS of Figure 13.55(d).

A **flatness tolerance** specifies a tolerance zone defined by two parallel planes within which the surface must lie. When a flatness tolerance is specified, the feature control frame is attached to a leader directed to the surface or to an extension line of the surface. It is placed in a view where the surface elements to be controlled are represented by a line. If the considered surface is associated with a size dimension, the flatness must be less than the size tolerance.

13.8.5 Circularity

Here, an element of a surface of revolution is a round or circular line [Fig. 13.55(e)]. **Circularity** is verified at various locations, independently and relative to the derived axis, on a surface of revolution. Circularity is a condition of a surface of revolution where:

1. For a cylinder or cone, all points of the surface intersected by any plane perpendicular to a common axis are equidistant from that axis.
2. For a sphere, all points of the surface intersected by any plane passing through a common center are equidistant from that center.

A **circularity tolerance** specifies a tolerance zone bounded by two concentric circles within which each circular element of the surface must lie, and applies independently at any plane described in the preceding list. The circularity tolerance must be less than the size tolerance, except for those parts subject to free state variation.

13.8.6 Cylindricity

Cylindricity is a condition of a surface of revolution in which all points of the surface are equidistant from a common axis [Fig. 13.55(f)]. A **cylindricity tolerance** specifies a tolerance zone bounded by two concentric cylinders within which the surface must lie. In the case of cylindricity, unlike that of circularity, the tolerance applies simultaneously to both circular and longitudinal elements of the surface, i.e., the entire surface. The leader from the feature control frame may be directed to either view. The cylindricity tolerance must be less than the size tolerance.

13.9 Profile Tolerances

A **profile** is the outline of a 2D part in a given plane. Profiles are formed by projecting a 3D figure onto a plane or by taking cross sections through the figure. The elements of a profile are straight lines, arcs, and other curved lines. If the drawing specifies individual tolerances for the elements or points of a profile, these elements or points must be individually verified. Such a procedure may be impractical in certain cases, particularly where accuracy of the entire profile, rather than elements of a profile, is a design requirement. With profile tolerancing, the true profile may be defined by basic radii, basic angular dimensions, basic coordinate dimensions, formulas, or undimensioned drawings.

Profile tolerances may be related to a datum, and although the considered feature may not be modified, a related datum of size may be specified at MMC. The profile tolerance specifies a uniform boundary along the true profile within which the elements of the surface must lie. It is used to control form or combinations of size, form, and orientation. If used as a refinement of size, the profile tolerance must be contained within the size limits. Profile tolerances are specified as follows:

1. An appropriate view or section is drawn showing the desired basic profile.
2. Depending on design requirements, the tolerance may be divided bilaterally to both sides of the true profile or applied unilaterally to either side of the true profile. If an equally disposed bilateral tolerance is intended, it is necessary to show only the feature control frame with a leader directed to the surface. For an unequally disposed or a unilateral tolerance, phantom lines are drawn parallel to the true profile to indicate the line is extended to the feature control

frame. The phantom line need extend only a sufficient distance to make its application clear.

3. If a profile tolerance applies all around the profile of a part, the symbol used to designate "all around" is placed on the leader from the feature control frame. If segments of a profile have different tolerances, the extent of each profile tolerance is indicated by the use of reference letters to identify the extremities or limits of each requirement. Similarly, if some segments of the profile are controlled by a profile tolerance and other segments by individually toleranced dimensions, the extent of the profile tolerance must be indicated.

13.9.1   Profile of a Line

If a datum is specified in conjunction with a profile tolerance, it orients the tolerance zone in a manner similar to the way a zone is oriented by a datum in parallelism. As an example, an element of a surface is made up of one or more basic curves, arcs, straight lines (may be at angles), or other shapes, all of which are described by BASIC dimensions [Fig. 13.55(g)].

13.9.2   Profile of a Surface

If the surface is made up of one or more basic curves, arcs, straight lines, or other shapes, all of which are described by BASIC dimensions [Fig. 13.55(h)], some segments of a surface may be controlled by profile tolerancing and other segments by different tolerances. Reference letters are used to define the extent of a controlled segment, such as FROM A TO B. Points A and B are directed to the appropriate location on the considered surface. If the relationship of features is to be zero at MMC, specify by placing a 0 in the control frame or with a note, e.g., PERFECT ORIENTATION REQUIRED AT MMC. The orientation tolerance may then be equal to or less than the amount the feature deviates from MMC, thus protecting the overall size envelope from virtual increase.

13.10   Orientation Tolerances

Orientation tolerances are parallelism, perpendicularity, and angularity. All require at least one datum specification. Some, such as perpendicularity, may use an additional (secondary) datum to stabilize the zone in the proper attitude. Orientation tolerances may use element controls rather than surface requirements. In this case, *each element* or *each radial element* is specified below the feature control frame to be invoked.

Angularity, parallelism, perpendicularity, and in some instances profile are orientation tolerances applicable to related features. These tolerances control the orientation of features to one another. They are sometimes referred to as **attitude tolerances.** In specifying orientation tolerances to control angularity, parallelism, perpendicularity, and in some cases profile, the considered feature is related to one or more datum features. Relation to more than one datum feature should be considered if required to stabilize the tolerance zone in more than one direction. Note that angularity, perpendicularity, and parallelism, when applied to plane surfaces, control flatness if a flatness tolerance is not specified.

Tolerance zones require an axis, or all elements of the considered surface, to fall within this zone. If it is a requirement to control only individual line elements of a surface, qualifying notation, such as EACH ELEMENT or EACH RADIAL ELEMENT, is added to the drawing. This permits control of individual elements of the surface independently in relation to the datum and does not limit the total surface to an encompassing zone.

If no variations of orientation, such as perpendicularity, are permitted at the MMC size limit of a feature, the feature control frame contains a zero for the tolerance, modified by the symbol for MMC. If the feature is finished at its MMC limit of size, it must be perfect in orientation with respect to the datum. A tolerance can exist only as the feature deviates from MMC. The allowable orientation tolerance is equal to the amount of such deviation.

13.10.1   Angularity

Angularity is the condition of a surface or axis at a specified angle other than 90° from a datum plane or axis [Fig. 13.55(i)]. An **angularity tolerance** specifies one of the following:

1. A tolerance zone defined by two parallel planes at the specified basic angle from a datum plane or axis within which the surface of the considered feature must lie.
2. A tolerance zone defined by two parallel planes at the specified basic angle from a datum plane or axis within which the axis of the considered feature must lie.

13.10.2   Perpendicularity

Perpendicularity is the condition of a surface, center plane, or axis at a right angle to a datum plane or axis [Fig. 13.55(j)]. A **perpendicularity tolerance** specifies one of the following:

1. A tolerance zone defined by two parallel planes perpendicular to a datum plane, or axis, within which the surface or center plane of the considered feature must lie.
2. A tolerance zone defined by two parallel planes perpendicular to a datum axis within which the axis of the considered feature must lie.
3. A cylindrical tolerance zone perpendicular to a datum plane within which the axis of the considered feature must lie.
4. A tolerance zone defined by two parallel lines perpendicular to a datum plane, or axis, within which an element of the surface must lie.

13.10.3   Parallelism

Parallelism is the condition of a surface equidistant at all points from a datum plane or an axis equidistant at all points from a datum plane or an axis equidistant along its length to a datum axis [Fig. 13.55(k)]. A **parallelism tolerance** specifies one of the following:

1. A tolerance zone defined by two planes or lines parallel to a datum plane, or axis, within which the line elements of the surface or axis of the considered feature must lie.

2. A cylindrical tolerance zone whose axis is parallel to a datum axis within which the axis of the considered feature must lie.

You May Complete Exercises 13.1 Through 13.4 at This Time

13.11   Runout Tolerances

Runout is a composite tolerance used to control the functional relationship of one or more features of a part to a datum axis. The types of features controlled by runout tolerances include those surfaces constructed around a datum axis and those constructed at right angles to a datum axis.

Runout tolerances control the composite form, orientation, and position relative to a datum axis [Fig. 13.55(l) and (m)]. Each considered feature must be within its runout tolerance when the part is rotated about the datum axis. This may also include the datum features as a part of the runout tolerance control where so designated. The tolerance specified for a controlled surface is the total tolerance or full indicator movement (FIM).

The two types of runout control are circular and total. The type used depends on design requirements and manufacturing considerations. Circular runout is normally a less complex requirement than total runout.

13.11.1   Circular Runout

Circular runout is the condition of a circular element on the surface with respect to a fixed point during one complete revolution of the part about the datum axis [Fig. 13.55(l)]. Circular runout provides control of circular elements of a surface. The tolerance is applied independently at any circular cross section as the part is rotated 360°. If applied to surfaces constructed around a datum axis, circular runout may be used to control the cumulative variations of circularity and coaxiality. If applied to surfaces constructed at right angles to the datum axis, circular runout controls circular elements of a plane surface (wobble).

13.11.2   Total Runout

Total runout [Fig. 13.55(m)] is the condition of a surface with respect to a perfect counterpart of itself, perfectly oriented and positioned. The indicator is moved across the feature, relative to the desired geometry, as the part is rotated about the datum axis.

Total runout provides composite control of all surface elements. The tolerance is applied simultaneously to all circular and profile measuring positions as the part is rotated 360°. If applied to surfaces constructed around a datum axis, total runout is used to control cumulative variations of circularity, straightness, coaxiality, angularity, taper, and profile of a sur-

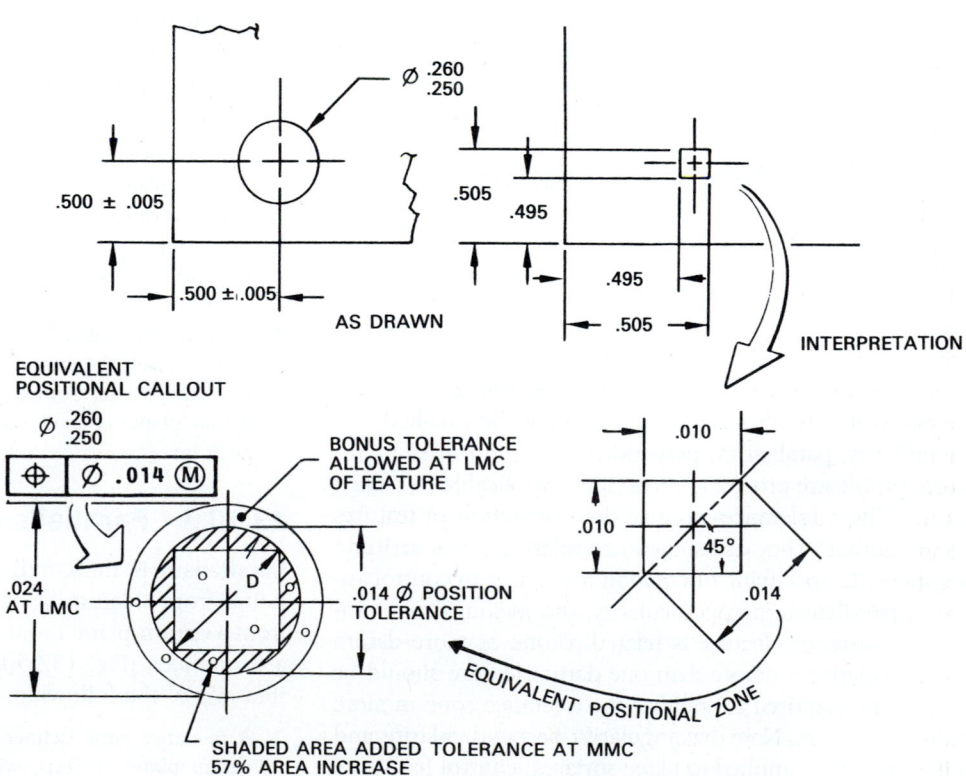

FIGURE 13.56 **Position Rectangular coordinate comparison**

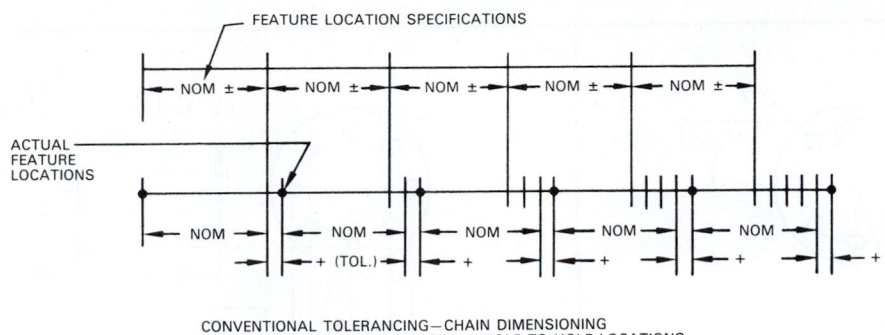

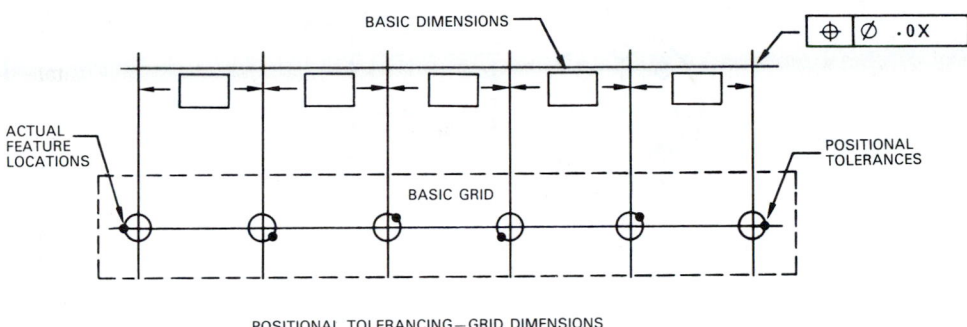

FIGURE 13.57 Conventional Chain Versus the Positional Grid System Comparison

face. If applied to surfaces constructed at right angles to a datum axis, total runout controls cumulative variations of perpendicularity to detect wobble and flatness to detect concavity or convexity.

13.11.3 Position

Position is a total zone specification such as a diameter or total width centered on the basic location of the axis, center plane, or center point of a feature from the true position with respect to datum(s) [Fig. 13.55(n)].

Locating a hole with rectangular coordinates and ± tolerances yields a square or rectangular zone. Provisions must be made for the worst case location for the axis of the mating features, at the diagonal. Inscribing this square with a circle does not change the mating relationship, but it does yield a 58% greater area. Additionally, positional tolerances apply at MMC thereby allowing a bonus tolerance as the feature deviates from MMC [Figs. 13.55(p) and 13.56].

Another improvement in the positional tolerancing system is the change from a "chain" or feature-to-feature basis to a "basic grid" system. Thus tolerance accumulations are avoided (Fig. 13.57). The grid for a pattern of zones is perfect in all respects. The locations of each of these zones are in

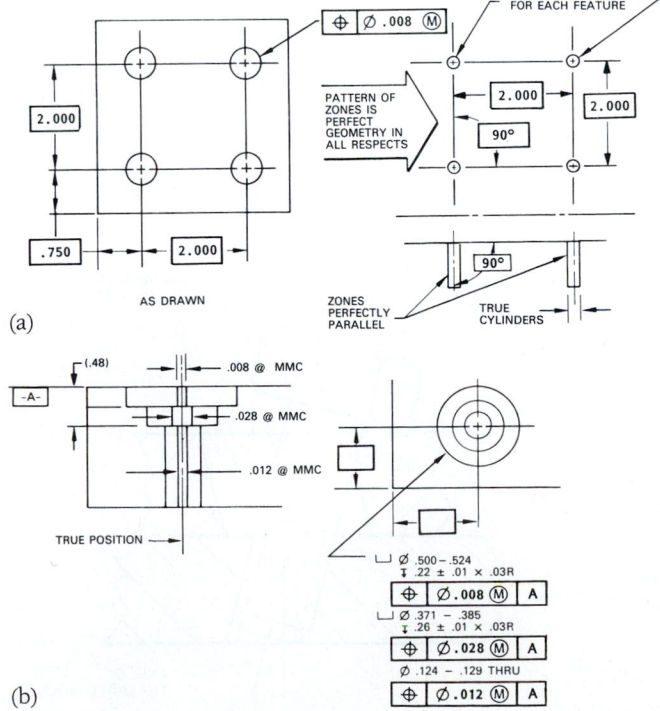

FIGURE 13.58 Positional Pattern—Grid Perfect Construction

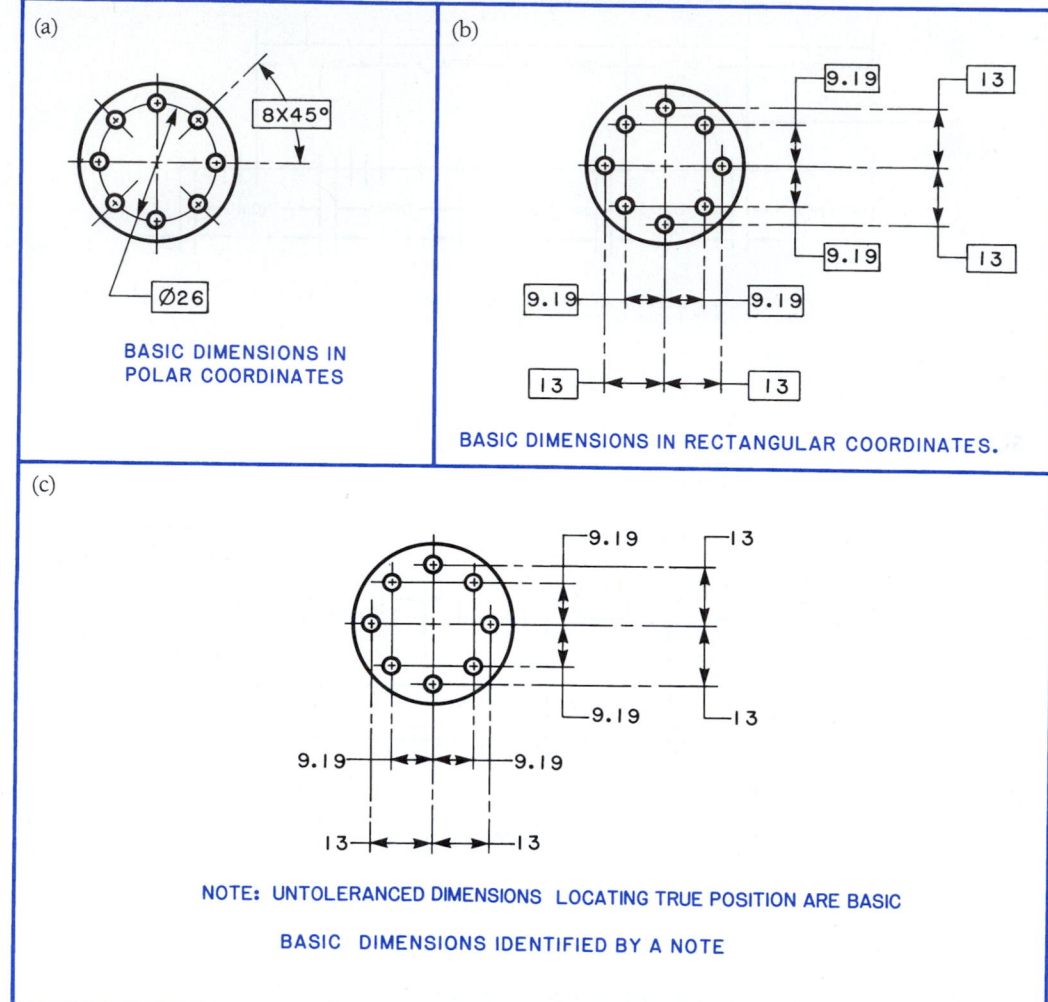

(a) BASIC DIMENSIONS IN POLAR COORDINATES

(b) BASIC DIMENSIONS IN RECTANGULAR COORDINATES.

(c) NOTE: UNTOLERANCED DIMENSIONS LOCATING TRUE POSITION ARE BASIC

BASIC DIMENSIONS IDENTIFIED BY A NOTE

FIGURE 13.59 Identifying Basic Dimensions

perfect relationship to each other. When the pattern of zones is located on a part, even though there may be a pattern locating tolerance, the pattern itself, regardless of its position on the part (tilted or offset), is constructed of perfect geometry (Fig. 13.58). A grid is established by placing **BASIC dimensions** between the features. Also notice that no matter how the BASIC dimensions are applied (in a chain, back and forth, etc.), once tied together with BASICS, they form a perfect grid (Fig. 13.58). Figure 13.59 shows examples of identifying basic dimensions for patterns.

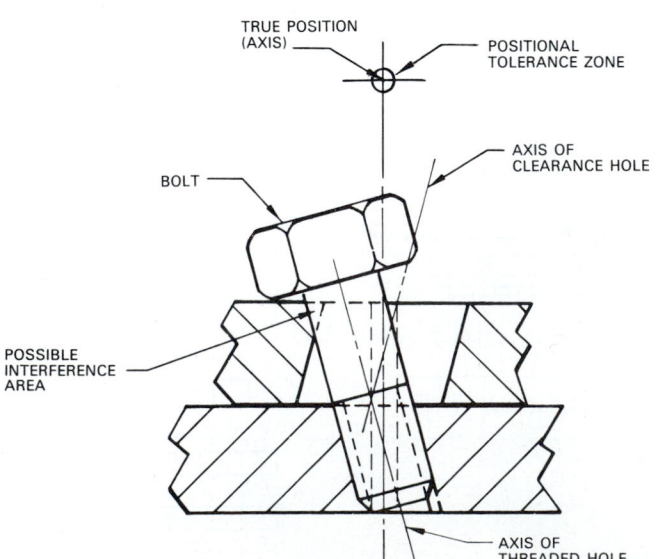

FIGURE 13.60 Interference Without Projected Zones on Tapped/Press Fit Holes

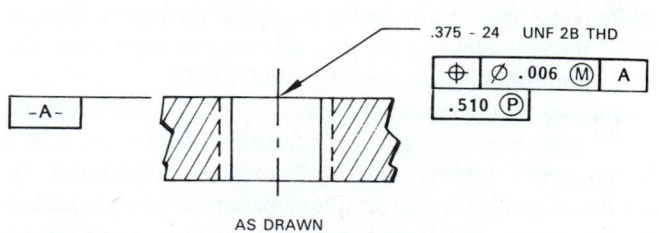

FIGURE 13.61 Projected Zone Specification

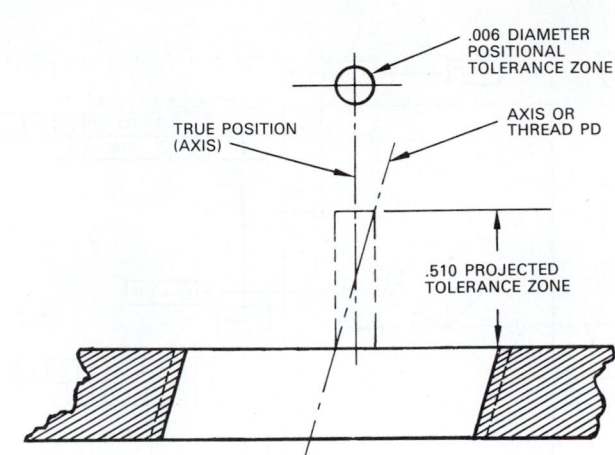

FIGURE 13.62 Projected Tolerance Zone

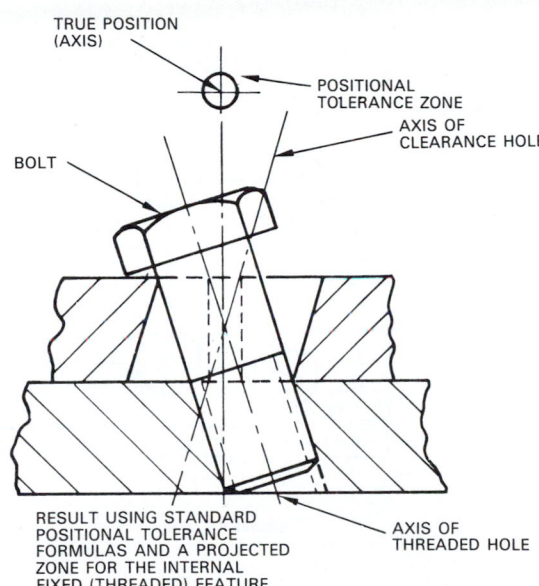

FIGURE 13.63 Projected Zone Eliminates Interference

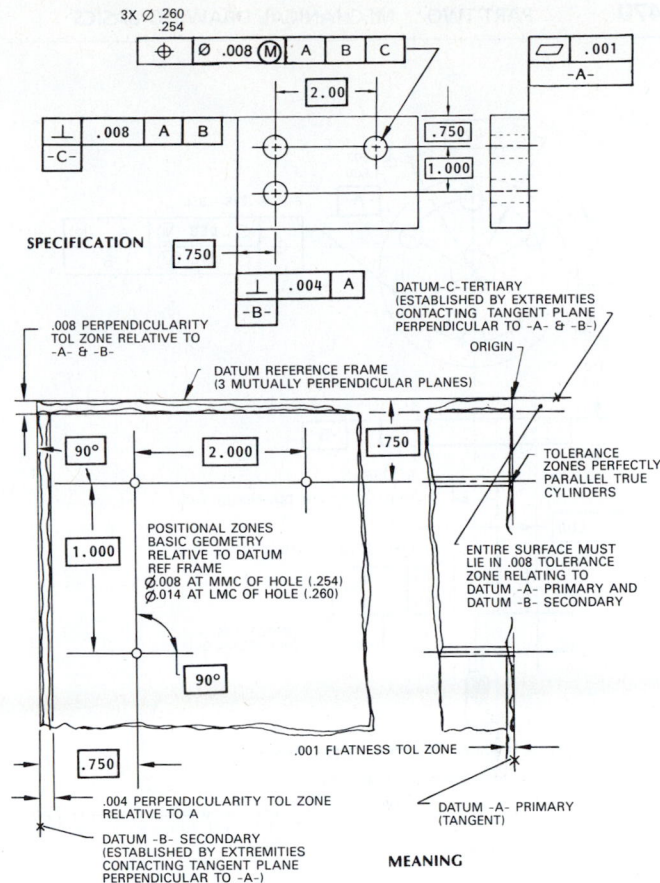

FIGURE 13.64 Positional Pattern Relative to a Datum Reference Frame

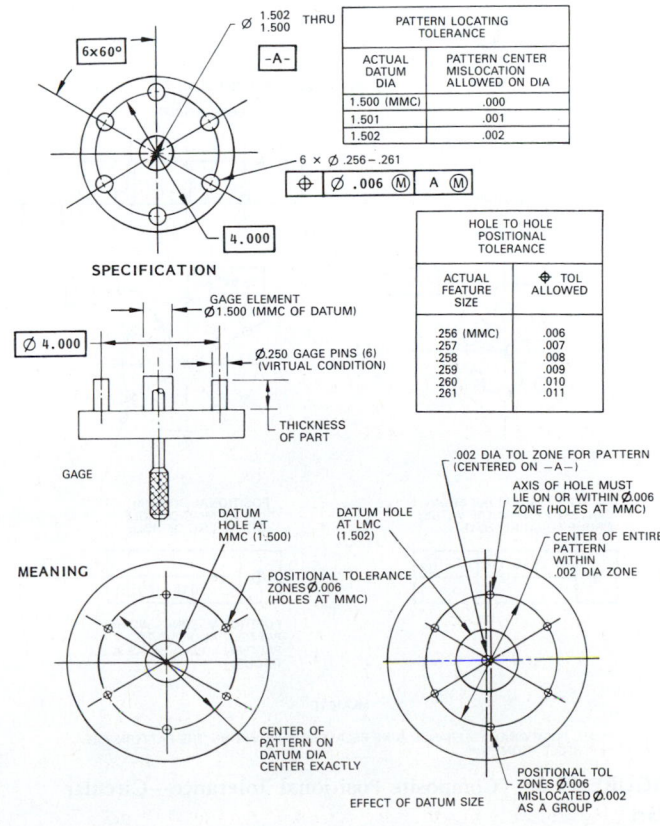

FIGURE 13.65 Pattern Related to Datum Diameter at MMC

To avoid perpendicularity errors, such as the one shown in Figure 13.60, tapped and press fit holes (not clearance holes) utilize projected zones (Fig. 13.61). The resulting zone is now only above the part (Fig. 13.62) and interchangeability is assured (Fig. 13.63).

13.11.4 Positional Patterns

Figures 13.64 through 13.67 are used to show how **patterns** are located on parts. The preference is for composite positional tolerancing, as depicted in Figures 13.66 and 13.67. The use of ± dimensions to locate a pattern is not recommended.

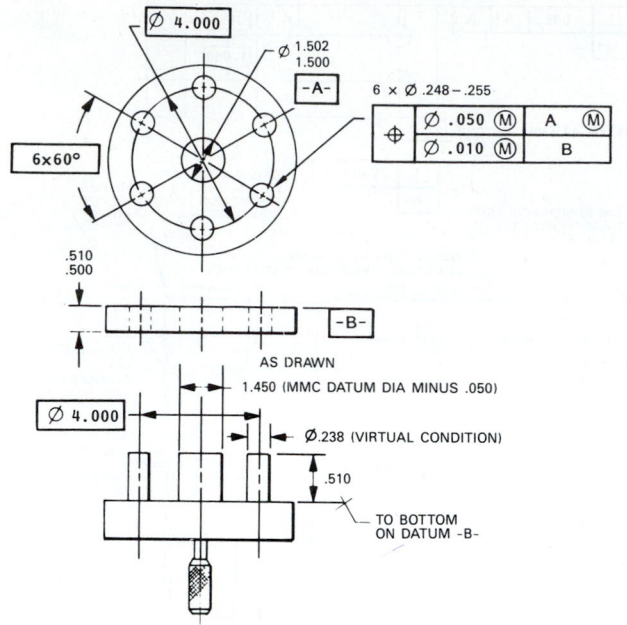

AS DRAWN

GAGE FOR COMPOSITE TOLERANCE

COMPOSITE POSITIONAL TOLERANCE

PATTERN OR GROUP LOCATION (ABOVE)
POSITIONAL ZONES WITHIN PATTERN
(BELOW)

(a)

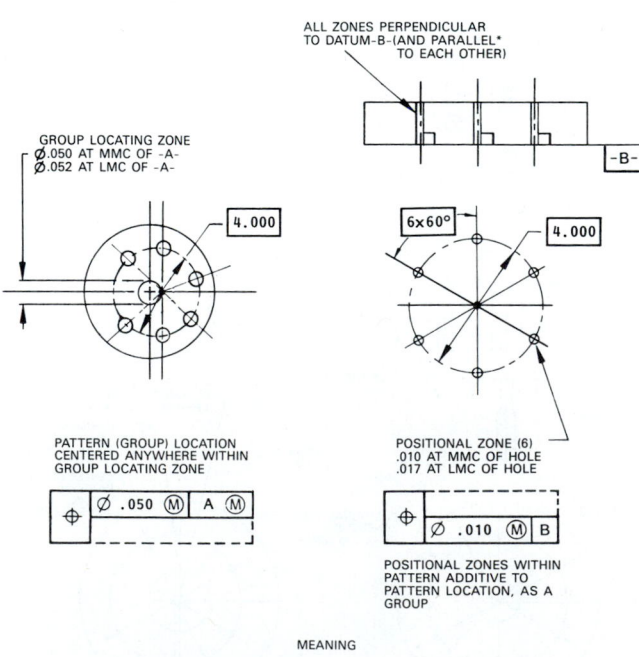

MEANING

* ALL POSITIONAL TOLERANCE ZONE RELATIONSHIPS WITHIN THE PATTERN ARE
PERFECT GEOMETRY

(b)

FIGURE 13.66 Composite Positional Tolerance—Circular Part

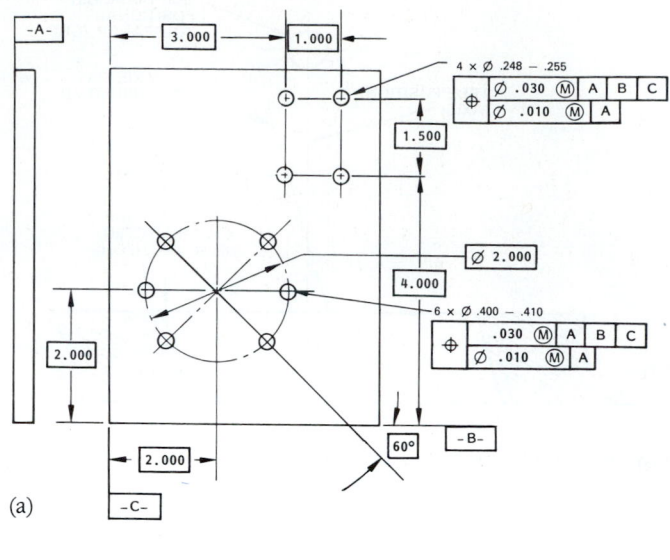

(a)

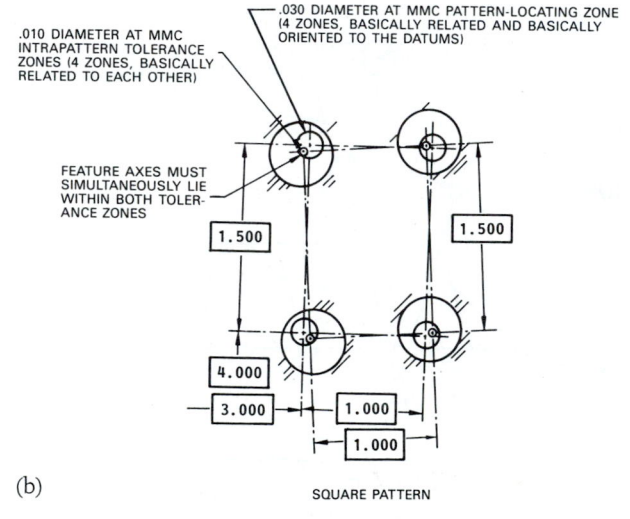

SQUARE PATTERN

(b)

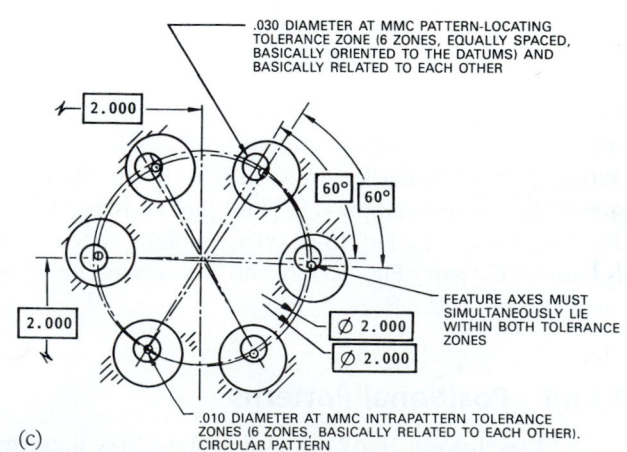

(c)

FIGURE 13.67 Composite Positional Tolerance to Datum Reference Frame

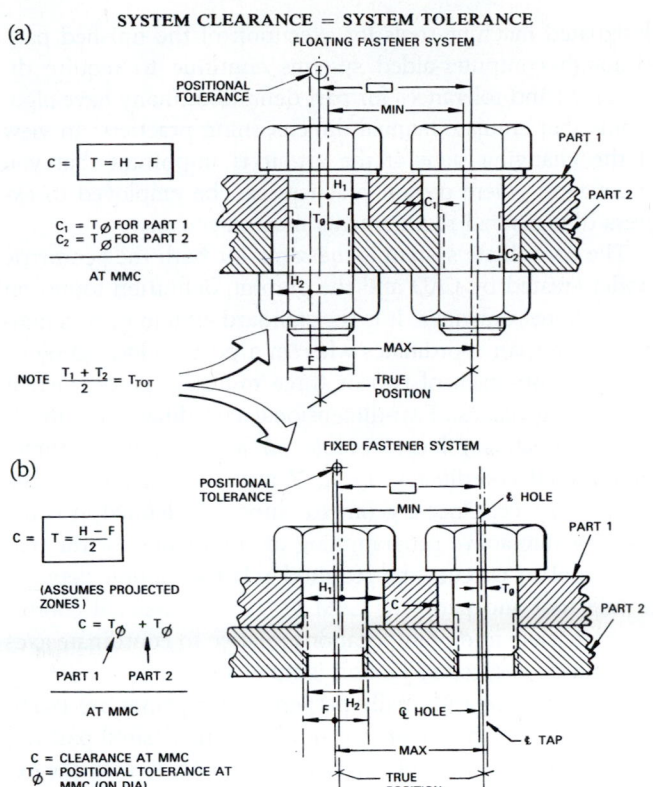

FIGURE 13.68 **Fixed Versus Floating Fastener System**
(a) Floating fastener system (b) Fixed fastener system

13.12 General Positional Tolerance Formulas

Positional tolerance formulas are normally presented in two ways: the **floating** and **fixed fasteners system series.** A floating fastener system is one in which both mating parts contain clearance holes. Therefore, the fastener may be freely "floated" into position between the holes for installation. In the fixed fastener system, one of the mating parts contains clearance holes and the other contains tapped holes or press fit holes or the like, which positively "fix" the position of the fastener during installation. Since there is no clearance between the tap or press fit hole and the fastener, there is only clearance at the clearance holes; in effect, only half the clearance one would find in a floating fastener system (Fig. 13.68).

13.12.1 Fixed and Floating Fastener Formulas

All formula values apply at MMC. In the case of fasteners, they apply at the virtual condition. All formulas (ANSI/ISO) result in a "line to line fit" (no clearance/no interference) worst case and should be used without further modification. The following formulas assume the free assembly of mating parts without restriction. Positional tolerances for tapped or press fit holes are to be projected. The variables are defined as follows:

$$H = \text{MMC Hole Size } \varnothing$$
$$T = \text{Positional Tolerance } \varnothing \text{ at MMC}$$
$$F = \text{Fastener Size } \varnothing \text{ at Virtual Condition}$$

(Aircraft quality fasteners will not virtually exceed nominal thread designations for their entire length.)

Floating Fastener Formulas – Equal Distribution

1. $T = H - F$
2. $H = F + T$

Example: Two parts, each with clearance holes
MMC $\varnothing$ = .264
Fastener Size = .250

$$T = H - F$$
$$T = .264 - .250$$
$$T = .014 \text{ (for all holes—both parts)}$$

Floating Fastener Formulas – Unequal Distribution

$T1 = \text{Positional Tolerance } \varnothing \text{ at MMC for part \#1}$
$T2 = \text{Positional Tolerance } \varnothing \text{ at MMC for part \#2}$
$H1 = \text{MMC Hole Size } \varnothing \text{ for part \#1}$
$H2 = \text{MMC Hole Size } \varnothing \text{ for part \#2}$

3. $T1 = (H1 + H2) - (2F + T2)$
4. $H1 = (T1 + T2) + (2F - H2)$

Example: Two parts, each with clearance holes
Part \#1: MMC $\varnothing$ = .262
Part \#2: MMC $\varnothing$ = .266 Positional Tolerance 0 = .010
Fastener Size = .250

$$T1 = (H1 + H2) - (2F + T2)$$
$$T1 = (.262 + .266) - (.500 + .010)$$
$$T1 = .528 - .510$$
$$\underline{T1 = .018}$$

Fixed Fastener Formulas – Equal Distribution

5. $T = (H - F)/2$
6. $H = F + 2T$

Example: Two parts, one with clearance holes and one with .250 tapped holes
MMC $\varnothing$ **Clearance Holes** = .264
Fastener Size = .250
Tap = .250 – 28 UNF 3B

$$T = (H - F)/2$$
$$T = .264 - .250/2$$
$$T = .007 \text{ (for all holes and taps—both parts projected on taps)}$$

Fixed Fastener Formulas—Unequal Distribution

T1 = Positional Tolerance $\emptyset$ at MMC for part #1
T2 = Positional Tolerance $\emptyset$ on taps for part #2
H1 = MMC Hole Size $\emptyset$ for part #1
H2 = Tapped Hole for part #2

$$7. \quad T1 = H1 - (T2 + F)$$
$$8. \quad H1 = T1 + T2 + F$$

Example: Two parts, one with clearance holes and one with .250 tapped holes

Part #1: Positional Tolerance $\emptyset$ = .008
Part #2: Tap = .250 − 28 UNF 3B
Positional Tolerance $\emptyset$ = .006
Fastener Size = .250

$$H1 = .008 + .006 + .250$$
$$\underline{H1 = .264}$$

13.13   System Tolerance Formulas

The **system tolerance formulas** are easier to use than the fixed or floating in that most cases of fit are covered. Consider the following logical statements:

	Statement	Result
9.	System Clearance = System Tolerance	Line to Line Fit
10.	System Clearance > System Tolerance	Clearance Fit
11.	System Clearance < System Tolerance	Interference Fit

Statement 9 results in a "line to line fit" (the fit, no clearance—no interference, used with the positional tolerance formulas) so this is all we really need to solve for fixed or floating situations and, in fact, most interchangeable situations. Consider the case of a mating precision shaft and hole of the same length. The shaft is .5000–.5008 and the hole is .5020–.5028. The system clearance (always at MMC) is .0012; therefore, we can allocate this amount as the system tolerance as follows: .0006 & .0006 straightness tolerance to each item or $\emptyset$ (at MMC) to the hole and .0012 to the shaft, etc., as long as the *total system clearance = system tolerance.* The same technique may be applied to positional tolerances.

13.14   Tolerancing Using CAD Systems

Industry acceptance of computer-aided design (CAD) and computer-aided manufacturing (CAM) systems for use in component design and fabrication is rapidly accelerating. Collectively, these highly sophisticated systems can be used to describe the desired part as a geometric model, interactively interject manufacturing data, and deliver this information to designated machine tools for execution of the finished part. Although computer-aided systems continue to require dimensions and tolerances for part definition, many have algorithms that emulate manual dimensioning practices. In view of the changing state of the art, it is important that you understand where certain practices can be employed to express dimensional requirements most effectively.

The coordinate system is the same for both the geometric model created by CAD and the graphic definition found on conventional drawings. It is the standard system of rectangular or Cartesian coordinates wherein a point is located by its distance from each of two or three mutually perpendicular intersecting planes. Two-dimensional coordinates (in the **X** and **Y** directions) locate points on a plane, while three-dimensional coordinates (in **X**, **Y** and **Z** directions) locate points in space. Once a geometric model is defined, it is the basis for interactive programming of commands for the machine tool to execute the required relative motion between cutting tool and part. For CAM usage, dimensional coordinates translate into point locations relative to coordinate axes since linear and rotary motion is involved.

For CAD, three mutually perpendicular planes are established from which a geometric model of the desired part can be constructed. These planes normally coincide with the exterior outline of parts having surfaces at right angles. If the part is cylindrical, two of these planes intersect along the axis of the cylinder and the third is perpendicular to it.

For CAM, three mutually perpendicular axes are established along which linear and rotary motions occur in the machine tool used for producing the desired part. Generally, these axes are designated as the basic coordinate axes of the equipment. Additional, or secondary, axes may also be designated, depending on machine capability and part configuration.

The intersection of the **X** axis and **Y** axis forms quadrants. These axes are normally aligned or coincident with appropriate surfaces or features on the desired part. When programming commands for the machine tool, the part should be positioned in a quadrant in such a way that a maximum of positive values will result. For example, if the part is positioned in Quadrant I, positive values will result. If the part is positioned in two or more quadrants, positive and negative values will result, and the potential for error is greater. This precaution is generally not necessary when programming on the computer, but helpful when programming without computer assistance. The considerations described above also apply to quadrants formed by intersections of the **X-Z** and **Y-Z** axes.

13.14.1   Guidelines for Dimensioning and Tolerancing

Recommended guidelines for dimensioning and tolerancing practices for use in defining parts using CAD/CAM are as follows:

1. Major features of a part are used to establish the basic coordinate system for initial part definition. These features may or may not be subsequently identified as datum features.

2. For final part definition, any number of subcoordinate systems may be used to locate and orient features of a part. These systems, however, must be geometrically related to the basic coordinate system of the given part.

3. Define part features in relation to three mutually perpendicular reference planes. Establish these planes along features that parallel the axes and motions of CAM equipment, wherever possible.

4. The assignment of datum features is based primarily on the functional requirements of the part.

5. Dimension the part so that its geometric shape is completely defined and mathematically precise.

6. Regular geometric profiles such as ellipses, parabolas, hyperbolas, etc., may be defined on the drawing by mathematical formulas. CAM equipment can be programmed to generate these profiles by linear interpolation, that is, a series of short straight lines whose endpoints are spaced close enough to approximate the desired profile within the specified profile tolerance.

7. A part surface whose profile is defined on the drawing by a mathematical formula should not be coordinately dimensioned unless specific dimensions are required for inspection or identified as reference information.

8. For arbitrary profiles, the drawing should specify appropriate points on the profile by coordinate dimensions or provide a table of coordinates. When determining the number of points needed to define the profile, keep in mind that the tighter the tolerance or the smaller the radius of curvature, the closer together the points should be.

9. Profiles may also be defined by other coordinate systems, such as polar, spherical, or cylindrical, as applicable. However, it is desirable to use the same coordinate system on a given drawing.

10. Any change in profile should be clearly defined with prime consideration given to design intent. Precise continuity of the profile is necessary for CAD.

11. A circular pattern of holes may be defined by polar coordinate dimensions. Location and orientation of the pattern must be clearly shown.

12. Where possible, express angular dimensions in degrees and decimal parts of a degree.

13. Limit dimensioning should be avoided except where limits are standardized—for example, preferred "limits and fits."

14. If plus and minus tolerancing is used, the tolerance should be bilateral and not unilateral. Equal plus and minus values are preferred. Positional tolerancing is recommended for locating features of size.

15. Geometric tolerances are specified in all cases where the control of specified geometric characteristics of part features is required. Where applicable, identifying datum features on the drawing and referencing them in an order of precedence will clearly indicate their usage for CAM.

Dimensional changes of small magnitude seldom require a change to the graphic definition on conventional drawings. Either the graphic definition remains within acceptable drawing accuracy, or the revised dimensional values are underlined, indicating that dimensions are not to scale. For CAD applications, dimension changes of any magnitude must be made in the database, which requires graphic reiteration. This must be done to ensure mathematical accuracy of changed values and to maintain the integrity of the CAD/CAM database.

Geometric tolerances may be added from a menu (Fig. 13.69) where the drafter specifies the tolerance on the screen

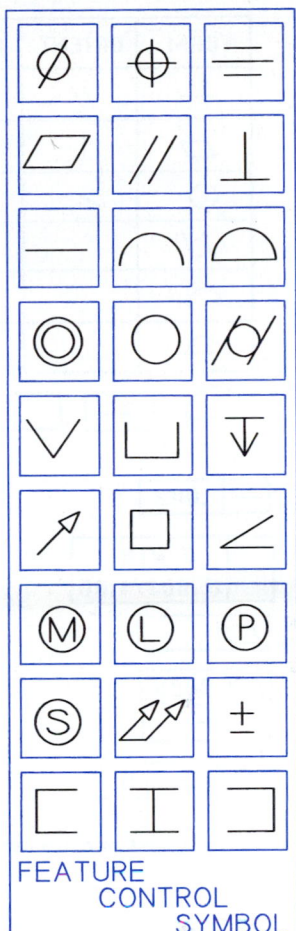

FIGURE 13.69   Geometric Tolerance Menu

(Fig. 13.70). Several versions are used on microcomputers. Completed feature control frames may be copied from a library that may be placed on the screen simultaneously with the considered drawing (Fig. 13.71). Figure 13.72 shows a geometric tolerancing feature control frame being added to a detail of a part using CAD commands.

13.15   Limits and Fits

Production, in general, and inspection, in particular, benefit from the use of standard limits. ANSI B4.2 and ISO 286 describe the system. The ISO system has more than 500 possible tolerance zones for holes and shafts, ANSI about 150. Many products may be standardized by using the system of limits and fits such as drills, reamers, clevis pins, bushings, keys, keyways, gages, and bolts. **Renard preferred numbers** are used in the metric system in conjunction with limits and fits to maximize the standardization. The tables presented herein are not restricted the preferred numbers. Sizes in design are sometimes determined predominantly by stress, weight, thermal considerations, and other factors besides cost.

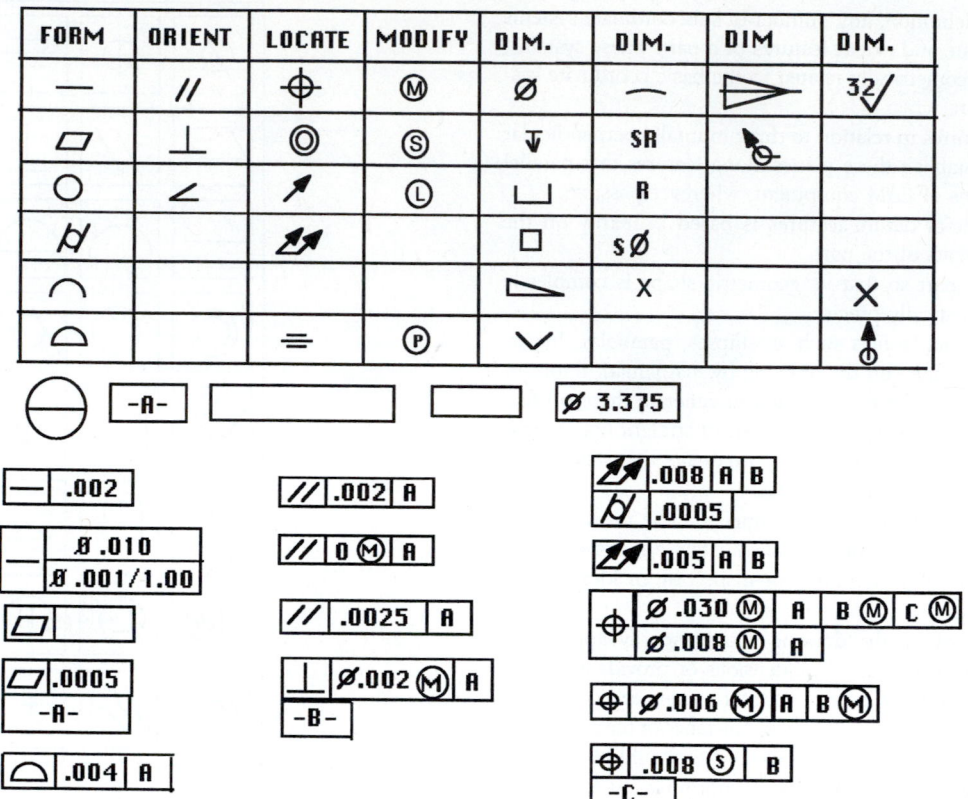

FIGURE 13.70   Placing Feature Control Frames for Geometric Tolerances

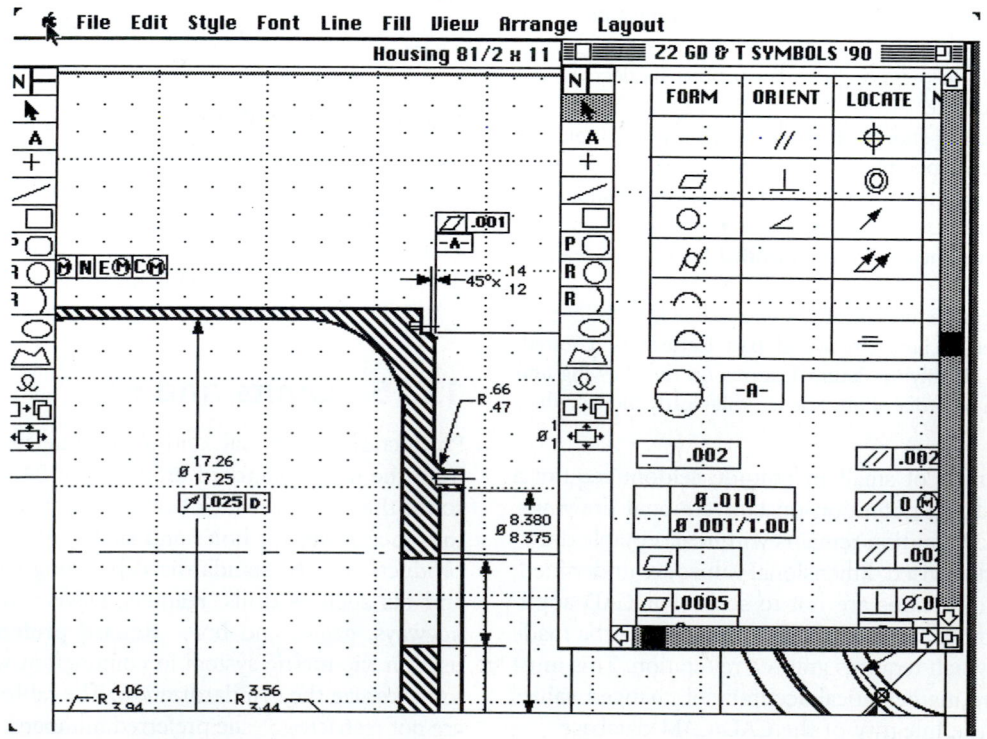

FIGURE 13.71   Geometric Tolerance Menu

(a)

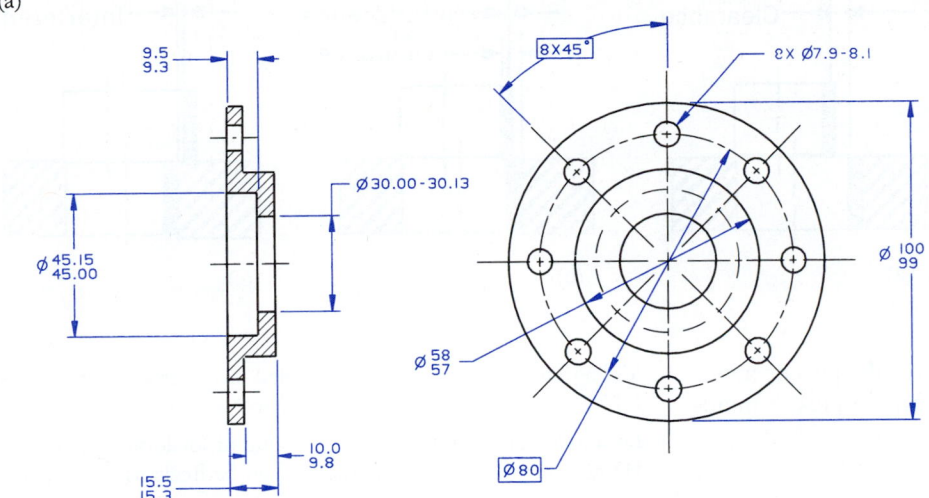

(b)

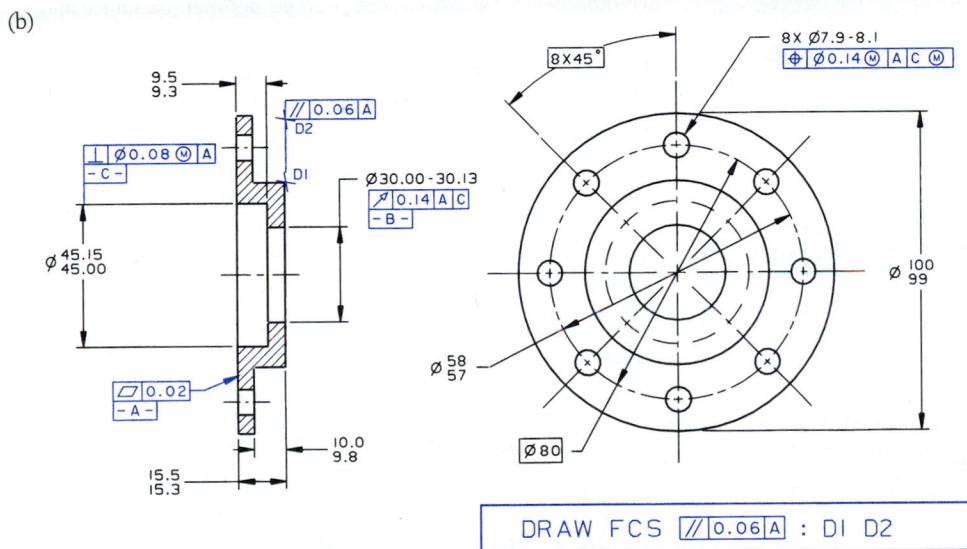

DRAW FCS //|0.06|A : D1 D2

FIGURE 13.72 Geometric Tolerance Frames and Symbols Placed on a Drawing
(a) Dimensions (b) Feature control symbols

Fits fall into three basic types: **clearance**, where there is always clearance; **transition**, where there may be clearance or interference based on where the parts fall in the tolerance range; and **interference**, where there is always interference (Fig. 13.73). The assumption used in "limits and fits" is the Taylor principle (or USA Rule 1)—each individual feature is in perfect form at MMC.

Limits and directly applied tolerance values are specified as follows:

1. **Limit dimensioning** The high limit (maximum value) is placed above the low limit (minimum value). When expressed in a single line, the low limit precedes the high limit and a dash separates the two values.
2. **Plus and minus tolerancing** The dimension is given first and is followed by a plus and minus expression of tolerance.

13.15.1 Single Limits

For **single limits**, MIN or MAX is placed after a dimension where other elements of the design definitely determine the other unspecified limit. Features such as depth of holes, length of threads, corner radii, chamfers, etc., may be limited in this way. Single limits are used where the intent will be clear, and the unspecified limit can be zero or approach infinity and will not result in a condition detrimental to the design.

13.15.2 Tolerance Expression

The conventions pertaining to the number of decimal places carried are different for metric and inch drawings. Where millimeter dimensions are used on the drawings, the following

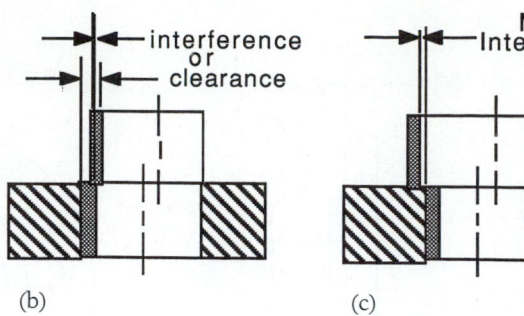

FIGURE 13.73 Basic Types of Fits (a) Clearance fit (b) Transition fit (c) Interference fit

applies. For **unilateral tolerancing**, when the plus or minus value is nil, a single zero is shown without a plus or minus sign:

Example:

$$32 \begin{matrix} 0 \\ -0.02 \end{matrix} \quad \text{or} \quad 32 \begin{matrix} +.02 \\ 0 \end{matrix}$$

Where **bilateral tolerancing** is used, both the plus and minus values have the same number of decimal places, using zeros where necessary:

Example:

$$32 \begin{matrix} +.25 \\ -.10 \end{matrix} \quad \text{not} \quad 32 \begin{matrix} +.25 \\ -.1 \end{matrix}$$

Where **limit dimensioning** is used and either the maximum or minimum value has digits following a decimal point, the other value has zeros added for uniformity:

Example:

$$\begin{matrix} 25.45 \\ 25.00 \end{matrix} \quad \text{not} \quad \begin{matrix} 25.45 \\ 25 \end{matrix}$$

Where **inch dimensions** are used on the drawing, both limit dimensions or the plus and minus tolerance and its dimension are expressed with the same number of decimal places:

Examples:

$$.500 + .005 \quad \text{not} \quad .50 + .005$$

$$\begin{matrix} +.005 \\ -.000 \end{matrix} \quad \text{not} \quad \begin{matrix} +.005 \\ 0 \end{matrix}$$

$$25.0 + .2 \quad \text{not} \quad 25 + .2$$

13.15.3   Preferred Metric Fits

For metric application of limits and fits, the tolerance may be indicated by a basic size and tolerance symbol. See ANSI B4.2 for complete information on this system. The preferred metric fits are defined as follows:

Loose Running H11/c11	suitable for wide commercial tolerances or allowances on external members
Free Running H9/d9	not suitable for use where accuracy is essential, but good for large temperature variations, high running speeds, or heavy journal pressures
Close Running H8/f7	suitable for running on accurate machines and for accurate location at moderate speeds and journal pressures

Sliding Fit H7/g6	not intended to run freely, but to move and turn freely and to locate accurately
Locational Clearance H7/h6	provides snug fit for locating stationary parts, but can be freely assembled and disassembled
Locational Transition H7/k6	suitable for accurate location; a compromise between clearance and interference
Locational Transition H7/n6	for more accurate location where greater interference is permissible
Locational Interference H7/p6	suitable for parts requiring rigidity and alignment with prime accuracy of location, but without special bore pressure required
Medium Drive H7/s6	suitable for ordinary steel parts or shrink fits on light sections, tightest fit usable with cast iron
Force Fit H7/u6	suitable for parts that may be highly stressed or for shrink fits where the heavy pressing forces required may be impractical

13.15.4   Preferred Inch Fits

The classes of fits are arranged in three general groups: running and sliding fits, locational fits, and force fits. **Running** and **sliding** fits provide a similar running performance, with suitable lubrication allowance, throughout the range of sizes. The clearances for the first two classes, used chiefly as slide fits, increase more slowly with the diameter than for the other classes, so the accurate location is maintained even at the expense of free relative motion. The first ten preferences for inch fits are as follows: RC 4, RC 7, RC 9, LC 2, LC 5, LT3, LT6, LN 2, FN2, and FN4. Running and sliding fits are described below:

RC 1   Close sliding fits are intended for the accurate location of parts that must assemble without perceptible play.

RC 2   Sliding fits are intended for accurate location, but with greater maximum clearance than class RC 1. Parts made to this fit move and turn easily but are not intended to run freely; in the larger sizes, they may seize with small temperature changes.

RC 3   Precision running fits are about the closest fits that can be expected to run freely, and they are intended for precision work at slow speeds and light journal pressures, but are not suitable where appreciable temperature differences are likely to be encountered.

RC 4   Close running fits are intended chiefly for running fits on accurate machinery with moderate surface speeds and journal pressures, where accurate location and minimum play is desired.

RC 5 and RC 6   Medium running fits are intended for higher running speeds, or heavy journal pressures, or both.

RC 7   Free running fits are intended for use where accuracy is not essential, or where large temperature variations are likely to be encountered, or under both these conditions.

RC 8 and RC 9   Loose running fits are intended for use where wide commercial tolerances may be necessary, together with an allowance, on the external member.

13.15.5   Locational Fits

Locational fits are fits intended to determine only the location of the mating parts; they may provide rigid or accurate location, as with interference fits, or provide some freedom of location, as with clearance fits. Accordingly, they are divided into three groups: **clearance fits (LC)**, **transition fits (LT)**, and **interference fits (LN)** and are described below:

LC   Locational clearance fits are intended for parts that are normally stationary, but which can be freely assembled or disassembled. They range from snug fits for parts requiring accuracy of location, through the medium clearance fits for parts such as spigots, to the looser fastener fits where freedom of assembly is of prime importance.

LT   Locational transition fits are a compromise between clearance and interference fits, for application where accuracy of location is important, but either a small amount of clearance or interference is permissible.

LN   Locational interference fits are used where accuracy of location is of prime importance and for parts requiring rigidity and alignment with no special requirements for bore pressure. Such fits are not intended for parts designed to transmit frictional loads from one part to another by virtue of the tightness of fit, because these conditions are covered by force fits.

13.15.6   Force or Shrink Fits

Force or **shrink** fits constitute a special type of interference fit, normally characterized by maintenance of constant bore pressures throughout the range of sizes. The interference therefore varies almost directly with diameter, and the difference between its minimum and maximum value is small, to maintain the resulting pressures within reasonable limits.

FN 1   Light drive fits are those requiring light assembly pressures, and they produce more or less permanent assemblies. They are suitable for thin sections or long fits, or in cast-iron external members.

FN 2   Medium drive fits are suitable for ordinary steel parts or for shrink fits on light sections. They are about the tightest fits that can be used with high-grade cast-iron external members.

FN 3   Heavy drive fits are suitable for heavier steel parts or for shrink fits in medium sections.

FN 4 and FN 5   Force fits are suitable for parts that can be highly stressed or for shrink fits where the heavy pressing forces required are impractical.

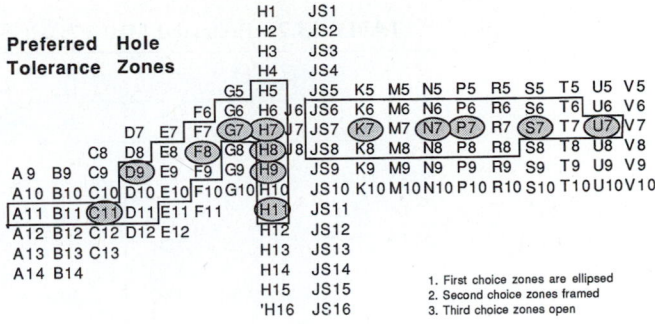

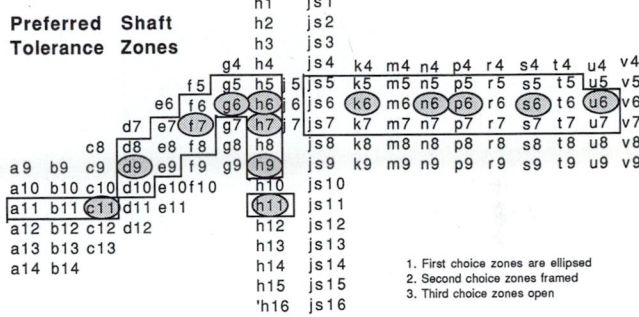

FIGURE 13.74   Preferred (Standardized) Tolerance Zones

13.15.7   Preferred Tolerance Zones

A profile tolerance may be applied to an entire surface or to individual profiles taken at various cross sections through the part. **Preferred tolerance zones** are shown in Figure 13.74. These two cases are provided for as follows:

1. For the profile of a surface, the tolerance zone established by the profile of a surface tolerance is three dimensional, extending along the length, width, or circumference of the considered feature or features. This may be applied to parts having a constant cross section to parts having a surface of revolution, or to parts defined by profile tolerances as applying **ALL OVER** indicated below the feature control frame, such as castings.

2. For the profile of a line, the tolerance is two dimensional, extending along the length of the considered feature. This applies to the profiles of parts having a varying cross section, such as the tapered wing of an aircraft, or to random cross sections of parts where the entire surface of the feature is not controlled as a single entity.

A **positional tolerance** defines a zone within which the center, axis, or center plane of a feature of size is permitted to vary from true position. Basic dimensions establish the true position from specified datum features and between interrelated features. A positional tolerance is indicated by the position symbol, a tolerance, and appropriate datum references placed in a feature control frame.

13.15.8   Metric Preferred Sizes

Metric preferred sizes are based on the Renard series of preferred numbers. The first choice is rounded off from the

TABLE 13.2 Preferred Metric Basic Sizes (B.S.4318)

Choice			Choice			Choice		
1st	2nd	3rd	1st	2nd	3rd	1st	2nd	3rd
1					23			122
	1.1				24		125	
1.2			25					128
		1.3			26	130		
	1.4			28				132
		1.5	30				135	
1.6				32				138
		1.7			34	140		
	1.8		35					142
		1.9			36		145	
2				38				148
		2.1	40			150		
	2.2			42				152
		2.4			44		155	
2.5			45					158
		2.6			46	160		
	2.8			48				162
3			50				165	
		3.2		52				168
	3.5				54	170		
		3.8	55				175	
4					56			178
		4.2		58		180		
	4.5		60					182
		4.8		62			185	
5					64			188
		5.2	65			190		
	5.5				66			192
		5.8		68			195	
6			70					198
		6.2		72		200		
	6.5				74			205
		6.8	75				210	
	7				76			215
		7.5		78		220		
8			80					225
		8.5			82		230	
	9			85				235
		9.5			88	240		
10			90					245
	11				92		250	
12				95				255
		13			98	260		
	14		100					265
		15			102		270	
16				105				275
		17	110					285
	18				108		290	
		19			112			295
20				115		300		
	21				118			
	22		120					

R10 series where succeeding numbers each increase by 25%. The second choice are rounded off from the R20 series, which has 12% increments. The rationale for first choice sizes is the selection of every second number in the series such as 1, 1.6, 2.5, etc. This series is rounded off from the R5 series of preferred numbers in which the increments are 60%. Preferred sizes from 1 to 300 are given in metric (Table 13.2) and .01 to 20.00 in inches (Table 13.3). To avoid unnecessary multiplicity of tools and gages, common fits, preferred tolerance zones, and preferred numbers should be selected from the tables. The **hole basis system** is the preferred system for selecting standard tools and gages.

TABLE 13.3 Preferred Basic Sizes in Inches

Decimal			Fractional					
0.010	2.00	8.50	1/64	0.015625	2¼	2.2500	9½	9.5000
0.012	2.20	9.00	1/32	0.03125	2½	2.5000	10	10.0000
0.016	2.40	9.50	1/16	0.0625	2¾	2.7500	10½	10.5000
0.020	2.60	10.00	3/32	0.09375	3	3.0000	11	11.0000
0.025	2.80	10.50	1/8	0.1250	3¼	3.2500	11½	11.5000
0.032	3.00	11.00	5/32	0.15625	3½	3.5000	12	12.0000
0.040	3.20	11.50	3/16	0.1875	3¾	3.7500	12½	12.5000
0.05	3.40	12.00	1/4	0.2500	4	4.0000	13	13.0000
0.06	3.60	12.50	5/16	0.3125	4¼	4.2500	13½	13.5000
0.08	3.80	13.00	3/8	0.3750	4½	4.5000	14	14.0000
0.10	4.00	13.50	7/16	0.4375	4¾	4.7500	14½	14.5000
0.12	4.20	14.00	1/2	0.5000	5	5.0000	15	15.0000
0.16	4.40	14.50	9/16	0.5625	5¼	5.2500	15½	15.5000
0.20	4.60	15.00	5/8	0.6250	5½	5.5000	16	16.0000
0.24	4.80	15.50	11/16	0.6875	5¾	5.7500	16½	16.5000
0.30	5.00	16.00	3/4	0.7500	6	6.0000	17	17.0000
0.40	5.20	16.50	7/8	0.8750	6½	6.5000	17½	17.5000
0.50	5.40	17.00	1	1.0000	7	7.0000	18	18.0000
0.60	5.60	17.50	1¼	1.2500	7½	7.5000	18½	18.5000
0.80	5.80	18.00	1½	1.5000	8	8.0000	19	19.0000
1.00	6.00	18.50	1¾	1.7500	8½	8.5000	19½	19.5000
1.20	6.50	19.00	2	2.000	9	9.0000	20	20.0000
1.40	7.00	19.50	....	.....	...	.....	....	....
1.60	7.50	20.00						
1.80	8.00	.....						

All dimensions are given in inches.

13.15.9 Standardized Tolerances

Standardized **metric tolerances** are given in Table 13.4. International tolerance (IT) grade values are used. The basis for these is the tolerance unit i, which is defined as follows: i equals .45 times the cube root of D plus .001 times D (where D equals the nominal dimension in millimeters).

Standardized **inch tolerances** are given in Table 13.5. The equivalent to IT values are based on the following formula (in inches): i equals .052 times the cube root of D plus .001 times D (where D equals the nominal dimension in inches).

IT grade versus machining is shown in Figure 13.75 for a rough approximation of the process that may be used in conjunction with the various IT grades. Production costs may be reduced by confining the use of limits to dimensions or grades for which gaging equipment is readily available. Doing so allows production personnel to apply "Go" (MMC) and "Not Go" (LMC) gages to the inspection of small parts, where micrometers and comparitors were previously required. A guide to the practical application of the eighteen IT grades is shown in Figure 13.76.

13.16 Calculating Limits and Fits

Metric tolerancing makes extensive use of limits and fits and uses the symbology extensively (Fig. 13.77). In the United States, the symbology is supplemented by the limits or, most likely, the limits are specified and the symbology referenced on drawings to prevent misinterpretation. Tables 13.6 and

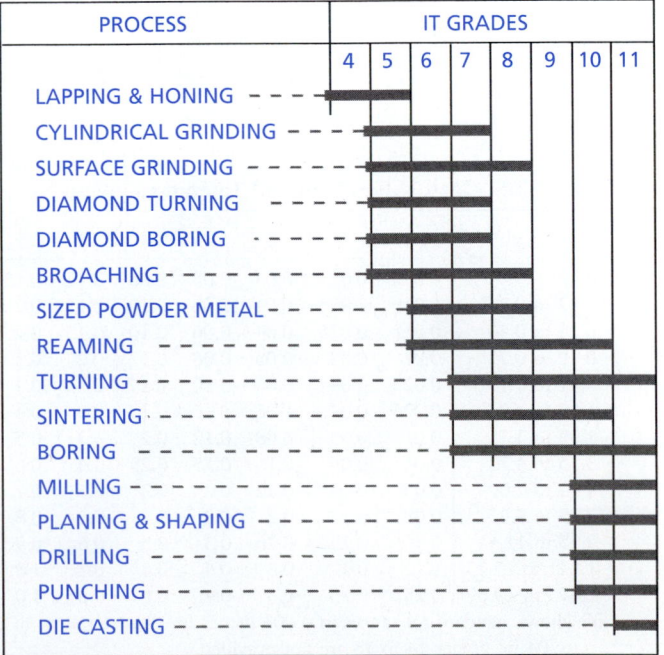

FIGURE 13.75 IT Grade Versus Manufacturing Process

TABLE 13.4 Metric Table-Standard Tolerances

Nominal¹ sizes Over mm	Up to and including mm	IT01	IT0	IT1	IT2	IT3	IT4	IT5	IT6³	IT7	IT8	IT9	IT10	IT11	IT12	IT13	IT14²	IT15²	IT16²
—	3	0·3	0·5	0·8	1·2	2	3	4	6	10	14	25	40	60	100	140	250	400	600
3	6	0·4	0·6	1	1·5	2·5	4	5	8	12	18	30	48	75	120	180	300	480	750
6	10	0·4	0·6	1	1·5	2·5	4	6	9	15	22	36	58	90	150	220	360	580	900
10	18	0·5	0·8	1·2	2	3	5	8	11	18	27	43	70	110	180	270	430	700	1100
18	30	0·6	1	1·5	2·5	4	6	9	13	21	33	52	84	130	210	330	520	840	1300
30	50	0·6	1	1·5	2·5	4	7	11	16	25	39	62	100	160	250	390	620	1000	1600
50	80	0·8	1·2	2	3	5	8	13	19	30	46	74	120	190	300	460	740	1200	1900
80	120	1	1·5	2·5	4	6	10	15	22	35	54	87	140	220	350	540	870	1400	2200
120	180	1·2	2	3·5	5	8	12	18	25	40	63	100	160	250	400	630	1000	1600	2500
180	250	2	3	4·5	7	10	14	20	29	46	72	115	185	290	460	720	1150	1850	2900
250	315	2·5	4	6	8	12	16	23	32	52	81	130	210	320	520	810	1300	2100	3200
315	400	3	5	7	9	13	18	25	36	57	89	140	230	360	570	890	1400	2300	3600
400	500	4	6	8	10	15	20	27	40	63	97	155	250	400	630	970	1550	2500	4000
500	630	—	—	—	—	—	—	—	44	70	110	175	280	440	700	1100	1750	2800	4400
630	800	—	—	—	—	—	—	—	50	80	125	200	320	500	800	1250	2000	3200	5000
800	1000	—	—	—	—	—	—	—	56	90	140	230	360	560	900	1400	2300	3600	5600
1000	1250	—	—	—	—	—	—	—	66	105	165	260	420	660	1050	1650	2600	4200	6600
1250	1600	—	—	—	—	—	—	—	78	125	195	310	500	780	1250	1950	3100	5000	7800
1600	2000	—	—	—	—	—	—	—	92	150	230	370	600	920	1500	2300	3700	6000	9200
2000	2500	—	—	—	—	—	—	—	110	175	280	440	700	1100	1750	2800	4400	7000	11000
2500	3150	—	—	—	—	—	—	—	135	210	330	540	860	1350	2100	3300	5400	8600	13500

Tolerance unit 0.001 mm
¹STANDARD TOLERANCE IN MICRONS (1μ = 0.001 mm)
²Not applicable to sizes below 1 mm
³Not recommended for fits in sizes above 500 mm
ISO TOLERANCE GRADE 6 IN ABBREVIATED FORM IS IT6

TABLE 13.5 Inch Values-Standard Tolerances

IT Grade	01	0	1	2	3	4	5	6	7	8	9	10	11	12	13	14*	15*	16*
≤ 0.12	0.012	0.02	0.03	0.05	0.08	0.12	0.15	0.25	0.4	0.6	1.0	1.6	2.5	4.0	6.0	10.0	16.0	25.0
> 0.12 to 0.24	0.015	0.025	0.04	0.06	0.10	0.15	0.2	0.3	0.5	0.7	1.2	1.8	3.0	5.0	7.0	12.0	18.0	30.0
> 0.24 to 0.40	0.015	0.025	0.04	0.06	0.10	0.15	0.25	0.4	0.6	0.9	1.4	2.2	3.5	6.0	9.0	14.0	22.0	35.0
> 0.40 to 0.71	0.02	0.03	0.05	0.08	0.12	0.2	0.3	0.4	0.7	1.0	1.6	2.8	4.0	7.0	10.0	16.0	28.0	40.0
> 0.71 to 1.19	0.025	0.04	0.06	0.10	0.15	0.25	0.4	0.5	0.8	1.2	2.0	3.5	5.0	8.0	12.0	20.0	35.0	50.0
> 1.19 to 1.97	0.025	0.04	0.06	0.10	0.15	0.3	0.4	0.6	1.0	1.6	2.5	4.0	6.0	10.0	16.0	25.0	40.0	60.0
> 1.97 to 3.15	0.03	0.05	0.08	0.12	0.2	0.3	0.5	0.7	1.2	1.8	3.0	4.5	7.0	12.0	18.0	30.0	45.0	70.0
> 3.15 to 4.73	0.04	0.06	0.1	0.15	0.25	0.4	0.6	0.9	1.4	2.2	3.5	5.0	9.0	14.0	22.0	35.0	50.0	90.0
> 4.73 to 7.09	0.05	0.08	0.12	0.2	0.3	0.5	0.7	1.0	1.6	2.5	4.0	6.0	10.0	16.0	25.0	40.0	60.0	100.0
> 7.09 to 9.85	0.08	0.12	0.2	0.3	0.4	0.6	0.8	1.2	1.8	2.8	4.5	7.0	12.0	18.0	28.0	45.0	70.0	120.0
> 9.85 to 12.41	0.10	0.15	0.25	0.3	0.5	0.6	0.9	1.2	2.0	3.0	5.0	8.0	12.0	20.0	30.0	50.0	80.0	120.0
> 12.41 to 15.75	0.12	0.2	0.3	0.4	0.5	0.7	1.0	1.4	2.2	3.5	6.0	9.0	14.0	22.0	35.0	60.0	90.0	140.0
> 15.75 to 19.69	0.15	0.25	0.3	0.4	0.6	0.8	1.0	1.6	2.5	4.0	6.0	10.0	16.0	25.0	40.0	60.0	100.0	160.0

Table shows standard tolerances in 0.001 inches for diameter steps in inches.
*Up to .04 in, grades 14 to 16 are not provided.

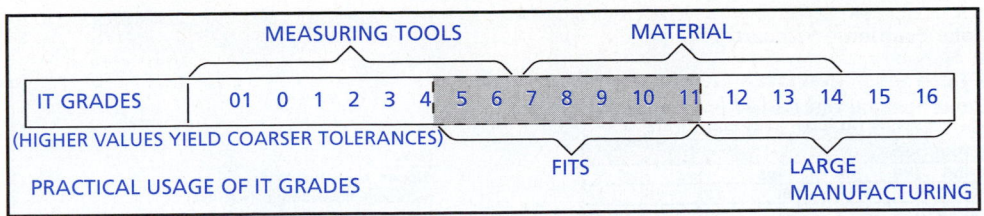

| MEASURING TOOLS | | | | | | | | MATERIAL | | | | | | | | |

FIGURE 13.76 Practical Uses for IT Grades

13.7 provide metric and inch shaft position tables, respectively. These are used in conjunction with Tables 13.4 and 13.5 to calculate limits and fits.

13.16.1   Calculating Metric Hole Limits

The hole basis system places the low limit of a hole at exactly the basic or design size. The high limit is calculated by adding the IT value (Table 13.4) to it. For example:

$\varnothing$ 80 H7 = 80 + 0.03, −0 (.03 from Table 13.4).

13.16.2   Calculating Inch Hole Limits

The low limit of the hole is again at exactly the basic or design size. The high limit is calculated by adding the IT value (Table 13.5) to it. For example:

$\varnothing$ 3.1500 H7 = 3.1500 + 0.0012, − .0000 (.0012 from Table 13.6).

13.16.3   Calculating Metric Shaft Limits

When using a hole basis system, unless the shaft is at h position (see figure at bottom right of Table 13.6), the value in Table 13.6 must be added algebraically to arrive at the upper limit of a shaft; subtracting the IT value (Table 13.4) from the upper limit yields the lower limit.

Example:

$\varnothing$ 80 k6 = 80 + .021, + .002 or 80.002 − 80.021 (.021 − .019 = .002; where .021 came from Table 13.6 and .019 from Table 13.4).

Example:

$\varnothing$ 80   c11 =   .80 − .150,   − 340   or   79.   660 − 79.850 (− .150 − .190 = − .340; where − .150 came from Table 13.6 and .190 from Table 13.4).

Note: Minus, minus and plus, plus are used in the system of limits and fits as well as the plus and minus used in the conventional customary inch system.

13.16.4   Calculating Inch Shaft Limits

When using a hole basis system, unless the shaft is at h position (see figure at bottom right of Table 13.7), the value in Table 13.7 must be added algebraically to arrive at the upper limit of a shaft; subtracting the IT value (Table 13.6) from the upper limit yields the lower limit.

Example:

$\varnothing$ 3.15 k6 = 3.1500 − .0008, − .0015 or 3.1485 − 3.14992 (− .0008 − .0007 = − .0015; where − .0008 came from Table 13.7 and .0007 from Table 13.6).

Example:

$\varnothing$ 12.00 d9 = 12.00 − .007, − .012 or 11.988 − 11.993 (− .007, − .005 = − .012; where − .007 came from Table 13.7 and .005 from Table 13.6).

13.16.5   Calculating Fits

Once the limits are computed, the **fit calculation** is relatively simple. A fit consists of two sets of limits and the maximum and minimum clearance. For the most part, except for interference, force, or shrink fits, the shaft is given a tolerance grade one number less than the hole (as in Fig. 13.77). Using the example in Figure 13.77 of $\varnothing$ 80 H7/k6 (LT3, clearance locational fit; see Table 13.6) the limits calculated above are:

    Hole   80.000 − 80.030
    Shaft   80.002 − 80.021

Subtracting the largest (MMC) shaft from the smallest (MMC)

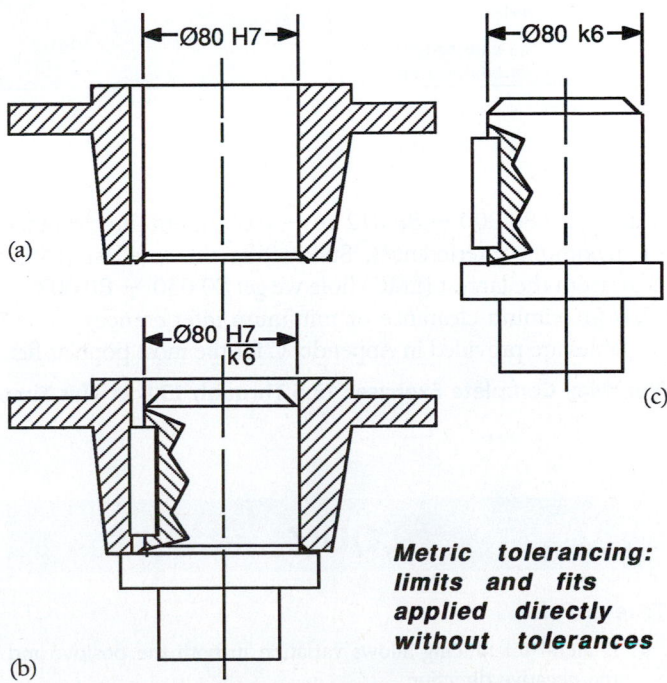

Metric tolerancing: limits and fits applied directly without tolerances

FIGURE 13.77 Metric Symbology for Limits and Fits

TABLE 13.6   Metric Tolerance Zone Position—Standard Fits

****************TABLE   5****************
METRIC-TOLERANCE ZONE POSITION TABLE-SHAFT UPPER LIMITS
FROM ZERO LINE (BASIC SIZE) SEE GRAPHIC AT LOWER RIGHT.

Loose, free & close running, sliding, locational, drive and force fits

Over-To	c11	d9	f7	g6	h6	k6	n6	p6	s6	u6
≤3	-60	-20	-6	-2	0	6	10	12	20	24
3 to 6	-70	-30	-10	-4	0	9	16	20	27	31
6 to 10	-80	-40	-13	-5	0	10	19	24	32	37
10 to 14	-95	-50	-16	-6	0	12	23	29	39	44
14 to 18	-95	-50	-16	-6	0	12	23	29	39	44
18 to 24	-110	-65	-20	-7	0	15	28	35	48	54
24 to 30	-110	-65	-20	-7	0	15	28	35	48	61
30 to 40	-120	-80	-25	-9	0	18	33	42	59	76
40 to 50	-130	-80	-25	-9	0	18	33	42	59	86
50 to 65	-140	-100	-30	-10	0	21	39	51	72	106
65 to 80	-150	-100	-30	-10	0	21	39	51	78	121
80 to 100	-170	-120	-36	-12	0	25	45	59	93	146
100 to 120	-180	-120	-36	-12	0	25	45	59	101	166
120 to 140	-200	-145	-43	-14	0	28	52	68	117	195
140 to 160	-210	-145	-43	-14	0	28	52	68	125	215
160 to 180	-230	-145	-43	-14	0	28	52	68	133	235
180 to 200	-240	-170	-50	-15	0	33	60	79	151	265
200 to 225	-260	-170	-50	-15	0	33	60	79	159	287
225 to 250	-280	-170	-50	-15	0	33	60	79	169	313
250 to 280	-300	-190	-56	-17	0	36	66	88	190	347

1. Basic hole system (unilateral hole basis) employed (table covers shafts).
2. Values are in thousandths of a millimeter (microns); sizes in mm.
3. Values represent the upper limit (relative to the zero line) of shafts
4. The selected fits indicated are recommended in ANSI B4.1.
these are somewhat similar to those in (UK standard) BS 4500.
5. Add value from table algebraically to basic size for upper shaft limit

USING THE TABLE ABOVE

Ø30 f7 (Shaft)

zero line   30.00
Basic size   "-20 (.02) from above "
                  table to get upper limit

	29.980
IT7 f	
	29.959

IT7 (other table)=.021

30.000-.020=29.980
29.980-.021=29.959

Clearance Fits

FIT	HOLE	SHAFT
loose	H11	c11
free	H9	d9
close	H8	f 7
sliding	H7	g6
locational	H7	h6

Transition Fits

FIT	HOLE	SHAFT
locational	H7	k6
locational	H7	n6

Interference Fits

FIT	HOLE	SHAFT
locational	H7	p6
med. drive	H7	s6
force	H7	u6

Note:
•Upper case letters
represent holes/bores. (e.g. H7).
•Lower case letters
represent shafts (e.g. f6).
•The letter (location symbol) represents
the position/distance to the
"zero line"/Basic size.
•H and h are on the zero line.
• The number (quality no.) represents
the tolerance grade. Higher no.s yield coarser fits.
•*See tolerance grade (IT) table
for limits not shown in these tables.
*Add IT to hole for max limit (Basic size is min hole)
*Subtract IT from shaft limit calc. from table for min.

METHODS OF INDICATING
1.   Ø30 f7
2.   Ø29.980 +.000, -.021 (Ø30 f7)
3.   Ø 29.959 - 29.980 (Ø30 f7)

INDICATING FITS
1.   Ø.30 H8/f7 (hole first)
2.   Ø30 H8 (30.000-30.033)
           f7 (29.959 - 29.980)

•BASIC size is min. hole size.
•Add IT(X) from table for max. hole. Upper limit from table

•Subtract value from table above
for one (high) limit of shaft.
•Subtract IT(X) from high limit
of shaft for low limit.

POSITIONS OF TOLERANCE ZONES TO ZERO LINE.

---

hole we get 80.000 − 80.012 = −.012 (minimum clearance or maximum interference). Subtracting the smallest (LMC) shaft from the largest (LMC) hole we get 80.030 − 80.002 = .028 (maximum clearance or minimum interference).

Tables are provided in Appendix C for the most popular fits.

You May Complete Exercises 13.5 Through 13.8 at This Time

QUIZ

True or False

1. Bilateral tolerancing allows variation in both the positive and the negative direction.
2. In a feature control frame, a separator is not required between the geometric characteristic and the tolerance.

3. A tolerance of 1.2−1.4 allows a feature of 1.202 to be accepted.
4. A tertiary datum may be established by a single point of contact.
5. The four basic types of fit are clearance, interference, transition, and running.
6. The ISO system of limits and fits has been standardized at about 500 fits.
7. Tolerances are understood to apply at 68°F unless otherwise specified.
8. A datum is identified, located, and established in a feature control frame.

Fill in the Blanks

9. A theoretically exact dimension is a _____ dimension.
10. A datum may be a _____ , a _____ , or a _____ .
11. The abbreviations for the modifiers are _____ , _____ , and _____ .
12. The surfaces of a feature must not extend beyond a _____ of _____ _____ at MMC.

TABLE 13.7   Inch Tolerance Zone Position — Standard Fits

*****************TABLE   6*****************
INCH -TOLERANCE ZONE POSITION TABLE-SHAFT UPPER LIMITS
FROM ZERO LINE (BASIC SIZE) SEE GRAPHIC ON METRIC TABLE PAGE.
RUNNING, SLIDING, CLEARANCE TRANSITION AND INTERFERENCE LOCATIONAL FITS

Over-To	c9&c10	d8	d9	e7&E8	e9	f6,f7	f8	g4,g5	g6	h5,6,7&9	js6	js7	k6	k7	n5	n6	n7	p6	r6	Sp-10	Sp-11	Sp-12
0-.12	-2.50	-1.0	-1.0	-.6	-.6	-.3	-.3	-.10	-.10	0	0.1	0.2	-	-	0.45	0.5	0.65	0.65	0.75	-4.0	-4.0	-5
.12-.24	-2.80	-1.2	-1.2	-.8	-.8	-.4	-.4	-.15	-.15	0	0.15	0.25	-	-	0.5	0.6	0.8	0.8	0.9	-4.5	-4.5	-6
.24-.40	-3.00	-1.6	-1.6	-1.0	-1.0	-.5	-.5	-.20	-.20	0	0.2	0.3	0.5	0.7	0.65	0.8	1	1	1.2	-5.0	-5.0	-7
.40-.71	-3.50	-2.0	-2.0	-1.2	-1.2	-.6	-.6	-.25	-.25	0	0.2	0.35	0.5	0.8	0.8	0.9	1.2	1.1	1.4	-6.0	-6.0	-8
.71-1.19	-4.50	-2.5	-2.5	-1.6	-1.6	-.8	-.8	-.30	-.30	0	0.25	0.4	0.6	0.9	1	1.1	1.4	1.3	1.7	-7.0	-7.0	-10
1.19-1.97	-5.00	-3.0	-3.0	-2.0	-2.0	-1.0	-1.0	-.40	-.40	0	0.3	0.5	0.7	1.1	1.1	1.3	1.7	1.6	2	-8.0	-8.0	-12
1.97-3.15	-6.00	-4.0	-4.0	-2.5	-2.5	-1.2	-1.2	-.40	-.40	0	0.3	0.6	0.8	1.3	1.3	1.5	2	2.1	2.3	-9.0	-10.0	-14
3.15-4.73	-7.00	-5.0	-5.0	-3.0	-3.0	-1.4	-1.4	-.50	-.50	0	0.4	0.7	1	1.5	1.6	1.9	2.4	2.5	2.9	-10.0	-11.0	-16
4.73-7.09	-8.00	-6.0	-6.0	-3.5	-3.5	-1.6	-1.6	-.60	-.60	0	0.5	0.8	1.1	1.7	1.9	2.2	2.8	2.8	3.5	-12.0	-12.0	-18
7.09-9.85	-10.00	-7.0	-7.0	-4.0	-4.0	-2.0	-2.0	-.60	-.60	0	0.6	0.9	1.4	2	2.2	2.6	3.2	3.2	4.2	-15.0	-16.0	-22
9.85-12.41	-12.00	-8.0	-7.0	-5.0	-4.5	-2.5	2.2	-.80	-.70	0	0.6	1	1.4	2.2	2.3	2.6	3.4	3.4	4.7	-18.0	-20.0	-28
12.41-15.75	-14.00	-10.0	-8.0	6	-5.0	-3.0	2.5	-1.00	-.70	0	0.7	1	1.6	2.4	2.6	3	3.8	3.9	5.9	-22.0	-22.0	-30

FORCE AND SHRINK FITS

Over-To	s6	t6	u6	x7	Sp-5
0-.12	0.85	-	0.95	1.3	0.5
.12-.24	1	-	1.2	1.7	0.6
.24-.40	1.4	-	1.6	2	0.75
0.4-.56	1.6	-	1.8	2.3	0.8
.56-.71	1.6	-	1.8	2.5	0.9
.71-.95	1.9	-	2.1	3	1.1
.95-1.19	1.9	2.1	2.3	3.3	1.2
1.19-1.58	2.4	2.6	3.1	4	1.3
1.58-1.97	2.4	2.8	3.4	5	1.4
1.97-2.56	2.7	3.2	4.2	6.2	1.8
2.56-3.15	2.9	3.7	4.7	7.2	1.9
3.15-3.94	3.7	4.4	5.9	8.4	2.4
3.94-4.73	3.9	4.9	6.9	9.4	2.6
4.73-5.52	4.5	6	8	11.6	2.9
5.52-6.30	5	6	8	13.6	3.2
6.30-7.09	5.5	7	9	13.6	3.5
7.09-7.88	6.2	8.2	10.2	15.8	3.8
7.88-8.86	6.2	8.2	11.2	17.8	4.3
8.86-9.85	7.2	9.2	13.2	17.8	4.3
9.85-11.03	7.2	10.2	13.2	20	4.9
11.03-12.41	8.2	10.2	15.2	22	4.9
12.41-13.98	9.4	11.4	17.4	24.2	5.5
13.98-15.75	9.4	13.4	19.4	27.2	6.1
15.75-17.72	10.6	13.6	21.6	30.5	7
17.72-19.69	11.6	15.6	23.6	32.5	7

1. Basic hole system employed (table covers shafts).
2. Values are in thousandths of an inch
3. Values represent the upper limit (relative to the zero line) of shafts
4. Values indicated "Sp-X" are not used in the ISO (International ISO 286) system
5. Add value from table algebraically to basic size for upper shaft limit.

Running and Sliding Fits

FIT	HOLE	SHAFT
RC 1	H5	g4
RC 2	H6	g5
RC 3	H7	f6
RC 4	H8	f 7
RC 5	H8	e7
RC 6	H9	e8
RC 7	H9	d8
RC 8	H10	c9
RC 9	H11	Sp-10

Clearance Locational Fits

FIT	HOLE	SHAFT
LC 1	H6	h5
LC 2	H7	h6
LC 3	H8	h7
LC 4	H10	h9
LC 5	H7	g6
LC 6	H9	f 8
LC 7	H10	e9
LC 8	H10	d9
LC 9	H11	c10
LC 10	H12	Sp11
LC 11	H13	Sp12

Clearance Locational Fits

FIT	HOLE	SHAFT
LT 1	H7	js6
LT 2	H8	js7
LT 3	H7	k6
LT 4	H8	k7
LT 5	H7	n6
LT 6	H7	n7

Interference Locational Fits

FIT	HOLE	SHAFT
LN 1	H6	n5
LN 2	H7	p6
LN 3	H7	r6

Force and Shrink Fits

FIT	HOLE	SHAFT
FN 1	H6	Sp5
FN 2	H7	s6
FN 3	H7	t6
FN 4	H7	u6
FN 5	H8	x7

Location on zero line (H)
|
Ø30 H7
|
Basic Size (Ø30)   **Hole Designation**   IT Grade (7)

Location to zero line (f)
|
Ø30 f7
|
Basic Size (Ø30)   **Shaft Designation**   IT Grade (7)

Note:
•Upper case letters represent holes/bores (e.g. H7).
•Lower case letters represent shafts (e.g. f6)..
•The letter (location symbol) represents the position/distance to the "zero line"/Basic size.
•H and h are on the zero line.
• The number (quality no.) represents the tolerance grade. Higher no.s yield coarser fits.
•See tolerance grade (IT) table for limits not shown in these tables
*Add IT(x) for hole limit (from 0). (Basic hole is min size.)
*Subtract IT from max shaft limit calculated from basic size and value in table for other limit.

METHODS OF INDICATING
1. Ø.30 f7
2. Ø.2995 +.000, -.0006 (Ø.30f7)
3. Ø.2989-.2995 (Ø.30f7)

INDICATING FITS
1.   Ø.30 H8/f7 (hole first)
2.   Ø.30 H8 (.3000-.3009)
      f7 (.2989-.2995)

---

13. _____ , _____ , and _____ are the basic types of fits.
14. In _____ and _____ tolerancing, the _____ is given first and is followed by a _____ and _____ expression of tolerance.
15. The classes of fits are arranged into three groups: _____ and _____ fits, _____ fits, and _____ fits.
16. _____ means producing parts relative to standard measures and forms.

Answer the Following

17. What is the difference between circularity and cylindricity?
18. What is a tolerance zone?
19. What does the following statement mean?: "In principle, every individual (single) feature of a part is perfect at MMC."
20. Define the three datum planes and how they are located.
21. What is the Taylor principle and how is it used?
22. What is title block tolerance and how is it applied to part features?
23. Explain virtual condition and its applications.
24. Summarize Rule 1 and how it is applied in tolerancing.

EXERCISES

Exercises may be assigned as sketching, instrument or CAD projects. Transfer the given information to an "A" size sheet of .25 in. grid paper. Exercises that are not assigned by the instructor can be sketched in the text to provide practice and understanding for the preceding instructional material. Complete all views by showing all hidden lines, centerlines, tolerances, datums, and dimensions.

After Reading the Chapter Through Section 13.10.3 You May Complete the Following Exercises

Exercise 13.1   The surface between points D and E must lie between two profile boundaries .001 apart, perpendicular to plane A, equally disposed about the true profile and positioned with respect to datum planes B and C. All dimensions given on the exercise sheet are basic.

Exercise 13.2   Specify different tolerances for each segment of the profile; between A and B use .005, between B and C use .004, and between C and D use .002. Complete the views and dimension the part.

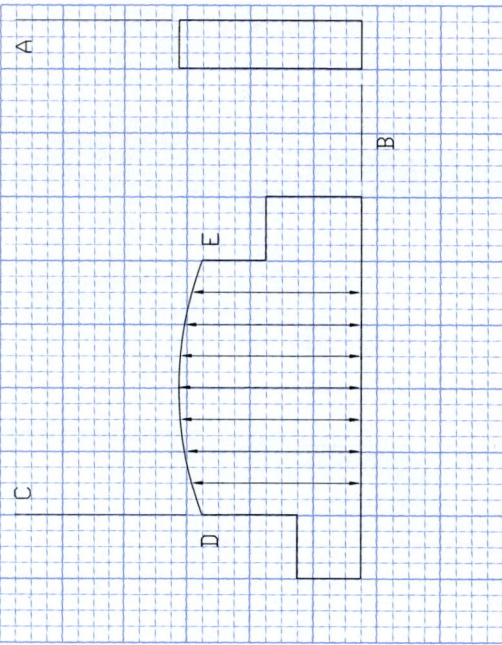

Exercise 13.1

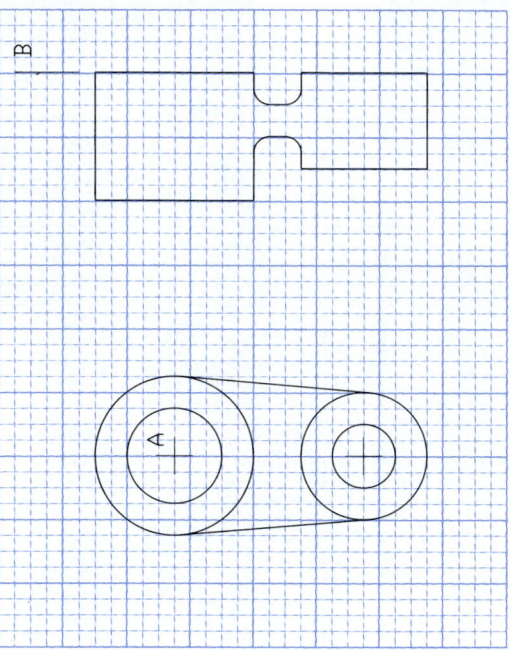

Exercise 13.3

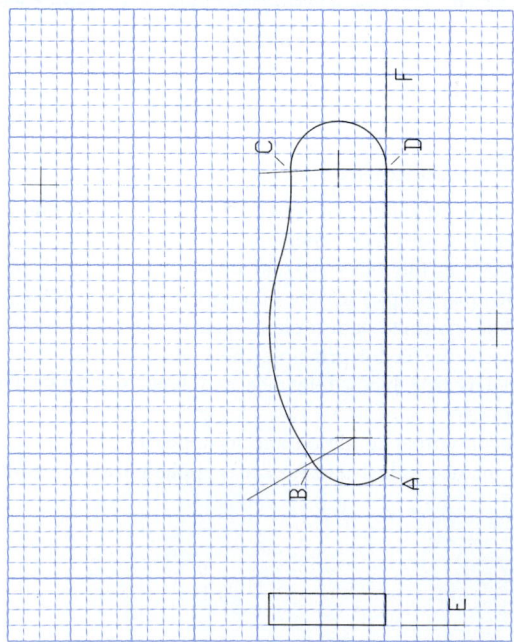

Exercise 13.2

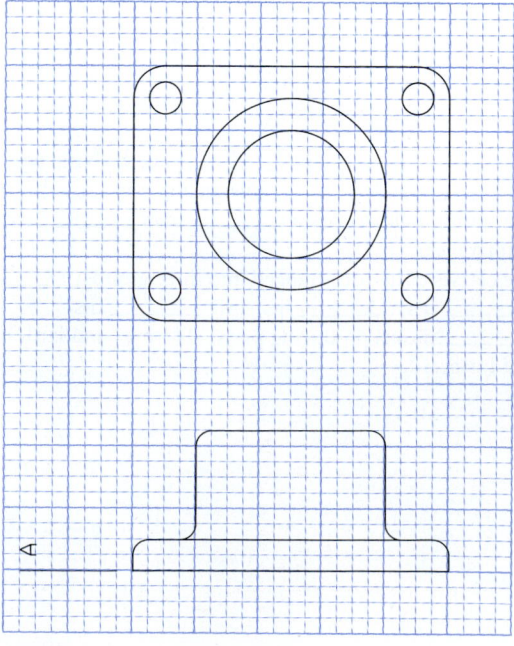

Exercise 13.4

Exercise 13.3 The two holes are to be parallel with a maximum tolerance of .002. Complete the views and dimension the part.

Exercise 13.4 Large hole at MMC is to be perpendicular to datum plane A with a maximum tolerance of .004. Complete the views and dimension the part.

After Reading the Chapter Through Section 13.16.5 You May Complete the Following Exercises

Exercise 13.5 Use positional tolerancing for the part. The holes are to be at a depth of ½ of the part thickness. Show the bolt circle diameter as a reference dimension.

Exercise 13.6 Use positional tolerancing for the part. The large hole is to be toleranced at .016 at MMC from datums A, B, and C. The small holes are to be toleranced at .001 at MMC from the large hole. Dimensions for the hole pattern are basic.

Exercise 13.7 Dimension the part using composite positional tolerancing. All hole patterns are to be basic. The bolt circle hole pattern is 6 × 60° basic.

Exercise 13.8 Dimension the part using positional tolerancing. Use symbology to call out the counterbored holes. The counterbores are to have a .001 diameter tolerance zone at MMC in relation to datum B.

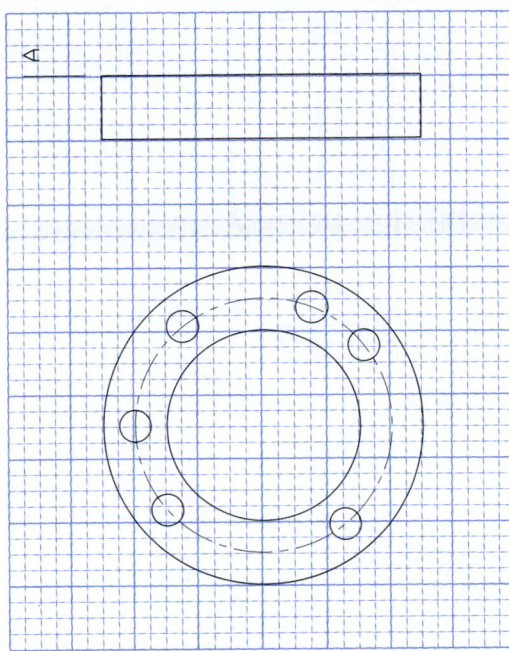

Exercise 13.5

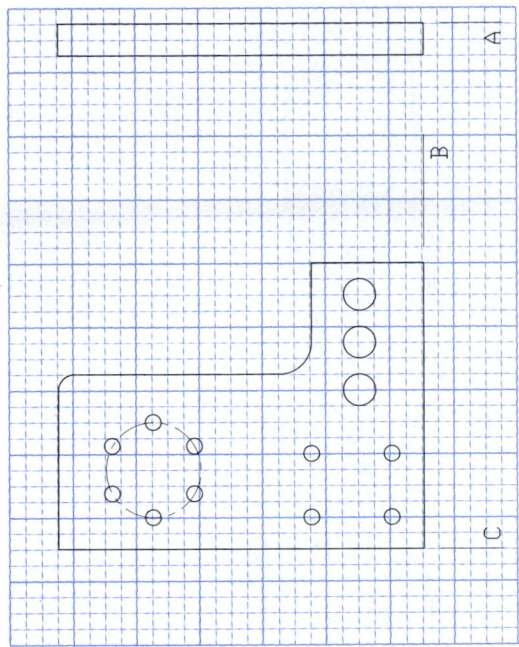

Exercise 13.7

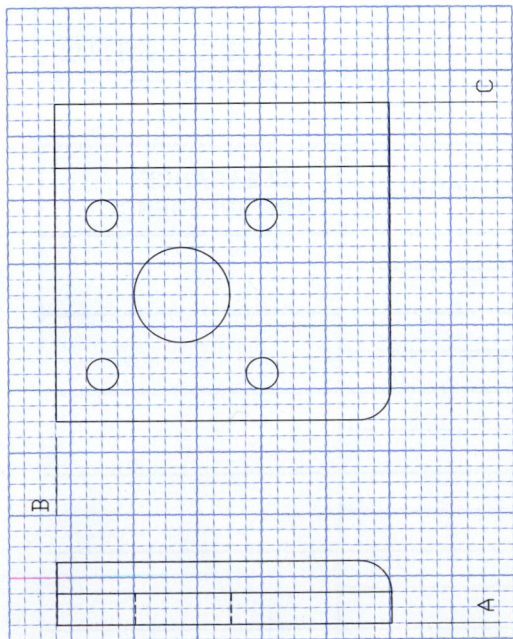

Exercise 13.6

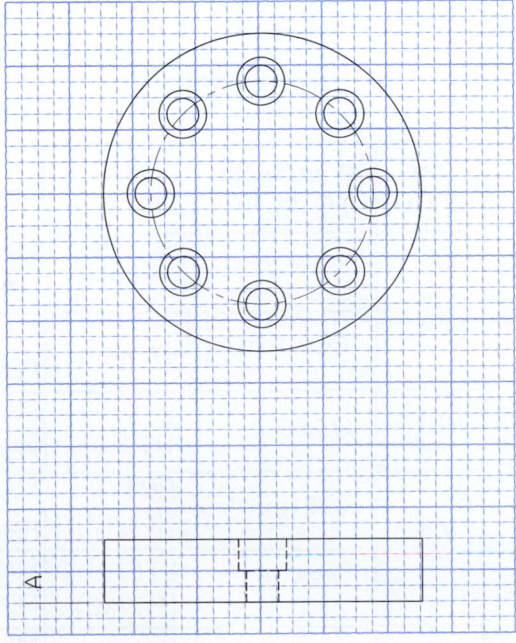

Exercise 13.8

PROBLEMS

The concepts and methods presented in the chapter should be applied for drawing projects throughout the text, especially those found in Chapter 18. The problems presented here are meant to introduce and familiarize you with simple geometric tolerancing situations. On problems that do not have units, use either metric or decimal-inch scales and transfer directly from the text using 2X scale.

Problem 13.1   Complete the table for each of the four cases. Use Tables 13.1 through 13.6 and Appendix C to check the results.

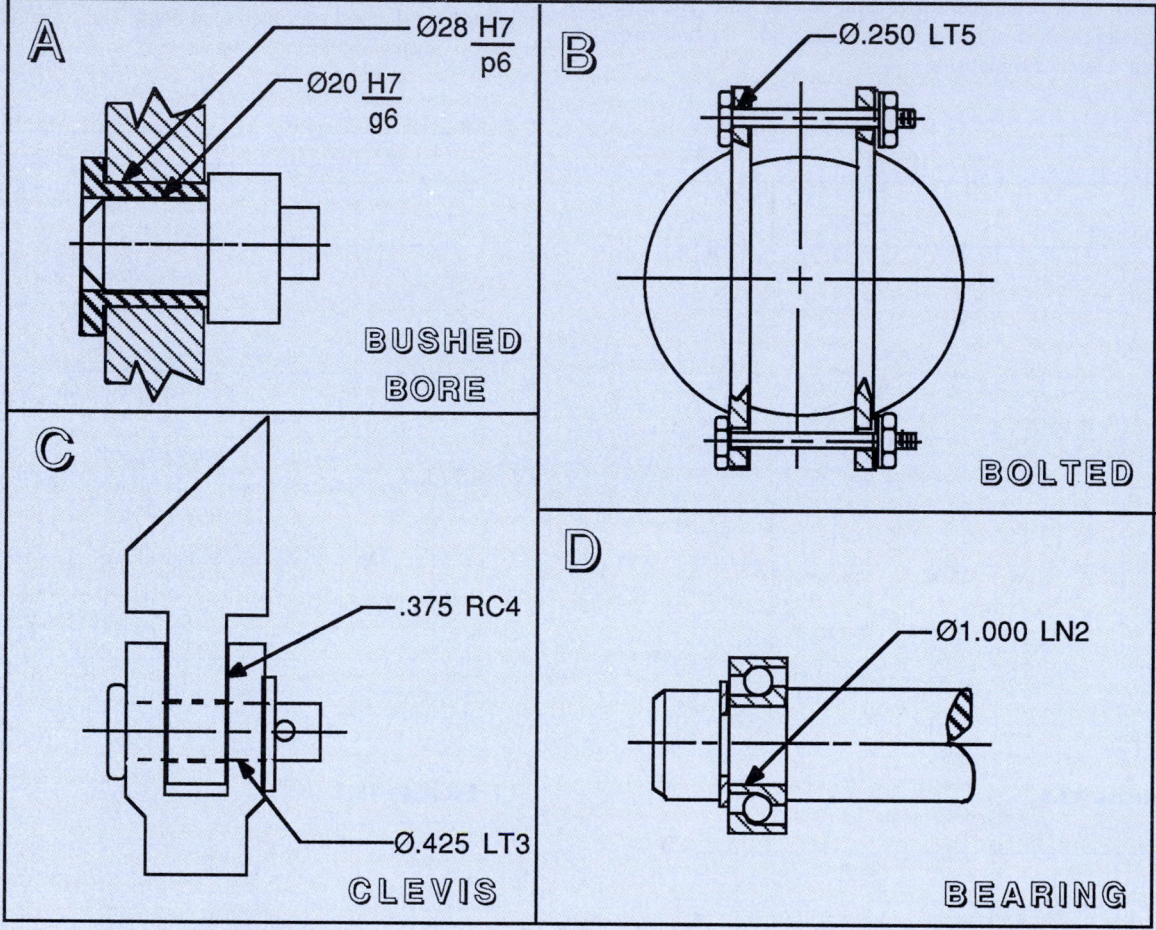

FIT IDENT	Ø or width mm or in.	FIT CALLOUT	FEATURE	SIZE LIMITS	CLEARANCE/ INTERFERENCE
A	Ø28 mm	H7/p6	MALE		
			FEMALE		
	Ø20 mm	H7/g6	MALE		
			FEMALE		
B	Ø.250 in.	LT5 (H7/n6)	MALE		
			FEMALE		
C	.375 in.	RC4 (H8/f7)	MALE		
			FEMALE		
	.425 in.	LT3 (H7/k6)	MALE		
			FEMALE		
D	1.00 in.	LN2 (H7/p6)	MALE		
			FEMALE		

Problem 13.2   Follow the instructions at the bottom of the figure.

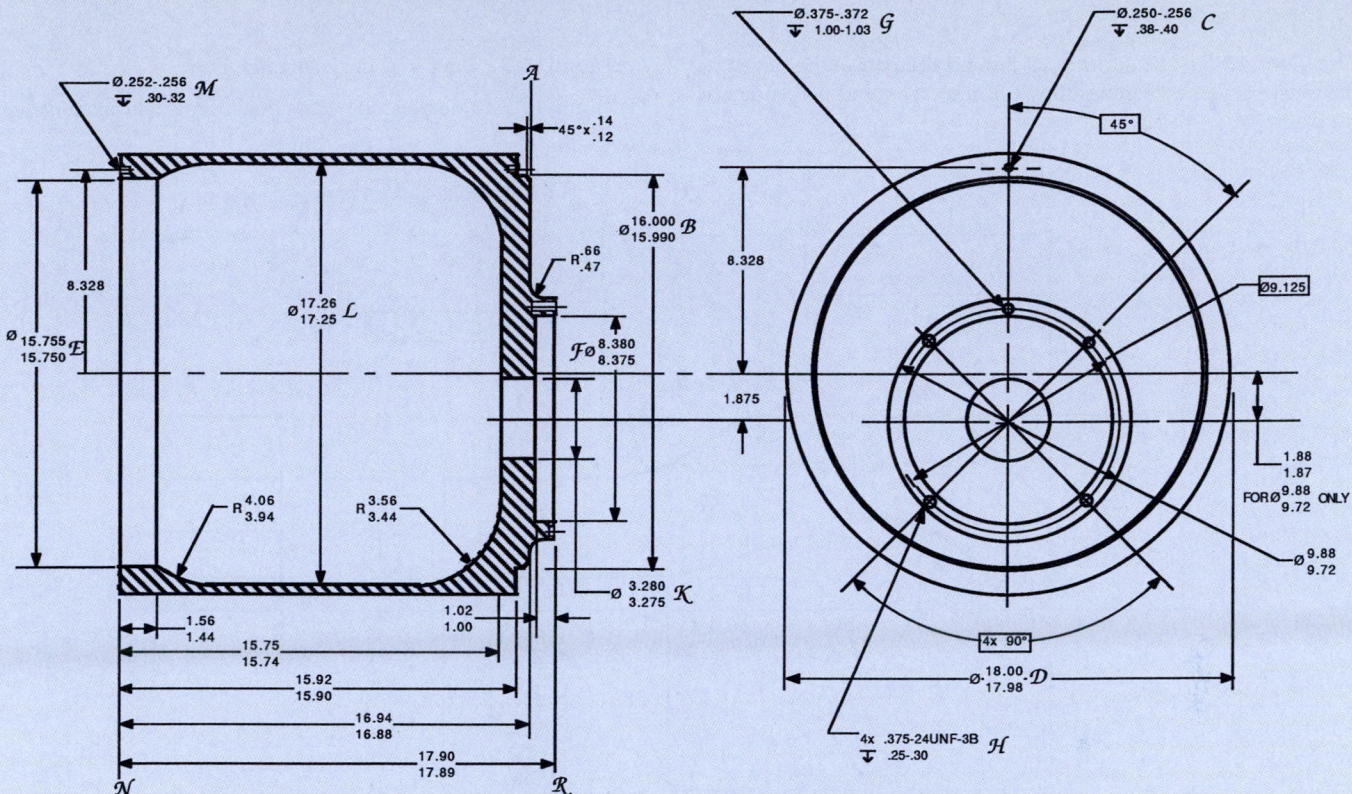

1. Establish a Datum Reference Frame using features A, B and C.
2. A is flat to .001, B is perpendicular to A within .010 at MMC. C is Positioned within .005 at MMC to A and B at MMC
3. Feature D has a Positional tol. of .020 at MMC to A and B at MMC.
4. E has an .008 Circ. Runout to A and B 5. F is positioned within .004 at MMC to R, B at MMC and C at MMC.

6. G is positioned to .005 at MMC to R, F at MMC and C at MMC.
7. H has a Composite Positional Tol. of .020 at MMC to R, F at MMC and G at MMC, and positioned to .006 at RFS to R the zone is projected .510.
8. K is positioned to .010 at MMC to R and F at MMC.   9. L has a Circ. Runout of .025 to D 10. M is Positioned to .008 at MMC to N, E at MMC and C at MMC.   11. N and R are parallel within .005 & .003 to A respectively.

Problems 13.3 and 13.4   Redraw each of the frames and note the parts of each.

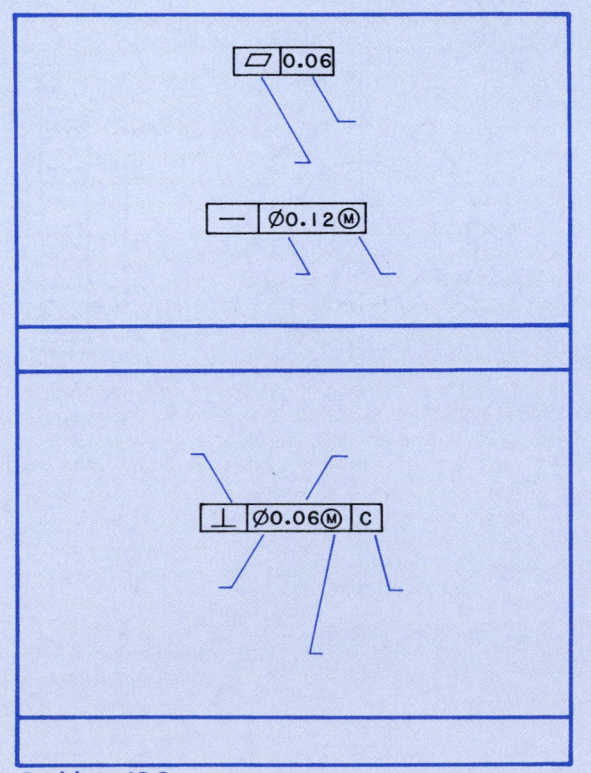

Problem 13.3

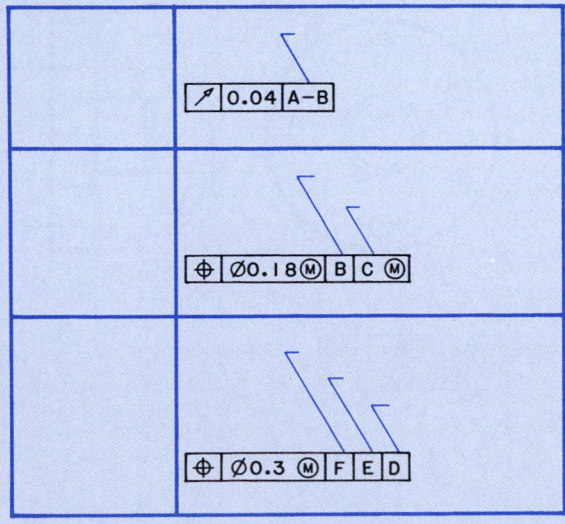

Problem 13.4

Problem 13.5 The surfaces all around the part outline must lie between parallel boundaries .06 (1.5 mm) apart and perpendicular to datum -A-.

Problem 13.6 Draw and dimension the part.

Problem 13.7 Complete the part's dimensions and tolerancing.

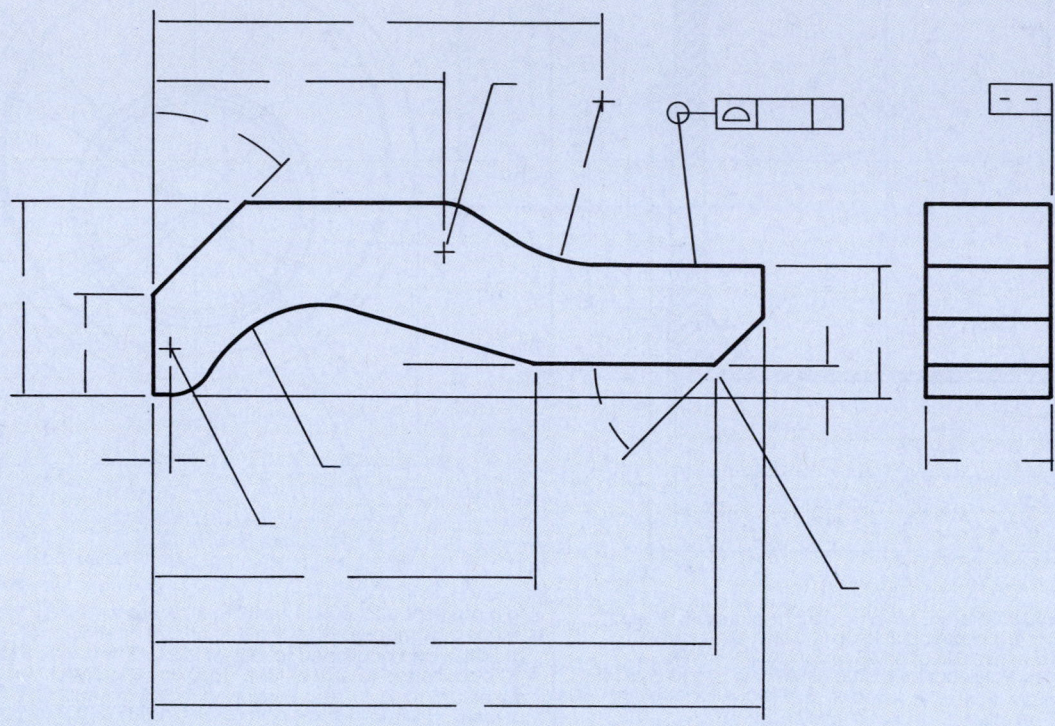

Problem 13.5

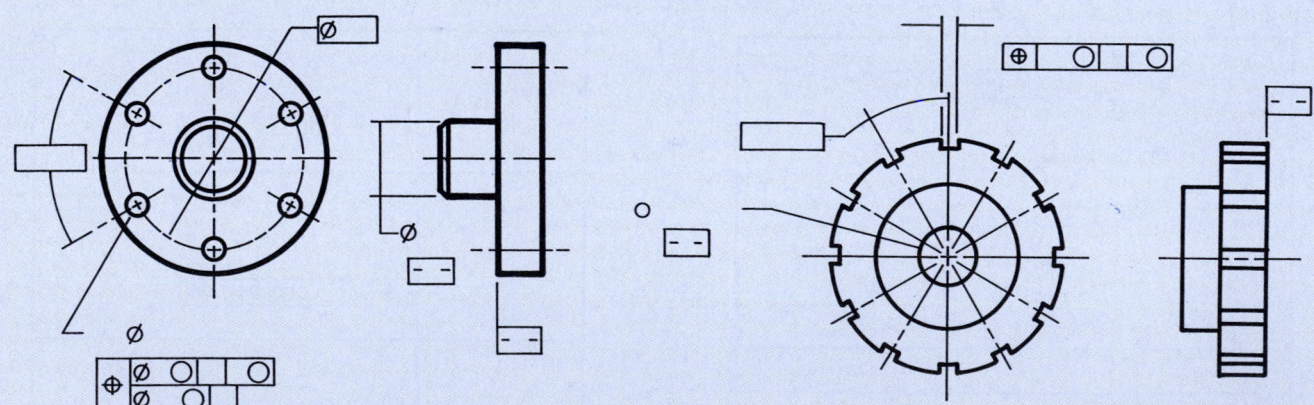

Problem 13.6

Problem 13.7

Problem 13.8 Draw the part and complete the dimensioning.   **Problem 13.9** Complete the part as required.

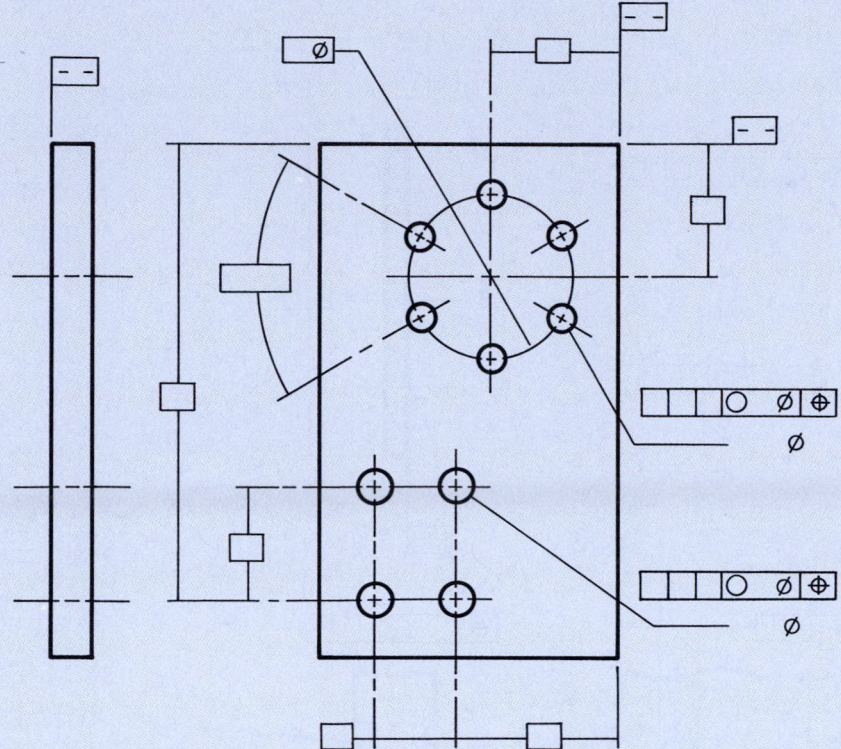

Problem 13.8

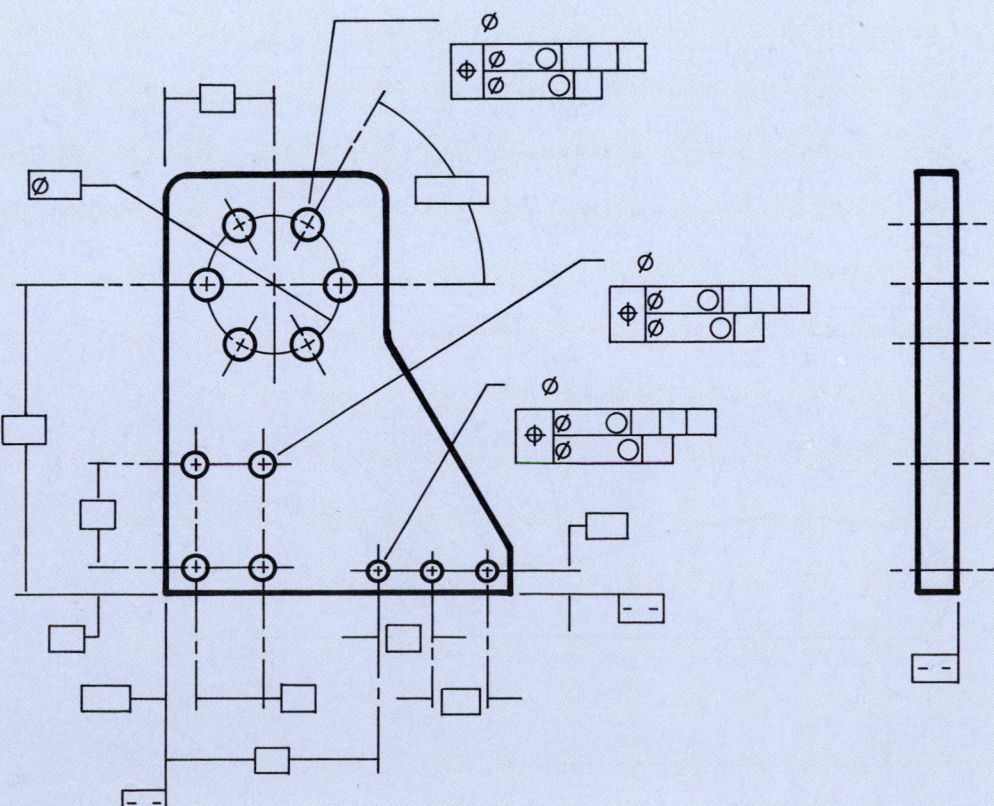

Problem 13.9

Problem 13.10 Draw and dimension the part as required.

Problem 13.11 Complete the portion of the part as shown.

Problem 13.12 Complete the project as required. Specify the different profile tolerances between the segments: .12 (3 mm) between A and B, .10 (2.5 mm) between B and C, and .05 (1.2 mm) between C and D.

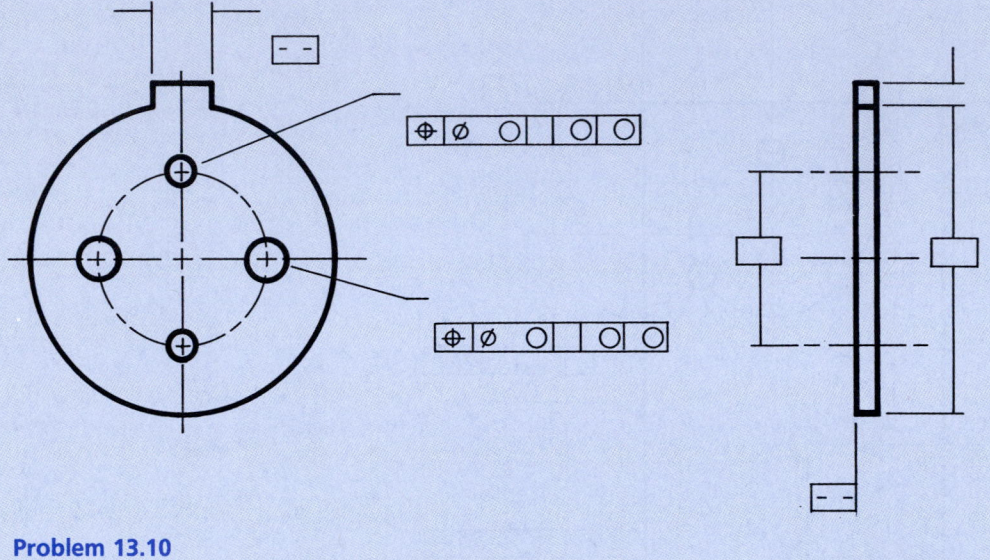

Problem 13.10

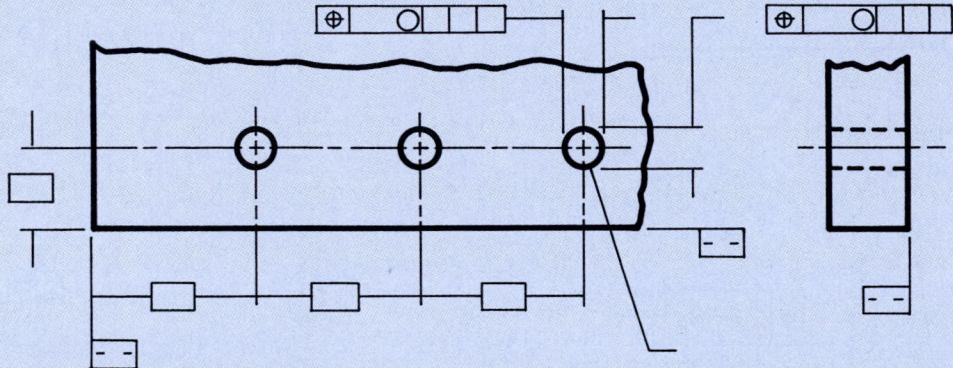

Problem 13.11

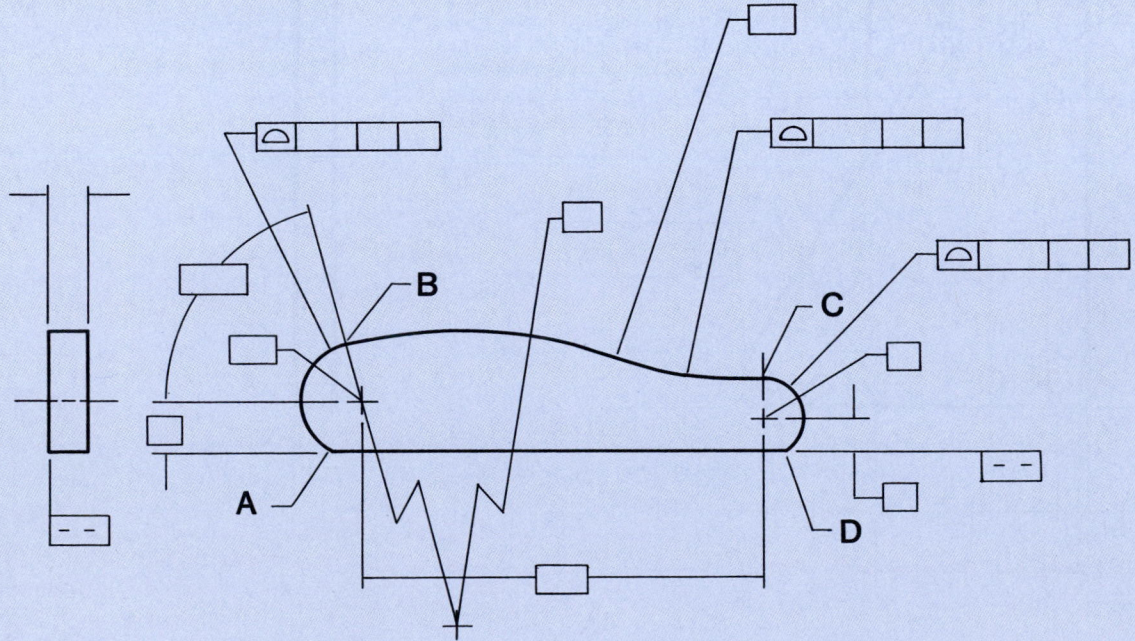

Problem 13.12

Problem 13.13 Redraw the rotor and show all dimensions.

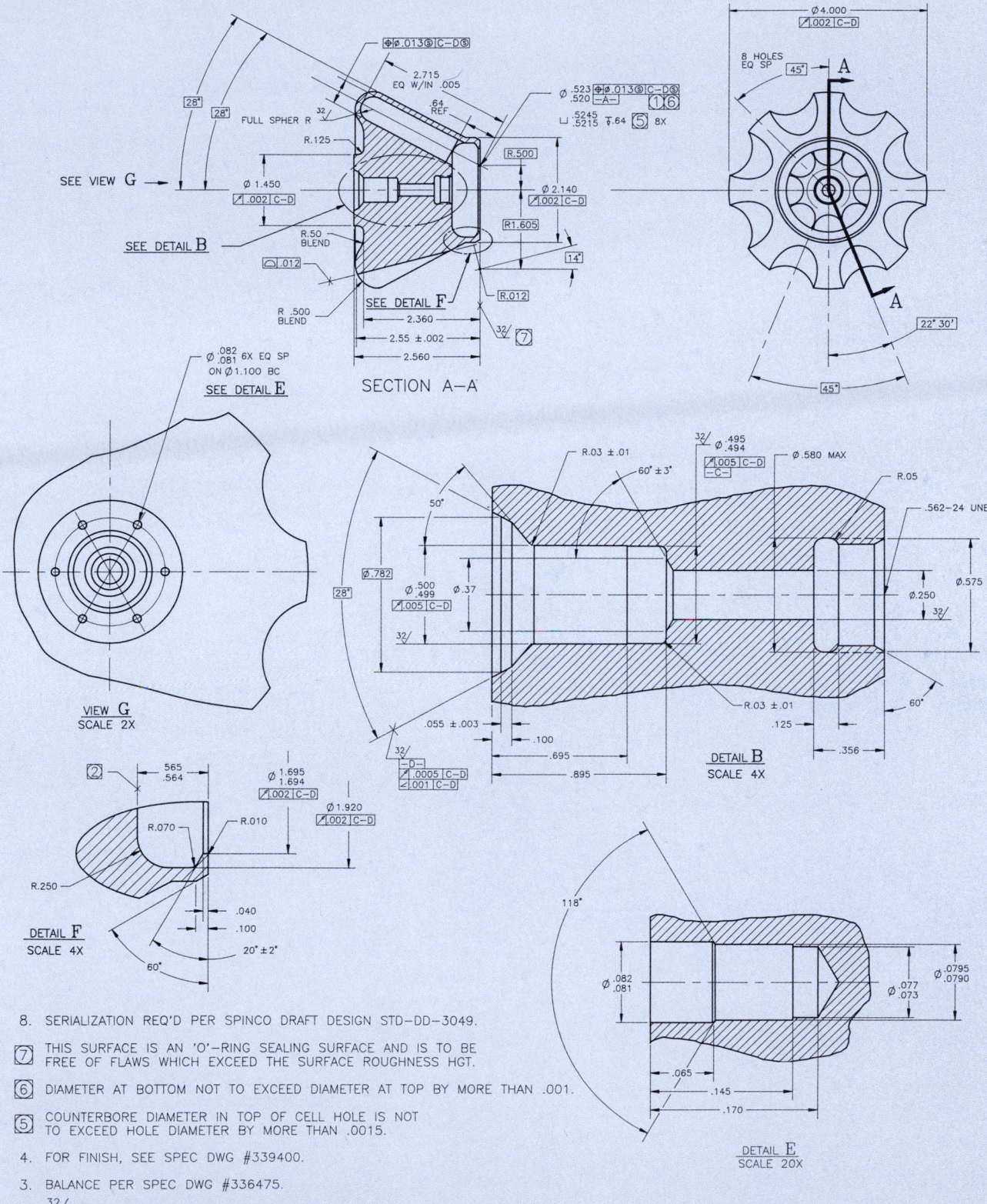

8. SERIALIZATION REQ'D PER SPINCO DRAFT DESIGN STD-DD-3049.

⑦ THIS SURFACE IS AN 'O'-RING SEALING SURFACE AND IS TO BE FREE OF FLAWS WHICH EXCEED THE SURFACE ROUGHNESS HGT.

⑥ DIAMETER AT BOTTOM NOT TO EXCEED DIAMETER AT TOP BY MORE THAN .001.

⑤ COUNTERBORE DIAMETER IN TOP OF CELL HOLE IS NOT TO EXCEED HOLE DIAMETER BY MORE THAN .0015.

4. FOR FINISH, SEE SPEC DWG #339400.

3. BALANCE PER SPEC DWG #336475.

② $\sqrt[32]{}$ PRIOR TO MARKING. THIS SURFACE IS AN 'O'-RING SEALING SURFACE AND IS TO BE FREE OF FLAWS WHICH EXCEED THE SURFACE ROUGHNESS HGT.

① TRUE POSITION OF DIAMETER $\boxed{-A-}$ TO BE WITHIN THE CONICAL ZONE AS SHOWN. THE MAX TRUE POSITION VARIATION BETWEEN CAVITIES TO BE .004.

NOTE: (UNLESS OTHERWISE SPECIFIED)

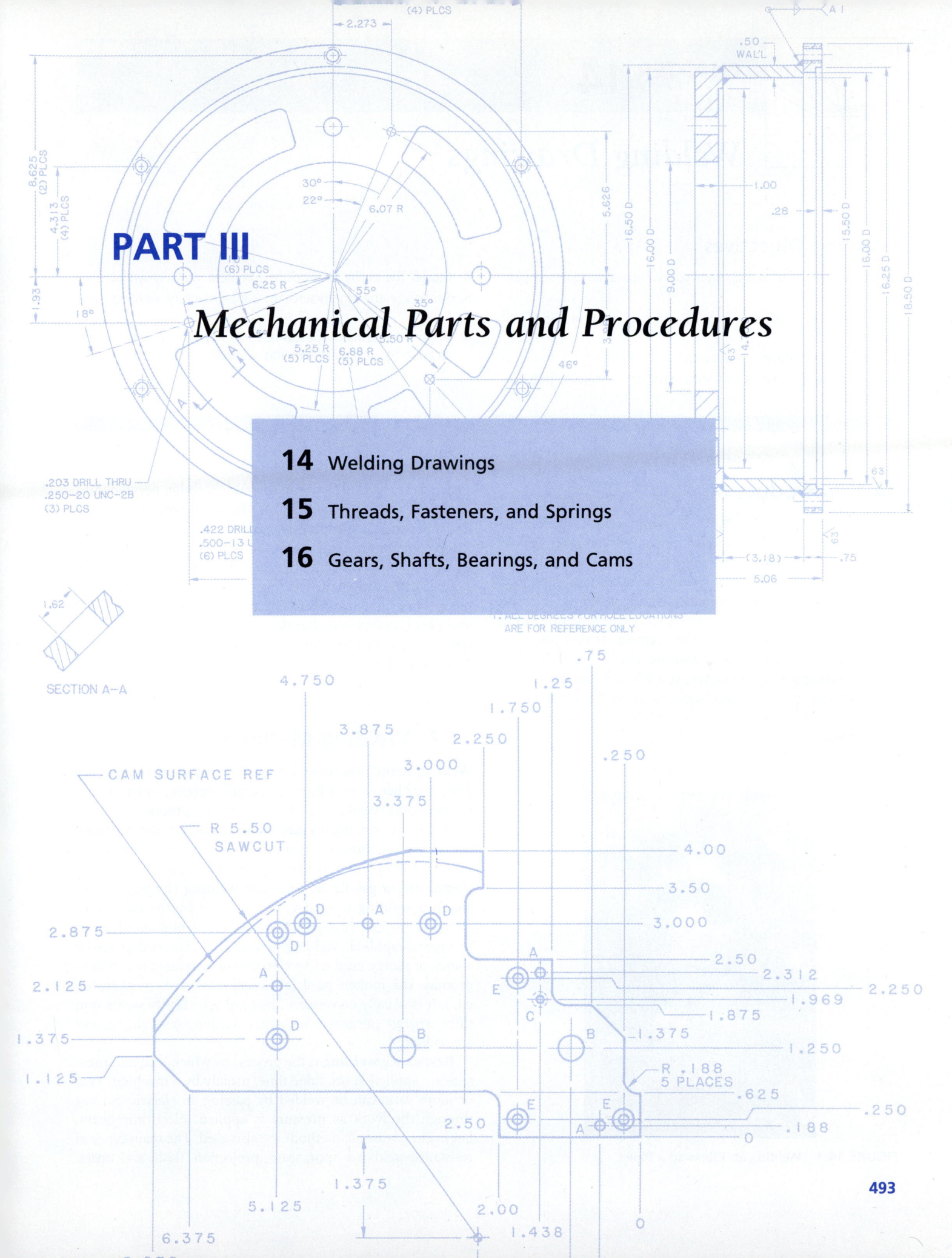

PART III

Mechanical Parts and Procedures

CHAPTER 14

Welding Drawings

Learning Objectives

Upon completion of this chapter you will be able to accomplish the following:

1. Develop an understanding of welding methods and processes.
2. Determine material weldability.
3. Identify various types of welds, symbols, and joint preparations.
4. Master the ability to produce complete welding symbols.
5. Recognize the significance of supplementary welding symbols.
6. Apply and position appropriate weld type, size, length, and location for complete welding symbols.

14.1   Introduction

Knowledge of welding (Fig. 14.1) is important to the drafter for many reasons. As a designer or drafter you will need to learn the essentials necessary to let the welder know the type, dimensions, and position of weld to be used. It is important to keep welds simple to eliminate misunderstanding. Intricate welds take time and are therefore expensive; moreover, time is often lost when interpreting the symbols. At first you need be familiar only with welds and their symbols. However, through training and experience, you will develop the knowledge of welding theory necessary for designing a system by determining adequate weld sizes, placement, and welding procedures.

FIGURE 14.1   **Welding an Elbow to a Pipe**

Welds are used to fasten an assembly together permanently. The parts to be fastened can be the same type of metal or dissimilar metals. Welding is used on assemblies (Fig. 14.2) that do not require disassembly for service or maintenance and when only one or a small number of assemblies is required. The heat used during the welding process will distort the work piece. Therefore, any machining that is required on a welded assembly is completed after the welding process. Other methods of fastening assemblies are covered in Chapter 15. See Chapter 18 for more information on welded assemblies.

14.2   Welding Methods

Welding is the procedure by which two pieces of metal are fused together along a line or a surface between them or at a certain point. Welding can be classified by process or source of energy. With **nonpressure welding** (fusion and brazing), no mechanical pressure is applied. The pieces of metal are welded at the point of contact by heat, which is created by an electric arc or gas flame. **Pressure welding** (forging) or **resistance welding** is used to form a joint by the passage of electrical current through the area of the joint as mechanical pressure is applied. Welding may also be classified as to the source of energy used to develop the temperatures required to produce the molten pool (chemical, electrical, mechanical, etc.). It is usually convenient, however, to classify welds into three separate categories: resistance welding, gas welding, and arc welding.

Resistance welding is the process by which heat and pressure are applied at the same time, usually by a machine. Two or more parts can be welded by passing an electric current through the work as pressure is applied. Electronic beam, laser, and ultrasonic methods are also used. The main types of resistance welds are spot, seam, projection, flash, and upset.

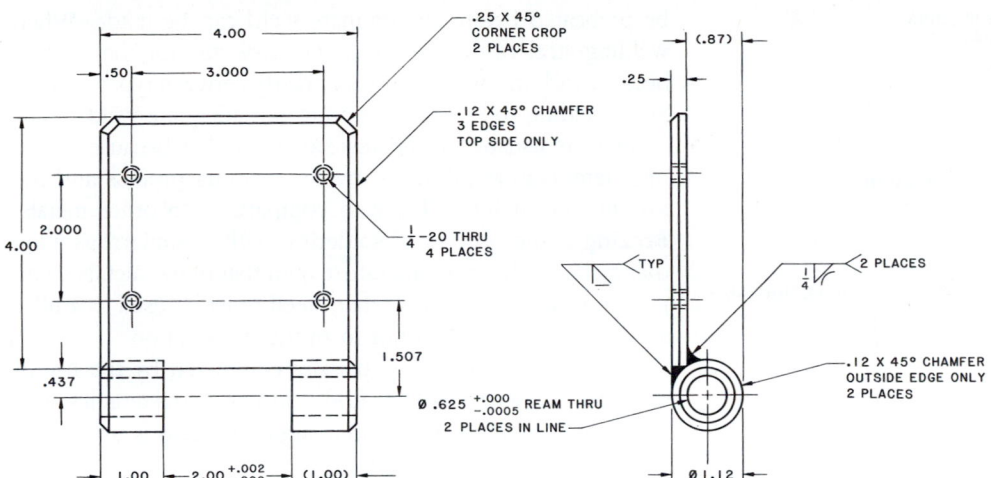

FIGURE 14.2   Weldment Detail

In **fusion welding**, also known as **gas or oxyfuel welding**, heat is created by the combustion of a gas and air or pure oxygen. In one form of gas welding—oxyacetylene welding—a flame is produced by the combustion of oxygen and acetylene gases. In today's technology, this type of welding is used less frequently (except in flame cutting) than the others and is manually applied. Besides guiding the torch, the welder may also introduce the filler rod as the welding material (Fig. 14.1).

14.2.1   Arc Welding

The third type of welding, which is the most common method, is **arc welding.** Arc welding processes include submerged arc welding, shielded arc welding, gas-metal arc welding and gas-tungsten arc welding.

In **submerged arc welding** coalescence is produced by the heating caused by an electric arc that is generated between the electrode and the work. The work is shielded by a blanket of granular, fusible material called **flux.** The flux protects the weld pool (floats on it). Leftover flux creates slag, which must be removed at the end of the process. The filler material is obtained from a supplementary welding rod or from the electrode itself. In this process, loose flux (also called melt or welding composition) is placed over the joint to be welded. After the arc is established, the flux melts to form a shield, which coats the molten metal (Fig. 14.3). A bare wire electrode is used in this process instead of a coated electrode, and the flux is supplied separately.

In **shielded arc welding**, the electric arc is produced by the passage of current from a coated metal electrode and the material to be welded. A gap exists between the electrode and the work piece. Fusion takes place by the intermingling of the molten metal. Figure 14.4 illustrates manual shielded arc welding. Note how slag is formed on top of the base metal or on top of the solidified weld metal. Slag must be removed after the welding process is completed. Figure 14.3, by way of contrast, showed how the electrode in submerged arc welding extends into the work itself and how the base materials are fused together in molten weld metal. The flux may have some additives that may become part of the weld. Note that the penetration is much deeper than in shielded arc welding.

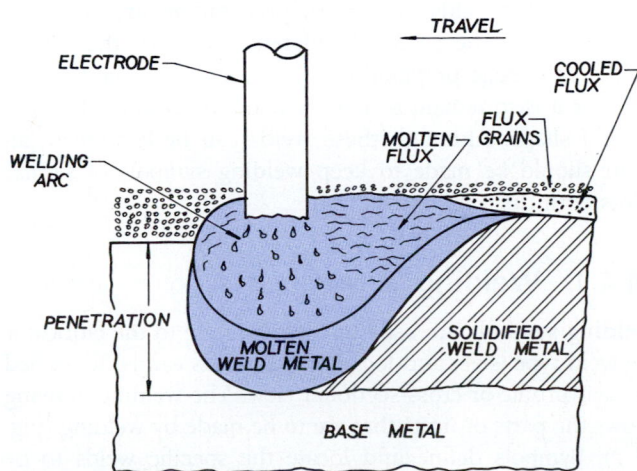

FIGURE 14.3   Submerged Arc Welding

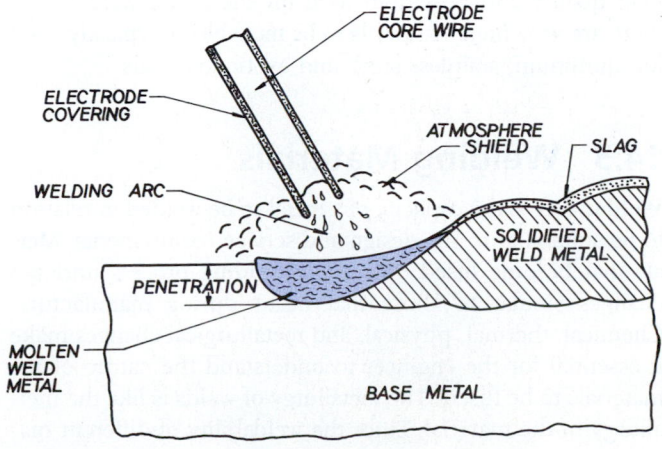

FIGURE 14.4   Manual Shielded Metal Arc Welding

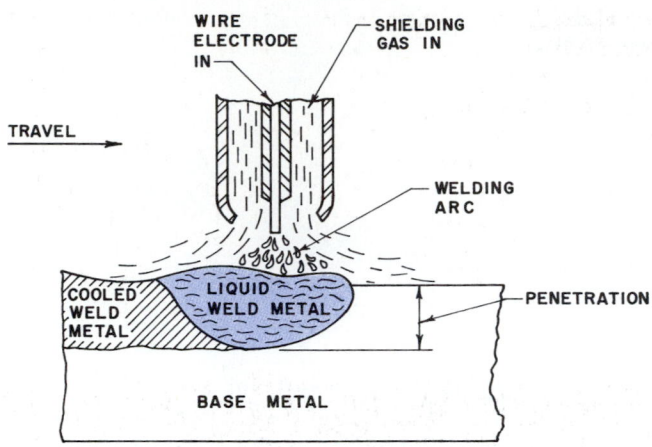

FIGURE 14.5   Gas-Metal Arc Welding

Shielded arc welding is almost always accomplished manually by a trained welder rather than an automated machine. It is used quite often in structural systems (see Fig. 14.10, p. 502) because of its ease of application in the field. It is also used for **tack welding**—holding parts in position prior to final welding.

In **gas-metal arc welding (GMAW)**, heat is created electrically as in the process just described, but the shielding is accomplished by a blanket of gas (Fig. 14.5). The term **MIG** is normally used when referring to this process, not GMAW. Pressure may or may not be used, but welding is generally pressureless. The electrode is the filler metal, becoming an integral part of the weld. The filler metal may also be added to the welding zone prior to welding. In this process, inert gases are fed into the welding area to form a blanket. This welding procedure is used for magnesium, aluminum, and carbon steel.

Gas-tungsten arc welding (GTAW) is different than GMAW because the electrode in GTAW is tungsten. The term **TIG** is commonly used when referring to this process, not GTAW. The electrode is used to transmit electric current and is not a filler metal. The TIG process produces root beads of high quality and is seldom used for the entire weld unless there are very high standards to be met. TIG is typically used for aluminum, stainless steel, and exotic materials.

14.3   Welding Materials

Weldability is the capacity of a metal to be welded in relation to its suitability to the design and service requirements. Metals that become fused during the welding process undergo changes similar to those that occur during manufacture. Chemical, thermal, physical, and metallurgical changes make it essential for the engineer to understand the nature of the materials to be fused. The metallurgy of welds is like the metallurgy of the material. Since the weldability of different materials varies greatly, so does the process by which the weld is completed. When welding cast iron to steel, for instance, cast iron rods are used as the welding material and the steel must

be preheated before an adequate weld can be made. When welding steel castings, there is no easy rule for the process because carbon content can vary greatly between types of steel. Steel welding rods usually produce an adequate weld.

Brass is usually brazed instead of welded because of the high temperature produced by the welding process and the low melting point of brass in comparison to other metals. **Brazing** is the process of soldering with a nonferrous alloy that melts at a lower temperature than that of the metals being joined. In welding copper, that metal must be used as a filler and care must be taken not to produce oxidation.

Carbon steel welding is usually completed by the use of shielded metal arc welding. Rod iron has characteristics similar to those of mild steel, and a similar process is used in its welding.

In aluminum and aluminum alloys, most of the commercial welding and brazing processes can be used, though the most common are GTAW and GMAW. Various problems are encountered when using the acetylene process to weld aluminum because of an oxide film that prevents metal flow at welding temperatures. Aluminum is characterized by its low melting point and high thermal conductivity.

As a beginning drafter you will not be required to know all the different kinds of welds and the reasons for using them, but it is essential to understand the different procedures by which the weld and the joint are created.

14.4   Types of Welds

As a drafter, you will be most concerned with symbols for the various welds and joint preparations. Weld symbols and types of welds are classified by process. Resistance weld symbols are grouped under flash or upset, projection, seam, and spot with supplementary descriptions such as contour weld and field weld.

Arc and gas weld symbols are divided into groove types (bevel, square, J, U, V), bead, fillet, plug, or slot welds. For bead and fillet welds, no special preparations are necessary for the metal. The essential difference between the groove welds is the edge preparation of the material to be welded, whether it is to remain square, beveled, or machined in a V, U, or J shape. Although these welds can be combined, an effort should be made to keep welding symbols of similar joints both the same and simple.

14.4.1   Welding Symbols

Welding symbols are used to communicate to the fabricator the weld type, size, and location. All welds can be identified by their profile or cross-sectional view. The welding drawing shows the parts or units that are to be made by welding (Fig. 14.2). Symbols define and locate the specific welds to be used. Each joint in the welding process must be fully described. The weld symbol (Fig. 14.6) denotes the desired type of weld: fillet, square, bevel, J, U, V, flare V, back, weld, arc

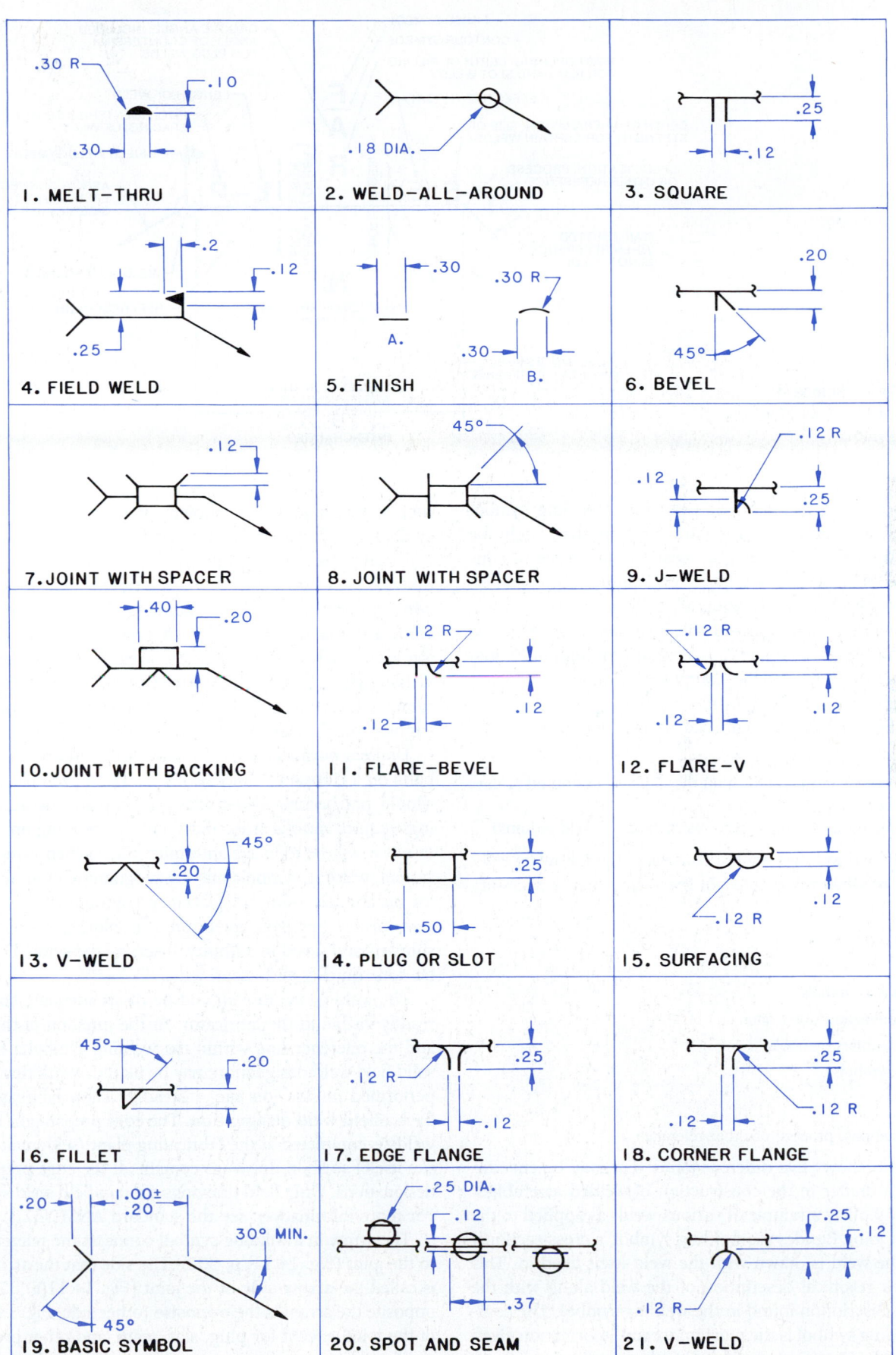

FIGURE 14.6 Weld Symbols

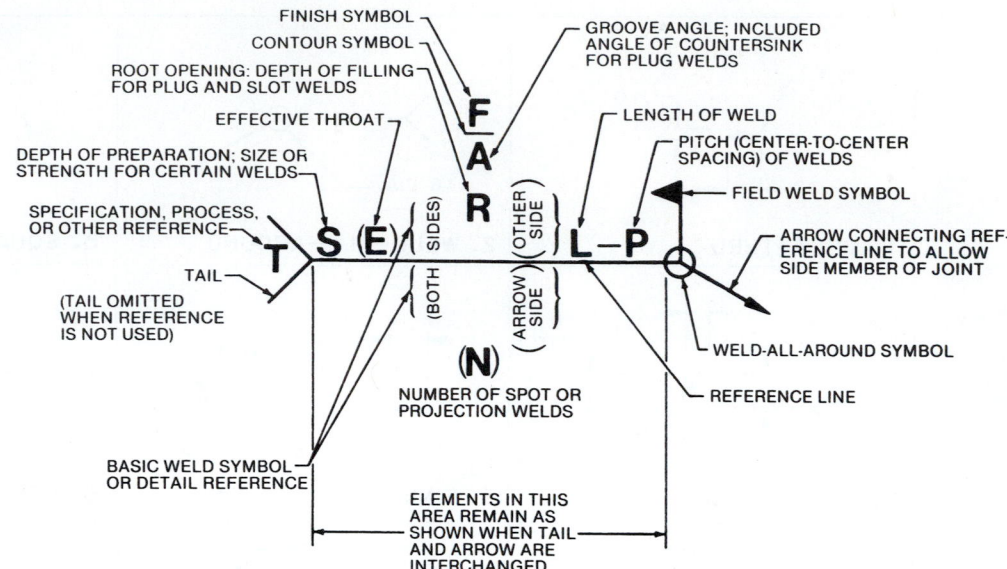

FIGURE 14.7   **Standard Location of Elements of a Welding Symbol**

seam, spot, plug, and slot. The complete welding symbol takes into account all welding information that might be needed: weld type, size, length, location, and place of construction (field or shop). Figure 14.7 shows the standard welding symbol and the location of its elements. This type of symbol, with the exception of the field weld flag which is used by only a few companies, is standard throughout industry. The components of the complete welding symbol and their location are provided in this figure.

Welding symbols are composed of three basic parts:

1. an **arrow** which points to the joint
2. a **reference line** upon which all the dimensions and other data are placed
3. the **weld symbol**, which indicates the type of weld required

The assembled welding symbol consists of the following eight elements or whatever number of these elements is necessary (Fig. 14.7):

Reference line

    Arrow

    Basic weld symbols

    Dimensions and other data

    Supplementary symbols

    Finish symbols

Tail

    Specifications, process, or other reference

Figure 14.8 shows five different joints that may be encountered by a drafter in the construction of welded assemblies. Figure 14.9 offers a sample of various welds as applied to the particular joint. Besides the welding symbol, a cross-sectional view of the weld is drawn with the weld itself filled in. This provides a graphical description of the weld along with the symbolic description found in the welding symbol. The complete welding symbol is the most important information given to the welder. In many applications, the graphic representa-

tion of the weld is not shown on the drawing—only the symbol (see, for example, Fig. 14.13, p. 503).

Usually the same welding process is used throughout a drawing as in Figure 14.10. If this is not the case, for instance, when the drawing contains submerged arc welding by machine and manual welding, each process must be noted on the symbol when pointing to the joint to be completed. The welding process should be placed at the tail of the welding symbol. The tail is omitted when references are not needed to supplement the symbol.

Drafters normally use templates (or a library of standard parts on a computer) for drawing welding symbols. But you should not become dependent on templates because drawings require various sizes of symbols, depending on whether or not it will be reduced onto microfilm. When using a CAD system, welding symbols may be programmed into the menu for instant selection and placement by digitizing or explicit coordinates. Symbols are created as blocks, subfigures, or subparts and saved in a library. Inserting the symbol can then be done quickly and accurately.

The welding symbol should be of an adequate size to be readily visible to the fabricator. At the junction of the arrow and the reference line within the welding symbol a flag or a solid field weld designation may be placed. Work that is to be performed on the job site, instead of shop fabricated, will have a **field weld designation**. The edge preparation for such welds is completed at the fabricating plant (seldom at the job site itself) so shop drawings contain all the edge preparation designations. Only field drawings contain field weld symbols. For more information, see the standard ANSI Y32.3.

The arrow in a welding symbol connects the reference line to the joint (Fig. 14.11, p. 502). The side that the arrow is on is called the **arrow side** of the joint [Fig. 14.11(a)]. The side opposite the arrow is the **opposite** [other side, Fig. 14.11(d)] of the joint, except for plug, slot, seam, and other projection welds where the arrow connects the symbol to the surface to

APPLICABLE WELDS

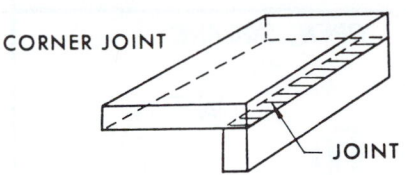

BUTT JOINT

SQUARE GROOVE	FLARE-V-GROOVE
V-GROOVE	FLARE-BEVEL-GROOVE
BEVEL-GROOVE	EDGE-FLANGE
U-GROOVE	BRAZE
J-GROOVE	

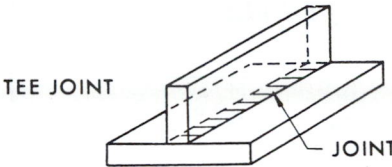

CORNER JOINT

FILLET	FLARE-V-GROOVE
SQUARE-GROOVE	CORNER FLANGE
V-GROOVE	EDGE-FLANGE
BEVEL-GROOVE	SPOT
U-GROOVE	PROJECTION
J-GROOVE	SEAM
	FLARE-BEVEL-GROOVE
	BRAZE

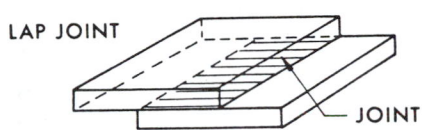

TEE JOINT

FILLET	FLARE-BEVEL-GROOVE
PLUG	SPOT
SLOT	PROJECTION
BEVEL-GROOVE	SEAM
SQUARE-GROOVE	BRAZE
J-GROOVE	

LAP JOINT

FILLET	BEVEL-GROOVE
PLUG	J-GROOVE
SLOT	FLARE-BEVEL-GROOVE
SPOT	PROJECTION
SEAM	BRAZE

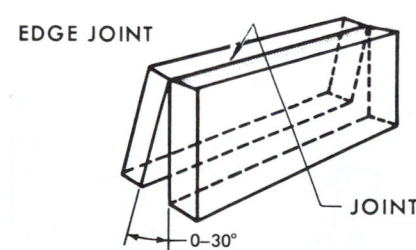

EDGE JOINT

SQUARE-GROOVE	J-GROOVE
V-GROOVE	EDGE-FLANGE
BEVEL-GROOVE	CORNER-FLANGE
U-GROOVE	SEAM
	EDGE

FIGURE 14.8 Basic Types of Joints

be acted on. The arrow side of the joint is always considered the near side. Welds on the arrow side of the joint are shown by placing the weld symbol on the side nearest to the reader. To show welds on both sides, the weld symbol is placed on both sides of the reference line [Fig. 14.11(e), p. 502].

In many situations one welding symbol is shown on the drawing and a note is included that specifies the type of weld to be used on the entire drawing—such as all welds to be $\frac{1}{4}$ in. unless otherwise noted. On welds that are to be on all sides of a particular joint, the **weld-all-around symbol** is used at the junction of the arrow line and the reference line, which may also contain a field weld symbol at the same joint (Fig. 14.12, p. 503). When welds must be finished or contoured, this requirement must be shown on the symbol (Fig. 14.12). It is also possible to combine different weld symbols in one welding symbol. Remember, the weld symbol is always placed according to the side of the joint on which the weld is to be made.

14.5 Welding Symbol Specifications

Weld symbols are to be drawn as in Figure 14.6. The sizes shown in this figure are used as a guide for symbol construction with their minimum values given. The actual size of the weld symbol and the welding symbol will vary according to the drawing size. Basic weld symbols on drawings are proportioned as shown in Figure 14.6 and are of a size to be compatible with microfilm reduction requirements.

When drawing welding symbols, no distinction is made between arc and gas welding. Weld symbols are shown only as part of the welding symbol. Symbols are drawn "on" the reference line. Fillet, bevel-groove, J-groove, flare-bevel-groove, and corner-flange weld symbols are shown with the *perpendicular leg always to the left.* Symbols are drawn a uniform size throughout the drawing. If the arrow is directed to the outer surface of one of the members of the joint (plug,

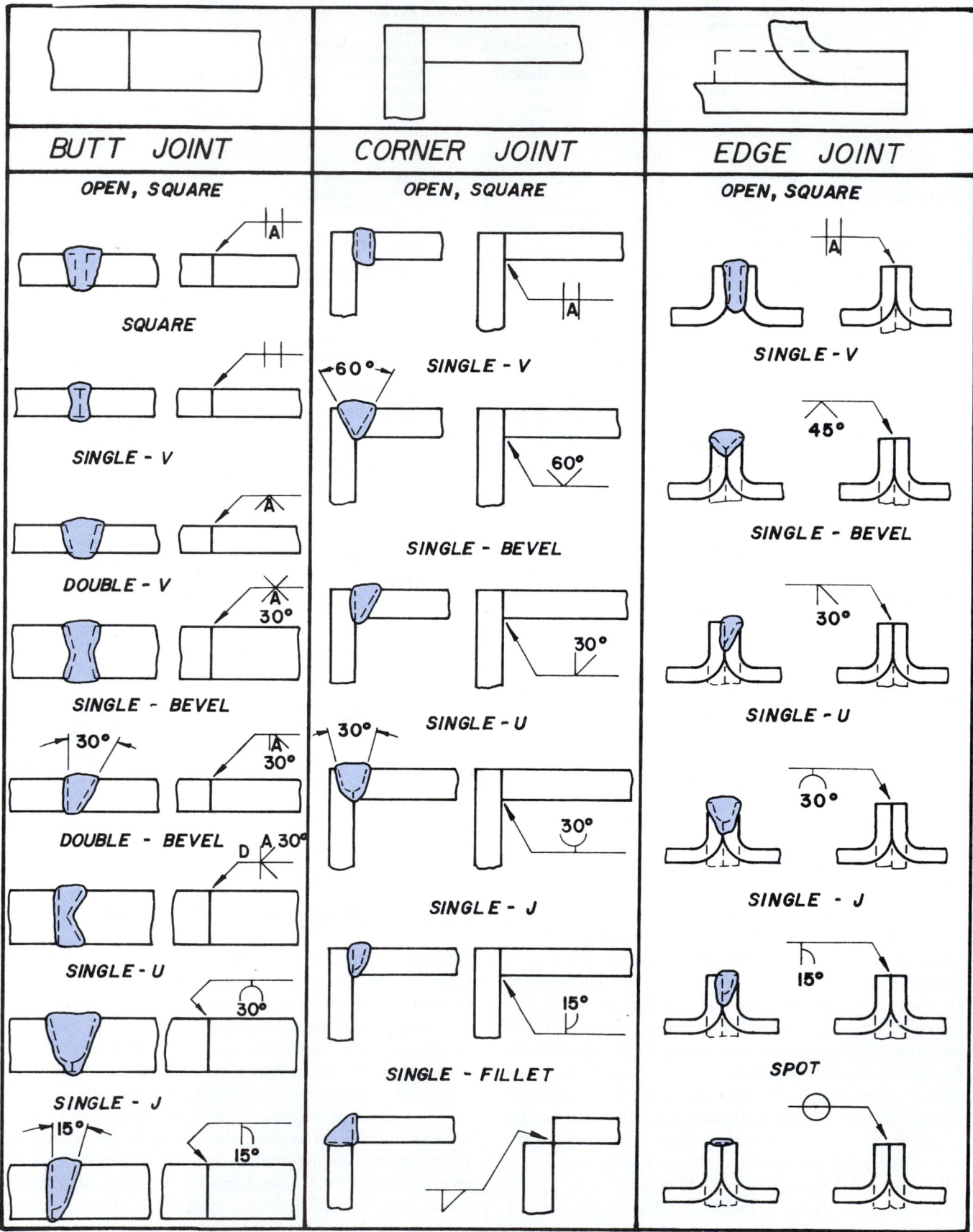

(a)

FIGURE 14.9 Joints and Appropriate Welds

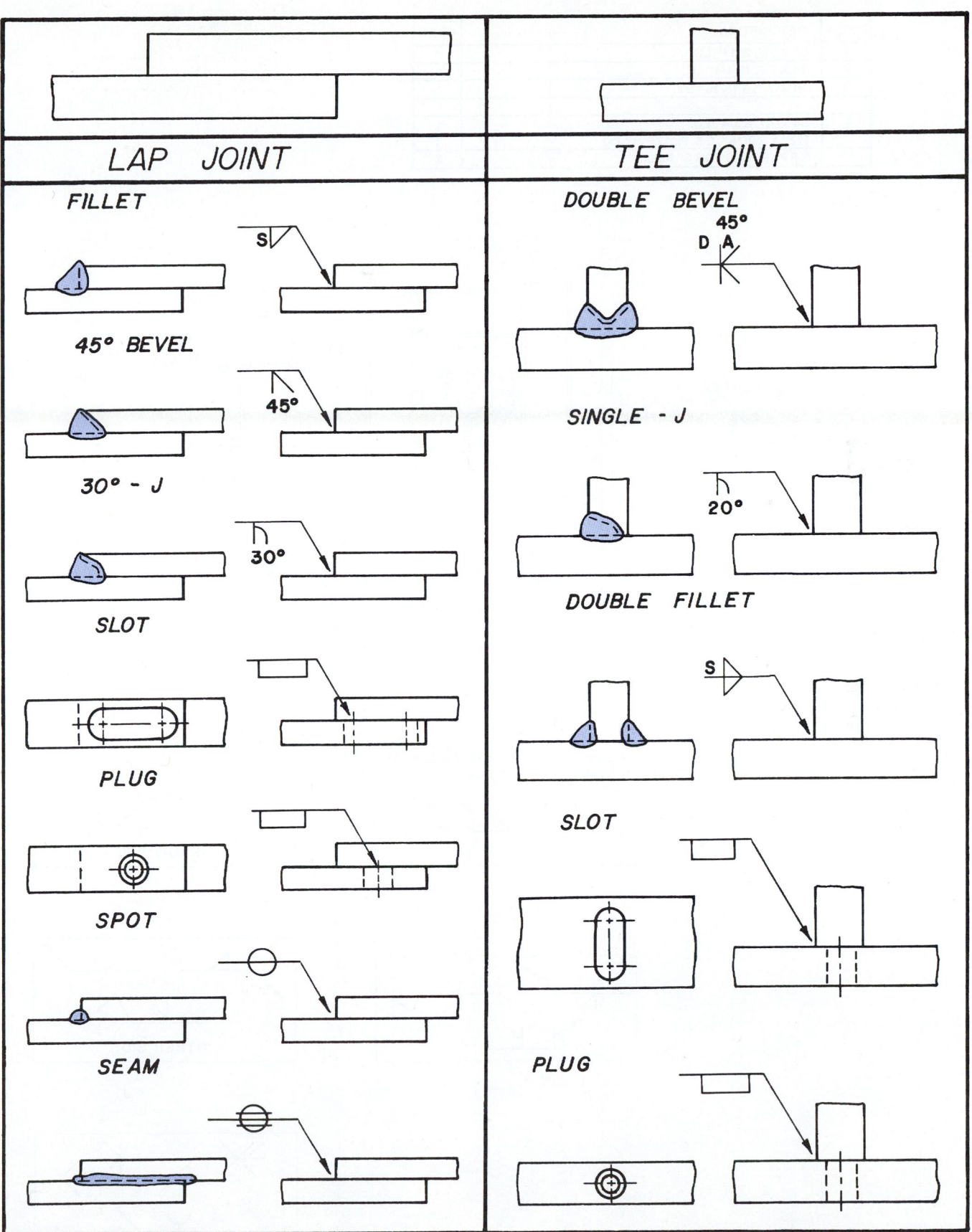

(b)

FIGURE 14.9—*Continued*

DET.#	DESCRIPTION	QUAN
1	54 X 7.7, 2'-11" LG.	1
2	54 X 7.7, 13-1/4" LG.	2
3	54 X 7.7, 6-13/16" LG.	1
4	54 X 7.7, 8-3/4" LG.	1
	1/2" X 2-9/16", C.S. PLATE, 4" LG.	3
	8-P PART 298 FOR 3" PIPE	2

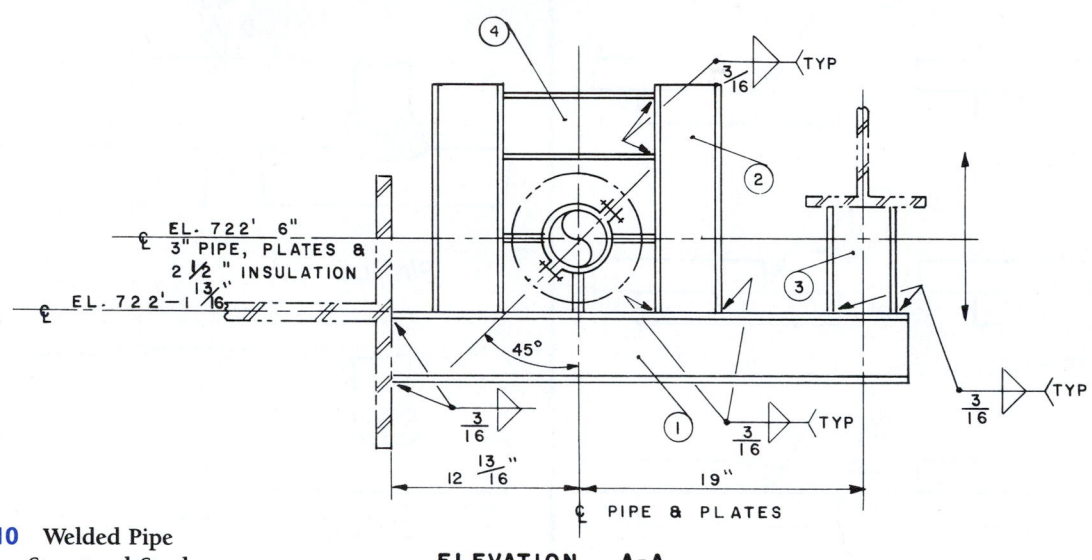

FIGURE 14.10 Welded Pipe
Support Using Structural Steel

ELEVATION A-A

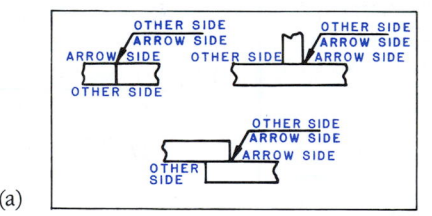

(a)

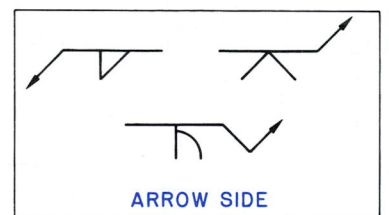

ARROW SIDE

(c)

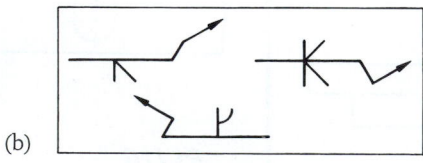

(b)

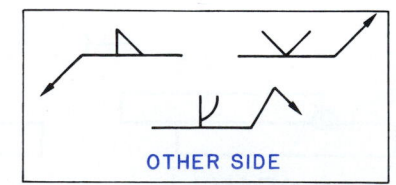

OTHER SIDE

(d)

FIGURE 14.11 Example of
Welding Symbol Element
Locations

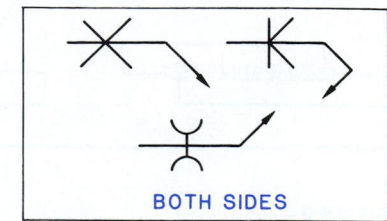

BOTH SIDES

(e)

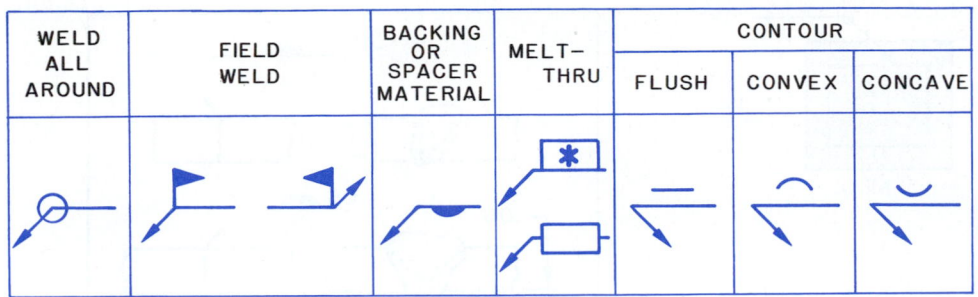

FIGURE 14.12 Supplementary Symbols

slot, seam, and projection welds) at the centerline of the desired weld, the member to which the arrow points is considered the arrow side member.

14.5.1 Supplementary Welding Symbols

Supplementary welding symbols are shown in Figure 14.12 and are used as applicable to define specific welding requirements. The *weld-all-around* symbol is used to indicate welds extending completely around a joint (Figs. 14.13 and 14.14). Welds completely around a joint in which the metal intersections at the points of welding are in more than one plane are also indicated by the weld-all-around symbol. The **melt-thru** symbol (Fig. 14.15) is used only where 100% joint or member penetration plus reinforcement is required in welds made from one side only. Reinforcement (melt-thru) height may be shown on the welding symbol [Fig. 14.15(a)]. Melt-thru that is to be made flush by mechanical means is shown by adding both the flush contour symbol and finish symbol [Fig. 14.15(b)]. Melt-thru that is to be mechanically finished to a convex contour is shown by adding both the convex *contour* symbol and *finish* symbol.

Contour symbols are used, as applicable, to indicate the appropriate weld contour (flax, convex, or concave) desired, either with (in conjunction with a finish symbol) or without

mechanical finishing. Finishing of welds, other than cleaning, are indicated by a suitable contour and finish symbol [Fig. 14.15(b) and (c)]. Welds indicated by symbols are continuous between abrupt changes in the direction of the joint except when the weld-all-around symbol is used, or as specified by length dimension on the welding symbol or dimension lines on the view. Welds extending beyond abrupt changes in direction are indicated by means of additional arrows pointing to each section of the joint to be welded. A symbol is shown for each weld on joints having more than one weld. When the basic weld symbols are inadequate to indicate the desired weld, the weld is shown by a cross section, detail, or other data, with a reference on the welding symbol.

The **pitch** (center-to-center spacing) of intermittent welds is shown to the right of the length dimension and separated from it by a hyphen [Fig. 14.16(a)]. The pitch indicates the distance between centers of the welds on one side of the joint. Chain and staggered intermittent weld dimensions are shown on both sides of the reference line [Fig. 14.16(b) and (c)]. When intermittent welding is called out by itself, the symbol indicates that welds are located at the ends of the joint. When intermittent welding is called out between continuous welding, the symbol indicates that spaces equal to the pitch minus the length of one increment are left between the end of the

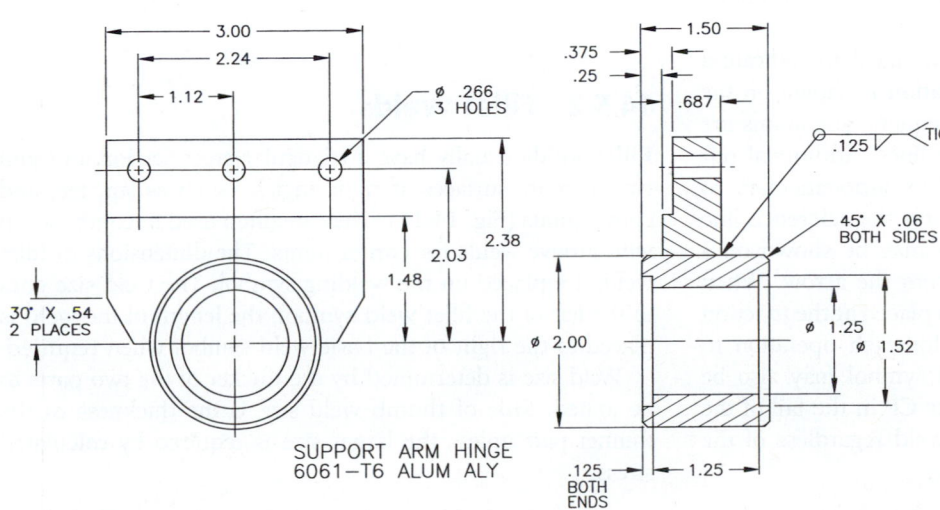

SUPPORT ARM HINGE
6061−T6 ALUM ALY

FIGURE 14.13 Detail Drawing of a Weldment

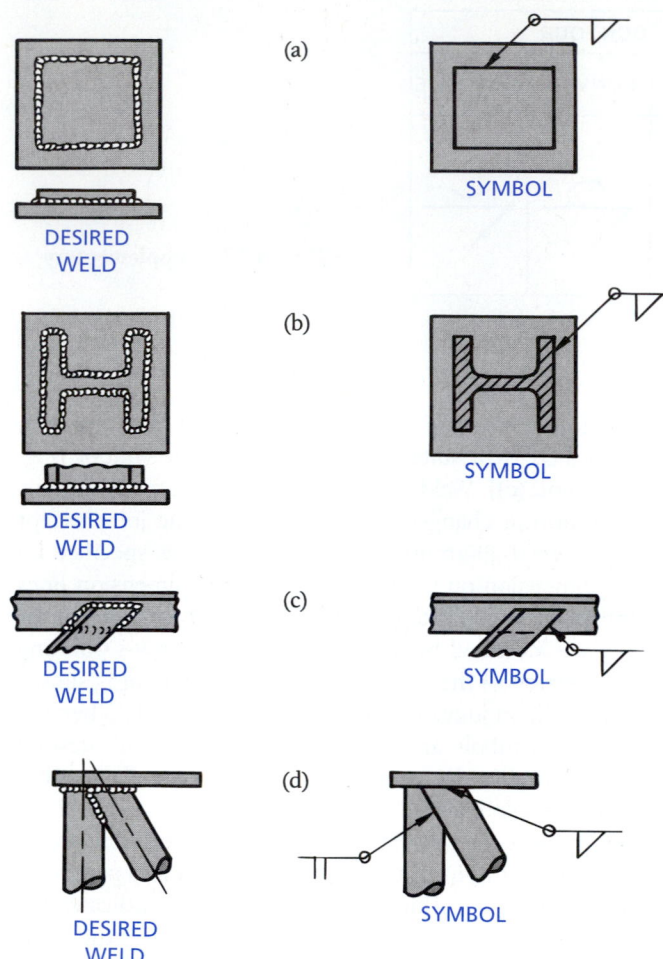

FIGURE 14.14 **Weld-all-around Symbols**

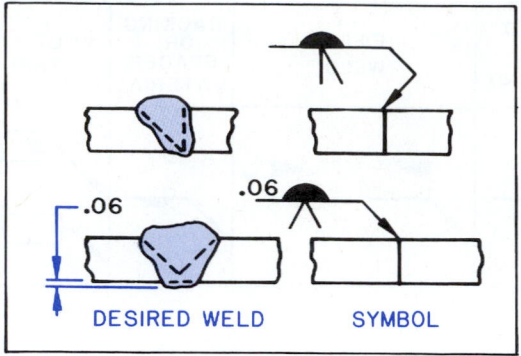

(a) Use of melt-thru symbol

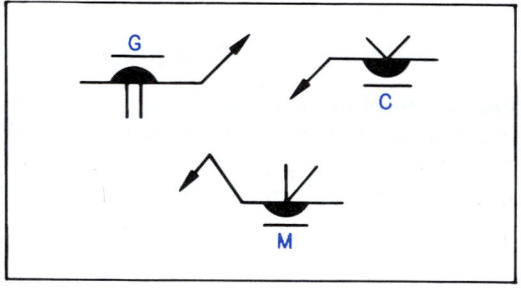

(b) Melt-thru finished flush

METHOD OF FINISH				
CHIP	GRIND	MACHINE	ROLL	HAMMER
C	G	M	R	H

(c) Weld finish symbols

FIGURE 14.15 **Melt-thru and Finish Symbols** (a) Use of melt-thru symbol (b) Melt-thru finished flush (c) Weld finish symbols

continuous weld and the intermittent weld [Fig. 14.16(c)]. Unless otherwise specified, staggered intermittent welds on both sides are symmetrically spaced as shown in Figure 14.16(c). Separate welding symbols are used for intermittent and continuous welding when the two are used in combination along one side of the joint.

Two or more reference lines may be used to indicate a sequence of operations. The first operation is shown on the reference line nearest the arrow. Subsequent operations are shown sequentially on other reference lines. Additional reference lines may be used to show data supplementary to welding symbol information included on the reference line nearest to the arrow. Test information may be shown on a second or third reference line away from the arrow. When required, the weld-all-around symbol is placed at the junction of the arrow line and reference line for each operation to which it is applicable. The field weld symbol may also be applied in the same manner. The letters CP in the tail of the arrow indicate a *complete penetration* weld regardless of the type of weld or joint preparation.

14.5.2 Fillet Welds

Fillet welds usually have a triangular cross section and join two or more surfaces at right angles—such as lap, tee, and corner joints (Fig. 14.17). They are often used in combination with groove welds for corner joints. The dimensions of fillet welds are placed on the welding symbol. The weld size goes to the left of the fillet weld symbol; the length of the weld is placed to the right of the basic weld symbol when required.

Weld size is determined by the thicker of the two parts to be joined. Rule of thumb weld size is the thickness of the thinner part unless the larger size is required by calculated stress.

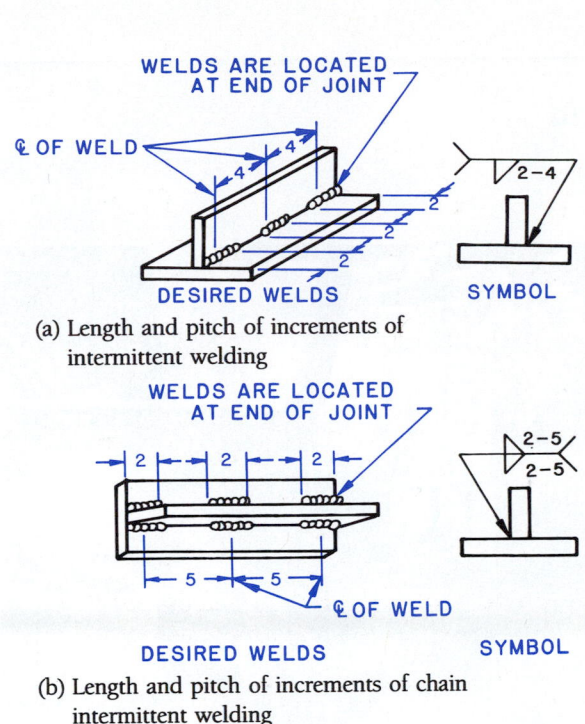

(a) Length and pitch of increments of intermittent welding

(b) Length and pitch of increments of chain intermittent welding

(c) Length and pitch of increments of staggered intermittent welding

FIGURE 14.16   Application of Dimensions to Intermittent Fillet Welding Symbols

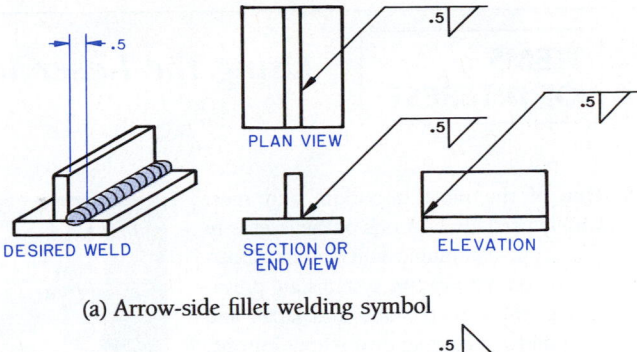

(a) Arrow-side fillet welding symbol

(b) Other-side fillet welding symbol

FIGURE 14.17   Application of Fillet Welding Symbols

Fillet welds are also used in larger holes and slots where plug and slot welds are inappropriate. Generally, fillet welds are not finished unless a specific finishing process is specified on the symbol. The two basic types of fillet welds are those with *equal legs* and those with *unequal legs*.

The size of fillet welds is shown on the same side of the reference line as the weld symbol and to the left of the weld symbol (Fig. 14.17). When welds on both sides of the joint have the same dimensions, both are dimensioned (Fig. 14.18). The size of a weld with unequal legs is shown in parentheses to the left of the weld symbol. Weld orientation is not shown by the symbol and is shown graphically on the drawing when required (Fig. 14.18). Fillet weld size can also be specified in a general note such as:

NOTE: UNLESS OTHERWISE SPECIFIED
ALL FILLET WELDS SHALL BE 20 MM SIZE

Specified lengths of fillet welding may be indicated by symbols in conjunction with dimension lines [Fig. 14.19(a) and (b)]. When necessary for clarity, the length of fillet welding

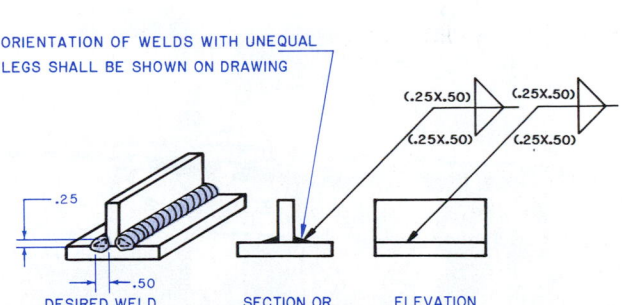

(a) Both sides fillet welding symbol for one joint

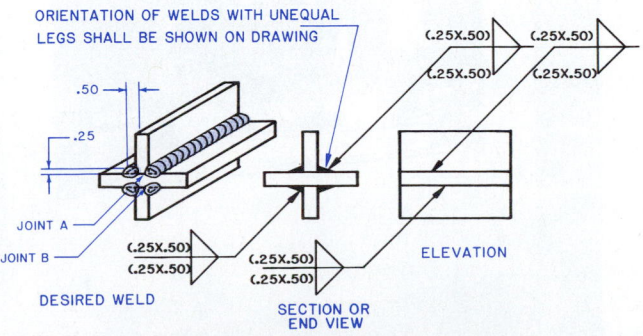

(b) Both sides fillet welding symbol for two joints

FIGURE 14.18   Fillet Welding Symbol Application

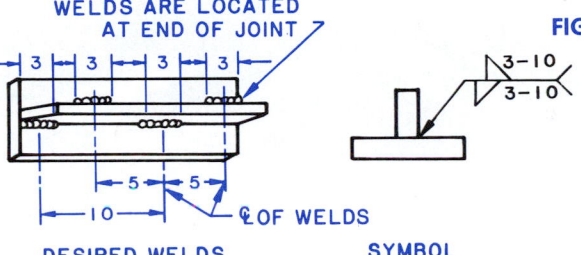

ITEMS
OF INTEREST

Using the Laser to Weld

One of the most important and most widely used applications of the laser is in fiber optic communication systems. Laser-based communication systems are prevalent in the United States and Japan and are rapidly spreading throughout Europe. Laser beams that are transmitted by glass fibers carry thousands of times more information than copper cables. Even though lasers are a relatively new technology (1960), they have become one of our most useful tools.

Laser applications in industry, ranging from manufacturing to the space program, have become quite popular. Laser-based tools are used for heat treating, cutting, drilling, and welding. Even though laser cutting and drilling is used, laser welding is by far the most often used process.

There are two different laser welding processes. One is conduction, which occurs at the surface of the material; the other is deep penetration, where heat is moved below the surface of the material.

Arc Welding with Robots

Laser Welding Machine

The conduction process is used to join thin sheets. The deep penetration process creates a more efficient weld with high tensile strength and hardness. Laser welding has been used with great success in shipbuilding, pipeline fabrication for the Arctic, nickel steels, and low alloy steels. The National Aeronautics and Space Agency developed a way to weld aluminum effectively using a laser. Aluminum is difficult to weld because it has a low melting temperature. Because of the developed process, aluminum vessels can now contain a high-pressure gas. Other precision aluminum pieces can be fabricated with the same process.

In laser welding, the welding rod is eliminated. The welding is accomplished without the excess heat that distorts and even destroys some materials in conventional welding. Even two dissimilar materials can be joined with laser welding. As larger and more powerful lasers are built, laser welding applications will grow in size and in number. Welding with lasers has made fabrications possible today that were impossible only forty years ago.

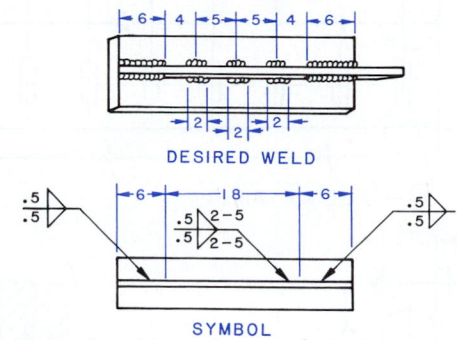

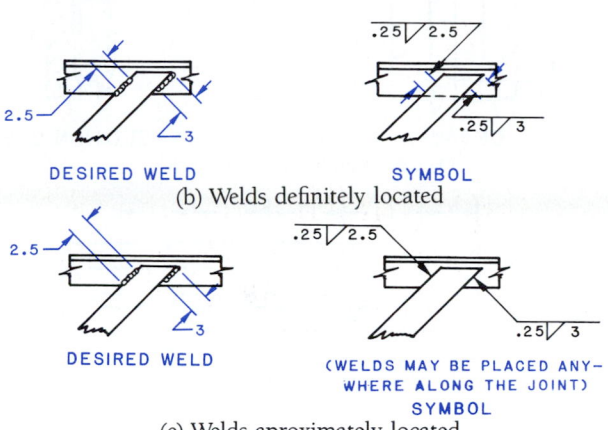

FIGURE 14.19 **Designation of Location and Extent of Fillet Welds**

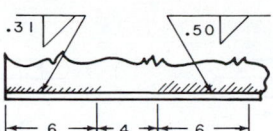

FIGURE 14.20 **Length of Fillet Welds**

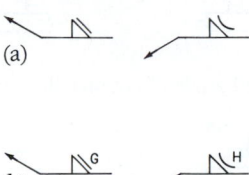

FIGURE 14.21 **Surface Contours for Fillet Welds** (a) Surface contoured without mechanical finish (b) Surface mechanically contoured

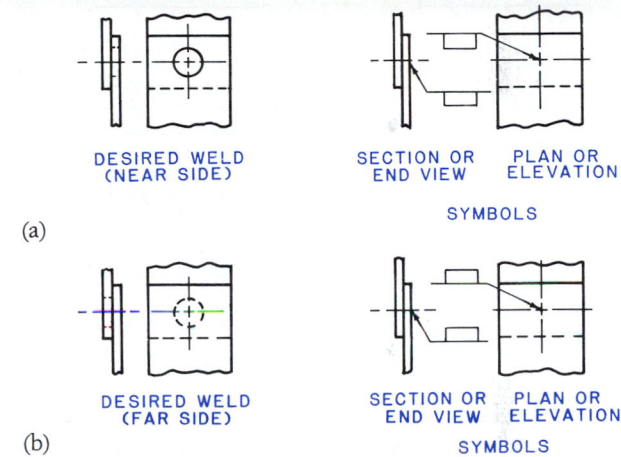

FIGURE 14.22 **Plug Welds**

may be graphically shown by *hatching* and dimensioned directly on the drawing (Fig. 14.20). No length dimension need be shown when the weld extends for the full distance between abrupt direction changes.

When a design requires fillet welds to be welded approximately flat-faced, convex-faced, or concave-faced, the contour symbol is added to the weld symbol [Fig. 14.21(a)]. If the weld is to be contoured mechanically, the weld finish symbol is added to the contour symbol [Fig. 14.21(b)].

14.5.3   Plug and Slot Welds

The rectangular basic weld symbol (Fig. 14.22) is used for designating **plug** and **slot welds**. All the rules for drawing symbols and their locations apply for this type of weld as well. Plug and slot welds are often used in butt joints and lap joints for reinforcement. When the slot or hole is too large to make plug or slot welds effective or economical, fillet welds are used.

Plug welding holes in the arrow-side member of a joint are indicated by placing the weld symbol below the reference line. Holes in the other-side member are indicated by placing the weld symbol above the reference line (Fig. 14.22). Plug weld dimensions are shown on the same side of the reference line as the weld symbol (Fig. 14.23). The diameter of the base of the hole is shown to the left of the weld symbol. The hole is cylindrical unless the included angle of countersink (taper) is shown above (other-side) or below (arrow-side) the weld

symbol [Fig. 14.23(c)]. Plug welds completely fill the holes unless depth of filling is shown inside the weld symbol. The pitch of plug welds is shown to the right of the weld symbol [Fig. 14.23(d)].

Length, width, spacing, included angle of countersink (taper), orientation, and location of slot welds cannot be shown on the welding symbol. This information is shown on the drawing with a detail referenced on the welding symbol (Fig. 14.24). Unless otherwise indicated, the depth of filling of slot welds is complete. When the depth of filling is less than smooth or complete, the depth of filling is shown inside the weld symbol [Fig. 14.24(b)].

14.5.4   Projection Welds

When **projection welding** is required, the spot weld symbol is used with the projection welding process reference in the tail of the welding symbol (Fig. 14.25). The spot weld symbol is placed above and below (never on) the reference line to

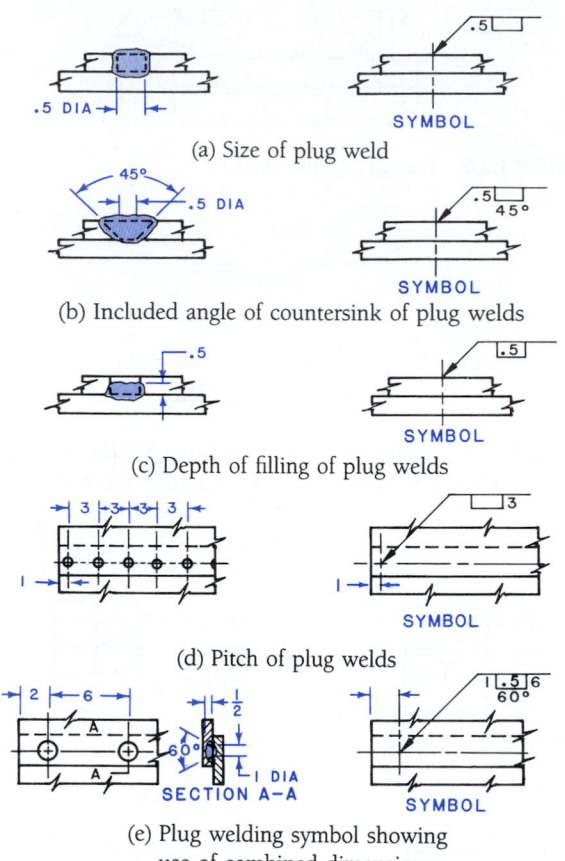

(a) Size of plug weld

(b) Included angle of countersink of plug welds

(c) Depth of filling of plug welds

(d) Pitch of plug welds

(e) Plug welding symbol showing
use of combined dimensions

FIGURE 14.23   Dimension on Plug Welding Symbols

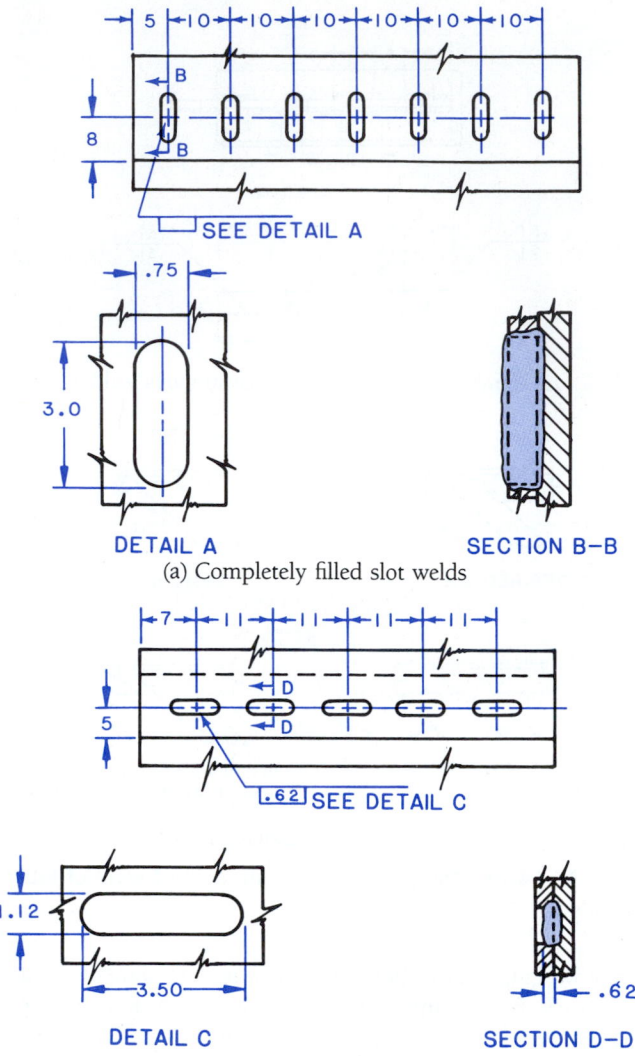

DETAIL A   SECTION B–B
(a) Completely filled slot welds

DETAIL C   SECTION D–D
(b) Partially filled slot welds

FIGURE 14.24   Dimension on Slot Welding Symbols

indicate in which member the *embossment* is placed. Dimensions are shown on the same side of the reference line as the weld symbol, or on either side when the symbol is astride the reference line and has no arrow-side or other-side significance. The strength of spot welds is designated as the minimum shear strength per spot and unless controlled by the applicable process specification is shown to the left of the weld symbol (Fig. 14.26).

The pitch of spot and projection welds is shown to the right of the weld symbol [Fig. 14.26(b)]. When spot welding extends less than the distance between abrupt changes in direction, or less than the full length of the joint, the extent is dimensioned on the drawing. When a definite number of spot welds is desired in a joint, the number is shown in parentheses either above or below the weld symbol [Fig. 14.26(c)].

14.5.5   Seam Welds

One symbol is used for all **seam welds** regardless of the welding process. The process reference is shown in the tail of the welding symbol. The weld symbol may or may not have location significance, depending on the welding process. Dimensions are shown on the same side of the reference line as the weld symbol, or on either side when the symbol is astride the reference line and has no arrow-side or other-side significance (Fig. 14.27).

Seam welds are dimensioned by either size or shear strength. Weld size is designated as the width of the weld. Shear strength is designated in pounds per linear inch minimum, and is shown to the left of the weld symbol [Fig. 14.27(b)]. The length of a seam weld that extends less than the full length of the joint or the distance between abrupt changes in direction is either shown to the right of the weld symbol or dimensioned on the drawing [Fig. 14.27(c)]. The flush contour symbol may be used to indicate flushness of the exposed surface of either member of a seam welded joint.

14.5.6   Groove Welds

The five basic **groove welds** are beveled, square, J, U, and V. However, various combinations are also used: single V, single bevel, single J, single U, double V, double bevel, double J, and double U. The edges in a groove weld are usually prepared by a flame cutting torch. Whether single or double, these are probably the easiest, most economical welded joints used to join two ends. With this type of joint preparation, the most

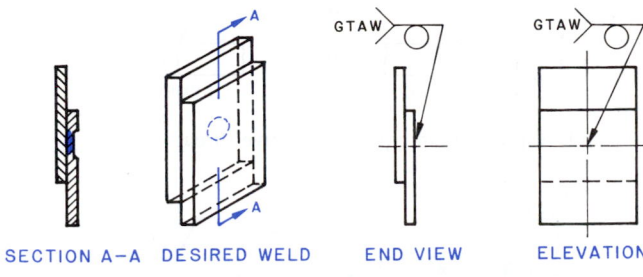

(a) Arrow-side spot weld symbol
(gas tungsten-arc spot)

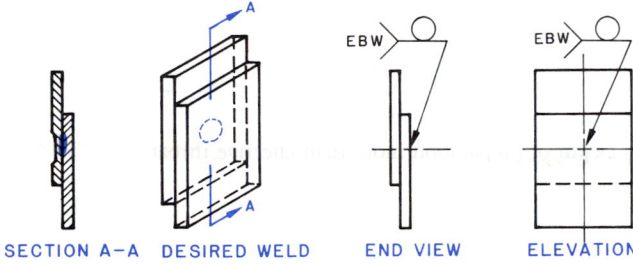

(b) Other-side spot weld symbol
(electron beam spot)

FIGURE 14.25 Spot Welding Symbol Applications

(a) Shear strength of spot welds (resistance spot)

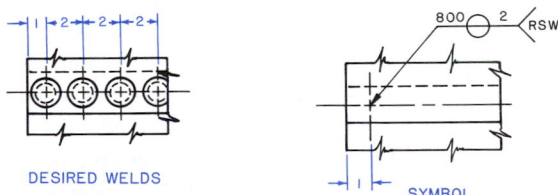

(b) Pitch of spot welds (resistance spot)

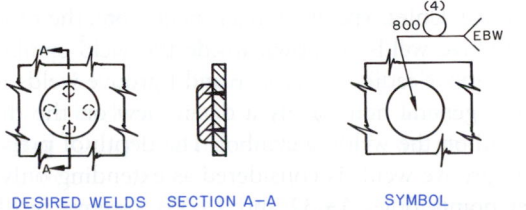

(c) Specified number of spot welds located at random
(electron beam spot)

FIGURE 14.26 Application of Dimension to Spot Welding Symbols

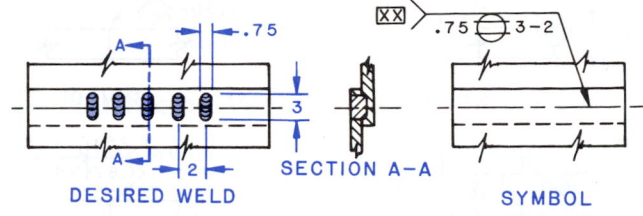

(a) Length and pitch of seam welds

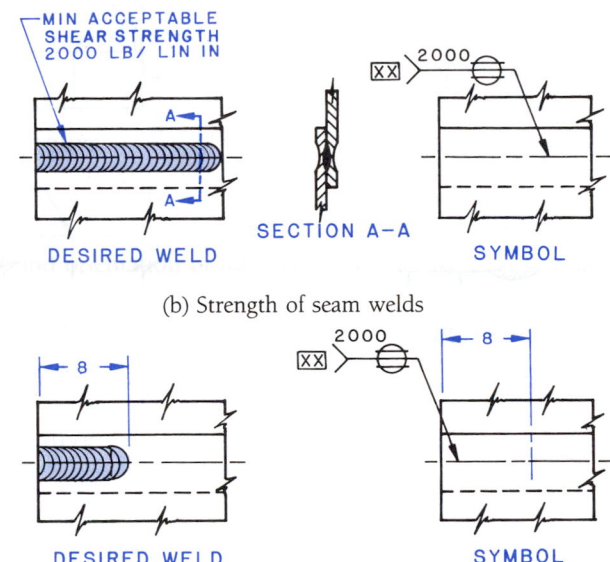

(b) Strength of seam welds

(c) Extent of seam welds

FIGURE 14.27 Application of Dimension to Seam Welding Symbols

common faulty connection, whether using submerged arc, shielded arc, or another process, is the lack of penetration that sometimes occurs at the root of the weld.

When a joint is prepared for welding, the thickness of the material must be taken into account. In small thicknesses such as $\frac{1}{16}$ to $\frac{1}{8}$ in. (1.5 to 3 mm), welding can be successful when the edges are square. When the edges are thicker than this, bevels must be made to assure full penetration and create an adequate joint. Otherwise the flame will not be hot enough to produce adequate fusion. A general rule to follow when material is thicker than $\frac{1}{8}$ in. (3 mm) is that the edges must be prepared for a groove channel, and during the welding process a filler material must be added.

In most cases, steel and iron are beveled at an angle of 45°. The included angle of the bevel is approximately 90° and V-shaped. Many groove welds use a *backing bar* or *backing weld*. The American Society of Mechanical Engineers (ASME) boiler code and other regulating codes require full penetration welds, especially for pressure vessels and piping services that are considered critical. *Backup rings* are therefore employed in the construction of vessels and pipe joints where full penetration is required. The ASME and the AWS (Amer-

(a)

(b)

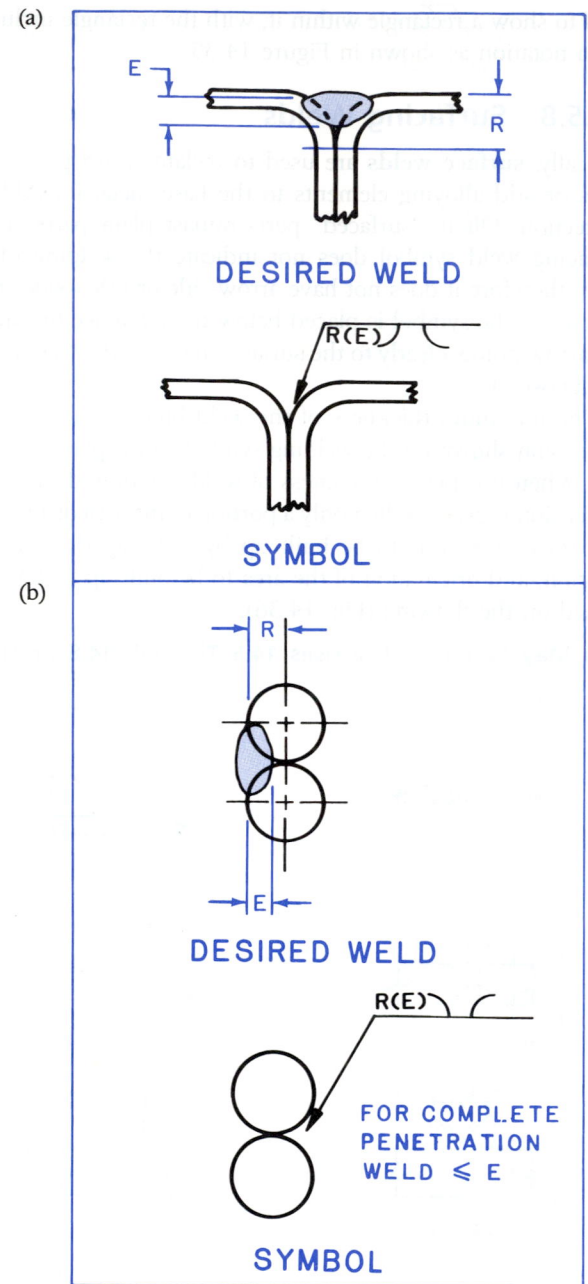

FIGURE 14.32 Bead Welds

(a)

(b)

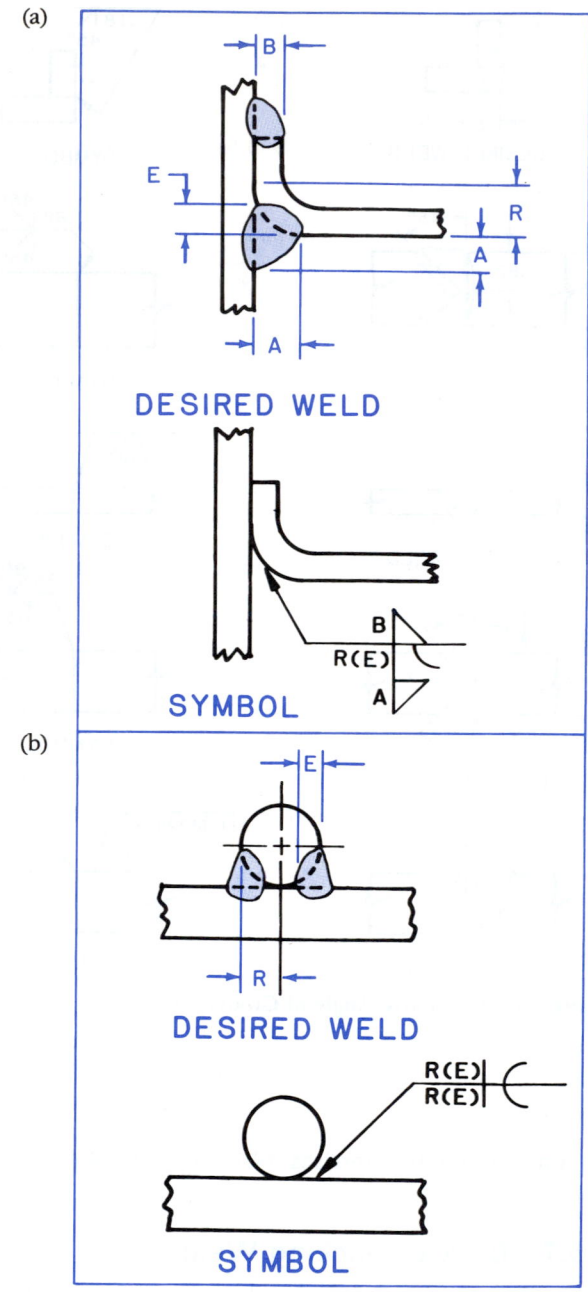

FIGURE 14.33 Bead Welds and Symbols

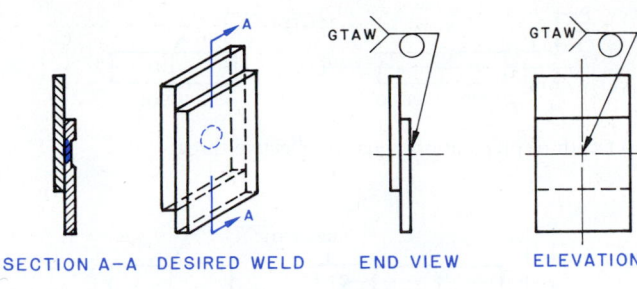

(a) Arrow-side spot weld symbol
(gas tungsten-arc spot)

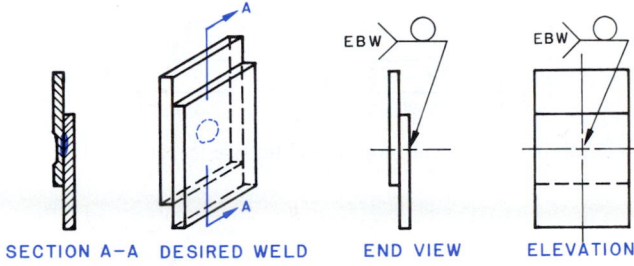

(b) Other-side spot weld symbol
(electron beam spot)

FIGURE 14.25   Spot Welding Symbol Applications

(a) Shear strength of spot welds (resistance spot)

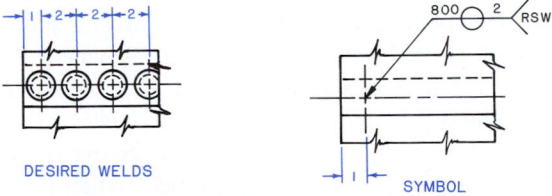

(b) Pitch of spot welds (resistance spot)

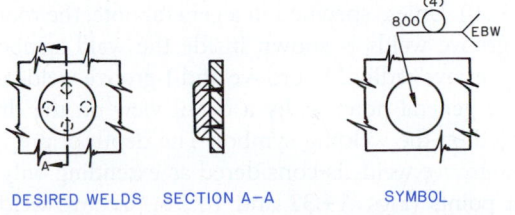

(c) Specified number of spot welds located at random
(electron beam spot)

FIGURE 14.26   Application of Dimension to Spot Welding Symbols

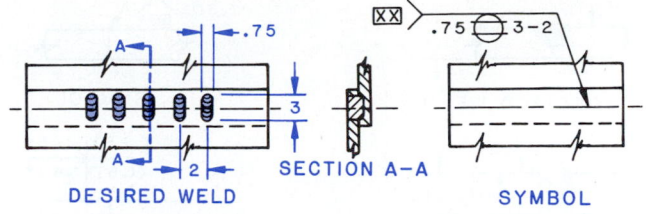

(a) Length and pitch of seam welds

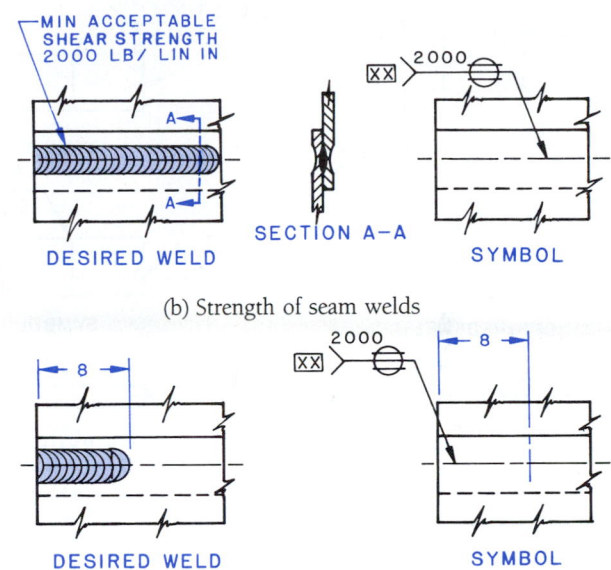

(b) Strength of seam welds

(c) Extent of seam welds

FIGURE 14.27   Application of Dimension to Seam Welding Symbols

common faulty connection, whether using submerged arc, shielded arc, or another process, is the lack of penetration that sometimes occurs at the root of the weld.

When a joint is prepared for welding, the thickness of the material must be taken into account. In small thicknesses such as $\frac{1}{16}$ to $\frac{1}{8}$ in. (1.5 to 3 mm), welding can be successful when the edges are square. When the edges are thicker than this, bevels must be made to assure full penetration and create an adequate joint. Otherwise the flame will not be hot enough to produce adequate fusion. A general rule to follow when material is thicker than $\frac{1}{8}$ in. (3 mm) is that the edges must be prepared for a groove channel, and during the welding process a filler material must be added.

In most cases, steel and iron are beveled at an angle of 45°. The included angle of the bevel is approximately 90° and V-shaped. Many groove welds use a *backing bar* or *backing weld*. The American Society of Mechanical Engineers (ASME) boiler code and other regulating codes require full penetration welds, especially for pressure vessels and piping services that are considered critical. *Backup rings* are therefore employed in the construction of vessels and pipe joints where full penetration is required. The ASME and the AWS (Amer-

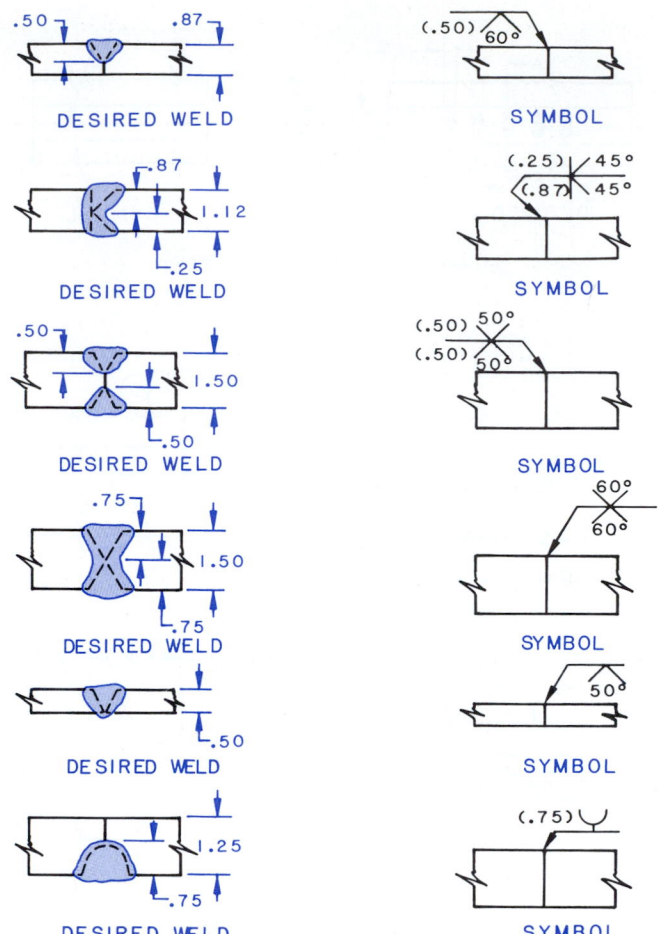

FIGURE 14.28 Designation of Size of Groove Welds with No Specified Root Penetration

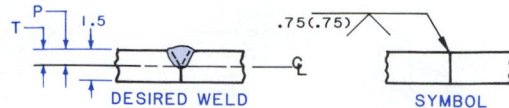

(a) Depth of preparation equal to effective throat

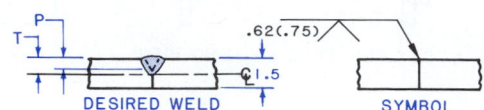

(b) Depth of preparation less than effective throat

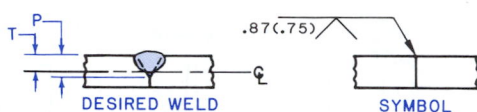

(c) Depth of preparation more than effective throat

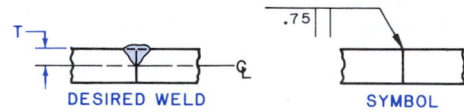

(d) No preparation

FIGURE 14.29 Depth of Groove Weld Preparation

ican Welding Society) provide standards for welding and should be consulted when necessary.

Complete (full) penetration is defined to have occurred when the weld and the base metal are fused through the entire depth of the joint. This way may or may not require backing bars or bead welds. Partial penetration groove welds are used when full penetration is not necessary because of stress levels to be carried by the joint. The only difference between the two penetrations is in the depth of the end preparation or edge preparation: Partial penetration does not cover the full thickness of the two materials to be joined. Root spacing is used to minimize lack-of-penetration notches caused by insufficient spacing or tight butting of joints. Root spacing is just one of the considerations that determine the quality of the joint. Alignment is also important, although slight imperfections are tolerable.

Often a drafter will be called on to detail different cross-sectional views of the joint geometry including backing, space, or extension bars and to show whether the weld is a full or partial penetration and its various angles and dimensions. **Joint geometry** is the basic cross-sectional shape of the joint prior to welding.

Dimensions of all types of groove welds [Fig. 14.28] are shown on the same side of the reference line as the weld symbol. If double-groove welds have the same dimensions, both are dimensioned. The depth of groove preparation and effective throat of a groove weld are shown to the left of the weld symbol with the effective throat in parentheses. The *effective throat* is the perpendicular depth of the groove cut. The total effective throat never exceeds the thickness of the thinner member of a joint. The effective throat is shown only for square groove welds in Figure 14.29, where **P** is the preparation thickness and **T** is the effective throat depth.

When no depth of groove preparation or effective throat is shown on the welding symbol for single-groove or symmetrical double-groove welds, complete penetration is required (Fig. 14.28). Unless specified in a general note, the groove angle or groove welds are shown outside the weld symbol (Fig. 14.30). Unless specified in a general note, the root opening of groove welds is shown inside the weld symbol (Fig. 14.31). Groove radii of U-groove and J-groove welds is specified in a general note, or by a detail view on the drawing, referenced on the welding symbol. The depth of preparation for flare-groove welds is considered as extending only to the tangent points (Figs. 14.32 and 14.33). Groove welds with contour requirements are indicated in the same manner as that prescribed for fillet welds.

The flush and convex supplementary weld symbols are also applied to groove welds, for instance, when the outer contour of the weld must be altered by grinding or machining.

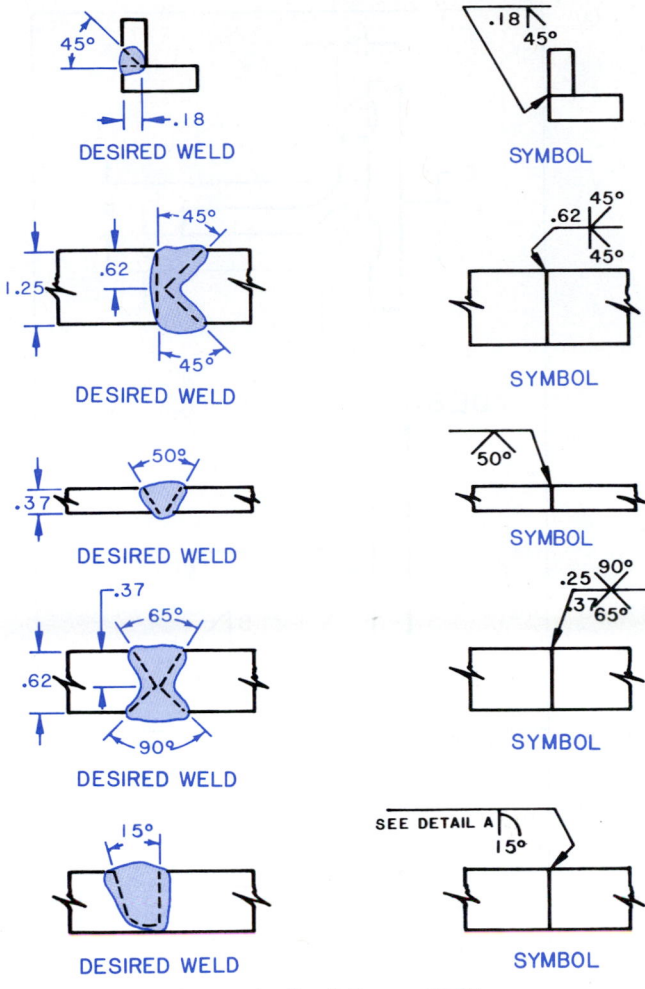

FIGURE 14.30 Groove Angle of Groove Welds

ified to show a rectangle within it, with the rectangle including a notation as shown in Figure 14.35.

14.5.8 Surfacing Welds

Basically, **surface welds** are used to reclaim worn part surfaces or add alloying elements to the base metal for added protection. Often, "surfaced" parts outlast plain parts. The surfacing weld symbol does not indicate the welding of a joint, therefore it does not have arrow-side or other-side significance. The symbol is placed below the reference line and the arrow points clearly to the surface on which the weld is to be deposited.

The minimum thickness of the weld buildup is the only dimension shown on the welding symbol and is placed to its left. When no specific thickness of weld is required, no size dimension is given. When only a portion of the area of a plane or curved surface is to be built up by welding, the extent, location, and orientation of the area to be built up is dimensioned on the drawing (Fig. 14.36).

You May Complete Exercises 14.5 Through 14.8 at This Time

You May Complete Exercises 14.1 Through 14.4 at This Time

14.5.7 Back or Backing Welds

The **back** or **backing welds** of single-groove welds are shown by placing a back or backing weld symbol on the side of the reference line opposite the groove weld symbol (Fig. 14.34). The welding symbol does not indicate the welding sequence (groove weld made before or after backing weld) or backing weld passes (single or multiple). The height of the weld bead is shown to the left of the backing weld symbol, when required. No other backing weld dimensions are shown on the welding symbol. Other dimensions may be shown pictorially on a drawing detail.

Back or backing welds that are to be welded flush without recourse to any method of finishing are shown by adding the flush contour symbol to the back or backing weld symbol. Those to be made flush by mechanical means are shown by adding the flush contour symbol and the finish symbol. A joint with spacer is shown with the groove weld symbol mod-

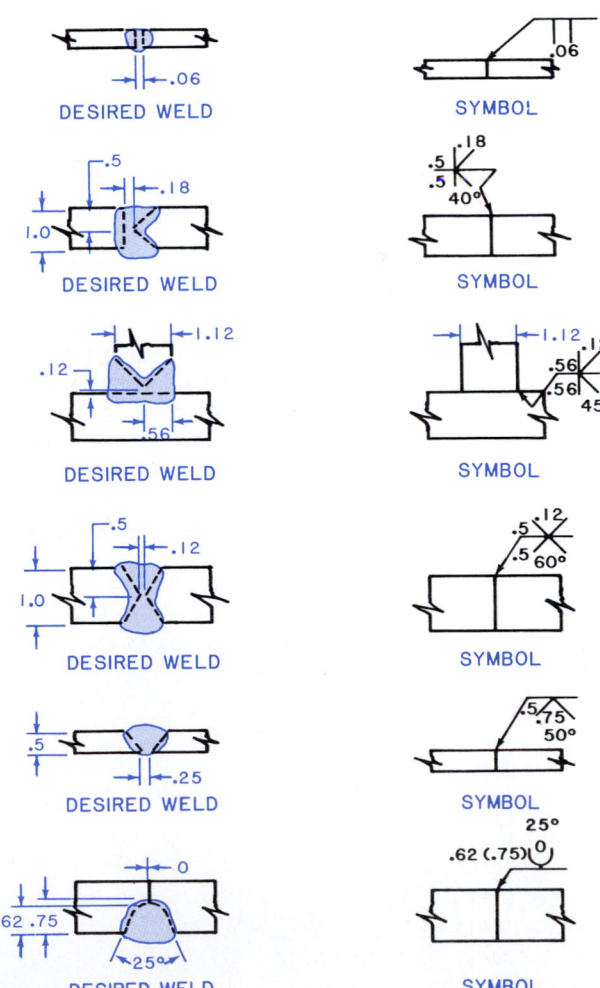

FIGURE 14.31 Root Opening of Groove Welds

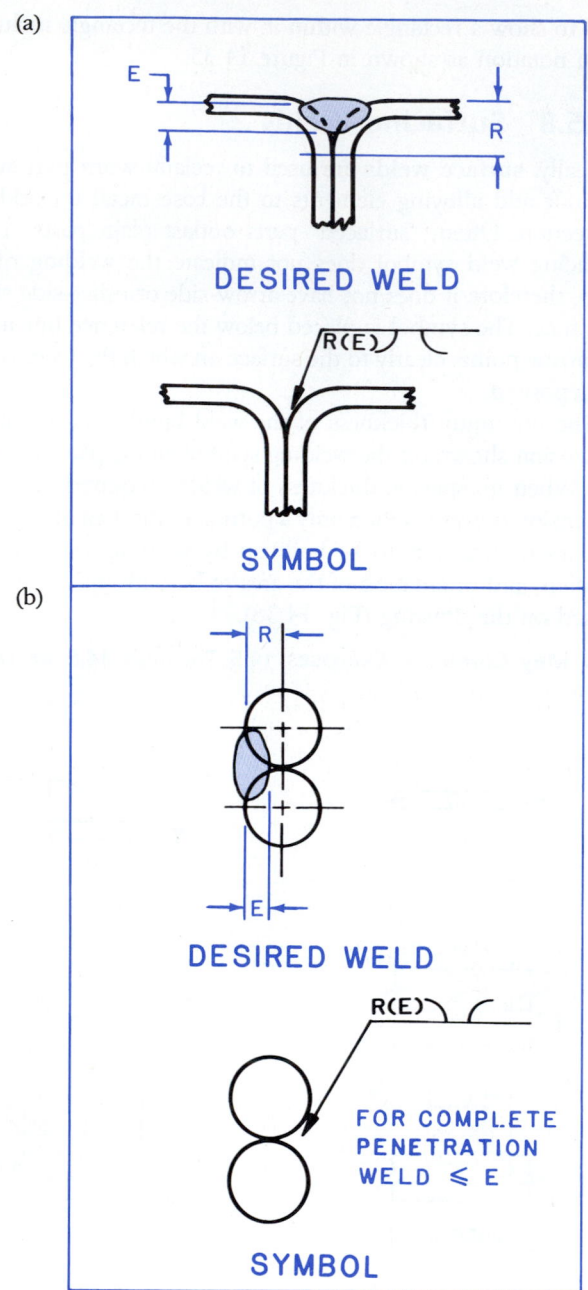

FIGURE 14.32 Bead Welds

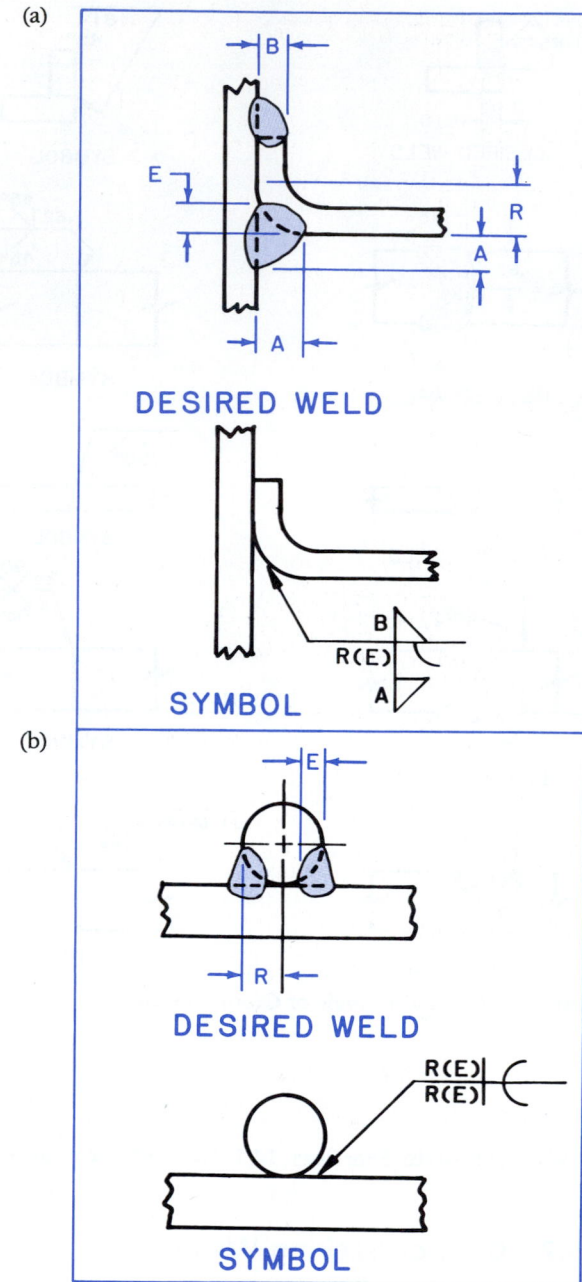

FIGURE 14.33 Bead Welds and Symbols

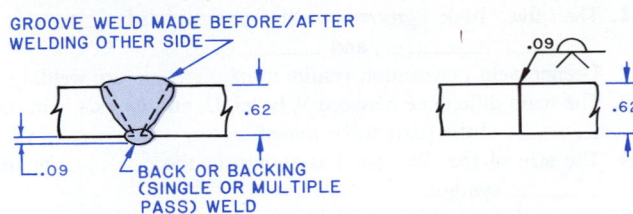

(a)   DESIRED WELD   SYMBOL

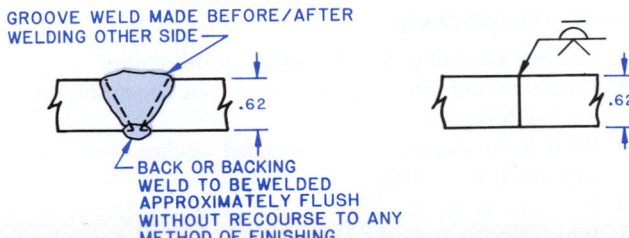

(b)   DESIRED WELD   SYMBOL

FIGURE 14.34   **Bead Weld Symbols Used to Indicate Bead-type Back and Backing Weld**

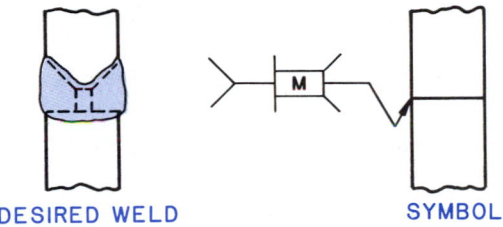

DESIRED WELD   SYMBOL

(a) Spacer in double-bevel-groove joint

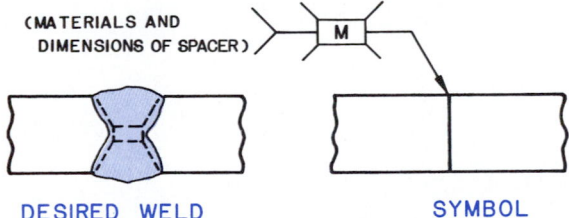

DESIRED WELD   SYMBOL

(b) Spacer in double-v-groove joint

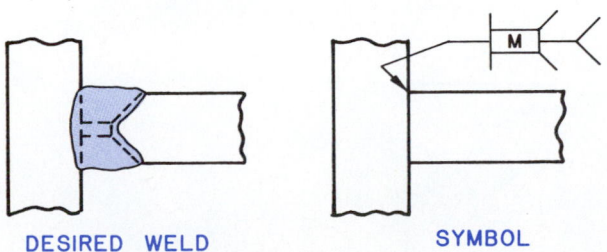

DESIRED WELD   SYMBOL

(c) Spacer in double-bevel-groove joint

FIGURE 14.35   **Spacers for Welds**

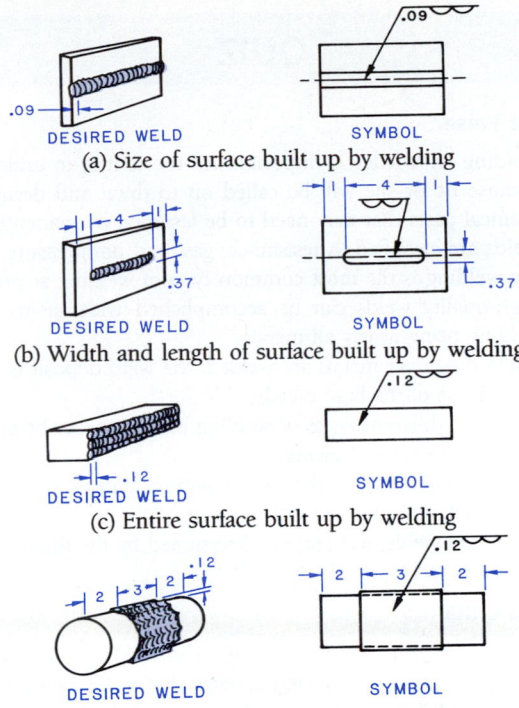

(a) Size of surface built up by welding

(b) Width and length of surface built up by welding

(c) Entire surface built up by welding

(d) Portion of surface built up by welding

FIGURE 14.36   **Dual Bead Weld Symbol to Indicate Surfaces Built Up by Welding**

QUIZ

True or False

1. Welding knowledge is important for the drafter to understand because he or she will be called on to draw and design mechanical parts that may need to be fastened permanently.
2. Welds are classified as resistance, gas, and nonpressure.
3. Arc welding is the most common type of welding at present.
4. High-quality welds can be accomplished with gas-metal arc welding using nearly all metals.
5. When dissimilar metals are welded, the weld deposit is always that of one of the base metals.
6. Normally, different types of welding processes can be encountered on the same drawing.
7. Lack of penetration is the most common type of problem encountered with groove welds.
8. With fillet welds, weld size is determined by the thinner of the two parts to be joined.

Fill in the Blanks

9. Dimensions for all types of groove welds are shown on _____ _____ of the reference line as the weld symbol.
10. The assembled welding symbol consists of the following eight parts: a reference line, _____ , _____ , _____ , _____ , _____ , _____ , and specifications.
11. The five basic groove welds are beveled, _____ , _____ , _____ , and _____ .
12. Deeper weld penetration results from _____ arc welding.
13. The main difference between V, bevel, U, and J welds is in the _____ of the parts to be joined.
14. The size of the fillet weld is shown to the _____ of the _____ symbol.
15. Plug and slot welds are used primarily in _____ joints.
16. The tail of the weld symbol should be omitted when _____ or _____ are not used.

Answer the Following

17. Describe slot and plug welds and their differences.
18. Explain the difference between shielded arc and unshielded arc welding processes.
19. What is the name for the granulated welding cover used in submerged arc welding?
20. What factors can affect the weldability of metals?
21. Which process is most commonly used to weld dissimilar materials?
22. Why is it important to bevel plates before groove welding?
23. Name the elements of a complete weld symbol.
24. What is meant by *arrow side* and *opposite side* and what is the tail of the symbol used for?

EXERCISES

Exercises may be assigned as sketching, instrument, or CAD projects. Transfer the given information to an "A" size sheet of .25 in. grid paper. Complete all views and solve for proper visibility, including centerlines, object lines, and hidden lines. Exercises that are not assigned by the instructor can be sketched in the text to provide practice and understanding of the preceding instructional material.

After Reading the Chapter Through Section 14.5.6 You May Complete the Following Exercises

Exercise 14.1   Draw the requested welding symbol, far side only. Complete the symbol including the arrowhead.

Exercise 14.2   Draw the requested weld and its associated symbol for each joint.

Exercise 14.3   Complete the welding symbol and draw the weld on the given views. The shaft weld requires a surface weld.

Exercise 14.4   Use .25 in. or 6 mm fillet welds and appropriate groove welds to construct the all-welded assembly. Show the welds and the welding symbols.

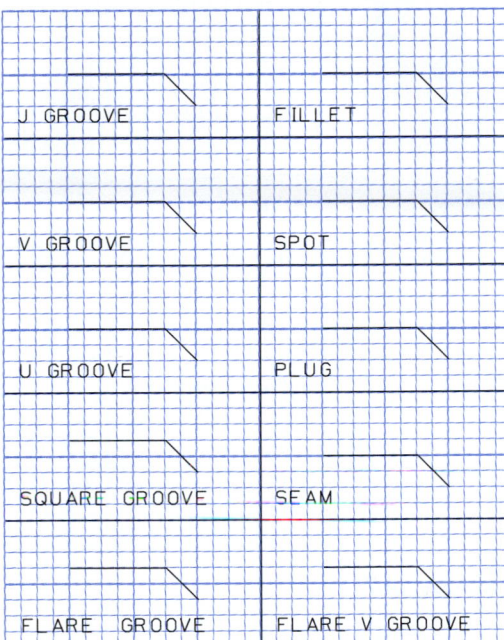

Exercise 14.1

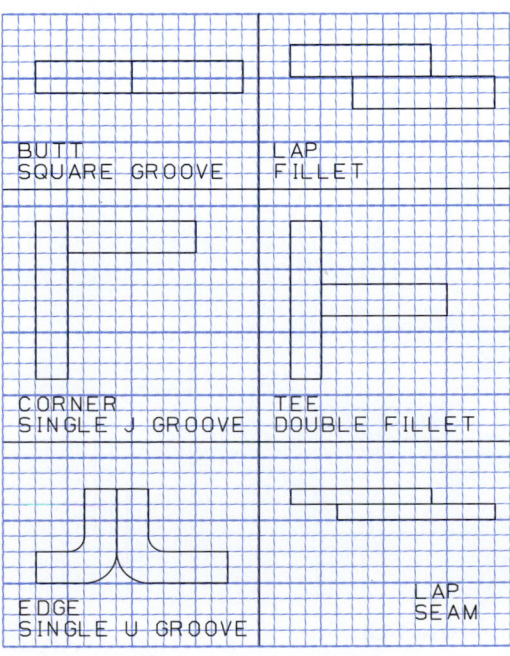

Exercise 14.2

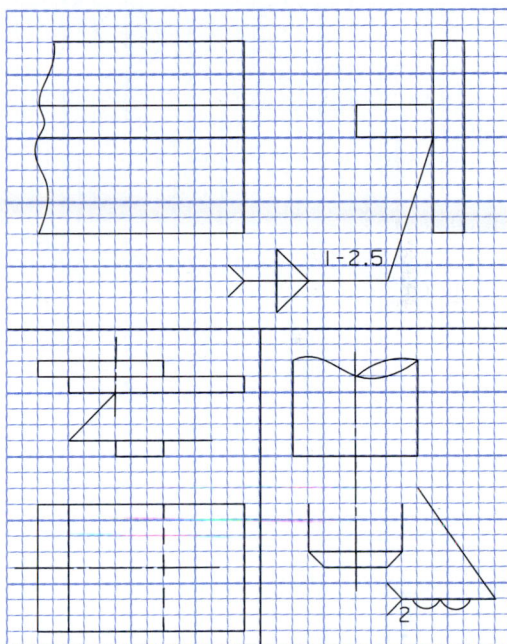

Exercise 14.3

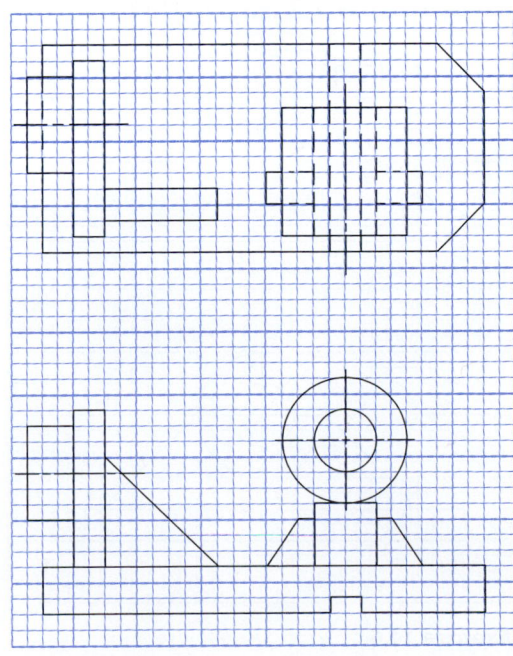

Exercise 14.4

After Reading the Chapter Through Section 14.5.8 You May Complete the Following Exercises

Exercise 14.5 Using .25 in. or 6 mm fillet welds show all symbols and welds for the part.

Exercise 14.6 Show appropriate welds and welding symbols for the all-welded assembly.

Exercise 14.7 Draw the welds and welding symbols for the all-welded assembly.

Exercise 14.8 Using spot welding for the angle and plate weldment, show the appropriate weld and welding symbol to attach the pieces with welds placed at 1 in. (25 mm) increments. For the two plates, use plug welds. Draw the welds and the welding symbols.

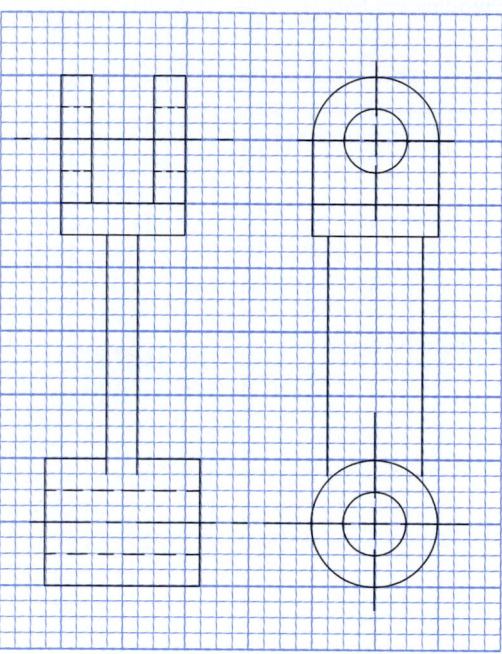

Exercise 14.5

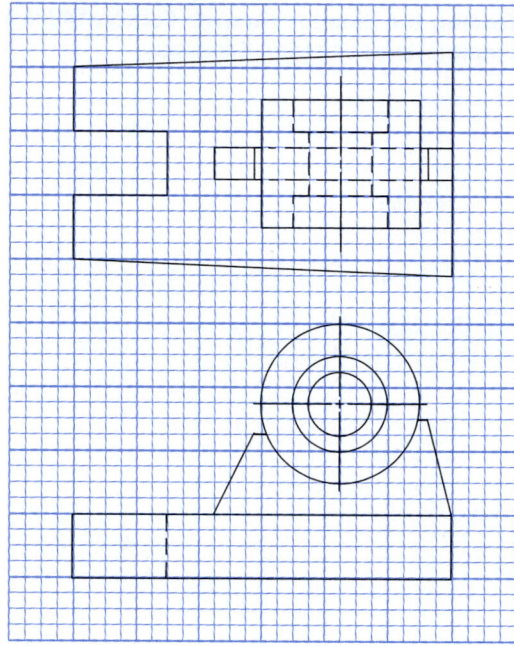

Exercise 14.7

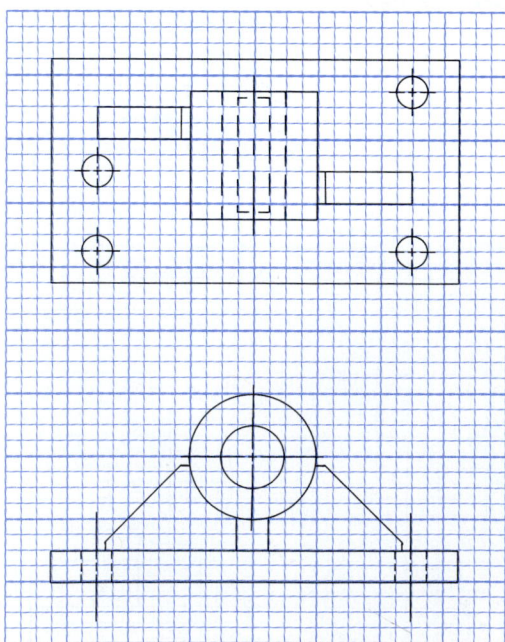

Exercise 14.6

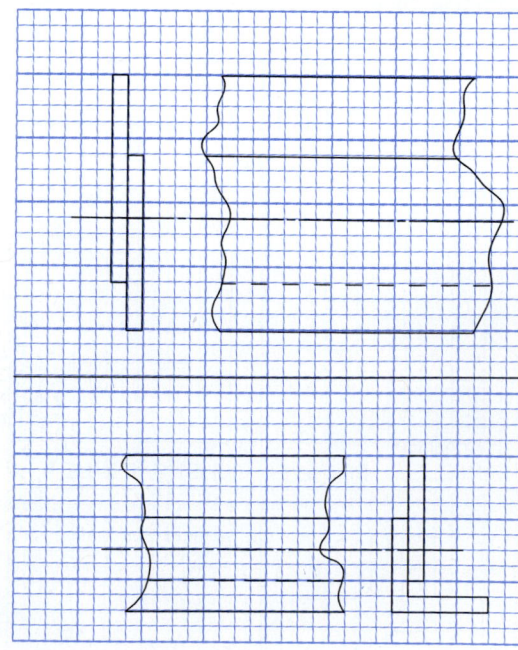

Exercise 14.8

PROBLEMS

Problems 14.1 through 14.8 Draw each of the given mechanical parts, dimension completely, and show all welds and welding symbols. Use the most recent ANSI dimensioning standards. Do a material or parts list for each project. Balloon and call out each separate weldment piece (see Chapter 18).

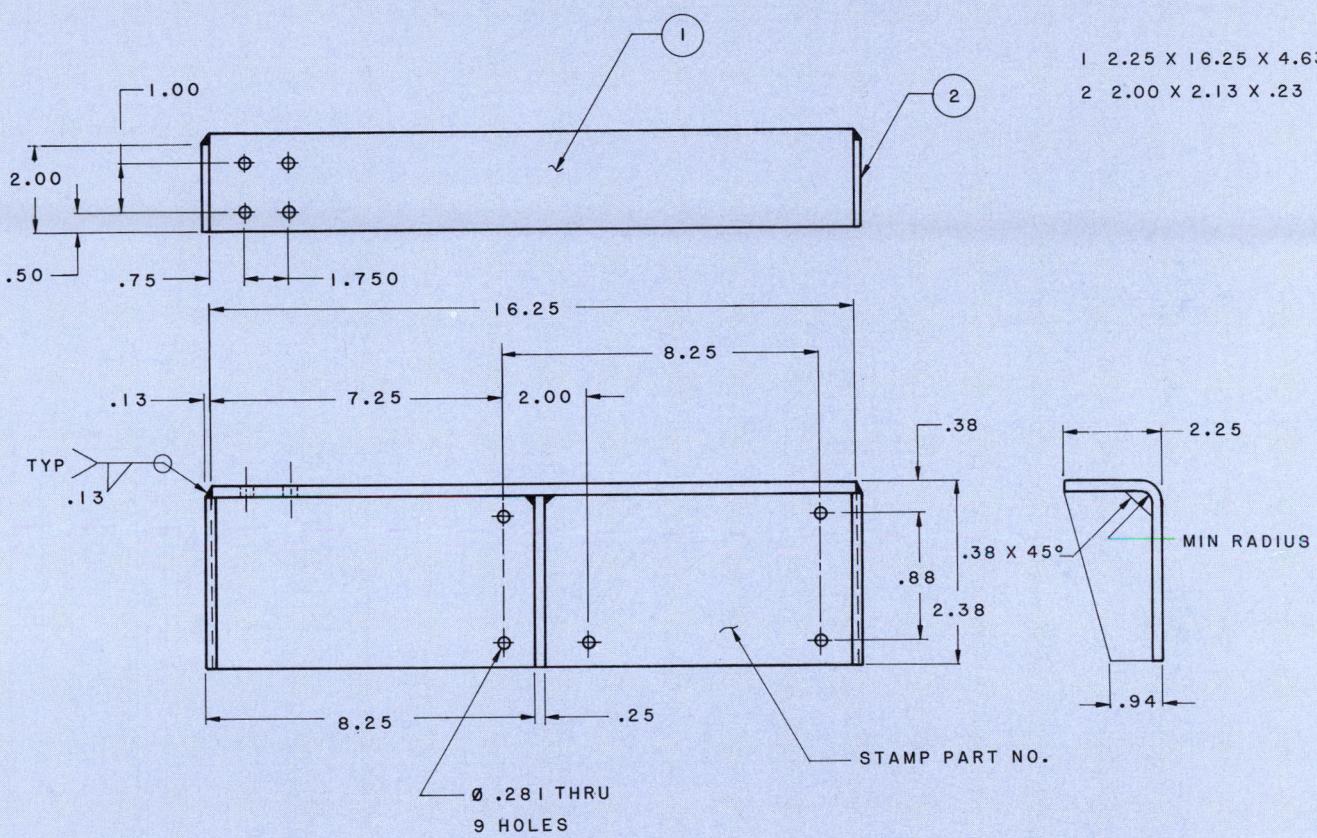

1 2.25 X 16.25 X 4.63
2 2.00 X 2.13 X .23

Problem 14.1 Sensor bracket

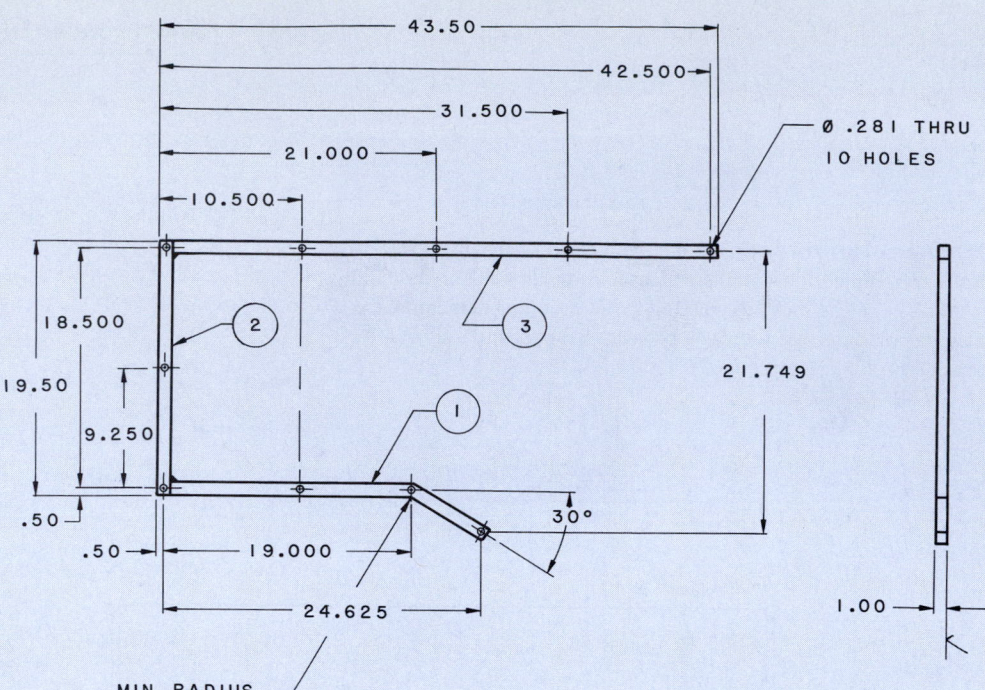

Problem 14.2 Form dam

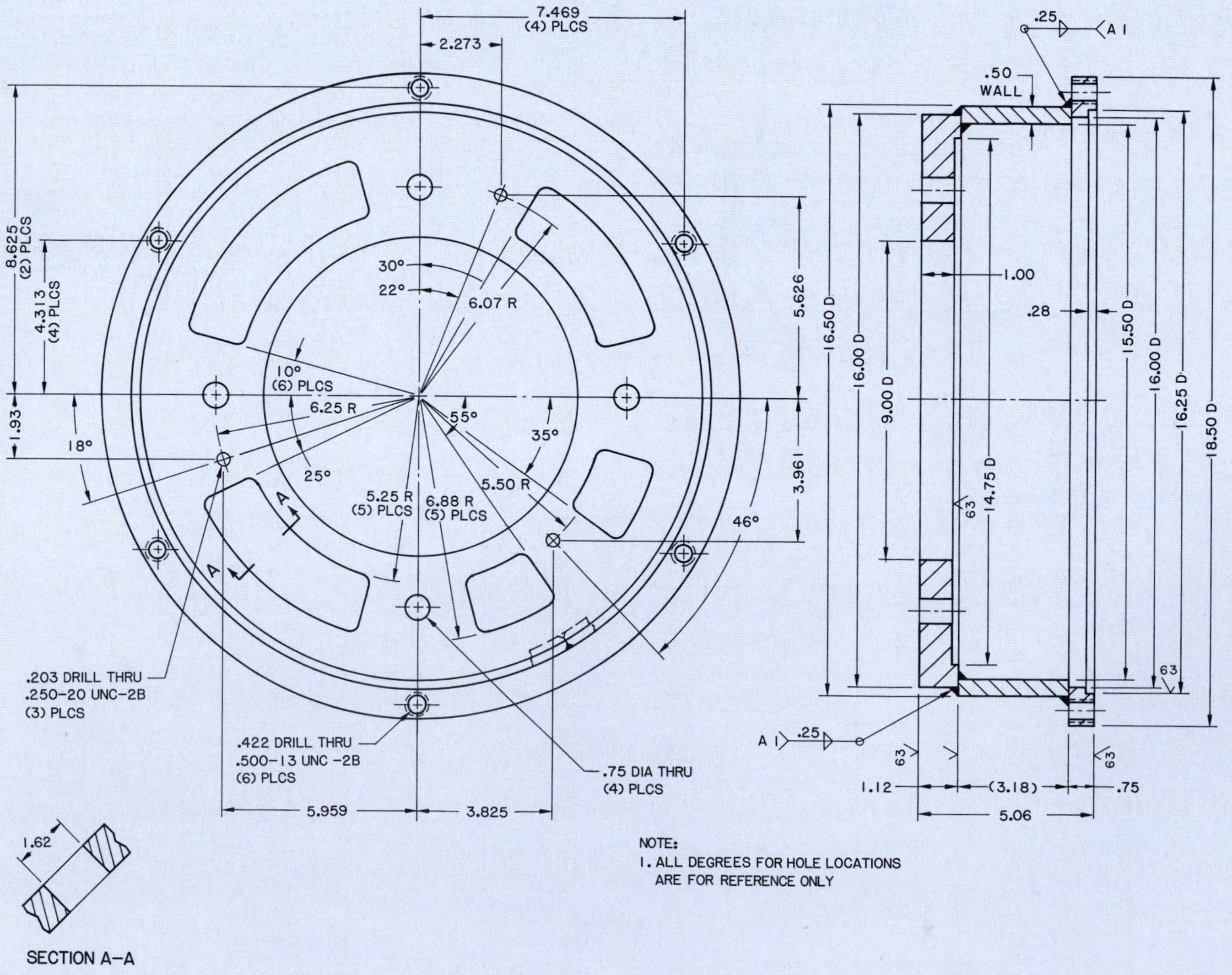

MIN RADIUS

7.469
(4) PLCS

2.273

.25   A 1

.50
WALL

8.625
(2) PLCS

4.313
(4) PLCS

1.93

30°
22°   6.07 R

10°
(6) PLCS

6.25 R   55°

18°

25°   35°

5.25 R   6.88 R
(5) PLCS   (5) PLCS   5.50 R

46°

.203 DRILL THRU
.250-20 UNC-2B
(3) PLCS

.422 DRILL THRU
.500-13 UNC-2B
(6) PLCS

.75 DIA THRU
(4) PLCS

5.959   3.825

5.626

3.961

16.50 D

16.00 D

9.00 D

14.75 D

1.00

.28

15.50 D

16.00 D

16.25 D

18.50 D

63

63

63

A 1   .25

1.12   (3.18)   .75

5.06

NOTE:
1. ALL DEGREES FOR HOLE LOCATIONS
   ARE FOR REFERENCE ONLY

1.62

SECTION A-A

Problem 14.3 Housing

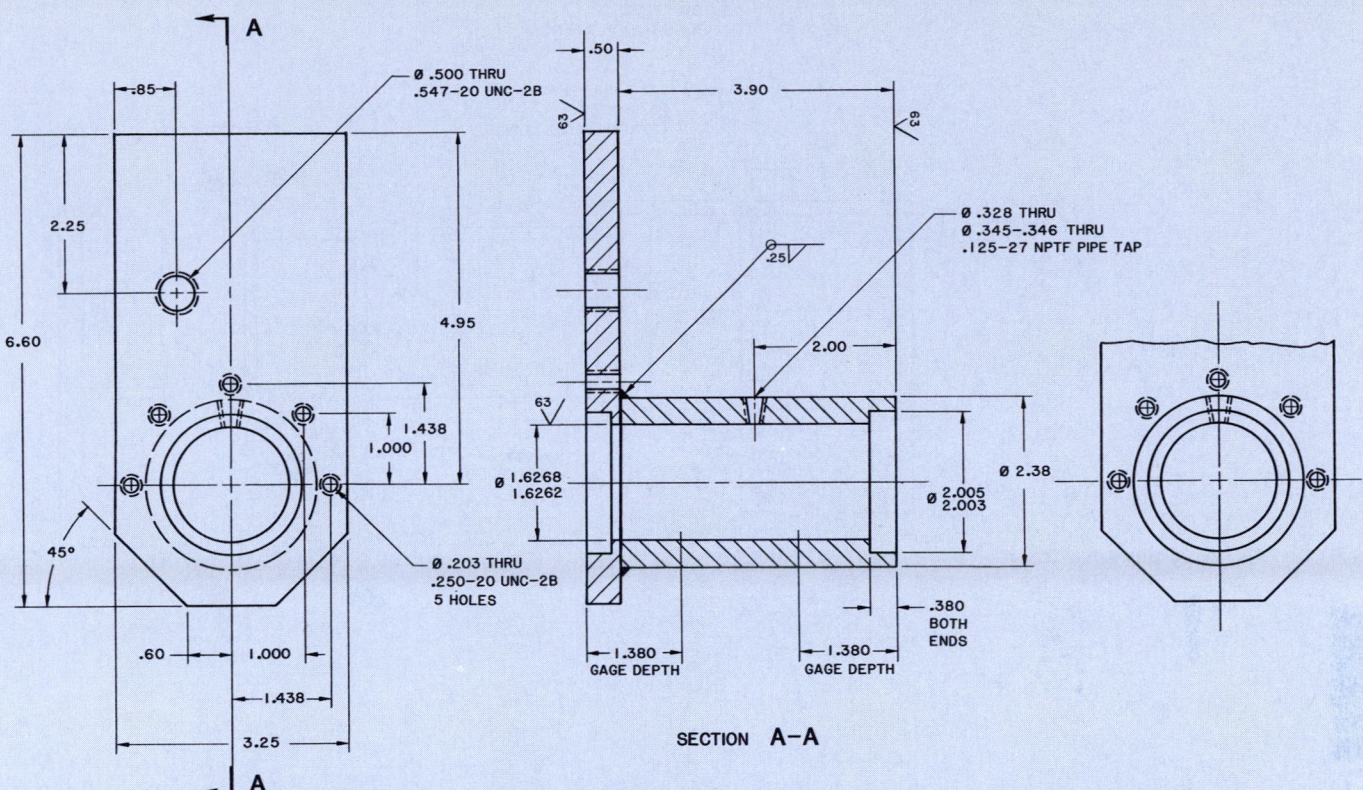

SECTION **A–A**

Problem 14.4   Weldment detail

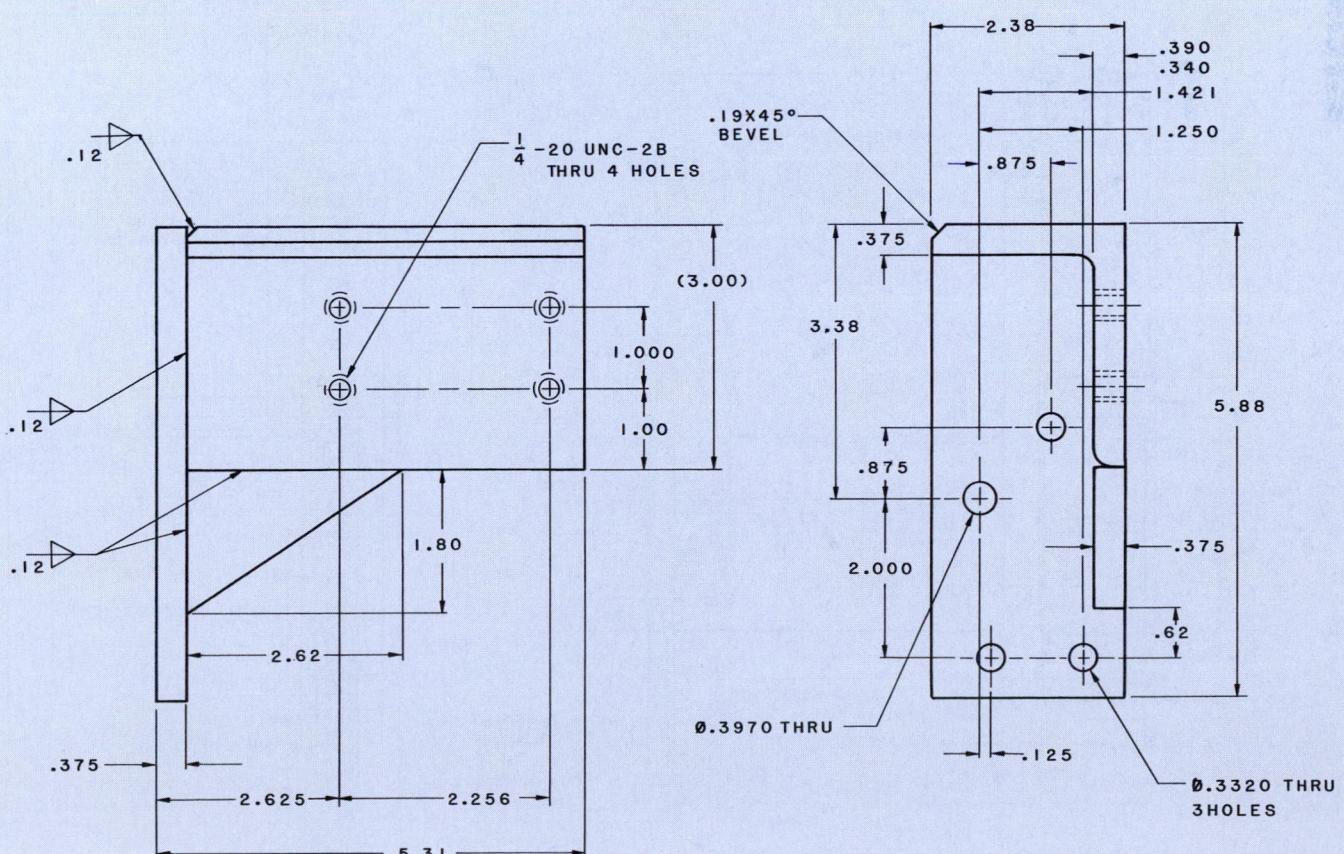

Problem 14.5   Weldment

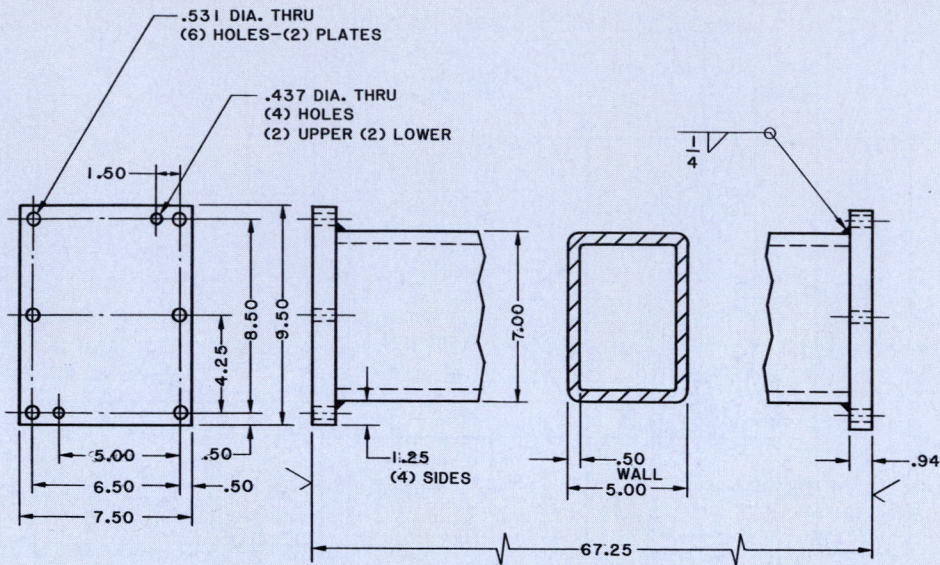

Problem 14.6   Column weldment

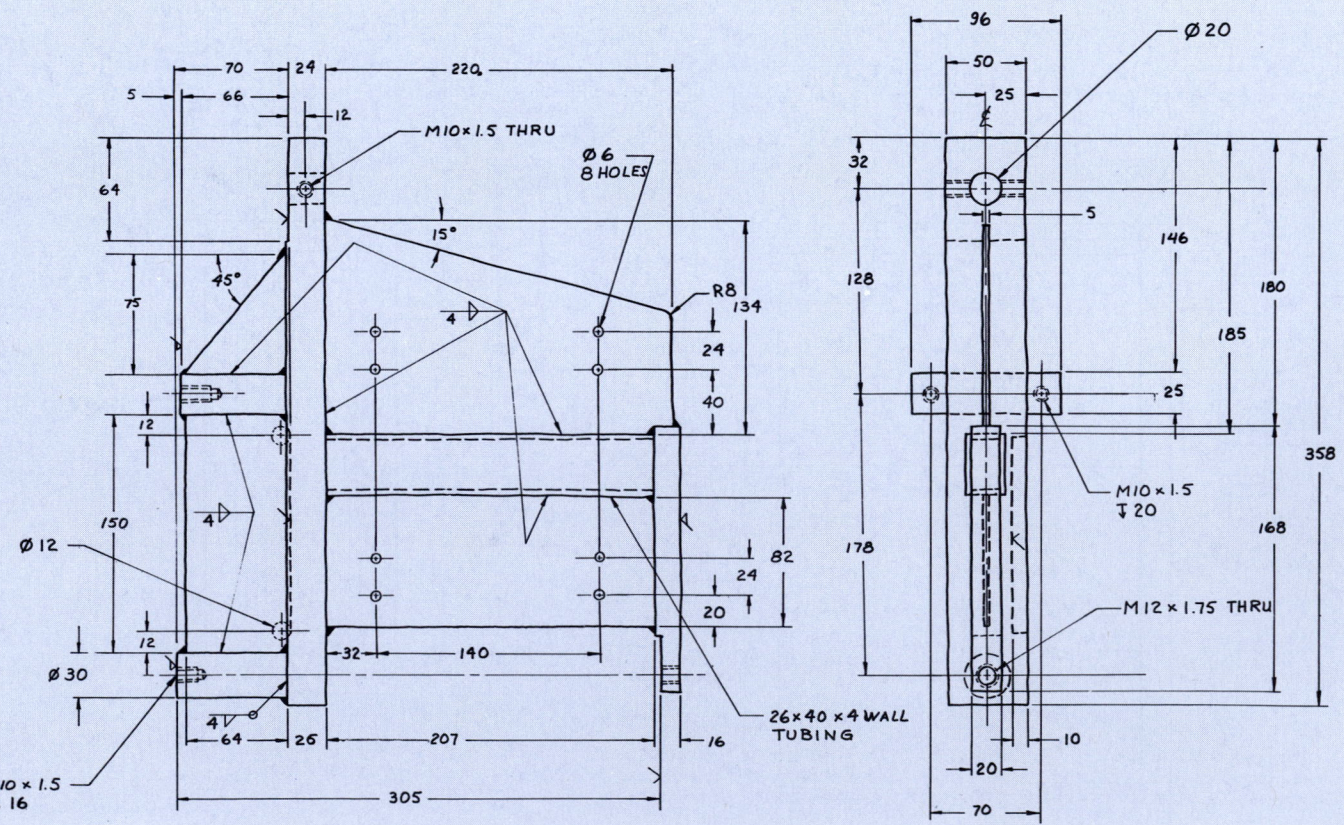

Problem 14.7   Sketch of profile machine

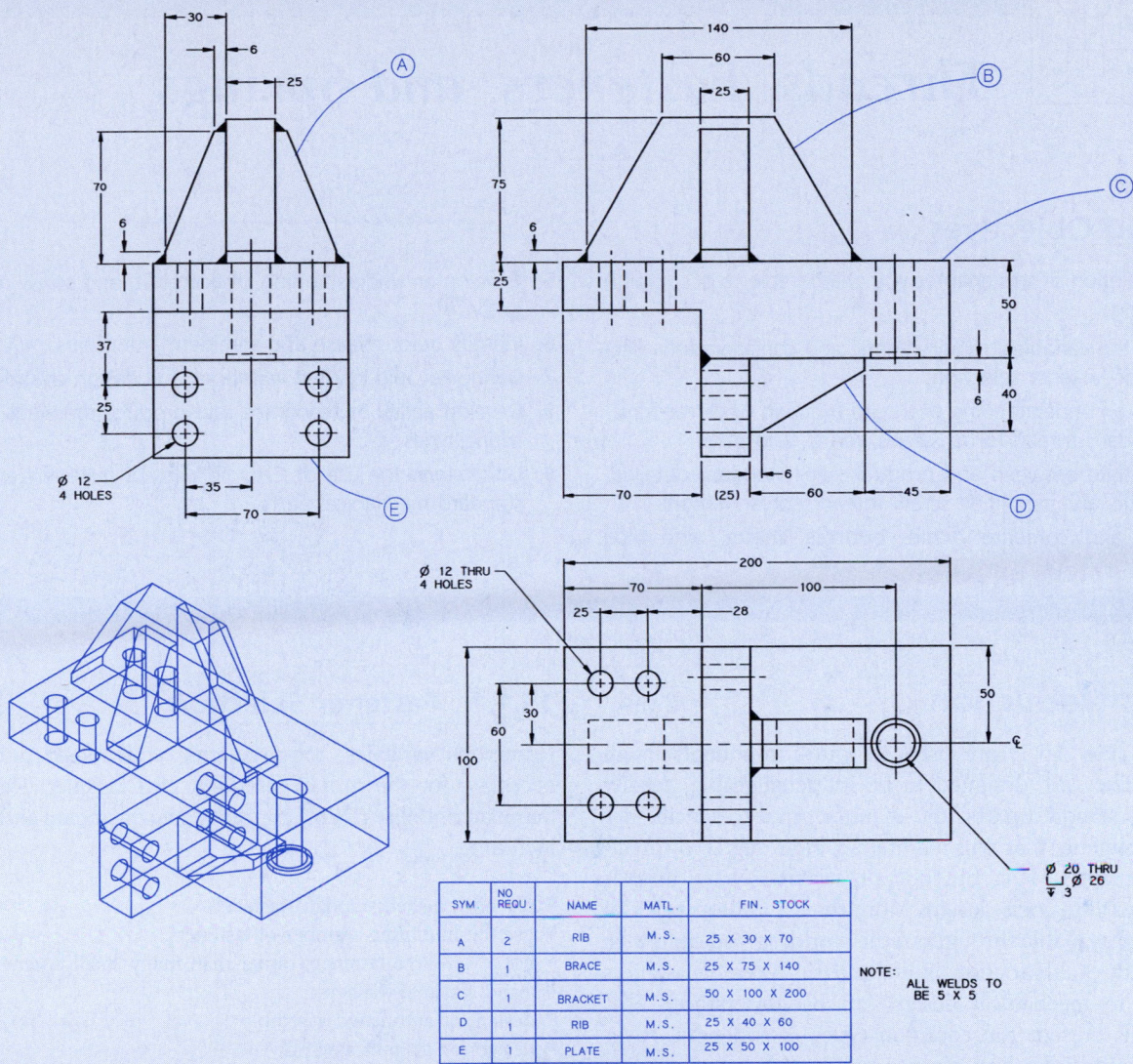

SYM.	NO REQU.	NAME	MATL.	FIN. STOCK
A	2	RIB	M.S.	25 X 30 X 70
B	1	BRACE	M.S.	25 X 75 X 140
C	1	BRACKET	M.S.	50 X 100 X 200
D	1	RIB	M.S.	25 X 40 X 60
E	1	PLATE	M.S.	25 X 50 X 100

NOTE: ALL WELDS TO BE 5 X 5

Problem 14.8   3D CAD model and weldment detail

Problem 14.9   Draw the five major joints and a cross-sectional view of two different welds applied to each.

Problem 14.10   Sketch five basic joints.

Problem 14.11   Sketch three basic welds.

Problem 14.12   Draw a cross section of a fillet weld and call out its basic parts.

Problem 14.13   Draw the basic arc and gas weld symbols.

Problem 14.14   Draw the basic resistance weld symbols.

Problem 14.15   Create the following symbols:

(a) $\frac{1}{4}$ in. (6 mm) continuous fillet weld on arrow side.

(b) $\frac{3}{8}$ in. (9 mm) intermittent fillet weld on other side. Each weld is 3 in. (75 mm) long spaced on 5 in. (15 mm) centers.

Problem 14.16   Create an appropriate symbol for a butt joint:

(a) Single V-groove weld.

(b) $\frac{3}{8}$ in. (9 mm) weld on opposite side.

(c) 60° groove weld on both sides.

(d) $\frac{1}{2}$ in. (12 mm) weld on arrow side.

(e) Work pieces to be placed $\frac{1}{8}$ in. (3 mm) apart.

(f) Grind welds flush with plate surface.

Problem 14.17   Using Figure 14.2, redraw the part and dimension completely.

Problem 14.18   Using Figure 14.13, redraw the part.

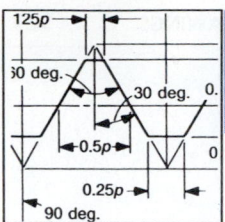

CHAPTER 15

Threads, Fasteners, and Springs

Learning Objectives

Upon completion of this chapter you will be able to accomplish the following:

1. Identify the variables, requirements, and considerations necessary for fastener selection.
2. Develop an understanding of thread function while recognizing standard thread forms, series, terms, and parts.
3. Differentiate between and produce ANSI standard detailed, schematic, and simplified screw thread representations.
4. Identify and compare Acme, buttress, metric, and pipe threads.

5. Develop an understanding of bolt, nut, and screw representation.
6. Identify quick-release and semipermanent pins.
7. Define key and keyseat variations and design considerations.
8. Develop ability to recognize and produce drawings of basic spring types.
9. Understand the use of CAD libraries of fasteners and other standard mechanical parts.

15.1 Introduction

Fasteners (Fig. 15.1) are used to join components in an assembly. They are designed to be interchangeable, readily available as standard parts, and manufactured to specific design requirements that will maintain a high degree of precision and quality. Most, but not all, fasteners have threads incorporated into their design. More than a million types of fasteners are available throughout the world, so you cannot be familiar with each variation. But the basic types of fasteners pertaining to mechanical design can be understood. This chapter will present the common types of fasteners, cover thread specifications, and discuss nonthreaded types of fasteners (and springs).

15.1.1 Fastener Selection

Numerous variables, requirements, and considerations are necessary for the proper selection of a fastener. Design for manufacturability (DFM) concepts are considered at this stage including:

- use off-the-shelf standard fasteners
- use the minimum number of fasteners
- use fewer large fasteners rather than many small fasteners
- avoid separate washers
- design for automated assembly
- design for drop-in assembly
- eliminate separate fasteners by design (e.g., snap fits)

The selection of the proper fastener for a project involves the following considerations during the design phase:

- assembly requirements for assembly and disassembly during manufacturing, shipping, installation, service, and maintenance
- conditions of operation: temperature, vibration, movement, corrosion, and impact
- quantity of fasteners required to secure the parts adequately
- variety of fasteners on the assembly
- function of the fasteners in the assembly: location, fastening

15.2 Screw Threads

A thread is one of the six simple machines. A **thread** is a helical or spiral groove formed on the outside (external) or on the inside (internal) surface of a cylinder. **Screw threads** support and transfer loads and in some cases transmit power. Most mechanical devices use threaded fasteners in their design. A variety of thread styles are used in the valve shown in Figure 15.2.

FIGURE 15.1 Fasteners

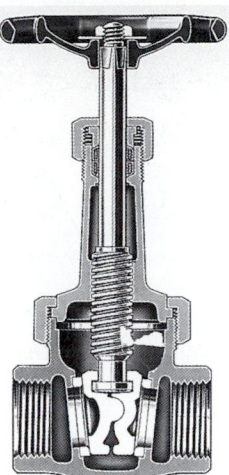

FIGURE 15.2   UNC, Acme, and NPT Threads Used in the Design of Rising Stem Gate Valve

FIGURE 15.4   Internal Threads

Threads on round parts such as shafts or bolts are **external threads** (Fig. 15.3), and threads on interior surfaces of a cylindrical hole are **internal threads** (Fig. 15.4). A *die* is used to cut most external threads and a *tap* is used to cut internal threads.

There are a number of different forms of threads, which are selected based on the requirements of the design. Eight standard styles are presented in Figure 15.5: (a) American National thread form, (b) the British Standard (Whitworth) thread form, (c) the worm thread form, (d) the square thread form, (e) the sharp V thread form, (f) the knuckle thread form, (g) the Acme thread form, and (h) the buttress thread form. The ISO metric thread form is shown in Figure 15.6, and the Unified National thread form in Figure 15.7.

The Acme and square thread forms are used to transmit power. The Acme threads in Figure 15.2 are used to move the valve stem up and down, opening and closing the valve. Worm threads are similar to Acme threads and are also used

to transmit power. Worm threads are typically regarded as a gear device (see Chapter 16).

The knuckle thread form is used for sheet-metal products such as the light bulb, bottle and jar tops, and plastic bottles and caps. Buttress threads are used in high-stress designs and to transmit power along the axis in one direction.

ISO metric threads (Fig. 15.6) are the internationally recognized standard for thread forms. The ISO thread is very similar to the Unified National thread form except that its thread depth is not as great. The ISO thread has the same basic profile as the Unified National thread form.

The **Unified National thread** form (Fig. 15.7) is used in the United States and is practically identical to the obsolete American National thread form. In fact, threads manufactured to either form are functionally interchangeable. American National threads are designated as N, NC, NF, NEF, or NS. Unified National threads are designated similarly: UN, UNC, UNF, UNEF, UNS, or UNM.

15.2.1   Thread Terms

The following terms are used throughout the chapter when describing threads:

Class of thread   An alphanumerical designation to indicate the standard grade of tolerance and allowance specified for a thread.

Crest   The top surface joining the two sides of the thread.

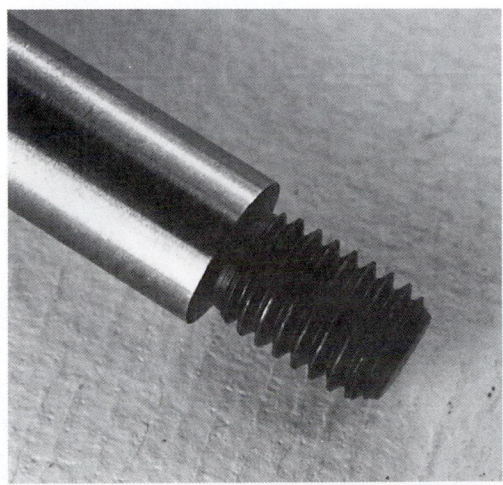

FIGURE 15.3   External Threads

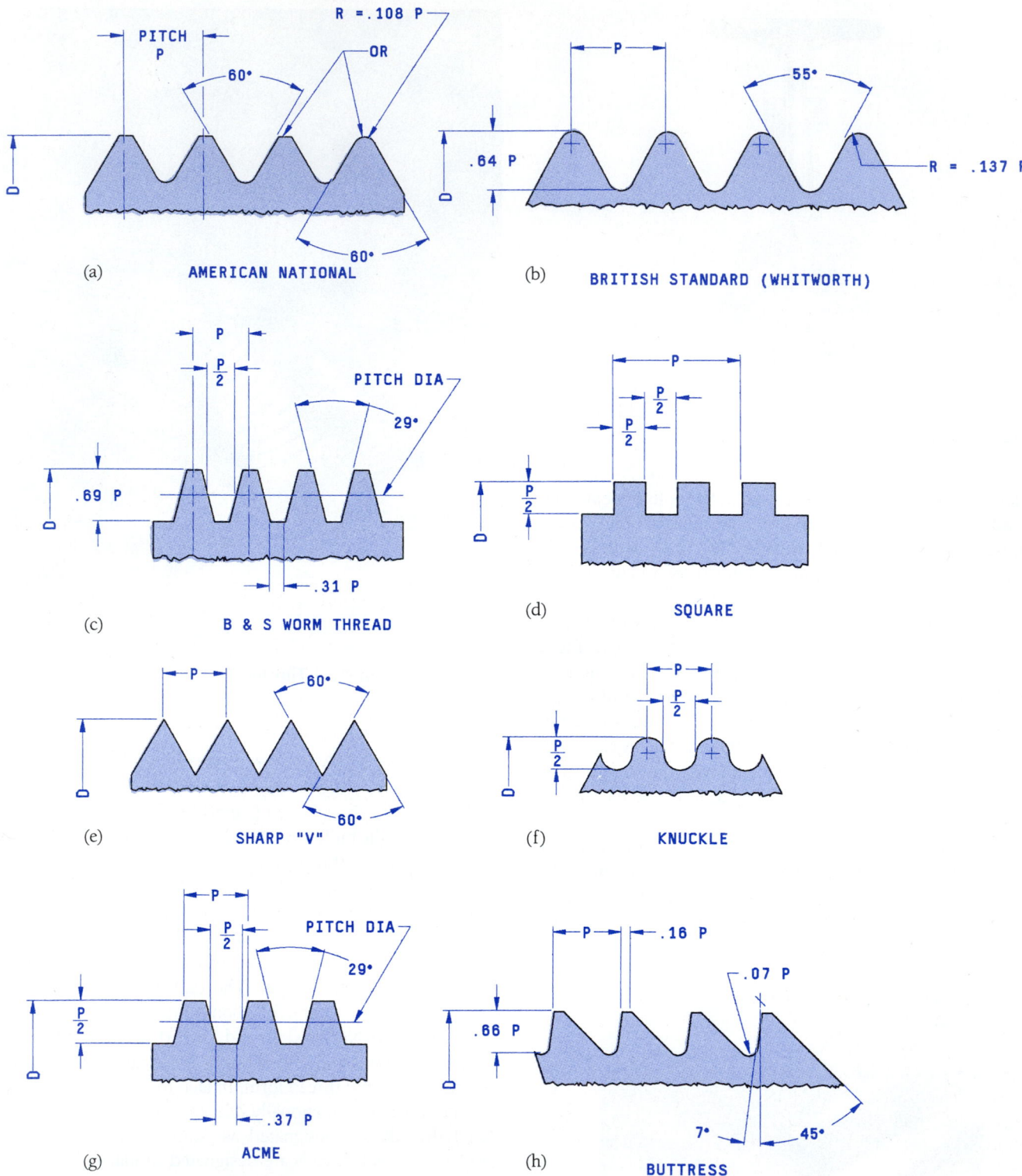

FIGURE 15.5 Standard Thread Forms

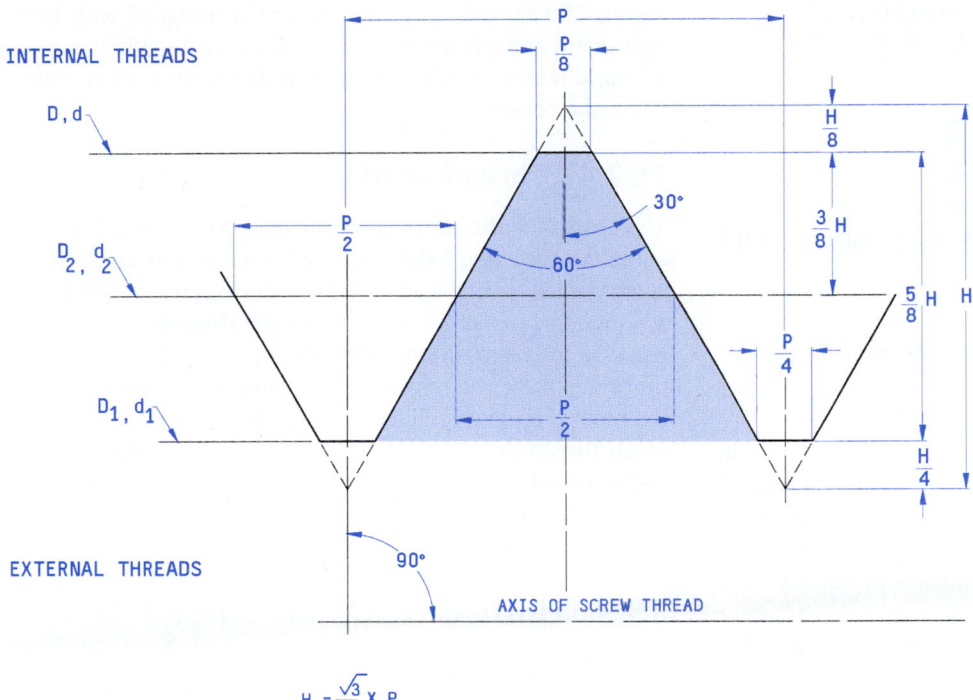

INTERNAL THREADS

EXTERNAL THREADS

AXIS OF SCREW THREAD

$$H = \frac{\sqrt{3}}{2} \times P$$

FIGURE 15.6   Basic M Thread Profile (ISO 68 Basic Profile)

Depth of thread engagement   The radial distance, crest to crest, by which the thread forms overlap between two assembled mating threads.

Major diameter   The major diameter is that of the major cylinder—distance across the crests of the thread.

Minor diameter   The minor diameter is that of the minor cylinder—the root diameter of the thread.

Nominal size   The designation that is used for general identification of a thread based on the major diameter.

Pitch   The axial distance from a point on one screw thread to the corresponding point on the next screw thread. Pitch is equal to the lead divided by the number of thread starts.

Profile of thread   The contour of a screw thread ridge and groove delineated by a cutting plane passing through the thread axis. Also called **form of thread.**

Root   The bottom surface joining the two sides of the thread.

Root diameter   The diameter of an imaginary cylinder bounding the bottom of the roots of a screw thread (minor diameter of the thread).

Thread designations   A capital letter abbreviation of names used to designate various thread forms and thread series.

Thread series   Groups of diameter/pitch combinations distinguished from each other by the number of threads per unit of measurement.

15.2.2   Thread Parts

The configuration of the thread in an axial plane is the **thread form** (profile). The three parts making the form of a thread are the **crest**, the **root**, and the **flank.** The crest of a thread is at the top, the root is on the bottom, and the flank joins them. The **fundamental triangle** (shaded part on Fig. 15.7) is the triangle formed when the thread profile is extended to a sharp

V at both crests and roots. The height of the fundamental triangle (*H*) is the distance between the crest and the root diameters (for Unified National threads, *H* equals .866025 times the thread pitch).

A thread having full form at both crests and roots is a complete or **full-form thread.** When either the crest or root is not fully formed, it is an **incomplete thread.** Such threads occur at the ends of externally threaded fasteners that are pointed (conical), at thread runouts where the threaded length blends into the unthreaded shank, and at the countersinks on the faces of nuts and tapped holes.

Thread pitch (*P*) is the distance, measured parallel to the thread axis, between corresponding points on adjacent threads. Unified screw threads are designated in **threads per**

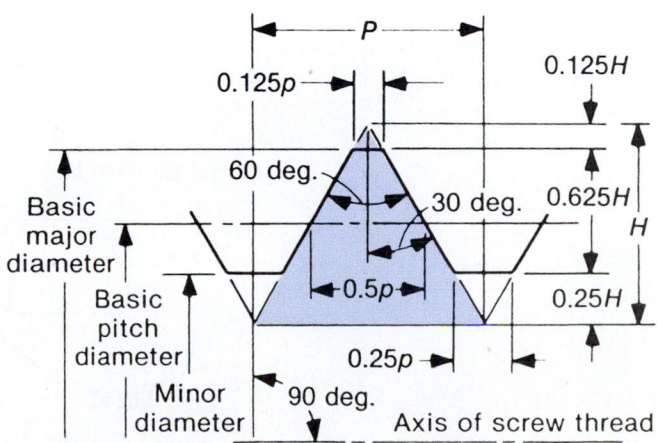

FIGURE 15.7   Basic Profile for UN and UNR Screw Threads

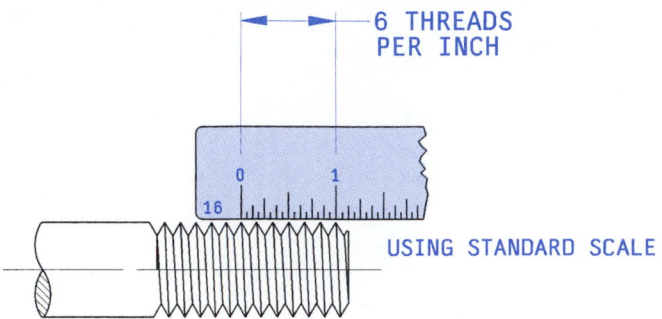

FIGURE 15.8   Using a Scale to Measure Threads per Inch

inch, which is the number of complete threads occurring in one inch of threaded length. Thread pitch is the reciprocal of threads per inch. The standard inch scale can be placed along the threads when a screw thread pitch gage is unavailable (Fig. 15.8). Counting the number of threads in one inch will give the threads-per-inch measurement.

The **pitch diameter** is the diameter of a theoretical cylinder that passes through the threads so that the widths of the thread ridges and thread widths would each equal one-half of the thread pitch (Fig. 15.9).

The combination of allowances and tolerances in mating threads is called the **fit** and is a measure of tightness or looseness between them. A **clearance fit** is one that always provides a free running assembly. An **interference fit** is one that always results in a positive interference between the threads when assembled.

When assembling externally threaded fasteners into internally threaded nuts or tapped holes, the axial distance of contact of the fully formed threads is the **length of thread engagement** (Fig. 15.10). The distance these threads overlap in a radial direction is the **depth of thread engagement.**

15.2.3   Right-hand and Left-hand Threads

Unless otherwise specified, threads are right hand. A left-hand thread turns counterclockwise to advance (Fig. 15.11).

Figure 15.12 shows a turnbuckle that is designed with both right-hand and left-hand threads. When the buckle is turned in one direction, it will pull both rods together, thus, tightening the connection.

15.2.4   Thread Lead

The **lead** of a thread is the axial distance it travels in one complete turn (the axial distance between two consecutive crest points). Since lead is the axial distance a point will advance in one complete turn, **single threads** have a lead equal to the pitch, **double threads** have a lead equal to two times the pitch, and **triple threads** have a lead of three times the pitch (Fig. 15.13). If a screw advances two times its pitch when turned one complete revolution, it has a double lead and is called a double thread. If it advances three times its pitch, it has a triple lead and is called a triple thread.

15.3   Unified National Thread Series

Thread series are groups of diameter pitch combinations, differing by the number of threads per inch. For fasteners, the popular thread series are Unified coarse, fine, and 8-pitch. The two general series classifications are *standard* and *special*.

The standard series consists of three series with graded pitches (coarse, fine, and extra-fine) and eight series with constant pitches (4, 6, 8, 12, 16, 20, 28, and 32 threads per inch).

15.3.1   Constant-Pitch Thread Series Applications

The various constant-pitch series (UN/UNR) with 4, 6, 8, 12, 16, 20, 28, and 32 threads per inch offers a comprehensive range of diameter-pitch combinations where the threads in the coarse, fine, and extra-fine series do not meet the particular requirements of the design.

The **8-thread series** (8UN) is a uniform-pitch series for large diameters or as a compromise between coarse and fine thread series. Although originally intended for high-pressure-

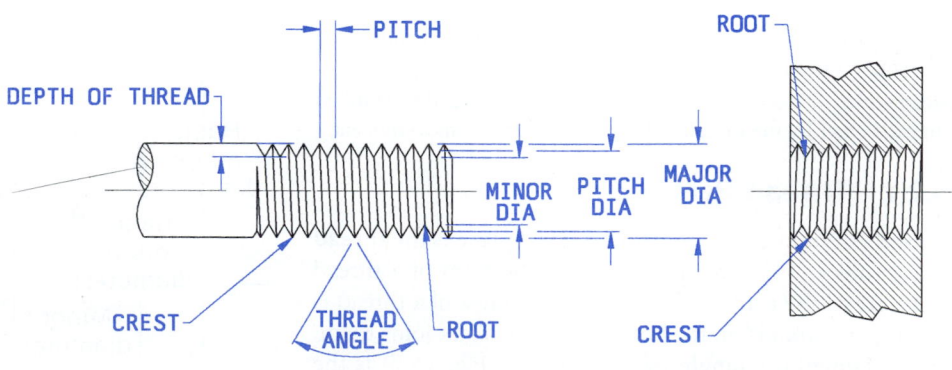

FIGURE 15.9   Unified National
Thread Terminology

EXTERNAL THREAD   INTERNAL THREAD

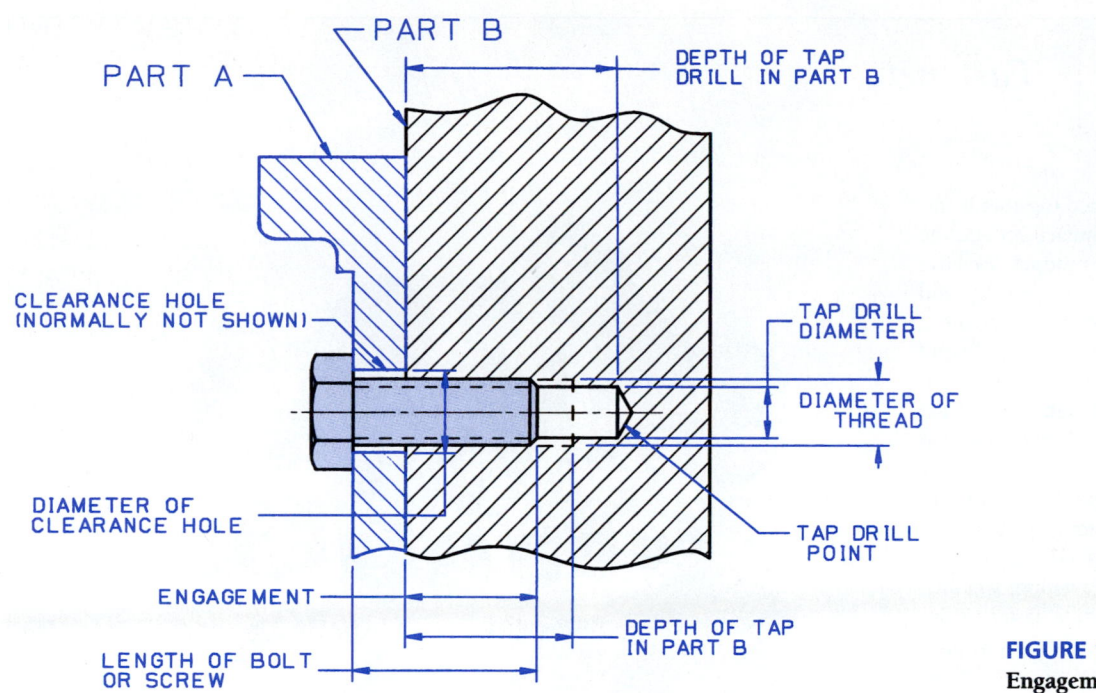

FIGURE 15.10 Thread Engagement

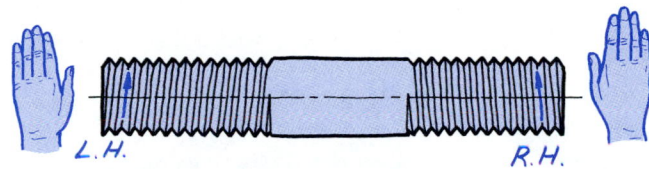

FIGURE 15.11 **Right-Hand and Left-Hand Threads**

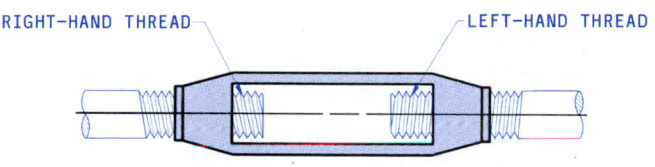

FIGURE 15.12 **Turnbuckle**

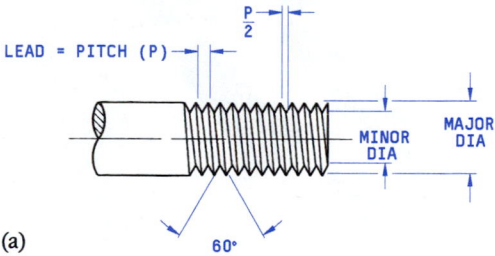

(a)

SINGLE THREAD

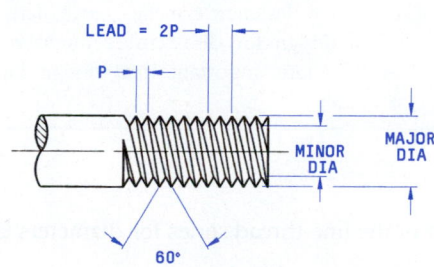

(b)   DOUBLE THREAD

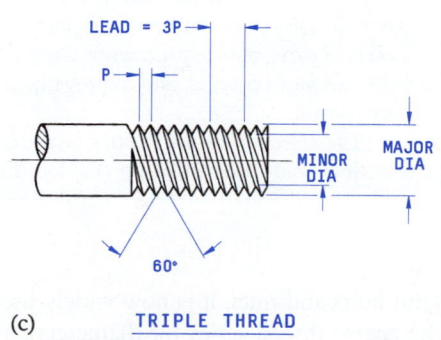

(c)   TRIPLE THREAD

FIGURE 15.13 **Single, Double, and Triple Threads**

Fasteners

How a product is fastened together is important to both the manufacturer and the customer or user of the product. We have all complained about the difficulty and cost to replace some minor component in an assembled product. Obviously, if rapid and easy disassembly were considered in the beginning in the design stage of the product, everyone would save time and money.

A fastener is any kind of device or method that is used to hold parts together. The permanent fastener choices are soldering, brazing, riveting, welding, and adhesives. Removable fasteners include nuts and bolts, screws, studs, pins, rings, or keys. Snap fits can also be designed into the part itself, eliminating the need for separate fasteners.

The choice of a suitable material for the fastener is also important. Because new materials, like carbon fiber composites, are being used, the choice of fastener material is becoming increasingly complex. Also, fasteners used on assemblies (for instance, aircraft and automobiles) must function in all weather conditions without deteriorating in a reasonable amount of time.

One of the most popular removable fasteners is the screw. Archimedes, the Greek mathematician, first used the idea in a screw conveyor to raise water. The threads on a screw provide a fast and easy method of fastening two parts together. However, screws are not the method of choice in automated assembly because of the complex motion required for insertion. Standards are being established to unify screw threads throughout the world. These standards would cut the costs of parts, reduce paperwork, simplify the inventory process, and improve quality control.

The selection of the proper fastening method and material is crucial for the

Industrial Fasteners

Various Fasteners

product to be an economic success. The cost of the fastener itself is small compared to the costs associated with that fastener over the lifetime of the assembly. Every designer and drafter in industry knows how complicated the proper selection of a fastener can be, particularly when design for disassembly might be as, or more important than design for assembly.

---

joint bolts and nuts, it is now widely used as a substitute for the coarse thread series for diameters larger than one inch.

The **12-thread series** (12UN) is a uniform-pitch series for large diameters requiring threads of medium-fine pitch. Although originally intended for boiler practice, it is now used

as a continuation of the fine-thread series for diameters larger than $1\frac{1}{2}$ inches.

The **16-thread series** (16UN) is a uniform-pitch series for large diameters requiring fine-pitch threads. It is suitable for adjusting collars and retaining nuts and also serves as a continuation of the extra-fine thread series for diameters larger than $1\frac{11}{16}$ inch.

15.4   Screw Thread Selection

The first consideration in determining screw thread selection is the *length of thread engagement* required between threaded components (Fig. 15.10). For fastenings and other general-purpose applications, the lengths of engagement can be derived from thread formulas based on the basic major diameter, nominal size of the thread, and the material of the internal threaded part. The basic diameter of the thread is "D." To determine the optimum strength of steel screws, the length of engagement in mating materials should equal D for steel; 1.50 $\times$ D for cast iron, brass, bronze, or zinc; 2.00 $\times$ D for forged aluminum; 2.50 $\times$ D for cast aluminum and forged magnesium; and 3.00 $\times$ D for cast magnesium or plastic.

Thread form is the second consideration. Normally, the choice will be limited to UNC, UNF, or SI metric for fasteners. Other thread forms such as square, Acme, buttress, knuckle, and worm are used for special applications such as power transmission.

Thread series is the third consideration in selecting screw threads. The Unified Screw Thread Standard Series gives preference to the coarse and fine thread series.

The **class of thread fit** is the fourth consideration in thread selection. The class of threads determines the degree of looseness or tightness between mating threads.

15.4.1   Thread Form

There are literally dozens of different screw thread forms. However, for inch-series mechanical fasteners, only three have significance: UN, UNR and UNJ. All are 60° symmetrical threads with essentially the same profile. The principal difference between them is the contour at the root of the external thread. For metric fasteners, SI metric threads are designated.

UNR applies only to external threads. The difference between UN and UNR threads, in addition to designation, is that a flat or optional rounded root contour is specified for UN threads, while only a rounded root contour is specified for UNR threads. The design of UNJ threads grew out of a search for an optimum thread form. This thread has root radius limits of .150 to .180 times thread pitch.

15.5   Standard Thread Fits

Standard thread fit specifications establish the size relation between two mating parts, with reference to the type of assembly. **Thread fit** is a measure of looseness or tightness between mating threads. **Classes of fit** are specific combinations of allowances and tolerances applied to external and internal threads.

For Unified inch screw threads, there are three thread classes for external threads: 1A, 2A, and 3A; and three for internal threads: 1B, 2B, and 3B. All are clearance fits, which means they assemble without interference. *The higher the class number, the tighter the fit.* The designator "A" denotes an external thread, "B" denotes an internal thread. The mating of class 1A and 1B threads provides the loosest fit, the mating of class 3A with 3B, the tightest.

Additionally, there is a Class 5 thread fit. Class 5 is an interference fit, which means that the external and internal threads are toleranced so that a positive interference occurs when they are assembled. Class 5 interference fits are standard only for coarse thread series in sizes of one inch and smaller.

The requirements of screw-thread fits are determined by use and should be specified by indicating the proper classes for the components. For example, a Class 2A external thread should be used with a Class 2B internal thread. When choosing a class fit for threads, no tighter thread fit should be selected than the function of the component's parts requires.

Classes 1A and 1B are very loosely toleranced threads, with an allowance applied to the external thread. These classes are ideally suited when quick and easy assembly and disassembly are a prime design consideration. They are standard only for coarse and fine thread series in sizes $\frac{1}{4}$ in. and larger. They are rarely specified for mechanical fasteners.

Classes 2A and 2B are by far the most popular thread classes specified for inch-series mechanical fasteners. Close to 90% of all commercial and industrial fasteners produced in North America have this class of thread fit.

Class 3A and 3B threads are suited for closely toleranced fasteners such as socket cap screws and set screws, and other high-strength fasteners. Classes 3A and 3B have restrictive tolerances and no allowance.

15.6   Thread Representation

On working drawings, threads are seldom drawn as they would actually appear; instead notes and specifications are used. The American National Standards Institute (ANSI) recognizes three conventions for representing screw threads on drawings: **detailed** (Fig. 15.14), **schematic** (Fig. 15.15), and **simplified** (Fig. 15.16) representations. One method is generally used within any one drawing. When required, however, all three methods may be used.

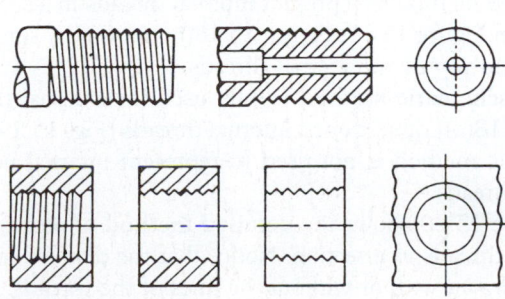

FIGURE 15.14   **Detailed Thread Representation**

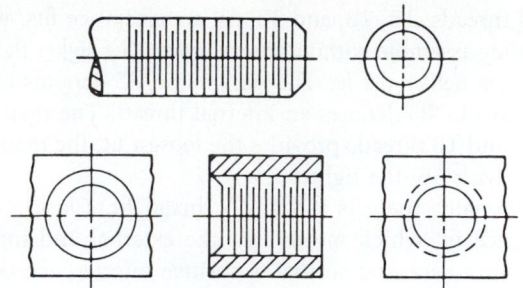

FIGURE 15.15 Schematic Thread Representation

FIGURE 15.16 Simplified Thread Representation

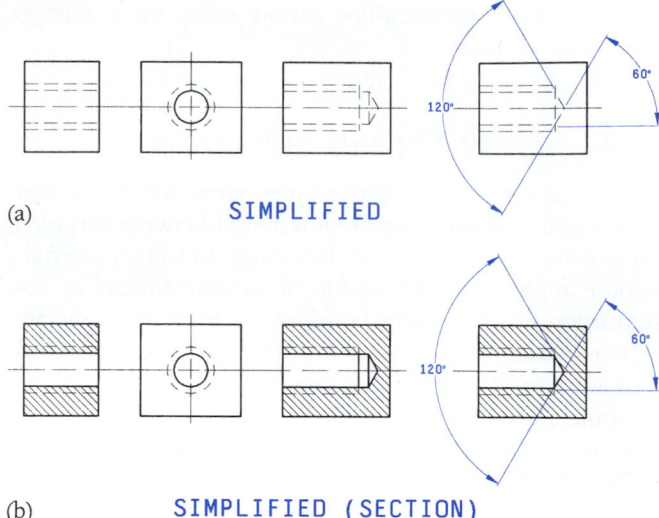

(a) SIMPLIFIED

(b) SIMPLIFIED (SECTION)

FIGURE 15.17 Internal Simplified Thread Representation

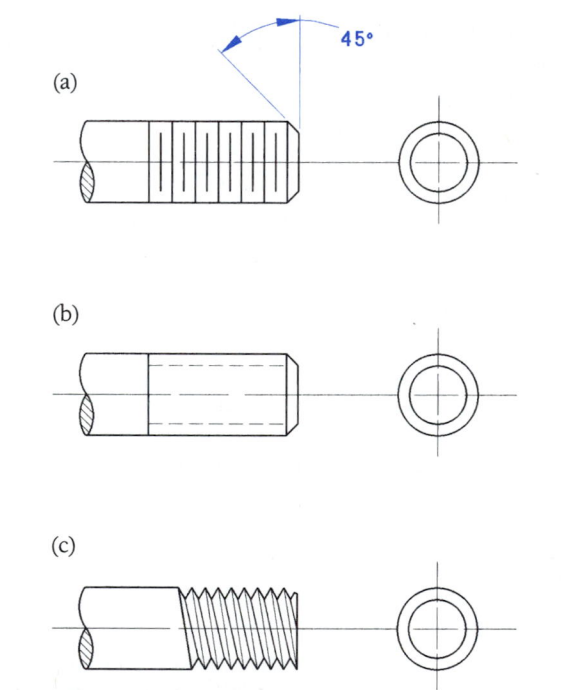

(a)

(b)

(c)

FIGURE 15.18 External Thread Representation
(a) Schematic (b) Simplified (c) Detailed

The detailed representation is an approximation of the actual appearance of screw threads. Minor modification includes showing the thread profile as a sharp V where the actual thread has flat crests and roots. Also, the normal helices are shown as straight lines connecting the thread, crest to crest and root to root. The detailed conventional representation is limited to where the basic diameter is over 1.00 inch and where detail or relation of component parts could be confused by less realistic thread representation. When internal holes are drawn using the detailed method, the lines representing the threads are sometimes omitted.

It is important to represent threads on drawings properly. The **simplified method** showing internal threads and the simplified method to represent internal threads in a section is shown in Figure 15.17. Figure 15.18(b) shows the simplified method to represent external threads.

The **schematic method** is only used for external threads [Fig. 15.18(a)] or sectioned internal threads (Fig. 15.19). The schematic method is not used to represent internal nonsectioned threads.

Figure 15.20 shows the **detailed method** of representing internal threads in a section. Notice that the detailed method can be drawn with or without the lines of the threads. Exter-

nal threads drawn with detailed representation are shown in Figure 15.18(c).

15.6.1 Drawing Threads Using Simplified Representation

The simplified method is drawn by following the steps in Figure 15.21. Both internal and external threads are drawn with this method. Here, external threads are being con-

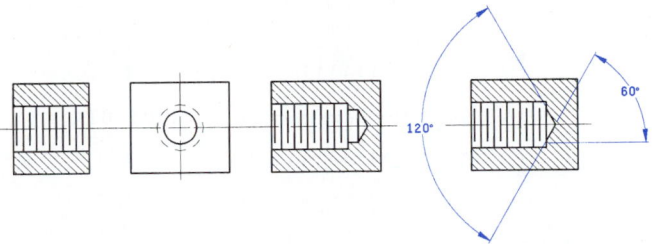

FIGURE 15.19   Internal Schematic Thread Representation

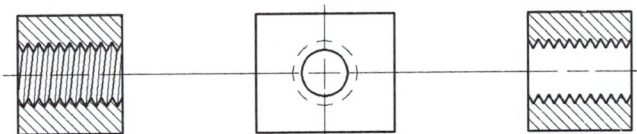

FIGURE 15.20   Internal Detailed Thread Representation

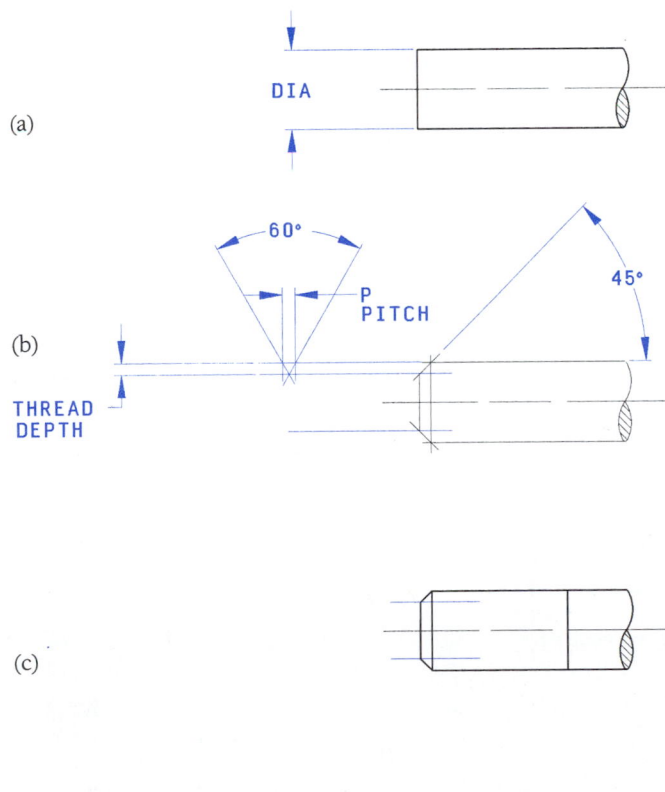

FIGURE 15.21   Drawing Threads Using Simplified Thread Representation

structed. The diameter of the screw is drawn and its end is established in Figure 15.21(a). The pitch P is measured as shown in (b). Lines are drawn at 60° through the pitch measurements. The thread depth is where the 60° lines cross. The thread depth is used to draw the chamfered end. The chamfer is drawn at 45° and the threaded length is established in Figure 15.21(c). The thread depth is used to draw the dashed lines that represent the minor diameter of the thread in (d).

15.6.2   Drawing Threads Using Schematic Representation

Schematic representation is nearly as visually effective as the detailed representation and is much easier to draw. The alternate lines, symbolic of the thread roots and crests, are usually drawn perpendicular to the axis of the thread or sometimes slanted to the approximate angle of the thread helix. This construction should not be used for internal threads or sections of external threads.

Drawing schematic threads is similar to the simplified method. The screw diameter and end are drawn first [Fig. 15.22(a)]. The chamfer is completed using 45° and the thread depth in (b). The pitch P is used to establish the spacing of the thread crests in Figure 15.22(c). The root lines are drawn up to the thread depth in (d) and the thread is completed by darkening in the lines in (e). This method is called the *uniform-line method*. The slope-line representation is shown in Figure 15.22(f). The slope angle is equal to one-half of the pitch. In actual industrial practice, drafters draw the screw diameter, construct a 45° chamfer, and use the chamfer depth to locate the thread root.

15.6.3   Drawing Threads Using Detailed Representation

The detailed thread representation is drawn only when a mechanical advantage must be calculated or analyzed graphically (or for illustrations). Figure 15.23 shows four steps in drawing threads with detailed representation. Step (a) is the same as for simplified and schematic thread representation. The diameter of the screw thread is layed out and one-half of the pitch is measured. Using the pitch P, the top and the bottom lines of the shaft are divided along its length into the required number of threads. The slope lines (crest lines) are drawn with an angle of one-half the pitch. The threads are drawn as sharp V's at 60° in Figure 15.23(b). The ends of the root lines will be established where the crest lines cross at the root. The root lines are drawn by connecting the roots [Fig. 15.23(c)]. In Figure 15.23(d), the threads are darkened.

15.6.4   How to Draw Acme Threads

A step-by-step procedure for drawing Acme threads is given in Figures 15.24 and 15.25. The Acme thread has a depth equal to one-half of its pitch. The drawing is started by drawing

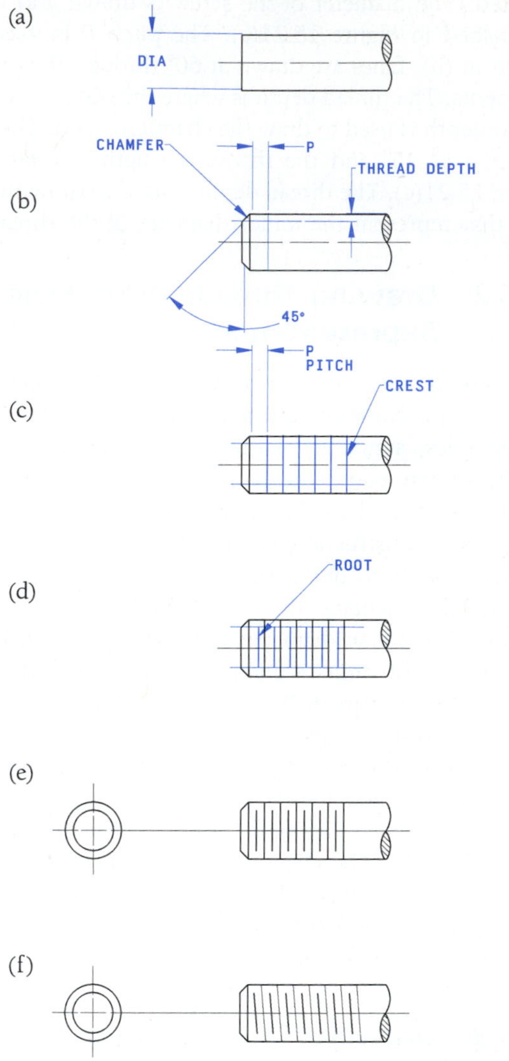

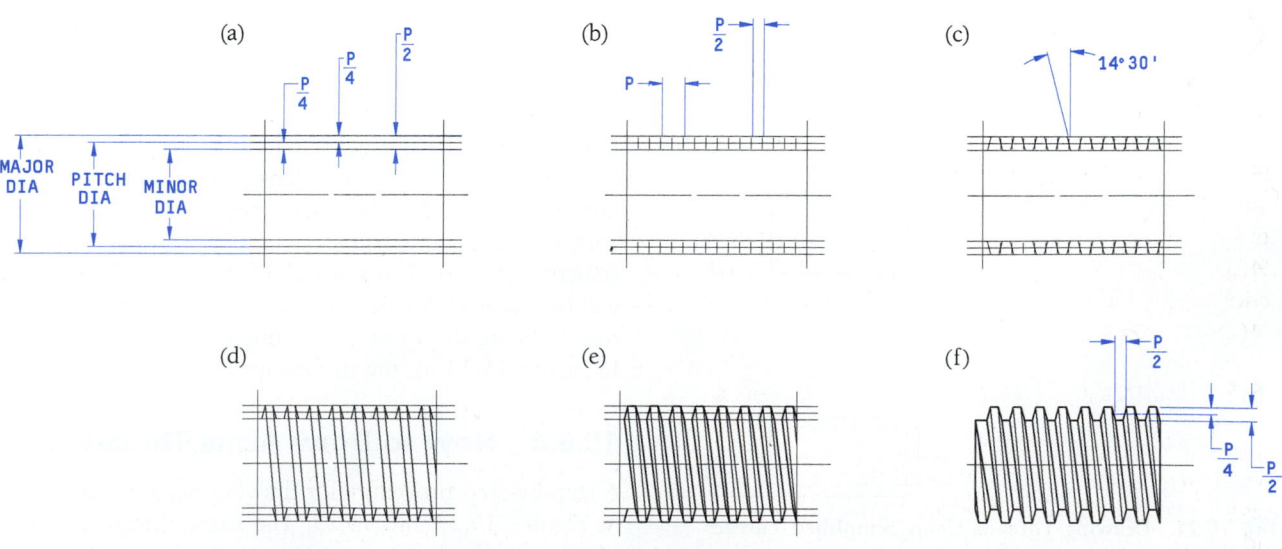

(a)

DIA

(b)

CHAMFER ← P

THREAD DEPTH

45°

P PITCH

(c)

CREST

(d)

ROOT

(e)

(f)

FIGURE 15.22 Drawing Threads Using Schematic Thread Representation

(a)

DIA ROOT DIA

P

60°

(b)

(c)

MAJOR DIA MINOR DIA

(d)

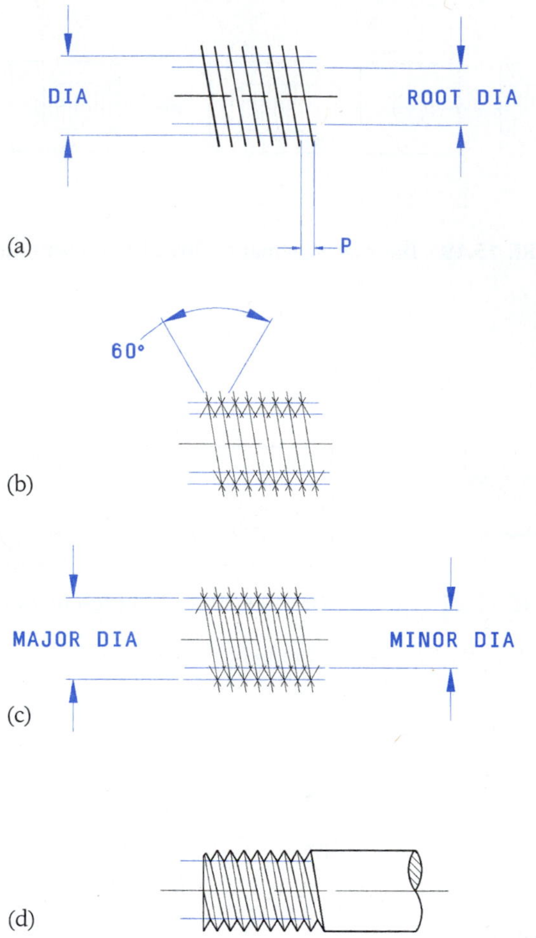

FIGURE 15.23 Drawing Threads Using Detailed Thread Representation

(a)

$\frac{P}{4}$ $\frac{P}{4}$ $\frac{P}{2}$

MAJOR DIA PITCH DIA MINOR DIA

(b)

$\frac{P}{2}$

P

(c)

14° 30'

(d)

(e)

(f)

$\frac{P}{2}$

$\frac{P}{4}$ $\frac{P}{2}$

FIGURE 15.24 Drawing Acme Threads Using Detailed Thread Representation

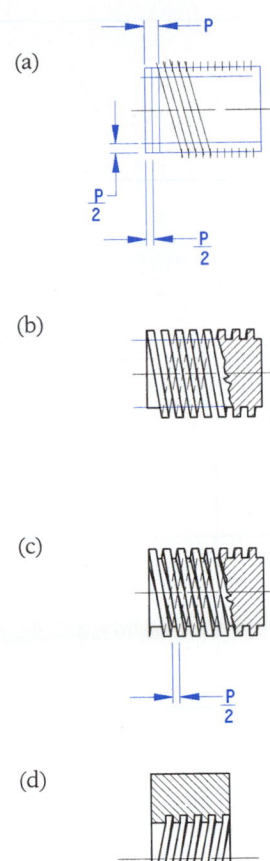

FIGURE 15.25   Detailed Acme Threads

the shaft diameter (major diameter), the minor diameter, and the pitch diameters with construction lines [Fig. 15.24(a)]. The pitch diameter lines are divided into segments equaling one-half the pitch in (b). The angle of the thread profile is one-half of 29° ($14\frac{1}{2}$°). Normally, 15° is used to simplify the procedure. The 15° lines are drawn through the half-pitch distances established along the pitch diameter lines [Fig. 15.24(c)]. The angled lines will fall between the major diameter and the minor diameter, as shown in Fig 15.24(d). The crests are completed and the root lines are then drawn in Fig. 15.24(e). The ends of the threads are completed, the construction lines erased, and the drawing is darkened [Fig. 15.24(f)].

15.6.5   Using a CAD System to Draw Threads

Drawing threads with a CAD system (in 2D) is similar to the process described above for detailed and Acme threads. The thread profile (of one thread) must still be constructed. Using commands, the drafter completes the project as shown in

Figure 15.26. The **ARRAY** command is used to create the threads. The following AutoCAD command was used in Fig. 15.26:

```
Command: ARRAY
Select objects: W (D1 and D2 are used to window the
entities)
Rectangular or polar array (R/P): R
Number of rows (---) <1>: Return/Enter
Number of columns (¦¦¦) <1>: 7
Unit cell or distance between rows (---):
Return/Enter
Distance between columns (¦¦¦): .125
```

The socket head cap screw in Figure 15.27 was drawn with Computervisions Personal Designer software. The command used to generate the threads is different (**MOVE COPY**), but the results are the same for both examples.

15.6.6   Tap Drills

Threaded holes are drilled first and then tapped (Fig. 15.28, p. 536). The tapping tool extends far enough into the hole to thread the required length of full threads. The **tap drill**, therefore, must extend beyond the required thread depth. The major diameter represents the outside diameter of the thread and the minor diameter represents the tap drill diameter.

Figure 15.29, p. 536 shows how to represent tapped holes using the simplified method. The drilled hole is drawn accurately with its diameter and depth as shown. The drill tip is normally 118°, but for simplicity it is drawn at 120° (30° from the horizontal). For drilled and tapped holes, the depth of the full thread is accurately drawn. Normally, the tap drill is drawn 3× the pitch below the threaded portion. This distance includes a number of incomplete threads created by the chamfer end of the tapping tool. Though normally drawn at 3× the pitch, this distance is determined by the drill size and whether a bottoming tap or a plug tap is used. In some cases, the thread will extend to the bottom of the drilled hole, or a **thread relief** will be required. An internal thread relief is slightly larger than the major diameter of the thread (Fig. 15.29). The circular views of the threaded holes show the tap drill as a solid line and the major thread (major diameter) as a dashed (hidden) line.

15.7   Designating Threads and Thread Notes

The thread designation includes the nominal diameter, the number of threads per inch (or the pitch and lead), the letter symbol of the thread series, the number and letter of the thread class, and any qualifying information. The thread length, the hole size, and the chamfer or countersink may be included in the note or dimensioned on the drawing of the part.

The series symbols and the class numbers identify the controlling thread standard and define the details of thread

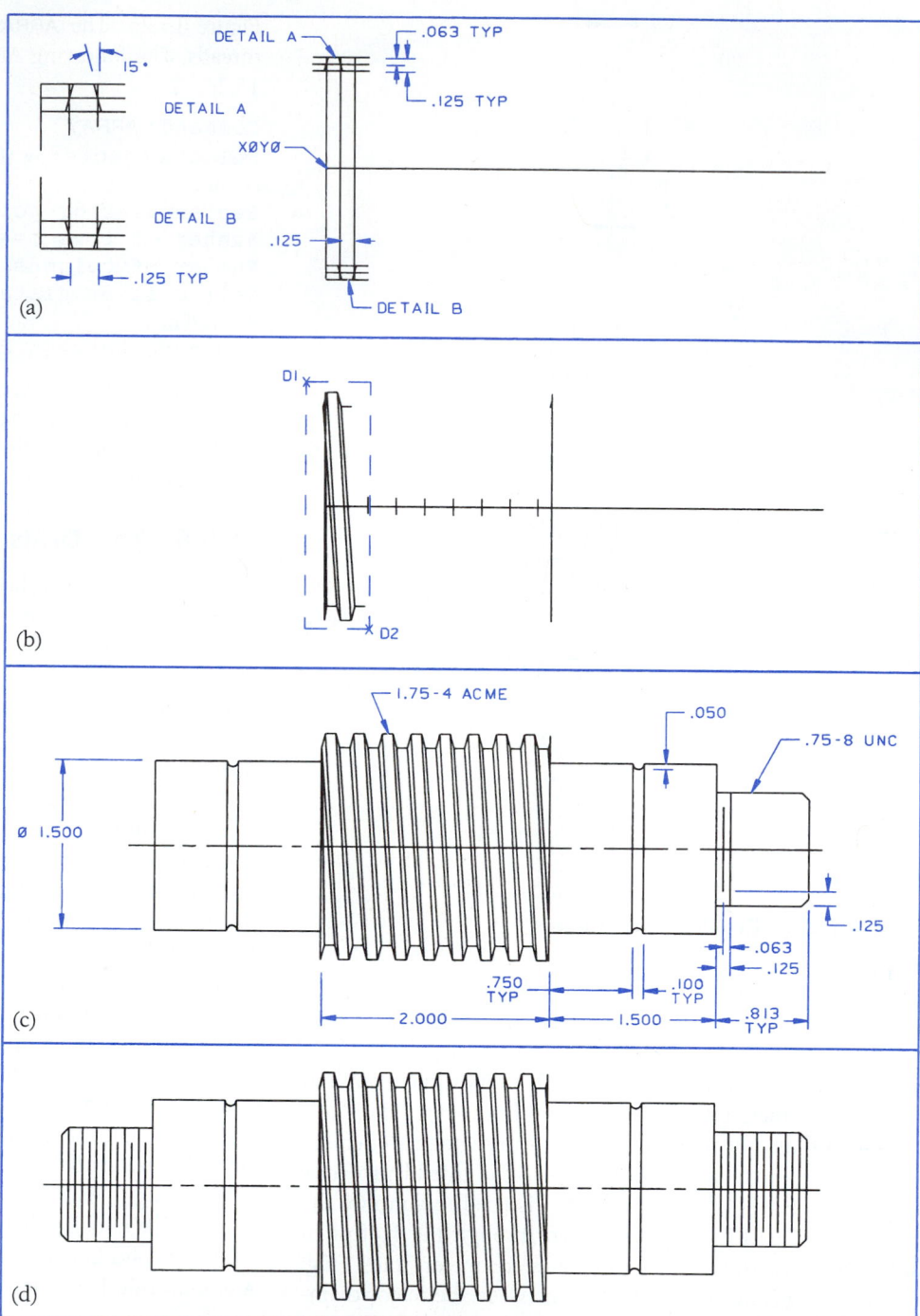

FIGURE 15.26 Using a CAD System to Draw Detailed Acme Threads

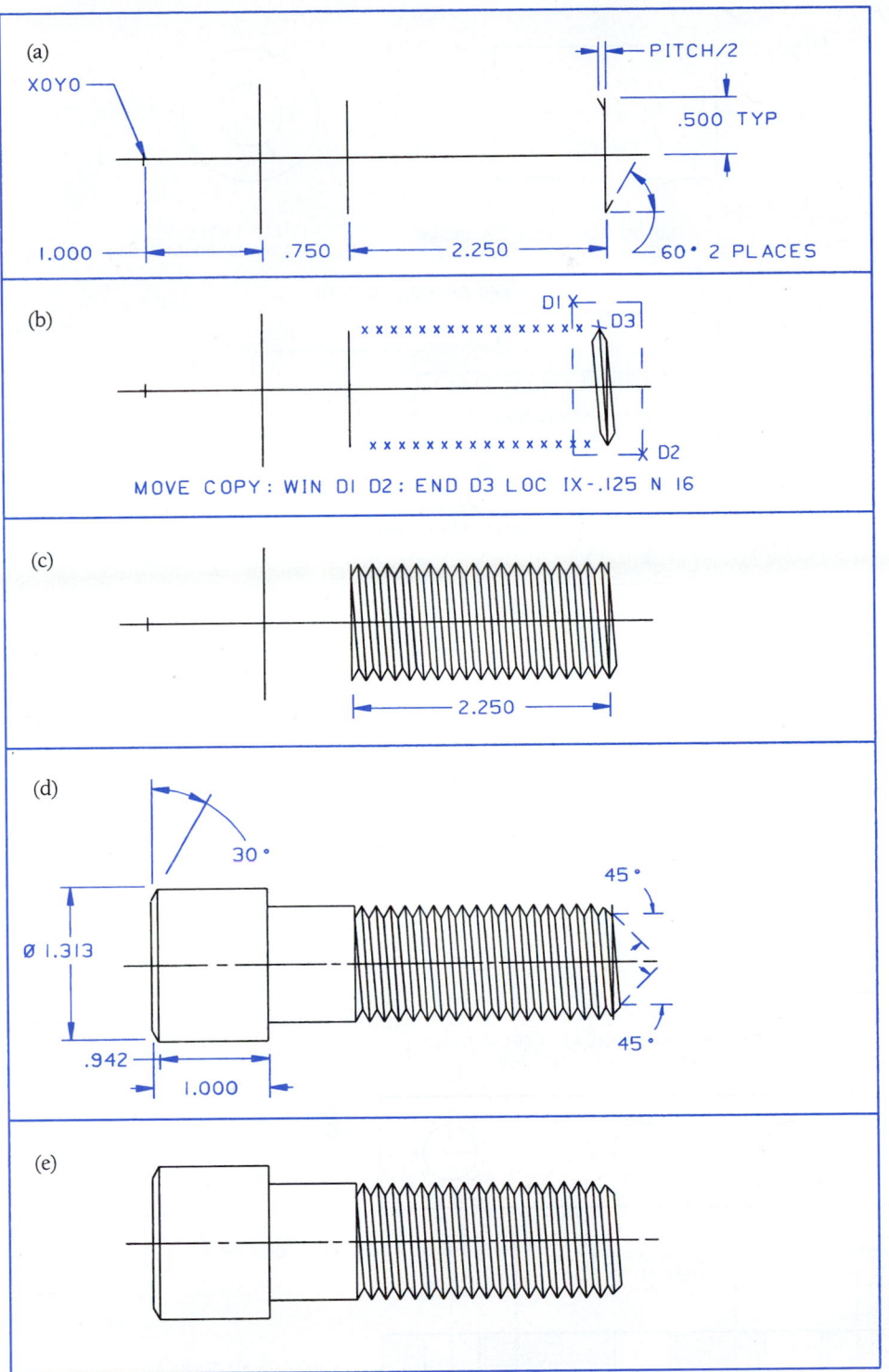

(a)

XOYO

PITCH/2

.500 TYP

1.000   .750   2.250   60° 2 PLACES

(b)

DI   D3

x x x x x x x x x x x x x x x x   x

x x x x x x x x x x x x x x   x   D2

MOVE COPY: WIN DI D2: END D3 LOC IX-.125 N 16

(c)

2.250

(d)

30°

45°

Ø 1.313

45°

.942

1.000

(e)

FIGURE 15.27   Using a CAD
System to Draw Detailed Threads

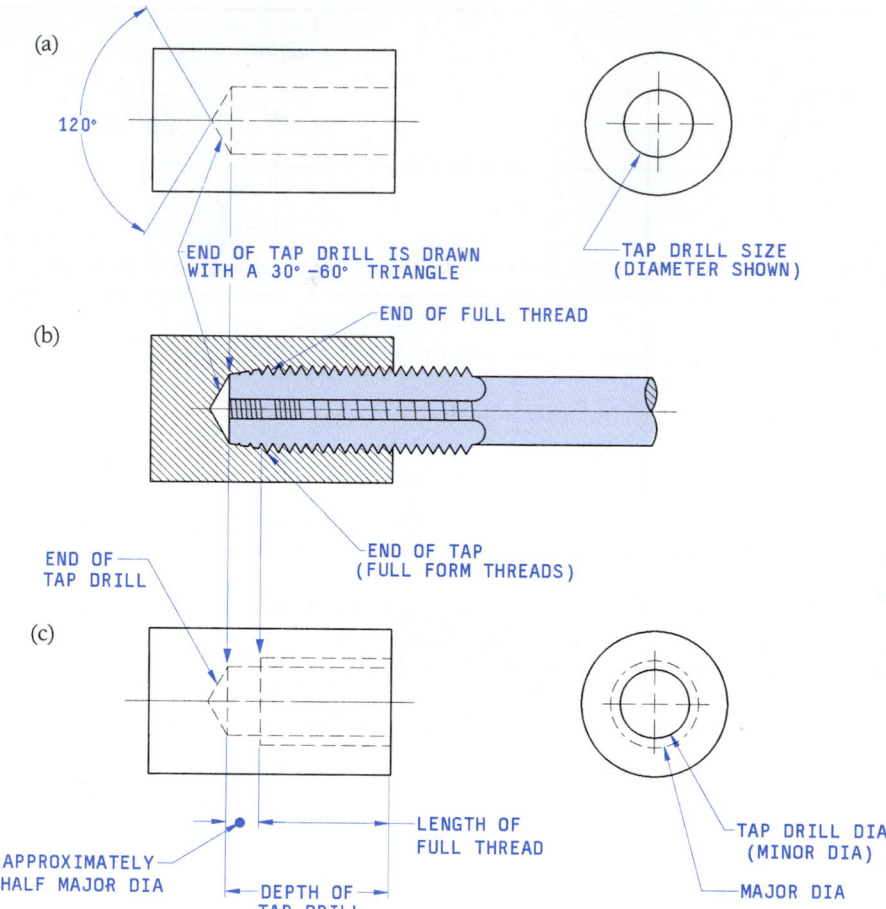

(a)

120°

END OF TAP DRILL IS DRAWN
WITH A 30°-60° TRIANGLE

TAP DRILL SIZE
(DIAMETER SHOWN)

(b)

END OF FULL THREAD

END OF TAP
(FULL FORM THREADS)

END OF
TAP DRILL

(c)

LENGTH OF
FULL THREAD

APPROXIMATELY
HALF MAJOR DIA

DEPTH OF
TAP DRILL

TAP DRILL DIA
(MINOR DIA)

MAJOR DIA

FIGURE 15.28 Blind Holes and
Taps

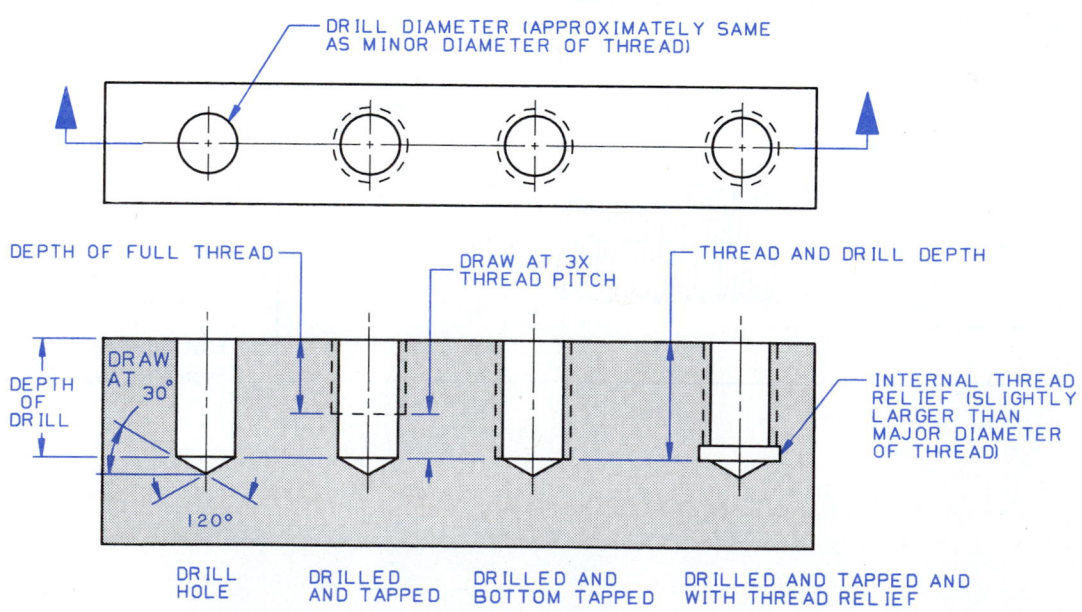

DRILL DIAMETER (APPROXIMATELY SAME
AS MINOR DIAMETER OF THREAD)

DEPTH OF FULL THREAD

DRAW AT 3X
THREAD PITCH

THREAD AND DRILL DEPTH

DEPTH
OF
DRILL

DRAW
AT 30°

120°

INTERNAL THREAD
RELIEF (SLIGHTLY
LARGER THAN
MAJOR DIAMETER
OF THREAD)

DRILL
HOLE

DRILLED
AND TAPPED

DRILLED AND
BOTTOM TAPPED

DRILLED AND TAPPED AND
WITH THREAD RELIEF

FIGURE 15.29 Drilling and Tapping Holes

design, dimensions, and tolerances not specifically covered on the drawing. Series, class, and dimensional letters in a thread designation are shown as follows:

A	— external, American, aeronautical
B	— internal
C	— coupling, coarse, or centralizing
EXT	— external
EF	— extra fine
F	— fine, fuel, and oil
G	— general-purpose, gas, pitch allowance
H	— house
I	— intermediate
INT	— internal
J	— controlled radius root
L	— lead, locknut
LE	— length of engagement
LH	— left hand (absence of LH indicates RH)
M	— metric, mechanical, microscope, miniature
MOD	— modified
N	— national
O	— outlet, objective
P	— pipe, pitch
R	— railing, rounded root, American National Class 1 allowance
RH	— right hand
S	— straight
SE	— special engagement
SPL	— special
T	— taper
UN	— unified

15.7.1   Thread Designation Examples

In general practice, the designation and the pitch diameter limits are in note form and referenced to the drawing of the thread with a leader line. The following example illustrates the elements of a designation of a screw thread:

.250-20 UNC-2A

where

```
.250 = NOMINAL DIAMETER IN DECIMAL FORM
  20 = NUMBER OF THREADS PER INCH OR
       PITCH AND LEAD
 UNC = THREAD FORM, SERIES, AND TOLERANCE
       FORMULATION SYMBOL
   2 = CLASS NUMBER
   A = INTERNAL OR EXTERNAL SYMBOL
       (A IS EXTERNAL)
```

Thread sizes are shown as decimal callouts except for fractional sizes. When specifying decimal sizes, a minimum of three or maximum of four decimal places, omitting any zero

in the fourth decimal place, should be shown as the nominal size as given below:

1.000-8 UNC-2A

$1\frac{3}{4}$-8 UN-2A

Numbered sizes may also be shown; the decimal equivalent should be in parentheses as shown below:

No. 10(.190)-32 UNF-2A

Unless otherwise specified, threads are right hand; a left-hand thread shall be designated **LH** as follows:

$\frac{1}{4}$-20 UNC-3A-LH

15.8   Acme Threads

There are four classes of general-purpose Acme threads and five classes of centralizing Acme threads. The general-purpose Acme threads have clearances on all diameters for free movement and may be used in assemblies where both internal and external members are supported to prevent movement.

There is only one class of stub Acme thread established for general usage. It is the Class 2G (general-purpose) thread using two threads with modified thread depths. Stub Acme threads are used for power applications.

When designating Acme threads, the designation covers the nominal size, the number of threads per inch, the thread form symbol, and the thread class symbol as shown here:

1.750-4 ACME-2G

where

```
1.750 = NOMINAL DECIMAL SIZE
    4 = NUMBER OF THREADS PER INCH
 ACME = THREAD FORM AND SERIES SYMBOL
   2G = THREAD CLASS SYMBOL
```

15.9   Buttress Threads

Buttress threads are used for high-stress applications where the stress is along its axis in only one direction. The buttress thread is designated **butt** or **push-butt**. Since the design of most components having buttress threads is so special, no diameter pitch series is recommended. There are two classes of buttress threads: Class 2 (standard grade) and Class 3 (precision grade).

When only the designation "butt" is used, the thread is a "pull"-type buttress with the clearance flank angle of 45° leading and the pressure flange angle of 7° following. Whenever possible, the designation should be confirmed by a view on the drawing of the product that has the buttress thread. In thread designations on drawings and in specifications, the designation should be shown as in the following example:

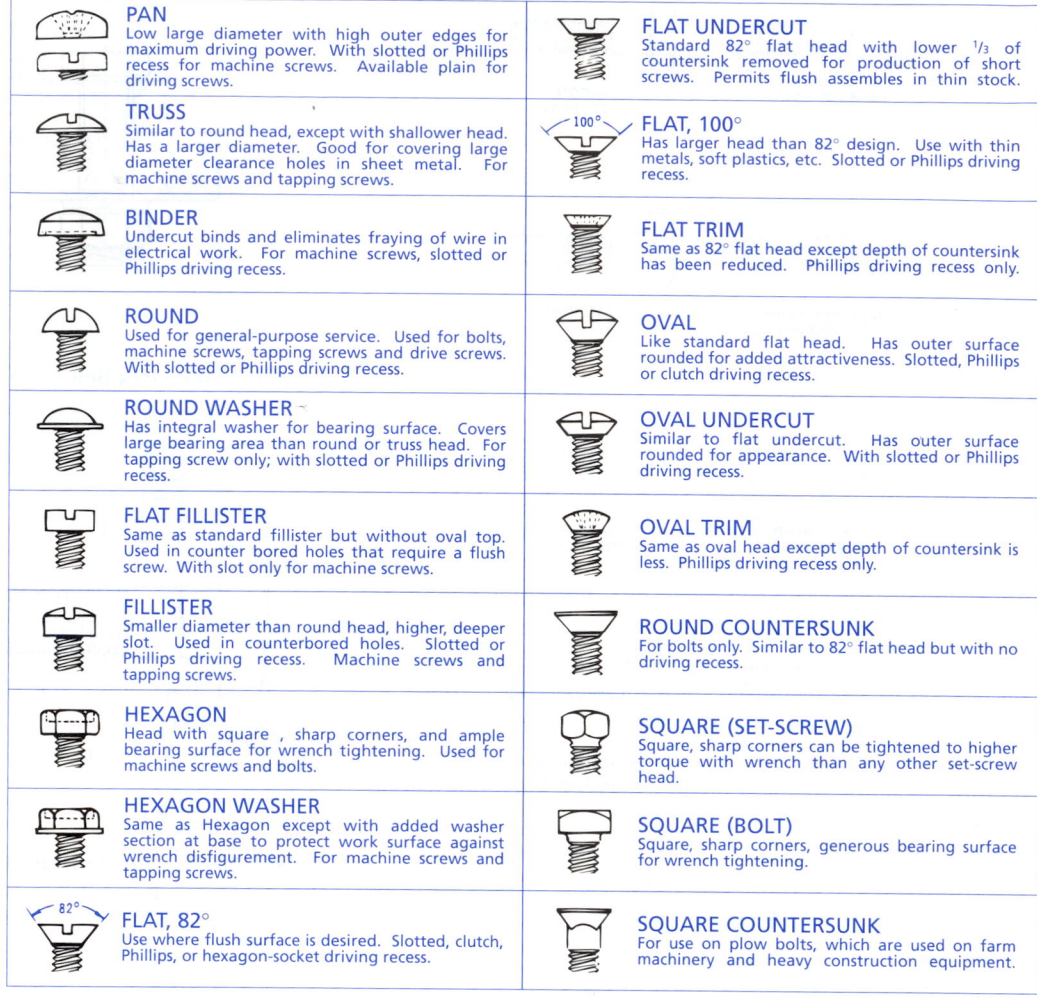

	PAN Low large diameter with high outer edges for maximum driving power. With slotted or Phillips recess for machine screws. Available plain for driving screws.		**FLAT UNDERCUT** Standard 82° flat head with lower 1/3 of countersink removed for production of short screws. Permits flush assembles in thin stock.
	TRUSS Similar to round head, except with shallower head. Has a larger diameter. Good for covering large diameter clearance holes in sheet metal. For machine screws and tapping screws.		**FLAT, 100°** Has larger head than 82° design. Use with thin metals, soft plastics, etc. Slotted or Phillips driving recess.
	BINDER Undercut binds and eliminates fraying of wire in electrical work. For machine screws, slotted or Phillips driving recess.		**FLAT TRIM** Same as 82° flat head except depth of countersink has been reduced. Phillips driving recess only.
	ROUND Used for general-purpose service. Used for bolts, machine screws, tapping screws and drive screws. With slotted or Phillips driving recess.		**OVAL** Like standard flat head. Has outer surface rounded for added attractiveness. Slotted, Phillips or clutch driving recess.
	ROUND WASHER Has integral washer for bearing surface. Covers large bearing area than round or truss head. For tapping screw only; with slotted or Phillips driving recess.		**OVAL UNDERCUT** Similar to flat undercut. Has outer surface rounded for appearance. With slotted or Phillips driving recess.
	FLAT FILLISTER Same as standard fillister but without oval top. Used in counter bored holes that require a flush screw. With slot only for machine screws.		**OVAL TRIM** Same as oval head except depth of countersink is less. Phillips driving recess only.
	FILLISTER Smaller diameter than round head, higher, deeper slot. Used in counterbored holes. Slotted or Phillips driving recess. Machine screws and tapping screws.		**ROUND COUNTERSUNK** For bolts only. Similar to 82° flat head but with no driving recess.
	HEXAGON Head with square, sharp corners, and ample bearing surface for wrench tightening. Used for machine screws and bolts.		**SQUARE (SET-SCREW)** Square, sharp corners can be tightened to higher torque with wrench than any other set-screw head.
	HEXAGON WASHER Same as Hexagon except with added washer section at base to protect work surface against wrench disfigurement. For machine screws and tapping screws.		**SQUARE (BOLT)** Square, sharp corners, generous bearing surface for wrench tightening.
	FLAT, 82° Use where flush surface is desired. Slotted, clutch, Phillips, or hexagon-socket driving recess.		**SQUARE COUNTERSUNK** For use on plow bolts, which are used on farm machinery and heavy construction equipment.

FIGURE 15.49 Machine Screw Head Styles

15.13.5 Machine Screws

Machine screws differ from cap screws mainly in range of basic diameters, head shapes, and driver provisions. Machine screws are so named because they are completely machined from bar stock. They are usually restricted to light assemblies such as instrument panel mountings, moldings, and clip fasteners. The size selection is determined by the tightness required of the parts to be fastened. Machine screws can be assembled into a nut or a threaded hole in a functional part. Figure 15.49 shows various screw head shapes available as standard parts. Screw selection is made by considering design needs such as surface condition, appearance, size of hole, cover clearance, driving provisions, and expected environmental exposure.

Machine screws come in either fine or coarse thread and are normally confined to light assembly applications. Machine screw sizes are divided into two categories: fractional sizes and numbered sizes. Numbered sizes are confined to those below $\frac{1}{4}$ in. diameter. Fractional sizes range between $\frac{1}{4}$ and $\frac{3}{4}$ inch. Number 0 has a diameter of .06 inches; .013 inches is added to each numbered size above number 0. Figure 15.50 shows

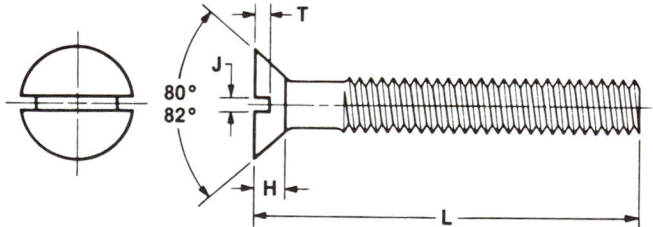

FIGURE 15.50 Slotted Flat Countersunk-Head Machine Screw

Nominal Size	Head Dia	H	J	T
#5 (.125)	.25	.075	.04	.03
.500	.875	.223	.10	.10

a slotted flat countersunk-head machine screw. Machine screws two inches and below in length come fully threaded. All lengths above two inches have $1\frac{3}{4}$ inch thread. Machine screws are called out the same as bolts as shown below:

.25-20 × 1.5 SLOTTED PAN HEAD MACHINE SCREW, STEEL, ZINC PLATED

6-32 × 1.50 SLOTTED FLAT COUNTERSUNK HEAD MACHINE SCREW

design, dimensions, and tolerances not specifically covered on the drawing. Series, class, and dimensional letters in a thread designation are shown as follows:

A	— external, American, aeronautical
B	— internal
C	— coupling, coarse, or centralizing
EXT	— external
EF	— extra fine
F	— fine, fuel, and oil
G	— general-purpose, gas, pitch allowance
H	— house
I	— intermediate
INT	— internal
J	— controlled radius root
L	— lead, locknut
LE	— length of engagement
LH	— left hand (absence of LH indicates RH)
M	— metric, mechanical, microscope, miniature
MOD	— modified
N	— national
O	— outlet, objective
P	— pipe, pitch
R	— railing, rounded root, American National Class 1 allowance
RH	— right hand
S	— straight
SE	— special engagement
SPL	— special
T	— taper
UN	— unified

15.7.1 Thread Designation Examples

In general practice, the designation and the pitch diameter limits are in note form and referenced to the drawing of the thread with a leader line. The following example illustrates the elements of a designation of a screw thread:

.250-20 UNC-2A

where

```
.250 = NOMINAL DIAMETER IN DECIMAL FORM
  20 = NUMBER OF THREADS PER INCH OR
       PITCH AND LEAD
 UNC = THREAD FORM, SERIES, AND TOLERANCE
       FORMULATION SYMBOL
   2 = CLASS NUMBER
   A = INTERNAL OR EXTERNAL SYMBOL
       (A IS EXTERNAL)
```

Thread sizes are shown as decimal callouts except for fractional sizes. When specifying decimal sizes, a minimum of three or maximum of four decimal places, omitting any zero

in the fourth decimal place, should be shown as the nominal size as given below:

1.000-8 UNC-2A

$1\frac{3}{4}$-8 UN-2A

Numbered sizes may also be shown; the decimal equivalent should be in parentheses as shown below:

No. 10(.190)-32 UNF-2A

Unless otherwise specified, threads are right hand; a left-hand thread shall be designated **LH** as follows:

$\frac{1}{4}$-20 UNC-3A-LH

15.8 Acme Threads

There are four classes of general-purpose Acme threads and five classes of centralizing Acme threads. The general-purpose Acme threads have clearances on all diameters for free movement and may be used in assemblies where both internal and external members are supported to prevent movement.

There is only one class of stub Acme thread established for general usage. It is the Class 2G (general-purpose) thread using two threads with modified thread depths. Stub Acme threads are used for power applications.

When designating Acme threads, the designation covers the nominal size, the number of threads per inch, the thread form symbol, and the thread class symbol as shown here:

1.750-4 ACME-2G

where

```
1.750 = NOMINAL DECIMAL SIZE
    4 = NUMBER OF THREADS PER INCH
 ACME = THREAD FORM AND SERIES SYMBOL
   2G = THREAD CLASS SYMBOL
```

15.9 Buttress Threads

Buttress threads are used for high-stress applications where the stress is along its axis in only one direction. The buttress thread is designated **butt** or **push-butt**. Since the design of most components having buttress threads is so special, no diameter pitch series is recommended. There are two classes of buttress threads: Class 2 (standard grade) and Class 3 (precision grade).

When only the designation "butt" is used, the thread is a "pull"-type buttress with the clearance flank angle of 45° leading and the pressure flange angle of 7° following. Whenever possible, the designation should be confirmed by a view on the drawing of the product that has the buttress thread. In thread designations on drawings and in specifications, the designation should be shown as in the following example:

2.500-8 BUTT-2A-LH

where

$$
\begin{aligned}
2.500 &= \text{NOMINAL SIZE (BASIC MAJOR} \\
 &\quad\ \text{DIAMETER IN INCHES)} \\
8 &= \text{THREADS PER INCH (TPI)} \\
\text{BUTT} &= \text{BUTTRESS FORM OF THREAD, PULL-TYPE} \\
2 &= \text{CLASS 2 (MEDIUM) THREAD} \\
\text{A} &= \text{EXTERNAL THREAD} \\
\text{LH} &= \text{LEFT HAND}
\end{aligned}
$$

15.10   Metric Threads

Many types of threaded fasteners are manufactured using metric threads. This section contains general metric standards for a 60° symmetrical screw thread with a basic ISO 68, profile designated "M".

The simplified, schematic, and detailed methods of thread representation also apply to metric screw thread drawing practices. The following additional definitions are used for metric threads:

Bolt thread (external thread)   Used in ISO metric thread standards to describe all external threads. All symbols associated with external threads are designated with lowercase letters.

Nut thread (internal thread)   Used in ISO metric thread standards to describe all internal threads. All symbols associated with internal threads are designated with uppercase letters.

15.10.1   Metric Classes of Thread Fit

There are two recognized classes of thread fit. One is for general-purpose applications and contains tolerance classes 6H/6g; the other is used where closer thread fits are required and contains tolerance classes 6H/4g–6g.

The **tolerance grade** is indicated by a number. The system provides for a series of tolerance grades for each of the four screw thread parameters: minor diameter, internal thread (4, 5, 6, 7, 8); major diameter, external thread (4, 6, 8); pitch diameter, internal thread (4, 5, 6, 7, 8); and pitch diameter, external thread (3, 4, 5, 6, 7, 8, 9).

The **tolerance position** is the allowance and is indicated by a letter. An uppercase letter is used for internal threads and a lowercase letter for external threads. The system provides a series of tolerance positions for internal and external threads:

Internal threads	G, H
External threads	g, h

The tolerance grade is given first, followed by the tolerance position: 4g or 5H. To designate the tolerance class, the grade and position of the pitch diameter is shown first followed by the major diameter (external thread) or the minor diameter (internal thread) — 4g6g for an external thread and 5H6H for an internal thread. If the two grades and positions are identical, it is not necessary to repeat the symbols. Therefore, 4g alone stands for 4g4g, and 5H alone means 5H5H.

15.10.2   Designation of Metric Screw Threads

Metric screw threads are identified by the letter **M** for the thread form profile, followed by the nominal diameter size and the pitch expressed in millimeters, separated by the × sign and followed by the tolerance class separated by the dash (-) from the pitch.

The simplified international practice for designating coarse pitch M profile metric screw threads is to leave off the pitch. Thus, a **M14 × 2** thread is designated just **M14**. However, to prevent misunderstanding, it is mandatory to use the value for pitch in all designations shown on drawings.

Thread acceptability gaging system requirements of ANSI B1.3M may be added to the thread size designation. The numbers are shown in parentheses: (22), (21). The following is an example of a close tolerance external thread designation:

M8 × 1.25-4g6g (22)

Two examples of internal thread designation are:

M6 × 1-6H (21)

M6 × 1-5H6H (21)

Unless otherwise specified in the designation, the screw thread helix is right hand. When a left-hand thread is specified, the tolerance class designation is followed by a dash and LH. The following example is of a left-hand external thread with an M profile:

M6 × 1-4g6g-LH,

where

$$
\begin{aligned}
\text{M} &= \text{METRIC THREAD SYMBOL, ISO 68} \\
 &\quad\ \text{METRIC THREAD FORM} \\
6 &= \text{NOMINAL SIZE IN MILLIMETERS} \\
1 &= \text{PITCH IN MILLIMETERS} \\
\text{4g6g} &= \text{TOLERANCE CLASS} \\
\text{4g} &= \text{MAJOR DIAMETER TOLERANCE SYMBOL} \\
 &\quad\ (4 = \text{TOLERANCE POSITION)} \\
 &\quad\ (\text{g} = \text{TOLERANCE GRADE)} \\
\text{6g} &= \text{PITCH DIAMETER TOLERANCE SYMBOL} \\
 &\quad\ (6 = \text{TOLERANCE POSITION)} \\
 &\quad\ (\text{g} = \text{TOLERANCE GRADE)} \\
\text{LH} &= \text{LEFT HAND}
\end{aligned}
$$

A fit between *mating threads* is indicated by the internal thread tolerance class, followed by the external thread tolerance class separated by a slash as shown below:

M6 × 1-6H/6g

M6 × 1-6H/4g6g

15.11   Dimensioning Threads

In addition to the drawing practices for representation and designation of screw threads, ANSI Y14.5 should be used in

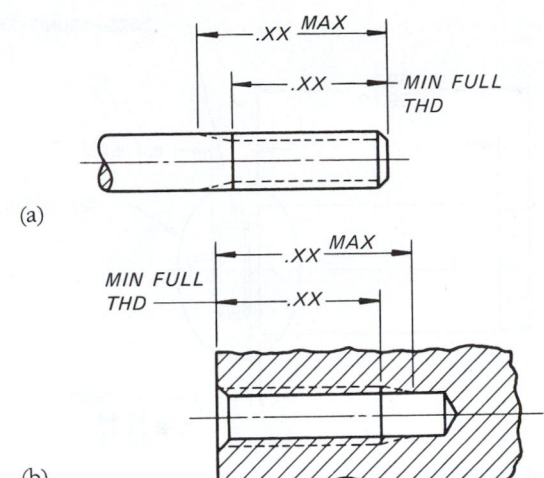

(a)

(b)

FIGURE 15.30 Dimensioning Thread Length

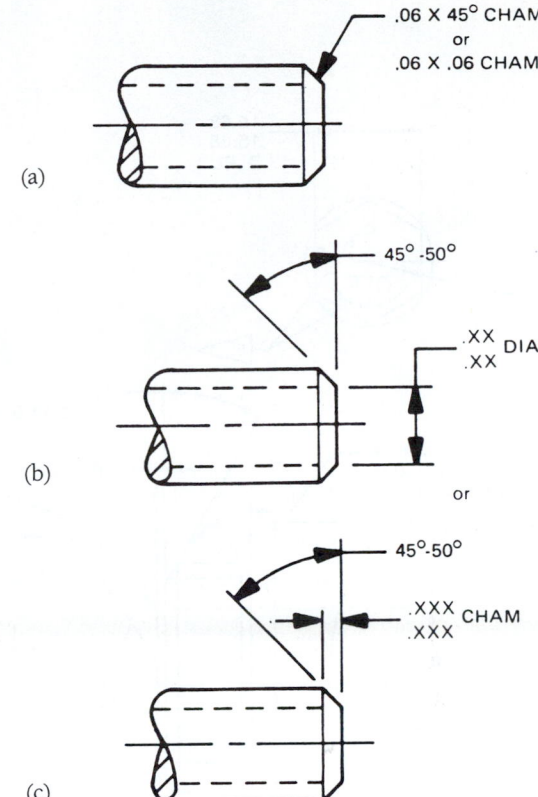

(a)

(b)

or

(c)

FIGURE 15.31 Dimensioning Chamfers at the End of External Threads

dimensioning as required (see Chapter 12). The thread length dimensioned on the drawing should be the gaging length or the length of threads having full form. That is, the incomplete threads are outside or beyond the length specified.

Should there be reason to control or limit the number of incomplete threads on parts having full body diameter shank, the overall thread length, including the vanish (runout or incomplete) threads, are represented and dimensioned on the drawing, in addition to the full thread length (Fig. 15.30). All representation of fully formed threads should indicate the *thread runout* (incomplete threads) as shown here. If essential to design requirements, the control of thread runout should be dimensioned. Overall thread length should be represented and dimensioned on the drawing and should include the thread runout.

15.11.1 Thread Chamfers

If required, thread **chamfers** or **countersinks** should be specified on the drawing. It is preferable to specify the chamfer by length and diameter to avoid confusion. Figure 15.31 shows three methods of dimensioning an external chamfer. The chamfer length should be .75 to 1.25 times the pitch, rounded off to a two- or three-place decimal. When a callout cannot properly or clearly designate an internal threaded hole, the depth, size, and countersink (chamfer) are dimensioned (Fig. 15.32). If the chamfer and minor diameter are very close to being the same, the minor diameter of a thread may be eliminated to improve clarity. On end views of countersunk threaded holes where countersunk diameters and the major diameters of threads are close to being the same, the major diameter may be eliminated for clarity.

15.11.2 Internal Thread Relief

If a design requires a **relief** or **undercut** at the bottom of a tapped hole, the minimum diameter of the relief should be

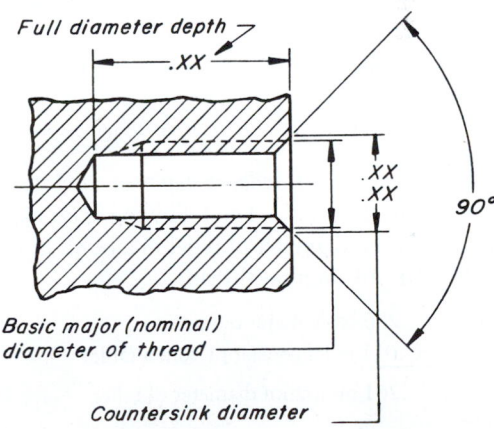

FIGURE 15.32 Dimensioning Countersink, Drill Depth, and Size on Internal Threaded Holes

greater than the maximum major diameter of the thread (Fig. 15.29). The relief should not be less than the diameter derived by adding the internal relief constant to the basic diameter of the internal thread. The internal relief constant is

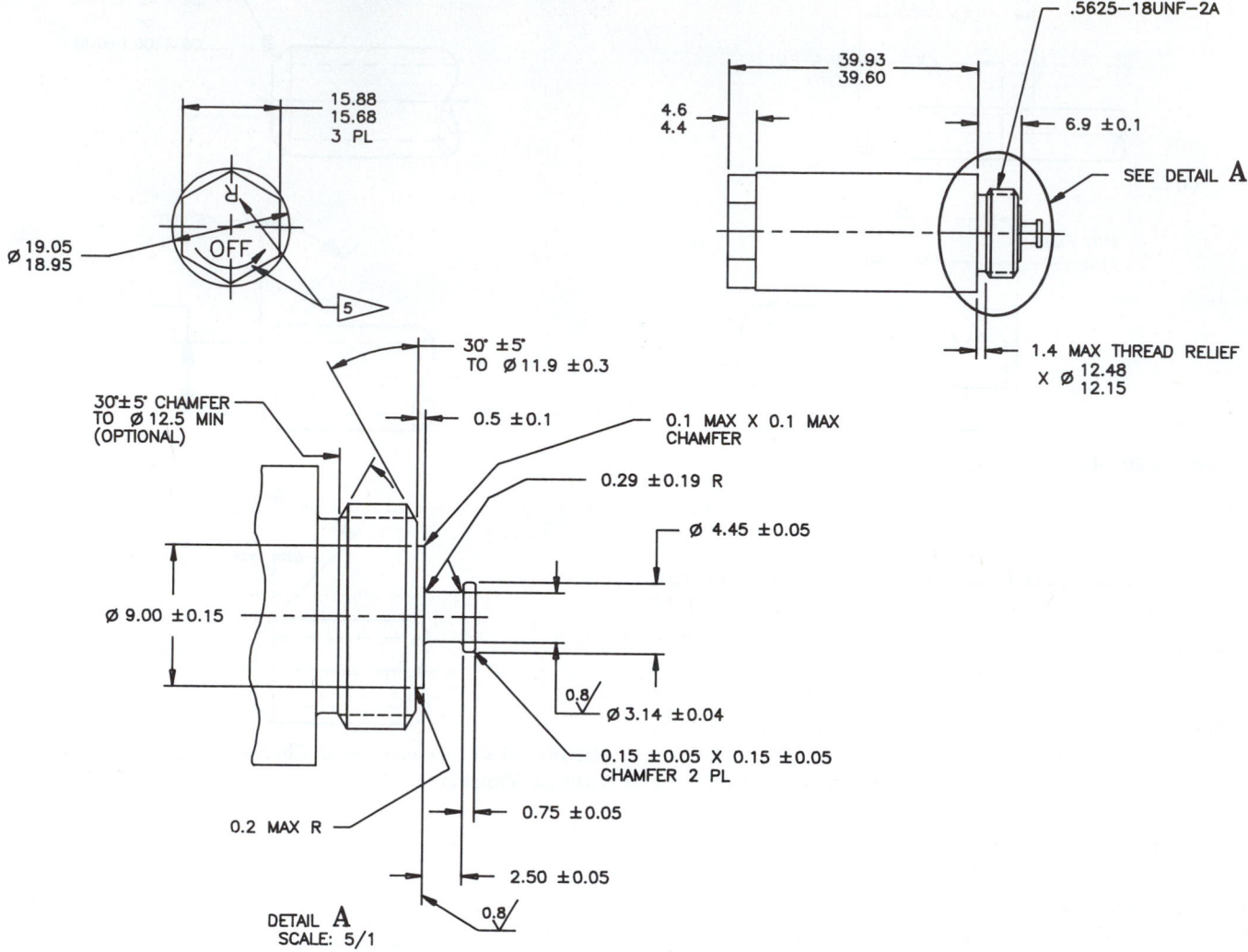

FIGURE 15.33   Plug Detail

found in the *Machinery's Handbook* table or an International Fasteners Institute (IFI) table. The following is an example of calculating minimum diameter of relief in a blind tapped hole for **.250-28 UNF-2B** internal thread:

$$
\begin{array}{r}
.250 \text{ basic major diameter} \\
\underline{+ .011 \text{ relief constant (from a table)}} \\
.261 \text{ minimum diameter of relief}
\end{array}
$$

15.11.3 External Thread Relief

The length of an external thread relief should be sufficient to allow for the chamfer on the threading tool. The maximum diameter of the relief should be less than the minor thread diameter. Figure 15.33 shows a metric part that has an external thread relief of 1.4 mm maximum width by a toleranced diameter of $\frac{12.48}{12.15}$. An optional 30° chamfer to a 12.5 diameter is provided next to the relief. Notice that the chamfer's small diameter is 12.5, whereas the thread relief diameter is a maximum of 12.48.

The following is an example of the calculations for the maximum diameter of the relief for a **.250-28 UNF-2A** external thread:

$$
\begin{array}{r}
.249 \text{ maximum major diameter} \\
\underline{- .053 \text{ relief constant(from a table—}} \\
\textit{Machinery's Handbook} \text{ or other source)} \\
.196 \text{ maximum diameter of relief}
\end{array}
$$

15.11.4 Threads on Drawings

Holes are located by their centers. Leaders have the arrowheads pointing toward the center in the circular views. When the circular view is not available, the arrow of the leader line should touch the axial centerline of the hole. Figure 15.34 shows an example of both metric and Unified National thread callouts (they are not meant to be equivalents in the example).

The full depth of the drilled hole for **blind tapped holes** should be specified on the drawing (Figs. 15.29 and 15.32).

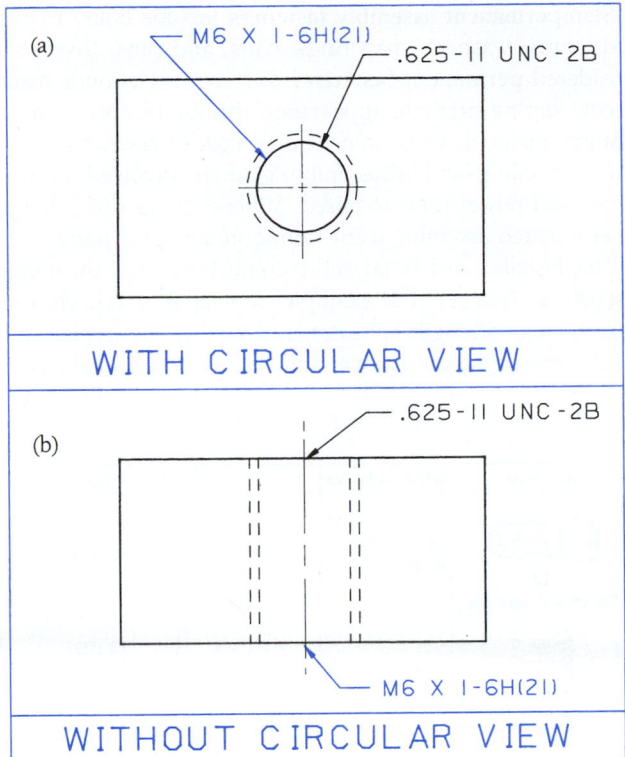

FIGURE 15.34 Calling Out Threads on Drawings

Blind holes do not go all the way through the part. If the wall at the drill point is the limiting consideration in addition to, or instead of, the full diameter depth, the drill point depth or the *wall thickness* may be dimensioned or stated in a note. In some cases, the depth may be specified as a minimum full-diameter depth and the note "**DO NOT BREAK THRU**" should be added. Hole size limits should be shown on the drawing.

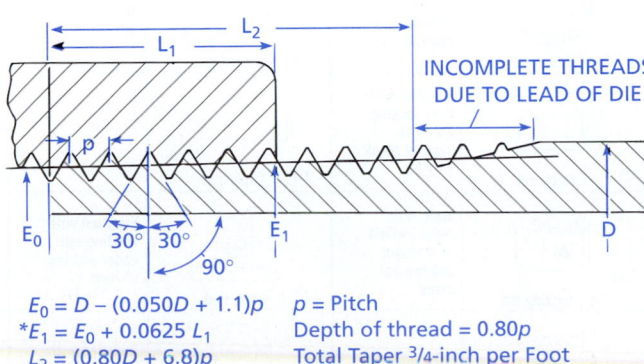

$$E_0 = D - (0.050D + 1.1)p \qquad p = \text{Pitch}$$
$$*E_1 = E_0 + 0.0625\, L_1 \qquad \text{Depth of thread} = 0.80p$$
$$L_2 = (0.80D + 6.8)p \qquad \text{Total Taper } 3/4\text{-inch per Foot}$$

FIGURE 15.35 American National Pipe Thread (NPT)

Nominal Pipe Size	D	TPI	P	EO	E1	L1	L2
.750	.840	14	.071	.758	.778	.320	.533
3.000	3.500	8	.125	3.340	3.388	.766	1.200

15.12 Pipe Threads

The American National Standard taper pipe thread is tapered $\frac{1}{16}$ in. per inch ($\frac{3}{4}$ in. per ft) to ensure a tight joint at the fitting (Fig. 15.35). The crest of the thread is flattened, and the root is filled so that the depth of the thread is equal to 80% of the pitch. The number of threads per inch for a given nominal diameter can be obtained from Appendix C (see also Chapter 22).

Pipe threads are designated in established trade sizes that signify a nominal diameter only. The designation of tapered threads include the nominal size, the number of threads per inch, the thread form, and thread series symbols as shown below:

6-8 NPT   **.125-27 NPT**

	Explanation	
6 =	nominal pipe diameter in inches	= .125
8 =	number of threads per inch	= 27
N =	American Standard National thread	= N
P =	pipe	= P
T =	taper	= T

.750-14 NPSL   **12-8 NPTR**

	Explanation	
.750 =	nominal pipe diameter in inches	= 12
14 =	number of threads per inch	= 8
N =	American National Standard thread	= N
P =	pipe	= P
S =	straight	
	taper	= T
L =	locknuts & locknut pipe threads	
	rail fittings	= R

15.12.1 Drawing Pipe Threads

Figure 15.36 shows a male (external) and female (internal) pipe thread drawn using simplified representation. The taper on a pipe thread is so slight that it does not show up on drawings unless it is exaggerated. In general, it is drawn to $\frac{1}{8}$ in. of taper per inch. The ANSI recommendation for representing pipe threads is the same as for all other threads. The simplified form is the most commonly used, the detailed form the least.

You May Complete Exercises 15.1 Through 15.4 at This Time

15.13 Fasteners

Basic industrial **fasteners** (Fig. 15.37) include square and hex bolts, cap screws, carriage bolts, machine screws, plow bolts, lag screws, studs, nuts, and rivets. Other fasteners have also been standardized over the years as to type, style, usage, properties, dimensions, and tolerances.

(a)

(b)

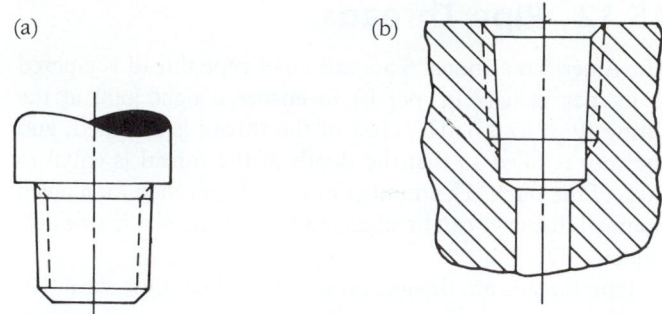

FIGURE 15.36 **Thread Representation** (a) External threads
(b) Internal threads

Semipermanent assembly fasteners include bolts, screws, studs, nuts, washers, snap rings, nails, and pins. Rivets are considered **permanent fasteners.** Fastener selection is made by considering strength, appearance, durability, corrosion resistance, materials to be joined, total cost of assembly parts, and assembling and disassembling labor involved or machines and power tools required. Whenever possible, design for automated assembly using common standard parts.

The *installed cost* is far more important than the initial cost of the fastener. For example, a rivet is much cheaper than the high-strength bolt, nut, and washer that replaced it, but the greater holding power and the lower installed cost of

Description	Military Reference	Description	Military Reference	Description	Military Reference
—1— Pan head	MS 35204 thru MS 35219 and MS 35221 thru MS 35236	—12— Socket head cap screw	MS 35455 thru MS 35461	—23— Flat washer	MS 15795
—2— 82° Flat head	MS 35188 thru MS 35203 and MS 35237 thru MS 35251 and MS 35262	—13— Set screw	AN 565	—24— Lockwasher-spring	MS 35337 MS 35338 MS 35339 MS 35340
—3— 100° Flat head	AN 507	—14— Self-locking	Plastic pellet can be applied to all types of screws	—25— Lockwasher-ext. tooth	MS 35335
—4— Fillister head	MS 35361 and MS 35366	—15— Hex nut	MS 35649 MS 35650 MS 35690	—26— Lockwasher-int. tooth	MS 35333 MS 35334
—5— Drilled fillister head	MS 35263 thru MS 35278	—16— Self-locking nut (non-metallic collar)	Can be supplied with fibre or plastic collar. All sizes and material	—27— Lockwasher-csk. tooth	MS 35336 MS 35790
—6— Slotted hex head	Made to order in 1020 Bright. 1035 Heat Treat and Alloy Steel	—17— Self-locking nut (deflected beam)	Can be supplied in Steel, Brass, Stainless - all sizes	—28— Spring pin	MS 9047 MS 9048 MS 171401
—7— Tapping screw-Type 1	AN 504 AN 506	—18— Clinch nut	Supplied to order for special applications	—29— Grooved pin	MS 35671 thru MS 35679
—8— Tapping screw-Type 23	AN 504 AN 506	—19— Clinch nut	Supplied with fibre locking collar in various shank lengths	—30— Taper pin	AN 385
—9— Tapping screw-Type 25	AN 530 AN 531	—20— Self-locking nut	Made with Nylon pellets in standard and special sizes	—31— Weld stud	Supplied with welding nibs under and top of head
—10— Drive screw	AN 535	—21— Semi-tubular	MS 20450	—32— Weld nut (self locating)	Supplied with standard thread sizes
—11— Sems	Supplied with all types of heads, also with Internal and External Lockwashers	—22— Shoulder	Made to specifications in steel and brass	—33— Weld nut	Supplied with standard thread sizes

FIGURE 15.37 **Industrial Fasteners**

the high-strength bolting system has for all practical purposes displaced riveting as standard fastening for structural joints.

When designating fasteners on a drawing, provide the following:

- **product name**
- **nominal** or **actual size** in fractions, decimal equivalent, or metric units
- **thread specification**, if appropriate
- **length** in fractions, decimal equivalent, or metric units
- **material** and **protective coating**, if applicable
- **finish**, where required

15.13.1 Representing Fasteners

In general, a template is used for construction of standard fasteners. When a CAD system is used, a standard library of parts is normally available for rapid and accurate insertion of standard fasteners on a 3D model or a 2D part (Fig. 15.38). Many standard parts are now available with 2D and 3D parts libraries for use with CAD systems. A library of standard parts eliminates the need to redraw each part. The part can be recalled and inserted as required anywhere on the design, in as many places as required. Library parts are a CAD system's version of a manual drafter's template.

Figure 15.39 shows two typical fasteners. The *head styles* shown here are the **hex** and **socket** varieties. The *bearing surface* is that portion of the fastener that is in contact with the part that is being fastened (or a washer when one is used). The *point* is at the opposite end from the head. The point is normally chamfered. The *threaded* part of the *body* extends from the point toward the bearing surface. Some fasteners are completely threaded (the whole body) and some are partially threaded.

15.13.2 Studs

Studs are fasteners with no head but with threads at both ends of the shank. Studs come in *continuous threaded* types and *double-ended* varieties. In most applications, the stud is screwed into a work piece on one end and a nut is used on the

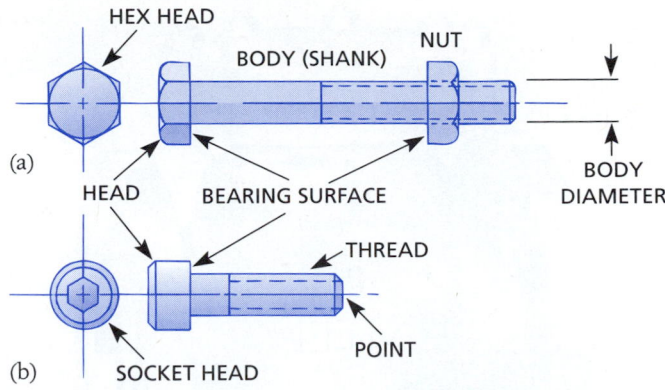

FIGURE 15.39 Bolt and Screw Terminology
(a) Bolt (b) Screw

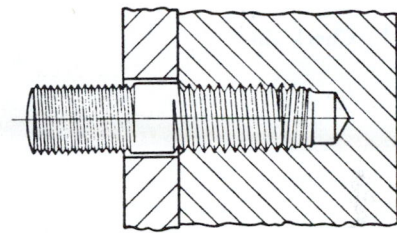

FIGURE 15.40 Threaded Stud in Blind Hole

other end (Fig. 15.40). In other applications, the stud has a nut on both ends and is used to secure two pieces. In Figure 15.41 the cover plate for the check valve has eight studs and sixteen nuts.

Continuous thread studs are threaded from end to end. Continuous threaded studs are often used for flange bolting with two nuts applied. Continuous threaded studs come in two types: Type 1 and Type 2. Type 1 is for general purposes and Type 2 is for pressure piping. If a stud is to be inserted into a tapped hole (Fig. 15.40), it is recommended that it be held in place by jamming it against the bottom of the hole. A Class 5 fit is recommended for such service. The thread engagement should be $1\frac{1}{4}$ times the diameter of the stud for steel, $1\frac{1}{2}$ times for cast iron, and $2\frac{1}{2}$ times for softer materials.

Double-ended studs come in four types: Type 1 is unfinished, Type 2 is finished and has an undersize body, Type 3 is full bodied and finished, and Type 4 is finished and is close-body, milled to specifications.

A typical stud application is shown in Figure 15.42 of the swivel-heel clamp assembly. Here, two studs are used in the design of this tooling component. Studs are designated on drawings as shown below

For Type 1 continuous:

CONTINUOUS THREAD STUD, $\frac{1}{2}$-13 × 8, ASTM A307, ZINC PLATED

For Type 2 continuous:

ANSI/ASME B16.5 STUD BOLT, .875-9 × 12, ASTM A 354, GRADE BD

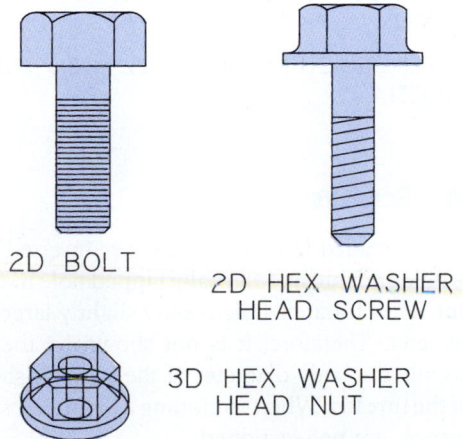

2D BOLT

2D HEX WASHER HEAD SCREW

3D HEX WASHER HEAD NUT

FIGURE 15.38 2D and 3D CAD Library Parts

FIGURE 15.41 Check Valve

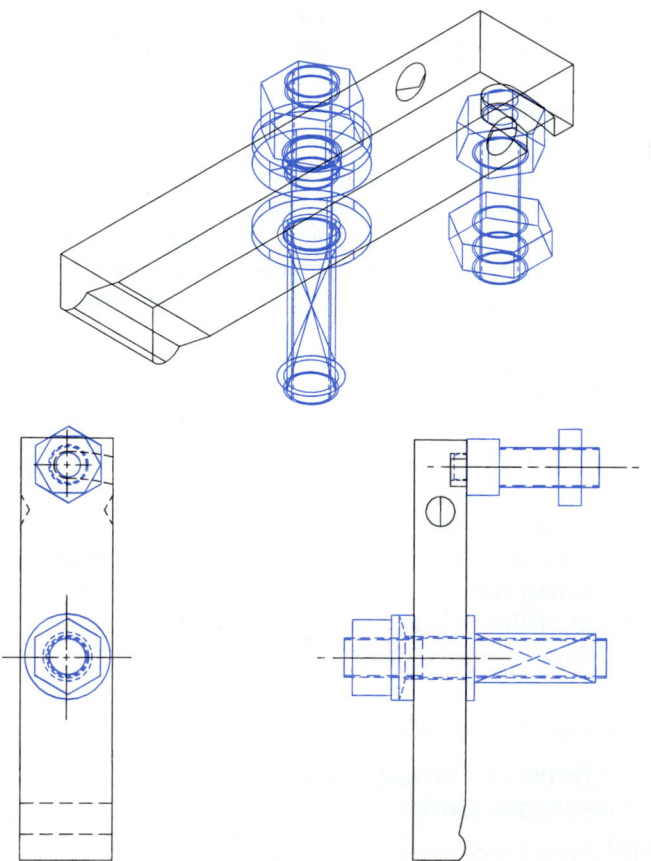

FIGURE 15.42 Swing Clamp for Tooling

For metric continuous:

> CONTINUOUS THREAD STUD, M24 × 3 × 200, ASTM F568 CLASS 8.8, ZINC PHOSPHATE AND OIL

For double-ended:

> TYPE 4 DOUBLE END STUD $\frac{3}{4}$-10 × 8.50, ASTM A499, CADMIUM PLATED

> TYPE 2 DOUBLE END STUD, M10 × 1.5 × 90, ASTM F568 CLASS 9.8, ZINC PLATED

15.13.3 Bolts

A **bolt** is a device with a head on one end of a shank or body and a thread opposite. Designed for insertion through holes in assembly parts, it is mated with a tapped nut. The diameter of all bolts is measured as the outside or major diameter of the thread. The length of a bolt is measured from under the head to the end of the bolt. The length of a bolt with a countersunk (flathead) head is the overall length. The point (tip) of a bolt is always included in the measured length.

Figure 15.43 illustrates the common types of bolts available. **Hexagon bolts** (Fig. 15.44) can be used in a threaded hole or with a nut. A typical application of a hexagon bolt is shown in Figure 15.45. Hexagon bolts are available with either plain or slotted heads, and also come in metric sizes.

Square-head (Fig. 15.46) and **round-head** (Fig. 15.47) bolts are usually made of low-carbon steel and are referred to as "black bolts." They are available in unfinished style and with coarse threads. Square-head bolts are adequate for heavy machinery, conveyors, and fixtures. Round-head bolts have variously shaped necks under the head that are embedded in wood or metal and act as a locking device. **Countersunk bolts** are shown in Figure 15.48. Bolts are designated on drawings as shown below:

> $\frac{1}{2}$-13 × 3$\frac{1}{2}$ HEX CAP SCREW, SAE GRADE 8 STEEL

> .625-11 × 2 ROUND HEAD SQUARE NECK BOLT, STEEL

For metric:

> HEX BOLT, M20 × 2.5 × 160, CLASS 4.6, ZINC PLATED

> HEAVY HEX STRUCTURAL BOLT, M22 × 2.5 × 160, ASTM A325M

15.13.4 Screws

A **screw** is a threaded fastener. Screws are inserted through a clearance hole and into an internally tapped hole in the mating part or nut. The clearance hole is only slightly larger than the screw diameter. Therefore, it is not shown on the assembly drawing. Only the body diameter of the screw is shown, as is the OD of the threads. When sectioning assemblies, screws and other fasteners are not sectioned.

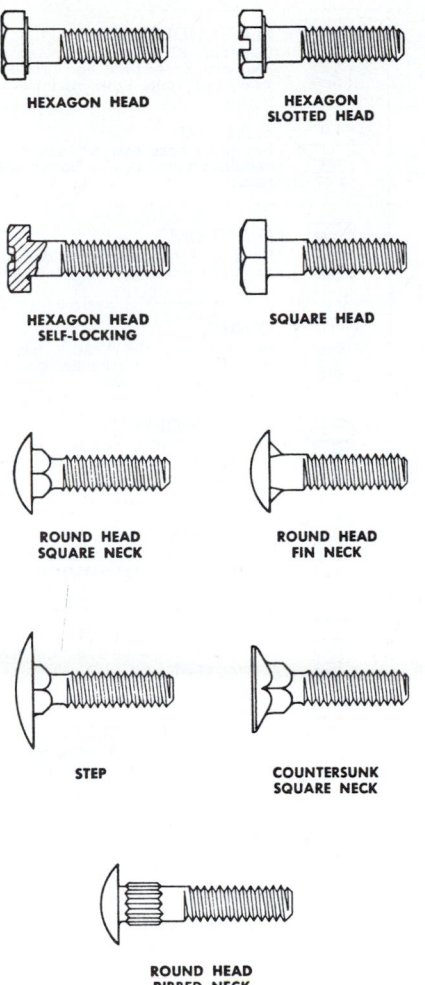

FIGURE 15.43   Bolt Head Types

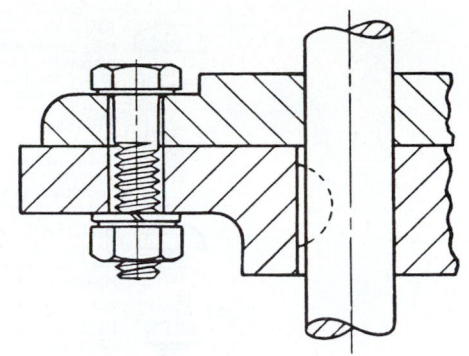

FIGURE 15.45   Hex Bolt Used on Assembly

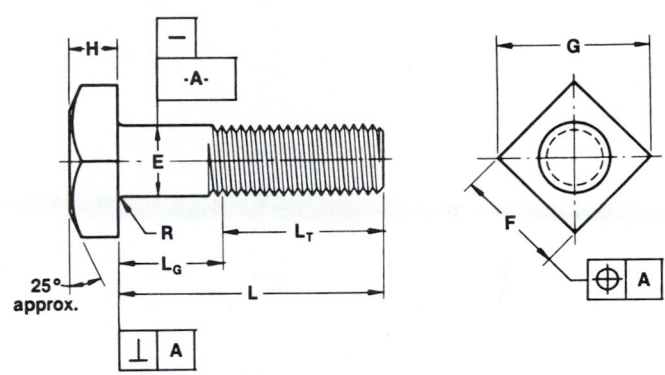

FIGURE 15.46   Square-Head Bolt

Nominal Size	E	F	G	LT	L
.875	.875	1.312	1.856	2.00	6.00 or less
1.500	1.50	2.250	3.182	3.25	6.00 or less

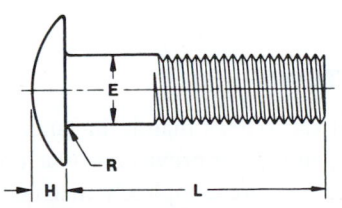

FIGURE 15.47   Round-Head Bolt

Nominal Size	A	E	H
.312	.719	.312	.176
.625	1.344	.625	.344

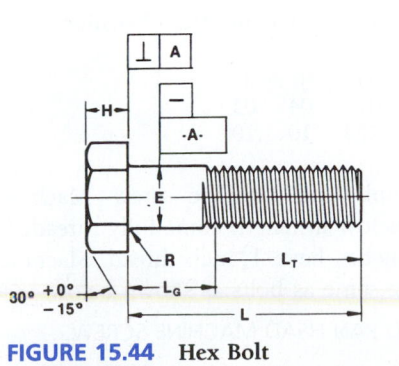
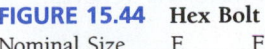

FIGURE 15.44   Hex Bolt

Nominal Size	E	F	G	LT	L
.627	.627	.938	1.08	1.50	6.00 or less
1.000	1.000	1.500	1.73	2.25	6.00 or less

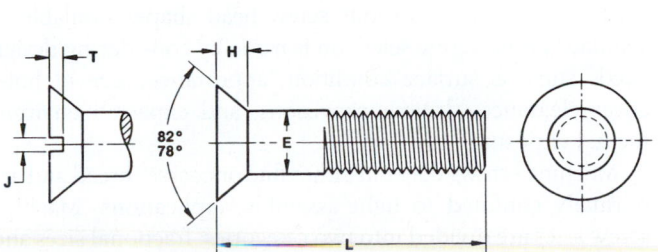

FIGURE 15.48   Countersunk Bolts

Nominal Size	Head Dia	E	H	J	T
.750	1.16	.750	.40	.14	.17
1.25	2.33	1.250	.67	.22	.29

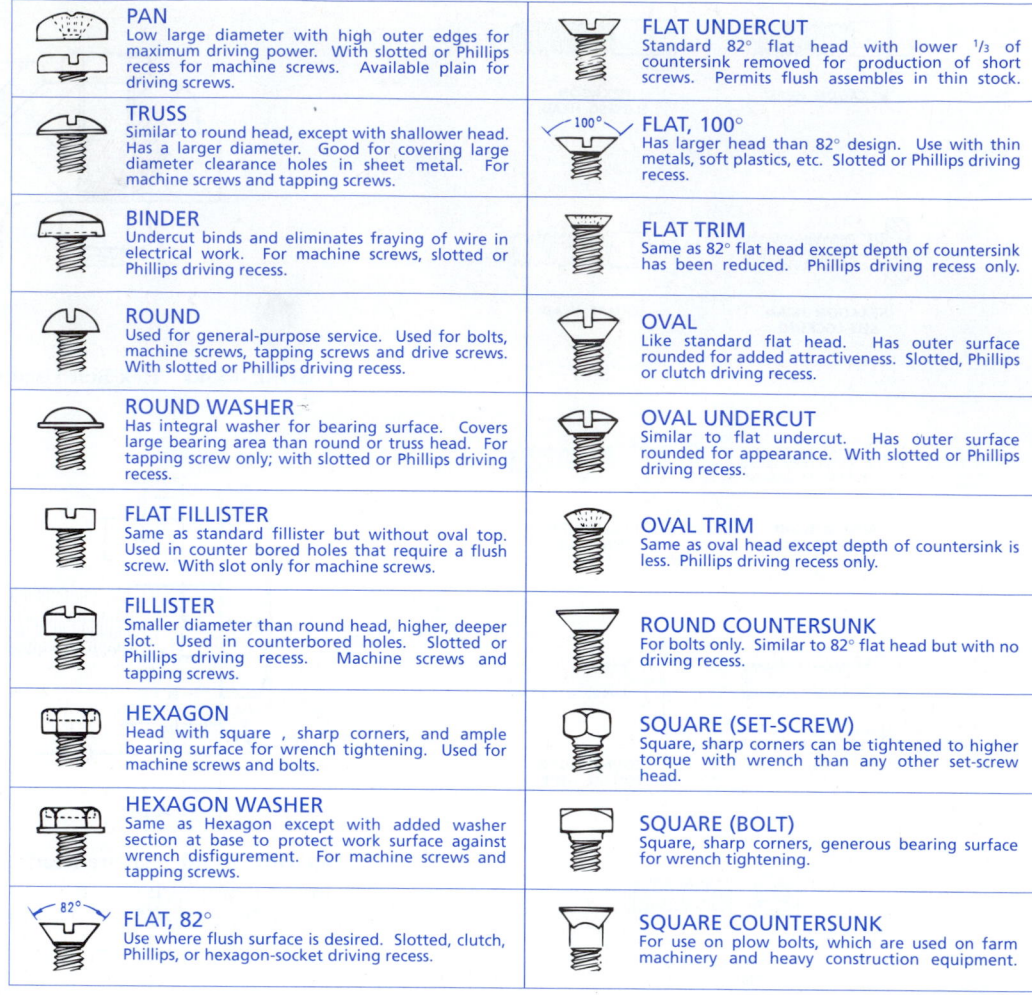

FIGURE 15.49 Machine Screw Head Styles

15.13.5 Machine Screws

Machine screws differ from cap screws mainly in range of basic diameters, head shapes, and driver provisions. Machine screws are so named because they are completely machined from bar stock. They are usually restricted to light assemblies such as instrument panel mountings, moldings, and clip fasteners. The size selection is determined by the tightness required of the parts to be fastened. Machine screws can be assembled into a nut or a threaded hole in a functional part. Figure 15.49 shows various screw head shapes available as standard parts. Screw selection is made by considering design needs such as surface condition, appearance, size of hole, cover clearance, driving provisions, and expected environmental exposure.

Machine screws come in either fine or coarse thread and are normally confined to light assembly applications. Machine screw sizes are divided into two categories: fractional sizes and numbered sizes. Numbered sizes are confined to those below $\frac{1}{4}$ in. diameter. Fractional sizes range between $\frac{1}{4}$ and $\frac{3}{4}$ inch. Number 0 has a diameter of .06 inches; .013 inches is added to each numbered size above number 0. Figure 15.50 shows

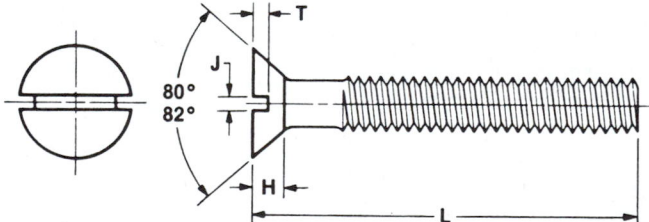

FIGURE 15.50 Slotted Flat Countersunk-Head Machine Screw

Nominal Size	Head Dia	H	J	T
#5 (.125)	.25	.075	.04	.03
.500	.875	.223	.10	.10

a slotted flat countersunk-head machine screw. Machine screws two inches and below in length come fully threaded. All lengths above two inches have $1\frac{3}{4}$ inch thread. Machine screws are called out the same as bolts as shown below:

.25-20 × 1.5 SLOTTED PAN HEAD MACHINE SCREW, STEEL, ZINC PLATED

6-32 × 1.50 SLOTTED FLAT COUNTERSUNK HEAD MACHINE SCREW

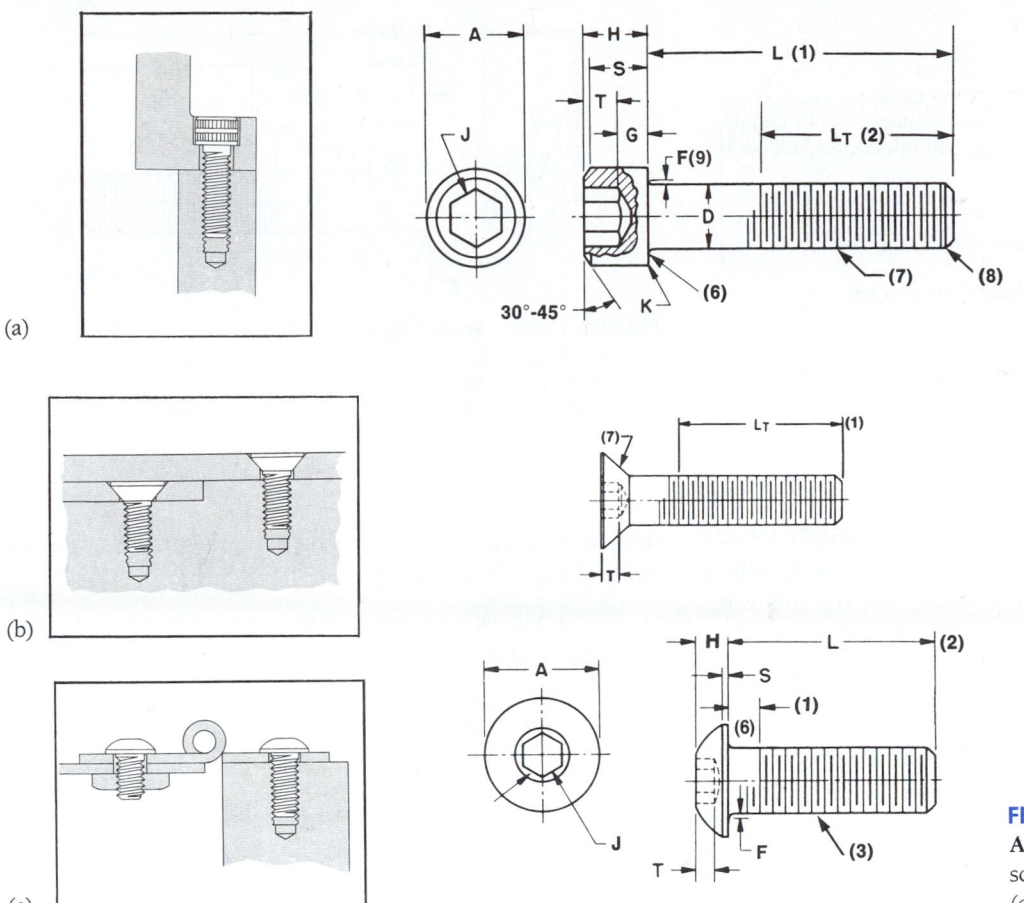

FIGURE 15.51 Cap Screw **Applications** (a) Socket head cap screw, (b) Flat head cap screw, (c) Round head cap screw

For metric:

M8 × 1.25 × 30 SLOTTED PAN HEAD MACHINE SCREW, CLASS 4.8 STEEL, ZINC PLATED

M4 × 0.7 × 40 RECESSED PAN HEAD MACHINE SCREW, BRASS

15.13.6 Cap Screws

Cap screws are similar to machine screws except that there are fewer head styles available. Cap screws have their heads cold-formed from smaller diameter stock. Cap screws are for applications that require closer tolerances and greater holding power per diameter. Figure 15.51 shows three examples of cap screws. Cap screws are finished and are more expensive than similar size bolts and machine screws. Cap screws come in coarse, fine, or special threads. Cap screws one inch in diameter and below have a Class 3A thread; those above one inch in diameter have a Class 2A thread.

Cap screws are available in steel, brass, bronze, aluminum, and titanium. Steel hex head cap screws (Fig. 15.52) are available in diameters from $\frac{1}{4}$ to 3 inches and have their strength indicated on their hex head by a geometric symbol. Slotted head cap screws come in round (Fig. 15.53), fillister (Fig. 15.54), or flat heads.

Socket head cap screws (Fig. 15.55) are used throughout industry for precision high-strength fastening and where the

head of the screw must be flush or below the part's surface. When this is the case, a clearance hole for the head is counterbored into the part (Fig. 15.51). Socket head cap screws are also made with socket button heads and socket flat heads.

The metric format for designating fasteners can be abbreviated. For example, **SOCKET HEAD SHOULDER SCREW** becomes **SHSS**. American standard fasteners can also have

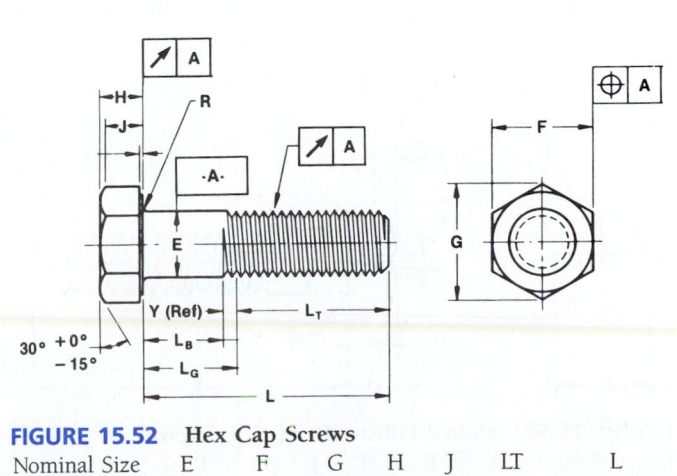

FIGURE 15.52 Hex Cap Screws

Nominal Size	E	F	G	H	J	LT	L
.500	.500	.750	.86	.32	.21	1.25	6.00 or less
.75	.750	1.125	1.29	.48	.32	1.75	6.00 or less

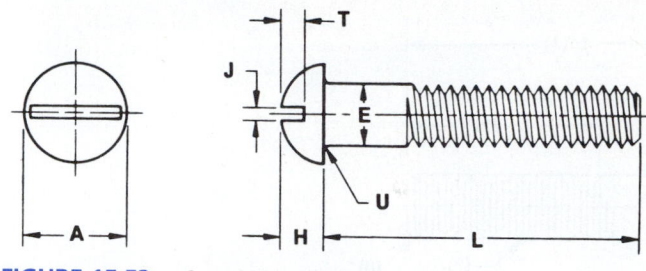

FIGURE 15.53 Slotted Round-Head Cap Screws

Nominal Size	A	E	H	J	T
.250	.437	.250	.19	.07	.11
.500	.812	.500	.35	.10	.21

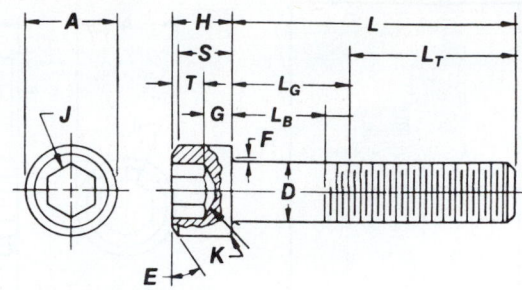

FIGURE 15.55 Socket Head Cap Screws

Nominal Size	A	D	H	J	LT
.375	.56	.375	.372	.312	1.25
1.000	1.50	1.000	1.000	.750	2.50

abbreviated designations. For example, **HEXAGON HEAD CAP SCREW** can be abbreviated **HEX HD CAP SCR**. When designating cap screws on your drawing, use the following format:

.138-32 × 1.00 HEXAGON SOCKET HEAD CAP SCREW, ALLOY STEEL, CADMIUM PLATED

$\frac{1}{4}$-28 × 1.75 HEXAGON SOCKET FLAT COUNTERSUNK HEAD CAP SCREW, ALLOY STEEL

For metric:

B18.3.1M-M6 × 1 × 20 HEXAGON SOCKET HEAD CAP SCREW

IFI-535 - 6 × 1 × 8 SOCKET COUNTERSUNK HEAD CAP SCREW, ZINC PLATED

Socket head shoulder screws are used for location and fastening by combining the features of dowels and screws, and for applications requiring a pivot. This type of screw has an enlarged, toleranced, unthreaded portion of the screw body called a *shoulder* (Fig. 15.56). The length of a shoulder screw is measured from under its head to the end of its shoulder. The threaded portion is not included in the length specification. When designating a shoulder screw on a drawing, give the nominal size or basic shoulder diameter in fractions or

decimal equivalent, shoulder length, product name, material, and finish as shown below:

$\frac{1}{4}$ × 1.250 HEX SOCKET HEAD SHOULDER SCREW, ALLOY STEEL

1.25 × 4.25 HEX SOCKET HEAD SHOULDER SCREW, ALLOY STEEL, PHOSPHATE COATED

For metric:

B18.3.3M-8 × 25 SOCKET HEAD SHOULDER SCREW

B18.3.3M-10 × 50 SHSS ZINC PLATED

15.13.7 Set Screws

Set screws come in three types: slotted, socket, and square head. In a set screw, there are three types of holding power: torsional (resistance to rotation), axial (resistance to lateral movement), and vibrational. Set screws are used for a variety of applications, such as securing components to shafts (Fig. 15.57).

Set screws are available in number sizes from 0 to 12 and in fractional sizes from $\frac{1}{4}$ to 2 inch. Metric set screws come in nominal diameters of 1.6, 2, 2.5, 3, 4, 5, 6, 8, 10, 12, 16, 20, and 24 millimeters.

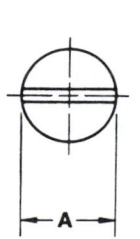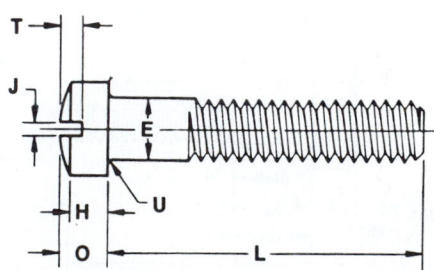

FIGURE 15.54 Slotted Fillister Head Cap Screws

Nominal Size	A	E	H	J	O	T
.312	.437	.312	.20	.08	.25	.11
.562	.812	.562	.37	.11	.46	.21

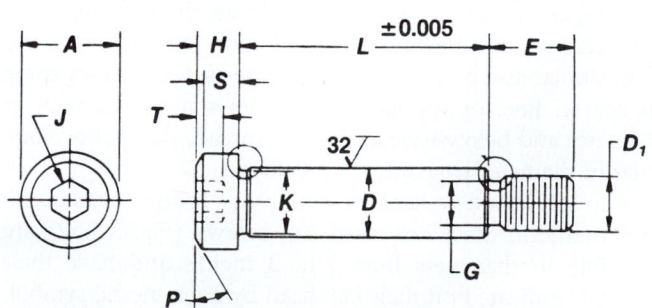

FIGURE 15.56 Hexagon Socket Head Cap Shoulder Screw

Nominal Size	A	D	D1	E	G	H	J	K
.500	.75	.500	.375	.625	.30	.31	.25	.47
1.000	1.31	.998	.750	1.000	.63	.625	.50	.97

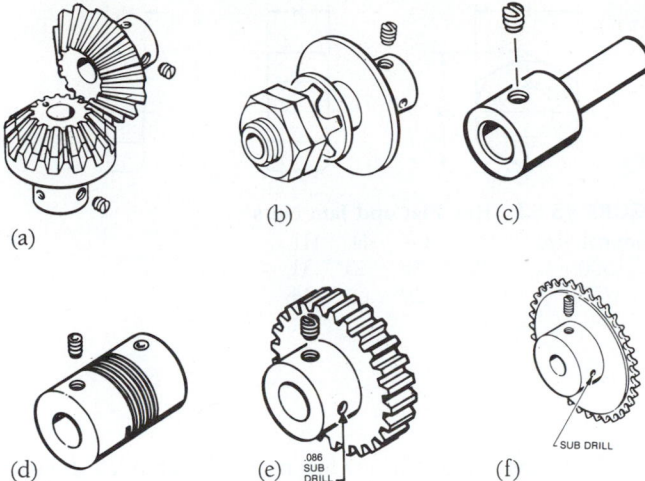

(a)   (b)   (c)

(d)   (e)   (f)

FIGURE 15.57   Set Screws in Use

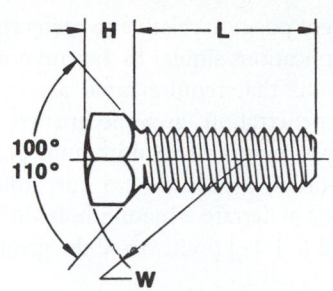

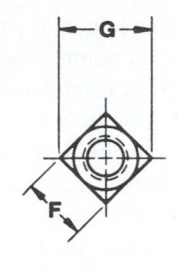

FIGURE 15.58   Square-Head Set Screws

Nominal Size	F	G	H	W
.250	.250	.35	.19	.62
.500	.500	.70	.38	1.25

The size of a set screw is an important factor in holding power. A rough rule of thumb is that the set screw diameter should be 25% (.25) of the shaft diameter. When more than one set screw is used, it should be placed near and in line with the first one. If the second set screw must be in the same location as the first, it should be staggered at an angle of 60°.

Square-head set screws protrude above the surface of the part (Fig. 15.58). Headless types disappear below the work surface when tightened. **Socket-head set screws** have spline or hex sockets (Fig. 15.59). **Slotted set screws** are tightened with screw drivers (Fig. 15.60). Figure 15.60 also shows examples of six standard point forms available for both socket and slotted set screws. The cone point is used where two parts

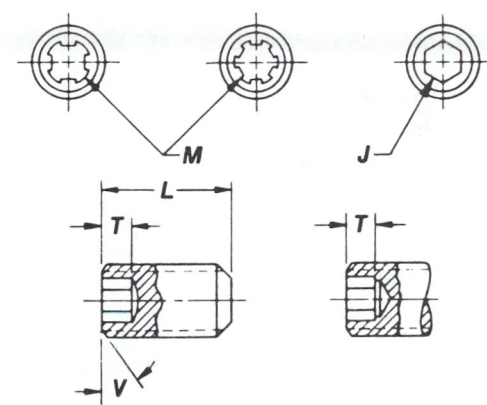

FIGURE 15.59   Socket-Head Set Screws

Nominal Size	J	M	T
.250	.125	.14	.12
.375	.188	.21	.18

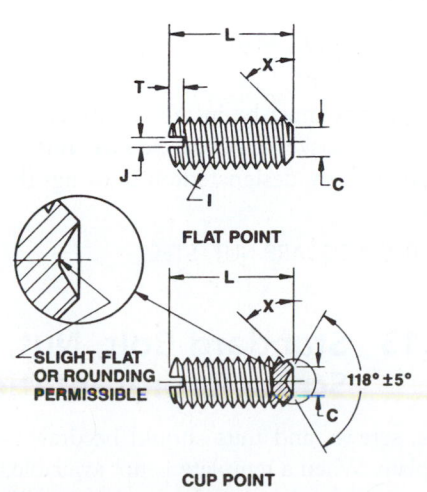

FLAT POINT

SLIGHT FLAT OR ROUNDING PERMISSIBLE

118° ±5°

CUP POINT

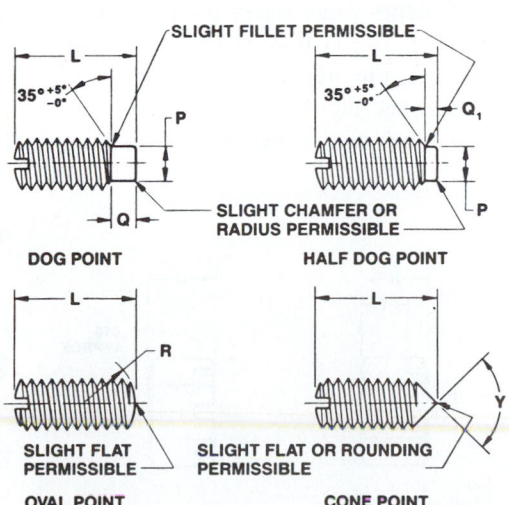

SLIGHT FILLET PERMISSIBLE

35° +5° −0°

SLIGHT CHAMFER OR RADIUS PERMISSIBLE

DOG POINT

35° +5° −0°

HALF DOG POINT

SLIGHT FLAT PERMISSIBLE

OVAL POINT

SLIGHT FLAT OR ROUNDING PERMISSIBLE

CONE POINT

FIGURE 15.60   Slotted Headless Set Screws

Nominal Size	J	P	Q	Q1	T
.250	.04	.15	.13	.06	.06
.375	.06	.25	.19	.09	.09

must be joined in a permanent position relative to each other. The oval point is used in applications similar to the cup point, which is used for applications that require rapid assembly. Cone points, with deepest penetration, give the greatest increase in holding power; oval points, with minimum penetration, the least. The flat point is used where fine adjustments are needed. Since they penetrate a mating hole drilled in the shaft, the half dog and full dog points have the greatest holding power.

A set screw is designated on a drawing by giving the nominal size, threads per inch, length, product name, point style, material, and protective coating (if needed) as shown below:

$\frac{1}{4}$-20 × .375 HEXAGON SOCKET SET SCREW, CUP POINT, ALLOY STEEL

.250-20 × .50 SLOTTED HEADLESS SET SCREW, HALF DOG POINT, STEEL

For metric:

B18.3.6M-10 × 1.5 CUP POINT SOCKET SET SCREW, ZINC PLATED

15.14 Nuts

Many types of nuts are available to satisfy specific design and functional requirements. Lock nuts, swivel nuts, hex nuts, flange nuts, coupling nuts, square nuts, slotted nuts, and jam nuts are just a few of the types used in industry. Most nuts are either hex head or square-head varieties. *Nuts are identified by the size of bolt they fit, not by their outside dimensions.*

Flange nuts incorporate a washer into the nut that increases the bearing area of the nut. **Hexagon nuts** are available as unfinished, plain, slotted, regular, heavy, and jam types. Semifinished hex nuts are available in plain, slotted, jam, thick plain, thick slotted, and castle varieties. Semifinished nuts have one side machined on the bearing side of the nut. Heavy nuts are .125 inches wider across the flats on the hexagon. **Slotted nuts** (Fig. 15.61) have slots for use with cotter pins, which prevent the nut from coming off or untightening. Regular hex nuts (Fig. 15.62) are thinner than their size designations. A $\frac{1}{2}$ inch regular hex nut is actually $\frac{7}{16}$

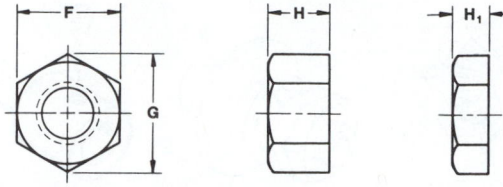

FIGURE 15.62 Hex Flat and Jam Nuts

Nominal Size	F	G	H	H1
.500	.75	.86	.43	.31
.750	1.12	1.29	.66	.44

inch thick, and a $\frac{1}{2}$ inch heavy hex nut is $\frac{31}{64}$ inch thick. Metric nuts are also thinner than their designated size. An M6 × 1 metric hex nut, Style 2, is 5.70 mm thick. There are two types of metric nuts, Style 1 and Style 2. The nominal size, threads per inch, product name, material, and protective finish are given to designate a hex nut on a drawing, as shown below:

$\frac{1}{2}$-13 HEX NUT, STEEL, ZINC PLATED

.750-20 HEX NUT, SAE J995 GRADE 5, CORROSION RESISTANT STEEL

For metric:

HEX NUT, STYLE 2, M20 × 2.5, ASTM A563 CLASS 9, ZINC PLATED

HEAVY HEX NUT, M30 × 3.5, ASTM A563M CLASS 10S, HOT DIP GALVANIZED

Jam nuts are thin hex nuts and are used where height is restricted, or as a means of locking the working nut, if assembled as in Figure 15.63. Jam nuts are designated the same as hex nuts as shown below:

.500-16 HEX JAM NUT, STEEL, ZINC PLATED

For metric:

HEX JAM NUT, M10 × 1.5, ASTM A563M CLASS 04, ZINC PLATED

Because they must be installed with an open-ended wrench and not a socket wrench, **square nuts** are less common. Square nuts are designated on drawings the same way as hex nuts:

1.000-8 SQUARE NUT, STEEL

15.15 Standard Bolt, Nut, and Screw Representation

Bolts, screws, and nuts should be drawn with the aid of a template. When a template is not available, use the fastener's dimensions for drawing the part. A simplified method is also acceptable (Fig. 15.64). The dimensions of Figure 15.64 are acceptable when constructing bolts and screws. The most

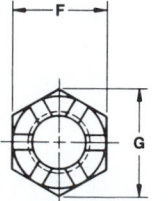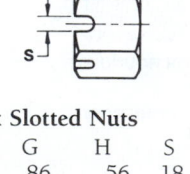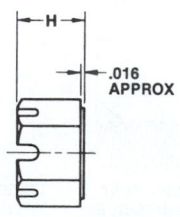

FIGURE 15.61 Hex Slotted Nuts

Nominal Size	F	G	H	S
.500	.75	.86	.56	.18
1.000	1.50	1.72	1.018	.30

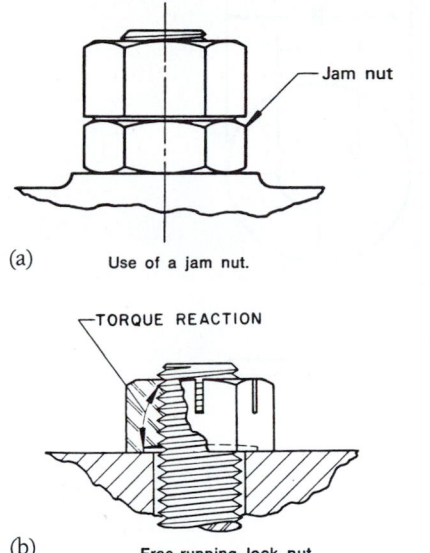

(a)   Use of a jam nut.

(b)   Free-running lock nut.

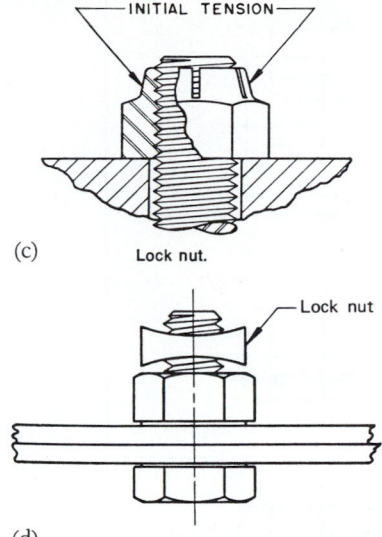

(c)   Lock nut.

(d)   Concave lock nut.

FIGURE 15.63   **Lock and Jam Nut Applications**

important dimensions on fasteners are diameter and length, which must be accurately constructed because they affect clearances.

Figure 15.64 shows some approximate dimensions that can be used to draw fasteners. Although they do not correspond exactly to the fastener's actual dimensions, it is standard practice to simplify the constructions. In this figure, *the basic sizes of each part of a fastener are given, relative to the diameter dimension.* Each dimension is a fraction of the diameter. Chamfered endpoints are normally drawn at 45°.

When drawing the end view of a slotted fastener, the slots are angled at 45°, not at 90 or 180°. The head of hex head

bolts and nuts is drawn so that three surfaces are visible from an elevation view. The depth of the hex on a hex socket head cap screw is not drawn. Figure 15.65 shows three steps in the construction of a hex head bolt and nut. Figure 15.66 shows the dimensions used to construct a square head bolt.

15.16   Washers

Washers are used in conjunction with threaded fasteners. The three basic types of washers are *plain, spring lock,* and *tooth lock.* Plain washers spread the bearing area of the

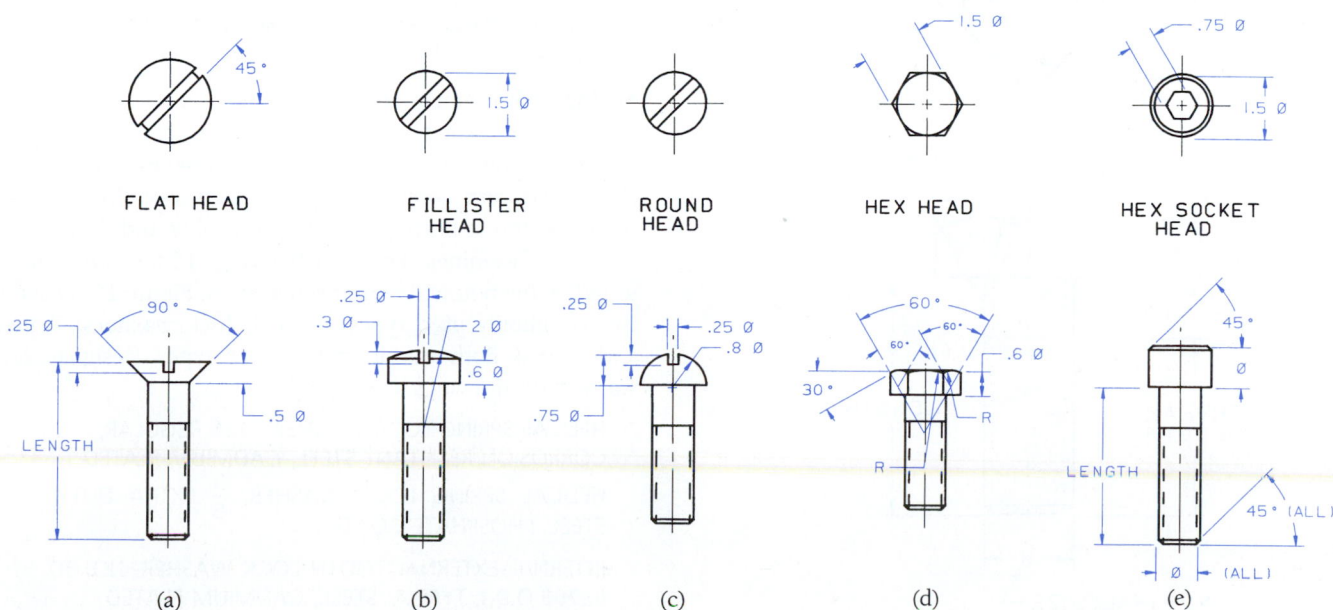

FLAT HEAD   FILLISTER HEAD   ROUND HEAD   HEX HEAD   HEX SOCKET HEAD

(a)   (b)   (c)   (d)   (e)

FIGURE 15.64   **Approximate Sizes for Drawing Screws**

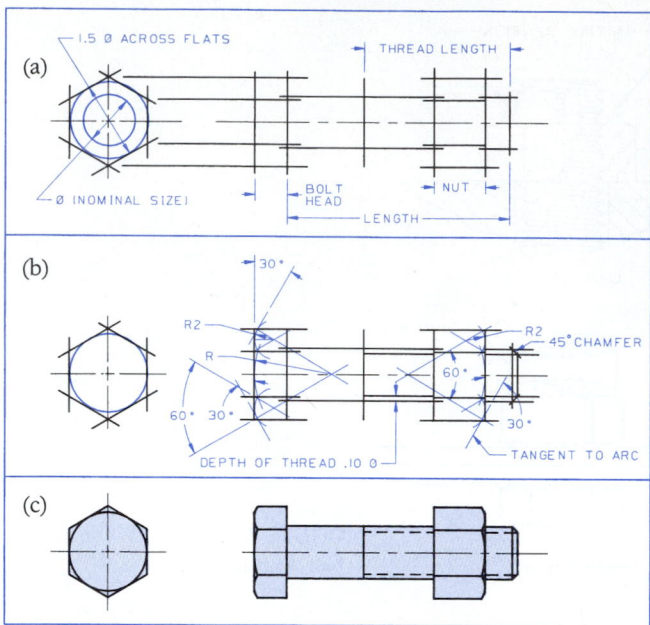

FIGURE 15.65 Drawing a Hex Bolts and Nut Without a Template

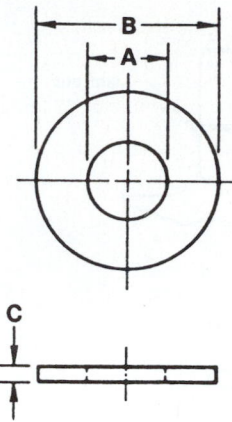

FIGURE 15.67 Plain Washers

Nominal Size	A	B	C
.500	.531	1.06	.09
1.000	1.062	2.50	.16

fastener head or nut and are normally used with soft metals. Spring washers maintain tension on the nut or bolt head, and tooth lock washers provide teeth that dig into the fastener and the part to prevent the fastener from loosening. **Plain washers** are flat and ring shaped (Fig. 15.67). Washers are designated on drawings by providing the product name and type, size (ID), material, and finish, as shown below:

TYPE A PLAIN WASHER, 1 $\frac{1}{2}$, STEEL, CADMIUM PLATED

TYPE B PLAIN WASHER, NO. 12, STEEL

For metric:

PLAIN WASHER, 6MM, NARROW, SOFT, STEEL, ZINC PLATED

Spring lock washers are split on one side and are helical in shape. They have the dual function of acting as a spring take-up to compensate for developed looseness and a loss of tension between component parts of an assembly and as a hardened thrust bearing to aid in assembly and disassembly of bolted fastenings. Lock washer (Fig. 15.68) sizes are selected by the nominal bolt or screw sizes. Figure 15.69 shows two commonly used types of **tooth lock washers:** Type A and Type B. Both are internal-external types. Designate lock washers on drawings as shown below:

HELICAL SPRING LOCK WASHER, .125 REGULAR, CORROSION RESISTANT STEEL, CADMIUM PLATED

HELICAL SPRING LOCK WASHER, $\frac{3}{8}$ EXTRA DUTY, STEEL, PHOSPHATE COATED

INTERNAL-EXTERNAL TOOTH LOCK WASHER, NO. 10 (0.760 O.D.), TYPE A, STEEL, CADMIUM PLATED

EXTERNAL TOOTH LOCK WASHER, .625, TYPE B, STEEL, PHOSPHATE COATED

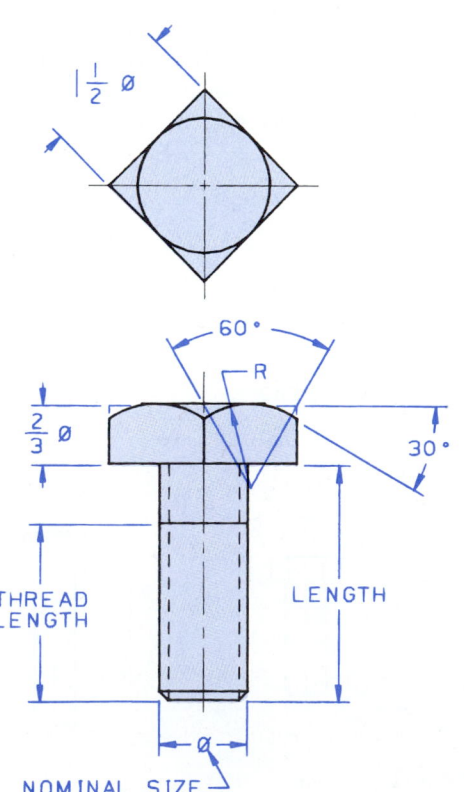

FIGURE 15.66 Drawing a Square Head Bolt Without a Template

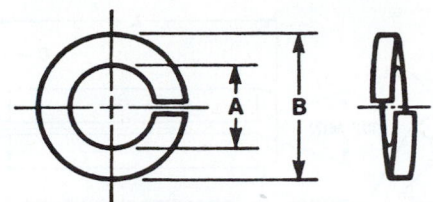

FIGURE 15.68 Spring Lock Washers

Nominal Size	A	B	Width
.500	.518	.87	.125
.625	.65	1.07	.156

For metric:

4MM INTERNAL TOOTH, TYPE A

You May Complete Exercises 15.5 Through 15.8 at This Time

15.17 Machine Pins

Standard machine pins are used throughout industry where there is a need for the assembly and alignment of mating parts, and for attaching gears, cams, collars, pulleys, sprockets, and other mechanical parts to shafts. Three types of pins are used to secure a gear to a shaft in Figure 15.70; (a) a straight pin, (b) a taper pin, and (c) a spring pin. Most of the

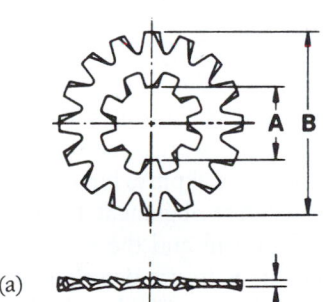

(a)

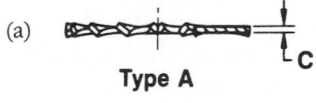

Type A

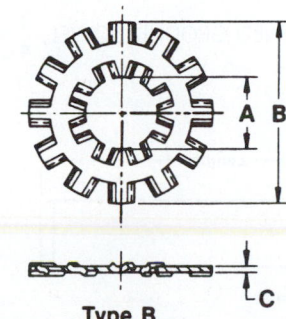

(b)

Type B

FIGURE 15.69 Tooth Lock Washers

Nominal Size	A	B	C
#10 (.190)	.20	.76	.04
.500	.53	1.41	.06

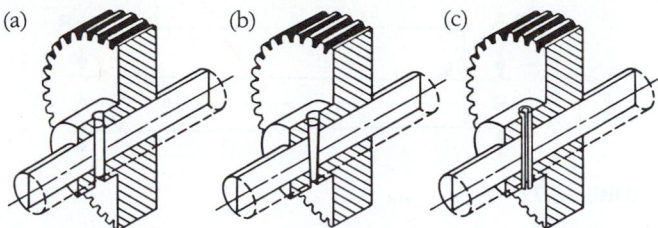

FIGURE 15.70 Pinning Applications

pin types have metric-sized standard equivalents. Seven common types of pins are found in industry and are recognized as American National standards:

- straight
- tapered
- spring
- grooved
- dowel
- cotter
- clevis
- push-pull

Pins can be either quick-release or semipermanent. **Quick-release pins** include cotter, clevis, push-pull, and positive locking varieties. Dowel, tapered, straight, grooved, and spring are **semipermanent** types because they all require some form of pressure to insert.

15.17.1 Straight Pins

Straight pins (Fig. 15.71) are somewhat difficult to align during assembly and must be a precise fit to make them secure. To designate a pin on a drawing the product name, nominal size, length, material, and the finish (if required) are given, as shown below:

$$\text{PIN, CHAMFERED STRAIGHT, } \frac{5}{16} \times 2, \text{ STEEL}$$

15.17.2 Tapered Pins

Tapered pins (Fig. 15.72) can be used for ease of assembly and disassembly. Taper pins fall out more easily than dowels. Taper pins come in sizes from $\frac{1}{16}$ to $1\frac{1}{2}$ inches and are normally steel. Taper pins are called out by a number from 0 (small diameter) to 14 (large diameter) and their length requirement. The large end of a taper pin is constant for a particular size pin, but the small end changes according to the length. Taper pins have a taper of $\frac{1}{4}$ inch per foot.

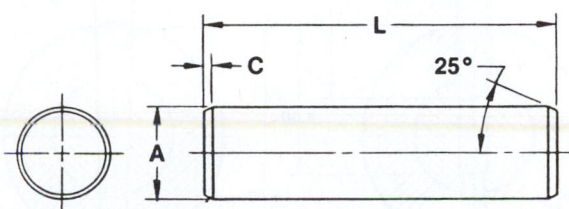

FIGURE 15.71 Straight Pins

Nominal Size	A	C
.250	.2500	.025
.375	.3750	.040

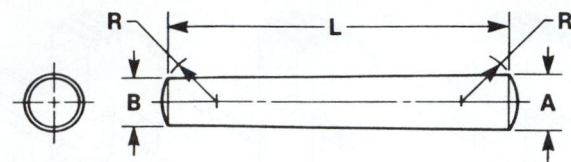

FIGURE 15.72   Taper Pins

Nominal Sizes	A	R
#4 (.2500)	.2500	.26
#8 (.4920)	.4920	.50

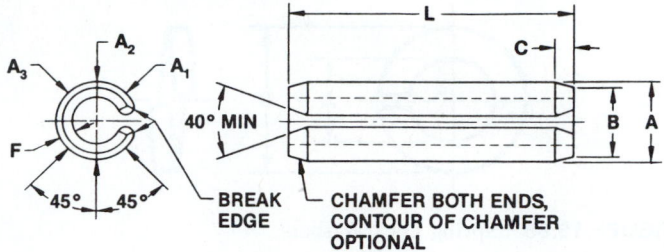

FIGURE 15.74   Slotted Spring Pins

Nominal Size	A	B	C
.375	.39	.36	.09
.500	.521	.48	.11

Step drilling or tapered reaming is required for taper holes. The information contained in Figure 15.73 should be provided on all taper details. Taper pins are designated as shown below:

> PIN, TAPER (COMMERCIAL CLASS) NO. 2 × 1 $\frac{1}{4}$, STEEL

15.17.3   Spring Pins

Since the spring force retains the pin in the hole, **spring pins** (rolled pins) also reduce the possibility of falling out during operation. The hole for a spring pin is drilled slightly smaller than the pin. Spring pins are reusable and can be repeatedly removed without distortion or losing their locking efficiency.

Spring pins come in two basic styles. One type has a slot throughout its length (Fig. 15.74) and the other is shaped in the form of a coil (Fig. 15.75). Spring pins are designated on drawings as shown below:

> PIN, COILED SPRING, $\frac{1}{2}$ × 2 $\frac{1}{4}$, STANDARD DUTY, STEEL, ZINC PLATED

> PIN, SLOTTED SPRING, .250 × .75, AISI 420 CORROSION RESISTANT STEEL

For metric:

> PIN, COILED SPRING, 10 × 40, HEAVY DUTY, STAINLESS STEEL, PHOSPHATE COATED

> PIN, SLOTTED SPRING, 20 × 60, STANDARD DUTY, CHROME-NICKEL AUSTENITIC STAINLESS STEEL, CADMIUM PLATED

15.17.4   Grooved Pins

Grooved pins (Fig. 15.76) are tapered or straight with longitudinal grooves pressed into the body. The pin will deform when pressed into the part. Since they hold securely even after repeated removal and reassembly, grooved pins are used in situations where repeated disassembly is required. Grooved pins are designated as shown below:

> PIN, TYPE B GROOVED, $\frac{5}{16}$ × 2, CORROSION RESISTANT STEEL

15.17.5   Dowel Pins

Dowel pins (Fig. 15.77) are heat-treated, precision ground pins. Dowels are used to align mating parts precisely or to retain parts in a fixed position; they are not used as fasteners. Since the dowels are press fit, holes for dowels are reamed and not drilled. In other words, the dowel is slightly larger than the hole and the dowel pin is forced ("press fit") into the hole to provide accurate alignment between mating parts. Dowels provide alignment and the screws are used for fastening. A general rule is to use dowels that are close to the same diameter as the screws. The length of the dowel should be 1 $\frac{1}{2}$ to 2 times its diameter in each plate or part to be doweled. Dowel pins are designated as shown below:

> PIN, HARDENED GROUND PRODUCTION DOWEL, .500 × 1.75, STEEL, PHOSPHATE COATED

> PIN, UNHARDENED GROUND DOWEL, $\frac{3}{4}$ × 1 $\frac{1}{2}$, STEEL

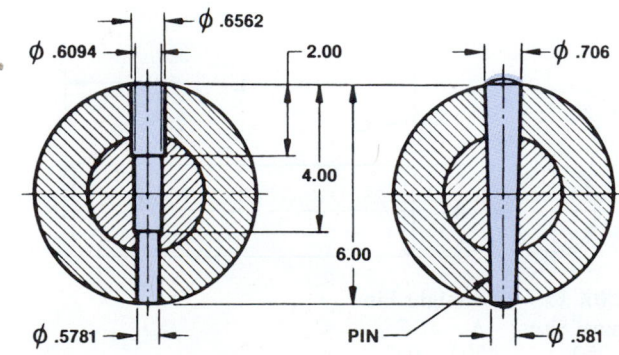

FIGURE 15.73   Dimensioning Taper Pins

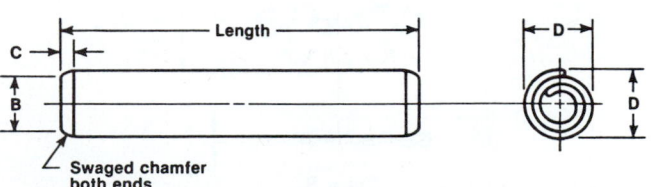

FIGURE 15.75   Metric Coiled Spring Pins

Nominal Size	B	C	D
10	9.75	2.5	10.80
20	19.6	4.5	21.10

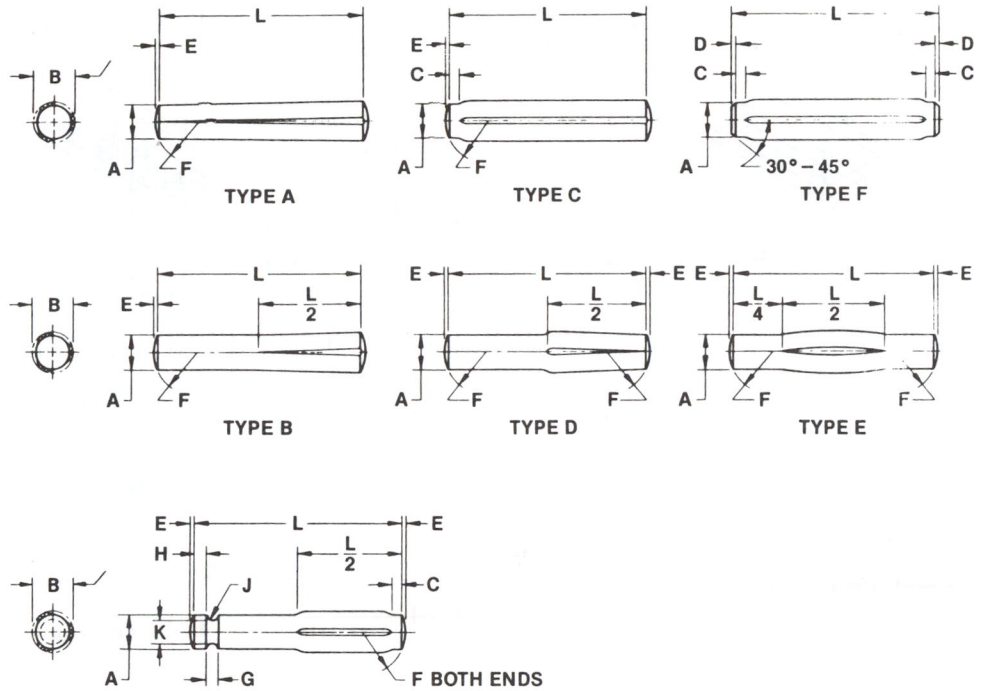

TYPE A

TYPE C

TYPE F

TYPE B

TYPE D

TYPE E

TYPE G

FIGURE 15.76   Grooved Pins

For metric:

PIN, DOWEL, 16 × 70, STAINLESS STEEL

15.17.6 Clevis Pins and Cotter Pins

Clevis pins (Fig. 15.78) are used with cotter pins to retain parts on a shaft or to lock a nut and bolt. **Cotter pins** (Fig. 15.79) are used with clevis pins to retain parts on a shaft or to lock a slotted nut and bolt. Cotter pins are used where quick and easy assembly and dissasembly are required. Clevis pins and cotter pins are designated as shown below:

PIN, CLEVIS, .438 × 1.19, STEEL, CADMIUM PLATED

PIN, CLEVIS, $\frac{1}{4}$ × .77, STEEL

PIN, COTTER, $\frac{1}{8}$ × 1$\frac{1}{2}$, EXTENDED PRONG TYPE, STEEL, ZINC PLATED

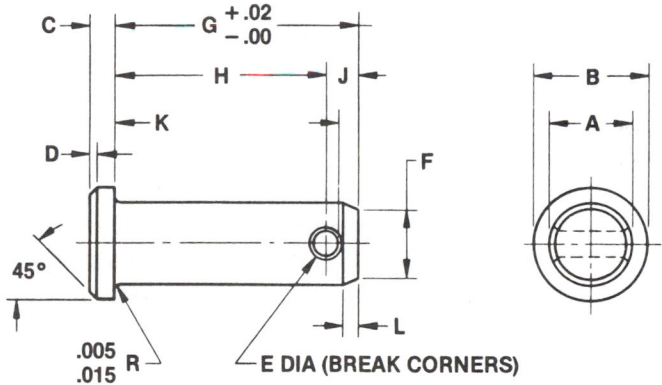

FIGURE 15.78   Clevis Pins

Nominal Size	A	B	C	D	F	G	H	J	L	Pin Size
.375	.37	.51	.13	.03	.33	1.06	.95	.12	.07	.093
.500	.49	.63	.16	.04	.44	1.36	1.22	.15	.08	1.250

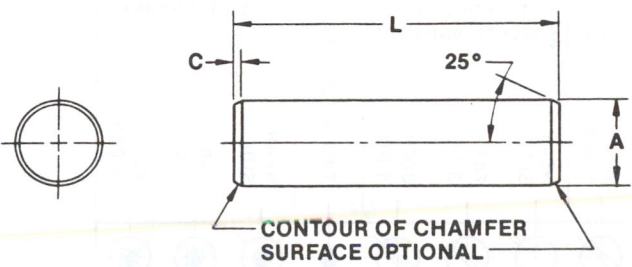

FIGURE 15.77   Dowel Pins

Nominal Size	A	C
.375	.371	.04
.500	.496	.04

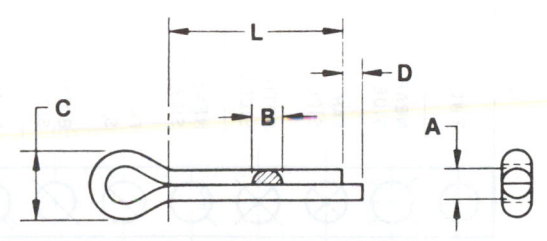

FIGURE 15.79   Cotter Pins

Nominal Size	A	B	C	D
.125	.12	.12	.25	.06
.188	.17	.17	.38	.09

INTERNAL	**BASIC** **N5000** For housings and bores — Size Range: .250—10.0 in. / 6.4—254.0 mm.	EXTERNAL	**BOWED** **5101** For shafts and pins — Size Range: .188—1.750 in. / 4.8—44.4 mm.	EXTERNAL	**REINFORCED** **5115** For shafts and pins — Size Range: .094—1.0 in. / ●	EXTERNAL	**TRIANGULAR NUT** **5300** For threaded parts — Size Range: 6-32 and 8-32 / 10-24 and 10-32 / 1/4-20 and 1/4-28
INTERNAL	**BOWED** **N5001** For housings and bores — Size Range: .250—1.750 in. / 6.4—44.4 mm.	EXTERNAL	**BEVELED** **5102** For shafts and pins — Size Range: 1.0—10.0 in. / 25.4—254.0 mm.	EXTERNAL	**BOWED E-RING** **5131** For shafts and pins — Size Range: .110—1.375 in. / 2.8—34.9 mm.	EXTERNAL	**KLIPRING** **5304** **T-5304** For shafts and pins — Size Range: .156—1.000 in. / 4.0—25.4 mm.
INTERNAL	**BEVELED** **N5002** For housings and bores — Size Range: 1.0—10.0 in. / 25.4—254.0 mm.	EXTERNAL	**CRESCENT®** **5103** For shafts and pins — Size Range: .125—2.0 in. / 3.2—50.8 mm.	EXTERNAL	**E-RING** **5133** For shafts and pins — Size Range: .040—1.375 in. / 1.0—34.9 mm.	EXTERNAL	**TRIANGULAR** **5305** For shafts and pins — Size Range: .062—.438 in. / ●
INTERNAL	**CIRCULAR** **5005** For housings and bores — Size Range: .312—2.0 in. / ●	EXTERNAL	**CIRCULAR** **5105** For shafts and pins — Size Range: .094—1.0 in. / ●	EXTERNAL	**PRONG-LOCK®** **5139** For shafts and pins — Size Range: .092—.438 in. / ●	EXTERNAL	**GRIPRING®** **5555** For shafts and pins — Size Range: .079—.750 in. / 2.0—19.0 mm.
INTERNAL	**INVERTED** **5008** For housings and bores — Size Range: .750—4.0 in. / 19.0—101.6 mm.	EXTERNAL	**INTERLOCKING** **5107** For shafts and pins — Size Range: .469—3.375 in. / 11.9—85.7 mm.	EXTERNAL	**REINFORCED E-RING** **5144** For shafts and pins — Size Range: .094—.562 in. / 2.4—14.3 mm.	EXTERNAL	**HIGH-STRENGTH** **5560** For shafts and pins — Size Range: .101—.328 in. / ●
EXTERNAL	**BASIC** **5100** For shafts and pins — Size Range: .125—10.0 in. / 3.2—254.0 mm.	EXTERNAL	**INVERTED** **5108** For shafts and pins — Size Range: .500—4.0 in. / 12.7—101.6 mm.	EXTERNAL	**HEAVY-DUTY** **5160** For shafts and pins — Size Range: .394—2.0 in. / 10.0—50.8 mm.	EXTERNAL	**PERMANENT SHOULDER** **5590** For shafts and pins — Size Range: .250—.750 / 6.4—19.0 mm.

FIGURE 15.87   Retaining Ring Styles

Radially assembled rings are designed to be snapped directly onto a shaft. Axially assembled rings require special tools to expand (for external rings) or to contract (for internal rings) the ring to slide over a shaft (external) or slip into a grooved housing (internal) while installing (see also Chapter 16).

15.20   Collars

A **collar** (Fig. 15.88) is a ring installed over a shaft and positioned adjacent to a machine element such as a pulley, gear, or sprocket. A collar is held in position, in most cases, by a set screw. The advantage of a collar lies in that axial location can be established virtually anywhere along the shaft to allow adjustment of the position at the time of assembly. Typical collar applications include:

1. spacer on a machine shaft
2. thrust collar on pillow block
3. hub or plate on a sprocket
4. adjustment for torsion spring
5. clutch part
6. locating a gear or cam on a shaft

15.21   Keys and Keyseats

A **key** is a machine component used to assemble a shaft and the hub of a power-transmitting element (gear, sprocket, pulley) to transmit torque. Keys are removable to facilitate assembly and disassembly of the shaft and components. A key is installed in an axial groove machined into the shaft, called a **keyseat** (Fig. 15.89). A similar groove in the hub of the power-transmitting element is usually called a **keyway** but is more properly called a keyseat (see also Chapters 12 and 16).

Square keys (the width and the height are equal) are preferred on shaft sizes up to a 6.50 in. diameter. Square keys (Fig. 15.90) are sunk halfway into the shaft and extend halfway into the hub of the assembly. Above 6.50 inches in diameter, rectangular keys are recommended. The **rectangular key** (flat key), is recommended for larger shafts and is used for smaller shafts where the shorter height is acceptable for the design requirements.

The **taper key** (Fig. 15.90) permits the key to be inserted from the end of the shaft after the hub is in position. If the opposite end of the key is not accessible to be driven out, the

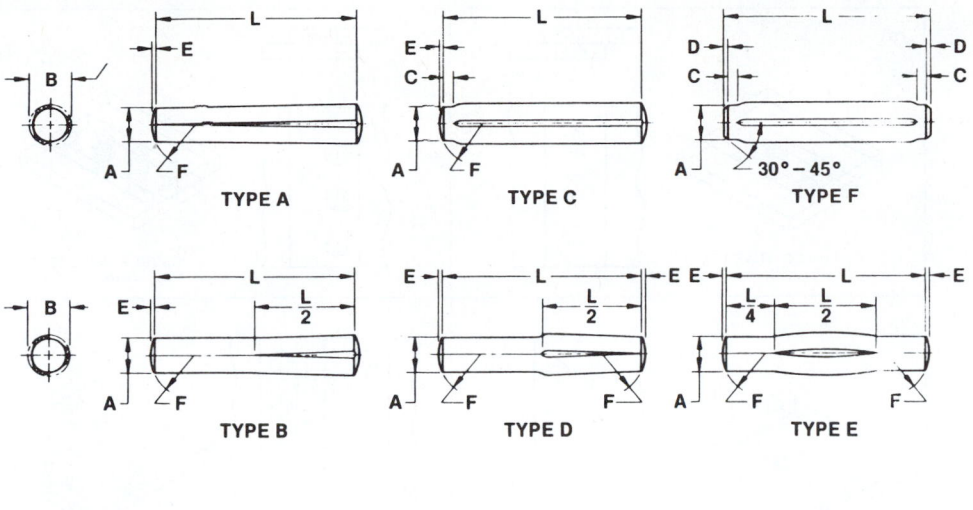

TYPE A TYPE C TYPE F

TYPE B TYPE D TYPE E

TYPE G

FIGURE 15.76 Grooved Pins

For metric:

PIN, DOWEL, 16 × 70, STAINLESS STEEL

15.17.6 Clevis Pins and Cotter Pins

Clevis pins (Fig. 15.78) are used with cotter pins to retain parts on a shaft or to lock a nut and bolt. **Cotter pins** (Fig. 15.79) are used with clevis pins to retain parts on a shaft or to lock a slotted nut and bolt. Cotter pins are used where quick and easy assembly and dissasembly are required. Clevis pins and cotter pins are designated as shown below:

PIN, CLEVIS, .438 × 1.19, STEEL, CADMIUM PLATED

PIN, CLEVIS, $\frac{1}{4}$ × .77, STEEL

PIN, COTTER, $\frac{1}{8}$ × $1\frac{1}{2}$, EXTENDED PRONG TYPE, STEEL, ZINC PLATED

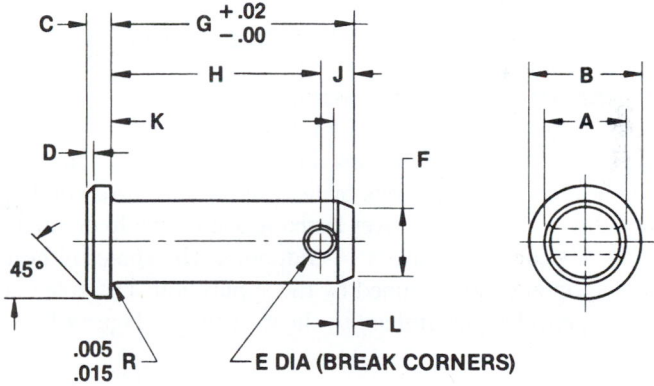

FIGURE 15.78 Clevis Pins

Nominal Size	A	B	C	D	F	G	H	J	L	Pin Size
.375	.37	.51	.13	.03	.33	1.06	.95	.12	.07	.093
.500	.49	.63	.16	.04	.44	1.36	1.22	.15	.08	1.250

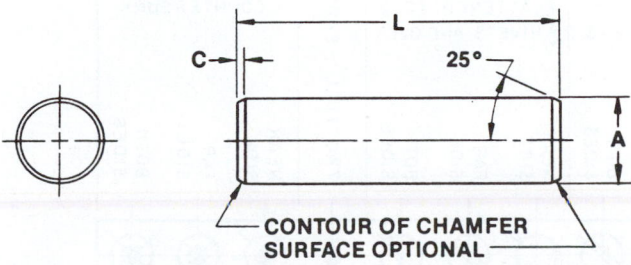

FIGURE 15.77 Dowel Pins

Nominal Size	A	C
.375	.371	.04
.500	.496	.04

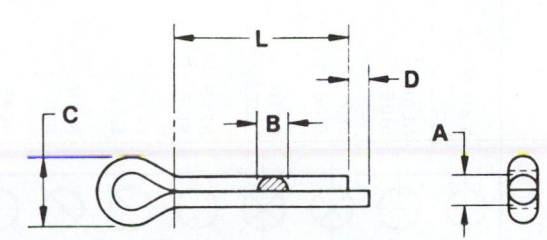

FIGURE 15.79 Cotter Pins

Nominal Size	A	B	C	D
.125	.12	.12	.25	.06
.188	.17	.17	.38	.09

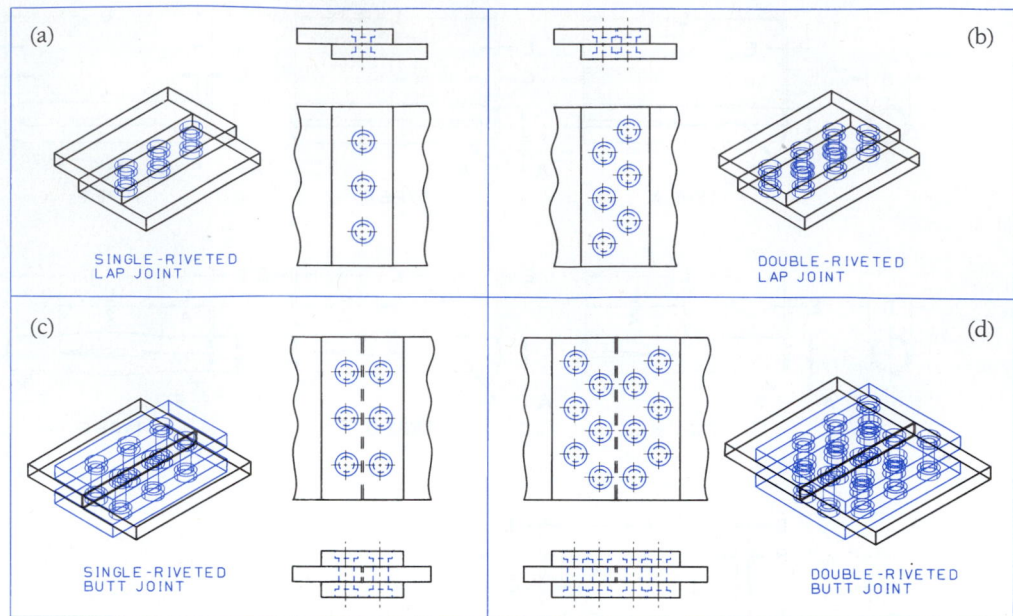

FIGURE 15.80 Riveted Joints

15.18 Rivets

Figure 15.80 shows four typical riveted joints; single-riveted lap, double-riveted lap, single-riveted butt, and double-riveted butt. The most common types of rivets are solid, tubular, split, and blind rivets.

Solid **rivets** are used in assembling parts not to be taken apart. Solid rivets are shown on drawings as in Figure 15.81. If plans, elevations, or sections show the conventional signs for the head of the shop rivets or field rivets, the corresponding lengthwise view of the rivet fastenings is normally omitted.

Rivets come in a variety of endpoints. The choice of head and endpoint is determined by the application. The hole size and type will be determined by the rivet choice. Figures 15.82 through 15.85 show four standard types of rivets. Designate rivets on drawings as shown below:

.146 × .500 SEMI-TUBULAR, OVAL HEAD, STEEL, CADMIUM PLATED

$\frac{1}{4}$ × $1\frac{1}{4}$ FLAT HEAD SMALL SOLID RIVET, STEEL, ZINC PLATED

15.19 Retaining Rings

Retaining rings are semipermanent fasteners found on many assemblies. Retaining rings are used as shoulders that can be located along a shaft (or pin) or in a recessed hole to keep the components of an assembly properly positioned, as shown in

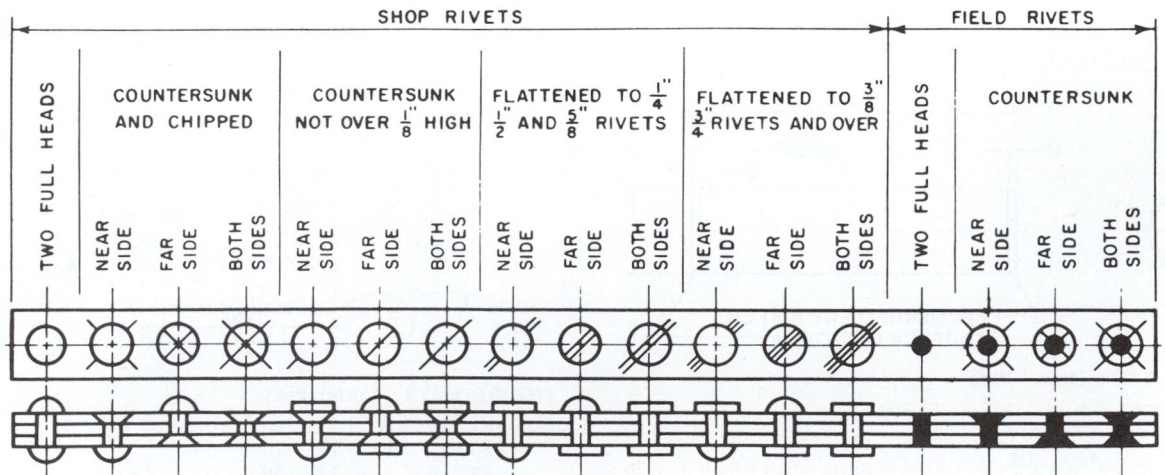

FIGURE 15.81 Drawing Conventions for Solid Rivets

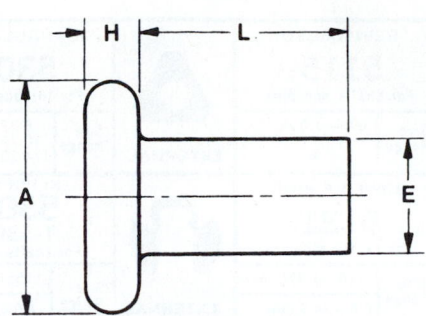

FIGURE 15.82   **Flat Head Rivets**

Nominal Size	A	E	H
.125	.125	.25	.04
.250	.250	.50	.09

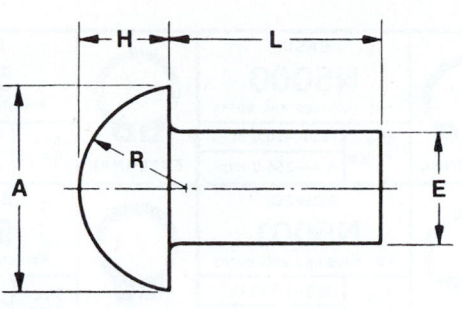

FIGURE 15.84   **Button Head Rivets**

Nominal Size	A	E	H	R
.094	.18	.094	.07	.08
.281	.51	.281	.22	.249

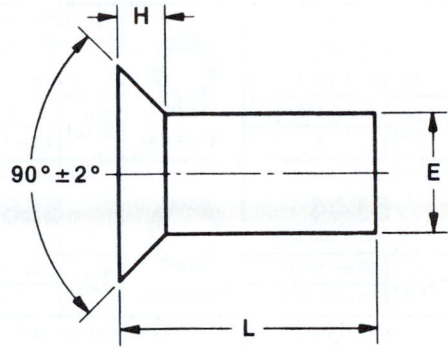

FIGURE 15.83   **Flat Countersunk Head Rivets**

Nominal Size	Head Dia.	E	H
.156	.29	.15	.06
.312	.58	.31	.13

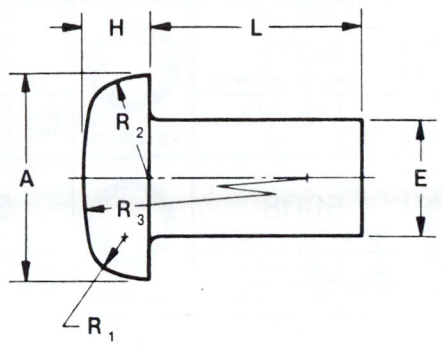

FIGURE 15.85   **Pan Head Rivets**

Nominal Size	A	E	H	R1	R2	R3
.188	.33	.187	.11	.05	.15	.64
.312	.55	.312	.18	.09	.26	1.07

Figure 15.86. Many different styles of retaining rings are available (Fig. 15.87).

Retaining rings can easily be installed in machined grooves, internally in housings, or externally on shafts or pins. Some styles of retaining rings do not require grooves but have a self-locking spring-type action. There are two types of retaining rings: *internal* and *external*.

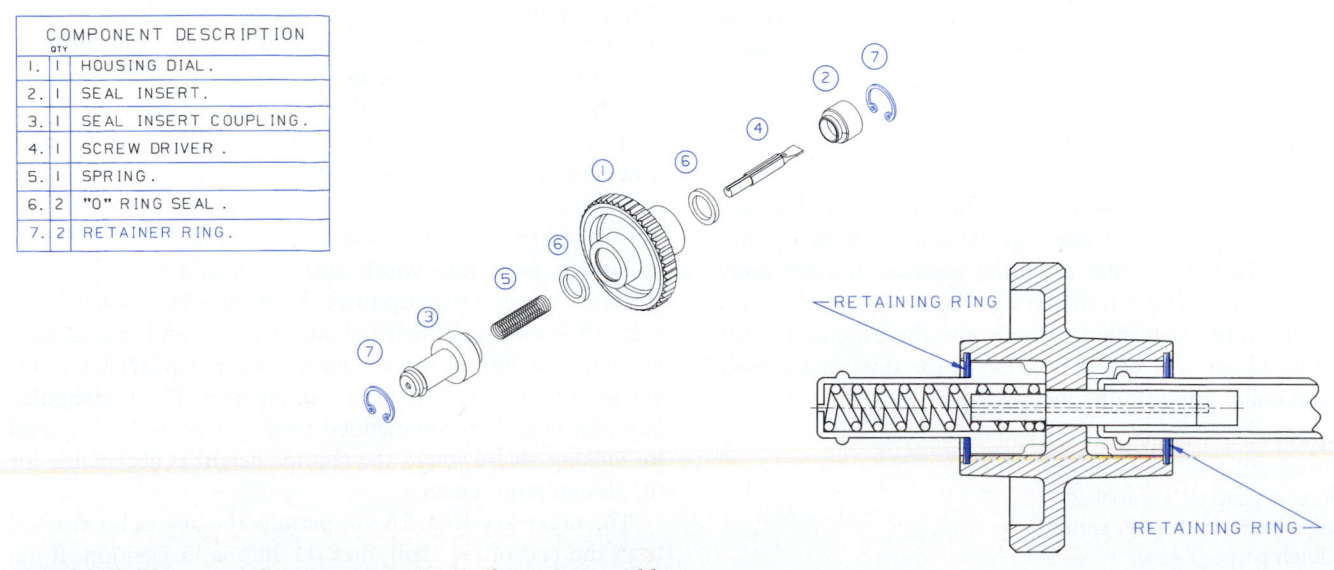

COMPONENT DESCRIPTION		
	QTY	
1.	1	HOUSING DIAL.
2.	1	SEAL INSERT.
3.	1	SEAL INSERT COUPLING.
4.	1	SCREW DRIVER .
5.	1	SPRING.
6.	2	"O" RING SEAL .
7.	2	RETAINER RING.

FIGURE 15.86   **Internal Retaining Rings Used on an Assembly**

INTERNAL	BASIC N5000 For housings and bores		EXTERNAL	BOWED 5101 For shafts and pins		EXTERNAL	REINFORCED 5115 For shafts and pins		EXTERNAL	TRIANGULAR NUT 5300 For threaded parts
	Size Range	.250—10.0 in.		Size Range	.188—1.750 in.		Size Range	.094—1.0 in.		Size Range	6-32 and 8-32 10-24 and 10-32
		6.4—254.0 mm.			4.8—44.4 mm.			●			1/4-20 and 1/4-28

INTERNAL	BOWED N5001 For housings and bores		EXTERNAL	BEVELED 5102 For shafts and pins		EXTERNAL	BOWED E-RING 5131 For shafts and pins		EXTERNAL	KLIPRING 5304 T-5304 For shafts and pins
	Size Range	.250—1.750 in.		Size Range	1.0—10.0 in.		Size Range	.110—1.375 in.		Size Range	.156—1.000 in.
		6.4—44.4 mm.			25.4—254.0 mm.			2.8—34.9 mm.			4.0—25.4 mm.

INTERNAL	BEVELED N5002 For housings and bores		EXTERNAL	CRESCENT® 5103 For shafts and pins		EXTERNAL	E-RING 5133 For shafts and pins		EXTERNAL	TRIANGULAR 5305 For shafts and pins
	Size Range	1.0—10.0 in.		Size Range	.125—2.0 in.		Size Range	.040—1.375 in.		Size Range	.062—.438 in.
		25.4—254.0 mm.			3.2—50.8 mm.			1.0—34.9 mm.			

INTERNAL	CIRCULAR 5005 For housings and bores		EXTERNAL	CIRCULAR 5105 For shafts and pins		EXTERNAL	PRONG-LOCK® 5139 For shafts and pins		EXTERNAL	GRIPRING® 5555 For shafts and pins
	Size Range	.312—2.0 in.		Size Range	.094—1.0 in.		Size Range	.092—.438 in.		Size Range	.079—.750 in.
		●			●			●			2.0—19.0 mm.

INTERNAL	INVERTED 5008 For housings and bores		EXTERNAL	INTERLOCKING 5107 For shafts and pins		EXTERNAL	REINFORCED E-RING 5144 For shafts and pins		EXTERNAL	HIGH-STRENGTH 5560 For shafts and pins
	Size Range	.750—4.0 in.		Size Range	.469—3.375 in.		Size Range	.094—.562 in.		Size Range	.101—.328 in.
		19.0—101.6 mm.			11.9—85.7 mm.			2.4—14.3 mm.			●

EXTERNAL	BASIC 5100 For shafts and pins		EXTERNAL	INVERTED 5108 For shafts and pins		EXTERNAL	HEAVY-DUTY 5160 For shafts and pins		EXTERNAL	PERMANENT SHOULDER 5590 For shafts and pins
	Size Range	.125—10.0 in.		Size Range	.500—4.0 in.		Size Range	.394—2.0 in.		Size Range	.250—.750
		3.2—254.0 mm.			12.7—101.6 mm.			10.0—50.8 mm.			6.4—19.0 mm.

FIGURE 15.87 Retaining Ring Styles

Radially assembled rings are designed to be snapped directly onto a shaft. Axially assembled rings require special tools to expand (for external rings) or to contract (for internal rings) the ring to slide over a shaft (external) or slip into a grooved housing (internal) while installing (see also Chapter 16).

15.20 Collars

A **collar** (Fig. 15.88) is a ring installed over a shaft and positioned adjacent to a machine element such as a pulley, gear, or sprocket. A collar is held in position, in most cases, by a set screw. The advantage of a collar lies in that axial location can be established virtually anywhere along the shaft to allow adjustment of the position at the time of assembly. Typical collar applications include:

1. spacer on a machine shaft
2. thrust collar on pillow block
3. hub or plate on a sprocket
4. adjustment for torsion spring
5. clutch part
6. locating a gear or cam on a shaft

15.21 Keys and Keyseats

A **key** is a machine component used to assemble a shaft and the hub of a power-transmitting element (gear, sprocket, pulley) to transmit torque. Keys are removable to facilitate assembly and disassembly of the shaft and components. A key is installed in an axial groove machined into the shaft, called a **keyseat** (Fig. 15.89). A similar groove in the hub of the power-transmitting element is usually called a **keyway** but is more properly called a keyseat (see also Chapters 12 and 16).

Square keys (the width and the height are equal) are preferred on shaft sizes up to a 6.50 in. diameter. Square keys (Fig. 15.90) are sunk halfway into the shaft and extend halfway into the hub of the assembly. Above 6.50 inches in diameter, rectangular keys are recommended. The **rectangular key** (flat key), is recommended for larger shafts and is used for smaller shafts where the shorter height is acceptable for the design requirements.

The **taper key** (Fig. 15.90) permits the key to be inserted from the end of the shaft after the hub is in position. If the opposite end of the key is not accessible to be driven out, the

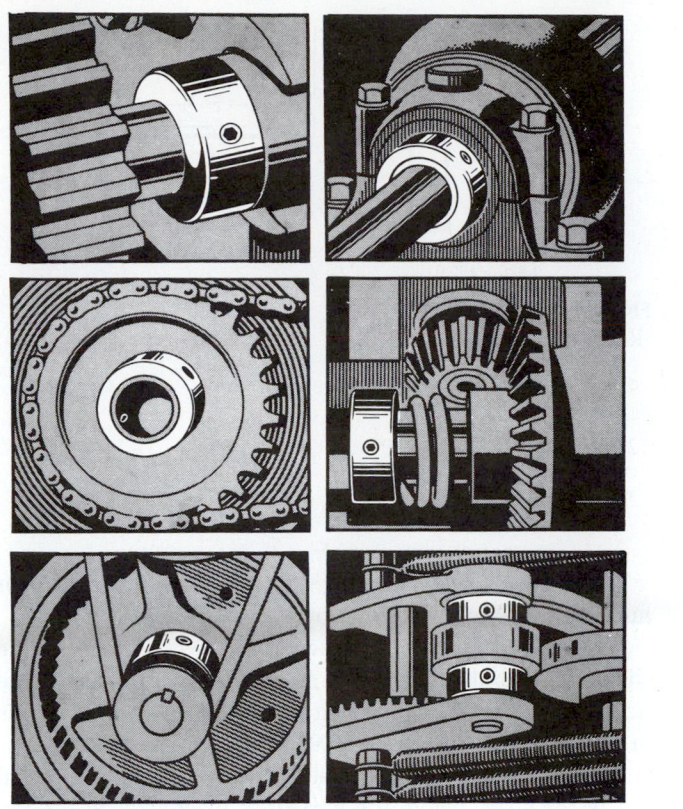

FIGURE 15.88   Coupling Applications

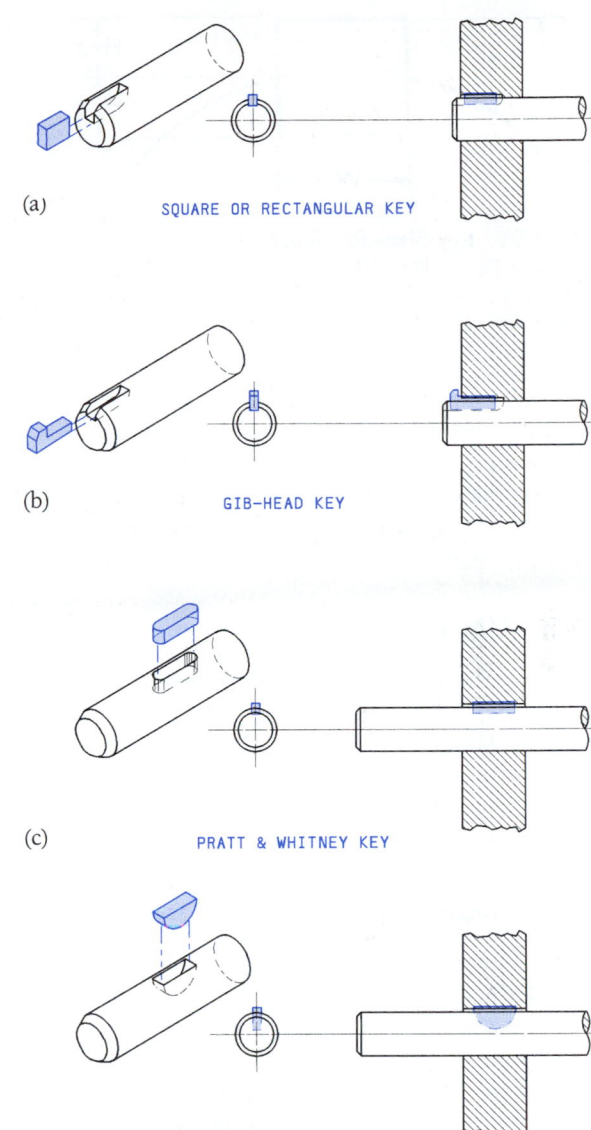

(a)   SQUARE OR RECTANGULAR KEY

(b)   GIB-HEAD KEY

(c)   PRATT & WHITNEY KEY

(d)   WOODRUFF KEY

FIGURE 15.89   Types of Keys

gib head key provides the means of extracting the key. On both the **plain taper** and the **gib head key**, the taper is $\frac{1}{8}$ inch per foot. The cross-sectional dimensions of the key, W and H, are the same as those used for parallel keys, with the height H measured at the position specified in Figure 15.90.

15.21.1   Key Size Versus Shaft Diameter

For a stepped shaft (one that has multiple diameters), the size of a key is determined by the diameter of the shaft at the point of location of the key, regardless of the number of different diameters on the shaft.

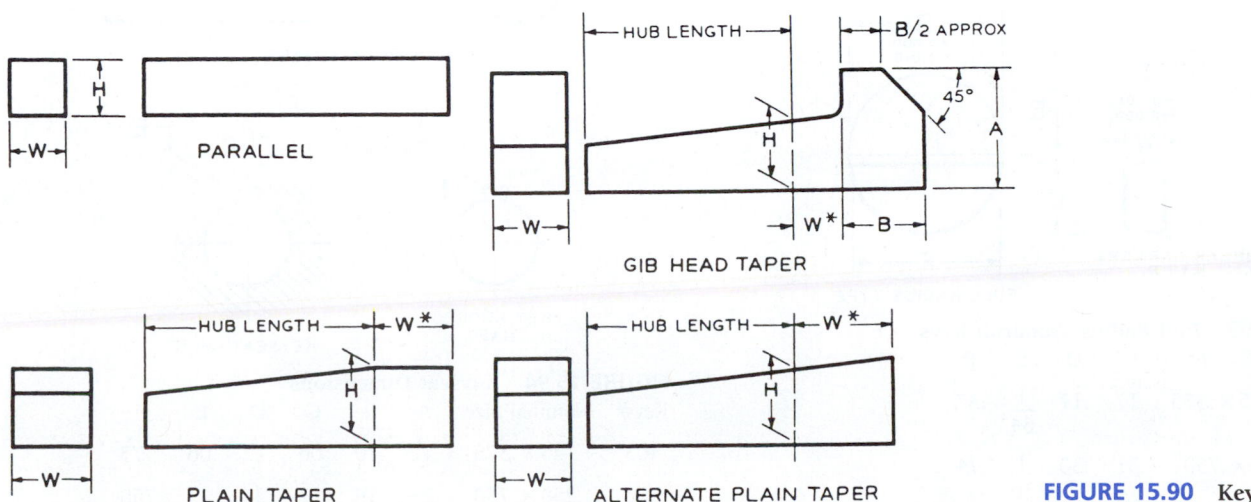

PARALLEL

GIB HEAD TAPER

PLAIN TAPER

ALTERNATE PLAIN TAPER

FIGURE 15.90   Keys

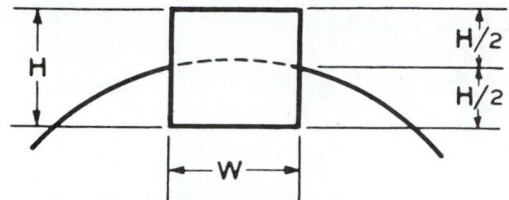

FIGURE 15.91   Key Sizes for Square Keys

Nominal Shaft Dia.	H	W
.875-1.25	.25	.25
1.750-2.25	.50	.50

Sizes and dimensions for keys are found in tables in the *Machinery's Handbook* and in ANSI B17.1. Figure 15.91 gives the preferred dimensions for parallel keys as a function of the shaft diameter. The width is normally one-fourth of the diameter of the shaft.

15.21.2   Woodruff Keys

Woodruff keys, which are almost in the shape of a half circle, are used where relatively light loads are transmitted. One advantage of Woodruff keys is that they cannot change their axial location on a shaft because they are retained in a pocket. Woodruff keys can be either the full radius or the flat bottom type and come in two styles (Figs. 15.92 and 15.93).

15.21.3   Design of Keys and Keyseats

The key and keyseat are designed after the shaft diameter is determined. Then, with the shaft diameter as a guide, the size of the key is selected from ANSI Standard B17.1 or ANSI B17.2. The only remaining variables are the length of the key and its material. One of these can be specified, and the requirements for the other can then be computed. Typically, the length of a key is specified to be the hub length of the element in which it is installed to provide for good alignment and stable operation. Figure 15.94 shows keyseat dimensions for

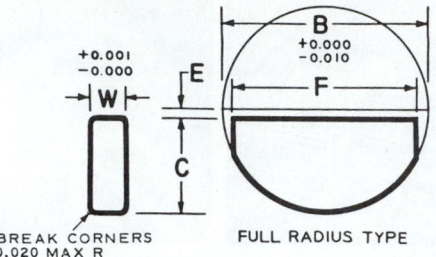

FIGURE 15.93   Woodruff Keys

Key#	W × B	C	D	E	F
817-1	.250 × 2.125	.40	.39	$\frac{21}{32}$	1.38
1217-1	.375 × 2.125	.40	.29	$\frac{21}{32}$	1.38

Woodruff keys. Keys are designed to fail before the shaft or hub fails, thus resulting in a lower cost for replacement.

If rectangular and square keys are used, keyseats in the shaft and the hub are designed so that exactly one-half of the height of the key is in the shaft keyseat and the other half is in the hub keyseat. Figure 15.95 shows the resulting geometry. The distance Y is the radial distance from the theoretical top of the shaft, before the keyseat is machined, to the top edge of the finished keyseat to produce a keyseat depth of exactly $H/2$. To assist in machining and inspecting the shaft or the hub, the dimensions S and T can be computed and shown on the part drawings. The equations are given in Figure 15.95. Tabulated values (Fig. 15.96) of Y, S, and T are available in the standard and in the *Machinery's Handbook*. Standard key sizes are listed in Appendix C.

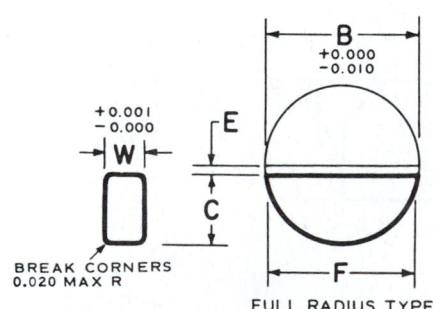

FIGURE 15.92   Full Radius Woodruff Keys

Key#	W × B	C	D	E	F
403	.125 × .375	.17	.17	$\frac{1}{64}$	.37
806	.250 × .7501	.31	.30	$\frac{1}{16}$	.74

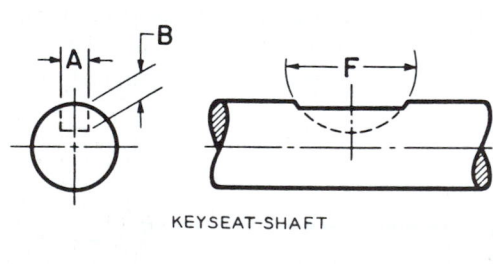

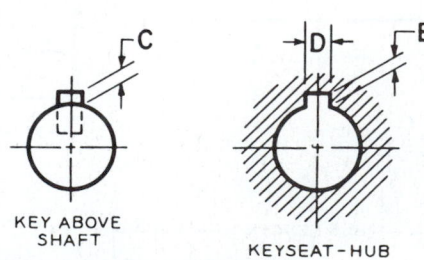

FIGURE 15.94   Keyseat Dimensions

Key#	Nominal Size	A	B	C	D	E	F
403	.125 × .375	.12	.10	.06	.12	.06	.375
806	.250 × .750	.24	.18	.12	.25	.13	.750

CHORDAL HEIGHT

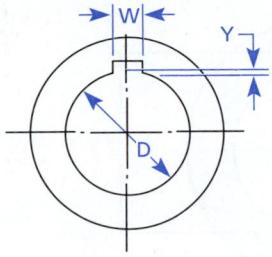

DEPTH OF SHAFT KEYSEAT

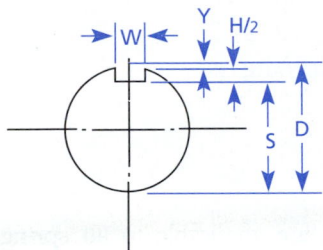

DEPTH OF HUB KEYSEAT

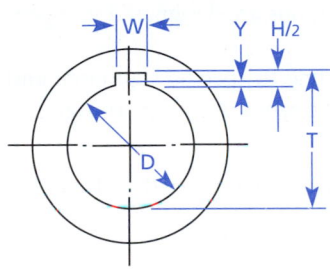

The chordal height Y is determined from the following formula:

$$Y = \frac{D - \sqrt{D^2 - W^2}}{2}$$

The distance from the bottom of the shaft keyseat to the opposite side of the shaft is specified by dimension S. The following formula may be used for calculating this dimension:

$$S = D - Y - \frac{H}{2} = \frac{D - H + \sqrt{D^2 - W^2}}{2}$$

The distance from the bottom of the hub keyseat to the opposite side of the hub bore is specified by dimension T. For taper keyseats, T is measured at the deeper end. The following formula may be used for calculating this dimension:

$$T = D - Y + \frac{H}{2} + C = \frac{D + H + \sqrt{D^2 - W^2}}{2} + C$$

Symbols
C = Allowance
  + 0.005 inch clearance for parallel keys
  − 0.020 inch interference for taper keys
D = Nominal shaft or bore diameter, inches
H = Nominal key height, inches
W = Nominal key width, inches
Y = Chordal height, inches

FIGURE 15.95   Calculating Keyseats

NOMINAL SHAFT DIAMETER	PARALLEL AND TAPER		PARALLEL		TAPER	
	SQUARE	RECTANGULAR	SQUARE	RECTANGULAR	SQUARE	RECTANGULAR
	S	S	T	T	T	T
1/2	0.430	0.445	0.560	0.544	0.535	0.519
9/16	0.493	0.509	0.623	0.607	0.598	0.582
5/8	0.517	0.548	0.709	0.678	0.684	0.653
11/16	0.581	0.612	0.773	0.742	0.748	0.717
3/4	0.644	0.676	0.837	0.806	0.812	0.781
13/16	0.708	0.739	0.900	0.869	0.875	0.844
7/8	0.771	0.802	0.964	0.932	0.939	0.907
15/16	0.796	0.827	1.051	1.019	1.026	0.994
1	0.859	0.890	1.114	1.083	1.089	1.058
1-1/16	0.923	0.954	1.178	1.146	1.153	1.121

FIGURE 15.96   Shaft Diameter and Keyseat Dimensions

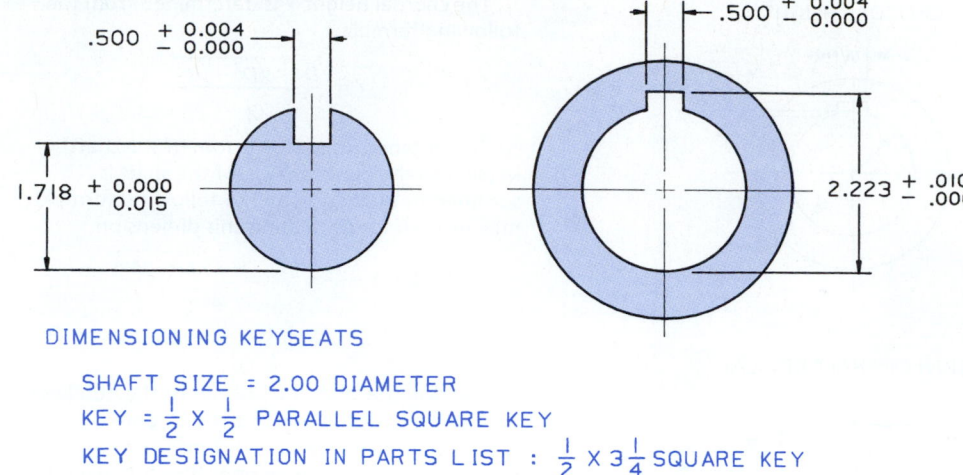

DIMENSIONING KEYSEATS

SHAFT SIZE = 2.00 DIAMETER

KEY = $\frac{1}{2}$ X $\frac{1}{2}$ PARALLEL SQUARE KEY

KEY DESIGNATION IN PARTS LIST : $\frac{1}{2}$ X 3$\frac{1}{4}$ SQUARE KEY

FIGURE 15.97 Dimensioning Keyseats

15.21.4 Dimensioning Keyseats

Keyseats (Fig. 15.97) are dimensioned by giving the width, depth, location, and, if required, length. For shafts, the width of the keyseat, the distance from the bottom of the shaft to the bottom of the keyseat, and the length are given. For the hub, give the width of the keyseat and the distance from the bottom of the shaft hole to the top of the keyseat. See Chapter 12 for methods used to dimension keyseats.

When designating keys on drawings, the key number or size, length, and product name are given, as shown in the following examples:

$\frac{1}{2}$ × 3 SQUARE KEY

NO. 403 WOODRUFF KEY

$\frac{1}{4}$ × 1 $\frac{1}{2}$ SQUARE GIB HEAD KEY

1$\frac{1}{4}$ × 4 SQUARE PLAIN TAPER KEY

NO. 8 PRATT & WHITNEY KEY

$\frac{1}{8}$ × $\frac{3}{32}$ × $\frac{3}{4}$ RECTANGULAR KEY

You May Complete Exercises 15.9 Through 15.12 at This Time

15.22 Springs

A **mechanical spring** is an elastic body whose mechanical function is to store energy when deflected by a force and to return the equivalent amount of energy on being released. Helical springs (Fig. 15.98) are similar to threads in that they are basically spiral-shaped.

Most springs are represented by their centerline and phantom lines defining their outside diameter. Seldom are springs drawn pictorially (i.e., coils are not usually drawn). At the end of the chapter, a step-by-step procedure for drawing spring coils is provided.

A number of requirements are applicable to all spring drawings, including material specifications and inspection notes. Since most springs are standard configurations and sizes, specifications and notes are more important than the drawing itself. Material specifications are designated in a general note on the drawing.

Springs are produced according to specific standards and specifications. There are six basic types of springs recognized by the ANSI:

1. **compression**—helical, cylindrical, volute, coned disk (Belleville)
2. **extension**—helical
3. **garter**—helical
4. **torsion**—helical, torsion bar, spiral
5. **flat**—cantilever
6. **constant force**—flat

15.22.1 Definition of Spring Terms

The following terms are used throughout this section and on drawings of mechanical springs:

Coils, active The number of coils used in computing the total deflection of a spring. Those coils that are free to deflect under load.

Deflection, total The movement of a spring from its free position to maximum operating position. In a compression spring, it is the deflection from the free length to the solid (compressed) length.

Force The force exerted on a spring to reproduce or modify motion, or to maintain a force system in equilibrium.

Helix The spiral form (open or closed) of compression, extension, and torsion springs.

Length, free The overall length of a spring in the unloaded position.

Length, solid The overall length of a compression spring when all coils are fully compressed.

Load The force applied to a spring that causes deflection.

Pitch The distance from center to center of the wire in adjacent active coils (recommended practice is to specify number of active coils rather than pitch).

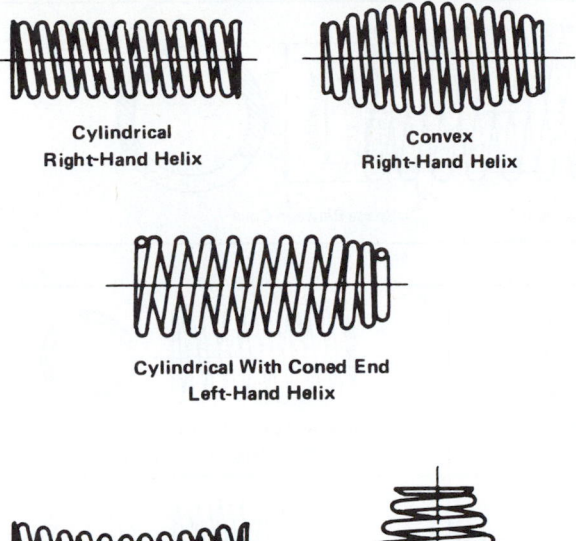

Cylindrical
Right-Hand Helix

Convex
Right-Hand Helix

Cylindrical With Coned End
Left-Hand Helix

Concave
Right-Hand Helix

Conical
Right-Hand Helix

FIGURE 15.98   Helical Compression Spring Forms

Set   Permanent distortion of the spring when stressed beyond its elastic limits.

Total number of coils   Number of active coils n plus the coils forming the ends.

15.22.2   Right-hand and Left-hand Springs

If dictated by design requirements, the direction of helix is specified as "**LEFT-HAND**" (**LH**) or "**RIGHT-HAND**" (**RH**). Otherwise, the direction of helix is specified as "**OP-TIONAL.**" In most cases, the direction is not important, except when a plug is screwed into the end or when one spring fits inside another. In the case of the latter, one spring is designated left hand and the other spring right hand. Figure 15.99 shows how the coils look for right-hand and left-hand springs. When looking at the back of your hands, the spring will coil to the left or right.

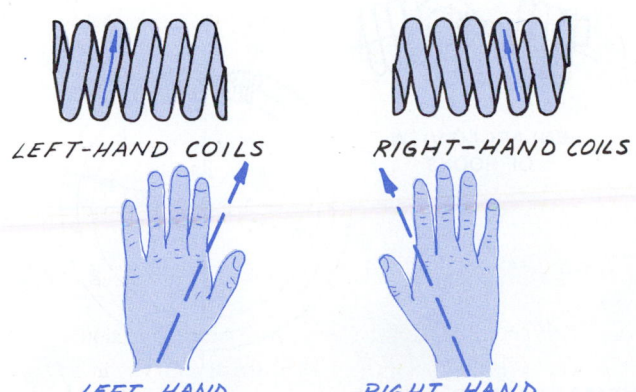

LEFT-HAND COILS   RIGHT-HAND COILS

LEFT HAND   RIGHT HAND

FIGURE 15.99   Left-Hand and Right-Hand Springs

15.22.3   Compression Springs

A **compression spring** is an open-coil helical spring that resists a compressive force applied along the axis. Compression springs are usually coiled as a constant-diameter cylinder. Other common forms of compression springs such as conical, tapered, concave, convex, or various combinations of these are used as required by the application (Fig. 15.98). While square, rectangular, or special-section wire may have to be specified, round wire is predominant in compression springs. In Figure 15.100 the recommended way to specify compression springs is shown.

There are four basic types of compression spring ends (Fig. 15.101). The particular type of ends specified affect the pitch, solid height, number of active and total coils, free length, and seating characteristics of the spring. The type of ends are specified on the drawing and dimensioned as required.

Depending on the application of the compression spring, the following requirements are specified:

TO WORK OVER _____ MAX DIAMETER ROD
TO WORK IN _____ MIN DIAMETER BORE
ID (WITH TOLERANCE) _____
OD (WITH TOLERANCE) _____

15.22.4   Extension Springs

Extension springs (Fig. 15.102) absorb and store energy by resisting a pulling force. Various types of ends are used to attach the extension spring to the source of the force. Most extension springs are wound with an initial tension, which holds the coils tightly together. The load necessary to overcome the internal force and just start coil separation is the same as the initial tension.

15.22.5   Helical Extension Springs

A **helical extension spring** is a close-wound spring, with or without initial tension, or an open-wound spring that resists an axial force trying to elongate the spring. Extension springs

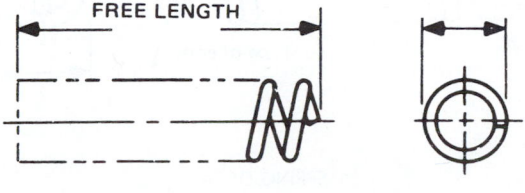

FREE LENGTH

SPRING DATA

MATERIAL SPECIFICATION ....
WIRE DIAMETER ....
DIRECTION OF HELIX ....
TOTAL COILS ....

FIGURE 15.100   Drawing Requirements for Helical Compression Springs

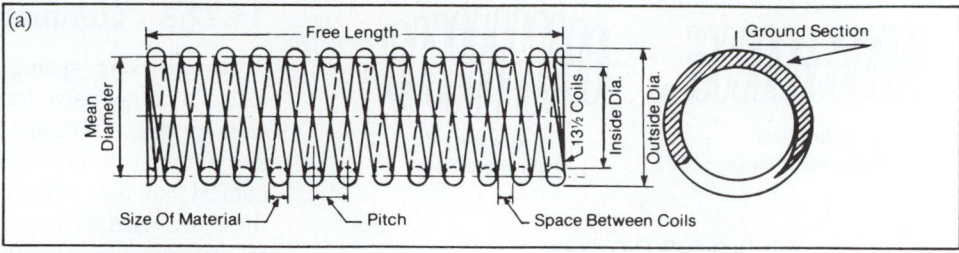

Type of End Finishes

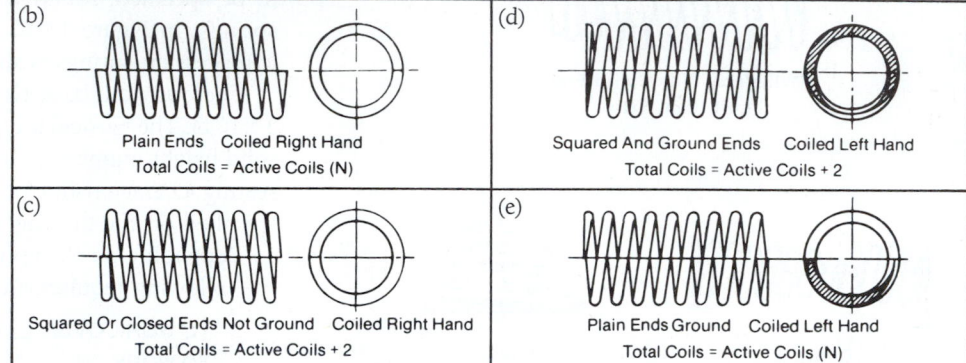

FIGURE 15.101 End Finishes for Compression Springs

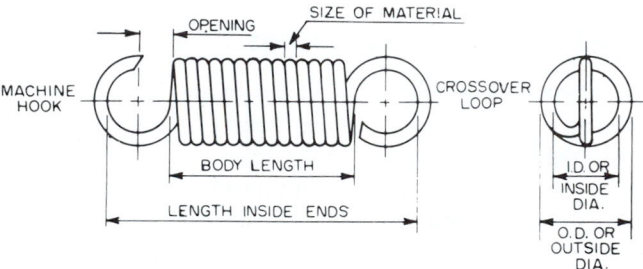

FIGURE 15.102 Extension Springs

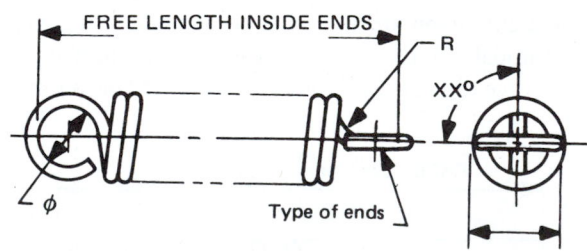

```
                                  SPRING DATA
MATERIAL SPECIFICATION . . . . . . . . . . . . . . . . . . . . . . . . . . . . . . . . . . . . . . .
WIRE DIAMETER . . . . . . . . . . . . . . . . . . . . . . . . . . . . . . . . . . . . . . . . . . . . . . .
DIRECTION OF HELIX . . . . . . . . . . . . . . . . . . . . . . . . . . . . . . . . . . . . . . . . . . . .
TOTAL COILS . . . . . . . . . . . . . . . . . . . . . . . . . . . . . . . . . . . . . . . . . . . . . . . . . . .
EXTENDED LENGTH WITHOUT PERMANENT SET . . . . . . . . . . . . . . . . . . .
RELATIVE POSITION OF ENDS . . . . . . . . . . . . . . . . . . . . . . . . . . . . . . . . . . . .
INITIAL TENSION . . . . . . . . . . . . . . . . . . . . . . . . . . . . . . . . . . . . . . . . . . . . . . .
FORCE AT OPERATING LENGTH OF_____
```

FIGURE 15.103 Drawing Requirements for Helical Extension Springs

are formed or fitted with ends that are used for attaching the spring to an assembly. Guidelines for specifying dimensional and force data on engineering drawings showing helical extension springs (Fig. 15.103) are similar to those established for helical compression springs. Usually, all coils in an extension spring are active. Exceptions are those with plug ends and those with end coils coned over swivel hooks. The total number of coils required is specified.

15.22.6 Garter Extension Springs

A **garter spring** (Fig. 15.104) is a long, close-coiled extension spring with its ends joined to form a ring. Garter springs are used principally in mechanical seals on shafting, to hold round segments together, as a belt, and as a holding device. The diameter over which the spring is to function is specified.

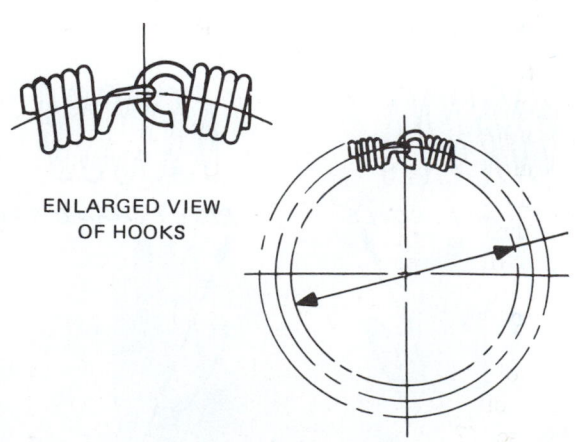

ENLARGED VIEW OF HOOKS

FIGURE 15.104 Drawing Requirements for Garter Springs

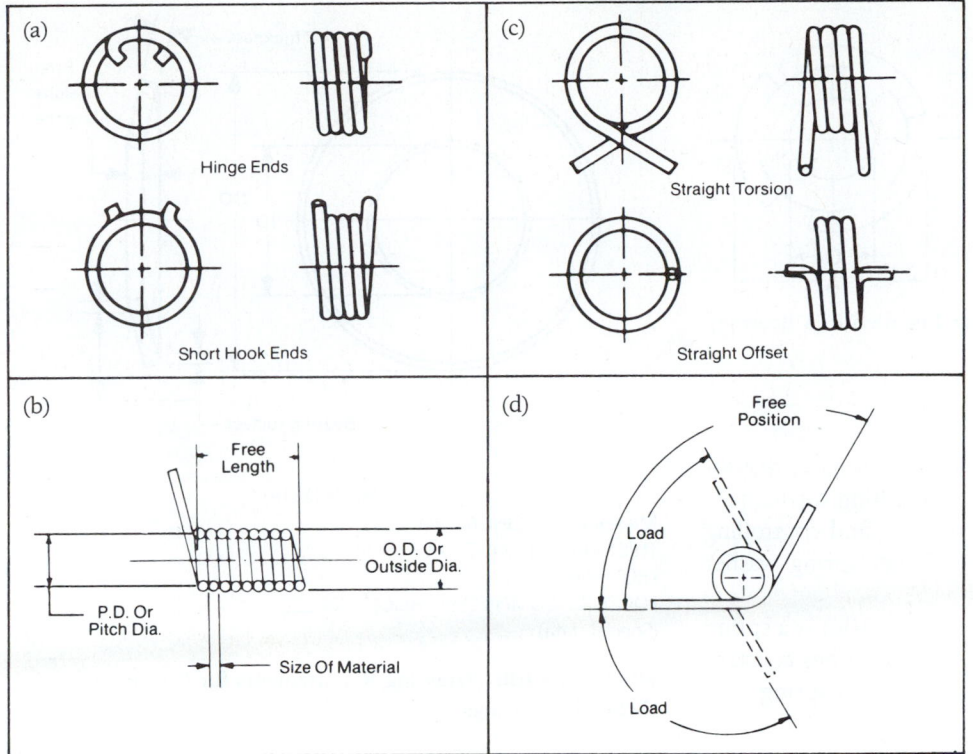

FIGURE 15.105 Drawing Requirements for Helical Torsion Springs

For example, a shaft diameter may be used, although other than an actual shaft may be involved.

15.22.7   Helical Torsion Springs

Helical torsion springs (Fig. 15.105) are springs that resist a force or exert a turning force in a plane at right angles to the axis of the coil. The wire is subjected to bending stresses rather than torsional stresses. Usually, all coils in a torsion spring are active. The total number of coils required and the length in the free position are specified. The helix of a torsion spring is important. Either "LEFT HAND" or "RIGHT HAND" is specified on the drawing.

15.22.8   Spiral Torsion Springs

Spiral torsion springs (Fig. 15.106), made of rectangular section material, are wound flat, with an increasing space between the coils. A spiral torsion spring is made by winding flat spring material on itself in the form of a spiral. It is designed to wind up and exert a force in a rotating direction around the spring axis. This force may be delivered as torque, or it may be converted into a push or pull force.

15.22.9   Spring Washers

Because of trends toward miniaturization and greater compactness of design, **spring washers** are becoming more widely used. They afford space and weight advantages over conventional wire springs and are often more economical.

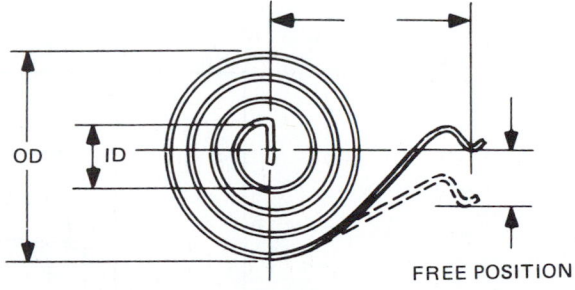

SPRING DATA

MATERIAL SPECIFICATION . . . .
MATERIAL SIZE . . . .
OUTSIDE DIAMETER . . . .
INSIDE DIAMETER . . . .
DEVELOPED LENGTH OF MATERIAL . . . .
ACTIVE LENGTH OF MATERIAL . . . .
NUMBER OF COILS IN FREE POSITION . . . .
TORQUE AT FINAL POSITION . . . .
MAXIMUM DEFLECTION BEYOND FINAL POSITION WITHOUT SET . . . . .
TYPE OF ENDS . . . .

FIGURE 15.106 Drawing Requirements for Spiral Torsion Springs

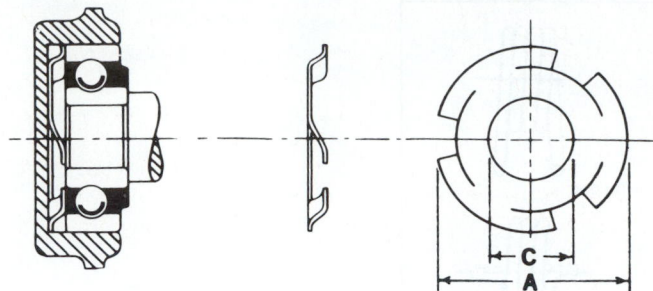

FIGURE 15.107 Finger Spring Washer Installed in a Bearing Housing

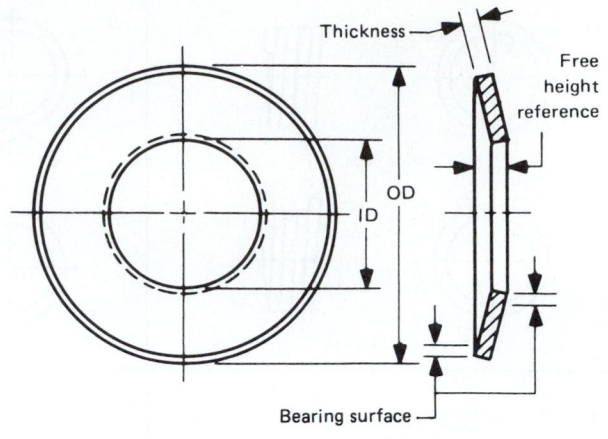

Their applications include keeping fasteners secure, distributing loads, absorbing vibrations, compensating for temperature changes, eliminating side and end play, and controlling end pressure. Figure 15.107 shows a finger spring washer used for preloading ball bearings.

A **coned disk (Belleville) spring** (Fig. 15.108) is a spring washer in the form of the frustrum of a cone. It has constant material thickness and is used as a compression spring.

15.22.10 Flat Springs

The term **flat springs** covers a wide range of springs or stampings fabricated from flat strip material. When deflected by an external load, they will release stored energy. Only a small portion of a complex shaped stamping may actually be functioning as a spring. Leaf springs used on the rears of cars and vans are examples of flat springs.

A flat spring includes all springs made of flat strip or bar stock that deflects as a cantilever or as a simple beam. Figure

```
SPRING DATA
MATERIAL SPECIFICATION  . . . . . . . . . . . . . . . . . . . . . . . . . . . . . . . . . . . . . .
THICKNESS OF MATERIAL  . . . . . . . . . . . . . . . . . . . . . . . . . . . . . . . . . . . . .
FREE HEIGHT . . . . . . . . . . . . . . . . . . . . . . . . . . . . . . . . . . . . . . . . . . . . . . .
FORCE AT COMPRESSED HEIGHT OF_____
(Special data)  . . . . . . . . . . . . . . . . . . . . . . . . . . . . . . . . . . . . . . . . . . . . . .
```

FIGURE 15.108 Drawing Requirements for Coned Disk (Belleville) Springs

15.109 is an example of a detail drawing of a flat spring. A pictorial view shows the part in its finished state and gives the bending angle in degrees. The dimensioned view is of the flat (unfolded) part.

15.22.11 Constant Force Springs

A **constant force spring** (Fig. 15.110) is a strip of flat spring material that has been wound to a given curvature so that, in

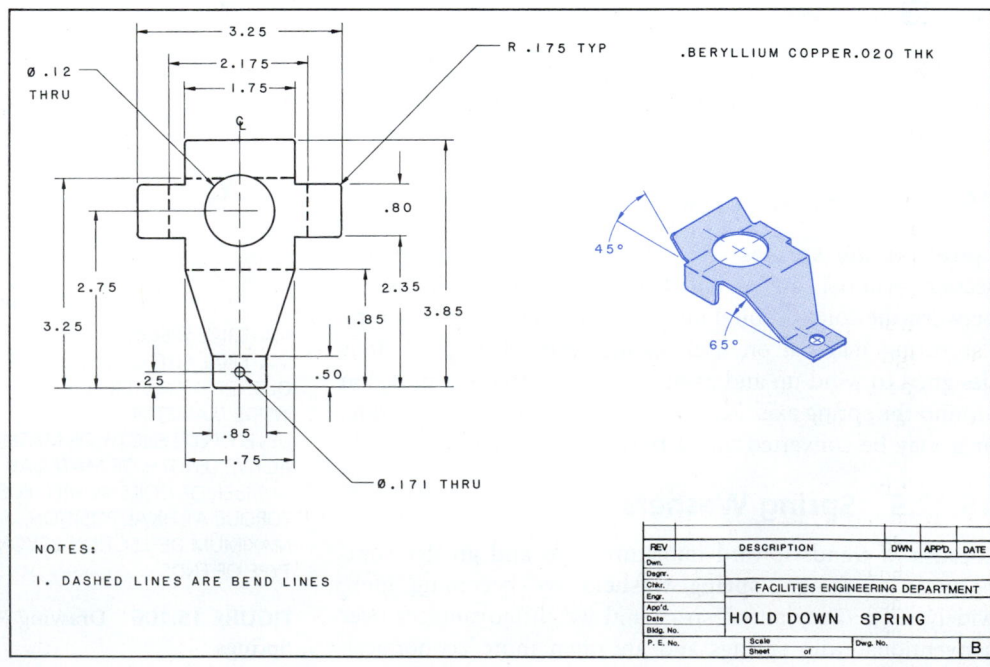

FIGURE 15.109 Hold Down Spring

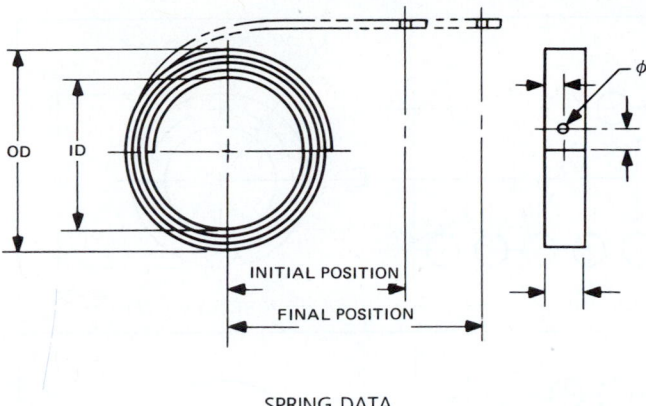

SPRING DATA

MATERIAL SPECIFICATION . . . .
MATERIAL SIZE . . . .
ACTIVE LENGTH . . . .
NUMBER OF COILS . . . .
FORCE . . . .
FITS OVER . . . .

FIGURE 15.110   Drawing Requirements for Constant Force Springs

its relaxed condition, it is in the form of a tightly wound coil or spiral. A constant force is obtained when the outer end of the spring is extended tangent to the coiled body of the spring. A constant torque is obtained when the outer end of the spring is attached to another spool and wound in either the reverse or same direction as originally wound. Because the material used for this type of spring is thin and the number of coils would be difficult to show in actual form, it is acceptable to exaggerate the thickness of the material and to show only enough coils to depict a coiled constant force spring.

15.23   Drawing Springs

Springs are drawn using simplified methods, except when the spring must be pictorially correct for dimensioning. Even when these situations occur, it is normal practice to show only a limited number of coils and use the simplified method for the remaining coils. The simplified method of representing springs uses phantom lines to establish the spring's outside diameter and a centerline to locate its axis. Figure 15.111 shows an industrial detail of a torsion spring. The ends are drawn true, and the coils are shown with phantom lines.

In Figure 15.112 six active coils were required along with plain open ends. The following steps are used to draw the coils of a *compression spring*:

1. The free length (overall length), coil centerline, and outside diameter of the spring are layed out. These dimensions are blocked-in with construction lines. The *mean diameter* is drawn as shown in the side view (end view) of the spring. The mean diameter equals the outside diameter of the coil minus the wire diameter.

One coil diameter (wire diameter) is drawn in the side view, as shown. The inside diameter and the outside diameter of the coil is drawn in the side view (end view).

The front view of the spring is divided into even spaces based on the total number of coils. Each of the coil cross-section diameters is lightly drawn along the top and bottom of the coil length, at the appropriate divisions.

2. The coil winding (left or right hand) is lightly drawn as shown. The appropriate end style is then constructed. The plain open end is used in this example.

3. The coil is darkened in, using appropriate line weights, and dimensioned accordingly (dimensions are not shown in this example—refer to previous examples throughout the chapter).

Drawing an *extension spring* is similar to constructing a compression spring except that the coils are solid in the relaxed (unloaded) position. In other words, the coils touch. The following steps were used to draw a full-loop-over-center extension spring [Fig. 15.113(a) through (e)]:

1. Centerlines and the outside and inside diameter are drawn in the end view. Then the end loops (they will be the same as the end view) are drawn at the required length and the construction completed.

2. Using a circle template and the appropriate diameter (wire size), the wire diameters are drawn on the top and the bottom.

3. A construction line is extended from the end of the edge of the wire diameter on the lower left to the edge of the upper left diameter. Lines are drawn parallel to the first construction line along the total length of the spring coils.

NOTES:

1. ASSOCIATED SPRING
   PART NO. T054-180-421-R

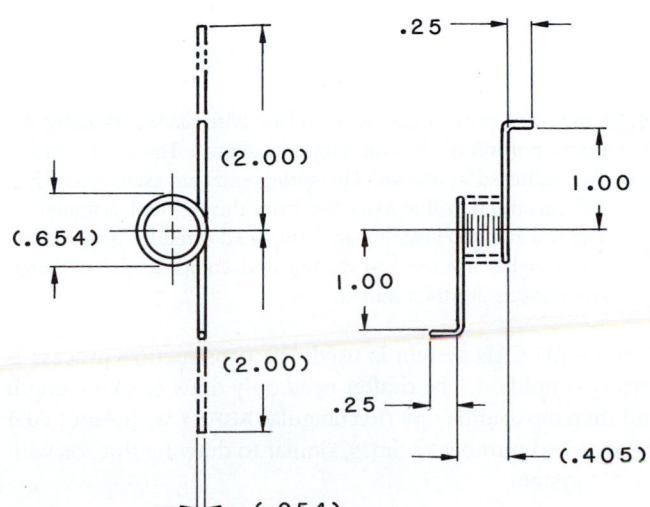

FIGURE 15.111   Torsion Spring Detail

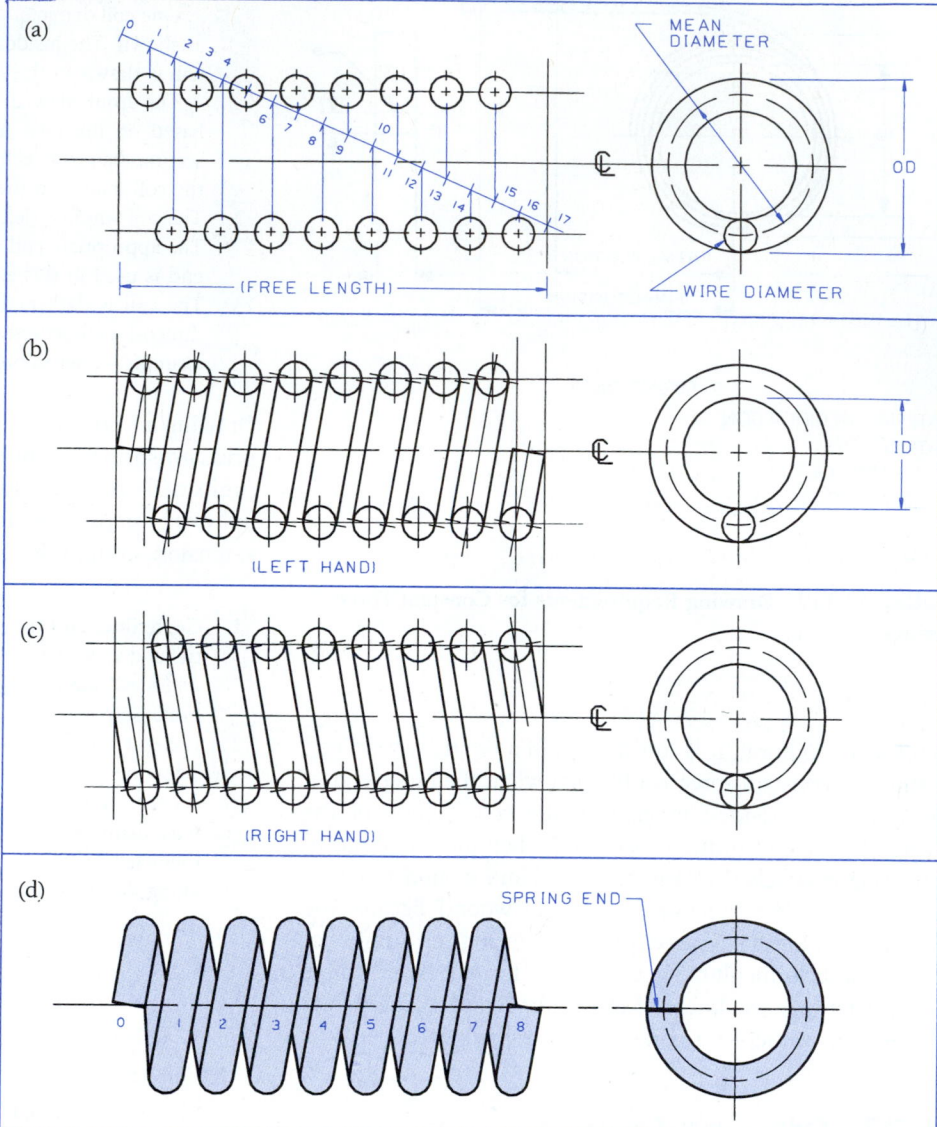

FIGURE 15.112 Drawing a Compression Spring

4. Circles are drawn that represent the wire diameters along the upper portion of the coil length as shown. The spring end is then adjusted as shown. The spring ends are established by a 30° construction line extended from the coil end diameter.
5. The coil and end visibility are completed carefully. Appropriate line weights are used to darken and complete the drawing. Dimensions are then added.

When a 2D CAD system is used, the construction process is greatly simplified. The drafter need only draw one coil length and then move and copy (Rectangular **ARRAY** with AutoCAD) the required number of times, similar to drawing threads with a CAD system.

You May Complete Exercises 15.13 Through 15.16 at This Time

QUIZ

True or False

1. M5 × 1.50-6g is a designation for an American National thread.
2. UNC means United National thread form.
3. The B symbol for threads indicates that the thread is external.
4. Dowel pins are used to align and locate parts.
5. Studs are fasteners that secure two left-handed parts together.
6. Black bolts have a square body under the head.
7. The term 13 "in .500-13 UNC-2B" means the number of threads per foot.
8. Taper pins are tapered $\frac{1}{8}$ inch per foot.

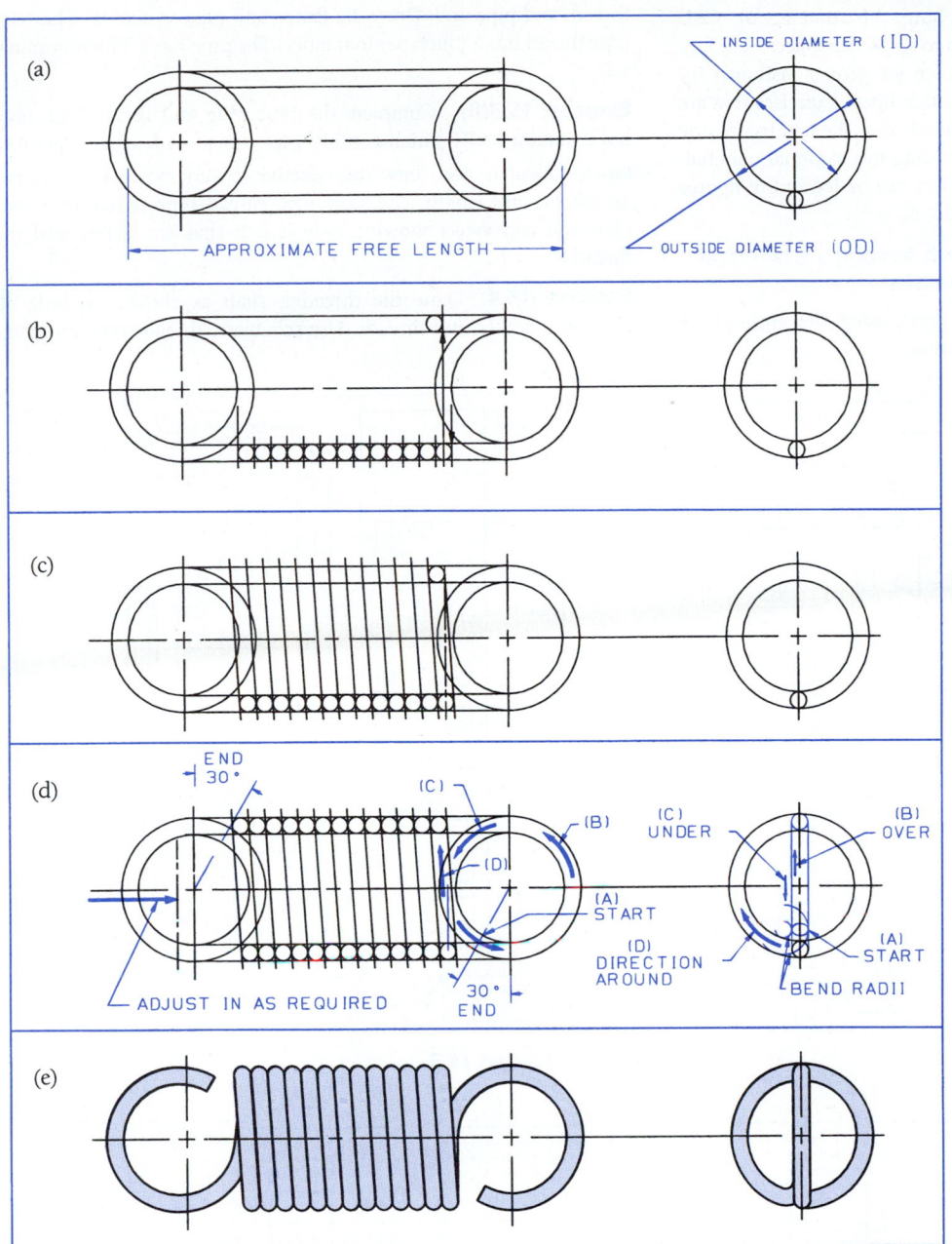

FIGURE 15.113   Drawing an
Extension Spring

Fill in the Blanks

9. _____ , _____ , and _____ are types of keys.

10. _____ , _____ , and _____ are primarily for power transmission.

11. _____ pins are used to retain parts such as slotted nuts and _____ pins.

12. _____ threads are used in place of the old _____ threads.

13. Compression springs come with _____ or _____ ends.

14. _____ _____ rings are installed on _____ machined grooves in housings.

15. A _____ key is shaped similar to a half circle.

16. _____ , _____ , and _____ are three types of end configurations used on extension springs.

Answer the Following

17. Describe how an axially assembled external retaining ring might be used in a design.

18. What is a set screw? Describe some of its possible design functions.

19. Name and describe three types of locating pins.

20. What are the meanings of UN, UNF, and UNC?

21. What is the difference between Class 1, 2, and 5 threads?

22. List four considerations in the selection of a fastener.

23. Describe three uses for springs.

24. What is the difference between the free length and the solid length of a spring?

EXERCISES

Exercises may be assigned as sketching, instrument, or CAD projects. Transfer the given information to an "A" size sheet of .25 in. grid paper. Complete all views and solve for proper visibility, including centerlines, object lines, and hidden lines. Exercises that are not assigned by the instructor can be sketched in the text to provide practice and understanding of the preceding instructional material. Dimensions for fasteners used on exercises can be located in figures throughout the chapter and in Appendix C.

After Reading the Chapter Through Section 15.12.1 You May Complete the Following Exercises

Exercise 15.1 Complete the three parts using the appropriate threads. Use detailed thread representation.

Exercise 15.2 Draw a detailed representation of the Acme threads.

Exercise 15.3(A) Calculate the normal engagement, effective thread, and pipe end. Draw the flange and pipe as shown. The NPT pipe thread has a $\frac{3}{4}$ inch per foot taper. The pipe has a 3 inch nominal size.

Exercise 15.3(B) Complete the pipe plug and flange. The plug has a standard NPT $\frac{3}{4}$ inch nominal pipe thread with a $\frac{3}{4}$ inch per foot taper. Calculate and draw the effective thread, normal thread engagement, and length. Use simplified thread representation. Complete the end views showing only details that are visible and the threads.

Exercise 15.4 Draw the threaded shaft as shown. Include all chamfers, reliefs, and threads. Use schematic thread representation.

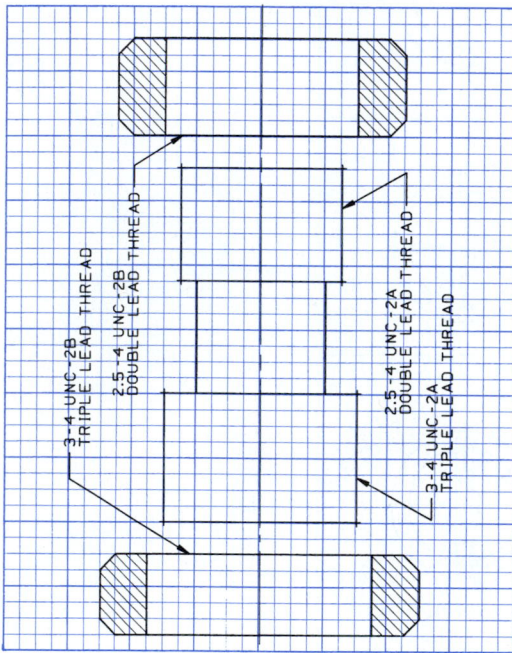

Exercise 15.1

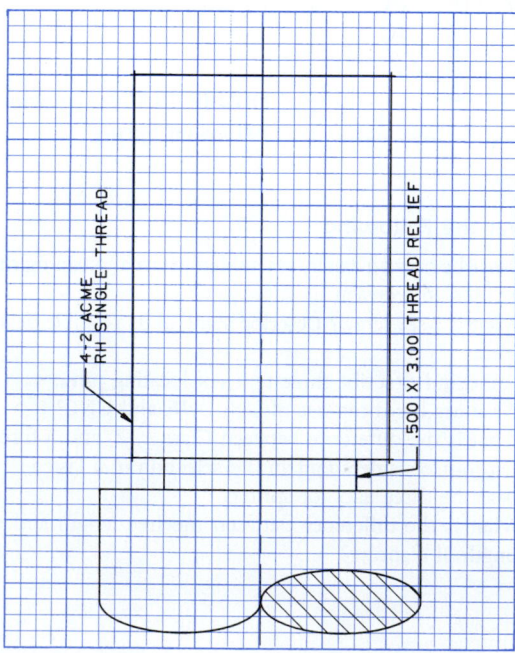

Exercise 15.2

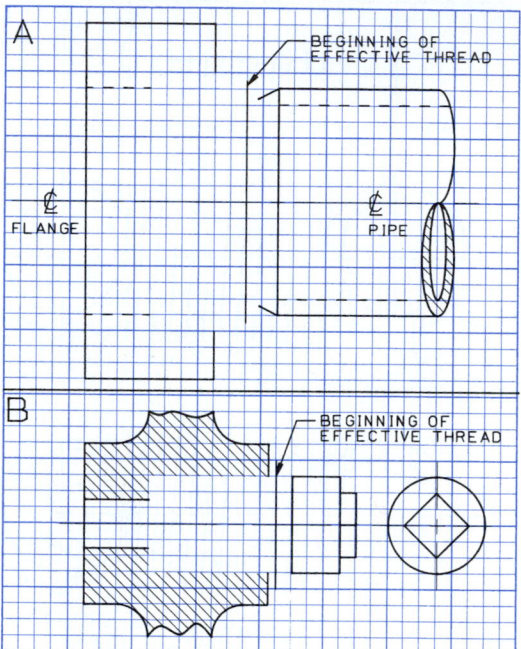

Exercise 15.3

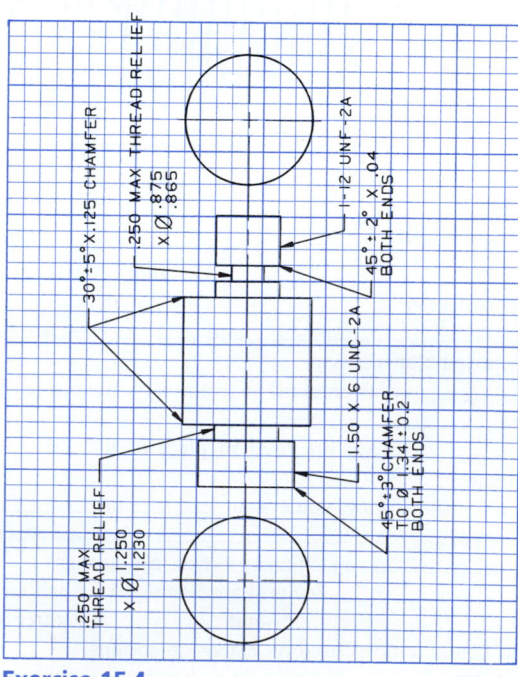

Exercise 15.4

After Reading the Chapter Through Section 15.16 You May Complete the Following Exercises

Exercise 15.5(A) Using detailed representation draw a 1.50-6 UNC-2A × 4 square head bolt. Draw only the axial (side) view in the given space.

Exercise 15.5(B) Draw a detailed representation of the 1-8 UNC-2A × 3 hex socket head cap screw. Show the side and end views in the given space and label the drawing correctly.

Exercise 15.6(A) Fasten the rest block to the plate with four $\frac{3}{8}$ inch diameter hex socket head cap screws (S) and two $\frac{3}{8}$ inch diameter steel dowel pins (D). Calculate the screw and dowel lengths. The plate will have threaded through-holes. The rest block will have clearance through holes for the screws to pass through. Calculate the screw's length of engagement and counterbore the block so that the screw's head will be flush with the top surface. Calculate the coun-terbore diameter and depth. The dowel will be press fit (interference fit) into the block and the plate. Calculate the ream hole diameter for the dowels.

Exercise 15.6(B) Dimension the hole pattern for the screws and the dowels. Call out the proper clearance hole size for the drilled clearance holes' screws and the reamed holes for the dowels.

Exercise 15.7 Draw the moving shaft pivot as shown. Use two hex socket head shoulder screws. Show the screws in both views. The screws have different diameters and lengths.

Exercise 15.8 Determine the proper diameter and length of the set screws as per shaft diameter. Two hex socket set screws are required for each shaft. They are installed 90° to one another. Use a cup point for the small set screws and a dog point for the two larger set screws.

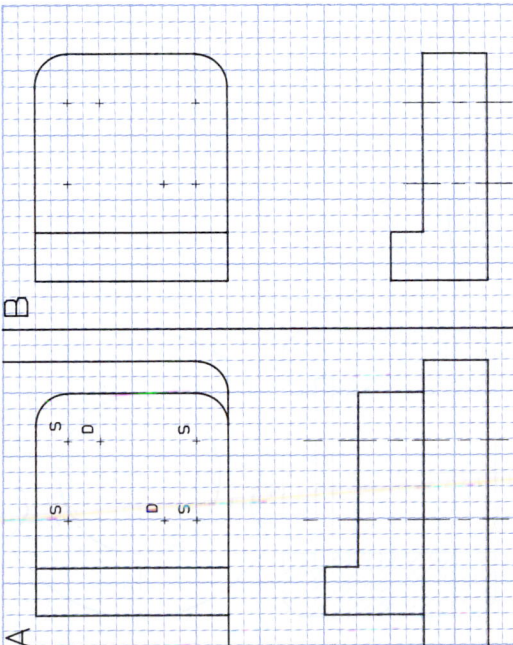

Exercise 15.6

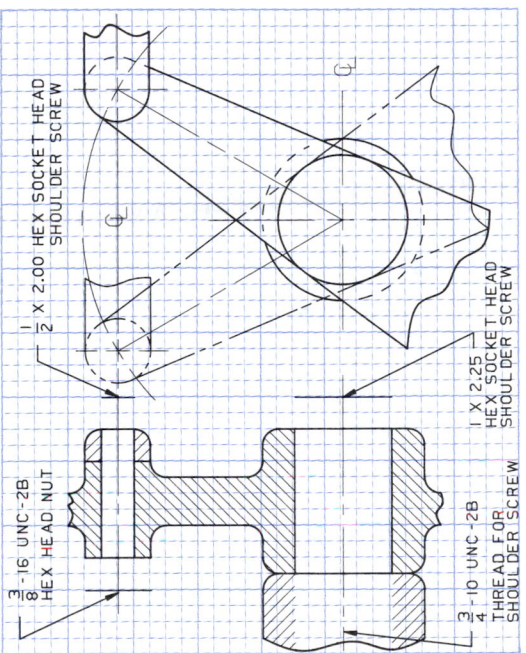

Exercise 15.7

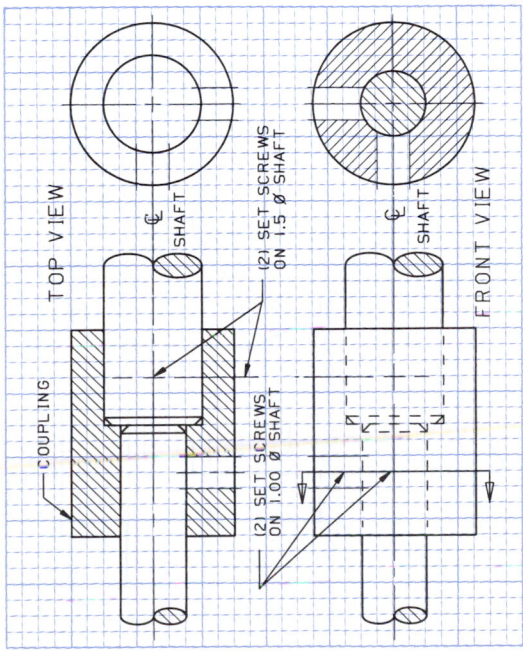

Exercise 15.8

Exercise 15.5

PROBLEMS

Problem 15.1 Draw a 1.00 inch pitch thread (two times size), of the following thread types: Acme, square, and UNC.

Problem 15.2 Draw 3-2 Acme thread with a length of 5.00 inches using detailed thread representation.

Problem 15.3 Draw a 1.25 × 4.50 hex socket head shoulder screw full size. Show length view, and end view of head. Use schematic method to display threads.

Problem 15.4 Fasten a 1.25 inch plate to a cast aluminum casting (3.00 inches thick) using a .500-13 UNC socket head cap screw. Calculate and show the screw in two views. Dimension and call out the tap drill, clearance hole, and tap size.

Problem 15.5 Connect a 1.50 inch and a 1.375 inch plate with a 1.00 inch socket head shoulder screw and appropriate nut. Show in two views and call out all hole sizes.

Problem 15.6 Bolt together two 1.50 inch thick steel plates with two 1.25 12 UNF hex head bolts. Use lock washers on both ends and the appropriate nut. Show in section. Construct a small parts lists for the hardware.

Problem 15.7 Fasten a 4.0 × 4.0 × 4.0 × 2.00 inch thick steel angle plate to a steel part using four .375-16 UNC socket head caps screws and two .375 inch diameter dowels. Design the bolt pattern and calculate all fastener sizes. Dimension and call out all fasteners. Counterbore the plate so that the screw heads will be below the surface.

Problem 15.8 Draw a 50 mm diameter shaft and a 74 mm wide collar (OD 100 mm/ID 51 mm). Fasten the collar to the shaft with two appropriately sized socket set screws with a dog point. Show in two views.

Problem 15.9 Draw a 2.50 inch diameter shaft and a 4.00 inch wide collar (OD 5.00 in./ID 2.51 in.). Connect the two parts with a square key 2.00 inches long. Calculate the key size and show in two views. Dimension the views as required.

Problem 15.10 Same as Problem 15.9 but use a Woodruff key and keyseat. Dimension the views as required.

Problem 15.11 Connect two sheets of .125 inch thick aluminum with a .125 inch diameter button head rivet. Show in two views at two times size.

Problem 15.12 Using a butt joint connect two .500 inch thick sheets (6.00 inches wide) of steel with twelve 1.125 inch diameter pan head rivets. Use double rivets on each side of the joint. Show in two views and dimension completely.

Problem 15.13 Using Exercise 15.13 as an example, draw a detailed representation of a compression spring. List all specifications on the drawing. The spring is steel, has a wire diameter of .200 inches, is right-hand wound with square ends, and has ten active coils and twelve total coils. Use the same OD.

Problem 15.14 Using Exercise 15.14 as an example, draw a compression spring showing five coils at each end and the remainder with phantom lines. The spring is left-hand wound, has a wire diameter of .125 inches, comes with plain ends, and has a total of twenty active coils (also twenty total coils). List all controlling specifications. Use the same OD.

Problem 15.15 Using Exercise 15.15 as an example, draw a helical extension spring. The spring is to be left-hand wound, has a .200 in. wire diameter, and comes with round ends. Draw all coils and list the specifications. Use the same OD.

Problem 15.16 Using Exercise 15.16 as an example, construct a helical torsion spring with a wire diameter of .187 inches and fifteen coils. The spring is right-hand wound. Draw all coils. List all specifications. Use the same OD.

Problem 15.17 Design and detail an extension spring with a full loop over center on the right end and a long hook over center on the left end. The spring is right-hand wound and has a free length of 180 mm with a 6 mm wire size. It should have fourteen total coils. The coil length is 80 mm with an OD of 50 mm. Show all dimensions.

Problem 15.18 Design and detail an extension spring with the following specifications:

Approximate free length = 1700 mm
Winding = left-hand (special)
Wire size = 5 mm
OD = 50 mm
Ends = Full loop over center for both

Problem 15.19 Draw and dimension a compression spring with plain closed ends and a wire diameter of 10 mm. The spring will be left-hand wound, with an OD of 48 mm. The free length is 160 mm. Calculate the solid length. There are ten total coils (eight are active).

Problem 15.20 Design and detail a compression spring with the following specifications:

Free length = 4.00 inch
Coils = 6 total
3 active
Wire size = .50 inch
Ends = closed ground
OD = 3.75 inch
Winding = Left-hand
Solid length = (calculate)

Problem 15.21 Design and detail a compression spring with the following specifications:

Free length = 190 mm
Coils = 14 total
12 active
Wire size = 6 mm
Ends = plain open
OD = 60 mm
Winding = Right-hand
Solid length = (calculate)

Problem 15.22 Design and detail a compression spring with the following specifications:

Free length = 5.00 inch
Coils = 7 total
5 active
Wire size = .375 inch
Ends = ground open
OD = 3.00 inch
Winding = Left-hand
Solid length = (calculate)

After Reading the Chapter Through Section 15.16 You May Complete the Following Exercises

Exercise 15.5(A) Using detailed representation draw a 1.50-6 UNC-2A × 4 square head bolt. Draw only the axial (side) view in the given space.

Exercise 15.5(B) Draw a detailed representation of the 1-8 UNC-2A × 3 hex socket head cap screw. Show the side and end views in the given space and label the drawing correctly.

Exercise 15.6(A) Fasten the rest block to the plate with four $\frac{3}{8}$ inch diameter hex socket head cap screws (S) and two $\frac{3}{8}$ inch diameter steel dowel pins (D). Calculate the screw and dowel lengths. The plate will have threaded through-holes. The rest block will have clearance through holes for the screws to pass through. Calculate the screw's length of engagement and counterbore the block so that the screw's head will be flush with the top surface. Calculate the coun-

terbore diameter and depth. The dowel will be press fit (interference fit) into the block and the plate. Calculate the ream hole diameter for the dowels.

Exercise 15.6(B) Dimension the hole pattern for the screws and the dowels. Call out the proper clearance hole size for the drilled clearance holes' screws and the reamed holes for the dowels.

Exercise 15.7 Draw the moving shaft pivot as shown. Use two hex socket head shoulder screws. Show the screws in both views. The screws have different diameters and lengths.

Exercise 15.8 Determine the proper diameter and length of the set screws as per shaft diameter. Two hex socket set screws are required for each shaft. They are installed 90° to one another. Use a cup point for the small set screws and a dog point for the two larger set screws.

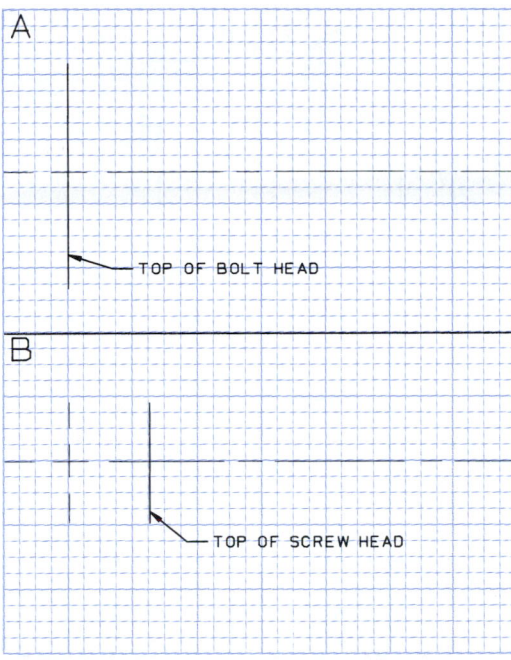

Exercise 15.5

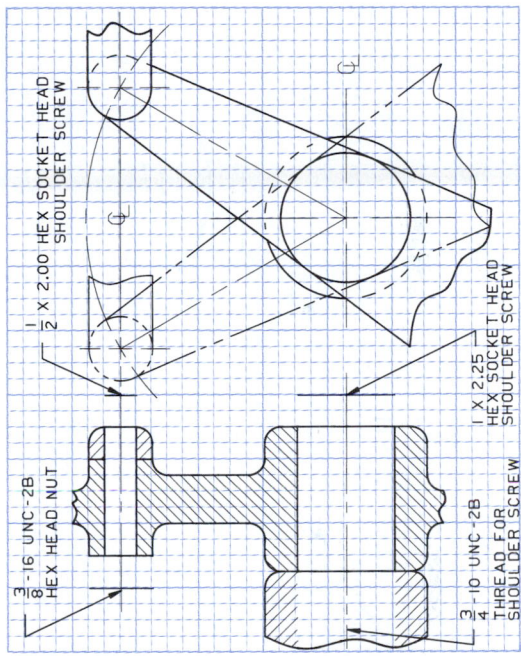

Exercise 15.7

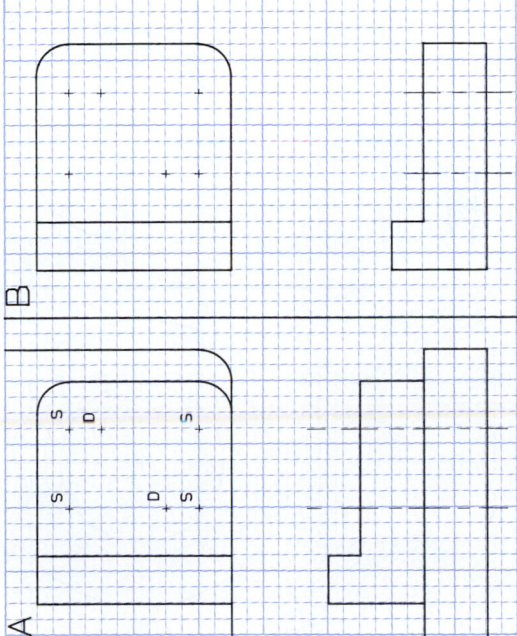

Exercise 15.6

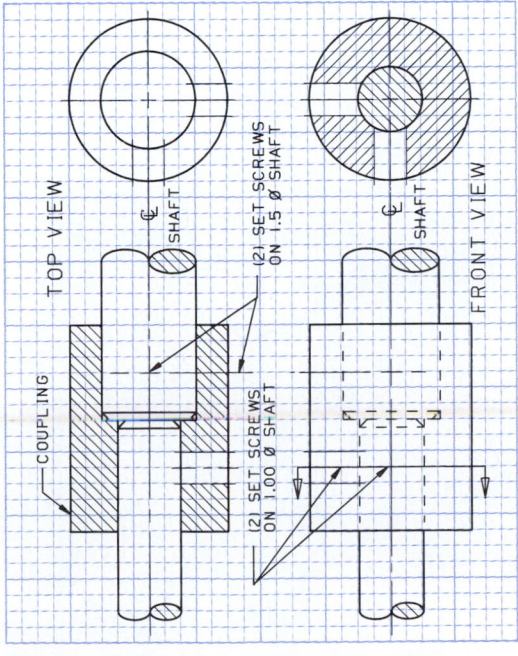

Exercise 15.8

After Reading the Chapter Through Section 15.21.4 You May Complete the Following Exercises

Exercise 15.9(A) Attach the collar to the shaft using one of the two following types of spring pins:

Pin, Coiled Spring, 10 × 100, Metric, Steel
Pin, Slotted Spring, .500 × 4.00, ANSI 302

Exercise 15.9(B) Attach the collar to the shaft with a tapered pin. Call out the hole size and dimensions for tapered holes and use the following pin: Pin, Tapered, No. 8 × 2.50, Steel.

Exercise 15.10 Fasten the hitch at point C with a .500 inch clevis pin. Use two .500 inch plain washers above and below the hitch and plate. Show a .125 inch diameter cotter pin to secure the clevis pin. Fasten the plates at point B with three .625 inch diameter hex bolts. Use lock washers on both sides and hex flat nuts on the bottom. Show fasteners in both views. You will need to determine the length of the bolts and the clevis pin based on the fastening requirements. Call out the clevis pin, cotter pin, washers, nuts, and bolts on a separate parts list and attach to the drawing.

Exercise 15.11(A) Calculate the size and length of a Woodruff key or a square key (ask your instructor). Draw the key in the view provided. The shaft has a 2.00 inch diameter.

Exercise 15.11(B) Secure the shaft to the sprocket using a tapered gib key or a taper key. Determine the size and length of a key for the 1.50 inch diameter shaft.

Exercise 15.12(A) Draw and dimension the shaft and a basic 5100 external retaining ring. See Appendix C or manufacturing catalogs for the ring dimensions.

Exercise 15.12(B) Same as Exercise 15.12(A) except use a N5000 basic 3 inch internal retaining ring for the housing. Draw and dimension completely.

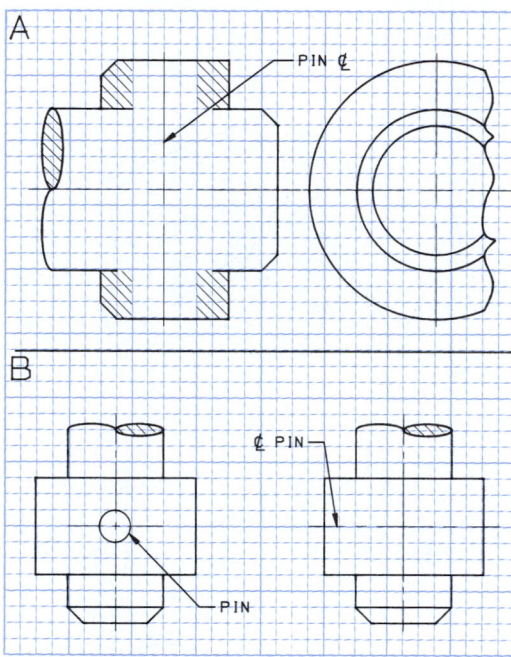

Exercise 15.9

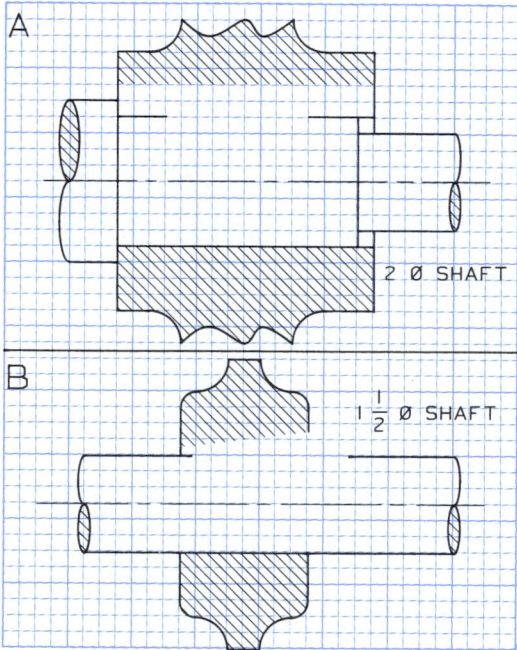

Exercise 15.11

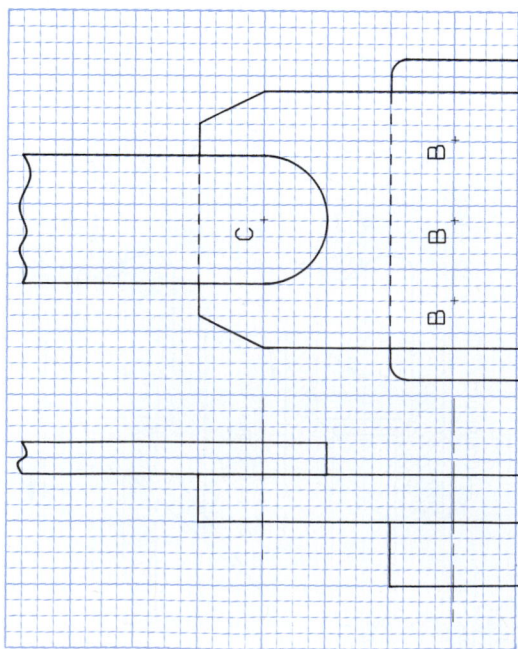

Exercise 15.10

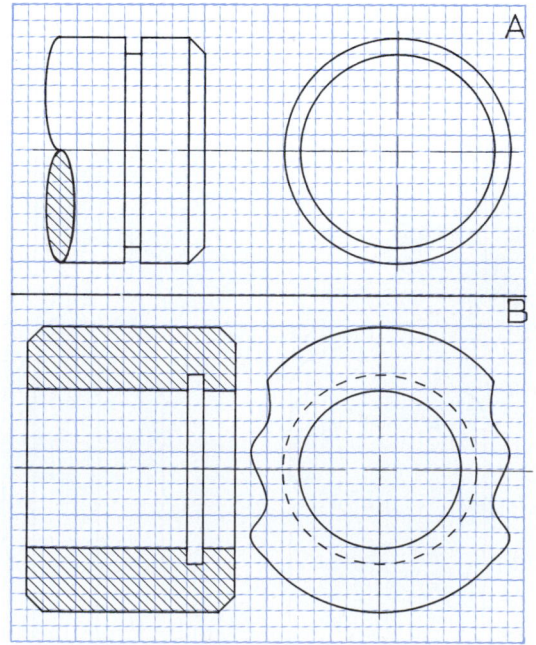

Exercise 15.12

After Reading the Chapter Through Section 15.23 You May Complete the Following Exercises

Exercise 15.13   Using detailed representation, draw the compression spring as shown. List all pertinent specifications on the drawing. The spring is steel, has a wire diameter of .250 inches, is left-hand wound with square ends, and has eight active coils and ten total coils.

Exercise 15.14   Draw all coils for the compression spring. The spring is right-hand wound, has a wire diameter of .187 inches, comes with plain ends, and has a total of eighteen active coils (also eighteen total coils). List all controlling specifications.

Exercise 15.15   Complete the helical extension spring. The spring is to be right-hand wound, has a .250 in. wire diameter, and comes with round ends as shown. Draw all coils. List all specifications.

Exercise 15.16   Complete the helical torsion spring using a wire diameter of .200 inches and seventeen coils. The spring is left-hand wound. Draw all coils. List all specifications.

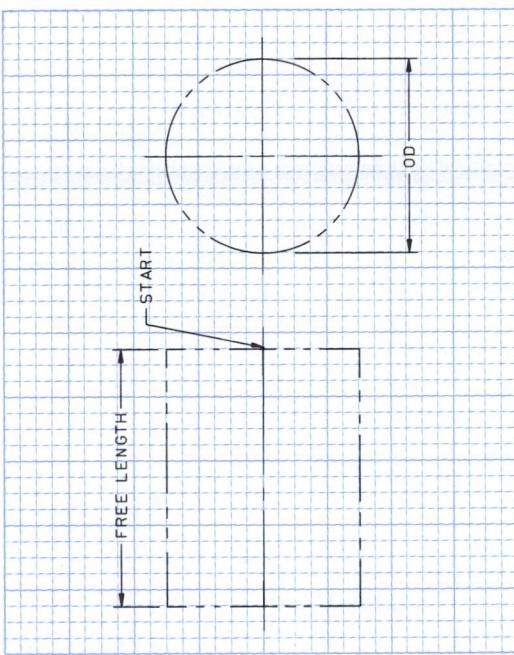

Exercise 15.13

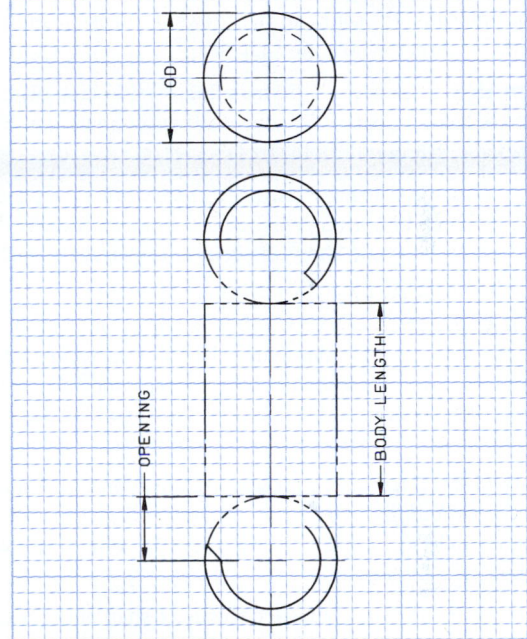

Exercise 15.15

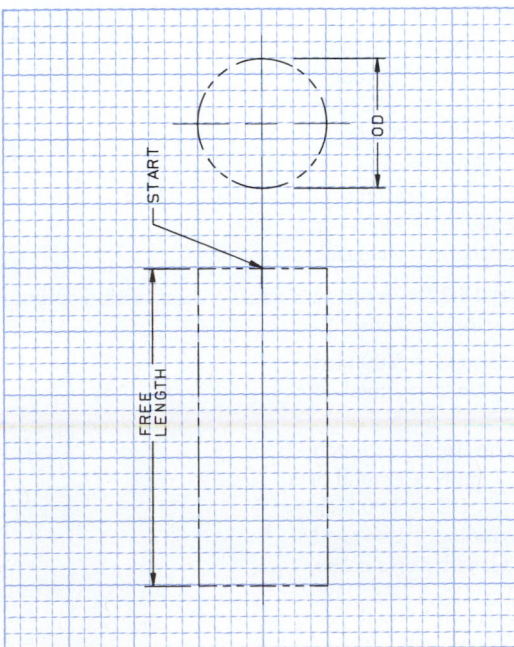

Exercise 15.14

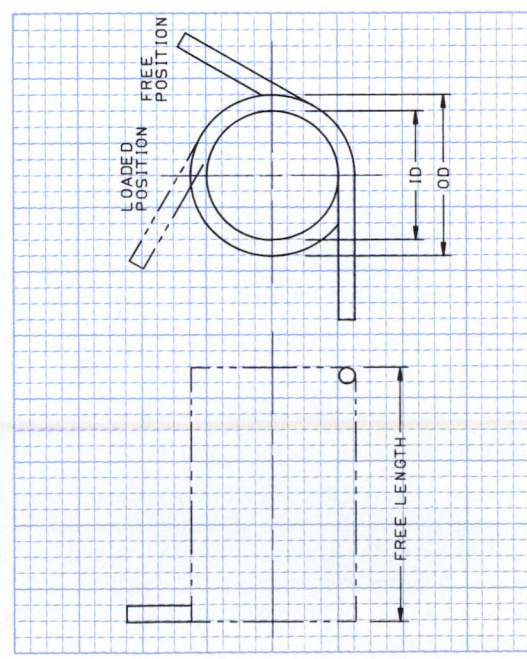

Exercise 15.16

PROBLEMS

Problem 15.1   Draw a 1.00 inch pitch thread (two times size), of the following thread types: Acme, square, and UNC.

Problem 15.2   Draw 3-2 Acme thread with a length of 5.00 inches using detailed thread representation.

Problem 15.3   Draw a 1.25 × 4.50 hex socket head shoulder screw full size. Show length view, and end view of head. Use schematic method to display threads.

Problem 15.4   Fasten a 1.25 inch plate to a cast aluminum casting (3.00 inches thick) using a .500-13 UNC socket head cap screw. Calculate and show the screw in two views. Dimension and call out the tap drill, clearance hole, and tap size.

Problem 15.5   Connect a 1.50 inch and a 1.375 inch plate with a 1.00 inch socket head shoulder screw and appropriate nut. Show in two views and call out all hole sizes.

Problem 15.6   Bolt together two 1.50 inch thick steel plates with two 1.25 12 UNF hex head bolts. Use lock washers on both ends and the appropriate nut. Show in section. Construct a small parts lists for the hardware.

Problem 15.7   Fasten a 4.0 × 4.0 × 4.0 × 2.00 inch thick steel angle plate to a steel part using four .375-16 UNC socket head caps screws and two .375 inch diameter dowels. Design the bolt pattern and calculate all fastener sizes. Dimension and call out all fasteners. Counterbore the plate so that the screw heads will be below the surface.

Problem 15.8   Draw a 50 mm diameter shaft and a 74 mm wide collar (OD 100 mm/ID 51 mm). Fasten the collar to the shaft with two appropriately sized socket set screws with a dog point. Show in two views.

Problem 15.9   Draw a 2.50 inch diameter shaft and a 4.00 inch wide collar (OD 5.00 in./ID 2.51 in.). Connect the two parts with a square key 2.00 inches long. Calculate the key size and show in two views. Dimension the views as required.

Problem 15.10   Same as Problem 15.9 but use a Woodruff key and keyseat. Dimension the views as required.

Problem 15.11   Connect two sheets of .125 inch thick aluminum with a .125 inch diameter button head rivet. Show in two views at two times size.

Problem 15.12   Using a butt joint connect two .500 inch thick sheets (6.00 inches wide) of steel with twelve 1.125 inch diameter pan head rivets. Use double rivets on each side of the joint. Show in two views and dimension completely.

Problem 15.13   Using Exercise 15.13 as an example, draw a detailed representation of a compression spring. List all specifications on the drawing. The spring is steel, has a wire diameter of .200 inches, is right-hand wound with square ends, and has ten active coils and twelve total coils. Use the same OD.

Problem 15.14   Using Exercise 15.14 as an example, draw a compression spring showing five coils at each end and the remainder with phantom lines. The spring is left-hand wound, has a wire diameter of .125 inches, comes with plain ends, and has a total of twenty active coils (also twenty total coils). List all controlling specifications. Use the same OD.

Problem 15.15   Using Exercise 15.15 as an example, draw a helical extension spring. The spring is to be left-hand wound, has a .200 in. wire diameter, and comes with round ends. Draw all coils and list the specifications. Use the same OD.

Problem 15.16   Using Exercise 15.16 as an example, construct a helical torsion spring with a wire diameter of .187 inches and fifteen coils. The spring is right-hand wound. Draw all coils. List all specifications. Use the same OD.

Problem 15.17   Design and detail an extension spring with a full loop over center on the right end and a long hook over center on the left end. The spring is right-hand wound and has a free length of 180 mm with a 6 mm wire size. It should have fourteen total coils. The coil length is 80 mm with an OD of 50 mm. Show all dimensions.

Problem 15.18   Design and detail an extension spring with the following specifications:

> Approximate free length = 1700 mm
> Winding = left-hand (special)
> Wire size = 5 mm
> OD = 50 mm
> Ends = Full loop over center for both

Problem 15.19   Draw and dimension a compression spring with plain closed ends and a wire diameter of 10 mm. The spring will be left-hand wound, with an OD of 48 mm. The free length is 160 mm. Calculate the solid length. There are ten total coils (eight are active).

Problem 15.20   Design and detail a compression spring with the following specifications:

> Free length = 4.00 inch
> Coils = 6 total
> 3 active
> Wire size = .50 inch
> Ends = closed ground
> OD = 3.75 inch
> Winding = Left-hand
> Solid length = (calculate)

Problem 15.21   Design and detail a compression spring with the following specifications:

> Free length = 190 mm
> Coils = 14 total
> 12 active
> Wire size = 6 mm
> Ends = plain open
> OD = 60 mm
> Winding = Right-hand
> Solid length = (calculate)

Problem 15.22   Design and detail a compression spring with the following specifications:

> Free length = 5.00 inch
> Coils = 7 total
> 5 active
> Wire size = .375 inch
> Ends = ground open
> OD = 3.00 inch
> Winding = Left-hand
> Solid length = (calculate)

Problem 15.23   Design and detail (draw two times size) a torsion spring with the following specifications:

Free length = .875 inch
Coils = 5
Wire size = .125 inch
Ends = straight and turned to follow radial lines to center of spring and extend .375 inch from outside diameter of spring
OD = 1.375 inch
Winding = Left-hand

Problem 15.24   Design and detail a torsion spring with the following specifications:

Free length = 50 mm
Coils = 10
Wire size = 6 mm
Ends = as assigned by instructor
OD = 70 mm
Winding = Right-hand

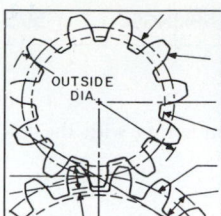

CHAPTER 16

Gears, Shafts, Bearings, and Cams

Learning Objectives

Upon completion of this chapter you will be able to accomplish the following:

1. Recognize mechanical devices that are designed to transmit motion from one machine element to another.
2. Analyze gear blank stock material, types of hubs, and methods of attaching gears to shafts.
3. Define the various gear categories and basic specifications for manufacture and inspection.
4. Explain common gear terms and symbols.
5. Demonstrate an understanding of gear and cam drawing practices.
6. Develop ability to communicate gear, shaft, bearing, and cam data by means of ANSI standard dimensioning and notation.
7. Define the types and purposes of bearings and their respective housings and mountings.
8. Demonstrate familiarity with cam and follower functions and terminology.
9. Identify cam motions.
10. Explore the use of CAD in gear and cam design.

16.1 Introduction

This chapter covers mechanical devices designed to transmit motion from one machine element to another (Fig. 16.1). Most gears and cams are mounted on shafts (Fig. 16.2), which, in turn, are secured by **bearings** installed in a variety of housings. **Gears** are designed to transfer rotary motion from one **shaft** to another. The speed of the motion can be increased or decreased by changing the size of the drive gear and the driven gear. The selection of gear types is based on the relative position of the shafts. The shafts will be either intersecting, nonintersecting, or parallel. Shafts can be posi-

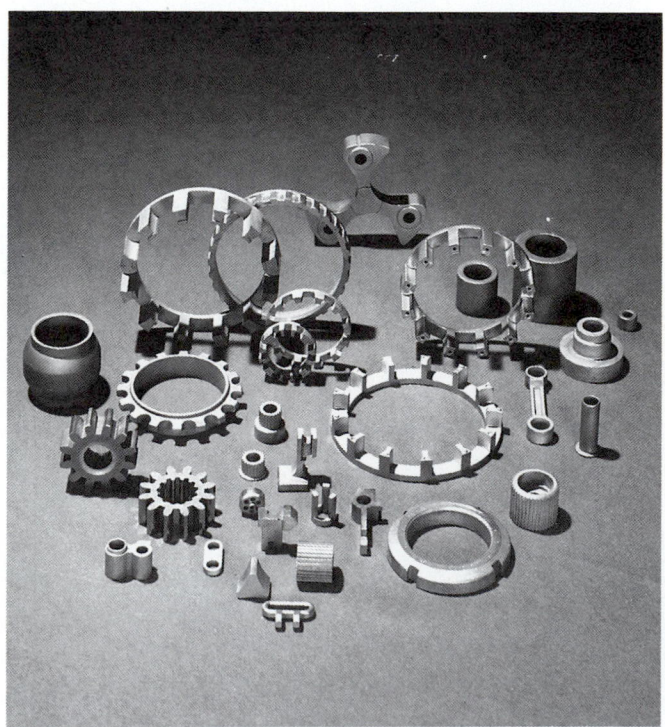

FIGURE 16.1 Gears and Machine Parts

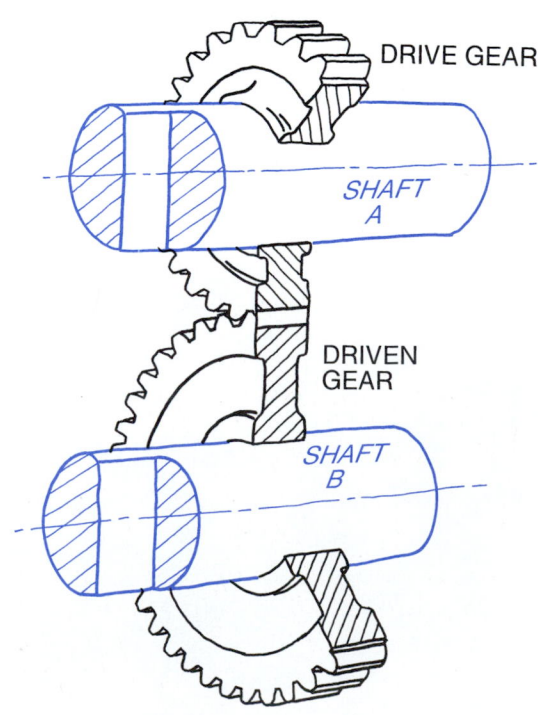

FIGURE 16.2 Gears and Shafts

tioned perpendicular, parallel, or at any given angle to each other, depending on the design application. Figure 16.2 shows two spur gears mounted on parallel shafts. Shaft A holds the *drive gear*; shaft B holds the *driven gear*. Spur gears are commonly used to transfer motion from one parallel shaft to another. In this example, the drive gear is smaller than the driven gear; therefore, the driven gear will take longer to complete one revolution and its speed will be less than that of the drive gear.

Some gears are designed to change rotary motion into reciprocating (linear—back and forth) motion. These machine elements are called **pinions** and **gear racks**. Another method of transmitting rotary motion into reciprocating (linear—up and down) motion utilizes a **cam** and **follower** assembly.

Whether the transfer of motion is rotary to rotary or rotary to linear, the rotary element must be mounted on some kind of a shaft and that shaft must rotate freely. Therefore, shafts ride on bearings.

16.2   Gears

This chapter introduces the most common types of gears, shows how they are represented on drawings, and provides methods for calling out their specifications. **Gear specifications** are the most important information to be supplied to the gear manufacturer. Gears come in many styles, including spur gears, pinions, ring gears, worm gears, bevel gears, miter gears, hypoid bevel gears, racks, and others. Gears are made of metals and nonmetals. Spur gears are the most common gear type manufactured. Color Plates 28 and 29 show examples of gear design using solid modeling on a CAD system.

The illustration of the gears in Figure 16.3 shows a manual grinder. The handle is turned, which rotates the drive gear. Since the drive gear is larger than the driven gear, the simple

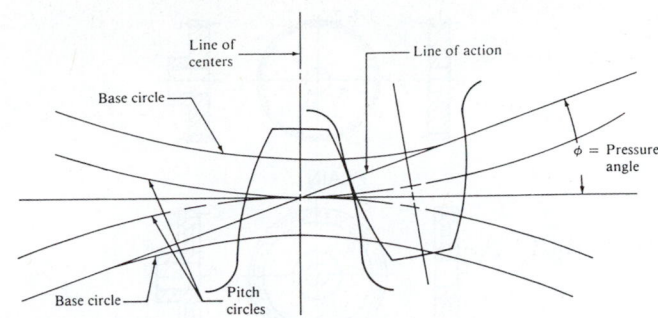

FIGURE 16.4   Pressure Angle and Line of Action

machine will increase the speed of the grinding wheel through a series of gears. Spur gears are used in this application.

16.2.1   Gear Teeth

Gear teeth are projections designed to fit into the tooth spaces of mating gears and contact mating teeth along a common line known as the **pressure line**, which is also called the **line of action** (Fig. 16.4). The most common form for the tooth flank is **involute**. The pressure line determines the particular involute shape. The American National Standards Institute (ANSI) has standardized two pressure angles, $14\frac{1}{2}°$ (now rarely used) and $20°$ (Fig. 16.5).

16.2.2   Gears, Splines, Racks, and Serrations

The following terms and descriptions define the general gear categories covered in the chapter:

Spur gears   Gears connecting parallel shafts and having straight teeth elements (parallel to the axis of the shafts). The smaller gear of a pair of gears is called a **pinion**.

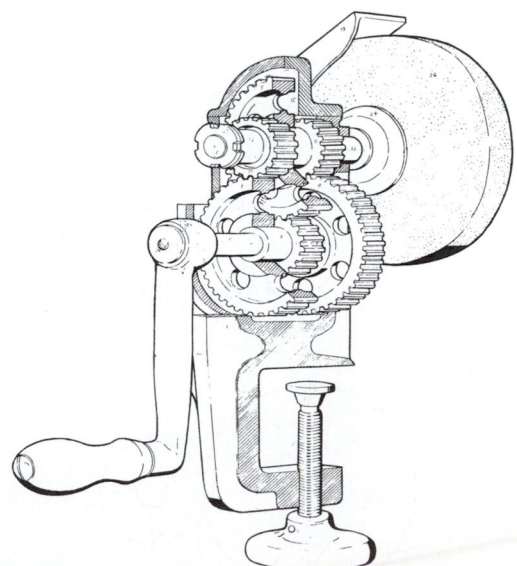

FIGURE 16.3   Illustration of Gear Train for Grinder

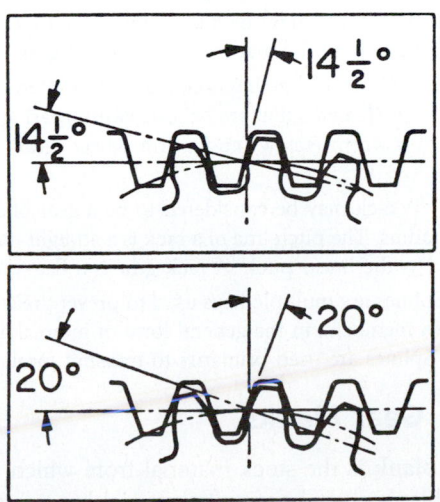

FIGURE 16.5   Pressure Angles

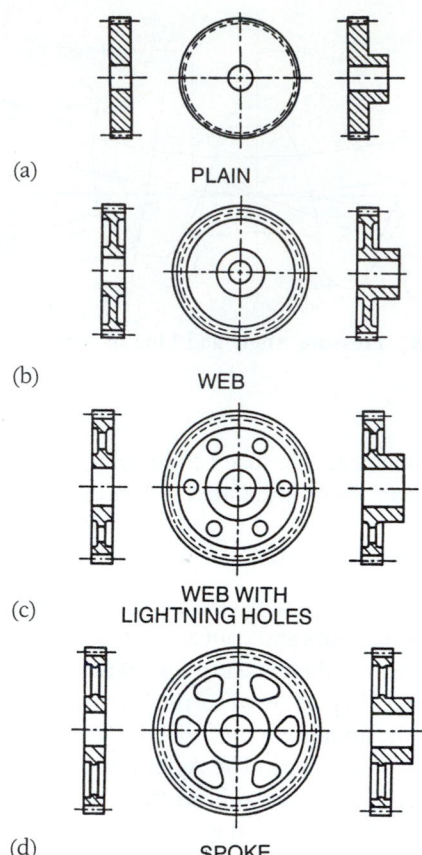

(a)   PLAIN

(b)   WEB

(c)   WEB WITH LIGHTNING HOLES

(d)   SPOKE

FIGURE 16.6   **Gear Blank Options**

Helical gears   Gears connecting shafts with projected nonintersecting centerlines. Helical gear teeth elements are spiral or helical in shape.

Bevel and miter gears   Gears that are conical in form and operate on shafts having projected intersecting centerlines. When the gears are different sizes, they are called bevel gears. Bevel gears of the same size (one-to-one ratio) with shafts intersecting at right angles, are called miter gears.

Internal gears   Gears connecting parallel shafts, with teeth elements that are either straight or helical and with a pitch circle that is tangent internally to the mating spur or spiral gear.

Worm gears   Gears connecting nonparallel, nonintersecting shafts. They have teeth elements that are helical. Worm gearing generally is composed of a worm (screw) and worm wheel (gear) in matched sets.

Rack gear   A rack may be considered to be a gear of an infinitely long pitch radius. The pitch line of a rack is a straight line; the pitch is described as the linear pitch. A rack gear is a flat spur gear.

Splines   Splines are multiple keys used to prevent relative rotation between two members, in the general form of internal and external gear teeth. Splines are used primarily to transmit torque.

16.2.3   Gear Blanks

The **gear blank** is the stock material from which the gear is cut. The blank must have sufficient rigidity to prevent distortion during tooth cutting. The type of *hub* (split, solid, or hubless) and the type of gear (spoked, flanged, or flat) must

also be determined. Hub variations are shown in Figure 16.6. Still another factor to consider in the selection of the gear blank is the method of attaching the gear to its shaft. Some of the more common methods employed are:

Key   Permits easy assembly and disassembly. The design must assure that the key is captive when the assembly is complete.

Pin   Requires drilling at assembly. This tends to weaken small shafts and does not permit replacement of gear or shaft. This method provides a positive engagement between gear and shaft.

Set screw   Permits easy assembly and disassembly. This method should always use two set screws at 45–90° to each other. Set screws at a 60° angle are the strongest. The design of the shaft should provide flats on the shaft as a bearing surface for the set screw. Some method of retaining the set screw must be provided. This method is not appropriate when large torque loads are transmitted.

Adhesive bond   Requires considerable care at assembly to assure a good bond. Adhesive has temperature and torque limitations. Disassembly is very difficult without destroying parts of the assembly. The adhesive chosen must be compatible with gear and shaft materials.

Mechanical stake   This method has moderate torque transmitting capacity and may not permit replacement of gear or shaft.

Clamp   Can only be used with split hub gears, are bulky in size, and have only moderate torque capacity. This method is easy to assemble and disassemble.

Press   Not acceptable when shaft cannot be isolated from the bearings as in a motor. Disassembly is difficult. Materials must not expand or contract and cause a loose fit at temperature extremes.

16.3   Spur Gears

Spur gears are mounted on parallel axes. Two friction wheels with surfaces in contact are shown in Figure 16.7. If one of the wheels is turned—and no slipping occurs—the other one will turn. To prevent slipping, gear teeth may be added to both wheels, with corresponding recesses in each wheel.

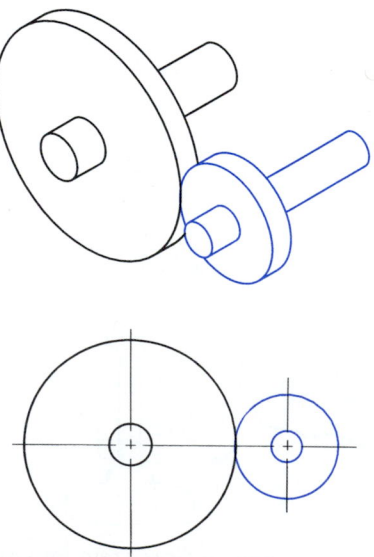

FIGURE 16.7   **Friction Wheels**

FIGURE 16.8   Spur Gears

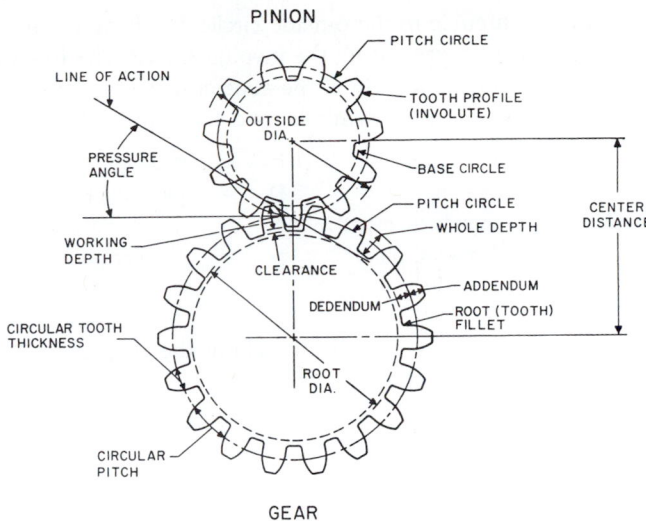

(a)

These are called **spur gears** (Fig. 16.8). Terms are given in Figure 16.9(a) and (b) for gears with the involute form of gear teeth. A gear and pinion are shown in this figure. A **pinion** is the smaller of two gears in a mating set. The **pitch circles** in Figure 16.9(a) are tangent and might be thought of as representing the friction wheels. The pitch circles on spur gears are tangent circles. Spur gears are manufactured in both internal and external versions.

16.3.1   Internal Spur Gear (Ring Gear)

An **internal gear** has greater tooth strength for a given tooth size. Internal spur gears permit a closer *center distance* that may enable a more compact design and allow input (drive) and output (driven) shafts to rotate in the same direction. Figure 16.10 illustrates the center-to-center distance between a **ring gear** and a **pinion gear**. Ring gears can have spur or helical tooth forms.

16.3.2   External Spur Gear

The **external spur gear** is the most common and best known type of gear. It transmits motion between parallel shafts that rotate in opposite directions. Spur gears generate radial bearing loads. Because of their availability and ease of manufacture, they should be given first consideration as the choice of gear type.

16.3.3   Spur Gear Specifications

The basic specifications for both manufacturing and inspection for a spur gear are shown below:

- pressure angle
- tooth form
- AGMA quality number
- diametral pitch
- tooth thickness, circular
- measuring-wire size
- total composite error
- testing pressure
- outside diameter
- number of pinion teeth
- material
- number of gear teeth
- face width
- pitch diameter
- measurement over wires
- gear testing radius
- surface finish

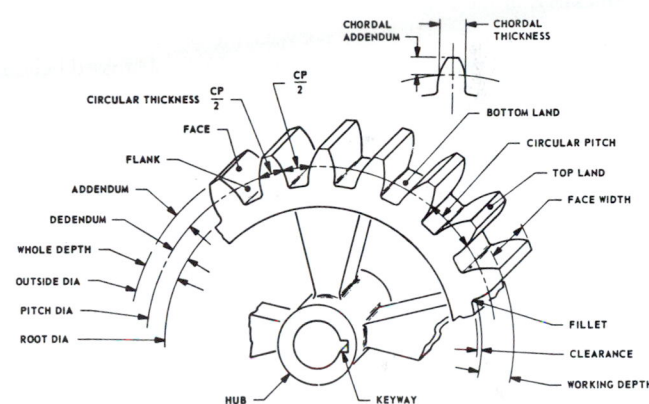

(b)

FIGURE 16.9   Spur Gear   (a) Spur gear and pinion (b) Spur gear terminology

To provide the required data listed above, certain application requirements must be known. This information should include speed, ratio, power, accuracy, life, temperature, and application.

16.3.4   Spur Gear Terms and Symbols

Many terms will be understood by an examination of Figure 16.9(a) and (b). The addendum is the height of the tooth,

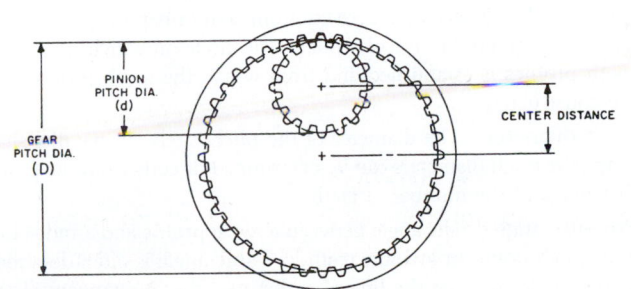

FIGURE 16.10   Ring Gear and Pinion

from the pitch circle to the outside circle. The **base circle** is the circle used for generating the involute curve. The **line of action** is the line along which the contact between the teeth takes place. Some of the symbols used for gears include:

a	=	addendum	b	=	dedendum
c	=	clearance	D	=	pitch diameter
OD	=	outside diameter	N	=	number of teeth
P	=	diametral pitch	p	=	circular pitch

The following terms are used throughout the chapter to describe spur and helical gears:

Addendum   The height that a tooth projects beyond the pitch circle or pitch line.

Base diameter   The diameter of the base cylinder from which the involute portion of a tooth profile is generated.

Backlash   The amount by which the width of a tooth space exceeds the thickness of the engaging tooth on the pitch circles.

Center distance   The distance between the parallel axis of spur gears and parallel helical gears, or the crossed axes of crossed helical gears.

Circular pitch   The distance along the pitch circle or pitch line between corresponding profiles of adjacent teeth.

Dedendum   The depth of a tooth space below the pitch line. It is normally greater than the addendum of the mating gear to provide clearance.

Diametral pitch   The ratio of the number of teeth to the pitch diameter in inches, which gives an indication of tooth size.

Face width   The length of the teeth in an axial plane.

Hub diameter   The outside diameter of a gear, sprocket, or coupling hub.

Hub projection   The distance the hub extends beyond the gear face.

Involute teeth   The teeth of spur gears, helical gears, and worms where the active portion of the profile in the transverse plane is the involute of a circle.

Lead   The axial advance of a helix for one complete turn, as in the threads of cylindrical worms and teeth of helical gears.

Normal diametral pitch   The value of the diametral pitch as calculated in the normal plane of a helical gear or worm.

Normal plane   The plane normal to the tooth surface at a pitch point and perpendicular to the pitch plane.

Outside diameter   The diameter of the addendum (outside) circle of a gear.

Pinion   A machine part with gear teeth. When two gears run together, the one with the smaller number of teeth is called the pinion.

Pitch circle   The circle derived from a number of teeth and a specified diametral or circular pitch. The circle on which spacing or tooth profiles is established and from which the tooth proportions are constructed.

Pitch diameter   The diameter of the pitch circle. In parallel shaft gears, the pitch diameters can be determined directly from the center distance and the number of teeth.

Pressure angle   The angle between a tooth profile and a radial line at its pitch point. In involute teeth, pressure angle is often described as the angle between the line of action and the line tangent to the pitch circle.

Root diameter   The diameter at the base of the tooth space.

Transverse diametral pitch   The ratio of the number of teeth to the pitch diameter, in inches, for a helical gear.

Whole depth   The total depth of a tooth space, equal to addendum plus dedendum, equal to the working depth plus variance.

Working depth   The depth of engagement of two gears.

16.3.5   Diametral Pitch System

All stock gears are made in accordance with the diametral pitch system. The **diametral pitch** of a gear is the number of teeth in the gear for each inch of pitch diameter. Therefore, the diametral pitch specifies the size of the gear tooth; a smaller diametral pitch indicates a larger tooth. An eight-pitch gear has eight teeth for each inch of pitch diameter (for a 6 in. pitch diameter, $6 \times 8 = 48$ teeth). The **circular pitch** is the distance from a point on one tooth to the corresponding point on the next tooth, measured along the pitch circle.

Gear teeth can be manufactured with a wide variety of shapes and profiles. The **involute profile** is the most commonly used system for gearing today, and most standard spur and helical gears are of involute form. An **involute** is a curve that is traced by a point on a taut cord unwinding from a circle, called a **base circle**. The involute is a form of spiral, the curvature of which becomes straighter as it is drawn from a base circle. Eventually, if drawn far enough, it would become a straight line. (See Chapter 5 for information on drawing the involute of a circle.)

16.3.6   Pressure Angle

Pressure angle (PA) (Fig. 16.5) is defined as the angle formed between the normal to the tooth profile at the pitch circle, and the tangent to the pitch circle at that point.

Standard gears are manufactured in both $14\frac{1}{2}°$ and 20° PA, involute, full-depth system gears. While 20° PA is generally recognized as having a higher load carrying capacity, $14\frac{1}{2}°$ PA gears still exist. The spur gear detail shown in Figure 16.11 has a pressure angle of $14\frac{1}{2}°$, a pitch diameter of 12.00 inches, and a diametral pitch of 4. Therefore, the gear has $12 \times 4 = 48$ teeth. *For gears to mesh, they must have the same diametral pitch.*

16.3.7   Spur Gear Formulas

Standard tooth proportions for the 20° fine-pitch system are as follows:

$$a = \text{addendum} = 1.000/P$$
$$b = \text{dedendum} = 1.200/P + 0.002$$
$$c = \text{clearance} = 0.200/P + 0.002$$
$$h_k = \text{working depth of tooth} = 2.000/P$$
$$h_t = \text{total depth of tooth} = 2.200/P + 0.002$$
$$D = \text{standard pitch diameter} = N/P$$
$$OD = \text{outside diameter} = D + 2/P$$
$$N = \text{number of teeth}$$
$$P = \text{diametral pitch} = N/D$$

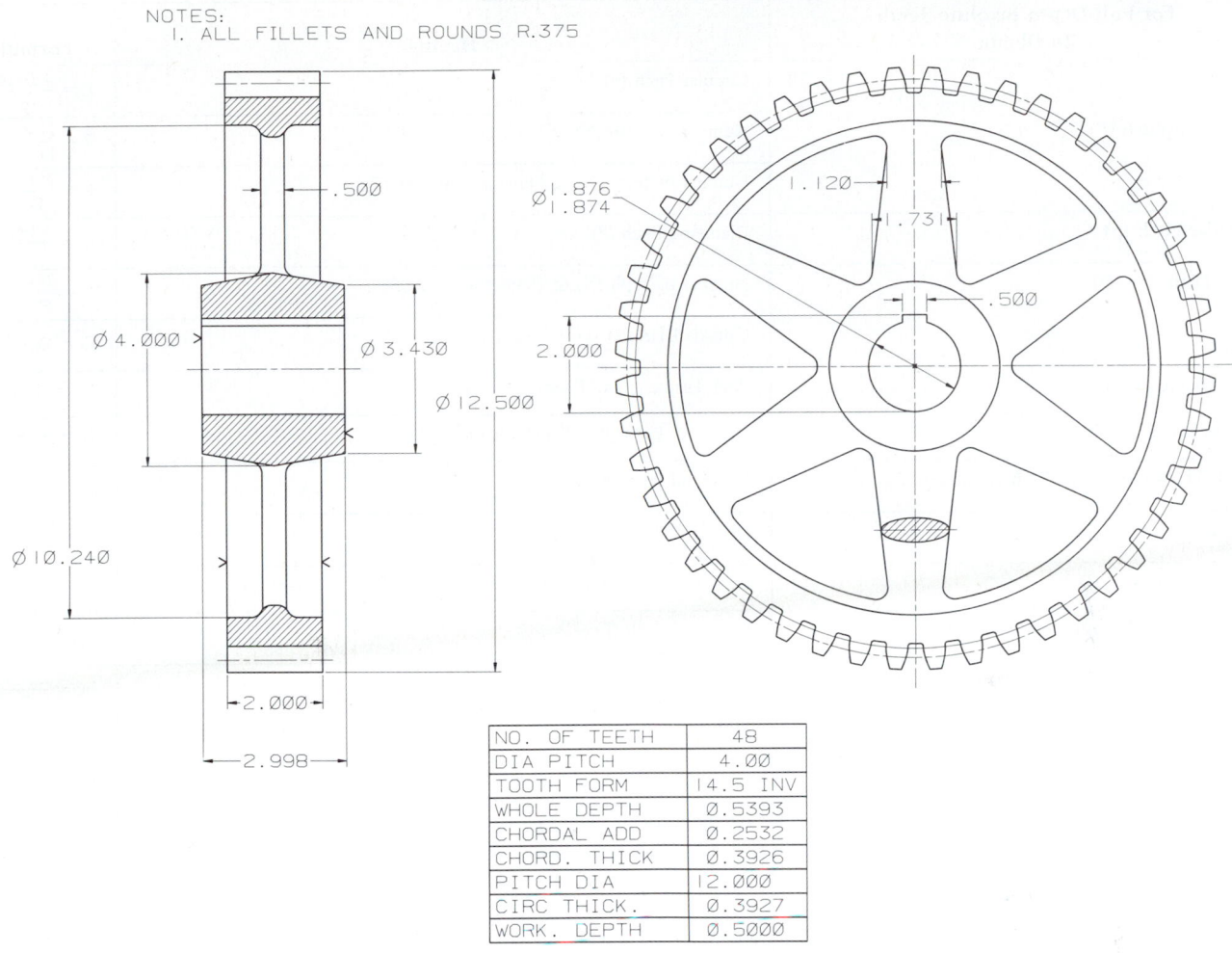

NOTES:
1. ALL FILLETS AND ROUNDS R.375

NO. OF TEETH	48
DIA PITCH	4.00
TOOTH FORM	14.5 INV
WHOLE DEPTH	0.5393
CHORDAL ADD	0.2532
CHORD. THICK	0.3926
PITCH DIA	12.000
CIRC THICK.	0.3927
WORK. DEPTH	0.5000

FIGURE 16.11 Spur Gear Detail

Tooth proportions for the standard $14\frac{1}{2}°$ full-depth involute system are as follows:

$$a = \text{addendum} = 1/P$$
$$b = \text{dedendum} = 1.157/P$$
$$c = \text{clearance} = 0.157/P$$
$$h_k = \text{working depth} = 2/P$$
$$h_l = \text{total depth} = 2.157/P$$
$$D = \text{pitch diameter} = N/P$$
$$OD = \text{outside diameter} = D + 2/P$$
$$N = \text{number of teeth}$$
$$P = \text{diametral pitch} = N/D$$

Figure 16.12 shows a complete set of spur gear formulae for full-depth involute teeth. Stock gears can be measured using a gage that measures the diametral pitch as shown in Figure 16.13.

16.3.8   Spur and Helical Gear Teeth Representation

Views of external spur and helical gears are drawn as shown in Figure 16.14(b). Gear tooth outlines can normally be omit-

ted from the drawing, except where needed for orientation with other features of the gear or where details, such as tip chamfers or reliefs, require dimensioning. Where required, one tooth may be shown [Fig. 16.14(a)]. Notice that all the teeth are shown in Figure 16.11. This is because a CAD system was used to draw the gear detail. The drafter drew only one tooth and then rotated and copied the tooth the required number of times (48 in the example). When gears are drawn manually, a template is almost always used to construct the gear teeth.

16.3.9   Gear Tooth Thickness

Circular or arc **tooth thickness** is the preferred specification; chordal tooth thickness may be used. Tooth thickness is normally specified at the referenced pitch circle. Figure 16.15 shows gear teeth terms in detail. If measurements such as with pins or balls (Fig. 16.15) are specified in addition to the actual tooth thickness, these measurements must be labeled "reference," or labeled as in Figure 16.16 (p. 584) where the

For Full-Depth Involute Teeth To Obtain	Having	Formula
Diametral Pitch (P)	Circular Pitch (p)	$P = \dfrac{3.1416}{p}$
	Number of Teeth (N) & Pitch Diameter (D)	$P = \dfrac{N}{D}$
	Number of Teeth (N) & Outside Diameter (D_o)	$P = \dfrac{N+2}{D_o}$
Circular Pitch (p)	Diametral Pitch (P)	$p = \dfrac{3.1416}{P}$
Pitch Diameter (D)	Number of Teeth (N) & Diametral Pitch (P)	$D = \dfrac{N}{P}$
	Outside Diameter (D) & Diametral Pitch (P)	$D = D_o - \dfrac{2}{P}$
Base Diameter (D_b)	Pitch Diameter and Pressure Angle	$D_b = D\cos\varnothing$
Number of Teeth (N)	Diametral Pitch (P) & Pitch Diameter (D)	$N = P \times D$
Tooth Thickness (t) @ Pitch Diameter (D)	Diametral Pitch (P)	$t = \dfrac{1.5708}{P}$
Addendum (a)	Diametral Pitch (P)	$a = \dfrac{1}{P}$
Outside Diameter (D_o)	Pitch Diameter (D) & Addendum (a)	$D_o = D + 2a$
Whole Depth (h_t) (20P & Finer)	Diametral Pitch (P)	$h_t = \dfrac{2.2}{P} + .002$
Whole Depth (h_t) (Coarser than 20P)	Diametral Pitch (P)	$h_t = \dfrac{2.157}{P}$
Working Depth (h_K)	Addendum	$h_K = 2(a)$
Clearance (c)	Whole Depth (h_t) Addendum (a)	$c = h_t - 2a$
Dedendum (b)	Whole Depth (h_t) & Addendum (a)	$b = h_t - a$
Contact Ratio (M_c)	Outside Radii, Base Radii, Center Distance and Pressure Angle $$M_c = \dfrac{\sqrt{R_o{}^2 - R_b{}^2} + \sqrt{r_D{}^2 - r_b{}^2} - C\sin\varnothing^*}{P_c\cos\varnothing}$$	
Root Diameter (D_r)	Pitch Diameter and Dedendum	$D_r = D - 2b$
Center Distance (C)	Pitch Diameter or Number of Teeth and Pitch	$C = \dfrac{D_1 + D_2}{2}$ or $\dfrac{N_1 + N_2}{2P}$

*R_o = Outside Radius, Gear
 r_o = Outside Radius, Pinion
 R_b = Base Circle Radius, Gear
 r_b = Base Circle Radius, Pinion

FIGURE 16.12 **Spur Gear Teeth Formulas**

dimension is given "**OVER PIN**." The diameter of pins or balls (Fig. 16.16) must be expressed beyond four decimal places as appropriate. The diameter of pins or balls is basic.

Tooth thickness must be designated "actual" or "functional." Functional tooth thickness is a specification at the referenced pitch circle for definitive backlash control. It may be used in place of, or in addition to, actual tooth thickness. However, if the actual tooth thickness is critical, it should be specified in addition to the functional tooth thickness. Figure 16.17 shows standard tooth dimensions for spur gears.

16.3.10 Backlash on Spur Gears

Backlash is the motion of a meshed gear when its mate is held fixed. An increase or decrease in center distance will cause an increase or decrease in backlash. Stock spur gears are cut to operate at **standard center distances** (Figs. 16.9 and 16.10). The standard center distance is defined by:

$$\text{Standard Center Distance} = \frac{\text{Pinion PD} + \text{Gear PD}}{2}$$

FIGURE 16.13 **Gear Tooth Gage** Shown full size

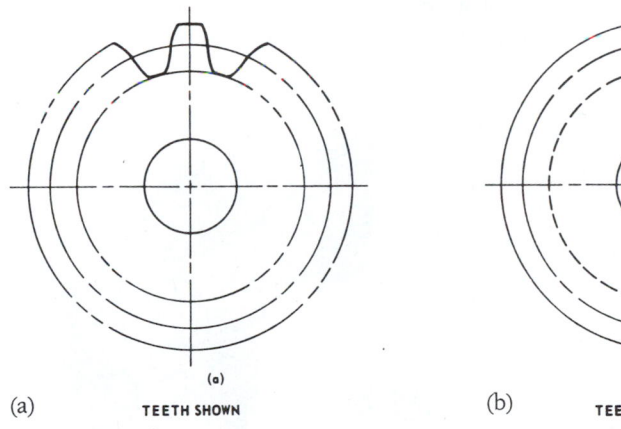

(a) TEETH SHOWN (b) TEETH NOT SHOWN

FIGURE 16.14 **Representing Gear Teeth** (a) One tooth shown (b) Teeth not shown

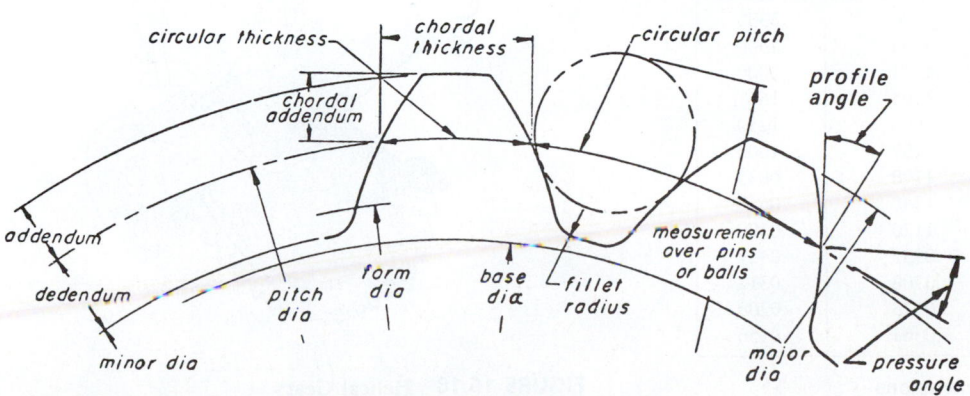

FIGURE 16.15 **Spur Gear Teeth Terminology**

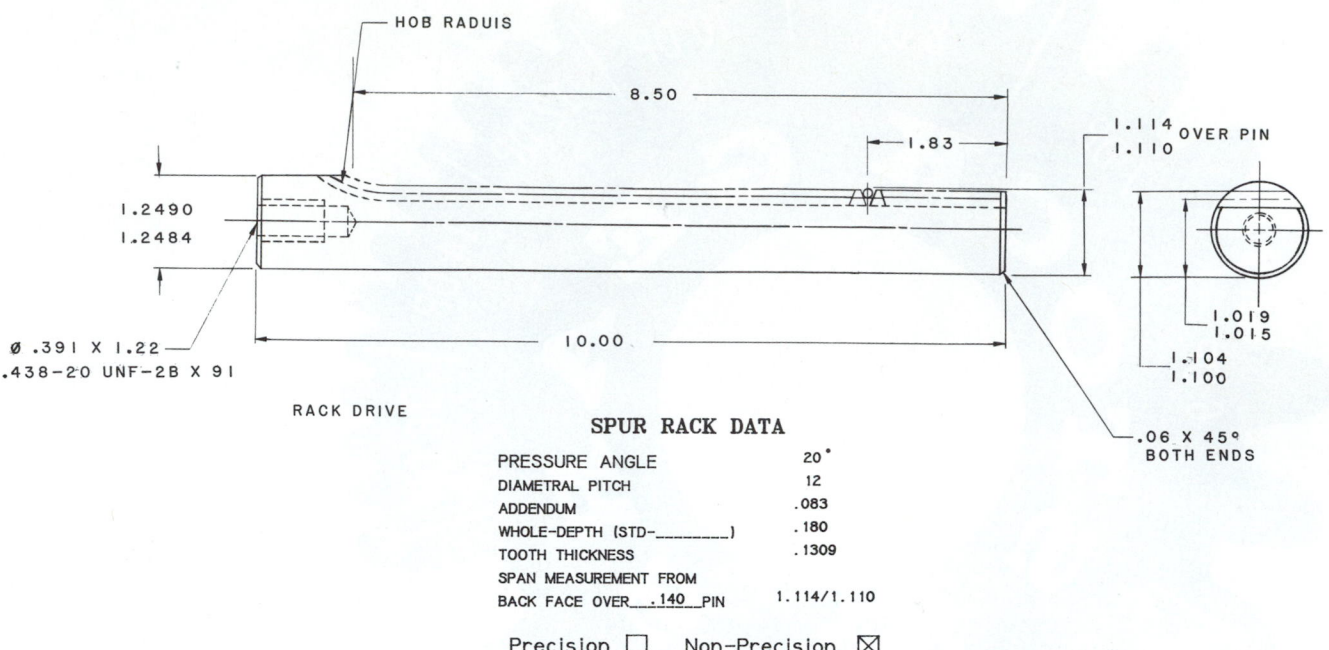

RACK DRIVE

SPUR RACK DATA

PRESSURE ANGLE	20°
DIAMETRAL PITCH	12
ADDENDUM	.083
WHOLE-DEPTH (STD-_____)	.180
TOOTH THICKNESS	.1309
SPAN MEASUREMENT FROM BACK FACE OVER ___.140___ PIN	1.114/1.110

Precision ☐   Non-Precision ☒

FIGURE 16.16 Spur Rack Detail

16.4 Helical Gears

The information contained in the spur gear section is also applicable to helical gears (Fig. 16.18) with the addition of helix angle and lead. **Helix angle** is the angle between any helix and an element of its cylinder. In helical gears (Fig. 16.19), it is at the pitch diameter, unless otherwise specified. **Lead** for helical gears is the axial advance of a helix for one complete turn, for instance, as in the threads of cylindrical worms and teeth of helical gears.

Many standard helical gears are cut to the diametral pitch system, resulting in a normal pitch that is smaller than the diametral pitch. **Normal diametral pitch** is the diametral pitch calculated in the normal plane.

Helical gears of the same hand operate at right angles. Helical gears of opposite hands run on parallel shafts.

Diametral Pitch	Circular Pitch (inches)	Thickness of Tooth on Pitch Line (inches)	Depth to Be Cut in Gear (inches) (Hobbed Gears)	Addendum (inches)
3	1.0472	.5236	.7190	.3333
4	.7854	.3927	.5393	.2500
5	.6283	.3142	.4314	.2000
6	.5236	.2618	.3565	.1667
8	.3927	.1963	.2696	.1250
10	.3142	.1571	.2157	.1000
12	.2618	.1309	.1798	.0833
16	.1963	.0982	.1348	.0625
20	.1571	.0785	.1120	.0500
24	.1309	.0654	.0937	.0417
32	.0982	.0491	.0708	.0312
48	.0654	.0327	.0478	.0208
64	.0491	.0245	.0364	.0156

FIGURE 16.17 Spur Gear Tooth Dimensions

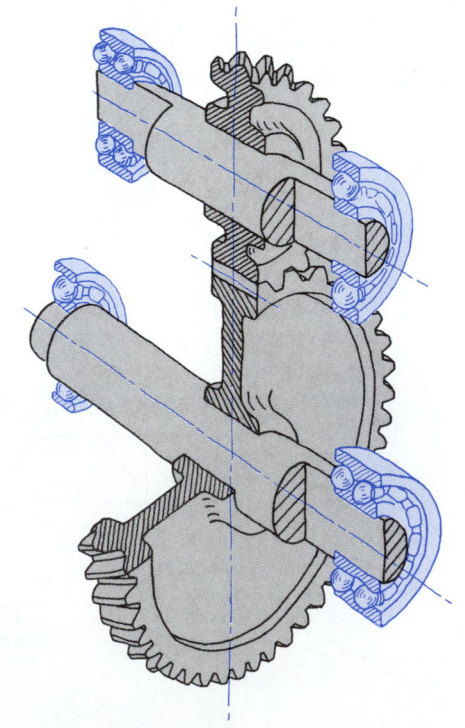

FIGURE 16.18 Helical Gears

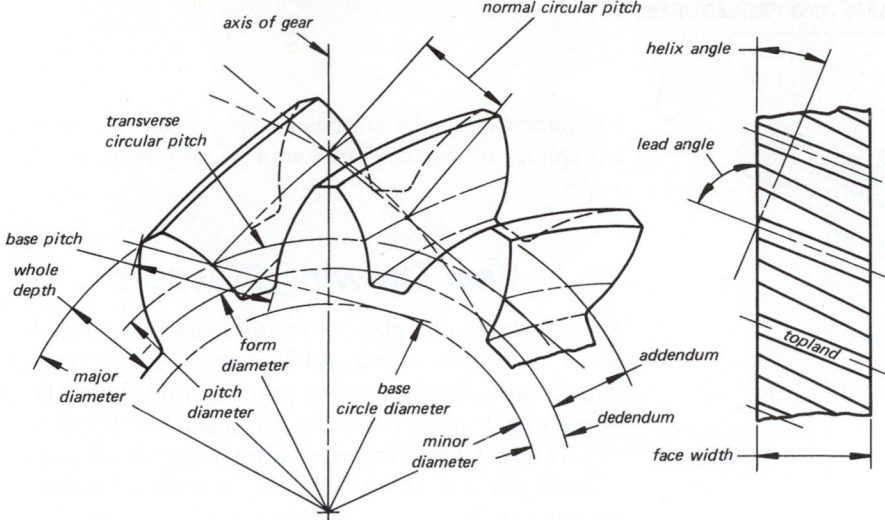

FIGURE 16.19 Helical Teeth Terminology

To Obtain	Having	Formula
Transverse Diametral Pitch (P)	Number of Teeth (N) & Pitch Diameter (D)	$P = \dfrac{N}{D}$
	Normal Diametral Pitch (P_N) Helix Angle (ψ)	$P = P_N \cos \psi$
Pitch Diameter (D)	Number of Teeth (N) & Transverse Diametral Pitch (p)	$D = \dfrac{N}{P}$
Normal Diametral Pitch (P_N)	Transverse Diametral Pitch (P) & Helix Angle (ψ)	$P_N = \dfrac{P}{\cos \psi}$
Normal Circular Tooth Thickness (τ)	Normal Diametral Pitch (P_N)	$\tau = \dfrac{1.5708}{P_N}$
Transverse Circular Pitch (p_t)	Diametral Pitch (P) (Transverse)	$p_t = \dfrac{\pi}{P}$
Normal Circular Pitch (p_n)	Transverse Circular Pitch (p)	$p_n = p_t \cos \psi$
Lead (L)	Pitch Diameter and Pitch Helix Angle	$L = \dfrac{\pi D}{\tan \psi}$

FIGURE 16.20 Helical Gear Formulas

The helical tooth form is involute in the plane of rotation and can be developed in a manner similar to that of the spur gear. However, unlike the spur gear, which may be viewed as two dimensional, the helical gear must be viewed as three dimensional to show changes in axial features. Formulas for helical gears are provided in Figure 16.20.

16.5 Racks and Pinions

A **rack** may be considered to be a gear of infinitely long pitch radius. The pitch line of a rack is a straight line; the pitch is described as the **linear pitch**. Racks can have spur or helical teeth. Figure 16.21 shows a standard rack detail (also see Fig. 16.16). Racks are designed to mate with a **pinion** (gear) and are used to transmit radial motion into linear motion or the reverse.

16.6 Splines

Splines (Fig. 16.22) are multiple keys, in the general form of internal and external gear teeth, used to prevent relative

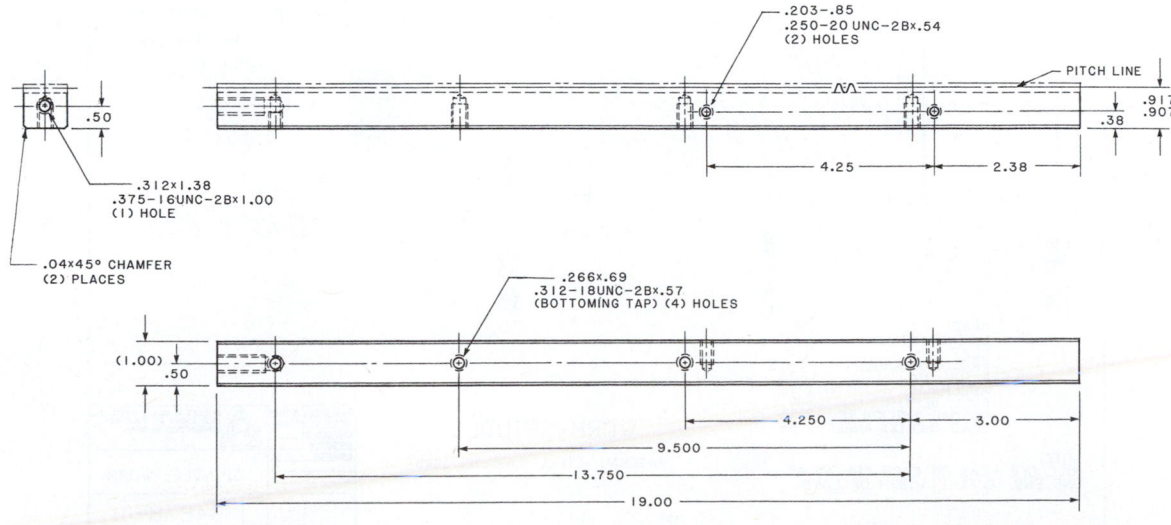

FIGURE 16.21 Rack Detail

NOTE:
MAKE FROM BOSTON P/N L2012-4 ITEM 37320
12 PITCH, 20° PRESSURE ANGLE APPROX. RACK·48.00 LG.

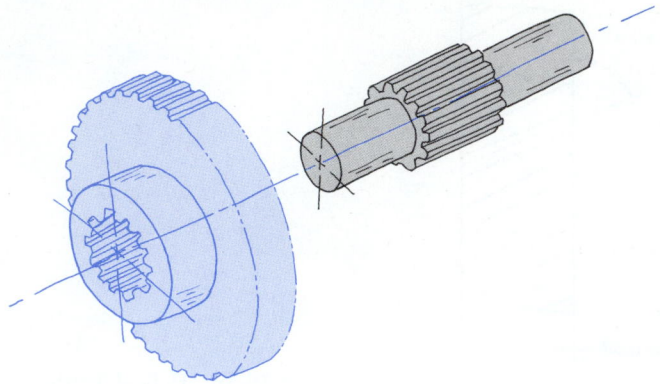

FIGURE 16.22 Spline and Gear

rotation between two members. Splines are used primarily to transmit torque and are usually integral with shafts that include other features. In Figure 16.23 the end of the shaft is a spline and the center is a worm (screw). Splines are normally used in three applications:

1. for coupling shafts when heavy torques are transmitted without slippage
2. for attaching parts that require removal for indexing or for change of angular position
3. for transmitting power to permanently fixed gears, pulleys, and other rotating devices

Involute splines (Fig. 16.24) are similar in form to external or internal involute gears. The general graphic format for depict-

ing spline teeth is the same as for spur gears. Standard involute splines are manufactured with 30, $37\frac{1}{2}$, and 45° pressure angles.

16.7   Gear Drawing Practices

An axial view and a plane of rotation view are generally sufficient to illustrate a gear. Additional views may be used to show construction and special features or relations. The axial view is usually made in section, on a plane parallel to the axis (Fig. 16.11). A gear, pinion, or worm integral with a shaft, or a helical gear is shown in full view, on a plane parallel to the axis (Fig. 16.24). In the axial view, visible lines are drawn to represent the outside diameter. The pitch diameter is shown by conventional centerlines and the root diameter by hidden lines. In an axial section view, visible lines are used to represent the outside and root diameter, and centerlines for the pitch diameter (see Fig. 16.11).

In views representing planes of rotation, the outside and root diameters are shown by phantom lines and, when several teeth are shown, the pitch diameter is shown by a centerline [Fig. 16.14(a)]. *When no teeth are shown,* the outside diameter is represented by a visible object line, and the root diameter by a hidden line [Fig. 16.14(b)]. The root diameter is still represented by a centerline. Figure 16.25 is an actual industry detail drawing of a gear.

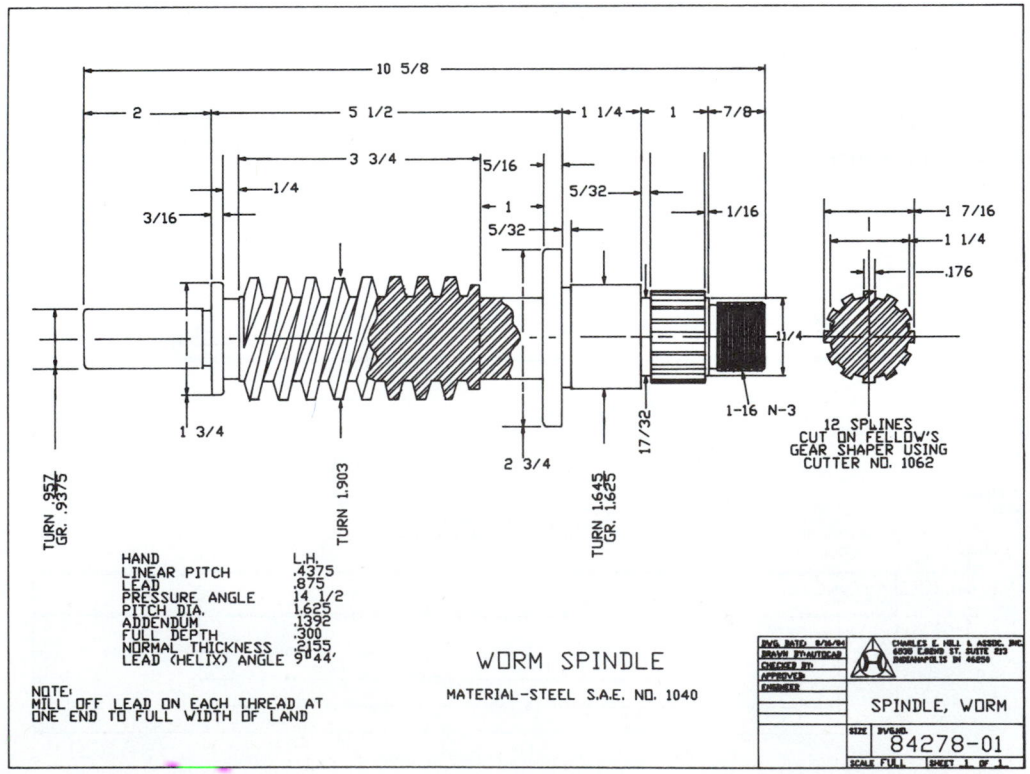

FIGURE 16.23 Worm Spindle

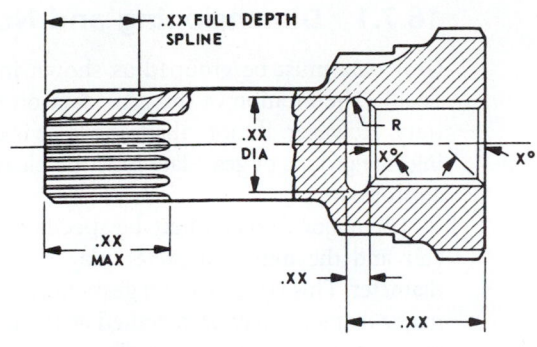

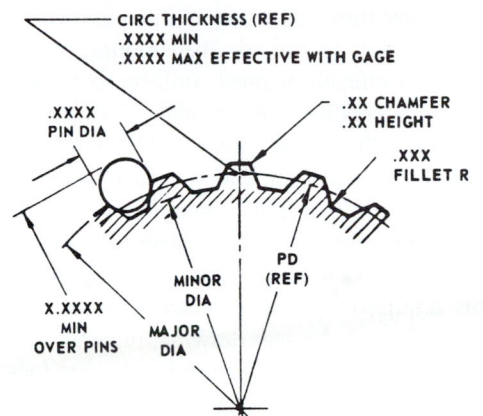

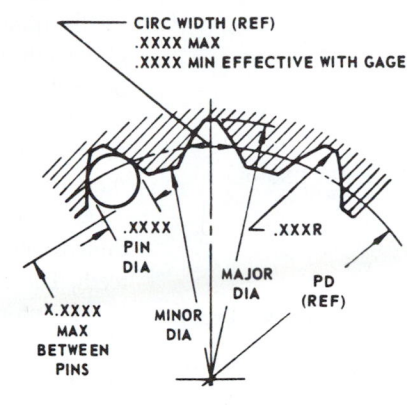

INVOLUTE SPLINE DATA – EXTERNAL	
NUMBER OF TEETH	XX
DIAMETRAL PITCH	XX/XX
PRESSURE ANGLE	XX°
PITCH DIA (REF)	X.XXXX
MAJOR DIA	X.XXXX – X.XXXX
MINOR DIA	X.XXXX – X.XXXX
TRUE INVOLUTE FORM DIA	X.XXXX
*MAX LEAD ERROR	.XXXX

INVOLUTE SPLINE DATA – INTERNAL	
NUMBER OF TEETH	XX
DIAMETRAL PITCH	XX/XX
PRESSURE ANGLE	XX°
PITCH DIA (REF)	X.XXXX
MAJOR DIA	X.XXXX – X.XXXX
MINOR DIA	X.XXXX – X.XXXX
TRUE INVOLUTE FORM DIA	X.XXXX
*MAX LEAD ERROR	.XXXX

FIGURE 16.24   Spline Dimensioning

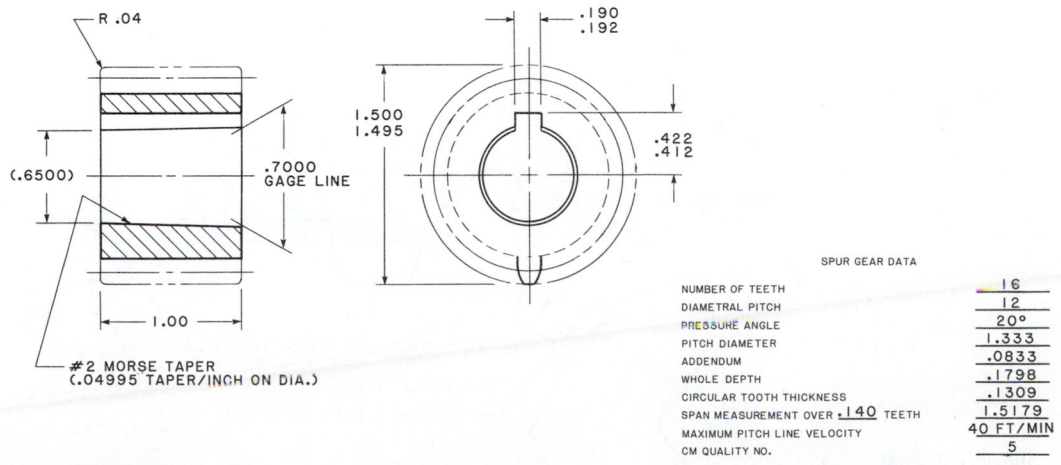

SPUR GEAR DATA	
NUMBER OF TEETH	16
DIAMETRAL PITCH	12
PRESSURE ANGLE	20°
PITCH DIAMETER	1.333
ADDENDUM	.0833
WHOLE DEPTH	.1798
CIRCULAR TOOTH THICKNESS	.1309
SPAN MEASUREMENT OVER ±140 TEETH	1.5179
MAXIMUM PITCH LINE VELOCITY	40 FT/MIN
CM QUALITY NO.	5

FIGURE 16.25   Spur Gear Detail

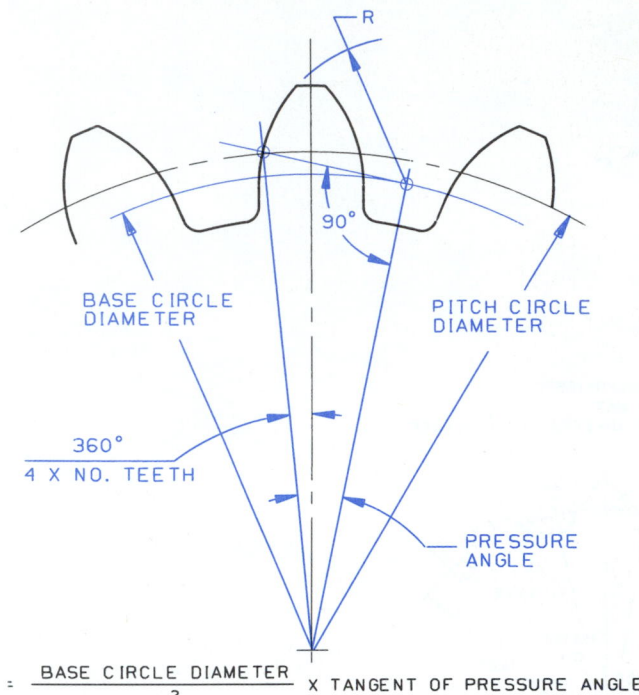

$$R = \frac{\text{BASE CIRCLE DIAMETER}}{2} \times \text{TANGENT OF PRESSURE ANGLE}$$

FIGURE 16.26 Drawing an Approximate Involute for Construction of Gear Teeth

Although it is not necessary to draw all gear teeth when detailing gears, if it is necessary to illustrate a relation to some other feature, such as a keyway or bolt hole, or to show dimensions across pins, one or more teeth may be shown. An enlarged view or section should be used to show special features of gear teeth or a gear profile. Gear teeth may be drawn by the approximate method shown in Figures 16.26 or 16.27. The relative size of gear teeth in terms of diametral pitch is illustrated full size in Figure 16.28.

16.7.1 Dimensioning and Notes

Gear data must be grouped as shown in Figures 16.25 and 16.11. The location of the gear data on the drawing is arbitrary. However, if more than one gear is depicted on a drawing, the groups of gear data must be clearly referenced to the appropriate gear.

The major diameter may be specified as the outside diameter and the minor diameter may be specified as the root diameter. This is for external gears only. On internal gears, the major diameter may be specified as the root diameter and the minor diameter may be specified as the inside diameter.

Illustrations show only those dimensions that control the gear teeth and their relation to the specified mounting. All other dimensions and specifications must conform to recommended drafting practice (ANSI). Dimensional values are indicated by X's on the rack illustration in Figure 16.29 to show the number of decimal places recommended in each instance.

A completely defined rack or gear contains two sets of dimensions: those of the gear blank and those of the gear teeth. This information is shown as a composite on one set of views. Information required for the production of a gear blank is shown on the face of the gear drawing, integral with the graphic depiction. Information required for the production of the gear teeth is shown on the same drawing in a data block. Local and general notes are added as required. Angular dimensions are expressed in degrees and decimal portions thereof (where desired, the angle may be given in degrees, minutes, and seconds).

The spur gear detail shown in Figure 16.30 is a company drawing of a standard gear set manufactured by Babcock Gear Works. Figure 16.31 is a gear assembly detail used on a milling machine detail featuring a standard Browning gear, a split bushing, and two socket head cap screws. All parts in this assembly are commercially available.

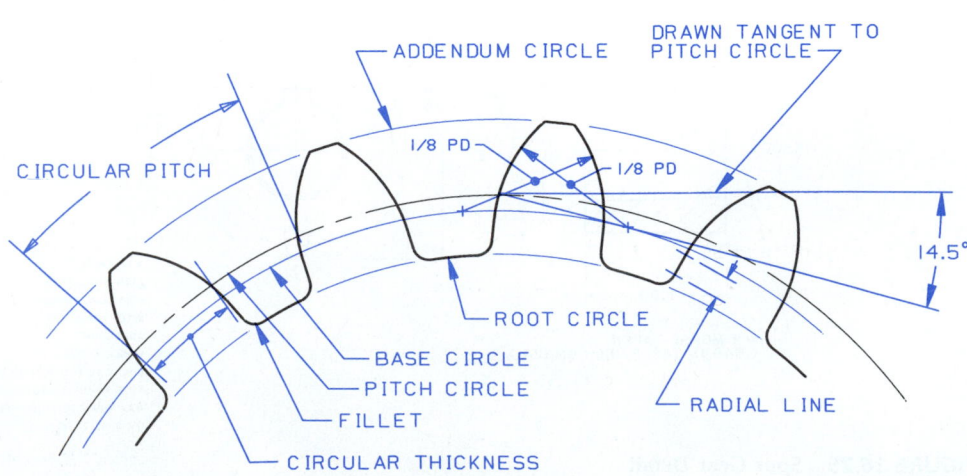

FIGURE 16.27 Simplified Gear Tooth Construction

FIGURE 16.28 **Spur Gear Teeth Outlines** Shown full size

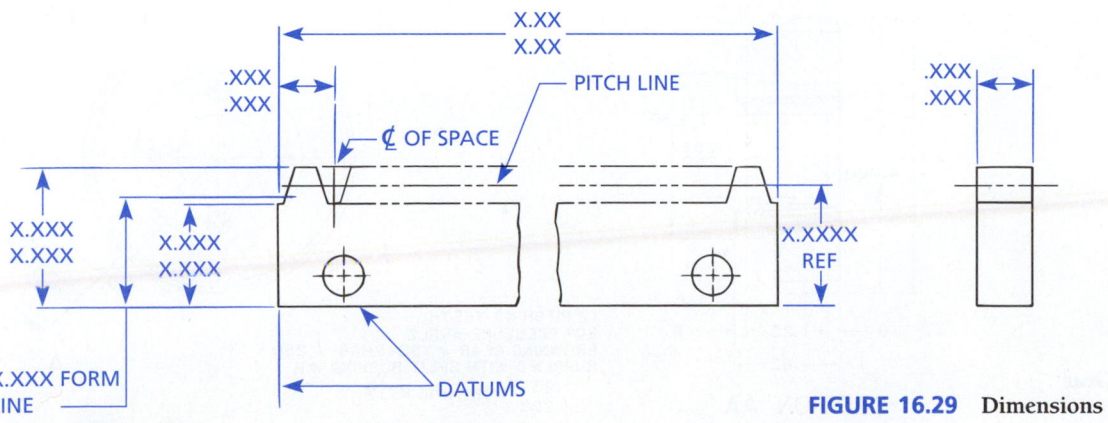

FIGURE 16.29 **Dimensions Required for Racks**

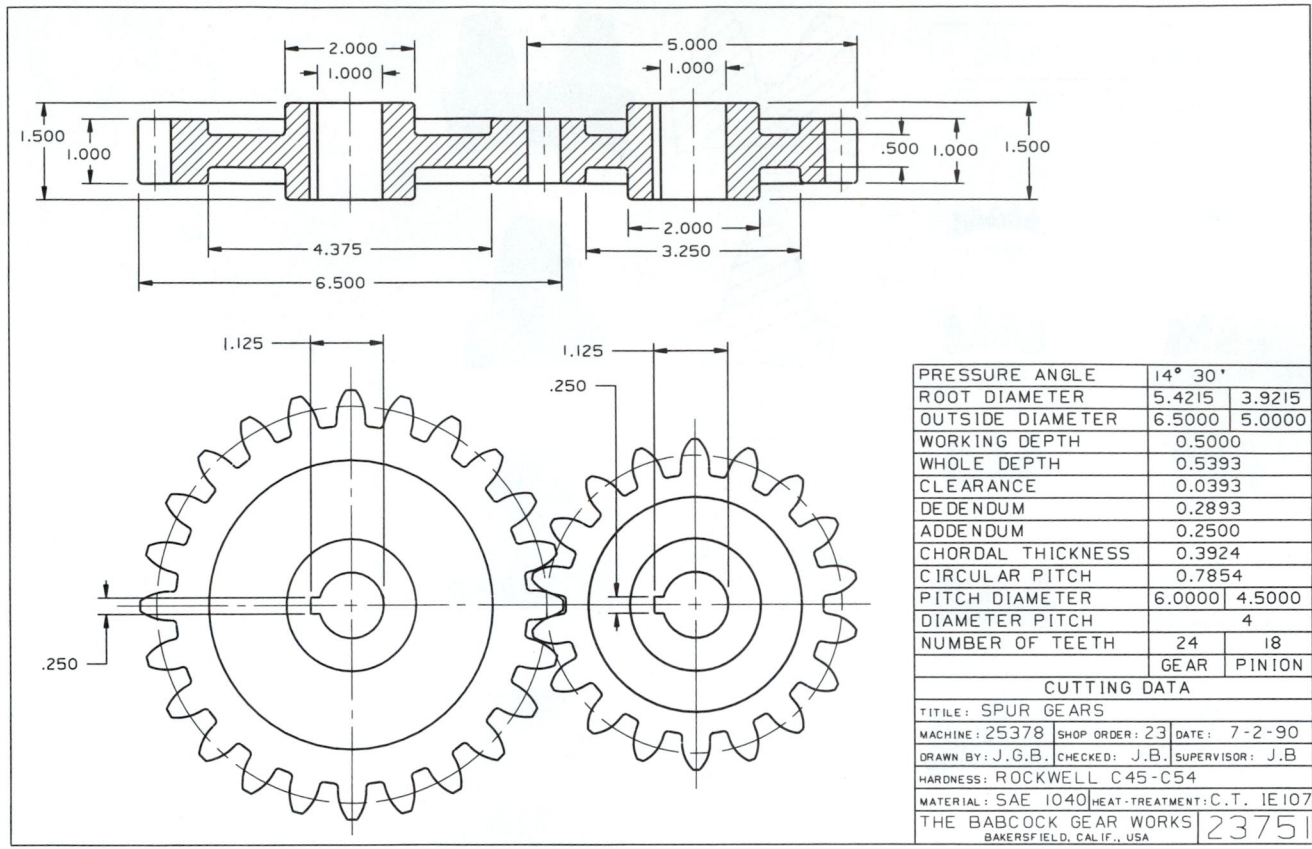

PRESSURE ANGLE	14° 30'	
ROOT DIAMETER	5.4215	3.9215
OUTSIDE DIAMETER	6.5000	5.0000
WORKING DEPTH	0.5000	
WHOLE DEPTH	0.5393	
CLEARANCE	0.0393	
DEDENDUM	0.2893	
ADDENDUM	0.2500	
CHORDAL THICKNESS	0.3924	
CIRCULAR PITCH	0.7854	
PITCH DIAMETER	6.0000	4.5000
DIAMETER PITCH	4	
NUMBER OF TEETH	24	18
	GEAR	PINION

CUTTING DATA

TITLE: SPUR GEARS		
MACHINE: 25378	SHOP ORDER: 23	DATE: 7-2-90
DRAWN BY: J.G.B.	CHECKED: J.B.	SUPERVISOR: J.B
HARDNESS: ROCKWELL C45-C54		
MATERIAL: SAE 1040	HEAT-TREATMENT: C.T. 1E107	
THE BABCOCK GEAR WORKS BAKERSFIELD, CALIF., USA		23751

FIGURE 16.30 Spur Gear Detail

16.8 Bevel Gears

Portions of two cones in frictional contact (Fig. 16.32) might be used to transmit motion from one shaft to another. However, to prevent slipping, teeth may be used. The cones then become **bevel gears** (Fig. 16.33). Two bevel gears of the same size, with shafts at right angles, are called **miter gears.** Bevel

gears are the most common method of transmitting motion between shafts with intersecting axes. The addendum and dedendum are measured the same as the spur gear and are measured on a cone, called the **back cone.** The diametral pitch, circular pitch, etc., are the same as for a spur gear.

The shafts for bevel gears may make any angle, called the **shaft angle**, with each other. The terms used for bevel gears are given in Figure 16.34.

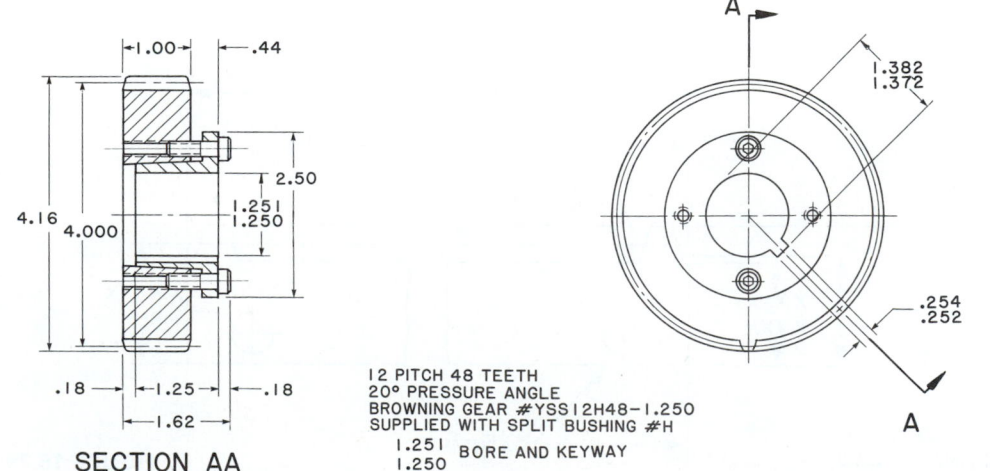

FIGURE 16.31 Spur Gear Assembly Detail

SECTION AA

12 PITCH 48 TEETH
20° PRESSURE ANGLE
BROWNING GEAR #YSS12H48-1.250
SUPPLIED WITH SPLIT BUSHING #H
1.251
1.250 BORE AND KEYWAY

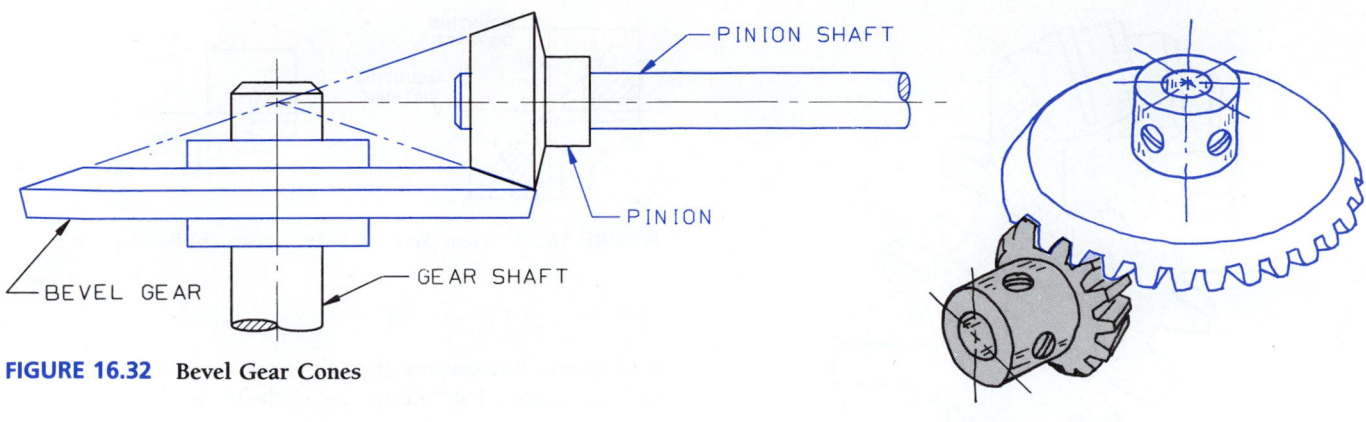

FIGURE 16.32   Bevel Gear Cones

FIGURE 16.33   Bevel Gears

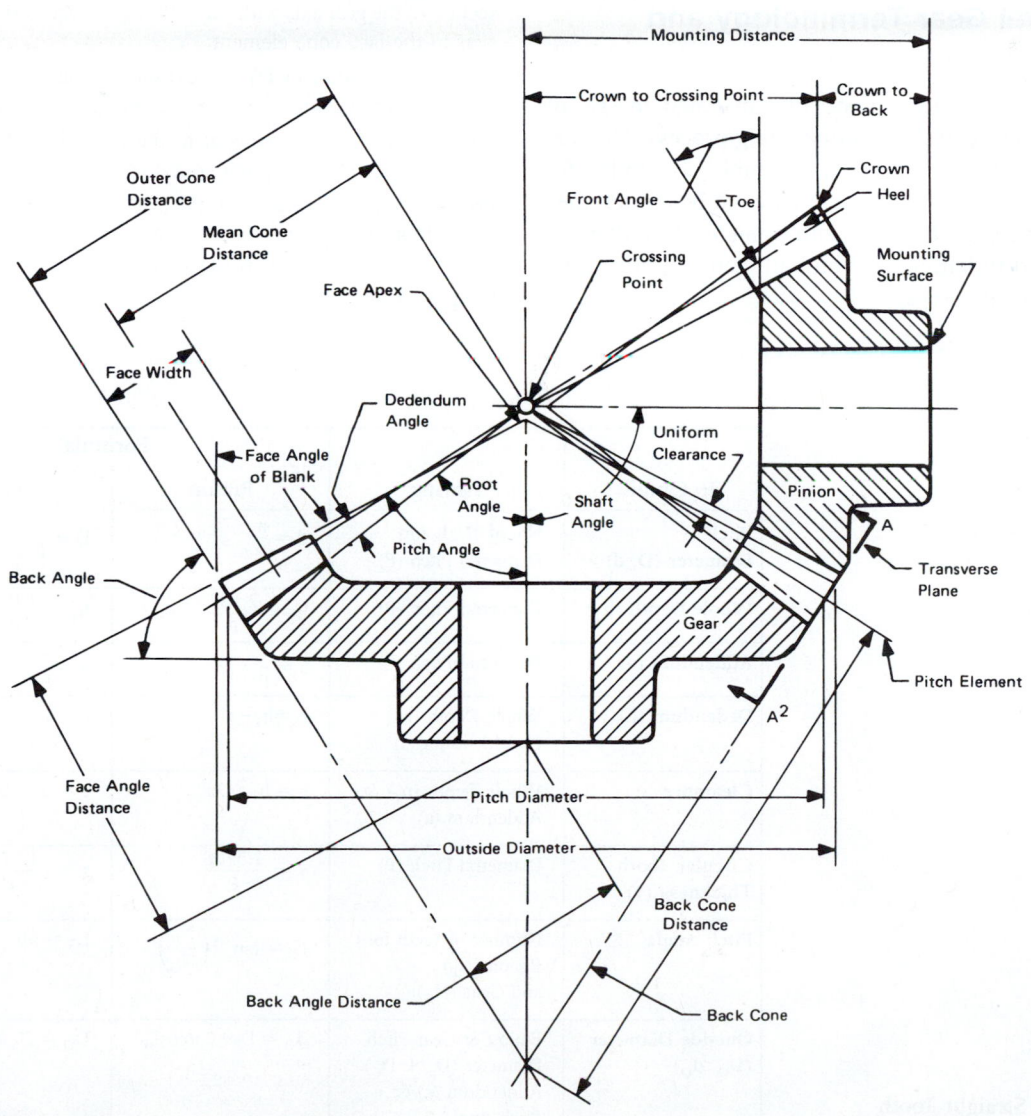

FIGURE 16.34   Bevel and Miter Gear Terminology

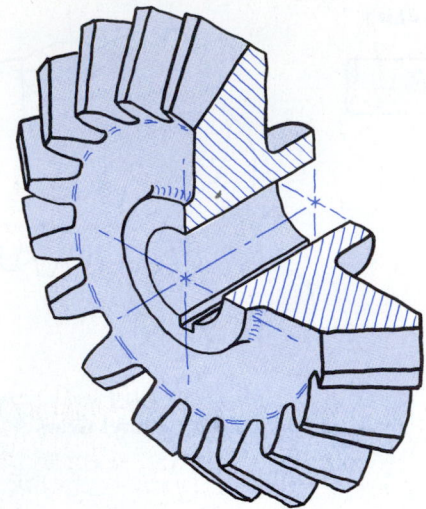

FIGURE 16.35 Bevel Gear

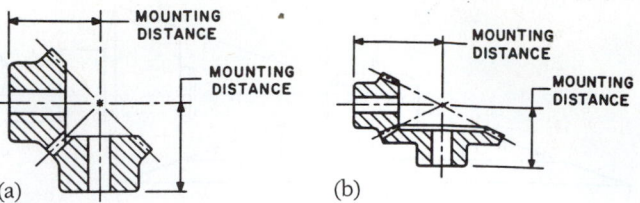

FIGURE 16.37 Gear Sets (a) Miter gears (b) Bevel gears

16.8.1 Bevel Gear Terminology and Formulas

Bevel gears (Fig. 16.35) are frequently matched in sets or pairs during sequence of the manufacturing process. They are maintained as a matched set in assembly. Formulas for straight bevel gears are given in Figure 16.36. Since they differ from spur gears, the gear tooth nomenclature that follows is presented to familiarize you with general terms used on the bevel gear drawings:

Addendum The distance from the pitch cone to the top of the tooth, as measured at the large end of the tooth.

Axial plane A plane that contains the gear axis.

Back angle distance The perpendicular distance from the intersection of the gear axis with the locating surface at the back of a bevel gear to the back cone element.

Circular thickness The length of arc between the two sides of a gear tooth on the pitch circle.

Face angle distance The perpendicular distance from the intersection of the gear axis with the locating surface at the back of a bevel gear to the face cone element.

Mounting distance (MD) The distance from the end of the hub of one gear to the centerline of its mating gear (Fig. 16.37).

Pitch plane A plane tangent to the gear pitch surface. The pitch plane is tangent to the pitch cone for bevel gears.

Pressure angle The angle at the pitch point between a line normal to the tooth profile and the pitch plane.

Spiral angle The angle between the tooth trace and an element of the pitch cone.

FIGURE 16.36 Straight Tooth Miter and Bevel Gear Formulas

		Formula	
To Obtain	**Having**	**Pinion**	**Gear**
Pitch Diameter (D, d)	No. of Teeth and Diametral Pitch (P)	$d = \frac{n}{P}$	$D = \frac{n}{P}$
Whole Depth (h_T)	Diametral Pitch (P)	$h_T = \frac{2.188}{P} = .002$	$h_T = \frac{2.188}{P} = .002$
Addendum (a)	Diametral Pitch (P)	$a = \frac{1}{P}$	$a = \frac{1}{P}$
Dedendum (b)	Whole Depth (h_T) & Addendum (a)	$b = h_T - a$	$b = h_T - a$
Clearance	Whole Depth (n_T) & Addendum (a)	$c = h_T - 2a$	$c = h_T - 2a$
Circular Tooth Thickness (τ)	Diametral Pitch (P)	$\tau = \frac{1.5708}{P}$	$\tau = \frac{1.5708}{P}$
Pitch Angle	Number of Teeth in Pinion (N_P) and Gear (N_G)	$L_P = \tan^{-1}\left(\frac{N_P}{N_G}\right)$	$L_G = 90 - L_P$
Outside Diameter (D_O, d_O)	Pinion & Gear Pitch Diameter ($D_p + D_G$) Addendum (a) & Pitch Angle ($L_P + L_G$)	$d_O = D_P + 2a(\cos L_P)$	$D_O = D_G + 2a(\cos L_G)$

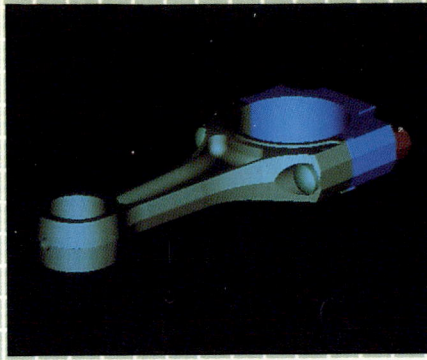

PLATE 1
Using simple interactive commands, the ICEM Solid Modeler assists the user in creating a connecting rod. The user constructs shaded, color images in true 3D perspective by combining 14 geometric primitives such as spheres, cones, and torioids.

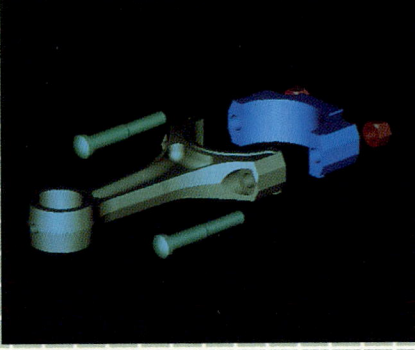

PLATE 2
Once the Geometric model is created, the ICEM Solid Modeler can be used to explode the connecting rod into component parts, rotate it for viewing from different angles, create a cross section, and check for interference with related parts.

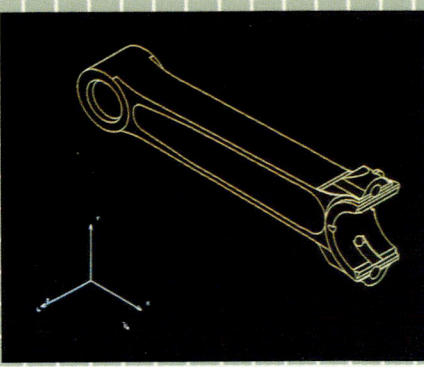

PLATE 3
The ICEM Solid Modeler automatically creates a wire frame model from the solid geometry of the connecting rod. Hidden line removal is also automatic; the resulting drawing can be used in drafting applications without reformatting the data.

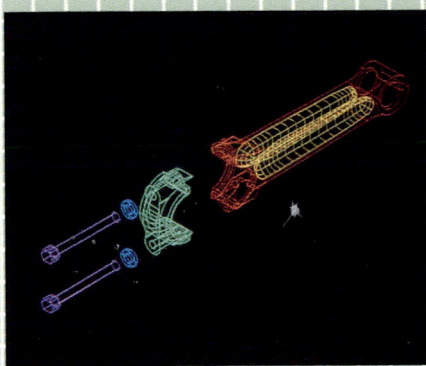

PLATE 4
The ICEM Solid Modeler creates an exploded view wire model. The geometric data can be automatically transferred to the ICEM design/drafting application, where it is used to determine weight, volume, surface area, moment of inertia, and radium of gyration of the design.

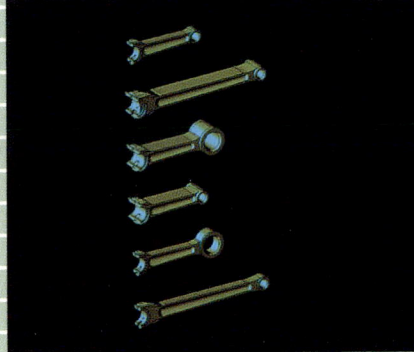

PLATE 5
The ICEM Solid Modeler application gives the user the ability to input multiple dimension parameters to automatically generate families of parts.

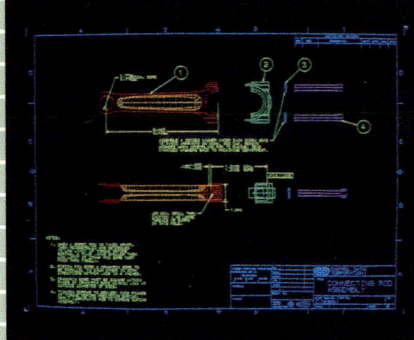

PLATE 6
The ICEM Engineering Data Library provides the design engineer with comprehensive, automatic, and security controlled progression of product documentation.

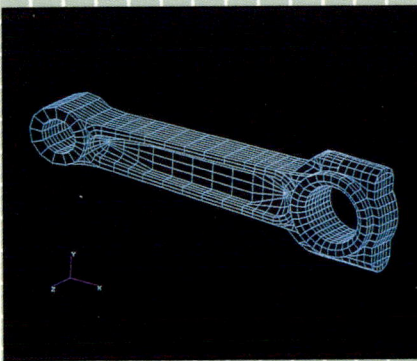

PLATE 7
The ICEM utilizes Control Data's UNISTRUC II system or Patran-G for automatic mesh generation of finite element models of up to 20,000 nodes or elements, with larger projects analyzed by segmenting the model into blocks. The resultant model can be rotated, sectioned, or viewed from different angles.

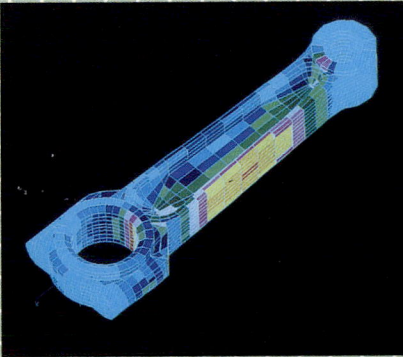

PLATE 8
ICEM provides the design engineer with a variety of mesh patterns and color schemes to depict a particular analysis. The brick-like mesh of this connecting rod displays gradations of stress measured at the centroid of each element.

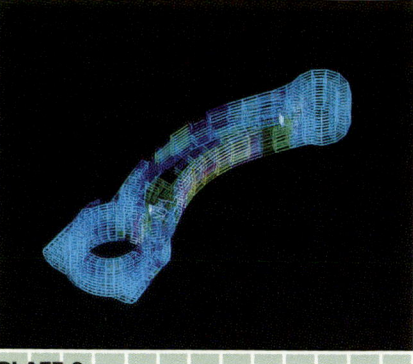

PLATE 9
Magnified deformation depicts stress data for connecting rod in motion.

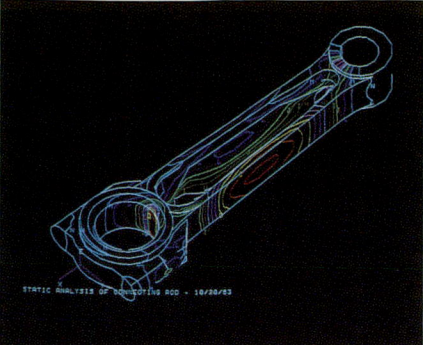

PLATE 10
Colored iso lines display uniform stress contours.

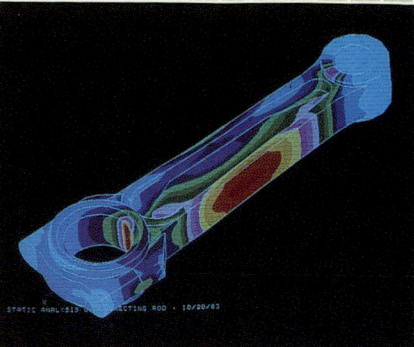

PLATE 11
Color regions indicate ranges of stress displacements.

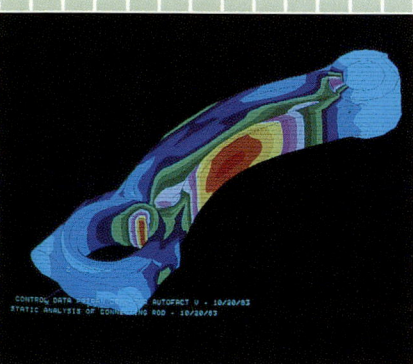

PLATE 12
Color regions are contoured to accurately display stress of connecting rod in motion.

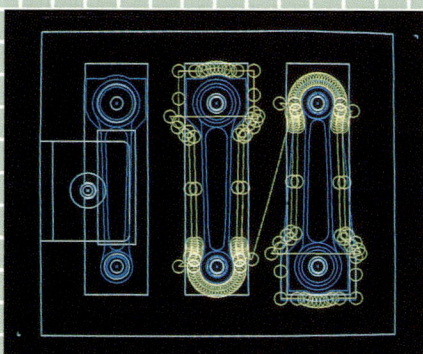

PLATE 13
Design engineers can preview cutter paths with ICEM and automatically input needed changes to insure the most accurate and precise paths before machining the actual part. This shortens many time-consuming processes in manually readjusting cutter paths to obtain optimum cutter path design.

PLATE 14
The ICEM numerical control capability allows generation of control tapes directly from design geometry. The NC output is used for the machining of the actual part.

PLATE 15
The ICEM assists design engineers in creating numerical control machining for complex surfaces of dies, molds, and finished parts. ICEM NC features point-to-point construction, pocketing, profiling, 3-axis machining, 5-axis swarf cutting, dynamic tool path display, and lace and non-lace cutting.

PLATE 16
HP 9000 Model 825SRX superworkstation used for design of products
by the individual engineer or a small team of designers.

PLATE 17
Solid modeling design and drafting system using a 2D concept to create
or modify 3D models.

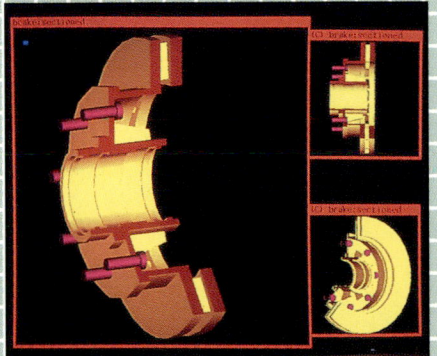

PLATE 18
Design model created with AutoSolid.

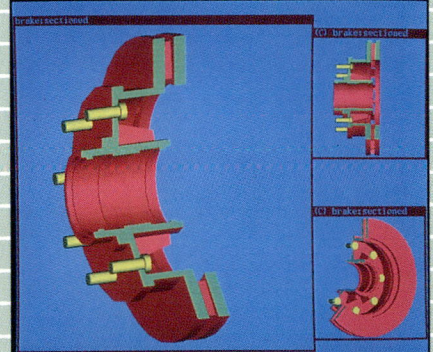

PLATE 19
Sectioned 3D solid model.

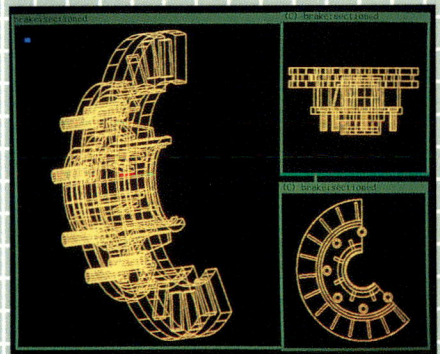

PLATE 20
Wire frame display of part.

PLATE 21
Solid model assembly.

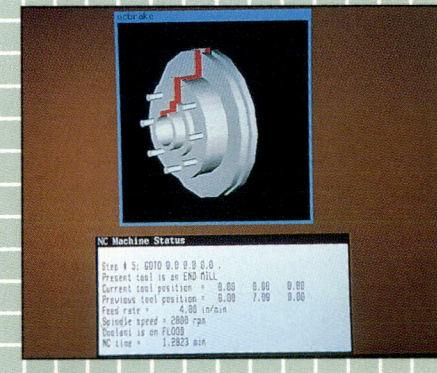

PLATE 22
NC machine status displayed on screen with
model.

PLATE 23
HP 9000 Model 350 TurboSRX engineering workstation can render photorealistic images and 3D interactive graphics.

PLATE 24
Artistic 3D rendering using CADKEY Renderman software.

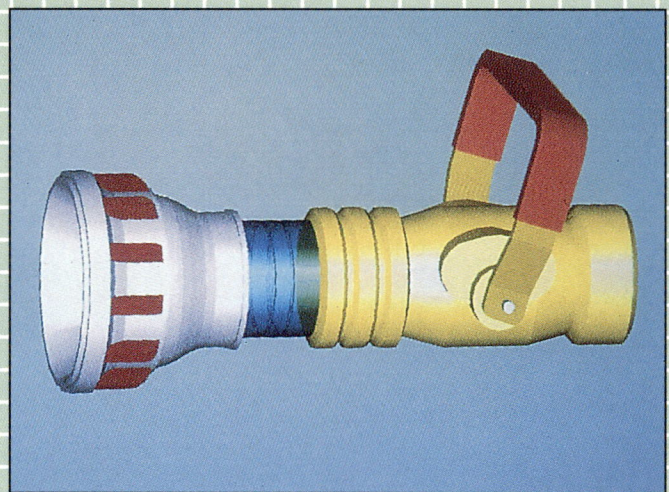

PLATE 25
Solid Model illustrated with AutoSolid software.

PLATE 26
Interior perspective of building.

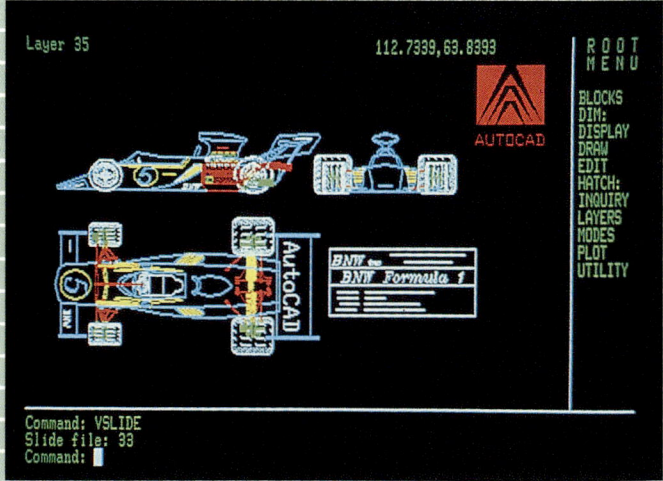

PLATE 27
Formula 1 race car. Designed on AutoCAD by Autodesk, Inc. Drawing Courtesy of BNW Inc., Los Gatos, California.

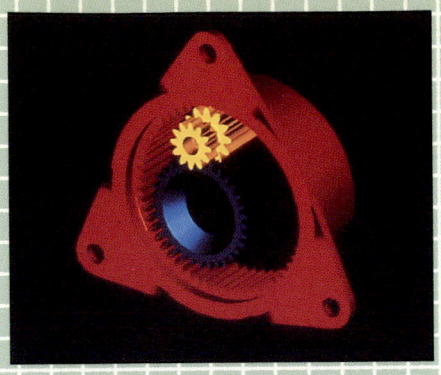

PLATE 28
Solid model of planetary gear system.

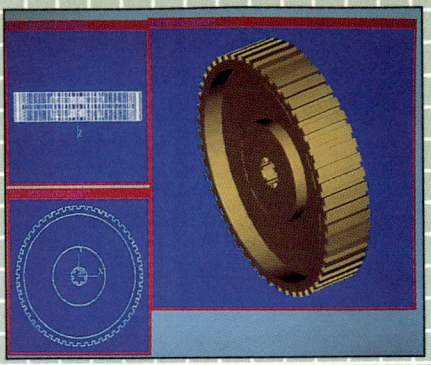

PLATE 29
Gear design using AutoSolid and shading.

PLATE 30
Designer models a human powered sail plane in 3D.

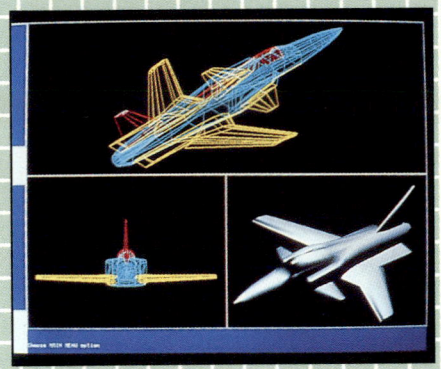

PLATE 31
Airplane design.

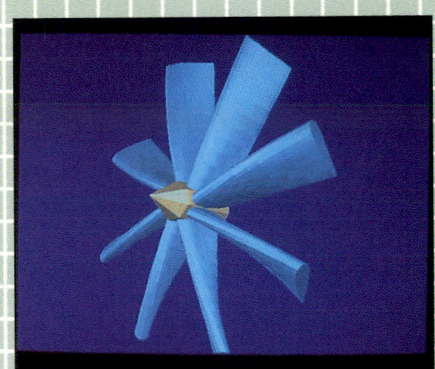

PLATE 32
Turboprop design.

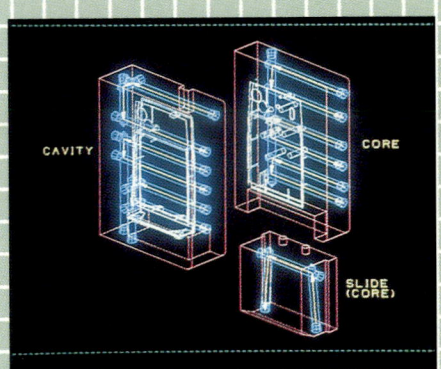

PLATE 33
3D wire frame of plastic mold design.

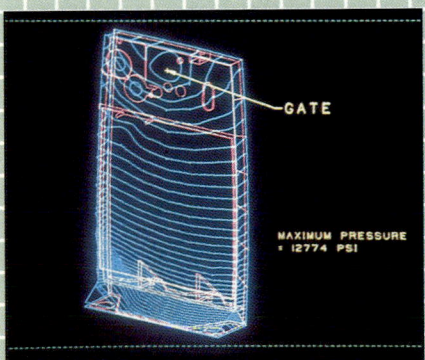

PLATE 34
Wire frame model of mold part undergoing analysis.

COLOR PLATES

5

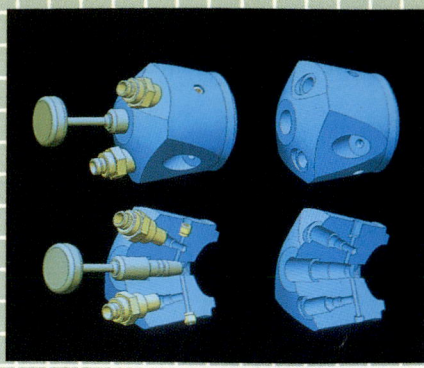

PLATE 35
Once the geometric model is created the solid modeler can be used to explode the valve housing into component parts, rotate it for viewing from different angles, create a cross section, and check for interference with related parts.

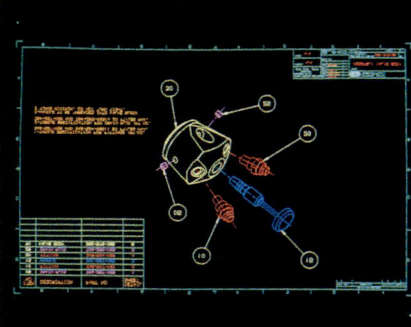

PLATE 36
Wire frame geometry can be automatically created from the solid model geometry of the valve housing. Exploded views, assemblies, hidden line removal, and design drawings can all be used in drafting format without altering the data generated in the modeling stage.

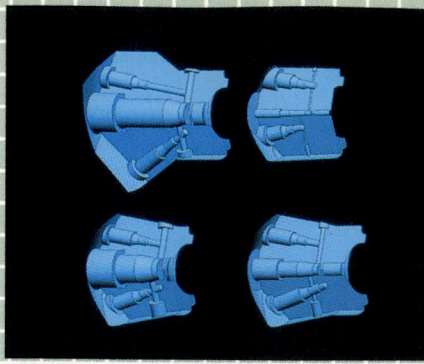

PLATE 37
The solid modeler gives the ability to input multiple dimension parameters to automatically generate families of parts.

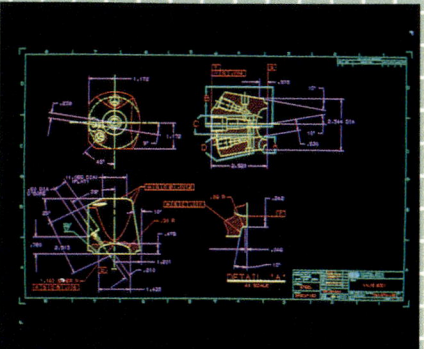

PLATE 38
Product drafting and detailing documentation is produced from common design geometry.

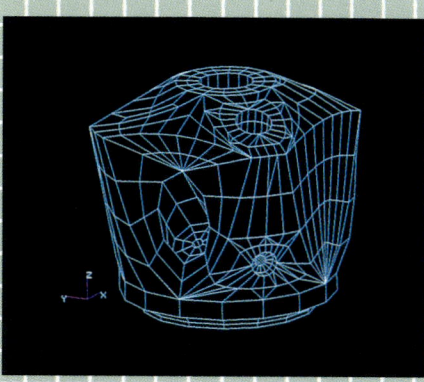

PLATE 39
A finite element model is generated from common geometry and analyzed to insure meeting design criteria.

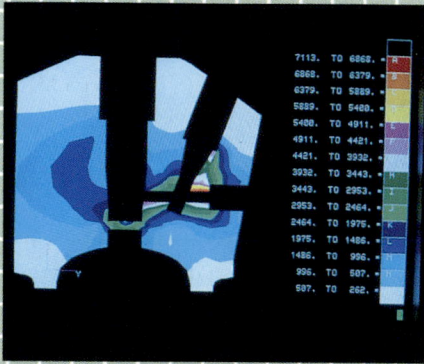

PLATE 40
A variety of color schemes can be called upon to depict a particular analysis.

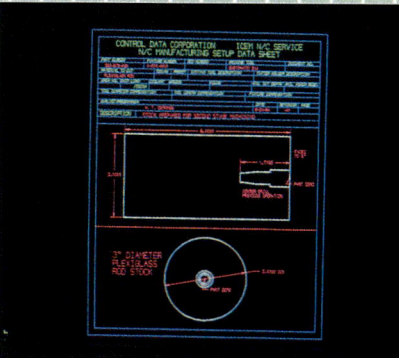

PLATE 41
Numerical control capability allows generation of control tapes directly from design geometry. The NC output is used for the machining of the actual part.

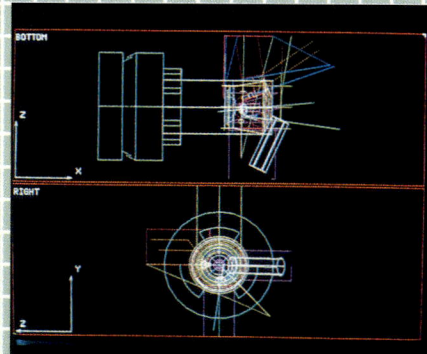

PLATE 42
Designers can preview cutter paths before machining the part to obtain optimum cutter path design.

PLATE 43
Finished valve housing.

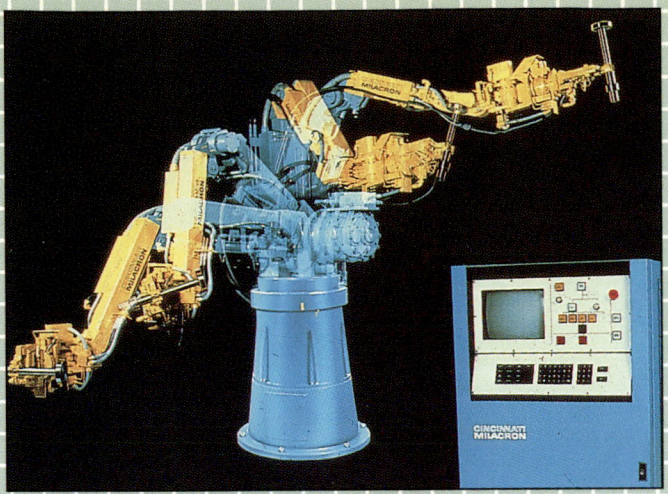

PLATE 44
Industrial robot.

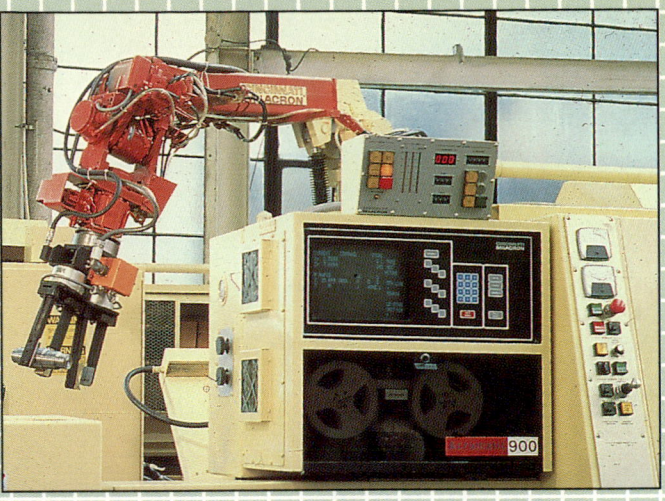

PLATE 45
Control panel and arm of an industrial robot.

PLATE 46
The work cell can be designed for welding, assembly, machine loading, and other manufacturing operations. This robot is performing material handling operations.

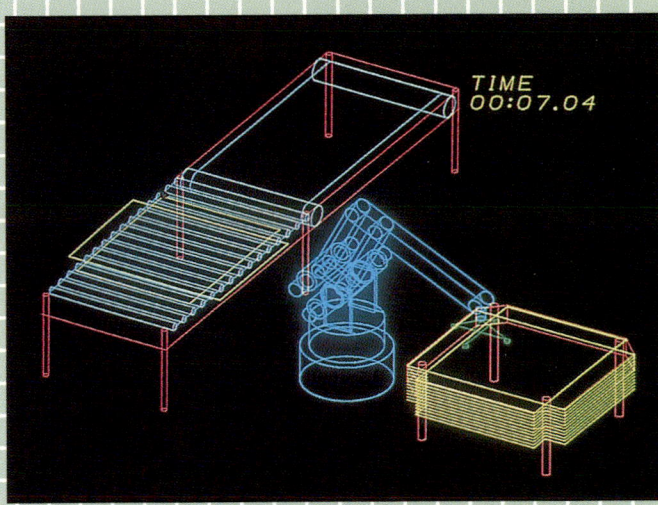

PLATE 47
During robot simulation, work cell cycle time is displayed on screen at the computer-aided design station. Throughout the simulation, ROBOT-SIM software allows the operator to check work cell design elements such as interferences in the motion of the robot or end affecter with other work cell components.

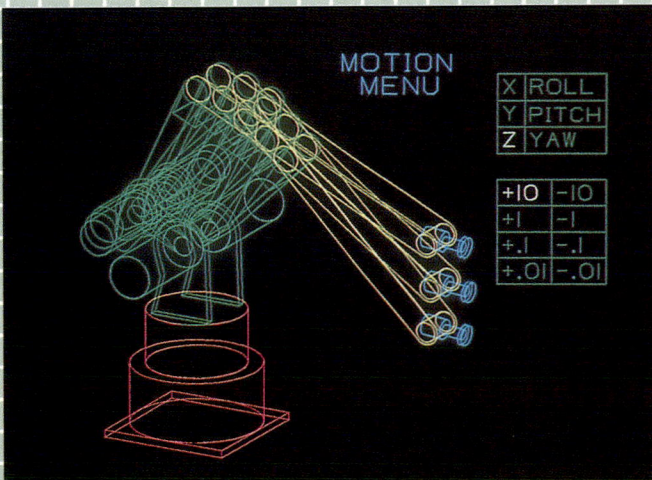

PLATE 48
Using the motion menu feature of Calma's ROBOT-SIM software, a work cell designer can analyze and simulate robot movement within its factory floor environment. This screen view shows superimposed robot images obtained from motion simulation.

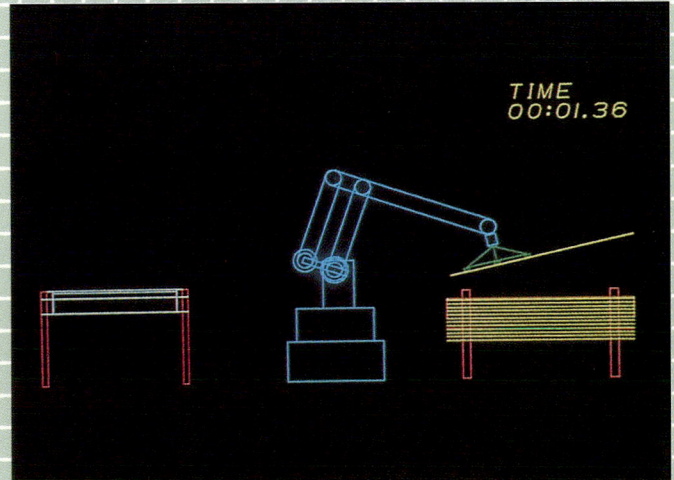

PLATE 49
This side view of a robot work cell was designed using Calma's ROBOT-SIM computer-aided design software. The conveyor (left), indexing pallet (right), and robot (center) are drawn from the robot library. Other robot and work cell components, such as the end effector (shown in green), may be added using 3D design, design, drafting and manufacturing core mechanical software, integrated with the ROBOT-SIM package.

PLATE 50
Interior view of British rail car.

PLATE 51
Interior view of rail car interior from different angle.

PLATE 52
Individual seating module.

PLATE 53
Seating design with one choice of many color and fabric options.

PLATE 54
Boundary display of back support.

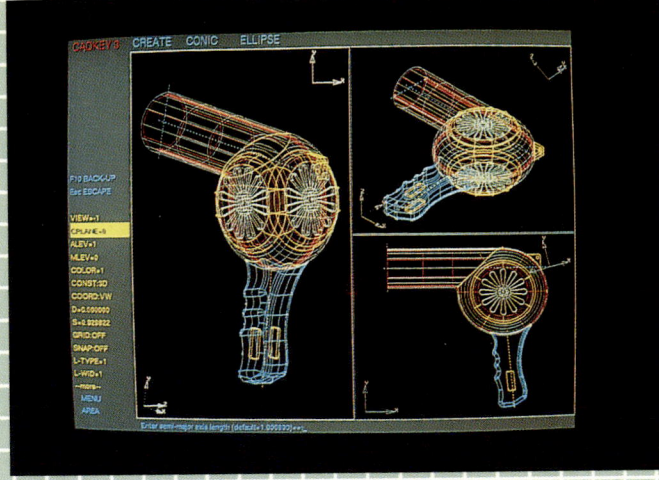

PLATE 55
3D wire frame design model of a hair dryer.

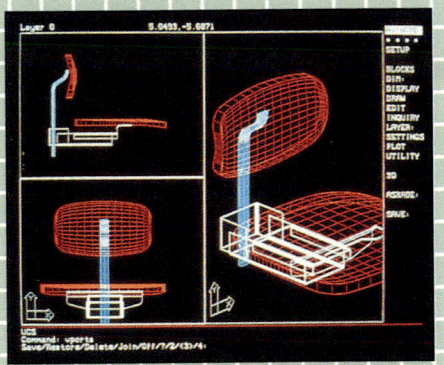

PLATE 56
Three views of chair seat modeled in 3D.

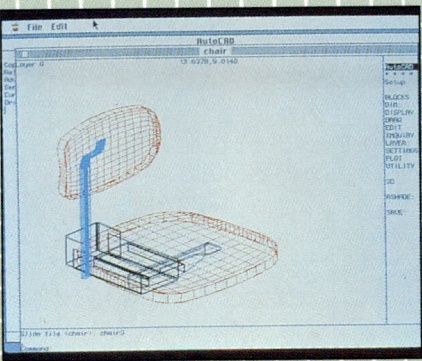

PLATE 57
Chair design using AutoCAD 3D modeling.

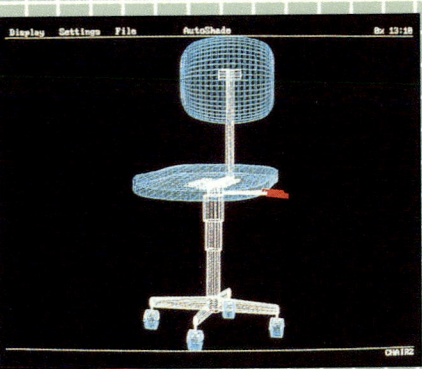

PLATE 58
Chair design.

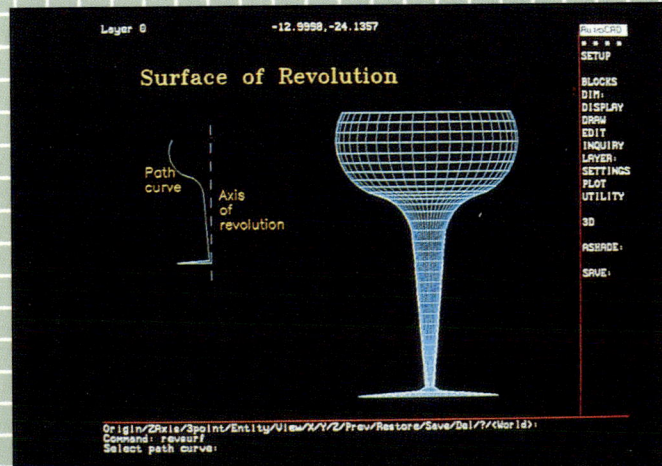

PLATE 59
Glass design using surface of revolution command.

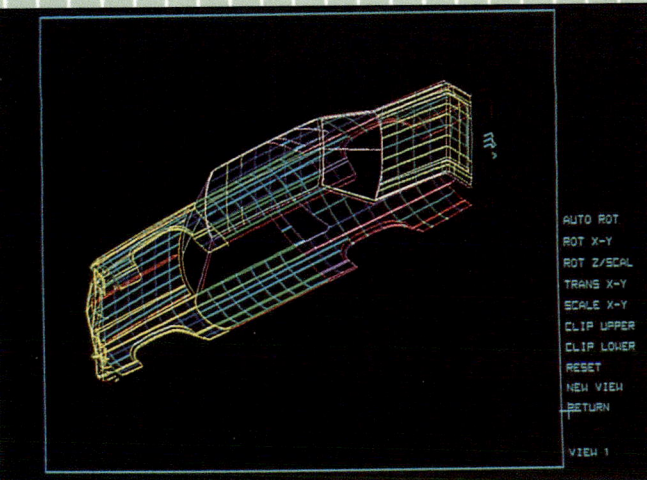

PLATE 60
Wire frame model of car.

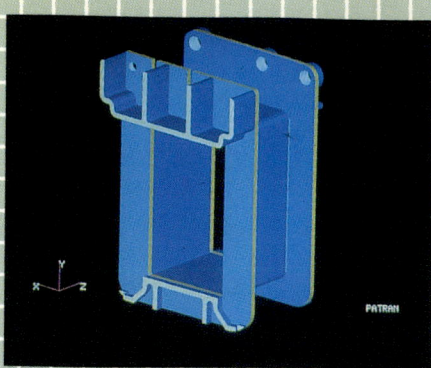

PLATE 61
Component modeling and solid shading of 3D part.

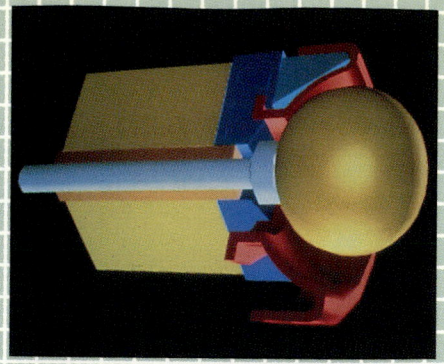

PLATE 62
Solid shaded model of a peach pitter assembly.

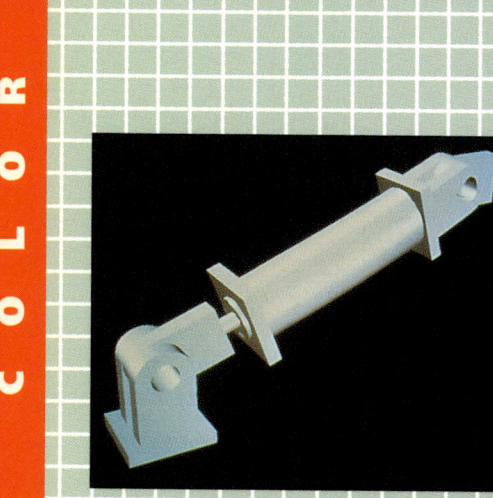

PLATE 63
3D modeling capability for defining kinematic relationships.

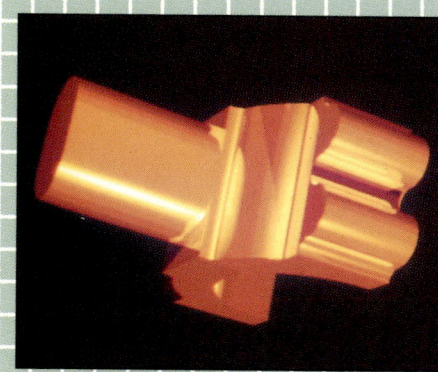

PLATE 64
Solid model of mechanical part.

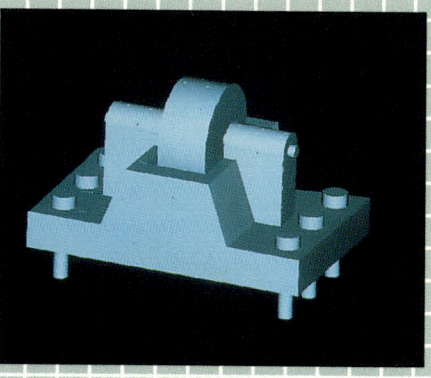

PLATE 65
Shaded 3D solid model assembly.

PLATE 66
Display showing a solid model assembly.

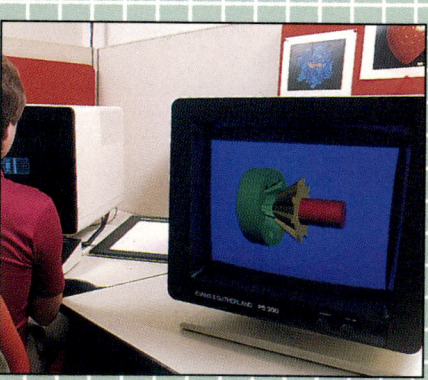

PLATE 67
Solid model of mechanical assembly.

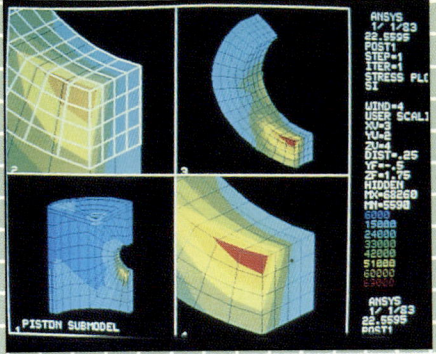

PLATE 68
Stress analysis using a 3D modeler.

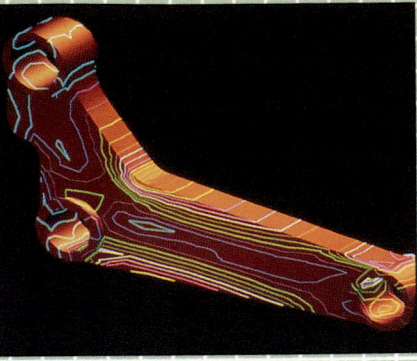

PLATE 69
Von Mises stress contours on light source shaded model of an acturator arm.

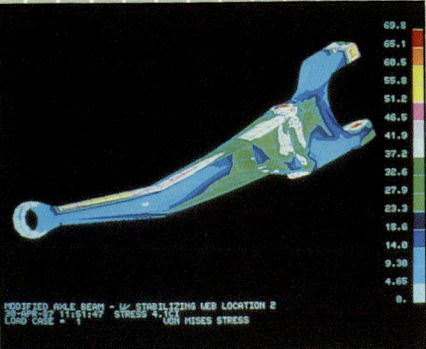

PLATE 70
Stress analysis of a connecting rod.

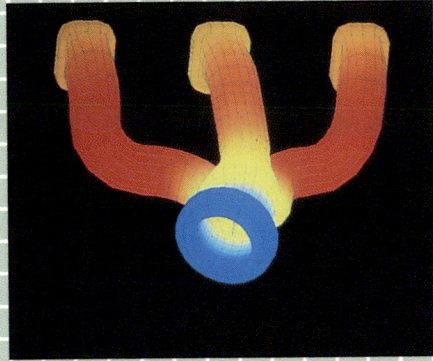

PLATE 71
Temperature contours for an engine exhaust manifold.

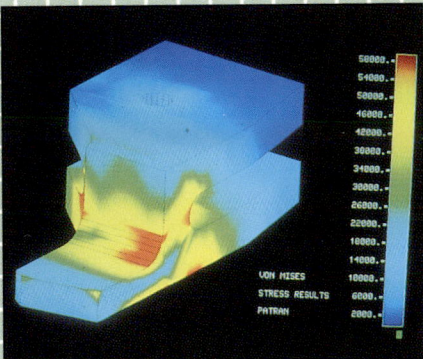

PLATE 72
3D stress analysis.

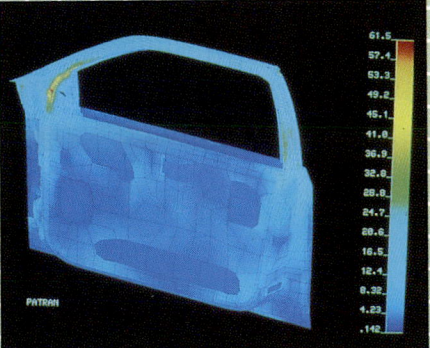

PLATE 73
Stress contours for a car door structural analysis.

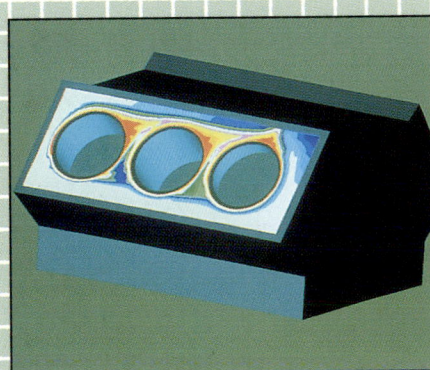

PLATE 74
Display showing laminar viscous flow.

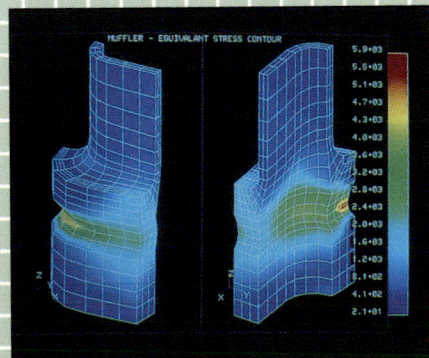

PLATE 75
Two views of the stress values for a component, shown by a continuous color fringe plot.

PLATE 76
Von Mises stress for a torsional analysis of a car's structural frame.

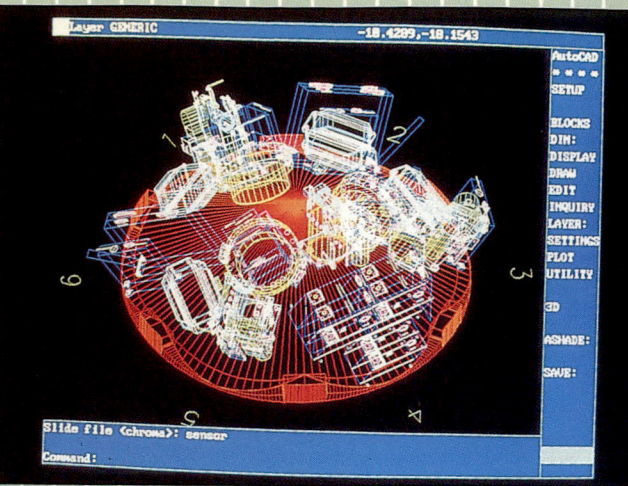

PLATE 77
Design of assembly using 3D wire frame modeling.

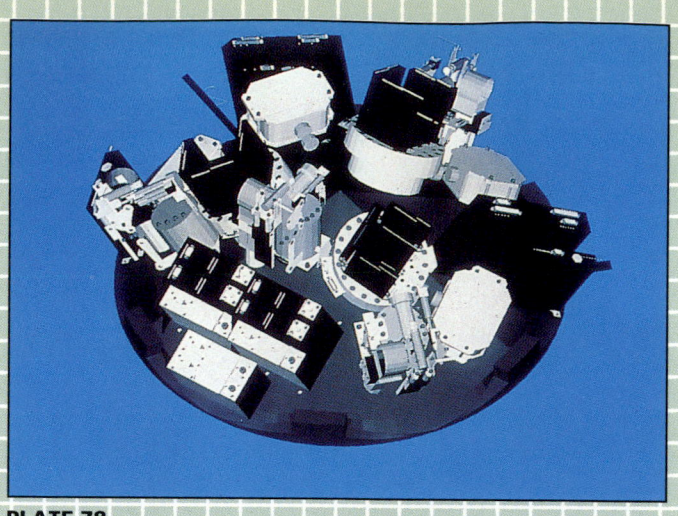

PLATE 78
Assembly shown with AutoShade.

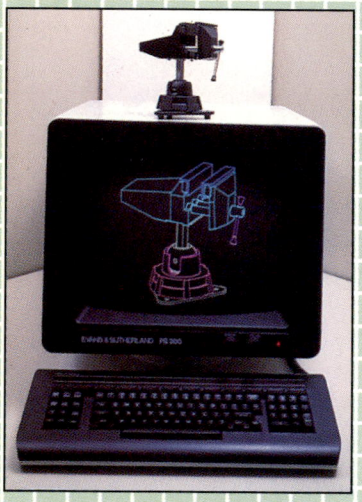

PLATE 79
Vice assembly shown on the display.

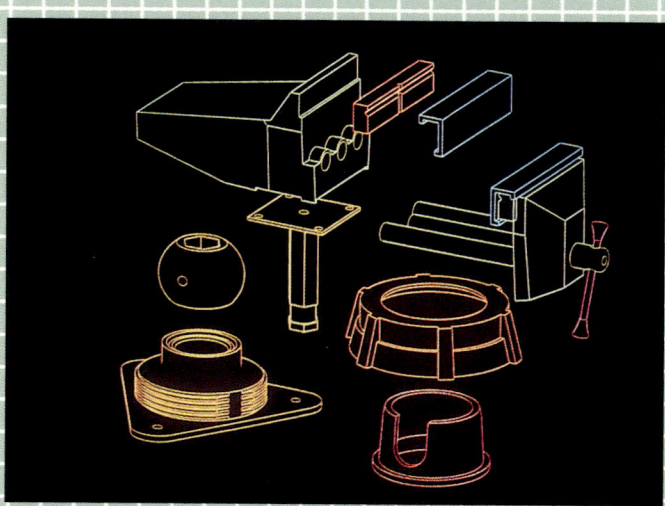

PLATE 80
Exploded view of vice assembly.

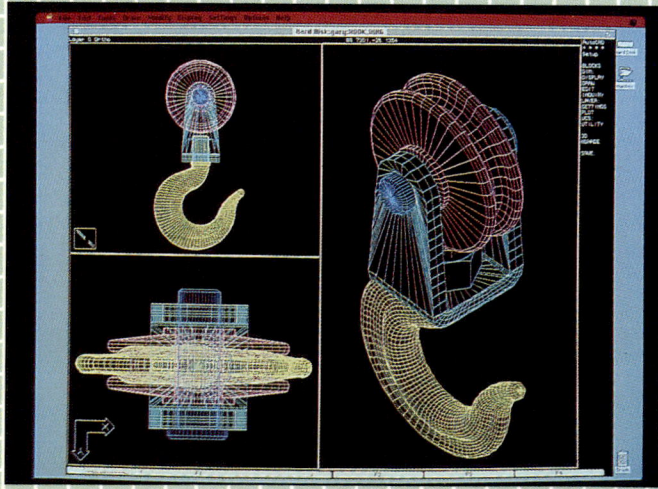

PLATE 81
3D assembly model.

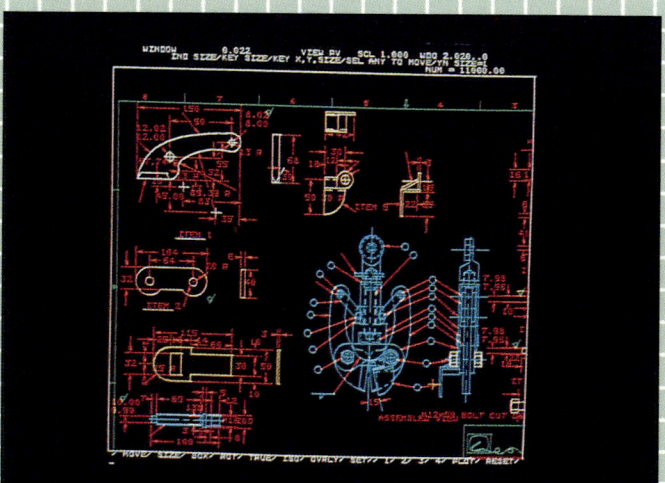

PLATE 82
Assembly and detail drawing of a mechanical part.

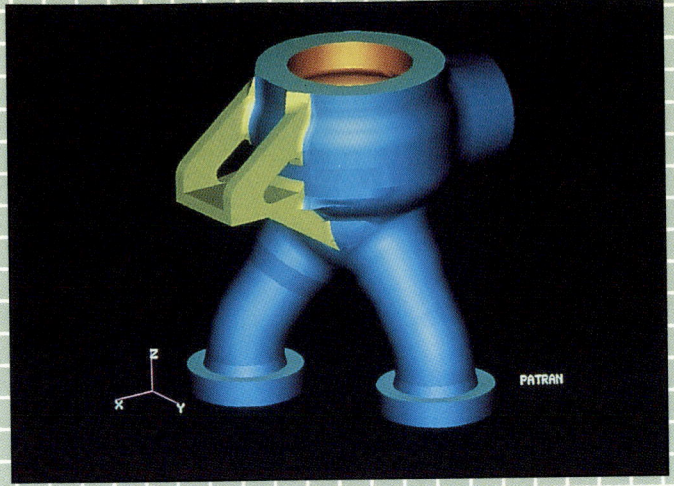

PLATE 83
Complex solid model of a pressure vessel and piping connections.

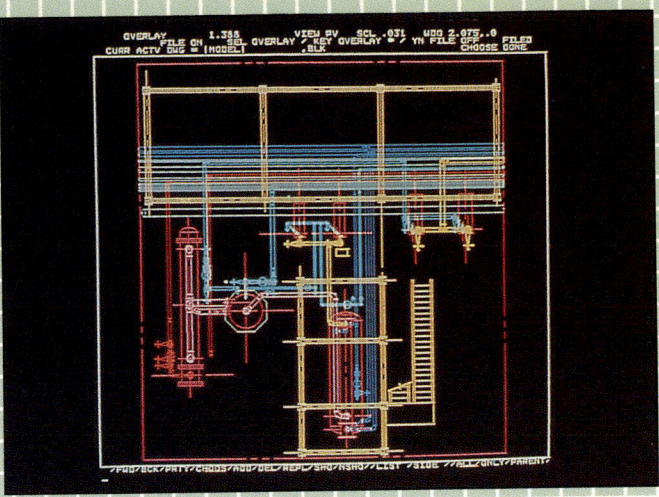

PLATE 84
Plan view of piping design project modeled in 3D.

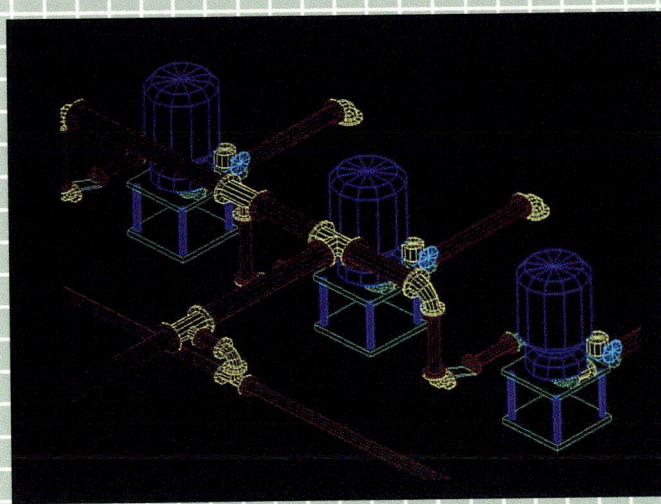

PLATE 85
Wire frame model of piping and equipment for plant design.

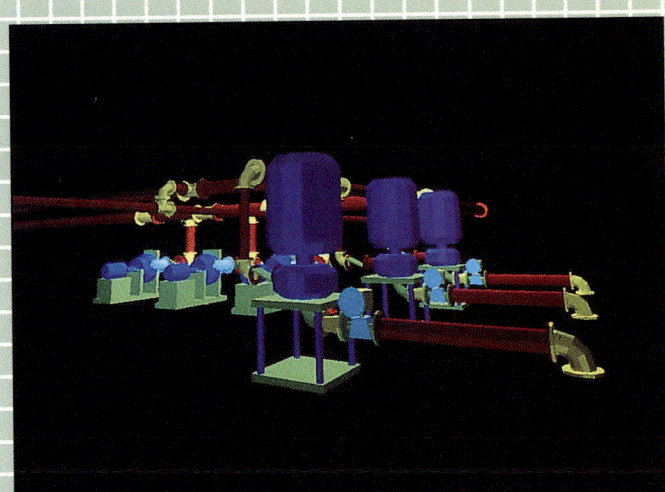

PLATE 86
Shaded image of piping and equipment.

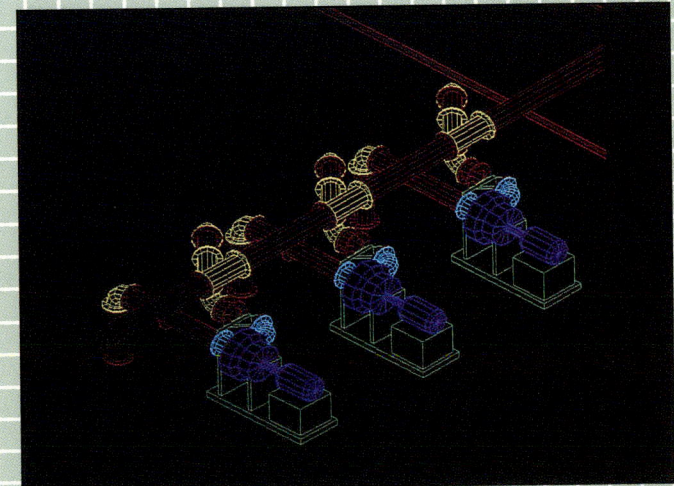

PLATE 87
3D model of pumping station.

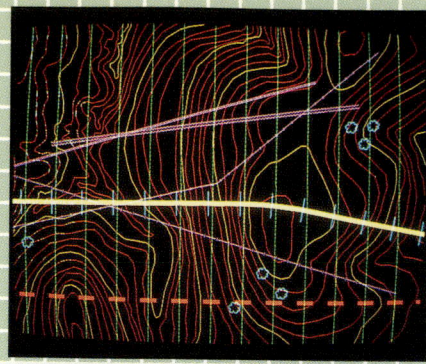

PLATE 88
Data collected from field measurements or contour maps becomes the base map upon which the civil engineer can graphically experiment with alternative horizontal alignments.

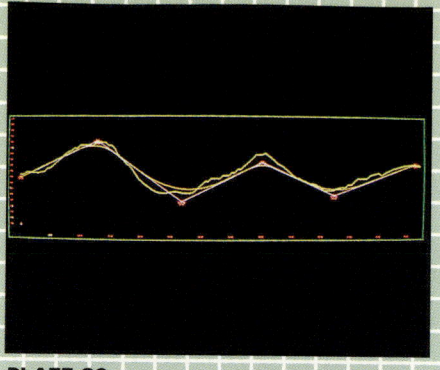

PLATE 89
Existing ground profile information along this horizontal alignment is automatically generated. To this, the engineer can add and graphically fine tune the proposed vertical control.

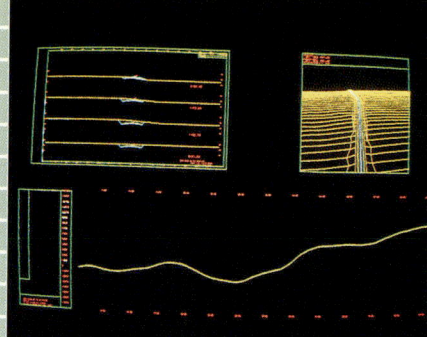

PLATE 90
Define typical roadway cross sections and the design is complete. Graphical options provide a variety of mechanisms for evaluation of this design, including cross-section plots, mass haul diagrams, perspectives, etc.

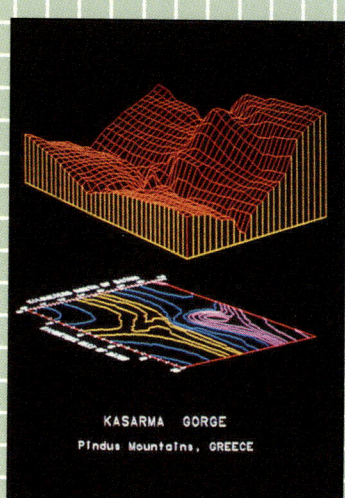

PLATE 91
3D section of mountain.

PLATE 92
3D topographic model using AutoShade.

PLATE 93
Bridge design.

PLATE 94
Golden Gate Bridge.

PLATE 95
Perspective at the McDonnell Douglas ISG Campus.

PLATE 96
Solids and color shading used to realistically show how the building will appear.

PLATE 97
Solids and color shading used with wire frame to view the building and its surroundings.

PLATE 98
Architectural modeling with AutoCad.

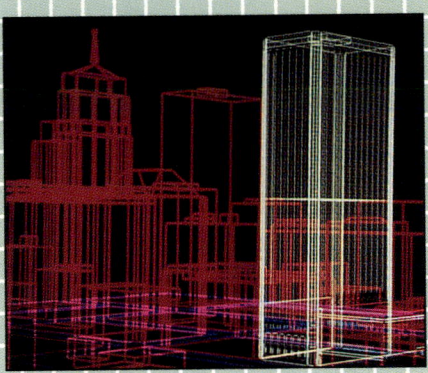

PLATE 99
Wire frame model of city with new architectural project highlighted.

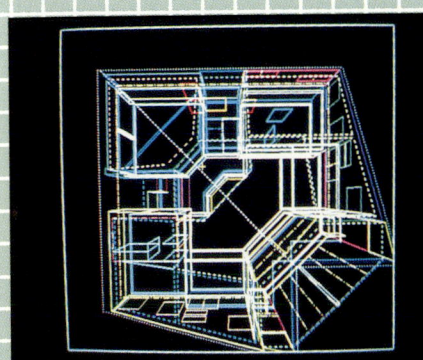

PLATE 100
Plan view of an architectural model.

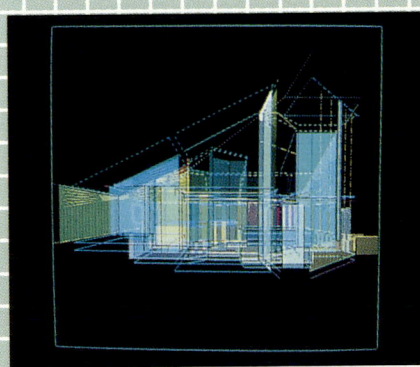

PLATE 101
3D wire frame of an architectural project.

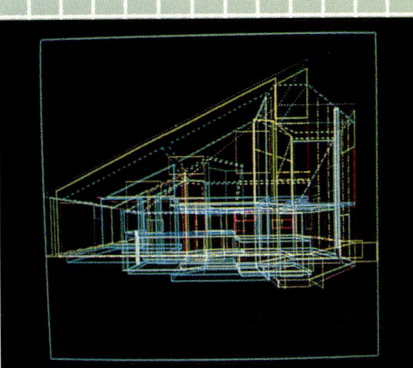

PLATE 102
Architectural design model.

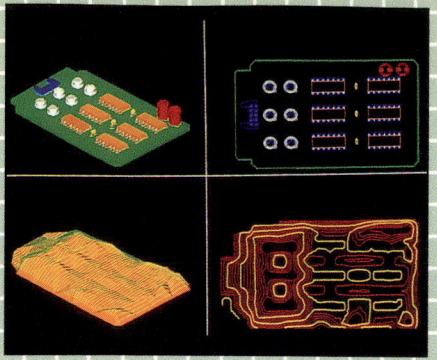

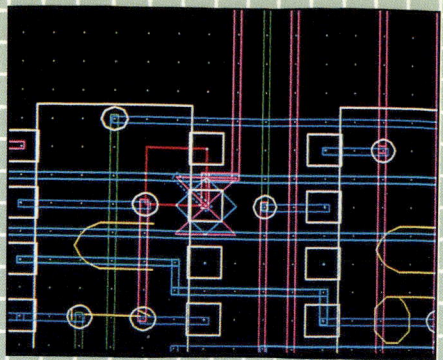

PLATE 103
3D model of a printed circuit board undergoing heat analysis.

PLATE 104
PCB layout.

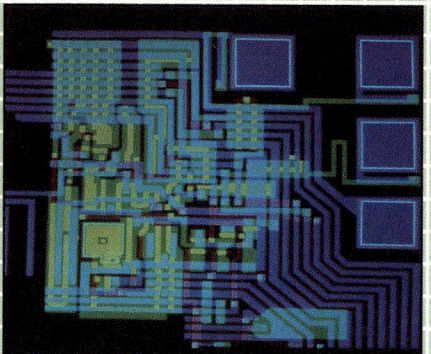

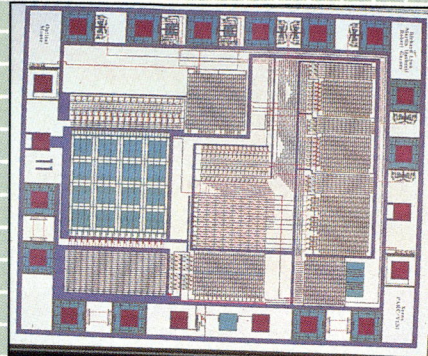

PLATE 105
Integrated circuit layout.

PLATE 106
IC design.

PLATE 107
Integrated circuit color plot.

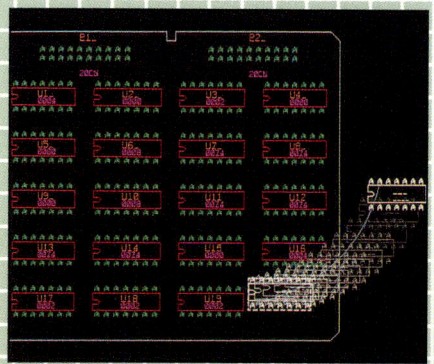

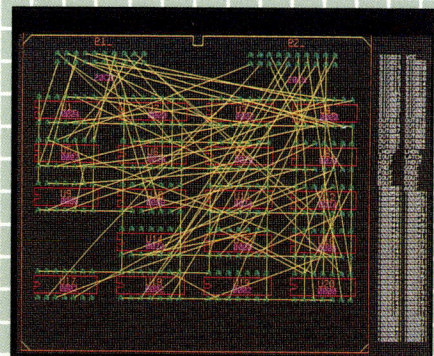

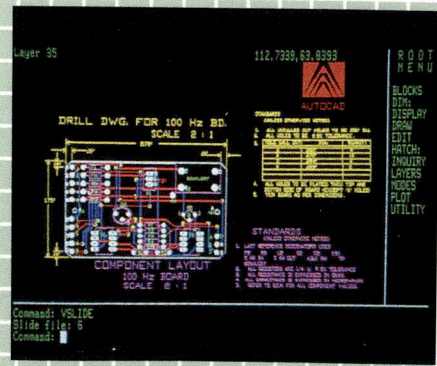

PLATE 108
Automatic component placement.

PLATE 109
Automatic routing of circuit board traces.

PLATE 110
PCB assembly.

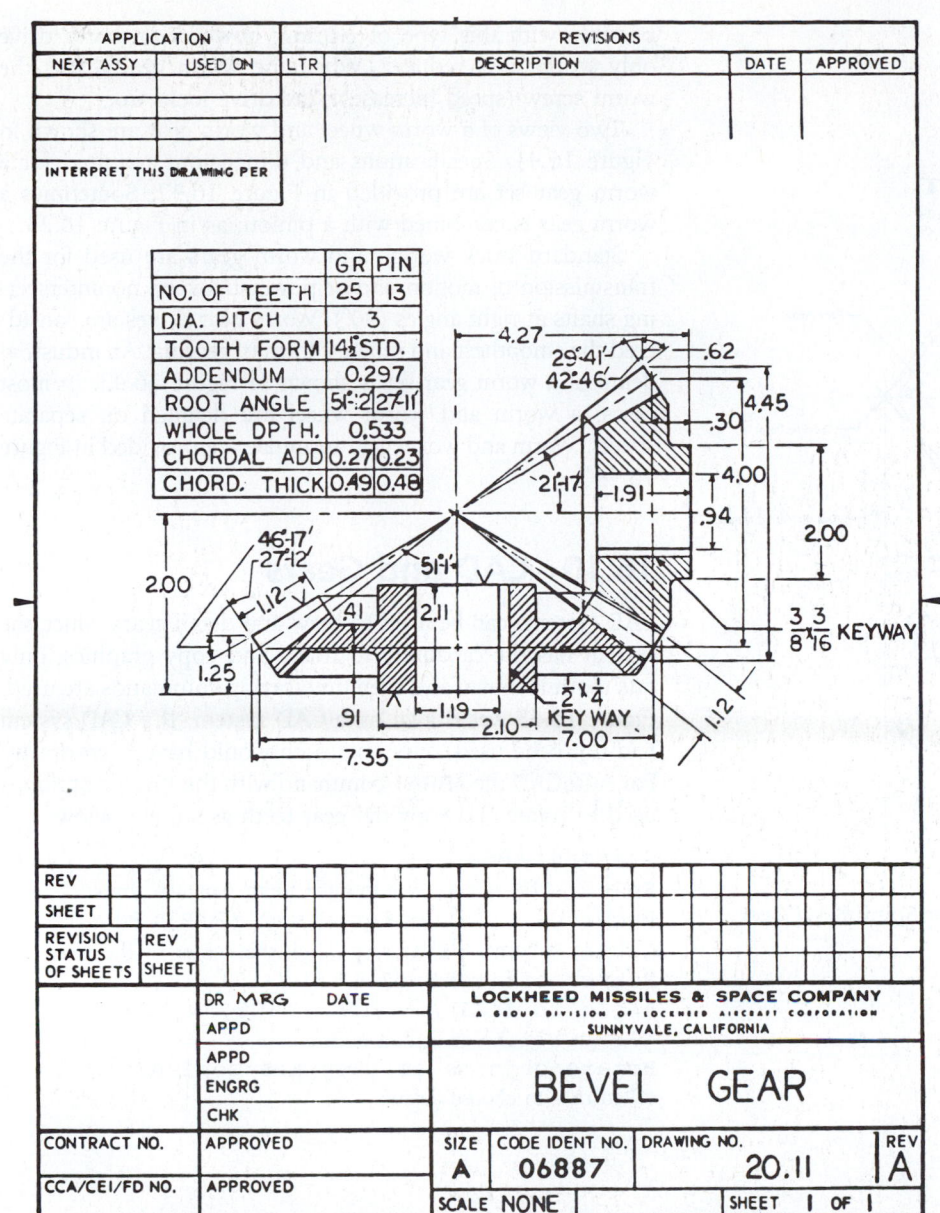

		GR	PIN
NO. OF TEETH		25	13
DIA. PITCH		3	
TOOTH FORM		14½ STD.	
ADDENDUM		0.297	
ROOT ANGLE		5f:2 27·11	
WHOLE DPTH.		0.533	
CHORDAL ADD		0.27	0.23
CHORD. THICK		0.49	0.48

LOCKHEED MISSILES & SPACE COMPANY
A GROUP DIVISION OF LOCKHEED AIRCRAFT CORPORATION
SUNNYVALE, CALIFORNIA

BEVEL GEAR

| SIZE A | CODE IDENT NO. 06887 | DRAWING NO. 20.11 | REV A |
| SCALE NONE | | SHEET 1 OF 1 | |

FIGURE 16.38 Bevel Gear Detail

Tooth form The shape of the tooth profile. Since bevel gears are manufactured with a variety of tooth forms, it is essential to specify the desired form on the gear drawing.

16.8.2 Drawing and Dimensioning Bevel Gears

A bevel gear drawing consists of a side view or axial section illustrating the general configuration and tabulated gear tooth data. An industrial detail of a set of bevel gears is shown in Figure 16.38. Generally, only one view is needed. A front view is used where necessary to show the relationship of the gear teeth to other features.

The gear illustration of Figure 16.39 shows only those dimensions that control the gear teeth and their relation to

the mounting surfaces. Dimensional values are indicated by X's to show the number of decimal places recommended in each instance.

16.9 Worms and Worm Gears

Worm gears (Fig. 16.40) are used to transmit motion from one shaft to another at a high speed. **Worm gears** (wheel) and **worm screws** are designed to transmit motion between non-intersecting, perpendicular shafts. A worm is, in effect, a screw. When a worm wheel (similar to a spur gear) has teeth shaped to fit the threads on the worm, the worm will turn the wheel. The worm may have single, double, or multiple threads, as explained in Chapter 15. A large speed ratio is

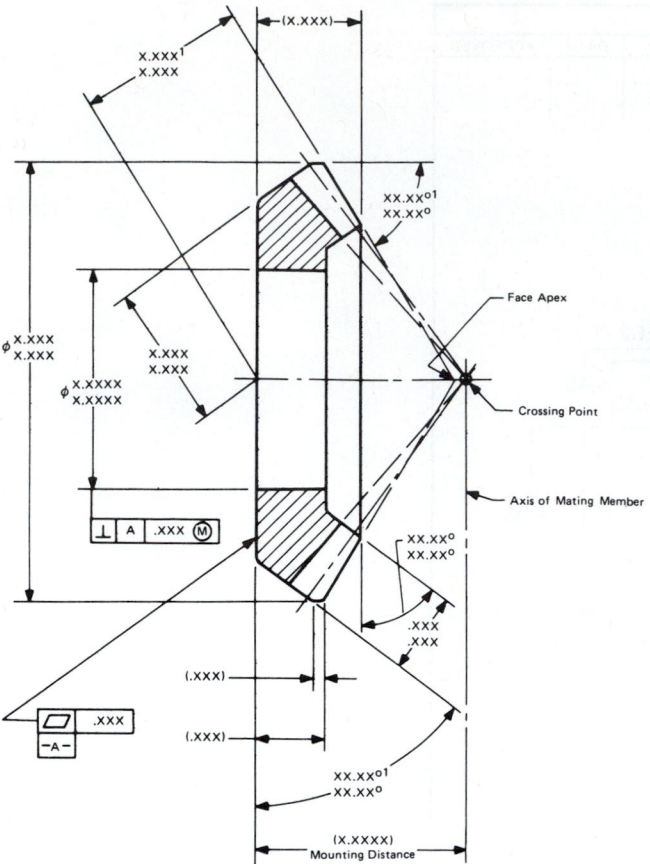

FIGURE 16.39   Dimensions Required for Spiral Bevel Gear

possible with this type of gearing; however, a worm drive only works as a reducer. When the worm gear drives the worm screw (speed increases), the drive locks up.

Two views of a worm wheel and worm gear are shown in Figure 16.41. Specifications and dimensions required for a worm gear set are provided in Figure 16.42. Sometimes a worm gear is combined with a pinion, as in Figure 16.23.

Standard stock worms and worm gears are used for the transmission of motion and/or power between nonintersecting shafts at right angles (90°). Worm gear drives are considered the smoothest and quietest form of gearing. An industrial detail of a worm gear set is shown in Figure 16.43. In most cases, a worm and worm wheel are detailed on separate sheets. Worm and worm gear formulae are provided in Figure 16.44.

16.10   CAD and Gears

CAD systems can be used to draw and detail gears. Since the system has the capability to rotate and copy graphics, only one tooth is drawn and then time-saving commands are used. Figure 16.43 was drawn on a CAD system. If a CAD system had not been used, only one tooth would have been drawn. For AutoCAD the **ARRAY** command with the `Polar` option is used to rotate and copy the gear teeth as shown below:

```
Command: ARRAY
Select Objects: Window the tooth that was drawn.
Rectangular or Polar Array (R/P): P
Center point of array: Pick the center of the gear.
Number of items: 32
Angle to fill (+=CCW, -=CW) <360>:
<Return> to choose default of 360.
Rotate objects as they are copied? <y>:
<Return> to choose default.
```

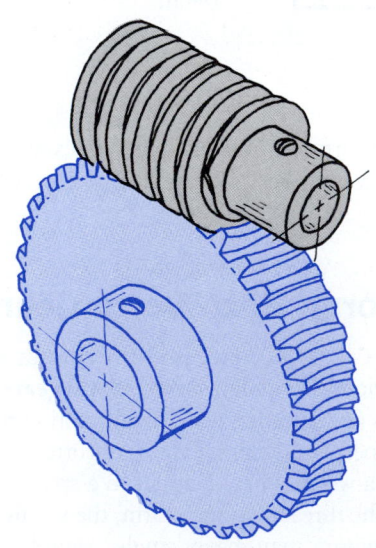

FIGURE 16.40   Worm Gear and Worm

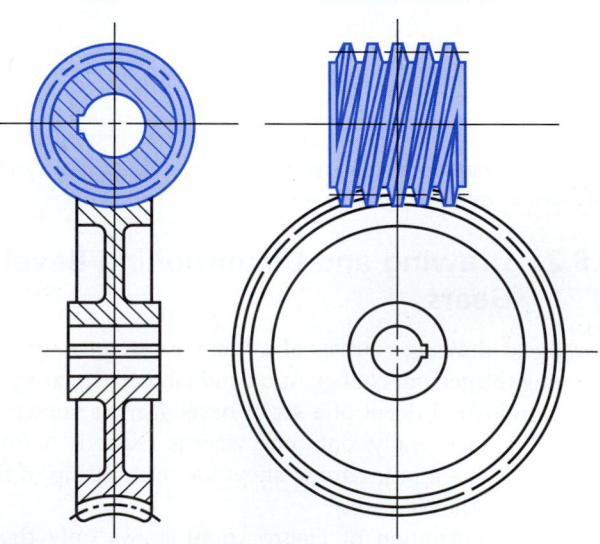

FIGURE 16.41   Worm Gear Set

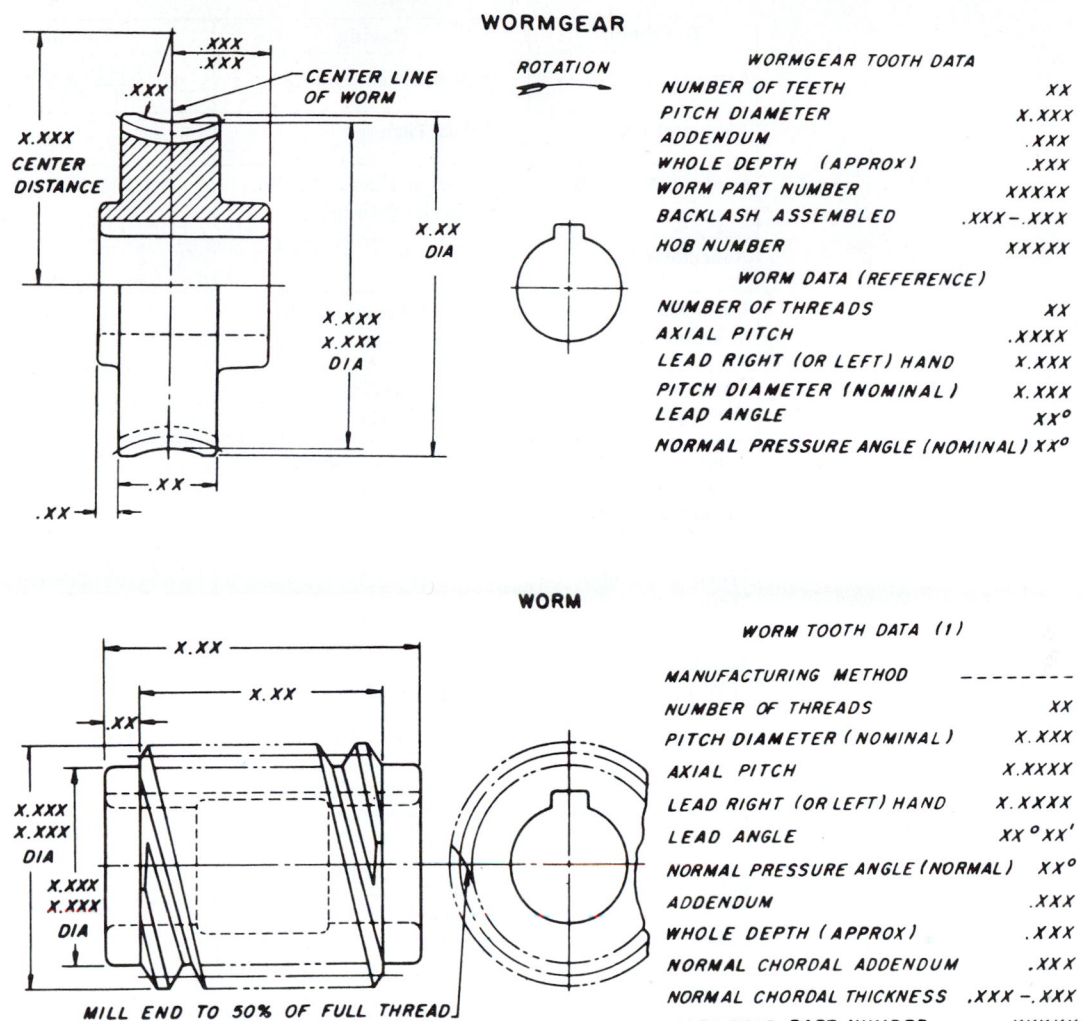

WORMGEAR

ROTATION

WORMGEAR TOOTH DATA	
NUMBER OF TEETH	XX
PITCH DIAMETER	X.XXX
ADDENDUM	.XXX
WHOLE DEPTH (APPROX)	.XXX
WORM PART NUMBER	XXXXX
BACKLASH ASSEMBLED	.XXX – .XXX
HOB NUMBER	XXXXX
WORM DATA (REFERENCE)	
NUMBER OF THREADS	XX
AXIAL PITCH	.XXXX
LEAD RIGHT (OR LEFT) HAND	X.XXX
PITCH DIAMETER (NOMINAL)	X.XXX
LEAD ANGLE	XX°
NORMAL PRESSURE ANGLE (NOMINAL)	XX°

WORM

WORM TOOTH DATA (1)	
MANUFACTURING METHOD	– – – – – –
NUMBER OF THREADS	XX
PITCH DIAMETER (NOMINAL)	X.XXX
AXIAL PITCH	X.XXXX
LEAD RIGHT (OR LEFT) HAND	X.XXXX
LEAD ANGLE	XX°XX'
NORMAL PRESSURE ANGLE (NORMAL)	XX°
ADDENDUM	.XXX
WHOLE DEPTH (APPROX)	.XXX
NORMAL CHORDAL ADDENDUM	.XXX
NORMAL CHORDAL THICKNESS	.XXX – .XXX
WORMGEAR PART NUMBER	XXXXX

MILL END TO 50% OF FULL THREAD

FIGURE 16.42   Dimensions Required for Worm and Worm Gears

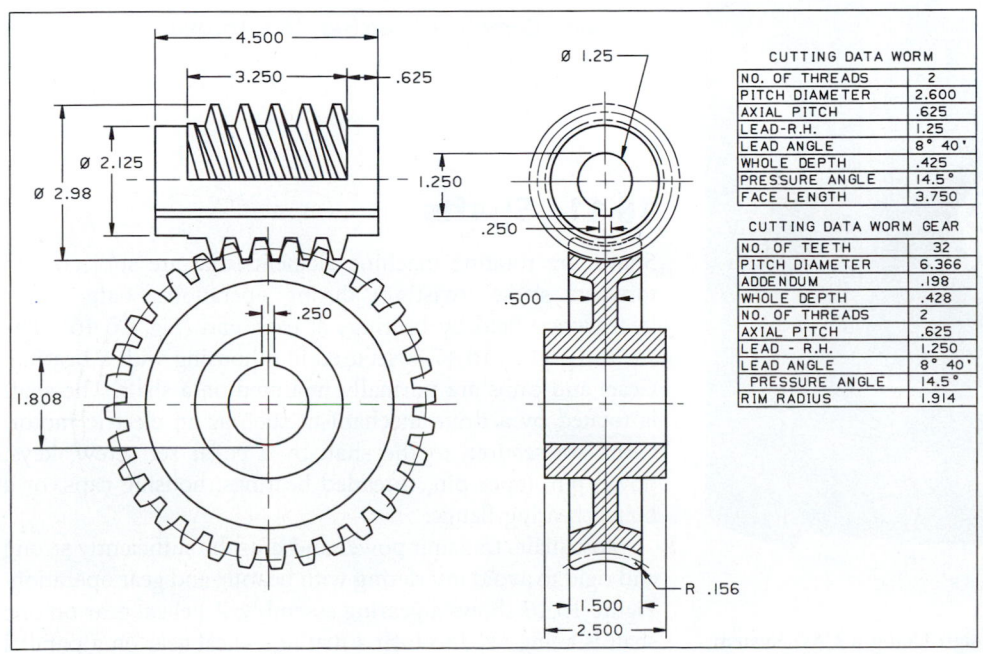

CUTTING DATA WORM	
NO. OF THREADS	2
PITCH DIAMETER	2.600
AXIAL PITCH	.625
LEAD-R.H.	1.25
LEAD ANGLE	8° 40'
WHOLE DEPTH	.425
PRESSURE ANGLE	14.5°
FACE LENGTH	3.750

CUTTING DATA WORM GEAR	
NO. OF TEETH	32
PITCH DIAMETER	6.366
ADDENDUM	.198
WHOLE DEPTH	.428
NO. OF THREADS	2
AXIAL PITCH	.625
LEAD - R.H.	1.250
LEAD ANGLE	8° 40'
PRESSURE ANGLE	14.5°
RIM RADIUS	1.914

FIGURE 16.43   Worm and Worm Gear Detail

To Obtain	Having	Formula
Circular Pitch (p)	Diametral Pitch (P)	$P = \dfrac{3.1416}{P}$
Diametral Pitch (P)	Circular Pitch (p)	$P = \dfrac{3.1416}{P}$
Lead (of Worm) (l)	Number of Threads in Worm & Circular Pitch (p)	$i = P$ (Number of Threads)
Addendum (a)	Diametral Pitch (P)	$a = \dfrac{1}{P}$
Pitch Diameter of Worm (D_W)	Outside Diameter (d_O) & Addendum (a)	$D_W = d_O - 2a$
Pitch Diameter of Worm Gear (D_G)	Circular Pitch (p) & Number of Teeth (N)	$D_G = \dfrac{N_p}{3.1416}$
Center Distance Between Worm and Worm Gear (CD)	Pitch Diameter of Worm (D_W) & Worm Gear (D_G)	$CD = \dfrac{P_W + D_G}{2}$
Whole Depth of Teeth (h_T)	Circular Pitch (p)	$h_T = .6866\,p$
	Diametral Pitch (P)	$h_T = \dfrac{2.157}{P}$
Bottom Diameter of Worm (d_r)	Whole Depth (hT) & Outside Diameter (d_w)	$d_r = d_O - 2\,h_T$
Throat Diameter of Worm Gear (D_T)	Pitch Diameter of Worm Gear (D) & Addendum (a)	$D_T = D + 2a$
Lead Angle of Worm	Pitch Diameter of Worm (D) & the Lead (L)	$= \tan^{-1}\left(\dfrac{L}{3.1416d}\right)$
Ratio	No. of Teeth on Gear (N_G) and Number of Threads on Worm	$\text{Ratio} = \dfrac{N_G}{\text{No. of Threads}}$

FIGURE 16.44 **Worm and Worm Gear Formulas**

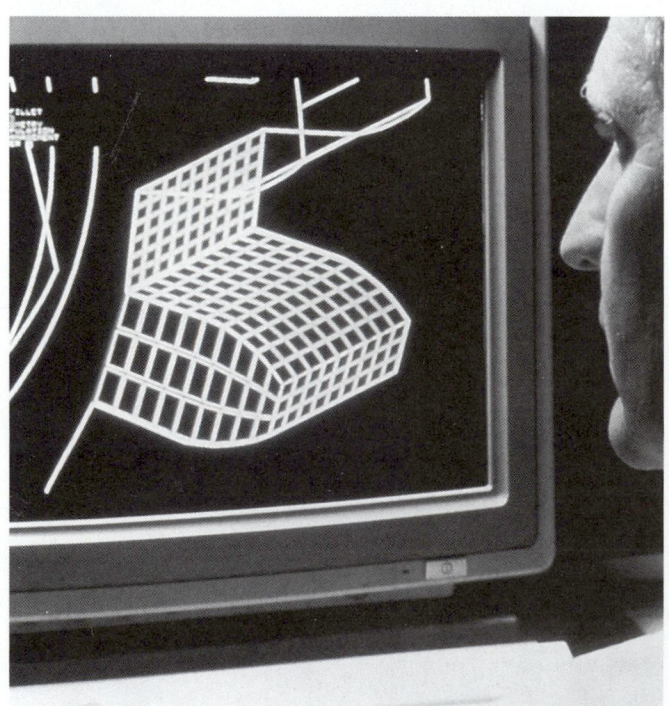

FIGURE 16.45 **Spur Gear Tooth Design Using a CAD System**

Gears are also designed in 3D using a CAD system. The designer in Figure 16.45 is working at his terminal creating a 3D surface model of a spur gear tooth.

You May Complete Exercises 16.1 Through 16.4 at This Time

16.11 Shafts

Shafts are rotating machine elements that are subjected to torsional stress (twisting) during operation. Shafts rotate freely when held by bearings at each end (Fig. 16.46). The shaft in Figure 16.47 is secured in a housing with a bearing. Gears and cams are normally mounted on a shaft. The shaft is rotated by a drive mechanism such as an electric motor. Gears are secured to the shaft by a collar set screw, keys, dowel pin, taper pin, threaded bearings, housing caps, or a bolted bearing flange.

Most shafts transmit power and must be sufficiently strong and rigid to avoid interfering with bearing and gear operation. Figure 16.18 shows a gearing assembly. A helical gear on one shaft is being used to turn a mating helical gear on a parallel

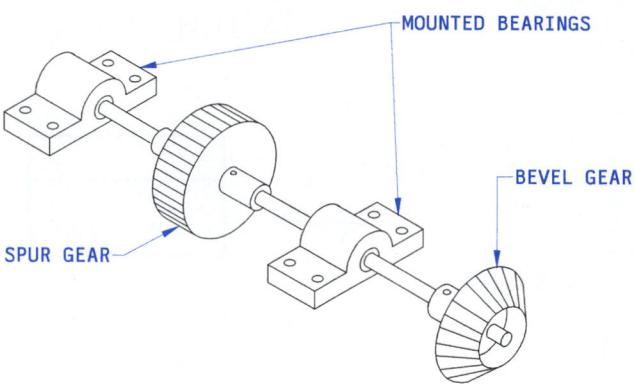

FIGURE 16.46   Shaft, Bearings, and Gear

FIGURE 16.48   Bearings and Housings

shaft. The shafts are held in place by bearings at both ends. A single-row ball bearing is at one end and a double-row ball bearing is at the other end of each shaft. Double-row ball bearings carry a greater load than single-row ball bearings. The two gears are of different sizes. Therefore, they provide reduced or increased shaft speed, depending on which shaft is the drive shaft and which is the driven shaft.

16.12   Bearings

Bearings (Fig. 16.48) are designed to take radial loads, axial loads, or a combination of the two. Bearings that are designed to resist a load perpendicular to the axis of the shaft are **radial bearings.** Those designed to resist an axial load (along the axis) are thrust bearings. Plain radial bearings are sometimes called journal bearings (bushing type). The portion of a shaft that is in contact with the bearing is called a journal. Figure

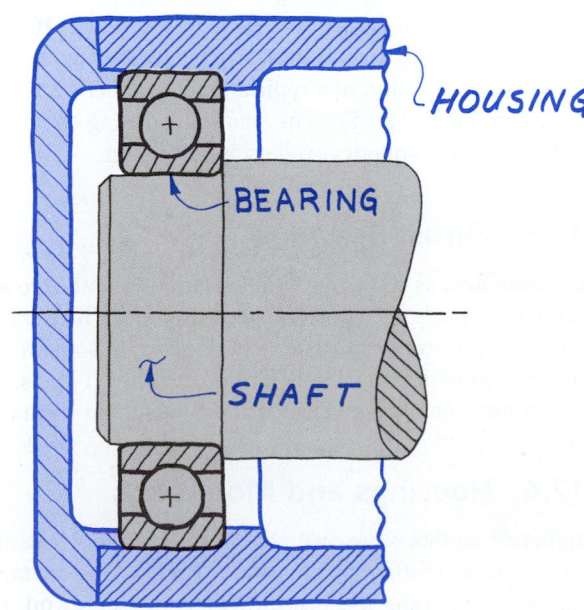

FIGURE 16.47   Ball Bearing, Shaft, and Housing

16.49 shows the difference between axial load and radial load. Bearings are manufactured using a variety of metals and plastics.

Bearing selection is based on shaft size, application, speed of rotation, required design life, load requirements, physical geometry, cost, and mounting requirements. When specifying bearings, you must consider the method of retaining the bearings, lubrication requirements, and sealing of the housing and the bearing. Shaft tolerance and diameter, shaft shoulder diameter, and the housing's internal bore and tolerance are also important. Many types of bearings are on the market and they can be divided into categories: **plain bearings** and **rolling-contact bearings.**

16.12.1   Plain Bearings

When two mechanical members rest on one another and move in relation to one another, they create a *bearing surface.* In general, bearings are separate mechanical devices that reduce friction between moving parts. The two basic types of **plain bearings** are those in which the parts in contact slide, and those in which the members revolve. Since the surfaces of each part or member make contact, bearings that do not incorporate some form of roller or ball are plain surface bearings.

Bearings that provide sliding contact between mating surfaces fall into three general classes: **radial bearings** that support rotating shafts or journals; **thrust bearings** that support axial loads on rotating members; and **guide** or **slipper bearings** that guide moving parts along a straight line.

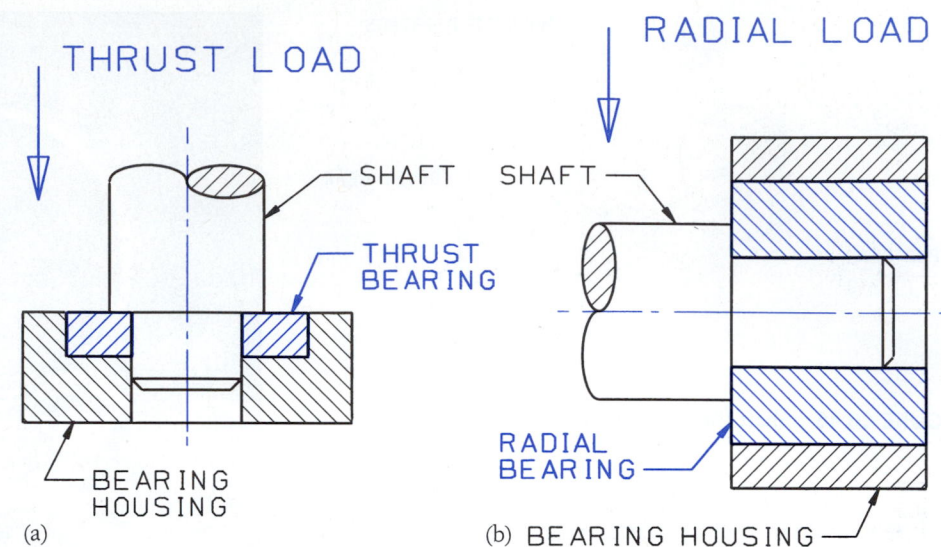

FIGURE 16.49 Bearing Loading
(a) Thrust load (b) Radial load

Radial sliding bearings, more commonly called **sleeve bearings**, may be of several types. The most common being the plain full journal bearing that has 360° contact with its mating journal, and the partial journal bearing that has less than 180° contact. Plain bearings look like bushings and, in many cases, what is referred to as a bushing is actually a plain bearing. Since the bearings (drawn sectioned) in Figure 16.49 do not have balls or rollers, they would be called plain bearings. Plain bearings are manufactured both with and without flanges.

FIGURE 16.50 Ball Bearing

Dimensions	A	B	C	R	Balls	Ball Dia.
	.500	1.125	.375	.025	7	.187
	1.000	2.000	.562	.035	10	.250
	1.312	2.562	.687	.035	9	.375

16.12.2 Rolling-Contact Bearings

Rolling-contact bearings substitute a rolling element, a ball (Fig. 16.50), or a roller for a hydrodynamic or hydrostatic fluid film to carry an impressed load without wear and with reduced friction. Because of their greatly reduced starting friction compared to the conventional journal bearing, they have acquired the common designation of antifriction bearings. The balls of a rolling ball bearing can be any size from 0.05 to 320 mm and can be manufactured from a wide variety of metals and plastics.

The most common antifriction bearing application is the deep-groove **ball bearing** (Fig. 16.50) with a ribbon-type separator in which sealed-grease lubrication is used to support a shaft with radial and thrust loads in rotating equipment. The two basic types of rolling bearings are those that use a **ball** as the rolling element and those that use a **roller.** Rollers may be either cylindrical, tapered, spherical, or needle shaped (Fig. 16.51). The construction of a typical tapered roller bearing is illustrated in Figure 16.52. The bearing housing in Figure 16.53 incorporates spherical rollers in its design.

16.12.3 Thrust Bearings

Thrust bearings, as the name implies, are used either to absorb axial shaft loads or to position vertical shafts. Thrust bearings are designed to take thrust loads alone or, in some cases, in combination with radial loads. Thrust bearings (Fig. 16.54) have been manufactured in sizes up to 8 meters in diameter.

16.12.4 Housings and Mountings

A number of methods are available to ensure that a bearing remains in place within a housing (Fig. 16.55). One common technique for retaining the bearing is to press or shrink the bearing in the housing with a light interference fit. Figure

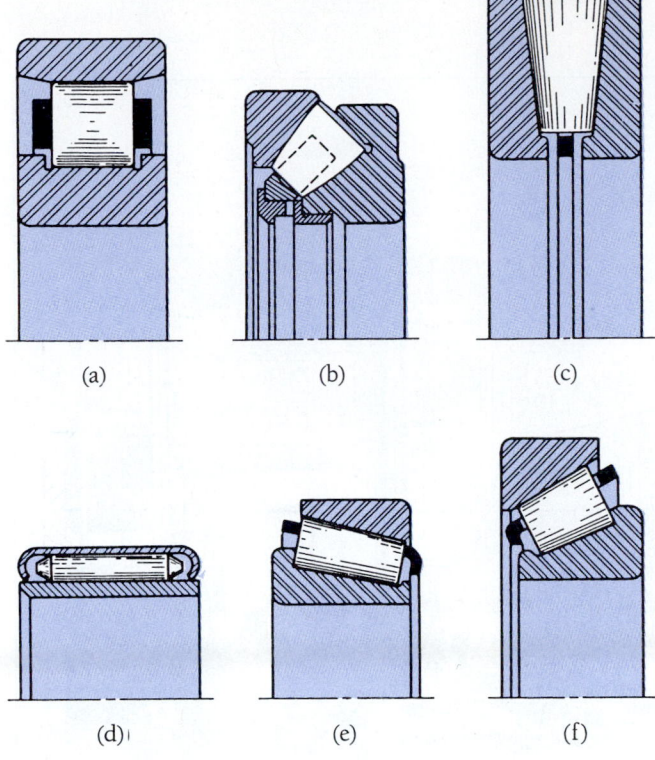

(a)   (b)   (c)

(d)   (e)   (f)

FIGURE 16.51   Roller Bearings   (a) Straight (b) Spherical thrust (c) Tapered thrust (d) Needle radial (e) Tapered radial (f) Steep-angle tapered

FIGURE 16.53   Spherical Roller Bearing in Housing

FIGURE 16.54   Large-Diameter Thrust Roller Bearing

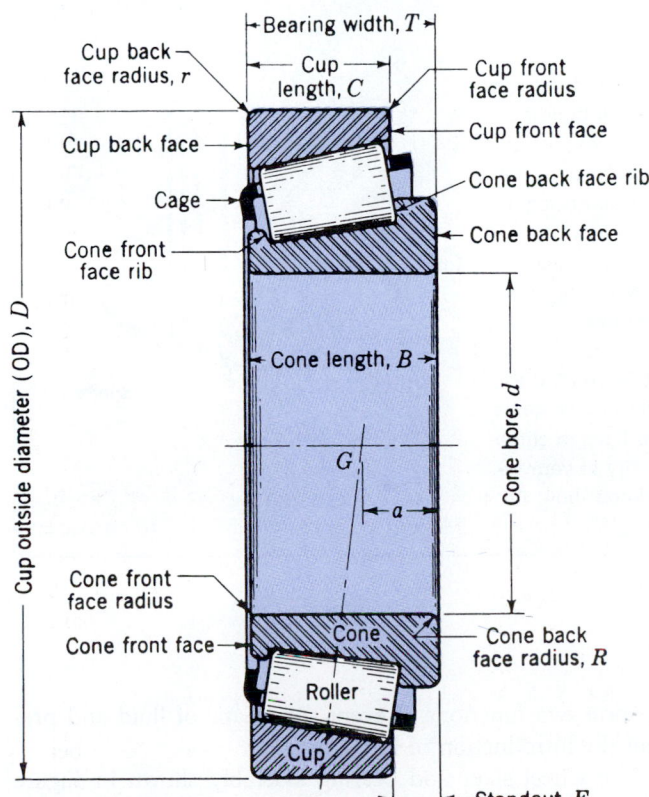

FIGURE 16.52   Tapered Roller Bearing

FIGURE 16.55   Bearing and Housing

Elevators

If asked, the average person would tell you that an elevator is a mechanical device used for moving people or objects to a higher or lower level. They might also tell you that it is a rectangular car that moves up and down on guides in a shaft, has doors that open onto each floor, has a mechanism of some sort, has controls, and uses safety devices. Virtually no one would think to tell you that the elevator is the world's most used and safest method of transportation. Many would consider automobiles, planes, and trains before the elevator. Most would not even consider the elevator at all.

The total number of passengers riding in elevators in any two-week period is more than the world's population. Records show that there are fewer than 1,000 accidents per year that involve elevators. However, if you have ever been stranded in an elevator during a malfunction, you know that the elevator is the kind of important technology no one notices until it malfunctions.

Elevators are based on the principle of the counterweight; the weight of one object can be used to balance the weight of another object.

In the early nineteenth century, the English were first to hook up a steam engine to a pulley, but it was not until 1853 that Elisha Graves Otis really improved the safety of the elevator. He displayed his spring safety elevator at the World's Fair in New York City at the Crystal Palace. He invented a governor that allowed the cable holding the car to be cut without moving the car. Everyone was amazed and wanted to know how he stopped the elevator from plunging to the ground.

In 1857, Otis installed the first commercial passenger elevator in a department store. This elevator took fifteen

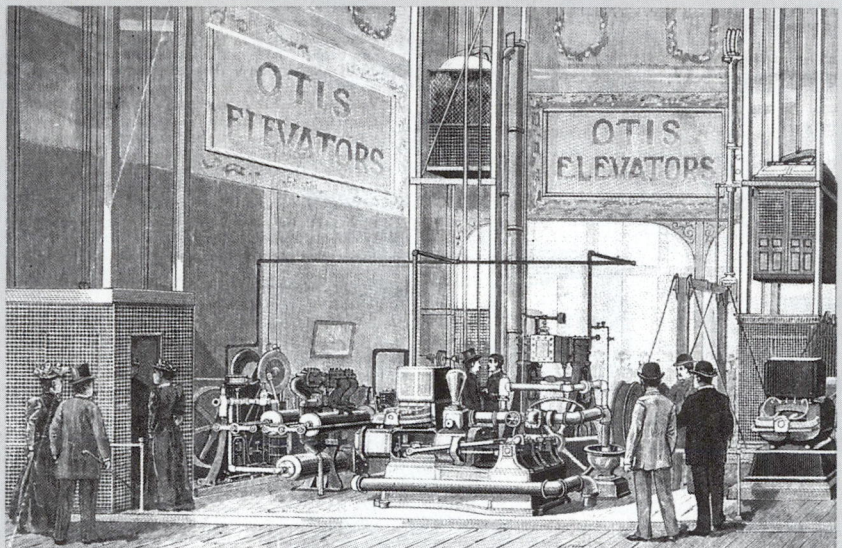

Early Steam Elevator

minutes to arrive at the top of a skyscraper, but back then that was fast! The elevator was one of the key factors in the development of our cities. Otis, because of his patents on the steam elevator, created the Otis Elevator Company—a familiar name because their products are very visible in our modern tall buildings.

Today, the manufacturing, installation, and use of elevators is regulated by the national code of the American Society of Mechanical Engineers, the American Institute of Architects, and the National Institute of Standards and Technology. One wonders if Otis could have imagined the impact his invention would have on us when he first exhibited it in 1853 at the World's Fair. It's one of those inventions you don't notice until you have to climb stairs to the twenty-fifth story of your office building. Then you know how important Otis is to your life.

Modern Elevator

16.56 shows a cast steel bearing unit for motors. The bearing was pressed into the housing.

In applications where lubricants or process fluids are utilized in operation, provision must be made to prevent leakage. This is accomplished by the use of a sealer. All seals must perform two functions: Prevent the escape of fluid and prevent the introduction of foreign matter.

The wheel shaft and bearing assembly shown in Figure 16.56 has both ends of the roller bearing sealed with a packing. The flanged bearing unit and the plummer-mounted

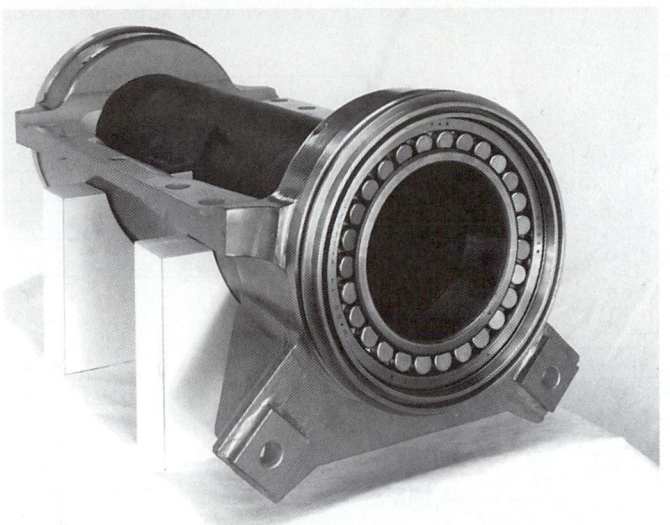

FIGURE 16.56   Cast Steel Bearing Unit Designed for Motors

FIGURE 16.58   Automobile Engine Crank Shaft Utilizing Lobe Cams in Its Design

(a)

(b)

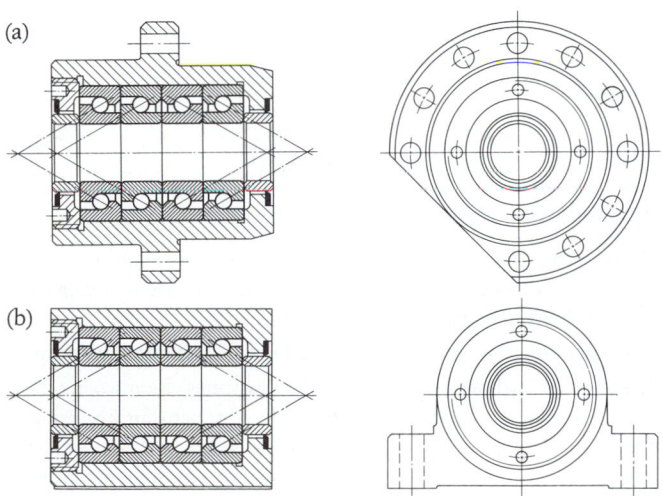

FIGURE 16.57   **Bearing Units**   (a) Flanged bearing (b) Plummer bearing unit

FIGURE 16.59   Cam Styles

bearing unit in Figure 16.57 are used for shaft ends of ball and roller screw assemblies. Each of these units incorporates four roller bearings and two packing seals into their design.

16.13   Cams and Cam Design

Cams are machine elements used to transmit or change motion by direct rolling or sliding contact with another part, called a **follower.** Cams can translate rotary into rotary or linear, and linear into rotary or linear motion. Cams are either *radial* or *cylindrical*. Radial cams move followers perpendicular to the cam shaft. Cylindrical cams move followers parallel to the shaft.

In general, most cams are designed to transform **rotary** motion into **reciprocating** motion. An example is the automobile engine cam shaft (Fig. 16.58). The cam raises and lowers the valve lifters of the motor. The movement of the cam imparts motion to the follower. Cams are designed to accomplish a wide variety of motion changes and are made in an almost unlimited number of configurations (Fig. 16.59). A detail of a cam is provided in Figure 16.60.

For most cams, the follower moves perpendicular to the axis about which the cam is rotating. This type of cam has a **translating follower**, but it might be a roller, and is normally a **flat plate cam**. A cam that moves the follower axially or parallel to the axis of the cam is called a **cylindrical cam** or **drum cam.** Follower systems of a cam mechanism usually

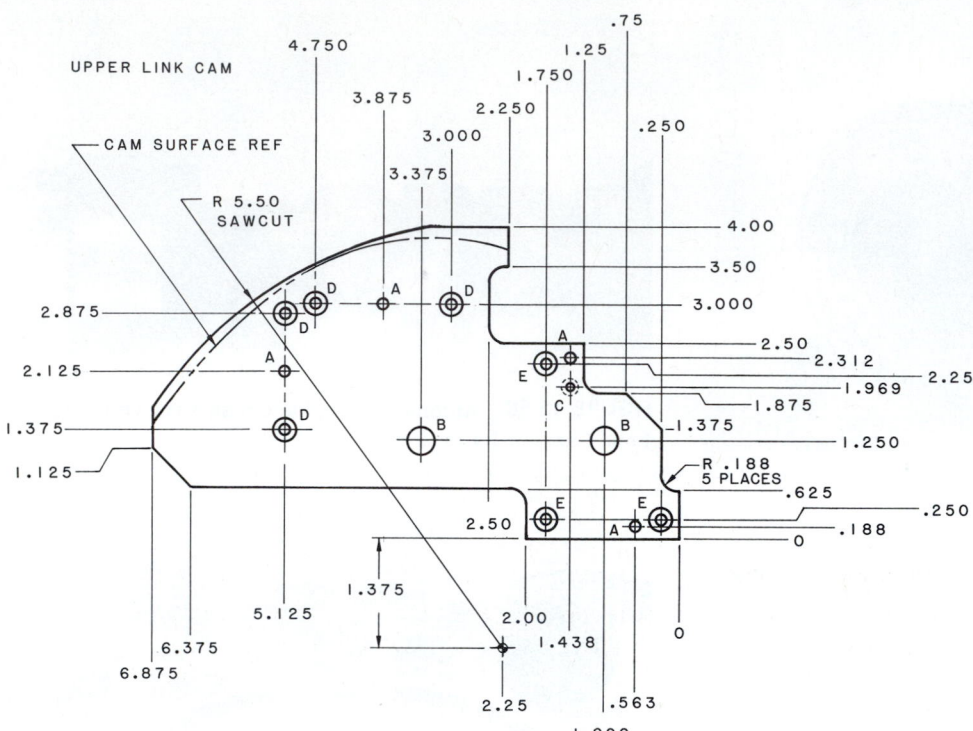

HOLE	DESCRIPTION	QTY
A	Ø .125 THRU	4
B	Ø .375 THRU	2
C	8–32 UNC–2B	1
D	Ø .149 Ø .266 CBORE X .138 DP	4
E	Ø .171 Ø .313 CBORE X .164 DP	3

FIGURE 16.60   Detail of a Cam

consist of one or more rods, gears, levers, springs, and/or other mechanical devices.

Cams are also used in designs to perform other types of work, such as clamping. Figure 16.61 shows a standard cam-clamp assembly that can be ordered off the shelf from a tooling fixture company. The cam design on the end of the clamp allows the machinist to secure and release quickly and easily a work piece requiring machining.

Cams are usually mounted on shafts with keys (Fig. 16.62). In some cases, the drive mechanism employs a gear. In Figure 16.63, a drive gear keyed to a shaft turns a cam that is also keyed to the shaft.

16.13.1   Cam Terminology

The following terms are used when describing cams:

Base circle   A circle drawn using the center of the shaft as its center and a radius equal to the distance to the center of the follower wheel when it is in its lowest position.

Cam profile   The cam surface edge on which the follower moves.

Displacement diagram   A curve that illustrates the movement of a cam. The diagram is drawn by laying out a stretch-out line equal to the circumference of the working circle, dividing the line into even units based on angular divisions on the cam, and then plotting a series of points corresponding to the cam's outline.

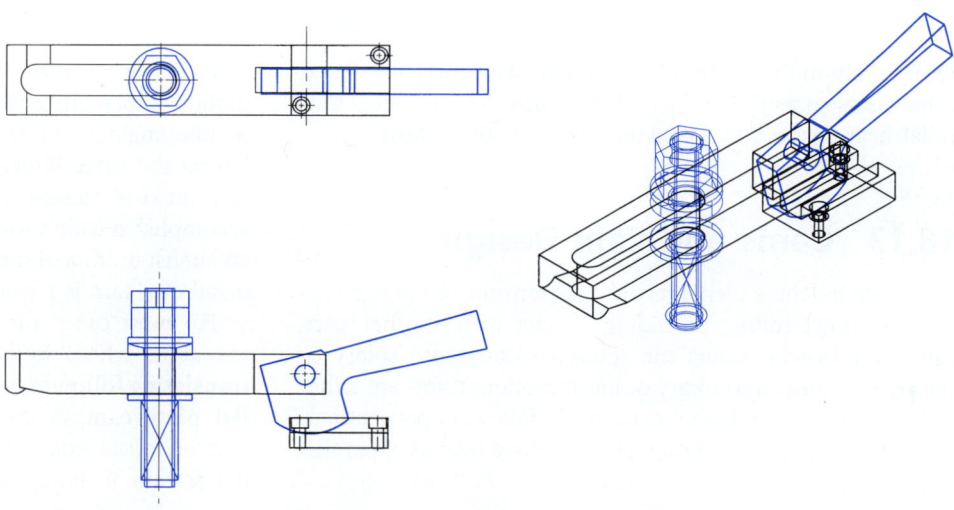

FIGURE 16.61   Cam-Clamp
Assembly

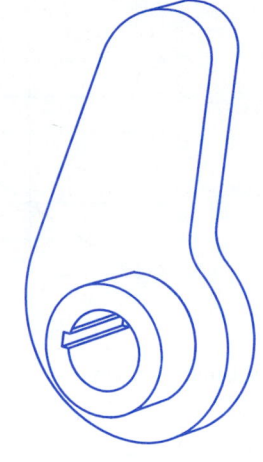

FIGURE 16.62 Cam Detail

Dwell When a cam's follower rests or stops movement. A dwell is designed into the cam profile by allowing the cam outline to be a constant distance from its center for a period of time.

Follower A machine element that moves with reciprocating movement by following the cam as it rotates. Followers usually move up and down, although followers on drum cams move back and forth.

Harmonic motion Harmonic motion produces a smooth start and stop with nonuniform speed.

Height The total vertical rise of the follower during operation of the cam. The height (the total rise of the follower) is found by subtracting the base circle from the working circle.

Pitch curve (pitch line) A curve generated by the motion of the follower about the cam. The distance between the shaft center and each position of the follower's center generates the pitch curve as it moves about the cam profile.

Reciprocating motion Linear movement, either back and forth or up and down, of the follower that is caused by the rotary movement of the shaft and cam assembly. A follower can also oscillate in rotation.

Rise and fall Movement of the cam through one cycle.

Roller A cylindrical element mounted at the end of a follower to follow the cam outline.

Time interval The time needed to move the follower from its lowest to its highest position.

Transition point The position where the acceleration changes from plus to minus and the follower reverses directions.

Uniform acceleration When the change in speed is constant throughout the cam movement.

Uniform velocity When a cam follower rises and falls at a constant speed.

Working circle A circle using the center of the shaft as its center and a radius equal to the distance to the center of the follower wheel when it is in its highest position. The working circle is usually not shown on the cam drawing. The distance between the base circle and the working circle is equal to the follower displacement (rise or height).

16.13.2 Classes of Cams

Cams can usually be divided into two classes: **uniform motion cams** and **accelerated motion cams.** The uniform mo-

tion cam moves the follower at the same speed from the beginning to the end of the stroke. Because the movement is started and stopped abruptly, a shock can occur. If the movement is rapid, there is a significant shock at the beginning and at the end of the stroke. Therefore, in high-speed machinery, cams must be designed so that sudden shocks are avoided throughout the motion of the follower. Cam motions are illustrated in diagrams (Fig. 16.64):

Uniform motion The equal distances are traveled in equal intervals of time; Figure 16.64(a).

Uniform motion modified A radius is introduced at the beginning and end to smooth starting and stopping; Figure 16.64(b).

Parabolic motion The displacement curve is created using parabolic construction; Figure 16.64(c).

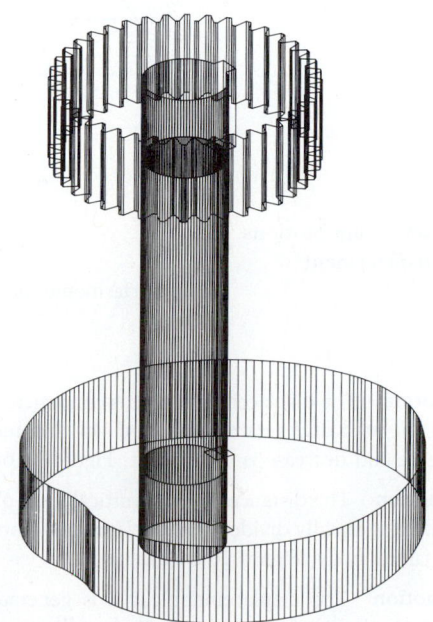

FIGURE 16.63 Cam, Shaft, and Gear Assembly

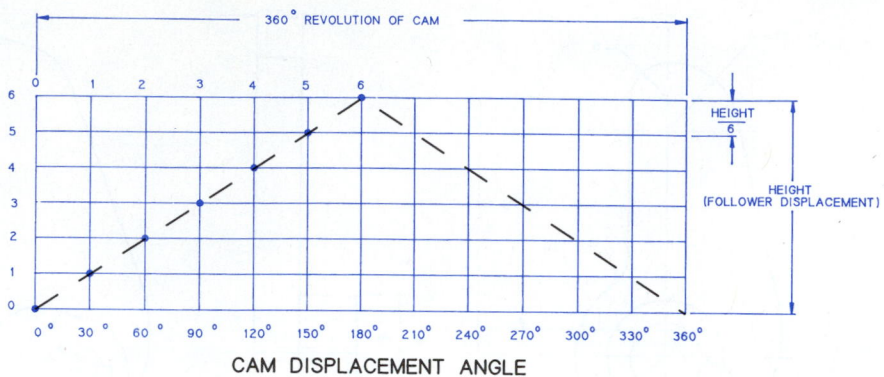

(a) Uniform motion

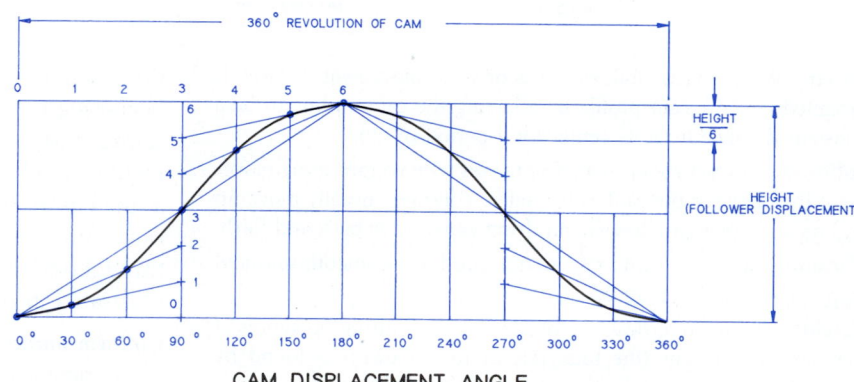

(c) Parabolic construction (parabolic motion)

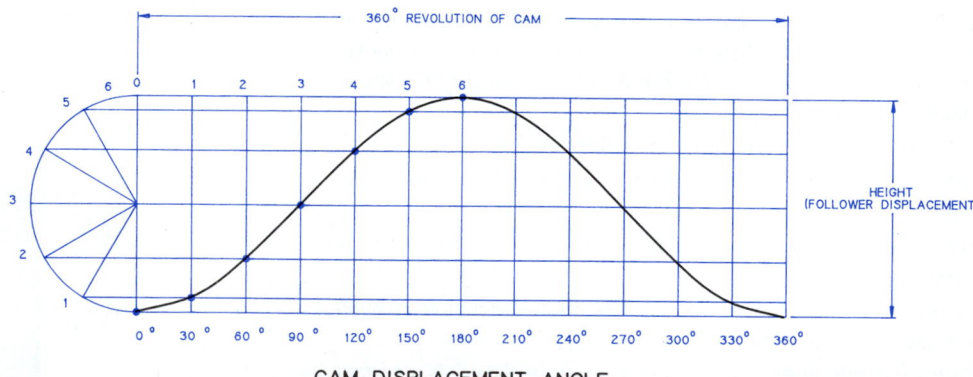

FIGURE 16.64 Cam Motions Shown on Displacement Diagrams

(e) Harmonic motion

Parabolic motion The displacement curve is constructed using the uniformly accelerated and retarded method. In this method, the ratio of increase and decrease is 1:3:5:5:3:1; Figure 16.64(d).

Harmonic motion The distances moved vertically are obtained by projecting from the equally divided semicircle; **gravity motion** is the motion of a falling body; Figure 16.64(e).

Cycloidal motion The displacement curve is generated from a cycloid that is the locus of a point on a circle rolling on a straight line; Figure 16.64(f).

A displacement diagram of a cam may utilize many types of motions to accomplish specific design tasks. Figure 16.65 shows a displacement diagram that has three dwells and three types of motion: modified, parabolic, and harmonic. *Modified motion* is simply a straight line that has radii introduced at each end. *Harmonic motion* is plotted by drawing a half circle and dividing it evenly. Each division corresponds to a division on the diagram (horizontally). The points are projected from the half circle to the vertical lines and connected with a

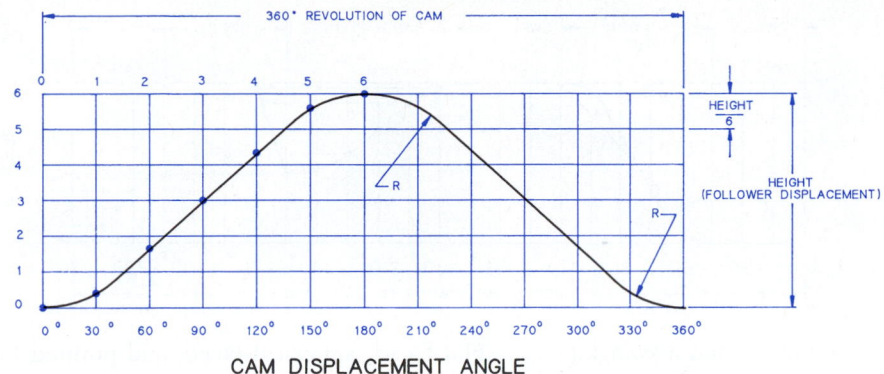

(b) Modified uniform motion

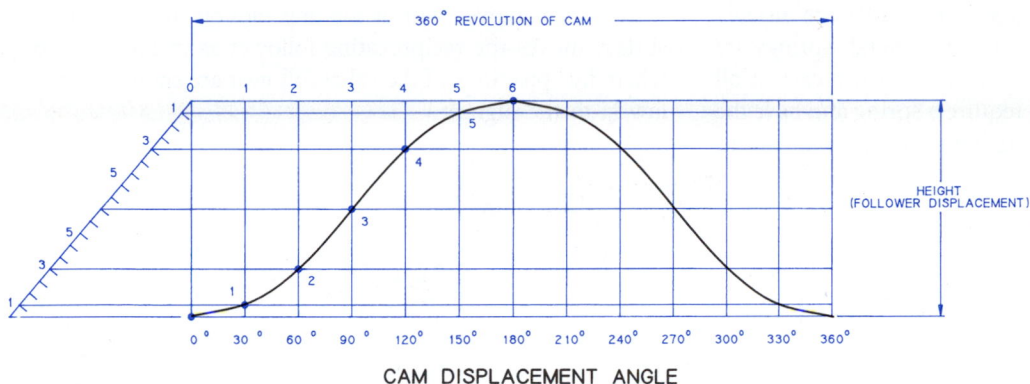

(d) Uniformly accelerated (parabolic motion)

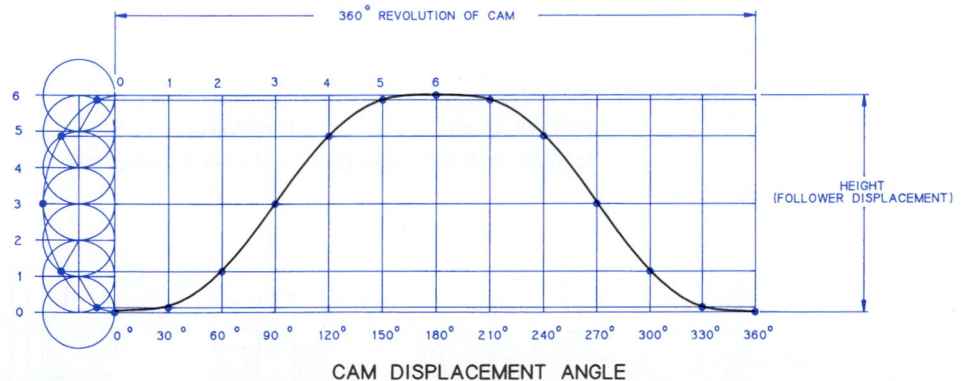

(f) Cycloidal motion

FIGURE 16.64 Cam Motions Shown on Displacement Diagrams—*Continued*

smooth curve (using an irregular curve). *Parabolic motion* is plotted by proportionally dividing the vertical distance of the rise or fall using a ratio of 1:3:5:5:3:1 and projecting the points to the vertical lines as shown.

Some cams use **gravity motion** in their design. Gravity motion is uniformly accelerated motion. The **uniformly accelerated motion cam** can be used in cam designs requiring moderate speeds. If sudden changes in acceleration occur at the beginning, middle, or end of the stroke, this type of cam

is not the best design. Since it results in low noise, a **cycloidal motion curve cam** produces no abrupt changes in acceleration and is often used in high-speed machinery.

16.13.3 Cam Followers

The three most used cam followers (Fig. 16.66) are (a) the **radial**, (b) the **offset translating**, and (c) the **swinging** roller follower. When the cam rotates, it imparts a translating

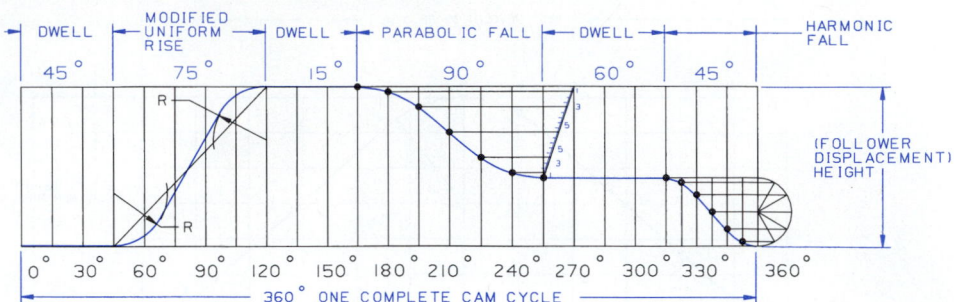

FIGURE 16.65 Cam Displacement Diagram Designed with a Variety of Motions and Dwells

motion to the roller followers in (a) and (b) and a swinging motion to the roller follower in (c).

The arrangement in Figure 16.67(a) shows a **closed-track single roller** cam. In (b), the roller is forced to move in a **closed-track double roller**. Open-track cams are usually smaller than closed-track cams, but, in general, springs are necessary to keep the roller in contact with the cam at all times. Closed-track cams do not require a spring and have the advantage of positive drive throughout the rise and return cycle.

Flat-faced, spherical-faced, and **pointed** followers (Fig. 16.68) are used when the cam is not moving at high speeds and when heat buildup and wear of the follower are not factors in the machine's design.

As a cam moves with a rotating motion, its curved-edge surface moves the reciprocating follower as in Figure 16.69, where five positions of the roller follower are shown from the lowest to the highest.

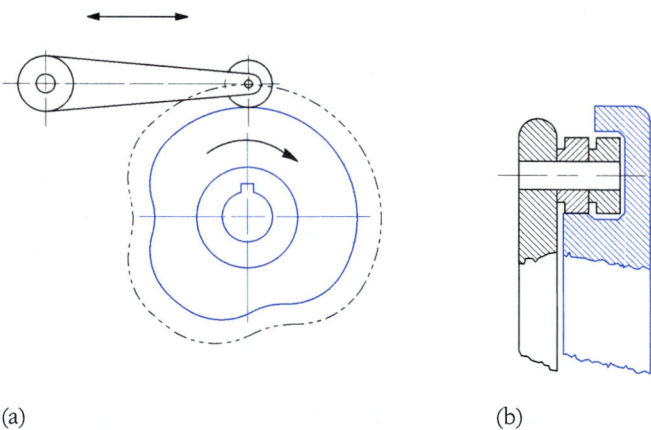

(a)

(b)

FIGURE 16.67 Closed-Track Followers (a) Closed-track follower with one roller (b) Closed-track follower with two rollers

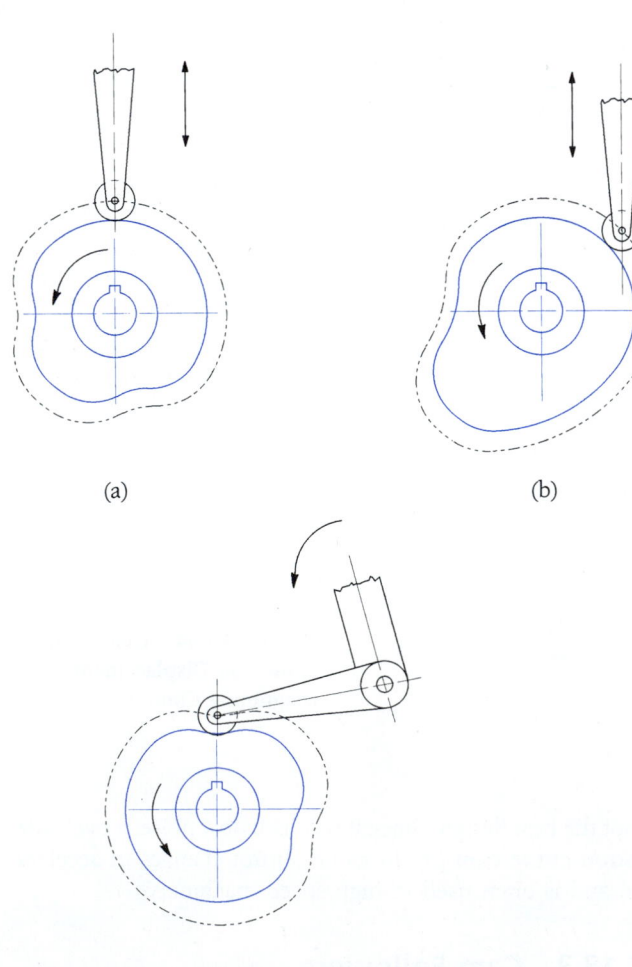

(a)

(b)

(c)

FIGURE 16.66 Styles of Roller Followers (a) Radial translating roller follower (b) Offset translating roller follower (c) Swinging roller follower

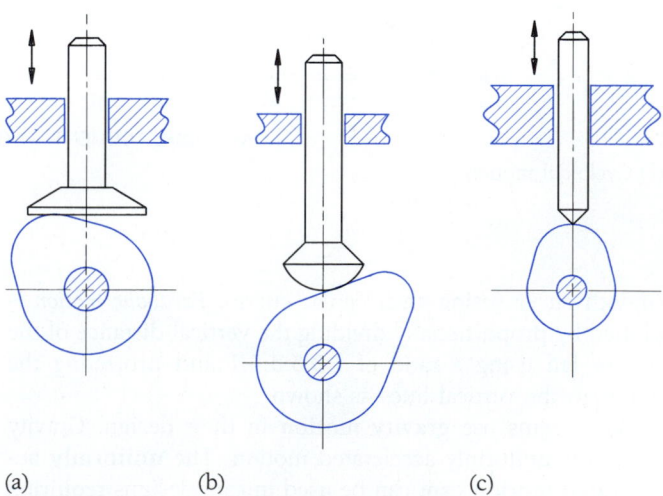

(a)

(b)

(c)

FIGURE 16.68 Nonrolling Cam Followers (a) Flat-faced follower (b) Spherical-faced (round) follower (c) Pointed follower

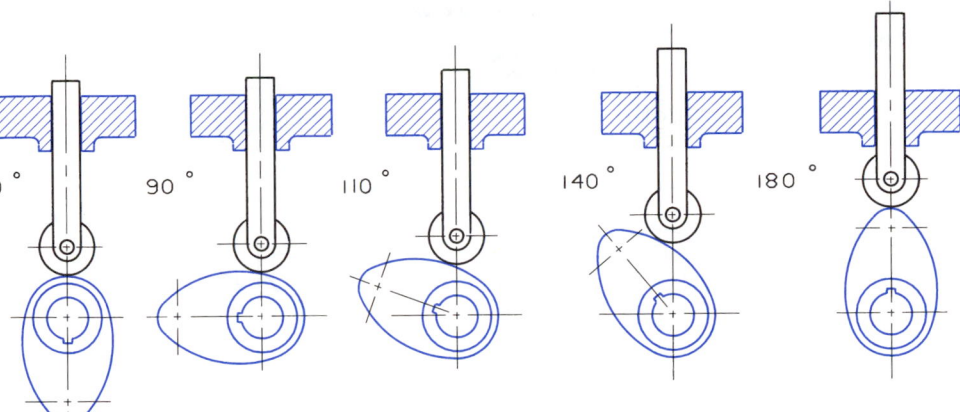

0°   90°   110°   140°   180°

FIGURE 16.69   Five Positions of
a Lobe Cam and Roller Follower

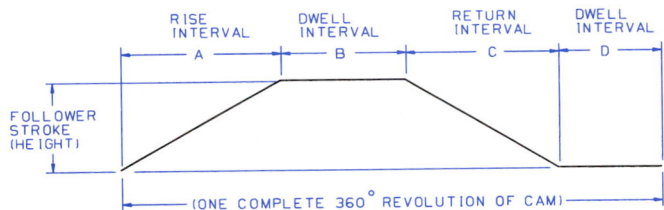

FIGURE 16.70   Simplified Displacement Diagram

position for 20° (BC), returns over 180° (CD), and finally
dwells in its lowest position for 60° (DE).

16.14   Drawing Cams

When drawing the cam and follower, instead of revolving the
cam, it is assumed that the follower rotates around the fixed
cam, which requires the drawing of many follower positions,
but because this is done more or less diagrammatically, it is
relatively simple.

When a roller is used as the follower instead of a point, the
cam outline will be smaller. The **pitch curve** (pitch line)
becomes the line of centers of the roller (Fig. 16.72). With the
radius of the roller and the centers on the pitch line, a number
of arcs are drawn to which a tangent working curve can be
drawn to give the cam outline. You can also transfer the
distances using a compass or dividers. The **cam pitch curve**
is the actual profile or working surface when a flat, pointed,
or spherical follower is used. To obtain the profile or working
surface for a cam with a roller follower, a series of circles with
centers on the pitch curve and radii equal to the radius of the
roller are drawn. The inner envelope drawn tangent to these
arcs is the cam working surface or profile.

16.13.4   Displacement Diagrams

The design of a cam usually begins with the **displacement
diagram**. A simplified displacement diagram is shown in
Figure 16.70. One cycle means one 360° revolution of the
cam. The horizontal distances A, B, C, and D are expressed
in units of time (seconds), radians, or degrees. The vertical
distance (height) represents the maximum "rise" or stroke of
the follower.

The time-displacement diagram for a cam with a radial
translating roller follower is shown in Figure 16.71(a). This
diagram is read from left to right as follows: For 100° of cam
shaft rotation, the follower rises (AB), dwells in its upper

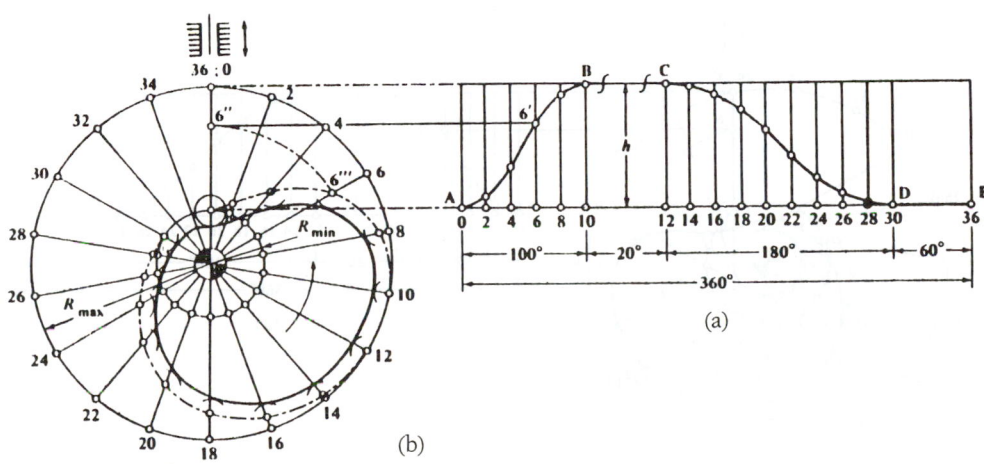

(a)

(b)

FIGURE 16.71   Displacement
Diagram and Cam Layout

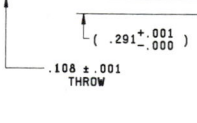

FIGURE 16.76

After Reading the Chapter Through Section 16.14.1 You May Complete the Following Exercises

Exercise 16.5   Using the bearing dimensions from Figure 16.50, design and draw a bearing housing to retain the bearings and support the stepped shaft.

Exercise 16.6   Draw the displacement diagram using the given cam motions, dimensions, and displacement. The cam is symmetrical about its vertical centerline. Use the diagram for both halves to construct the cam in Exercise 16.7.

Exercise 16.7   Using the displacement diagram in Figure 16.6, lay out the cam and follower as shown. Calculate the proper keyway and set screw for the shaft. The set screw is to be at 90° to the keyway.

Exercise 16.8   Lay out the offset cam with the following specifications:

   0–90° modified uniform motion rise, total 1.50 displacement
   90–120° dwell
   120–180° parabolic motion fall, 1.00
   180–300° harmonic motion rise, .50
   300–330° dwell
   330–360° harmonic fall, 1.00

Construct a displacement diagram on a separate sheet to establish the cam's outline. Show the follower at 30° intervals. Design a proper size keyseat and secure the cam to a shaft with two set screws at 90° to the keyseat.

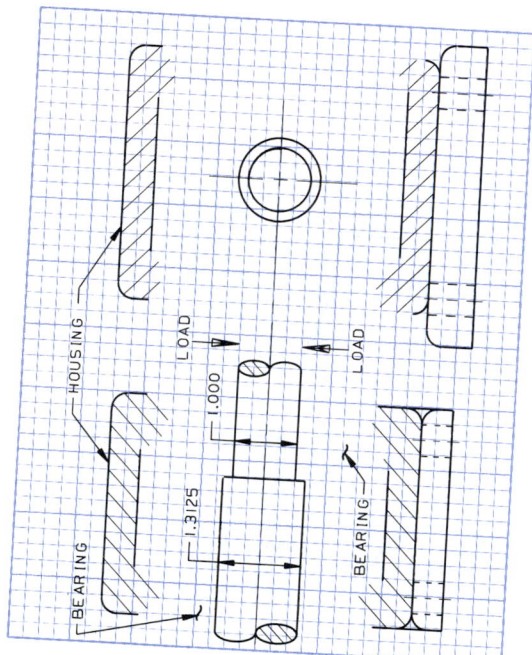

Exercise 16.5

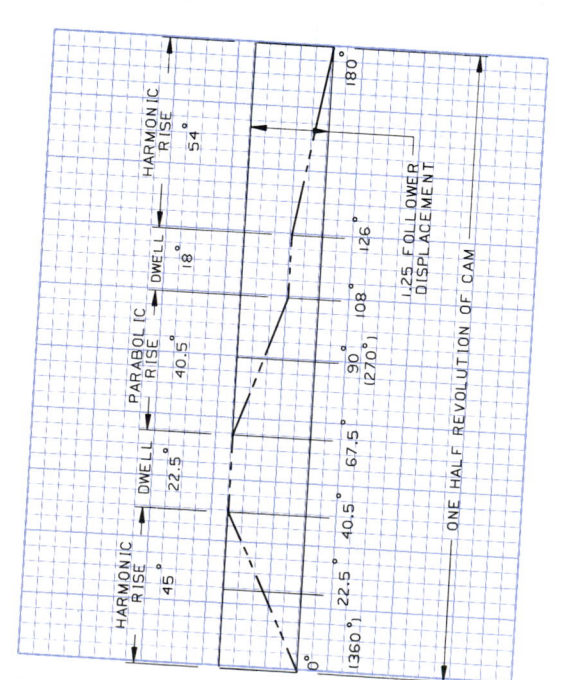

Exercise 16.6

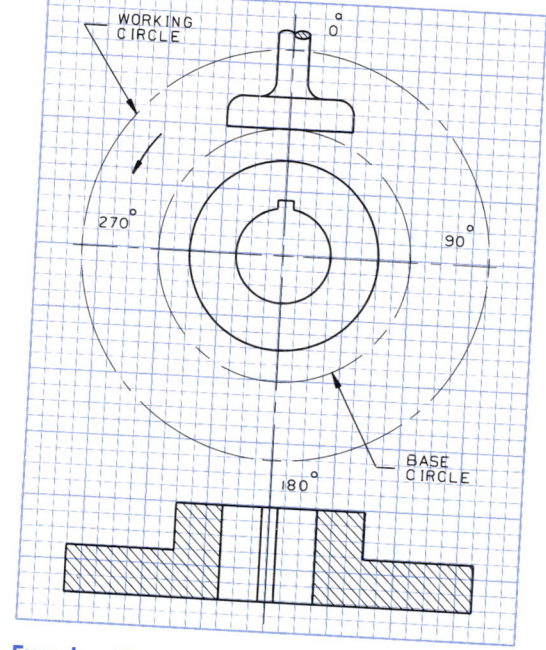

Exercise 16.7

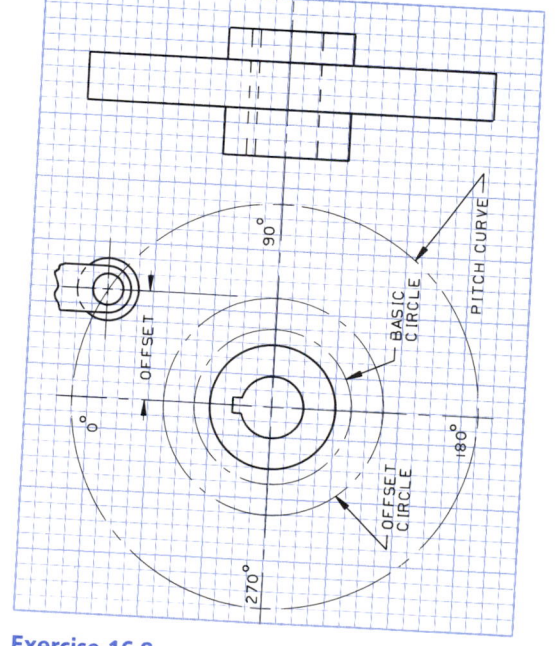

Exercise 16.8

provided, the detail must show all radii for the cam profile outline. In this detail, the cam's shaft hole must be perpendicular to surface A within .002 in. The cam is held in place on the shaft with a keyseat and set screw design. The eight 1.00 in. diameter holes reduce the total mass weight of the cam. In Figure 16.76, a cylindrical drum or cam is detailed and a displacement diagram is provided. This is a typical industrial cam detail.

You May Complete Exercises 16.5 Through 16.8 at This Time

QUIZ

True or False

1. Cams are used to change reciprocating motion into revolving motion.
2. A journal is that portion of a bearing that touches the balls or rollers.
3. A rolling follower is a machine element that is used on designs that operate at a high speed, where there is considerable wear, and when friction (heat) buildup is a factor in the operation of the machine.
4. All needle bearings provide sealed housings.
5. Gear teeth are seldom drawn on the gear detail unless the gear is a special order.
6. Some thrust bearings can carry a radial load.
7. The working circle of a cam is the distance from the shaft centerline to the highest position on the edge of the cam profile.
8. Cylindrical cams transmit motion perpendicular to the cam's shaft.

Fill in the Blanks

9. An _____ _____ is not in line with the cam centerline.
10. _____ bearings are the most common type of bearing used in industry.
11. A _____ is a straight machine element that has teeth cut into its surface that engage with a _____ gear to produce linear movement.
12. _____ gears connect parallel shafts, _____ gears connect shafts whose axes intersect, and _____ gears are used to connect shafts whose axes are not parallel and do not intersect.
13. _____ are used to support and align _____ .
14. A _____ gear is the same as a spur gear, but is usually smaller and has less _____ .
15. A _____ is designed to transmit power and is under _____ stress.
16. Harmonic motion of a cam is _____ , but the _____ is not _____ .

Answer the Following

17. Describe the difference between a thrust and a radial bearing.
18. What information is needed on a bevel gear drawing in addition to the graphical representation?
19. Name four types of cam motion and give a short description of each.
20. Why do plain bearings require special lubrication?
21. What are displacement diagrams and why are they used in cam design?
22. How do worm screws and worm gears work, and what type of motion is transmitted during operation?
23. What are the types of roller bearings?
24. Describe four common gear types.

Exercises may be assigned as sketching, instrument, or CAD projects. Transfer the given information to an "A" size sheet of .25 in. grid paper. Complete all views and solve for proper visibility, including centerlines, object lines, and hidden lines. Exercises that are not assigned by the instructor can be sketched in the text to provide practice and understanding of the preceding material.

After Reading the Chapter Through Section 16.10 You May Complete the Following Exercises

Exercise 16.1   Draw a standard spur gear. Show three teeth. The cast iron spur gear has a pressure angle of 20°, 48 teeth, 6.000 pitch diameter, 1.00 bore diameter, 2.00 hub diameter (1.00 hub projection), 8 diametral pitch, with a gear face width of 1.50, and a total width of 2.50. Design the gear to have a standard keyseat per the shaft diameter (see Chapter 15). The gear hub is to have a set screw at 90° to the keyway. Determine the set screw size based on the shaft diameter (see Chapter 15).

Exercise 16.2   Draw the spur gear and rack. Show three teeth on the rack and the gear. Design the gear's keyseat and set screw per Exercise 16.1. The steel rack has the following specifications: 20° pressure angle, 5 diametral pitch, 1.500 overall thickness, 1.300 pitch line to back, 2.500 face width. The steel gear has the following specifications: 20° pressure angle, 5 diametral pitch, 1.125 shaft bore diameter, 20 teeth, .750 hub projection, 2.500 face width, 3.25 total width, and a 3.00 hub diameter.

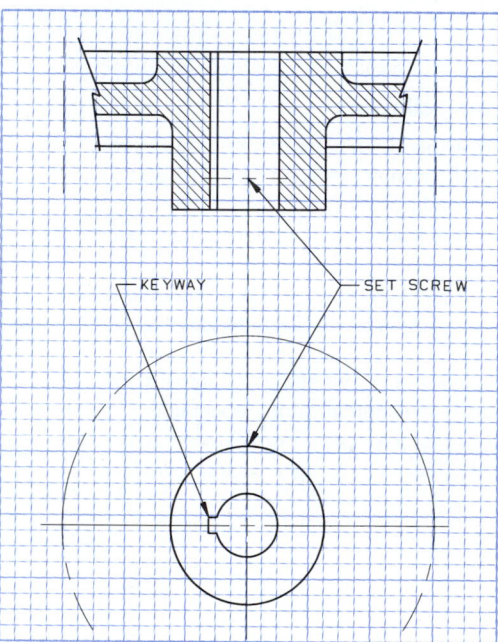

Exercise 16.1

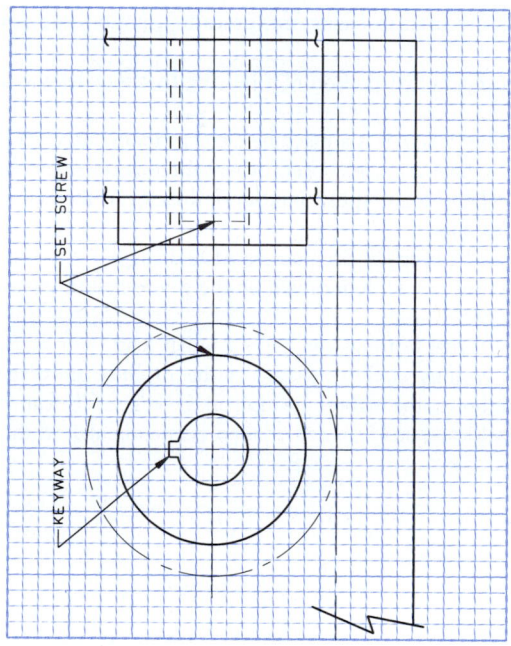

Exercise 16.2

Exercise 16.3   Design and draw bevel gears with the following specifications:

Gear A		Gear B
6	Diametral pitch	6
18	Teeth	36
2:1	Ratio	2:1
1.06	Face width	1.125
3.500	Mounting distance	4.750
2.25	Gear width	2.75
2.50	Hub diameter	3.25
6.00	Pitch diameter	3.00
1.125	Hub bore diameter	1.125
calculate	Keyway	calculate
calculate	Set screw	calculate

Exercise 16.4   Design and draw the worm and the worm gear as in Figure 16.43. The worm (screw) is to have a $14\frac{1}{2}°$ pressure angle, 4 diametral pitch, 3.500 face width, .7854 lead, 4.76° lead angle, 1.250 bore shaft diameter, 3.000 pitch diameter. Design the keyway per the shaft size. The worm gear is to have a $14\frac{1}{2}°$ pressure angle, 4 diametral pitch, 20 teeth, 5.000 pitch diameter, 1.00 diameter bore for a shaft, 2.50 hub diameter, 1.250 hub projection, and a face width of 1.500. Design an appropriate size keyway for the shaft.

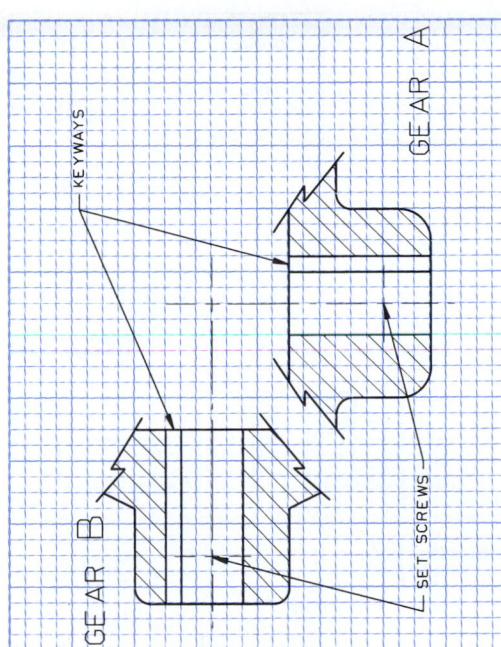

Exercise 16.3

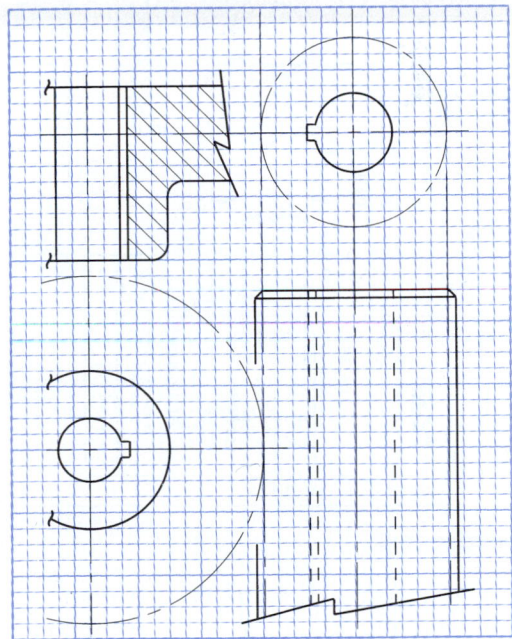

Exercise 16.4

After Reading the Chapter Through Section 16.14.1 You May Complete the Following Exercises

Exercise 16.5 Using the bearing dimensions from Figure 16.50, design and draw a bearing housing to retain the bearings and support the stepped shaft.

Exercise 16.6 Draw the displacement diagram using the given cam motions, dimensions, and displacement. The cam is symmetrical about its vertical centerline. Use the diagram for both halves to construct the cam in Exercise 16.7.

Exercise 16.7 Using the displacement diagram in Figure 16.6, lay out the cam and follower as shown. Calculate the proper keyway and set screw for the shaft. The set screw is to be at 90° to the keyway.

Exercise 16.8 Lay out the offset cam with the following specifications:

0–90° modified uniform motion rise, total 1.50 displacement
90–120° dwell
120–180° parabolic motion fall, 1.00
180–300° harmonic motion rise, .50
300–330° dwell
330–360° harmonic fall, 1.00

Construct a displacement diagram on a separate sheet to establish the cam's outline. Show the follower at 30° intervals. Design a proper size keyseat and secure the cam to a shaft with two set screws at 90° to the keyseat.

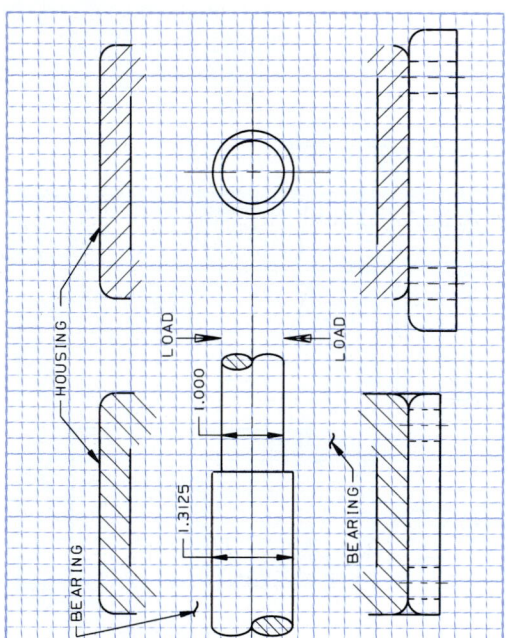

Exercise 16.5

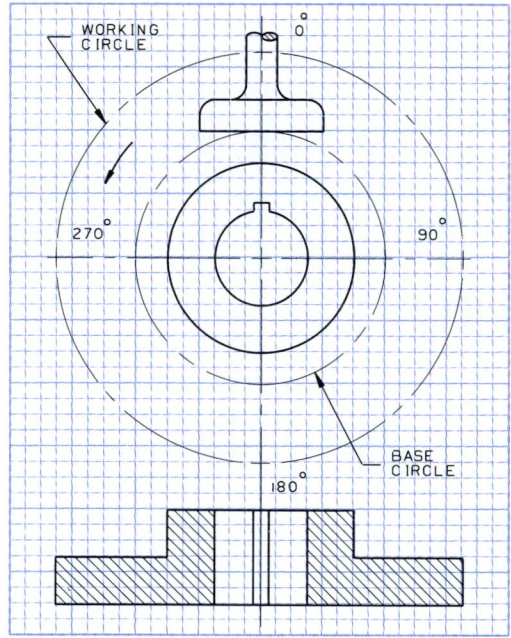

Exercise 16.7

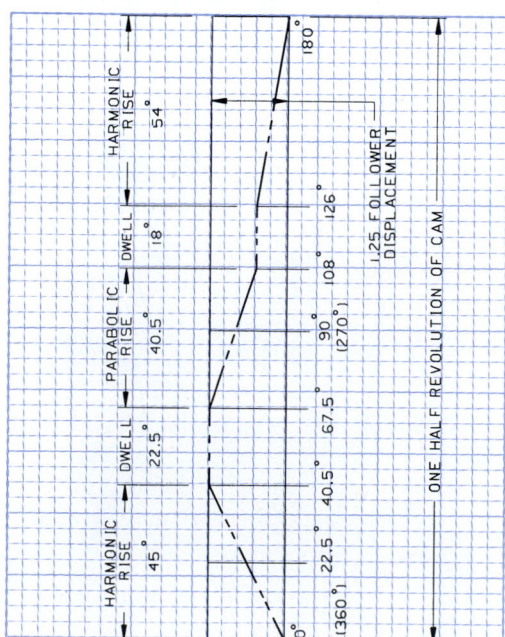

Exercise 16.6

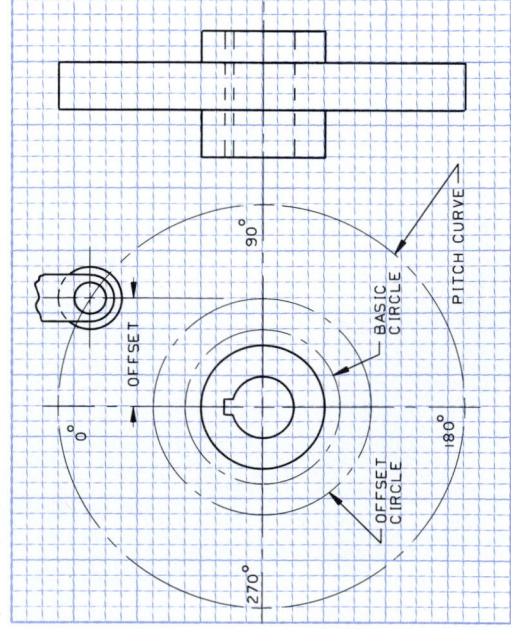

Exercise 16.8

PROBLEMS

For gear problems completed manually, show only one tooth. For projects drawn on a CAD system, show all teeth.

Problem 16.1   Redraw the spur gear detail in Figure 16.11.

Problem 16.2   Draw the spur rack detail shown in Figure 16.16.

Problem 16.3   Detail the rack shown in Figure 16.21.

Problem 16.4   Draw the worm spindle detail provided in Figure 16.23.

Problem 16.5   Detail the spur gear in Figure 16.25.

Problem 16.6   Redraw the detail shown in Figure 16.30.

Problem 16.7   Detail the spur gear assembly shown in Figure 16.31.

Problem 16.8   Redraw the bevel gears in Figure 16.38.

Problem 16.9   Redraw the worm and worm gear shown in Figure 16.43. Split the two into separate details and also draw an assembly. Use Figure 16.42 as a guide for dimensioning.

Problem 16.10   Design a spur gear rack and mating gear with the following specifications:

1. Gear—6 inch pitch diameter
   20° pressure angle (20° involute teeth)
   2.00-inch face width
   Keyway in hub
   1.25 diameter shaft
   Spoked gear blank
2. Rack—will move laterally 5 inches

Compute the required specifications for the rack and gear. Show all information data blocks on the drawing. Draw an assembly of the gear and rack using appropriate ANSI dimensioning.

Problem 16.11   Using the same format as Problem 16.10, complete a spur gear and rack assembly with 20° involute teeth, a gear face width of .75 inches, solid gear blank, shaft diameter of 2.00 inches, 7 inch pitch diameter for the gear, 56 teeth, and a diametral pitch of 8. The rack will move 8 inches laterally.

Problem 16.12   Design spur gears with the following specifications:

Gear A—Spur Gear
1. 44 teeth
2. 20° full-depth involute teeth
3. Diametral pitch of 12
4. Spoke gear blank
5. 1.00 face width
6. Keyway in hub
7. 2.00 diameter shaft

Gear B—Spur Gear
1. 18 teeth
2. 20° full-depth involute teeth
3. Diametral pitch of 8
4. Webbed hub with lightning holes
5. .750 face width
6. Keyway in hub
7. 1.00 diameter of shaft

Gear C—Internal Ring Gear
1. 32 teeth
2. $14\frac{1}{2}°$ teeth
3. 32 diametral pitch
4. 2.00 pitch diameter
5. 2.75 OD
6. 1.96 ID
7. .315 face width

Problem 16.13   Design bevel gears with the following specifications. Show all dimensions, and detail per Figure 16.38. Design the appropriate keyway for each gear.

	Gear A	Gear B	Gear C	Gear D
1. Teeth	20	45	16	20
2. Pitch diameter	2.000	7.500	4.000	50 mm
3. Diametral pitch	10	6	4	10
4. Face	.570	1.070	1.400	18 mm
5. Bore	.750	1.125	1.125	30 mm
6. Hub diameter	1.750	3.250	3.250	40 mm
7. Hub projection	1.000	1.250	1.875	24 mm
8. Hub width	1.500	2.125	3.500	36 mm

Problem 16.14   Design mating miter gears with the following specifications. Show all dimensions, and detail per Figure 16.38. Design the appropriate keyseat for each gear.

	Set A	Set B	Set C
1. Teeth	36	32	30
2. Pitch diameter	1.500	2.000	2.500
3. Diametral pitch	24	16	12
4. Face	.220	.400	.540
5. Bore	.3125	.500	.625
6. Hub diameter	.6875	1.250	1.625
7. Hub projection	.3125	.375	.843
8. Hub width	.609	.875	.484
9. Mounting distance	1.188	1.562	2.312

Problem 16.15   Design and detail a worm gear set with the following specifications: Worm— 1.250 pitch diameter, diametral pitch of 10, $14\frac{1}{2}°$ pressure angle. Worm gear— 40 teeth, .750 face width.

Problem 16.16   Design and detail a worm gear set with the following specifications: Worm— 1.000 pitch diameter, diametral pitch of 12, $14\frac{1}{2}°$ thread. Worm gear— 30 teeth, .625 face width, .750 bore, 2.50 pitch diameter.

Problem 16.17   Design and detail a helical gear with the following specifications: normal diametral pitch = 12, 20° pressure angle, 48 teeth, face width = 1.75, helix angle of 45°.

Problem 16.18   Redraw the upper link cam shown in Figure 16.60.

Problem 16.19   Using a CAD system, model the cam in Figure 16.62 in 3D and dimension completely using geometric tolerancing.

Problem 16.20   Design a cam using the displacement diagram shown in Figure 16.65. The cam will have a shaft diameter of 1.50 and an appropriately sized keyway. The cam will be .75 thick and have a 1.50 thick shaft hub with a 3.00 diameter. Design the shaft hub to have two appropriately sized set screws to secure the cam to the shaft. The cam will employ a radial translating roller follower. The roller is 1.25 in diameter. Show the roller in 12 positions using phantom lines. The height of the displacement diagram (the rise of the follower) is 4.00. The working circle is 10.00 diameter, and the base circle is 6.00. Completely dimension the cam using two views. If using a 3D CAD system, model the part and display it as a rotated (pictorial, isometric) view. The radius value used for modifying the uniform rise is a radius value of $\frac{1}{3}$ the rise. The harmonic fall will be 1.625, and the parabolic fall will be 2.375.

Problem 16.21   Redraw the cam shown in Figure 16.75 and construct a displacement diagram for the cam.

Problem 16.22   Redraw the cylindrical cam detail shown in Figure 16.76.

Problem 16.23   Draw a displacement diagram and construct a cam with the following specifications:

1.	Rise	120°, harmonic motion, 50 mm
2.	Dwell	30°
3.	Rise	60°, harmonic motion, 24 mm
4.	Dwell	30°
5.	Fall	60°, modified uniform motion, 40 mm
6.	Dwell	15°
7.	Fall	45°, harmonic motion, to starting level

A.	Height	100 mm
B.	Working circle	280 mm
C.	Base circle	100
D.	Cam rotation direction	Clockwise
E.	Shaft diameter	40 mm
F.	Shaft hub diameter	78 mm
G.	Shaft hub thickness	60 mm
H.	Keyset and set screws	As per shaft size
I.	Follower type	Pointed
J.	Cam plate thickness	30 mm
K.	Cam cutouts	Six at 24 mm diameter

Problem 16.24   Draw a displacement diagram and cam with the following specifications (for metric cam use SI dimensions in parentheses):

1.	Rise	90°, harmonic motion, 1.50 (38)
2.	Dwell	15°
3.	Rise	60°, uniform acceleration, 1.50 (38)
4.	Dwell	15°
5.	Fall	60°, harmonic motion, 1.00 (25)
6.	Dwell	15°
7.	Rise	30°, uniform acceleration, 2.00 (25)
8.	Dwell	15°
9.	Fall	60°, harmonic motion, to starting level

A.	Height	4.00 (100)
B.	Working circle	12.50 (318)
C.	Base circle	4.50 (114)
D.	Cam rotation direction	Counterclockwise
E.	Shaft diameter	1.75 (45)

F.	Shaft hub diameter	2.75 (70)
G.	Shaft hub thickness	2.50 (64)
H.	Keyseat and set screws	As per shaft size
I.	Follower type	Flat face
J.	Cam plate thickness	1.00 (25)
K.	Cam cutouts	Six holes at .75 (20) diameter

Problem 16.25   Draw a displacement diagram and cam with the following specifications (for metric cam use SI dimensions in parentheses):

1.	Rise	45°, modified uniform motion, 2.00 (50)
2.	Dwell	45°
3.	Fall	45°, harmonic motion, .75 (19)
4.	Dwell	45°
5.	Fall	45°, modified uniform motion, 1.00 (25)
6.	Dwell	15°
7.	Rise	60°, harmonic motion, 1.50 (38)
8.	Dwell	15°
9.	Fall	45°, parabolic motion, to starting level

A.	Height	2.00 (50)
B.	Working circle	7.50 (187)
C.	Base circle	3.50 (89)
D.	Cam rotation direction	Clockwise
E.	Shaft diameter	1.00 (25)
F.	Shaft hub diameter	1.875 (48)
G.	Shaft hub thickness	1.75 (45)
H.	Keyway and set screws	As per shaft size
I.	Follower type	Radial translating roller
J.	Cam plate thickness	.75 (18)
K.	Cam cutouts	None

Problem 16.26   Draw a displacement diagram and cam with the following specifications:

1.	Fall	75°, modified uniform motion, 90 mm
2.	Dwell	30°
3.	Rise	45°, harmonic motion, 60 mm
4.	Dwell	15°
5.	Fall	60°, uniformly accelerated motion, 50 mm
6.	Dwell	30°
7.	Rise	105°, harmonic motion, to starting level

A.	Height	310 mm
B.	Working circle	270 mm
C.	Base circle	100 mm
D.	Cam rotation direction	Clockwise
E.	Shaft diameter	50 mm
F.	Shaft hub diameter	70 mm
G.	Shaft hub thickness	60 mm
H.	Keyway and set screws	As per shaft size
I.	Follower type	Offset translating roller; offset 50 mm to the right side of cam center

J. Cam plate thickness   30 mm
K. Cam cutouts   Four holes at 20 mm diameter

Problem 16.27   Draw a displacement diagram and cam with the following specifications:

1. Rise   45°, harmonic motion, 4.00 (100)
2. Dwell   30°
3. Fall   60°, gravity motion, 3.50 (90)
4. Dwell   15°
5. Rise   90°, parabolic motion, 3.00 (76)
6. Dwell   30°
7. Fall   90°, uniformly accelerated, to starting level

A. Height   4.00 (100)
B. Working circle   14.00 (355)
C. Base circle   6.00 (127)
D. Cam rotation direction   Clockwise
E. Shaft diameter   2.00 (50)
F. Shaft hub diameter   4.00 (100)
G. Shaft hub thickness   3.00 (76)
H. Keyway and set screws   As per shaft size
I. Follower type   Swinging roller follower
J. Cam plate thickness   2.00 (50)
K. Cam cutouts   Six at .50–1.00 (12–24) diameter

Problem 16.28   Design and lay out a shaft and bearing assembly cabable of supporting any of the gear sets described in Problems 16.10, 16.11, 16.14, 16.15, or 16.16. Use standard mounted bearings or design a housing for the bearings in Figure 16.50.

PART IV

Design and Layout

CHAPTER 17

The Design Process

Learning Objectives

Upon completion of this chapter you will be able to accomplish the following:

1. Recognize the options of material, instrumentation, manufacturing technology, and fabrication personnel involved in the design process.
2. Interpret the criteria for product and manufacturing engineering that result in design for manufacturability.
3. Identify and define design parameters and considerations.
4. Analyze and utilize the stages involved in the design process while recognizing their flexibility.
5. Develop an understanding of critical-path scheduling and just-in-time production concepts.
6. Integrate CAD applications into the design process.

17.1 Introduction

The **design process** is an organized, interactive engineering activity that results in a well-defined concept and a specific plan to turn that concept into reality. The design process is basically a logical and planned sequence that can be used by an individual or a team to develop a solution to a specific problem. The stages in the design process are not intended to be hard and fast rules or procedures that are appropriate for all design situations. They can be considered as a guide to the design process, which is normally more fluid than described here.

Though the end product is specified in the form of drawings, computer images, sketches, and engineering specifications, designing involves more than simply putting a drawing together and having the part made in the shop. Designing should be an interactive process with planned steps and checkpoints. Every design involves solving a particular problem, analyzing what is needed to do the job, and planning the series of steps and activities that will make the concept a concrete object. Each design involves making choices in materials, instrumentation, manufacturing processes, and fabrication personnel. Finally, every design should have the input of several people, each of whom can offer advice, assistance, guidance, constructive critiques, and support.

With the advent of **design for manufacturability (DFM)** the design process is now understood to be the incorporation of procedures and considerations formerly left to manufacturing. Throughout this chapter you will be introduced to a variety of DFM concepts and ideas that will show the design process to be a fluid and dynamic process of integrating manufacturability into the design. For more information, see Chapter 3 and *Design for Manufacturability* by David M. Anderson (CIM Press, Lafayette, CA).

Few people understand the complexity of a particular product or the amount of effort required to bring a product to

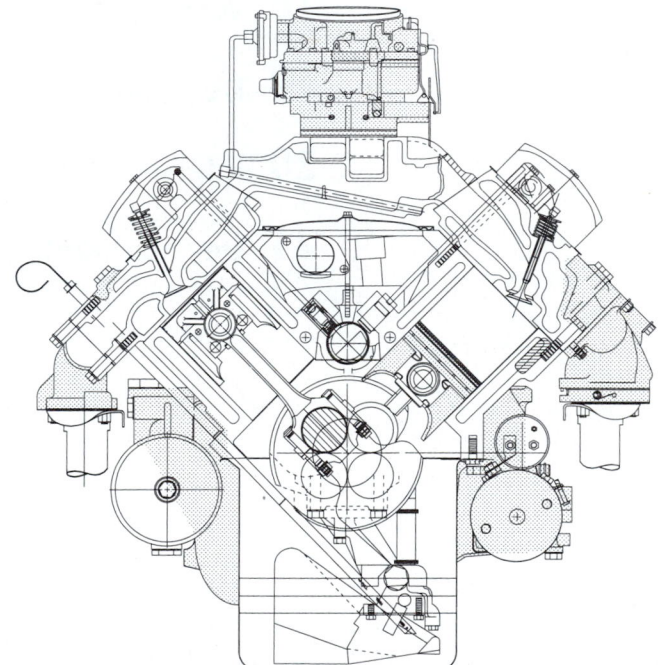

FIGURE 17.1 Automobile Engine

market. The automobile engine in Figure 17.1 is an example of an extremely complex piece of machinery that we all take for granted when we get in our cars. The complexity of a typical system design, such as a nuclear power plant, petrochemical facility, or an industrial building is more obvious. But, even in these types of projects, the general public does not fathom the complexity of and the time devoted to the design process.

A typical consumer product, such as a household appliance, hand tool, or other item for the general public, can

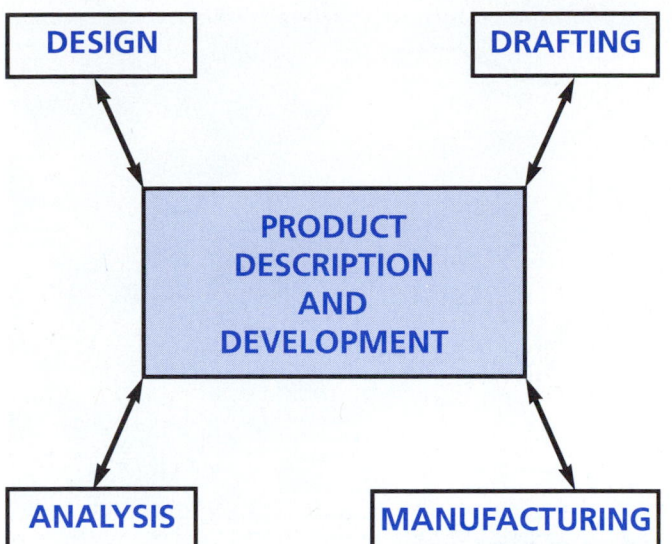

FIGURE 17.2   Product Description and Development

appear deceptively simple. In reality, however, the design concerns, engineering requirements, and manufacturing procedures are extremely complicated and time-consuming. Obviously, all products are the result of many hours of intense work. Product description and development include design, drafting, analysis, and manufacturing (Fig. 17.2). If the part design is generated on a CAD system, it can be used in all subsequent stages of the design-through-manufacturing sequence (Fig. 17.3).

It is impossible to describe how to design every item. It has been said that you cannot teach design in a school, but a thorough presentation of design concepts leading to the understanding of the conceptualization process involved in design and mastery of the stages involved in the design process will lay a solid foundation for anyone aspiring to become a designer. Specific design parameters for a product or system are mastered on the job through trial and error and the accumulation of experience.

The two main divisions of engineering design are **system design** and **product design**. Although systems design is an

important field, a majority of this text is devoted to product and mechanical design and drafting techniques. Therefore, this chapter is primarily a detailed analysis of the design process as it relates to product development and mechanical design. Figure 17.4 shows an example of a mechanical design done on a CAD system (see also Color Plates 1 through 22, 28, 29, 35 through 43, and 61 through 82).

17.2   Design Engineering

The design effort encompasses both **product engineering** and **manufacturing engineering**. Product and manufacturing engineering include a wide range of activities from the creative description of the item to its production. To design and produce a product efficiently, the **manufacturability** of the part must be built into the design from the beginning. Therefore, the product engineering and the manufacturing engineering of a successful project integrates the activities shown below:

Product Engineering
- Product description
- Specifications
- Models
  Test
  Prototype
  Fit and function
  Presentation
- Analysis
  Stress/Strain
  Fatigue/corrosion
  Movement/kinematics
  Load-forces/dynamics
  Heat-energy/thermodynamics
- Layout and detail drawings
- Redesign

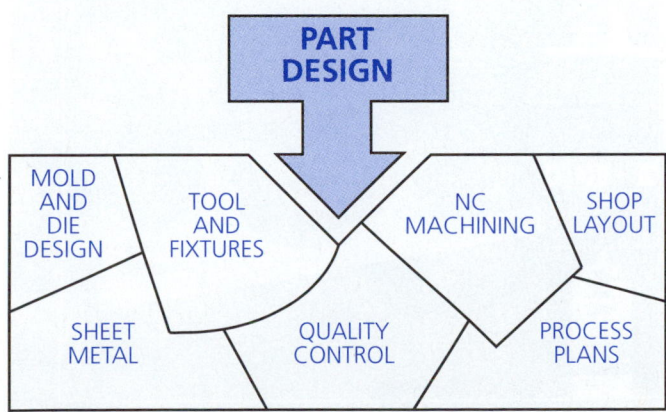

FIGURE 17.3   Part Design Using CAD

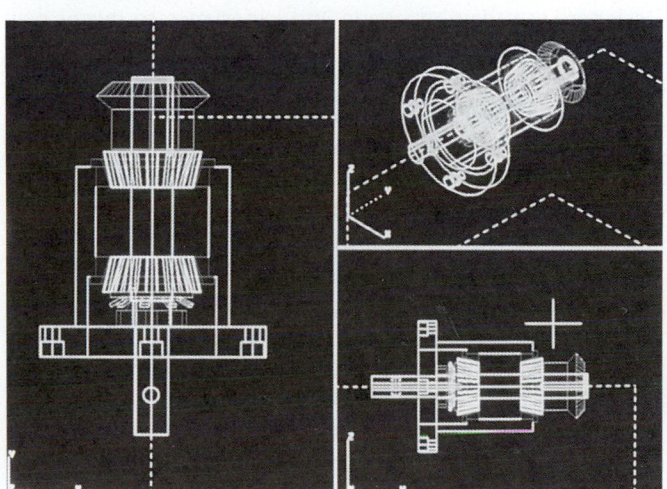

FIGURE 17.4   3D Design Using CAD

Manufacturing Engineering

- Production method
- Costs
- Quantity
- Tooling
  Dies
  Tools
  Jigs and fixtures
- Robot workcells
- Material management
  and movement
- Ordering
- Production planning
- Manpower requirements
- Testing
- Inspection
- Quality control
- Distribution
  Packaging
  Shipping
  Storing/stacking
- Facility management

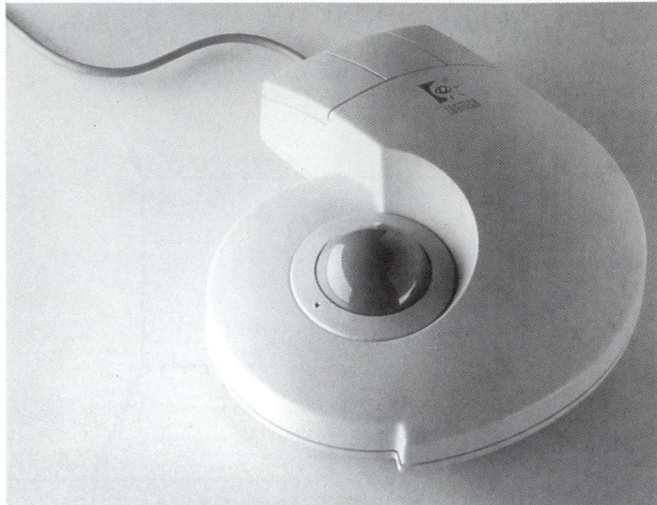

FIGURE 17.5 Trackman

The end result of the design activity is the most useful and economic product or system. To achieve success, the designer must consider multiple factors and make decisions based on compromises. Seldom is a design everything that the designer wanted when the project was started. The true test of a successful design is if the design is *functional* and *manufacturable*. Designs are functional when they satisfy a need and are available to the public in some form or quantity that is cost-effective and profitable for the company. Before a design is accepted, it must be tested and researched thoroughly. After the development and testing of a product or mechanical design, the design data is released to the factory for production.

17.2.1 The Designer and Designing

Designers use their education and experience to invent new products, create new systems, or take existing products or systems and add innovations. The process of design involves creativity and the ability to discover new solutions to existing problems or invent new products to fill a need. Being a designer has less to do with natural talent than with cultivating an eye for detail, accumulating knowledge from education, and gathering experience with a design.

Designing is an intellectual activity that has no hard and fast rules. Most good designers develop their expertise through time and experience. The best designers keep their minds open to new concepts and learn from co-workers, journals, magazines, and past failures. They are well informed; they choose the best features from several approaches for their designs. When you approach a new problem, study existing, related designs to try and understand the rationale and reasoning that have gone into their creation.

Since the item being designed or invented often does not exist before the process starts, **product design** (Fig. 17.5) involves more creativity. Product design involves the creation of commercially profitable, useful, or desirable items and devices. **Mechanical design** includes a wide range of industrial products (Fig. 17.6) and tools used in manufacturing (jigs and fixtures, dies, molds). The systems designer is a problem-solver and innovator. They use existing standard parts, combined in a unique functional manner, to satisfy a need or industrial requirement.

During the design process, the designer uses many different types of documents and consults a variety of specialists (Fig. 17.7). Customers communicate their needs through the contract and program office, which in turn releases the job to the engineering team. During the design process the designer has many responsibilities including:

- geometric arrangement of the components or design configuration
- effects of motion, forces, heat, and environment

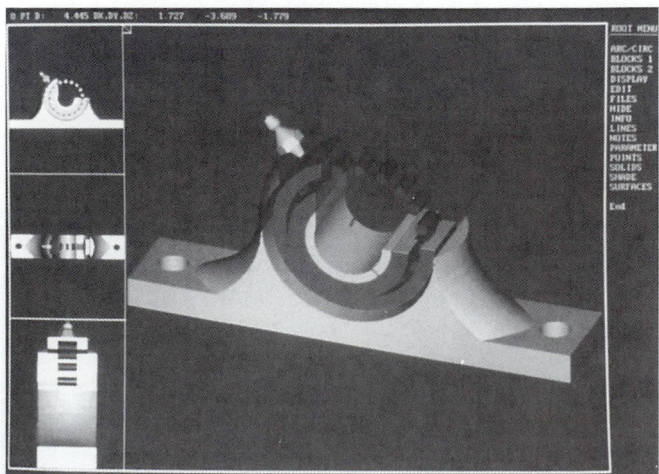

FIGURE 17.6 Bearing Design

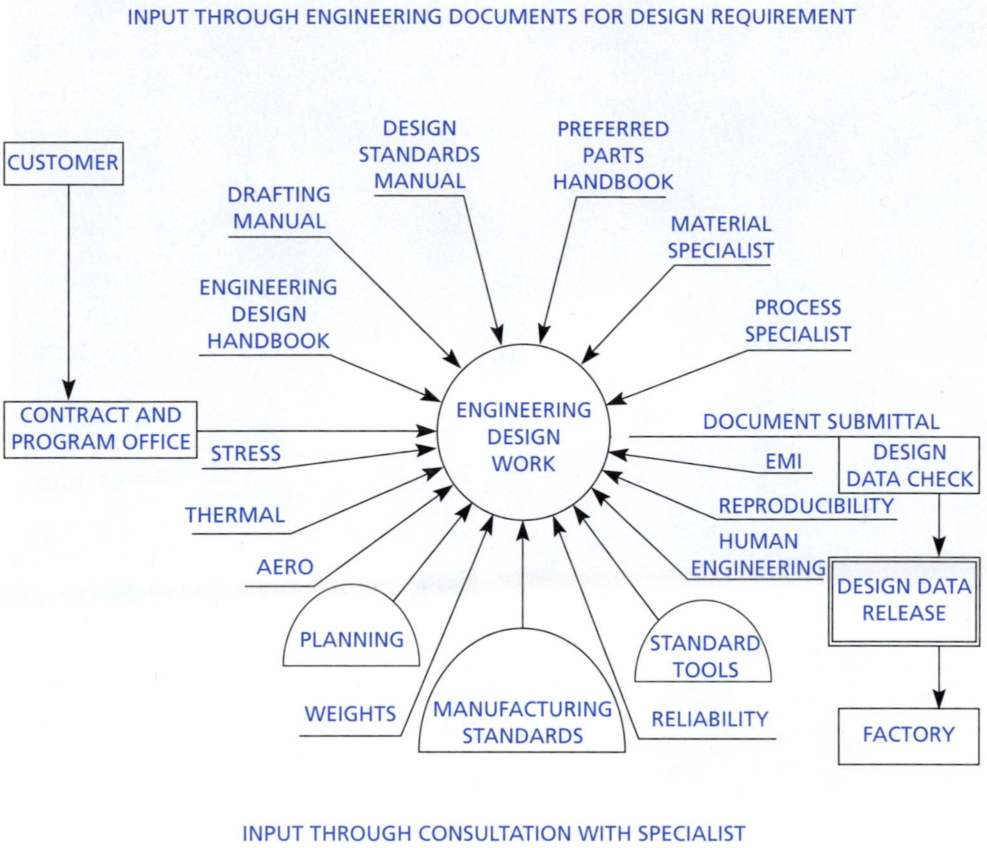

INPUT THROUGH ENGINEERING DOCUMENTS FOR DESIGN REQUIREMENT

INPUT THROUGH CONSULTATION WITH SPECIALIST

FIGURE 17.7   Engineering Design Flow Diagram

- human capabilities, limitations, and requirements (human factors)
- manufacturing and production processes
- material selection

To understand a design situation and bring the problem to a succsessful conclusion, the designer needs to possess basic creative instincts, an inquisitive mind, and the ability to communicate verbally, in the written form, and graphically. Successful designer traits include the following:

- intuition
- good communication skills—written, verbal, graphic
- open mind to problem-solving
- inquiring mind
- understanding of fundamental principles of design
- ability to integrate and balance several ideas and solutions
- ability to do self-evaluation
- concentration skills
- visualization skills
- ability to think and communicate in 3D
- mathematical skills

Cultivating successful designer traits can be done by 2D sketching, 3D visualization techniques, and the scrutiny of existing mechanical items and products. Developing memory skills, encouraging an investigative mind, practicing written and verbal descriptions of designs, and specific organizational skills are also essential.

The space program (Fig. 17.8) is an excellent example of where designers had to create new designs for exploration in entirely unique environments. Space exploration required designers who were not captive to preconceived notions, a limited vision, or afraid to push the frontiers of knowledge.

17.3 Systems Design

Systems design and **drafting** involve a variety of engineering disciplines that use standard parts in an assembled configuration to accomplish a task. Systems design revolves around the use of standardized parts that can be assembled in unique ways to solve particular problems or meet specialized needs. Each system is a combination of parts designed to fit into a specialized environment. Many systems are themselves combinations of systems. A building, for example, is not just a structural and architectural system. The typical building has a structural system to support it, a plumbing and piping system to provide water and remove waste, a gas system for heating, an electronic system for communications and security, an electrical system for power and lighting, a heating distribution system, a mechanical system for moving people and materials, and a ventilation and air conditioning system for controlling the temperature and air filtration of the structure. The larger the building, the more complex the systems.

Power generation, construction/structural, mass transportation (public and military), and electronic systems including computers are all system designs. The radio telescope in Figure 17.9 is an example of a combination of structural,

FIGURE 17.8   Space Station

mechanical, and electronic systems. The petrochemical plant model, shown in Figure 17.10, is an example of a system used to produce consumable energy products. A refinery is composed of electrical, heating and ventilation, structural, mechanical, electronic, instrumentation, and piping systems—all integrated into a complex facility. Piping systems are covered in Chapter 22 and electronic systems in Chapter 23.

FIGURE 17.9   Tracking Antenna

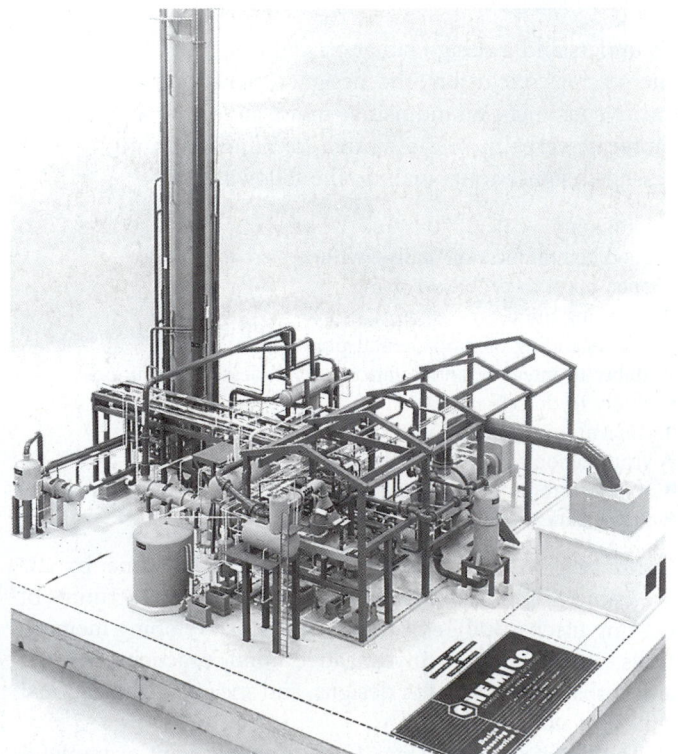

FIGURE 17.10   Model of Chemical Plant

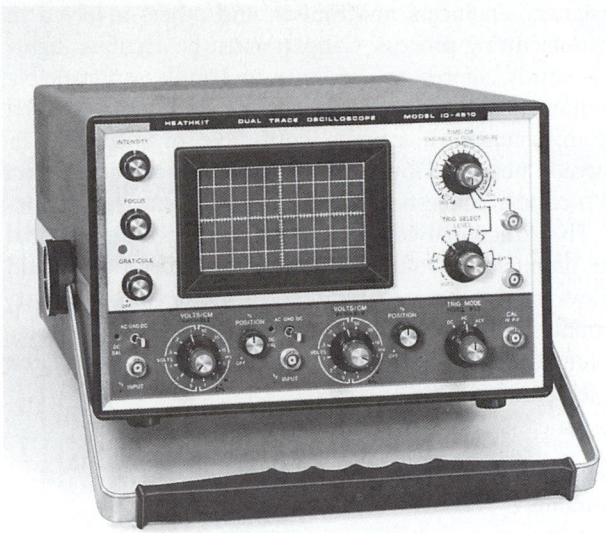

FIGURE 17.11   Oscilloscope

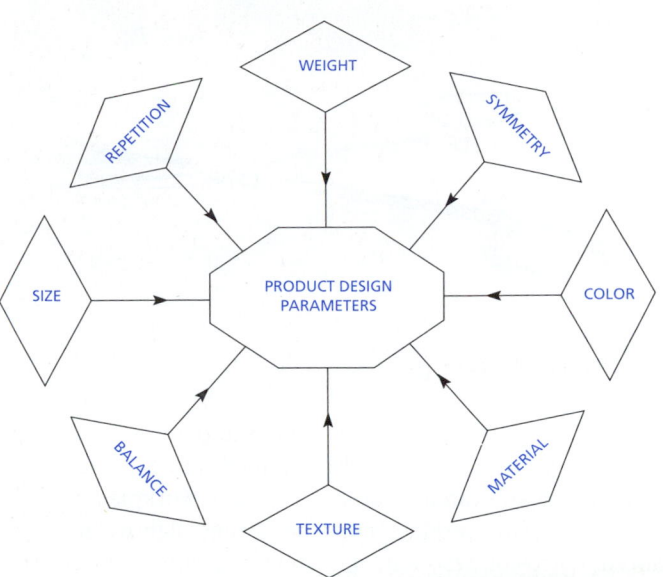

FIGURE 17.13   Product Design Parameters

17.4   Product and Industrial Design

Product design is done by an **industrial designer** who works in conjunction with the engineering, manufacturing, and marketing departments to develop and create a useful and profitable product. Products are mass produced for the consumer, educational, or industrial market. Figure 17.11 is an example of an **industrial product.** Its function is far more important than its visual appeal. The oscilloscope is sold to industry, military, and educational markets. The hairdryer, shown in Color Plate 55, and the computer office chair in Color Plates 56, 57, and 58, are consumer products. The gas generator, in Figure 17.12, is a product that has both individual consumer and industrial markets. Since its design is

functional and mechanical in nature, we could say that it is more of an industrial product. The rollerball pointing device used for computer input (Fig. 17.5) is an example of a consumer product.

17.4.1   Product Design Parameters

All design decisions must be made after careful consideration of the factors influencing the product. **Product design parameters** (Fig. 17.13) determine manufacturing and production methods and include the following:

- **weight**
- **material**
- **symmetry**
- **size**
- **texture**
- **color**
- **repetition**
- **balance**

Each design parameter affects the other parameters. For instance, the weight of the product is influenced by its material and size. The color will be influenced by the material. The material influences the texture or surface quality. Since the texture of a product may in some cases be more important than other factors, the surface feel or *texture* requirements, in return, affect the material choice. The weight and size of a product affect its ease of use.

The shape of the product should be considered with regard to its symmetry, proportion, repetition, and balance. Geometric proportions that are pleasing to the eye and appear balanced are used to provide a repetitive shape to the part. Curves, lines, and contours all influence this balance and symmetry. Remember, the best selling product is not always the best product. An extremely reliable, completely functional, long lasting product will not necessarily sell if it is also poorly proportioned and unappealing in color and shape. All of the above factors are interdependent. A good designer determines the proper mix of factors based on their relative importance to the project.

FIGURE 17.12   10-kW Gas Generator Mockup

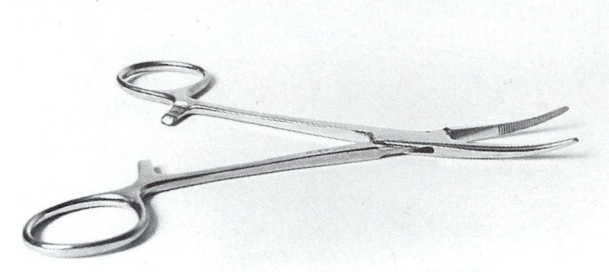

FIGURE 17.14   Forceps

The forceps in Figure 17.14 is an example of a small product. Though normally considered a medical instrument, this clamping device can be found in industrial workplaces and in the home. This product must be strong, lightweight, balanced, corrosion resistant, and come in a variety of sizes and shapes. Since the main requirement is that it can be sterilized, its color is not important. The material itself dictates most of its characteristics. Stainless steel is used because it satisfies the design requirements.

17.4.2   Design Considerations

Design considerations require proper and timely decisions by the designer. A careful and systematic overview of a product's design considerations will lead to a successful final product.

The calipers in Figure 17.15 are an example of a product that was designed with a very specific use. Calipers are used

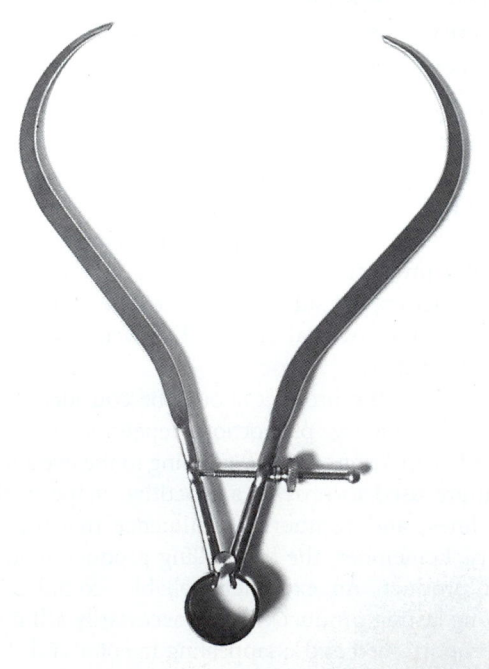

FIGURE 17.15   Calipers

by designers, engineers, machinists, and others involved in the manufacturing process. Calipers must be accurate, lightweight, sturdy, simple to use, easy to handle, unbreakable within limits, have an extremely long life, and not be affected by the environment. Inaccurate, corrodible, or breakable calipers would not sell. Obviously, the **function** of this product is the foremost concern—it must *accurately* measure something. This functional consideration determines the material choice; nonmetals would be inappropriate since they would not allow for the accuracy required of the finished product. Appearance is not a major consideration. The requirement for corrosion resistance limits the material choices, as will the strength considerations.

Design considerations include the following:

- **function**
- **constraints**
- **materials**
- **appearance**
- **environmental effect** on product and product on environment
- **product life**
- **reliability**
- **safety** requirements
- **interchangeability** and **standardization** of components
- **maintenance** and **service** requirements
- **costs**

Function   The actual functions of a product must be defined early in the design process. Unnecessary functions or extra features (sometimes called "bells and whistles") should be eliminated if they do not substantially increase the value or salability of the product. The designer must determine whether the product could be used for more than the original function described by the customer. Could the product be less complicated? Could it serve more than one purpose?

The function of a product will always be its primary consideration. If the product does not function properly, then it is not marketable. The function of a product will be influenced by its complexity. A basic rule is *to minimize the complexity of a design*. The simpler a product, the easier and cheaper it is to manufacture. Strength requirements will be influenced by the product's function. Reducing rotational stress, bending, and other complex movements is the goal. The designer considers these factors when designing for strength. Interference between moving parts is also an aspect of function. The function of a product determines the movements and how many individual parts are required. Attempt *to minimize the number of parts* in the design.

Constraints   *Design for simplicity* within the constraints. What are the **constraints** of the project? Are the size, weight, and volume of the product adequate? Could they be reduced to create a better design? The projected cost of the product is also a constraint. A "widget" that performs 24 different functions, but costs five times more than the consumer will pay, is not a well-designed product. Size, weight, and volume will be influenced by handling, shipping, and marketing considerations.

ITEMS OF INTEREST

Ballpoint Pens

Before the invention of the fountain pen, man used the sharpened shaft of a feather as a standard writing instrument. The earliest form of a fountain pen was found in a 6,000-year-old Egyptian tomb. It was a reed into which ink was poured and was used to write on parchment and papyrus. In 1884, the fountain pen, as we now know it, was invented. Because of the leaks and breaks in the nibs, you could always spot users of these pens from their ink-stained hands. It became obvious—there had to be a better way to write than this.

People began experimenting using a ball bearing point. A Hungarian, Ladisloa Biro (a journalist), and his brother Gerry (a chemist) worked on the problem of the ink on the ball point clotting and not running smoothly. When the war broke out, the Biro brothers emigrated to Argentina and in 1943 formed a new company to perfect and produce the pen.

They finally worked out a formula for the ink. In 1944 the tube for the ink and the ball bearing point were combined to form a new pen. An Englishman spotted

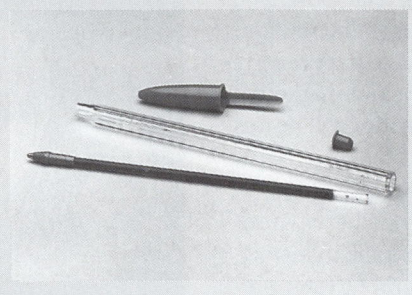

Bic Pen

one of the new pens and knew about the problem the wartime aircraft crews were having with the fountain pen leaking at high altitudes. An instant market was available for the new pen!

After the war, the Biro brothers' invention (which had been sold earlier to their financial backer) was sold in the United States as Eversharp and in Europe as Bic. The Biro name became a household word, but the inventors disappeared into obscurity. A medium-point Bic pen produces more than two miles of writing.

The French company sells more than 12 million ballpoint pens per year.

The ballpoint pen is a simple design. A precision ground ball, usually stainless steel and $\frac{1}{32}$ in. in diameter, is the main component. It is ground to an accuracy of a few millionths of an inch. The ball can also be a tungsten and a carbon compound almost as hard as diamond.

The ball is fitted into a housing that allows rotation in all directions. The tip of the housing is bent over the edge of the ball so it does not fall out of the pen. Ink is fed through a narrow tube from the reservoir to the ball housing. If the reservoir is not open to the air, a small hole is made in the housing to prevent a partial vacuum from forming and preventing the ink from flowing. The ink is distributed evenly around the ball by ridges inside the housing.

Ballpoint pens remain the most popular, inexpensive, and efficient writing tool of today. The Biro brothers gave us another important invention we hardly notice, but would not want to live without.

The size of a product will also be influenced by who uses the item. A child's hand is smaller than an adult's and, in most cases, a woman's hand will be smaller than a man's. If the item is sex-determined (used by only one sex), then research at the marketing level defines many of the constraints.

Materials   The **material** used for the design is determined by a multitude of factors. In fact, much of the success of a design might be determined by the material choice. The following is a partial list of *material properties* that are considered during the design process:

Strength   A measure of a material's capacity to resist different types of forces.

Elasticity   The stiffness of a material and its capacity to deflect under load.

Ductility   The ability of a metal to deform before fracturing.

Fatigue   When a material fails after many load cycles.

Bearing characteristics   The suitability of a material to be used as an element resting on another part and in motion.

Hardness and brittleness   Opposite of ductility; a characteristic of a material to shatter before deforming.

Damping   Ability of a material to dissipate energy caused by vibration.

Temperature   Effective range where the material properties will be suitable.

Toughness   Ability of a material to absorb energy before fracturing.

Resilience or elasticity   Ability of a material to store energy when permanently deforming.

Wearing   Ability of a material to withstand rubbing motion, causing removal of material.

Corrosion   Ability of a material to resist deterioration caused by a reaction to the environment.

Toxicity   The possibility of producing a poisonous effect. Material safety data sheets (MSDS) are now required documentation for products.

Machinability   The relative ability of a material to be machined.

Forgeability   Ability of a material to be forged.

Formability   The ability of a material to be formed.

Castability   The ability of a material to be cast.

Weldability   The ease with which a material can be welded.

Many times, the function of the item determines the material; in other cases, there is more leeway in the material choice. The material that best suits the design and manufacturing requirements is sometimes a compromise. **Availability** is also a factor in material selection. An exotic material may be the best choice, but if it is hard to procure, another material may be better for adequate production runs.

Appearance   Appearance is one of the most important considerations in consumer product design and usually the least important for industrial product design. The look, feel, shape (symmetry, modernness, roundness, smoothness), and eye appeal of a product have to be given consideration early in the design phase. Sometimes, for the successful marketing of a product, the function and other characteristics will be less important than the appearance.

Environment   The effect of the product on the environment is now more important than at any other time in history. Industrial history is full of examples of how profit took precedence over the protection of the environment. An environmental impact report is mandatory, in most places, for large systems design.

The effects of the environment on the product are also a concern for the designer as with the tractor in Figure 17.16. The effects of temperature variations during operation must be considered in the design phase of a product. Dust and dirt must be excluded from many products to ensure proper operation. Vibration also affects the operation and life of a product and, therefore, must be limited by dampening devices and other methods. The moisture level in an operating environment will be a concern for many products; excess moisture can cause corrosion. *Designing any product starts with the understanding of when, how, by whom, and where a product is to be used.*

The oscilloscope (Fig. 17.11) was designed to be carried. The electronics inside must be shielded properly by the packaging. Heat must be allowed to escape from the package. Therefore, vents are provided in the sheet metal on the sides of the package. The ruggedness of the product will obviously

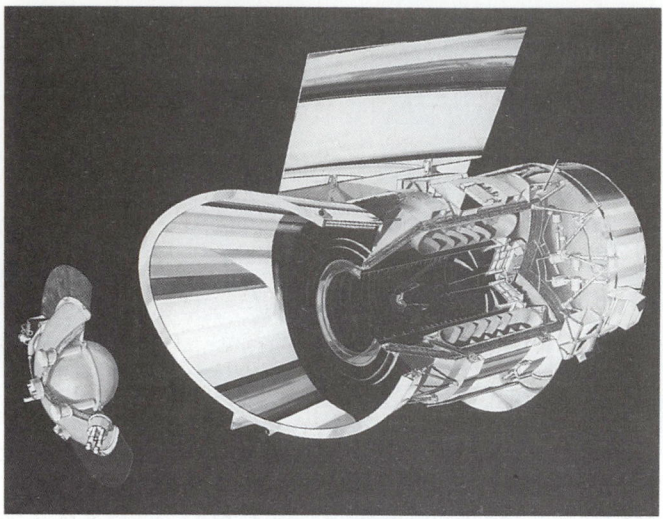

FIGURE 17.17   Infrared Astronomical Satellite

affect its reliability, life, and the effects of the environment on its operation.

The space shuttle was designed to withstand heat measured in thousands of degrees while reentering the atmosphere. The shuttle tiles had to be made of ceramics that could handle this type of repeated environmental assault. Most of the shuttle's components were designed to operate in a dust-free environment. Therefore, the manufacturing and assembly stages of production for its components were done in *clean rooms.*

The space telescope in Figure 17.17 must be cooled to eliminate its own heat radiation, which could interfere with infrared reception from the stars. The telescope and its associated measuring equipment were designed so that they are cooled to 4° F above absolute zero. Environmental considerations are one of the most demanding aspects of this design.

Product Life   The **operation life** of a product is its time of operation before it fails. The **shelf life** of a product is the period of time it can be in storage and still operate correctly. The designer can influence the life of a product by choice of material, features, manufacturing methods, and assembly methods. Often, it is the intention of the designer to have the product wear out at a given life length.

An industrial product's life may be longer and provide for easier replacement of worn parts. The tractor in Figure 17.16 is an example of a product that is designed to be maintained over a long period of use.

The Viking lander (Fig. 17.18) had to have an extremely long life in order to operate effectively in a hostile environment. Service, replacement, and maintenance were not considered in this design because the lander could not be reached to perform these functions. The original parts had to have extremely long operational lifetimes and had to operate error-free for an extended period while undergoing extensive environmental attack—temperature variation, dust, and solar radiation. In other words, it had to be extremely reliable.

FIGURE 17.16   Case Tractor

FIGURE 17.18 Viking Lander

Reliability

The reliability of a product is influenced by the number of moving parts, complexity, and sensitivity to the environment. **Reliability** is a product's ability to function properly during each operation. Reliability affects both the life and the cost of the product. An unreliable product will not enjoy continued sales. Each product is designed to have adequate reliability to last the average expected life. The higher the quality of the components used in a product, the longer its life and the higher its reliability. However, it is not cost-effective to design something that has components with more reliability than the item itself. Parts designed for the military and for space exploration must have the highest reliability.

Safety

Safety involves the correct performance of a product. Some sensitive or dangerous products have fail-safe designs so as to prevent any injury or harm to the environment. **Fail-safe** means that a product incorporates features for automatically counteracting the effect of an anticipated possible source of breakdown. Products can be dangerous when they do not perform correctly, when they are operated incorrectly, or when they are performing correctly but there is insufficient protection for the operator. Each of these three considerations influences the design. The first and last are the easiest to prevent. Protective shields, housings, and guards can be incorporated into the design. The product can be rigorously tested for safe operation and incorporation of any safety features.

Standardization and Interchangeability

By using standard, off-the-shelf items, the cost of the product can be reduced. Systems design is, in reality, the assembly of standard components in unique configurations that accomplish a specific task—such as producing power or creating a chemical. Products also benefit from the incorporation of standard parts in their design. The use of standard parts and previously designed parts is an important factor in DFM, thereby saving time and cost.

The ability of a unit to use similar parts or have different components that can be substituted is called **interchangeability**. The product is designed so that different sizes of fasteners or other standard components can be used. This will reduce the production costs and eliminate possible shortage problems and delays in production.

Maintenance

Design for simplicity in disassembly and maintenance. Some, if not most, products are now designed as throwaways. *Design with recycling* in mind whenever the product is to be a throwaway.

Products that require repair, service, and maintenance are designed to be disassembled at specific intervals of operation or stages of wear; therefore, *design for disassembly.* Providing clearance for tools and hands during maintenance and repair is a consideration for many industrial products. As an example, the valve in Figure 17.19 is designed to allow for the removal of the handwheel, stem, bonnet, and disk to replace the composition ring. This service can be accomplished without cutting or disassembling the pipeline.

Costs

The number of parts produced could influence the **cost** of the product. In general, the greater the quantity manufactured, the lower the overall unit cost of the product. If you had to purchase each part separately, the average automobile would cost about 100 times more than they do now. Most of us have had this experience when we needed a repair on our car. The cost of each replacement part far exceeded its

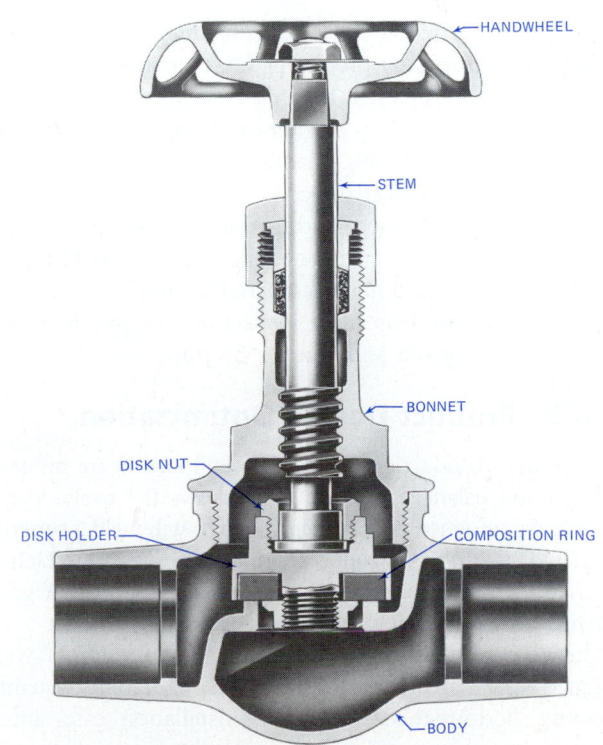

FIGURE 17.19 Composition Disk Globe Valve

FIGURE 17.20 Product Design Optimization

cost as part of the whole car. Most consumer products can be made much cheaper by producing large quantities. Industry has realized that they must hold down costs and at the same time increase quality. The designer can be an important factor in this equation. Materials, manufacturing methods, equipment, and labor all affect the cost of a product.

The design, production, and marketing costs of a product must be estimated early in the design process to bring the product to market and make a fair return on the investment. *Designing in quality* instead of inspecting out problems will ensure a greater profit and a better product.

17.4.3 Product Design Optimization

The optimum product is created when all factors are properly analyzed and balanced. Figure 17.20 shows the twelve major influences that, when properly considered, will yield a superior product. This process is called **product optimization.** Each of the twelve factors affects the success of the product. A good designer factors in each to develop an optimum product.

The pipe insulation covers shown in Figure 17.21 were designed using many of these factors. Durability, quality, economy, performance, simplicity, installation ease, interchangeability, safety, and manufacturability were all considered in the design and production of the covers. Although the

FIGURE 17.21 Zestron Pipe Insulation Covers

FIGURE 17.22   **Insulating a Pipeline**

insulation of a pipeline (Fig. 17.22) that uses covers does not require the aesthetic considerations required of consumer products, it does require proper industrial considerations that will affect design and production.

17.4.4   The Design Tree

The **design tree** (Fig. 17.23) is useful in analyzing a particular project. The design tree can be used to illustrate the decision process during the crucial initial design or redesign phase of a project. Although the physical configuration, materials, manufacturing methods, assembly procedures, and equipment costs may be altered and balanced between selections, stages occur along the design process of a new product in which equal function, quality, and performance levels can be obtained. The goal is to maximize the product's advantages while maintaining the critical specifications.

The design tree starts with the trunk (product idea). The two main branches are the material selection and the physical configuration. The left limb in the illustration depicts the

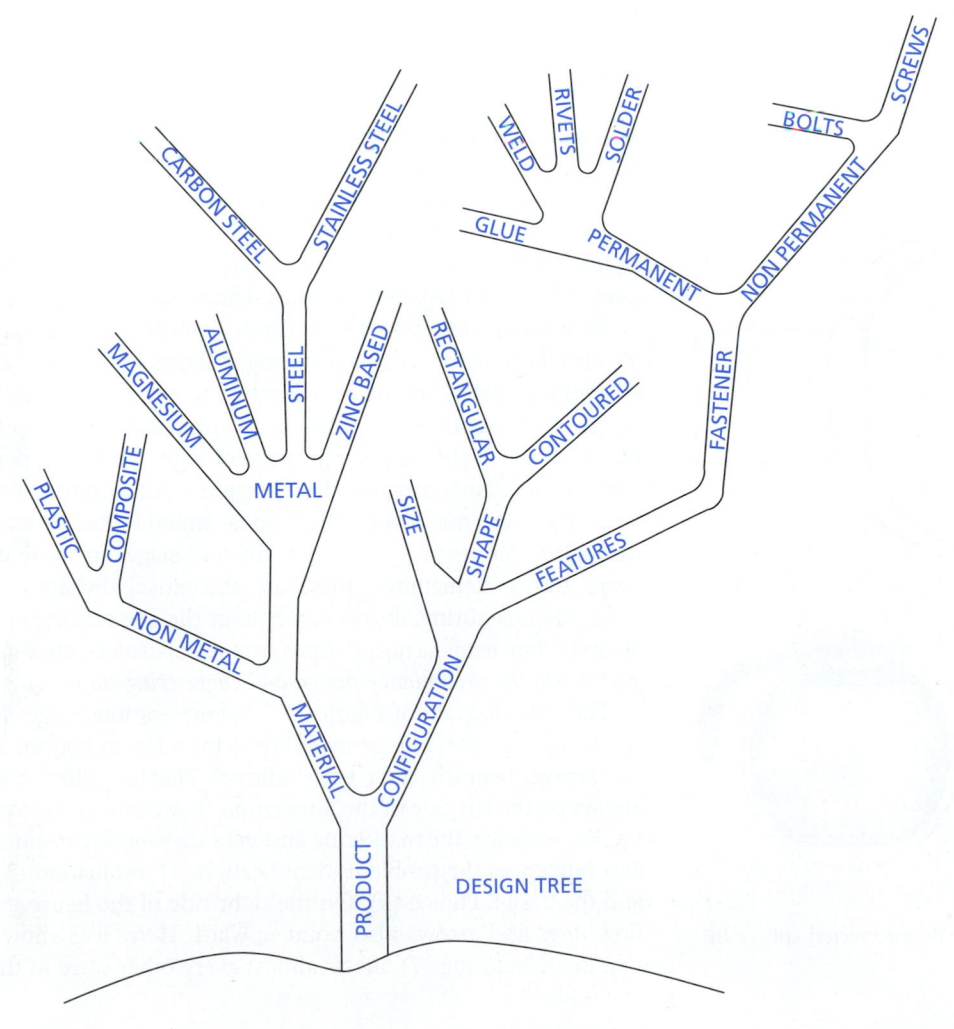

FIGURE 17.23   **Design Tree**

material choices and splits at metal and nonmetal. Many questions must be answered at this juncture. If metal is chosen, what grades and types should be considered? If nonmetal is considered the best choice, the same questions are asked. The physical shape of the product will be determined by taking the right branch and selecting its size, shape, and features. The branching process can continue to include possible modifications and enhancements. The design tree can also help to see where a particular option or feature may actually threaten the product's integrity.

17.4.5   Product Design Example

A sphere is considered the perfect geometric shape. However, if a sphere is penetrated or truncated by some other geometric shape, it tends to lose its distinctive shape and appears either ellipsoidal or flattened, as Figure 17.24(a) shows. Of course, if,

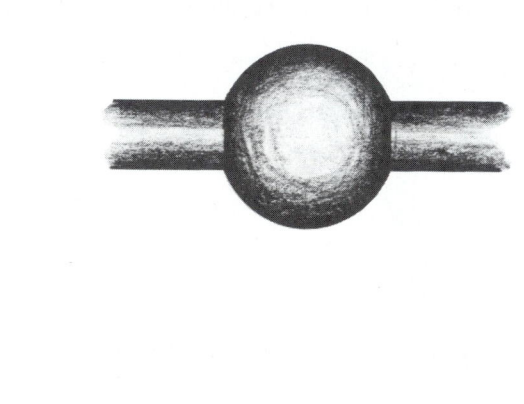

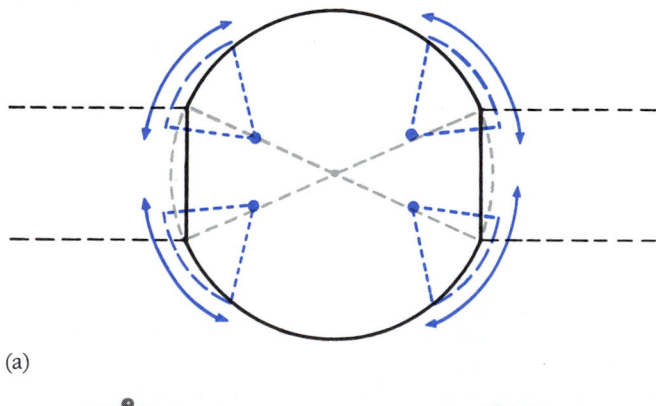

(a)

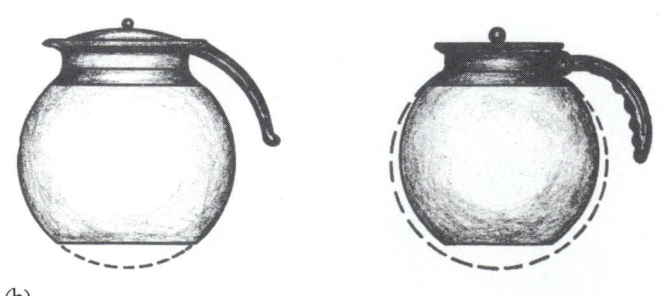

(b)

FIGURE 17.24   Product Design   (a) The intersected sphere in design (b) Spheres in product design

in this case, the penetrating cylinder had been much smaller in diameter, this optical illusion would not have occurred.

Figure 17.24(b) is an enlargement of the sphere in outline form. Notice that the surface seems flattened at those places where the penetrating cylinder passes through it. The difficulty with which the designer must cope, in this situation, is clear. How can the sphere be made to look like a sphere instead of an ellipsoid? The dashed lines show the sphere as it would be without the penetrating cylinder.

Designers overcome this optical illusion by subtle changes in shape. To create the illusion that the flattened sides are not flattened, the designer must first change the shape of the sphere around the flattened area. This is done by laying out four radii. The designer "builds up" or "swells" the sphere and, thus, negates the flattened look. In other words, the designer creates an ellipsoid that appears to be a sphere when penetrated along its long axis.

When a sphere is truncated, as in this design for a coffee carafe [Fig. 17.24(b)] the same process is used. The drawing on the left shows the squat, flattened look the carafe would have if the designer did not modify the basic sphere. On the right, the designer subtly uses the ellipsoidal shape—shown here by the solid line—to give the finished product a spherical appearance.

17.5   The Design Process

The **design process** begins when a customer expresses a need for a product. Working with the customer, you define the project and formulate its requirements.

For simplicity, the design process has been separated into eight individual stages (Fig. 17.25). This is not to be taken as a set of hard-and-fast steps or rules. The actual design process is more flexible and is not as linear as described here. *Design for manufacturability* requires the eight stages not to be considered separately, but, as an integrated whole in which each "stage" is constantly being considered within each other stage. Many of the eight stages represented here are being performed simultaneously by the design/manufacturing team. The stages do not always flow in a straight line from 1 through 8. Sometimes, there are different stages or more or fewer stages. Remember, these are theoretical divisions of tasks. Manufacturing always comes after the engineering and analysis, but *manufacturing decisions and capabilities are integrated into the preliminary design and engineering stage.*

The flow diagram of Figure 17.25 shows various stages in the design process. The general flow is from top to bottom as the arrows beneath each box indicate. The flow lines and arrows on the left side of the illustration flow from the bottom up. For instance, the marketing and sales division is consulted and influences the problem identification (1), evaluation (3), and the design choice (5). On the right side of the figure the flow lines and arrows also point upward. Here, it is shown that manufacturing (7) affects almost every other stage in the

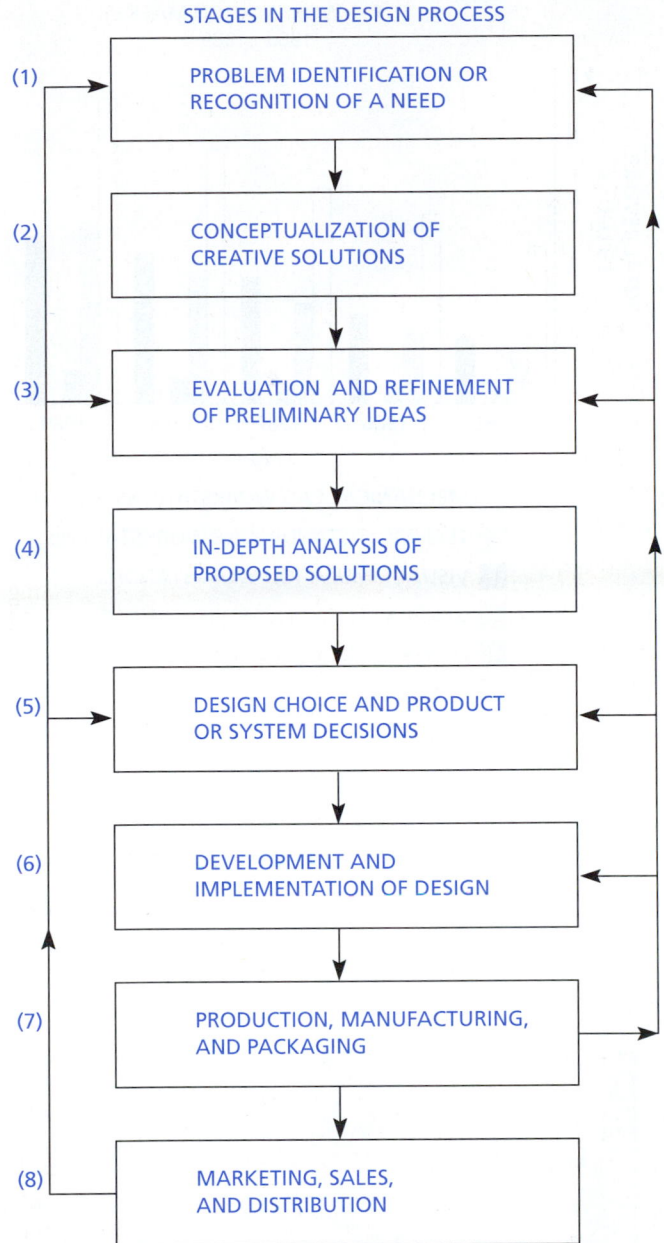

FIGURE 17.25 Stages in the Design Process

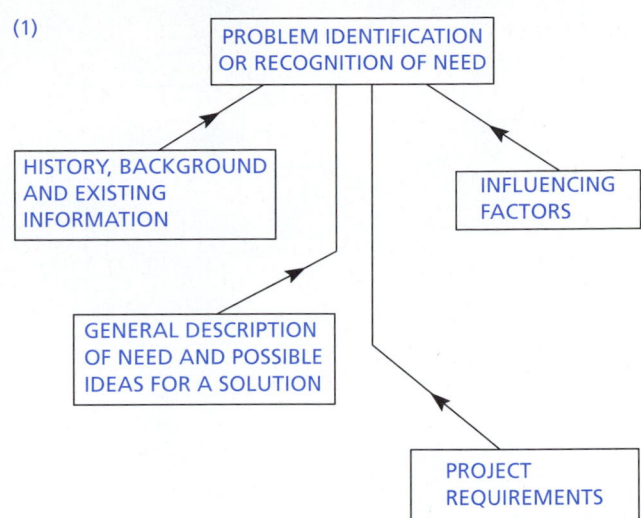

FIGURE 17.26 Stage 1 in the Design Process

process. The following portion of this chapter will take each stage in sequence and indicate the specific influencing factors and tasks associated with it.

17.5.1 Problem Identification or Recognition of a Need

The design process starts with the **identification** of a problem (Fig. 17.26), an observed need, or a potential new idea for a product or system. The problem identification or recognition of need stage is the starting point of all design efforts. The identification or recognition stage requires that the designer or design team be thoroughly acquainted with the problem or

need. You should attempt to answer the following at this stage of the project:

- *Who* needs it?
- *What* is needed?
- *Where* is it needed?
- *When* is it needed?
- *Why* is it needed?
- *How* many are needed?

History, Background, and Existing Information The **background** of the project is presented to the design team by a concerned party: the company management, an outside client, or a company inventor who has a new idea. The marketing department may be asked to do a survey on the potential for a particular product. Let us say, for example, a computer company that has a well-received product line servicing the private sector with personal computers wishes to enter the engineering workstation market. Surveys may be needed to determine the total sales of computers in that sector and create a forecast for the future. The marketing and research department will probably create a series of charts and graphs to present their findings visually. The company's management, along with the design team, then discusses the potential for their firm to enter—and be successful in—this market. Figure 17.27(a) is an example of an analysis of the past sales in the engineering workstation market. The forecast for workstation type is shown in Figure 17.27(b).

A number of questions can be asked at this stage of the process:

- What exists now?
- How was the problem faced in the past?
- Is this a new problem?

The answers to these questions may not be complete at this stage and, in fact, they may create more questions.

(a)

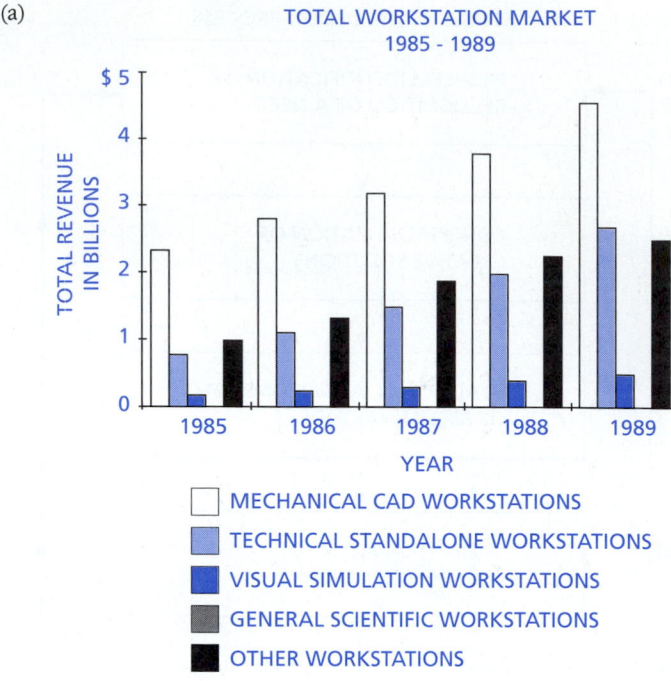

TOTAL WORKSTATION MARKET
1985 - 1989

☐ MECHANICAL CAD WORKSTATIONS
▨ TECHNICAL STANDALONE WORKSTATIONS
■ VISUAL SIMULATION WORKSTATIONS
▩ GENERAL SCIENTIFIC WORKSTATIONS
■ OTHER WORKSTATIONS

(b)

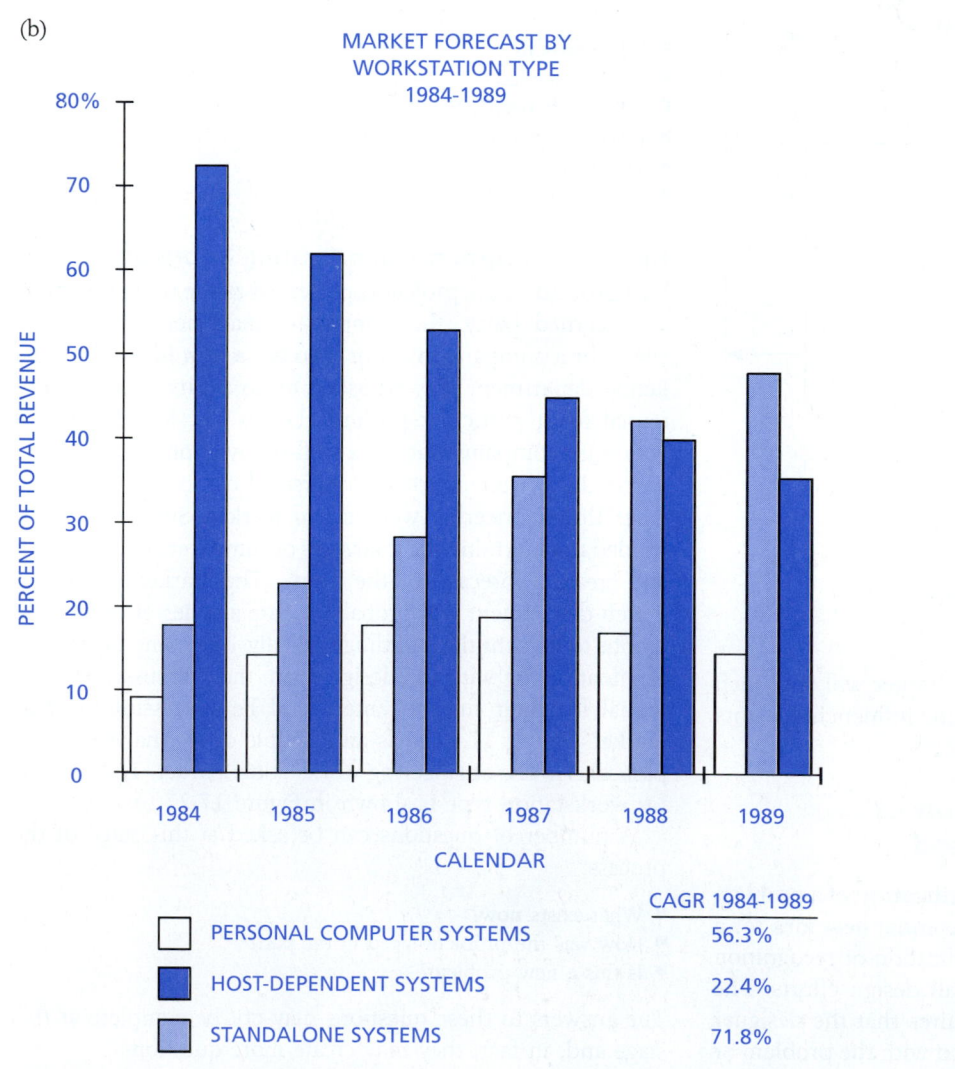

MARKET FORECAST BY
WORKSTATION TYPE
1984-1989

	CAGR 1984-1989
☐ PERSONAL COMPUTER SYSTEMS	56.3%
■ HOST-DEPENDENT SYSTEMS	22.4%
▨ STANDALONE SYSTEMS	71.8%

FIGURE 17.27 Example of a Market Analysis (a) Graph depicting workstation market data (b) Market forecast data in graph form

FIGURE 17.28   48 in. Gate Valve for Transalaska Pipeline

General Description of a Need and Possible Ideas for a Solution

The **general description** and possible solutions to the problem flow from a series of meetings conducted with the design team. Let us say a company that has been manufacturing small, residential, plumbing valves (Fig. 17.19) and medium-sized industrial valves has an opportunity to bid on a large job requiring pipeline-sized valves (Fig. 17.28). The new product line will affect the manufacturing equipment, facility space, manpower requirements, shipping, and storage areas of the firm. The size of the valve alone may necessitate a total retooling of the facility. The job may also be a one-time opportunity and have little continued sales after the project is complete. The economics of the project is of primary concern. How will it affect existing product lines? Is it worth the risk? Will the company turn a profit for its effort? Will the company be able to sustain a continued presence in this market after the project is complete?

Influencing Factors

The design of a product or system does not happen in a vacuum. All products and systems have an effect on the users of the product or system and, possibly, society in general. The cost of a project determines its feasibility. All factors that may influence the total cost and the economic feasibility of the design must be considered before the project is initiated.

Environmental constraints and concerns may be important for many product designs. Systems design is influenced by the environmental constraints and effects imposed on it by the government and special interest groups. The design of a power plant, chemical facility, hydroelectric plant, bridge, housing complex, or a building, to name a few, is defined by the acceptable effect it has on the environment. An environmental impact report may be needed before much of the design effort is begun. The valve of Figure 17.28 is on the Alaskan pipeline (Fig. 17.29). Environmental impact reports were a major part of the design effort and were used to convince the public that the pipeline was feasible and safe. The actual conditions under which the pipeline and valves operate stretched the limits of pipeline technology.

The economics of a particular solution must be understood at an early part of this stage. Can the product or system make money? Is the existing budget adequate? Will the project involve new markets or will the product be replacing an existing one? When economics is concerned, input from all other departments is important. The marketing and manufacturing departments have considerable input that must be integrated into the total economic analysis of the project if it is to be successful.

Project Requirements

Basic parameters can be identified at this stage. All ideas and suggestions should be recorded as notes and rough sketches. The project's size, shape, color, material, and general configuration can be discussed. No decisions should be made at this point. Requirements dictated by a client or purchaser of the product or system must be added to the list of known influencing factors and project requirements. If a project must be a certain color or weight, this must be understood at the earliest stage of the process. If the product is to be efficiently produced, design for manufacturability must be integrated into the project from the onset.

FIGURE 17.29   Gate Valve Being Installed on Transalaska Pipeline

(2)

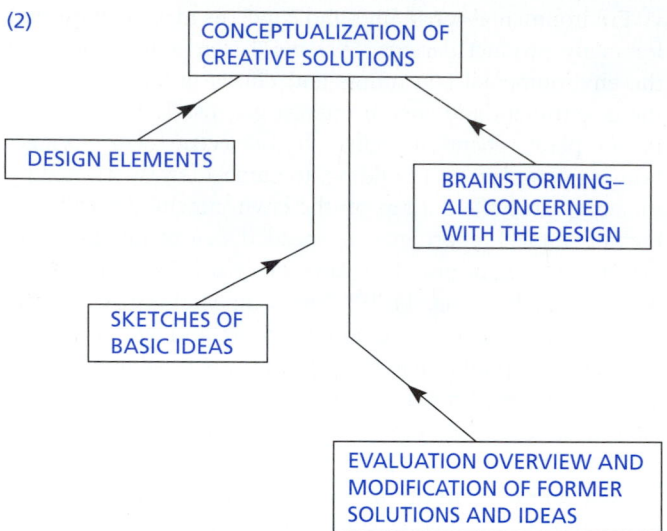

FIGURE 17.30 Stage 2 in the Design Process

17.5.2 Conceptualization of Creative Solutions

Before the design process goes any further, **creative possibilities** for a solution to the design problem should be purposely investigated. Knowing background information and the research of pertinent data help the designer see clearly the range of possible answers to the design problem.

This stage (Fig. 17.30) includes researching every available source of information about the project. Each of the design elements listed in Stage 1 is now analyzed thoroughly. The influencing factors, general parameters, and project requirements are now used to investigate possible solutions. Even at this stage, attempt should *not* be made to find a complete final solution. Data from outside sources is integrated into the design process during this stage. Former solutions to the same or a similar problem can be discussed and expanded on now.

Although the past experience and education of a designer are extremely important for the success of a project, the proper research of all existing information on the subject is no less important. Since the research process helps build a professional "database" that can be tapped for other projects, a new or inexperienced designer benefits from any existing information. Oddly enough, it is not the lack of background sources but the overabundance of information that is a problem. The designer must differentiate between what is useful and important and what is nonessential. The following list provides some sources for acquiring information on a design problem:

- textbooks
- periodicals—technical magazines
- library search
- engineering standards
- technical reports
- published papers presented at conferences
- manufacturing specifications
- catalogs of parts
- patents
- handbooks
- previous designs in the company
- co-workers—other designers and engineers

Design Elements   The **elements of design** must be identified by the designer early in this stage of the project. The identification and classification of design elements helps to clarify and divide important or vital elements from minor or nonvital concerns. A creative choice for a design solution must flow from a deep understanding of the design elements related to the project. Listing the design elements helps to

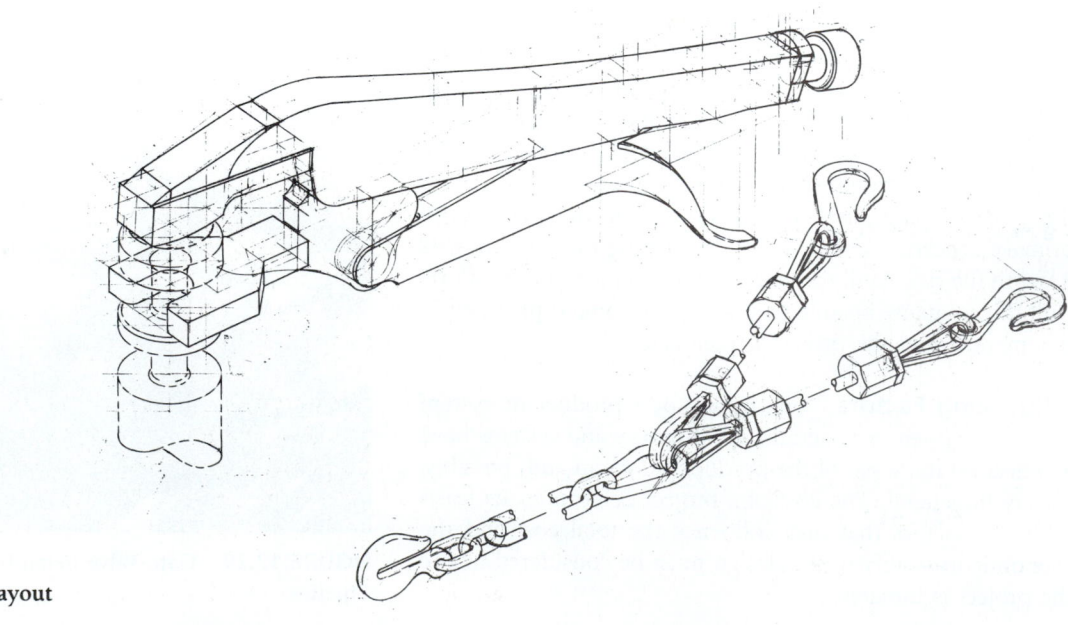

FIGURE 17.31 Pictorial Layout

clear any misconceptions regarding the project. The following is a list of steps that will help identify the design elements:

1. Define the *basic design problems* relevant to the solution.
2. Define the *secondary design problems* that are not the designer's concern but still need to be solved.
3. Identify *perceived problems* that are not really important. This alleviates false concerns.
4. Identify *obstructions* to the design, i.e., significant obstacles to the design solution that must be avoided or circumvented.
5. Find and discuss all *hidden difficulties*. These are obstructions to the solution that are not clearly seen or understood.
6. Scrutinize any *hindrances* to the design that are really not important enough to justify much time.

Sketches and Layouts of Basic Ideas   Although a few rough sketches may have been made during Stage 1, more developed sketches and pictorial layouts (Fig. 17.31) are used to better define any preliminary ideas. All notes and preliminary sketches should be kept on file. Nothing created at this stage should be destroyed. Sketches and layouts help refine the design. They also define physical aspects of the problem and help spin off creative or new solutions. All those concerned with the project should bring the notes and sketches developed to this point to the next meeting where a short brainstorming session may introduce creative solutions to the problem.

Brainstorming   A brainstorming session would be appropriate at this time. **Brainstorming** is a group problem-solving technique that elicits a spontaneous contribution of ideas from all members of the group. No idea is rejected at this point, and all members of the group are considered equal. Ideas are not explored in depth at this time. All suggestions are recorded and used later to evolve certain ideas. The acceptance of the project or design choice is a long way off at this stage of the project. Creative solutions are given as much merit as practical or obvious solutions.

Many aspects of the design background must be understood *before* the brainstorming session so that it does not become a useless exercise. Brainstorming may help find a unique or unthought of set of possibilities. Multiple products or variations of one product or solution should be thoroughly investigated before the next stage.

Review and Modification   After the brainstorming session, all notes, sketches, surveys, marketing analysis, and research data should be reviewed. Any ideas that show no merit are filed at this point. The basic thrust of the design effort starts to take shape. Many possible answers to the problem are still considered, but a basic or general idea of the direction of the project will be sought so as not to linger at this stage.

17.5.3   Evaluation and Refinement of Ideas

The **evaluation** of possible solutions and their **refinement** into an end product (Fig. 17.32) is done in this stage. Refinement of

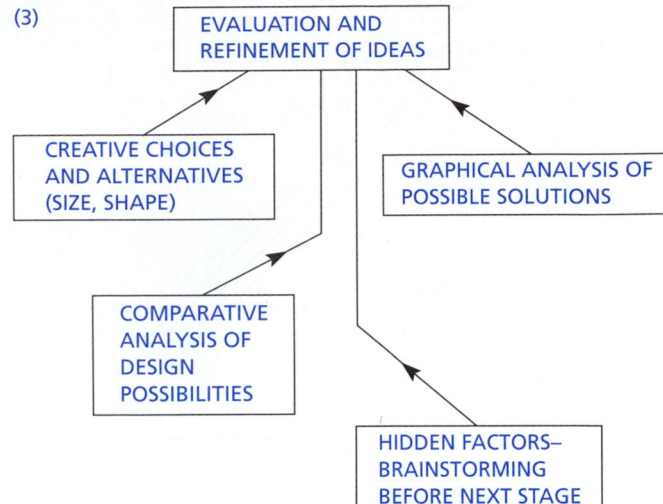

(3)

FIGURE 17.32   **Stage 3 in the Design Process**

a design is more restrictive at this point. More than one solution is still pursued, but the basic parameters of the project have been used to control the breadth of the design effort. An analysis of the project includes graphical analysis using descriptive geometry, statics, and vector analysis. Human factors engineering is also an aspect of this analysis.

Creative Choices and Alternatives Size and Shape
Before a formal proposal is formulated, a number of possibilities for the project should be sketched and evaluated to determine size and shape. The basic parameters determined here help define the engineering and scientific analysis needed and what must be understood before the final decision design choice is made.

The size and shape of the design will narrow the choice of materials that can be used. Specific design requirements, elements, and parameters are now solidified into a complete description of the problem and the thrust of a solution.

Comparative Analysis of Design Possibilities   To be successful, the analysis of a problem must include both its requirements and limitations in order. The restraints and limitations of a design problem help define the boundaries of the solution. Any analysis of the data gathered to this time must include the possibility of a compromise solution to the problem. From this analysis, a decision must be made to proceed with any graphical analysis that may be needed to better define the project.

Graphical Analysis of Possible Solutions   **Engineering analysis** includes the use of graphics to define a number of possible solutions and analyze them using descriptive geometry, vector analysis, layout drawings, and 3D modeling with a CAD system. Figure 17.33 is an example of descriptive geometry being used to find a clearance between a pipeline and a fixed point in space. Piping systems, as in Figure 17.34,

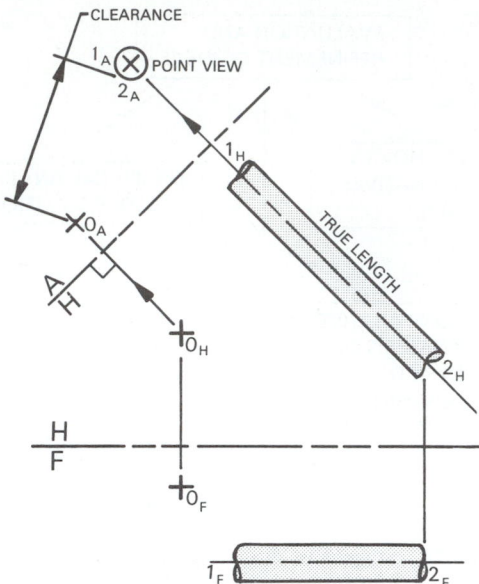

FIGURE 17.33 Descriptive Geometry Problem-Solving for the Shortest Distance Between a Pipe and a Fixed Point

FIGURE 17.34 Insulated Piping System

are one part of a complete building or plant. The interferences between pipelines and other systems, e.g., electrical, heating/cooling, and the structure, require a detailed analysis. Sketches and descriptive geometry drawings are created with instruments or on a computer—to scale. A selection of the "best possible solutions" is rendered for **graphic analysis.**

Human Engineering and Graphical Analysis   Product design includes consideration of **human engineering** requirements. Human engineering involves analyzing how people are affected by performing specific tasks and the man-machine interface. The first concern is normally referred to as **ergonomics** and the second as **human factors.** Both concerns are important to the successful design of a product or a system.

Ergonomics is primarily concerned with the study of physiological responses to physically demanding work; environmental stress caused by temperature, noise, and lighting; motor skills for assembly; and visual-monitoring tasks. Human factors is the modeling of the human body in a work-related setting. Human factors data is useful in the design of a factory workstation in order to provide a comfortable environment and thereby increase work output and decrease job stress. As an example, three views of a man at work are shown in Figure 17.35. The seating and standing heights of a typical male, the comfortable reaching distance from both positions, and the maximum and minimum working area are defined graphically. Industrial design requires the study of body dimensions and movements. Simple products, such as hand tools, to complex system products, such as auto-

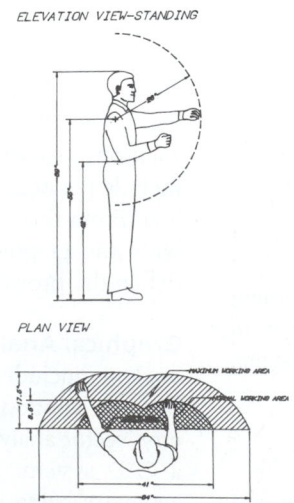

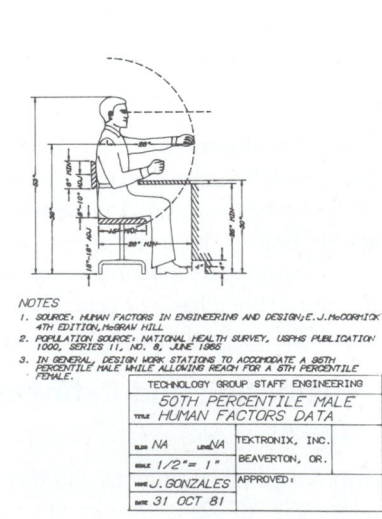

FIGURE 17.35 Male Human Factors Data

mobiles, require extensive use of human factors and ergonomic studies and recommendations.

Human engineering also considers a person's behavior within a work environment. The interaction of workers with their tools, equipment, or workstation is the focus of human engineering design. Strength capabilities relative to the equipment and workplace design are also essential factors in a functional and sound design. Much of the research human engineering design has come from the space program. The space program spawned the first intensive study of human physiology of man in the healthy state. Many of the tasks associated with space travel required intensive study of adverse environments to create appropriate designs for equipment and living or workstations. The restrictive work environment of a spaceship required designs incorporating the findings of human factors and ergonomic research.

The human factors dummy in Figure 17.36 was used to study and design an ejection seat for an airplane. The dummy is attired in a pressurization suit and is fitted into an ejection seat for engineering tests. Notice the foot clamps, arm guards, and stabilizing fins on the seat. The seat was designed by engineers to have a stable supersonic ejection with maximum projection for the pilot.

The design of products and systems used and operated by people incorporates human factors analysis as an important part of the research and analysis stage of the project. Typically, the operation of a system or product must incorporate the following objectives:

1. Minimize the possibility of injury caused by improper use of the product or system. Designs must incorporate safety features that make normal usage error free. Avoiding injury to others adjacent to the user of the product is also important, as is anticipating misuse of the product.

2. The design should be as efficient as possible. Limiting user fatigue and stress due to repetition is essential to proper design.

3. Systems or products should be designed with physical attractiveness, operational ease, and error-free operation in mind. These factors contribute to the overall satisfaction by the user and the desire to purchase the unit and maintain it.

4. The product or system should be designed with a positive, efficient, and functional user interface.

5. Products and systems must be designed to prevent catastrophic failures and must fail in a relatively safe mode at the end of their useful life. The end of a product's useful life must come with subtle and safe warnings.

The designing of controls for crane operation is an example of a system that requires the study and analysis of human engineering. The cranes in Figures 17.37 and 17.38 are operated by means of a center-post joystick. The design of such a control starts with the establishment of the physical

FIGURE 17.36   **Human Factors "Dummy"**

FIGURE 17.37   **Model of Crane**

FIGURE 17.38 Model of Pipe Laying Ship

movements required by the operator and variations in a typical operator's body dimensions. Figure 17.39 shows a set of sketches that were used to establish the maximum movements required for proper operation. Reach, seat clearance, stick height, lateral movement, and arm height are graphically described in this illustration. The given dimensions are rough estimates of the design requirements that were refined in a later step.

Descriptive geometry methods were used to solve graphically for potential interferences and to verify the degrees–of–freedom of movement of the control stick. If the operator's cab included the ability to drive the machine, the human factors and ergonomic studies would include design of a space envelope [Figs. 17.40(a) and (b)]. The cab is designed for optimal, comfortable operation and safety during movement over rough surfaces. The determination of whether the operator is standing or sitting would also have to be made in this stage of the design.

Product Design and Human Factors The mechanical factors, anthropometric (human dimensions) and anatomical considerations (body and limb rotational and movement characteristics), ergonomic factors, and the work environment must also be considered in the design of consumer products. Hand tools require the study and utilization of these principles. The tool must be designed to be strong, functional, easy to carry, safe to operate, easy to store, compact, insulated from electrical shock, and slip resistant.

The design of the long-nose pliers in Figure 17.41 required the designer to align the center of gravity with the grasping hand so that the user does not have to overcome rotational movement or torque of the tool. The tool handle is oriented so that the user's wrist remains in the most comfortable and natural position while applying force. The sketches in Figure 17.42 show variations in designs for handle orientation. The handle must be long enough to accommodate the average

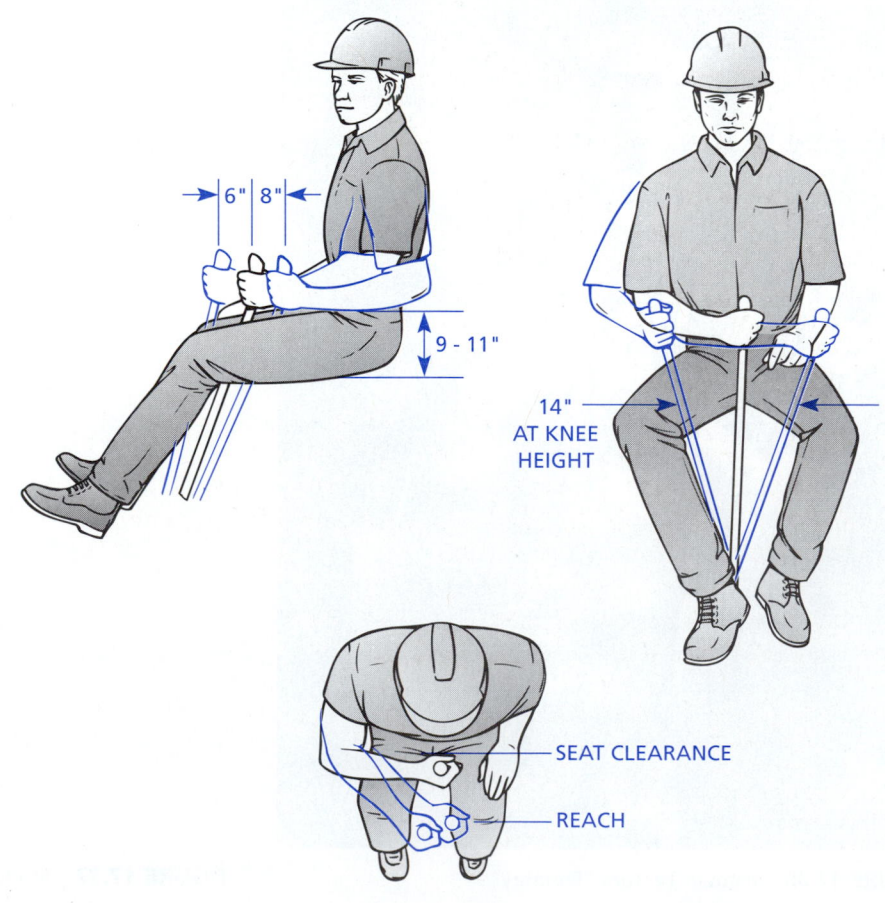

FIGURE 17.39 Control Stick Movement Studies

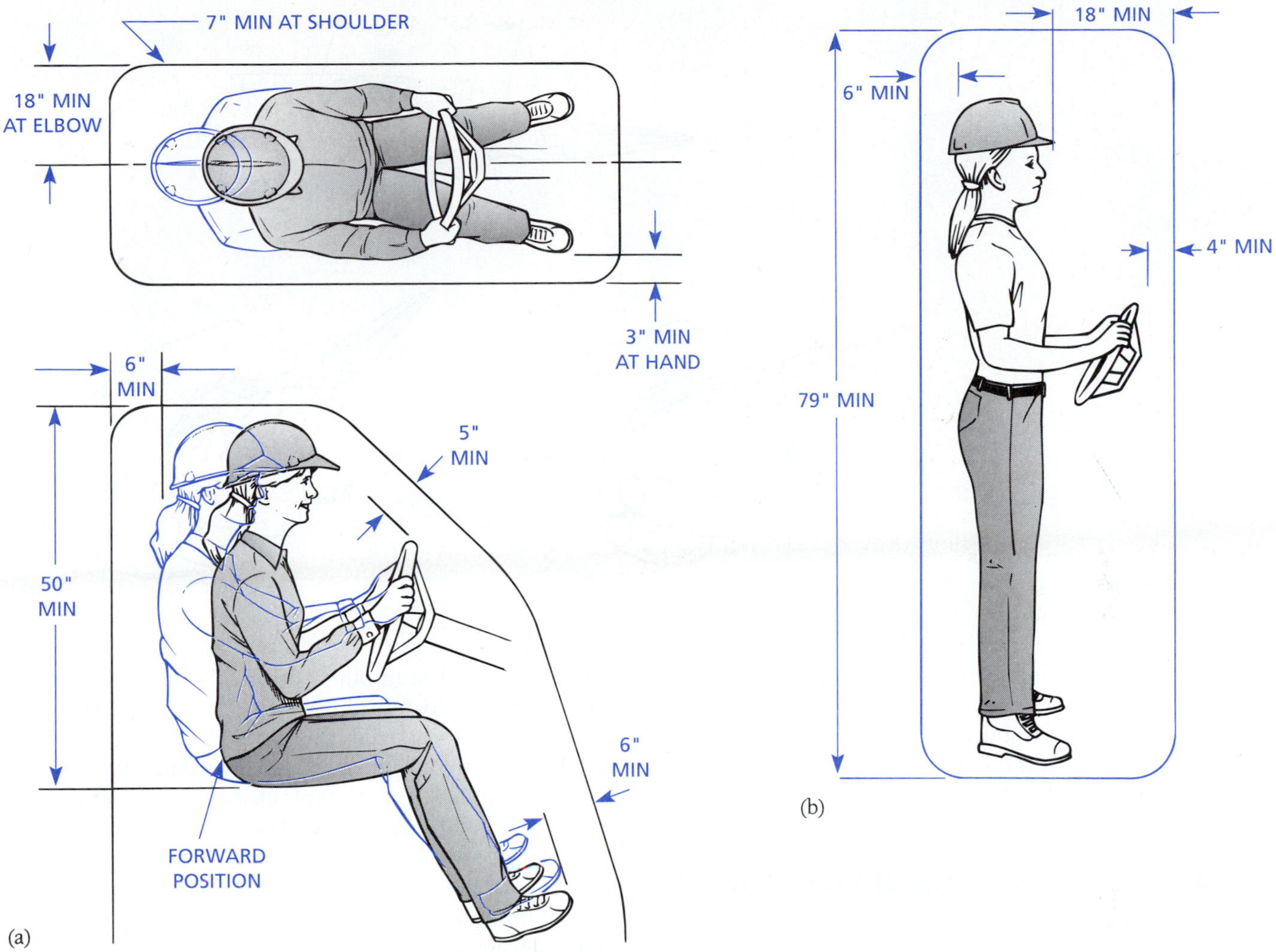

7" MIN AT SHOULDER

18" MIN AT ELBOW

3" MIN AT HAND

6" MIN

5" MIN

50" MIN

6" MIN

FORWARD POSITION

(a)

18" MIN

6" MIN

4" MIN

79" MIN

(b)

FIGURE 17.40 **Human Factors Study of Cab Design** (a) Sitting (b) Standing

male hand so that the user's grip includes all fingers and provides proper leverage during operation. On the other hand, the maximum handle spread must not be so great that a small hand could not fully open the tool's jaws during operation.

Hidden Factors What possible factors may have been overlooked in the design? Are there any aspects of the design that are suspect? If these and other pertinent questions are not satisfactorily answered, the design team should go back to the beginning of the design process and review each step. The design proposal cannot be accepted without the consensus of the total team and all departments in the company. Solutions to any problems must be solved here, not later when they could prove costly.

A variety of pertinent questions should be honestly and openly discussed at this point in the project:

- What could go wrong?
- Will the product work?
- Will it sell?
- Will the company lose money?

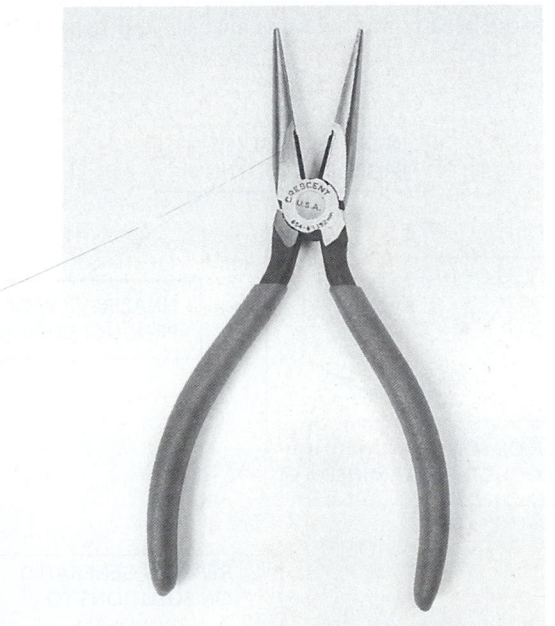

FIGURE 17.41 **Needle-Nose Pliers**

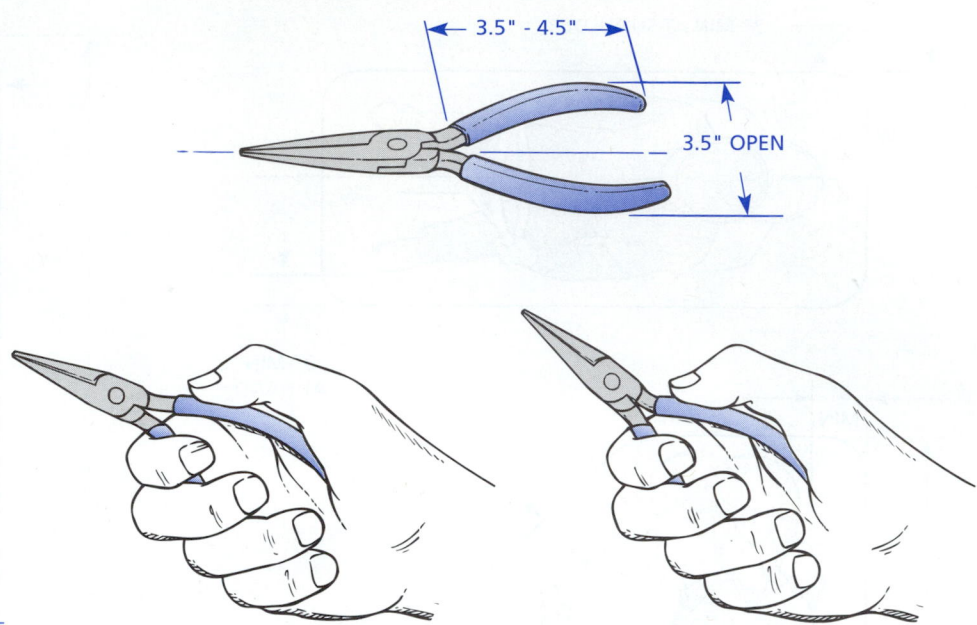

FIGURE 17.42 Design Studies of Pliers Handles

Often, at this juncture the business managers will determine that although the product will sell, the company, with its current assets, cannot produce the item. A startup company may then be formed with the design team becoming the core of a new company. The impact of potential failure is minimized while success produces a diversification of assets.

17.5.4 In-Depth Analysis of Proposed Solutions

The **analysis and evaluation** (Fig. 17.43) of possible design solutions is normally done through a thorough investigation of the data that pertain to it. The use of graphs, charts, and diagrams can greatly improve this analysis and help in com-

municating the data to others involved in the project. Data can be categorized into three divisions: **survey data**, data gathered by the marketing department evaluating a design's possible acceptance by the public; **design data**, data gathered by analyzing the performance characteristics of the test model; and **comparison data**, data used to balance two or more design solutions against each other based on material, manufacturability, or exclusive design features.

Data presented graphically can also help a designer determine the adequacy of a design based on environmental conditions or the reaction of the materials to stresses created during operation. As an example, a typical piping system is

(4)

```
        ┌─────────────────────────┐
        │  IN-DEPTH ANALYSIS OF   │
        │   PROPOSED SOLUTION     │
        └─────────────────────────┘

  ┌──────────────────┐        ┌──────────────────┐
  │ ANALYSIS OF DATA │        │ FINAL REVIEW OF  │
  └──────────────────┘        │ PRODUCT CHOICES  │
                              └──────────────────┘

┌──────────────────────────┐
│ NUMBER OF SOLUTIONS      │
│ AND PRODUCTS DETERMINED  │
└──────────────────────────┘

        ┌─────────────────────────┐
        │ REPORTS GENERATED       │
        │ ON SOLUTIONS TO         │
        │ ALL PROPOSALS           │
        └─────────────────────────┘
```

FIGURE 17.43 Stage 4 in the Design Process

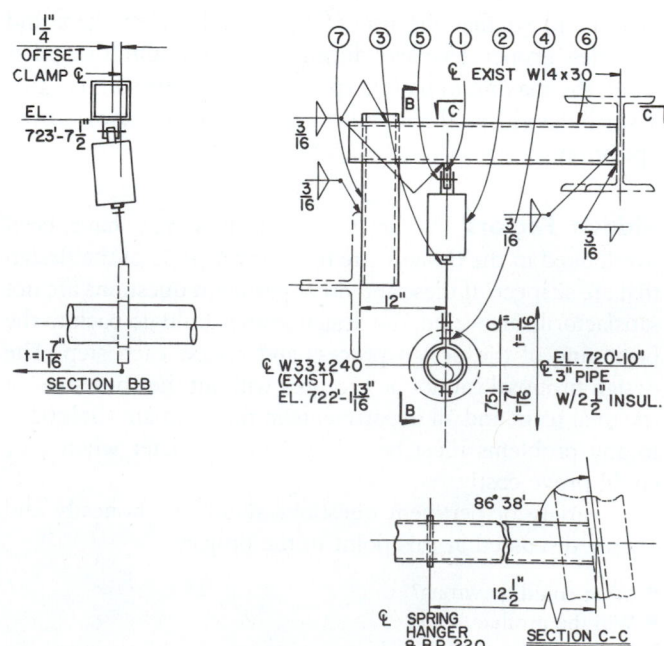

FIGURE 17.44 Spring Hanger Used in Pipe Support Design

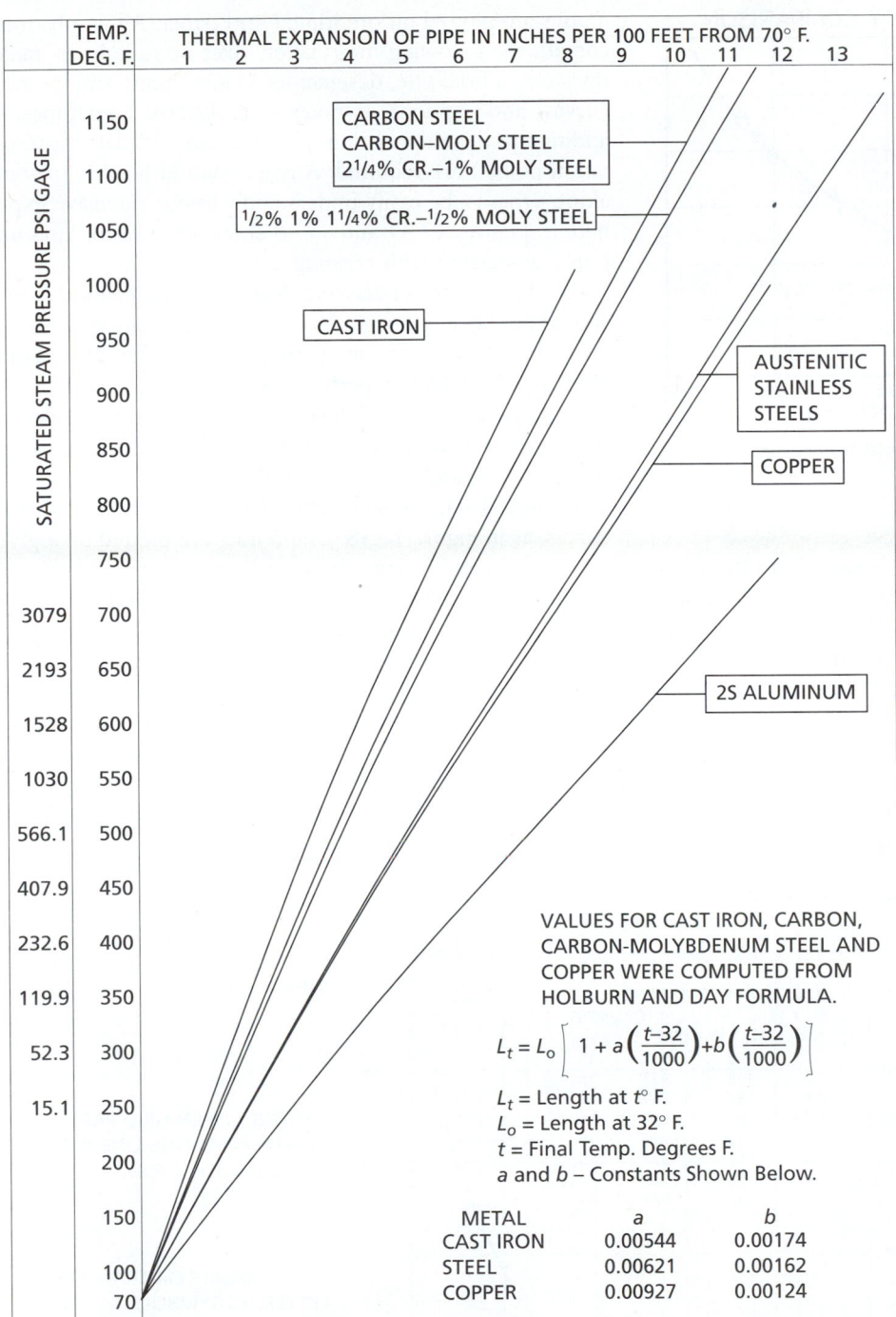

FIGURE 17.45 Thermal Expansion of Pipe

designed to operate under specific temperatures. A steam line or a chemical process line may have a high operating temperature. The designer must create a piping system that not only transfers the line contents from one place to another, but also is flexible enough to handle expansion and contraction of the system during operation. Pipe supports must handle the full weight of the system and at the same time allow for restricted movement of the line caused by thermal expansion or earthquakes.

The pipe support shown in Figure 17.44 incorporates a spring hanger in its design. Spring hangers can adjust the load of the pipe and allow for limited safe movement. The graph in Figure 17.45 was used in the design of the pipe support. The thermal expansion of a pipe for a steam line at various temperatures is graphed. Six separate materials have been plotted. The expansion characteristics of the pipeline being designed are determined so as to meet the operating conditions.

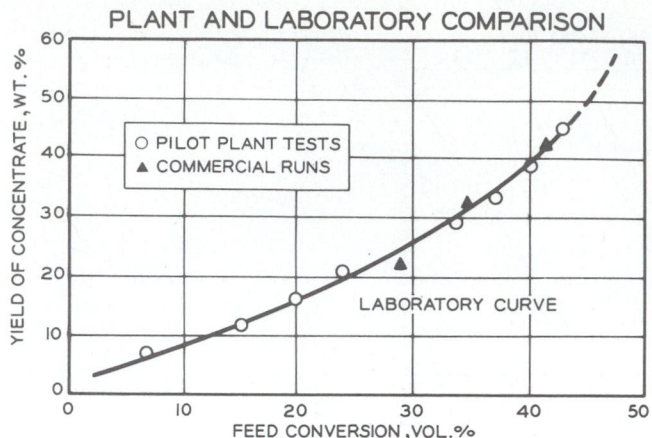

FIGURE 17.46   Graph Layout for Publications

graphs are plotted on preprinted grid paper. All graphs must contain the following information: axes or scale lines, major divisions, a brief title, designators on axes, units, one or more curves, and captions or notes (Fig. 17.46). Sometimes, in addition to this information, plotting symbols (data representation points) are required. A graph should be able to stand alone—that is, be easily understood without extensive explanation. Figures 17.47 and 17.48 show some of the do's and don'ts associated with creating a graph.

The importance of drawing clear, easily understood graphs should not be overlooked. Much of the information needed to do a design is shown in graphical form. This information includes characteristic performance curves of devices, stress input response curves of devices and entire systems, relationships of one quantity to another, waveforms, thermal expansion of items, and project schedules.

Graphical data is sometimes represented by noncircular curves, as in Figure 17.48. Graph lines are plotted on a given grid pattern on rectangular coordinate paper, representing two variables. When a CAD system is used for the graph, spline or smooth curves are used to connect the data points. The horizontal coordinate on a graph is usually plotted as the independent variable and the dependent variable is plotted vertically. The horizontal, or **X**, axis is called the **abscissa** and the vertical, or **Y** axis, the **ordinate**. The origin of the data may be located at a number of different places on the graph, such as the lower left corner of the graph with 0,0 as in Figure 17.48, or the center, as in Figure 17.49.

Analysis of Data   **Marketing data** is useful in identifying features and capabilities desired by the public. Marketing data will, at times, drive the project design. The performance characteristics of a possible design solution are determined by analyzing the data generated from hardware testing. The use of graphs and charts is an integral part of this process.

Graphs and Charts   Throughout this text, information about the fundamentals of drafting and design is sometimes displayed on **graphs, charts, and diagrams**. Most technical

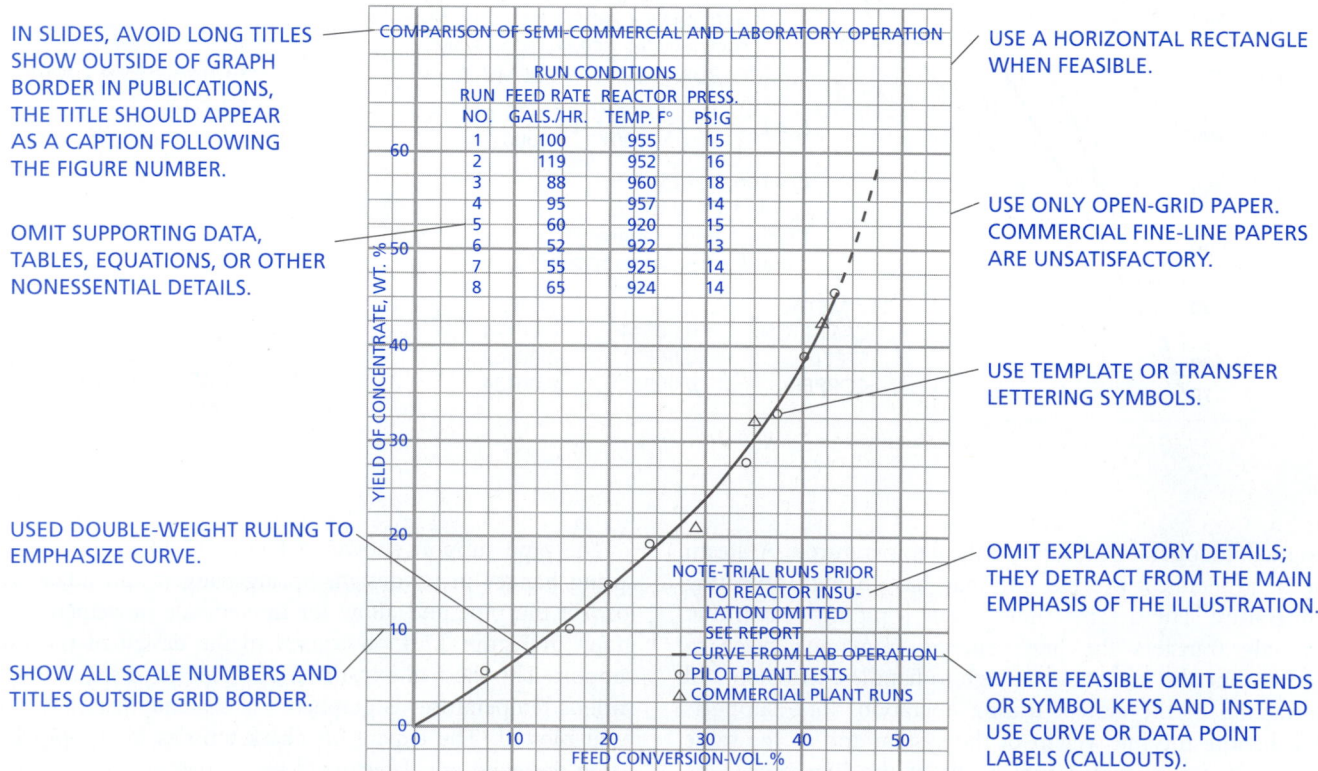

FIGURE 17.47   Example of Poor Illustration of Graph

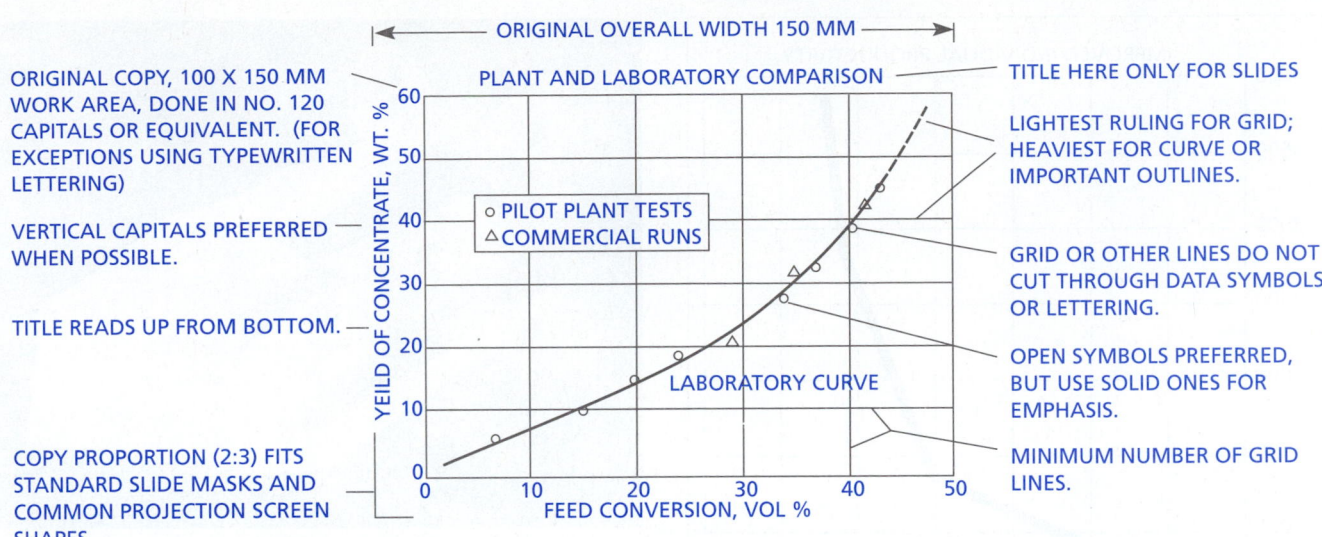

FIGURE 17.48 Example of Good Illustration of Graph

Figure 17.50 shows lines and symbols on a graph. Clear, accurate graphs and charts are essential for communicating data in this stage of the design process. At present, almost all graphs and charts are now generated with the help of a computer (Fig. 17.51).

Number of Solutions and Products Determined The process of creating a new design always gives rise to more than one solution. Often the different solutions involve trade-offs between cost, reliability, and time. Design for manufacturability concepts and procedures help ensure a design that is functional, cost-effective, and timely. If the design process has given birth to more than one solution or product, whether or not the project should be separated into different proposals should be determined. Each possible solution may

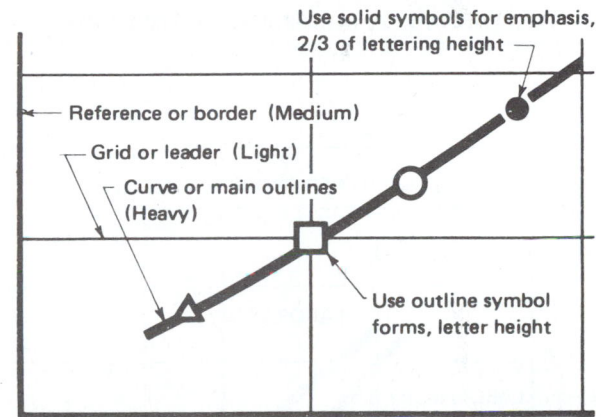

FIGURE 17.50 Lines and Symbols on Graphs

produce a valid marketable item. A record of each design possibility should be kept, including all sketches, written descriptions, and other data. It is appropriate to investigate more than one solution at a time. If a team is working on a project, it may need to be divided into subunits, with each subunit investigating different solutions. A variety of different designs should be created and developed to a point where they are sufficiently defined. They should then be evaluated and compared during the next stage of the project. Duplication of competing teams should be minimized by the sharing of data and resources.

In Figure 17.52 the model of the hovercraft is one of many design solutions being investigated by a ship building company. The surface-effect ship, in Figure 17.53, is a more detailed design alternative. The Coast Guard hovercraft shown in Figure 17.54 is a full-scale test prototype. The design of simple products or complex systems (like the hovercraft) requires a complete analysis of design alternatives and a comparison of performance capabilities before production.

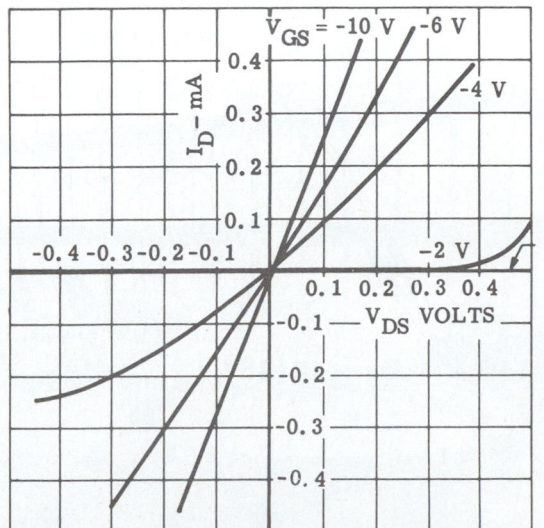

FIGURE 17.49 Voltage Versus Current Characteristics for an FET

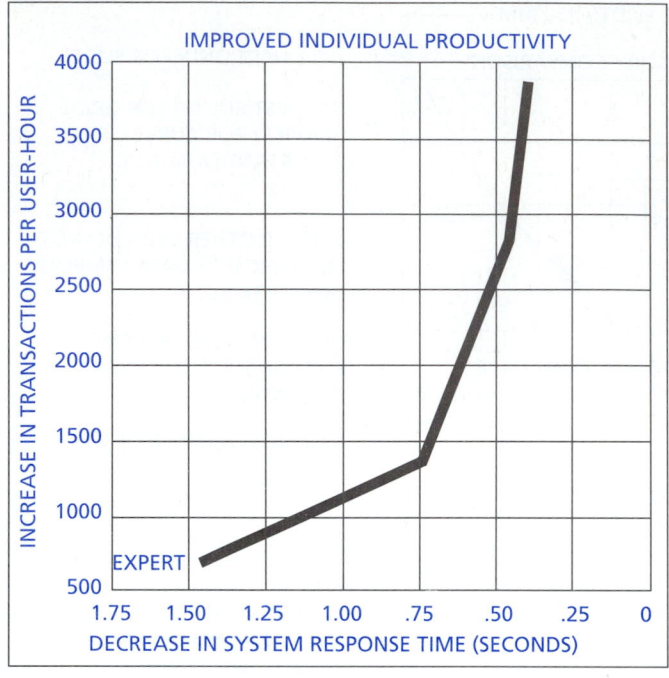

(a)

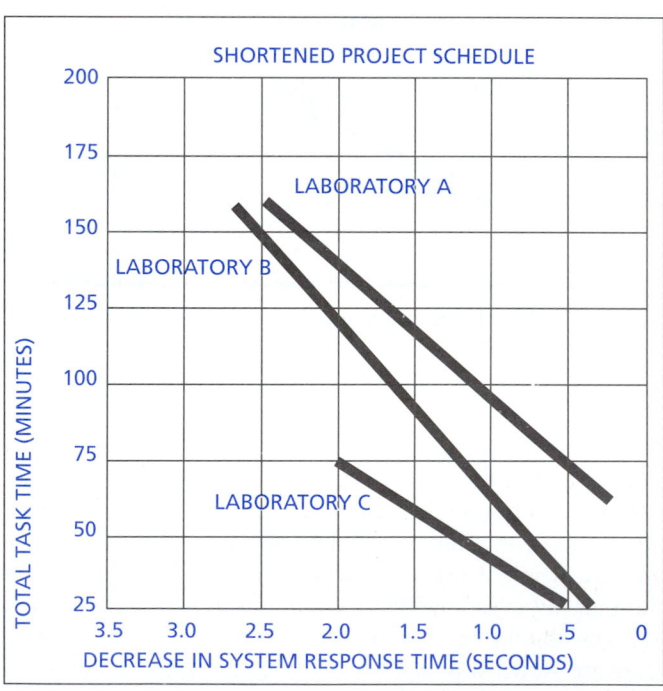

(b)

FIGURE 17.51 Computer-Generated Graphs

FIGURE 17.52 Model of Hovercraft Produced by Carving Artfoam

FIGURE 17.53 Surface-Effect Ship Model

FIGURE 17.54 Coast Guard Hovercraft Test Model

Reports Generated on Solutions to All Proposals

Technical reports containing design data on each possible solution must be generated at this point in the process. All pertinent factors, both positive and negative, must be clearly defined before the project is further developed. The design team does not want to enter the decision stage of the project ill prepared or with incomplete findings. Management will not pursue a project that is poorly defined. Properly presented projects need complete graphic descriptions and well-written reports.

Final Review of Product Choices

The design department must evaluate each of the possible solutions before submitting their findings and suggestions to the management during Stage 5. Two or more design solutions should be prepared by the design team. During a team meeting, each of the designs should be compared. The merits of each design solution should be clearly presented, as well as any drawbacks to the design. Each of the features incorporated into the design should be compared to those of other possible solutions. A list should be prepared ranking the relative importance of each feature.

Materials, manufacturing, and facility requirements should be discussed at this meeting to balance each solution's effectiveness against others based on cost and company capabilities. At this point, select the best designs and prepare for the next stage of the project.

17.5.5   Design Choice and Product or System Decisions

After all the data have been gathered on the design problem and the remaining possible solutions have been clearly defined, the last step in the decision process is addressed (Fig. 17.55). Management has the final say on which project design solution to pursue. The designers, engineers, and other company personnel involved in the project present their findings and design choices to management for a decision. The choice depends on many variables. A project may even be abandoned at this point, or more than one product or solution may be accepted.

The development and design of supersonic aircraft required extensive research leading to the development of new and unconventionally shaped wings. These wings were designed to offset the effects of the abrupt and erratic changes in air flows encountered at the speed of sound. One of the solutions was the swept-back wing shown in Figure 17.56 being prepared for experiments. Resembling the tip of an arrow, this wing is more efficient because there is a sharp reduction in the drag created by the formation of shock waves at and near the speed of sound. Earlier designs for wings were also modeled and tested in a wind tunnel to determine their in-flight characteristics. Each of these designs was eventually

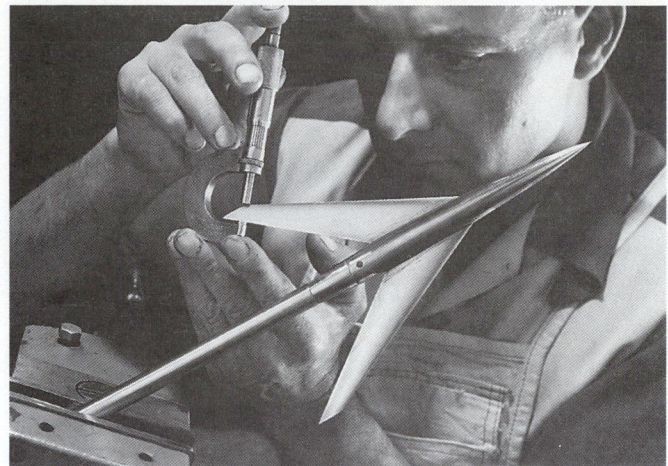

FIGURE 17.56   Model Being Prepared for Research and Development of Air Flows and Wing Design

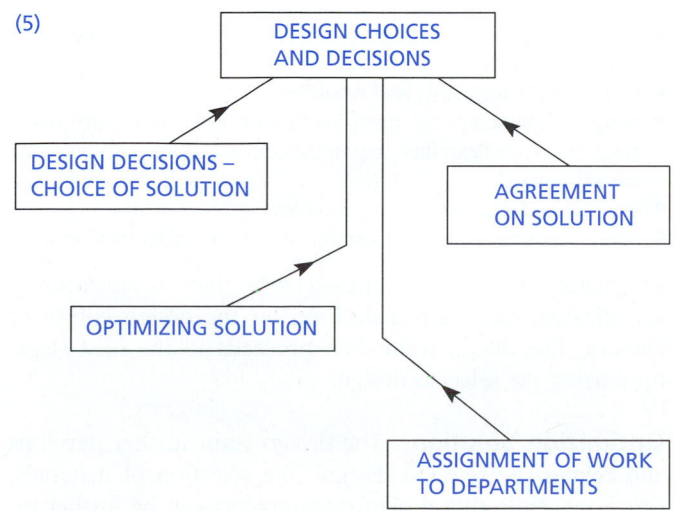

FIGURE 17.55   Stage 5 in the Design Process

FIGURE 17.57   Aircraft Model Being Prepared for Wind Tunnel Studies

FIGURE 17.58 World's Largest Experimental Test Aircraft

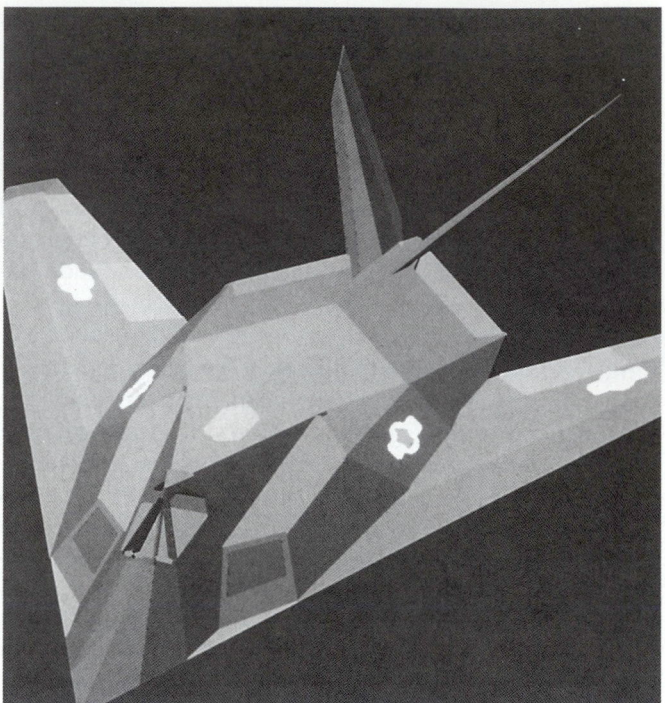

FIGURE 17.59 Stealth Bomber

incorporated into modern military and commercial aircraft. The sharp wing style was also tested in a full-size mockup, shown in a wind tunnel experiment in Figure 17.57. The eventual prototype aircraft, shown in Figure 17.58, was the world's largest experimental aircraft. The B70 project was never produced because of cost factors, materials research, government decisions, and improvements in the accuracy of ICBMs, which made the aircraft obsolete. The development work was later used in the design of the Concord SST. The Stealth bomber (Fig. 17.59) involved using technology and research developed for previous aircraft, but also incorporated high-tech materials and design concepts to enable it to fly undetected by conventional radar.

At present, a revival of interest in supersonic transport is occurring. The years of research and development that seemed for naught may eventually bring an efficient, well-designed product to the market—a supersonic aircraft used for commercial passengers.

Over the last 20 years, new materials such as composites have been developed. A new generation of materials will fly with the X-30, an experimental plane that will pioneer hypersonic travel in the late 1990s. To withstand the environmental impact of travel at 17,000 mph (Mach 2.5) and an orbit near that of the present-day space shuttle, carbon-composite materials coated with ceramics will be used for the airplane.

Sometimes the concept of a design exceeds the known capabilities of science and technology. In this case, the development of a design may have to wait for the technology to catch up with the concept. History has many examples of designs that were developed before they could be effectively, safely, and profitably brought to market. The Soviet Union's 2000-mph transport and the French-English Concorde jet may have been premature efforts, considering design flaws and cost of operation.

Design Decisions A complete technical report on each solution must be submitted at this juncture by the design group. The report consists of a design proposal and a timetable for completion of the project. All pertinent data regarding the design solutions must accompany the proposal, including cost analysis, time studies, capital requirements (personnel, equipment, and facility), design layouts, and other materials that may help in the decision process.

The management decision team, which includes members from the design, manufacturing, and marketing departments, evaluates the merits of each solution submitted by the design department. The evaluations of competing designs consider the following:

Design Comparison

- capability to satisfy the original statement of the design intent and project definition
- cost, manufacturability, and reliability
- design requirements for precision (which will affect cost), operating efficiency/flexibility, maintenance projections, and environmental impact
- material and manufacturing processes
- effect of configuration and complexity on manufacturing costs

The management team, after each of the above is satisfactorily investigated, can reach a decision on the design choice or choices. The design team then proceeds to the next stage, optimizing the selected design.

Optimizing Solution The design team further develops and refines the selected design. The selection of materials, processes, and other design requirements can be further refined at this stage. Each feature and capability of the design

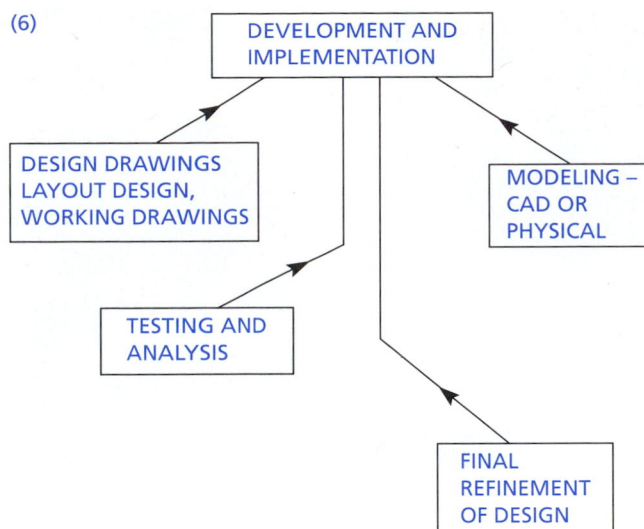

(6)

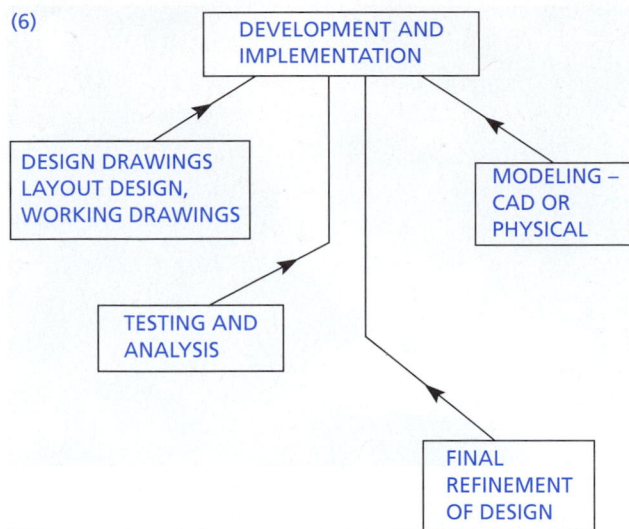

FIGURE 17.60 Stage 6 in the Design Process

should be analyzed and evaluated. Any changes should be made at this point so that, during Stage 6 (development and implementation), there are no drastic changes in the design that hinder its completion. Any new desirable features or capabilities should be evaluated. A list of concerns and considerations should include the following:

Design Refinements

- Should any new or desired features be added at this time?
- Should the effective life of the design be extended or decreased?
- Are there any aspects of the design's appearance that need to be changed or better defined?
- Based on the design's potential configuration and operating conditions, what materials should be considered acceptable?
- Is the design manufacturable?
- Can the design be more flexible and interchangeable without cost increases?
- What are the basic cost parameters for the design?
- What are the tolerance requirements?
- Have the stress factors and alignment problems that may be encountered been determined?
- Has the need for study models, prototypes, and test models for motion, stress, or other design studies been established?

Agreement on Solution After the choice of solutions is determined, it is important that all of the concerns of each department be addressed. A concencus must be reached on the acceptability of the solution. There should be complete agreement as to the direction and choice of management's decision. Reservations by one or more of the departments in the company about the product's feasibility are addressed and eliminated at this time, so as not to undermine the design's success. All basic features and design requirements are now solidified into an accepted solution.

Assignment of Work The project work schedule is determined after the final design is chosen and the **project**

launch is given the go-ahead by management. Several methods of project scheduling are used in industry. One method is the **Project Evaluation and Review Technique (PERT).** This method is used to coordinate the many activities associated with a successful design project. All departments must be coordinated efficiently to move the project from design through production in a smooth and error-free environment.

The success of the project depends on this coordination. At the project launch, each department is given specific work assignments and time requirements. The **critical-path method** of scheduling project work assignments is used in conjunction with PERT to control the project. The critical-path method was used in the design and manufacturing of the trackball input device, shown at the end of this chapter.

17.5.6 Development and Implementation of Design

The **development and implementation** stage of the design process includes the drawing, modeling, testing, analysis, and refinement of the design (Fig. 17.60). The actual documentation of the project can be done manually or on a CAD system.

Physical models are used for design and testing (Fig. 17.61). Actual full-scale prototypes, developed from design drawings, are used to test for strength and design flaws. The rotor mount, in Figure 17.62, failed during the test of a prototype design. Other models are used for testing aspects of the design, such as the all-brass antenna model on the destroyer used for reflectivity studies (Fig. 17.63).

The design and development of a project takes many forms while weaving through a series of trials and errors, testing, and refinement. The space shuttle started as a design concept and proposal [Fig. 17.64(a)]. This pictorial rendering is quite

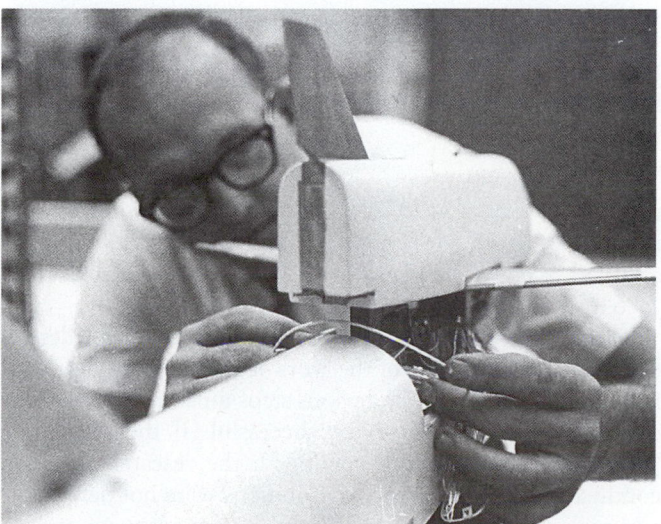

FIGURE 17.61 Shaker Test Being Prepared for the Space Shuttle Using $\frac{1}{100}$ Scale Model

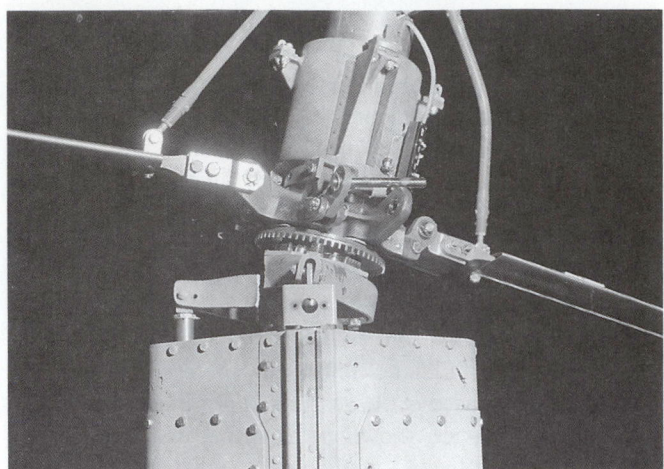

FIGURE 17.62 Rotor Test Failure

(a)

FIGURE 17.63 All-Brass Antenna Model of Destroyer Used for Reflectivity Studies

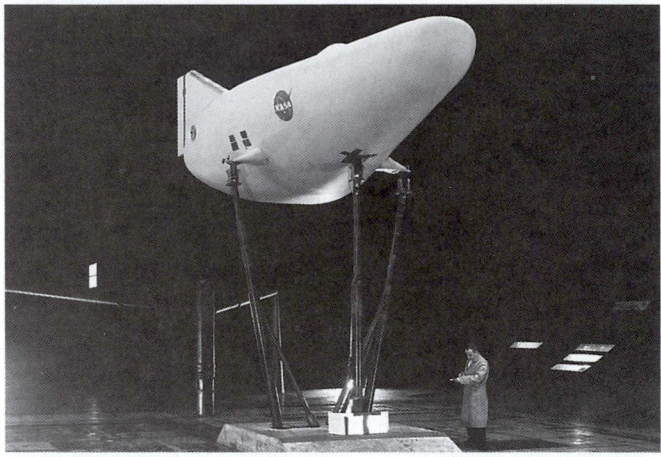

(b)

FIGURE 17.64 **Development of Space Shuttle Design**
(a) Space shuttle concept (b) Wind tunnel study of original space shuttle concept (c) Space shuttle concept with astronaut window (d) Flow studies in wind tunnel using oil (e) Full-scale test prototype of reentry spacecraft shown here before being dropped from a B-52 in 1966! (f) Space shuttle model being tested in wind tunnel in 1975 (g) Illustration of final space shuttle design in 1979

unlike the final vehicle. The original designs were drawn, modeled [Fig. 17.64(b) and (c)], and tested [Fig. 17.64(d) and (e)] many times before the design was refined [Fig. 17.64(f)] and brought to completion [Fig. 17.64(g)].

Stage 6 in the design process is the heart of all design efforts. It is when most of the work is done, and the project is brought to fruition. All previous steps must have been done effectively for this step to be successful. If the system or product was not properly identified, the research was not conducted correctly, alternative solutions were not developed and analyzed, the analysis of all data was not adequate, and all departments involved in the project were not incorporated in the first five stages, the development and implementation of the design may not come to a successful conclusion. The sixth

stage starts with the creation of design drawings, either manually or with a CAD system.

Design, Layout, and Working Drawings   At this step in the design process, it is important for all preliminary work to be complete and for the design to have been accepted. No major changes in the design should be implemented at this point. The acceptance of the project by all parties is essential.

A majority of this text has been devoted to this stage of the design process. Manual or CAD-generated technical drawings are the primary means of communicating design and manufacturing information at this time. Drawings are also required before the construction of physical models: test, prototype, mock-ups, presentation, process, system, or product.

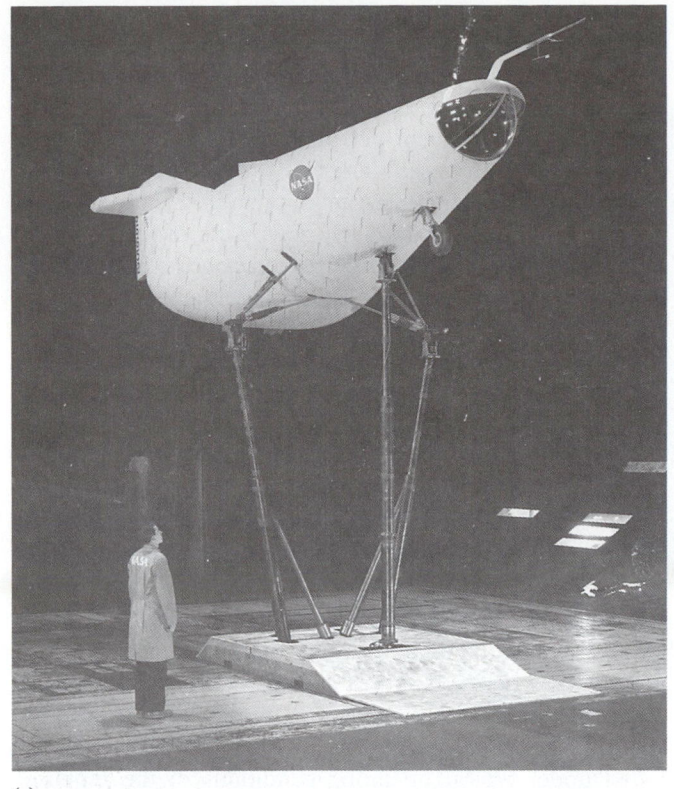

(c)

(f)

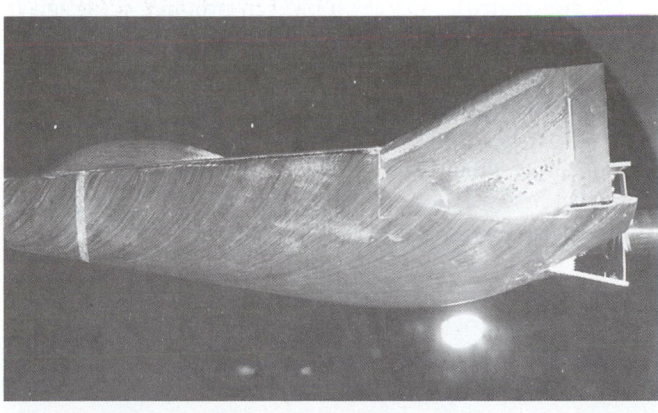

(d)

(g)

(e)

Similar designs and previous work are useful guides for product improvement design work. The designer must be familiar with existing documents. There are many situations where the redesign of an existing item or refitting of an existing system necessitates the use of older drawings that have been completed using previous standards. Most design work rarely involves original design work from concept to production but is instead a continual evolution of an existing product. Each member of a design team works only on a small portion of the total effort.

FIGURE 17.65 Tractor-Trailer Models

Physical Models Models are used throughout the industry as scaled representations of systems design and for refinement and testing of product designs. A **systems model** shows an installation: components, structure, and instrumentation, as in the model of the petrochemical plant shown in Figure 17.16. A model provides a better understanding of any installation and can be used as a tool for design and checking. **Product models** are used in many stages of the design process to establish scale, appearance, and function of a product. Scale models of tractor-trailer designs are shown in Figure 17.65.

The designer can request a model at almost any stage of the design process. The type of models requested depends on the product or system and the availability of modeling facilities. Outside vendors are, at times, called on to complete a model. Regardless of who does the modeling or where it is done, the designer will be an important part of its creation.

Engineering systems models are a design tool that can eliminate unnecessary problems, bad design, inefficient planning, and other expensive, time-loss situations. They are used throughout the petrochemical, nuclear, and conventional power-generation industries. They are also used in food and beverage processing, pulp and paper manufacture, pharmaceutical processing, and other fields of systems design. Product design uses models throughout the design process including research and development.

When working with a three-dimensional model (Fig. 17.66), the designer can visualize the design sequences and operations that are necessary for the project. This may not be possible when using a large assortment of drawings.

Models are most advantageous if they are used as a working tool, from the beginning stages of a project through the entire design phase. The beginning or preliminary models may look nothing like the final design model. Many stages may be needed in between to provide the designer with the necessary three-dimensional information to solve any problems that may be encountered.

Mock-up models are full-size models. They are used primarily to determine the appearance of the product. The size, configuration, color, and artistic considerations can be determined with the use of a mock-up. This type of model is not often used for movement or operation design. A mock-up is a replica of the proposed design.

Product models are used more often in mechanical engineering fields to help design various parts of machinery or other mechanical devices, such as components that must be manufactured. In some cases, these models are built to a scale larger than that of the project itself.

Prototype models are basically similar to product models, but are sometimes working simulations of the product [Fig. 17.64(e)]. In the case of an airplane, the company may build an actual full-scale prototype to gain knowledge of its aerodynamic characteristics, and also as a "feeler" in estimating public acceptance and sales. Some prototype models are mock-ups of the eventual product. 3D prototypes are sometimes required in the design of mechanisms to test their performance and capabilities. A prototype will often be close to the same configuration as the finished product. Therefore, the prototype model is used in the design stage of the project, after much of the design data have already been determined and the choice of designs has been made. Prototypes are tested under typical operating conditions of the proposed product.

Presentation models, such as the one shown in Figure 17.67, are created to display a project, product, or design to the general public, or for sales.

CAD Modeling Modeling with a 3D CAD system allows the designer to create multiple options for a design. A CAD model can be altered much easier than a layout on paper or a physical model. The CAD model can be used in every phase of the design decision process.

FIGURE 17.66 Designer Modeling Turbine Crane for a Power Plant

FIGURE 17.67   Display Model of Offshore Buoy

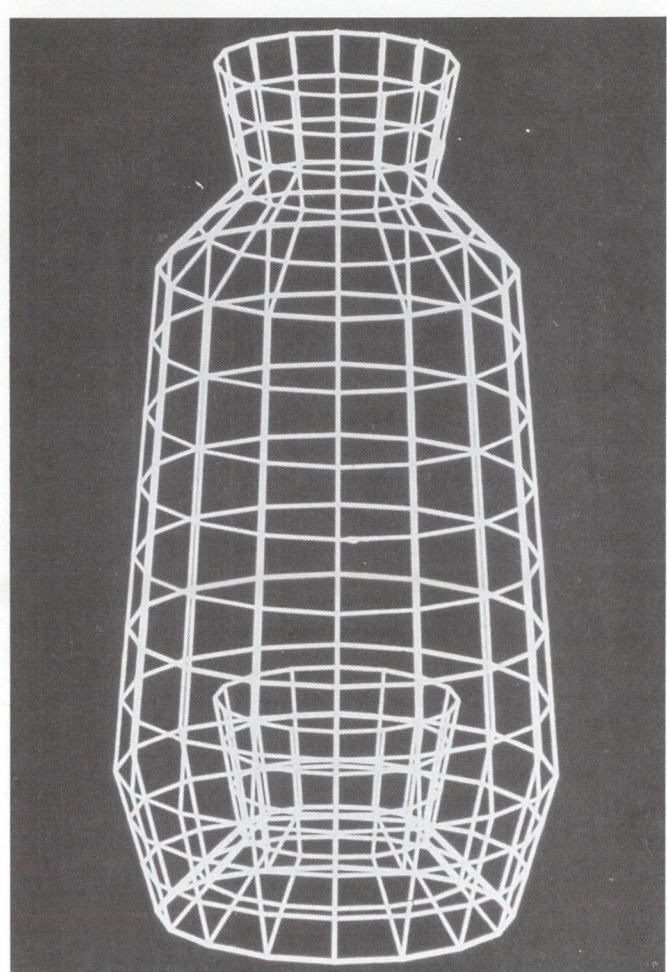

FIGURE 17.68   Finite Element Model of a Bottle

Three-dimensional modeling capabilities are grouped into three basic categories: 3D wireframe models (Color Plate 81); 3D surface models (Color Plates 31 and 96); and solid models (Color Plates 18, 19, and 61 through 65).

1. Wireframe Models   As the name signifies, a wireframe model is one in which the part geometry is represented by interconnected edges (Fig. 17.68). These edges may be lines, arcs, or splines (see Color Plate 20). Most CAD systems with 2D drafting capabilities may be used to create 2D wireframe models that can be used for 2D numerical control or to generate drawings. Three-dimensional systems, however, provide better modeling capability than the 2D systems.

Three-dimensional wireframe models (Fig. 17.69) use the same basic elements as the 2D model but add the **Z** coordinates. The visualization and ease of use is much better with the 3D wireframe model than with the 2D wireframe model.

2. Surface Models   Three-dimensional surface models are constructed by stretching a transparent membrane over the wireframe model (Color Plate 96). These membranes then become the faces of the model. These faces may be simple surfaces such as planes, cylinders, and spheres or they may be more complex surfaces such as ruled surfaces, extrusions, rotations of spline curves, and sculpted surfaces.

Three-dimensional surface models (Fig. 17.70) are used to represent shapes that are difficult to construct with wireframes. Examples of these shapes are: styled surfaces, such as the outer skins of automobiles and airplanes (Color Plate 31), and function surfaces, such as turbine blades and gears (Color Plate 28).

3. Hybrid Models   Most of the 3D modeling systems on the market are a combination of wireframe and surface modeling (Color Plates 1 through 14). The addition of the surfaces eliminates some of the deficiencies of the wireframe model. Specifically, the model can be unambiguous and complete (Fig. 17.71).

FIGURE 17.69   3D Wireframe Model

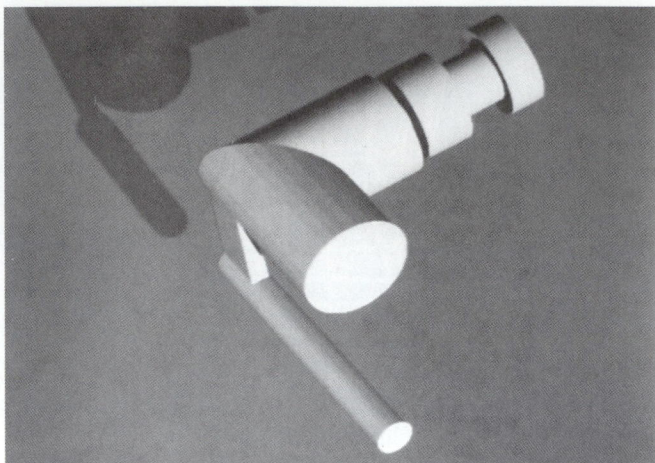

FIGURE 17.70   3D Shaded Model

4. Solid Models   The major requirement of a solid modeler is to be able to construct an unambiguous representation of parts or assemblies (Fig. 17.72) (Color Plates 63, 65, 66, 67, 85 through 87). Constructive solid geometry (CSG) and boundary representation (b-rep) are the two popular methods used to create a solid model.

A solid design model (Color Plate 62) forms the master representation of a part in contrast to using the engineering drawing as the master design representation. The main output of a design/drafting office is a solid model (Color Plate 35) of the part together with all the associated information that is contained on the engineering drawing. Engineering drawings are a secondary function when this system is used (Color Plate 38). In particular, the drawings, if required, are generated from the model. The combination of a solid model and the necessary tolerance and associated technical data is called the **product model.** Functions downstream of the design

FIGURE 17.72   Solid Model

office take the product model (Color Plates 1 through 14) as their primary input.

Physical Models from a CAD Database   Conceptual models are an important part of the product design process. Industrial designers and packaging engineers use CAD/CAM/CAE to get a computer representation of their idea. Sometimes, however, seeing the part on a 2D high-resolution graphic screen, or even the stereoscopic monitors that project a 3D view, is not enough. The "soft" touch of the physical design can bring to life a design, sometimes revealing unanticipated problems. By quickly forming 3D conceptual models from design ideas, engineers can evaluate a design, demonstrate its feasibility, and sell the concept.

Building conceptual models, prototypes, and patterns for castings are necessary—but expensive and time-consuming—steps in product design, often accounting for over half of the design effort. **Rapid Prototyping (RP)** is changing the way products are currently designed and brought to market. The ability to create plastic model parts (Fig. 17.73) in a matter of hours without tooling, using the same CAD database, created while designing the part using a CAD system, is revolutionizing design. CAD/CAM/CAE software, chemistry, laser, and optical scanning technologies have been combined to form this unique process. Rapid Prototyping is a process that creates 3D plastic parts from CAD/CAM/CAE data in a matter of hours, is producing parts for the automotive, aerospace, computer, medical, consumer, and electronic components industries. Applications of this technology include conceptual designs, prototypes, testing models, and casting master patterns (Fig. 17.73).

Conventional model making proves to be time-consuming as well as expensive. Typically, a design engineer creates a 3D

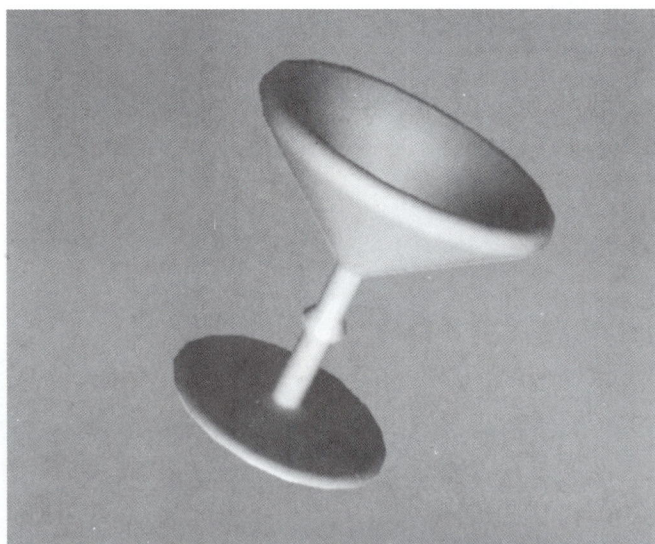

FIGURE 17.71   Wine Glass 3D Model with Shading and Highlights

FIGURE 17.73   Parts Produced with Stereolithography

model on a mechanical CAD system or on a drafting table. Then, paper drawings are plotted and passed to a model maker, who interprets them to create a prototype. Traditional methods include creating models from wood, clay, or a block of solid material, which is sculptured, cut, or machined.

Stereolithography is one of the most common Rapid Prototyping methods used in industry today. Stereolithography is used to make conceptual models, plastic prototypes, soft tooling for silicone and sand molds, and patterns for metal castings. Models created with stereolithography are being used to visualize designs, to verify engineering changes, and to check form, fit, and function.

Stereolithography Process   A 3D model database produced on a CAD format is sliced into a stack of thin layers using the stereolithography software. The layers are then redrawn on the surface of a vat of liquid photopolymer by a computer-controlled ultraviolet laser projector. Using a stereolithography apparatus (SLA), solid or surface data (from a CAD database) are sliced by software into very thin cross sections. A laser then generates a small intense spot of ultraviolet (UV) light that is moved across the top of a vat of liquid photopolymer by a computer-controlled optical scanning system. The laser changes the liquid photopolymer to a solid where it touches, as it precisely prints each cross section. A vertical elevator system lowers the newly formed layer, while a recoating and leveling system establishes the next layer's thickness. Successive cross sections, each of which adheres to the one below it, are built one on top of another to form the part from the bottom up. After the last layer is made, the part is removed from the SLA and given a high-intensity flood of ultraviolet light to complete the polymerization process. The part can then be finished by sanding, sand blasting, painting, or dying.

Testing and Analysis   One of the primary responsibilities of the designer is to create a design that will withstand the

stresses under which the product, part, or system will function. If the design is to be operated safely, the proper amount of strength becomes the designer's major concern. The size and configuration of a structural member, the ability of the part to withstand loads without breaking, deforming, or fracturing, the safe design of rotating machinery, the shielding of radical temperatures in operation of a system, and the stress produced by the application of external stress during operation are all in the domain of the designer. After the product or system is designed, it must undergo testing and analysis. Lab testing for strength of materials and finite element analysis using a CAD system (Fig. 17.74) are both used throughout industry to determine the adequacy of the design (Color Plates 8 through 11, 40, 68 through 76).

Finite Element Method   To design an optimal structure or to determine the cause of failure after manufacture, design engineers commonly use computerized design and analysis methods. One such method, which is supported by the CAD system, is the **finite element method** (FEM). The finite element method is an engineering tool that provides a mathematical simulation of the behavior of a part. Using this method, the designer can determine the amount and location of stress in a design, without building a test prototype (Color Plates 68 through 76).

A typical finite element modeling program allows the designer/engineer to create the model and prepare it for analysis, and then graphically display the results (Color Plates 7 through 12). As an integral part of a CAD system, the FEM program takes full advantage of all graphics and dynamics features. It also uses part information (since the part design information already exists), thus reducing the likelihood of errors and speeding the entire analysis cycle. *Finite element analysis starts with finite element modeling* (Color Plate 7).

Finite element analysis is the second part of the finite element method. It is generally a mainframe computer program

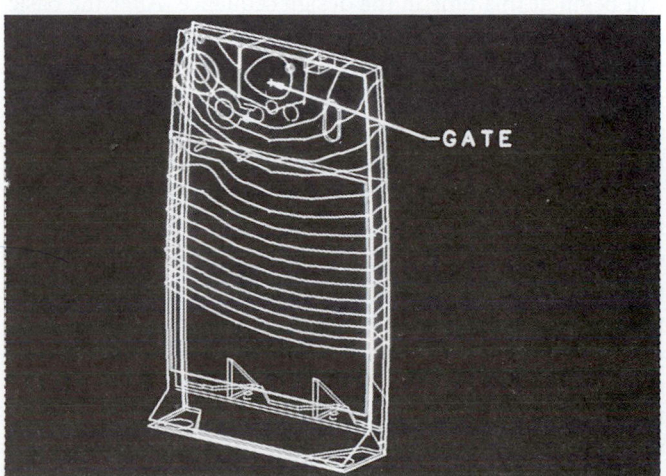

FIGURE 17.74   Mold Design Going Through Thermal Analysis

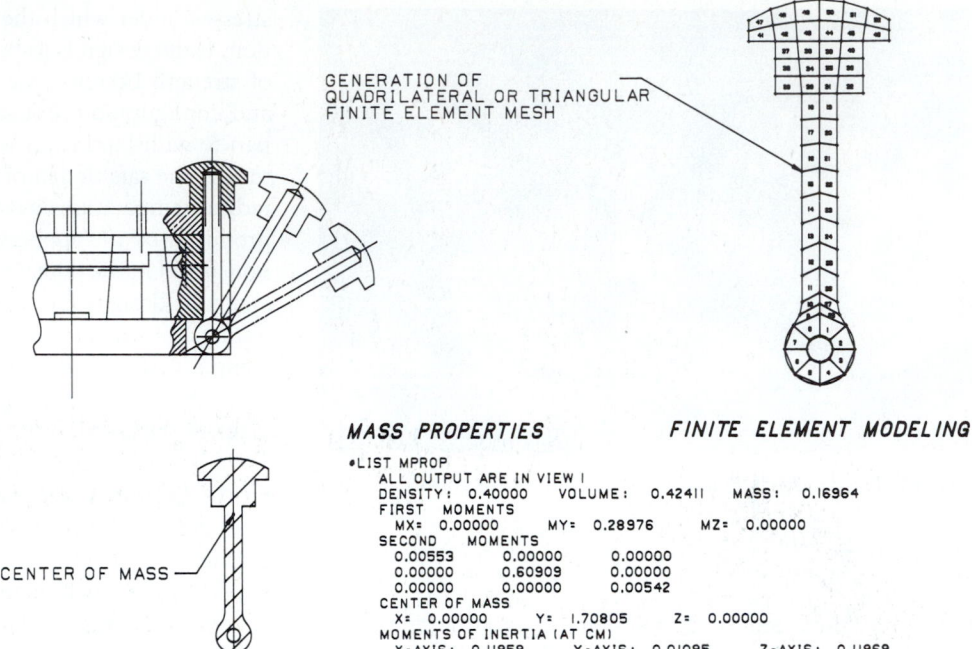

FIGURE 17.75 Finite Element Modeling and Analysis Using a CAD System

that analyzes the information from the text file to determine the amount and location of stress. Mass properties, including weight, volume, and center of gravity, can also be calculated (Fig. 17.75). Color Plate 70 shows stress analysis; Color Plate 71 is an example of temperature analysis; and Color Plate 74 is an example of turbulent flow, heat transfer, and viscous flow analysis. Color Plate 76 shows tortional analysis of the structural frame of a car.

Once the analysis is performed, numerical results are returned to the CAD system and the finite element analysis postprocessing phase begins. This involves reviewing the analysis results, determining problem areas, and modifying the design.

Final Refinement of Design The finalization of a design will begin at this time in the design sequence. After the basic design decisions have established an acceptable product, and it has been drawn, modeled, and tested, the final design refinements are made. Any alterations and refinements in this stage require many hours of manual drawing changes or alteration of the design database on a CAD system.

When complete, the final design is evaluated for potential new technology, innovation, and patent possibilities. A patent can be granted for a process or a unique invention or discovery. A patent is only granted to an individual, not to a company. The patent law states "any person who invents or discovers any new and useful process, machine, manufacture, composition of matter, or any new or useful improvement thereto, may obtain a patent." A patent is established with a written description of the invention or process and is normally accompanied by drawings.

Patent drawings must be included as one portion of a patent application. The drawings are done on standard patent drawing sheets. Figure 17.76 shows a typical patent drawing. Inking is required and shading is normally used on patent drawings to show the invention realistically. The patent drawing will be the last drawing created for a design project. After the product is designed, other drawings may be required for tooling and production. A patent drawing should be very general and present concepts only and not specific size, shape, and material details in order to prevent theft of the idea. The patent secures to the inventor exclusive production rights for up to fourteen years.

17.5.7 Production, Manufacturing, and Packaging

At this point (Fig. 17.77), the design must be presented to all interested, involved, and essential parties. The presentation will involve the designers, engineers, and other company personnel. The configuration of the design is presented in drawings, renderings, and possibly a prototype or presentation model. All aspects of the design are discussed at this meeting. The limitations, restraints, and capabilities of the design, as well as the new or improved features, problems in the design process of the product and validation of all research, scientific, and engineering aspects of the project must be available to answer questions, defend decisions, and demonstrate the appropriateness of the developed design. Graphs, charts, notes, sketches, models (of rejected design alternatives), and design calculations used to establish the solution may all be needed at this meeting. The production department will require much of this information to establish manufacturing requirements and a production schedule.

Detail drawings of each aspect of the product, assemblies, and any other graphic documentation are complete at this

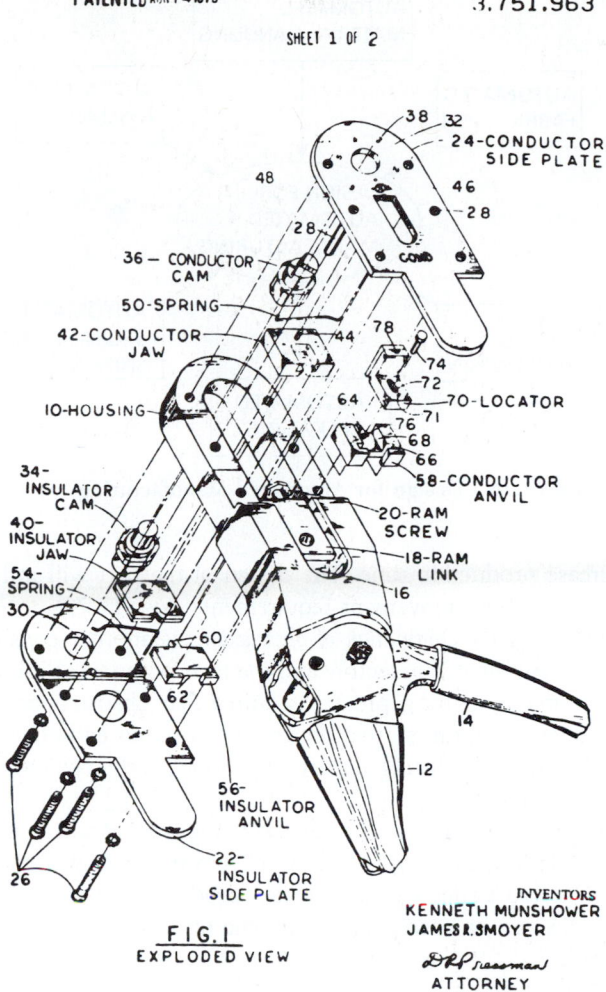

FIGURE 17.76   **Patent Drawing**

limitations of each one. The designer must be familiar with these capabilities and limitations to select the proper material and the manufacturing method.

Of course, the selection of materials in Stage 5 determines many of the manufacturing methods used in the production of the part or product. The part itself helps determine the material and, therefore, the manufacturing methods. Each of the factors listed below is critical to the manufacturability of a particular material and must be considered during this design stage:

- **size** limitation
- **configuration**
- **thermal** characteristics
- **tolerance** requirements
- **hardness**

- **weight** limits
- required ultimate **strength**
- **elasticity**
- surface **texture**—roughness
- **precision**

A variety of manufacturing processes is available. The choice of a process is determined by the part's material and whether or not the process will create an acceptable part. Regardless of the process or the material, the designer should design to facilitate the most efficient and cost-effective process. The following processes are used in manufacturing and were covered in more detail in Chapter 11:

- **machining**
  drilling
  boring
  milling
  planing
  reaming
  broaching
  turning

- **welding**
- **casting**
- **forging**
- **forming**
- **stamping**
- **extruding**
- **bending**

Assembly of the part is partially determined by the material selection. The estimated maximum number of parts and the minimum run is also a factor in the selection of the process. Since a simple part is easier to create and assemble, the part's

stage. Remember, this is not the first time these parties have been consulted about the design. There has been continuous communication throughout the design process, and, although this is the seventh step in a formal explanation of the design process, the flow of information has been back and forth between these steps throughout the process.

Manufacturing Considerations in Design

The design of a particular part or product usually determines the material and the manufacturing process. Failure to understand the limits and possibilities of the material and the manufacturing options will doom the project from the start. Design for manufacturability is therefore essential to the success of a product. The stress, vibration, environmental operating conditions, tolerance requirements, and surface finish are determined during previous stages in the design process. Therefore, by the time the material selection and the manufacturing methods are selected, they are almost defined by default. The decisions by the designers at this stage are merely refinements. An overview of possible materials and processes to be used must include an understanding of the capabilities and

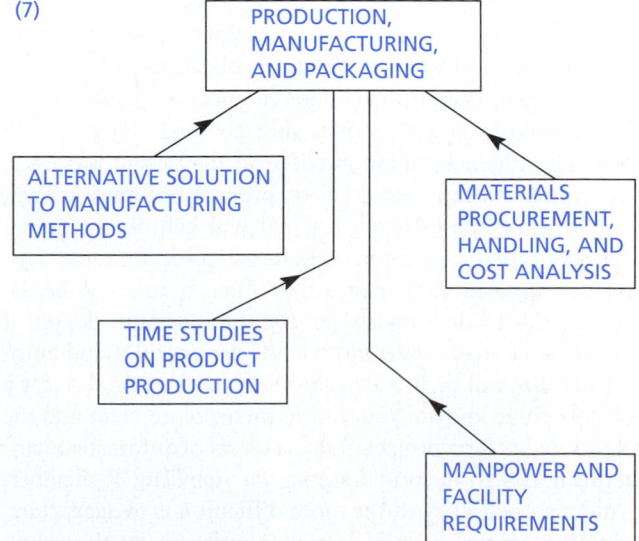

FIGURE 17.77   **Stage 7 in the Design Process**

complexity influences the selection as well. Manufacturing assembly processes include:

- brazing
- welding
- riveting
- gluing
- bolting

The following is a partial list of concerns and suggestions for the designer. If these conditions are met, the chance of a successful, manufacturable part is greatly increased.

1. Design for standard machines and processes.
2. Design within the cost-effective limits of available and effective manufacturing procedures.
3. Design to limit the number of manufacturing processes.
4. Design to permit efficient production in acceptable quantities and within time requirements.
5. Design for the most cost-effective process that will deliver a product meeting the design parameters.
6. Design for ease of assembly.

Although the above discussion centers on the designer's responsibilities and the design requirements, it should be understood that the actual selection of manufacturing processes be made by the manufacturing engineer in conjunction with the product designer.

Alternate Solutions to Manufacturing Methods

Automated manufacturing is the design of a product or part so that it can be readily manufactured, fabricated, assembled, handled, tested, quality controlled, packaged, stored, and shipped using automated methods. Since much of today's manufacturing involves the use of robot and automated assembly systems, the part itself should be designed to facilitate these methods. A typical designer has always been concerned with materials and manufacturing methods, including fabrication and assembly. Increased productivity requirements, brought on by foreign competition and profitability margins, have made automated manufacturing methods essential to the survival of a company. Ever-increasing overhead, labor, and material costs have driven industry's desire to automate. An understanding of the new methods of robotic production and automated manufacturing methods requires the knowledge of their capabilities as well as their shortcomings. Figure 17.78 shows the influences of automation on the design process.

As a new concept, material, or process becomes known, you can begin to establish a list that will help in the design process of a particular project. Material considerations, processes, automated technology, and other factors can be assembled to provide a review list for the optimum design. If they are to be up to date and useful, design rules and autofacturing tips will be in a constant state of flux. As data for a project become known, you should incorporate them into the design rule list for a project. Some aspects of automated manufacturing design include *designing for simplicity*. Remember, the more complex a part, the more difficult it is to *autofacture*. A simple part will require less manipulation by the robot. Thus, keeping the robot's movements short and efficient will

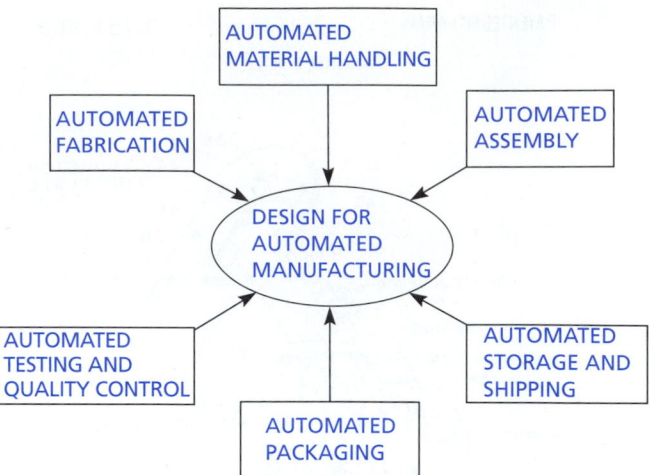

FIGURE 17.78 Design for Automated Manufacturing

decrease production time. The design of the part will influence the robot's movement requirements (Fig. 17.79).

Designing for elimination of obstructions is another consideration. Automated assembly and the incorporation of robots in the manufacturing process requires that obstructions be kept to a minimum so that the robotic arm and end-effector can move freely during material handling, part positioning, and part removal.

Designing with automated manufacturing in mind takes more initial design time, but you will be rewarded with a more efficient, cost-effective, and better product. The following checklist can be used to maximize the results of your design effort:

1. Incorporate every design aid available to reduce manufacturing costs, without adversely influencing the product's essential features.
2. Understand the basic capabilities and limitations of your in-house production and outside vendors' capabilities pertaining to the part's manufacturing and materials.

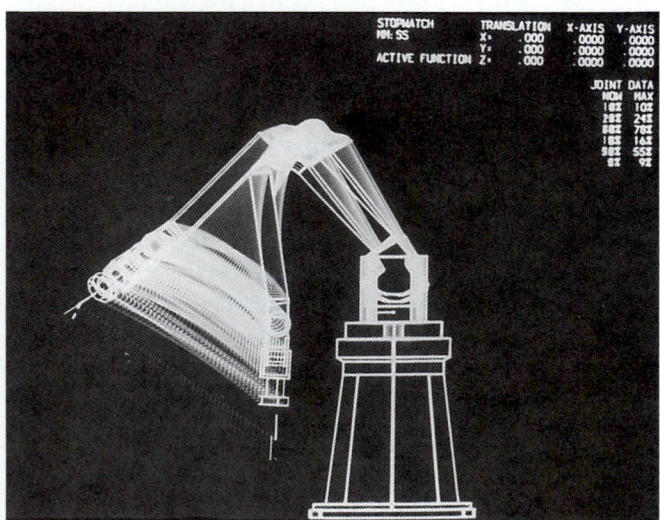

FIGURE 17.79 Robot Simulation

3. Determine the manufacturing methods—whether manually produced, automated production, or a combination of the two—early in the design process so as to maximize the successful creation of the product.

4. Use a design review process that maximizes the effect of any design rules created in the design process. Be willing to review the results and redefine any design requirements based on new knowledge and automated capabilities. Keep an open mind about the material, process, and the automated manufacturing methods.

5. Keep up to date on new and developing automated processes, machinery, time and production studies, advanced materials, and new technology.

Time Studies on Product Production   Studies are required of all processes required to produce a part. The rate of production has a direct effect on the profitability of a product. **Time studies** are conducted to optimize a product's manufacturing cycle. Material handling, production elapsed time (manufacturing and assembly), and part removal (and transportation) are all in this study. Time analysis affects the determination of manufacturing methods, assembly fastening choice, and, sometimes, the material itself.

Materials Procurement, Handling, and Cost Analysis
The **availability** of a material or standard part will influence its selection as much as design requirements. **Material procurement and handling** are an essential part of the total design effort. If the specified standard part is temporarily out of stock or not available, a product can be delayed in the manufacturing stage.

The designer must be aware of the material cost, as well as its availability. The increased cost of substituting one material for another at the manufacturing stage can completely destroy the product's profitability. The introduction of **just-in-time** manufacturing, where the traditional warehousing of large amounts of materials and standard parts is limited by efficient management of the procurement of the materials and parts and their arrival at the manufacturing station exactly when needed in the assembly or production process, requires extensive coordination of all departments. The manufacturing facility must be able to procure, store, and handle the material and standard parts if the production run is to be trouble free.

Manpower and Facility Requirements   Often, a company's facility and workforce will determine when and where the part or product should be made and assembled. The design process includes decisions based on available space, machinery, and trained personnel. One pressing problem in many industries is the lack of an educated, trainable workforce. The implementation of automated methods has been influenced by this lack of high-quality personnel, as well as by foreign competition. The use of robots in the manufacturing stage will also affect personnel, facility, and equipment considerations.

Robots and Manufacturing   Robots (Fig. 17.79) are increasingly used for efficient, safe, cost-effective manufacturing

processes including material and finished product handling and storage, as well as the actual processes involved in the production of the item. CAD robotics packages are a computer-aided design and manufacturing (CAD/CAM) tool for robotic simulation and robot workcell design. Much of all robotics workcell design is simulated remotely on a CAD system before it is used on the factory floor.

Robot workcells consist of the robot itself, robot end-effectors (hands), part orienters, the part being operated on, fixtures, and the surrounding equipment with which the robot interacts. By means of a robot-simulator package, automation engineers can consult libraries of robots and equipment to design a workcell and simulate actual robot motion within the cell. From the simulation, an engineer can accurately determine the workcell cycle time and check for interferences in the motion of the robot with other workcell components.

Industrial Packaging   The field of packaging design includes design of boxes to hold consumer items such as perfume, electronic products, food products, and general household items. It also includes industrial packaging for mechanical and electronic designs (sheet-metal enclosures). The artistic design of boxes for consumer items is considered under Stage 8. Here, the discussion is confined to sheet-metal enclosures required for mechanical and electronic systems. The electronic meter in Figure 17.80(a) is composed of electronic components housed in a sheet-metal enclosure [Fig. 17.80(b)].

A typical sheet-metal design can be created, in 3D, on a CAD system (Fig. 17.81). The 3D model can be automatically unfolded in a flat pattern development. Chapter 20 covers flat pattern developments and their use in the packaging industry in more detail.

The enclosure for any mechanical or electronic system considers the many factors that influence other areas of design. Space requirements, safety, function, operation, service, and environmental conditions are all determining factors. Most of these requirements are known in the early portion of the design process so as to provide sufficient leeway in the packaging when this step is reached.

17.5.8   Marketing, Sales, and Distribution

Marketing, sales, and distribution are an essential aspect of the total design effort (Fig. 17.82). The product or system may never exist without a thorough economic analysis. The cost of advertising, marketing, packaging, shipping, and distribution greatly affects the cost to bring the product to market. The input of the sales and marketing department, the packaging department, and the shipping and storage facility make the important connection to the real world of business and affect profit margin. Products that have been brought to market without a proper understanding of the business aspects of the design process are many times doomed to fail—even good products.

(a)

(b)

FIGURE 17.80   **Example of Industrial Packaging**   (a) Meter face (b) Meter panel and package

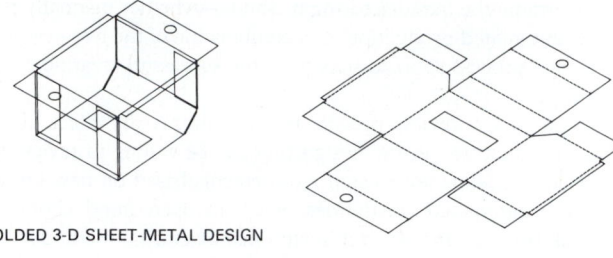

FOLDED 3-D SHEET-METAL DESIGN

UNFOLDED SHEET-METAL DESIGN

FIGURE 17.81   **Sheet-Metal Packaging and Development Using 3D CAD**

Advertising, Budgets, and Marketing Direction   The marketing department may participate in preliminary project work. Marketing is responsible for an accurate product survey before the product is designed. A poor design decision with respect to customer needs on the part of the designers would leave the marketing department with the job of selling an unusable or undesirable product. Sometimes the advertising campaign can create a need for a product in the minds of the public or sell an inferior product with slick advertising. In general, marketing will help determine many function requirements of the product before the final design is accepted. Surveys that help determine the need, size, color, shape, feel, and acceptable cost can be completed well before the engineers and designers are through with their work. The rough preliminary ideas of an inventor/engineer/designer may be refined and altered by the input of the marketing department.

Cost Estimating of Product   The **cost analysis** of the product includes the expenses generated by the engineering, design, manufacturing, sales, and shipping departments. Each department must submit a detailed cost estimate for the

(8)

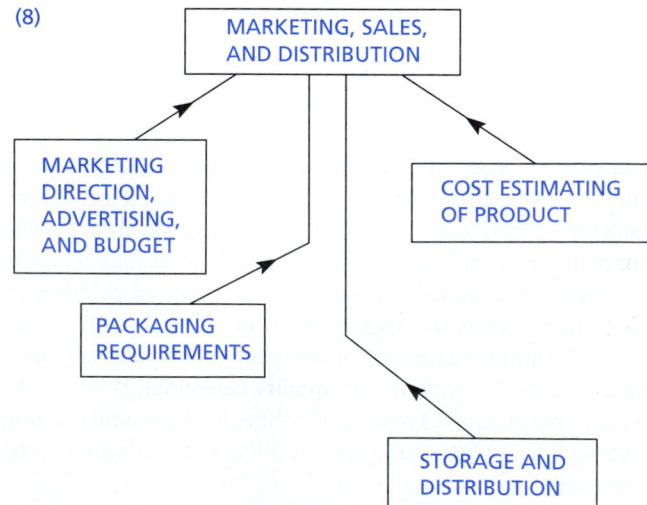

FIGURE 17.82   **Stage 8 in the Design Process**

man-hours, materials, and overhead cost for each stage of the design development process in which it is involved. Design costs include modeling and drafting; sales costs include advertising and marketing; packaging costs include art design and box design. Since they include personnel, equipment, facility, and material considerations, manufacturing costs may be the largest single cost of the product.

Cost estimation of the product affects many of the other department's decisions. The choice of materials, the choice of manufacturing methods, such as fastening, the choice of packaging materials and art design, and the level and extent of sales and advertising are all influenced by the item's cost and profit margin. Cost estimating includes how long it takes to generate an acceptable return and how many items must be sold before the product is considered an economic success.

Packaging Requirements   The design of a product does not end with the product itself. Without proper presentation, the product may fail to achieve the required sales to be successful. **Packaging** is almost as important as the product, especially in the world of mass marketing and international sales.

Packaging also includes new concepts of green-packaging or environmental packaging—using biodegradable packaging and eliminating overpackaging. Too much packaging creates unnecessary amounts of waste when the product is used.

A simple box may not be so simple. As a matter of fact, it can be rather complex. Size must be considered, along with shape, text, color, art, and competition from other boxes. Most packaging for consumer products must be designed for appearance, as well as function.

Although packaging is normally part of Stage 7, most of the design input about the appearance comes from the advertising and marketing departments. The actual design of the dies and patterns is the domain of the manufacturing group. The marketing department, in conjunction with the packaging designers assigned to the manufacturing department, must agree on a box design that is functional, attractive, and producible, within cost restraints.

Designing a box with a specific purpose can be even more complex—french fry boxes have unusual shapes and curves; deodorant boxes use die cuts to display the product inside; and medicine boxes are designed to be tamper resistant. Technology is minimizing complications while providing greater control, particularly over prototyping, through CAD/CAM.

Software programs have been designed specifically for the packaging industry. Software is available that offers a library of parametric designs for creating standard box configurations. The designer simply provides appropriate dimensions to any box design (for example, the standard reverse tuck—a common design with simple end flaps connected to the front of one side of the box and back of the other side to tuck it closed), and the CAD program automatically draws the required shape.

CAM programs can send instructions to devices such as a plotter. This machine cuts out the box and makes creases at the folds of the prototype, saving hours of tedious work. Instructions can also be sent to a laser that cuts a plywood die to hold the steel rules used to cut multiple boxes once the final design is determined.

Once the individual box design is complete [Fig. 17.83(a)], copies are *nested* together [Fig. 17.83(b)], mirroring and duplicating the images and interlocking them like jigsaw puzzle pieces to produce as many boxes as possible from a single sheet of cardboard. The software performs automatic *bridging,* a technique in which gaps are left during the process of cutting the plywood so that it doesn't fall apart. The die manufacturer then inserts steel blades into the plywood, bridging the gaps with blades so that the boxes will fall out like shapes from a cookie cutter.

The heaviest potential for CAD/CAM packaging lies with large food and pharmaceutical companies wanting more direct control over the prototyping phase for the hundreds of packages fabricated for their products. By combining packaging software with devices such as a PLANTAGRAM, in which a shelf environment is recreated, designers can see how the box will look against the competition. The decision can then be finalized before the die is cast.

While the ability to connect CAD box design to CAM machining has been available for some time, the concept of integrating the process with packaging graphics is a new idea that offers major advantages. The capability to prepare the entire design [Fig. 17.83(c)], including the structure, graphics, and machine codes on a single computer, not only speeds and simplifies the prototyping phase, it also eliminates expensive mistakes.

Shipping and Distribution   **Just-in-time** manufacturing is a process where the component parts of a system design arrive at the assembly line station at the time of installation. This process requires careful control of materials, equipment, and fabrication processes and subassembly transportation to the site at the appropriate time. **Field fabrication** of parts of the system also depends on the timely arrival of appropriate materials. The planners of any project have most of the responsibility for this stage of the project. The designers and procurement department must be in constant communication at almost every stage to prevent shortfalls or overstocking of suppliers. It is the coordination between all involved departments that make a project meet both time constraints and cost estimates.

Shipping and distribution of a product include storing and warehousing the product. Many times, the timely arrival of a consumer product on the market greatly affects its sales performance. If the greatest opportunity for sales of consumer goods occurs in the three months before Christmas, what would happen if the product showed up on store shelves on December 28?

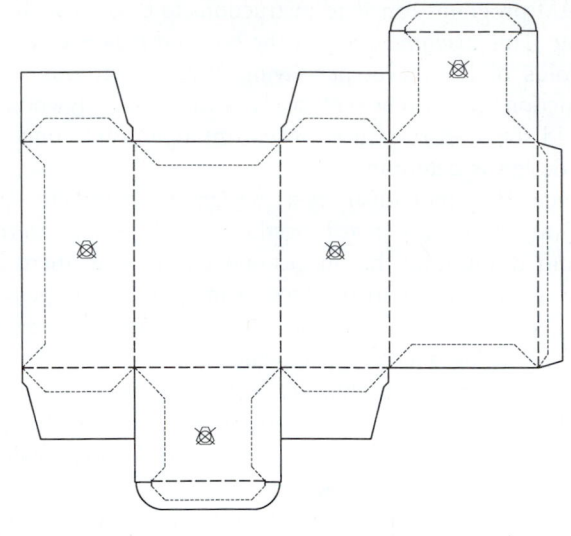

(a)

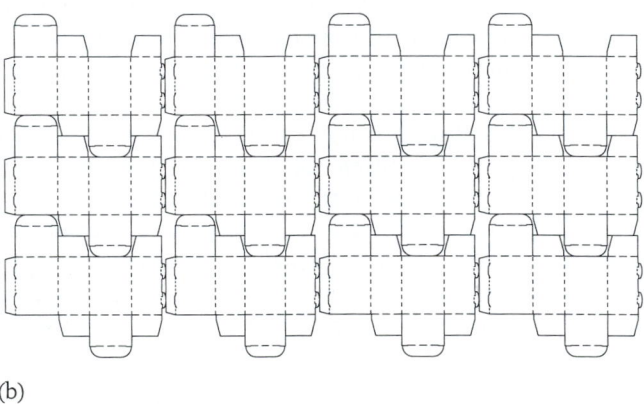

(b)

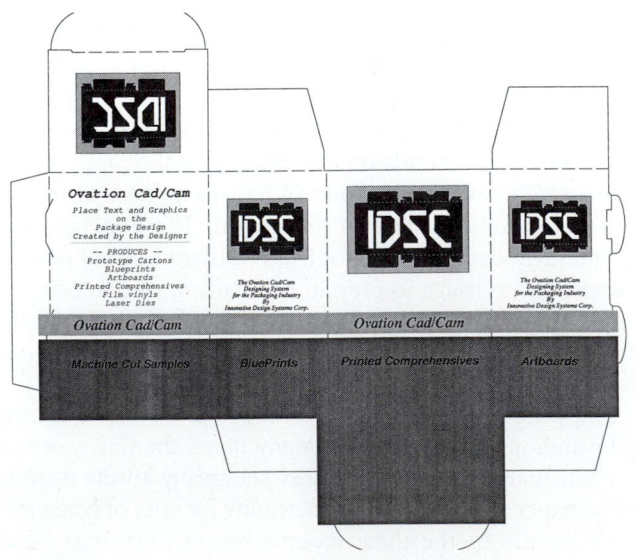

(c)

FIGURE 17.83 **Packaging Design Example**   (a) Die design using ovation CAD/CAM (b) Nested design layout (c) Package graphics

The shipping department must be aware of the product's size, weight, and any factors that would influence the method of shipment. Is the product fragile? Is it bulky? Is it perishable? Does it need any special considerations, such as refrigeration? Will it be affected by heat or cold?

If the product is to be stored at the facility, will there be enough warehouse space? Should the warehouse be automated to handle the product with robotic systems? How many of the product should be available at any one time? These are questions that must be asked early in the design process and solved by the time this last stage is reached.

The quantity of items to be handled and stored is also an important consideration. *Design for stacking* whenever possible. If the product is to be shipped to the general public, contracting with outside shipping sources must also be done. Other concerns at this stage include such things as, will the product be shipped overseas? If so, are there any packaging, duty, tariff, or handling factors that must be considered? As we can see, designing for storing, stacking, and shipping goes far beyond just how to move the product from the manufacturing and packaging facility to the trucking dock.

Illustrations for Presentation, Sales, Advertising, and Catalogs   Pictorial illustrations are used in this stage of the design process to present the product, system, or concept to a nontechnical or purchasing audience. Renderings of products and concepts provide a realistic illustration of the proposed item [Figs. 17.17 and 17.64(a) and (g)].

Renderings and models help introduce a product, concept, or system design to the general public or an interested potential customer. Using the 3D CAD database, an illustrator can now create a pictorial illustration without redrawing the assembly or part. Illustrations for presentations, sales, and catalogs were covered in detail in Chapter 8.

17.6   Design Project Example

The device shown in Figure 17.84(a) is an example of a well-designed consumer product created on a CAD system. Logitech manufactures a variety of mouse devices for computers. You may even have one of their products in your school on your CAD system. Over the years the designers at Logitech became aware of some of the shortcomings of a traditional mouse. Since the ball is on the bottom of a typical mouse, the user must move the device across a flat surface. This meant that the mouse must always rest on a clean flat pad or other acceptable surface. The position of the mouse, either on the right or left of the computer is dependent on whether the user was right-handed or left-handed. If the surface was not flat and clean, the mouse was susceptible to skipping. The user always had to have the device lying flat.

The new device solved many of these problems. The ball was moved to the top of the device to be rotated by the user's hand, not by contact between the ball and a flat surface. The user was now free to hold the input device in their hands. Of course, since it could be operated by either hand without a

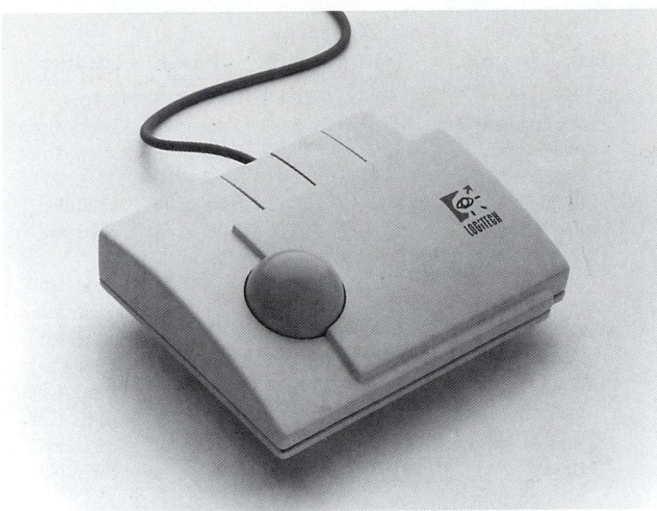

(a)

FIGURE 17.84   **Trackman Mouse**   (a) Trackman roller ball mouse (b) Critical-path schedule for trackman roller ball mouse (c) Trackball subassembly (d) Trackball assembly (e) Detail of skeleton, Tball (f) Top enclosure of Tball (g) Bottom enclosure of Tball (h) Bottom plate for Tball

flat area, the device did not have to be on the right or left side of the computer. Logitech called this product Trackman.

The **critical-path method** of scheduling is documented in Figure 17.84(b). Here, a computer program was used to keep track of the critical and noncritical tasks in the design sequence. The major headings are shown below:

- product management
- mechanical design
- software development
- software quality assurance (QA)
- publications
- product engineering
- test engineering
- materials
- manufacturing

Each of the major headings is subdivided into specific tasks. The duration of each task is estimated and noted as its *Duration Time*. The *Resource* of each task was the specific employee assigned to oversee and complete the task by the scheduled date. The *Scheduled Start* and *Scheduled Finish* dates were also noted on this list. Last, the *Status* was tracked for each task. *In Progress, Scheduled,* and *Completed* notations are shown as well as whether or not this was a critical task. For the product to be on the market before Christmas, all tasks had to be completed by 10-24-89. The critical-path method of scheduling project tasks throughout the design-through-manufacturing process is used in many companies.

Figure 17.84(c) is an enlargement of the subassembly skeleton (part 4). Figure 17.84(d) shows the assembly of Trackman. Figure 17.84(e) is the detail of the Tball skeleton, which is part of the subassembly (part 4). Figure 17.84(f) is the detail of the top enclosure (part 1). Figure 17.84(g) is the detail of the bottom enclosure (part 2), and Figure 17.84(h) is the detail of the button plate. Trackman was completely designed on an AutoCAD system and is an excellent example of the critical-path method of scheduling project activities and using CAD in the design process.

Heading Task Resource	Dur	Schd Start	Schd Finish	Status
TRACKMAN.PJ	148	03-27-89<	10-24-89	
PRODUCT MGMT	51	05-01-89	07-14-89	In Prog.
Rel Wood Model	0	05-01-89	05-01-89	Comp./Crit.
Rel Prototype	0	05-26-89	05-26-89	Comp./Crit.
Rel SalesForecst	0	06-01-89<	06-01-89	Comp./Crit.
Rel IntlShipInfo	0	07-14-89<	07-14-89	Scheduled
MECHANICAL DSGN	140	03-27-89	10-12-89	In Prog.
Rel Case Drawing	0	05-17-89	05-17-89	Comp./Crit.
Rel PWAPartsList	0	06-21-89	06-21-89	Comp./Crit.
SubmitPCBartwork	0	06-13-89<	06-13-89	Comp./Crit.
Rel PCB Layout	0	06-26-89	06-26-89	Comp./Crit.
Tooling	69	03-27-89<	07-07-89	Comp./Crit.
Tooling Support	69	03-27-89	07-07-89	Comp./Crit.
Josef	69	03-27-89	07-07-89	Critical
Rec CaseIstArtcl	0	07-07-89	07-07-89	Comp./Crit.
Rel Proto to Pkg	0	07-13-89	07-13-89	Comp./Crit.
Debug Parts	1w	07-10-89	07-14-89	In Prog.
Josef	1w	07-10-89	07-14-89	
Make 60 PCB's	13	06-27-89	07-17-89	In Prog./Crit.
Rec PWA Compents	0	07-14-89<	07-14-89	Scheduled
Rec 60 PWA's	0	07-27-89	07-27-89	Schd./Crit.
Build DVT1 Units	1w	07-28-89	08-03-89	Schd./Crit.
Rel DVT1 Units	0	08-03-89	08-03-89	Schd./Crit.
Run DVT1 Test	2w	08-04-89	08-17-89	Schd./Crit.
Josef	2w	08-04-89	08-17-89	Critical
Run DVT2 Test	1w	08-18-89	08-24-89	Scheduled
Josef	1w	08-18-89	08-24-89	
Texture Tool	1w	08-25-89	08-31-89	Scheduled
Make PVT units	3	09-01-89	09-06-89	Scheduled
Evaluate PVT	2w	09-22-89	10-05-89	Schd./Crit.
Mftr M-P Units	1w	10-06-89	10-12-89	Schd./Crit.
SOFTWARE DEVELOP	94	05-01-89	09-13-89	In Prog.
Rel Prelim Spec	0	05-05-89	05-05-89	Comp./Crit.
Rel Final Spec	0	07-14-89	07-14-89	Scheduled
Driver	56	05-01-89	07-20-89	In Prog.
Trackball Driver	1w	05-01-89<	05-05-89	Comp./Crit.
Joe	1w	05-01-89	05-05-89	Critical
Control Panel	4w	05-01-89<	06-29-89	Comp./Crit.
Bang	4w	05-01-89	06-29-89	Critical
Dual Mode-Driver	2w	06-15-89	07-06-89	Comp./Crit.
Joe	2w	06-15-89	07-06-89	Critical
WORD Fix	16	06-19-89	07-14-89	In Prog.
Mark	16	06-19-89	07-14-89	
ADI Driver	1w	07-14-89	07-20-89	Scheduled
Mark	1w	07-14-89	07-20-89	
Rel for Alpha	0	07-14-89	07-14-89	Scheduled
Alpha Test	8	07-14-89	07-25-89	Scheduled
Rel for Beta	0	07-25-89	07-25-89	Scheduled
Beta Evaluation	4w	08-09-89	09-06-89	Scheduled
Rel for Final	0	09-13-89	09-13-89	Scheduled
SOFTWARE QA	54	07-07-89	09-22-89	In Prog.
Alpha Phase	12	07-07-89	07-25-89	In Prog.
Rec A-Materials	4	07-07-89	07-14-89	In Prog.
Rec Alpha Manual	0	07-07-89	07-07-89	Comp./Crit.
Rec Mouse Units	0	07-14-89	07-14-89	Scheduled
Rec Alpha SW	0	07-14-89	07-14-89	Scheduled
Run Alpha Test	8	07-14-89	07-25-89	Scheduled
Luis	8	07-14-89	07-25-89	
Manual FdbackDue	0	07-17-89	07-17-89	Scheduled
Beta Phase	30	07-25-89	09-06-89	Scheduled
Rec B-Materials	7	07-25-89	08-03-89	Scheduled
Rec Beta SW	0	07-25-89	07-25-89	Scheduled
Rec Beta Manuals	0	07-27-89	07-27-89	Scheduled

(b)

Heading / Task Resource	Dur	Sched Start	Sched Finish	Status
Rec Beta HW	0	08-03-89	08-03-89	Scheduled
Run Beta Test	23	08-04-89	09-06-89	Scheduled
Luis	23	08-04-89	09-06-89	
Mail Materials	3	08-04-89	08-08-89	Scheduled
Angie	3	08-04-89	08-08-89	
Beta Evaluation	4w	08-09-89	09-06-89	Scheduled
Final Phase	7	09-13-89	09-22-89	Scheduled
Rec Final SW	0	09-13-89	09-13-89	Scheduled
Run Final Tests	1w	09-14-89	09-20-89	Scheduled
Rel Master Disks	0	09-20-89	09-20-89	Scheduled
Write SWQA Reprt	2	09-21-89	09-22-89	Scheduled
PUBLICATIONS	103	05-05-89	10-03-89	In Prog.
Rec Prelim Spec	0	05-05-89	05-05-89	Comp./Crit.
Rec Final Spec	0	07-14-89	07-14-89	Scheduled
Getting Started	77	05-17-89	09-06-89	In Prog.
Alpha Phase	49	05-17-89	07-27-89	In Prog.
Write Alpha	7w	05-17-89	07-07-89	Comp./Crit.
Bob G.	7w	05-17-89	07-07-89	Critical
Release Alpha	0	07-07-89	07-07-89	Comp./Crit.
AlphaFeedbackDue	0	07-17-89<	07-17-89	Scheduled
Correct Alpha	8	07-18-89	07-27-89	Scheduled
Bob G.	8	07-18-89	07-27-89	
Beta Phase	28	07-27-89	09-06-89	Scheduled
Release Beta	0	07-27-89	07-27-89	Scheduled
Beta FeedbackDue	0	08-03-89	08-03-89	Scheduled
Correct Beta	2w	08-04-89	08-17-89	Scheduled
Bob G.	2w	08-04-89	08-17-89	
Beta Test	4w	08-09-89	09-06-89	Scheduled
Final Phase	7	08-17-89	08-28-89	Scheduled
Rel Final Doc	0	08-17-89	08-17-89	Scheduled
Final Review	2	08-18-89	08-21-89	Scheduled
Correct Final	1w	08-22-89	08-28-89	Scheduled
Bob G.	1w	08-22-89	08-28-89	
Blueline #1	1w	08-29-89	09-05-89	Scheduled
Blueline #2	1w	09-06-89	09-12-89	Scheduled
Print Manuals	3w	09-13-89	10-03-89	Scheduled
PRODUCT ENG'G	114	05-02-89	10-12-89	In Prog.
Rec PCB Artwork	0	07-14-89	07-14-89	Scheduled
Rec TrackManUnit	0	08-04-89	08-04-89	Scheduled
Rec Master Disks	0	09-20-89	09-20-89	Scheduled
Rec SWQA Report	0	09-22-89	09-22-89	Scheduled
Rec HWTestReprts	0	10-09-89	10-09-89	Scheduled
Rec Blueline #2	0	09-12-89	09-12-89	Scheduled
BOM	78	06-21-89	10-12-89	In Prog.
Rec PrePartsList	0	06-21-89	06-21-89	Comp./Crit.
Prepare Pre BOM	2	06-22-89	06-23-89	Comp./Crit.
Issue Prelim BOM	0	06-28-89	06-28-89	Comp./Crit.
ECO Final BOM	0	10-12-89	10-12-89	Scheduled
HWQA Testing	7	08-04-89	08-14-89	Scheduled
Run HWQA Test	1w	08-04-89	08-10-89	Scheduled
Write HWQA Reprt	2	08-11-89	08-14-89	Scheduled
Safety Tests	42	08-04-89	10-03-89	Scheduled
FCC Test	2	08-04-89	08-07-89	Scheduled
Rec FCC Approval	0	08-07-89	08-07-89	Scheduled
UL Test	6w	08-04-89	09-15-89	Scheduled
Rec UL Approval	0	09-15-89	09-15-89	Scheduled
Rec FCC Letter	0	10-03-89	10-03-89	Scheduled
Packaging	89	05-02-89	09-07-89	In Prog.
Rec Wood Model	0	05-02-89	05-02-89	Comp./Crit.
Rec Drawings: MD	0	05-18-89	05-18-89	Comp./Crit.

Heading / Task Resource	Dur	Sched Start	Sched Finish	Status
Tray	66	05-26-89	08-30-89	In Prog.
RecTrckballProto	0	05-26-89	05-26-89	Comp./Crit.
Make Proto Drwgs	2w	05-26-89	06-14-89	Comp./Crit.
Build Tooling	4w	07-17-89	08-11-89	Scheduled
Rec Hand Samples	0	08-11-89	08-11-89	Scheduled
Approve Samples	1w	08-14-89	08-18-89	Scheduled
Finalize Drwgs	3	08-21-89	08-23-89	Scheduled
Manufacture Tray	1w	08-24-89	08-30-89	Scheduled
Carton	62	06-09-89	09-07-89	In Prog.
Define Packaging	2w	06-09-89	06-15-89	Comp./Crit.
Rec Hand Sample	0	07-13-89	07-13-89	Comp./Crit.
Sample Approved	0	07-14-89	07-14-89	Scheduled
Draw PackageSpec	1	07-14-89	07-14-89	Scheduled
Make Die Vinyl	3	07-17-89	07-19-89	Scheduled
Rel Die Vinyl	0	07-19-89	07-19-89	Scheduled
Rec 1st Articles	0	08-11-89	08-11-89	Scheduled
Approve 1stArtcl	3	08-14-89	08-16-89	Scheduled
Artwork	20	07-19-89	08-16-89	Scheduled
Rec Die Vinyl	0	07-19-89	07-19-89	Scheduled
Design Artwork	20	07-20-89	08-16-89	Scheduled
Beth	20	07-20-89	08-16-89	
Rel Films	0	08-16-89	08-16-89	Scheduled
Die—	10	07-27-89	08-09-89	Scheduled
PURCHASING				
Select Vendor	1w	07-27-89	08-02-89	Scheduled
Carol B.	1w	07-27-89	08-02-89	
Make Die	1w	08-03-89	08-09-89	Scheduled
Carol B.	1w	08-03-89	08-09-89	
Mftr Carton	3w	08-17-89	09-07-89	Scheduled
ECO	40	08-17-89	10-12-89	Scheduled
Process PWA ECO	2	08-18-89	08-21-89	Schd./Crit.
Approve PWA ECO	1	08-22-89	08-22-89	Schd./Crit.
Process Pkg ECO	2	08-17-89	08-18-89	Scheduled
Approve Pkg ECO	1	08-21-89	08-21-89	Scheduled
Process SW ECO	2	09-25-89	09-26-89	Scheduled
Approve SW ECO	1	09-27-89	09-27-89	Scheduled
Process FinalECO	2	10-10-89	10-11-89	Scheduled
Approve FinalECO	1	10-12-89	10-12-89	Scheduled
TEST ENGINEERING	99	05-18-89	10-09-89	In Prog.
Case Evaluation	5	08-17-89	08-24-89	Scheduled
Rec Plastics	0	08-17-89	08-17-89	Scheduled
Eval Plastics	1w	08-18-89	08-24-89	Scheduled
PCB Evaluation	2	07-17-89	07-19-89	Scheduled
Rec PCB	0	07-17-89	07-17-89	Scheduled
Evaluate PCB	2	07-18-89	07-19-89	Scheduled
Product Testers	73	05-18-89	08-31-89	In Prog.
Develop Plan	7	05-18-89<	07-14-89	In Prog.
Bus BON Test	35	07-14-89	08-31-89	Scheduled
Rec PCB Layout	0	07-14-89	07-14-89	Scheduled
Layout & Design	4w	07-14-89	08-10-89	Scheduled
Build Fixture	3w	08-11-89	08-31-89	Scheduled
Bus Test Ready	0	08-31-89	08-31-89	Scheduled
Serial BON Test	35	07-14-89	08-31-89	Scheduled
Rec PCB Layout	0	07-14-89	07-14-89	Scheduled
Layout & Design	4w	07-14-89	08-10-89	Scheduled
Build Fixture	3w	08-11-89	08-31-89	Scheduled
Serial TestReady	0	08-31-89	08-31-89	Scheduled

FIGURE 17.84 Trackman Mouse—*Continued* (b) Critical-path schedule for trackman roller ball mouse—*Continued*

Heading Task Resource	Dur	Schd Start	Schd Finish	Status
Final Test	35	07-14-89	08-31-89	Scheduled
Rec Case Drawing	0	07-14-89	07-14-89	Scheduled
Layout & Design	4w	07-14-89	08-10-89	Scheduled
Build Fixture	3w	08-11-89	08-31-89	Scheduled
Final Test Ready	0	08-31-89	08-31-89	Scheduled
PVT—Trackball	12	09-22-89	10-09-89	Scheduled
PVT Build	1w	09-22-89	09-28-89	Scheduled
PVT Evaluation	1w	09-29-89	10-05-89	Scheduled
Give PWA Approvl	0	10-05-89	10-05-89	Scheduled
Write PVT Report	2	10-06-89	10-09-89	Scheduled
MATERIALS	59	07-14-89	10-05-89	Scheduled
Rel MPS	0	07-14-89	07-14-89	Scheduled
Rel PWA Schedule	0	07-20-89	07-20-89	Scheduled
Rel SW DupeSched	0	07-27-89	07-27-89	Scheduled
SW Duplication	5	09-27-89	10-04-89	Scheduled
Rec SW ECO Aprvl	0	09-27-89	09-27-89	Scheduled
Duplicate Disks	1w	09-28-89	10-04-89	Scheduled
PWA Builds	31	08-22-89	10-05-89	Scheduled
PWA PreProd	21	08-22-89	09-21-89	Schd./Crit.
PWA ECO Approval	0	08-22-89	08-22-89	Schd./Crit.
PCB Artwork>Mftr	0	08-22-89	08-22-89	Schd./Crit.
Make 300Barebrds	2w	08-23-89	09-06-89	Schd./Crit.
QC Bareboards	2	09-07-89	09-08-89	Schd./Crit.
Kit 300 PWAs	1	09-11-89	09-11-89	Schd./Crit.
Make PWAs	6	09-12-89	09-19-89	Schd./Crit.
QC PWAs	2	09-20-89	09-21-89	Schd./Crit.
PWA MassProd	31	08-22-89	10-05-89	Scheduled
PWA ECO Approval	0	08-22-89	08-22-89	Scheduled
Make Bareboards2	4w	08-23-89	09-20-89	Scheduled
Rec Bareboards 2	0	09-20-89	09-20-89	Scheduled
QC Bareboards 2	2	09-21-89	09-22-89	Scheduled
Kit PWAs 2	1	09-25-89	09-25-89	Scheduled
Make PWAs 2	6	09-26-89	10-03-89	Scheduled
QC PWAs 2	2	10-04-89	10-05-89	Scheduled
Intl. Shipping	40	07-14-89	09-08-89	Scheduled
Rec IntlShipInfo	0	07-14-89	07-14-89	Scheduled
Prepare Applictn	2w	07-14-89	07-27-89	Scheduled
License Approval	6w	07-28-89	09-08-89	Scheduled
Rec Approval	0	09-08-89	09-08-89	Scheduled
MANUFACTURING	47	08-18-89	10-24-89	Schd./Crit.
Rel AssemblyPlan	0	08-18-89<	08-18-89	Scheduled
Preproduction	24	08-31-89	10-05-89	Scheduled
Rec Test Equip	0	08-31-89	08-31-89	Scheduled
Rec Cases	0	09-08-89	09-08-89	Scheduled
Rec PWA's #1	0	09-21-89	09-21-89	Schd./Crit.
Run PreProductn	2w	09-22-89	10-05-89	Schd./Crit.
PreProductn Done	0	10-05-89	10-05-89	Scheduled
Mass-Production	33	09-07-89	10-24-89	Schd./Crit.
Final ECO Aprovl	0	10-12-89	10-12-89	Scheduled
Rec Packaging	0	09-07-89	09-07-89	Scheduled
Rec SW Diskettes	0	10-04-89	10-04-89	Scheduled
Rec PWA's #2	0	10-05-89	10-05-89	Scheduled
Rec Final Manual	0	10-03-89	10-03-89	Scheduled
Rec Cases	0	10-12-89	10-12-89	Schd./Crit.
Run MassProductn	1w	10-16-89	10-20-89	Schd./Crit.
Inspect FinalPkg	2	10-23-89	10-24-89	Schd./Crit.
MassProductnDone	0	10-24-89	10-24-89	Schd./Crit.
PRODUCT AVAIL:	0	10-24-89	10-24-89	Schd./Crit.

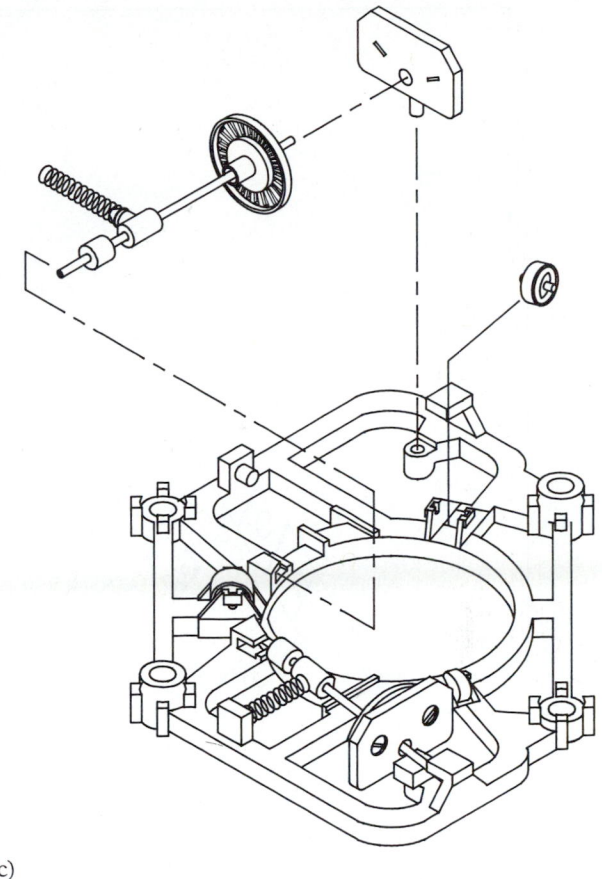

(c)

FIGURE 17.84   Trackman Mouse—*Continued*   (b) Critical-path schedule for trackman roller ball mouse—*Continued* (c) Trackball subassembly

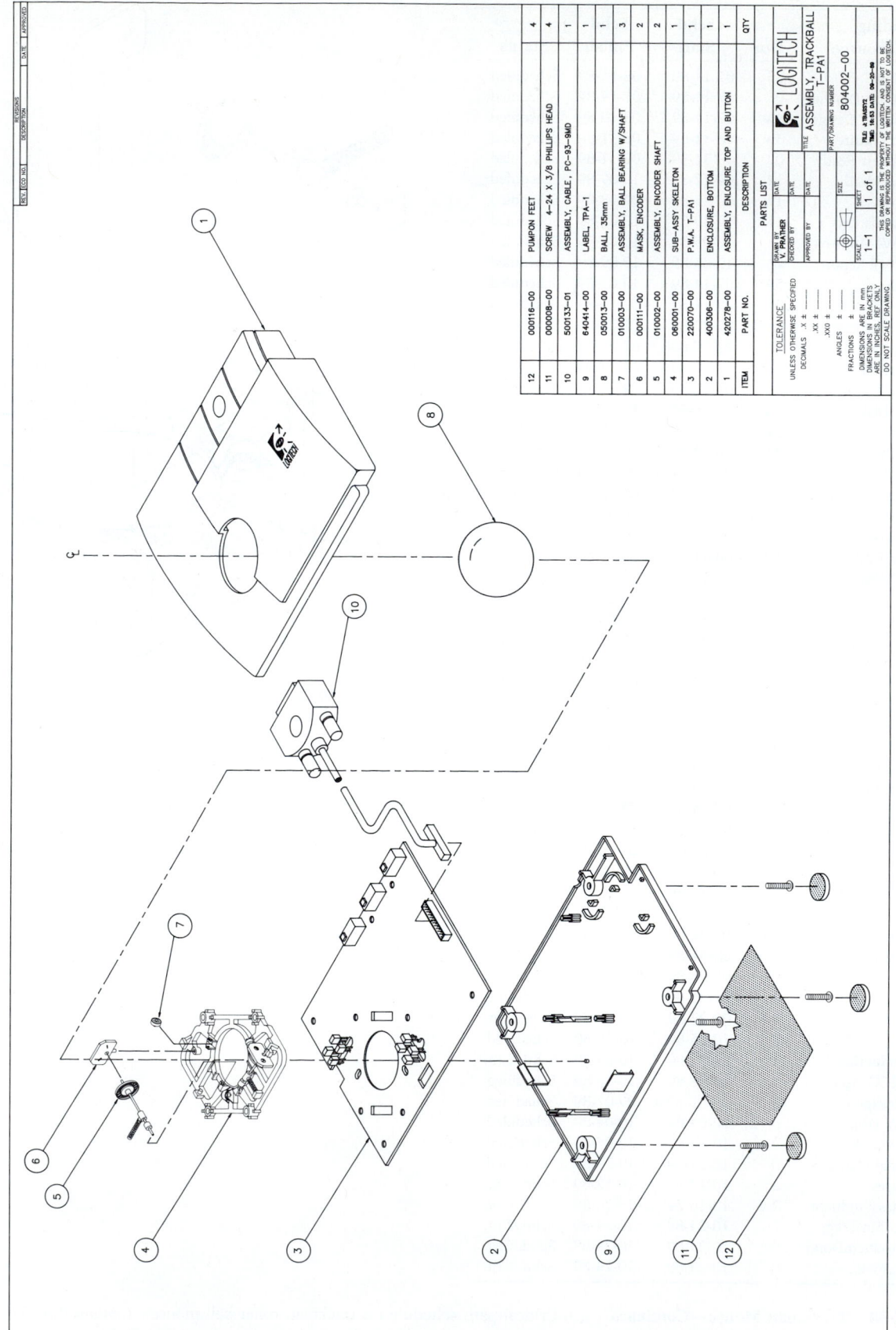

ITEM	PART NO.	DESCRIPTION	QTY
12	000116–00	PUMP/ON FEET	4
11	000008–00	SCREW 4–24 X 3/8 PHILLIPS HEAD	4
10	500133–01	ASSEMBLY, CABLE, PC–93–9MD	1
9	640414–00	LABEL, TPA–1	1
8	050013–00	BALL, 35mm	1
7	010003–00	ASSEMBLY, BALL BEARING W/SHAFT	3
6	000111–00	MASK, ENCODER	2
5	010002–00	ASSEMBLY, ENCODER SHAFT	2
4	060001–00	SUB–ASSY SKELETON	1
3	220070–00	P.W.A. T–PA1	1
2	400306–00	ENCLOSURE, BOTTOM	1
1	420278–00	ASSEMBLY, ENLOSURE TOP AND BUTTON	1

PARTS LIST

LOGITECH

ASSEMBLY, TRACKBALL
T–PA1

PART/DRAWING NUMBER

804002–00

FIGURE 17.84 Trackman Mouse—*Continued* (d) Trackball assembly

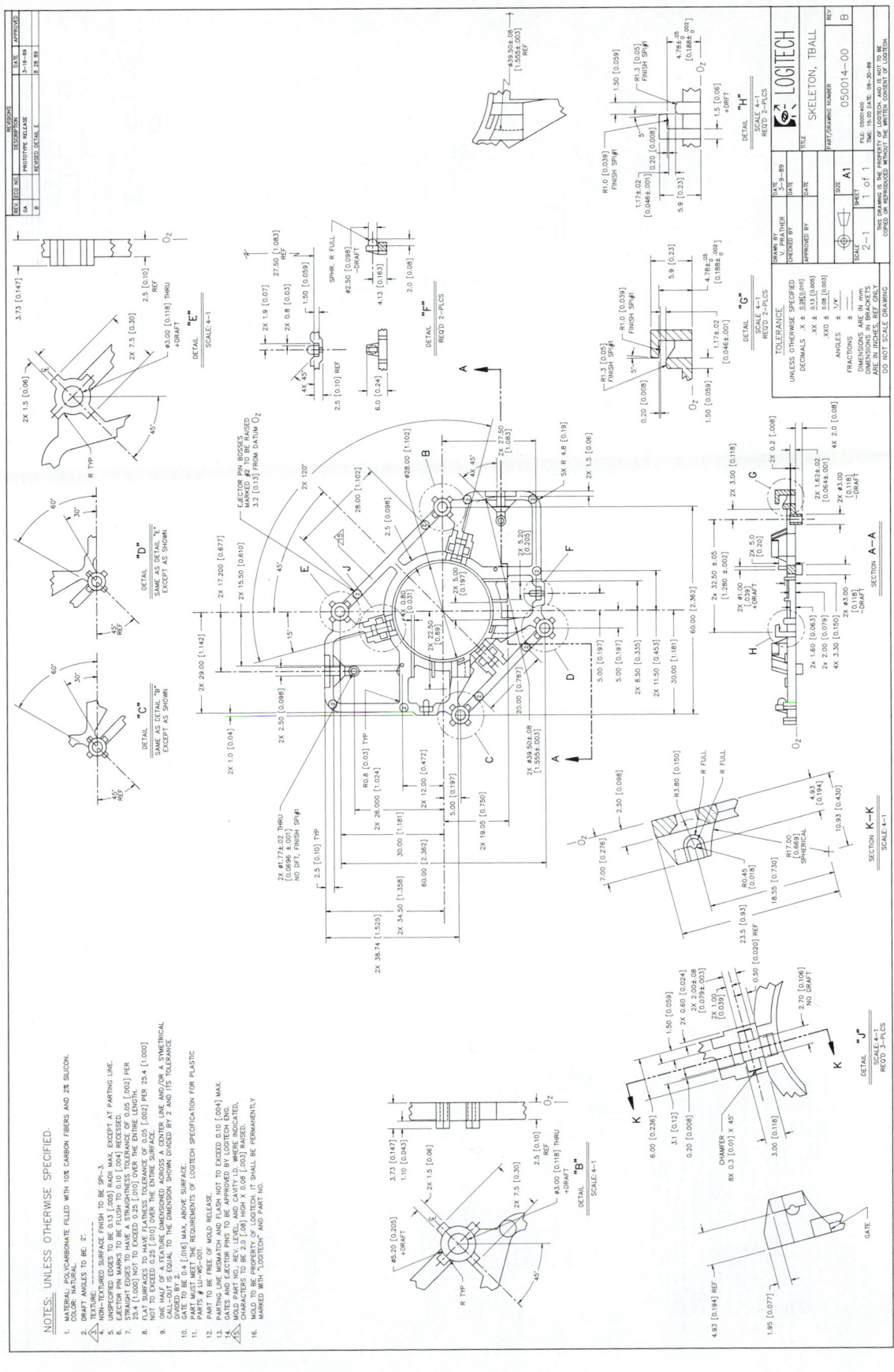

(e)

FIGURE 17.84 Trackman Mouse—*Continued*   (e) Detail of skeleton, Tball

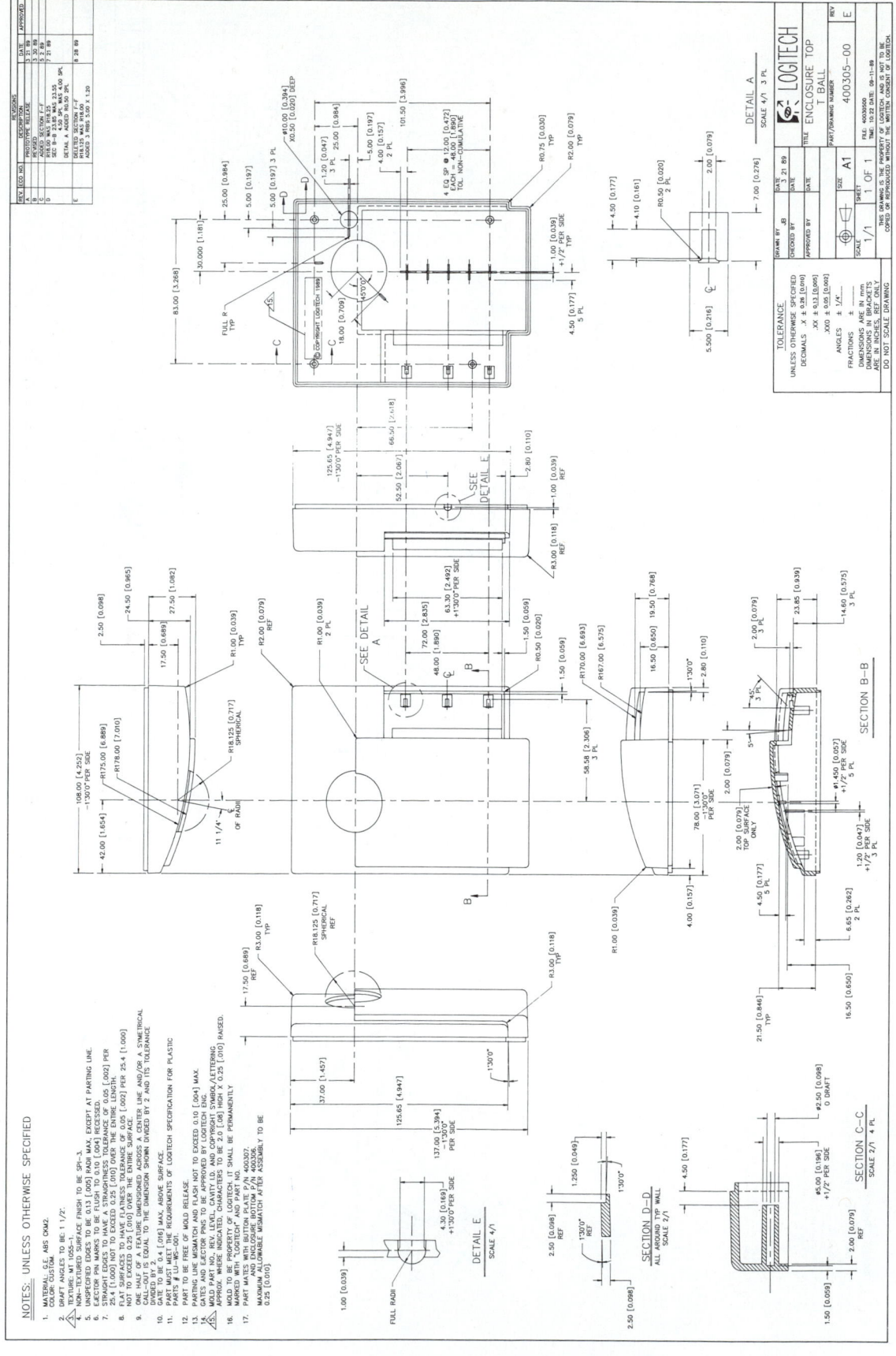

FIGURE 17.84 Trackman Mouse—*Continued* (f) Top enclosure of Tball

(f)

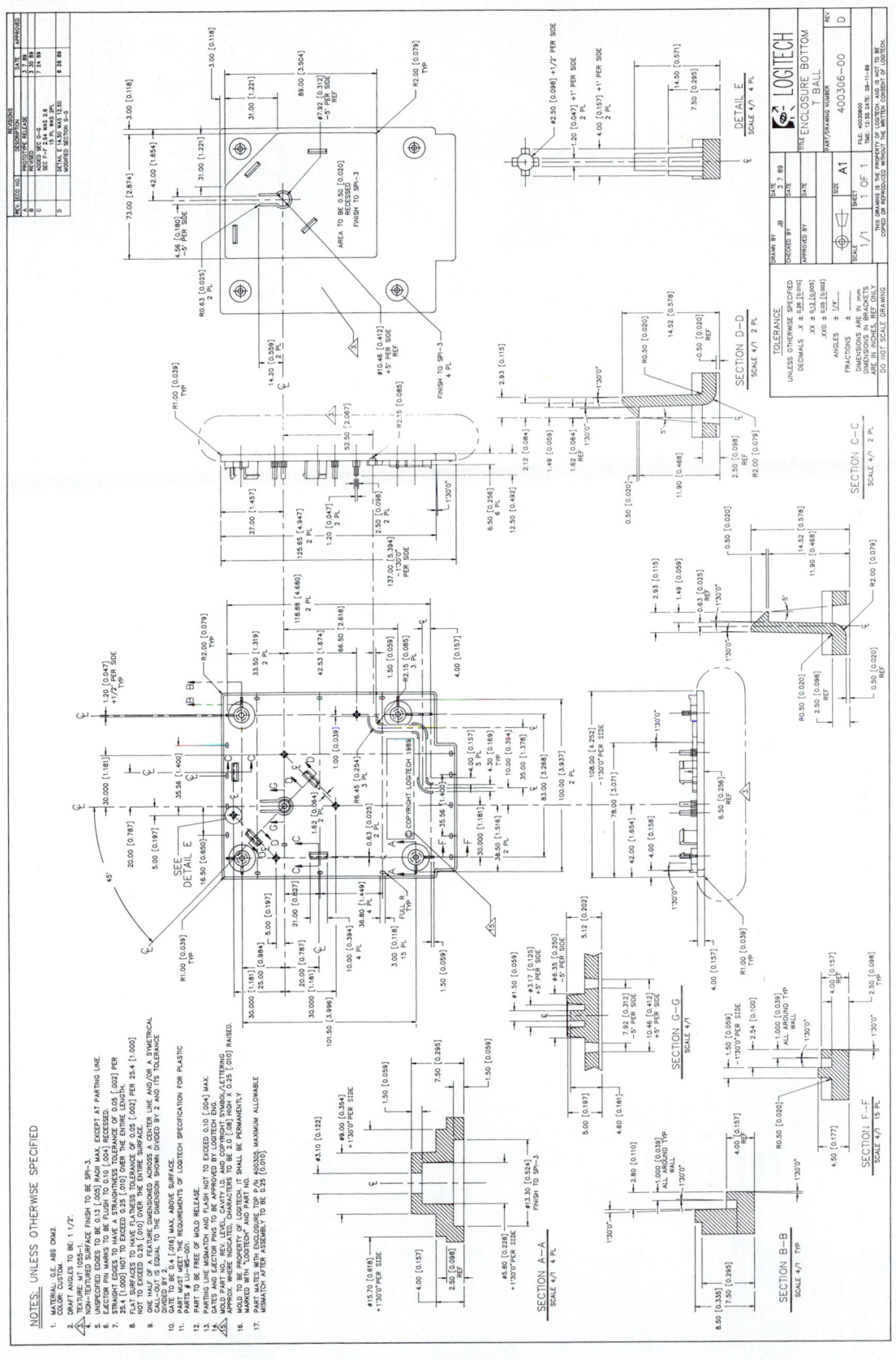

FIGURE 17.84   **Trackman Mouse—***Continued*   (g) Bottom enclosure of Tball

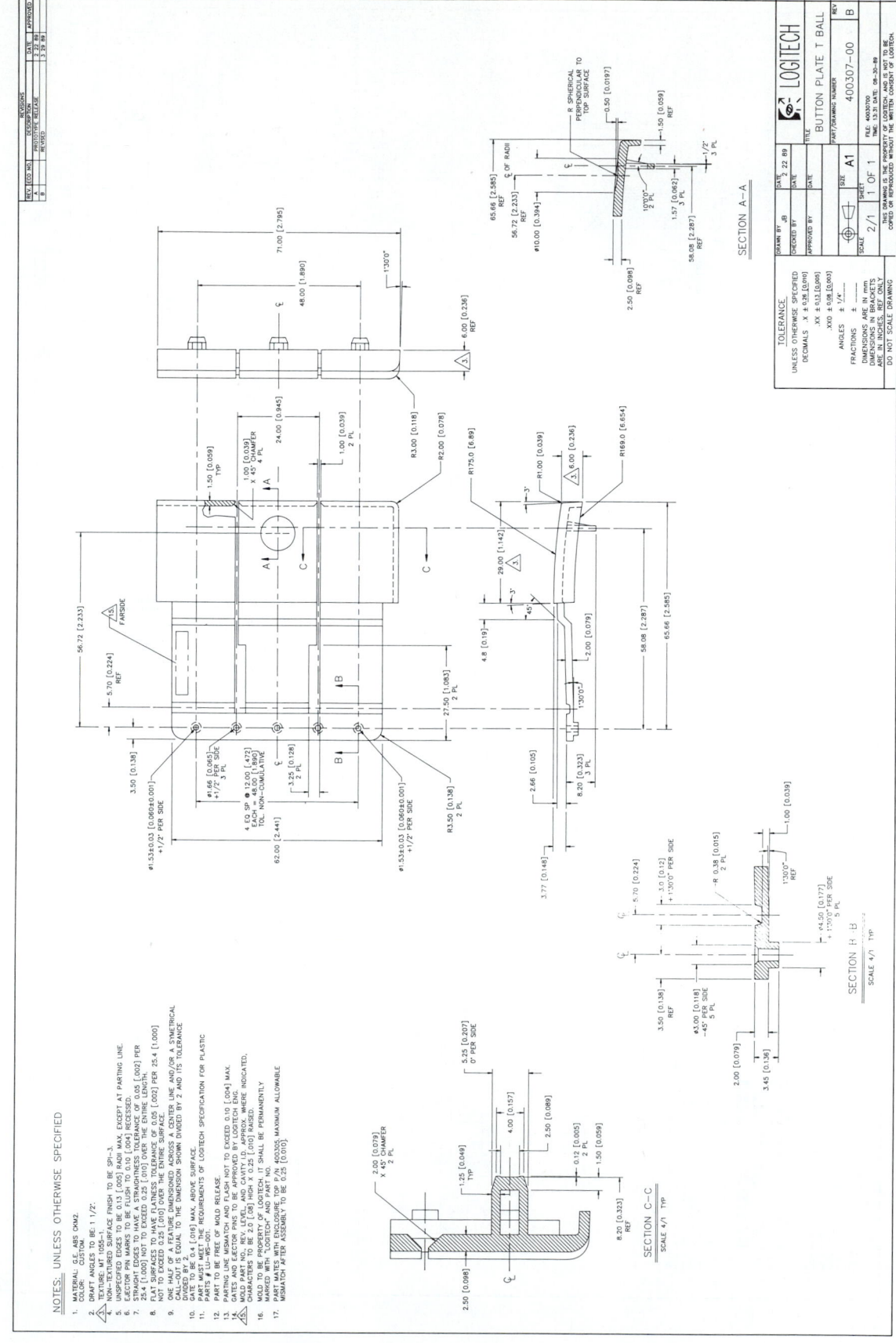

FIGURE 17.84 Trackman Mouse—*Continued* (h) Bottom plate for Tball

(h)

17.7 General Problem Instructions and Design Process Summary

The lists of design projects provided in this chapter are intended as a guide to both instructor and student, indicating some possibilities and alternatives for further work in design. Since the lists are hardly definitive and should not be used to restrict the student's creativity, the student may wish to choose, with the approval of the instructor, an unlisted design project in which they are personally interested. The major objective and importance of the project should be for the student to do some original thinking in the use of design principles and using DFM concepts. Since they outline a project from the abstract to actuality, the following design considerations should be carefully evaluated.

Design Process Summary

1. *Identification:* Defining the design objective
   a. Making a list of known facts and existing information.
   b. Ask the following questions: What? Why? Where? Whom? How? and When?
2. *Conceptualization:* Brainstorming, creative solutions
   a. How many ways can it be solved?
   b. Thought starters, make a list of values.
   c. Similarities, environmental requirements.
   d. Checklist, brainstorming, material options.
   e. Is there a simpler way?
3. *Evaluation:* Application, functional requirements, synthesis
   a. What makes the design good—economy, simplicity, reliability, durability, usefulness, attractiveness, manufacturability, easy to promote in sales, easy to service?
   b. What are the alternatives to the design?
4. *Decision:* Design optimization
   a. What materials should be used?
   b. Should the parts be interchangeable?
   c. Should we use standard parts?
   d. Is it an economical manufacturing process?
   e. How easy is it to operate?
5. *Development:* Implementation of design
   a. Create working drawings and details.
   b. Model the part—CAD, physical, types, number of models.
   c. Check the design.
   d. Testing and analysis—modeling, debugging.
   e. Improve and redesign for aesthetic or functional refinements.
6. *Production:* Manufacturing, packaging, handling the product
   a. Facility needs.
   b. Personnel requirements.
   c. Materials and processes for manufacturing.
   d. Packaging design.
   e. Material handling and product handling.
7. *Marketing:* Sales and distribution
   a. Staff training.
   b. Servicing the product.
   c. Low maintenance costs, customer acceptance.
   d. Sales strategy on how to present.
   e. Product and main features.
   f. Distribution of the product. Who? How?

Problem solutions may be completely freehand, a combination of freehand and instrument (or CAD) drawings, or all instrument-prepared accurate design layouts. The method used is dependent on the project size, the facility capabilities, and the class requirements.

A final report may include a whole or partial design, idea sketches, layouts, details, assemblies, exploded pictorials, patent drawings, graphical solutions, investigation reports, sales promotion suggestions, proposed newspaper announcements, graphs, charts, and a model. The laboratory sessions should be devoted mainly to the development of ideas by graphical documentation, unless a model shop is available. Depending on the size and complexity of the project, the instructor may choose to form design teams of two to four students.

Table 17.1 is a product design checklist that covers a variety of areas, not all of which apply to every design. It is suggested that any projects completed from the text use the checklist as a guide during the design process.

TABLE 17.1   Product Design Checklist

A. Customer Requirements	Comment	Yes	No
1. Functionality			
a. Does the product meet customer requirements?			
b. Does it deliver the required performance?			
c. Does it satisfy emergency conditions?			
d. Have the important functions of the overall system and subsystems been agreed on?			
e. Is there a consensus between customers and designers?			
2. Safety Provisions			
a. Were provisions made for both intended use and foreseeable misuse?			
b. Was the product analyzed for hazards?			
c. Are there interlocks and safety devices?			
d. Does it meet applicable DOE and ME safety standards?			
e. Are complete safety instructions provided?			
f. Are warning, hazard, and severity signs properly identified?			
g. Have all possible radiation, toxicity, or corrosivity problems been considered?			
h. Was the product subjected to overstress tests?			
i. Has Hazards Control reviewed the design?			
j. Are there any high-voltage, high-pressure, or high-explosive sources?			
k. Are there other stored-energy sources?			
3. Operation and Maintenance Provisions Requested by Customer			
a. Does the product come with clear and concise instructions?			
b. Is it simple to operate?			
c. Are the controls operable and understandable?			
d. Does the product accommodate differing physical characteristics of operators?			
e. Is it easily maintained?			
f. Will spare parts be available?			
g. Can product be misused?			
h. Are operating or maintenance manuals needed?			
i. Are controls foolproof, so a hazardous condition cannot be inadvertently created?			
4. Cost and Schedule Requirements			
a. What is the basic cost to design and produce the product?			
b. What will the cost be over the total life of the product?			
c. What will spare parts cost?			
d. What are the major cost items and drivers?			
e. Could cost savings be realized with alternate designs?			
f. Are costs reasonable and realistic?			
g. Has a detailed schedule been determined for the design release or for long lead-term items?			
5. Potential Environmental Effects on Product Performance and Reliability			
a. Could the product be affected by any of the following extremes at the customer's place of business:			
i. Voltage surges?			
ii. Service water hardness?			
iii. Pressure?			
iv. Temperature?			
v. External vibration?			
vi. External shock?			
vii. Ambient temperature?			
viii. Humidity?			
ix. Magnetic or electrical fields?			
x. Ambient sound?			
xi. Weather?			
b. Will operation be affected if the product is contaminated by foreign materials (sand, grit, oil, lint, dirt, etc.)?			
c. Will it be affected by corrosive ambients (salt, humid air, sea water, acids, cooling fluids, etc.)?			
d. Can radio interference affect operation?			
e. Can radiation affect the product?			
f. Can supplementary products (detergents, bleaches, oils, grease, solvents, lubricants, etc.) affect the product?			
g. How would an earthquake affect the product?			

Continued

TABLE 17.1   Product Design Checklist—*Continued*

A. Customer Requirements—*Continued*	Comment	Yes	No

6. Potential Product Effect on Customer's Personnel and Environment
  a. Does the product have a pleasant appearance? Is it compatible with its surroundings?
  b. Is it noisy?
  c. Does it give off objectionable odors?
  d. Will it affect the temperature of the area it is used in? Will it affect other equipment?
  e. Does it vibrate?
  f. Does it produce objectionable light?
  g. Does it emit radiation?
  h. Does the exhaust give off noxious fumes?
  i. Will waste materials require special disposal? Have provisions been made for their handling, storage, and shipping?
7. Reliability and Performance Provisions
  a. Is the estimated reliability adequate?
  b. Was the reliability estimating method valid?
  c. Could performance deteriorate with wear or environmental change?
  d. Are the controls stable?
  e. What were the design provisions for minimizing likely failures?
  f. Have the methods of calibration and determining the performance been verified?
  g. Have emergency shutdown provisions been provided for?
  h. Have provisions been made for power or water supply failures?
  i. Are there provisions for periodic inspection and in-service nondestructive evaluation?			

B. Good Design Practices			

1. Parts Breakdown
  a. Can several parts be combined into one?
  b. Can cost savings be realized by breaking a complex part into smaller, simpler, or less costly components?
  c. Is the Bill of Materials structure logical?
  d. Will the Bill of Materials suit the needs of manufacturing personnel?
  e. Is the drawing numbering system logical?
2. Safety Practices
  a. Does the product conform to the Design Safety Standards Manual?
  b. Is it free of sharp edges, burrs, or corners?
  c. Are the safety factors reasonable and defensible?
  d. Is a Safety Note needed? Has it been prepared according to the DSS?
  e. Is an Operational Safety Procedure needed?
  f. Has a failure modes and effects analysis been performed?
  g. Was a fault-tree analysis performed?
  h. Were all likely hazards identified and eliminated?
3. Assembly and Installation
  a. Can any part be assembled incorrectly?
  b. Is the assembly sequence simple and logical?
  c. Is there space for tooling access, insertion, etc.?
  d. Can likely repairs be diagnosed without disassembly?
  e. Are special tools needed for assembly and installation?
  f. Are common fasteners used?
  g. Will corrosion be readily apparent? If not, can the design be changed to ensure visibility?
  h. Will the method of inspection really validate the correctness of the assembly or installation work?
  i. Are written assembly or installation procedures required?
4. Parts and Components
  a. Does the design make use of proven standardized parts (fasteners, washers, clips, connectors, snap rings, etc.)?
  b. Are the raw materials specified in standard sizes, types, or forms (e.g., standard plate or sheet metal thicknesses, rod sizes, composition)?
  c. Are standard parts or raw materials readily available in the shop where the design will be fabricated?
  d. Were the components proven by use in an earlier, related design?			

Continued

TABLE 17.1   Product Design Checklist—*Continued*

B. Good Design Practices—*Continued*	Comment	Yes	No

5. Design Selection
    a. Was the design scope properly defined?
    b. Were the selection criteria properly balanced and valid?
    c. Did the criteria respect customer requirements?
    d. Were alternate designs, concepts, or processes identified and documented?
6. Measurements and Control
    a. What needs to be measured, recorded, monitored, or alarmed? Why?
    b. What alternate sensors can be considered?
    c. What functions are to be controlled? Why? How?
    d. What provisions were made for instrumentation recalibration?
    e. How should data be recorded?
    f. Have requirements for resolution, repetition, and accuracy of measurements been determined?
    g. What should be automated? Why? How?
    h. How and when should instruments or controls be tested?
    i. How can you tell when controls are working properly?
7. Nondestructive Evaluation
    a. Are nondestructive evaluation inspections required?
    b. Are appropriate techniques and equipment available?
    c. If not, can the design be modified?
    d. If not, can new NDE equipment or techniques be developed?			

C. Minimizing Costs			

1. Has an engineering analysis been performed to investigate:
    a. The use of alternate, less expensive materials?
    b. Redesigning to reduce initial costs?
    c. The cost of maintenance, repairs, or operation?
2. How reliable is the cost estimate?
3. Is a service warranty provided by the manufacturer?
    a. Is the manufacturer's reputation for service good?
    b. How quickly will service be provided?
4. Have manufacturing and production costs been optimized:
    a. To utilize existing processes, equipment, and facilities?
    b. To minimize tooling costs?
    c. To make the most use of standard parts?
    d. To utilize more efficient new processes, equipment, and facilities?
    e. To minimize inspection and testing?
5. Can an alternate component be procured with a substantially better warranty?			

D. Improving Reliability			
1. Are the maximum stresses within limits through the full range of travel, load, voltage, etc.? 2. Are the safety factors used reasonable? 3. Is the design as simple as possible? 4. Were failure modes of critical elements analyzed? 5. Did you make optimum use of standard, proven components and subassemblies? 6. Was the reliability data of similar devices considered? 7. Were design integrity tests successfully completed (life, safety, simulated stress environments, etc.)? 8. Are drawings clear and unambiguous? 9. Is the equipment available when needed? 10. Were steps taken to minimize electrolysis, corrosion, dirt, etc.?			

Continued

TABLE 17.1   Product Design Checklist—*Continued*

E. Manufacturability and Production	Comment	Yes	No
1. Does the design use existing equipment for fabrication, finishing, assembly, inspection, calibration, testing, packaging, etc.?			
2. If not, are new processes, equipment, and facilities more effective?			
3. Does the design avoid hazardous operations?			
4. Are tool and piece costs optimized?			
5. Does the design use existing acceptable tooling where possible?			
6. Does it permit maximum standardization?			
7. Are the tolerances and surface finishes specified consistent with acceptable processes and equipment?			
8. Does the design correct or avoid known manufacturing problems?			
9. Are the operations requiring special skills, new equipment, or special attention minimized?			
10. Are critical dimensions or parameters to be controlled during procurement and manufacturing clearly identified?			
11. Do the materials specified conform to standards?			
12. Are specifications clearly and completely described on drawings?			
13. Could inspection be accomplished easier and cheaper by changing the design?			

F. Shipping and Storage Requirements			
1. Will the product be transported with standard packaging?			
2. Is additional special packing material required?			
3. Will the package withstand applicable transportation tests for:			
a. Shock?			
b. Vibration?			
c. Temperature extremes?			
d. Humidity extremes?			
e. Handling equipment?			
f. Sand and dust?			
4. Have you considered the available transport and storage equipment?			
5. Has the shape and size of packaged product been optimized for rail and truck transportation?			
6. Are clear instructions for handling and lifting provided on the outside of the package?			
7. How will used packaging material be disposed of?			
8. How will moveable parts be secured during transport?			

G. Maintenance and Serviceability			
1. Are there any potential safety hazards during installation, repair, disassembly, or maintenance?			
2. Is special test or service equipment needed? If so, have provisions been made to procure it?			
3. Can the product be satisfactorily installed quickly?			
4. Are items requiring frequent maintenance easily accessible?			
5. Are new or nonstandard items minimized?			
6. Are servicing instructions clear? Are they adequate? Are they the result of a fault-tree analysis or failure mode and effects analysis?			
7. How will performance be verified after repair?			
8. Are periodic nondestructive inspections required?			

H. Applicable Laws and Agency Requirements			
1. Does the product comply with applicable laws and agency requirements such as:			
a. Local ordinances?			
b. State or federal laws?			
c. Environmental Protection Agency laws and guidelines?			
d. Department of Energy (DOE) guidelines?			
e. Department of Transportation (DOT) rules for shipping?			
f. Others?			

Continued

TABLE 17.1 Product Design Checklist—*Continued*

H. Applicable Laws and Agency Requirments—*Continued*	Comment	Yes	No

2. Does the product comply with applicable agency standards or guidelines such as:
  a. Underwriter's Laboratory (UL)?
  b. American Gas Association?
  c. Military specifications?
  d. Environmental Protection Agency (EPA)?
  e. Occupational Safety and Health Act (OSHA)?
  f. Consumer Product Safety Act?
  g. American National Standards Institute (ANSI)?
  h. American Society of Mechanical Engineers (ASME)?
  i. National Electronics Manufacturers Association (NEMA)?
  j. Institute of Electrical and Electronics Engineers (IEEE)?
  k. American Welding Society?
  l. DOE or others?
3. Are permits required for installation or operation, e.g., for venting gas or hazardous material?			

I. Patent and Classification Requirements	Comment	Yes	No
1. Has a search been conducted to learn of recent, related patents? 2. For patent protection, have any inventions been promptly disclosed? 3. Is any portion of the design, analysis, or documentation classified? Has an authorized classifier reviewed the preliminary and final designs? 4. Have steps been taken to safeguard the classified information? Are all personnel working on classified portions aware of the rules regarding the handling, dissemination, and disposal of classified information?			

J. Human Factors	Comment	Yes	No
1. Are controls and displays well organized? 2. Are controls conveniently located for efficient operation? 3. Can monitoring or diagnostic devices be easily and accurately read? 4. Are instructions clear, legible, and complete? 5. Can all operations be performed safely without danger to the user or the product? 6. Have the physiological and psychological characteristics (age, education, size, strength, or handicap) of the user been considered? 7. Can maintenance be performed easily? 8. Have the human factors of similar devices been analyzed?			

K. Appearance	Comment	Yes	No
1. Is the product compatible with its environment? 2. Are the color and finish logical for its environment and usage? 3. Are rating and instruction plates clear, concise, complete, and legible? 4. Are instruction books, operating manuals, or repair manuals easy to read and understand?			

L. Potential Design Modifications	Comment	Yes	No
1. Will it be possible to upgrade performance in the future? 2. Are other modifications likely? Will present design features allow for quick, low-cost changes later on?			

M. Installation	Comment	Yes	No
1. Is the selected installation site suitable? 2. Is a new building design needed? Will an existing site be modified? 3. Are written installation instructions needed? Are they complete and clear? 4. Is special installation equipment required? 5. Is there a schedule for building construction or modification? 6. Is the installation site easily accessible by truck, crane, etc.?			

N. Disposal	Comment	Yes	No
1. What are the safety and environmental concerns for decommissioning, shipping, and disposal? 2. Are permits required for disposal? 3. Will hazardous materials accumulate?			

QUIZ

True or False

1. The design process is a series of eight rules that should be followed exactly.
2. All designs developed by a company's design team eventually get manufactured or produced.
3. Function is the most determining factor in design.
4. Human engineering is the study of people and how they engineer/design projects in industry.
5. The project cost and the profit margin are two of the most important factors in any design.
6. Reliability is the length of time a product will operate properly.
7. Human factors play an important role in all product design.
8. "Off-the-shelf" refers to a mechanical item that is too large for shelf storage.

Fill in the Blanks

9. _____ design uses standard components arranged in a unique configuration.
10. _____ _____ is the first stage of the design process.
11. Durability, life, quality, economy, and simplicity are all factors in product _____ _____ .
12. The _____ _____ can be used to describe and determine the material and configuration requirements of a design.
13. _____ design and _____ design are the two main divisions of design projects.
14. The effects of motion, heat, _____ , and environment are some of a designer's concerns.
15. Design parameters include weight, size, _____ , _____ , _____ color, _____ , and _____ .
16. Machinability, castability, _____ , _____ , and _____ are all factors in the selection of a product's material.

Answer the Following

17. Compare systems design with product design. Describe both and explain their differences.
18. Name ten factors that influence design at the onset of the project.
19. Describe the use of models in the design process.
20. How are graphs and charts used in the design process?
21. What is human engineering and how do human factors and ergonomics influence design?
22. What is DFM and how does it affect the design process?
23. List six sources of information available to the designer.
24. What is critical-path scheduling?

PROBLEMS

Problem 17.1 *Play Yard Toy.* Design a child's backyard play toy. Include a slide, ladder, swing, tunnel, rope climb, and tire walk. Design for safety, strength, and creative play situations. Make sure that all aspects of the design are sized for the child.

Problem 17.2 *Small Tools.* Do a short survey on the variety of small tools, such as screw drivers, pliers, and saws. Attempt to redesign an existing product to better suit the needs of the user. Improve the design; attempt to find creative and aesthetically pleasing alternatives.

Problem 17.3 *Packaging Machine.* Take a small household product and design a packaging machine to load and box the item.

Problem 17.4 *Garbage Dumper.* Design a garbage can and a lift device that could empty the can into the dump truck. Expand on this idea by designing stackable recycling containers for glass, cans, plastic, and paper products.

Problem 17.5 *Fishing Rod Holder.* Create a series of fishing rod holders that will accommodate all sizes and shapes of handles. One version should be for a boat-mounted holder, the other a shore fishing model.

Problem 17.6 *Face Guard.* Design a face guard for baseball hitters to use while batting. Do a study on the typical human face and how to protect it without reducing visibility or inhibiting the batter.

Problem 17.7 *Trailer Hitch.* Design an interchangeable hitch that could be used for all size balls and every class of hitch, if possible. Research should include the ball sizes, weight limits, classifications, and materials of existing hitches.

Physically Challenged Problems

Most colleges have a department devoted to the physically challenged. An excellent design project would include the research and analysis of how the life of a physically challenged person is determined by the man-made items found in daily life. Contact your physically challenged program and request to interview a number of wheelchair-bound persons. Other types of physical limitations could also be studied. Design projects for the blind, hearing impaired, or seeing impaired could also be considered.

Since the physically challenged use many of the existing facilities, this is an excellent area in which to research, analyze, and design products and fixtures. Do some research and tabulate your findings as in Figure 17.84, where the number of fixtures and the number of users of a facility are displayed on a graph. Determine the number of users for a particular facility, and chart the information, as in Figure 17.85. Figure 17.86 is an example of a sketch used to determine the proper heights of restroom facilities for the physically limited. Your problems should have rough sketches, development layouts, and accurate CAD or manual assemblies and details.

Many products will require studies involving human factors and ergonomics. The student should research the project by consulting the *Human Factors Design Handbook* by Wesley E. Woodson (McGraw-Hill Book Company) and *Ergonomic Design for People at Work* (Eastman Kodak Company, Lifetime Learning Publications). Both of these volumes contain pertinent data regarding designs for the physically limited.

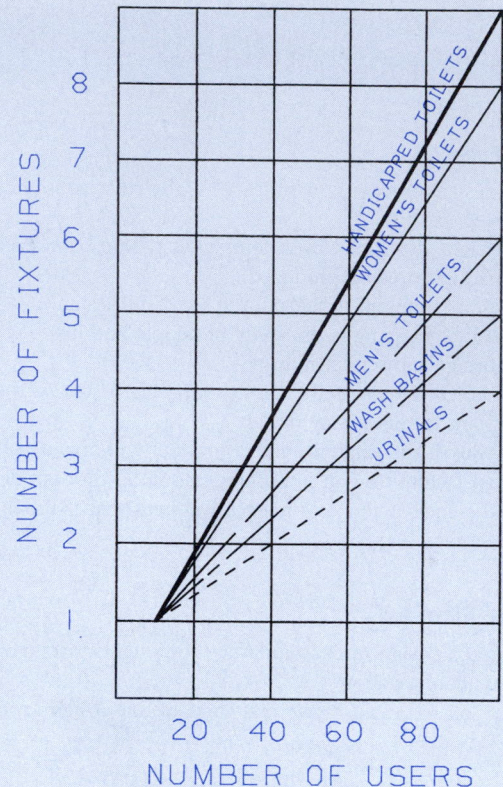

FIGURE 17.85 Graphical Analysis of Research Data on Facility Use of Restroom

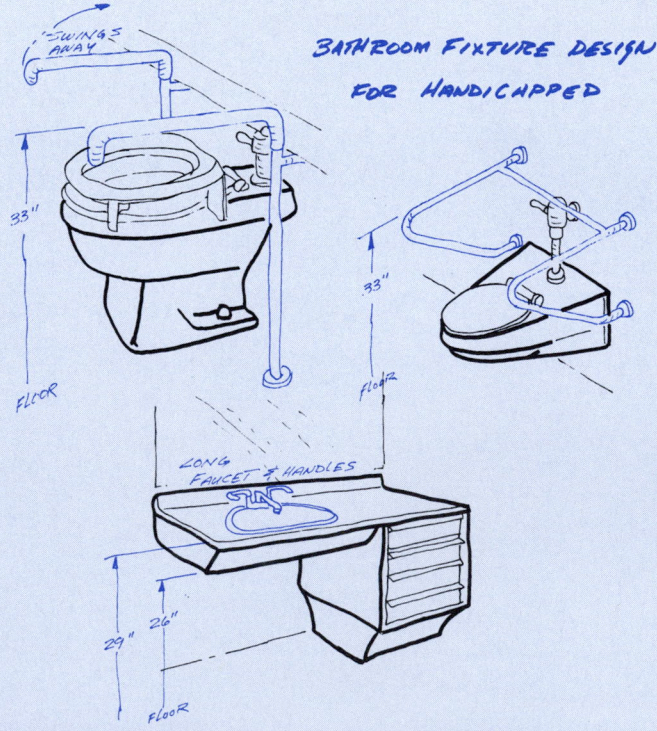

FIGURE 17.86 Bathroom Fixture Design for Handicapped

Problem 17.8 *Bathroom or Restroom Layout.* The bathroom or restroom configuration includes a number of appliances. Wash basins, commodes, mirrors, tubs, showers, faucets, lights, dryers, handtowel dispensers, soap dispensers, cabinets, and floor space must all be considered. Figure 17.86 shows some design alternatives for commodes and a sink. In addition to taking notes about the facility, bring along a tape measure and roughly determine the optimum height and size for a well-designed restroom or bathroom.

One way of researching the needs and capabilities of a physically limited person is to imagine yourself in their place. If possible, borrow a wheelchair and spend some time taking notes as to where and what difficulties are encountered during a typical day. If a wheelchair is unavailable, then use a chair with wheels (such as a computer chair) and move around your home while being confined.

When researching a restroom or a bathroom, take notice of each detail. First, do what you would normally do in that facility. Upon entering, is there enough room for your wheelchair? Is there sufficient clearance for your hands, for the chair, for your extended feet? How difficult is it to get on and off the commode? Can you reach the basin and the faucets? How difficult is it to perform simple grooming procedures? Are the switches and the electrical plugs accessible? Combing and drying hair, applying makeup, washing the face and hands should all be investigated.

Problem 17.9 *Kitchen Design.* Complete an analysis of the kitchen area as described for the bathroom. Can the stove and oven be safely operated by a wheelchair-bound person? Are the freezer and refrigerator accessible? Could someone get a beer or pop from the refrigerator's top shelf? Are the small appliances (microwave, blender, toaster) easily operated from a chair? Could the dishes be washed by hand from a wheelchair? Measure the kitchen cabinets and the placement of each appliance, major and minor. A rolling chair can be used to do the research in this area. Design special cabinets to hold small appliances. Redesign a refrigerator and freezer for a physically limited person. Sketch a variety of design improvements for the layout of the total kitchen.

Problem 17.10 *Car Jack.* Design a jack that could be easily used by a physically limited person who has limited use of their legs. The jack must be easy to operate and a convenient size. Possibilities include the incorporation of the jack into the car design itself.

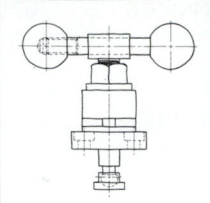

CHAPTER 18

Working Drawings

Learning Objectives

Upon completion of this chapter you will be able to accomplish the following:

1. Convey engineering information for production while recognizing basic types of assembly and drawing categories.
2. Produce assembly and detail drawings with appropriate view selection and dimensions.
3. Compile parts lists and supply information for notes and pre-printed drawing sheets.
4. Identify and apply simplification and checking procedures.
5. Develop an understanding of drawing reproduction and storage methods.
6. Use CAD to generate jig, fixture, die, and tooling designs.

18.1 Introduction

The primary purpose of a drawing is to convey engineering requirements to produce a finished product or part. **Working drawings** include the **assembly drawing** and associated **detail drawings** of a project. Parts are drawn manually or are modeled on a CAD system (Fig. 18.1). Drawings are required for all product design, production requirements, and manufacturing specifications. Each of the parts in Figure 18.2 required working drawings—detail drawings for each separate piece, and an assembly drawing to fit them together. A set of drawings for a system, tool, or a product contains sufficient engineering information so that the following functions may be performed by those who are responsible:

- order material
- plan manufacturing operations, tooling, and manufacturing facilities
- process material
- inspect and control product quality and reliability
- assemble
- test and model
- package, box, and ship
- determine cost
- catalog
- install and service
- conduct final acceptance test
- make alterations
- record for duplication, repair, or replacement

18.2 Assembly Design Considerations

The way the product will be assembled must be considered early in the design phase because of demands each type of assembly places on the design. This is one of the many rea-

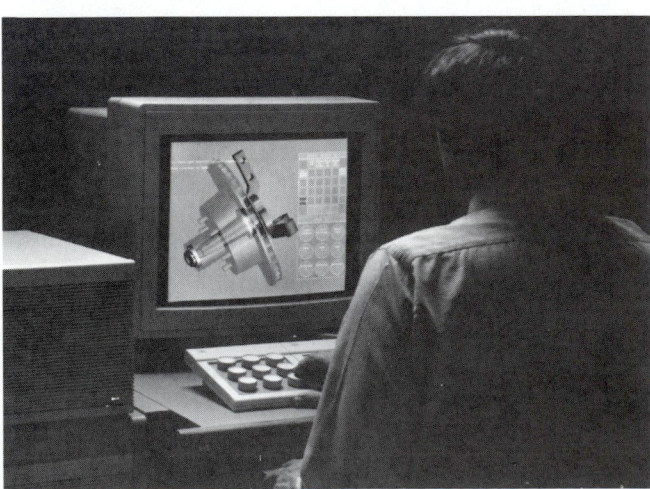

FIGURE 18.1   Solid Model of an Assembly

FIGURE 18.2   Disassembled Boiler Feed Pump

sons why the design of the product and the process must occur simultaneously. The optimal method of assembly can be chosen early in the design process if the product and the production-assembly process are designed at the same time. There are five basic types of assembly:

1. **Manual assembly** is performed manually with only the assistance of hand tools.
2. **Semiautomatic assembly** includes a combination of manual and automated processes. The operator loads the product manually, the machine then performs one or more assembly operations, and the operator then unloads the product.
3. **Adaptive assembly** involves programming the system to adapt itself automatically to certain variations based on sensor information.
4. **Automatic assembly** means that all operations are automatically performed without human intervention or decisions. Automatic assembly places constraints on the design for both the assembly of the product and the orientation, presentation, and gripping of the parts.
5. **Flexible assembly** uses flexible manufacturing equipment, which builds families of related products or subassemblies on the same setup or with quick, automated setup changes built into the process. Flexible assembly places the greatest constraints on the designer since not only do the products have to be designed for automation but all of the parts and the products must be similar enough to be built on the same machinery or at the same workstation.

18.3 Categories of Drawings

Engineering drawings can be classified in three broad categories:

- layout and design study drawings
- engineering and production detail drawings
- assembly drawings

18.3.1 Layout and Design Study Drawings

Layout and design drawings depict proportions, dimensions, materials, and the relationship of parts in new or modified designs. Usually, they precede production drawings, are drawn to scale, and are useful in preparing and checking part drawings and assemblies.

Layout drawings are often effective in establishing patent claims. Layouts are completed by designers and or layout drafters working closely with the lead designer and engineer. When practical, layouts should be prepared in a form suitable for use in manufacturing, especially in situations where prototype or developmental models of equipment (Fig. 18.3) are required.

18.3.2 Engineering and Production Detail Drawings

Detail drawings provide complete engineering definition of the finished system, assembly, or part (Fig. 18.4). This includes reference to supplementary information such as design

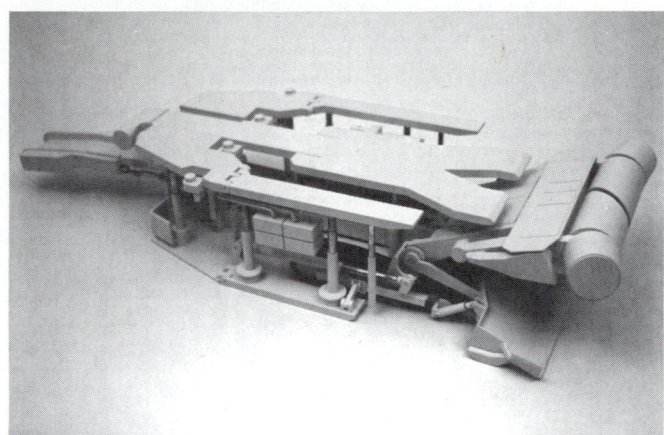

FIGURE 18.3 Industrial Prototype Model of a Lift

data references, laboratory instructions, and engineering specifications. These drawings are prepared for the shop floor and are used in the production of the desired product.

Individual parts of an assembly are machined separately during the manufacturing stage of the project. Parts are also called **work pieces**. A typical work piece is detailed so the fixture designer can produce appropriate tools for holding and locating the work piece during the machining operations.

Engineering production drawings are not prepared to accommodate a particular method of manufacture and do not include information relating to manufacturing workstations. Engineering production drawings are prepared so that, regardless of location of manufacture, they can be used without additional explanation. Manufacturing or processing instructions may also be provided, but this information is for reference purposes only, unless such data are vital to the end definition and engineering control of the product.

18.3.3 Assembly Drawings

An **assembly drawing** defines the complete end item requirements and establishes item identification for the assembled configuration of two or more pieces, parts, subordinate assemblies, or any combination joined together to form an assembly (Fig. 18.5, p. 684). Assembly drawings always include a **parts list** or **bill of materials**. The sleeve valve in Figure 18.6, p. 685 required an assembly drawing to show the proper relationship of the parts. During the design phase, a design layout was used to establish and control the relationship between the parts with regard to tolerancing and fits (see Color Plates 62 through 67 and 77 through 82).

18.4 Assembly Drawings and the Design Process

In most cases, the assembly is conceived as a whole (layout assembly) and broken into individual pieces (detail drawings)

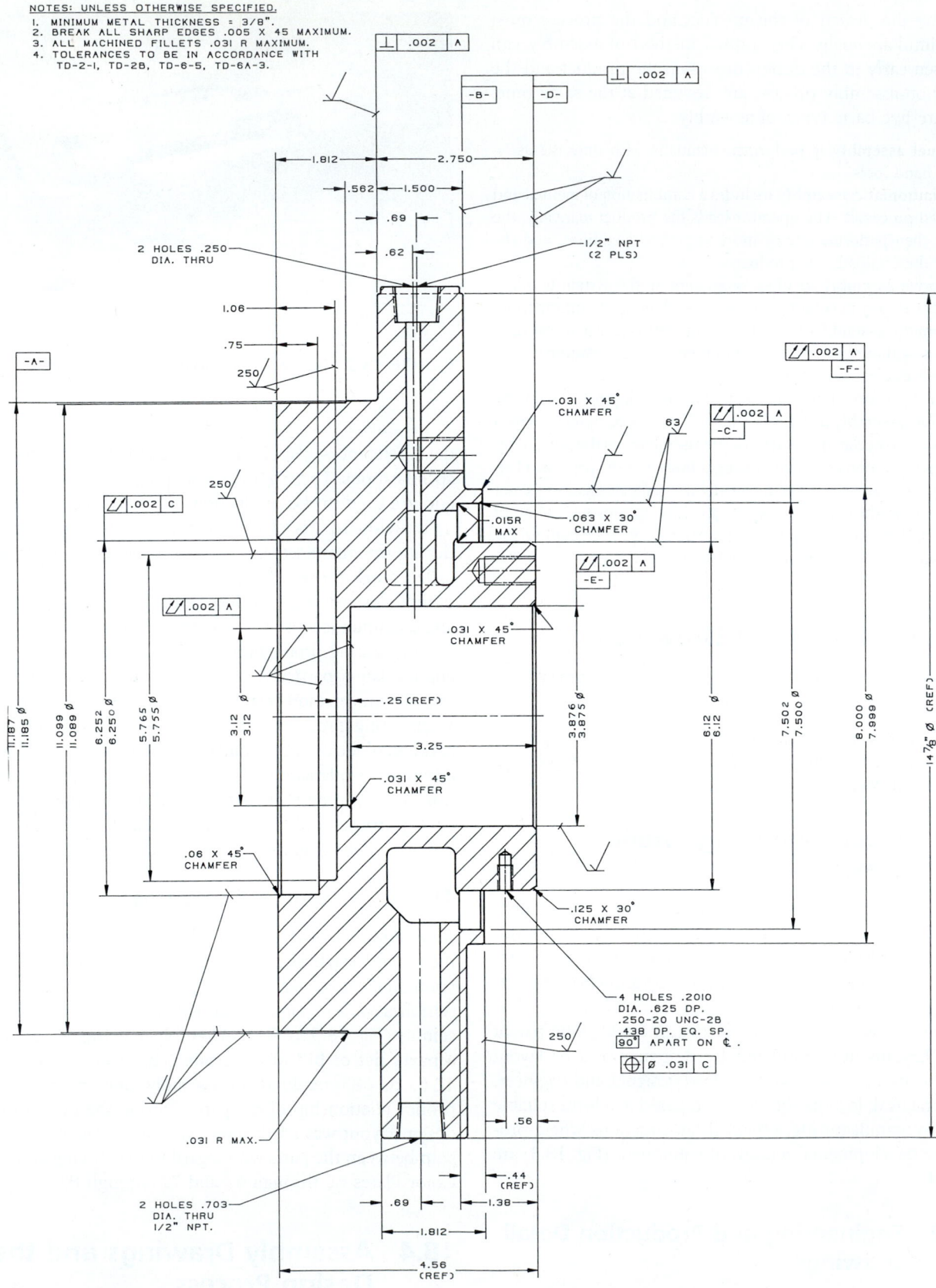

NOTES: UNLESS OTHERWISE SPECIFIED.
1. MINIMUM METAL THICKNESS = 3/8".
2. BREAK ALL SHARP EDGES .005 X 45 MAXIMUM.
3. ALL MACHINED FILLETS .031 R MAXIMUM.
4. TOLERANCES TO BE IN ACCORDANCE WITH
   TD-2-1, TD-2B, TD-6-5, TD-6A-3.

(a)

FIGURE 18.4   Cover Detail

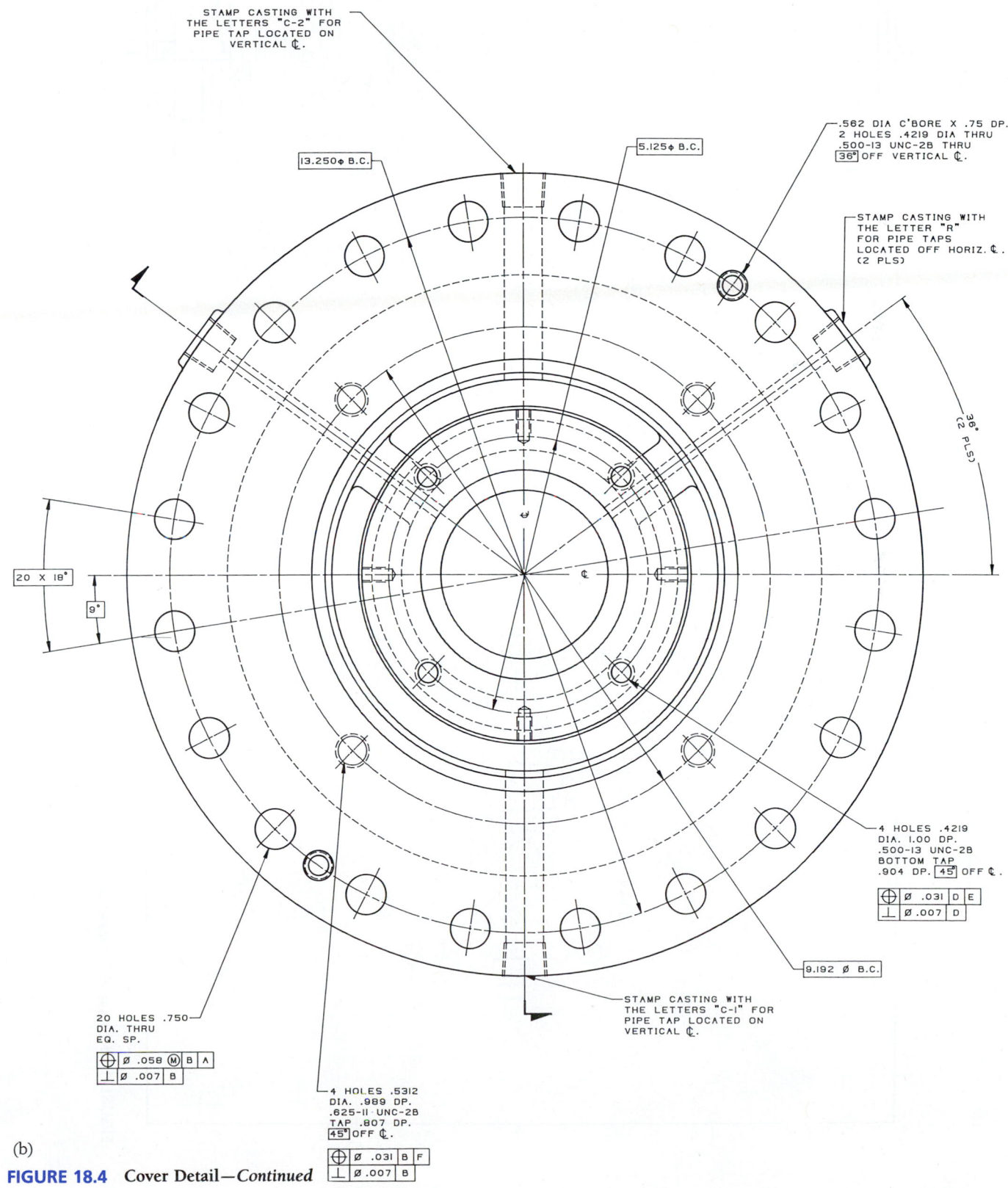

STAMP CASTING WITH
THE LETTERS "C-2" FOR
PIPE TAP LOCATED ON
VERTICAL ℄.

.562 DIA C'BORE X .75 DP.
2 HOLES .4219 DIA THRU
.500-13 UNC-2B THRU
36° OFF VERTICAL ℄.

STAMP CASTING WITH
THE LETTER "R"
FOR PIPE TAPS
LOCATED OFF HORIZ. ℄.
(2 PLS)

13.250ϕ B.C.

5.125ϕ B.C.

36°
(2 PLS)

20 X 18°

9°

4 HOLES .4219
DIA. 1.00 DP.
.500-13 UNC-2B
BOTTOM TAP
.904 DP. 45° OFF ℄.

| ⊕ | ∅ .031 | D | E |
| ⊥ | ∅ .007 | D |

9.192 ∅ B.C.

STAMP CASTING WITH
THE LETTERS "C-1" FOR
PIPE TAP LOCATED ON
VERTICAL ℄.

20 HOLES .750
DIA. THRU
EQ. SP.

| ⊕ | ∅ .058 Ⓜ | B | A |
| ⊥ | ∅ .007 | B |

4 HOLES .5312
DIA. .989 DP.
.625-11 UNC-2B
TAP .807 DP.
45° OFF ℄.

| ⊕ | ∅ .031 | B | F |
| ⊥ | ∅ .007 | B |

(b)

FIGURE 18.4   **Cover Detail—*Continued***

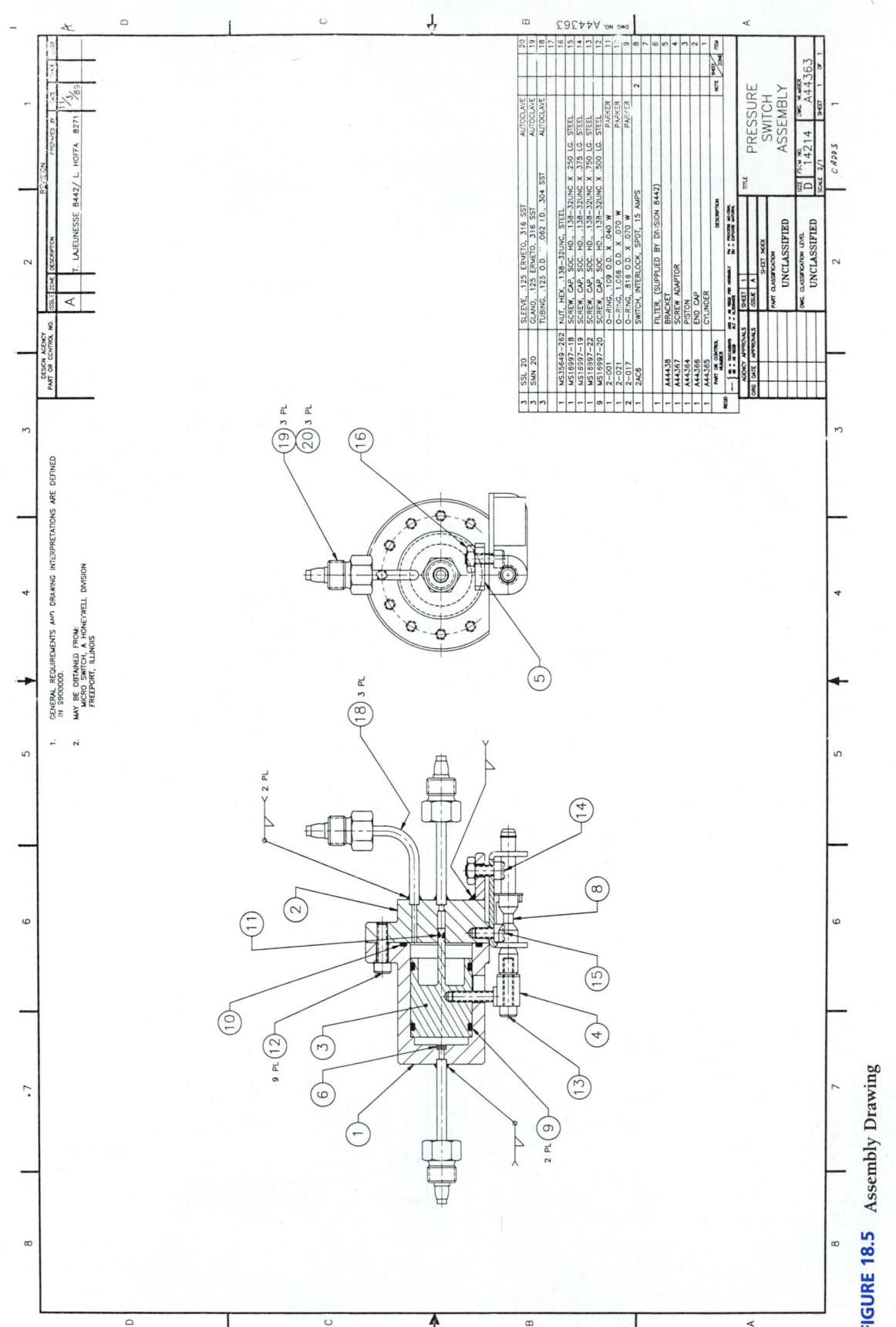

FIGURE 18.5 Assembly Drawing

FIGURE 18.6   Disassembled Grove Flexflo Flexible Rubber Sleeve Valve

for manufacturing and later assembly. This is called the **top-down approach** to design.

Assemblies are seldom designed from the bottom-up, unless the individual parts are standard items that are to be assembled into a unit. **Bottom-up design** means that each component of a unit is designed separately and then put together in an assembly.

The sleeve valve in Figure 18.6 comes in four pieces. The design is *limited to the minimum number of parts*. Each piece fits inside the other. Since each piece was toleranced in relationship to the housing, the product was *designed as a unit*. The housing and endcap hold the other parts together. The bolts and nuts needed for assembly are not shown in the figure.

After the design and layout of the project is complete, a detail drafter pulls separate parts from the assembly and draws them on individual sheets. This process is called **detailing**. Details include appropriate views and dimensions.

Standard items that can be purchased off the shelf are shown on the assembly drawing and listed in the parts list. They do not require a separate detail, unless they are to be modified in some way. Standard parts include bolts, screws, nuts, retaining rings, dowels, pins, springs, gears, bearings, clamps, and purchased subassemblies and assemblies.

As the product is designed and detailed, the manufacturing department will begin to determine the tooling requirements. The design and detail of the jigs, fixtures, dies, and other tools necessary for the production of the product is an extremely important process in the manufacturing of a product.

Tool designers create appropriate fixtures to hold the individual parts during the manufacturing processes. Machining involves the use of fixtures to locate, hold, and position the part for accurate, economical, and efficient production. A majority of the drafting and design time is devoted to the production requirements and tooling design, not product design. Jigs and fixtures are also assemblies and are designed, laid out, and detailed similar to product assemblies.

18.4.1   Assembly Drawing Types

An assembly drawing may contain the detailed design requirements for one or more parts used in the assembly. It is prepared for each group of items that is to be joined together to form an assembly and reflects either:

- a logical level in the assembly or disassembly sequence
- a functional unit
- a stocked standard off-the-shelf purchased item

The assembly may be shown on the same drawing sheet on which the details are shown or on a separate sheet. Color Plate 82 is a combined assembly and detail drawing. If the assembly is shown on a separate sheet, it will be sheet number one and the details shown on sheet number two, etc. All sheets will bear the same drawing number.

An assembly drawing may define either a **separable** or **inseparable** assembly. **Welded assemblies** are inseparable assemblies. Figure 18.7 is an example of a welded assembly. The parts list is actually a **material stock list** and simply lists the stock steel sizes of each piece. On most weldments, the assembly is considered a detail of a part and each piece is dimensioned on the drawing. The detail of the weldment in Figure 18.8 is such a case. Here, even though the weldment is three separate pieces of aluminum joined together by welding, it is not considered an assembly. This drawing is simply a detail of the weldment. Each piece is not separately called out, ballooned, or listed in a material stock list. Instead, it is dimensioned on the sheet. (See Chapter 14 for more information concerning weldments and welded assemblies.)

18.4.2   Mechanical Assemblies and Drawing Requirements

A mechanical assembly may have parts made from sand, permanent mold, or die castings (Fig. 18.9, p. 688); rolled, extruded or pressed shape forgings; plates; bars; sheet metal; or a combination of any two or more of these materials. These parts may be assembled into a complete unit by welding, brazing, soldering, riveting, bolting, or other fastening devices. After assembly, additional work, such as machining, may be necessary to make a completed item.

The function of an assembly drawing is to provide a complete specification for joining together, in proper relationship, two or more detail parts or subassemblies to form an assembly. This type of drawing usually includes a graphic layout of component parts, necessary notes, and, if a separate list or bill of material is not used, a tabulated list of parts. It should show the spatial relation of each part or subassembly, the method of fastening, and type of fasteners.

When necessary, the assembly drawing indicates subsequent operations to be performed on the assembly to form the completed item. For example, heat treatment, machining dimensions, and finishes are specified here. If a mechanical assembly is made entirely from cut shapes with sufficient

ITEM	QTY	MATERIAL SIZE
6	1	.75 X 1.75 X 4.75
5	1	.62 X 1.50 X 2.38
4	1	.38 X 1.00 X 1.25
3	1	.62 X 1.00 X 3.50
2	2	.62 X 1.00 X 1.31
1	1	.19 X 9.06 X 23.50

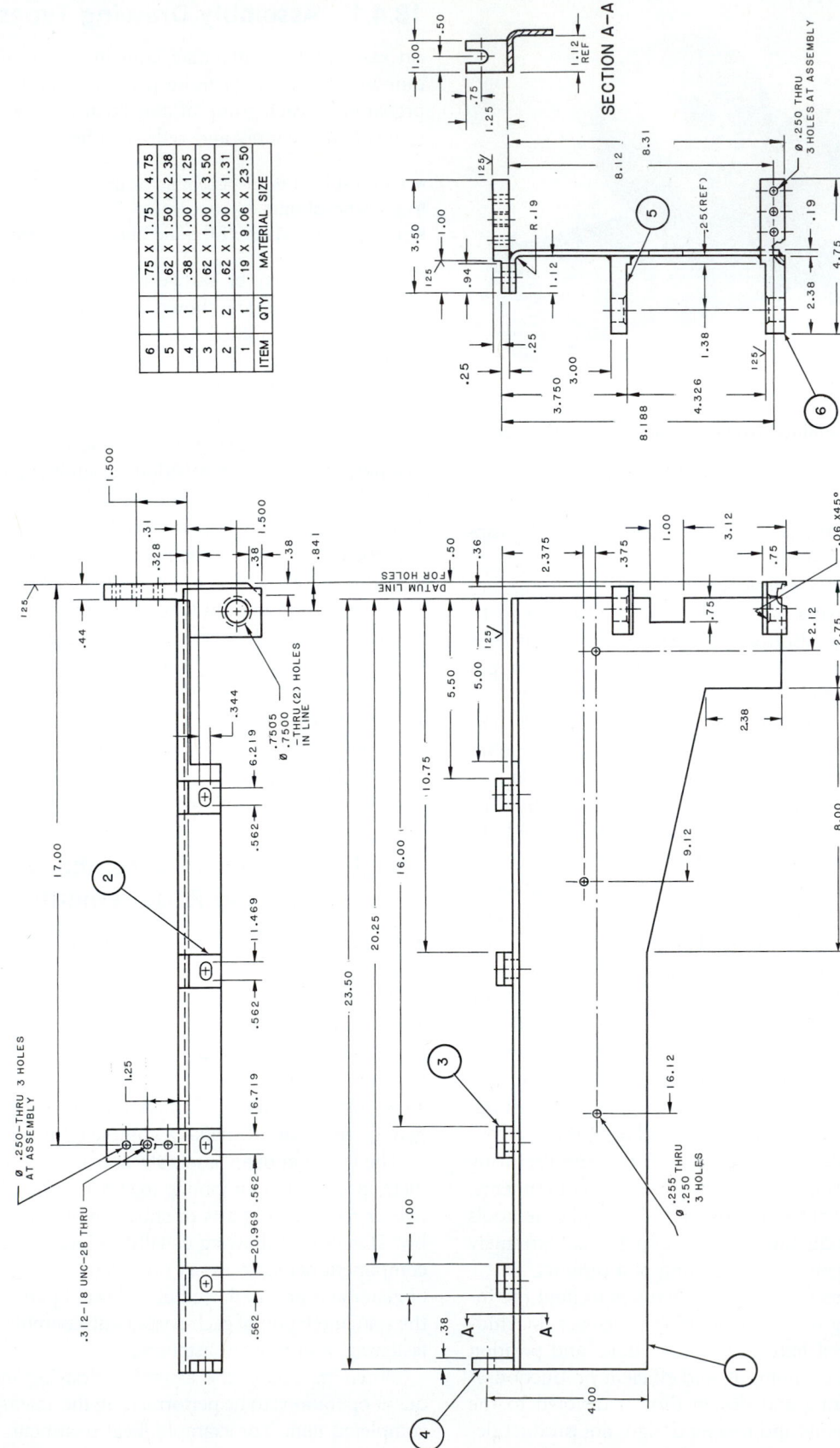

FIGURE 18.7 Welded Assembly

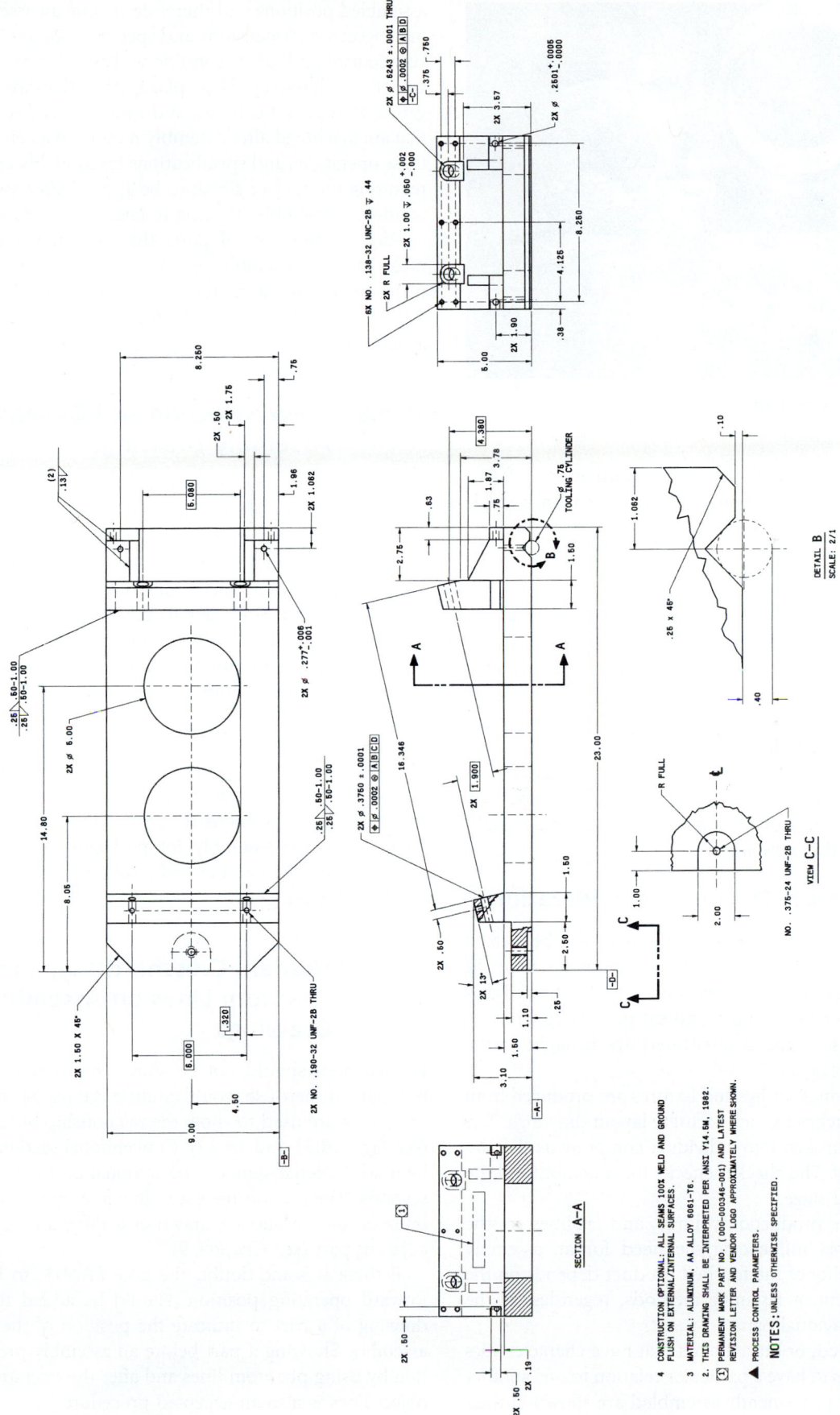

FIGURE 18.8 Welded Assembly Detail

FIGURE 18.9   Die Cast Parts

information for cutting each piece, the information to fasten them together and finish them might be given on a single drawing.

18.4.3   Detail Drawings

Detail drawings are fully dimensioned, accurately laid-out engineering drawings of individual parts (Fig. 18.10). All information needed to manufacture and produce the part must be included. Adequate view description, correct dimensioning and tolerancing, accurate notes, and material designation are shown on the detail drawing. Projection methods, dimensioning, and tolerancing for detail drawings are covered in Chapters 7, 9, 10, 12, and 13. Components may appear on the assembly drawings or on separate details, or be established by written description.

18.4.4   Assembly Drawing Considerations

Assembly drawings for production parts may also be created from the detail drawings *after they have been approved by the checker*. This procedure gives a final check of the detail drawings for space clearances, limits, and satisfactory function in assembly. Any discrepancies discovered are brought to the attention of the designer.

Assembly drawings for jigs and fixtures are produced from the designer's sketches that are accurate layout drawings. The final assembly is broken into individual components that are detailed separately. The checker checks the assembly and the details in the final stage.

Product design, production volume, and facilities are the determining factors influencing the need for an assembly drawing. The quality of the finished product depends on the effective attachment or fastening methods, regardless of the quality of the individual parts.

Welded, soldered, or brazed parts that have characteristics requiring the parts to have a particular relation to one another and parts that are permanently assembled are shown in their

assembled positions and therefore require an assembly drawing. Necessary dimensions and specifications are included for size control and other conditions. Parts that are pressed together and line-reamed in place; parts that are secured together with pins, bushings, and similar assemblies; and parts that are machined after assembly require an assembly to show these operations and specifications for assembly control. Parts requiring the surface finish to be applied after assembly may require an assembly drawing to ensure proper overall finish.

Any combination of parts that is purchased assembled must have an assembly drawing to show working arrangements, clearances, and other requirements. The vice in Figure 18.11 and the drain assembly in Figure 18.12 are examples of assembled devices.

18.4.5   View Selection and Dimensions on Assembly Drawings

The selection of the appropriate views for an assembly is important. Choice of views depends on the configuration and orientation. Usually, the views are chosen to depict the assembly in its natural position in space, to define clearly how the parts fit together, and to describe the functional relationship of the parts. Since details provide the physical description of each part, actual physical description of the parts is the last concern. The minimum number of views needed to define the assembly should be used. Often only one view is required.

Dimensions on assembly drawings are confined to setup dimensions, dimensions needed for assembly, dimensions required for machining after assembly, and clearance dimensions. Overall dimensions (height, width, and depth) may be included on the assembly for packaging assistance. When necessary, the open and closed positions of movable parts on the assembly are given.

18.4.6   Hidden, Crosshatching, and Phantom Lines on Assembly Drawings

Hidden lines should not be shown on assembly drawings, especially if their use would confuse the reader. Instead, section views are used to show the relationship of internal parts (see Figs. 18.31 and 18.32). Conventional section lining may be used. Material symbols are optional on assembly drawing sections. The section lines are drawn at angles to the object outlines and should be drawn at a different angle for each adjacent part (see Chapter 9).

If there is some doubt, the note **FRONT**, to indicate the forward operating position, should be added to the detail drawing of a part to indicate the position of the part in the assembly. Showing a part before an assembly process operation by using phantom lines and after the operation by using object lines is also an accepted procedure.

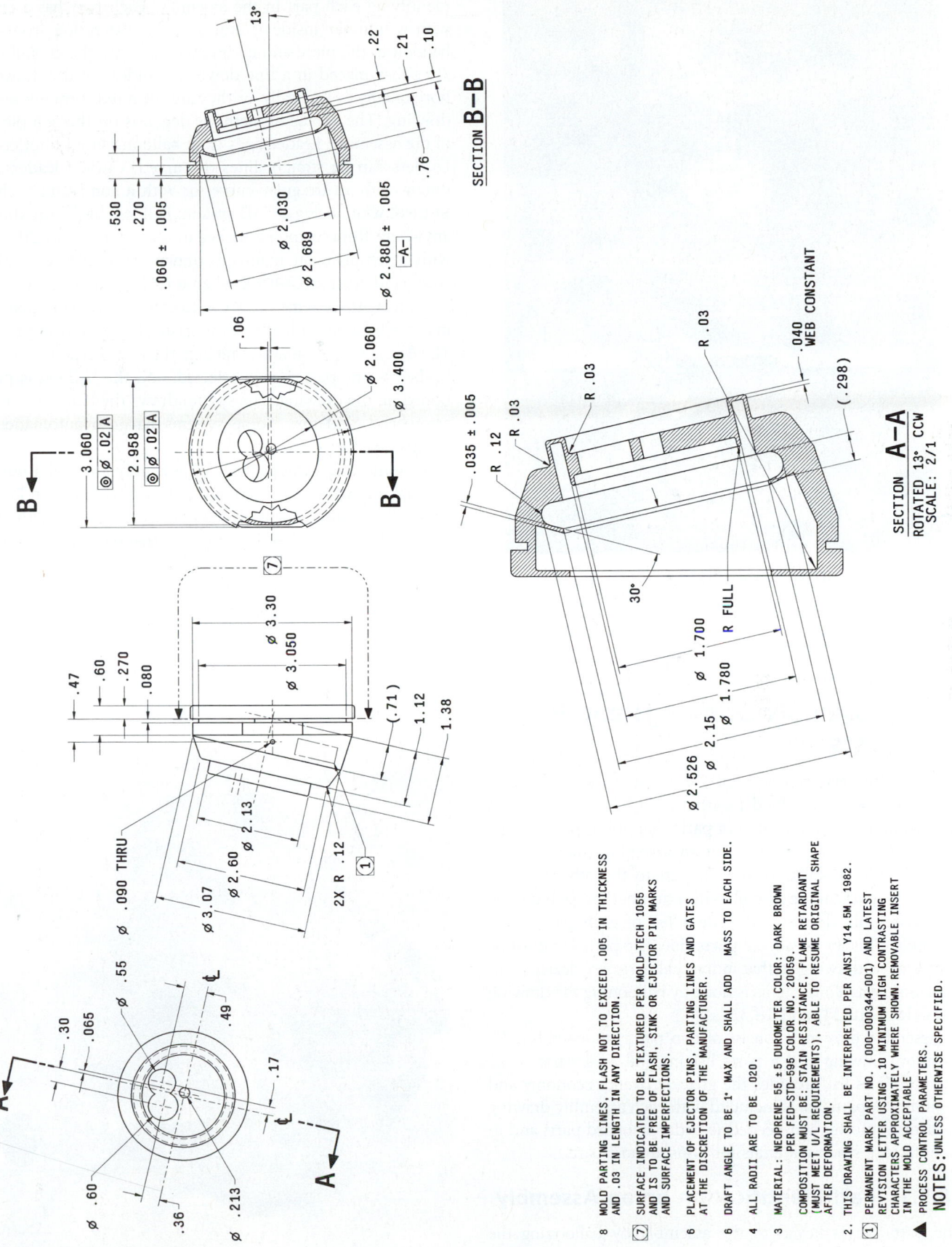

FIGURE 18.10   Acoustic Microphone Cup

SECTION **B-B**

SECTION **A-A**
ROTATED 13° CCW
SCALE: 2/1

8   MOLD PARTING LINES, FLASH NOT TO EXCEED .005 IN THICKNESS
    AND .03 IN LENGTH IN ANY DIRECTION.

7   SURFACE INDICATED TO BE TEXTURED PER MOLD-TECH 1055
    AND IS TO BE FREE OF FLASH, SINK OR EJECTOR PIN MARKS
    AND SURFACE IMPERFECTIONS.

6   PLACEMENT OF EJECTOR PINS, PARTING LINES AND GATES
    AT THE DISCRETION OF THE MANUFACTURER.

5   DRAFT ANGLE TO BE 1° MAX AND SHALL ADD   MASS TO EACH SIDE.

4   ALL RADII ARE TO BE .020.

3   MATERIAL: NEOPRENE 55 ± 5 DUROMETER COLOR: DARK BROWN
    PER FED-STD-595 COLOR NO. 20059.
    COMPOSITION MUST BE: STAIN RESISTANCE, FLAME RETARDANT
    (MUST MEET U/L REQUIREMENTS), ABLE TO RESUME ORIGINAL SHAPE
    AFTER DEFORMATION.

2. THIS DRAWING SHALL BE INTERPRETED PER ANSI Y14.5M, 1982.

1   PERMANENT MARK PART NO. (000-000344-001) AND LATEST
    REVISION LETTER USING .10 MINIMUM HIGH CONTRASTING
    CHARACTERS APPROXIMATELY WHERE SHOWN. REMOVABLE INSERT
    IN THE MOLD ACCEPTABLE

▲   PROCESS CONTROL PARAMETERS.
NOTES: UNLESS OTHERWISE SPECIFIED.

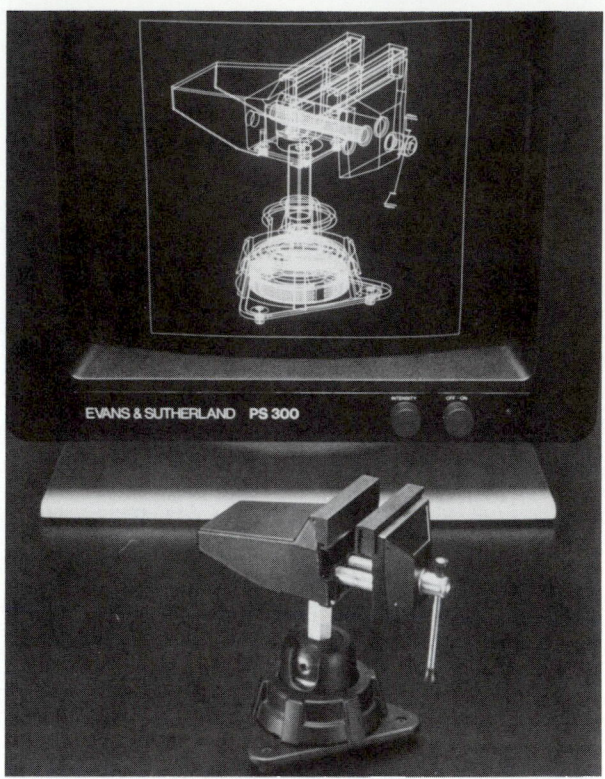

FIGURE 18.11 3D Vice Assembly

identifying each part in the assembly. Each part has a circle with a number inside it and a leader extending from the balloon to the piece and ending with an arrowhead. Balloons are either placed in a line down the middle of the drawing, horizontally or vertically, or they are scattered throughout the drawing. The choice of methods depends on the complexity of the assembly. Leader lines from balloons should not cross. Leaders can be straight lines or curved. Curved leaders are drawn with an irregular curve, or with a command such as **SPLINE** when using a CAD system. Balloon circles are drawn anywhere from .5 to .75 inches in diameter (12 to 20 mm) with a template on manually drawn assemblies or with a command such as **CIRCLE** when a CAD system is used.

Many CAD systems allow you to enter a command that will insert a balloon with the appropriate text within the circle. The **BALLOON** command is picked, the text is typed using the keyboard, the part edge is selected, and the balloon is positioned on the drawing. The system draws the balloon, leader, arrowhead, and text. Some systems have an automatic sequence number capability.

In some cases, the parts of an assembly are called out on the drawing without the aid of numbered balloons. In Figure 18.13 the shutter assembly has been displayed pictorially. Each of the parts is described in notes that have leaders pointing to the part. (See also the problem section of this chapter for other examples of assemblies.)

18.5 Assembly Drawings and Parts Lists

An **assembly** has been described as a combination of two or more parts that are joined together in one working unit. A **subassembly** is an assembly of parts that aid in producing a larger assembly. The purpose of an assembly drawing is to show the spatial relation of each part to the others and to identify all parts in the assembly by a number for each unique part. Assembly drawings include a list of each part of the assembly. This list is called a **parts list**. The parts list must be keyed to the drawing so that individual parts are clearly identified on the assembly. This is done by ballooning the drawing (Figs. 18.5, 18.31, and 18.32).

Assembly drawings consist of two parts: an assembly delineation drawing and a parts list integral or separate. The separate parts list provides the greatest overall economy and flexibility. A parts list is included with each assembly drawing to furnish information needed to order standard parts and to manufacture stock materials for nonstandard parts.

18.5.1 Part Identification on an Assembly

The parts list is keyed to the assembly by ballooning the individual pieces of the unit. **Ballooning** is the process of

FIGURE 18.12 Multiport Drain

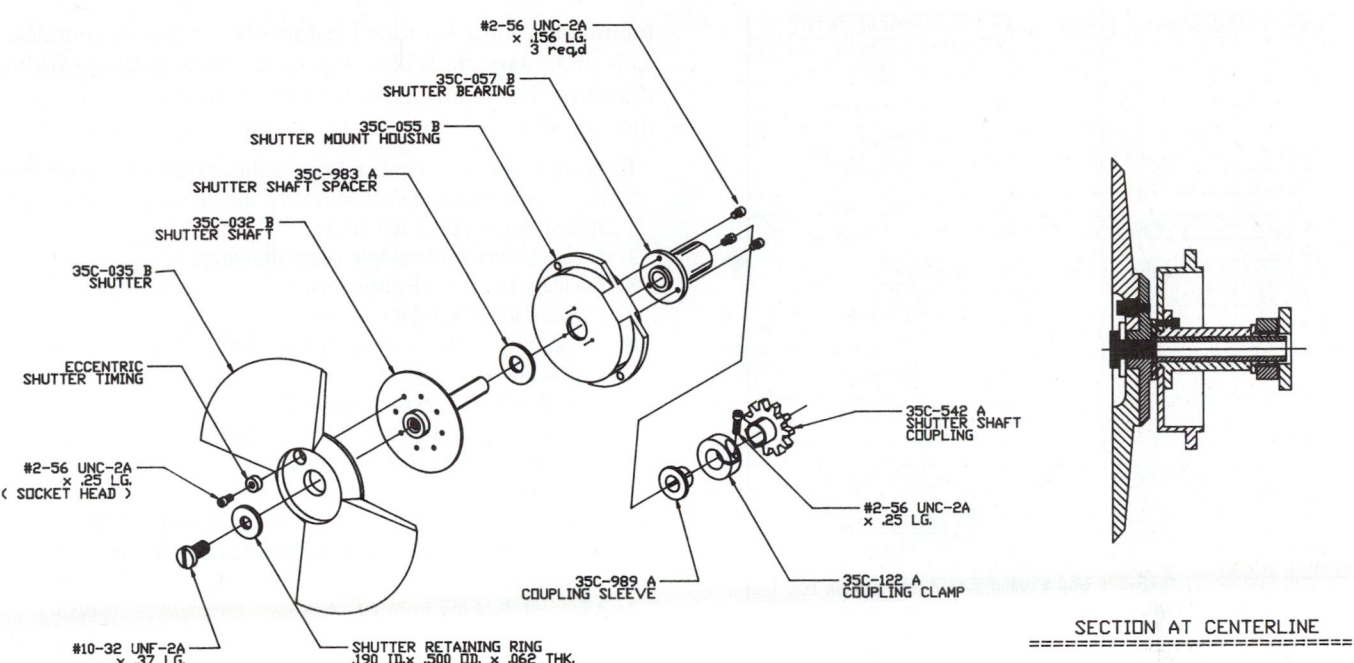

FIGURE 18.13 UltraCam Shutter Assembly

18.5.2   Parts Lists

The assembly drawing must have a complete **parts list**. Each parts list includes individual part numbers, name and description of each part, and the material and quantity of all items required for one complete assembly (Fig. 18.14).

On tool and die drawings, the parts list is sometimes called a **stock list.** Here, material allowance is added for purchase information. Die drawings also have a stock list on the assembly drawing sheet.

The assembly parts list is placed above the title block when on the same sheet as the drawing. The part numbers are arranged to read upward so that new parts can be added if needed. The precise method of listing parts varies with companies. The parts or stock list sometimes uses the vertical line divisions of the revision record (block at top right of the drawing form). The spacing of horizontal divisions is uniform in both revision blocks and the parts list.

Parts List Heading Arrangement When an integral parts list is included on a drawing sheet the heading **PARTS LIST** is placed on the bottom of the list and the part numbers read upward. Figure 18.15 is an example of a company title block with a parts list. The quantity, item number (balloon number), part number, and the description are shown.

When the parts list is separate from the part drawing or on a computer list, the heading **PARTS LIST** is at the top and the list is constructed from the top down. The following describes

the four basic columns (Fig. 18.16) used on a parts list and what entries are to be made in each:

- **QUANTITY REQUIRED** The number entered in this column denotes the quantity, volume, length, or other unit of measure required to complete one of the items to which the column applies. When this number applies to other than quantity, the unit of measure is entered here or in an optional unit of measure column.
- **FSCM** The Federal Supply Code for Manufacturer's number assigned to the originating design activity whose part or identifying number appears in column 3 is shown in this column. Notice that many company title blocks do not include this entry.
- **PART OR IDENTIFYING NUMBER** The identifying number for each item on the parts list is shown in this column.
- **NOMENCLATURE OR DESCRIPTION** The assigned noun or name of the item whose identifying number appears in the part number column appears in this column.

18.5.3   Drawing Sheets

Drafting sheets are preprinted sheets with the border, title block (Fig. 18.17), and revision block preprinted on polyester film, vellum, bond, or other type of paper. **Drafting formats** are predefined blocks or subdrawings available for quick insertion on an assembly drawing created on a CAD system. In either case, you need not draw the sheet, but you must know what each aspect of the drawing sheet means and what

ITEM	QTY	PART NO.	DESCRIPTION
55	1	664-359239	CABLE, ASSY - MONOCHRONOMETER, YEL
54	1	664-359238	CABLE, ASSY - MONOCHRONOMETER, GRN
53	1	664-359237	CABLE, ASSY - MONOCHRONOMETER, RED
52			
51			
50	1	693-349584	BOARD, P.W. – U.V. SCANNER
49	1	301-961283	SPRING, CPRSN-.063 OD X 1 LG CRES
48			
47			
46	12	165-359506	WASHER, FLT .127 TFL-
45			
44	1	125-362041	PIN, DOWEL –.1553 DIA X .450L CRES
43	4	125-811591	PIN, DOWEL –.1251 DIA X .375L CRES
42	4	125-824305	PIN, DOWEL –.0626 DIA X .312L CRES
41			
40			
39	3	130-961281	RING, RETAINING - EXT. .073 ID
38	2	105-828447	NUT, HEX 2-56 S-BK
37			
36			
35	6	101-827620	SCREW, CAP 4-40 X 1" S-HXSO
34	2	101-961013	SCREW, CAP 2-56 X 1-3/8 S-HXSO
33	2	101-803947	SCREW, CAP 2-56 X .875 S-HXSO
32	1	101-961282	SCREW, CAP 2-56 X .750 S-HXSO
31	2	101-961201	SCREW, MACH 2-56 X 1" FL-S-SL
30	2	101-828409	SCREW, MACH 2-56 X .375 P-S-BK-SL
29	3	101-828408	SCREW, MACH 2-56 X .25 P-S-BK-SL
28			
27			
26	2	201-361974	GEAR, (MODIFIED) 42 TEETH
25	1	201-359899	GEAR, (MODIFIED) 84 TEETH
24	3	201-349033	GEAR, (MODIFIED) 132 TEETH
23			
22			
21	1	150-359263	BUSHING, MIRROR HOUSING
20	6	145-863274	BEARING
19			
18			
17	1	201-356344	RACK, GEAR U.V. MODIFICATION
16	1	520-348987	GRATING
15	1	333-349032	PLATFORM, GRATING
14	1	223-356345	SHAFT, CROSSOVER U.V. MODIFICATION
13	4	223-349019	SHAFT, GEAR
12			
11	1	548-361969	ASSY. FILTER
10			
9	1	499-348983	SPUD
8	1	105-348982	NUT, RETAINER
7	1	178-348984	EXTENSION TUBE #1, U.V. SCANNER
6	1	178-349027	EXTENSION TUBE #2, U.V. SCANNER
5	1	178-347010	EXTENSION TUBE #3, U.V. SCANNER
4	1	299-348981	HOUSING, MIRROR
3			
2	1	299-349023	DIRECTION CHAMBER U.V. LIGHT (LEFT)
1	1	299-348989	DIRECTION CHAMBER U.V. LIGHT (RIGHT)

DWG. NO. 223-356367

SIZE E

	BY	DATE
DR	D.M.DUARTE	1/18/90
CHK		
DSGN		
ENGR		

BECKMAN
BECKMAN INSTRUMENTS, INC.
SPINCO DIVISION
1050 PAGE MILL ROAD
PALO ALTO, CALIFORNIA 94304

TITLE
MONOCHRONOMETER
ASSEMBLY

E SIZE | CODE IDENT NO. 07978 | DWG NO. 223-356367

| MOD L10-A | SCALE 1/2 | 1st USE 355899 | SHEET 1 OF 1 |

FIGURE 18.14   Monochronometer Assembly Parts List

information must be added before the project is complete. This understanding is also important when reading existing drawings. The following list describes each part of a typical drawing sheet, as shown in Figure 18.18(a) and (b):

1. Ancillary drawing number. Permits the drafter to file print copies so that, when folded correctly, all drawing numbers will appear in the upper left corner.
2. Sheet number for multiple sheet drawings.
3. Ancillary revision identification.
4. Revision identification symbol.
5. Description of the revision or the identification of the change authorization document.
6. Issue date of the revised drawing.
7. Required approval signatures for revisions.
8. Microfilm alignment arrowheads.
9. DSJ—distribution key or code, if used.
10. Company name and address. Must agree with FSCM number for companies with multidivisions and departments.
11. Drawing title.
12. Assigned drawing number.
13. Weight record. Should indicate whether it is actual, estimated, or calculated, when required, and if it is gross (before machining) or net (after machining).
14. FSCM number. If required for identification of the company or design activity whose drawing number is used.
15. Predominant scale of the drawing.
16. Drawing size letter designation.
17. The signature of the drafter and the date the drawing was started.
18. The signature and date of the responsible person who checked the drawing.
19. The signature and date of the responsible engineer to signify the approval of the design by engineering.
20. Signature of responsible issuing person and initial date of issue.
21. Notes.
22. Approval by an activity other than those described above.
23. The appropriate surface texture designation that applies.
24. The general tolerances that apply to the overall document.
25. The appropriate material specification that should include type, grade, class, or other classifications as applicable.
26. Zones: letters vertically (bottom up, starting with A) and numbers horizontally (right to left, starting with 1).

18.6   Notes

Notes are used on drawings (Fig. 18.19, p. 696) to supply information that cannot be presented in any other descriptive way. Notes are used for such a large variety of purposes that it is not practical to establish standard notes for every condition.

A standard method of applying, placing, and revising notes on engineering drawings is used to maintain company-wide uniformity. Many of the text's illustrations were taken directly from industry so as to show the variety and differences you may encounter. Although there are standard formats, placements, and sequences for notes on the drawing, each company will have their own **company standards**.

2	13	140-862005-606	STUD,SELF-CLINCH-FH, NO. 10-32 X.750 LG
2	12	140-862005-206	STUD,SELF-CLINCH-FH, NO.4-40 X .750
4	11	104-044042-014	FASTENER,SELF-CLINCHING, NO. 10-32
26	10	140-862005-404	STUD SELF-CLINCH-FH, NO.8-32 X .500
22	9	104-044042-002	FASTENER,SELF-CLINCHING, NO. 8-32
4	8	106-044316-006	WASHER EXTERNAL TOOTH, NO. 6
8	7	102-044729-003	LOCKNUT, HEX, NO. 2-56
2	6	140-017322-011	FASTENER,SELF-CLINCHING SS NO. 4-40
8	5	102-044629-001	NUT, SADDLE
7	4	104-045364-001	NUT, HEX JAM, NO. 1/4-20
6	3	104-044356-003	INSERT,THREADED STAINLESS STEEL,NO. 8-32 X.248 LG
3	2	140-021009-001	NUT-HEX, NO. 8 LIGHT
1	1	000-012345-051	COVER,CONTROL,FREQUENCY PANEL (13)
-001	ITEM NO.	VERSATEC PART NO.	DESCRIPTION

QUANTITY PER VERSION

PARTS LIST

PROPRIETARY The contents of this document are PROPRIETARY TO VERSATEC INC. and are not to be disclosed to others or used for purposes other than intended without the written approval of Versatec.

MATERIAL: SEE ABOVE P/L DATA BASE B.O.M AVAILABLE.

UNLESS OTHERWISE SPECIFIED DIMENSIONS ARE IN INCHES. ALL PARTS TO BE DEBURRED AND EDGES BROKEN .010 MAXIMUM

TOL.	1PLC.	2PLC.	3PLC.	ANG.
±	.1	.03	.010	1°--

THIRD ANGLE PROJECTION

FINISH: (7)

SIGNATURE	DATE
DRN. VALENZUELA	9-10-90
CHK.	- -
APPV.	- -
APPV.	- -
APPV.	- -

VERSATEC A XEROX COMPANY   SANTA CLARA CALIFORNIA 95051

TITLE: **COVER, CONTROL, FREQUENCY PANEL**

SIZE E	CODE IDENT. 50804	DRAWING NO. 000-012345	REV. 17

DO NOT SCALE DRAWING   SCALE: 1/2 , AS NOTED   SHEET 1 OF 1

A

FIGURE 18.15   Parts List

QTY REQD	FSCM	PART OR IDENTIFYING NO.	NOMENCLATURE OR DESCRIPTION
PARTS LIST			

(a) COLUMNAR ARRANGEMENT FOR INTEGRAL PARTS LIST

PARTS LIST			
QTY REQD	FSCM	PART OR IDENTIFYING NO.	NOMENCLATURE OR DESCRIPTION

(b) COLUMNAR ARRANGEMENT FOR SEPARATE PARTS LIST

FIGURE 18.16   **Parts List Arrangement**   (a) Columnar arrangement for integral parts list (b) Arrangement for separate parts list

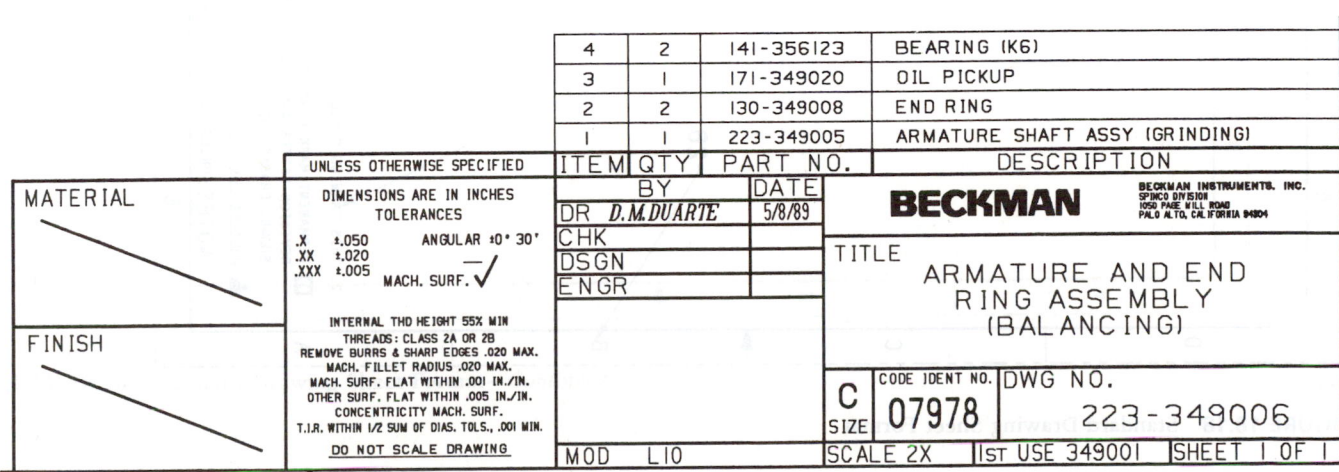

FIGURE 18.17   Armature and End Ring Assembly Title Block and Parts List

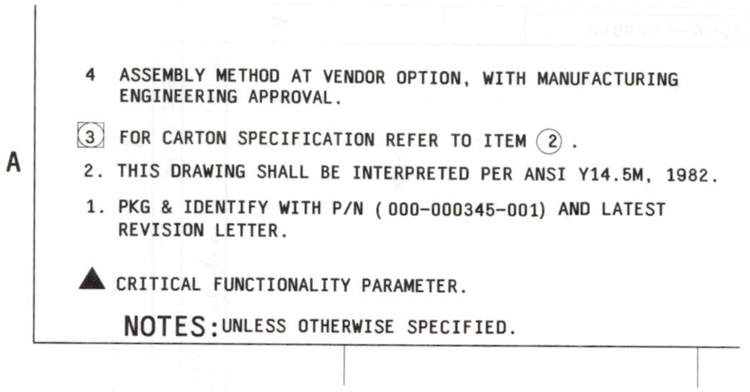

```
A    4   ASSEMBLY METHOD AT VENDOR OPTION, WITH MANUFACTURING
         ENGINEERING APPROVAL.
    [3]  FOR CARTON SPECIFICATION REFER TO ITEM (2).
     2.  THIS DRAWING SHALL BE INTERPRETED PER ANSI Y14.5M, 1982.
     1.  PKG & IDENTIFY WITH P/N ( 000-000345-001) AND LATEST
         REVISION LETTER.
     ▲   CRITICAL FUNCTIONALITY PARAMETER.
      NOTES: UNLESS OTHERWISE SPECIFIED.
```

FIGURE 18.19 General Notes

General notes (Fig. 18.19) are those that apply to the total drawing and, if placed on the drawing at each point of application, would be repetitive and time-consuming to apply. **Local notes** are those that apply to a specific portion, surface, or dimension on a drawing. Local notes indicate local or specific characteristics of a part, assembly, or diagram. The following rules can be used as a guide when putting notes on a drawing:

Use notes to:

- Clarify features that can be more accurately defined by words than by graphical delineation and dimensions.
- Give instructions for applying special treatments.
- Give instructions for utilization of specific processes.
- Describe instructions to supplement standard symbols.
- Provide additional information to the drawing document or to its use.
- Add notes to clarify so that the part will be made correctly the first time.

Notes should be:

- Clear and concise.
- In the present tense.
- Positioned parallel to the bottom edge of the drawing.
- Carefully composed to relay one message; capable of only one interpretation.
- Preprinted on appliques or, if the drawings are computerized, entered in a standard library for repeated use.

Notes should not:

- Be underlined on the drawing.
- Contain abbreviations other than the most commonly understood shop trade terms or words.
- Duplicate information recorded on an associated parts list or shop practices reference document.
- Contain dimensions that are already documented elsewhere on the drawing.
- Describe complex processes. This kind of information should be documented in either a specification or process document.
- Reference information that is given elsewhere in the product documentation.

18.6.1 General Notes

General notes on drawing sizes "B" through "F" are placed in the upper left-hand or lower left-hand corner of the sheet. Some companies construct their note sequence from the bottom-up (Fig. 18.20); others from the top-down (Fig. 18.21). Notes at the top of a sheet are numbered top-down; those at the bottom part of a sheet are numbered bottom-up. The width of the general note column should not exceed 6 to 8 inches (150 to 200 mm).

When the drawing is completed with a CAD system, it is possible to reuse notes that are common to a number of situations and designs. The notes are saved as a **text file** and inserted as blocks on the drawing. Text files can be edited; therefore, variations and changes can be incorporated before insertion.

18.6.2 Local Notes

The placement of **local notes** on the drawing must be outside the outline of the part. Position the note close to the item that is being referenced, or to the surface/area where an operation is to be performed.

Fabrication operations such as **BEND, DRILL, TAP, PUNCH,** or **BORE** are not shown on the drawing. This permits manufacturing to determine the type of operation required to produce the part within the required tolerances. Features

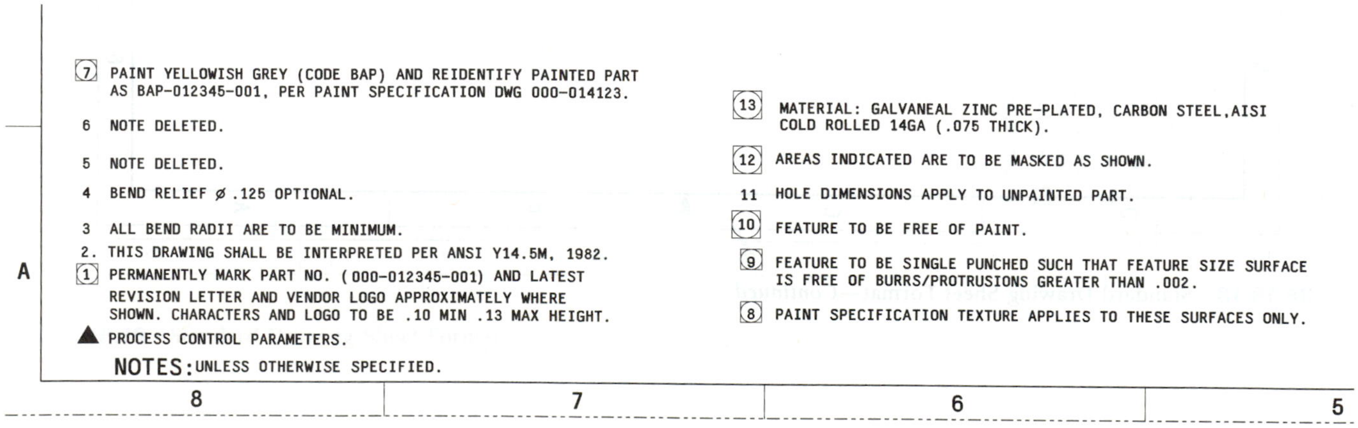

```
    [7]  PAINT YELLOWISH GREY (CODE BAP) AND REIDENTIFY PAINTED PART
         AS BAP-012345-001, PER PAINT SPECIFICATION DWG 000-014123.
     6   NOTE DELETED.
     5   NOTE DELETED.
     4   BEND RELIEF ∅ .125 OPTIONAL.
     3   ALL BEND RADII ARE TO BE MINIMUM.
     2.  THIS DRAWING SHALL BE INTERPRETED PER ANSI Y14.5M, 1982.
A   [1]  PERMANENTLY MARK PART NO. ( 000-012345-001) AND LATEST
         REVISION LETTER AND VENDOR LOGO APPROXIMATELY WHERE
         SHOWN. CHARACTERS AND LOGO TO BE .10 MIN .13 MAX HEIGHT.
     ▲   PROCESS CONTROL PARAMETERS.
      NOTES: UNLESS OTHERWISE SPECIFIED.
         8              7                    6               5

   [13]  MATERIAL: GALVANEAL ZINC PRE-PLATED, CARBON STEEL, AISI
         COLD ROLLED 14GA (.075 THICK).
   [12]  AREAS INDICATED ARE TO BE MASKED AS SHOWN.
    11   HOLE DIMENSIONS APPLY TO UNPAINTED PART.
   [10]  FEATURE TO BE FREE OF PAINT.
    [9]  FEATURE TO BE SINGLE PUNCHED SUCH THAT FEATURE SIZE SURFACE
         IS FREE OF BURRS/PROTRUSIONS GREATER THAN .002.
    [8]  PAINT SPECIFICATION TEXTURE APPLIES TO THESE SURFACES ONLY.
```

FIGURE 18.20 Notes Listed from Bottom-up

-001	ITEM NO.	VERSATEC PART NO.	DESCRIPTION
2	13	140-862005-606	STUD, SELF-CLINCH-FH, NO. 10-32 X .750 LG
2	12	140-862005-206	STUD, SELF-CLINCH-FH, NO.4-40 X .750
4	11	104-044042-014	FASTENER, SELF-CLINCHING, NO. 10-32
26	10	140-862005-404	STUD SELF-CLINCH-FH, NO.8-32 X .500
22	9	104-044042-002	FASTENER, SELF-CLINCHING, NO. 8-32
4	8	106-044316-006	WASHER EXTERNAL TOOTH, NO. 6
8	7	102-044729-003	LOCKNUT, HEX, NO. 2-56
2	6	140-017322-011	FASTENER, SELF-CLINCHING SS NO. 4-40
8	5	102-044629-001	NUT, SADDLE
7	4	104-045364-001	NUT, HEX JAM, NO. 1/4-20
6	3	104-044356-003	INSERT, THREADED STAINLESS STEEL, NO. 8-32 X.248 LG
3	2	140-021009-001	NUT-HEX, NO. 8 LIGHT
1	1	000-012345-051	COVER, CONTROL, FREQUENCY PANEL ⑬

QUANTITY PER VERSION

PARTS LIST

PROPRIETARY
The contents of this document are PROPRIETARY to VERSATEC INC. and are not to be disclosed to others or used for purposes other than intended without the written approval of Versatec.

MATERIAL:
SEE ABOVE P/L DATA BASE B.O.M AVAILABLE.

UNLESS OTHERWISE SPECIFIED
DIMENSIONS ARE IN INCHES. ALL PARTS TO BE DEBURRED AND EDGES BROKEN .010 MAXIMUM

TOL. | 1PLC. | 2PLC. | 3PLC. | ANG.
± | .1 | .03 | .010 | 1°

THIRD ANGLE PROJECTION

FINISH: ⑦

SIGNATURE | DATE
DRN. VALENZUELA | 9-10-90
CHK. | - -
APPV. | - -
APPV. | - -
APPV. | - -
DO NOT SCALE DRAWING

VERSATEC A XEROX COMPANY   SANTA CLARA CALIFORNIA 95051

TITLE:
COVER, CONTROL, FREQUENCY PANEL

SIZE E | CODE IDENT. 50804 | DRAWING NO. 000-012345 | REV. 17

SCALE: 1/2 , AS NOTED | SHEET 1 OF 1

A

2 | 1

FIGURE 18.15   Parts List

QTY REQD	FSCM	PART OR IDENTIFYING NO.	NOMENCLATURE OR DESCRIPTION

PARTS LIST

(a) COLUMNAR ARRANGEMENT FOR INTEGRAL PARTS LIST

PARTS LIST			
QTY REQD	FSCM	PART OR IDENTIFYING NO.	NOMENCLATURE OR DESCRIPTION

(b) COLUMNAR ARRANGEMENT FOR SEPARATE PARTS LIST

FIGURE 18.16   **Parts List Arrangement**   (a) Columnar arrangement for integral parts list (b) Arrangement for separate parts list

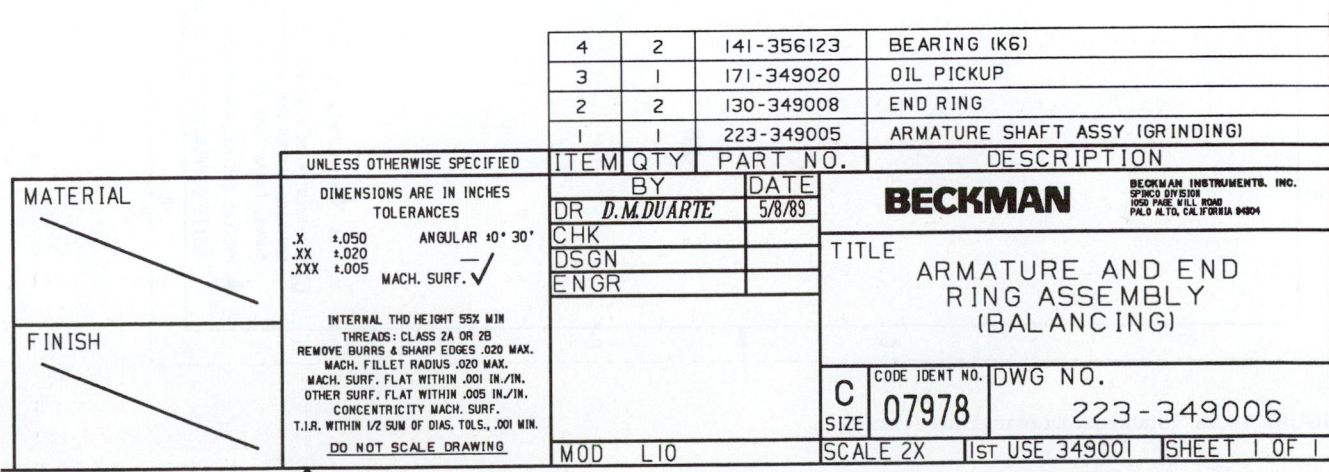

ITEM	QTY	PART NO.	DESCRIPTION
4	2	141-356123	BEARING (K6)
3	1	171-349020	OIL PICKUP
2	2	130-349008	END RING
1	1	223-349005	ARMATURE SHAFT ASSY (GRINDING)

MATERIAL

FINISH

UNLESS OTHERWISE SPECIFIED
DIMENSIONS ARE IN INCHES
TOLERANCES
.X   ±.050   ANGULAR ±0° 30'
.XX ±.020
.XXX ±.005   MACH. SURF. ✓

INTERNAL THD HEIGHT 55% MIN
THREADS: CLASS 2A OR 2B
REMOVE BURRS & SHARP EDGES .020 MAX.
MACH. FILLET RADIUS .020 MAX.
MACH. SURF. FLAT WITHIN .001 IN./IN.
OTHER SURF. FLAT WITHIN .005 IN./IN.
CONCENTRICITY MACH. SURF.
T.I.R. WITHIN 1/2 SUM OF DIAS. TOLS., .001 MIN.

DO NOT SCALE DRAWING

	BY	DATE
DR	D.M.DUARTE	5/8/89
CHK		
DSGN		
ENGR		

BECKMAN   BECKMAN INSTRUMENTS, INC. SPINCO DIVISION 1050 PAGE MILL ROAD PALO ALTO, CALIFORNIA 94304

TITLE
ARMATURE AND END RING ASSEMBLY (BALANCING)

SIZE C | CODE IDENT NO. 07978 | DWG NO. 223-349006

MOD L10 | SCALE 2X | 1st USE 349001 | SHEET 1 OF 1

PART: 04.ME.2235.349006   DRAW: A   05-08-89 15:41:13

FIGURE 18.17   **Armature and End Ring Assembly Title Block and Parts List**

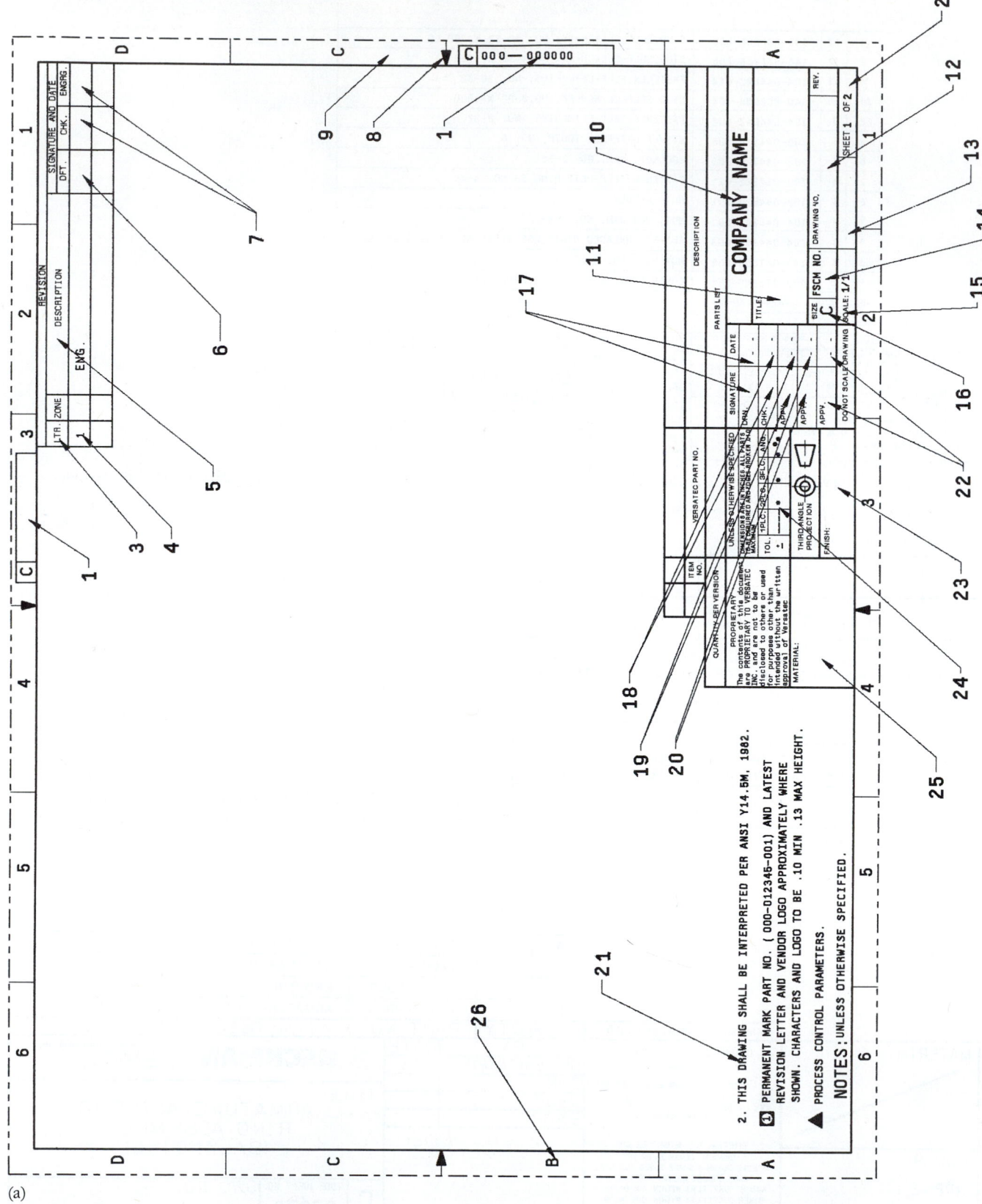

FIGURE 18.18 Standard Drawing Sheet Format

(a)

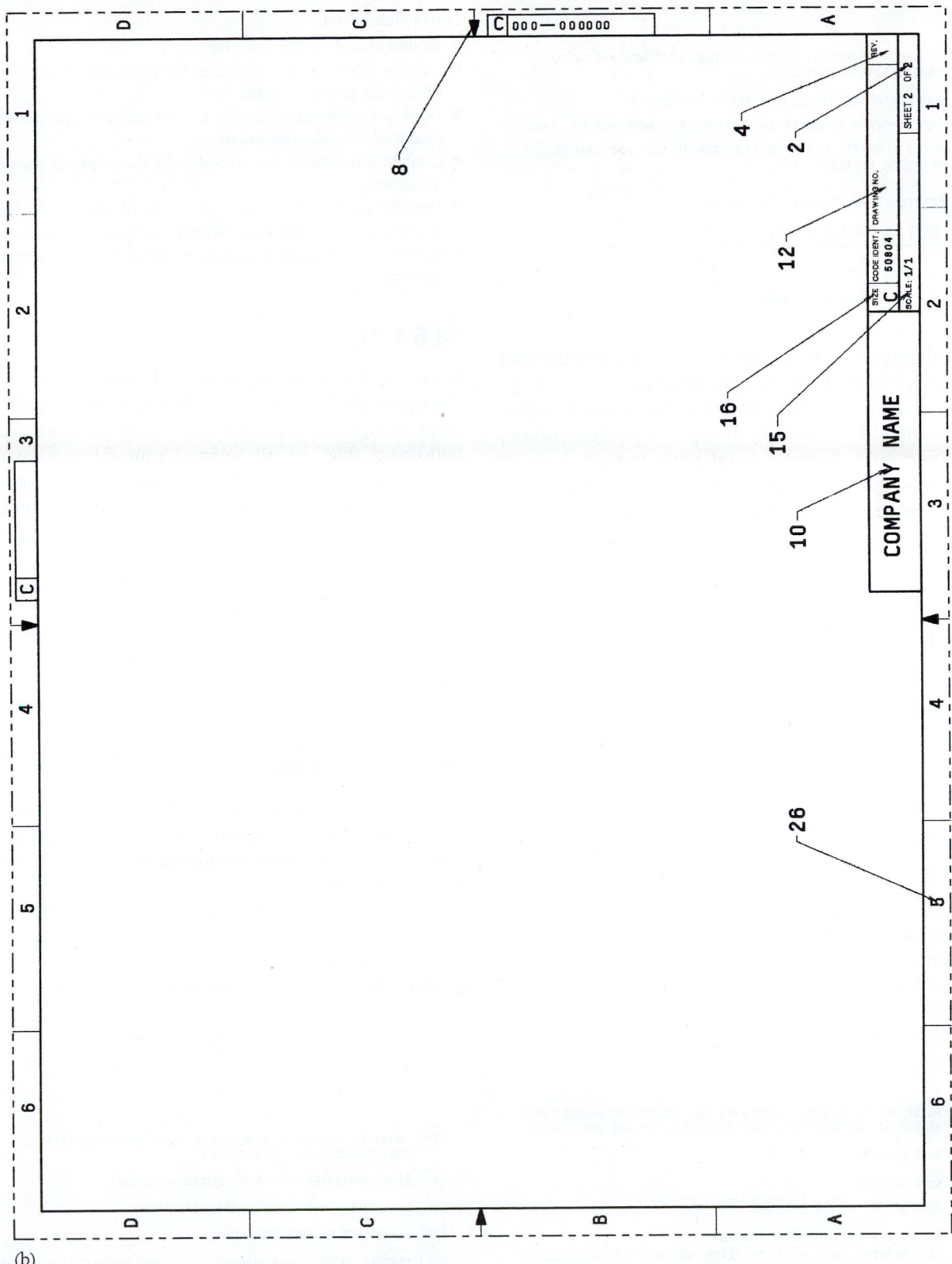

(b)

FIGURE 18.18   Standard Drawing Sheet Format—*Continued*

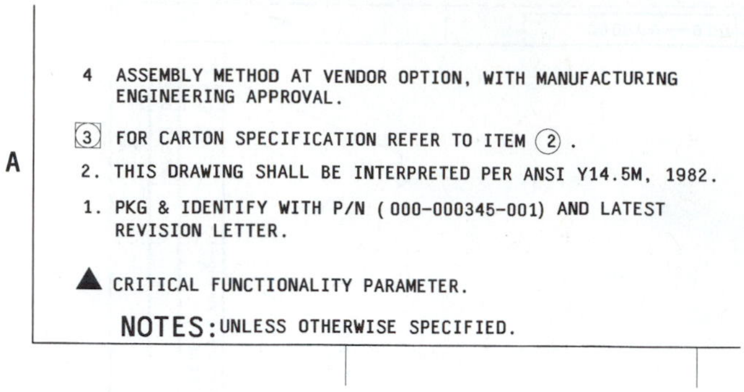

```
A   4   ASSEMBLY METHOD AT VENDOR OPTION, WITH MANUFACTURING
        ENGINEERING APPROVAL.

    ③   FOR CARTON SPECIFICATION REFER TO ITEM ②.

    2.  THIS DRAWING SHALL BE INTERPRETED PER ANSI Y14.5M, 1982.

    1.  PKG & IDENTIFY WITH P/N ( 000-000345-001 ) AND LATEST
        REVISION LETTER.

    ▲   CRITICAL FUNCTIONALITY PARAMETER.

        NOTES: UNLESS OTHERWISE SPECIFIED.
```

FIGURE 18.19   General Notes

General notes (Fig. 18.19) are those that apply to the total drawing and, if placed on the drawing at each point of application, would be repetitive and time-consuming to apply. **Local notes** are those that apply to a specific portion, surface, or dimension on a drawing. Local notes indicate local or specific characteristics of a part, assembly, or diagram. The following rules can be used as a guide when putting notes on a drawing:

Use notes to:

- Clarify features that can be more accurately defined by words than by graphical delineation and dimensions.
- Give instructions for applying special treatments.
- Give instructions for utilization of specific processes.
- Describe instructions to supplement standard symbols.
- Provide additional information to the drawing document or to its use.
- Add notes to clarify so that the part will be made correctly the first time.

Notes should be:

- Clear and concise.
- In the present tense.
- Positioned parallel to the bottom edge of the drawing.
- Carefully composed to relay one message; capable of only one interpretation.
- Preprinted on appliques or, if the drawings are computerized, entered in a standard library for repeated use.

Notes should not:

- Be underlined on the drawing.
- Contain abbreviations other than the most commonly understood shop trade terms or words.
- Duplicate information recorded on an associated parts list or shop practices reference document.
- Contain dimensions that are already documented elsewhere on the drawing.
- Describe complex processes. This kind of information should be documented in either a specification or process document.
- Reference information that is given elsewhere in the product documentation.

18.6.1   General Notes

General notes on drawing sizes "B" through "F" are placed in the upper left-hand or lower left-hand corner of the sheet. Some companies construct their note sequence from the bottom-up (Fig. 18.20); others from the top-down (Fig. 18.21). Notes at the top of a sheet are numbered top-down; those at the bottom part of a sheet are numbered bottom-up. The width of the general note column should not exceed 6 to 8 inches (150 to 200 mm).

When the drawing is completed with a CAD system, it is possible to reuse notes that are common to a number of situations and designs. The notes are saved as a **text file** and inserted as blocks on the drawing. Text files can be edited; therefore, variations and changes can be incorporated before insertion.

18.6.2   Local Notes

The placement of **local notes** on the drawing must be outside the outline of the part. Position the note close to the item that is being referenced, or to the surface/area where an operation is to be performed.

Fabrication operations such as **BEND**, **DRILL**, **TAP**, **PUNCH**, or **BORE** are not shown on the drawing. This permits manufacturing to determine the type of operation required to produce the part within the required tolerances. Features

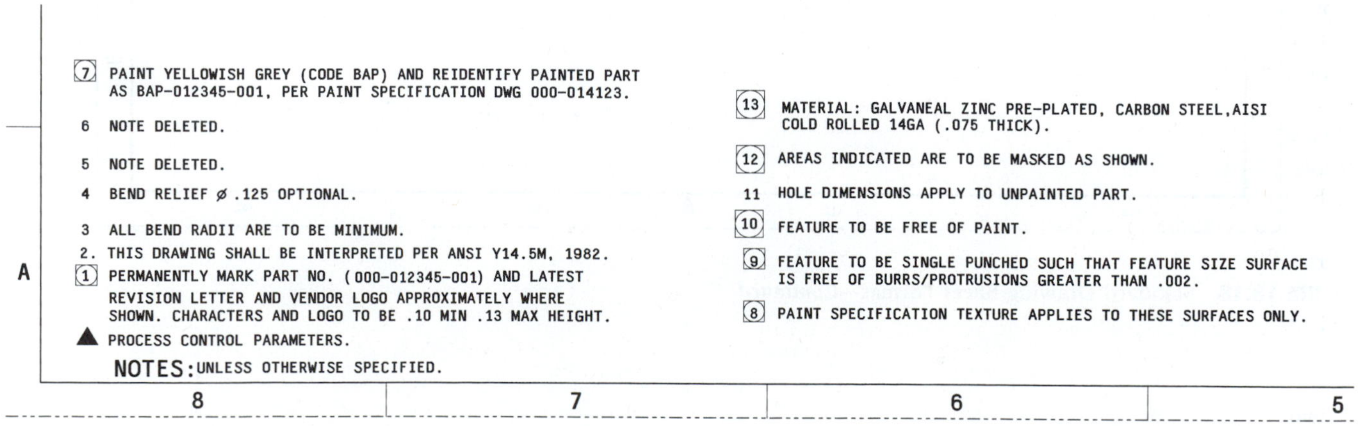

```
A   ⑦   PAINT YELLOWISH GREY (CODE BAP) AND REIDENTIFY PAINTED PART
        AS BAP-012345-001, PER PAINT SPECIFICATION DWG 000-014123.

    6   NOTE DELETED.

    5   NOTE DELETED.

    4   BEND RELIEF ∅ .125 OPTIONAL.

    3   ALL BEND RADII ARE TO BE MINIMUM.

    2.  THIS DRAWING SHALL BE INTERPRETED PER ANSI Y14.5M, 1982.

    ①   PERMANENTLY MARK PART NO. ( 000-012345-001 ) AND LATEST
        REVISION LETTER AND VENDOR LOGO APPROXIMATELY WHERE
        SHOWN. CHARACTERS AND LOGO TO BE .10 MIN .13 MAX HEIGHT.

    ▲   PROCESS CONTROL PARAMETERS.

        NOTES: UNLESS OTHERWISE SPECIFIED.
```

```
⑬  MATERIAL: GALVANEAL ZINC PRE-PLATED, CARBON STEEL,AISI
    COLD ROLLED 14GA (.075 THICK).

⑫  AREAS INDICATED ARE TO BE MASKED AS SHOWN.

11  HOLE DIMENSIONS APPLY TO UNPAINTED PART.

⑩  FEATURE TO BE FREE OF PAINT.

⑨  FEATURE TO BE SINGLE PUNCHED SUCH THAT FEATURE SIZE SURFACE
    IS FREE OF BURRS/PROTRUSIONS GREATER THAN .002.

⑧  PAINT SPECIFICATION TEXTURE APPLIES TO THESE SURFACES ONLY.
```

| 8 | 7 | 6 | 5 |

FIGURE 18.20   Notes Listed from Bottom-up

```
NOTES: (UNLESS OTHERWISE SPECIFIED)
  ①  BALANCE TO WITHIN 3 MILLIGRAM-INCHES BY
      DRILLING BETWEEN ALUMINUM BARS AS SHOWN
      (BOTH ENDS).  DEBURR HOLES AS REQUIRED.
  ②  .020 DIA (REF) IN ITEMS 1 AND .040 DIA (REF) IN
      ITEM (3) TO BE ASSEMBLED ALIGNED.
  ③  MAX DEPTH OF MATERIAL REMOVED
      FOR BALANCING TO BE .035.
  ④  BEARING PRESS FORCE TO BE BETWEEN
      100 AND 300 LBS.
  ⑤  LETTERING SIDE OF BEARING TO FACE OUTWARD.
  ⑥  OPTION: BEARING 356122 (K5) MAY BE USED
      ON TOP AND/OR OPTIONAL BEARING 356124
      (K1419) MAY BE USED ON BOTTOM AS REQUIRED
```

FIGURE 18.21   Notes Listed from Top-down

FIGURE 18.22   Revision Block

LTR.	ZONE	DESCRIPTION	DFT.	CHK.	ENGRG.
1		ENGRG.	VICTOR.V 2/22/89		
2	E5	ADDED ITEM 5 THRU 7 AND HOLES MFG.	VICTOR.V 3/07/89		
3	B2	ADDED HOLE CHART & PAGE 2 INPUT MFG.	VICTOR.V 3/12/89		
4	C7	REVISED SHT 1 & 2 PER ENG. CHANGES	VICTOR.V 3/26/89		
5	D3	ADDED BOTTOM VIEW & DETAIL F REV TOP VIEW LOCATION AND ADDED V15 THRU V22 ON HOLE CHART	VICTOR.V 4/03/89		
6	A5	REVISED LOCATION U1 ON CHART AND SHT 2 REV RADII WAS:.313 IS: .375	VICTOR.V 4/07/89		
7	F4	ADDED N5, N6, R2, R3, Y3 AND Y4	VICTOR.V 9/18/89		
8	C2	INCORP PROTO CHANGES PILOT RELEASE	VICTOR.V 9/18/89		
9	D6	REVISED PER ACO NO. 147	VICTOR.V 11/01/89		
10	E5	REVISED DIMENSIONS WAS: 3.50 & 6.25 IS: 4.00 & 6.00	VICTOR.V 11/16/89		
11	G8	ADDED ITEMS 2 & 3	VICTOR.V 12/06/89		
12	H3	REVISED ITEM 4 & 5 PER DETAILED PART	VICTOR.V 1/26/90		
13	F7	REVISED QTY OF ITEMS 7 & 9	VICTOR.V 3/08/90		
14	A6	ADDED SECTION A-A AND DETAIL B	VICTOR.V 6/01/90		
15	C5	REVISED NOTES 4, 7 AND 9	VICTOR.V 6/25/90		
16	E6	DELETED NOTES 5 AND 6	VICTOR.V 8/06/90		
17	G4	REVISED PER ACO NO. 353	VICTOR.V 9/10/90		

such as **SPOTFACE, COUNTERBORE, COUNTERSINK, UN-DERCUT,** and **THREAD** may be used in notes. See Chapters 12 and 15 for a detailed discussion on the construction, wording, and placement of local notes.

18.7   Revision of Engineering Drawings

The **revision block** (Fig. 18.22), located in the upper right-hand corner of the drawing, is used to record changes to the drawing. The revision of engineering drawings and associated lists is one of the most important links in the engineering documentation structure because of the far-reaching effects of the action. Revisions initiate a substantial number of change documents in all functions of a business. Therefore, the need for accuracy and completeness in the revision process should not be underestimated.

18.7.1   Revision Terminology

The following terms are used to describe the process of revising drawings and are found in revision blocks on drawings:

Added   A new feature or view introduced to the document.

Approval   An endorsement attesting to a revision made on a drawing or parts list.

Change   A specific alteration made as part of a revision of a drawing. A revision may include one or more changes.

Deleted   A feature or view removed from the document.

Obsolete (inactive, cancelled)   A condition where the drawing has been discontinued by the design activity. The words inactive or cancelled may be used.

Redrawn   A new original drawing with the same drawing number that has been substituted for a previous drawing.

Revision (revised)   One or more changes to a drawing, made after distribution or release, according to an established revision procedure.

Revision designation   Alphabetic, numeric, or alphanumeric characters that identify a revision.

18.7.2   Revising Drawings

Revisions are made by erasure, crossing out, addition, redrawing, or for the case of CAD-generated drawings, by editing. When evaluating the method to be used to revise a drawing, you must first give consideration to achieving and maintaining the best possible quality, legibility, and reproducibility by the most economical means. Unless otherwise specified, when revising an existing drawing, the most recently approved graphics symbols, designations and letter symbols, abbreviations, and drawing practices are used. The exception to this is the use of geometric and position tolerance symbols that may be different from the latest issue of ANSI Y14.5. If use of the latest symbol is desired, an explanatory note should be provided on the drawing. Superseded symbology on the drawing should remain unchanged, provided that the interpretation is clear.

18.7.3   Incorporating Changes

Dimensional changes entered on a drawing are made to the same scale as the portion of the drawing undergoing revision. If the drawing is not to scale, and the pictorial portion of the drawing is made to proportion, all dimensional changes are made to the proportions of the delineation affected.

When information is added to a drawing, the additions must match the lettering style and line weight of the existing drawing as closely as possible. The possibility of further additions should always be considered when locating additions on the drawing. If the drawing was originally prepared by

America's First Automobile

Who produced America's first automobile? One might be tempted to name Henry Ford or maybe even Thomas Edison because of his electric car. However, the first car manufactured in the United States was the creation of Charles Duryea in Springfield, Massachusetts, in 1895.

Duryea was born on a farm in 1861 at a time when people relied on mechanical devices to accomplish their farm work. At seventeen, he began to cultivate his mechanical aptitude by assembling discarded farm parts into bicycles. Later on, he sold bicycles built from parts manufactured to his specifications.

He first saw a gasoline engine while he was displaying bicycles at the Ohio State Fair. The engine was much larger than could possibly be used in an automobile, but he knew that smaller engines were possible. He also knew that a German, Karl Benz, had recently patented the first automobile. He decided to build and patent the first American automobile.

After many years of thinking about his horseless carriage, Duryea and his brother finally built their first car in 1892. It had a gasoline-powered internal combustion engine with an electric ignition. The engine was attached to a converted horse buggy.

In 1893, the Duryeas produced a prototype called the *buggaut* and established themselves as the makers of the first successful American automobile. By 1895, they offered an improved 700-pound version for $2,000.

Charles Duryea continued work on his dream machine and obtained nineteen patents, one of which was the first automobile patent issued to an American manufacturer. In 1896, the Duryea Motor Wagon Company produced thirteen cars of the same design. They were the first manufacturers to produce many copies of a single design. The car won several races against domestic and foreign automobiles.

Modern Internal Combustion Engine

computer-aided methods, and the change is to be made manually (not considered a good practice), extra care may be required to minimize the differences in appearance without compromising clarity and legibility.

18.7.4 Simplifying the Drafting Process and Saving Time

Saving time on a project may mean bringing it to market ahead of the competition. Overdrawn and detailed designs add time and cost to a project. The following list can be used to check for simplicity in drawing and time-saving methods:

1. Use text description wherever possible to eliminate drawing completely.
2. Use text description wherever practical to eliminate projected views.
3. Eliminate views where the shape can be given by description, e.g., HEX, SQ, DIA.
4. Show partial views of symmetrical objects.
5. Avoid the use of elaborate, pictorial, or repetitive detail.
6. When necessary to detail threads, do not show them over the full length of the stud, bolt, or tapped hole.

7. Eliminate detail of nuts, bolt heads, and other standard hardware. Show outlines when it is necessary to show position.

8. Reduce detail of parts on assembly drawings. Simply show the part position.

9. Avoid the use of unnecessary hidden lines that do not add clarification.

10. Sectioning should be used only when it is necessary for the clarity of the drawing.

11. Simplify graphics for holes and tapped holes by use of symbols.

12. Omit views with no dimensional or written instruction.

13. Within limits, a small drawing is usually easier and quicker to make than a large one.

14. When two parts are only slightly different, complete graphical representation of both parts is not required. The note "same as except _____", or "otherwise same as _____" may be used.

15. Drawings made to modify stock or commercial parts should be as plain as possible. Avoid detail.

16. Use standard abbreviations wherever possible.

17. When necessary, enlarge small details on larger parts for clarity.

18. Draw small parts large enough to avoid crowding so that they may be easily read, but not unnecessarily large so as to waste space on the drawing.

19. Do not duplicate dimensions.

20. Substitute recognized standard symbols to simplify the drawing of commonly used objects.

21. Eliminate repetitive data by use of general notes.

22. When drafting, use as much freehand drawing as the work permits in preference to using instruments.

23. Where practical, use geometric symbols instead of notes.

24. Where acceptable, use rectangular coordinate or tabular dimensioning instead of dimension lines.

18.8   A Checklist for Drafters and Designers

A drawing should be checked after it has been completed. It should be looked at as others will—as though you had never seen it before and had no prior knowledge of its function. Then, apply it to the following questions:

Readability

1. Is the drawing easy to read?
2. Are the part outlines distinct from dimension lines?
3. Is the lettering neat and clear?
4. Is all of the information on the drawing?
5. Will the drawing make a good print?
6. Have all the rules of standard drafting practice been followed?
7. Is the nomenclature correct? Will everyone understand it the same way?
8. Is the drawing title truly descriptive?

Completeness

9. Are all necessary views given?
10. Are some views unnecessary?

Notes

11. Are the general notes properly located?
12. Are any exceptions to the general notes clearly explained?
13. Are any notes crowded or hard to find?
14. Could any of the notes be misunderstood?
15. If a specially purchased item is required, is procurement information given?
16. If special procedures are required in making or assembling, have they been noted on the drawing?

Parts List

17. Does the parts list agree with the drawing?
18. Have overall dimensions been given?
19. Are standard parts specified correctly?

Dimensioning

20. Are out-of-scale dimensions (if any) clearly marked?
21. Is it necessary to leave a dimension out of scale?
22. Are all dimensions given?
23. Are there any duplicate dimensions?
24. Are dimensions kept well away from the outline of the part as much as possible?
25. Is the scale designated?

Tolerances

26. Have all tolerances given been carefully considered?
27. Are all tolerances to the maximum possible?
28. Are any tolerances too large? Too small?
29. Has the drawing been checked for possible tolerance stackups?

Finishes

30. Are all machine finishes given, and do they conform to applicable specifications?
31. Are all paint and plating finishes specified?

Processes

32. Is heat treatment needed?
33. Have standard manufacturing processes been followed?
34. Can the part be simply and economically produced?

Materials and Parts

35. Are standard or purchased parts used to the maximum extent?
36. Are all special or reworked parts noted?

Assembly

37. Have you made sure there are no mechanical interferences?
38. Will parts assemble without difficulty?
39. Does the work agree with associated mechanisms?
40. Are all parts properly numbered or designated?

Cost

41. Could the function have been accomplished at less expense with the same results?
42. Could the design have contained fewer parts?
43. Have you given thought as to how this could be built?

Reliability

44. Have you checked the design for possible failure?
45. Have you considered safety factors?

18.9   Reproduction and Storage of Drawings

The last step in the design-detailing process is outputting the drawings of the project. Reproduction of manual or CAD drawings involves a process called whiteprinting. Before a CAD drawing can be printed, it must be plotted using one of many types of plotters available.

18.9.1   Whiteprinting

Whiteprinters (Fig. 18.23) are used to make copies of drawings. The drawings must be drawn or plotted on a translucent medium. The whiteprinter is still referred to as a "blueprint machine" by many people. As a drafter you can expect to run prints of drawing projects both at school and on the job.

Regardless of the type of "paper," the whiteprinter makes a "positive" image of the drawing on whiteprint paper. The process depends on the transmission of light through the drawing paper and onto the developing surface. The lines, lettering, or other graphics must block the light in order for a positive image to be developed on the print. Because of the necessity to block light, your drawing must be drawn with high-quality, crisp, dark lines. CAD-plotted drawings use

black ink so the drawing's lines and lettering block light well. On the other hand, when projects are drawn manually, use an H or HB grade lead and press sufficiently hard to create a dark crisp drawing. Chapter 2 covered the methods and techniques used to achieve this quality of drawing.

18.9.2   Plotting

Output devices include printers, plotters, and photocopy equipment. The **plotter** allows the user to produce drawings on paper, vellum, or drafting film in a multitude of colors. Some plotters are limited by the size of the plotting surface. Others can plot drawings of any length, although they are limited to standard paper widths. Pen plotters can use ball-point pens, felt-tip pens, or liquid-ink pens. When plotting a drawing, the operator has many options: to scale the drawing, rotate it, select the colors to plot, and select different line widths. After the drawing is plotted on vellum or polyester film, a whiteprinter can be used to make copies. Multiple copies can also be made from the plotter, but plotting is a slow and tedious process. For this reason, many companies use electrostatic plotters instead of pen plotters. Electrostatic plotters are much faster and can plot a drawing without the mess of wet ink technical pens. Figure 18.24 shows the newest innovation in plotting technology. A laser plotter is

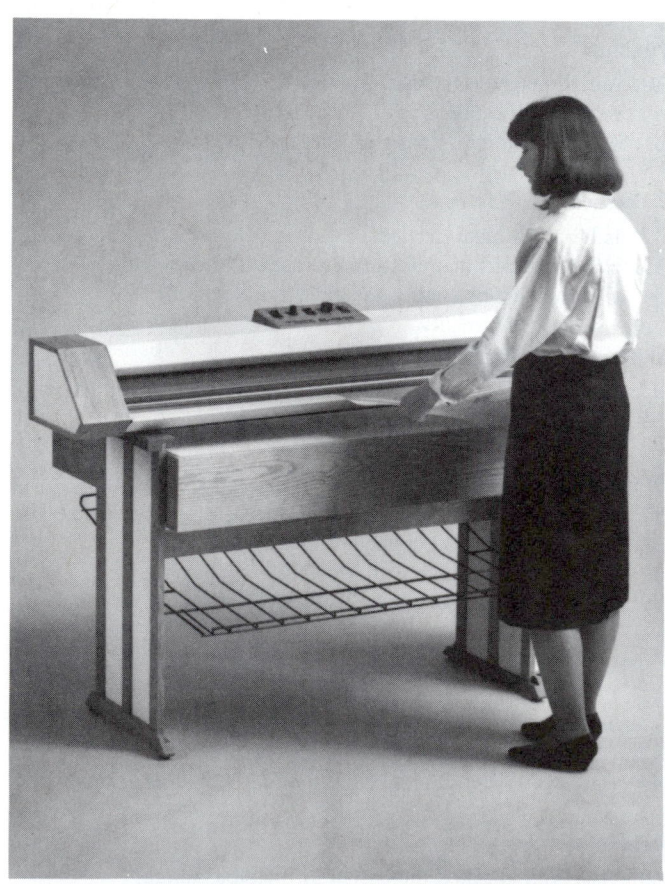

FIGURE 18.23   **Running Prints**

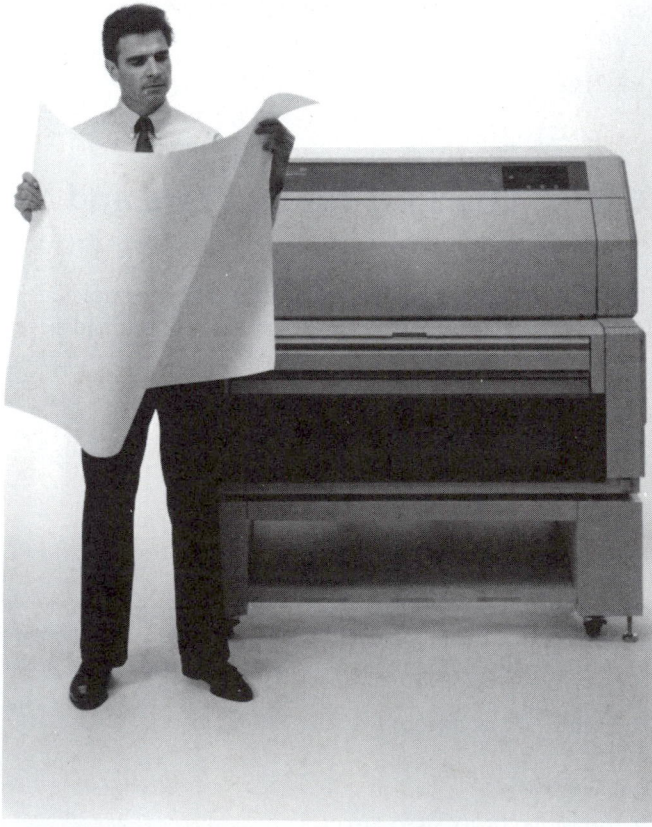

FIGURE 18.24   **COM Units**

faster than an electrostatic plotter, and is as accurate as a pen plotter.

Unlike manual drawings which have only one original, a CAD-plotter can output as many high-quality ink originals as required. However, having more than one original of a project could cause considerable document control problems! The "old" original must be removed from circulation or destroyed to prevent it from being used by persons or departments that are unaware of the new plot.

After the checker checks the drawing, the drafter can make changes on the screen and replot a new original. With a manual drawing, the checker works from a whiteprint and then the drafter does "checker changes" on the original. This method involves considerable erasing and redrawing of portions of the part or assembly.

18.9.3 Computer-Output Microfilm (COM) Units

COM units provide fast and accurate plotting of drawings. The microfilm is usually mounted on an aperture card. The CAD-generated database is transferred from the system to a

FIGURE 18.26 Aperture Card Reader-Plotter

graphics controller [Fig. 18.25(a)], and the laser film plotter creates the aperture card directly from a variety of data formats [Fig. 18.25(b)]. The microfilm can be enlarged to whatever size print is desired. In Figure 18.26 an operator is using an aperture card system to plot a drawing. An electrostatic plotter is used in this system.

18.10 Preparing Assemblies and Details with a CAD System

A 3D CAD system makes it easier to check the spatial relationship between parts in an assembly (Fig. 18.27). The assembly can be rotated to view it from any angle to examine it for interferences (Fig. 18.28). With a 2D system, as with manual drafting, complex projections are required to achieve the same results. Since the 3D system can view a part from any angle, isometric and perspective views can be created with little extra effort (Fig. 18.29).

(a)

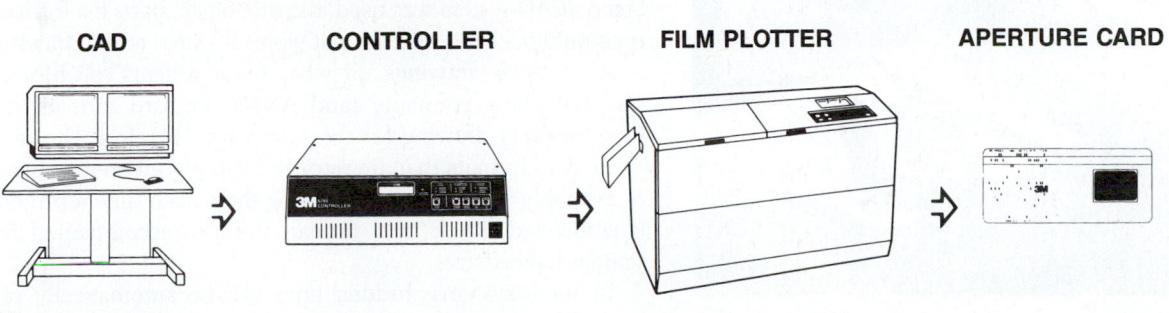

(b)

FIGURE 18.25 Aperture Card Film Plotter   (a) Laser plotter (b) Aperture card output

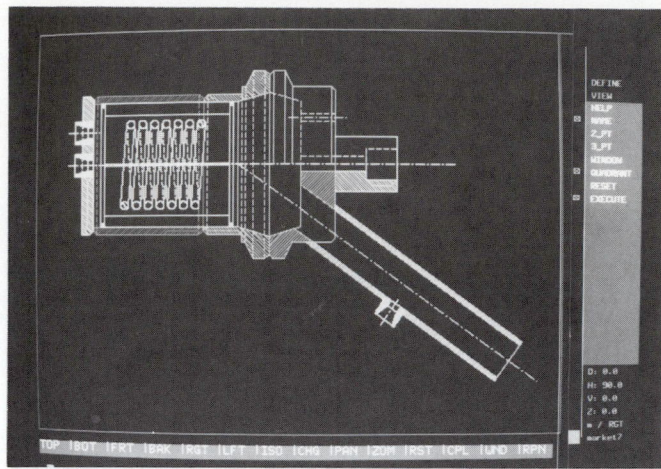

FIGURE 18.27 CAD Assembly

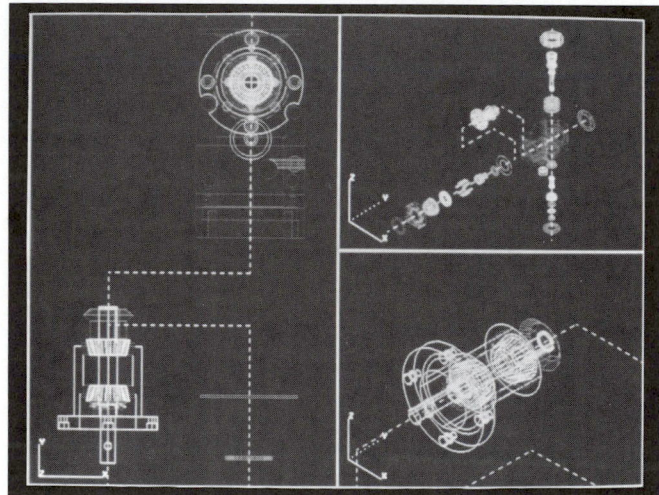

FIGURE 18.28 Assembly

FIGURE 18.29 Exploded Assembly Created on a CAD System

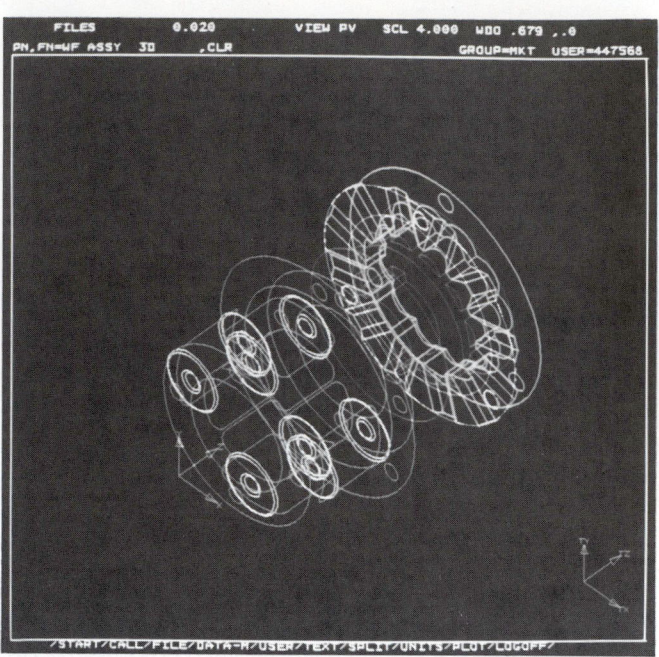

FIGURE 18.30 Exploded Mechanical Assembly

Exploded views of the assembly are easy to create from a 3D assembly model (Fig. 18.30). In Figure 18.31 the assembly was modeled on a CAD system and plotted on an electrostatic plotter. The assembly was displayed pictorially, which enhances the assembly because each part is realistically depicted in its assembled position. Since the pictorial illustration clearly displays the parts of the assembly and each part is ballooned appropriately, separate views were not required. A separate section (**VIEW A–A**) is provided in Figure 18.31.

The assembly in Figure 18.32 was also created with a CAD system. Here, the traditional method of providing appropriate views of the assembly and ballooning is used. The notes are in the lower left corner, the parts list is above the title block, and the revision information is in the upper right of the page. Since a CAD system was used, the title block, parts list format, revision block, and note format were all added to the drawing as subparts or drawings, or what some systems call **blocks** (ACAD). These company (and ANSI) standard formats are used on every drawing for this company. Therefore, they are predefined formats that are retrieved and placed on any detail or assembly without reconstructing them each time a project is completed. Predefined formats are also accompanied by standard sheet sizes.

In some systems, hidden lines can be automatically removed from the assembly. For solid modeling systems, the combined parts can be displayed with proper visibility as

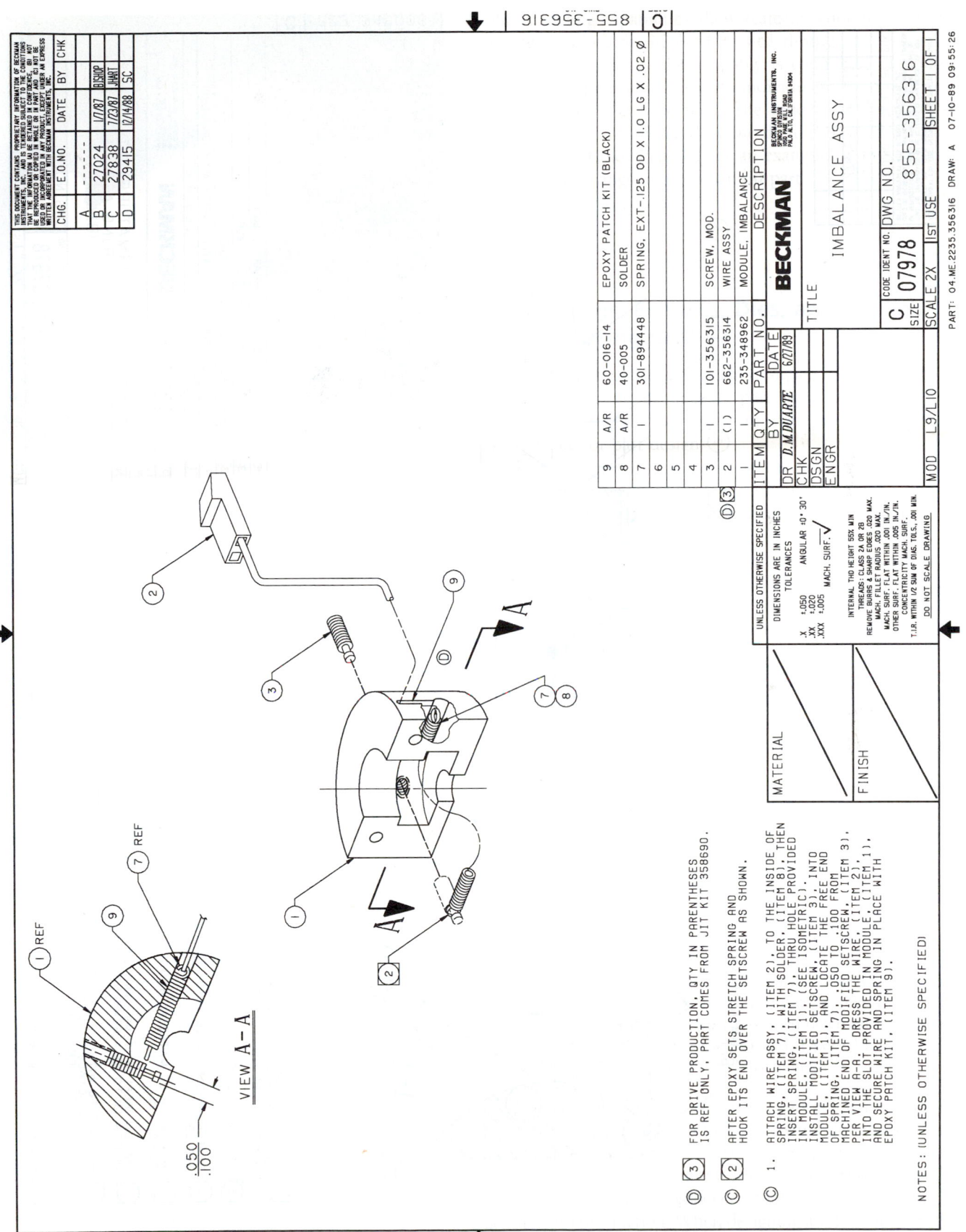

FIGURE 18.31 Imbalance Assembly

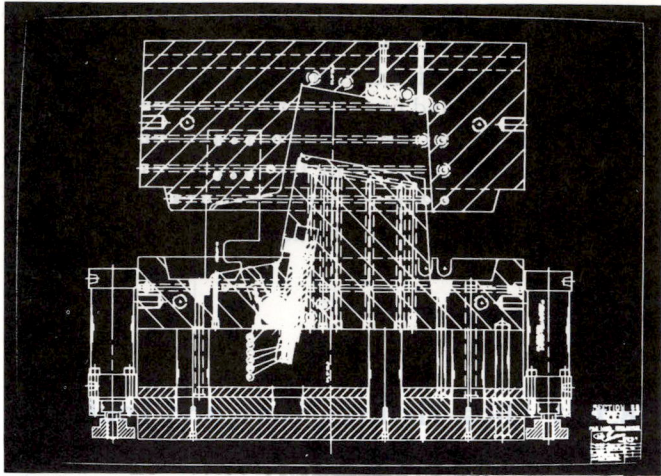

FIGURE 18.35 Mold Design Using a CAD System

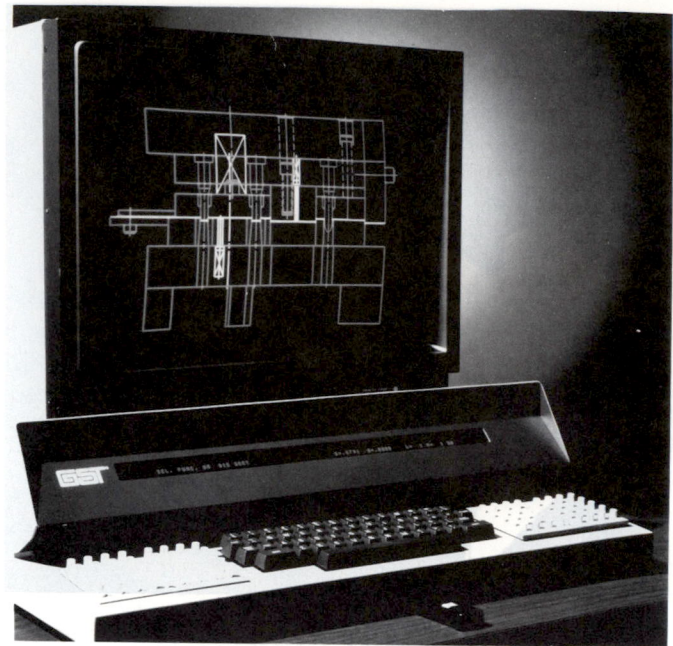

FIGURE 18.36 Tooling Fixture Designed on a CAD System

product. The tool or fixture is then designed directly on the system (Fig. 18.36).

Since duplicating the design for CAM-related purposes is eliminated, time is saved. This also helps eliminate errors caused by misinterpreting design information. A CAD system handles large amounts of information that the engineer, de-

signer, or drafter uses to determine complex relationships between the tool/fixture and the part. The visual representation of the tool/fixture on the display, as it relates to the part, provides an important link between engineering and manufacturing. This eliminates the tedious work of interpreting the detailed part drawing and then manually calculating individual

FIGURE 18.37 Planning Machine Operations on a CAD System

PART NO: 190105 PART NAME: FRONT PLATE FORMAT: NCS.1	
PLNG REV: 1 DWG REV: A PLANNER: ADAMS	
CODE ● 8798-3711-1189-3433-1400-0000-0000-00	
0040 5002 MACHINE PER TAPE ●1	
SET UP IN FIXTURE ●1	
WITH STD ANGLE PLATE	
●A123 PER SKETCH	
ROUGH & FINISH FACE	
- HOLD .25 +-.02 DIM.	
USE 4" DIA FACE MILL	
C-DRILL (3) HOLES	
DRILL (1) HOLE 3/8 DIA.	
DRILL (2) TOOLING HOLES	
5/16 DIA.	
DRILL (2) TOOLING HOLES	
.365/.370 DIA	
AND REAM TO .376/.370 DIA.	
SET UP = 2.50	
PIECE TIME =.350	

fits and tolerances of the tool or fixture required to produce the finished part. If product design changes are necessary, the tool fixture design is modified and updated.

Once the tool fixture is designed, a detail drawing to provide a geometric description of each part of the fixture is prepared. Detail drawings, an integral part of all steps in the design-through-manufacturing process, can represent the tool/fixture design in any view and include dimensions, surfaces, hidden lines, and other appearance control features. These drawings may be used for marketing, design, review, and manufacturing approval, or as input to the documentation, purchasing, and production departments.

To list the parts and materials needed to produce a tool/ fixture designed on the system, CAD systems can automatically output a bill of materials for the planning and purchasing departments.

18.10.2 Visual Simulation to Verify Tool and Fixture Design

To provide clearances between the tool fixture and the part, the designer can check and verify the minimum clearance needed by enlarging the view on the graphics display with the **ZOOM** and **MEASURE** commands. This ensures optimum use of materials. Color is used to discriminate components for ease of viewing and highlighting.

To evaluate a tool design, a CNC programmer generates a toolpath (cutter path) and visually simulates the movement of a cutting tool around a part. The simulated cutter moves on the display screen to verify the result of the toolpath definition. The toolpath is plotted on a drawing along with the part and the fixture (see Color Plates 12 through 15 and 42). This reduces costs for test machining, machine setup, and prototype creation by eliminating reruns. Process planners can then use this information to create process instructions and plans for the same part (Fig. 18.37).

18.10.3 Tool Design Using Standard Library Parts and CAD

Fixture design is an important application for computer-aided design. Tool designers can often benefit more than anyone from CAD/CAM. Since part size and shape are key factors in deciding how to locate and clamp, one obvious advantage of using a CAD system for tool design is that work piece geometry is already stored on the system. The ability to use and reuse a **standard library** of tooling components, made up of standard components plus in-company standards, is important to fixture layout and design.

Figure 18.38(a) through (i) demonstrate the steps taken to design a fixture using standard components from a tooling library of parts. In the following example, CARR LANE components are used. The CARR LANE library of parts has more than 5,000 standard items available in 2D and 3D versions. CARR LANE provides schools with the library of parts free of charge. CARR LANE supports micro-based CAD systems

including AutoCAD, CADKEY, VersaCad, and Personal Designer, as well as workstation systems such as Computervision and Anvil. The following describes a set of steps in the design of a fixture using standard components already modeled on the CAD system and saved as a parts library:

1. Work Piece Geometry [Fig. 18.38(a)]
Part geometry, before and after machining, is the key to deciding how to hold a part. Our sample part will be pocket milled, then drilled. When parts are designed on a CAD system and represented graphically, there is an extra advantage. After retrieving the work piece, drawing layers containing unneeded dimensions and notes are turned off. Parts are normally shown in phantom lines and/or different colors. Parts are not a component of the fixture itself. Before proceeding further, tool sizes and cutting forces must be considered.

2. Fixture Base [Fig. 18.38(b)]
In our example, we use a standard off-the-shelf *mill fixture base*. Whether you use a premachined base or make your own tooling plate, it must be big enough to hold the work piece and any clamps you plan to use. Usually, you should allow some gap under the part for supports. The base must be thick enough to resist distortion from clamping forces and vibration from cutting forces. Standard cast angles, cubes, and other sections are also available off-the-shelf, and can be easily modified for fixtures. For cylindrical parts, the "fixture base" may be a set of blank chuck jaws, custom-shaped to fit the part.

3. Supports [Fig. 18.38(c)]
For proper part location, designers commonly use multiple fixed support points and occasionally some adjustable supports. In this example, three *rest buttons*, all underneath the work piece, are the fixed supports. Geometric tolerancing considerations may dictate where the rest buttons are placed. Although you would usually place the supports by eye, you could also use your CAD system's center-of-mass function for heavy or complicated parts in order to distribute weight evenly. If the parts are thin and require additional backup against machining forces, you could add adjustable supports (hydraulically operated if you want the greatest accuracy).

4. Locators [Fig. 18.38(d)]
Next, we locate our part laterally. In the example, we bring in three *round pins*, tangent to the part's side reference surfaces, to orient it correctly.

We choose locators strong enough to resist anticipated lateral cutting forces. Three *spring stop buttons* hold the work piece firmly against the round pins while we clamp.

5. Clamps [Fig. 18.38(e)]
Cutter forces are considered when choosing the type, size, and number of clamps. In this example, we use three simple *clamp strap assemblies*, placed directly above the supports to avoid part distortion. We keep our clamps clear of the areas to be machined. If the entire top surface were to be milled, we could use *edge clamps* to keep the top totally clear.

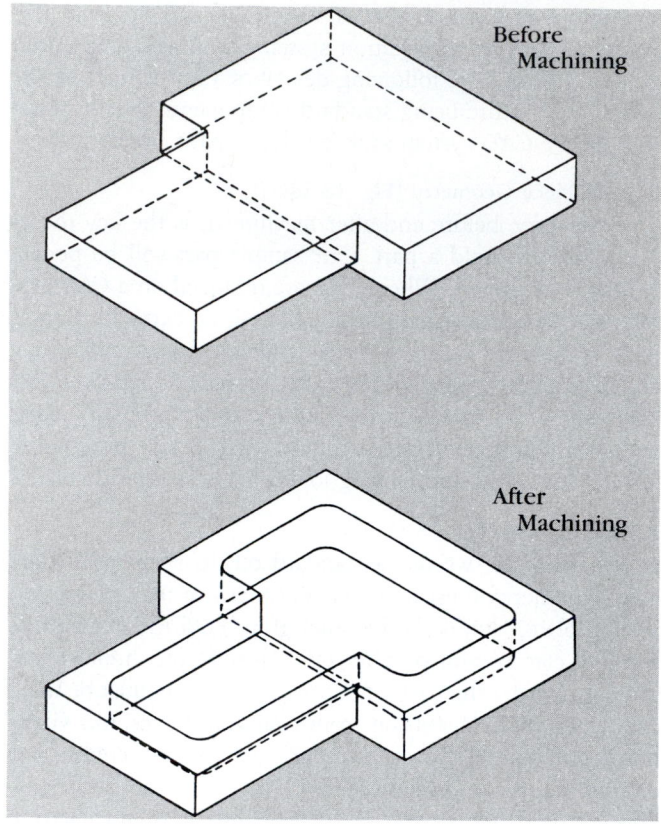

(a)

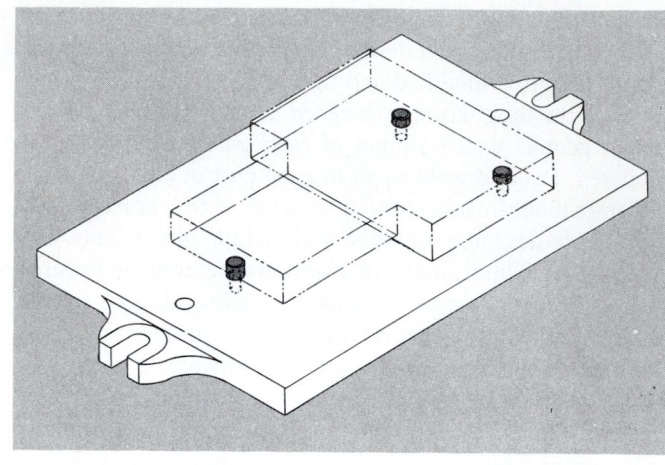

(c)

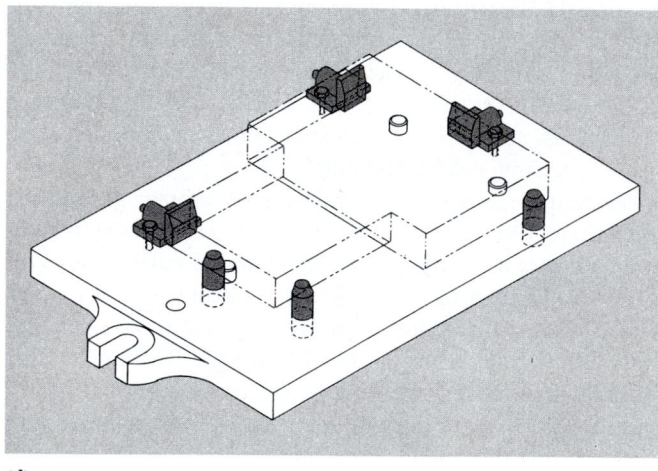

(d)

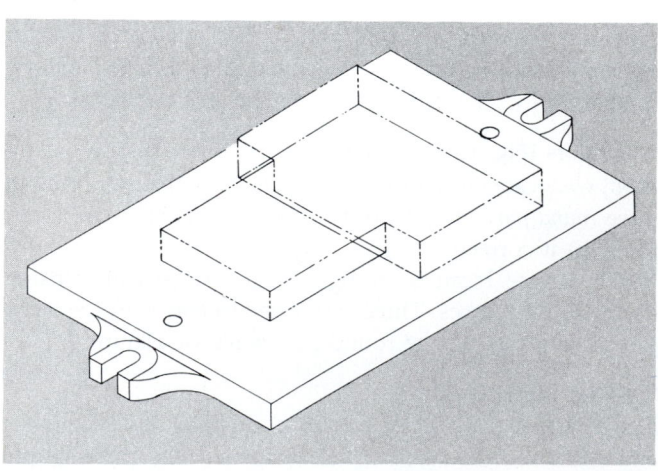

(b)

FIGURE 18.38 **Tool Design Process Using a CAD System and a Component Library of Parts** (a) Work piece geometry (b) Fixture base (c) Supports (d) Locators (e) Clamps

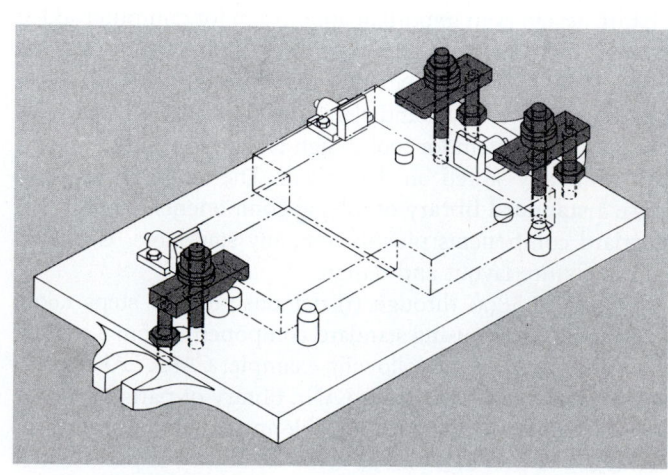

(e)

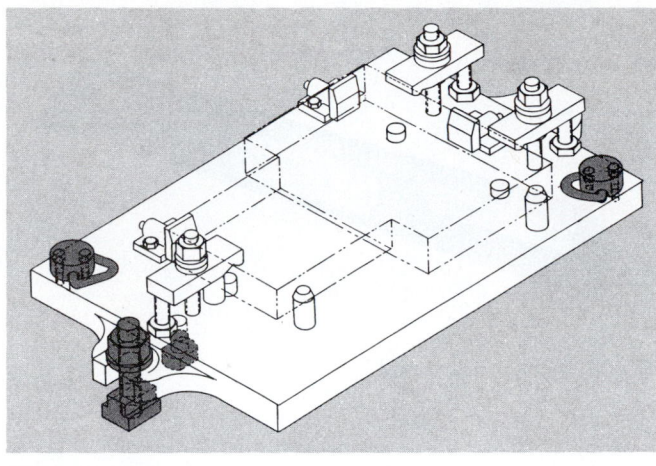

(f)

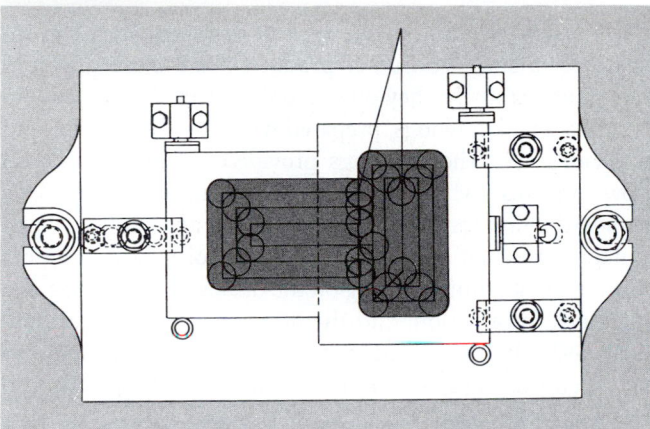

(g)

ITEM	QTY.	PART NO.	DESCRIPTION
1	2	CL-4-FN	FLANGE NUT
2	2	CL-5/8-11X2.50	STUD
3	2	CL-10-TN	T-NUT
4	4	48223	SOCKET HEAD CAP SCREW
5	2	CL-20-HR	HOIST RING
6	6	53896	HEX HEAD CAP SCREW
7	3	CL-20C-SSB	SPRING STOP BUTTON
8	2	CL-6-RB	REST BUTTON
9	3	CL-12-SHA-1	CLAMP STRAP ASSEMBLY
10	2	CL-687-SLFK	FIXTURE KEY
11	3	CL-5-RP	ROUND PINS
12	1	CL-7-RB	REST BUTTON
13	1	CL-4-MFB	MILL FIXTURE BASE

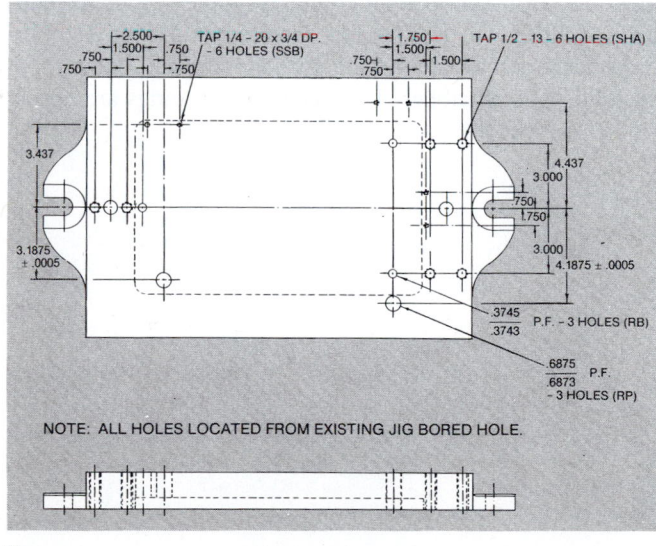

(h)

FIGURE 18.38   (f) Fixture accessories (g) Checking tool clearance (h) Assembly drawing and parts list (i) Base detail drawing

6. Fixture Accessories [Fig. 18.38(f)]

Fixture accessories are the final components we select. We choose two *hoist rings* to help lift our fixture into place. Two *sure-lock fixture keys* accurately locate the fixture base on the machine table. Two *T-nuts*, studs, and *flange nuts* fasten the base to the machine.

7. Checking Tool Clearance [Fig. 18.38(g)]

After tentatively placing all fixture components, you can check tool clearance. Using the CNC graphics capabilities of your CAD/CAM system, you can determine tool paths then, ultimately, generate CNC programs. This machining verification step ensures that the part is entirely machined and that tools do not interfere with the fixture.

8. Assembly Drawing and Parts List [Fig. 18.38(h)]

The first step in documenting the fixture design is an assembly drawing. Assembly drawings are easily produced by turning off the drawing layer containing the work piece. You can then use your system's capabilities to add item callouts and create a bill of material.

(i)

9. Base Detail Drawing [Fig. 18.38(i)]

A detail drawing of the fixture base is also easy to produce by turning off the drawing layers containing other components. Here, two views, top and front, were selected to add machining dimensions. As a final step, we could generate a CNC program to machine the base.

18.11   Working Drawing Example for a Consumer Product

The recalibratible electronic level, shown in Figure 18.39, is capable of reading all angles through 360°, rather than only traditional level and plumb measurements. The "SmartLevel" is designed to increase the speed, accuracy, and efficiency of standard leveling tasks, as well as providing a tool for tasks requiring direct measurement of angles, slopes, grades, and pitches.

A SmartLevel is composed of two components: an electronic sensor module, which contains the functions and display readout for the tool, and an ergonomically designed rail, which is available in lengths of 2, 4, and 6 feet. The sensor module may be used alone or may be locked into any rail handhold.

Made of a waterproof polycarbonate resin, the sensor module is designed to withstand the construction environment, as well as a wide range of temperatures. The rails are made of aircraft-grade aluminum and teak, the most durable and weatherproof wood available. This combination of materials ensures that each rail is extremely strong and shock-resistant.

18.11.1   Working Drawings for the SmartLevel

Figure 18.40(a) through (l), pp. 711—721 show assembly drawings (from the sensor module), computer-generated parts list, and individual details for the SmartLevel. This product has parts made of teak, aluminum, ABS high impact, polycarbonate, and silicone rubber. The electronic drawings are not included in this set.

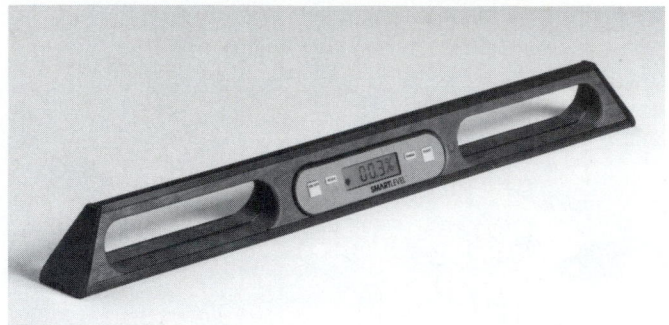

FIGURE 18.39   **SmartLevel**

This is an example of the type of drawings found in industry for a small consumer product. Since these drawings were done manually, they do not look perfect. Compare them to the trackball drawings, prepared with AutoCAD, at the end of Chapter 17. The drawings provided for the SmartLevel show erasures (which were made during revisions). Line quality, dimensioning, and overall appearance suffer, when compared to CAD drawings. The choice of views, assembly pictorial views, dimensioning on the details, the revisions, the title block information, and the notes of each drawing (material designations, production and manufacturing requirements, and finishes) should be examined carefully.

You May Complete Exercises 18.1 Through 18.4 at This Time

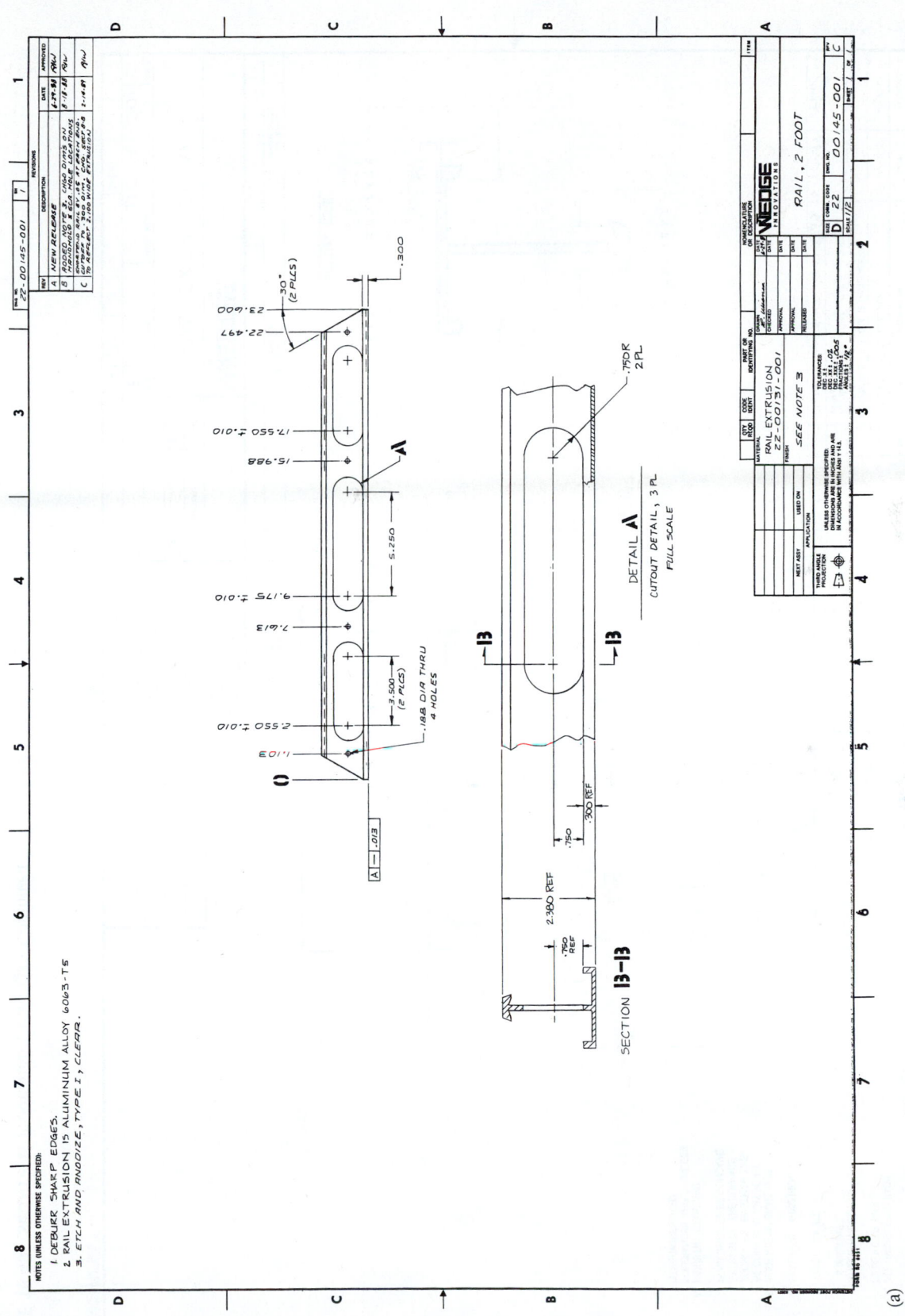

FIGURE 18.40 **SmartLevel Production Drawings** (a) Rail detail (b) Rail extrusion (c) Wood insert (d) End cap (e) Module assembly (f) Computer-generated parts list for the module assembly (g) Parts list for front panel assembly (h) Parts list for front panel assembly (i) Housing detail assembly (j) Housing detail (k) Front panel detail (l) Keytop detail

(a)

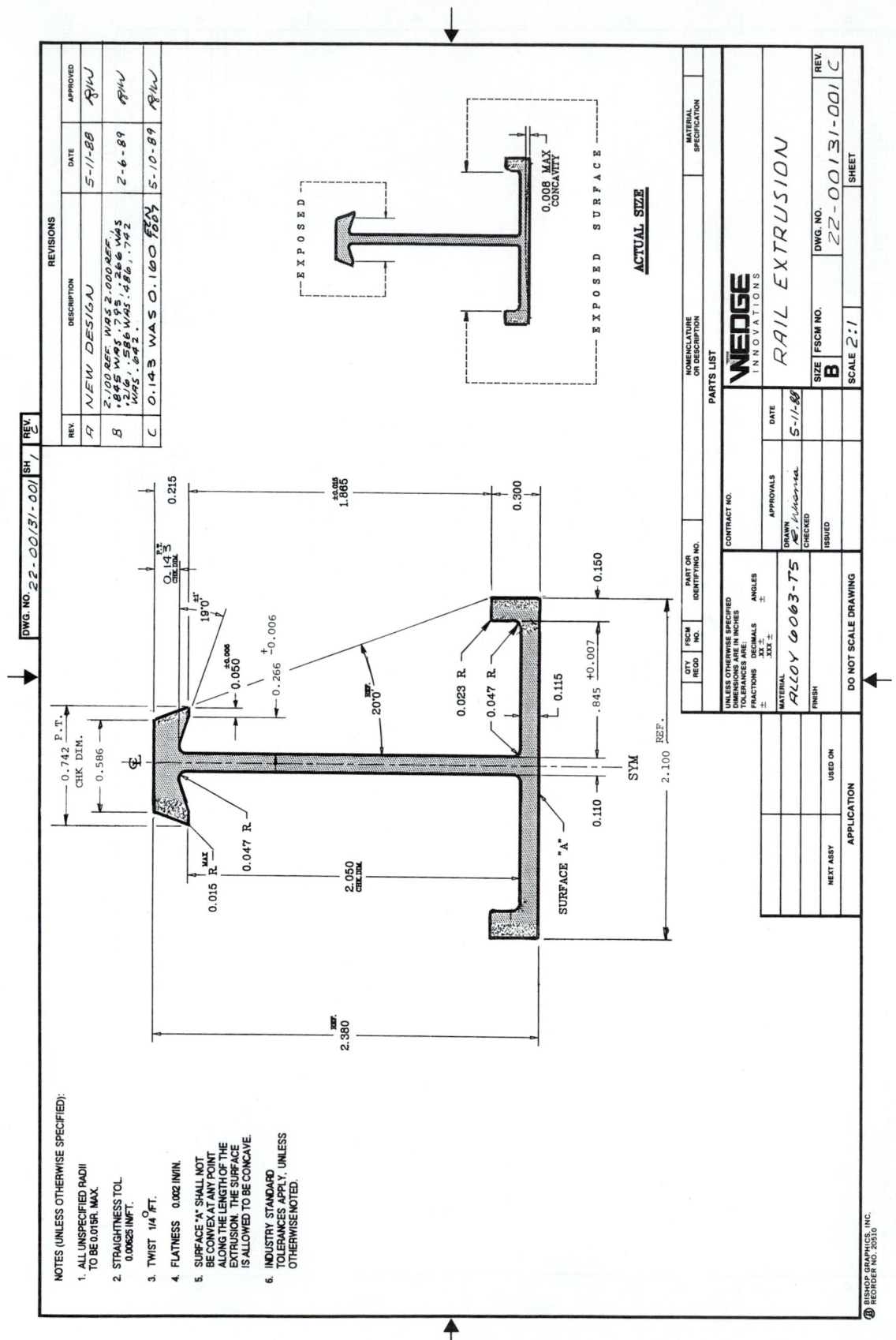

FIGURE 18.40 SmartLevel Production Drawings—*Continued*   (b) Rail extrusion

(b)

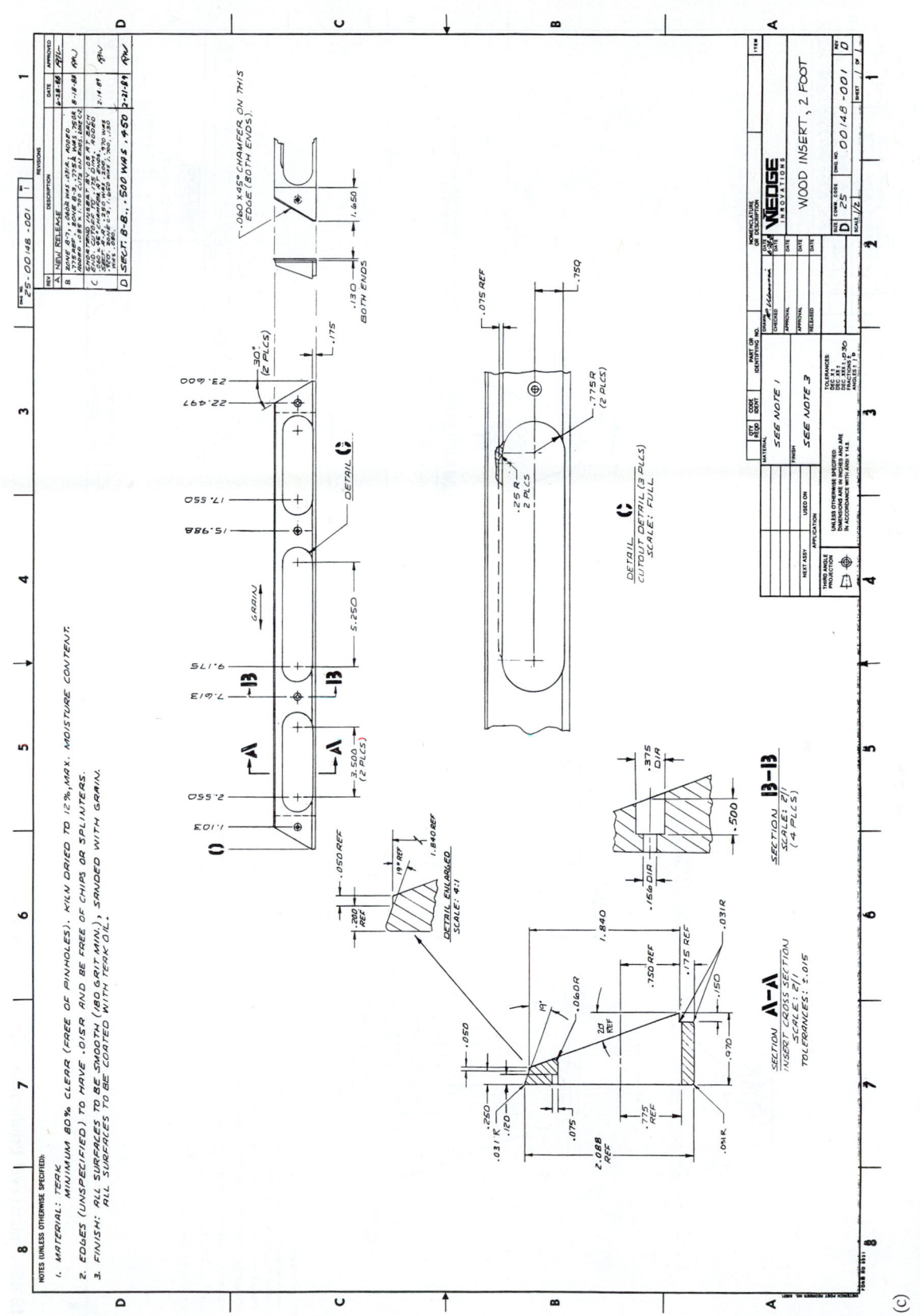

FIGURE 18.40 SmartLevel Production Drawings—*Continued* (c) Wood insert

(c)

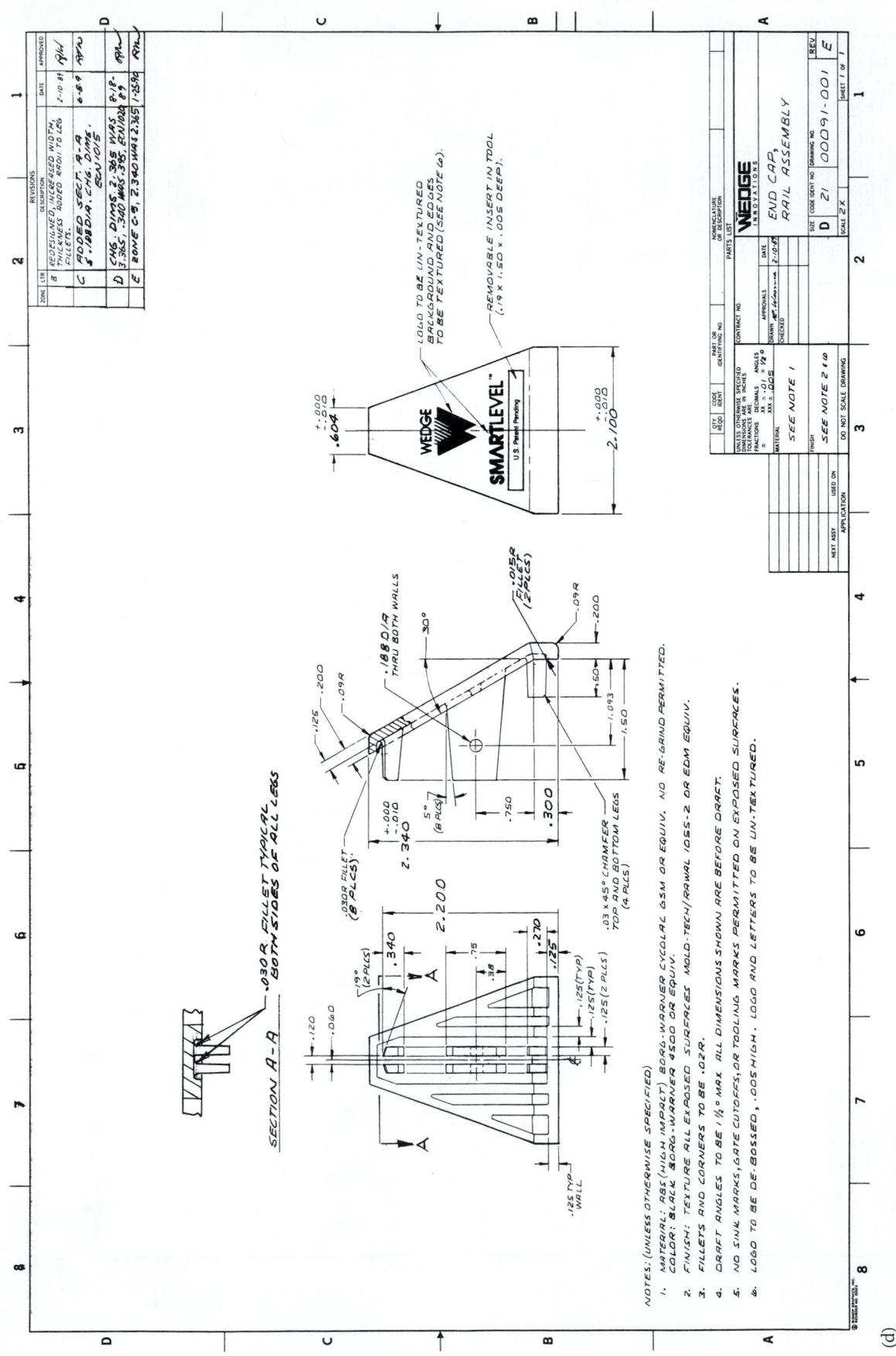

(d)

FIGURE 18.40 SmartLevel Production Drawings—Continued (d) End cap

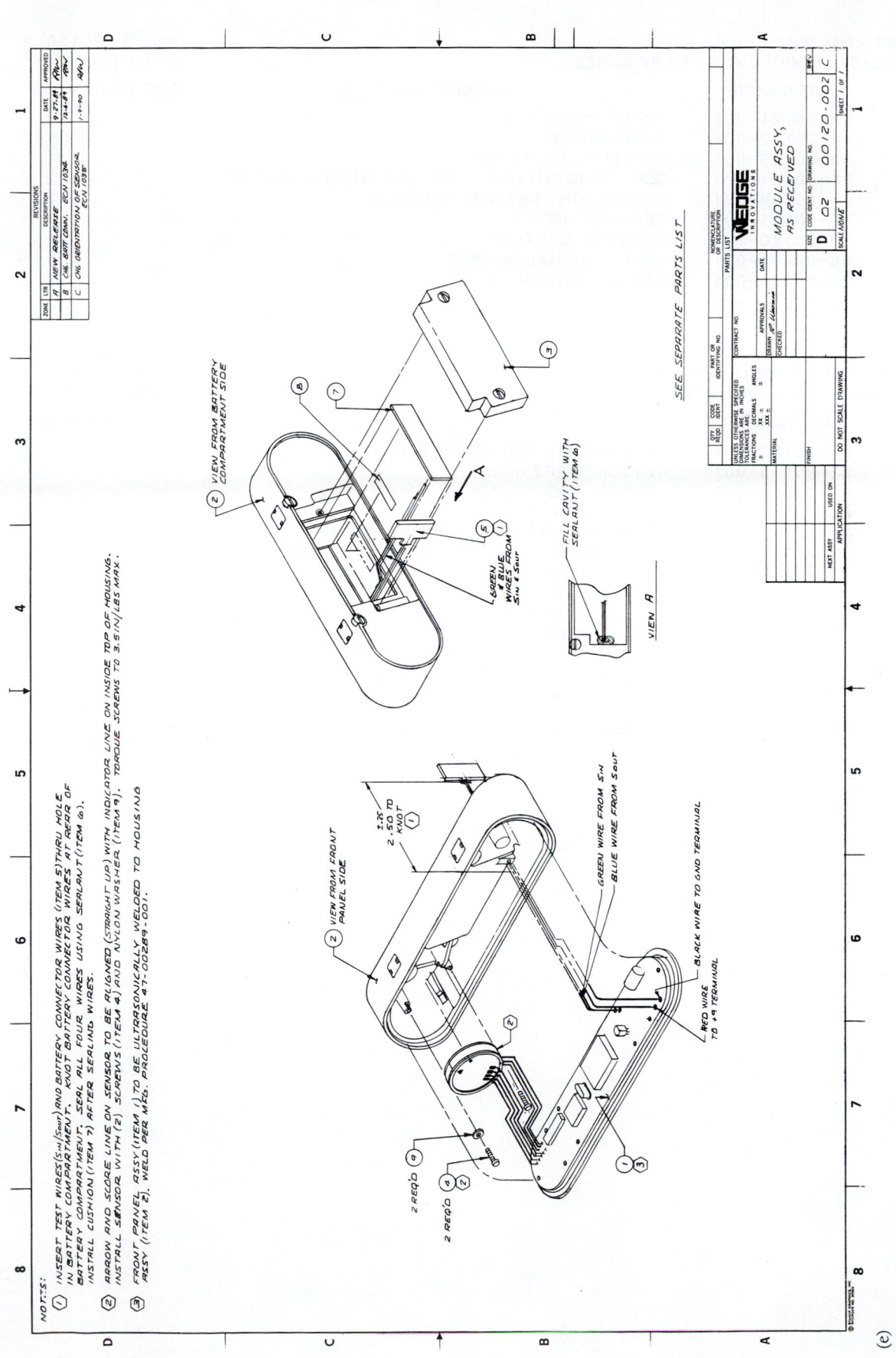

FIGURE 18.40 Smart Level Production Drawings—*Continued* (e) Module assembly

PARENT PART NUMBER: 02-00120-002 REV. B, PL120.2
PARTS LIST: MODULE ASS, AS REQUIRED DATE: 12-5-90

ITEM	PART NUMBER	DESCRIPTION	REF. DESIGN QTY	U/M
1	03-00121-001	FRONT PANEL ASSY	1	EA
2	03-00122-001	HOUSING ASSY	1	EA
3	03-00123-001	BATTERY CIVER ASSY	1	EA
4	81-00124-007	SCR, THRD CUTTING (TYPE 25) PH, CR, #2X1/2	2	EA
5	54-00399-001	CONNECTOR, BETTERY, MOLDED	1	EA
6	51-00141-001	SEALANT, RTV	A/R	OZ
7	23-00140-001	CUSHION, BATTERY	1	EA
8	26-00291-001	LABEL, SERIAL NUMBER	1	EA
9	82-00321-001	WASHER, NYLON, #1	2	EA

(f)

PARENT PART NUMBER: 03-00121-001 REV. F, FR. PNLASSY
PARTS LIST: FRONT PANEL ASSY DATE: 6-20-89

ITEM	PART NUMBER	DESCRIPTION	REF. DESIGN QTY	U/M
1	21-00112-001	FRONT PANEL (SILKSCREENED)	1	EA
2	23-00113-001	KEYTOP, LEFT HAND	1	EA
3	23-00113-002	KEYTOP, RIGHT HAND	1	EA
4	62-00250-001	LCD, 15 PIN	1	EA
5	23-00030-001	ELASTOMETRIC CONNECTOR STRIP, ACTIVE	1	EA
6	23-00030-002	ELASTOMETRIC CONNECTOR STRIP, DUMMY	1	EA
7	03-00183-001	PCB/SENSOR ASSY	1	EA
8	81-00124-002	SCR, THRD CUTTING (TYPE 25), PH, CR, #2X3/16	8	EA
9	81-00124-003	SCR, THRD CUTTING (TYPE 25), PH, CR, #2X1/4	2	EA
10	21-00223-001	PRESSURE BAR	1	EA
11	24-00246-001	INSULATOR, KEYPAD, RIGHT HAND	1	EA
12	24-00246-002	INSULATOR, KEYPAD, LEFT HAND	1	EA

(g)

FIGURE 18.40 **SmartLevel Production Drawings—***Continued* (f) Computer-generated parts list for the model assembly (g) Parts list for front panel assembly

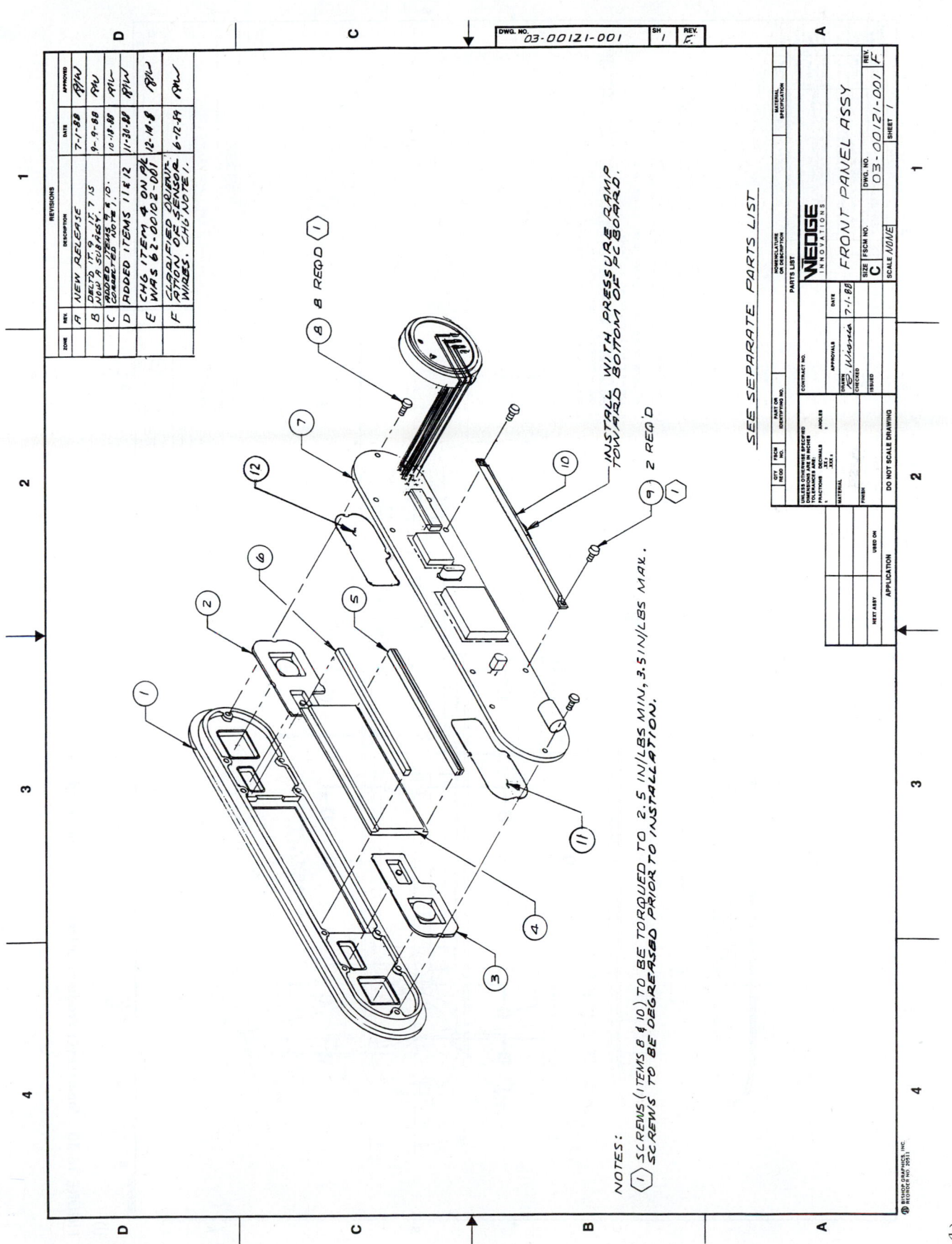

FIGURE 18.40   SmartLevel Production Drawings—*Continued*   (h) Front panel assembly

(h)

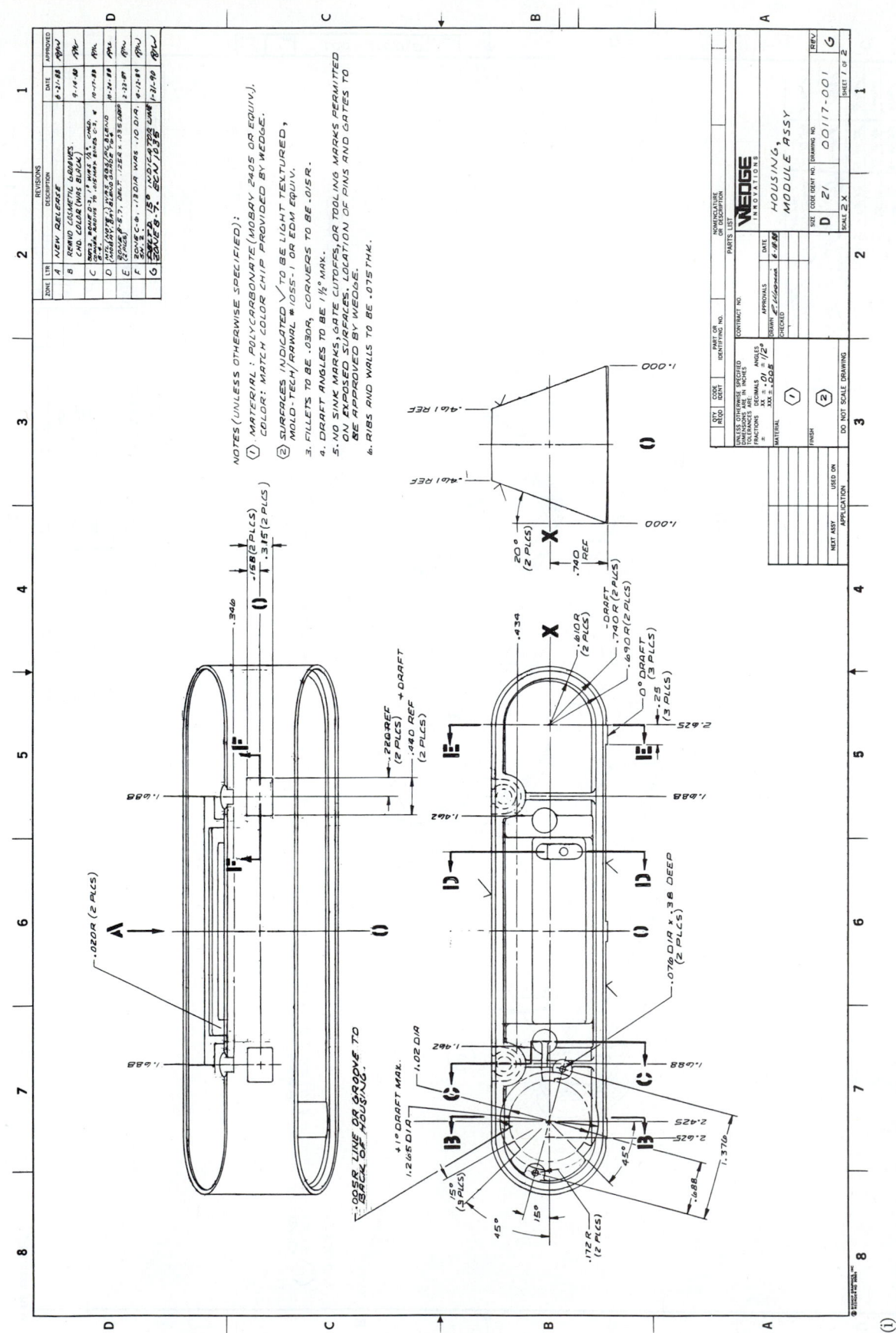

FIGURE 18.40 SmartLevel Production Drawings—*Continued* (i) Housing detail

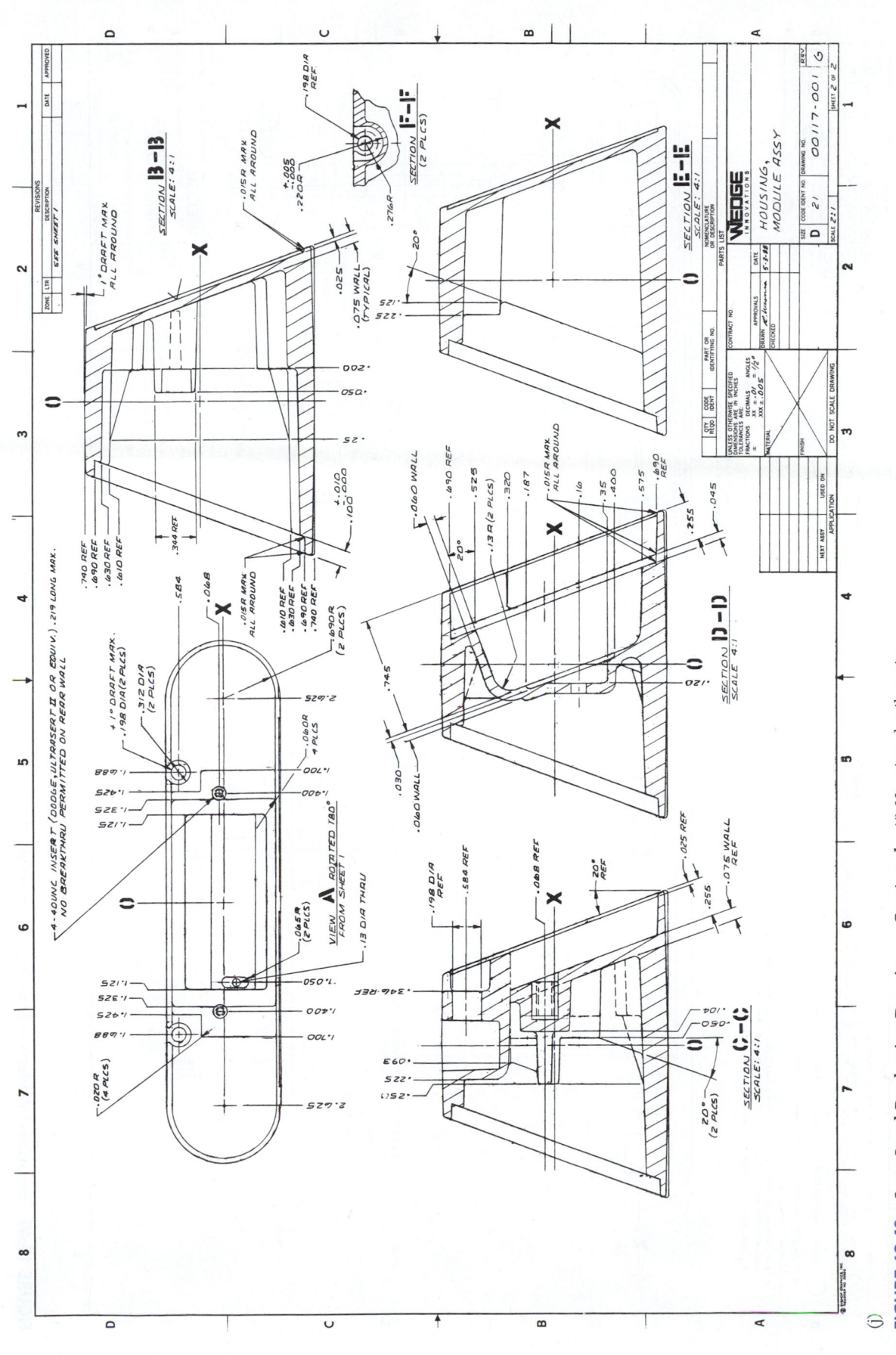

FIGURE 18.40   SmartLevel Production Drawings—*Continued*   (j) Housing detail sections

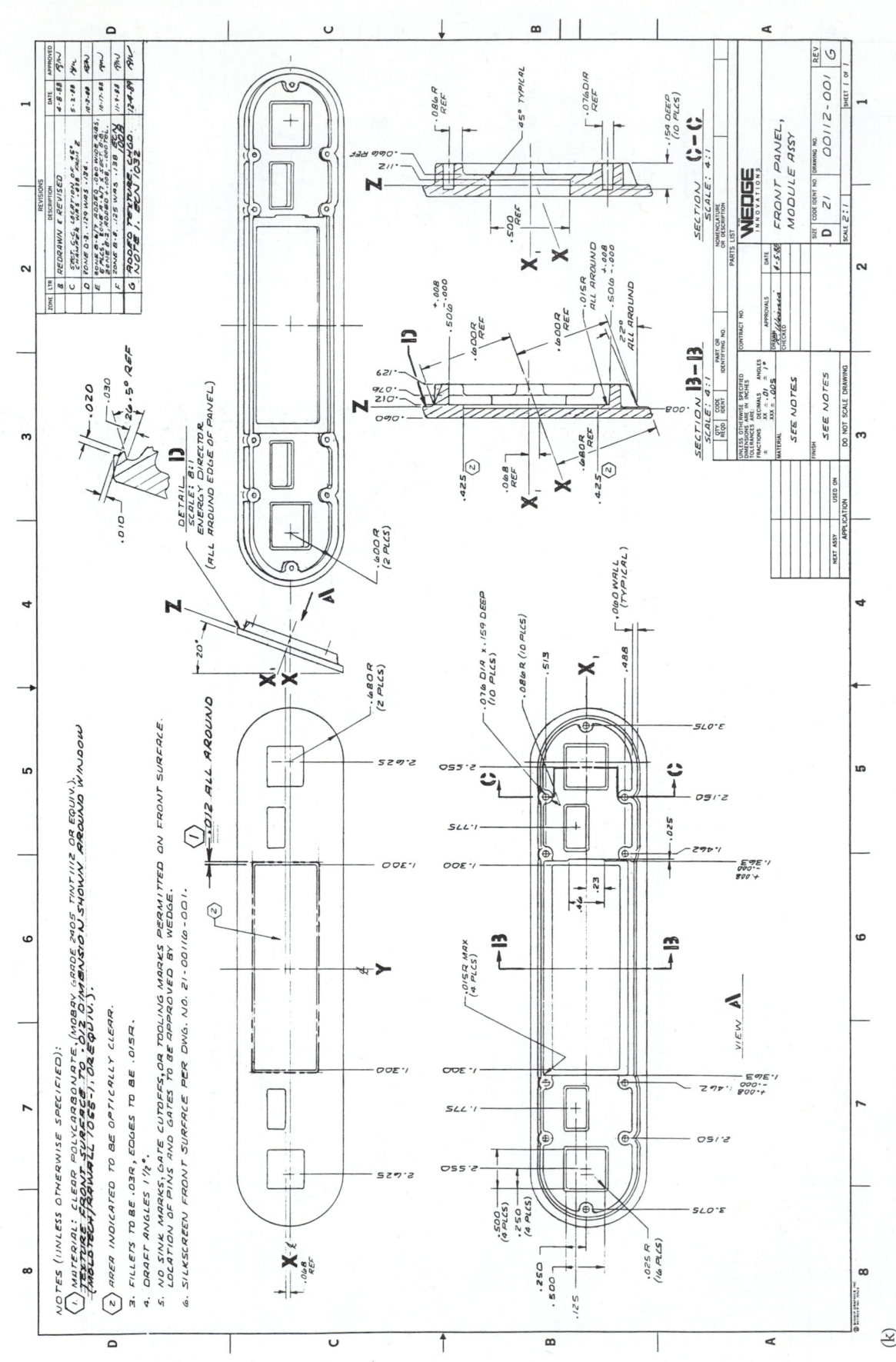

FIGURE 18.40   SmartLevel Production Drawings—*Continued*   (k) Front panel detail

(k)

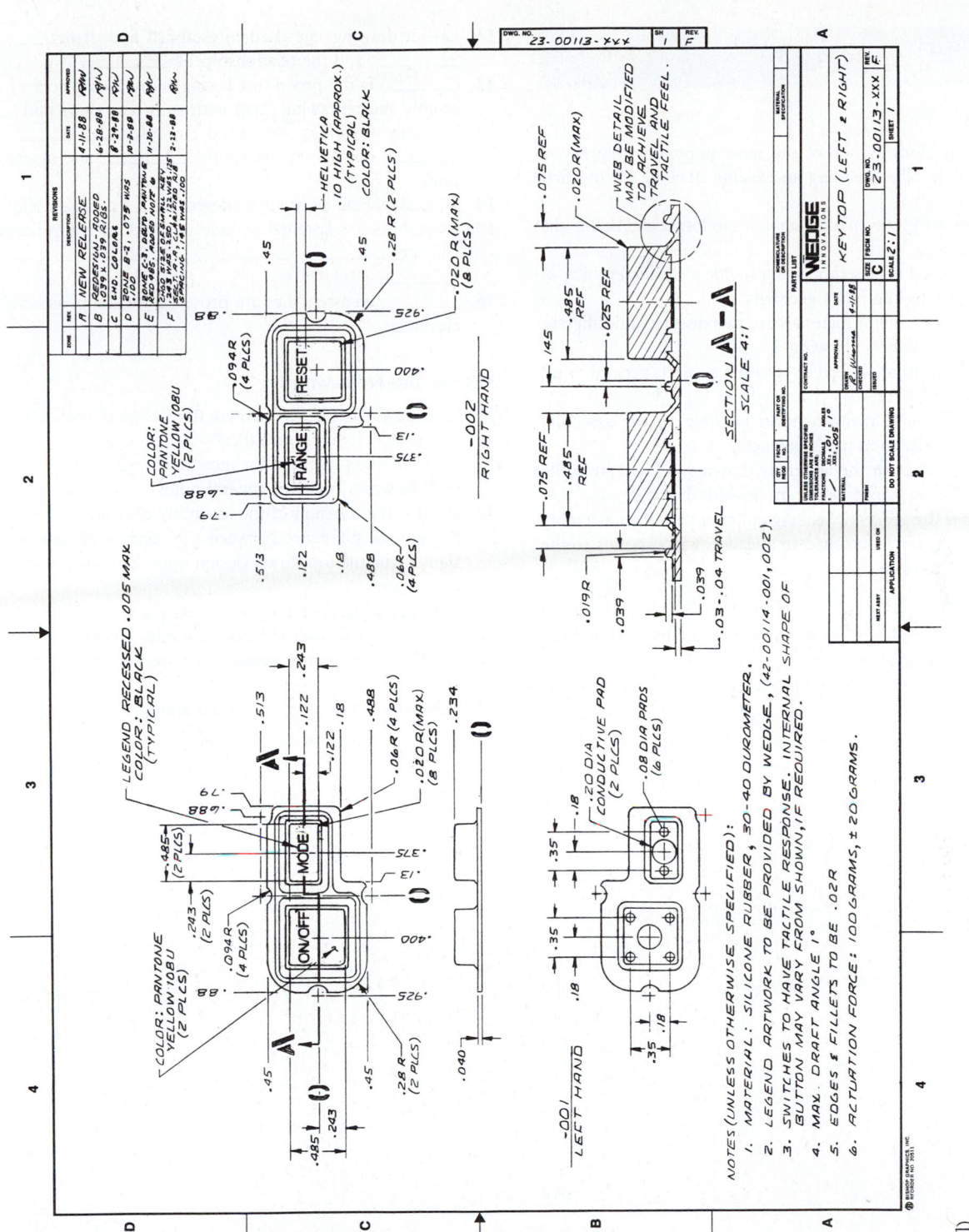

FIGURE 18.40   SmartLevel Production Drawings—Continued   (I) Keytop detail

QUIZ

True or False

1. The revision block is one of the most important things you should look at when reading an existing drawing for the first time.
2. Dimensions are given on all assemblies to locate and define the part's geometry.
3. Sections are used on assemblies to provide a convenient way of clearly displaying the unit's geometry.
4. A parts list and a bill of materials are two distinct and different aspects of an assembly drawing.
5. Since they will normally differ for each project, general notes are seldom standardized.
6. Hidden lines are shown whenever possible on the assembly drawing to clarify each part's geometry.
7. A parts list that is on the assembly drawing is listed from the top-down and is placed below the revision block.
8. Ballooning is the process of calling out each part of an assembly by providing a circle attached to a leader, which points to the piece on the drawing.

Fill in the Blanks

9. A _____ provides prints of a drawing that have white lines with a blue background.
10. _____ are used to hold and locate a part during machining operations.
11. Layout drawings are used to establish and depict _____ , _____ , and the relationship of _____ .
12. _____ is the process of taking individual pieces of an assembly and redrawing them with sufficient views and _____ .
13. Working drawings are used to order _____ , plan _____ operations, determine _____ , and assemble the unit.
14. Welded assemblies are considered _____ assemblies.
15. Assemblies are fastened by one or more of the processes including _____ , _____ , _____ , _____ , and _____ .
16. _____ on assemblies are provided for setup, assembly, and clearance.

Answer the Following

17. How do CAD systems facilitate the design of tools for production of jigs, fixtures, and dies?
18. Why are notes required for most drawings? What is the difference between local and general notes?
19. What is the function of the assembly drawing?
20. Explain the difference between the concept of bottom-up design versus the top-down design approach when constructing an assembly.
21. Describe a parts list and each of its major headings.
22. How are views selected for an assembly drawing?
23. Explain the difference between a separable and an inseparable assembly.
24. Name three ways that you could simplify a drawing.

EXERCISES

Exercises may be assigned as sketching, instrument or CAD projects. Transfer the given information to an "A" size sheet of .25 in. grid paper. Exercises that are not assigned by the instructor can be sketched in the text to provide practice and understanding for the preceding instructional material. Draw the drawing format, title block, and other standard information for the exercise. If using AutoCAD or another system that provides standard formats use them instead of the one provided here or in the worksheets.

After Reading the Chapter Through Section 18.11.1 You May Complete the Following Exercises

Exercise 18.1 Do a complete parts list for Problem 18.27 or 18.22.

Exercise 18.2 Do a complete parts list for Problem 18.28 or 18.23.

Exercise 18.3 Do a complete parts list for Problem 18.29 or 18.24.

Exercise 18.4 Do a complete parts list for Problem 18.30 or 18.25.

ITEM	QTY	PART NO.	DESCRIPTION

Exercise 18.1

ITEM	QTY	PART NO.	DESCRIPTION

Exercise 18.3

ITEM	QTY	PART NO.	DESCRIPTION

Exercise 18.2

ITEM	QTY	PART NO.	DESCRIPTION

Exercise 18.4

PROBLEMS

Jig and Fixture Assembly Design Projects

Design a jig and fixture to hold the following parts while machining. Do a layout of the fixture, a finalized assembly, a parts list, and details of each nonstandard item in the assembly. Show the work piece part in phantom lines or plot in a second color. Use Chapter 15, Threads, Fasteners, and Springs and Appendix C (and CARR LANE parts if available) for standard parts.

Figure 18.41 shows an example of a student-designed fixture. The journal bearing housing provided in Problem 18.7 was used as the part to be machined. A wireframe model was completed first [Fig. 18.41(a)]. A surface model of the part was completed next [Fig. 18.41(b)]. Figure 18.41(c) shows a dimensioned detail of the journal bearing housing. An assembly was designed using standard CARR LANE parts [Figure 18.41(d)] and an assembled detail was completed along with a parts list as shown in Figure 18.41(e).

Detail Drawings

For detail drawings use appropriate ANSI standards for dimensioning and tolerancing for all problems. Complete a rough sketch of the part before drawing it with instruments or on a CAD system. Choose an appropriate size drawing sheet for each project. If a 3D system is available, model the part first and then generate a dimensioned detail.

For all drawings, use ANSI or ISO standard sheet sizes, parts list format, revision block, and title blocks, as shown in this chapter, and on the inside covers of the text. The dimensions given for individual part's are, in most cases, for construction of the part's geometry only. The problems shown here are by no means meant to represent the correct way of dimensioning the part. The given dimensions will enable you to draw the part. *It will be your responsibility to select the proper views and place the dimensions, notes, and other information on the drawing.* Show all finish marks and use symbology wherever possible. See Chapters 12 and 13 for proper methods.

All pictorial drawings are to be converted to multiview details with appropriate view selection and proper dimensioning methods. In most cases, the drawings presented here as projects can be drawn full scale. If a project prohibits full-scale rendering, a reduced scale can be used. All projects done on a CAD system are to be modeled/drawn full scale and then plotted according to your instructor and the limitations of your plotter.

Decimal-inch projects and metric drawings are provided. You may convert any of the projects to the other measurement system. In many cases, you will find that converting the dimensions will give odd and inappropriate sizes. You may redesign any of the parts using even and logical sizes for that measurement system. As an example, a 1.00 inch measurement converts to 25.4 mm. It is acceptable to change the metric dimension into 25 mm or 24 mm. The same is true for standard parts such as screws, nuts, washers, and other off-the-shelf items; look up the closest standard size before ordering the item (placing on the parts list).

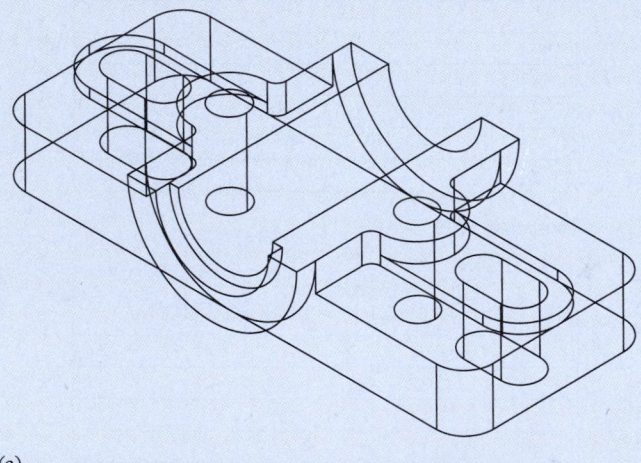

(a)

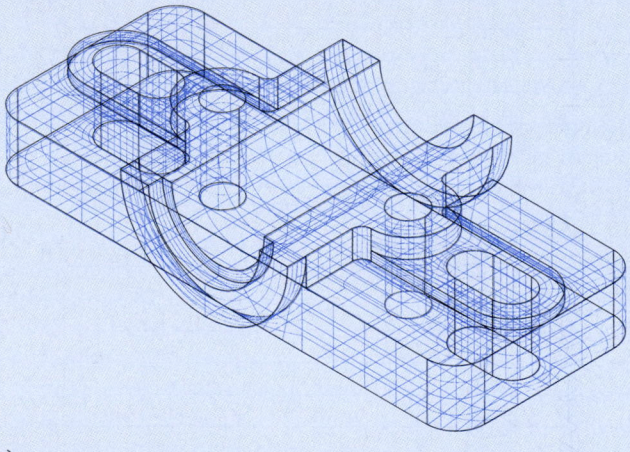

(b)

FIGURE 18.41   Journal Bearing Fixture   (a) Wireframe model of the journal bearing housing shown in Problem 18.7 (b) Surfaced model of the journal bearing housing (c) Dimensioned detail of the journal bearing housing (d) Machining fixture for the journal bearing housing (e) Assembly drawing of the fixture for the journal bearing housing

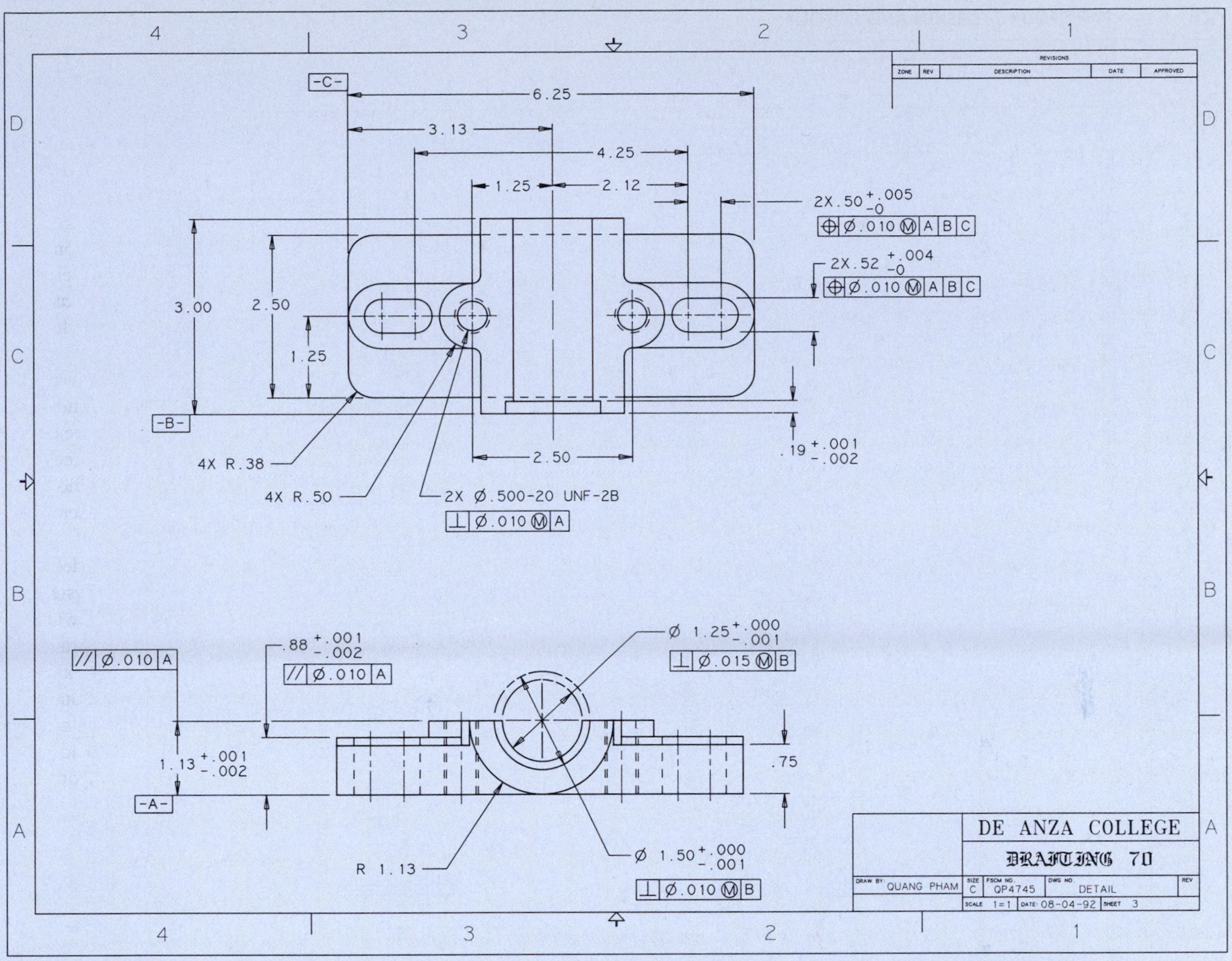

REVISIONS
ZONE
REV
DESCRIPTION
DATE
APPROVED
-C-
6.25
3.13
4.25
1.25
2.12
2X .50 +.005 -0
⌖ Ø.010 Ⓜ A B C
2X .52 +.004 -0
⌖ Ø.010 Ⓜ A B C
3.00
2.50
1.25
-B-
.19 +.001 -.002
2.50
4X R.38
4X R.50
2X Ø.500-20 UNF-2B
⊥ Ø.010 Ⓜ A
// Ø.010 A
.88 +.001 -.002
// Ø.010 A
Ø 1.25 +.000 -.001
⊥ Ø.015 Ⓜ B
1.13 +.001 -.002
-A-
.75
R 1.13
Ø 1.50 +.000 -.001
⊥ Ø.010 Ⓜ B
DE ANZA COLLEGE
DRAFTING 70
DRAW BY: QUANG PHAM
SIZE C
FSCM NO. QP4745
DWG NO. DETAIL
REV
SCALE 1=1
DATE: 08-04-92
SHEET 3
4
3
2
1
D
C
B
A

(c)

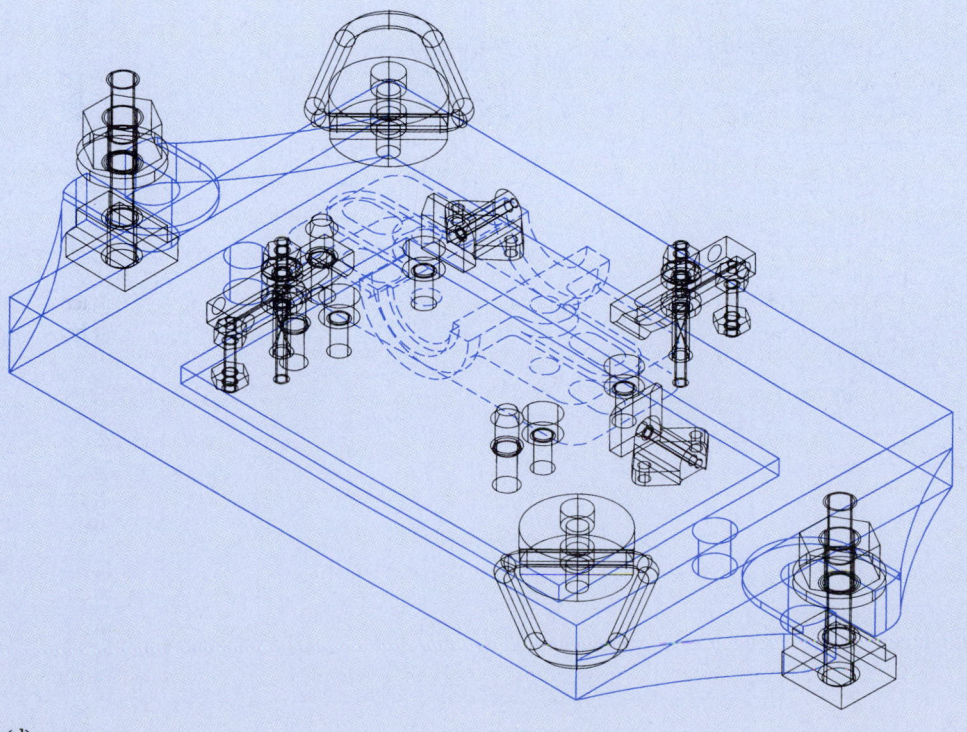

(d)

FIGURE 18.41 Journal Bearing Fixture—*Continued*
(c) Dimensioned detail of the journal bearing housing
(d) Machining fixture for the journal bearing housing

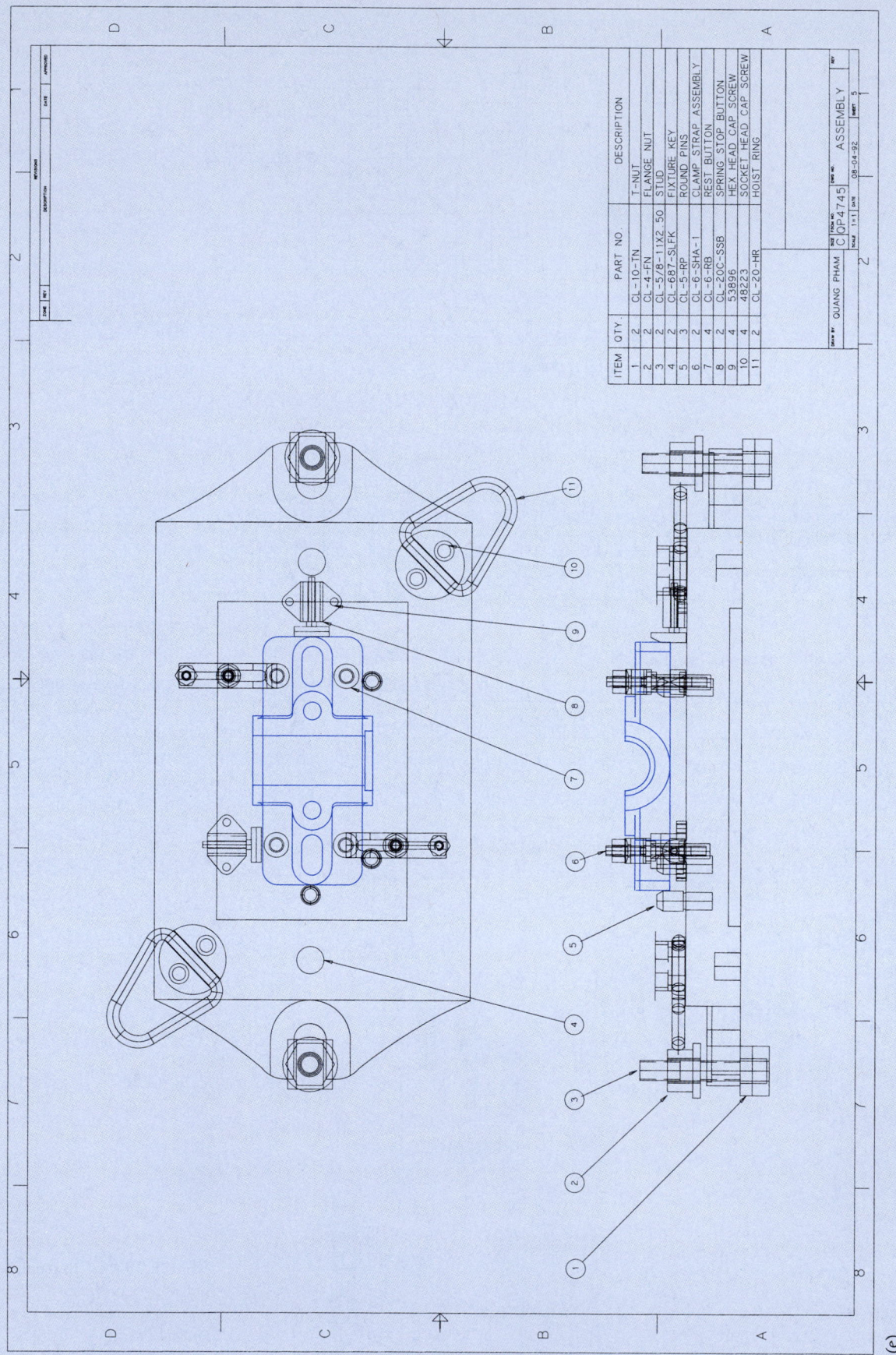

ITEM	QTY	PART NO.	DESCRIPTION
1	2	CL-10-TN	T-NUT
2	2	CL-4-FN	FLANGE NUT
3	2	CL-5/8-11X2 50	STUD
4	2	CL-687-SLFK	FIXTURE KEY
5	3	CL-5-RP	ROUND PINS
6	2	CL-6-SHA-1	CLAMP STRAP ASSEMBLY
7	4	CL-6-RB	REST BUTTON
8	2	CL-20C-SSB	SPRING STOP BUTTON
9	4	53896	HEX HEAD CAP SCREW
10	4	48223	SOCKET HEAD CAP SCREW
11	2	CL-20-HR	HOIST RING

FIGURE 18.41   Journal Bearing Fixture—*Continued*   (e) Assembly drawing of the fixture for the journal bearing housing

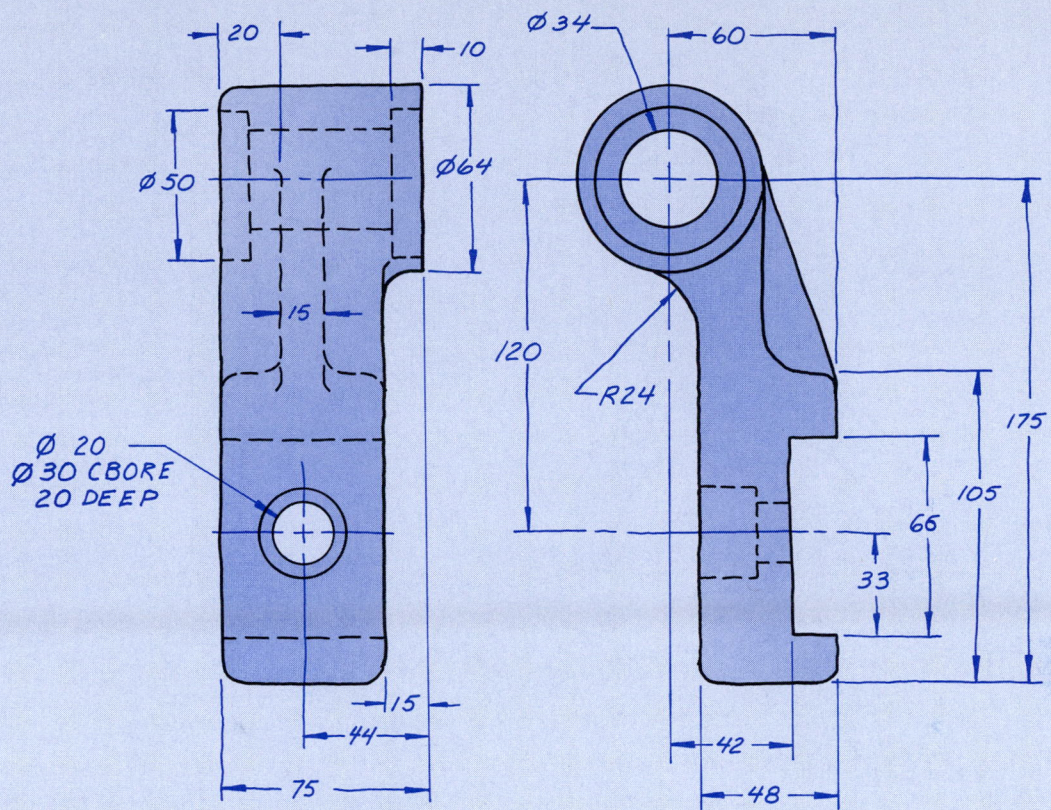

Problem 18.1   Draw and detail the adjustable guide.

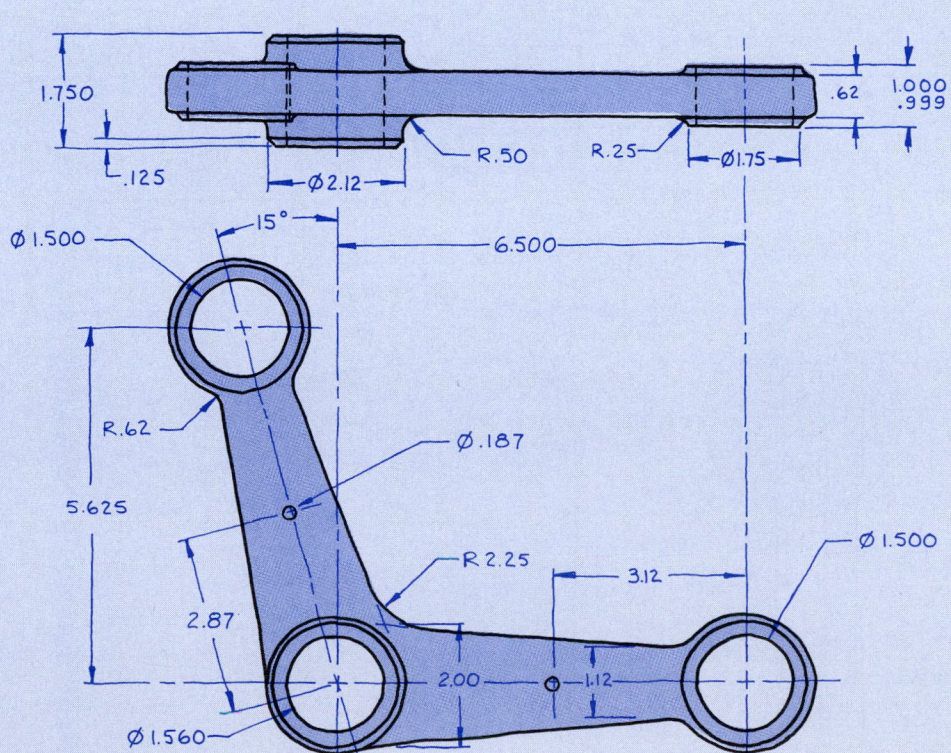

Problem 18.2   Do a detail drawing of the crank arm.

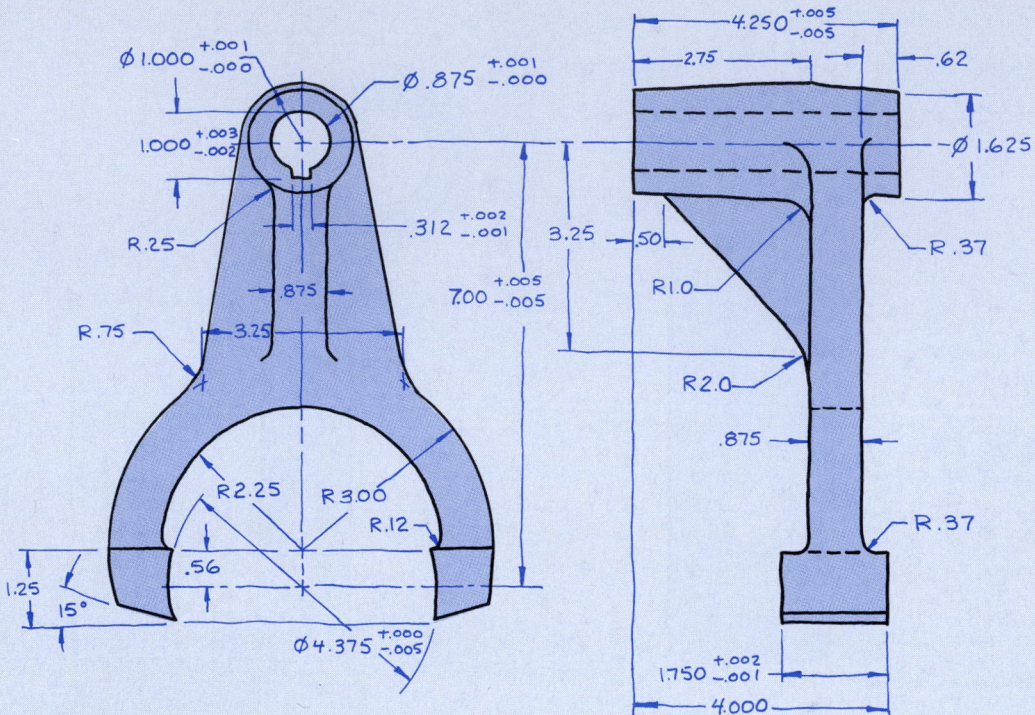

Problem 18.3 Draw and detail the shifter fork.

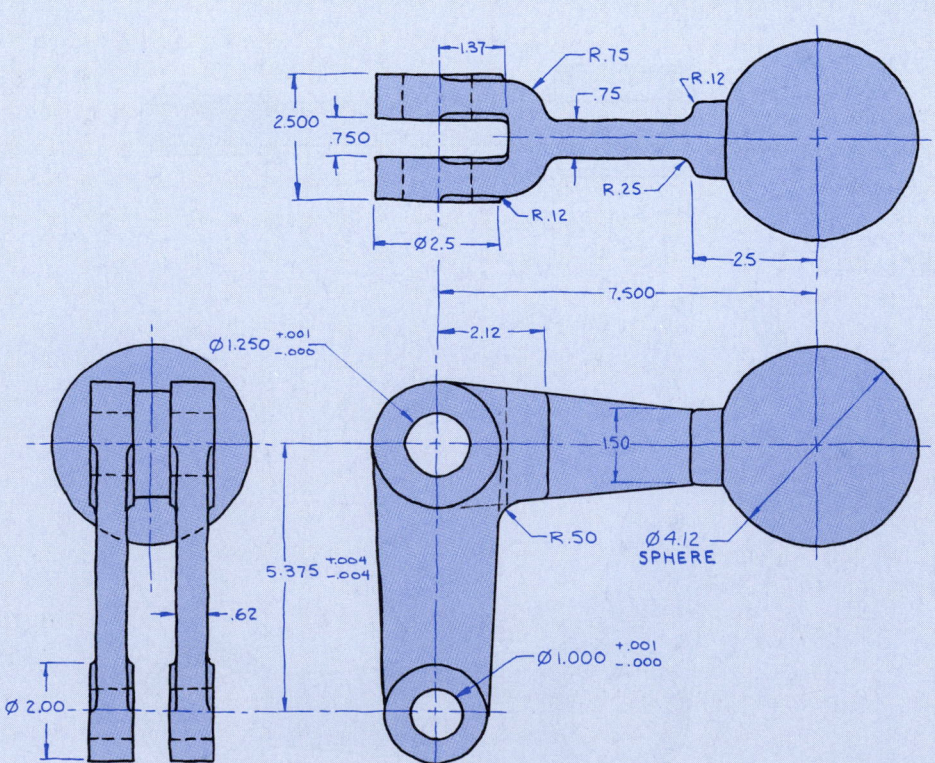

Problem 18.4 Draw and detail the flywheel.

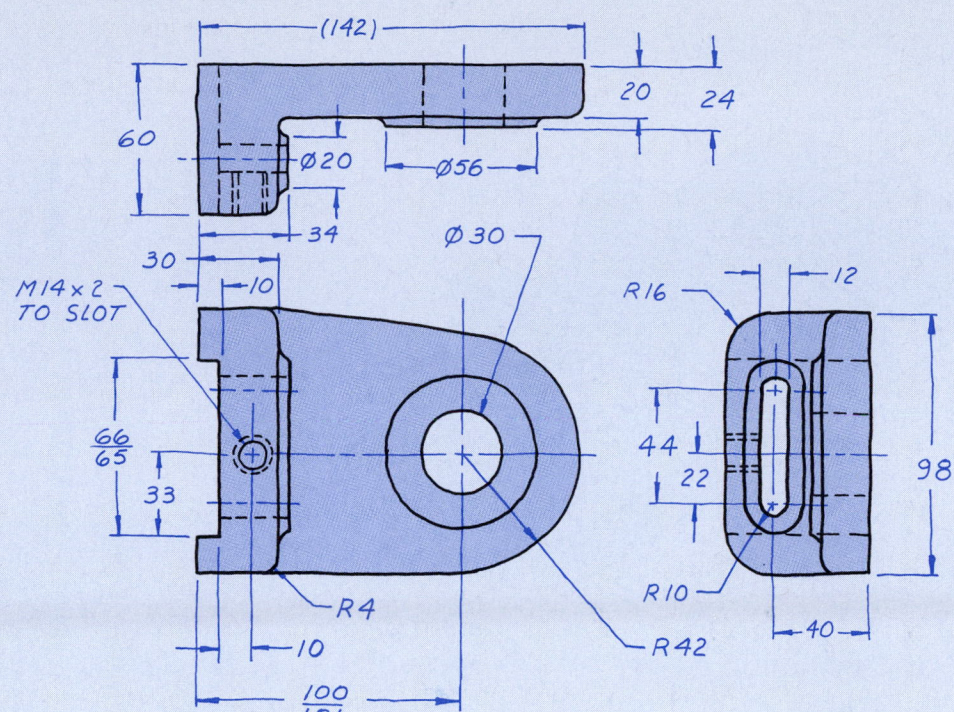

Problem 18.5 Do a detail drawing of the bearing adjustment.

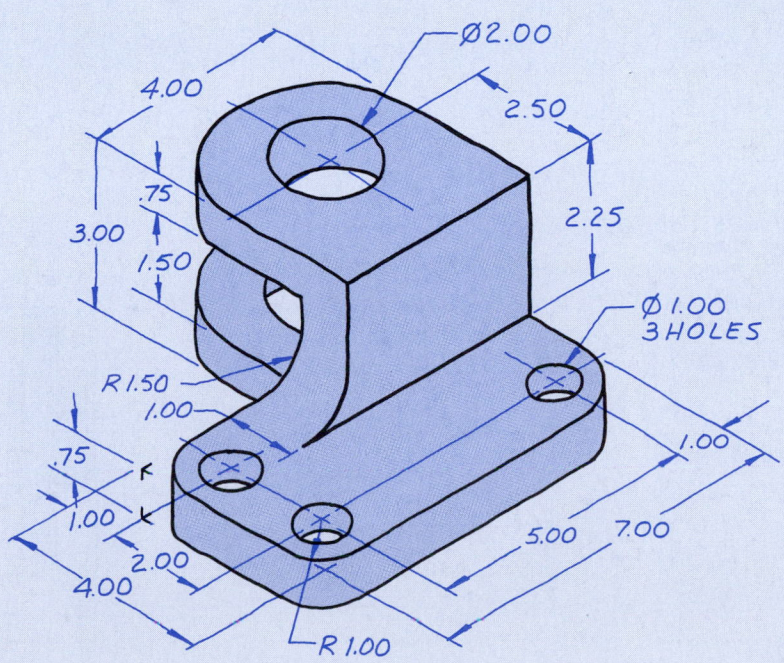

Problem 18.6 Draw and detail the guide bracket.

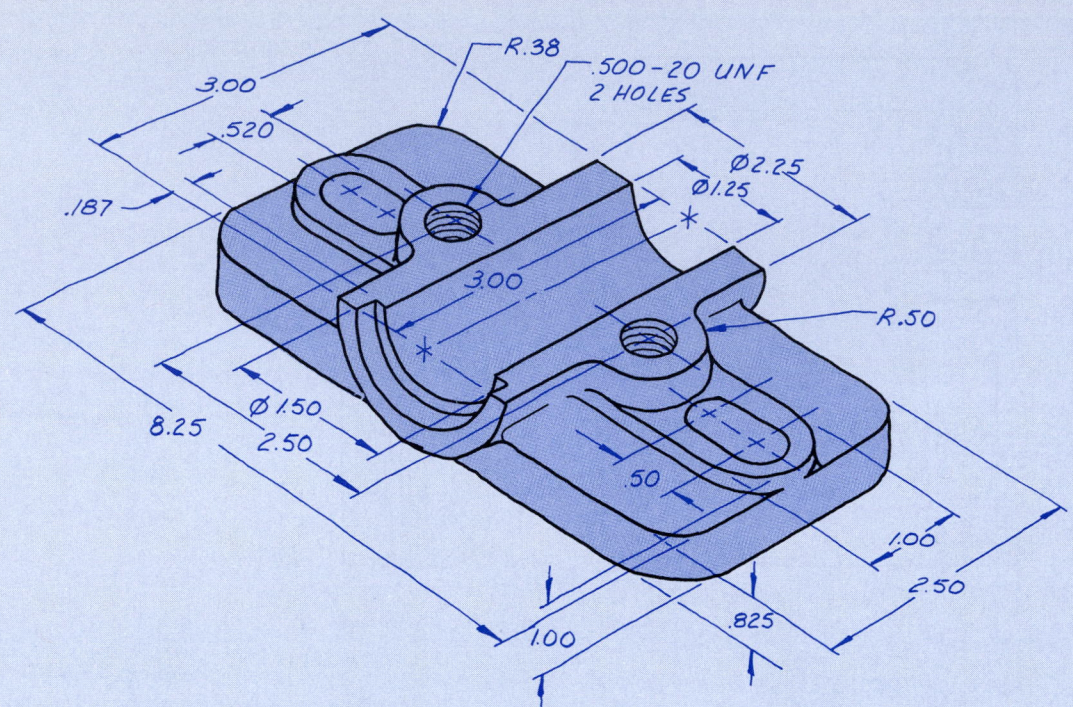

Problem 18.7 Detail the journal bearing housing.

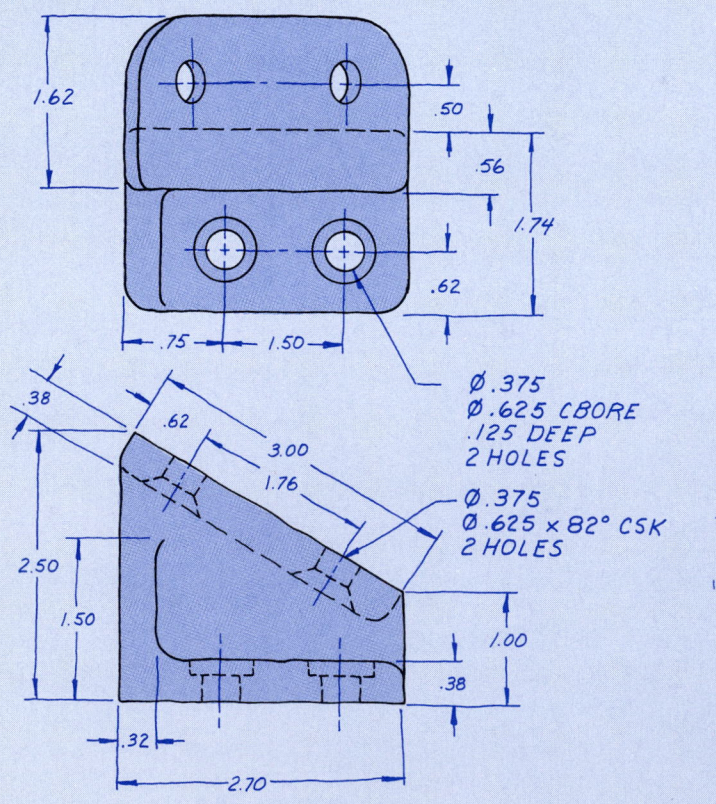

NOTE: ALL FILLETS AND ROUNDS R .18

Problem 18.8 Draw and detail the offset bracket.

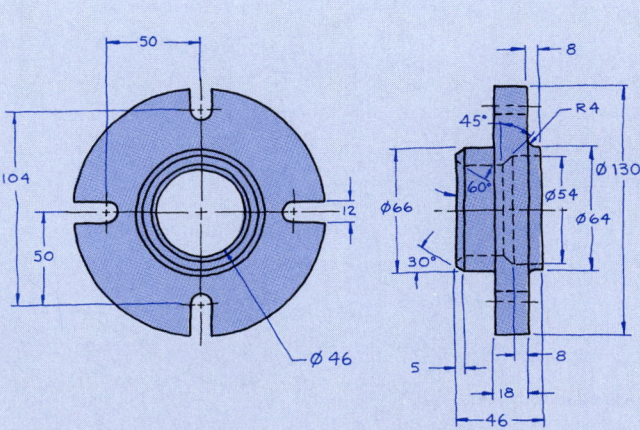

Problem 18.9 Complete a detail of the thrust bearing cap.

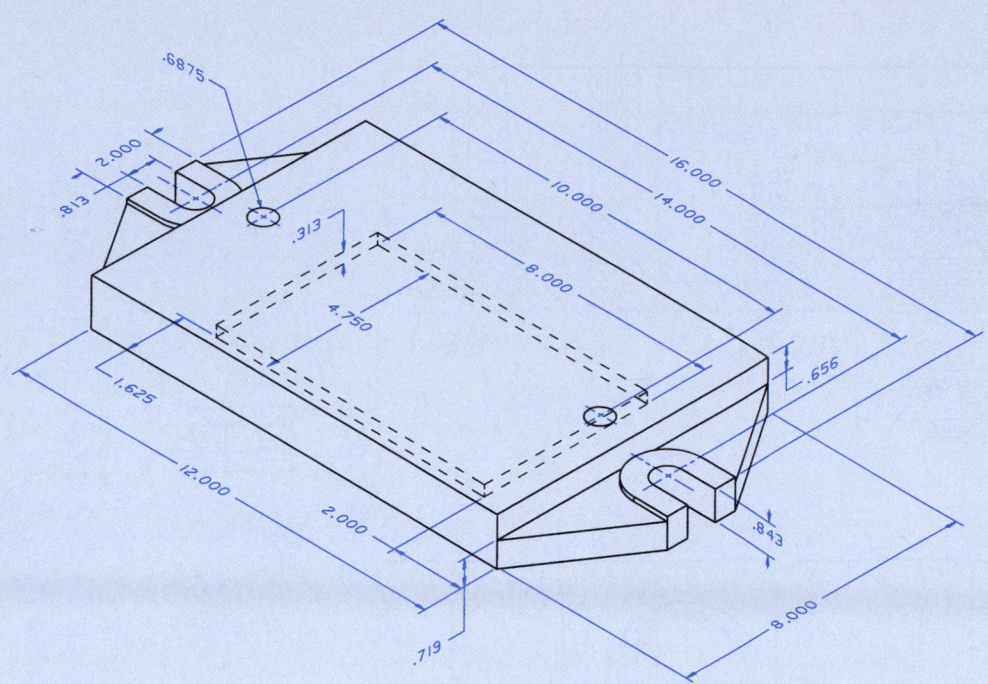

Problem 18.14   Draw and detail the CARR LANE mill base.

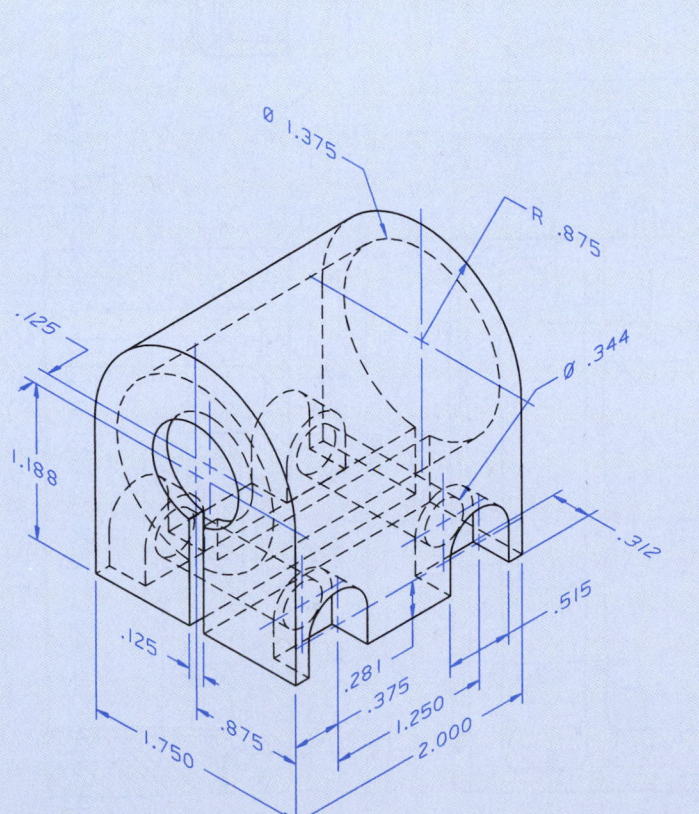

Problem 18.15   Draw and detail the CARR LANE cylinder mount.

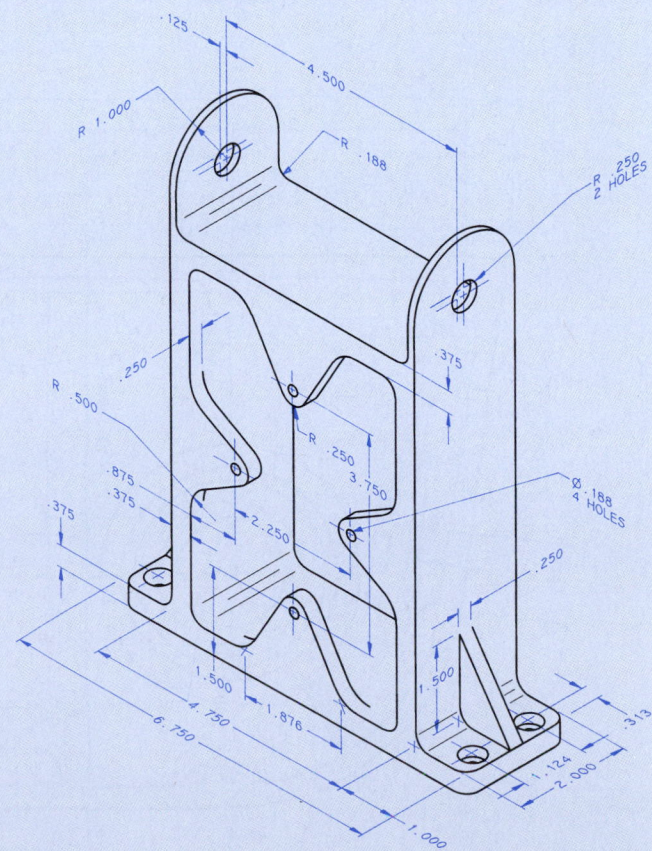

Problem 18.16   Draw and detail the casting.

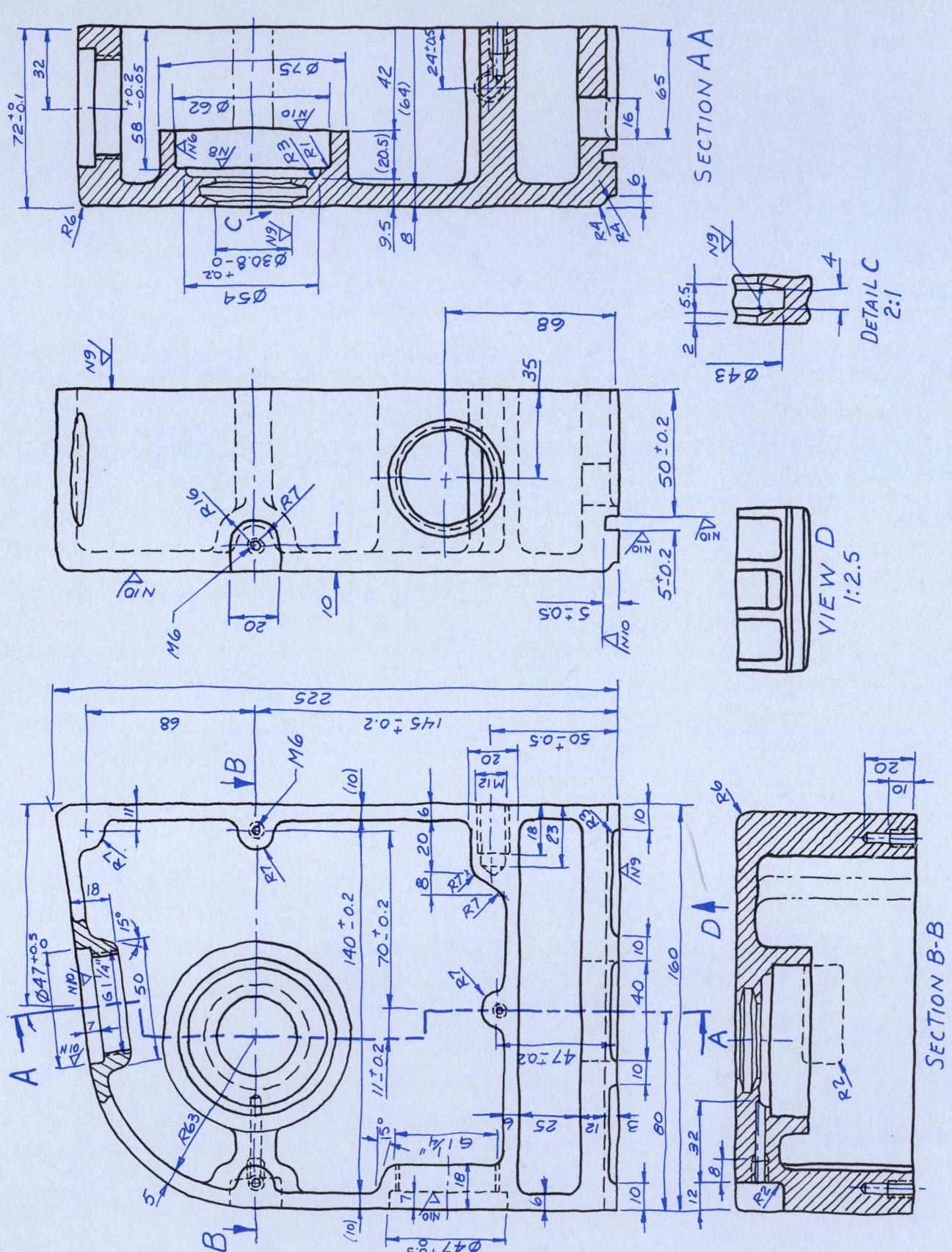

Problem 18.17 Draw and detail the casting.

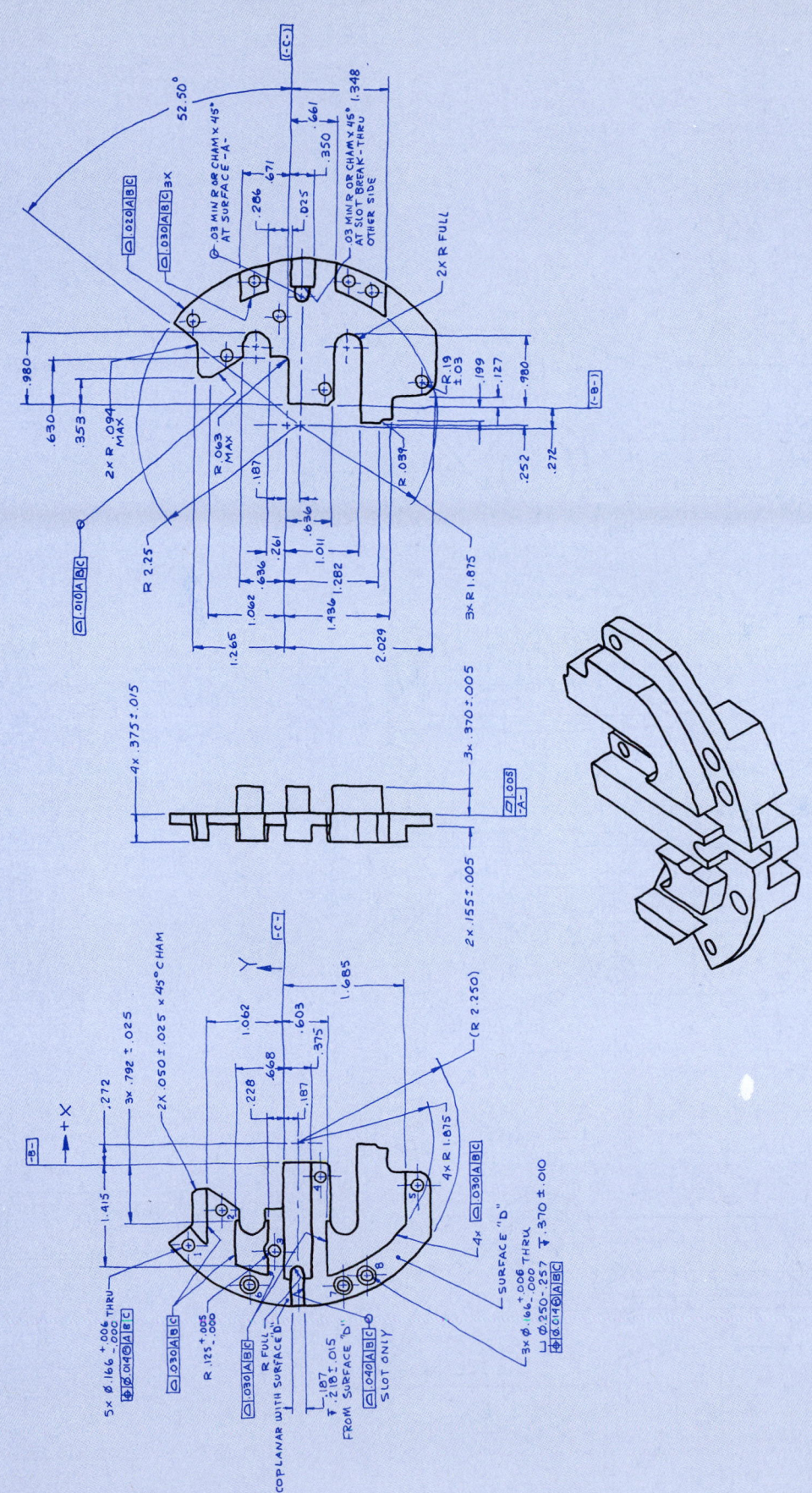

Problem 18.18 Draw and detail the safety shield.

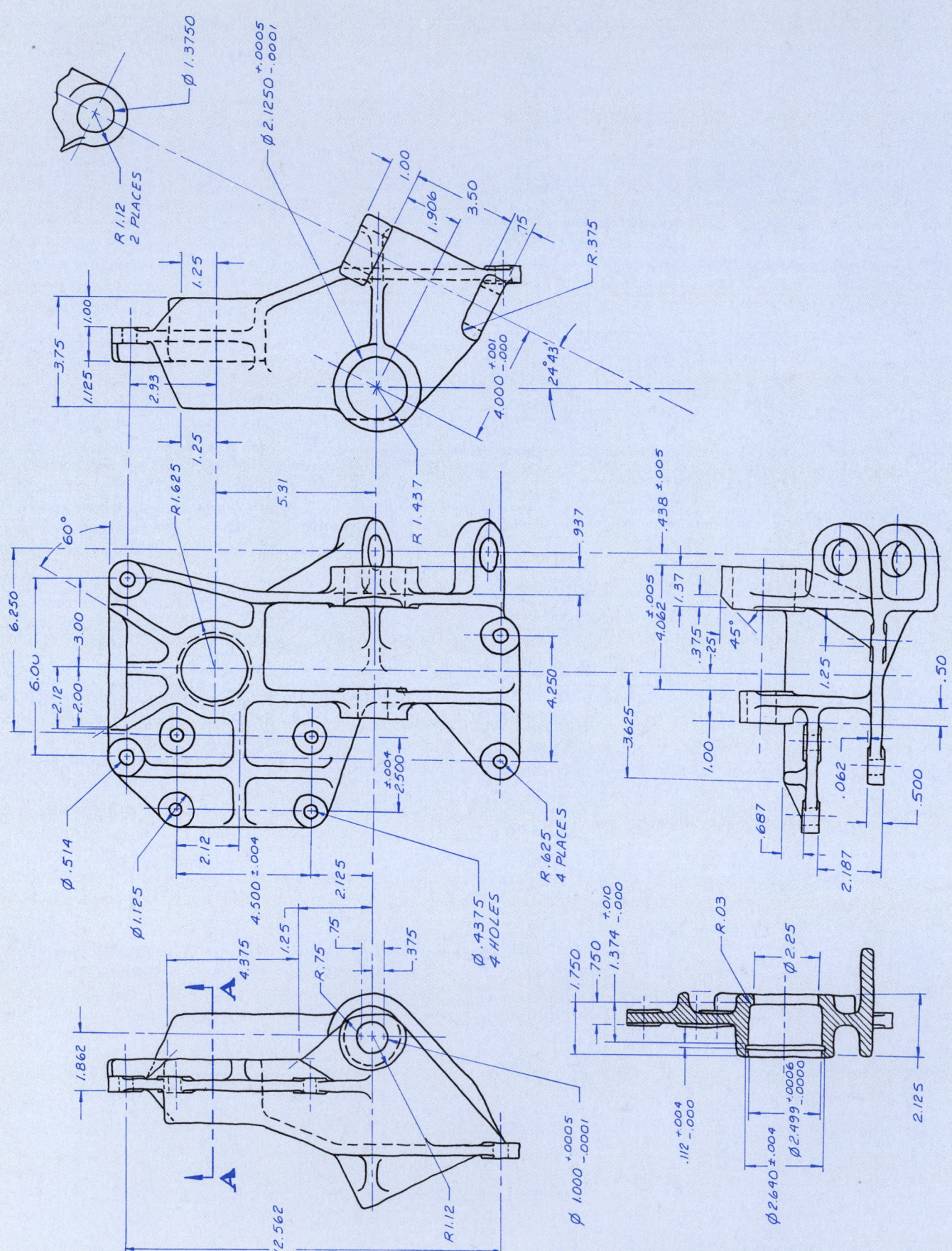

Problem 18.19 Draw and detail the actuator.

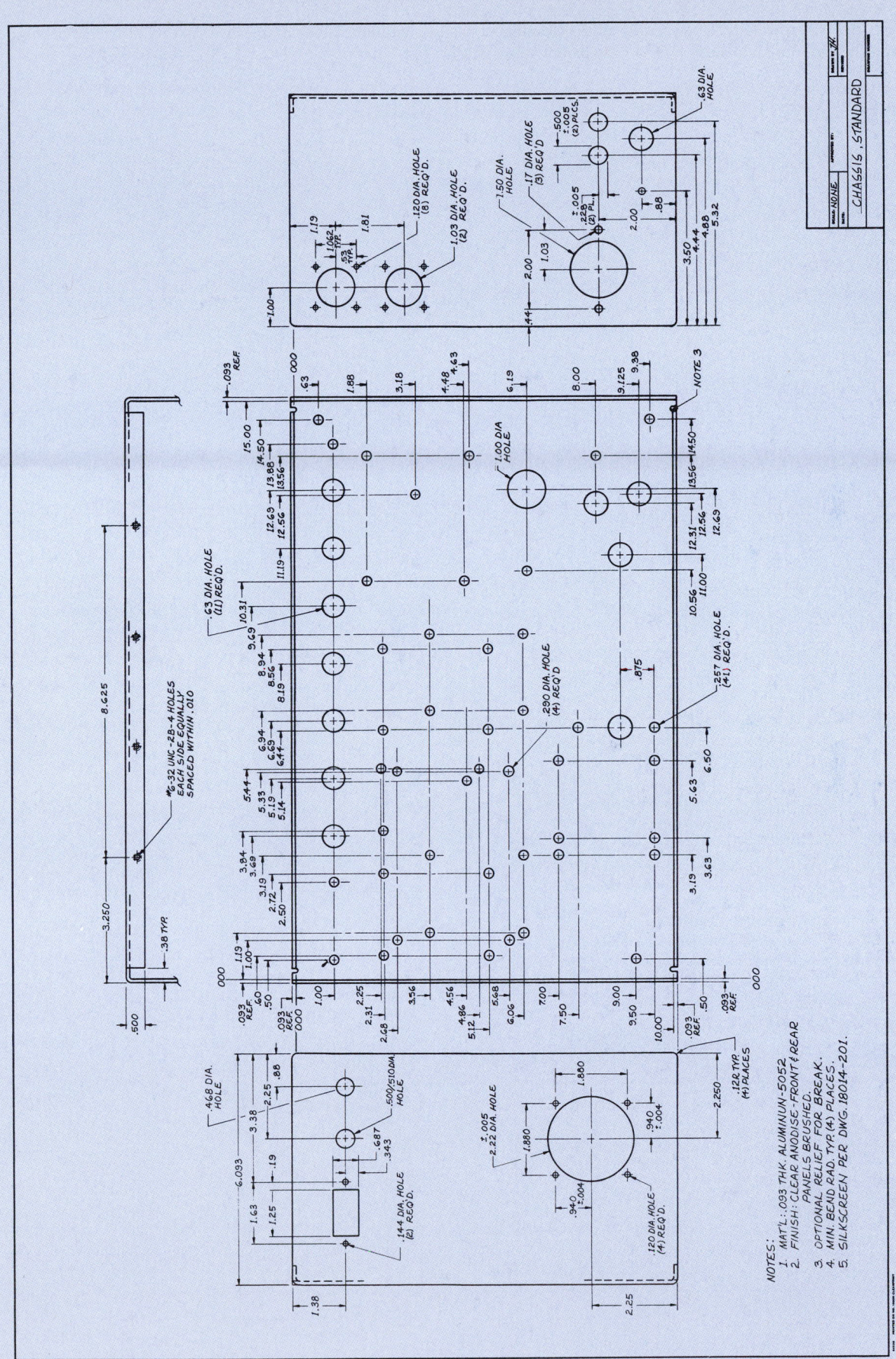

Problem 18.20   Redraw the chassis.

Problems 18.21(A) and (B)   Draw and detail the cleaning kit package and dimension completely. Make a full-size model of the box using cardboard. This project could also be used for Chapter 21.

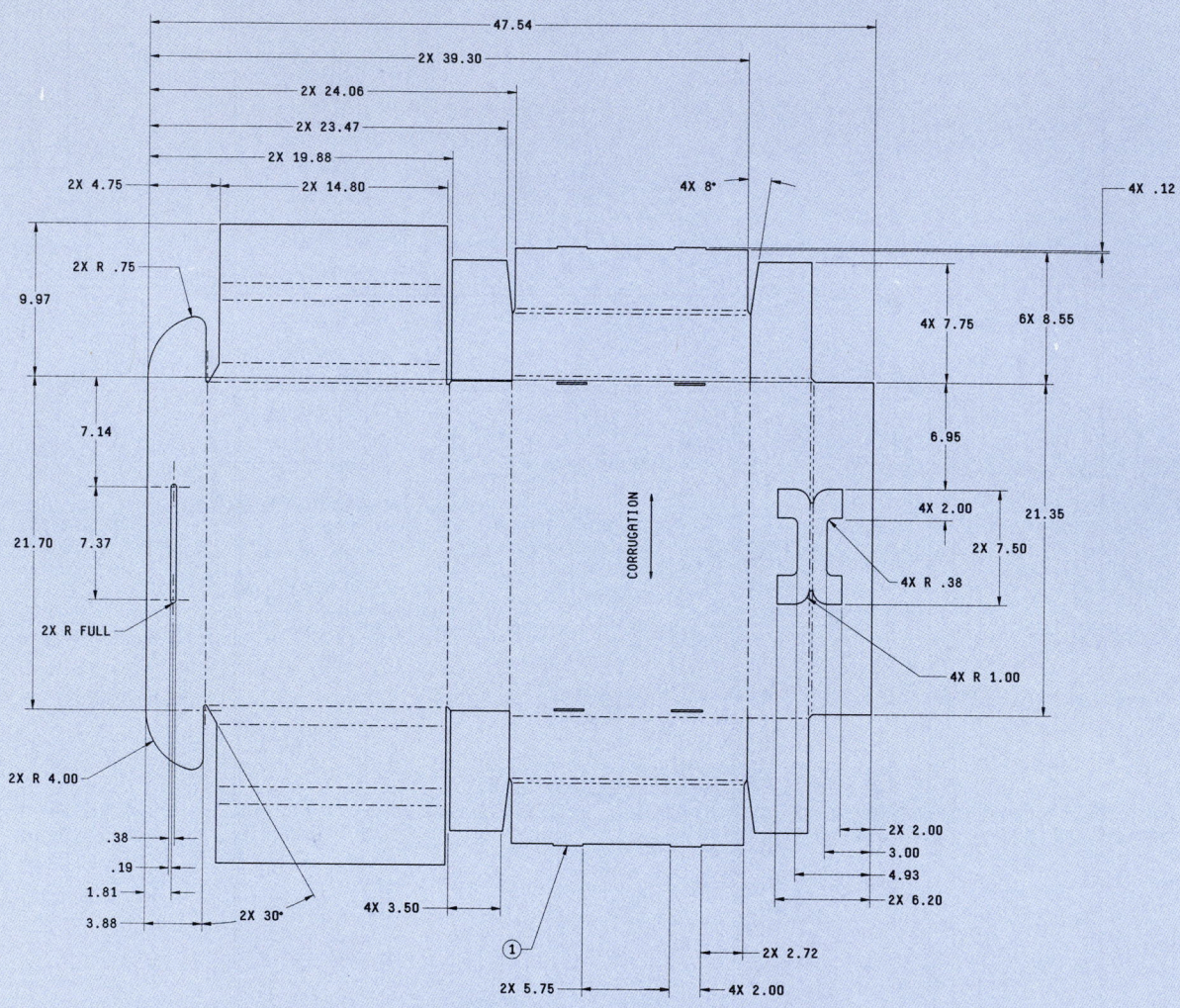

4   ASSEMBLY METHOD AT VENDOR OPTION, WITH MANUFACTURING
    ENGINEERING APPROVAL.

3   BOX MATERIAL: 200 B FLUTE NO. 3 WHITE

2. THIS DRAWING SHALL BE INTERPRETED PER ANSI Y14.5M, 1982.

1. PKG & IDENTIFY WITH P/N (000-000345-001) AND LATEST
   REVISION LETTER.

▲ CRITICAL FUNCTIONALITY PARAMETER.

   NOTES: UNLESS OTHERWISE SPECIFIED.

BOX, CLEANING KIT

Problem 18.21 (A)

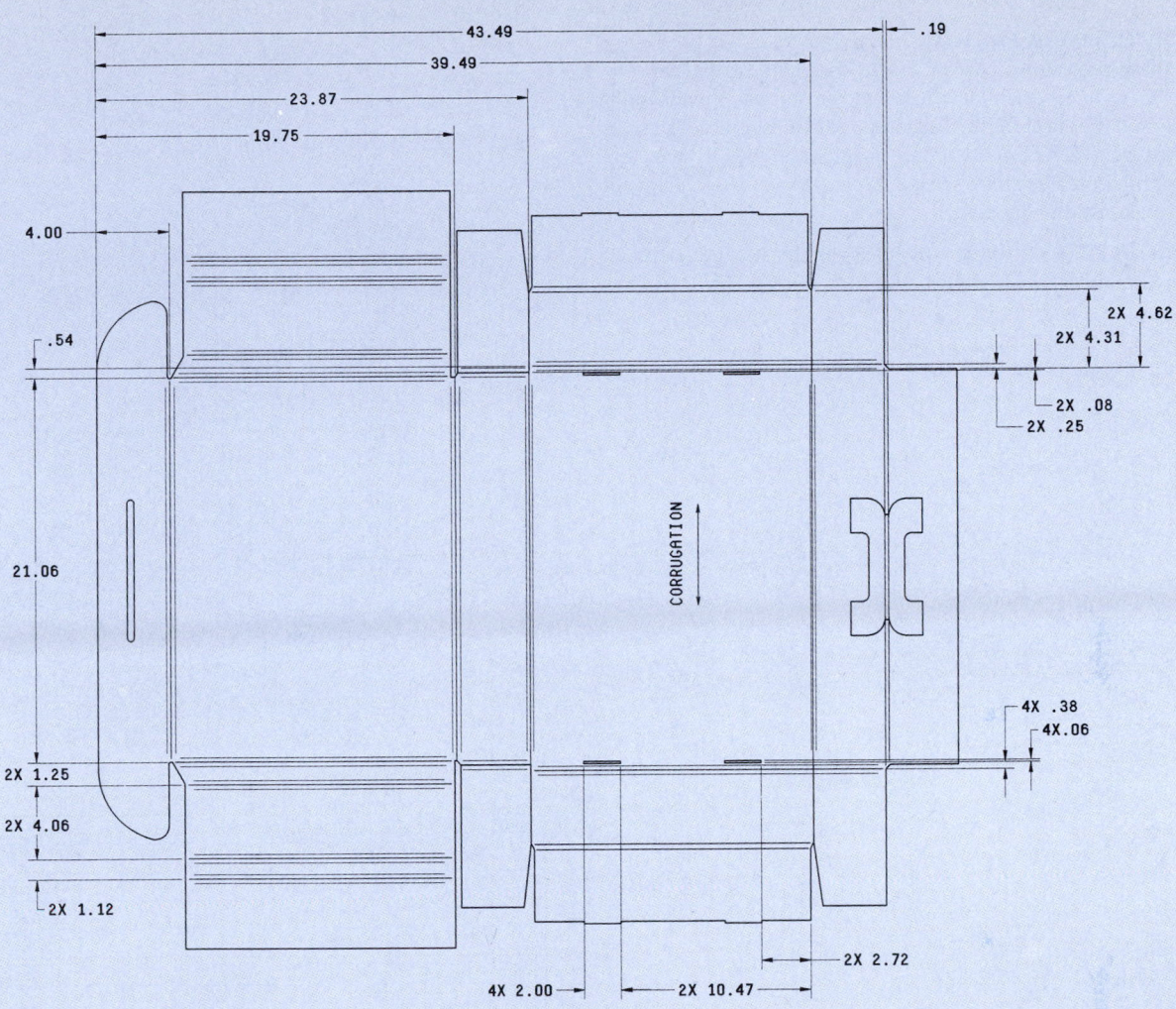

FOLDING DIMENSIONS

Problem 18.21 (B)

Assembly Drawings Projects

For assembly projects, prepare a layout assembly of the parts by blocking them in for each view required. Be sure to provide sufficient space on the sheet for the assembly and the parts list. The parts list can be generated on a wordprocessor or a CAD system and plotted/printed on a separate sheet. Check with your instructor for permission to use this method.

Problems 18.22 (A) and (B) Do an assembly (A) and details (B) for the hydraulic valve assembly.

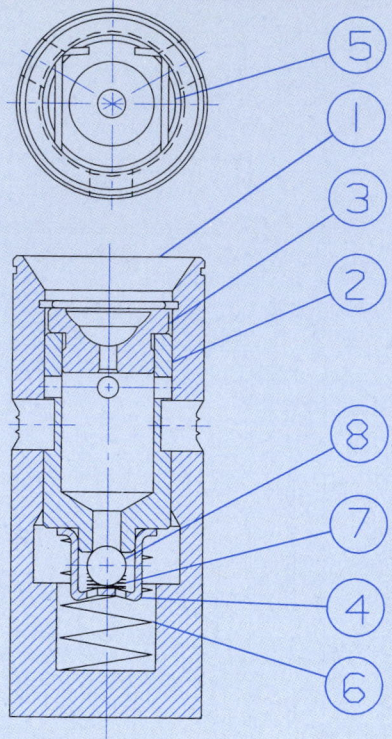

8	BALL BEARING Ø 3/16	1	STEEL
7	BALL CHECK VALVE SPRING	1	SPG STL
6	PLUNGER SPRING	1	SPG STL
5	RETAINER RING	1	SPG
4	BALL RETAINER	1	STL
3	PUSH ROD SEAT	1	STL
2	PLUNGER	1	STL
1	LIFTER BODY	1	STL
NO.	PART NAME	REQD	MATL

Problem 18.22 (A)

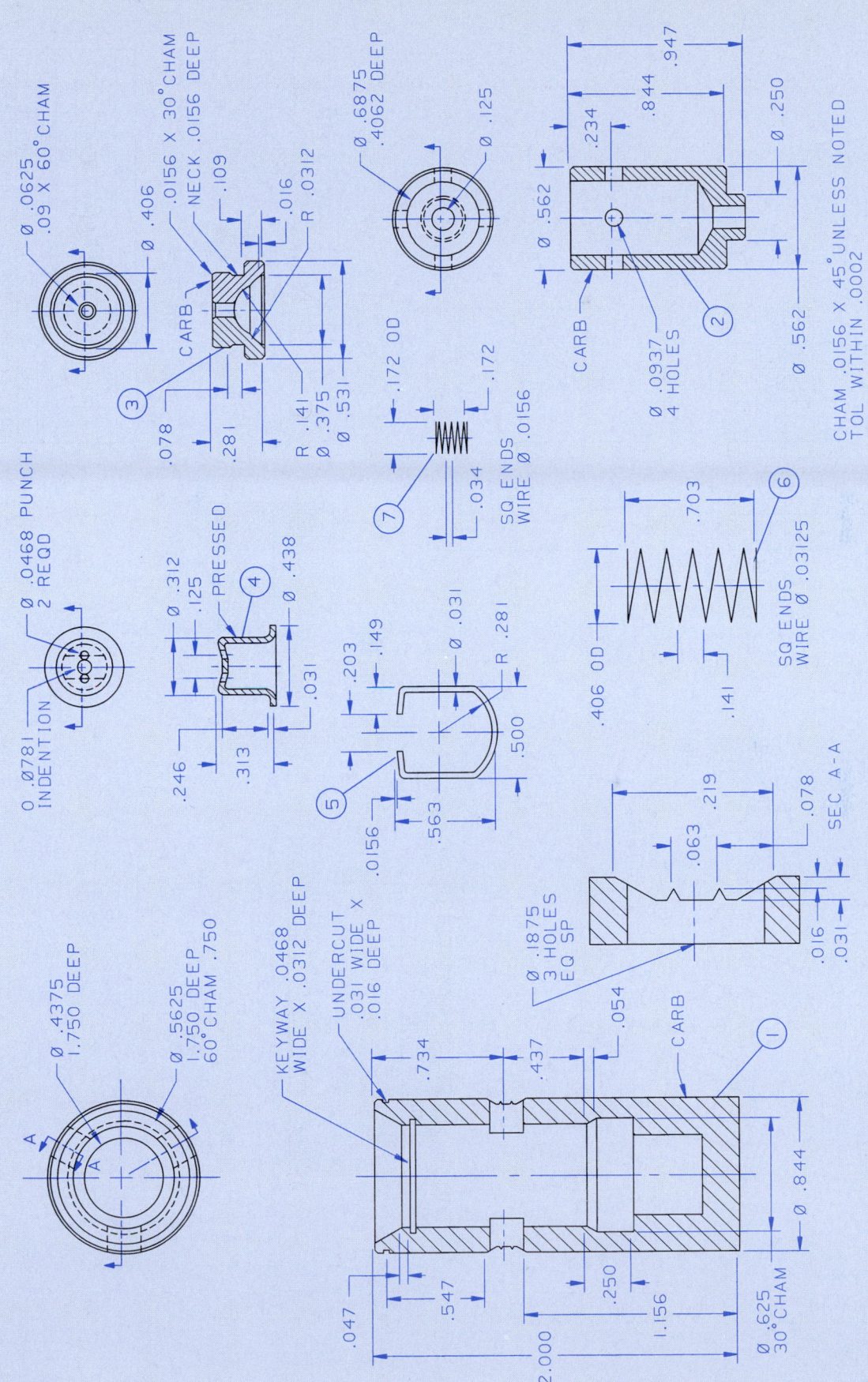

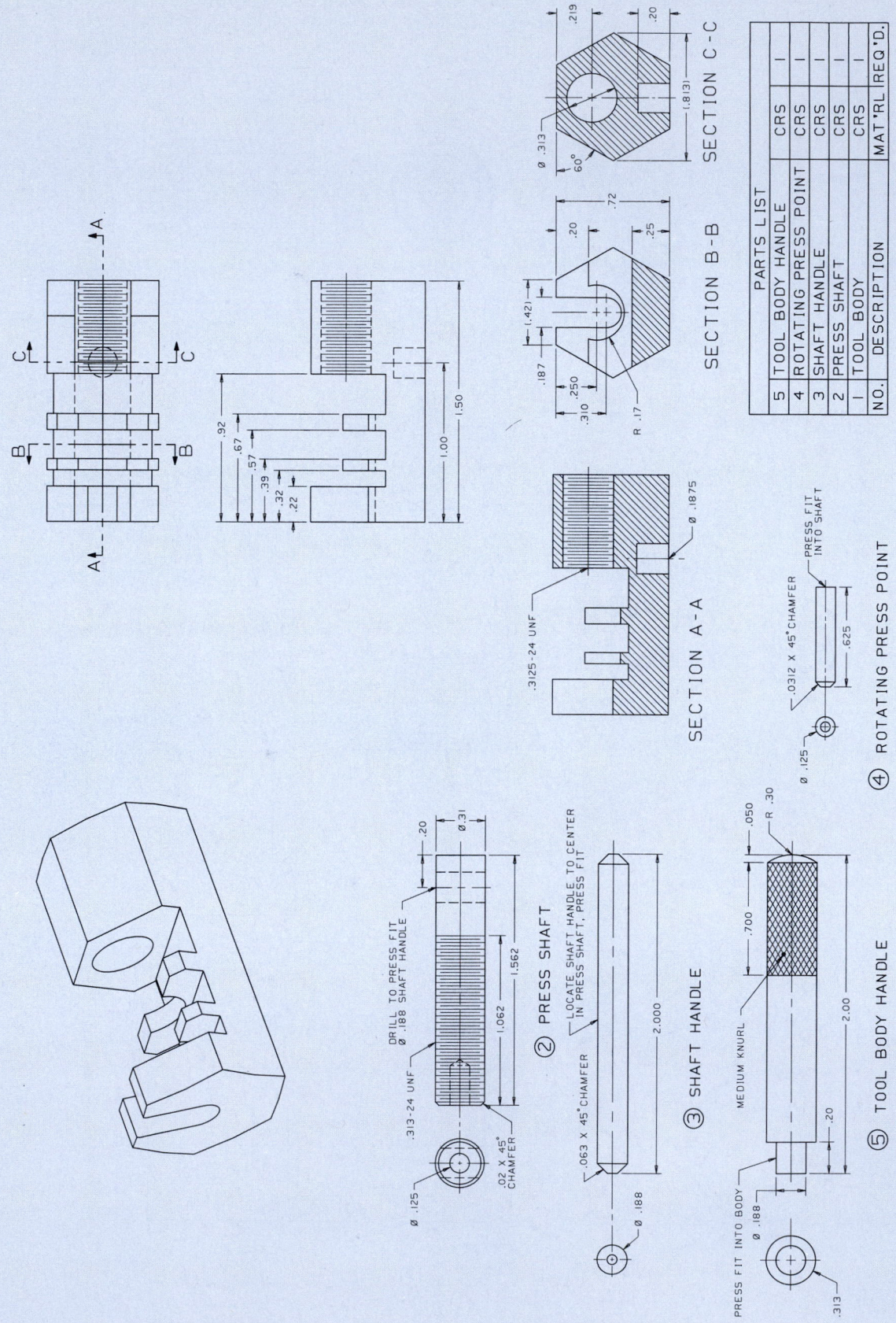

		PARTS LIST		
5	TOOL BODY HANDLE		CRS	1
4	ROTATING PRESS POINT		CRS	1
3	SHAFT HANDLE		CRS	1
2	PRESS SHAFT		CRS	1
1	TOOL BODY		CRS	1
NO.	DESCRIPTION		MAT'RL	REQ'D.

SECTION C-C

SECTION B-B

SECTION A-A

④ ROTATING PRESS POINT

② PRESS SHAFT

③ SHAFT HANDLE

⑤ TOOL BODY HANDLE

Problem 18.23   Do an assembly and details of the bike chain puller assembly.

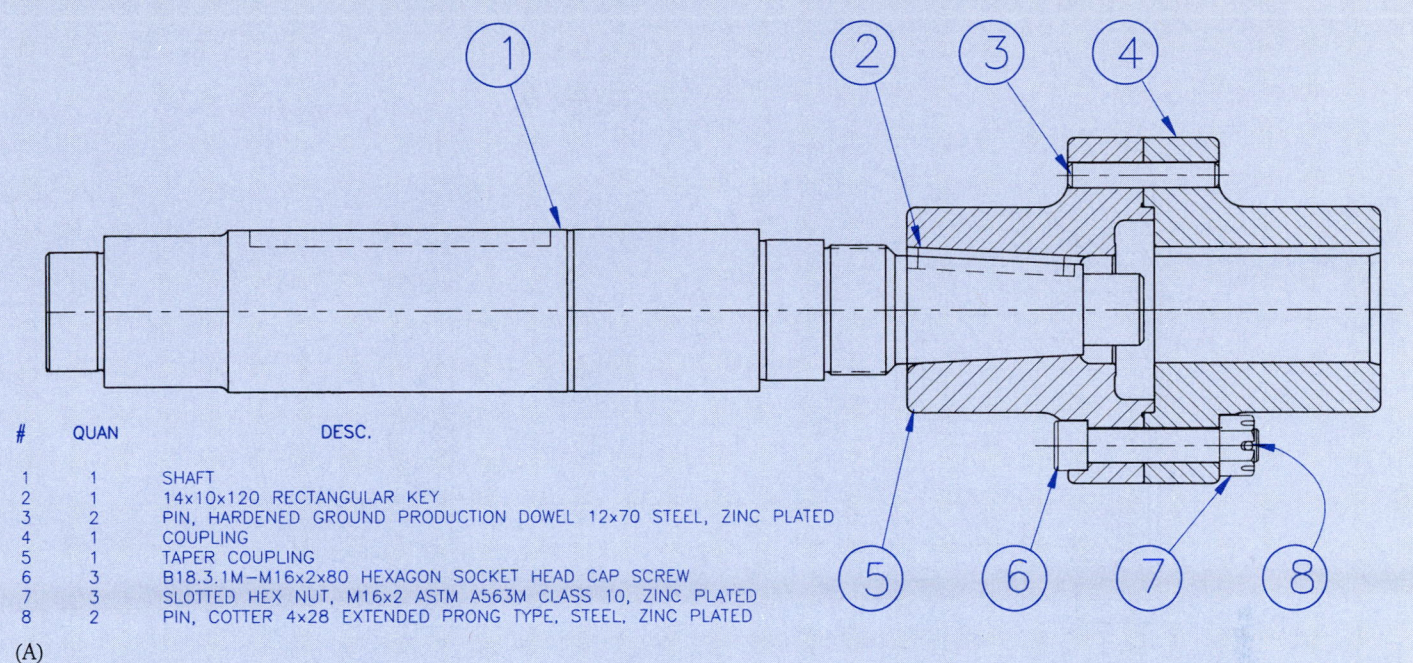

#	QUAN	DESC.
1	1	SHAFT
2	1	14x10x120 RECTANGULAR KEY
3	2	PIN, HARDENED GROUND PRODUCTION DOWEL 12x70 STEEL, ZINC PLATED
4	1	COUPLING
5	1	TAPER COUPLING
6	3	B18.3.1M—M16x2x80 HEXAGON SOCKET HEAD CAP SCREW
7	3	SLOTTED HEX NUT, M16x2 ASTM A563M CLASS 10, ZINC PLATED
8	2	PIN, COTTER 4x28 EXTENDED PRONG TYPE, STEEL, ZINC PLATED

(A)

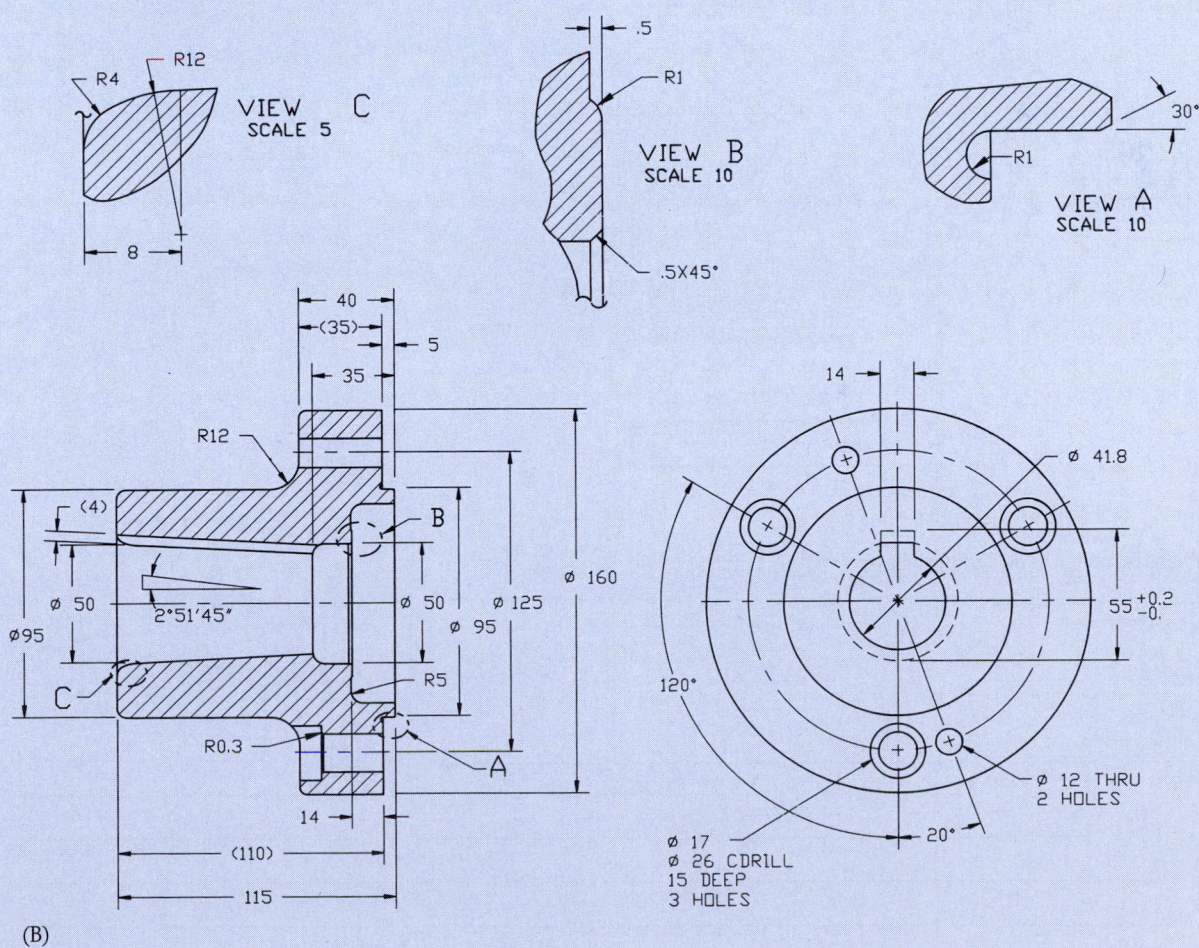

(B)

Problems 18.24 (A) and (B)   Draw and detail the assembly and details for the coupling.

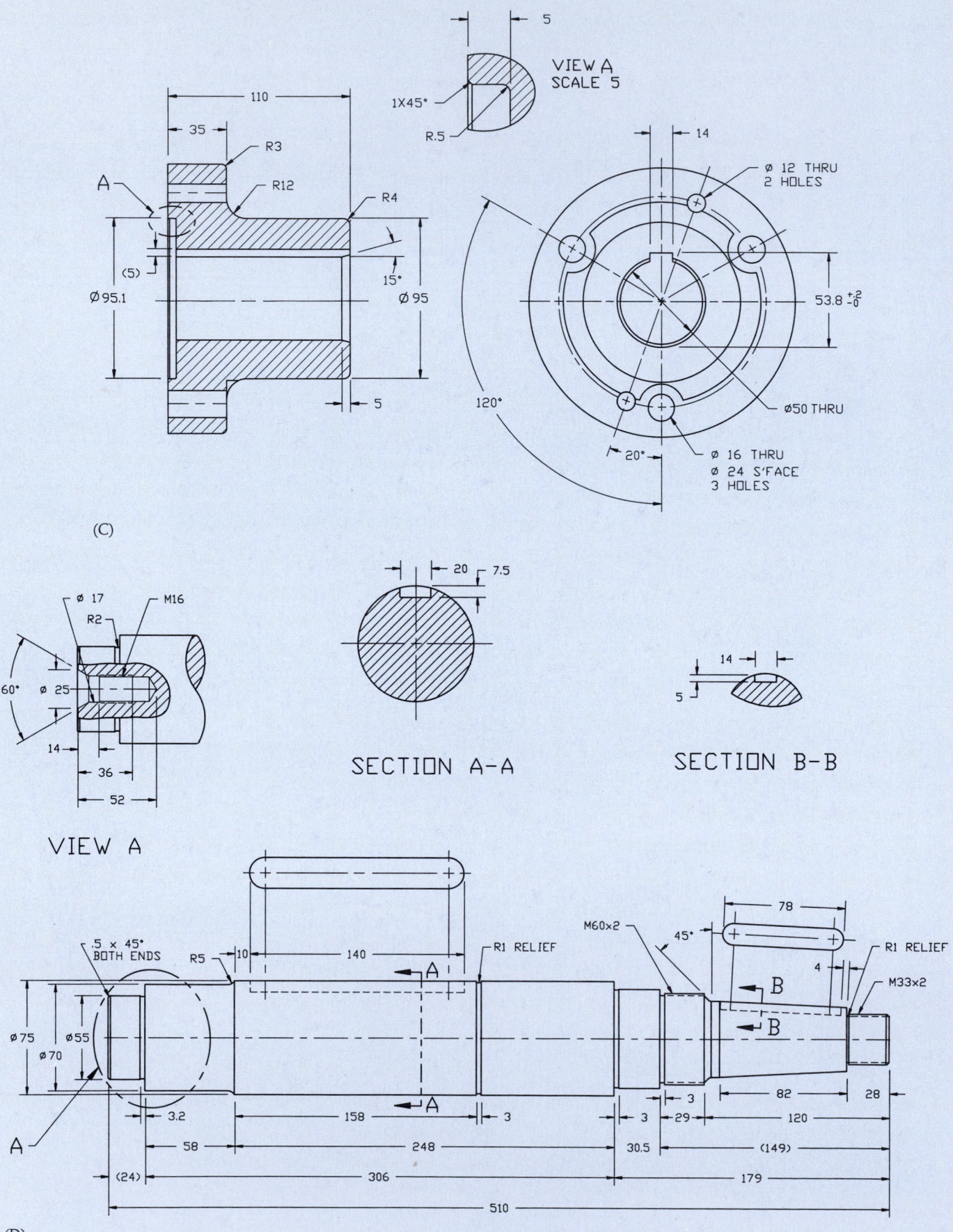

(C)

VIEW A

SECTION A-A

SECTION B-B

(D)

Problem 18.24 (C) and (D)   Draw and detail the assembly and details for the coupling.

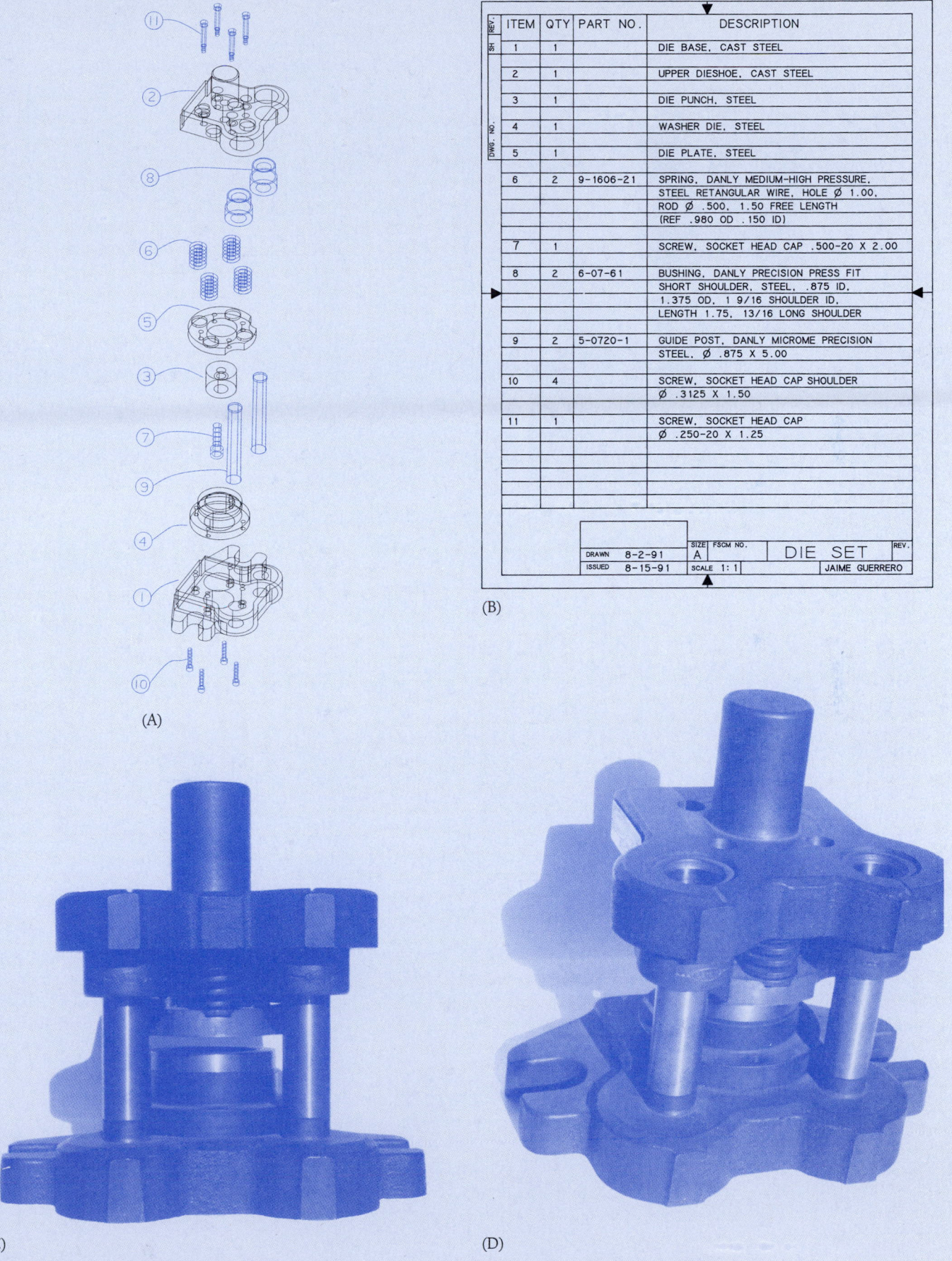

		ITEM	QTY	PART NO.	DESCRIPTION
REV.	SH	1	1		DIE BASE, CAST STEEL
		2	1		UPPER DIESHOE, CAST STEEL
		3	1		DIE PUNCH, STEEL
	DWG. NO.	4	1		WASHER DIE, STEEL
		5	1		DIE PLATE, STEEL
		6	2	9-1606-21	SPRING, DANLY MEDIUM-HIGH PRESSURE, STEEL RETANGULAR WIRE, HOLE Ø 1.00, ROD Ø .500, 1.50 FREE LENGTH (REF .980 OD .150 ID)
		7	1		SCREW, SOCKET HEAD CAP .500-20 X 2.00
		8	2	6-07-61	BUSHING, DANLY PRECISION PRESS FIT SHORT SHOULDER, STEEL, .875 ID, 1.375 OD, 1 9/16 SHOULDER ID, LENGTH 1.75, 13/16 LONG SHOULDER
		9	2	5-0720-1	GUIDE POST, DANLY MICROME PRECISION STEEL, Ø .875 X 5.00
		10	4		SCREW, SOCKET HEAD CAP SHOULDER Ø .3125 X 1.50
		11	1		SCREW, SOCKET HEAD CAP Ø .250-20 X 1.25

DRAWN	8-2-91	SIZE A	FSCM NO.	DIE SET	REV.
ISSUED	8-15-91	SCALE 1:1			JAIME GUERRERO

(A)

(B)

(C)

(D)

Problem 18.25 (A) Through (J) Draw and detail the die set. Do a complete assembly and set of details.

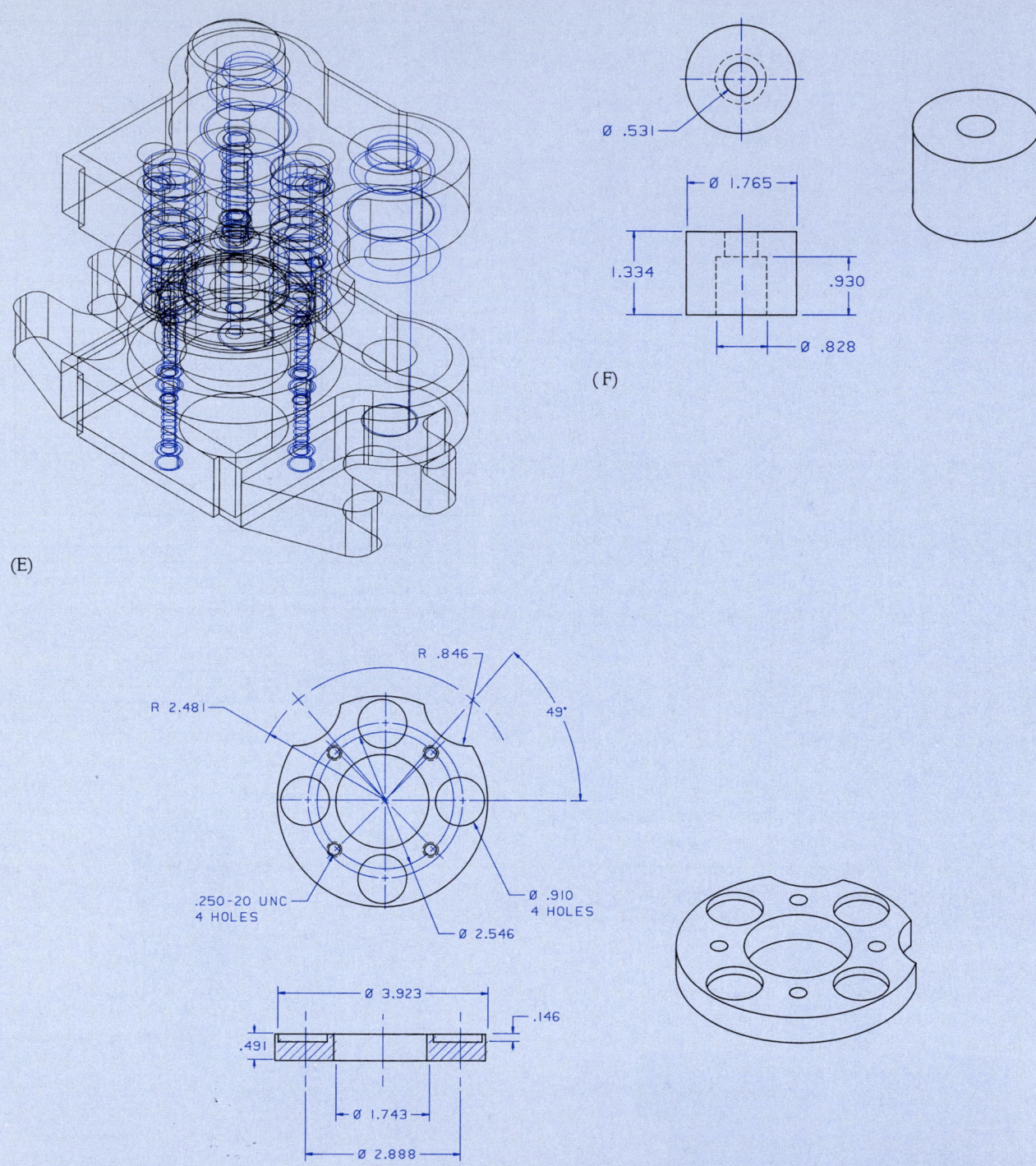

(E)

(F)

Ø .531

Ø 1.765

1.334

.930

Ø .828

R .846

R 2.481

49°

.250-20 UNC
4 HOLES

Ø .910
4 HOLES

Ø 2.546

Ø 3.923

.146

.491

Ø 1.743

Ø 2.888

(G)

Problem 18.25—*Continued*

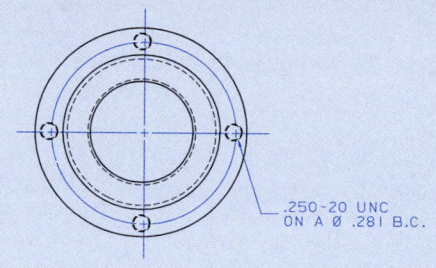

.250-20 UNC
ON A Ø .281 B.C.

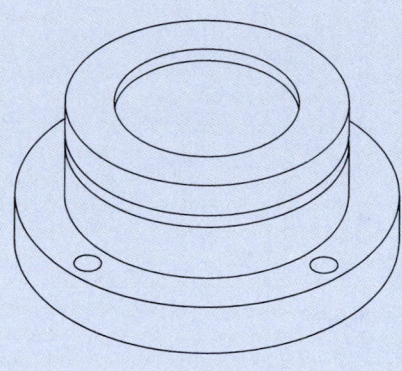

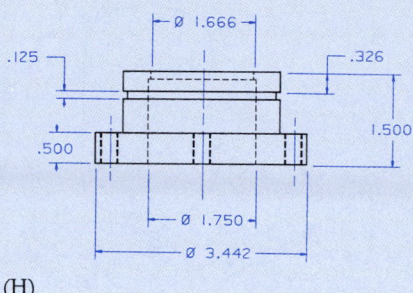

Ø 1.666
.125
.326
1.500
.500
Ø 1.750
Ø 3.442

(H)

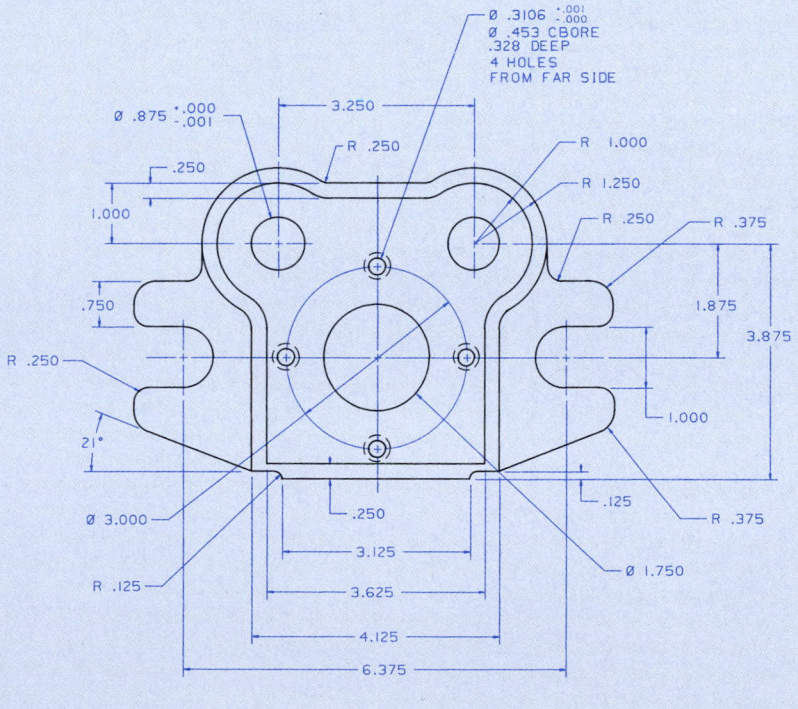

Ø .3106 +.001/-.000
Ø .453 CBORE
.328 DEEP
4 HOLES
FROM FAR SIDE

Ø .875 +.000/-.001

3.250

R .250

R 1.000

R 1.250

.250

1.000

R .250   R .375

.750

1.875

3.875

R .250

R .375

Ø 3.000

1.000

21°

.125

.250

R .375

Ø 1.750

3.125

R .125

3.625

4.125

6.375

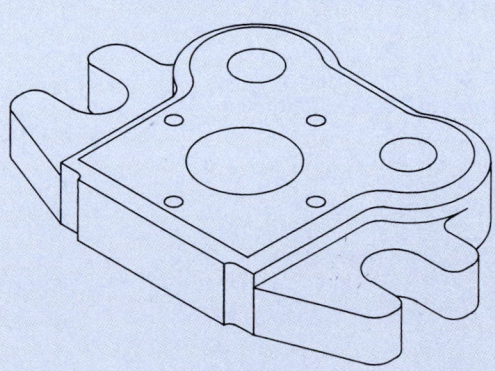

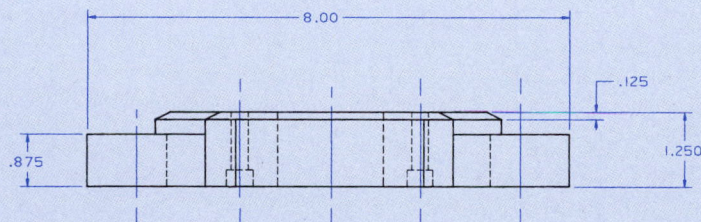

8.00

.125

.875

1.250

(I)

Problem 18.25—*Continued*

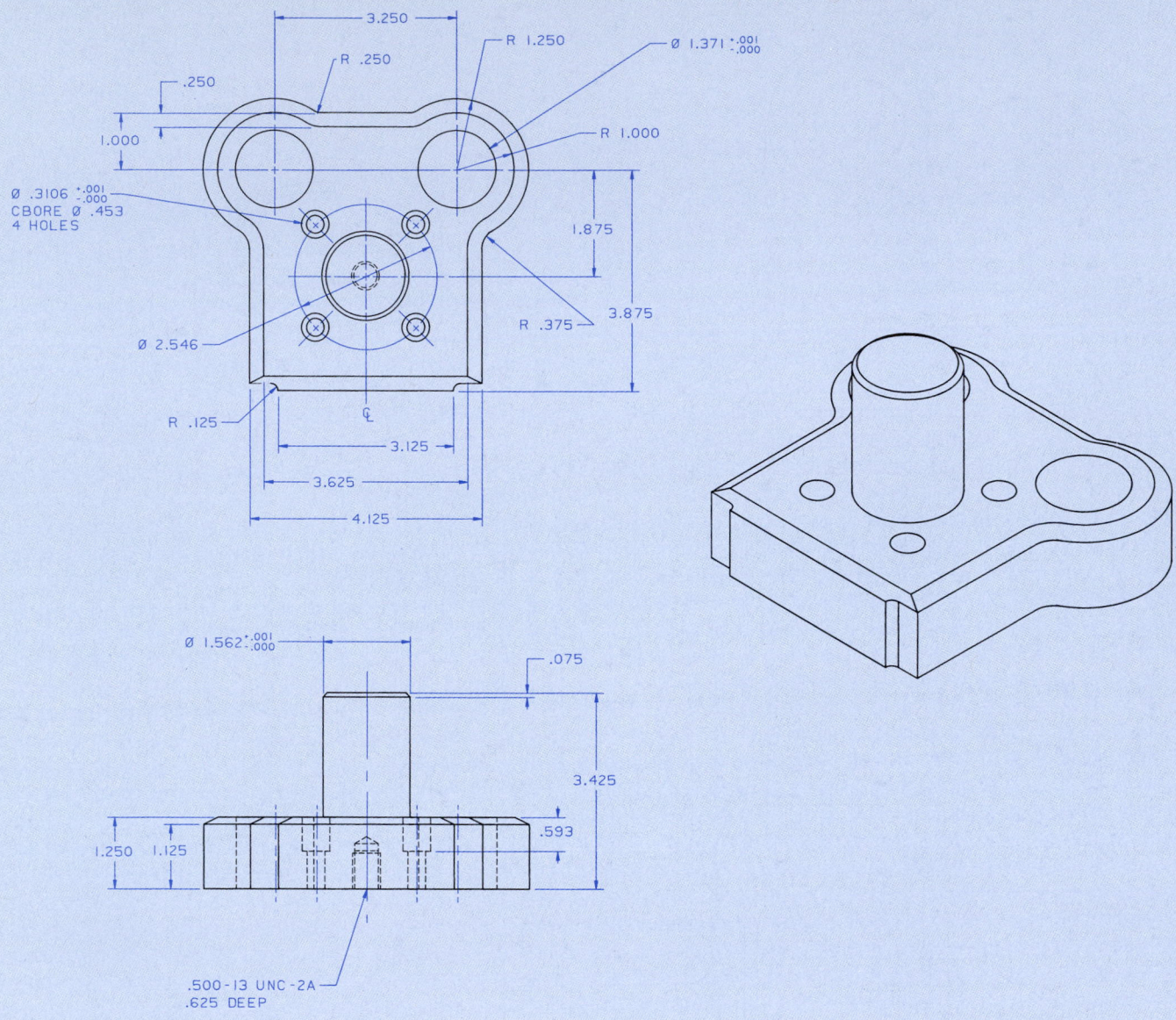

(J)

Problem 18.25—*Continued*

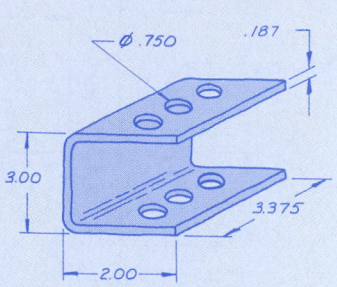

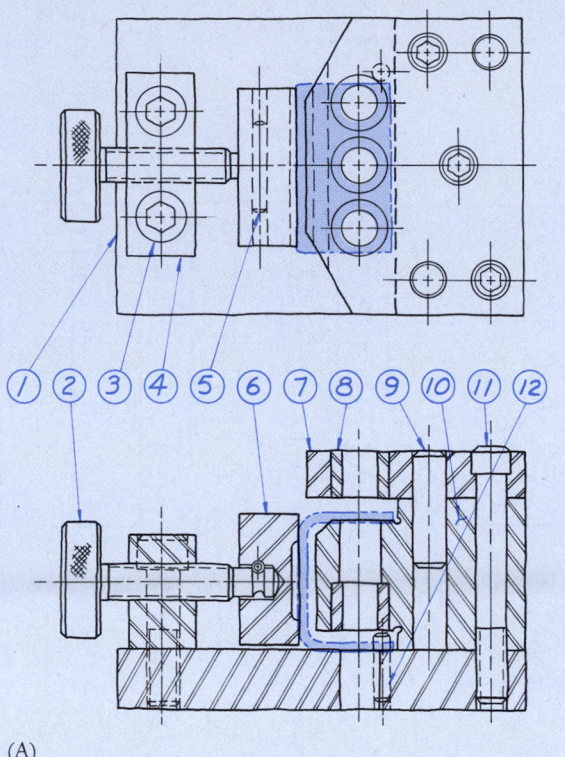

(A)

	ITEM	QTY	PART NO.	DESCRIPTION
	1	1		BASE PLATE. 1.375 X 6.50 X 9.00, STEEL
	2	1		SCREW, KNURLED HEAD, STEEL
	3	2		SCREW, HEX SOC HD CAP, .750-10 X 3.00
	4	1		CLAMP BLOCK, 1.50 X 2.50 X 4.00, STEEL
	5	1		PIN, MACHINE DOWEL, Ø .250 X 2.00
	6	1		CLAMP, 1.375 X 3.00 X 3.50, STEEL
	7	1		BUSHING PLATE, 1.00 X 4.75 X 6.50, STEEL
	8	6		BUSHING, TYPE P HEADLESS PRESS FIT MODIFIED ID = .750, 1.25 OD X 1.00 LG
	9	2		PIN, MACHINE DOWEL, Ø .750 X 2.50
	10	1		LOCATOR BLOCK, 3.25 X 4.50 X 6.50
	11	3		SCREW, HEX SOC HD CAP, .625-11 X 5.00
	12	1		PIN, MACHINE DOWEL, Ø .375 X 1.50

DRAWN 3-4-91	SIZE A	FSCM NO.	PLATE JIG, DRILL	REV.
ISSUED 7-30-91	SCALE 1 : 1			

(B)

Problem 18.26 (A) Through (H)   Draw and detail the jig and fixture assembly.

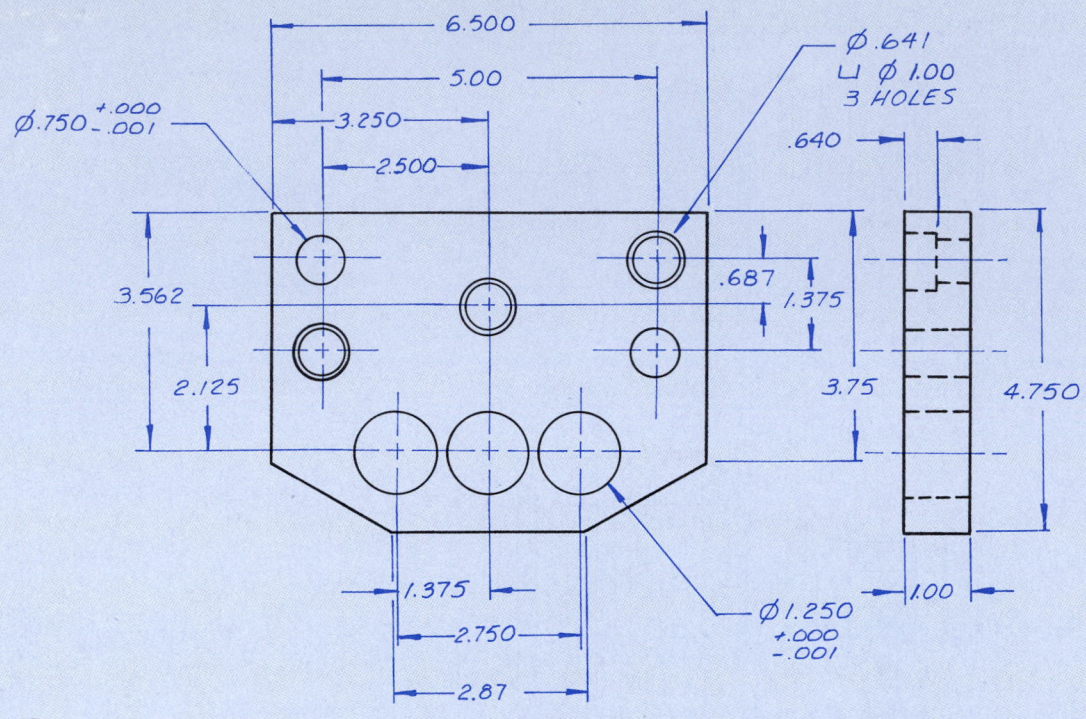

(C)

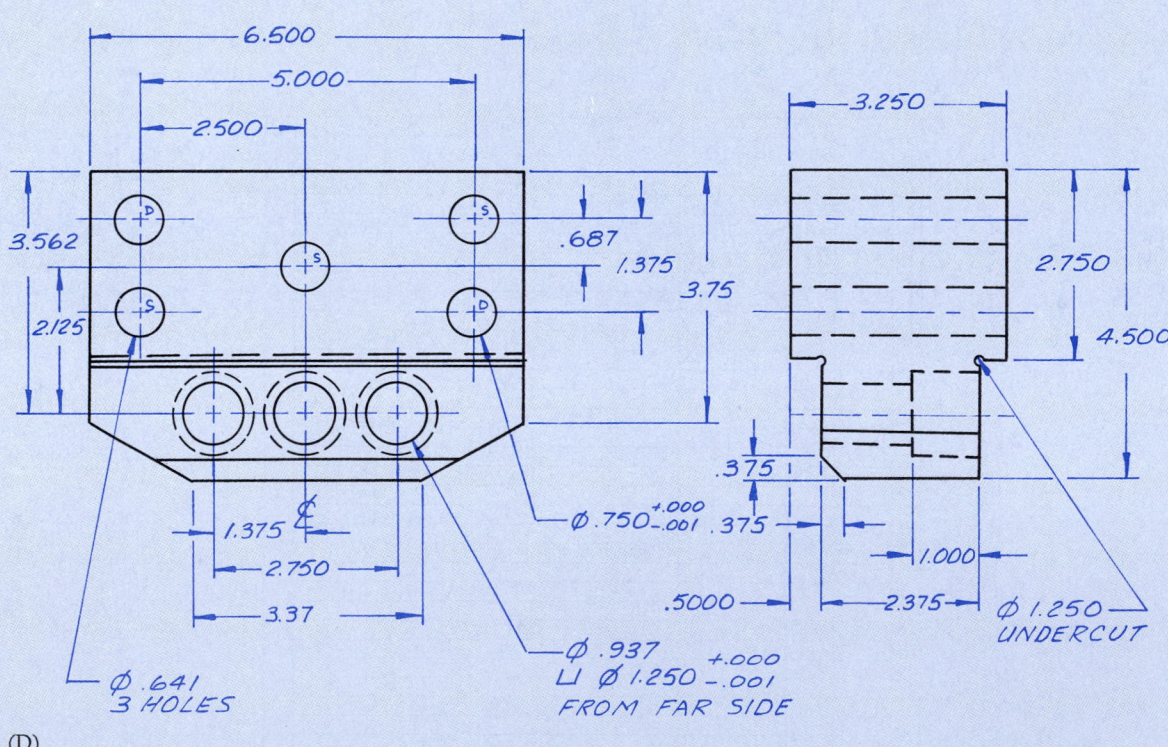

(D)

Problem 18.26—*Continued*

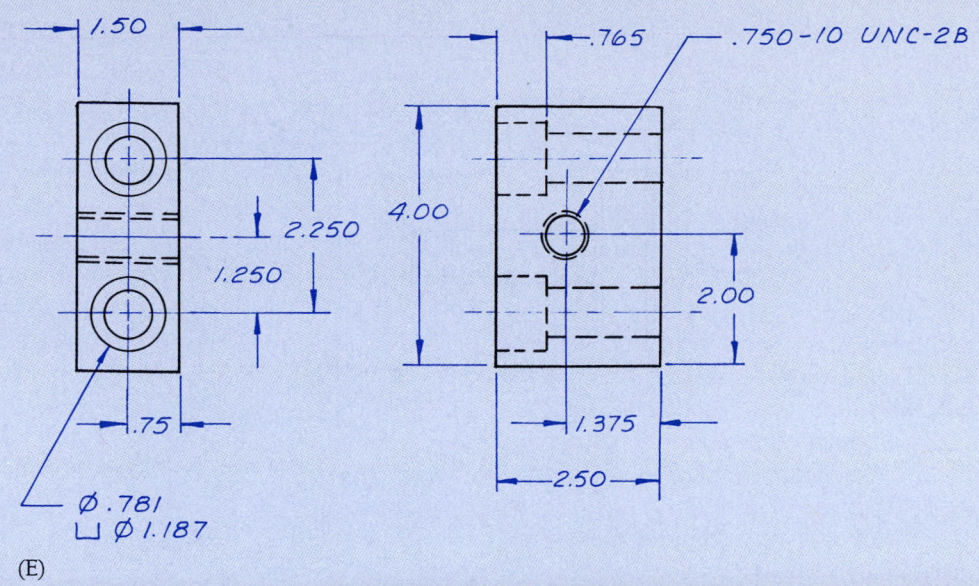

(E)

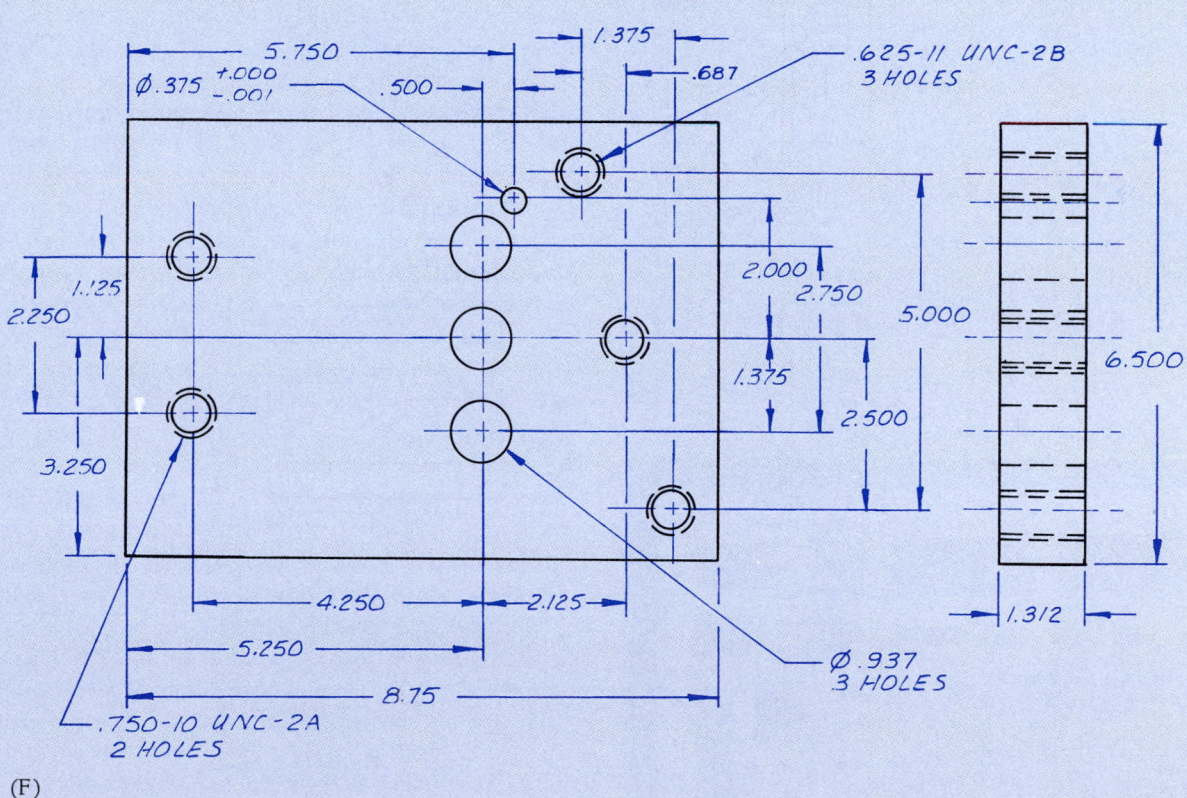

(F)

Problem 18.26—*Continued*

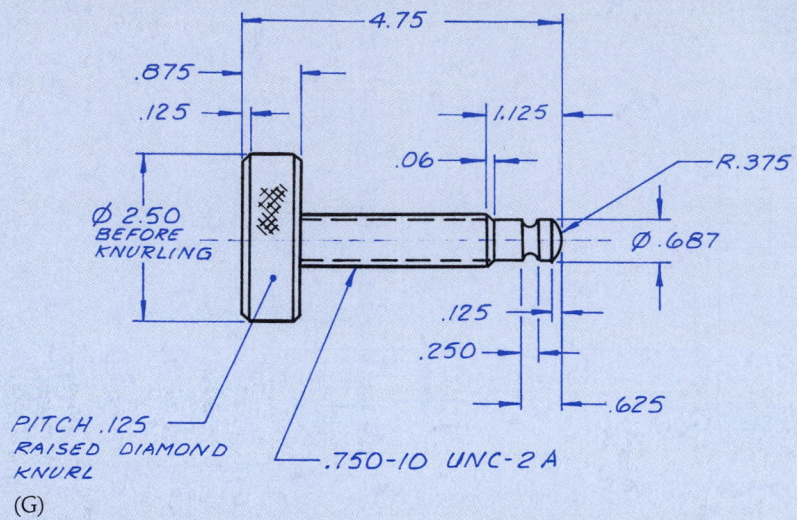

(G)

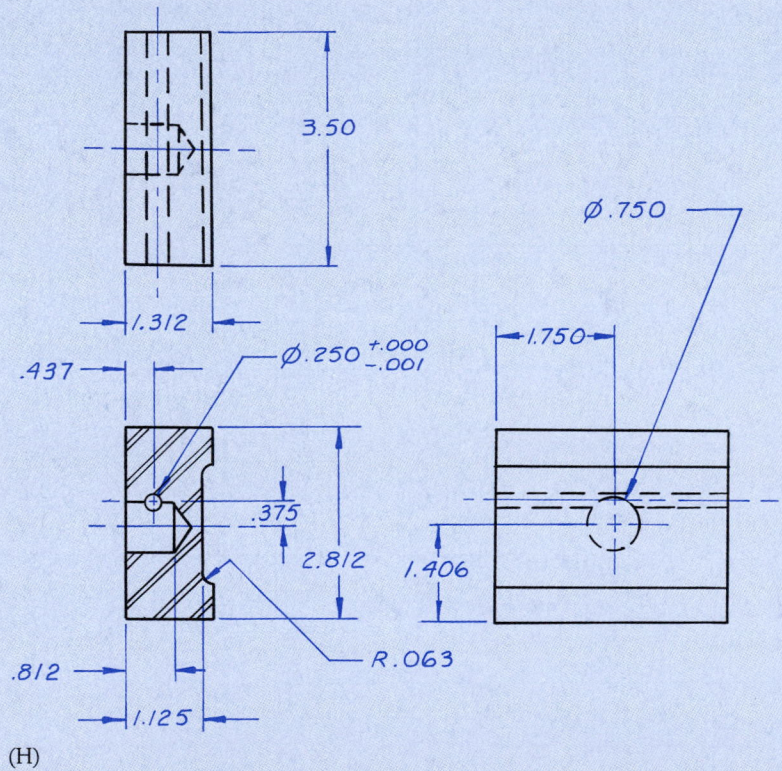

(H)

Problem 18.26—*Continued*

Assembly Grid Problems

The following five assembly projects are not dimensioned. Instead, a scale (inch and metric) is provided on the drawing. Use dividers to transfer the parts sizes and/or use the .25 inch grid to determine dimensions.

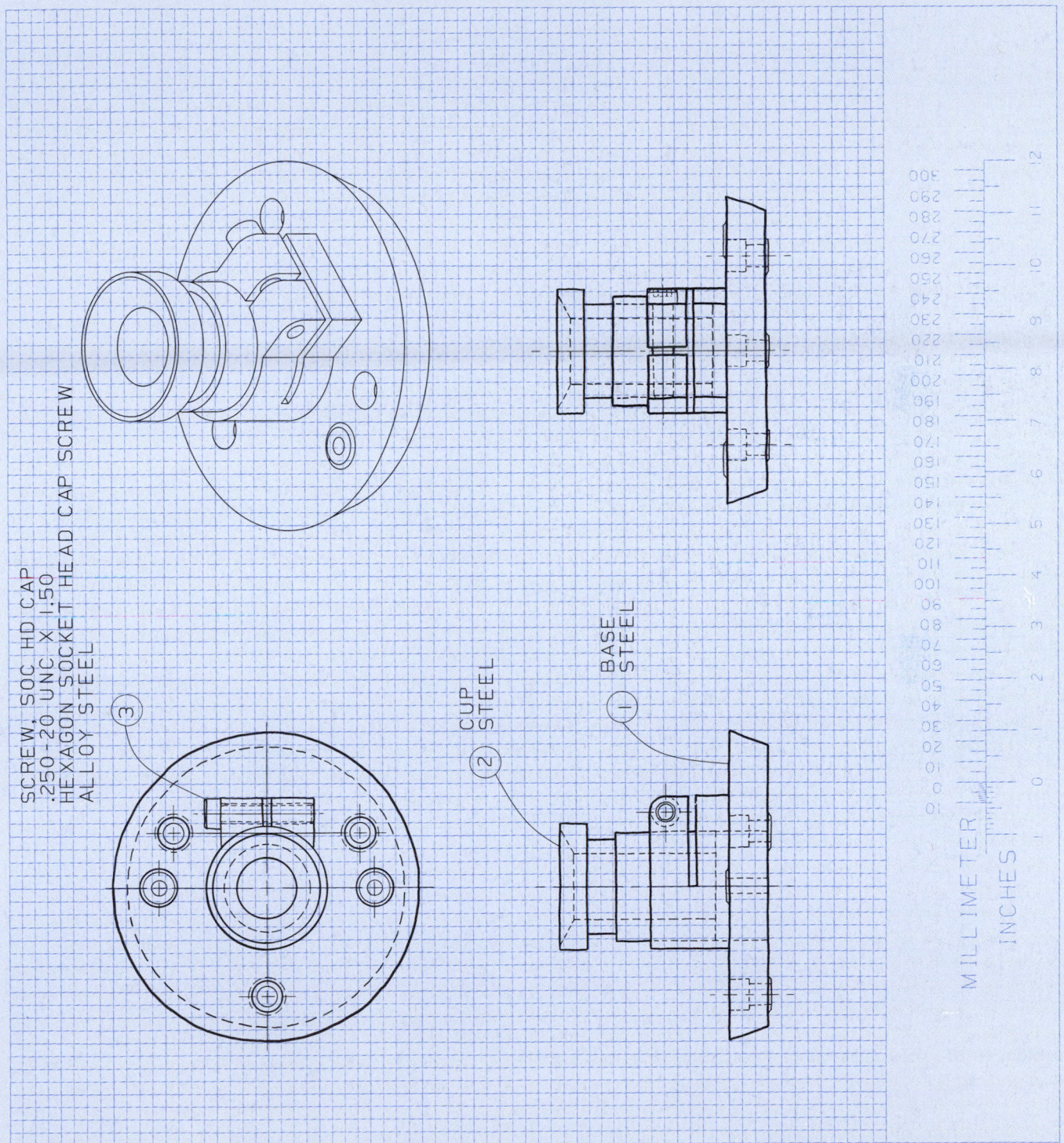

SCREW, SOC HD CAP
.250-20 UNC X 1.50
HEXAGON SOCKET HEAD CAP SCREW
ALLOY STEEL

CUP
STEEL

BASE
STEEL

MILLIMETER

INCHES

Problem 18.27   Draw and detail the optical cup mount assembly.

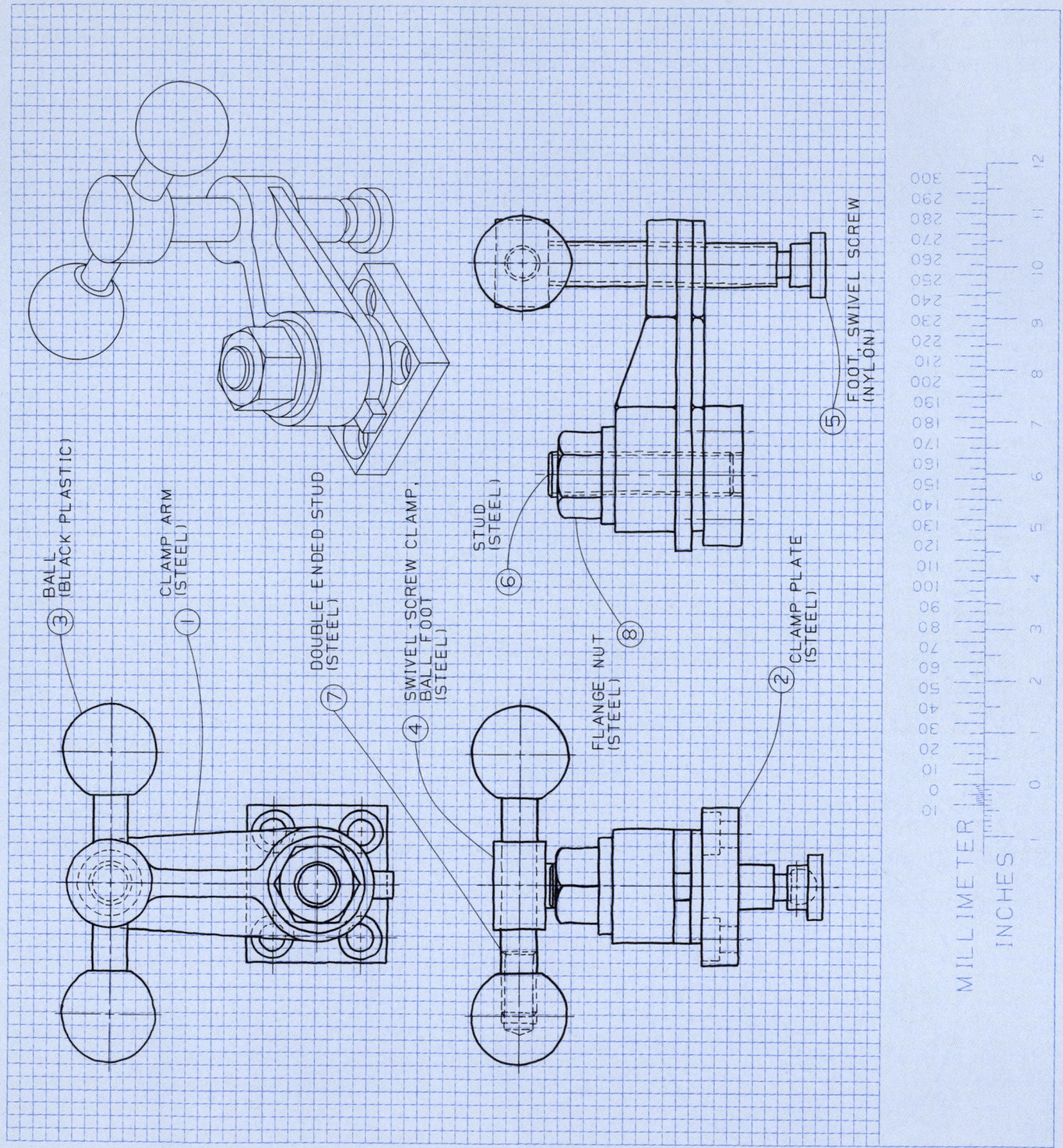

Problem 18.28 Draw and detail the swing clamp flange base assembly.

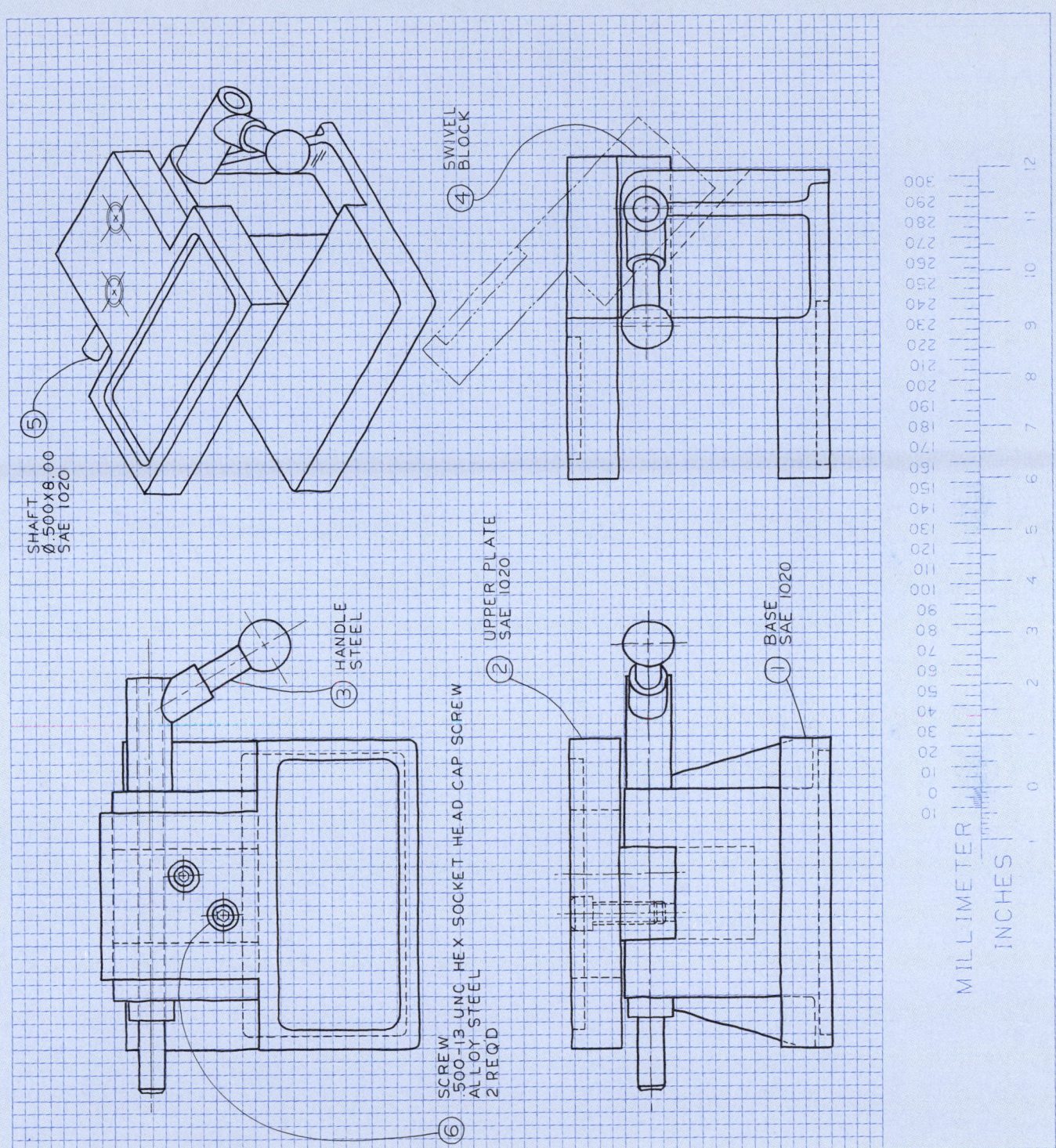

SWIVEL
BLOCK
④

SHAFT
Ø.500X8.00
SAE 1020
⑤

UPPER PLATE
SAE 1020
②

BASE
SAE 1020
①

HANDLE
STEEL
③

SCREW
.500-13 UNC HEX SOCKET HEAD CAP SCREW
ALLOY STEEL
2 REQD
⑥

MILLIMETER
INCHES

Problem 18.29 Draw and detail the swivel block fixture assembly.

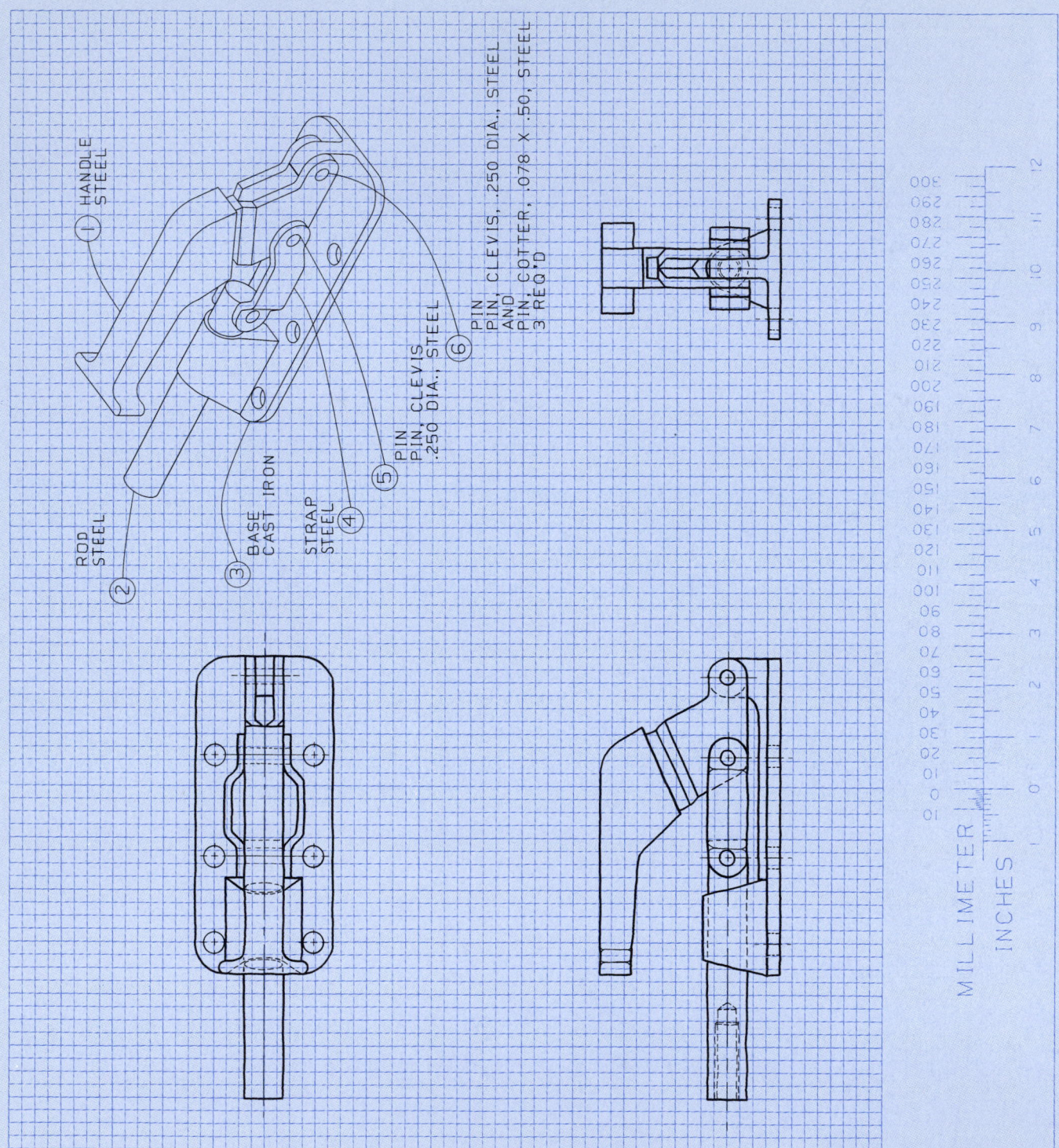

Problem 18.30   Draw and detail the connecting rod assembly.

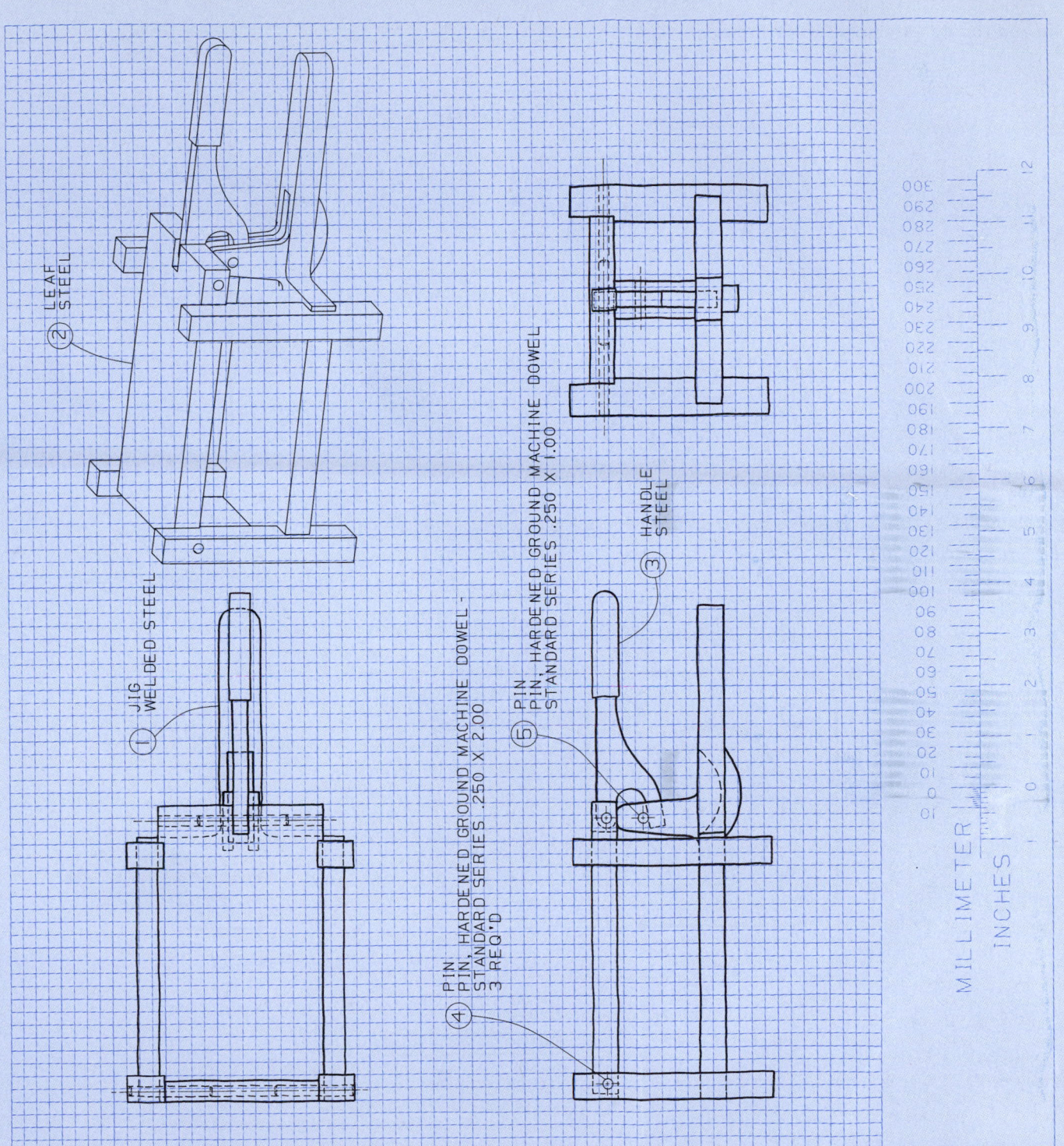

Problem 18.31 Draw and detail the leaf jig assembly.

Jig and Fixture Assembly Design Projects

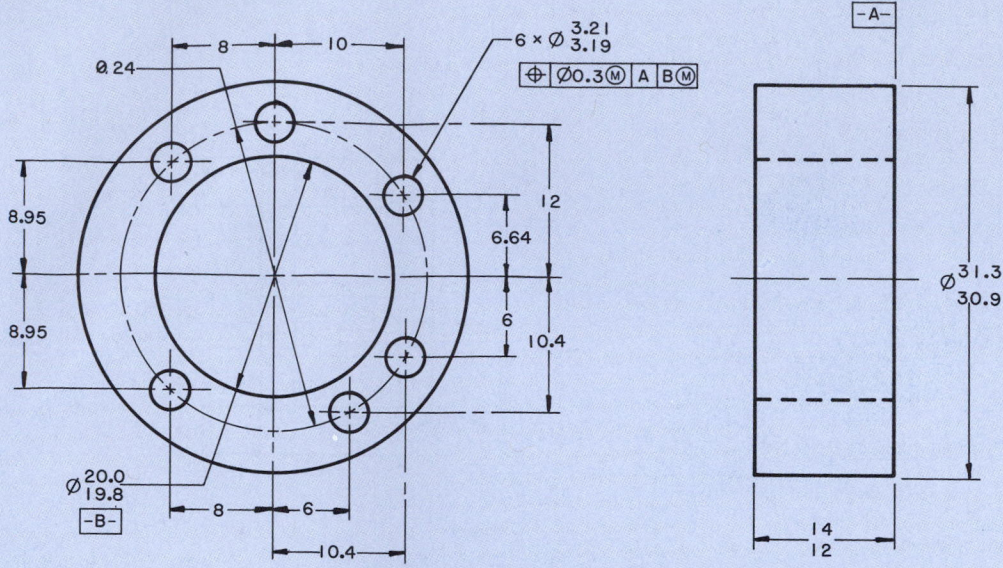

Problem 18.32 Design a fixture to hold the ring while machining the center hole and the six small holes.

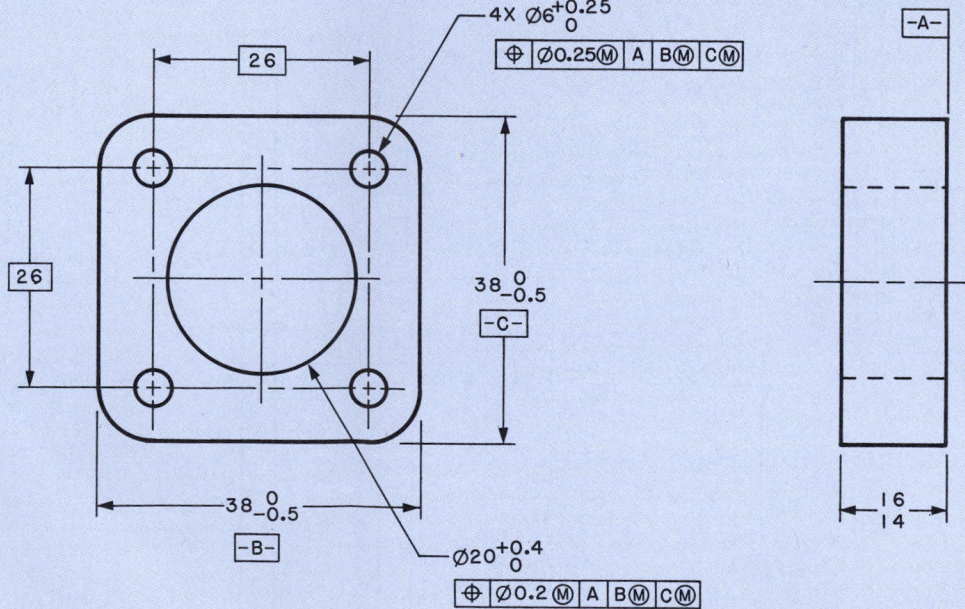

Problem 18.33 Design a fixture to hold the plate while machining the 6 mm and 20 mm holes.

Problem 18.34 Design a jig and fixture to hold the adjustable guide shown in Problem 18.1 while machining the slot.

Problem 18.35 Design and detail a jig and fixture to hold the crank arm shown in Problem 18.2. The three holes are to be created during this machining operation.

Problem 18.36 Design a fixture to hold the shifter fork shown in Problem 18.3, while machining the bottom of the part.

Problem 18.37 Design a fixture to hold the flywheel while machining the clevis ends, not the holes, using the part in Problem 18.4.

Problems from Figures in the Chapter

Problem 18.38 Redraw the welded assembly shown in Figure 18.7.

Problem 18.39 Draw and dimension the weldment in Figure 18.8.

Problem 18.40 Redraw the acoustic cup in Figure 18.10.

Problem 18.41 Model the SmartLevel rail [Fig. 18.40(a)], the wood insert [Fig. 18.40(c)], and the end cap [Fig. 18.40(d)]. Put all parts into an assembly, balloon, and complete a parts list.

Problem 18.42 Draw and detail the housing module shown in Figure 18.40(i) and (j).

Problem 18.43 Draw and detail the front panel shown in Figure 18.40(k).

Problem 18.44 Model and detail the keytop in Figure 18.40(l).

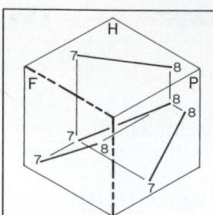

Descriptive Geometry

Learning Objectives

Upon completion of this chapter you will be able to accomplish the following:

1. Apply descriptive geometry solutions to three-dimensional problems.

2. Recognize the importance of notational elements used in descriptive geometry.

3. Define and differentiate between principal lines and line types.

4. Develop an understanding of spatial description and coordinate dimensions.

5. Identify the basic conditions for plane representation and projection.

6. Apply the concepts of parallelism and perpendicularity.

7. Recognize the significance of 2D and 3D CAD integration into geometric problem-solving.

19.1 Introduction

Descriptive geometry (Fig. 19.1) is the use of orthographic projection to solve three-dimensional problems on a two-dimensional surface. Practical industrial applications include sheet-metal layout, piping clearances, intersections of heating and air-conditioning ducting, transition pieces for farm product systems, range of movement studies in mechanical design, structural steel design and analysis, topographical and civil engineering projects, and a variety of mechanical engineering problems. Descriptive geometry is not only a means to communicate a particular aspect of a technical problem, it is the actual solution in graphical form. The descriptive geometry worksheet or drawing is equivalent to the final numerical answer when using a mathematical method.

Linework, lettering, and drawing standards are no less important here than for other forms of drafting. Lettering and notation are the primary means of communication on drawings. No matter how accurate and precise the drawing, if it is poorly lettered and inadequately labeled, it cannot communicate a solution or present ideas properly. Therefore, concise well-formed lettering, properly positioned notes, and sufficient labeling are essential to the solution of a descriptive geometry worksheet or drawing.

Figure 19.2 is a typical descriptive geometry drawing using the special language and notation that has been developed for this subject. It is essential that the format, symbols, and notation become part of your technical vocabulary. As you progress through the chapter, frequent referrals to this figure will reinforce this new language.

Figure 19.3 presents a line and symbol key that defines the type and thickness of the lines and symbols used in descriptive geometry. Many of the line weights and line types are similar to those found in mechanical/engineering drafting. Two unique lines are also shown—the fold line and the development element. The **fold line** as discussed in Chapter 10 is used to divide each view and to establish a reference from which to take dimensions when projecting from view to view.

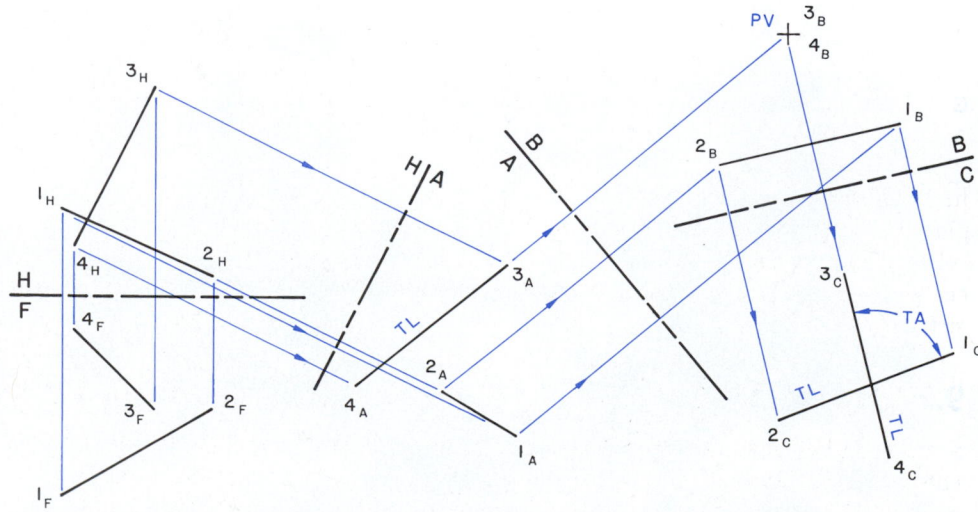

FIGURE 19.1 Descriptive Geometry Problem

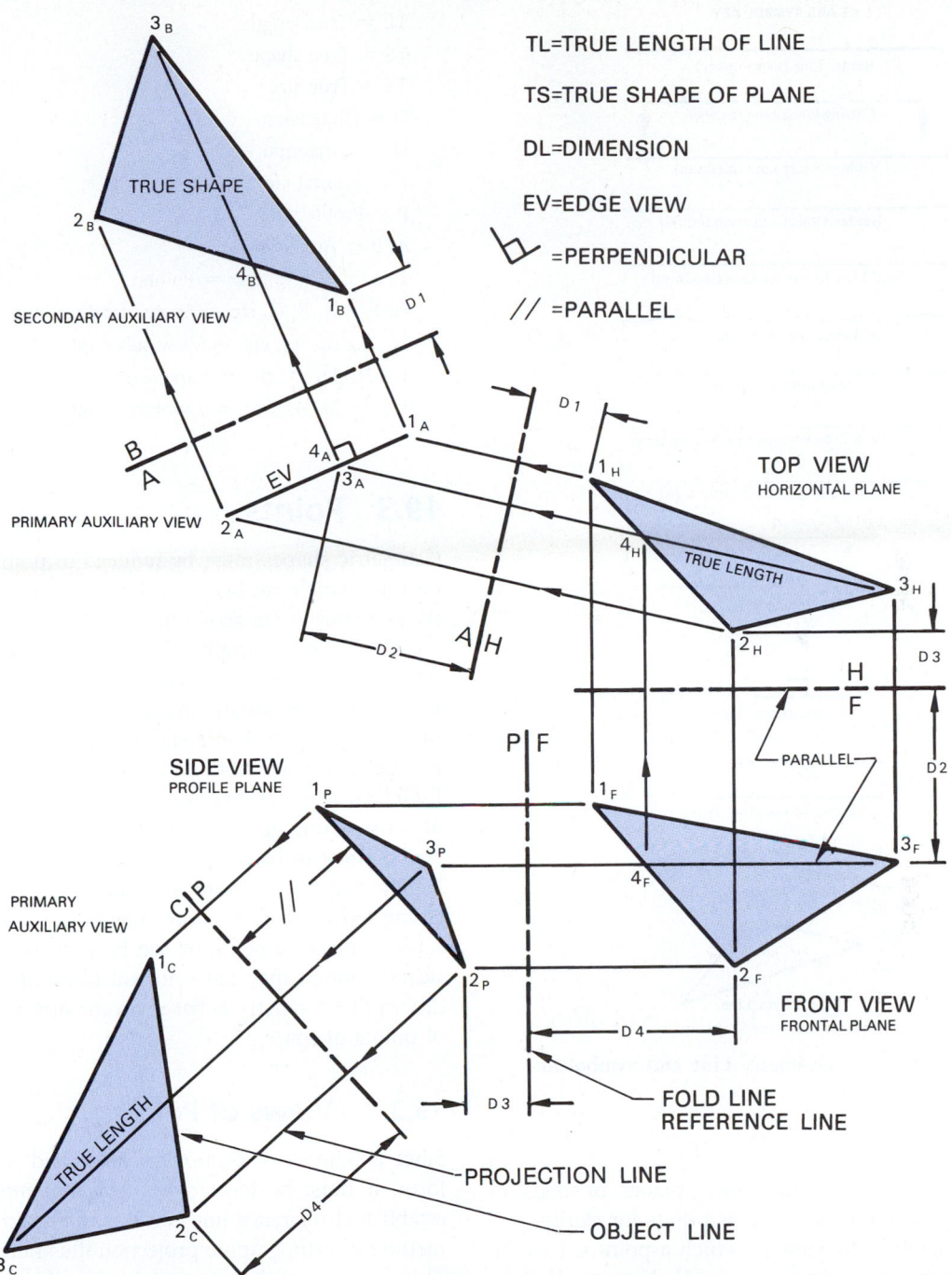

TL=TRUE LENGTH OF LINE

TS=TRUE SHAPE OF PLANE

DL=DIMENSION

EV=EDGE VIEW

∟ =PERPENDICULAR

// =PARALLEL

FIGURE 19.2 Descriptive Geometry Problem Setup and Notation

The **development element** is used extensively when developing curved surfaces and for triangulation of surfaces; it is explained in Chapter 21. Both development lines and fold lines are used in the solution of a variety of descriptive geometry problems.

19.2 Notation

The notation key gives the abbreviations and notational elements used throughout descriptive geometry problems. **EV** is the edge view of a plane. **IP** refers to the intersection of a line

and surface, whereas **PP** is the piercing point of a line (that is, part of a plane) and another surface; theoretically, IP and PP are the same. **PV** is the point view of a line. True shape and true size mean the same thing and are abbreviated as **TS. TL** is the true length of a line. **D** has been used to note a dimension.

H, F, and **P** are used to identify the three primary views in orthographic projection: horizontal (top), frontal (front), and profile (side). "**A**" will always be the first auxiliary view on a problem, followed by "**B**", "**C**", "**D**", etc.

Whole numbers 1, 2, 3, 4, 5, 6, etc., establish points in space. They can be individual points, or they can be used

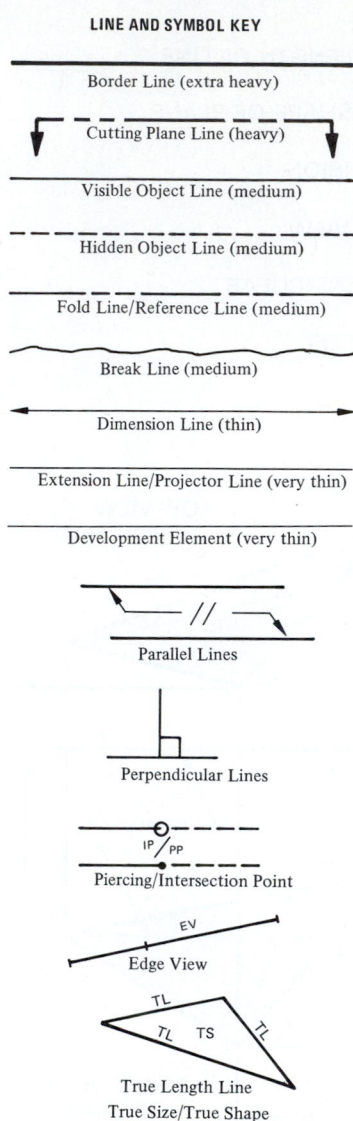

LINE AND SYMBOL KEY

Border Line (extra heavy)

Cutting Plane Line (heavy)

Visible Object Line (medium)

Hidden Object Line (medium)

Fold Line/Reference Line (medium)

Break Line (medium)

Dimension Line (thin)

Extension Line/Projector Line (very thin)

Development Element (very thin)

Parallel Lines

Perpendicular Lines

IP / PP
Piercing/Intersection Point

EV
Edge View

TL
TL   TS   TL

True Length Line
True Size/True Shape

FIGURE 19.3   **Descriptive Geometry Line and Symbol Key**

TL = True length

TS = True shape

TS = True size

D = Dimension

H = Horizontal view

F = Frontal view

P = Profile view

A, B = Auxiliary views

1, 2, 3, 4, 5, 6, etc. = Points

H, F, P, A, B, C, etc. = View identifications

1_H, 2_F, 3_P, 4_A, etc. = View subscript

1^1, 2^1, 3^2, 4^2, etc. = Superscript

1_R, 2_R, 3_R, 4_R, etc. = Revolved points

19.3   Points

Geometric shapes must be reduced to points and their connectors, which are lines. In descriptive geometry **points** are the most important geometric element and the primary building block for any graphical projection of a form. All projections of lines, planes, or solids can be physically located and manipulated by identifying a series of points that represent the object or part. Understanding this concept will help you to draft and design both on the board and with a CAD system. Establishing endpoints in space is one of the primary means of constructing geometry on a CAD system.

A point can be located in space and illustrated by establishing it in two or more adjacent views. Two points that are connected are called a **line**. Points can also be used to describe a plane or solid, or can be located in space by themselves, though they have no real physical dimension. All of descriptive geometry is based on the orthographic projection of points in space.

19.3.1   Views of Points

Since a point is a location in space and not a dimensional form, it must be located by measurements taken from an established reference line, such as that used in the glass box method of orthographic projection illustrated in Figure 19.4. This figure represents the projection of point 1 in the three principal planes, frontal (1_F), horizontal (1_H), and profile (1_P). In the glass box method, it is assumed that each mutually perpendicular plane is hinged so as to be revolved into the plane of the paper. *The intersection line of two successive (perpendicular) image planes is called a fold line/reference line.* All measurements are taken from fold lines to locate a point (line, plane, or solid) in space. A fold line/reference line can be visualized as the edge view of a reference plane as explained in Chapter 7 and Chapter 10.

A point can be located by means of verbal description by giving dimensions from fold/reference lines. In Figure 19.4, point 1 is below the horizontal plane (D1), to the left of the profile plane (D2), and behind the frontal plane (D3). D1 establishes the elevation or height of the point in the front and

together to determine the extent of lines, planes, or solids. In a few cases, capital letters are used as points for clarity.

Subscripts establish the view in which a point is located, such as 2_H, which means point 2 in the H (horizontal) view. Superscripts are used where an aspect of a point appears in more than one place in a view, for instance, when a line of a prism is called $3\text{-}3^1$, or where for clarity the piercing point of a line is noted as an aspect of the original point, e.g., 2^1.

After reading the text and completing a few of the problems, these notations will become second nature and enable you to label, notate, and communicate using descriptive geometry and its specialized language.

Notation Key

EV = Edge view

IP = Intersection point

PP = Piercing point

PV = Point view

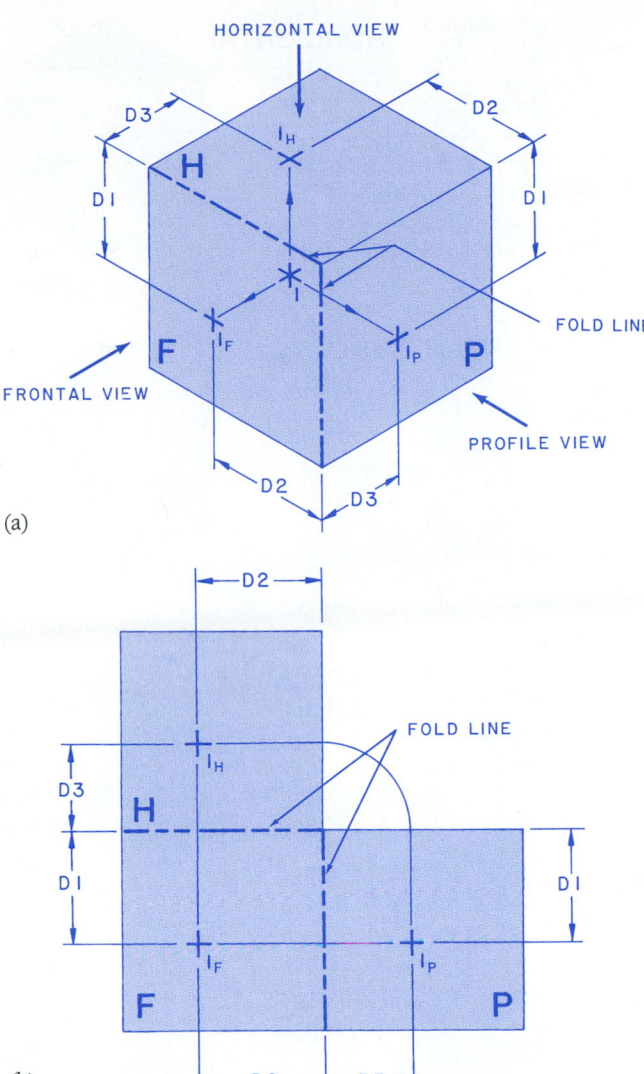

(a)

(b)

FIGURE 19.4   Three Views of a Point in Space.   (a) Shown here as an isometric pictorial (b) and in orthographic projection.

19.4   Lines

Lines can be thought of as a series of points in space, having magnitude (length) but not width. A line is assumed to have a thickness so as to draw it. Though a line may be located by establishing its endpoints and may be of a definite specified length, all lines can be extended in order to solve a problem. Therefore, a purely theoretical definition of a line could be as follows: lines are straight elements that have no width, but are infinite in length (magnitude); they can be located by two points that are not at the same location. When two lines lie in the same plane they will either be parallel or intersect.

Throughout the text, numbers have been used to designate the endpoints of a line. The view of a line and its locating

points are labeled with a subscript corresponding to the plane of projection, as in Figure 19.5, where the endpoints of line 1-2 are notated 1_H and 2_H in the horizontal view, 1_F and 2_F in the frontal view, and 1_P and 2_P in the profile view. For many figures in the chapter, subscripts are eliminated if the view is obvious, or only one point may be labeled per view.

19.4.1   Multiview Projection of a Line

Lines are classified according to their orientation to the three principal planes of projection or how they appear in a projection plane. They can also be described by their relationship to other lines in the same view. As with points, lines are located from fold lines/reference lines.

In Figure 19.5, line 1-2 is projected onto each principal projection plane and located by dimensions taken from fold lines. The end points of line 1-2 are located from two fold lines in each view, using dimensions or projection lines that originate in a previous (adjacent) view. Dimensions D1 and D2 establish the elevation of the endpoints in the profile and

side view, D2 the right-left location or width in the front and top view, and D3 the distance behind (depth) the frontal plane in the top and side view.

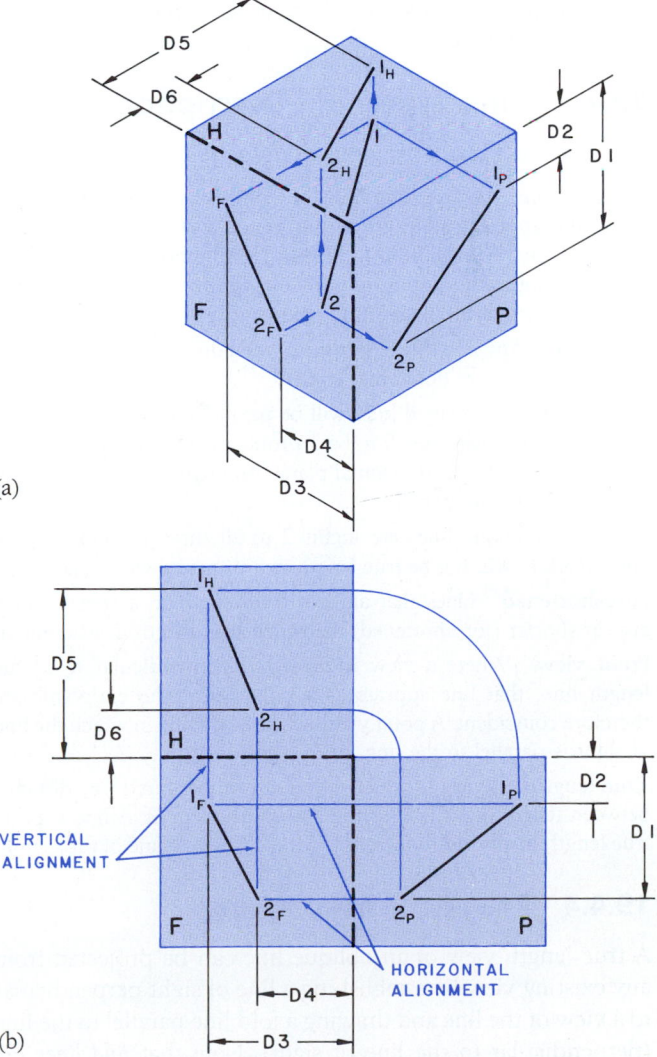

(a)

(b)

FIGURE 19.5   Three Views of a Line in Space

frontal view, since these points are horizontally in line in these two views. D3 and D4 locate the endpoints in relation to the F/P fold line (to the left of the profile plane), in both the frontal and horizontal views, since these points are aligned vertically. D5 and D6 locate each endpoint in relation to the H/F and the F/P fold lines since these dimensions are the distance behind the frontal plane and will show in both the horizontal and profile views.

19.4.2 Principal Lines

A line that is parallel to a principal plane is called a **principal line,** and is *true length* in the principal plane to which it is parallel. Since there are three principal planes of projection, there are three principal lines: horizontal, frontal, and profile, (Fig. 19.6):

1. A **horizontal line** is parallel to the horizontal plane and true length in the horizontal view.
2. A **frontal line** is parallel to the frontal plane and true length in the frontal view.
3. A **profile line** is parallel to the profile plane and true length in the profile view.
4. An **oblique line** is at an angle to the frontal, horizontal, and profile planes and therefore does not show true length in any of these projections.

19.4.3 Line Types and Descriptions

The following terms are used to describe lines:

Vertical line   Vertical lines are perpendicular to the horizontal plane and appear true length in the frontal and profile views (consequently, they will be both frontal and profile principal lines). Vertical lines appear as a point (point view) in the horizontal view and show true length in all elevation views.

Level line   Any line that is parallel to the horizontal plane is a level line. Level lines are horizontal lines.

Inclined lines   Inclined lines will be parallel to the frontal or profile planes (and will therefore be a profile or frontal principal line) and at an angle to the horizontal plane. An inclined line is always at an angle to the horizontal.

Oblique   Oblique lines are inclined to all three principal planes and therefore will not be true length in a principal view (Fig. 19.6).

Foreshortened   Lines that are not true length in a specific view appear shorter (foreshortened) than their true length measurement.

Point view   Where a view is projected perpendicular to a true length line, that line appears as a point view; the endpoints are therefore coincident. A point view is a view of a line in which the line of sight is parallel to the line.

True length   A view in which a line can be measured true distance between its endpoints shows the line as true length. A line appears true length in any view where it is parallel to the plane of projection.

19.4.4 True Length of a Line

A true length view of an oblique line can be projected from any existing view by establishing a line of sight perpendicular to a view of the line and drawing a fold line parallel to the line (perpendicular to the line of sight). Note that *fold lines are always drawn perpendicular to the line of sight.* The following

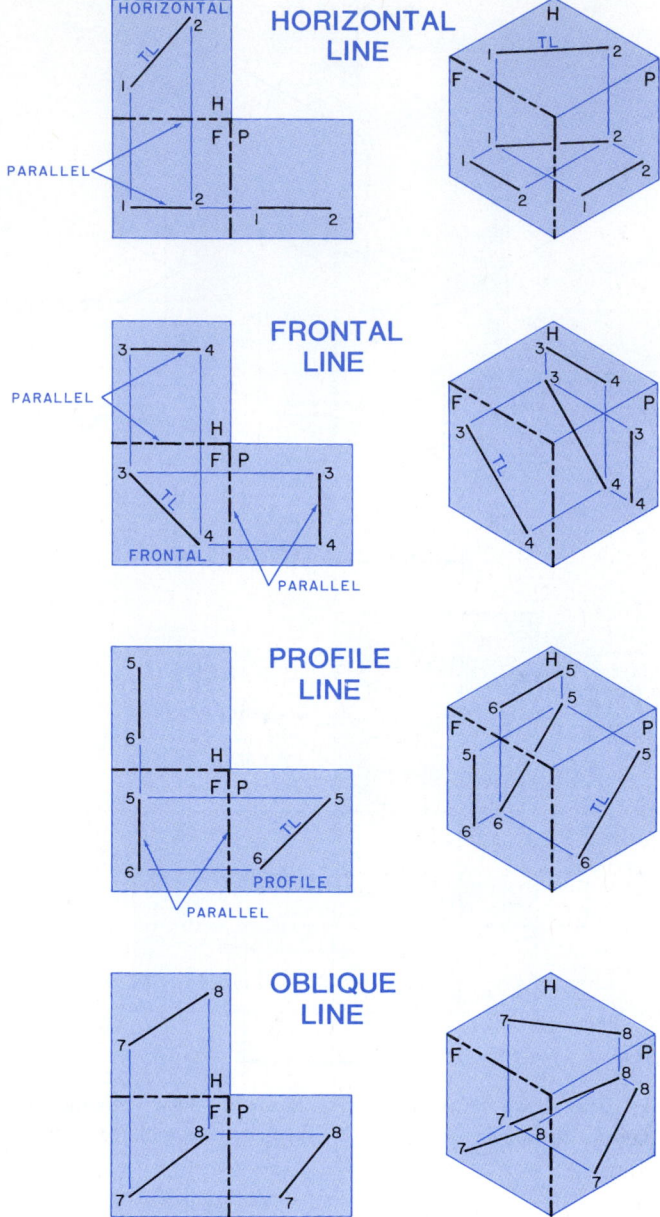

FIGURE 19.6   **Types of Lines**

steps describe the procedure for drawing a true length projection of an oblique line from the frontal view (Fig. 19.7):

1. Establish a line of sight perpendicular to oblique line 1-2 in the frontal view.
2. Draw fold line F/A perpendicular to the line of sight and parallel to oblique line 1-2.
3. Extend projection lines from points 1 and 2 perpendicular to the fold line (parallel to the line of sight). The distance from line 1_F-2_F is random.
4. Transfer the endpoints of the line from the horizontal view to locate points 1_A and 2_A along the projection lines in auxiliary view A.
5. Connect points 1_A and 2_A. This is the true length of projection of line 1-2.

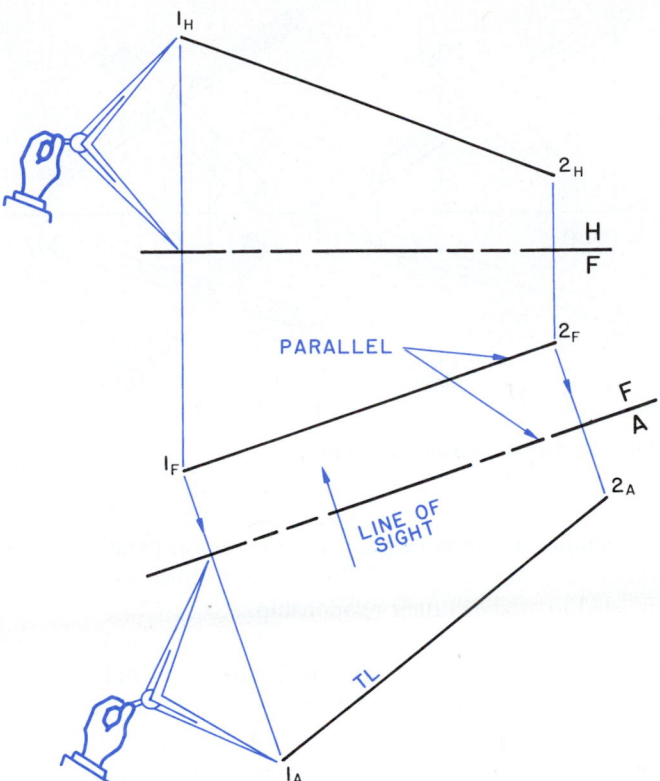

FIGURE 19.7   Oblique Line Shown in Horizontal Frontal and Auxiliary Views.   Note that auxiliary view A shows the lines and a true length projection.

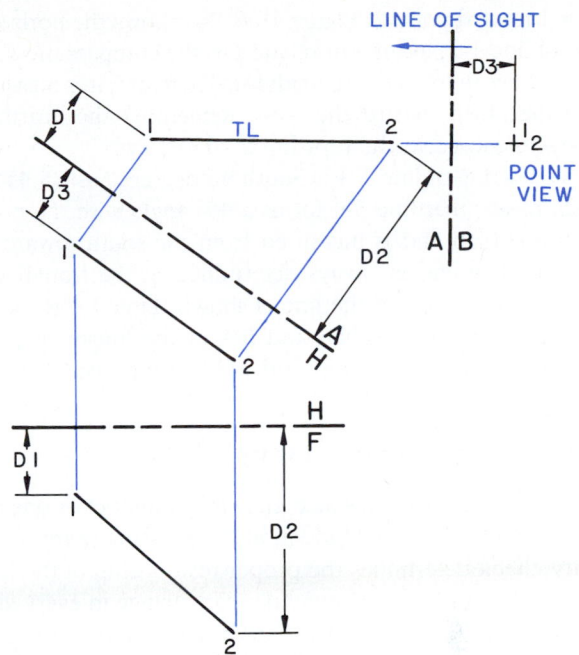

FIGURE 19.8   True Length and Point View of a Line

19.4.5   Point View of a Line

A line will project as a **point view** when the line of sight is parallel to a true length view of the line. In other words, the point view is projected on a projection plane that is perpendicular to the true length line. Finding the true length and the point view of a line is required for many situations involving the application of descriptive geometry to engineering problems. The first requirement for a point view is that the line be projected as true length. This procedure has been discussed previously.

The point view of an oblique line can be drawn only after the line is projected as true length in an auxiliary view. In Figure 19.8 line 1-2 is projected as true length in auxiliary view A. To establish the point view, a secondary auxiliary view (B) is projected perpendicular to the true length line. The following steps describe this process:

1. Project a TL view of line 1-2.
2. Establish a line of sight parallel to the true length line 1-2.
3. Draw the fold line (A/B) perpendicular to the line of sight. Note that the fold line is perpendicular to the true length line.
4. Transfer dimension D3 from the horizontal view to locate both points along the projection line in auxiliary view B.

19.4.6   Bearing of a Line

The angle that a line makes with a north-south line in the horizontal view is the **bearing** of that line. *The bearing can only be measured in the horizontal view and is always measured from the north or south.* Since the bearing of a line is the angle that the line makes with the north-south meridian, it can be measured from the north or south toward the east or west. The bearing is the map direction of a line and is measured in degrees with a protractor or compass from the north or south. The bearing indicates the quadrant in which the line lies.

Normally, the originating point is the lowest numerical value such as line 1-2, which will start at point 1. The **low end** is the lowest point on a line as seen in a frontal or elevation view. In some cases, the bearing is measured from the high end of the line toward the low end, as is done, for instance, for a sloping cross-country pipeline.

In Figure 19.9 line 1-2 has a bearing of North 73° West (N 73° W), measured from the north, 73° toward the west. The bearing is measured from the north toward the west, from

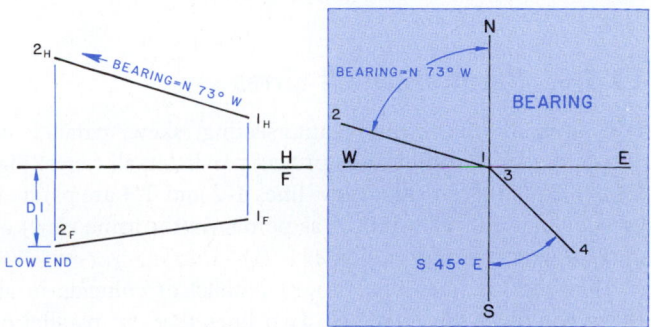

FIGURE 19.9   Bearing of a Line

point 1 toward point 2. Figure 19.9 also shows the horizontal view of line 1-2, located in relation to the compass meridian. Line 1-2 lies in the second quadrant. Therefore, it is measured from the north toward the west. Remember the bearing is always measured in the top (horizontal) view.

The bearing of line 3-4 is South 45 degrees East (S 45° E), which means that line 3-4 forms a 45° angle with the north-south meridian and is measured from the south toward the east. The low end is always determined in the frontal view where the elevation of the line is shown. Line 3-4 is located in relation to the meridian and lies in the fourth quadrant since it measured from the south toward the east.

19.4.7 Visibility of Lines

When two lines cross in space, they may intersect or one may be visible and the other hidden at the crossing point. A **visibility check** determines the proper relationship of the lines. Note that the visibility of two lines can change in every view; first one line may be visible, then in the next view the other line, or the same line may be visible in adjacent views. As an example, when two pipes or structural members cross in a construction project, one will be above or in front of the other. This relationship of construction elements is one of the applications of descriptive geometry in industry.

In Figure 19.10(a) lines 1-2 and 3-4 cross. It must be determined which line lies in front of the other in the frontal view and which line is on top in the horizontal view. A visibility check must be made. The following steps describe this process:

1. Where line 1_H-2_H crosses line 3_H-4_H in the horizontal view, extend a sight line perpendicular to H/F until it meets one of the lines in the frontal view [Fig. 19.10(b)]. Here, line 1_F-2_F is the first line to be encountered; therefore, line 1_H-2_H is the visible line in the horizontal view.
2. Extend a sight line from the crossing point of line 1_F-2_F and 3_F-4_F in the frontal view until it meets the first line in its path in the horizontal view. Since line 3_H-4_H was encountered first, it will be the visible line in the frontal view.
3. Complete the visibility of lines by showing the proper solid (visible) and dashed (hidden) lines in both views. The visible line has been shaded for clarity, though this is not standard practice. Note that line 1-2 is visible in the horizontal view (is above line 3-4), and line 3-4 is visible in the frontal view (is in front of line 1-2).

19.4.8 Parallelism of Lines

Two lines in space will be intersecting, skew, parallel, or perpendicular. **Parallel lines** project parallel in all views (Fig. 19.11). Note that in each view, lines 1-2 and 3-4 are parallel. Parallel lines may also appear as points (in the same view) or their projections may coincide.

Two oblique lines that project parallel or coincide in all views will always be parallel. Two lines that are parallel or

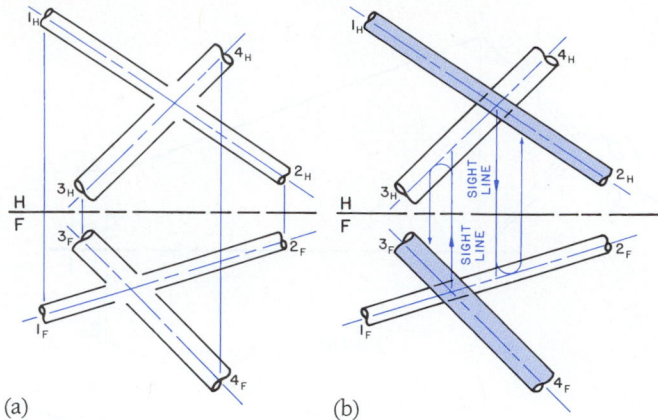

(a)   (b)

FIGURE 19.10   Visibility of Lines

perpendicular to a principal plane and appear parallel to each other may not be parallel lines, and a third view will be needed to establish their relationship.

The true distance between two parallel lines is shown in a view where the lines appear as points. In Figure 19.11 oblique lines 1-2 and 3-4 are parallel. Auxiliary view A is projected parallel to both oblique lines from the frontal view (fold line F/A is drawn parallel to 1-2 and 3-4). View A shows both lines as true length. *Note that parallel lines show true length in the same view.* Auxiliary view B is then projected perpendicular to the true length lines (fold line A/B is drawn perpendicular to true length lines 1-2 and 3-4). In auxiliary view B both lines appear as point views, therefore, true distance (shortest distance) between the lines can be measured here.

You May Complete Exercises 19.1 Through 19.4 at This Time

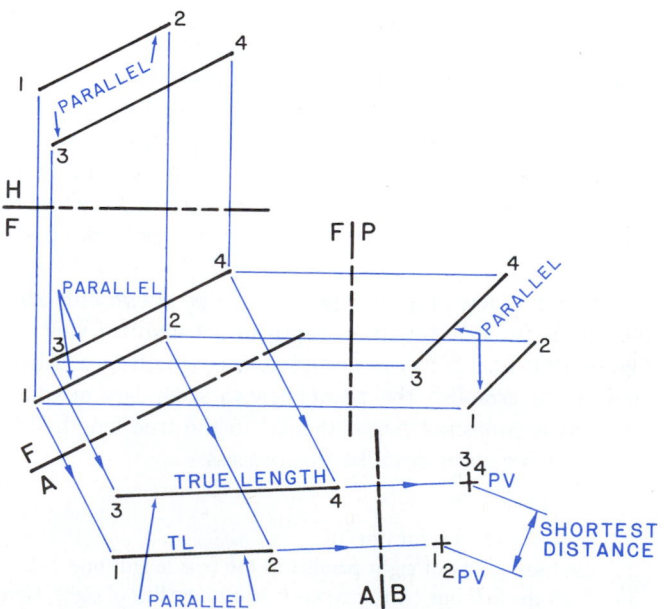

FIGURE 19.11   Solving for the Shortest Distance Between Two Lines

to the right or left of a given point. The horizontal view locates a point to the front or back and to the right or left of a given point, and the profile view locates a given point above or below and to the front or back of a given point. Notice that each view has one location direction in common with an adjacent view: in the frontal and horizontal views, the left/right distance; in the frontal and profile views, the above/below distance; and in the horizontal and profile views, the front/back distance.

In Figure 19.16 point 3 is on line 1-2. To locate the point we need to know only one coordinate distance and its spatial description. Point 3 can be said to lie on line 1-2 at distance D1 behind point 1. This would fix the point in all views by measurement or projection. Another way of describing the location of point 3 would be to say point 3 is on line 1-2, distance D2 below point 1; or point 3 is on line 1-2, distance D3 to the right of point 1. Of course, point 3 could also be located in respect to point 2. The distance dimension would be given in specific units of measurement.

If point 3 were to lie midpoint of line 1-2, then it would only be necessary to state that fact, since a point on the midpoint of a line is at its midpoint in every view. The above description allows for the spatial description of a point as referenced from an existing point. The new point need not lie

on the line to use this method. Also note that a point on a line can be simply projected from view to view since the point will remain on the line. A point on a line divides the line in the same proportions in every view.

19.4.14 Shortest Distance Between a Point and a Line

A perpendicular line between a given point and line is the shortest connection (distance). The **shortest distance** between a point and a line is measured along a perpendicular connector in a view where the line appears as a point view.

In Figure 19.17 oblique line 1-2 and point 3 are given. The shortest connector between the line and the point is required. This connector must be shown in all views. The following steps describe the procedure for finding the shortest distance between a point and a line:

1. Draw auxiliary view A parallel to oblique line 1-2. Start by drawing fold line F/A parallel to the line.
2. Project line 1-2 and point 3 into auxiliary view A. Line 1-2 shows true length.
3. Draw a perpendicular connector between point 3 and true length line 1-2, and label this new point 4.

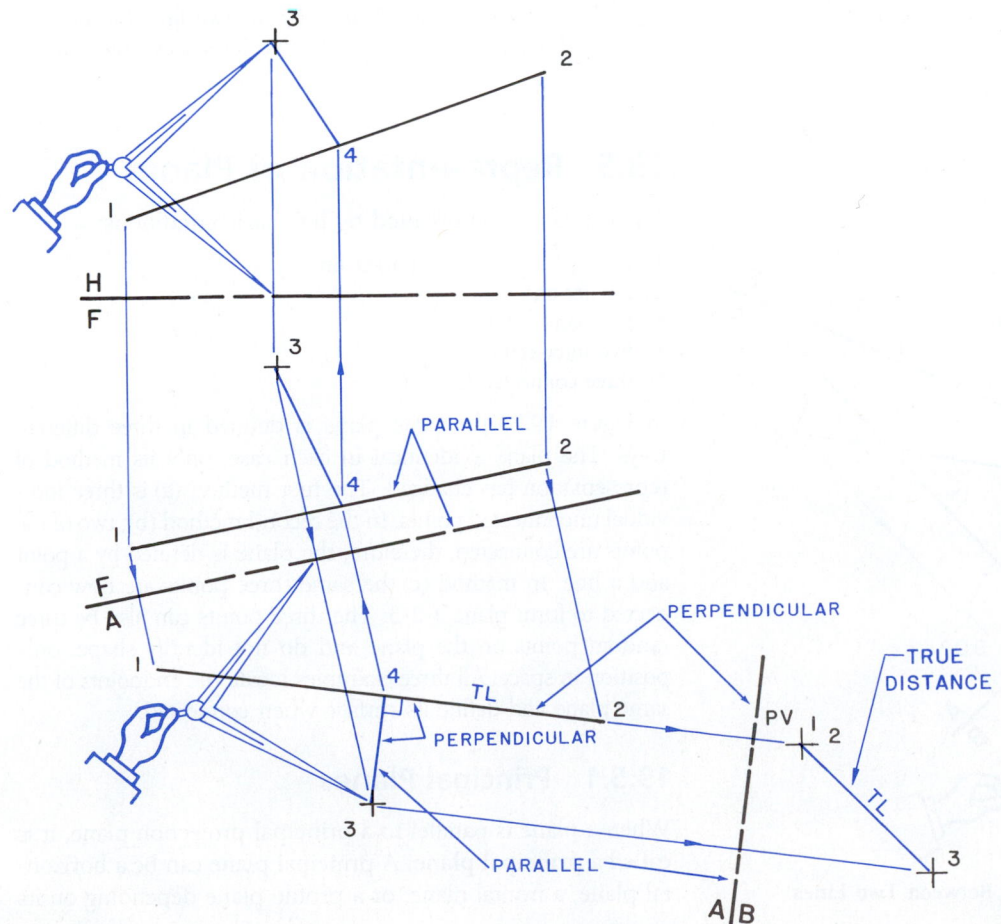

FIGURE 19.17 Shortest Connector (True Distance) Between a Point and a Line

4. Project auxiliary view B parallel to line 3-4 (and perpendicular to true length line 1-2). Note that fold line A/B is parallel to line 3-4 and perpendicular to line 1-2.
5. Auxiliary view B shows line 1-2 as a point view and line 3-4 (the shortest connector) as true length. The true distance between the point and the line can be measured here.
6. Project line 3-4 back into each view.

19.4.15 Shortest Distance Between Two Skew Lines

Two nonparallel, nonintersecting lines are called **skew lines.** The shortest distance between two skew lines is a line that is perpendicular to both lines. Therefore, only one solution is possible. This common perpendicular is shown as true length in a view where one line appears as a point view and the other oblique or true length. Given lines 1-2 and 3-4 in the horizontal and frontal view, the following steps describe how to solve for the shortest distance between skew lines (Fig. 19.18):

1. Draw fold line F/A parallel to line 3-4, and project auxiliary view A. Line 3-4 is true length and line 1_A-2_A is oblique.

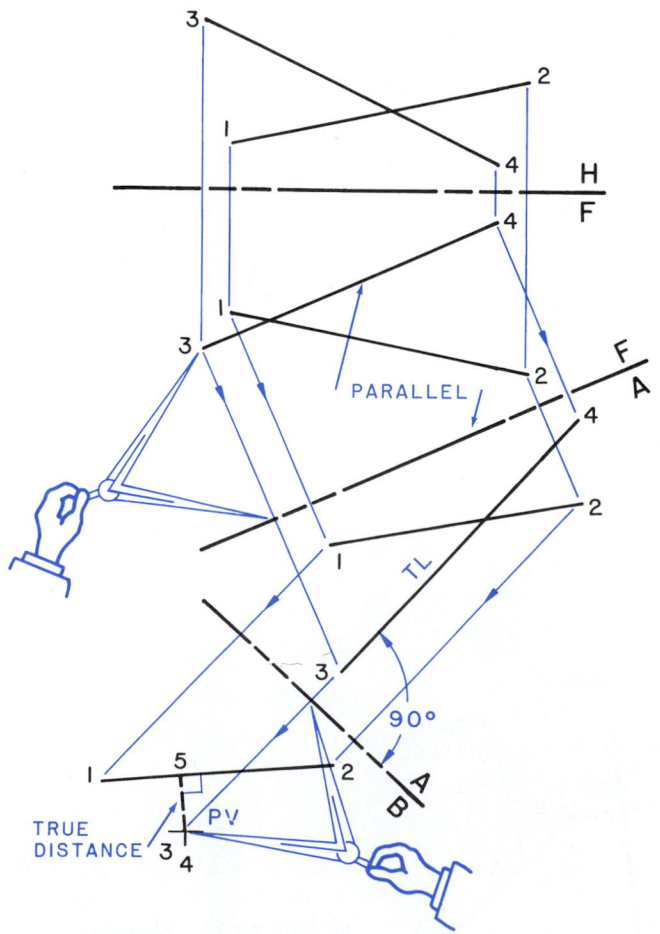

FIGURE 19.18 **Shortest Connector Between Two Lines**

2. Draw fold line A/B perpendicular (90°) to true length line 3_A-4_A, and complete auxiliary view B. Line 3-4 projects as a point view and line 1-2 as oblique.
3. Draw a line from point view 3_B-4_B perpendicular to line 1_B-2_B. Point 5_B is on line 1_B-2_B. This is the shortest distance between the two skew lines. Note that this shortest distance line is perpendicular to *both* skew lines. The distance between PV 3-4 and point 5 is the true distance between line 1-2 and line 3-4.

19.4.16 Angle Between Two Skew Lines

The angle formed by two skew lines is measured in a view where both lines appear as true length. In Figure 19.19 skew lines 1-2 and 3-4 are given in the F and H views; the angle formed by the two lines is required. The following steps were used to solve the problem:

1. Fold line F/A is drawn parallel to line 3_F-4_F.
2. Project primary auxiliary view A. Line 1_A-2_A is oblique and line 3_A-4_A shows as true length.
3. Draw fold line A/B perpendicular to true length line 3_A-4_A.
4. Complete secondary auxiliary view B. Line 1_B-2_B is oblique and line 3_B-4_B appears as a point view.
5. Draw fold line B/C parallel to oblique line 1_B-2_B.
6. Project auxiliary view C. Auxiliary view C is projected parallel to oblique line 1_B-2_B. Line 1_C-2_C therefore shows as true length in auxiliary C. Lines 1-2 and 3-4 both show as true length lines in this view.
7. The true angle (acute) formed by the two lines can be measured in auxiliary view C since both lines show true length.

19.5   Representation of Planes

A plane can be represented by five basic conditions:

1. three points not in a straight line
2. a point and a line
3. two parallel lines
4. two intersecting lines
5. three connected lines

In Figure 19.20 the same plane is defined in three different ways. The plane is identical in each case; only its method of representation has changed. The first method (a) is three individual unconnected points. In the second method (b), two of the points are connected; therefore, the plane is defined by a point and a line. In method (c) the same three points are now connected to form plane 1-2-3. The three points can also be three random points on the plane and do not identify shape, only position in space. All three examples locate the endpoints of the same plane and define its surface when connected.

19.5.1   Principal Planes

When a plane is parallel to a principal projection plane, it is called a **principal plane.** A principal plane can be a horizontal plane, a frontal plane, or a profile plane depending on its

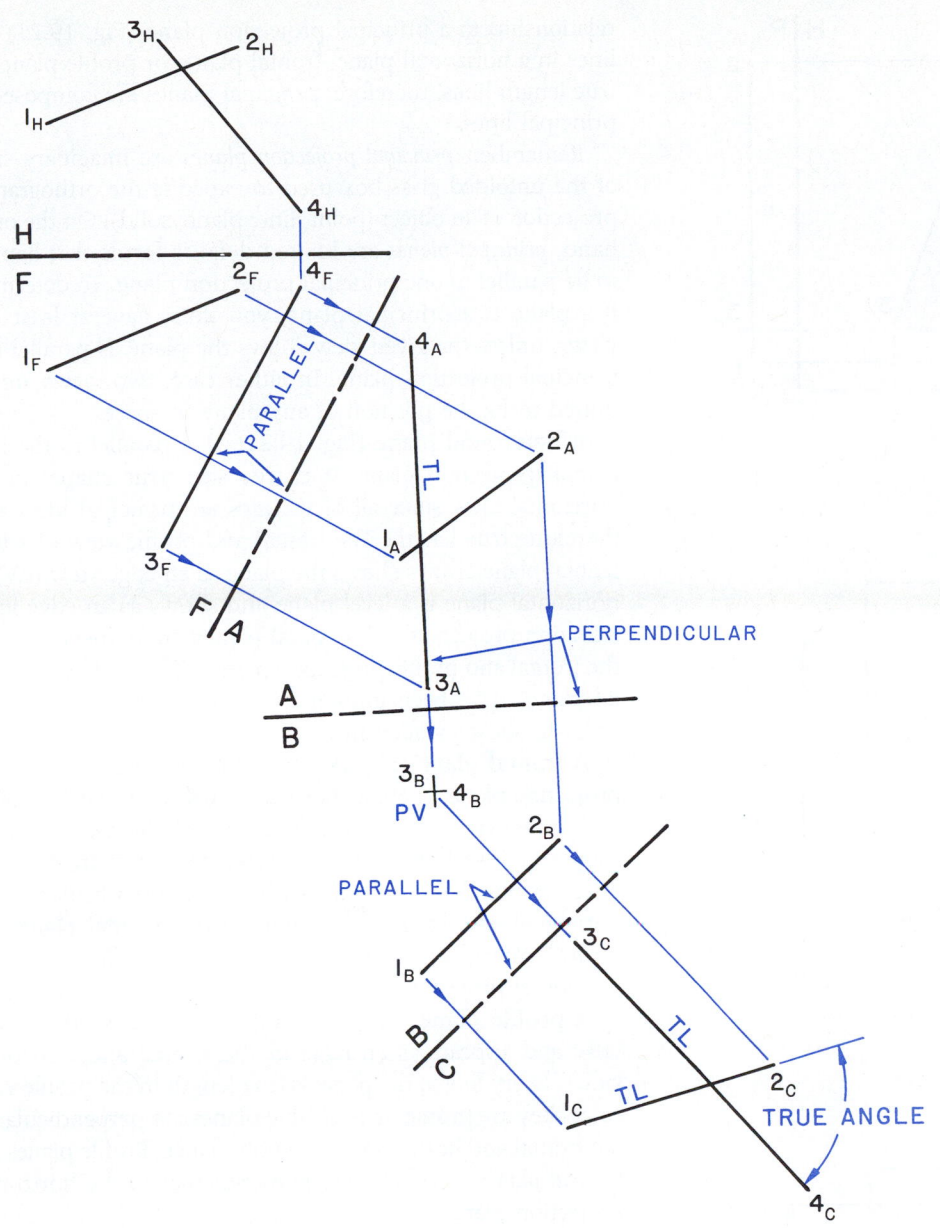

FIGURE 19.19 Angle Between
Two Skew Lines

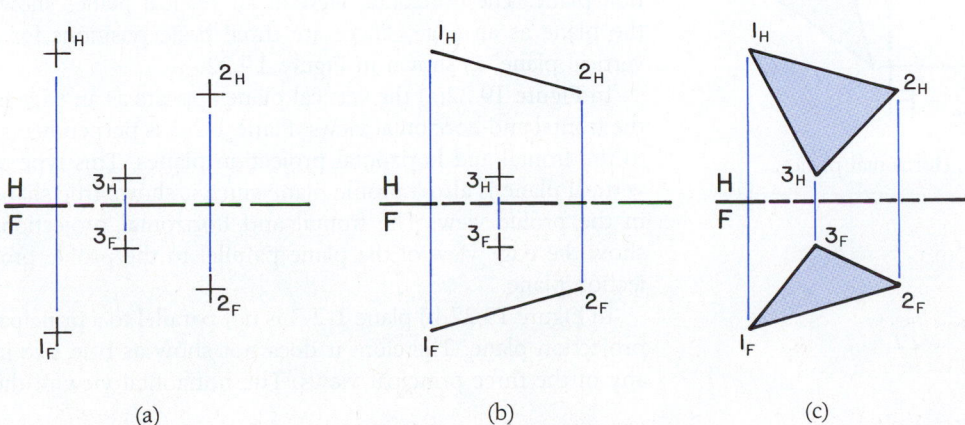

(a)   (b)   (c)

FIGURE 19.20 Representation
of a Plane Using   (a) Three
points (b) A line and a point
(c) Three lines

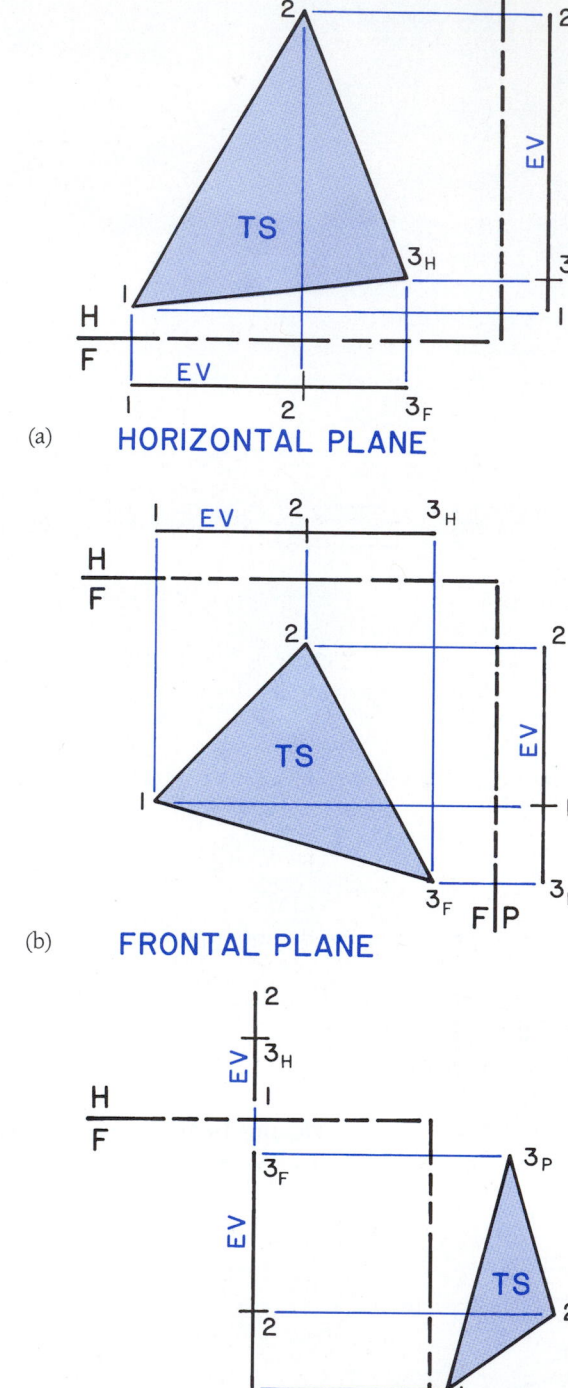

(a)   **HORIZONTAL PLANE**

(b)   **FRONTAL PLANE**

(c)   **PROFILE PLANE**

FIGURE 19.21   Principal Planes   (a) Horizontal plane
(b) Frontal plane (c) Profile plane

relationship to a principal projection plane (Fig. 19.21). All lines in a horizontal plane, frontal plane, or profile plane are true length lines; therefore, principal planes are composed of principal lines.

Remember, *principal projection planes* are imaginary sides of the unfolded glass box used to expedite the orthographic projection of an object (point, line, plane, solid). On the other hand, *principal planes* are limited definite forms that happen to lie parallel to one principal projection plane. To determine if a plane is a principal plane, you must have at least two views, unless the given view shows the plane as parallel to a principal projection plane. In either case, two views are required to fix the position of any plane in space.

A **horizontal plane** [Fig. 19.21(a)] is parallel to the horizontal projection plane. It is true size (true shape) in the horizontal view since all of its lines are principal lines and, therefore, true length. The frontal and profile view of a horizontal plane always shows the plane as an edge view (EV). A horizontal plane is a level plane and shows as an edge in all elevation projections. Horizontal planes are perpendicular to the frontal and profile projection planes. The profile and frontal planes have been unfolded from the horizontal plane in order to show parallelism.

A **frontal plane** [Fig. 19.21(b)] lies parallel to the frontal projection plane where it shows as true size. In the horizontal and profile views the plane appears as an edge view. All lines show true length in the frontal view, since they are principal lines (frontal lines). A frontal plane is perpendicular to the horizontal and profile projection planes. Frontal planes are *vertical planes,* since they are always perpendicular to the horizontal projection plane.

A **profile plane** [Fig. 19.21(c)] is true size in the profile view and appears as an edge in the frontal and horizontal views. Every line in the plane is true length in the profile view since they are profile lines. Profile planes are perpendicular to the frontal and horizontal projection planes. Profile planes are *vertical planes* since they are perpendicular to the horizontal projection plane.

19.5.2   Vertical Planes

Vertical planes are perpendicular to the horizontal projection plane. The horizontal view of all vertical planes shows the plane as an edge. There are three basic positions for a vertical plane, as shown in Figure 19.22.

In Figure 19.22(a) the vertical plane appears as an edge in the frontal and horizontal views. Plane 1-2-3 is perpendicular to the frontal and horizontal projection planes. This type of vertical plane is also a profile plane since it shows true shape in the profile view. The frontal and horizontal projections show the edge view of the plane parallel to the profile projection plane.

In Figure 19.22(b) plane 1-2-3 is not parallel to a principal projection plane. Therefore it does not show as true size in any of the three principal views. The horizontal view of the

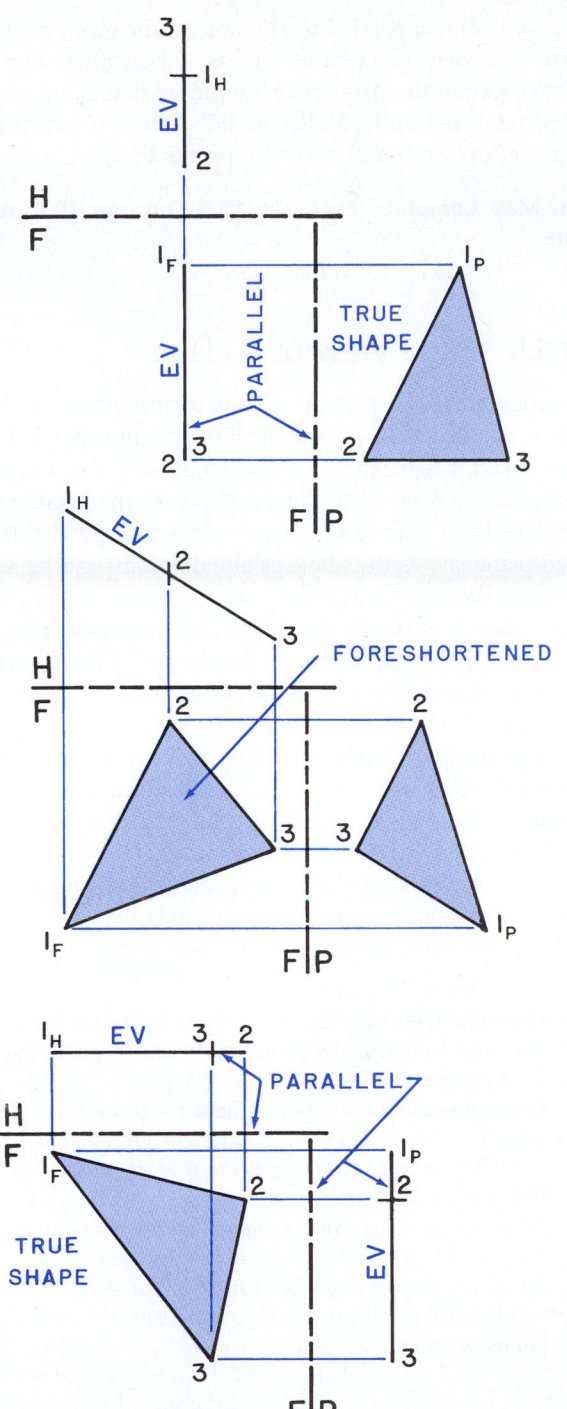

FIGURE 19.22   Vertical Planes

19.5.3   Oblique Planes

The classification of planes is determined by their relationship to the three principal projection planes: frontal, horizontal, or profile. Principal planes (normal planes) appear as true size in one of the three principal projections and as edges in the other two. An **oblique plane** is inclined to all three principal projection planes, which results in each view being foreshortened (distorted). *Oblique planes do not appear true size in any of the three principal views.*

Oblique planes are not vertical or horizontal (level) and will not be parallel to a principal projection plane. In Figure 19.23 an example of an oblique plane is shown in isometric and orthographic projection.

19.5.4   True Length Lines on Planes

Throughout descriptive geometry, the true length line that lies on an oblique plane needs to be found to solve for a particular

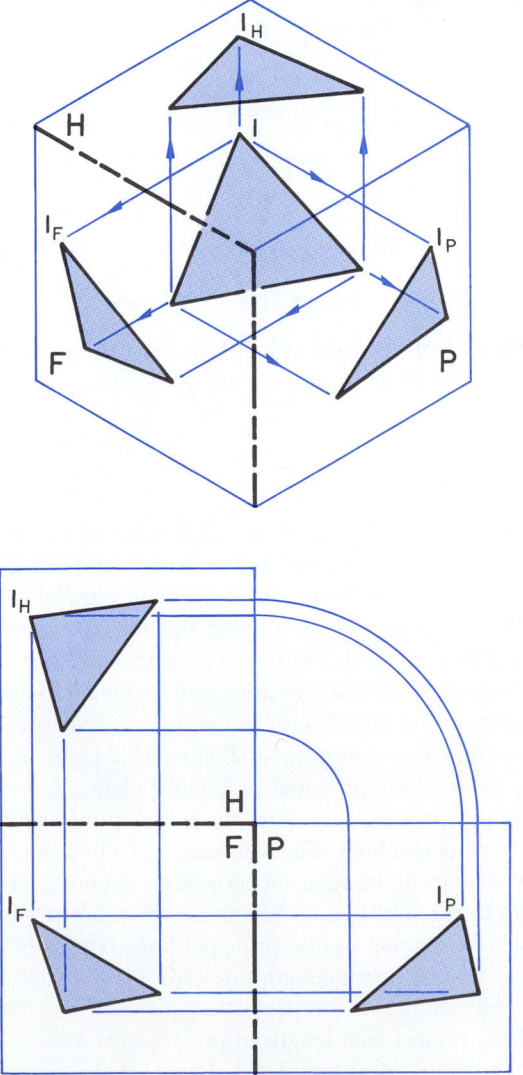

FIGURE 19.23   Three Views of a Plane in Space

plane establishes it as a vertical plane since it appears as an edge. The frontal and profile projections are foreshortened.

The third example of a vertical plane [Fig. 19.22(c)] is a frontal plane since it is true size in the frontal view. The horizontal and profile views show the plane as an edge and parallel to their adjacent projection planes.

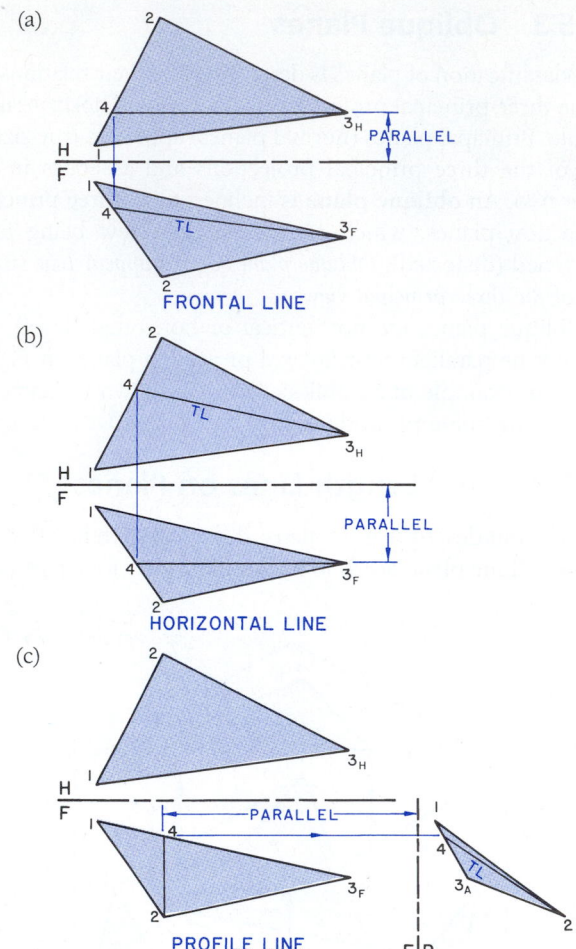

FIGURE 19.24   Principal Lines (True Length) on Planes
(a) Frontal line (b) Horizontal line (c) Profile line

problem, such as the edge view and true size of a plane, or the angle between two planes. A true length line can be established by drawing a line on the given plane parallel to the fold line. The adjacent projection shows the line as true length and on the given plane. In Figure 19.24 lines have been located in each example so that they are parallel to the fold line in one view and project true length in the adjacent view.

Note that the examples of Figure 19.24 are of oblique planes in the three principal projection planes: frontal, horizontal, and profile. Therefore, these newly introduced lines must be principal lines. The true length of a line can be found in any view using its adjacent projection to construct the line parallel to the fold line. When these views are not principal views, the lines will not be principal lines. The only requirement to finding a true length line on a plane is that the line be drawn parallel to the projection plane in one view and, therefore, project true length in the adjacent view.

In Figure 19.24(a) line 3-4 is drawn on the given oblique plane and parallel to H/F. The frontal projection of the line is on the plane and true length (a frontal line). In example (b),

line 3-4 is drawn parallel to H/F and on the given plane. The horizontal view shows the line as a horizontal line (true length) and on the plane. In example (c) line 2_F-4_F is drawn on plane 1-2-3 and parallel to F/P. Line 2-4 appears true length in the profile view; it is a profile line.

You May Complete Exercises 19.5 Through 19.8 at This Time

19.5.5   Edge View of a Plane

The **edge view** of a plane is seen in a view where the line of sight is parallel to the plane. The line of sight is parallel to the plane when it is parallel to a true length line that lies on the plane. Since a projection plane is always perpendicular to the line of sight, it follows that a view drawn perpendicular to a given plane shows the plane as an edge. This can be seen in a vertical plane, which appears as an edge in the horizontal view, since it is perpendicular to the horizontal projection plane. A horizontal plane is perpendicular to the frontal and profile projection planes and thus appears as an edge in these two views.

When the given plane is oblique, an auxiliary projection is needed to show the edge view. To establish a line of sight parallel to the plane, a true length line that lies on the plane needs to be drawn. An auxiliary view where the line appears as a point view shows the plane as an edge. In Figure 19.25 plane 1-2-3 is given and an edge view is required. The following steps were used in the solution:

1. Draw line 1_F-4_F on plane 1-2-3 in the frontal view, parallel to H/F, and complete the horizontal view by projection. Line 1_H-4_H is true length.
2. Project auxiliary view A perpendicular to plane 1-2-3 (perpendicular to line 3-4). The line of sight for this projection is parallel to the plane and parallel to true length line 1-4. Draw H/A perpendicular to 1-4 and complete auxiliary view A by projection. Auxiliary view A shows line 1-4 as a point view and therefore plane 1-2-3 appears as an edge view.
3. A true size view can now be projected from view A by drawing fold line A/B parallel to the EV of the plane and projecting the points as shown.

19.5.6   True Size (Shape) of an Oblique Plane

When the line of sight is perpendicular to the edge view of a plane, it projects as **true size (shape)**. The true size view is projected parallel to the edge view of the plane. Therefore, the fold line between the views is drawn parallel to the edge view. An oblique plane does not appear as true size in any of the principal projection planes. Therefore, a primary auxiliary and secondary auxiliary view are needed to solve for the true shape of an oblique plane.

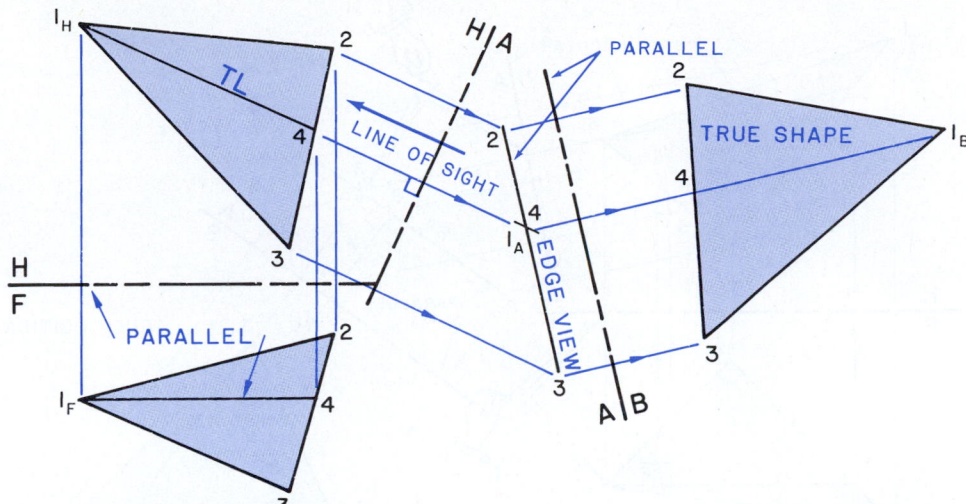

FIGURE 19.25 Edge View and
True Size of an Oblique Plane

In Figure 19.26 oblique plane 1-2-3 is given and its true
shape is required. The following steps were used to solve the
problem:

1. Draw horizontal line 3-4 parallel to H/F and project as true
length in the horizontal view.
2. Draw H/A perpendicular to line 3_A-4_A and complete auxiliary
view B. Line 3_A-4_A is a point view and plane 1_A-2_A-3_A an edge.
3. Project secondary auxiliary view B parallel to the edge view of
plane 1-2-3. Draw A/B parallel to the edge view.
4. Complete auxiliary view B; plane 1-2-3 projects true size
(shape).

19.5.7 Shortest Distance Between a Point
and a Plane

In Figure 19.27 plane 1-2-3 and point 4 are given. The
shortest connector is required. The shortest distance between a point and a plane is a perpendicular line drawn
between the point and the plane. A line drawn from a point
to a plane is its shortest connector if drawn perpendicular to
an edge view of the plane. In a view where the plane is an
edge, the shortest distance is measured as the perpendicular
distance between the point and the plane. The following steps
were used to solve the problem:

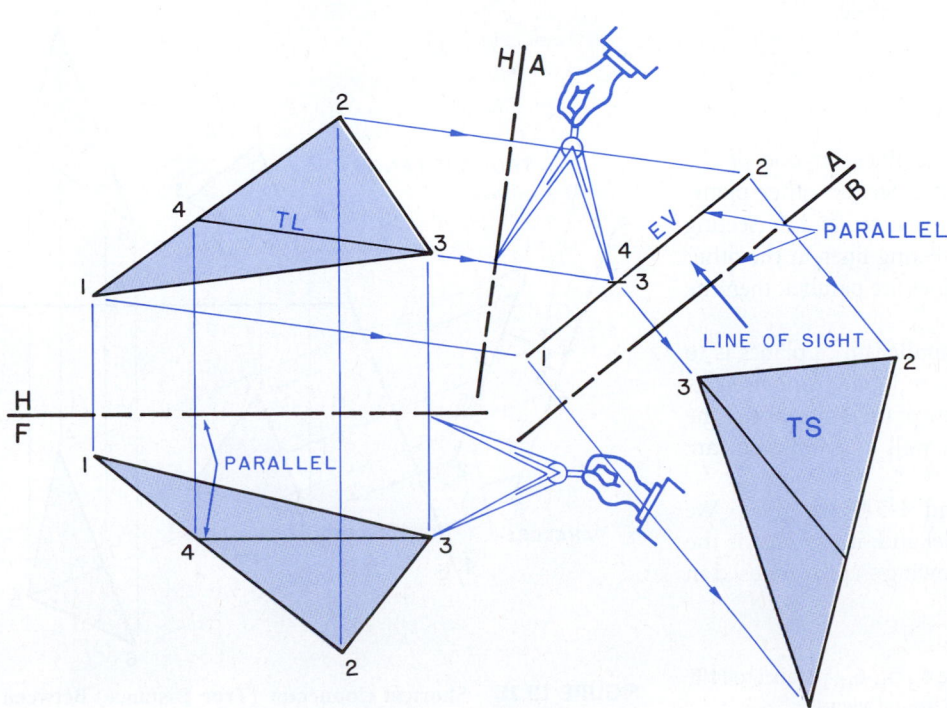

FIGURE 19.26 True Shape View
of an Oblique Plane

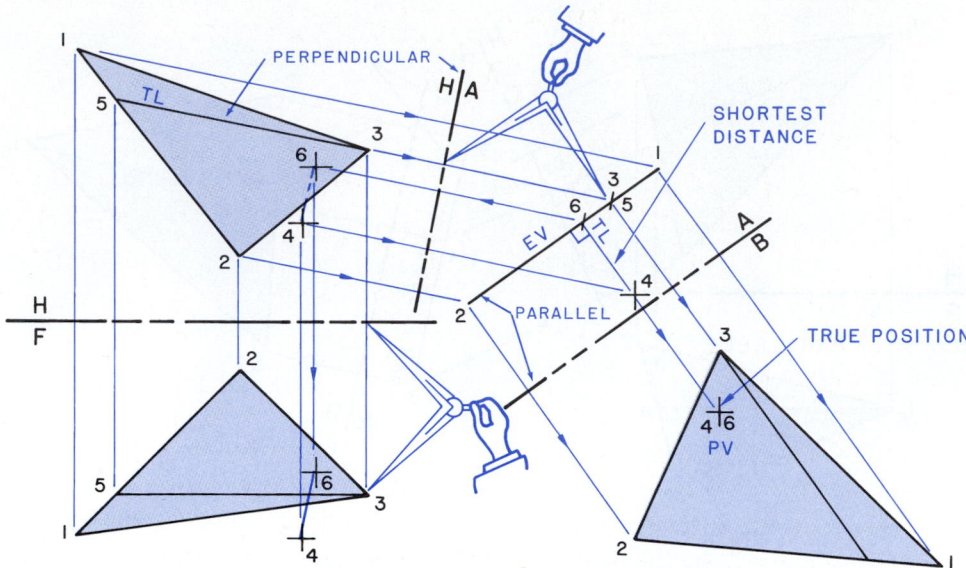

FIGURE 19.27 Shortest Connector (Shortest Distance) Between a Point and a Plane

1. Draw horizontal line 3_F-5_F parallel to H/F, and project as true length in the horizontal view.
2. H/A is drawn perpendicular to horizontal line 3-5. In auxiliary view A, plane 1-2-3 appears as an edge. Draw a line from point 4 perpendicular to the edge view of the plane. Point 6 lies on the plane (at the point where the line pierces the plane). Line 4_A-6_A is the shortest distance between the point and plane.
3. Line 4_A-6_A is true length in auxiliary view A; therefore, it projects to the horizontal view parallel to H/A. Point 6 is fixed by projection from auxiliary view A. Point 6 is located by transferring from auxiliary view A along its projection line in the frontal view.
4. Project auxiliary view B to establish the true shape of the plane and the true position of the line on the plane.

19.5.8 Parallelism of Planes

Two planes are parallel if intersecting lines on one of the planes are parallel to intersecting lines on the other plane. **Parallelism** is determined by drawing a set of intersecting lines parallel to any two of the intersecting lines in the other plane. If the two sets of intersecting lines are parallel, then the planes are parallel.

Another method of establishing parallelism of planes is to project an edge view of one of the planes. If one plane projects as an edge *and parallel* to the edge view of the other plane, the true distance between the planes as well as parallelism are established.

In Figure 19.28 planes 1-2-3 and 4-5-6 are given. We want to know if the planes are parallel and, if so, what is the true distance between them? The following steps were used in the solution:

1. Draw horizontal line 5_H-7_H on plane 4_H-5_H-6_H, parallel to H/F. It will project as true length in the frontal view.

2. Project auxiliary view A perpendicular to line 5-7 by drawing F/A perpendicular to it.
3. In auxiliary view A, both planes show as edges and also parallel to one another. The true distance between the planes is measured as the perpendicular distance between the two planes.

19.5.9 Angle Between Two Planes

The angle between two planes can be found in a projection where both planes are seen as edge views. The true angle

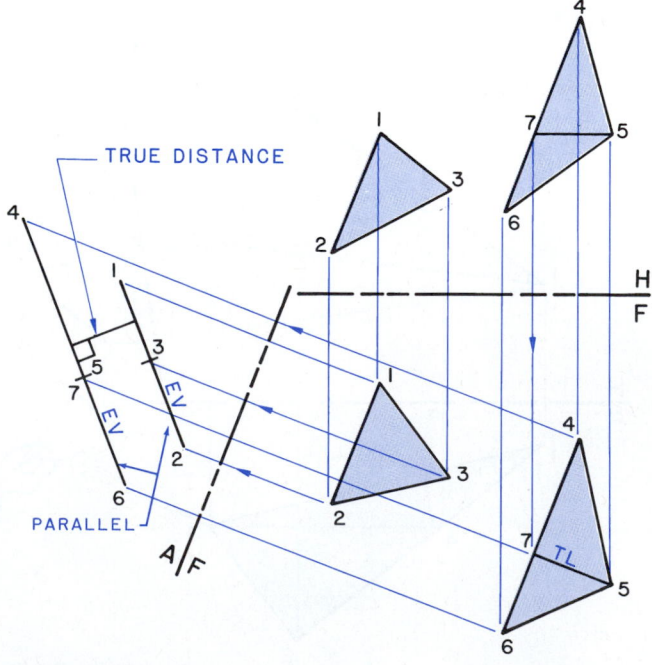

FIGURE 19.28 Shortest Connector (True Distance) Between Two Parallel Planes

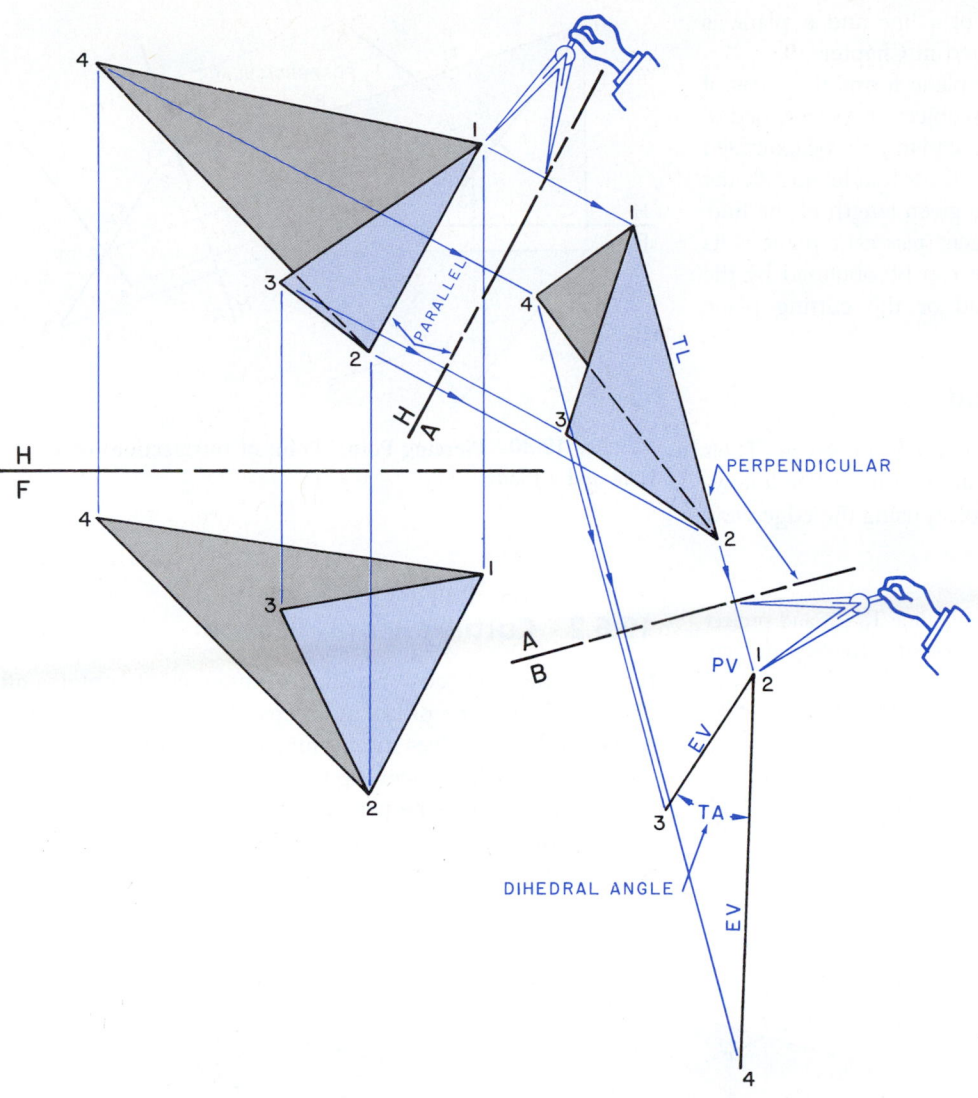

FIGURE 19.29   True Angle Between Connected Planes

between two intersecting planes is normally called a **dihedral angle.** To solve for the angle between two intersecting planes, a view is necessary where the common line (intersecting line) appears as a point view. In this view both planes show as edges and the angle between them can be measured. The first step in finding the angle between two planes involves projecting an auxiliary view where the common line is true length. An auxiliary view projected perpendicular to this true length intersection line shows the common line as a point and both planes as edges. The true angle between the planes is measured in this secondary auxiliary view.

In Figure 19.29 two oblique planes with a common line are given. The dihedral angle formed by these two intersecting planes is required. The following steps were used to solve the problem:

1. Draw H/A parallel to line 1-2. Line 1-2 is the common (intersection) line of the two oblique planes.
2. Complete auxiliary view A. Line 1-2 is true length in this projection.

3. Draw A/B perpendicular to true length line 1-2 and complete auxiliary view B by projection and transferring dimensions from the horizontal view.
4. The true angle between the planes is measured in auxiliary view B, since both intersecting planes appear as edges. This is the dihedral angle formed by the two planes.

19.6   Piercing Points

A line and a plane have three possible relationships:

1. A line can lie on a plane.
2. A line can be parallel to a plane.
3. A line can intersect (pierce) a plane.

The procedure for finding the intersection of a line and a plane can be applied to intersections in all categories. If divided into specific types of intersections—line and a sphere, plane and cone, cylinder and pyramid—the list is endless. In this chapter only the intersection of a line and a plane is presented. All other types are covered in Chapter 20.

The intersection of a line and a plane forms the basis of intersections of all forms, since most objects are composed of lines and planes. Both the line and the plane can be extended to solve for theoretical intersections—those that lie outside the given bounded plane or beyond the given length of the line.

The point at which a line intersects (*pierces*) a plane is its **piercing point**. This piercing point can be obtained by the edge view (auxiliary view) method or the cutting plane method.

19.6.1 Edge View Method

In Figure 19.30 plane 1-2-3 and line 4-5 are given. Their piercing point and proper visibility are required. The following steps were used to solve the problem using the **edge view method**:

1. Draw H/A perpendicular to horizontal line 1_H-2_H and project auxiliary view A. Plane 1-2-3 appears as an edge view and line 4-5 as oblique.
2. The piercing point (point 6) is where the line crosses the edge line of the plane.
3. Project point 6 to the horizontal and frontal views as shown.
4. Proper visibility is determined by inspection of auxiliary view A for the horizontal view and by the visibility test for the frontal view.

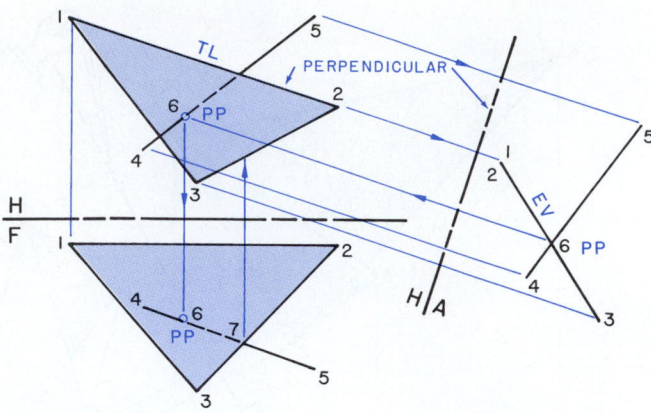

FIGURE 19.30 Piercing Point (Point of Intersection) of a Line and a Plane

19.6.2 Cutting Plane Method

If two planes intersect, their line of intersection contains all lines that lie on one plane and pierce the other. The **cutting plane method** involves the forming of a new plane that contains the given line. A cutting plane is used that shows as an edge view in one of the principal projection planes.

In Figure 19.31 a vertical cutting plane (VCP) was formed by passing a plane through line 1-2. Line 1-2 represents the

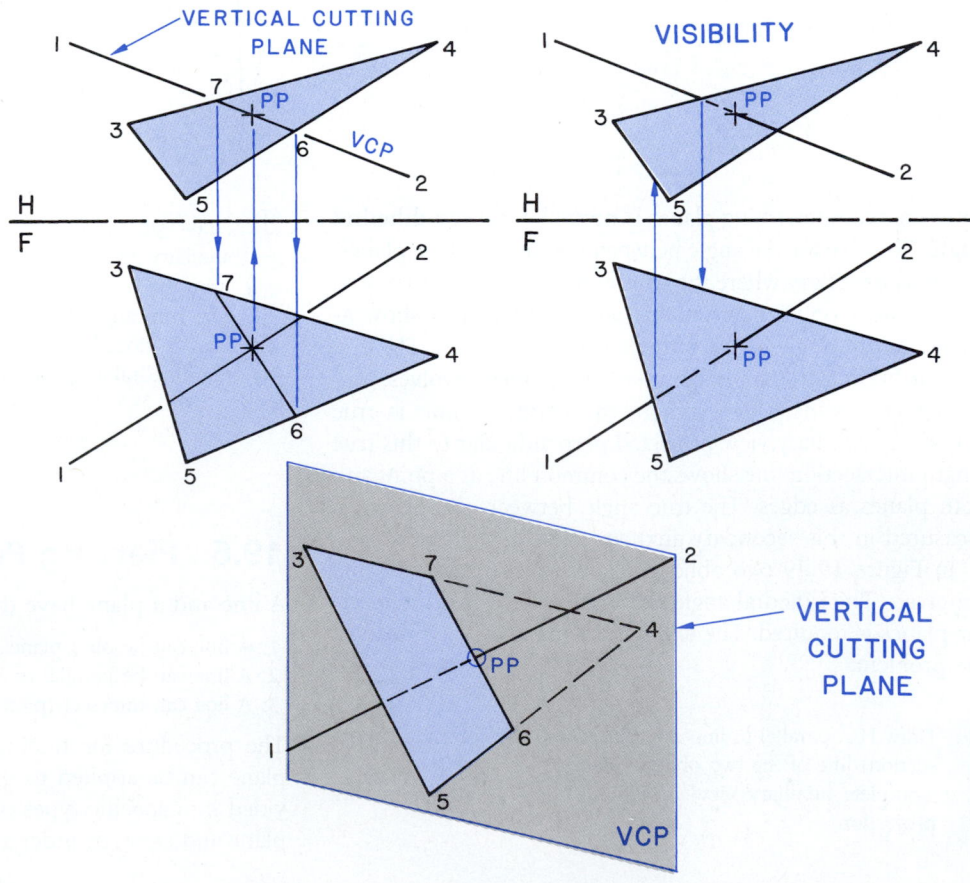

FIGURE 19.31 Intersection of a Line and a Plane Using the Cutting Plane Method

edge view of the VCP. Where this VCP "cuts" plane 3-4-5 it forms a line of intersection, line 6-7, common to both planes. This line of intersection is projected to the adjacent view, where it lies on both planes. The line of intersection between the two planes must be parallel or intersect the given line. If the line of intersection intersects the given line in the adjacent projection, then it will establish the piercing point of the line and the plane, PP.

When using a vertical cutting plane the piercing point is established by projecting the line of intersection from the horizontal view. Points 6 and 7 are projected to the frontal view where they form line 6_F-7_F. Line 6-7 crosses line 1-2 at PP. The horizontal view of PP can be located by projection. Visibility is determined using the visibility test, since inspection of an edge view is not possible.

If the line of intersection does not cross the given line, the line and plane do not intersect. In this case, the given line is parallel to the given plane and lies in front of or behind and above or below the plane.

In Figure 19.31 a pictorial view of this problem is also provided. The vertical cutting plane contains line 1-2. VCP cuts plane 3-4-5 along a line of intersection, line 6-7. Line 6-7 lies on both planes, i.e., it is a common line. Where line 6-7 crosses line 1-2 they will intersect at PP, which is the piercing point of line 1-2 and plane 4-5-6.

The piercing point problem shown in Figure 19.32 was completed using a CAD system. The cutting plane method was used to solve for the piercing point. This example was modeled in 3D but the piercing point was established using 2D drafting techniques.

You May Complete Exercises 19.9 Through 19.12 at This Time

19.7 Descriptive Geometry Using CAD

Traditionally, engineers, designers, and drafters have conceptualized a design in three dimensions and then presented the concept by constructing 2D views on paper. When using the manual method of projection and solving problems with descriptive geometry, you must rely on the accuracy of your linework and projection proficiency instead of the quality of the 3D model database. Designing with a 3D CAD system is a much more realistic way to produce the model of a part. The 3D model is the starting point for engineering analysis, drafting, and manufacturing. Using computer commands, you mold or model the part. The part exists in 3D space and is defined mathematically within the computer by 3D coordinates.

Even though 2D systems are limited when compared to 3D systems, the use of 2D CAD in descriptive geometry and in projects requiring orthographic projection is still advantageous. Verifying, measuring, and calculating are very accurate with a CAD system, whereas the manual methods of scaling and calculating are prone to errors and inaccuracies.

Model geometry is constructed in a 3D coordinate system. Therefore, all spatial relationships of the design can be determined accurately from the model itself, not a 2D representation of the part. Since information such as the location and the true length of each element, the size and area of each face

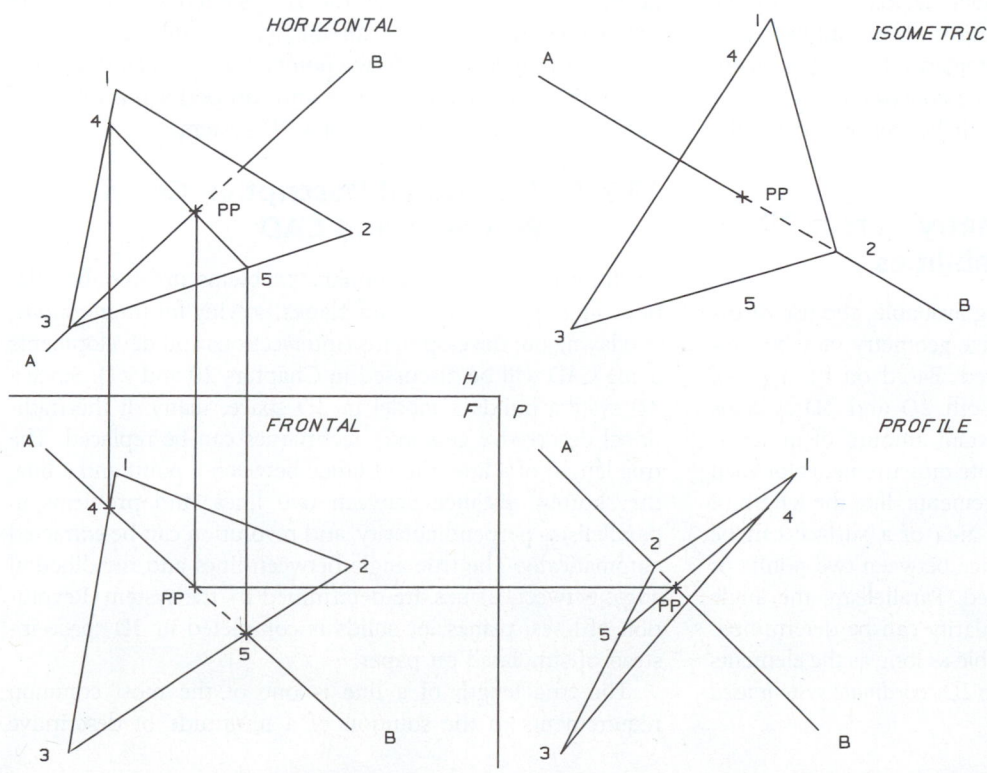

FIGURE 19.32 Using CAD to Solve for the Intersection of a Line and Plane. Note that the problem shows three views and an isometric projection.

Have you ever heard the phrase "Let George do it"? If you have, you may have wondered about George. That phrase refers to a bit of advice from World War II that encouraged someone to avoid a burdensome or demanding task by "letting George do it." George is the name given to the automatic pilot on aircraft, which is a device that removes some of the burden from the pilot and keeps the airplane on course during a flight to a particular destination. Automatic navigation is a concept unheard of until recently. For those who once sailed the seas by stars and by plotting complex navigational charts, it must have appeared magical indeed.

The magic is performed by gyroscopes. Gyroscopes have been around a long time (since the early 1800s), but they weren't applied to useful purposes until the 1900s. At that time, Elmer Sperry was convinced that they had great commercial possibilities. Sperry developed the gyrocompass from the elementary gyroscope. This invention filled an

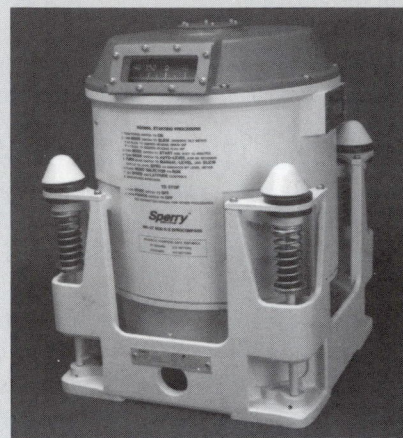

A Gyrocompass

immediate need by the Navy for a compass that would be unaffected by steel ships.

By World War II, 200 of the merchant fleets in the world were guided by the Sperry gyrocompass. Other devices that

used the gyroscope were developed, but the most important application was "George," the turn indicator and automatic pilot.

The autopilot relieves the pilot from the physical effort of flying the plane. Today autopilots are found in almost every size aircraft. Electronic navigation and control are used extensively on all modern aircraft. Modern commercial airplanes give George much of the duties involved in navigation and control. If you tell George where you want to go, he can navigate the plane so that it stays on that course.

After you have studied descriptive geometry, you will probably be able to appreciate the relationship between points, lines, and planes in 3D. You may also be able to appreciate navigation at sea during eras before the gyrocompass. Electronic navigation and control play a large part in piloting a modern aircraft. Most pilots will be happy to tell you that life is a lot nicer now that George is around.

---

plane, and the intersections of surfaces or shapes can be determined directly from the model database, descriptive geometry and orthographic projection have limited use. Views of the part are generated automatically by the system from the model. Sections can also be constructed automatically by the system and analysis can be performed on the computer part.

19.7.1 Descriptive Geometry Versus 2D and 3D CAD Capabilities

Depending on the type of modeling available, the use of orthographic projection and descriptive geometry may be similar, lessened, or possibly eliminated. Based on the type of computer model that was built, both 2D and 3D systems allow automatic extraction of a certain amount of information. A 2D system will extract accurate measurements for each view of the part. Therefore, measurements, like the length of a line, can be easily verified. The area of a surface can be calculated automatically. The distance between two points or a point and a line can be extracted. Parallelism, the angle between two lines, and perpendicularity can be determined. All of these measurements are possible as long as the elements being measured *lie in the plane of the 2D coordinate system used by the system.*

A 3D system can also perform any of the above-mentioned 2D measurements. However, the 3D system offers many more capabilities. A 3D system can calculate volume. It can measure the distance between two points, lines, or planes regardless of their placement in space and can perform a variety of tasks beyond the capabilities of a 2D system.

19.7.2 Traditional Descriptive Geometry Problems and CAD

Traditional descriptive geometry problems involve the relationship of points, lines, and planes, solving for intersections, and laying out developments (intersections and developments using CAD will be discussed in Chapters 20 and 21). Since a 3D system builds a model in 3D space, many of the traditional descriptive geometry techniques can be replaced. The true length of a line, the distance between a point and a line, the shortest distance between two lines, and problems in parallelism, perpendicularity, and revolution can be extracted automatically. The true angle between lines and the dihedral angle between planes are determined by the system. Revolution of lines, planes, or solids is completed in 3D space instead of simulated on paper.

The true length of a line is one of the most common requirements to the solution of a multitude of descriptive

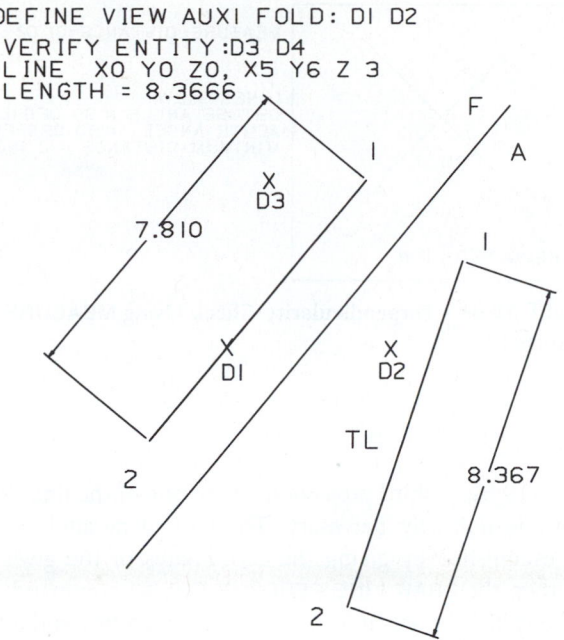

FIGURE 19.33   Solving for the True Length of an Oblique Line Using CAD

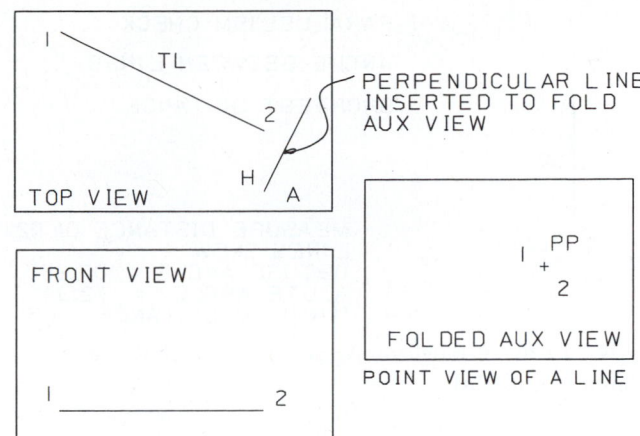

FIGURE 19.34   Point View Using CAD

geometry problems. For a solution, a minimum of a three-view drawing with an auxiliary projection is required. The true length of an oblique line is solved for in Figure 19.33. The auxiliary true length projection is simply folded from a view of the line. In the CAD-generated solution, the true length is established by verifying the entity. **Verifying** (**LIST** command on AutoCAD) an entity is a process in which you request the data establishing the entities, type, layer, color, position in space, and size. In Figure 19.33 the line is oblique in the given F view. The line is folded about F/A. The verification establishes the length at 8.3666 inches. Measurements were placed on the F and the A views as shown. Notice that the F view shows the line's length to be 7.810. This is the oblique view of the line, therefore it shows as foreshortened. The dimension in the A view establishes the true length measurement as 8.367 (rounded). Originally, the line was input using coordinates and the system responds to the verify command with the precise location of the endpoints of the line and its length. The auxiliary projection showing the line as true length was not necessary to extract the line's length and location. When using AutoCAD, verification of an entity is accomplished with the **LIST** command. **LIST** provides the **X**, **Y**, and **Z** location of the endpoints of the line, the length of the line, the angle the line makes with the **X-Y** plane, and the layer.

Typically, the next step after the projection of the true length of a line is to solve for the point view. A second auxiliary projection is necessary for lines that are oblique in the given view. In Figure 19.34 the CAD solution required inputting of the coordinates of the line and folding each successive view from the model view that was first created.

To establish the relationship of lines in space, a minimum of two views is necessary in traditional descriptive geometry, and often three projections will be required. The CAD solution requires inputting of the line's coordinates and picking the **MEASURE ANGLE** command. In Figure 19.35 the front view and the top view are included, but only one view was really necessary. The **MEASURE ANGLE** command extracted the obtuse and acute angles between the lines and the relationship of the lines in space.

Lines in space can have any of three spatial relationships: intersecting, parallel, or skew. When two lines appear parallel in a view, a second or third view is necessary to prove parallelism. In Figure 19.36 the profile view would normally be needed when using descriptive geometry. The CAD solution requires inputting of the lines using coordinates and selecting the **MEASURE DISTANCE** command. Besides extracting the

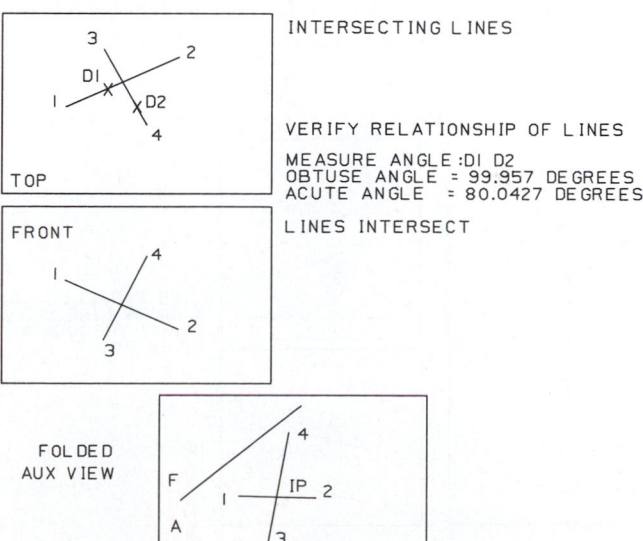

FIGURE 19.35   Angle of Two Lines in Space Using the **MEASURE** Command

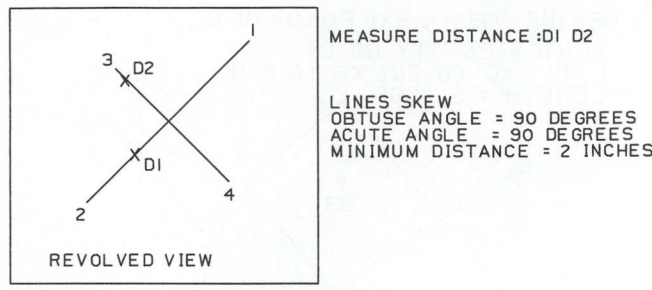

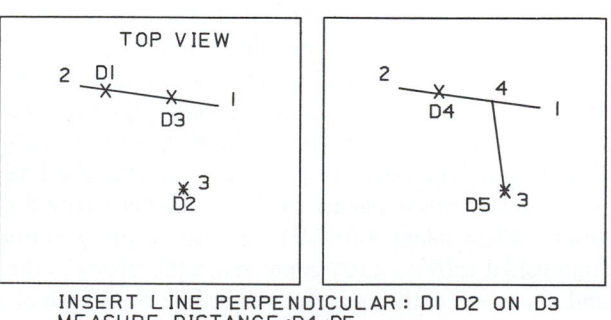

PARALLELISM CHECK
ANGLE BETWEEN LINES
SHORTEST DISTANCE

MEASURE DISTANCE :DI D2
LINES SKEW
OBTUSE ANGLE = 107.65°
ACUTE ANGLE   = 72.34°
MINIMUM DISTANCE = 1.5

FIGURE 19.36 Parallelism, Angle, and Shortest Distance Solutions Using CAD

MEASURE DISTANCE :DI D2

LINES SKEW
OBTUSE ANGLE = 90 DEGREES
ACUTE ANGLE = 90 DEGREES
MINIMUM DISTANCE = 2 INCHES

REVOLVED VIEW

FIGURE 19.38 Perpendicularity Check Using **MEASURE** Command

relationship of the lines (skew), the system provided the angle between the lines and the minimum distance. AutoCAD uses a similar command called **DISTANCE**, which asks you to pick the endpoints of the entities that you wish to measure. The distance, angle in the **X-Y** plane, and the angle from the **X-Y** plane are then provided.

To draw a line parallel to a given line and through a point (Fig. 19.37) is a fairly simple, but typical, problem in descriptive geometry. The CAD-generated solution requires inputting of the **X, Y, Z** locations of the given line and point as shown in Figure 19.37 (left). The **DRAW LINE PARALLEL** command or an **OFFSET** command is input. The given line is selected (D1), then the side of the line where the parallel line is to be drawn is established (D2). Last, the endpoints of the new line (D3 and D4) are picked [Fig. 19.37 (right)]. The line will show in all views since this was drawn on a 3D system (Computervision's Personal Designer).

In Figure 19.38 only one view of the lines in space is provided. Since the measurement command establishes that they are at 90°, they are perpendicular lines. Therefore, the lines are nonintersecting (skew).

The procedure for constructing a line perpendicular to a given line and through an established point is provided in

Figure 19.39. A third projection where one of the lines is true length is normally necessary. The CAD-generated solution was established by giving the coordinates of the given line and then the **DRAW LINE PERPENDICULAR** command. This is also called the shortest distance between a line and a point and is a common problem in descriptive geometry. The manual solution normally requires the use of two auxiliary projections. The CAD solution simply requires the insertion of a perpendicular line between the point and the given line. The **DRAW LINE PERPENDICULAR** command required selecting the original line (D1), the given point (D2), and the given line again with the **ON OSNAP** option (mask) (D3). The system constructed the line from the point to the line (on the line). The views for this solution show the lines skew. Since a 3D CAD system was used, it was not necessary to draw the lines in a view where they show perpendicular. The **MEASURE DISTANCE** command then provides the length of the shortest connector, which is the normal distance.

The angle between two planes (Fig. 19.40) is called the dihedral angle. The CAD solution requires the projection of the common line (1-2) as length (TL) and then as a point view

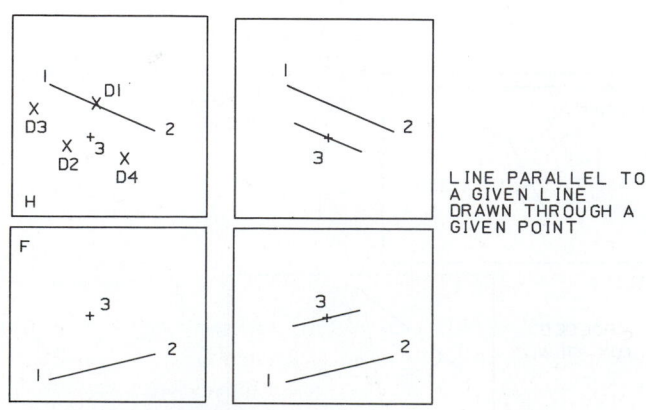

INSERT LINE PARALLEL :DI D2 :D3 D4

FIGURE 19.37 Inserting a Line Parallel to Another Line and Through a Given Point Using CAD

INSERT LINE PERPENDICULAR : DI D2 ON D3
MEASURE DISTANCE :D4 D5

NORMAL DISTANCE 1.75

1. SHORTEST DISTANCE BETWEEN A LINE AND A POINT
2. LINE DRAWN PERPENDICULAR TO A LINE AND THROUGH A GIVEN POINT
3. LINE 3-4 IS THE SHORTEST (PERPENDICULAR) CONNECTOR

FIGURE 19.39 Inserting a Line Perpendicular to a Given Line and Through a Given Point Using CAD

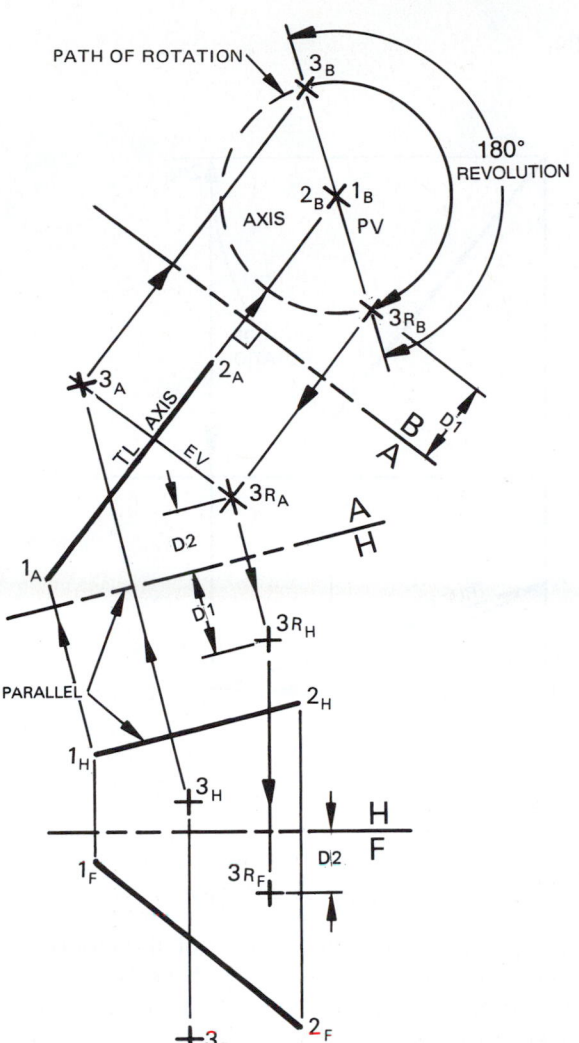

FIGURE 19.46   Rotation of a Point About an Oblique Axis Line

along its projection line. The location of point $3R_F$ is established by drawing its projection line and transferring D2 from auxiliary view A to the frontal view.

19.8.3   Revolution of a Line

A line can be revolved in the same manner as a point. The axis must be established before a line can be revolved. The axis can be through the endpoint of a line, a point on the line, or a point off the line. In the first case, the line revolves about a single endpoint and generates a cone. In the second case, both ends revolve and change position. Each endpoint remains in the same plane created by their paths of rotation.

One of the most common uses of revolution is to find the true length of an oblique line without the use of an auxiliary view. Since revolution changes the position of a line, but not its length, it is possible to revolve an oblique line so that it is parallel to the adjacent projection plane. The line will then project as true length in the adjacent view. The axis can be located through an endpoint or on the line and revolved in either given view. The axis line is a point view in one view and assumed true length in the other, though it need not have a specific length.

Figure 19.47 compares the auxiliary view method (a) with the revolution method (b). The auxiliary view method [Fig. 19.47(a)] requires the projection of a new view. In (b) point 2_H is revolved about a vertical axis line passed through point 1_H until it is parallel to H/F in position $2R_H$. Point 2 is located in the frontal view by projection since it falls on the edge view of the path of rotation. A construction line (which is really a portion of the edge view of the path rotation) is drawn parallel to H/F until it intersects the projection line and locates $2R_F$. Note that the revolution of point 2 changes its position in the horizontal and frontal view, *but does not alter its elevation since it must remain in a plane perpendicular to the true length axis of revolution.* Line 1_F-$2R_F$ is true length.

19.8.4   Revolution of an Oblique Line

When a line is revolved about another line, it generates a cylinder if the lines are parallel, a circle if they are perpendicular, a cone if intersecting, or a hyperboloid of revolution if oblique. In Figure 19.48 oblique line 1-2 is revolved clockwise 110° about vertical line 3-4. Line 3_H-4_H is a point view in the horizontal view and true length in the frontal view. Line 1_H-2_H is revolved about the point view of axis line 3_H-4_H in the horizontal view by rotating both endpoints 110°. Because the whole line is revolved, it does not change its oblique shape in the horizontal view; only its position ($1R_H$-$2R_H$) is altered. The frontal projection of the revolved line is located by moving points 1_F and 2_F perpendicular to the true length axis 3_F-4_F until it intersects the projection line drawn from each revolved point in the horizontal view.

generated by moving the point creates a circular plane in this view. Point $3R_A$ can be located in the horizontal plane by simple projection since it falls on the edge view of the path or rotation. The frontal position of point $3R$ is located by transferring D1 from auxiliary view A to the frontal view along its projected line.

In Figure 19.46 point 3 is to be revolved 180° about oblique line 1-2. The following describes the procedure used to solve the problem:

1. Draw H/A parallel to line 1_H-2_H and project auxiliary view A. Axis line 1_A-2_A is true length.
2. Draw A/B perpendicular to the true length axis line 1_A-2_A and complete auxiliary view B. Axis line 1_B-2_B is a point view.
3. In auxiliary view B revolve point 3_B 180° about axis 1_B-2_B to position $3R_B$.
4. Locate point $3R_A$ in auxiliary view A by projection, where it falls on the edge view of the path of rotation. The horizontal view of point $3R_H$ is found by transferring D1 from auxiliary B

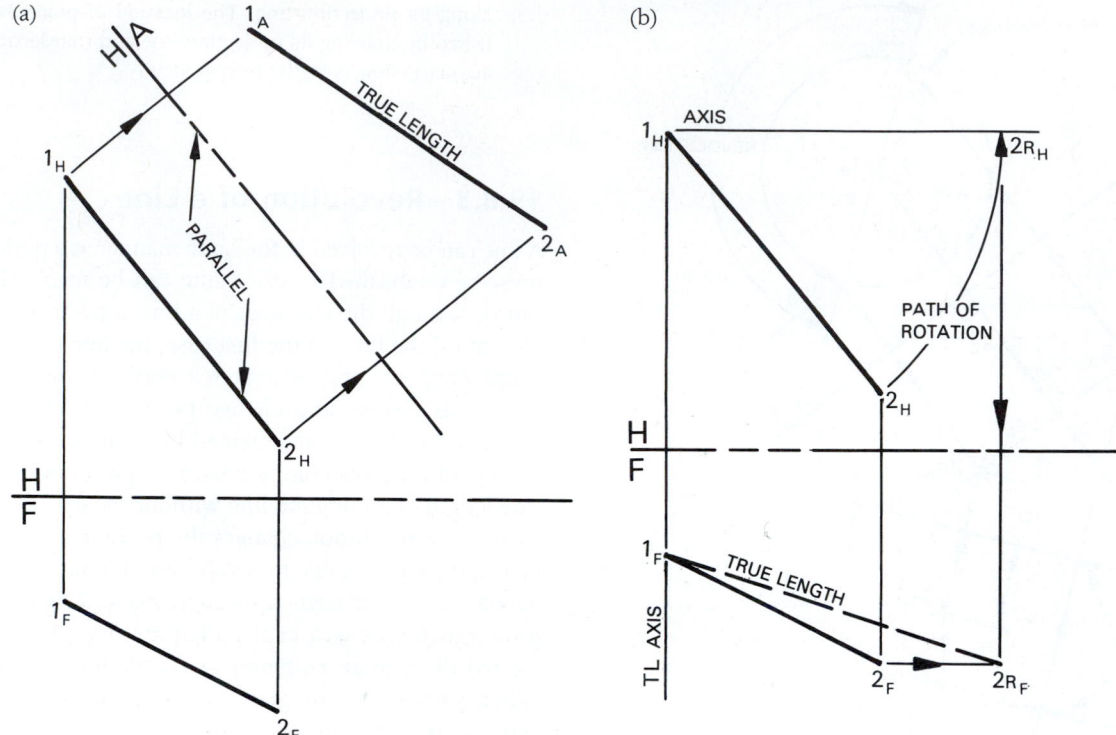

FIGURE 19.47   True Length of a Line by (a) Auxiliary View and (b) Revolution

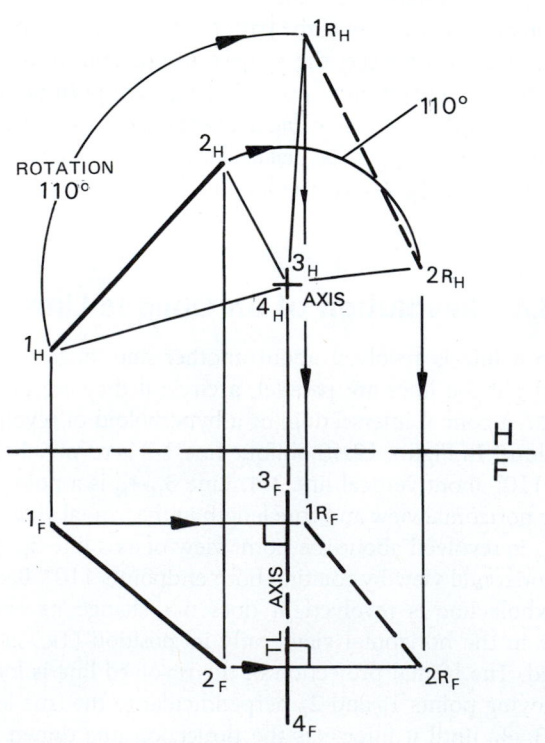

FIGURE 19.48   Revolution of a Line About a Vertical Axis

19.8.5   Cone Locus of a Line

The **locus** of a point or line is the set of all possible points (positions) formed by the movement of the line or point as determined by specified conditions. A circle results if a point is revolved to all possible positions around a given line axis. If the axis is a point, the resulting movement of the point generates a sphere. When a line is revolved into all possible locations about a parallel axis line, the resulting generation produces a cylinder since all lines on the surface are the same distance from the center axis line. When an oblique line is revolved about an axis line that is not parallel to or intersecting the given line, a hyperboloid of revolution is formed.

The most commonly used locus of a line is generated by the revolving of a line about an axis that passes through (intersects) an endpoint of the given line and is called a **cone locus** of a line (Fig. 19.49). The cone represents all possible positions that the line could be in, given a specified angle and a true length element. The true angle that the line makes with the edge view of the path of rotation is called the **base angle** (slope angle). The angle formed by the axis line and given line in a true length position is the **vertex angle.** The true length of the line is called the **slant height.** The slant height and the base form the *true angle* in Figure 19.49.

19.9   Revolution of Planes

The revolution of planes involves the same basic procedure used for revolution of points and lines. Revolution is an ex-

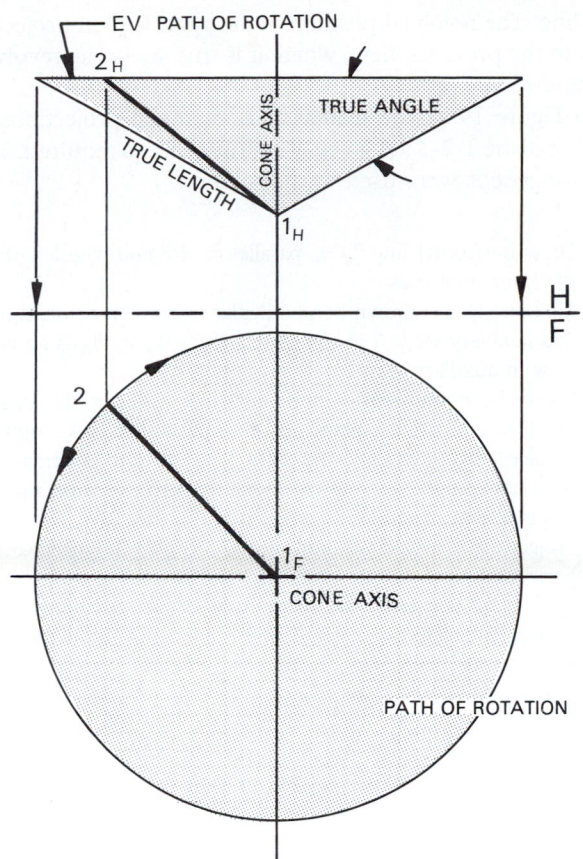

FIGURE 19.49   Cone Locus of a Line

cellent method for solving graphical problems in fewer views by eliminating time-consuming auxiliary projections. A variety of industrial applications involving revolving parts on machinery and aircraft or for showing clearance between moving parts and mechanisms must be solved by graphical revolution.

Revolution of any object (point, line, plane, solid) requires that each individual point that makes up the form be revolved about an established axis line. Each point of a given form is revolved through the same number of specified degrees, in the same direction.

19.9.1   Edge View of a Plane Using Revolution

The edge view of a plane is found in a view where a line in the plane appears as a point view. Normally an auxiliary projection is needed to solve for the edge view of a plane. Revolution can also be used to establish an edge view. By revolving a plane until it is perpendicular to a principal projection plane, its adjacent view will show the plane as an edge.

In Figure 19.50 the edge view of oblique plane 1-2-3 is required. The following steps were used in its solution:

1. Draw frontal line 3_H-4_H on the plane and parallel to H/F. Project as true length in the frontal view. Using point 3_F as an axis, revolve plane 1_F-2_F-3_F clockwise until frontal line 3_F-4_{R_F} is perpendicular to the horizontal projection plane.

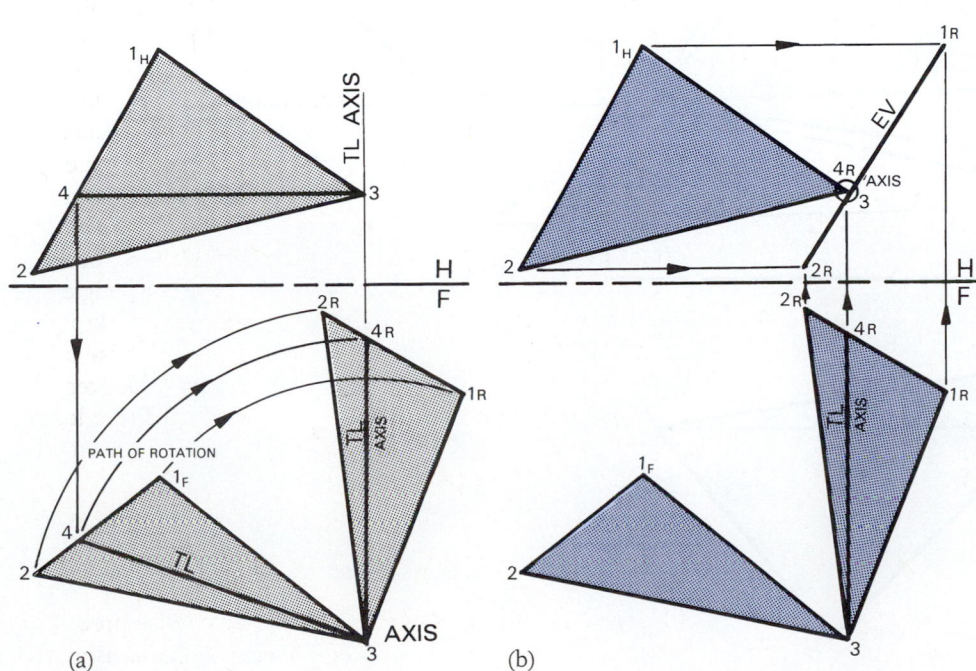

(a)   (b)   **FIGURE 19.50   Edge View by Revolution**

2. Project the revolved position of the plane to the horizontal view. Line 3-4R is a vertical line and appears as a point view. Point 1_{R_H} and 2_{R_H} are located by projection from the frontal view and by moving each point perpendicular to the axis (parallel to the adjacent fold line). Plane 1_{R_H}-2_{R_H}-3_H is an edge view.

19.9.2   True Size of a Plane by Revolution

The true size/shape of a plane can be determined by revolving the plane about a true length axis line that lies on the plane. The plane is revolved about the axis in a view where the plane appears as an edge and the axis line is a point view. The edge view of the plane is revolved until it is parallel to an adjacent projection plane. The revolved plane will then be parallel to the fold line and perpendicular to the line of sight for its adjacent projection.

Given two principal views of an oblique plane, the first step is to project the plane as an edge view. This can be done by establishing a principal (true length) line that lies on the plane in either view and projecting an auxiliary view perpendicular to it. The plane appears as an edge in this primary auxiliary view. The second step is to revolve the edge view of the plane about the point view of the axis line (principal line) that lies on the plane, until the plane is parallel to the adjacent

fold line. The revolved position of the plane is then projected back to the previous view, where it is true size in its revolved location.

In Figure 19.51 the frontal and horizontal projections of oblique plane 1-2-3 are given. The true shape is required. The following steps were used in the solution:

1. Draw horizontal line 2_F-4_F parallel to H/F and true length in the horizontal view.
2. Fold line H/A is drawn perpendicular to horizontal line 2_H-4_H and auxiliary view A is completed. Plane 1_A-2_A-3_A is an edge view in auxiliary view A.
3. Using the point view of horizontal line 2_A-4_A as the axis of revolution, rotate the plane until it is parallel to H/A. Point 1_A revolves to position 1_{R_A} and point 3_A revolves to position 3_{R_A}. Both points move counterclockwise through the same angular displacement.
4. Project the revolved position of plane 1_{R_A}-2_A-3_{R_A} back to the horizontal view. Locate point 1_{R_H} and 3_{R_H} by moving points 1_H and 3_H perpendicular to the true length axis line 2_H-4_H, until they intersect projection lines extended from the revolved points in auxiliary view A.
5. Connect points 1_{R_H}, 3_{R_H}, and 2_H. Plane 1_{R_H}-2_H-3_{R_H} is the true shape of the plane.

You May Complete Exercises 19.13 and 19.14 at This Time

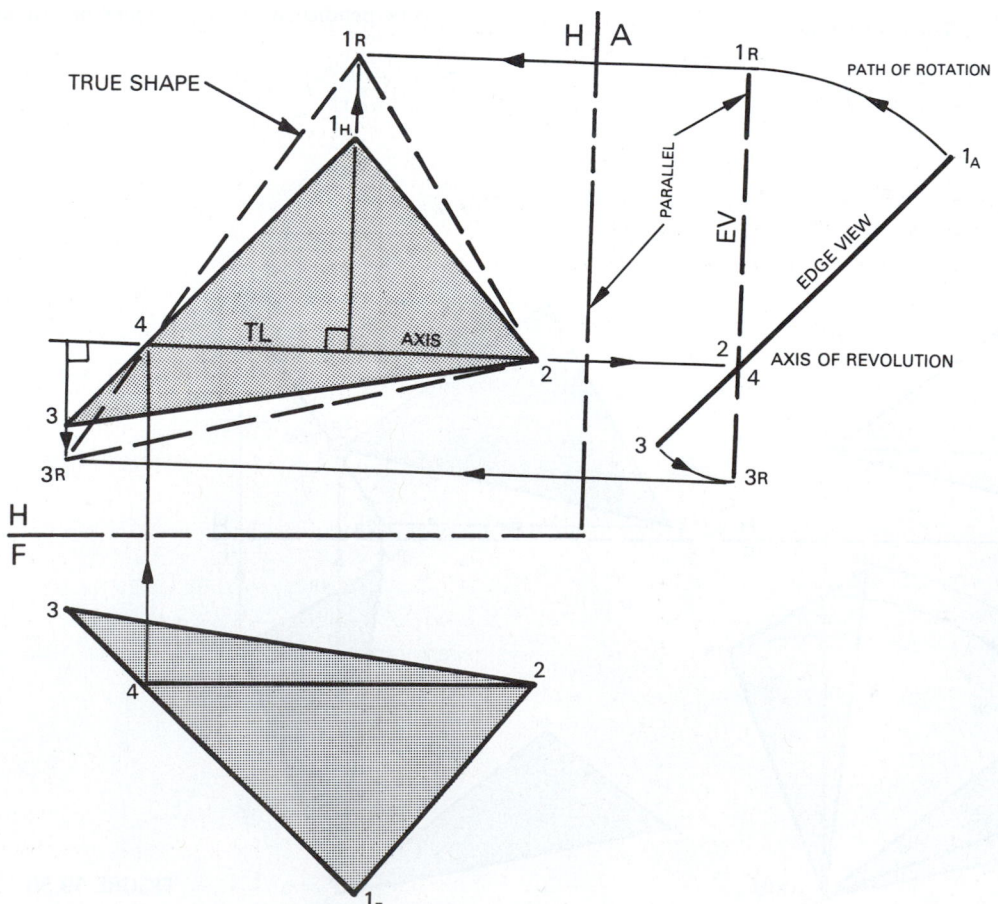

FIGURE 19.51   Edge View and True Shape by Revolution

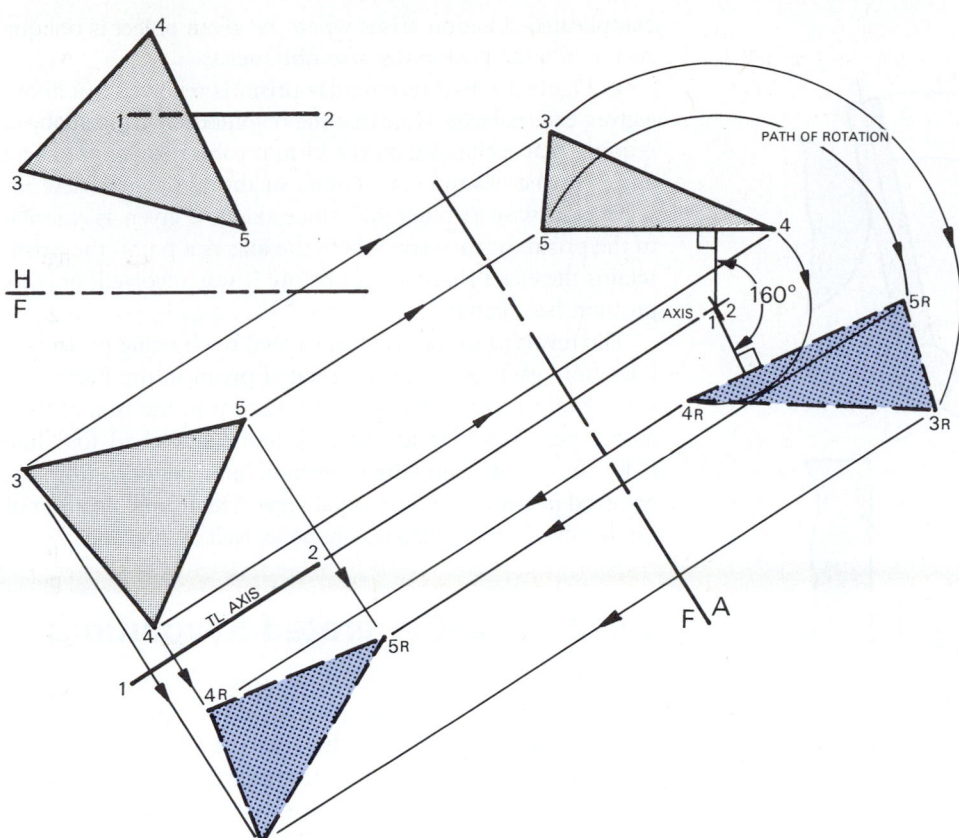

FIGURE 19.52   Revolution of a Plane About a Given Axis

19.9.3   Revolution of a Plane About a Given Line

A plane is revolved about a given external line in a view where the line appears as a point view. The true length of the line must be found before the point view can be established. The point view of the line is projected in a view taken perpendicular to the true length line.

In Figure 19.52 line 1-2 and plane 3-4-5 are given. The plane is to be revolved 160° clockwise about the line. Line 1-2 is a frontal line, therefore true length in the frontal view. Plane 3-4-5 is oblique. The following steps were used to solve the problem:

1. Draw fold line F/A perpendicular to frontal line 1_F-2_F. The line of sight for auxiliary view A is parallel to frontal line 1_F-2_F.
2. Project auxiliary view A. Line 1_A-2_A is a point view. Plane 3_A-4_A-5_A appears oblique.
3. Using line 1_A-2_A as the axis of revolution, revolve every point in the plane clockwise 160°. Since all points of the plane are external to the axis line, they move through the same angular displacement. Plane $3R_A$-$4R_A$-$5R_A$ is the revolved position of the given plane.
4. The revolved position of the plane is projected back to the frontal view where each of its points moves perpendicular to the axis line 1_F-2_F, parallel to F/A. Plane $3R_F$-$4R_F$-$5R_F$ is the frontal position of the revolved plane. Note that the horizontal position of the plane is not shown, but could be located by projection and measurement.

19.10   Restricted Revolution and Clearance

When a machine part or any type of mechanical device must be free to rotate about an axis through a circle or circular arc, revolution is used to find the extent of the piece's movement. The circular arc created by the extreme point of the revolving part determines its *clearance* with surrounding surfaces. The circular plane created by the rotating part scribes an arc, which equals the extreme line of intersection. If the part is to move through its prescribed angular displacement, all surrounding surfaces must lie outside the circular plane scribed by the outer edge of the part.

The lever in Figure 19.53 can move in a circular arc of 132° before it hits an obstruction. Its forward position is fixed by a dowel pin. The clearance between the moving lever and the steel beam is measured as the perpendicular distance between the beam and the circular line of intersection, along a line passing through the axis.

19.11   Revolution of a Solid

A designer may find it necessary to revolve an object/solid about a given axis line. Most often, the object will be revolved to a new position where some operation can be performed on it or with it. Usually, the revolved position shows the object in a normal (true shape) or edge view perspective. A more

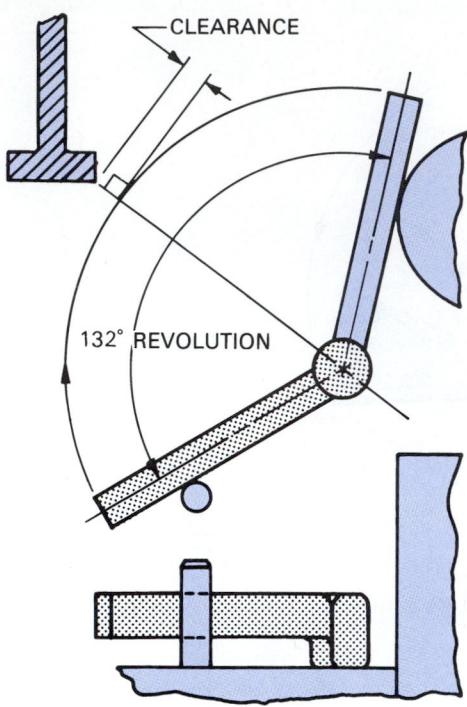

FIGURE 19.53 Restricted Revolution and Clearance

complicated situation arises when the given object is oblique and its rotated position is also oblique.

In Figure 19.54 a rectangular prism is revolved 90° about a given external axis. Note that the revolution of a given object requires that each point on the form revolve through the same angle. In the example, all points in the horizontal view revolve clockwise through 90°, since axis A is given as external to the prism. In the view where the axis is a point, the prism retains the exact shape it had before it was revolved, only its position has changed.

The revolved frontal view is located by drawing projection lines from each point on the rotated prism in the horizontal view. Every point of the given projection in the frontal view moves perpendicular to the axis line (parallel to fold line H/F), until intersecting the projection lines extended from the revolved prism in the horizontal view. The frontal position of the revolved prism changes shape as well as position.

19.12 CAD-Generated Revolutions

2D CAD systems will require the same techniques as described for the manual construction of revolutions. 3D CAD systems enable the designer/drafter to revolve the part into any position by executing the appropriate command. The part in Figure 19.55 is shown in six separate revolved positions. This figure is a wireframe 3D model, which displays all

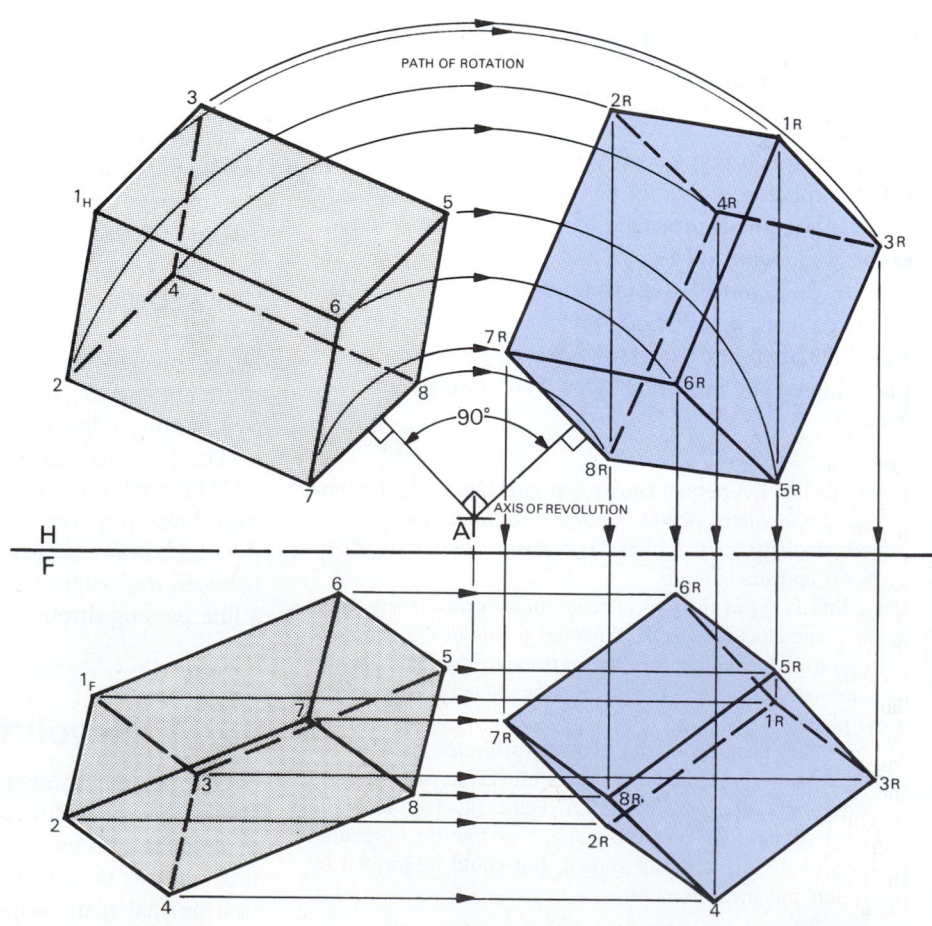

FIGURE 19.54 Revolution of a Solid at a Specified Angle

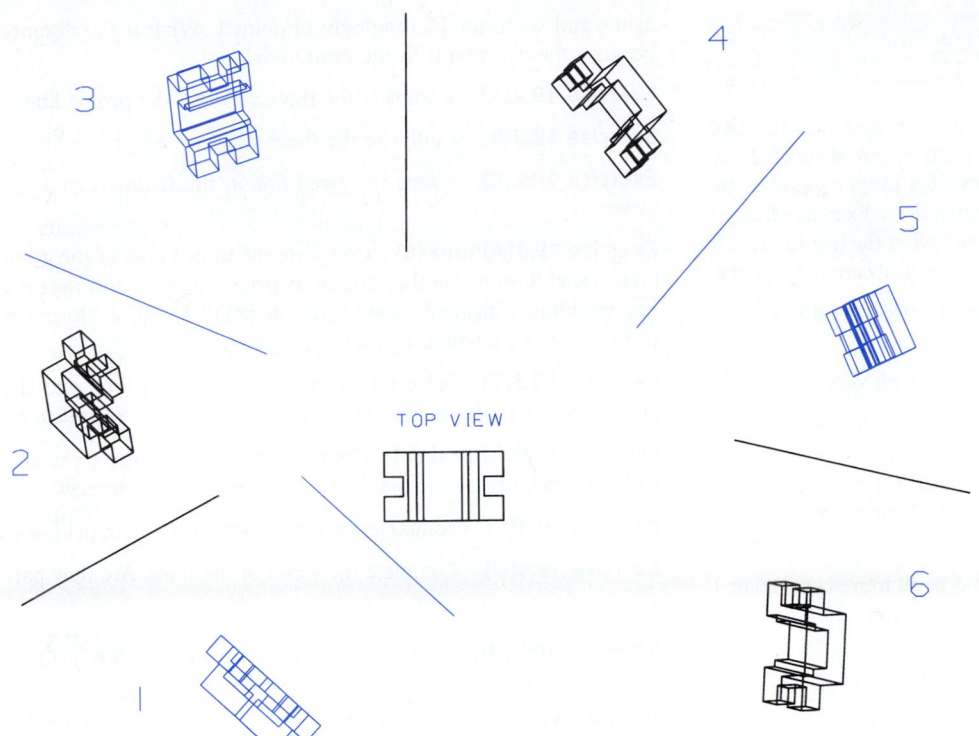

3

4

5

TOP VIEW

2

6

1

FIGURE 19.55   Revolution of a Part Using 3D CAD

edges as visible. The proper visibility is not established for this illustration. Many systems offer a hidden line removal capability that would show the part with the correct visible and hidden lines. Without the hidden line removal capability, the views would require editing to establish proper visibility.

After the original 3D model has been created, the designer can establish an unlimited number of views. The rotated views in Figure 19.55 were created quickly and with a minimum of effort. The manual projection of the six rotated views would have required many hours of effort by an experienced drafter.

You May Complete Exercises 19.15 and 19.16 at This Time

QUIZ

True or False

1. Perpendicular lines show in any view where one or both of the lines is true length.
2. Parallelism of two lines can always be established with only two views.
3. The bearing of a line is measured from the north toward the east or west.
4. Revolutions will in many cases eliminate the need for an auxiliary view.
5. Parallel planes can be determined in a view where both planes project as edges.
6. The shortest distance between two parallel lines can be measured in a view where the lines appear as point views.
7. Oblique lines are never true length in a principal view.
8. The cutting plane method for solving for the intersection of a line and a plane requires only two views.

Fill in the Blanks

9. Two oblique lines that appear _____ in two or more views will always be _____ .
10. The angle between two intersecting lines can be measured in any view where the _____ both appear _____ _____ .
11. Two lines on the same plane must be either _____ or _____ .
12. To establish the angle between a line and a plane, the plane must appear as an _____ _____ and the line _____ _____ .
13. To establish the point of intersection between a line and a plane, project a view where the plane is shown as an _____ _____ .
14. A point view of a line can be projected in a view where the _____ _____ is parallel to a true length view of the _____ .
15. Frontal lines and frontal planes are _____ to or lie in the frontal _____ _____ .
16. The path of a point as it is revolved about an _____ _____ will scribe a _____ arc.

Answer the Following

17. How many views are necessary to fix the position of a point or line in space?
18. Define a vertical line. In what views will it appear vertical?
19. What is the function of an axis line when drawing a revolved projection of a part?
20. What is the bearing of a line?
21. How do you solve for the edge view of a plane?
22. Explain how to solve for the piercing point of a line and a plane.
23. Explain how to check for perpendicularity of two lines.
24. Describe the difference between using 3D CAD for a revolution versus drawing one manually or with a 2D CAD system.

EXERCISES

Exercises may be assigned as sketching, instrument, or CAD projects. Transfer the given information to an "A" size sheet of .25 in. grid paper. Complete all views and solve for proper visibility, including centerlines, object lines, and hidden lines. Exercises that are not assigned by the instructor can be sketched in the text to provide practice and understanding of the preceding instructional material.

After Reading the Chapter Through Section 19.4.8 You May Complete the Following Exercises

Exercise 19.1(A)   Locate the three points in all views.

Exercise 19.1(B)   Locate the following three points in the given views. Point 1 is seven units below point 2. Point 2 is two units behind point 1. Point 3 is three units to the left of point 2. Point 1 is given in the H view, point 2 is given in the F view, and point 3 is given in the P view.

Exercise 19.1(C)   Locate points 1 and 2 in all four views. Point 1 is given. Point 2 is .25 in. (6 mm) in front of, .75 in. (20 mm) to the right of, and 1 .25 in. (32 mm) below point 1.

Exercise 19.1(D)   Locate the following points: Point 1 is four units behind the frontal plane, nine units to the left of the profile plane, and twelve units below the horizontal plane. Point 2 is three units behind the frontal plane, seven units below the horizontal

plane, and seven units to the right of point 1. What is the distance between the two points in the front view?

Exercise 19.2(A)   Complete the three views of the profile line.

Exercise 19.2(B)   Complete the three views of the profile lines.

Exercise 19.2(C)   Locate the given line in the required auxiliary views.

Exercise 19.3(A) and (B)   Complete the three views of the given lines. Label lines where they appear as principal lines, and note if a line is oblique, inclined, true length, or parallel with a projection plane. Show all possible solutions.

Exercise 19.3(C)   Solve for the true length of the line and the point view. Note the bearing of the line. Point 1 is above point 2.

Exercise 19.4(A) and (B)   Complete the views of the pipes and solve for visibility. Shade the pipe that is visible in each view.

Exercise 19.4(C)   Complete the three views of the parallel lines.

Exercise 19.4(D)   Complete the views of the lines. Are they parallel?

After Reading the Chapter Through Section 19.5.4 You May Complete the Following Exercises

Exercise 19.5(A)   Complete the views of the two lines. Line 3-4 shows as a point view in the horizontal view. Are they perpendicular? Note all TL lines.

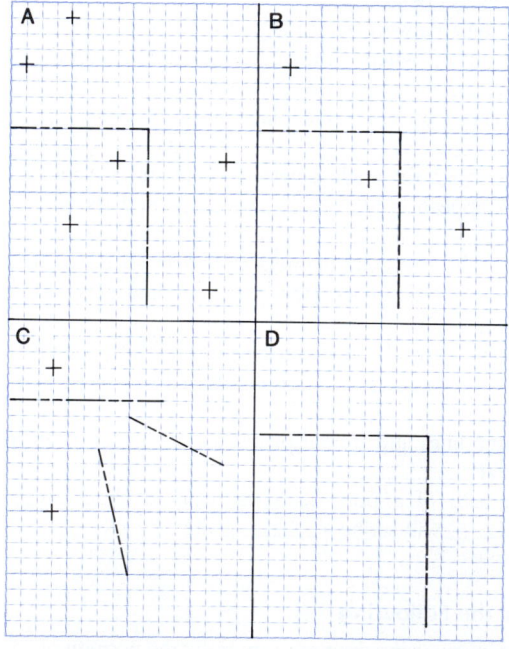

Exercise 19.1

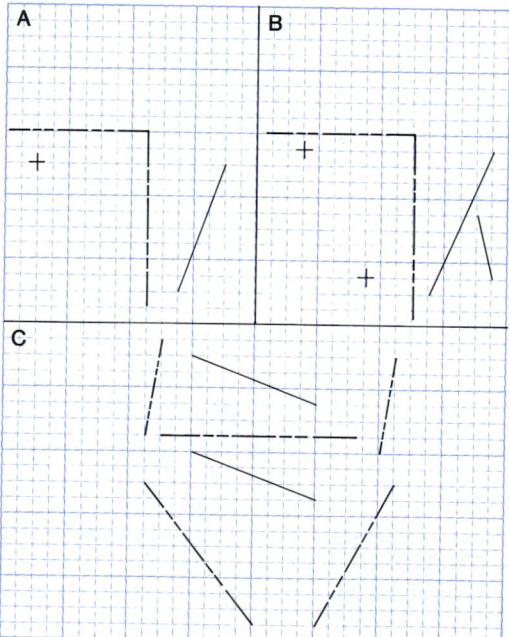

Exercise 19.2

Exercise 19.5(B) Project the three views of the two intersecting perpendicular lines.

Exercise 19.5(C) Construct a line through the point, perpendicular to and on the given line.

Exercise 19.5(D) Draw a line through the point and perpendicular to the line in the horizontal view.

Exercise 19.6(A) Draw the given line in each view and locate the points on the line in each projection.

Exercise 19.6(B) Locate point 3, which is three units to the right of point 1 and lies on the line. Point 4 is eight units below point 1 and on line 1-2. Point 1 is above point 2.

Exercise 19.6(C) Solve for the true length distance between the lines. Show the connector and the point in each view.

Exercise 19.6(D) Find the shortest (perpendicular) distance between the two lines. Project the line back into all views.

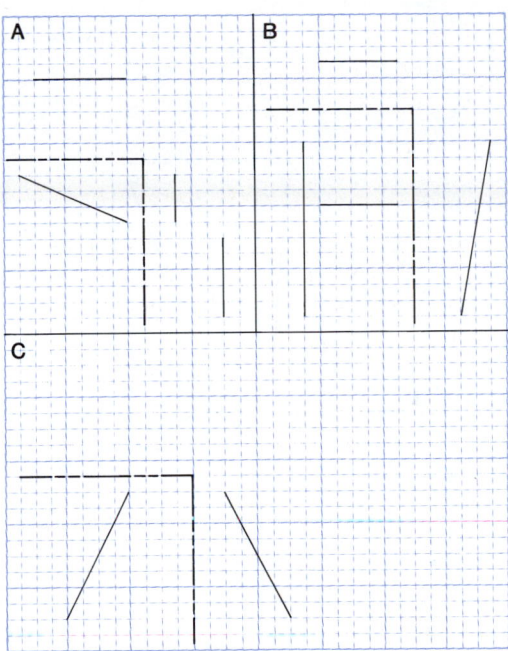

Exercise 19.3

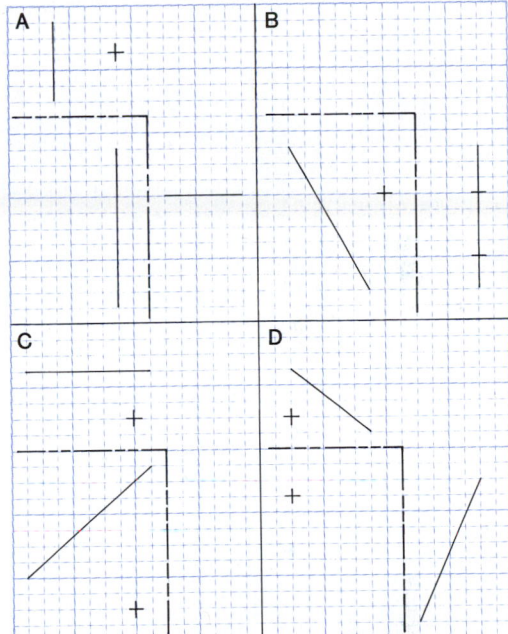

Exercise 19.5

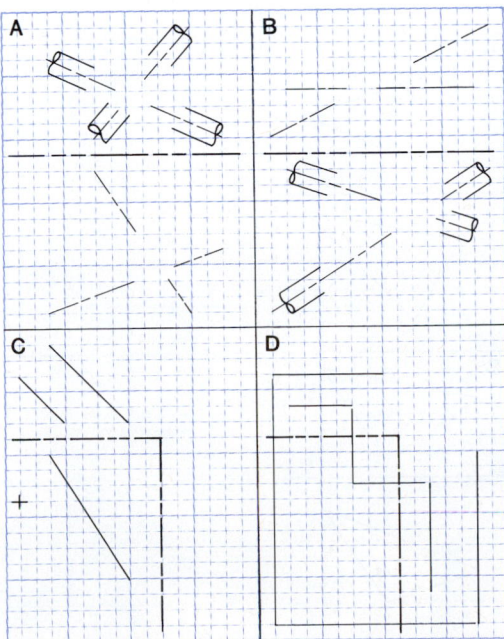

Exericse 19.4

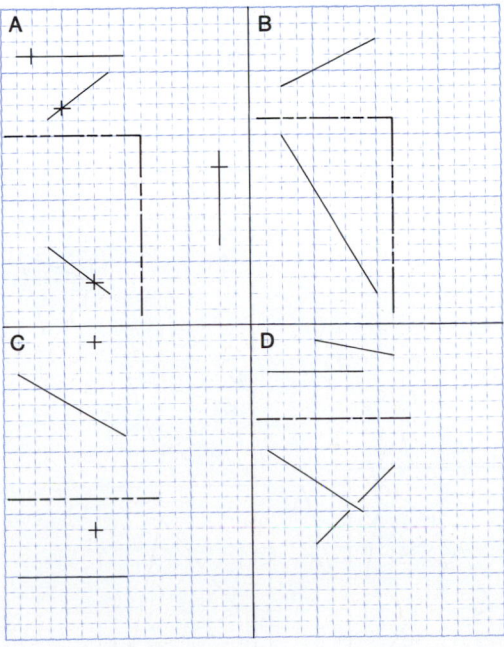

Exercise 19.6

Exercise 19.7 Solve for the angle between the nonintersecting lines. Show the shortest connector in all views.

Exercises 19.8(A) through (D) Complete the views of the planes in each problem. Label for the type of plane: vertical, inclined, oblique, and principal.

After Reading the Chapter Through Section 19.6.2 You May Complete the Following Exercises

Exercise 19.9(A) Project the front view of the plane. Draw three evenly spaced frontal lines on the plane and show in all views.

Exercise 19.9(B) Establish a profile, horizontal, and frontal line on the plane.

Exercise 19.9(C) Show the points and lines on the plane and project in all views.

Exercise 19.9(D) Solve for the EV of the plane.

Exercise 19.10(A) Solve for the largest circle within the plane. Establish an EV view from the horizontal view.

Exercise 19.10(B) Solve for the edge view and true shape of the plane. Project the EV from the frontal view.

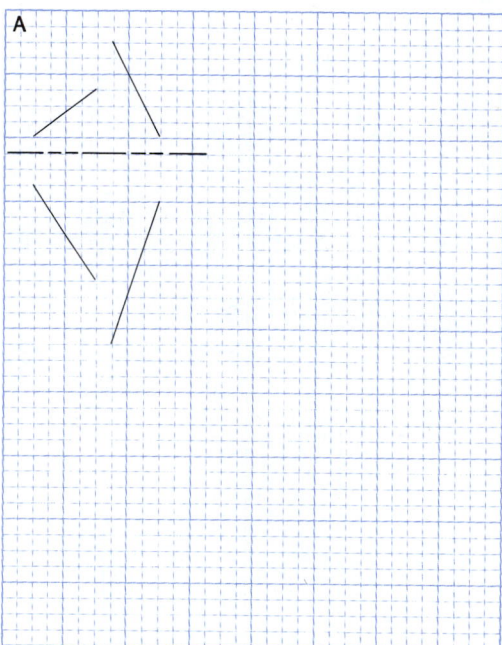

Exercise 19.7

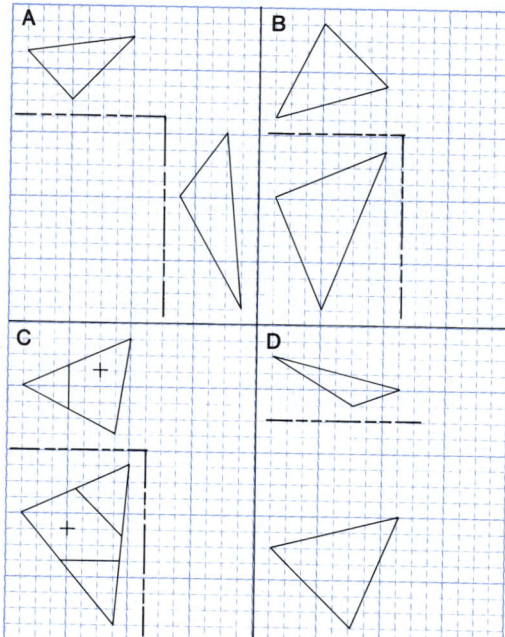

Exercise 19.9

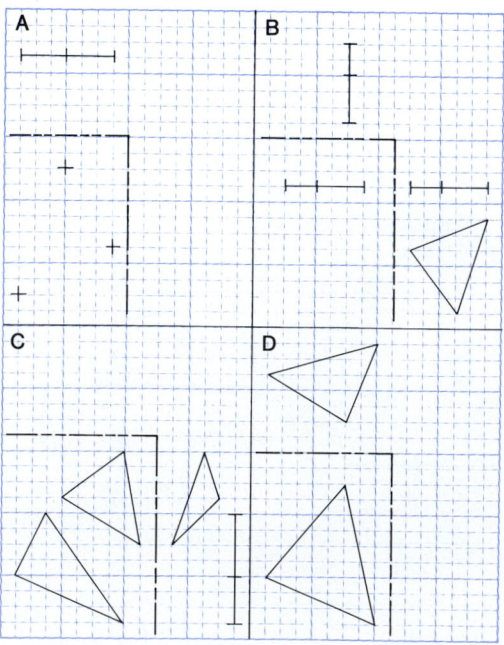

Exericse 19.8

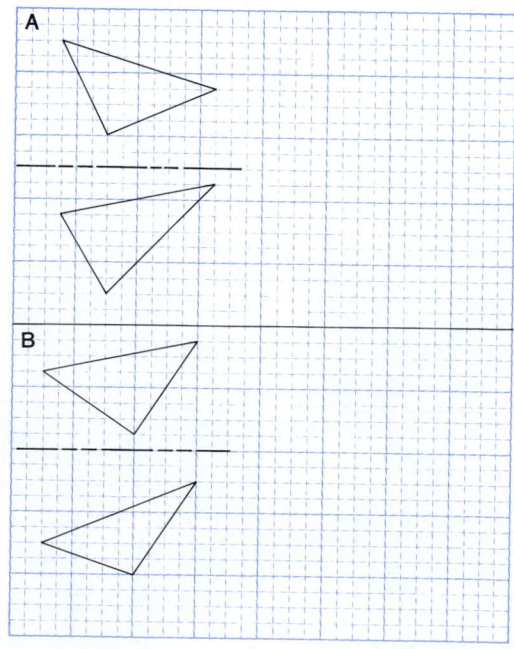

Exercise 19.10

Exercise 19.11(A) Determine the shortest distance between the point and the plane. Show the connecting line in all views. What is the bearing of the line? North is always at the top of the drawing.

Exercise 19.11(B) Construct a plane parallel to the given plane and through the point.

Exercise 19.11(C) and (D) Project and measure the true angle between the two connected planes.

Exercise 19.12(A) and (C) Using the edge view method, determine the piercing point and show in all views along with the proper visibility.

Exercise 19.12(B) Using the cutting plane method, solve for the piercing point of the line and the plane. Complete all views and show the proper visibility.

After Reading the Chapter Through Section 19.9.2 You May Complete the Following Exercises

Exercise 19.13(A) Rotate the point 200° clockwise around the frontal line. Show in all views.

Exercise 19.13(B) Rotate the point around the line 100° counterclockwise.

Exercise 19.13(C) Project an auxiliary view to establish a true length of the given line. Then solve for a point view of the line and rotate the given point 180°. Show in all views.

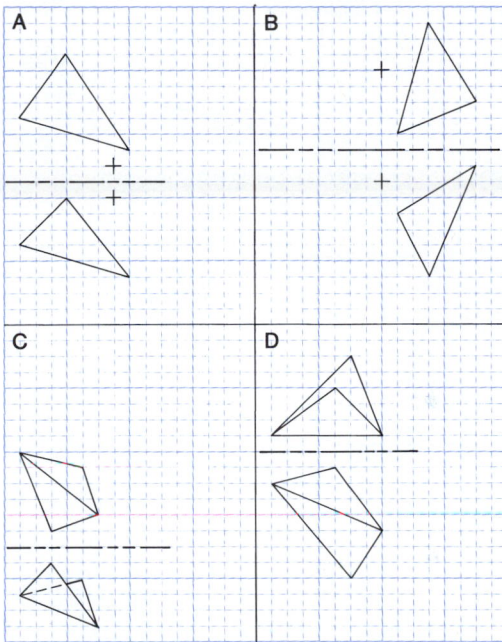

Exercise 19.11

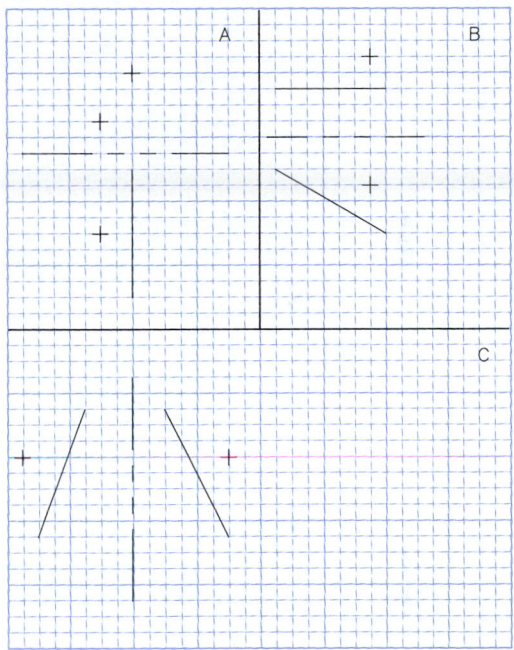

Exercise 19.13

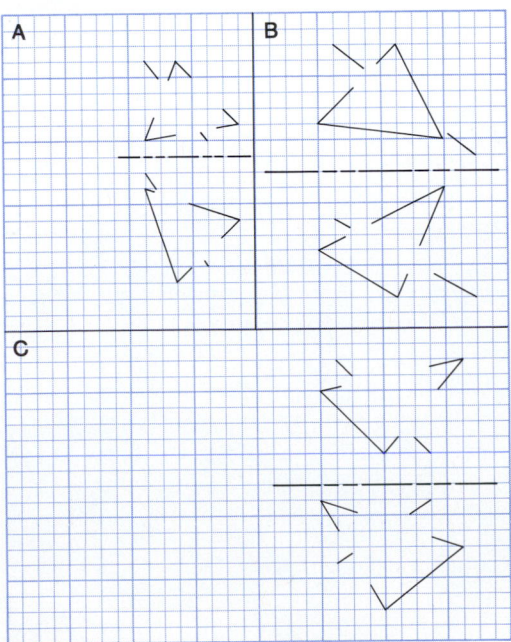

Exercise 19.12

Exercise 19.14(A)   Using revolution, determine the true length of the line and the angle the line makes with the horizontal plane. Verify by projection of an auxiliary view.

Exercise 19.14(B)   Determine the angle between the line and the profile plane.

Exercise 19.14(C)   Using revolution, project and measure the true lengths of the sides of the given figure.

Exercise 19.14(D)   Using revolution, solve for the angle that the line makes with the F view and its true length.

After Reading the Chapter Through Section 19.12 You May Complete the Following Exercises

Exercise 19.15(A)   Solve for the true shape of the plane by double revolution. The edge view will show in the P view.

Exercise 19.15(B)   Using double revolution, solve for the true shape of the plane. The edge view appears in the F view. Construct the largest circle that can be inscribed in the triangle using geometric construction.

Exercise 19.16   Project a point view of the true length line and revolve the plane 90° downward around the line. Show the revolved position in all views.

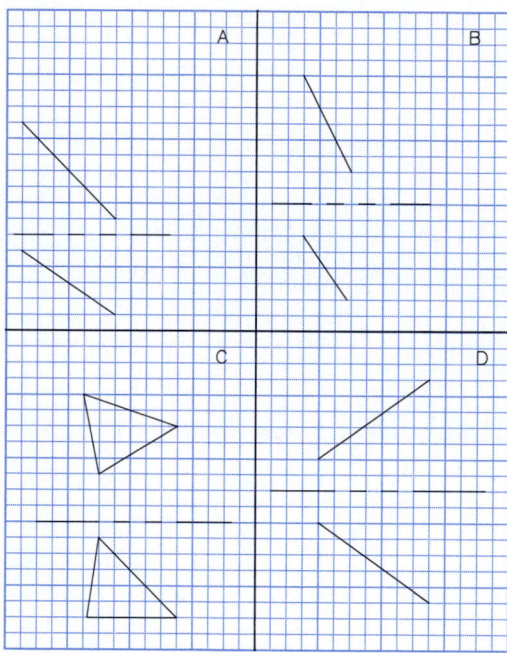

Exericse 19.14

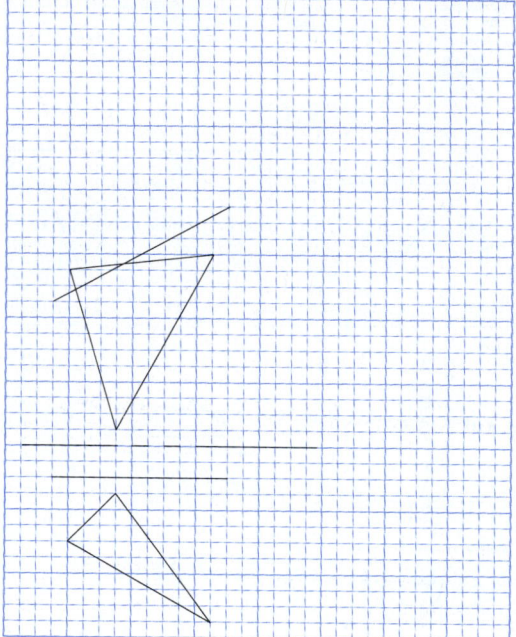

Exercise 19.16

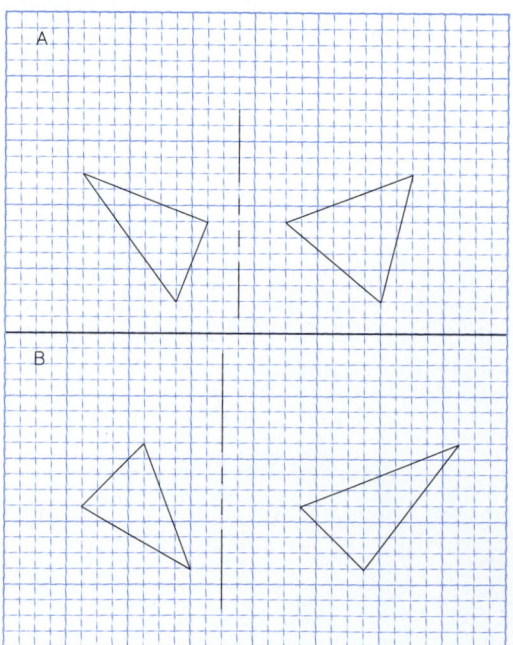

Exercise 19.15

PROBLEMS

Problems may be assigned as sketching, instrument, or CAD projects. For Problems 19.1 and 19.2, transfer the given problem to a separate "A" size sheet. Complete all views and solve for proper visibility, including centerlines, object lines, and hidden lines. Use dividers to transfer the positions of the points and lines. Note that a 1.5/1 scale is suggested but a 2/1 scale could also be used. Two problems can be put on each sheet. Make a rough trial sketch of the problem and the solution before finalizing its position on drafting paper. This will avoid placement of the problem without enough work space to complete the project.

Problem 19.1(A)   Project the profile view of point 1. Locate a point 2 that is .75 in. (1.9 cm) in front of, .50 in. (1.27 cm) to the right of, and 1 in. (2.54 cm) below point 1. Show point 2 in all views.

Problem 19.1(B)   Project three views of the line 1-2. Point 2 is .75 in. (1.9 cm) in front of, 1 in. (2.54 cm) to the right of, and 1.25 in. (3.17 cm) below point 1. If there is a true length projection of line 1-2, label it TL.

Problem 19.1(C)   Complete the three views of line 2-3 and project an auxiliary view showing the line as true length. Take the auxiliary projection from the frontal view.

Problem 19.1(D)   Complete the profile view of line 5-6. Solve for the true length of the line in two separate auxiliary projections and label as TL.

Problem 19.1(E)   Solve for the correct visibility of the pipes. Note that the fold line is not shown.

Problem 19.1(F)   Project the missing view of the two horizontal lines. Are they parallel? Label any true length projections.

Problem 19.1(G)   Construct line 1-2 perpendicular to line 3-4. Point 2 will lie on line 3-4. Project the profile view.

Problem 19.1(H)   Construct line 3-4 perpendicular to line 1-2. Point 4 will be at the midpoint of line 1-2.

Problem 19.1(I)   Project the shortest connector, line 3-4, between the two skewed lines. Point 4 is to be on line 7-8. Show line 3-4 in the H and F views.

Problem 19.2(A)   Project three views of profile line 1-2. Then draw three views of a 1 in. (2.54 cm) line 3-4. The two lines must intersect at their midpoints with line 3-4 appearing as a point in the profile view.

Problem 19.2(B)   Project an auxiliary view of line 1-2 so that its projection will be seen in true length. Label TL. Note the bearing of the line.

Problem 19.2(C)   Project an auxiliary view of plane 1-2-3 where edge line 1-2 will appear as true length. Label all true length edges TL.

Problem 19.2(D)   Determine the bearing and length of the line. The line is assumed to start from point 1. North is at the top of the page. The scale is 1 in. = 50′ (or 1 cm = 30 m). List the answers on the plate as below:

a. bearing =
b. length =

Problem 19.2(E)   Project the true size of plane 1-2-3 and label it TS.

Problem 19.2(F)   Solve for the true shape of the plane. What is the angle between plane 1-2-3 and the F plane?

Problem 19.2(G)   Determine the dihedral angle between the two connected planes.

Problem 19.2(H)   Solve for the angle between line 1-2 and plane 3-4-5. Does the line pierce the plane? Show the piercing point and the proper visibility in each view.

Problem 19.2(I)   Solve for the intersection of the line and the plane.

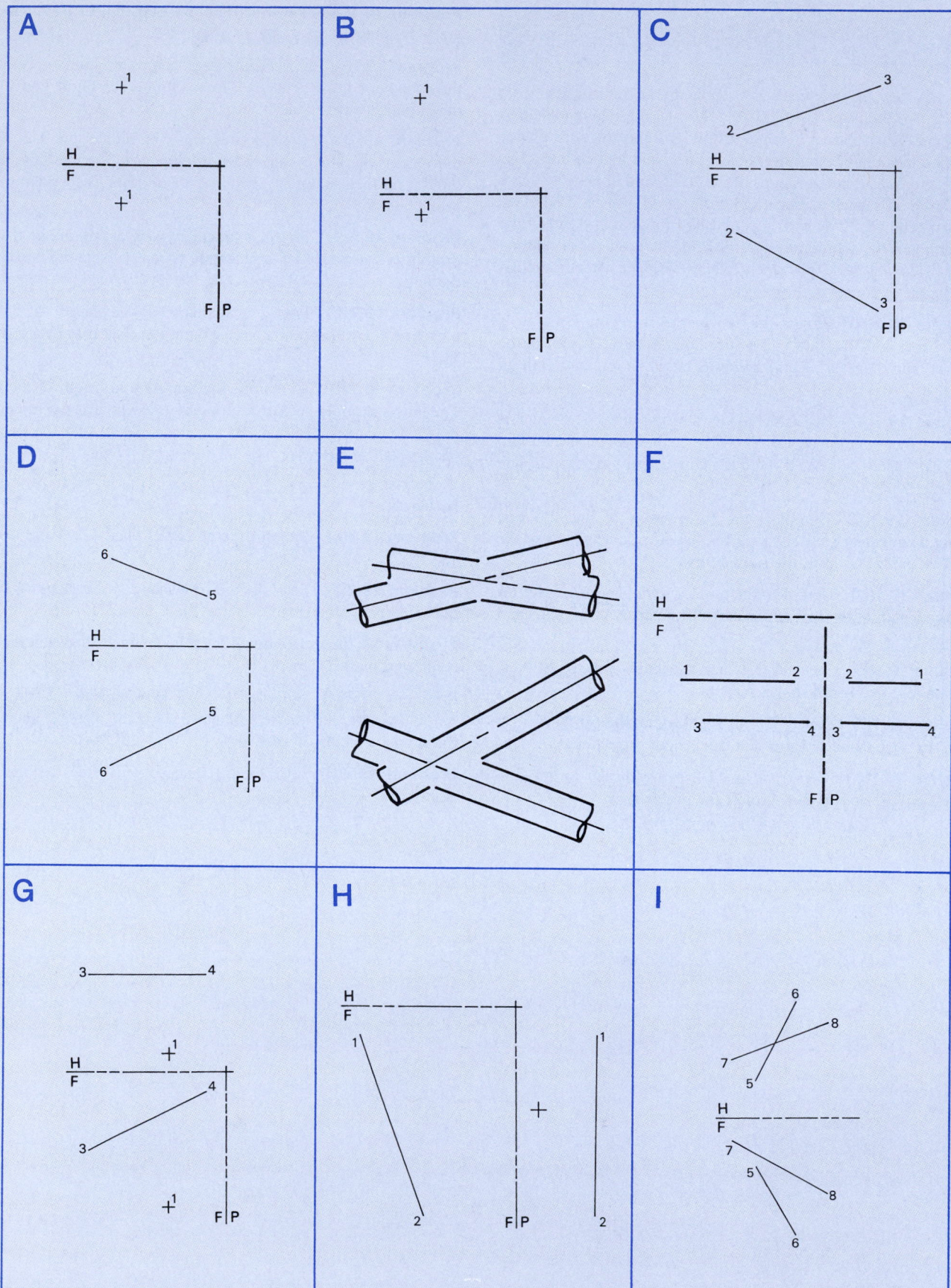

Problem 19.1

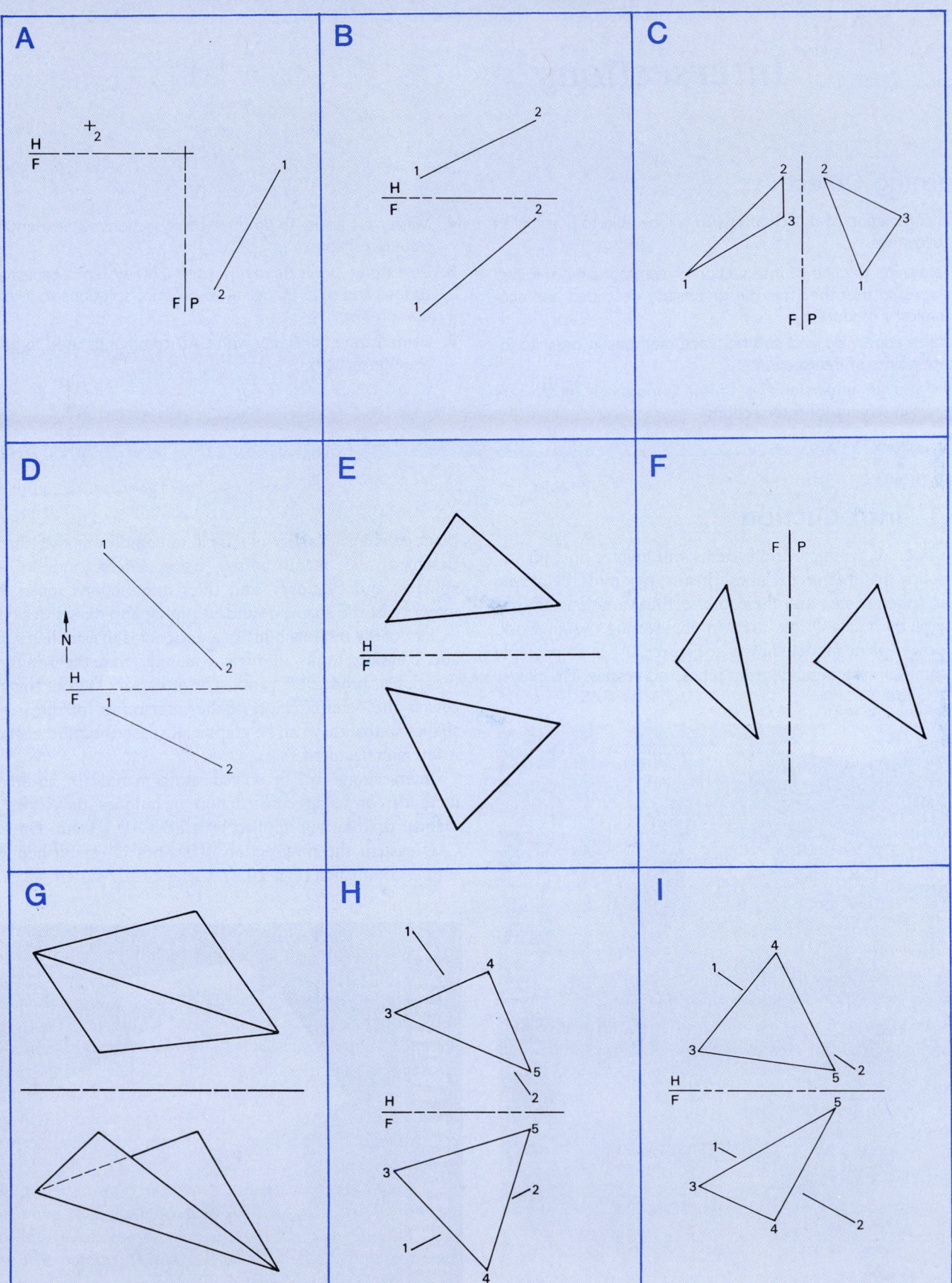

Problem 19.2

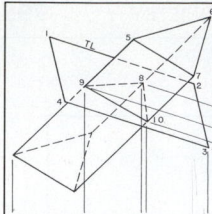

CHAPTER 20

Intersections

Learning Objectives

Upon completion of this chapter you will be able to accomplish the following:

1. Determine the line of intersection or common line of joined shapes so that they may be graphically described and economically produced.
2. Utilize edge view and cutting plane methods in order to locate points of intersection.
3. Develop an understanding of the importance of auxiliary views in solving for intersections.
4. Master the ability to produce conic sections while identifying resulting shapes.
5. Develop an understanding of the CAD system's capacity for surface and solid modeling to produce solutions to intersection problems.
6. Demonstrate familiarity with CAD commands used to generate intersections.

20.1 Introduction

The design of products and systems will involve line, planes, and solids that intersect. Cubes, prisms, pyramids, cylinders, cones, spheres, etc., and their intersecting variations are just a few of the many forms used in engineering design work. The power plant model shown in Figure 20.1 is an example of a complex system made from pipes and vessels. The power plant contains a variety of simple to complex shapes that are designed and manufactured using intersections. Cones, spheres, and cylinders, and their intersections make up a majority of the shapes found in piping and vessel design.

Part of the responsibility of a designer is to establish simple and complex forms in such a manner that the result is a functional, producible product. A necessary step in this process is the determination of the intersection of the various shapes so that they can be graphically described and economically manufactured.

Intersections can be solved using manual or automated methods, or using construction techniques developed for manual drafting but applied by a 2D CAD system. On a 3D CAD system the intersection of shapes is established with simple commands (Fig. 20.2). Using a CAD system gives the

FIGURE 20.1 Power Plant Model

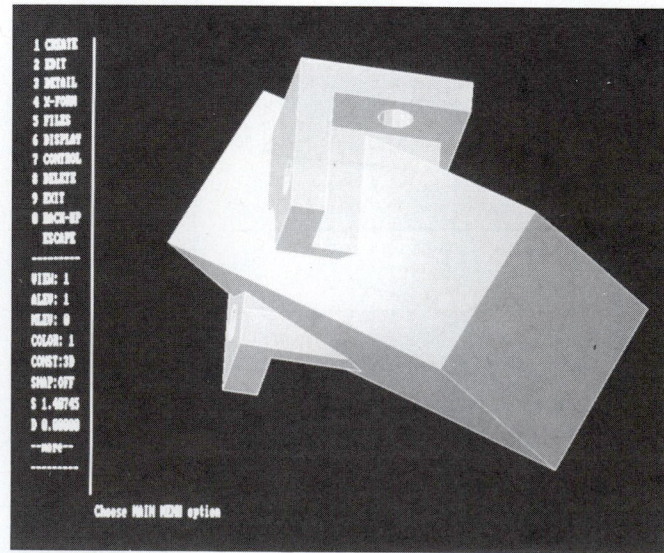

FIGURE 20.2 Solid Intersection

drafter/designer the ability to put a plane through a part at any orientation to create any desired cross section for detail drawings or for establishing the intersection and union of solid shapes.

The intersection of two shapes forms a line of intersection or common line. A basic step in finding the line of intersection between two geometric shapes is to determine the intersection of a line and a plane (piercing point), which was presented in the last chapter. The points of intersection are located by the projection of an edge view of the plane and/or the introduction of cutting planes of known orientation. These two methods may be utilized separately or together, depending on the requirements of the problem.

20.2 Intersection of Planes

The intersection of two or more planes can be determined by finding the edge view of one of the planes. Where any two lines on one plane pierce the edge view of any plane, they will determine the endpoints of the **line of intersection.** Both lines and planes can be considered *unlimited in size or length* for construction purposes. Therefore, both given planes and their line of intersection can be extended as required. The actual intersection of two defined planes will have a limited line of intersection that must be common to both planes.

20.2.1 Intersection of Two Planes

To establish the intersection of two planes, it is necessary to find two points common to both planes. These points of intersection form a straight line. In Figure 20.3 the line of intersection and correct visibility are required. The following steps were used to solve the intersection:

1. Plane 1-2-3-4 and plane 5-6-7 are given. Plane 1-2-3-4 appears as an edge in the frontal view [Fig. 20.3(a)].
2. Lines 5-6 and 5-7 pierce the edge view of plane 1-2-3-4 at points 8 and 9, respectively [Fig. 20.3(b)]. Project these two

piercing points to the horizontal view where they form line 8-9, which is the line of intersection. Visibility is determined by inspection.

20.2.2 Intersection of Two Oblique Planes (Edge View Method)

When the intersection of two oblique planes is required, an auxiliary projection showing one of the planes as an edge is needed. In Figure 20.4 oblique planes 1-2-3-4 and 5-6-7 are given. The following steps were used in the solution:

1. Lines 1-3 and 2-4 are horizontal lines [Fig. 20.4(a)]. Draw H/A perpendicular to line 2-4 and project auxiliary view A. Plane 1-2-3-4 appears as an edge view and plane 5-6-7 is oblique in view A.
2. Line 5-7 pierces the edge view of plane 1-2-3-4 at point 8 [Fig. 20.4(b)]. Line 5-6 pierces plane 1-2-3-4 at point 9. Project points 8 and 9 to the horizontal view where they form the common line of intersection between the two planes, line 8-9. Locate intersection line 8-9 in the frontal view by projection. The portion of the plane formed by line 8-9 and point 5 is in general above and in front of plane 1-2-3-4; therefore, it appears visible in the frontal and horizontal view.

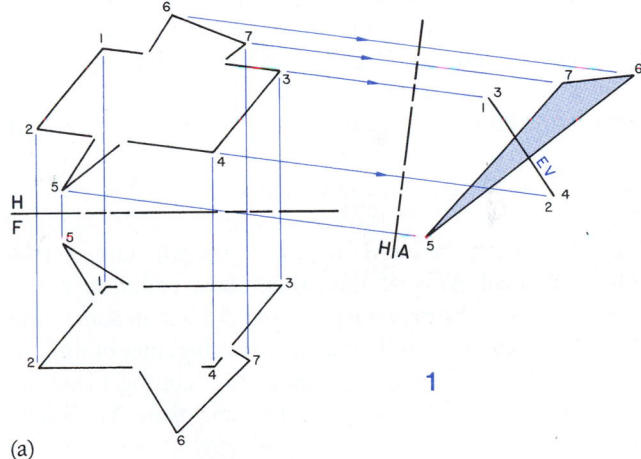

(a)

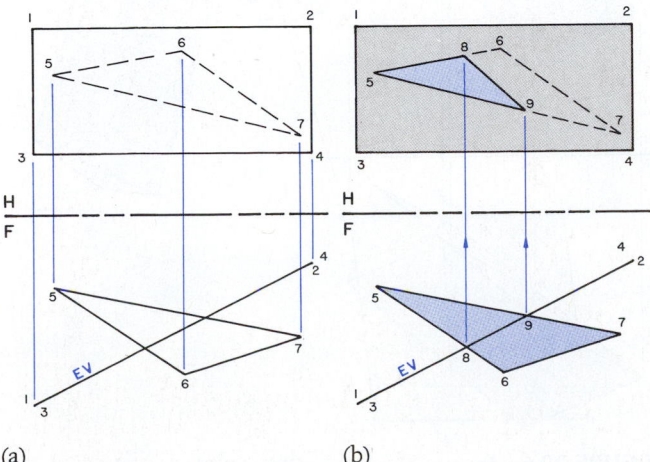

(a)

FIGURE 20.3 Intersection of Two Planes Using the Edge View Method

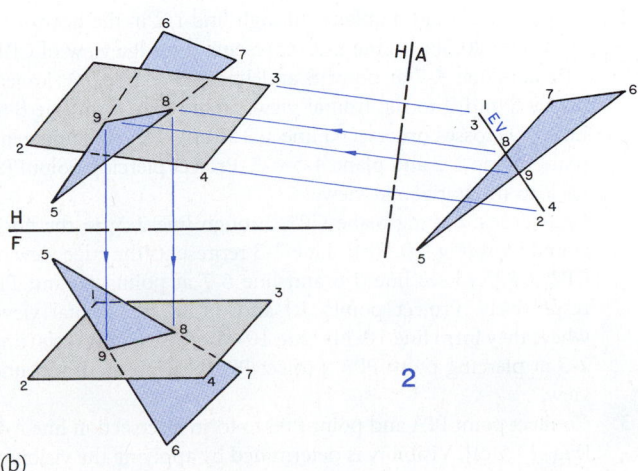

(b)

FIGURE 20.4 Intersection of Two Oblique Planes Using the Edge View Method

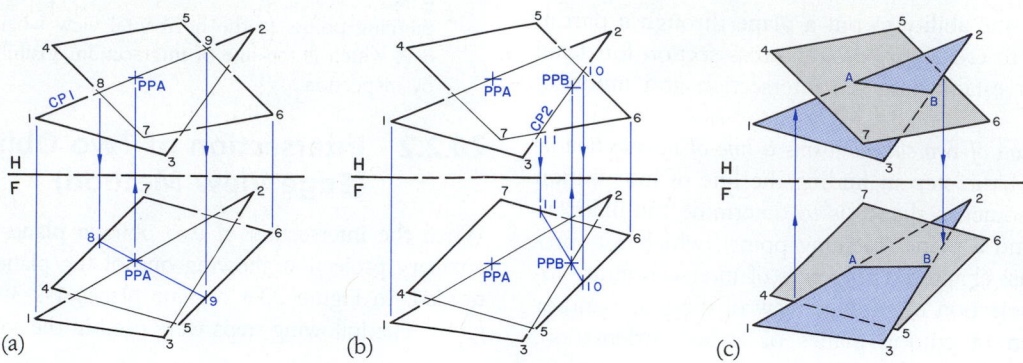

FIGURE 20.5   Intersection of Two Planes Using the Cutting Plane Method

20.2.3 Intersection of Two Planes (Cutting Plane Method)

The cutting plane method for finding the intersection of a line and a plane can be used to establish two common piercing points as covered in the previous chapter. Each piercing point is found individually and then projected to the adjacent view. Using cutting planes to solve for the piercing point of a line and a plane in each view, instead of projecting located points from view to view, is called the **individual line method.**

In Figure 20.5 oblique planes 1-2-3 and 4-5-6-7 are given. Their line of intersection is to be determined using the cutting plane method. Note that some lines make better cutting planes than others. Suitability is determined by trial and error. Some lines will obviously not cross the other plane and, therefore, cannot be used (unless extended). Others cross only very small parts of the other plane and may not be adequate. It may be necessary to extend a line in some cases. Also, cutting planes can be established using lines of different planes in the same view. In Figure 20.5 cutting planes are passed through different lines on the same plane. The following steps were used to solve the problem:

1. Pass a vertical cutting plane through line 1-2 in the horizontal view [Fig. 20.5(a)]. Line 1-2 represents the edge view of CP1. CP1 cuts line 4-7 at point 8 and line 5-6 at point 9. Project points 8 and 9 to the frontal view, where they form line 8-9. Line 8-9 crosses (intersects) line 1-2 at PPA. PPA is the piercing point of line 1-2 and plane 4-5-6-7. Project piercing point PPA back to the horizontal view.
2. Pass vertical cutting plane CP2 through line 2-3, in the horizontal view [Fig. 20.5(b)]. Line 2-3 represents the edge view of CP2. CP2 crosses line 5-6 and line 6-7 at points 10 and 11, respectively. Project points 10 and 11 to the frontal view, where they form line 10-11. Line 10-11 crosses (intersects) line 2-3 at piercing point PPB. Project PPB back to the horizontal view.
3. Connect point PPA and point PPB to form intersection line A-B [Fig. 20.5(c)]. Visibility is determined by applying the visibility test as shown.

20.3 Intersection of a Plane and a Prism (Edge View Method)

An auxiliary view showing the plane as an edge is required if the plane is oblique in the given views. In Figure 20.6 plane 1-2-3-4 and prism 5-6-7 are both oblique in the given frontal and horizontal views. The intersection and correct visibility are required. The following steps were used to solve the problem:

1. Lines 1-2 and 3-4 are horizontal lines (true length in the horizontal view). H/A is drawn perpendicular to line 1-2. Complete auxiliary view A.
2. Plane 1-2-3-4 represents the edge view of a cutting plane in view A. Plane 1-2-3-4 intersects the prism at points 8, 9, and 10. In other words, the edge lines of the prism pierce the plane

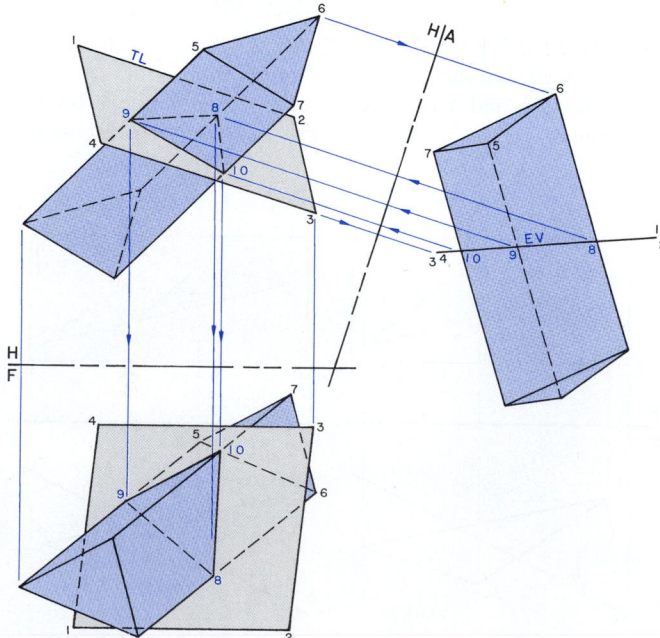

FIGURE 20.6   Intersection of an Oblique Plane and an Oblique Prism Using the Edge View Method

at points 8, 9, and 10. Project all three piercing points to the horizontal view. The horizontal view of the piercing points determines the plane section cut from the prism, which in turn corresponds to the intersection of the plane and prism.

3. Project points 8, 9, and 10 to the frontal view. The frontal location of each piercing point can also be fixed by transferring distances from auxiliary A along projection lines drawn from each point in the horizontal view. This method will ensure the accurate location of the intersecting points, and should be used to check the placement of the piercing points.

4. Visibility is determined by inspection of auxiliary view A and or the visibility test.

20.3.1 Intersection of a Plane and a Right Prism (Cutting Plane Method)

The line of intersection between two surfaces is a common line defined by connected piercing points located by the introduction of cutting planes. In Figure 20.7 the intersection of plane 1-2-3-4 and a right prism is required. The following steps were used to solve the problem:

1. Plane 1-2-3-4 and a prism defined by edge lines 5, 6, 7, and 8 are given [Fig. 20.7(a)].

2. Pass a vertical cutting plane (CP1) through the vertical plane represented by edge lines 5 and 8, and CP2 through edge lines 6 and 7 [Fig. 20.7(b)]. CP1 intersects lines 1-4 and 2-3 at points 9_H and 10, respectively. CP2 intersects line 1-4 at point 11 and line 2-3 at point 12. Project all four points to the frontal view where they form lines 9-10 and 11-12. Line 9-10 intersects edge lines 5 and 8 at points A and B, and line 11-12 intersects edge lines 6 and 7 at points C and D. A, B, C, and D are the piercing points of the edge lines of the prism and the plane. Piercing points A, B, C, and D are connected to establish the lines of intersection between the plane and prism.

3. Vertical cutting planes CP3 and CP4 could be used instead of CP1 and CP2 or as a check [Fig. 20.7(c)].

20.3.2 Intersection of an Oblique Plane and an Oblique Prism (Cutting Plane Method)

The line of intersection of an oblique prism and oblique plane can be located by the cutting plane method. *Cutting planes can be introduced at any angle, in any view.* Vertical, horizontal, and front edge view cutting planes passed through existing lines are the most convenient. In Figure 20.8 the plane and the prism are given. The line of intersection is required. The following steps were used in the solution:

1. Pass vertical cutting plane CP1 through line 4 in the horizontal view.

2. CP1 intersects line 1-2 at point 8, and line 2-3 at point 7. Project points 7 and 8 to the frontal view where they form line 7-8.

3. Line 7-8 intersects line 4 at point 14. Point 14 is the piercing point of line 4 and plane 1-2-3.

4. Project piercing point 14 to the horizontal view.

5. Pass vertical cutting planes CP2 and CP3 through line 5 and 6, respectively.

6. CP2 intersects line 2-3 at point 9 and line 1-2 at point 10. CP3 intersects lines 2-3 and 1-2 at points 11 and 12, respectively. Project points 9 and 10 and points 11 and 12 to the frontal view where they form lines 9-10 and 11-12.

7. Line 9-10 intersects line 5 at piercing point 13. Line 11-12 intersects line 6 at piercing point 15. Project piercing points 13 and 15 to the horizontal view.

8. Connect all three piercing points in both views to establish the line of intersection between the plane and the prism and solve for visibility.

Note that all three vertical cutting planes are parallel in the horizontal view and, therefore, cut parallel lines on the plane in the frontal view.

You May Complete Exercises 20.1 Through 20.4 at This Time

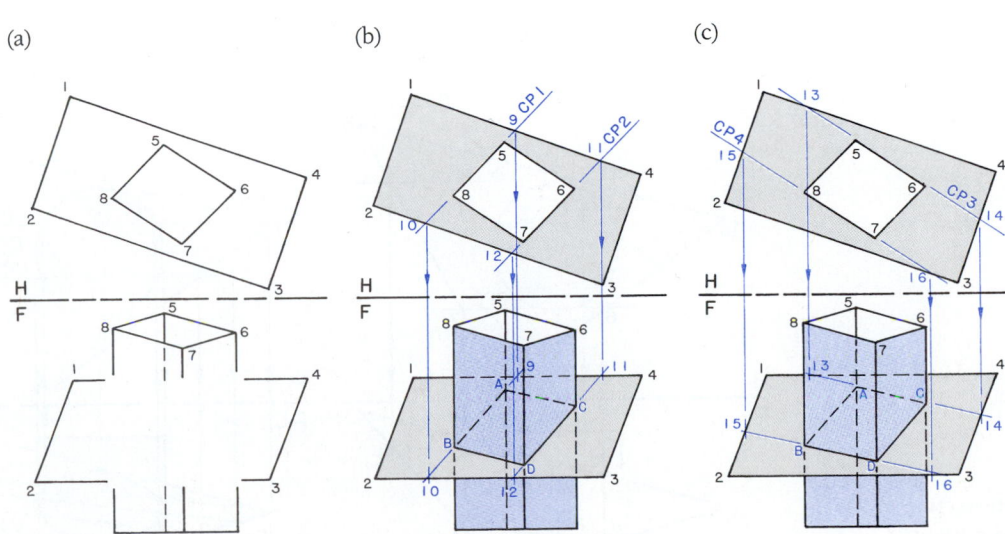

(a) (b) (c)

FIGURE 20.7 Intersection of a Plane and a Right Prism Using the Cutting Plane Method

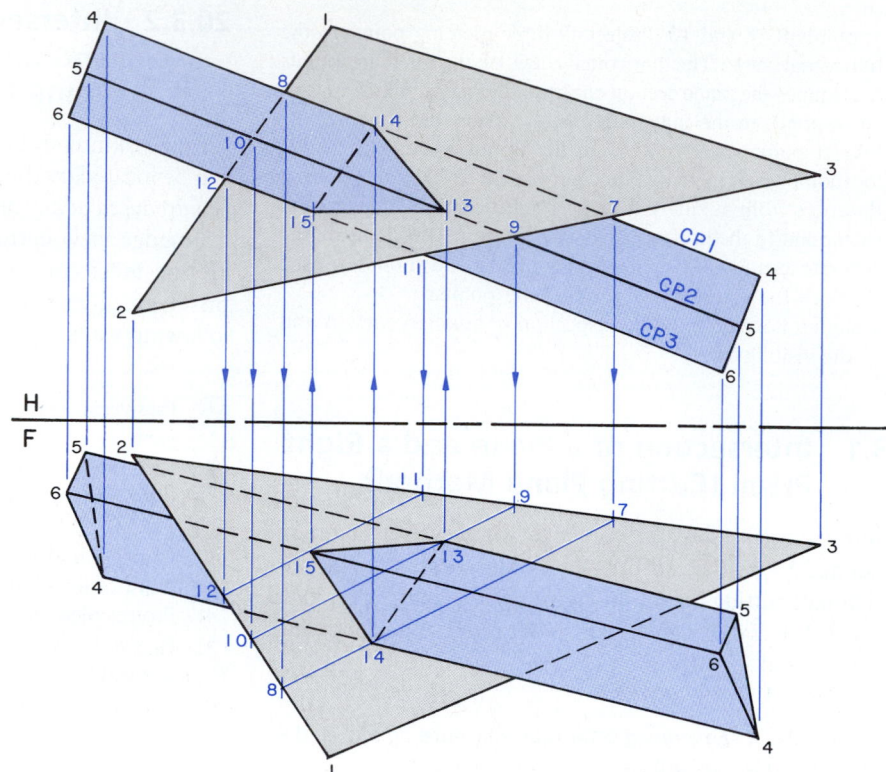

FIGURE 20.8 Intersection of an Oblique Plane and an Oblique Prism Using the Cutting Plane Method

20.4 Cylinders

A **cylinder** is a tubular form that is generated by moving a straight line element around and parallel to a straight line axis. A cylinder is considered to be composed of an infinite number of elements. A right section cut perpendicular to the axis line shows the true shape of the cylinder. Most cylinders are **cylinders of revolution,** that is, cylinders generated by an element moving in a circle, parallel to the axis line. Cylinders are represented by their axis line and two extreme elements.

20.4.1 Intersection of a Plane and a Cylinder (Cutting Plane Method)

The line of intersection of a plane and a cylinder can be determined by passing a series of cutting planes parallel to the axis of the cylinder. Each CP cuts elements on the cylinder, which pierce the plane to form an elliptical line of intersection. Accuracy increases with the number of cutting planes used.

In Figure 20.9 a series of vertical cutting planes is passed parallel to the axis and through the cylinder. Each cutting

(a)   (b)

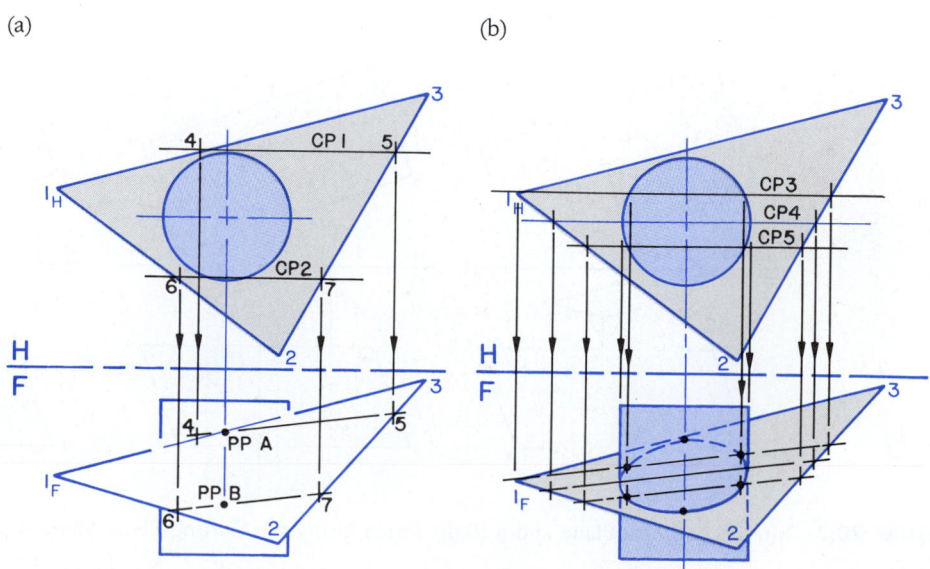

FIGURE 20.9 Intersection of an Oblique Plane and a Right Cylinder Using the Cutting Plane Method

plane establishes two elements on the cylinder and a line on the plane. Where these related lines and elements intersect, they establish the required piercing points. The following steps were used to solve the problem:

1. Draw CP1 and CP2 parallel to the axis line (and parallel to the H/F fold line) [Fig. 20.9(a)]. CP1 intersects line 1-3 at point 4 and line 2-3 at point 5. CP2 intersects line 1-2 at point 6 and line 2-3 at point 7. Both CPs establish an element on the cylinder. Project the elements to the frontal view along with lines 4-5 and 6-7. Line 4-5 intersects its element at piercing point A and line 6-7 intersects its corresponding element at point B.
2. Repeat step 1 using CP3, CP4, and CP5 [Fig. 20.9(b)]. Note that each of these cutting planes cuts *two* elements on the cylinder. Therefore, each locates two piercing points. Connect the piercing points in sequence to form a smooth curve. Since point 2 is in front of the cylinder, lines 1-2 and 2-3 are visible, as is point B.

20.5   Cones

A **cone** is a single-curved surface formed by line segments/elements connecting the vertex with all points on the perimeter of the base. Figure 20.10 shows a solid cone generated on a CAD system. A cone is generated by the movement of a

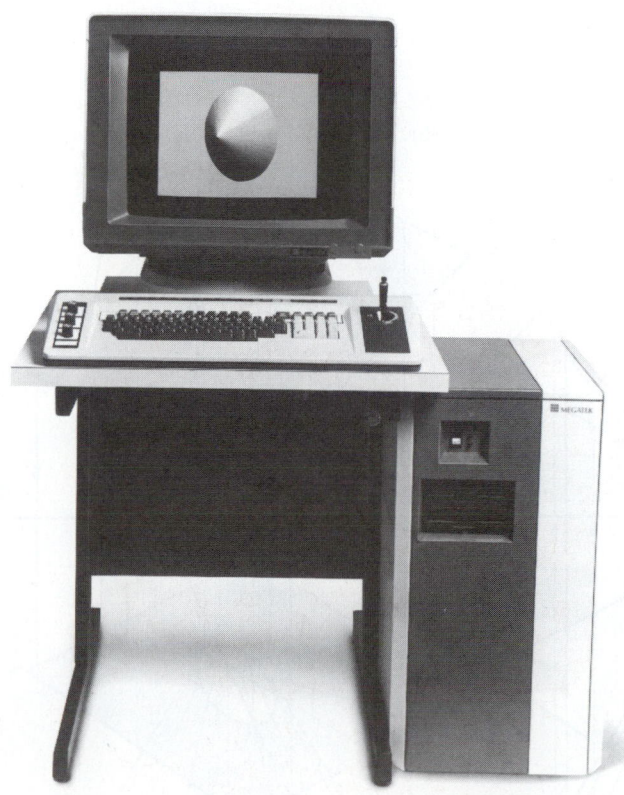

FIGURE 20.10   **Solid Model of a Cone Generated on a CAD System**

straight line element passed through the vertex and moving around the boundary of the base. A cone generated by a right triangle rotating about one of its legs is a **right cone** or **cone of revolution**. If a right section cut from the cone is an ellipse, the cone is an **elliptical cone**. A cone with a circular base whose right section is an ellipse is sometimes referred to as an **oblique circular cone**. If a cone is cut below its vertex, it is termed a **truncated cone**.

20.5.1   Conic Sections

The intersection of a plane and a right cone is called a **conic section**. Five types of shapes can result from this intersection (Fig. 20.11).

1. **Parabola**   A plane parallel to an extreme element of the cone, therefore forming the same base angle, cuts a parabola (1).
2. **Hyperbola**   A plane passed through the cone, at a greater angle than the base angle results in a hyperbola (2).
3. **Ellipse**   A plane that cuts all the elements of the cone, but is not perpendicular to the axis, forms a true ellipse (3).
4. **Isosceles triangle**   A plane passed through the vertex cuts an isosceles triangle (the frontal view).
5. **Circle**   A plane passed perpendicular to the axis forms a circular intersection. A series of horizontal cutting planes has been introduced in the frontal view, which project as circles in the horizontal view (Fig. 20.11).

The intersection of a cone and a plane is established by passing a series of horizontal cutting planes perpendicular to the axis of the cone. In Figure 20.11 the frontal and horizontal views of the cone are given along with the edge view of three theoretical unlimited planes that intersect the cone. The horizontal view and the true shape of each intersection are required. The following steps were used to solve the problem:

1. Pass a series of evenly spaced horizontal cutting planes through the cone, CP1 through CP12.
2. Each cutting plane projects as a circle in the horizontal view.
3. EV1 intersects cutting planes 3 through 12 in the frontal view. Project each intersection point to the horizontal view. The intersection of EV1 and the cone forms a parabola.
4. The true shape of the parabola is seen in a view projected parallel to EV1. The centerline of the parabola is drawn parallel to EV1 and the intersection points of the plane (EV1) and each cutting plane are projected from the frontal view. Distances are transferred from the horizontal view, as is dimension A.
5. Repeat steps 3 and 4 to establish the intersection of EV2 and EV3 with the cone. EV2 projects as a line in the horizontal view and as a hyperbola in a true shape view (2). EV3 forms an ellipse in the horizontal view and projects as a true ellipse in a true shape view (3).

20.5.2   Intersection of an Oblique Plane and a Cone (Cutting Plane Method)

The cutting plane method can be used to determine the intersection of a plane and a cone if the plane is oblique in its given views. A series of evenly spaced vertical cutting planes

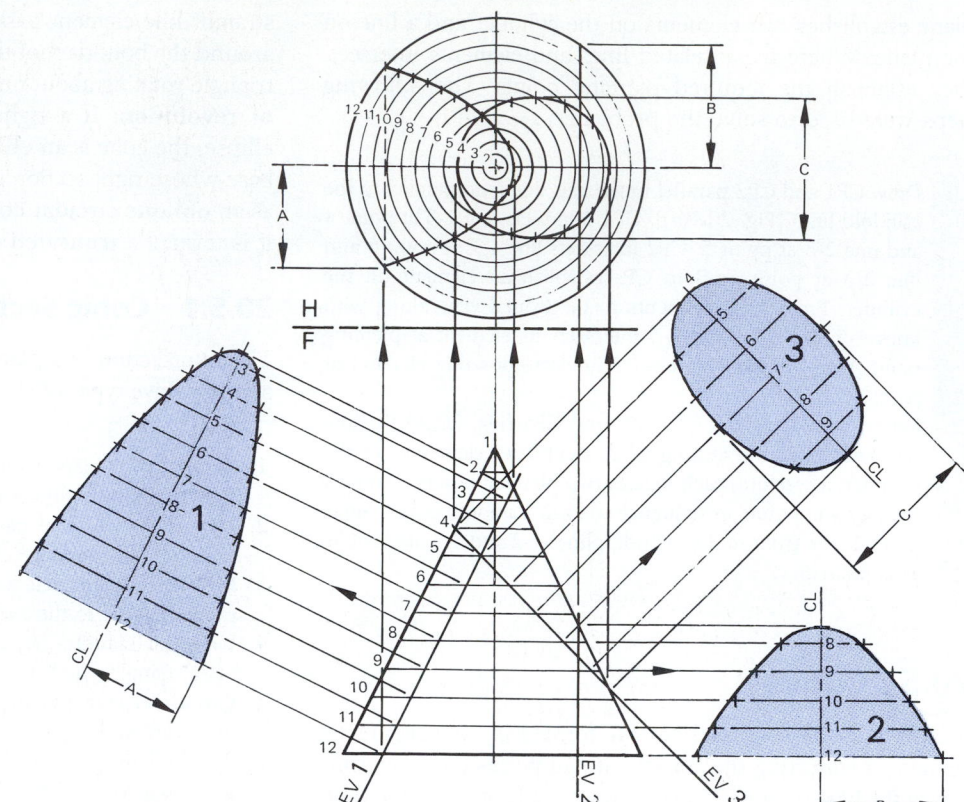

FIGURE 20.11 Conic Sections
The intersection of a plane and a right cone forms one of the following: (1) parabola, (2) hyperbola, and (3) ellipse.

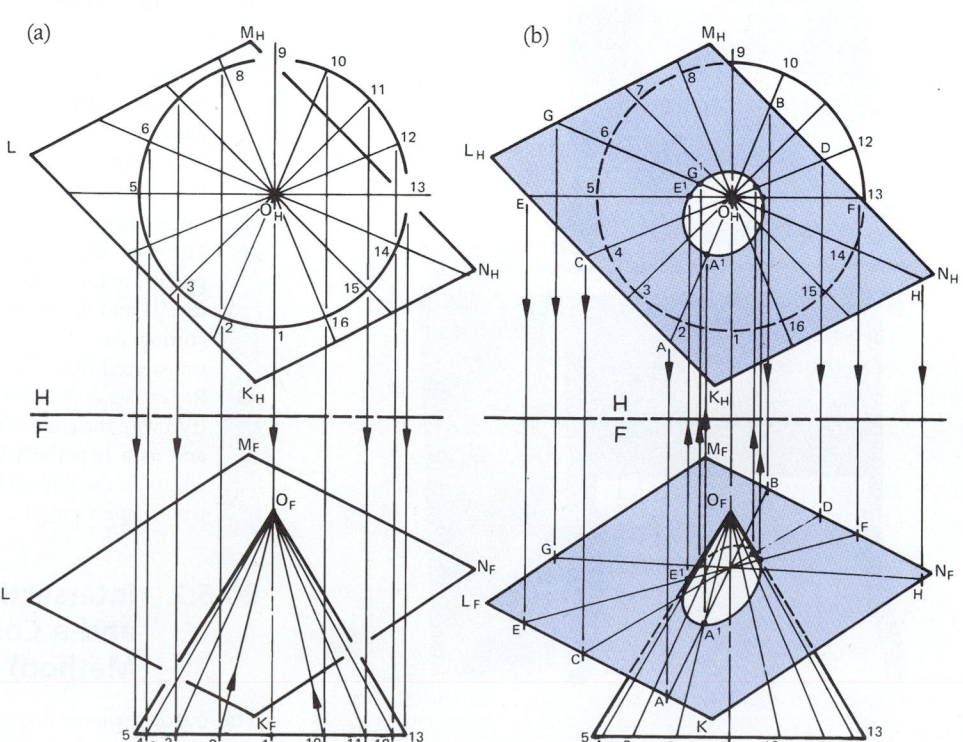

FIGURE 20.12 Intersection of an Oblique Plane and a Right Cone Using the Cutting Plane Method

is passed through the vertex of the cone and the plane. The cutting planes intersect the cone and the plane as straight line elements (lines) that lie on the plane. Each element intersects its corresponding line along the line of intersection of the plane and the cone. The point at which an element intersects its corresponding line on the plane locates a point on the line of intersection. This intersection point lies on the plane and on the cone's surface.

In Figure 20.12 oblique plane K-L-M-N and the right cone are given and their intersection line is required. The following steps were used in the solution:

1. Pass a series of evenly spaced vertical cutting planes through the cone's vertex [Fig. 20.12(a)]. Project the elements to the frontal view and label as shown.

2. Each element corresponds to a cutting plane that intersects the cone and the plane [Fig. 20.12(b)]. As an example, a cutting plane passed through the cone and intersecting the plane forms elements $0_H\text{-}2_H$ and $0_H\text{-}10_H$, and also intersects the plane at points A_H and B_H. Points A_H and B_H form line $A_H\text{-}B_H$, which lies on the plane and represents the intersection of the cutting plane and the given plane. Line A-B is projected to the frontal view where it intersects element $0_F\text{-}2_F$ at piercing point A^1. Each line formed by the intersection of the cutting plane and the plane intersects two corresponding elements on the cone. The line of intersection is determined by connecting the piercing points with a smooth curve. The piercing points are projected to the horizontal view to locate the line of intersection in that view. Visibility is then determined for both views using inspection or the visibility check.

FIGURE 20.13   Space Station

20.6   Spheres

A **sphere** can be defined as a geometric form bounded by a surface containing all possible points at a given distance from a given point. A sphere is generated by rotating a circle around an axis line that passes through the sphere's center. Spheres are **double-curved surfaces** and contain no straight lines. Spheres are represented as circles equal to their diameter in all projections.

Spheres or portions of spheres are found in the design of a variety of industrial products, consumer goods, toys, buildings, and vessels. In Figure 20.13 the space station uses cylindrical and spherical shapes in its design.

A plane passed through the center of a sphere and at an angle to the adjacent projection plane creates an elliptical line of intersection [A and B in Fig. 20.14(a)]. This type of intersection is known as a **great circle** of a sphere. A plane passed parallel to the adjacent projection plane and not through its center cuts a **small circle** [C and D in Fig. 20.14(b)].

20.6.1   Intersection of a Plane and a Sphere

The intersection of a plane and a sphere results in a **circular line of intersection.** If the plane is inclined, the line of intersection appears as an ellipse (Fig. 20.15). The extreme

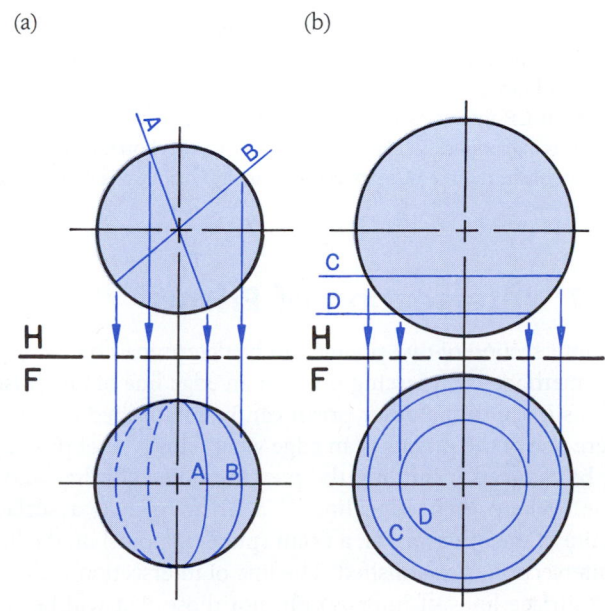

FIGURE 20.14   Great and Small Circles of a Sphere

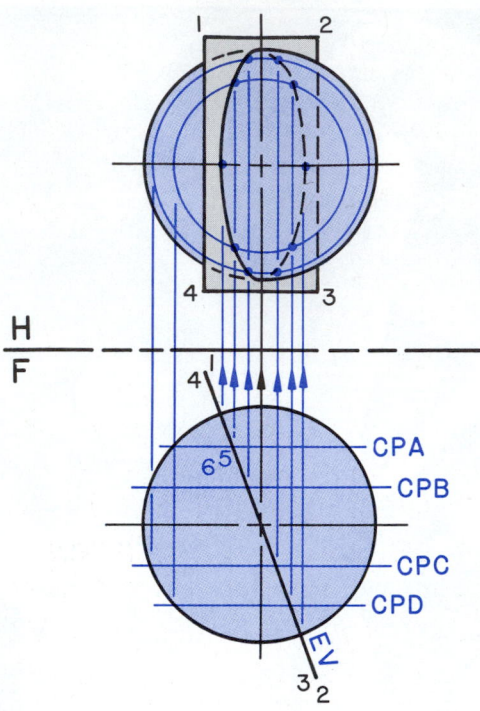

FIGURE 20.15 Intersection of a Plane and a Sphere Using Cutting Planes

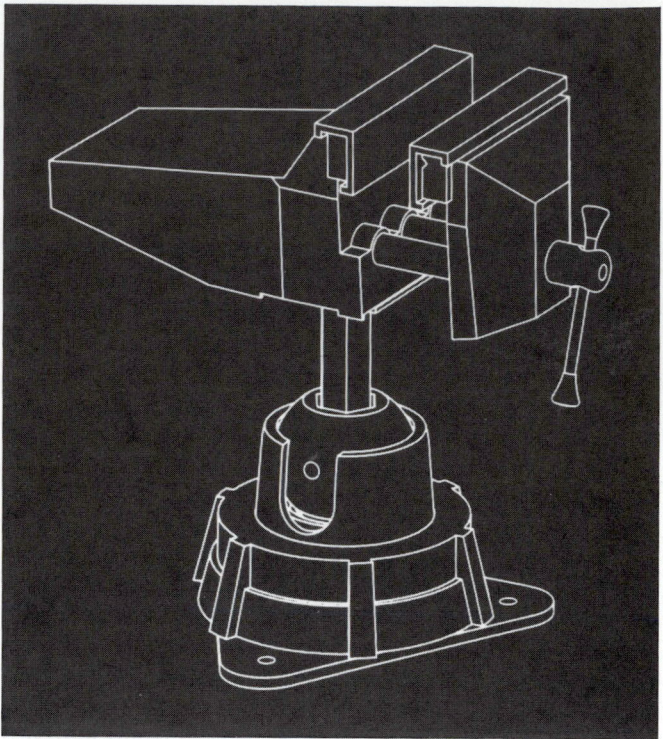

FIGURE 20.16 3D Model of a Vise

piercing points and, therefore, the major and minor axes must first be found using the edge view or cutting plane method. The actual ellipse can be constructed by means of an ellipse template using the major and minor axes, plotting a series of piercing points established by cutting planes in a view showing the plane as an edge, or passing a series of cutting planes through the sphere and the plane where the plane is inclined.

In Figure 20.15 the intersection of the sphere and plane is required. The following steps were used to solve the problem:

1. Pass a series of evenly spaced horizontal cutting planes through the sphere and project to the horizontal view. Each CP cuts a small circle section.
2. Each CP intersects the edge view of the plane and locates two piercing points, which are projected to the horizontal view to establish the line of intersection. Finally, visibility is determined.

20.7 Intersection of Prisms

The intersection of two prisms can be determined by the edge view method. The piercing point of an edge line of one prism and a surface of the other prism can be established in a view where one of the prisms is an edge view. This type of problem can be reduced to finding the piercing point of a line and a plane. Where each edge line of a prism pierces a surface (plane) of the other prism, a point (piercing point) on the line of intersection is established. The line of intersection includes only surface lines of intersection, not those that will be "inside" the prisms. Figure 20.16 is an example of an assembly

pictorial of a vise drawn with a CAD system. A variety of intersections was required in this design.

In Figure 20.17 two right prisms intersect at right angles. The horizontal view shows the edge view of the rectangular prism and the profile view shows the triangular prism as an edge view. The following steps were used in the solution:

1. The edges of the triangular horizontal prism pierce the vertical prism in the horizontal view at points 1 through 6. Edge line A pierces the surface bounded by lines D and G at piercing

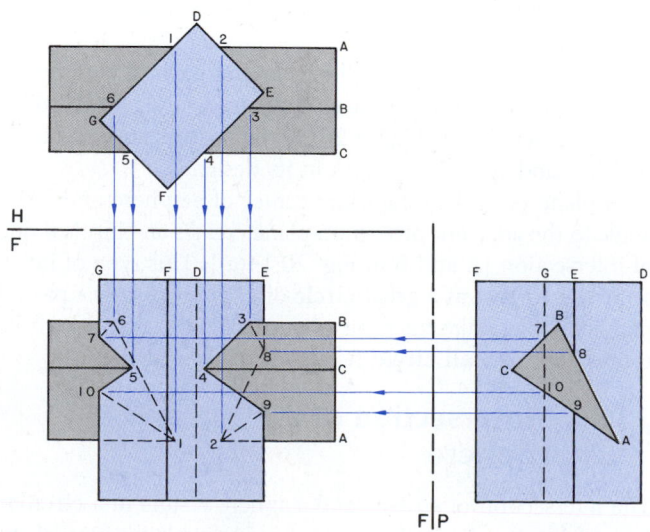

FIGURE 20.17 Intersection of Two Prisms

point 1 and at piercing point 2 on the surface bounded by lines D and E.
2. Project points 1 and 2 to the frontal view until they intersect line A.
3. Repeat this procedure to locate piercing points 3, 4, 5, and 6 in both views.
4. The edges of the vertical rectangular prism pierce the surfaces of the horizontal prism in the profile view at points 7, 8, 9, and 10. Edge line G pierces the surface bounded by lines B and C at piercing point 7.
5. Project point 7 to the frontal view until it intersects line G.
6. Repeat step 5 to locate piercing points 8, 9, and 10.
7. Determine visibility and connect the piercing points to form the line of intersection.

20.7.1   Intersection of Two Prisms (Edge View Method)

The line of intersection of two prisms is established by finding the piercing points of the edge lines of one prism with each surface of the other prism. This process is repeated using the lines of the second prism and is theoretically the intersection of individual lines and planes or the intersection of two planes. Each prism must be shown as an edge view. If only one prism is given as an edge view, an auxiliary view must be projected showing the other prism as an edge view.

In Figure 20.18 the horizontal and frontal views of the two prisms are given. The line of intersection is required. The following steps were used to solve the problem:

1. Draw an auxiliary view showing the triangular prism as an edge view. Each of the edge lines of the triangular prism is a frontal line (true length in the frontal view). Therefore, draw F/A perpendicular to line 1 and project auxiliary view A.

2. In the horizontal view, edge line 1 pierces the surfaces bounded by lines A and D at point 1. The surface bounded by line A and B is pierced by line 2 at point 2 and line 3 at point 3.
3. Project points 1, 2, and 3 to the frontal view to establish the endpoints of lines 1-1, 2-2, and 3-3.
4. In auxiliary view A, corner line A intersects two of the surfaces of the triangular prism at points 4 and 5.
5. Project piercing points 4 and 5 to the frontal view until they intersect corner line A.
6. Visibility is determined by inspection of the profile and horizontal view. Connect the piercing points in the proper sequence. In the frontal view, intersection lines 3-2 and 2-4 are visible; all others are hidden.

You May Complete Exercises 20.5 Through 20.8 at This Time

20.8   Intersection of Cylinders

The intersection of two cylinders (Fig. 20.19) is a common industrial problem in piping and vessel design and in duct design for HVAC. Two intersecting perpendicular right cylinders of the same diameter intersect as shown in Figure 20.20. The line of intersection can be determined by showing each cylinder as an edge view and passing a series of equally

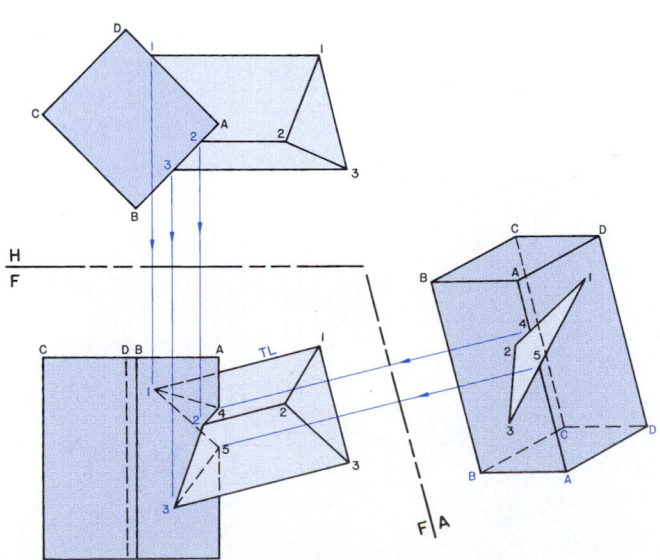

FIGURE 20.18   **Intersection of Two Prisms Using the Edge View Method**

FIGURE 20.19   **Sheet Metal Model of Intersecting Cylinders**

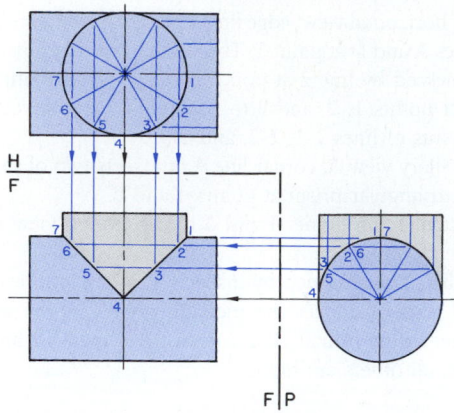

FIGURE 20.20   Intersection of Two Cylinders at 90°

determined by simply drawing the straight lines from point 1 to point 4 to point 7.

To solve for the perpendicular intersection of two cylinders, regardless of their diameters, a series of elements is drawn on the surface of one cylinder by equally dividing the edge view of the vertical cylinder (Fig. 20.20). Each vertical cutting plane passes parallel to the cylinder's axis and cuts a straight-line element on both surfaces. Points 1 through 7 represent the intersection of related elements established by the intersection of a cutting plane and each cylinder. The profile view can also be used to divide the horizontal cylinder equally and establish vertical cutting planes as shown.

20.8.1   Intersection of Two Cylinders (Not at Right Angles)

To find the intersection of two cylinders not at right angles, an edge view of both cylinders is necessary. Project an edge view of the cylinder, if it does not appear as an edge in a given view. Pass a series of cutting planes; each cutting plane intersects both cylinders as elements on their surface. Related elements intersect along the line of intersection of the two cylinders. Accuracy increases proportionally to the number of cutting planes and therefore piercing points. Piercing points are connected by means of a smooth curve. In Figure 20.21 an industrial drawing of two pipes intersecting at 45° is given. The line of intersection and the **development** is shown.

spaced cutting planes through both cylinders. Each cutting plane intersects a cylinder as an element on its surface. The intersection of related elements determines the line of intersection. Each intersection point is actually the piercing point of an element of one cylinder and the surface of the other cylinder.

In Figure 20.20, both cylinders are the same diameter and intersect one another at right angles. The resulting curved line of intersection appears as straight lines in the frontal view. Therefore, in this case the line of intersection could have been

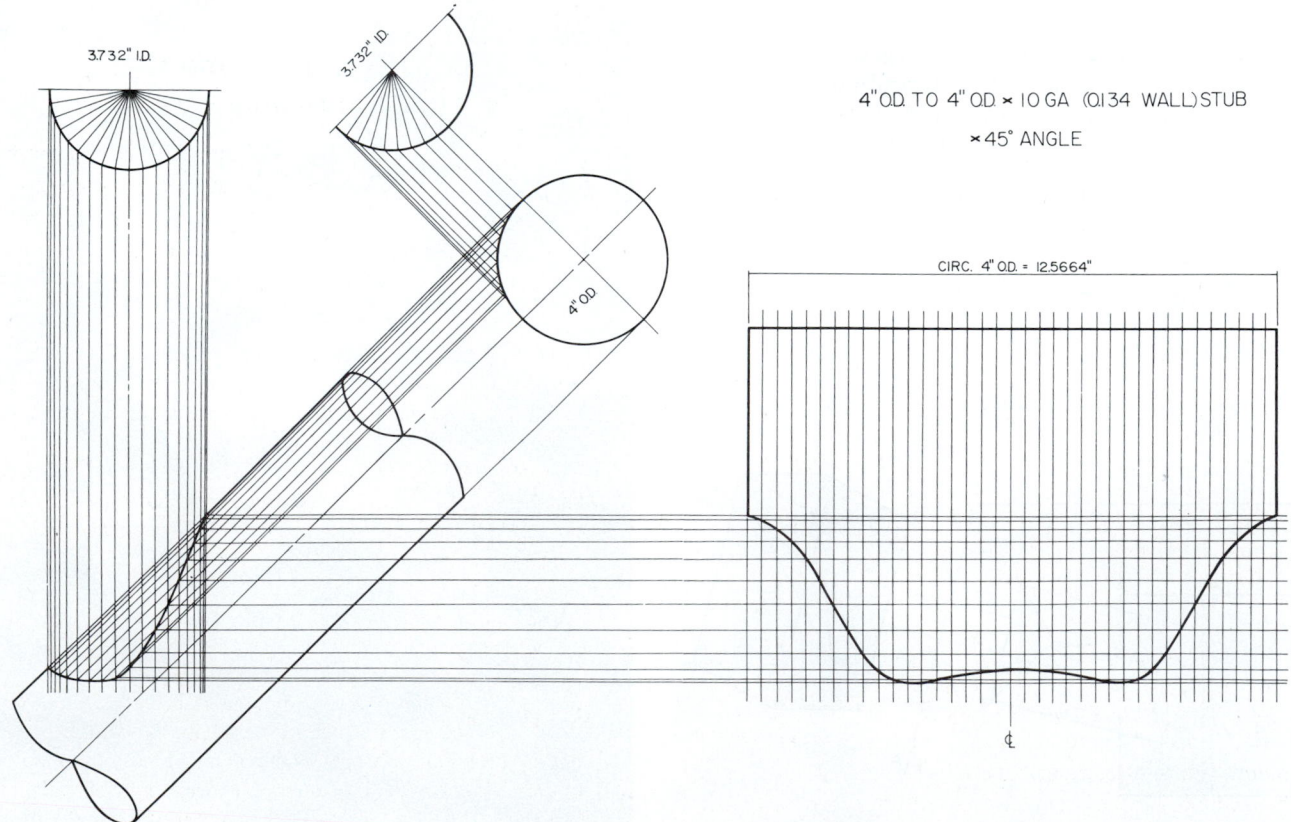

FIGURE 20.21   4 inch OD to 4 inch Stub-in at 45° Shown Along with Template Development

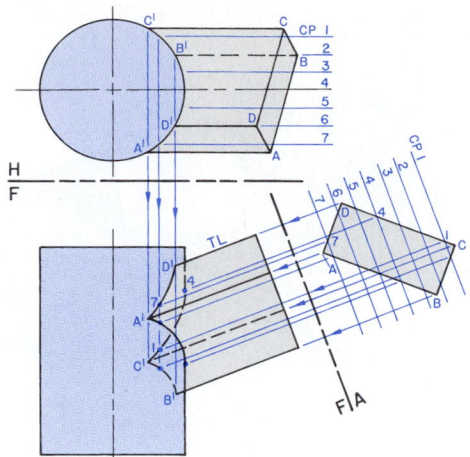

FIGURE 20.22   Intersection of a Cylinder and a Prism at an Angle

20.8.2   Intersection of a Cylinder and a Prism at an Angle

In Figure 20.22 the vertical right cylinder and the inclined prism are given in the frontal and horizontal views. A series of cutting planes is drawn through an end view of the prism (right section) and parallel to the axis of the cylinder. In Figure 20.23 a sheet-metal model of a similar intersecting cylinder and prism is given. The following steps were used to solve the problem in Figure 20.22:

1. Draw F/A perpendicular to the true length lines of the prism in the frontal view. Project auxiliary view A. The cylinder need not be shown.
2. Pass a series of evenly spaced vertical cutting planes through the right section of the prism in auxiliary view A. Show the cutting planes in the horizontal view.
3. The edge lines of the prism intersect the cylinder in the horizontal view. Project piercing points A, B, C, and D to the frontal view.
4. Project elements established on the prism in auxiliary view A and elements established on the cylinder in the horizontal view to the frontal view. Note that each cutting plane cuts two elements on the prism and one on the cylinder. Therefore, each cutting plane locates two points on the line of intersection.
5. Connect the intersection points in proper sequence after determining visibility.

20.9   Intersection of Cones

Conical shapes are used in the design of a wide variety of industrial products, structures, and commercial applications. In general, the right circular cone and the frustrum of a right circular cone are the most common. Oblique cones with circular bases are sometimes used as transition pieces and in ducting HVAC designs.

FIGURE 20.23   Sheet Metal Model of a Cylinder and a Prism at an Angle

20.9.1   Intersection of a Cone and a Horizontal Cylinder

The intersection of a cone and a cylinder can be determined by passing a series of CPs through the cylinder's axis in a view where the cylinder appears as a right circular section. In Figure 20.24 the intersection of a cone and a cylinder is required. The following steps were used in the solution:

1. Project the profile view to show the right section of the cylinder.
2. Evenly divide the cylinder as shown. Each division corresponds to a horizontal cutting plane, CP1 through CP7. Extend the cutting planes to the frontal view.
3. The highest and lowest points of the intersection are established in the frontal view where CP1 intersects the cone at point 1 and CP7 at point 7. Project points 1 and 7 to the horizontal view as shown.
4. Project the cutting planes to the horizontal view. Each CP appears as a *circle element* on the cone and a straight-line element on the surface of the cylinder.
5. The intersection of related elements determines a point on the line of intersection. Locate the points in both views.
6. With the exception of points 1 and 7, each common point is used to plot a line of intersection that is symmetrical to the axis of the cylinder in the horizontal view. Determine visibility and connect the points as a smooth curve representing the line of intersection.

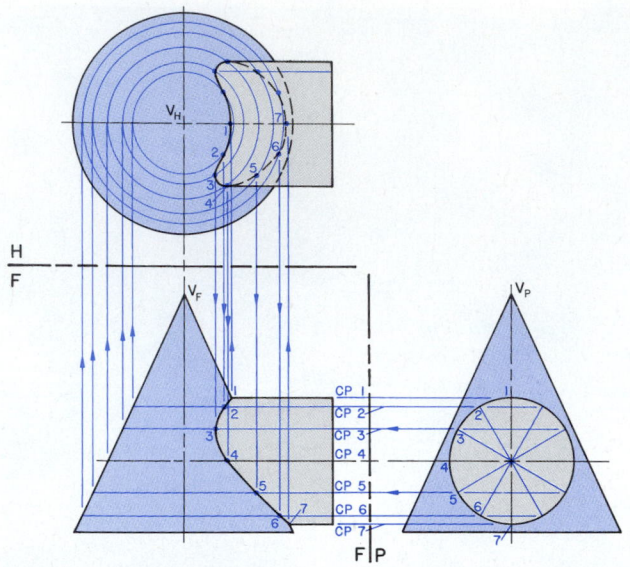

FIGURE 20.24   Intersection of a Cone and a Horizontal Cylinder

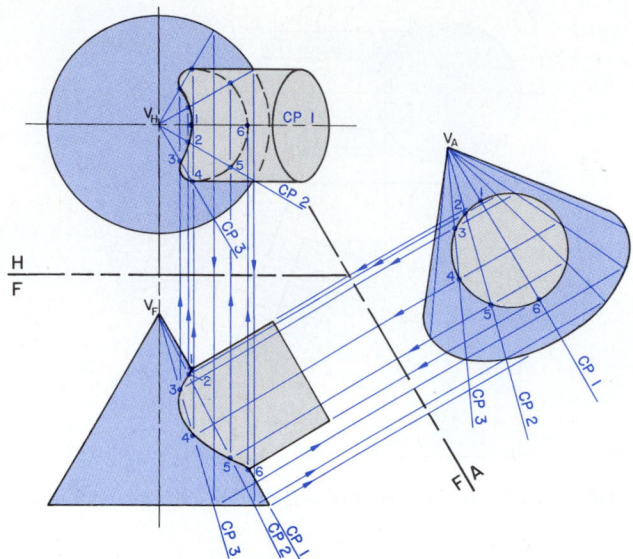

FIGURE 20.25   Intersection of a Cone and a Cylinder at an Angle

20.9.2   Intersection of a Cone and a Cylinder at an Angle

A vertical cutting plane passed through the vertex of the cone and parallel to its axis intersects both the cone and cylinder as straight-line elements on their surfaces. A right section view of the cylinder is required to fix the position of the elements along its surface. In Figure 20.25 the intersection of a cone and a cylinder is required. The following steps were used to solve the problem:

1. Project auxiliary view A perpendicular to the cylinder. The cylinder appears as a right section.
2. Evenly divide one-half of the circumference of the cone's base in the horizontal view. Since the intersection is symmetrical about the cylinder's axis, only the front divisions need be used as cutting planes. Each division corresponds to a vertical CP passed through the vertex of the cone.
3. Each CP cuts a straight line element along the surface of the cone. Locate the CPs in each view by projection of the elements of the cone.
4. The intersection of the CPs and the cylinder in auxiliary view A establish related elements along the surface of the cylinder. Project the cylinder's elements to the frontal view.
5. The intersection of related elements in the frontal view determines points along the line of intersection. CP1 locate points 1 and 6 at the extremes of the intersection line. CP2 locates points 2 and 5 as shown.

20.9.3   Intersection of a Cone and a Prism

The intersection of a cone and a prism can be established by passing a series of cutting planes through the shapes. When the prism is a vertical prism, horizontal cutting planes per-

pendicular to the cone's axis should be used (Fig. 20.26). When the prism is horizontal, vertical CPs passed through the axis of the cone or horizontal CPs perpendicular to the axis of the cone can be used (Fig. 20.27).

In Figure 20.27 the intersection of a prism and a right circular cone is required. The following steps were used to solve the problem:

1. Pass horizontal CP1 and CP2 through the upper and lower horizontal planes of the prism. Project the CPs to the horizontal view where they appear as circle elements.

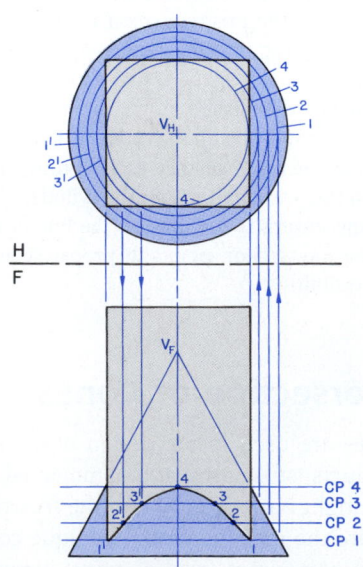

FIGURE 20.26   Intersection of a Cone and a Vertical Cylinder

2. Since the upper and lower surfaces of the prism are horizontal planes, the line of intersection coincides with the circle elements cut by the CPs.

3. When the prism's surfaces are not horizontal planes, vertical CPs passed through the axis of the cone in the horizontal view are used. CPs 3, 4, 5, and 6 cut elements along the cone's surface. Their intersection with the prism in the frontal view cuts two elements each on the prism. Intersecting elements determine the line of intersection in the horizontal view.

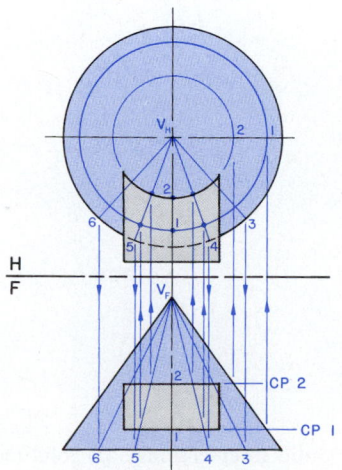

FIGURE 20.27   **Intersection of a Cone and a Horizontal Prism**

20.10   Intersection of a Sphere and a Cylinder

By passing a series of cutting planes parallel to the axis of a cylinder and through a sphere, points along the line of intersection can be determined. A cutting plane drawn parallel to the axis of a cylinder will cut straight-line elements along its surface. Therefore, the intersection of a related circle and straight-line elements establishes points on the line of intersection. Each point represents a point common to both the sphere and the cylinder. Cutting planes are conveniently passed parallel to the axis of a cylinder where the cylinder appears as an edge (right section). A right section shows the cylinder's axis line as a point view.

In Figure 20.28 the frontal and horizontal view of a sphere, and the horizontal view of a sphere and of a horizontal cylinder are given. The line of intersection is required. The following steps were used in the solution:

1. Draw H/A perpendicular to the cylinder's axis and project auxiliary view A. The cylinder appears as a right section with its axis line as a point view.

2. Pass a series of conveniently spaced horizontal cutting planes through the edge view of the cylinder and the sphere in auxiliary view A. Show the cutting planes in the frontal view. Project the cutting planes to the horizontal view, where they appear as circles on the sphere.

3. CP1 cuts a straight-line element along the upper surface of the cylinder and a circular element on the surface of the sphere. The intersection of the sphere's circular element and the cylinder's

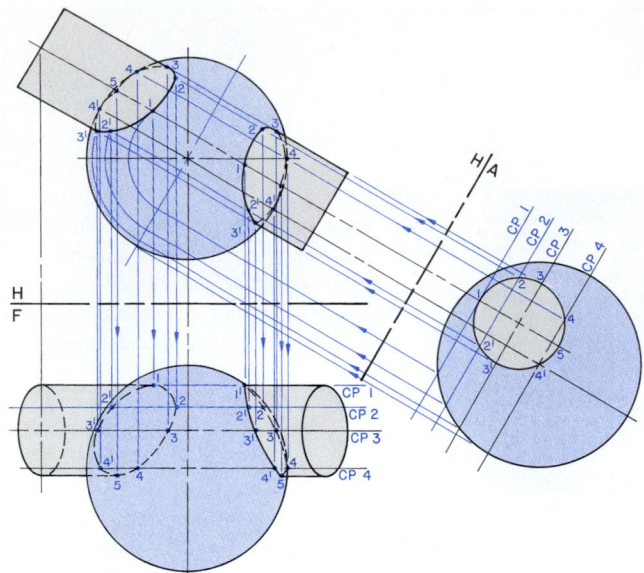

FIGURE 20.28   **Intersection of a Sphere and a Horizontal Cylinder**

straight-line element in the horizontal view locates a point on the line of intersection, point 1.

4. CP2 and CP3 intersect the sphere as circular elements and cut two straight-line elements each on the surface of the cylinder.
5. Project all points to the frontal view to their corresponding cutting planes.
6. Determine visibility and connect the points in proper sequence to establish the line of intersection. Since the cylinder goes through the sphere (pierces it), two curved lines of intersection result.

This chapter has provided many examples of simple to complex intersections of surfaces. The type and number of intersections found in industry is infinite, but the basic procedures and techniques found in this chapter can be applied to all intersecting forms.

You May Complete Exercises 20.9 Through 20.12 at This Time

20.11   Intersection Solutions Using CAD

Intersections of surfaces can be determined by using a number of different techniques such as Boolean operations where the system combines simple objects such as a cone and a prism or a cone and a cylinder. The basic primitives are combined automatically by the system, without the need to do descriptive geometry drawings. Both surface and solid modeling provide complete capabilities for intersection problems.

Piercing points and intersections of lines, planes, and solid shapes can be generated automatically with 3D CAD using commands such as **CUT SURFACE**, **INTERSECT SURFACE**, **CUT PLANE** and **SOLUNION**. Figure 20.29 shows an example of a solid modeling system used to solve for the union of two solids. The figure displays the two solids together and sepa-

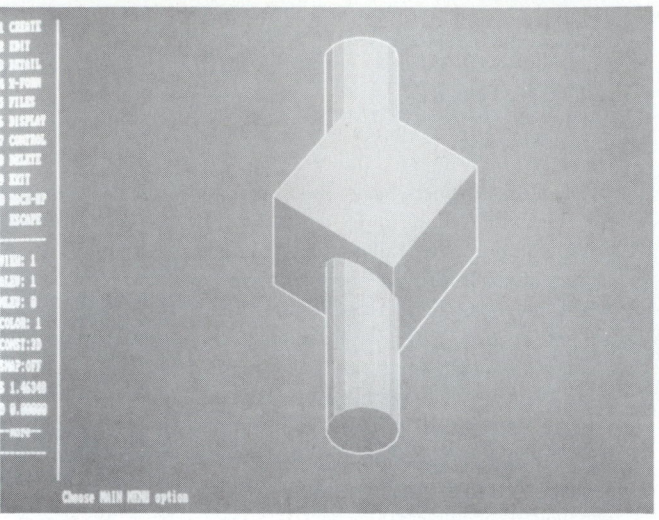

(a)

(b)

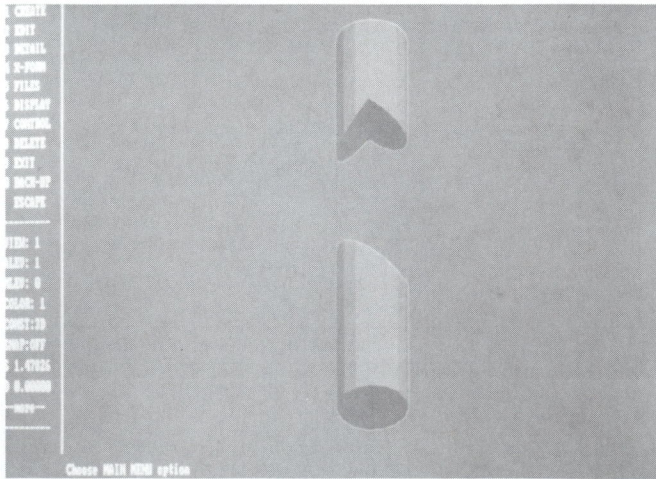

(c)

FIGURE 20.29   **Solid Intersections**   (a) Solid model of an intersecting cylinder and block (b) Solid model of a block with the cylinder removed, thereby creating a hole (c) Solid model of cylinder with block removed

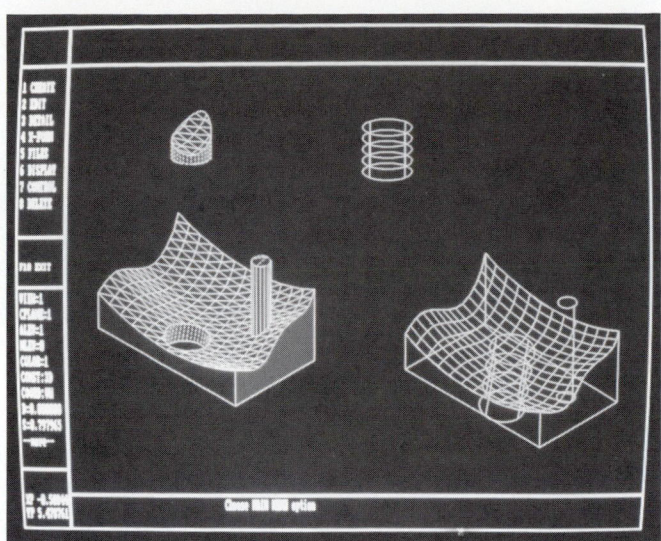

FIGURE 20.30   Solid Intersection of a Sculpted Surface and a Cylinder

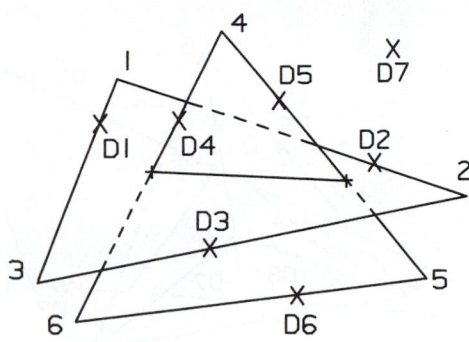

CUT PLANE :DI D2 D3,D4 D5 D6
HIDE PART :D7

FIGURE 20.31   CAD-Generated Solution for the Intersection of Two Planes

rately on the screen. Figure 20.30 shows an example of a complex shape and its intersection with a solid cylindrical shape. This type of modeling uses the power of the computer to merge the two solids automatically.

The intersection of two planes (Fig. 20.31) requires a minimum of two views when using the cutting plane method and three views with the edge view method. The CAD solution requires that a **CUT PLANE** command be given and the two planes picked. The system automatically generates the intersection points. However, depending on the system, the line of intersection may need be put in with a command to draw a line. The system may also require that the operator give a **HIDE** command in order to show proper visibility.

The intersection of a plane and a prism is another type of problem encountered (Fig. 20.32). The manual solution re-

quires a great deal of time and effort along with the ability to visualize the part. The CAD-generated solution involves giving a **CUT PLANE** command after the prism and the plane are established in 3D space.

The intersection of a plane and a pyramid is shown in Figure 20.33. The **CUT PLANE** command was used and correct visibility was established. The intersection of the plane and the cylinder (Fig. 20.34) required the addition of elements along the surface of the cylinder in the manual method. The curved line of intersection is generated automatically with the **CUT PLANE** command. Correct visibility was not established in this problem. Conic sections can be automatically generated with a 3D CAD system as shown in Figure 20.35. The rotated view shows the intersections with crosshatching used to highlight the sections.

The intersection of a cone and an oblique plane is shown in Figure 20.36. The manual method required the introduction of multiple cutting planes forming lines on the plane and

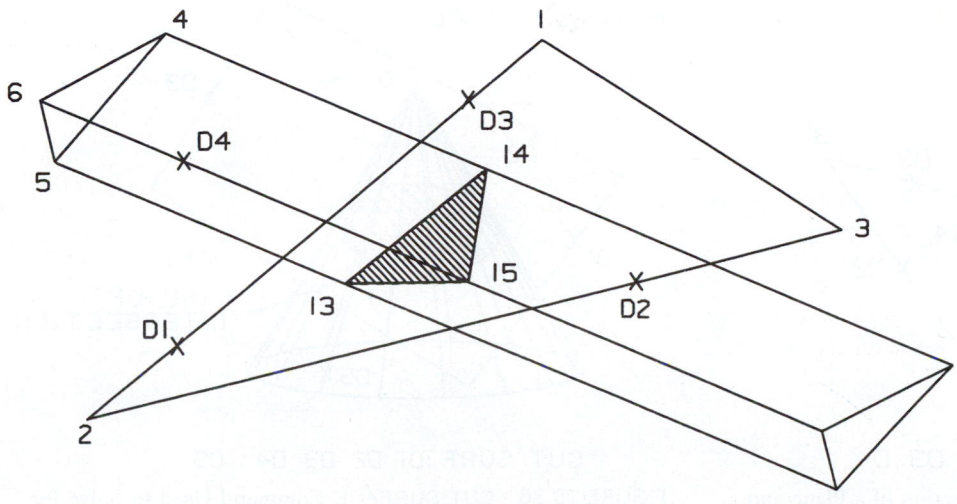

CUT PLANE :END DI D2 D3 ; D4

FIGURE 20.32   CUT PLANE Command Used to Solve for the Intersection of a Plane and a Prism

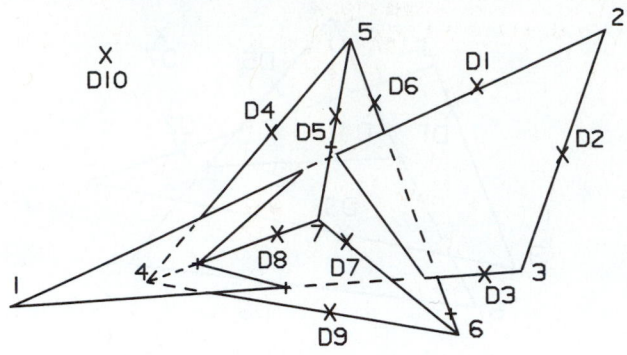

CUT PLANE :DI D2 D3, D4 D5 D6 D7 D8 D9
HIDE PART :DIO

FIGURE 20.33 CAD-Generated Solution for the Intersection of a Plane and a Pyramid

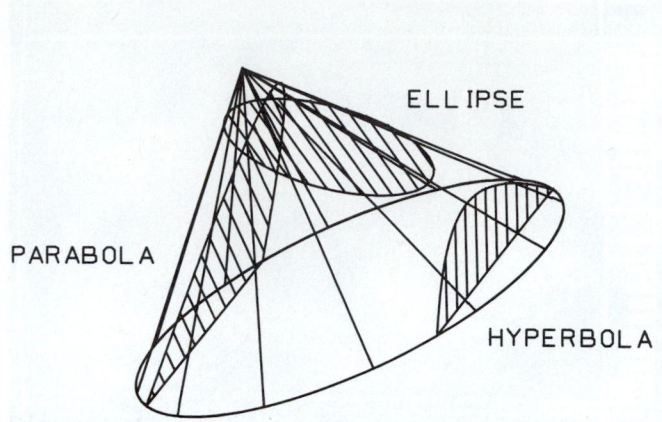

FIGURE 20.35 CAD-Generated Conic Sections

elements on the surface of the cone. The CAD solution required the entering of the **CUT SURFACE** command. The plane is identified by picking its edges and then selecting the cone. The system establishes the line of intersection (visibility is not determined). Figures 20.31 through 21.36 were generated on a Computervision system.

20.11.1 Intersection Using CAD Solid Modeling

The intersection of two solids is one of the most difficult problems encountered in descriptive geometry. The following examples were modeled on AutoCAD 12 using their **advanced modeling extension (AME)** program for solids.

In Figures 20.37 through 20.46 a series of projects using AutoCAD and AME is provided. Each figure includes a three-step piece of art (A, B, and C) and illustrates how to input the command to create the solids and to solve for their intersection using a **SOLUNION** command. The second piece of art in each sequence has an example of what the art (all three steps—A, B, and C) would look like if the **SOLMESH** and **HIDE** commands were applied to the illustration. If you have an AutoCAD system with AME, try each of the commands and plot the art.

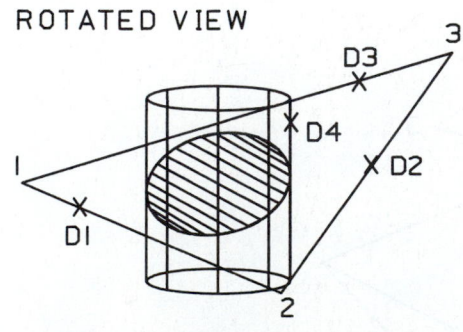

CUT PLANE :DI D2 D3 D4

FIGURE 20.34 CAD-Generated Intersection of a Plane and a Cylinder

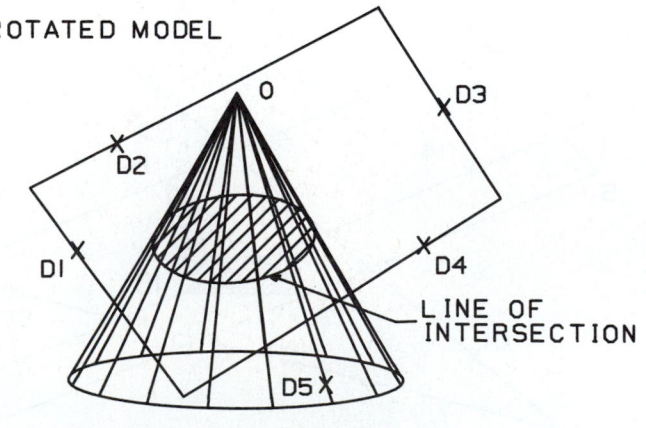

CUT SURF :DI D2 D3 D4 : D5

FIGURE 20.36 CUT SURFACE Command Used to Solve for the Intersection of a Plane and a Cone

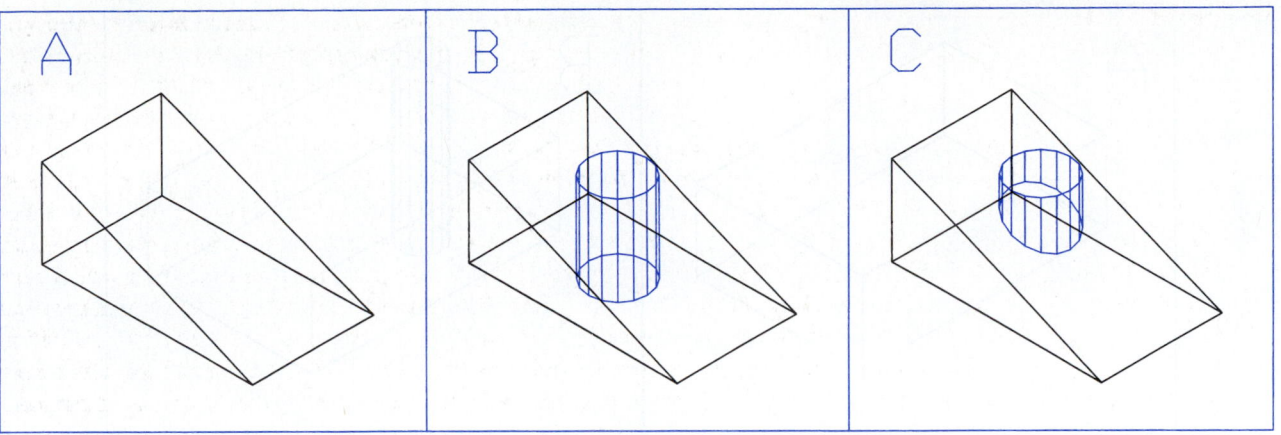

FIGURE 20.37   Union of a Cylinder and a Wedge Using AutoCAD

```
Command: VPOINT
Rotate/<View point> <0.0000, 0.0000, 1.0000>: 1,-1,1
Command: PAN
Displacement: 0,0
Second point: 5,4
Command: SOLWEDGE
Baseplane/<Corner of wedge> <0,0,0>: Press Enter
Length/<Other corner>: 7,4,3
Command: COLOR
New entity color <BYLAYER>: Blue
Command: SOLCYL
Baseplane/Elliptical/<Center point> <0,0,0>: 3,2,0
Diameter/<Radius>: 1
Center of other end/<Height>: 3
Command: SOLUNION
Select objects: Pick the wedge and the cylinder
Command: ZOOM
All/Center/Dynamic/Extents/Left/Previous/
Vmax/Window/<Scale(X/XP)>: All
```

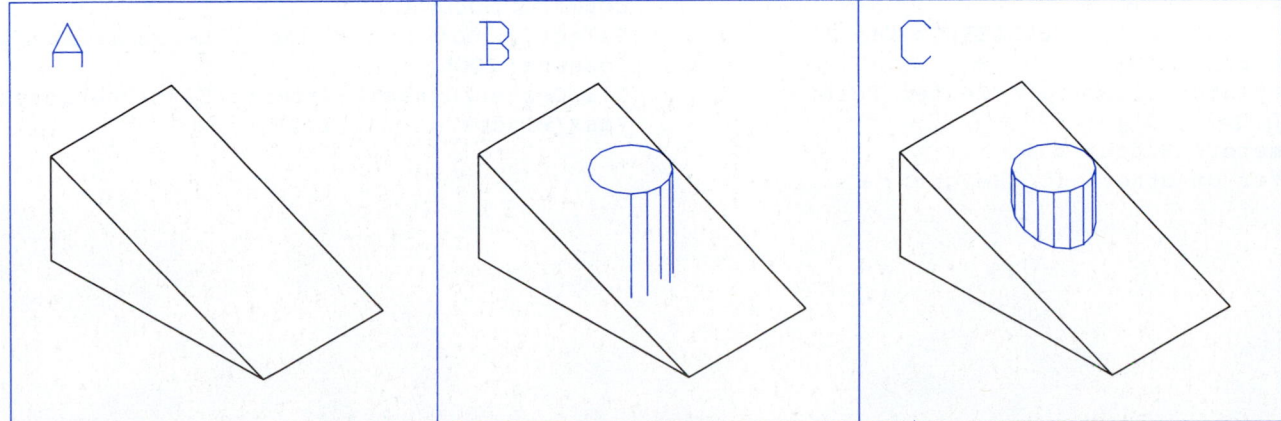

FIGURE 20.38   Union of a Cylinder and a Wedge Using AutoCAD's HIDE Command

```
Command: SOLMESH
Select objects: Pick the object
Command: HIDE
```

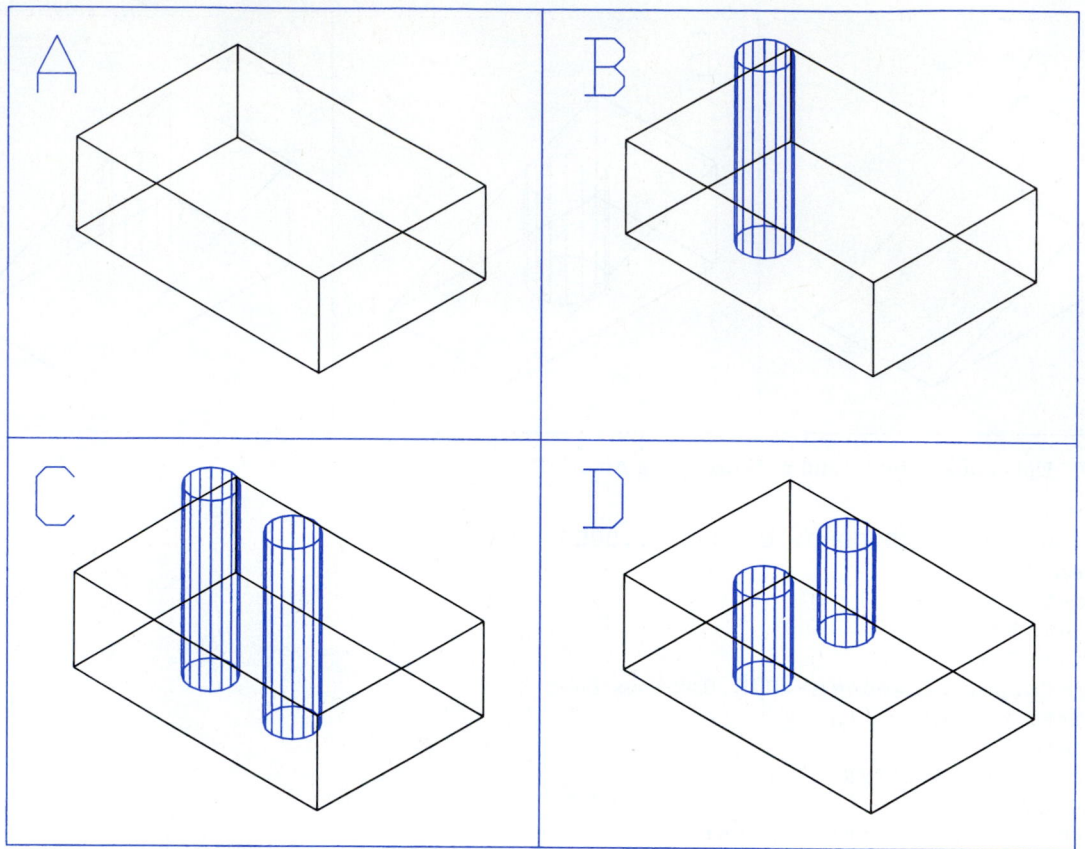

FIGURE 20.39   Union of Two Cylinders and a Box Using AutoCAD

Command: **VPOINT**
Rotate/<View point> <0.0000, 0.0000,
1.0000>: 1,−1,1
Command: **PAN**
Displacement: 0,0
Second point: 5,4
Command: **SOLBOX**
Baseplane/Center/<Corner of box> <0,0,0>:
Press Enter
Cube/Length/<Other corner>: 6,4,2
Command: **COLOR**
New entity color <BYLAYER>: Blue
Command: **SOLCYL**
Baseplane/Elliptical/<Center Point>
<0,0,0>: 2,2,0
Diameter/<Radius>: .5
Center of other end/<Height>: 4

Command: **SOLCYL**
Baseplane/Elliptical/<Center Point>
<0,0,0>: 4,2,0
Diameter/<Radius>: .5
Center of other end/<Height>: 4
Command: **SOLSUB**
Source objects. . .
Select objects: Pick the box
Objects to subtract from them. . .
Select objects: Pick the first cylinder
Command: **SOLUNION**
Select objects: Pick the box and the second cylinder
Command: **ZOOM**
All/Center/Dynamic/Extents/Left/Previous/
Vmax/Window/<Scale(X/XP)>: All

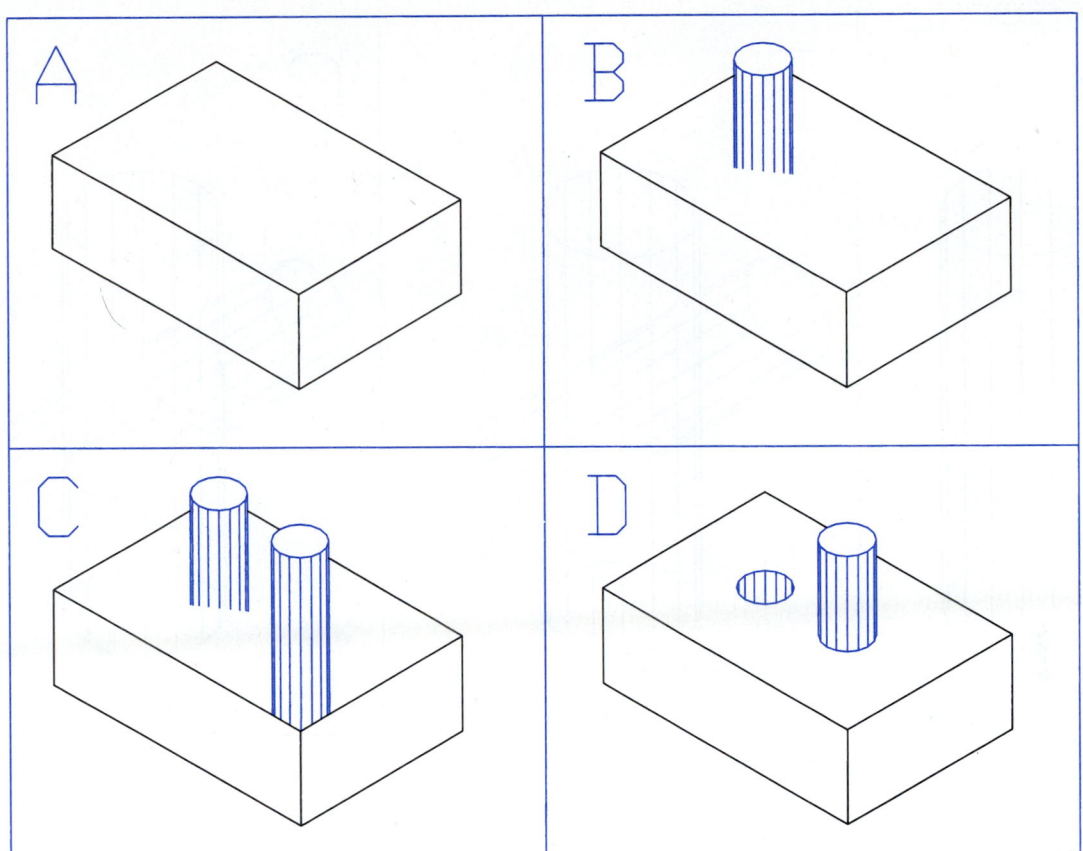

FIGURE 20.40   Union of Two Cylinders and a Box Using AutoCAD's HIDE Command

Command: SOLMESH
Select objects: Pick the object
Command: HIDE

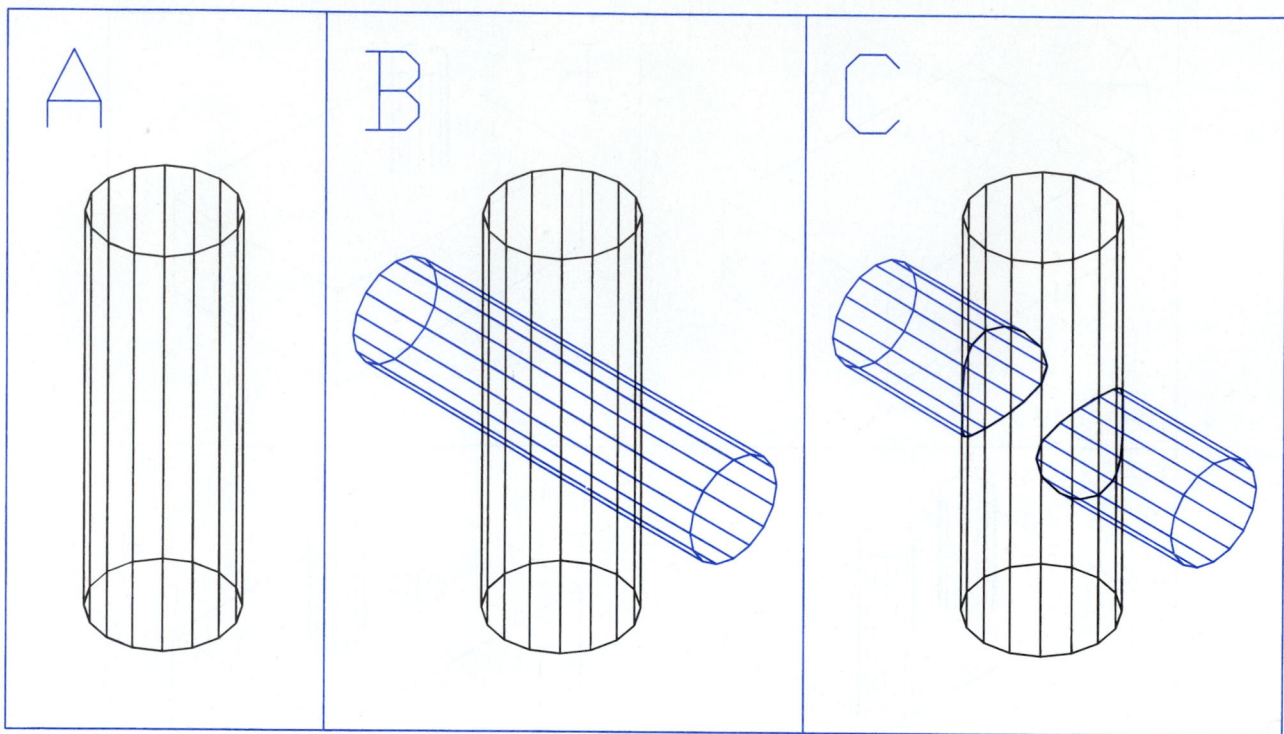

FIGURE 20.41 Union of Two Cylinders Using AutoCAD

```
Command: VPOINT
Rotate/<View point> <0.0000, 0.0000,
1.0000>: 1,-1,1
Command: PAN
Displacement: 0,0
Second point: 5,4
Command: SOLCYL
Baseplane/Elliptical/<Center Point>
<0,0,0>: 0,0,-5
Diameter/<Radius>: 1
Center of other end/<Height>: 10
Command: COLOR
New entity color <BYLAYER>: Blue
Command: UCS
Origin/ZAxis/3point/Entity/View/X/Y/Z/Prev/
Restore/Save/Del/?/<WORLD>: Y
Rotation angle about Y axis <0>: 90
Command: SOLCYL
Baseplane/Elliptical/<Center Point>
<0,0,0>: 0,0,-5
Diameter/<Radius>: 1
Center of other end/<Height>: 10
Command: SOLUNION
Select objects: Pick the two cylinders
Command: ZOOM
All/Center/Dynamic/Extents/Left/Previous/
Vmax/Window/<Scale(X/XP)>: All
```

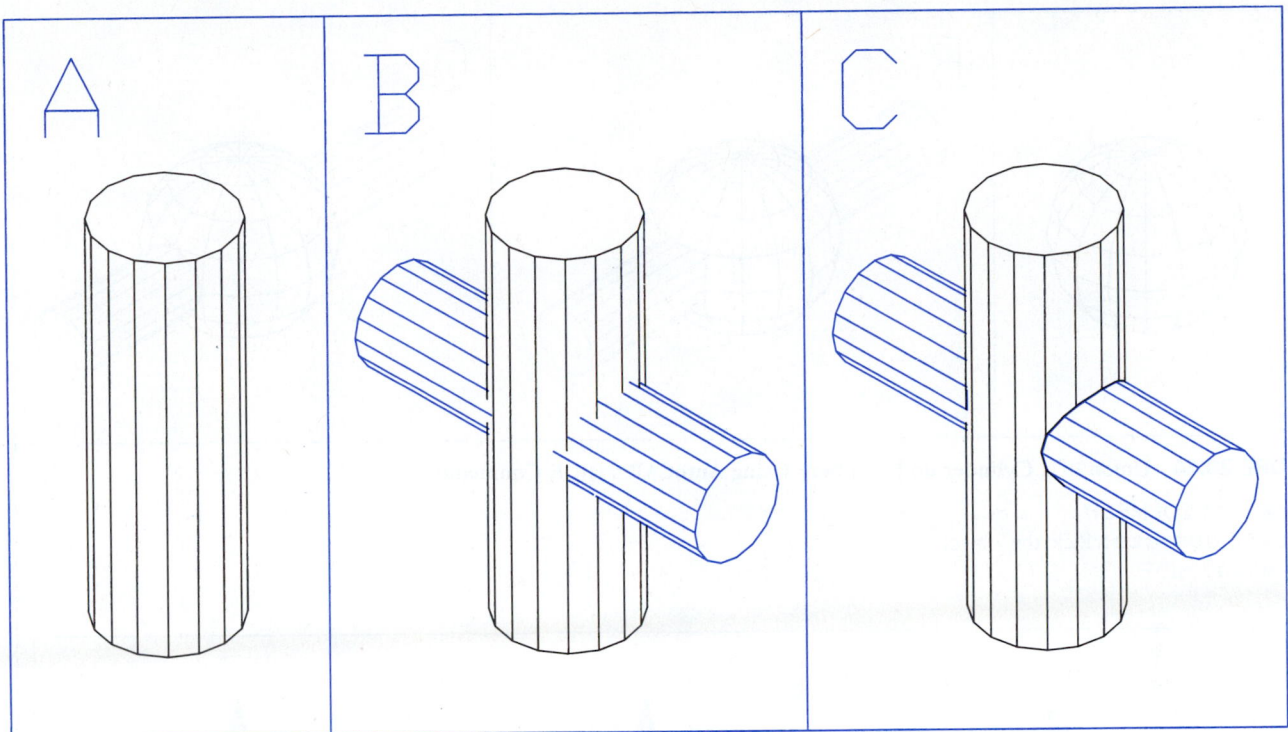

FIGURE 20.42   Union of a Two Cylinders Using AutoCAD's HIDE Command

```
Command: SOLMESH
Select objects: Pick the object
Command: HIDE
```

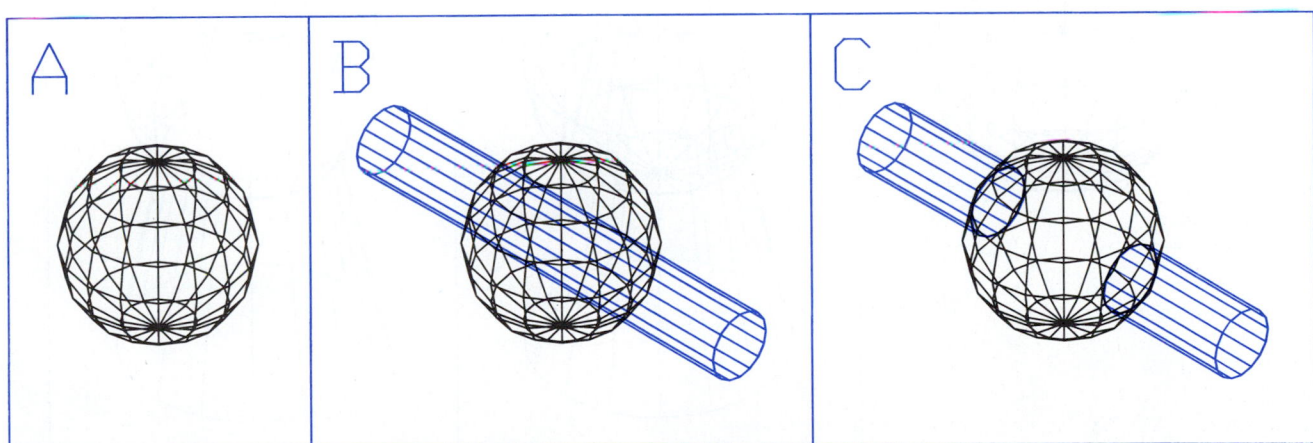

FIGURE 20.43   Union of a Cylinder and a Sphere Using AutoCAD

```
Command: VPOINT
Rotate/<View point> <0.0000, 0.0000,
1.0000>: 1,-1,1
Command: PAN
Displacement: 0,0
Second point: 5,4
Command: SOLSPHERE
Baseplane/<center of sphere> <0,0,0>: Press
Enter
Diameter/<Radius> of sphere: 2
Command: COLOR
New entity color <BYLAYER>: Blue
```

```
Command: UCS
Origin/ZAxis/3point/Entity/View/X/Y/Z/Prev/
Restore/Save/Del/?/<WORLD>: Y
Rotation angle about Y axis <0>: 90
Command: SOLCYL
Baseplane/Elliptical/<Center point>
<0,0,0>: 0,0,-5
Diameter/<Radius>: .75
Center of other end/<Height>: 10
Command: SOLUNION
Select objects: Pick the sphere and the cylinder
Command: ZOOM
All/Center/Dynamic/Extents/Left/Previous/
Vmax/Window/<Scale(X/XP)>: All
```

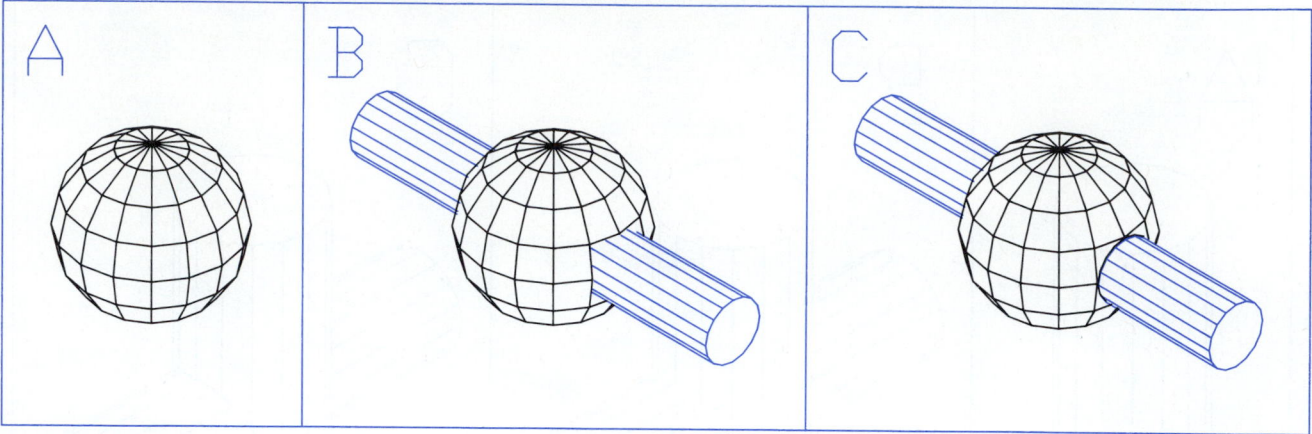

FIGURE 20.44   Union of a Cylinder and a Sphere Using AutoCAD's HIDE Command

```
Command: SOLMESH
Select objects: Pick the object
Command: HIDE
```

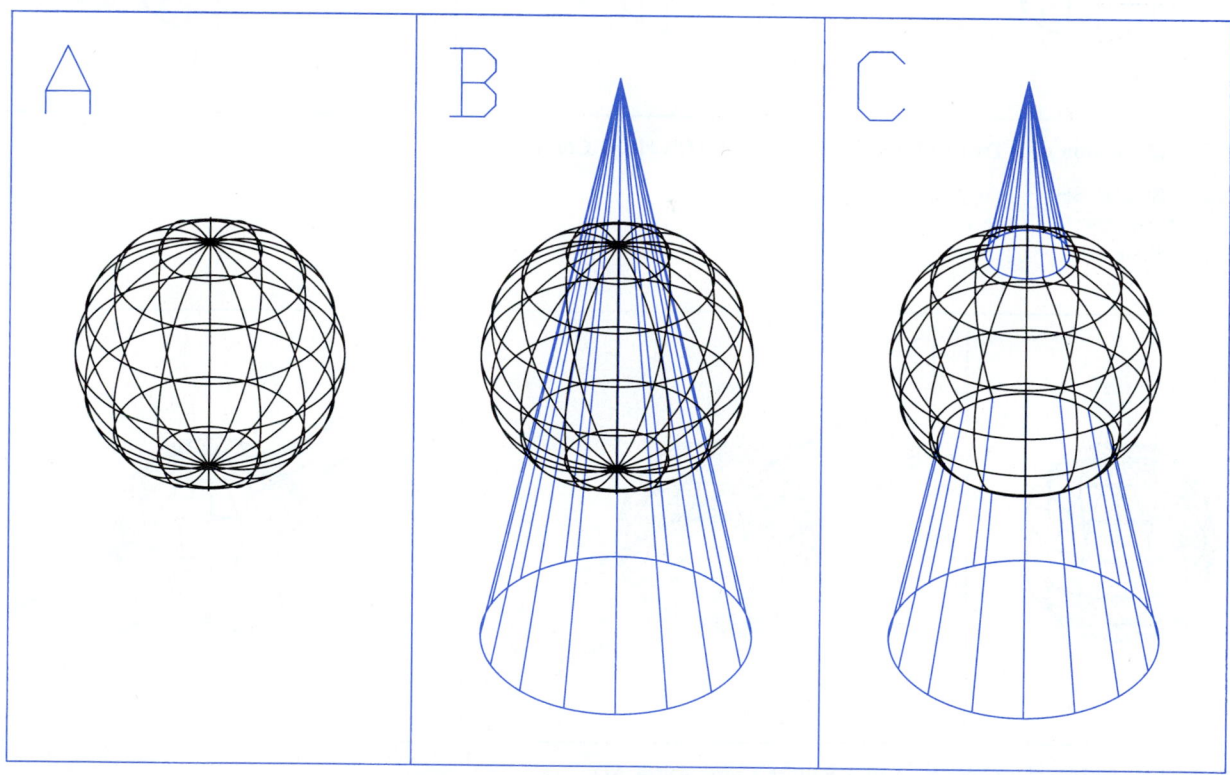

FIGURE 20.45   Union of a Cone and a Sphere Using AutoCAD

```
Command: VPOINT
Rotate/<View point> <0.0000, 0.0000,
1.0000>: 1,−1,1
Command: PAN
Displacement: 0,0
Second point: 5,4
Command: SOLSPHERE
Baseplane/<center of sphere> <0,0,0>: Press
Enter
Diameter/<Radius> of sphere: 2
```

```
Command: COLOR
New entity color <BYLAYER>: Blue
Command: SOLCONE
Baseplane/Elliptical/<Center point>
<0,0,0>: 0,0,−5
Diameter/<Radius>: 2
Apex/<Height>: 10
Command: SOLUNION
Select objects: Pick the sphere and the cone
Command: ZOOM
All/Center/Dynamic/Extents/Left/Previous/
Vmax/Window/<Scale(X=XP)>: All
```

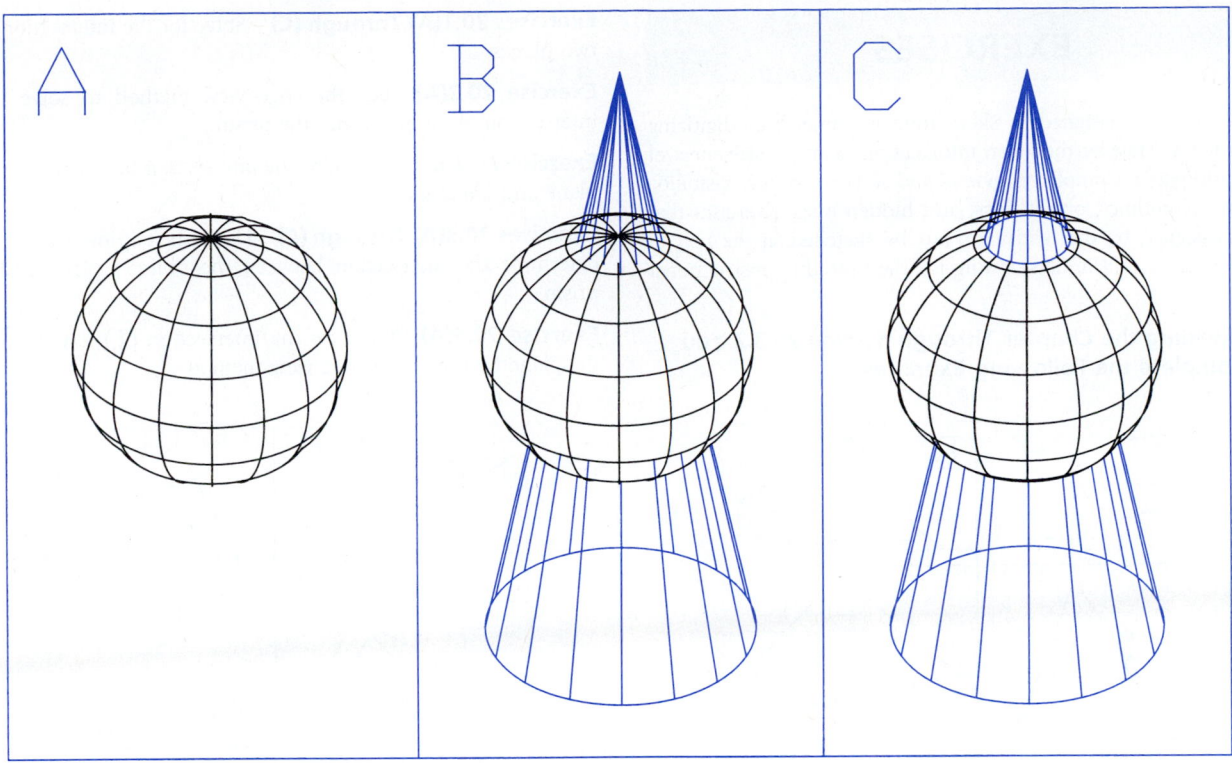

FIGURE 20.46 **Union of a Cone and a Sphere Using AutoCAD's HIDE Command**

```
Command: SOLMESH
Select objects: Pick the object
Command: HIDE
```

QUIZ

True or False

1. A cutting plane can be introduced at any angle and in any view.
2. A cone is generated by a straight-line element passed through the axis and at a specific distance from the vertex.
3. A piercing point and an intersection point are the same thing.
4. Most cylinders are cylinders of revolution.
5. The intersection of a plane and another shape can be established in a view where the plane appears as an edge.
6. An isosceles triangle is established by passing a plane through a triangular prism.
7. A plane passed parallel to the adjacent projection plane and not through its center cuts a small circle from a sphere.
8. The intersection of a sphere and a plane results in a circular line of intersection.

Fill in the Blanks

9. The cutting plane method needs only _____ adjacent _____ to solve for the intersection.
10. The line of intersection between two surfaces is defined by a series of _____ _____ representing the _____ of _____ .

11. A cylinder is a _____ _____ surface.
12. A sphere is a _____ _____ surface.
13. Passing a plane through a sphere's center results in a _____.
14. A right cone is generated by revolving a _____ about one of its legs.
15. An _____ is the result of a plane cutting all the elements of a cone.
16. A double curved surface contains no _____ _____ .

Answer the Following

17. Define the term *conic section*.
18. Describe the cutting plane method and the edge view method of solving for intersections.
19. Name three specific engineering applications for intersecting shapes.
20. When a plane intersects a circular cylinder at an angle to the cylinder's axis, the resulting intersection makes what type of shape?
21. Explain what is meant by common line or the line of intersection.
22. What is a cylinder of revolution?
23. Name the five types of sections resulting from a plane intersecting a cone.
24. What is a sphere and how is it generated?

EXERCISES

Exercises may be assigned as sketching, instrument, or digitizing CAD projects. Transfer the given information to an "A" size sheet of .25 in. grid paper. Complete all views and solve for proper visibility, including centerlines, object lines, and hidden lines. Exercises that are not assigned by the instructor can be sketched in the text to provide practice and understanding for the preceding instructional material.

After Reading the Chapter Through Section 20.3.2 You May Complete the Following Exercises

Exercises 20.1(A) Through (C)   Solve for the intersection of the two planes.

Exercise 20.2(A)   Use the edge view method to solve for the intersection of the plane and the prism.

Exercise 20.2(B)   Determine the intersection between the oblique plane and oblique prism.

Exercises 20.3(A) Through (C)   Using the cutting plane method, determine the intersection between the oblique plane and right prism.

Exercise 20.4(A)   Solve for the intersection of the pyramid and the plane by use of the edge view method.

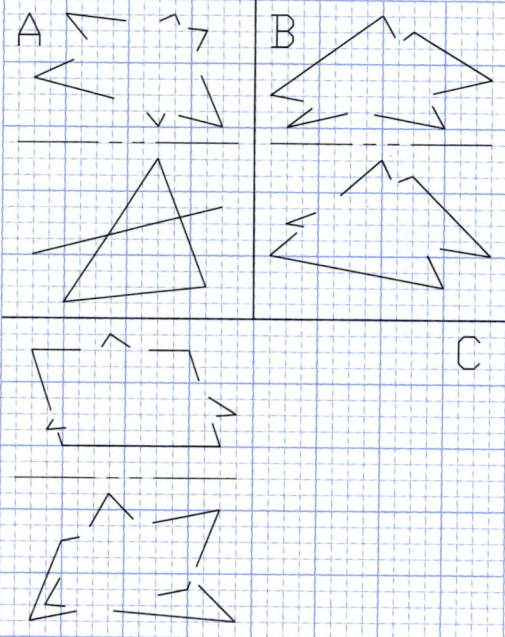

Exercise 20.1

Exercise 20.3

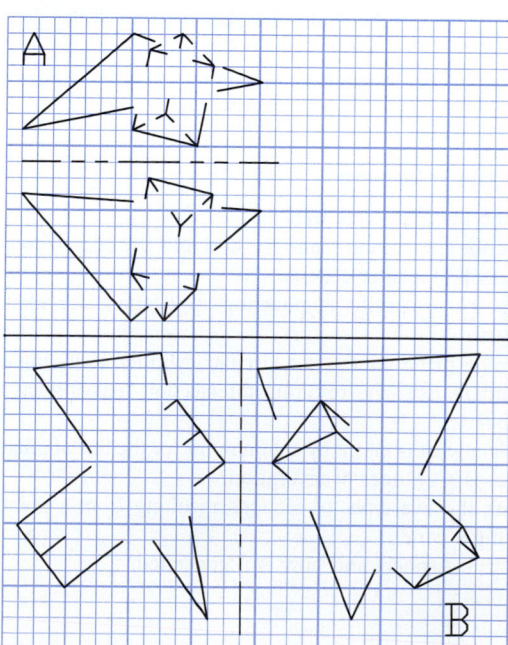

Exercise 20.2

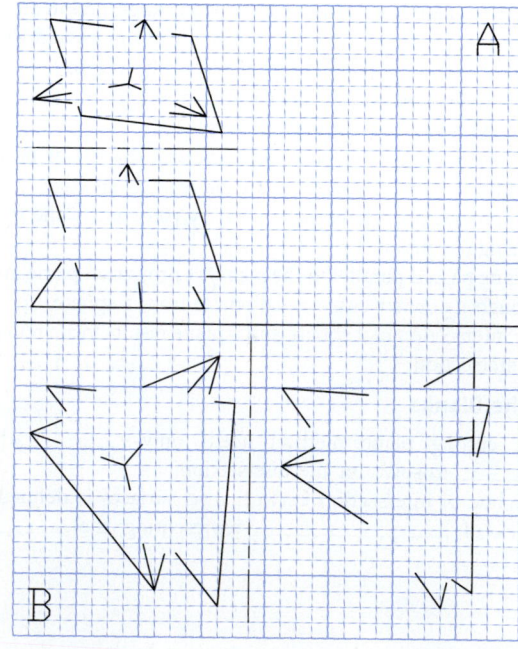

Exercise 20.4

Exercise 20.4(B) Determine the intersection of the oblique plane and pyramid using the cutting plane method.

After Reading the Chapter Through Section 20.7.1 You May Complete the Following Exercises

Exercise 20.5(A) Complete the two views of the intersection plane and cylinder.

Exercise 20.5(B) Solve for the intersection of the plane and the cone. Use the cutting plane method.

Exercise 20.6 The front view of the right cone is cut by three separate planes. Show the resulting true shape conic sections and the intersection lines in the H view.

Exercises 20.7(A) and (B) Solve for the intersection of the plane and sphere.

Exercise 20.7(C) Complete the views and determine the intersection of the two prisms.

Exercise 20.8(A) Using the edge view method, complete the views and solve for the intersection of the two prisms.

Exercise 20.8(B) Solve for the intersection of the pyramid and prism. Use the cutting plane method.

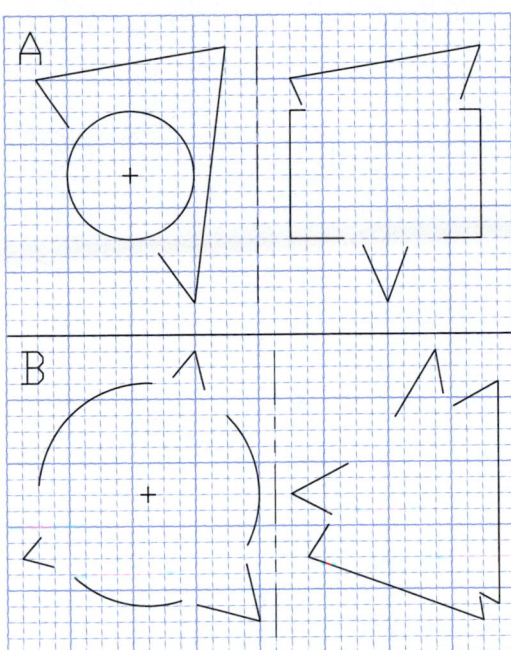

Exercise 20.5

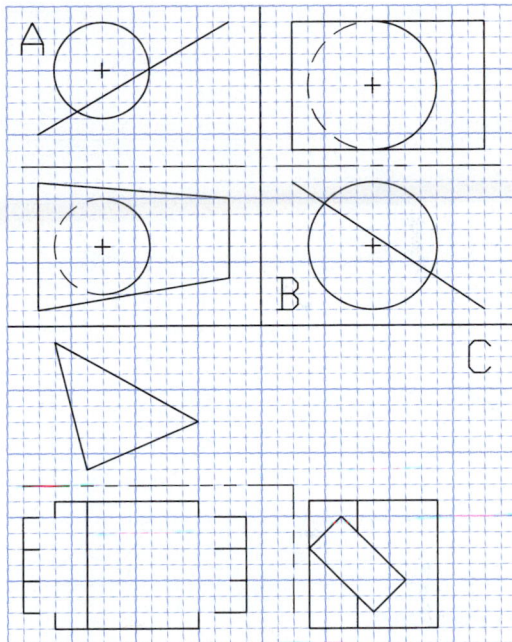

Exercise 20.7

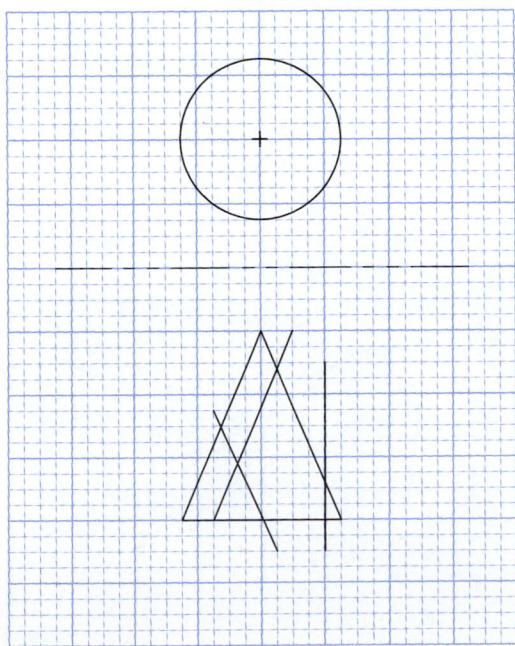

Exercise 20.6

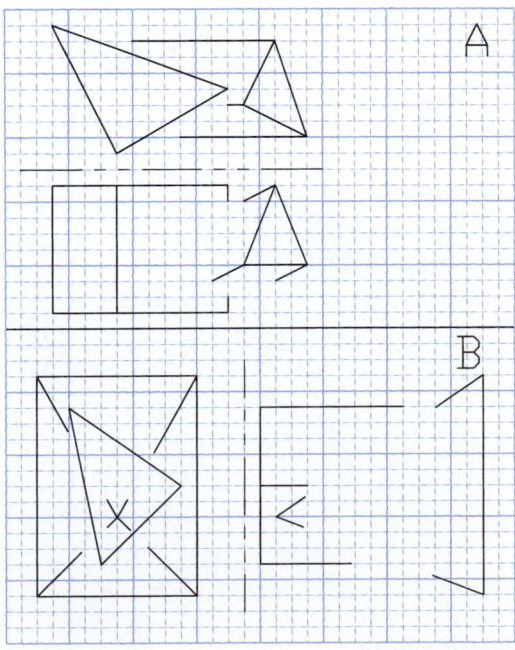

Exercise 20.8

After Reading the Chapter Through Section 20.10 You May Complete the Following Exercises

Exercise 20.9 Complete the given views and solve for the intersection by means of an edge view.

Exercise 20.10(A) Solve for the intersection between the given cylinders.

Exercise 20.10(B) Determine the intersection between the prism and the cylinder.

Exercise 20.11 Complete the three views of the cone intersected by the cylinder.

Exercises 20.12(A) and (B) Complete the views of the intersecting shapes.

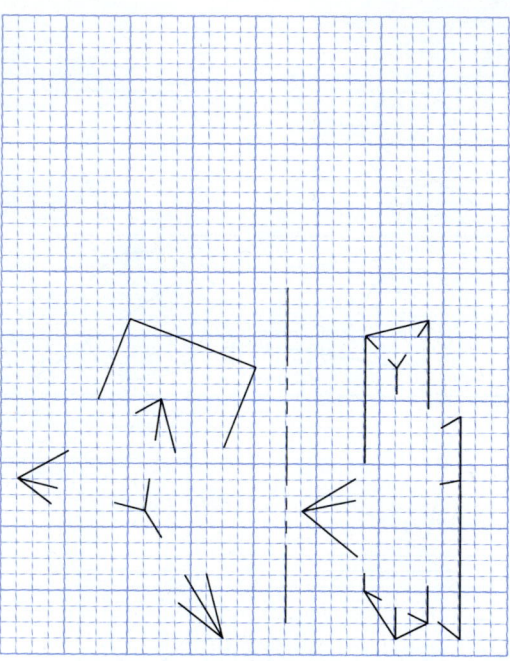

Exercise 20.9

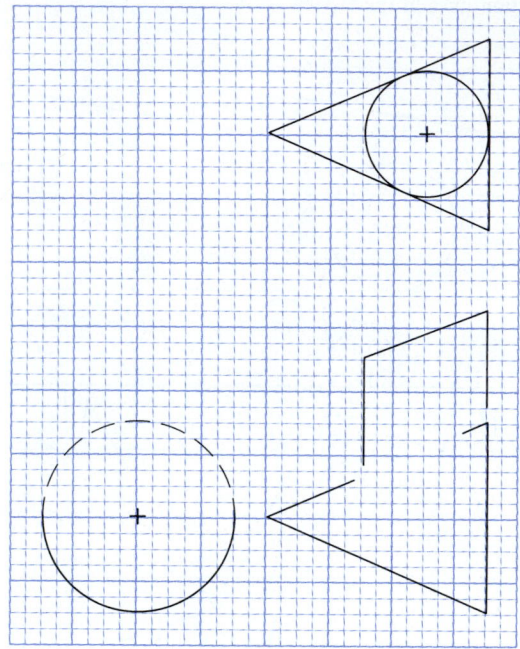

Exercise 20.11

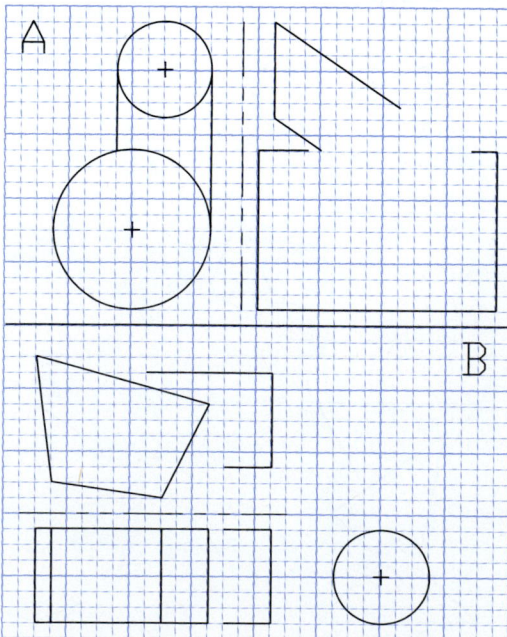

Exercise 20.10

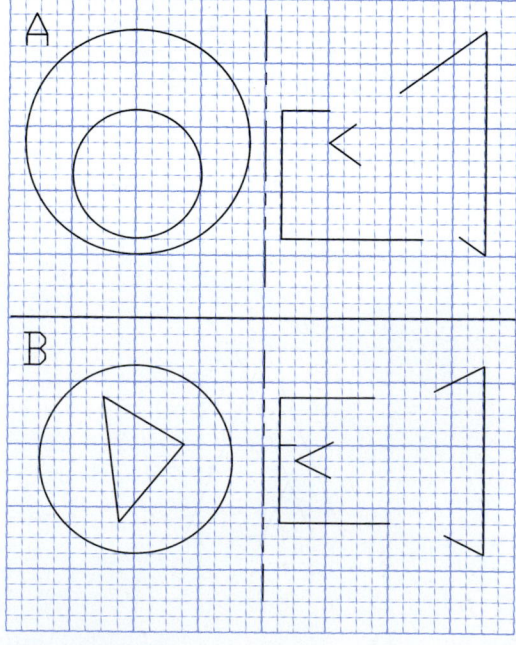

Exercise 20.12

PROBLEMS

Problems may be assigned as sketching, instrument, or CAD projects.

Problems 20.1(A) Through (L) Transfer the problem to another sheet. Most problems will fit on an "A" size drawing format. Complete the views of each intersection project. Add any view needed to complete the project. Use the edge view or the cutting plane method. Instructor may assign some projects for development problems after Chapter 21 is completed. Models of any of the problems can also be assigned.

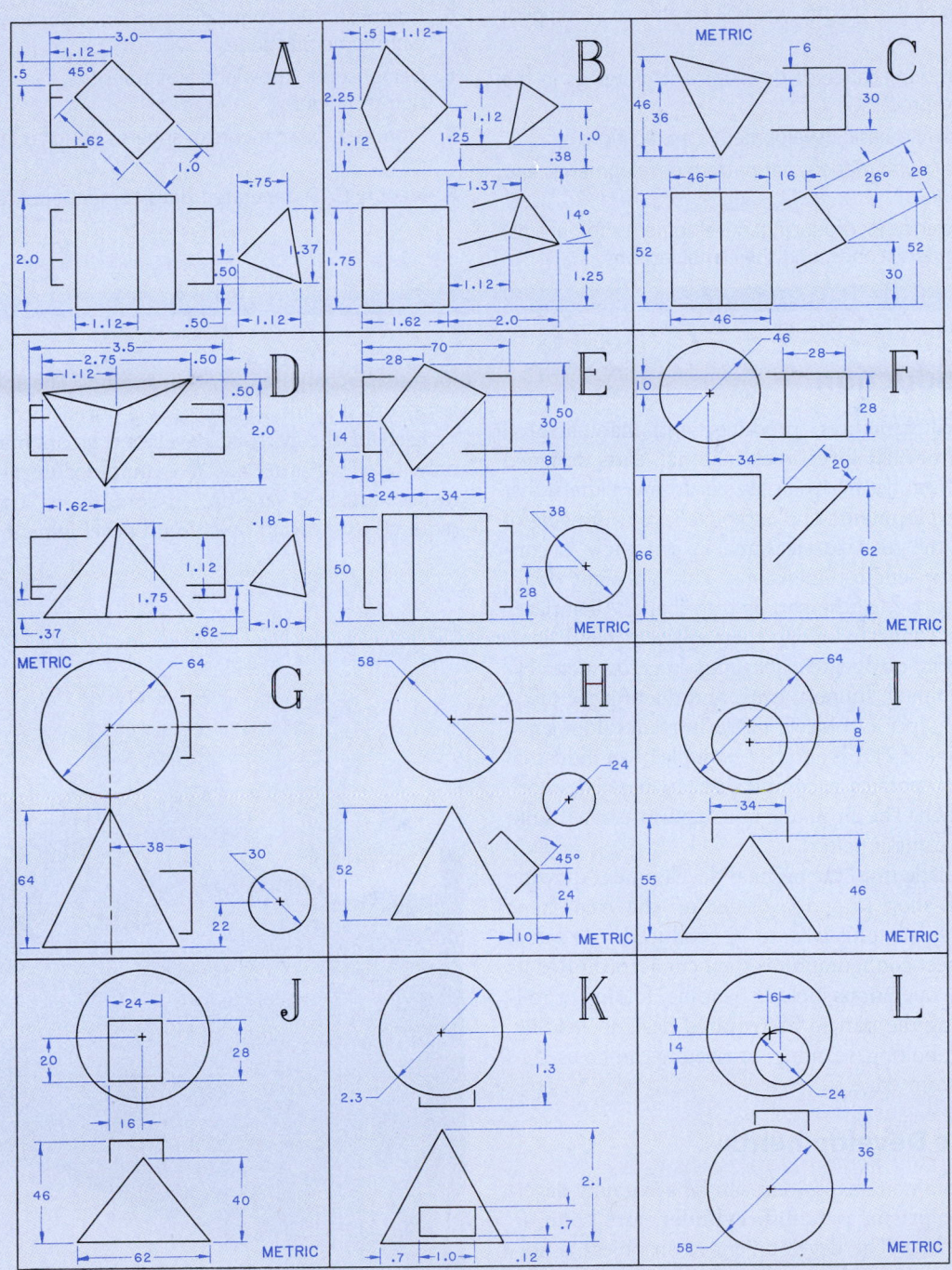

Problem 20.1

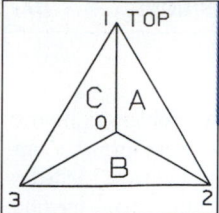

Developments

Learning Objectives

Upon completion of this chapter you will be able to accomplish the following:

1. Recognize the significance of development drawings in the manufacturing process.
2. Identify and define basic development classifications.
3. Become familiar with models, flat pattern developments, and joining techniques.
4. Acquire proficiency in producing developments for prisms, pyramids, cylinders, cones, and their intersections.

5. Comprise true length diagrams in order to develop surfaces with numerous edges.
6. Demonstrate knowledge of transition pieces and triangulation techniques.
7. Produce developments of spheres using zone and gore methods.
8. Identify CAD-generated development applications.

21.1 Introduction

Various industrial structures, products, and manufactured parts are made from flat sheet stock material. Parts designed to be produced from flat materials are cut from a pattern that is drawn as a **development**. The complete layout drawing of a part showing the total surface area in one view is constructed using true length dimensions. This flat plane drawing shows each surface of the part as true shape. All surfaces of the object are connected along their adjacent bend lines. Sheet metal objects, cardboard packaging, large-diameter cylindrical vessels/piping, funnels, cans, and ducting are just a few of the many types of objects made from developments. The turbine in Figure 21.1 is another example of an industrial product that incorporates a complex sheet metal development into its design. The air intake housing was created from a sheet of metal using a pattern.

A **pattern** is made from the original development drawing and used in the shop to scribe or set up the true shape configuration of a part, plus tabs, to be produced. The actual developed flat sheet configuration is then cut according to its pattern. The final operations include bending, folding or rolling, and stretching the part to its required design. Welding, gluing, soldering, bolting, seaming, or riveting can be used to join the piece's seam edge.

21.1.1 Basic Developments

The four most common shapes that can be accurately developed include the **prism**, **pyramid**, **cylinder**, and **cone**, in variations (Fig. 21.2). The development of an object is normally done by unfolding or unrolling its surfaces onto the plane of the paper. The actual drawing of the object consists of showing each successive surface as true shape and connected along common edges. One edge line serves as a **seam**

for a shape composed of plane surfaces. The seam or break line for a curved shape will be along a line/element on its surface.

Each of the parts is developed as an **inside-up** pattern drawing. That is to say, it is unfolded/unrolled so that the inside surface is face-up. In some cases a pattern may be required to show an outside-up development. The difference

FIGURE 21.1 Turbine

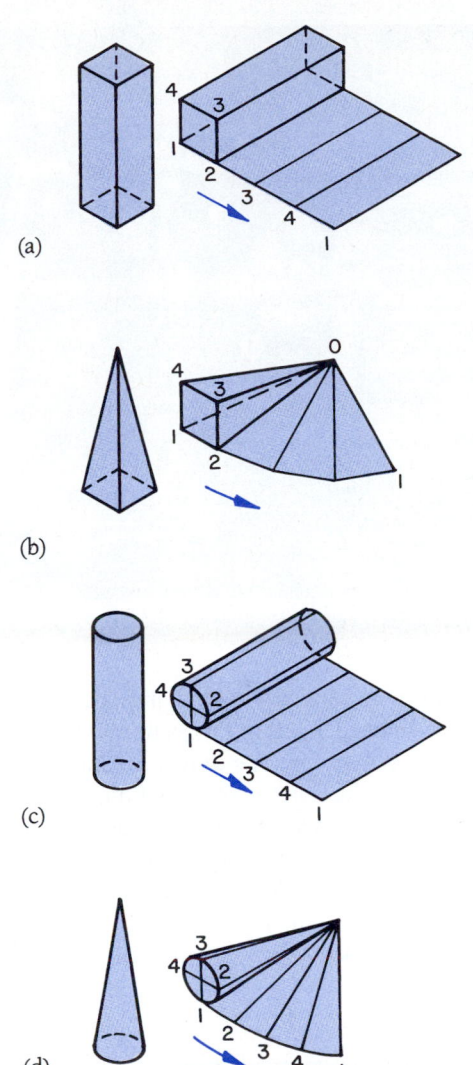

FIGURE 21.2   **Basic Developments**   (a) Prism (b) Pyramid
(c) Cylinder (d) Cone

in drawing this variation is shown in the representation of the bend lines.

In Figure 21.2(a) and (b), the prism and pyramid have been unfolded inside-up so that each surface is laid flat and connected along common edges. The first and last line of any development represents the same line, because they are joined together along the seam. A right prism unfolds as a rectangle. The length of the rectangle is equal to the perimeter of the base and its width is equal to its altitude.

In Figure 21.2(c) and (d), the cylinder and the cone have been unrolled (inside-up). A seam edge for these figures is along a specified line or element on its surface. A cylinder unfolds/unrolls as a rectangle with its length equal to its circumference ($\pi \times$ diameter) and its height equal to the altitude. A cone develops as a portion of a circle (sector).

The edges of a prism and pyramid correspond to the bend lines of the development. For a cylinder and cone,

elements are established along the surface and bend lines are not required.

Parts that are composed of flat surfaces, such as prisms and pyramid shapes, along with single-curved surfaces, such as cylinders and cones, are developable. In other words, they can be laid flat and constructed of one single piece of material. Double-curved and warped surfaces on the other hand are considered to be undevelopable. **Spheres, paraboloids, oblique helicoids,** and **cylindroids** are examples of undevelopable surfaces. Approximate methods can be used to develop these types of surfaces adequately.

21.2   Types of Developments

There are four types or classifications of developments. The division of developments is based on the shape of the surface and/or the method employed to construct its development.

1. **Parallel line**   Forms that are composed of parallel straight-line elements or edges: cylinders, prisms. The cylindrical shape of the exhaust ducting for the power plant turbine is a parallel line surface (Fig. 21.3).
2. **Radial line**   Forms whose edges or elements define triangular surface areas: pyramids, cones. Many of the tunnel sections shown in Figure 21.4 are radial line surfaces created from the frustrums of a cone.
3. **Triangulation**   Forms whose surfaces must be broken into triangular areas. Transition pieces are the most common type of development for this category. The scrubber system shown in Figure 21.5 uses a variety of transition pieces which required triangulation for developing.
4. **Approximate**   Forms whose surfaces cannot be truly developed, such as warped and double-curved surfaces (spheres). The water tower shown in Figure 21.6 is an example of a surface that would require an approximate development.

FIGURE 21.3   **Power Plant Model**

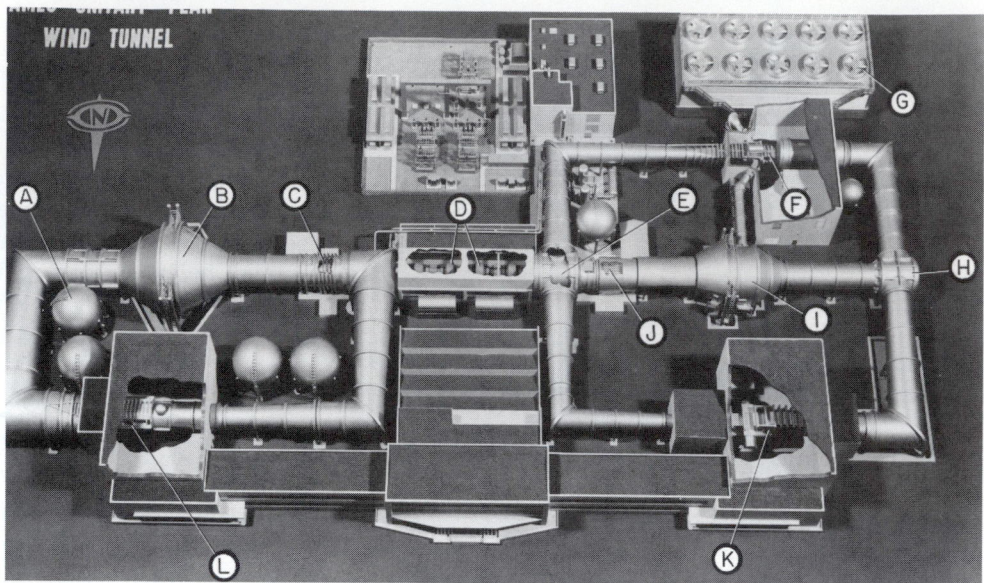

FIGURE 21.4   Wind Tunnel

21.2.1   Sheet Metal Developments

Many complex three-dimensional shapes are fabricated from flat sheet materials. The shape to be formed is subdivided into its simplest elements, which individually have the shapes of prisms, cylinders, cones, pyramids, and spheres. All of these shapes can be formed from a two-dimensional sheet of material by first cutting to the proper pattern and then folding or rolling the material into the three-dimensional form. Sheet metal is a typical material used for developable products or parts. HVAC ducting, transition pieces, and aircraft and spacecraft bodies are made from sheet metal developments.

The fabricator, working from drawings and specifications, develops pattern drawings of each component to be produced in the fabrication shop. These patterns are usually made to the full size of the object and can only be made after the true lengths of all lines that will lie on the pattern have

been determined. A pattern is a drawing composed entirely of true length lines. Therefore, all patterns are true shape/size. Each development must be drawn accurately so that the final product is of the correct shape within given tolerance limits. A **bend allowance** is usually added to the pattern drawing to accommodate the space taken by the bending process. A **tab** or **lap** is added to the pattern so that the two adjoining edges that form the seam may be attached. The width of this tab/lap depends on the type of joining

FIGURE 21.5   Air Filtration System Design with Right Vertical Prism and a Transition Piece

FIGURE 21.6   Ellipsoidal-Shaped Water Tower

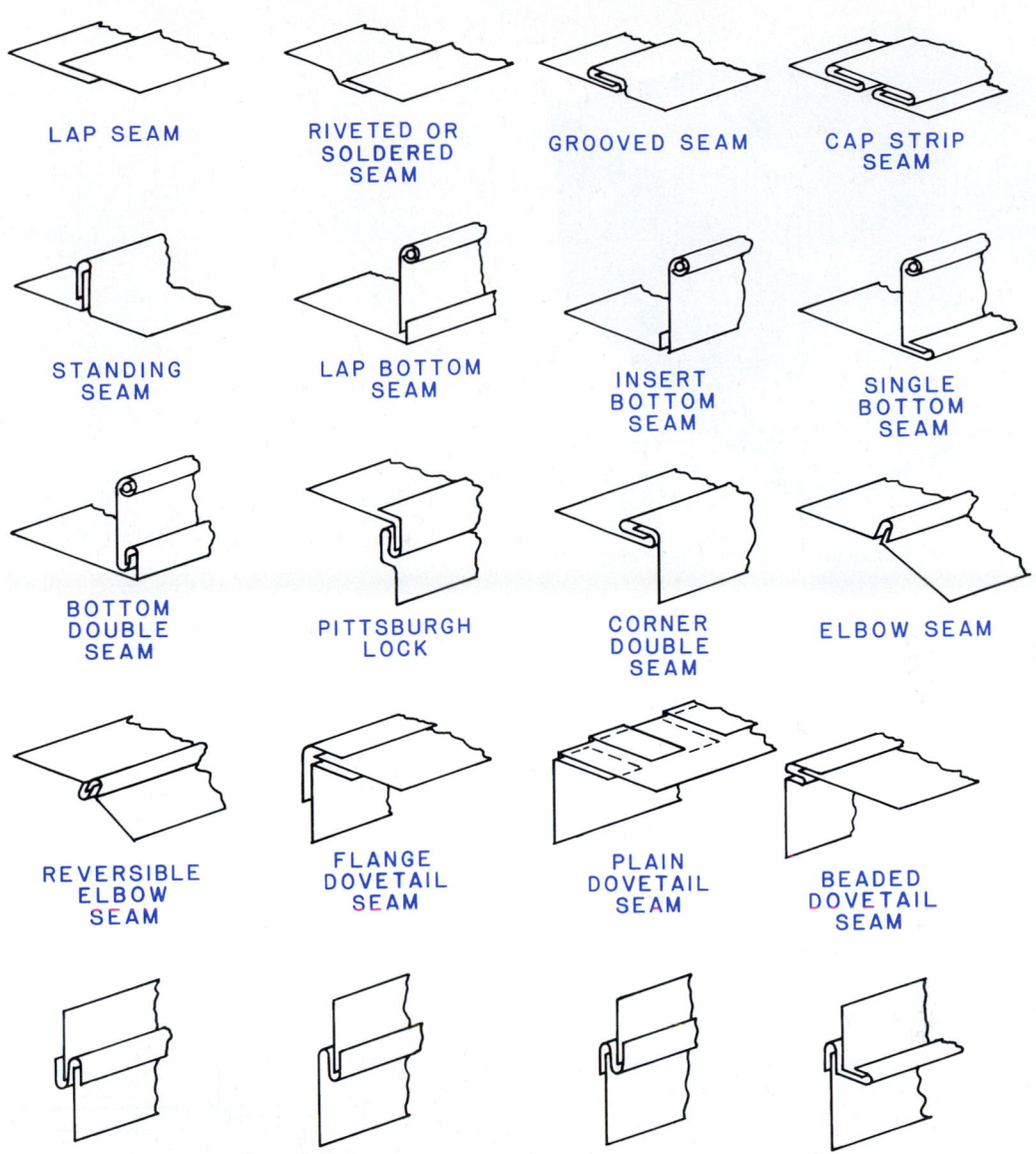

LAP SEAM   RIVETED OR SOLDERED SEAM   GROOVED SEAM   CAP STRIP SEAM

STANDING SEAM   LAP BOTTOM SEAM   INSERT BOTTOM SEAM   SINGLE BOTTOM SEAM

BOTTOM DOUBLE SEAM   PITTSBURGH LOCK   CORNER DOUBLE SEAM   ELBOW SEAM

REVERSIBLE ELBOW SEAM   FLANGE DOVETAIL SEAM   PLAIN DOVETAIL SEAM   BEADED DOVETAIL SEAM

SLIP "S" HOOKS FOR CROSS SEAM

FIGURE 21.7   **Standard Types of Seams Used in Sheet Metal Fabrication**

process. The length of the lap is normally established along the *shortest edge* so as to limit the amount and length of the seam. Throughout this chapter a bend allowance and a lap have been eliminated from the problems and example illustrations so as not to confuse the beginner. Each development will be a true development; one without bend allowances.

Typical seams used for sheet metal are shown in Figure 21.7. Seams are divided into mechanical or welded. The choice of seams is determined by the thickness of metal to be used, the type of metal, and the cost of fabricating the item. Welded and riveted seams are considered permanent and are used in applications where the pieces to be joined are thicker and are of heavier gage metals. Metal thicknesses are designated by gage number. From .25 in. and above, the thickness is designated by inches or metric sizes. See Appendix C for sheet metal sizes of common gage metals.

Much of electronic packaging involves the use and fabrication of sheet-metal parts to be used for chassis, panels, mounting plates, and a variety of enclosures and envelopes (Fig. 21.8). Sheet metal parts are normally made from a **blank** of sheet metal. Panels, mounting plates, and other parts are normally flat sheets of metal cut to the functional outline with the proper slots and holes punched out or machined as required. These flat, thin pieces of metal can be a variety of thicknesses, determined by the needs of packaging design.

Sheet metal configurations such as enclosures, chassis, cages, and some cabinets are laid out as developments of the original design. The industrial drawing of the chassis enclosure shown in Figure 21.9 has been developed as an inside-up pattern in Figure 21.10. The dashed lines on the pattern development are **bend lines**, lines along which the flat sheet metal will be bent. Another example of industrial

FIGURE 21.8 Sheet Metal Enclosure Used for Electronics Packaging

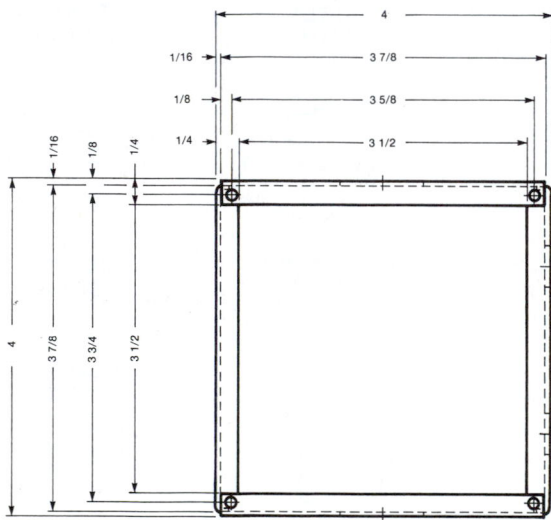

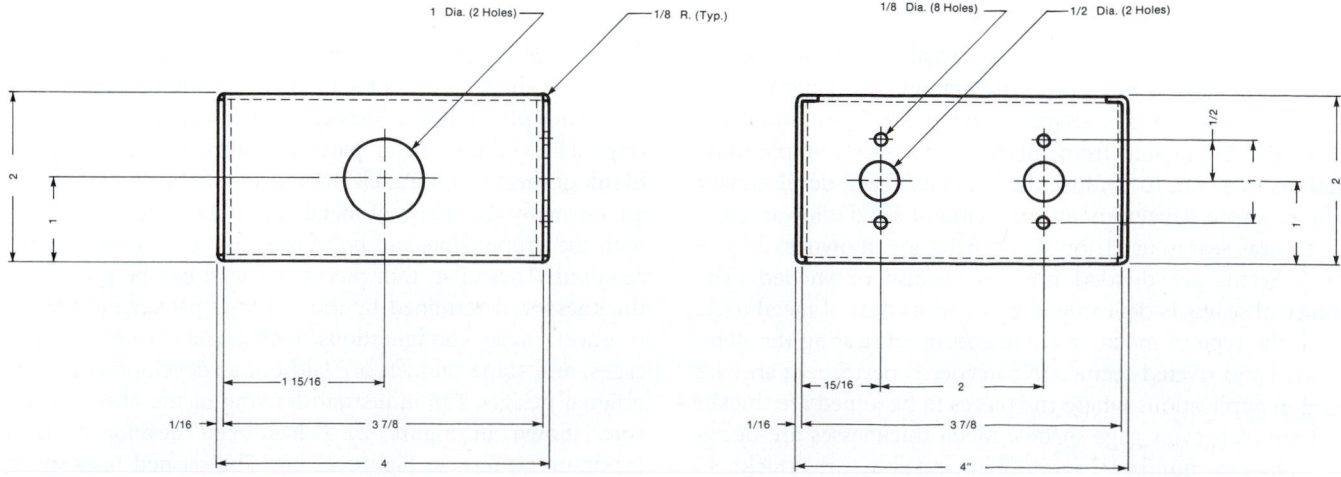

FIGURE 21.9 **Sheet Metal Chassis for Electronic Equipment** This item was developed from a single sheet of metal shown as a pattern in Figure 21.10.

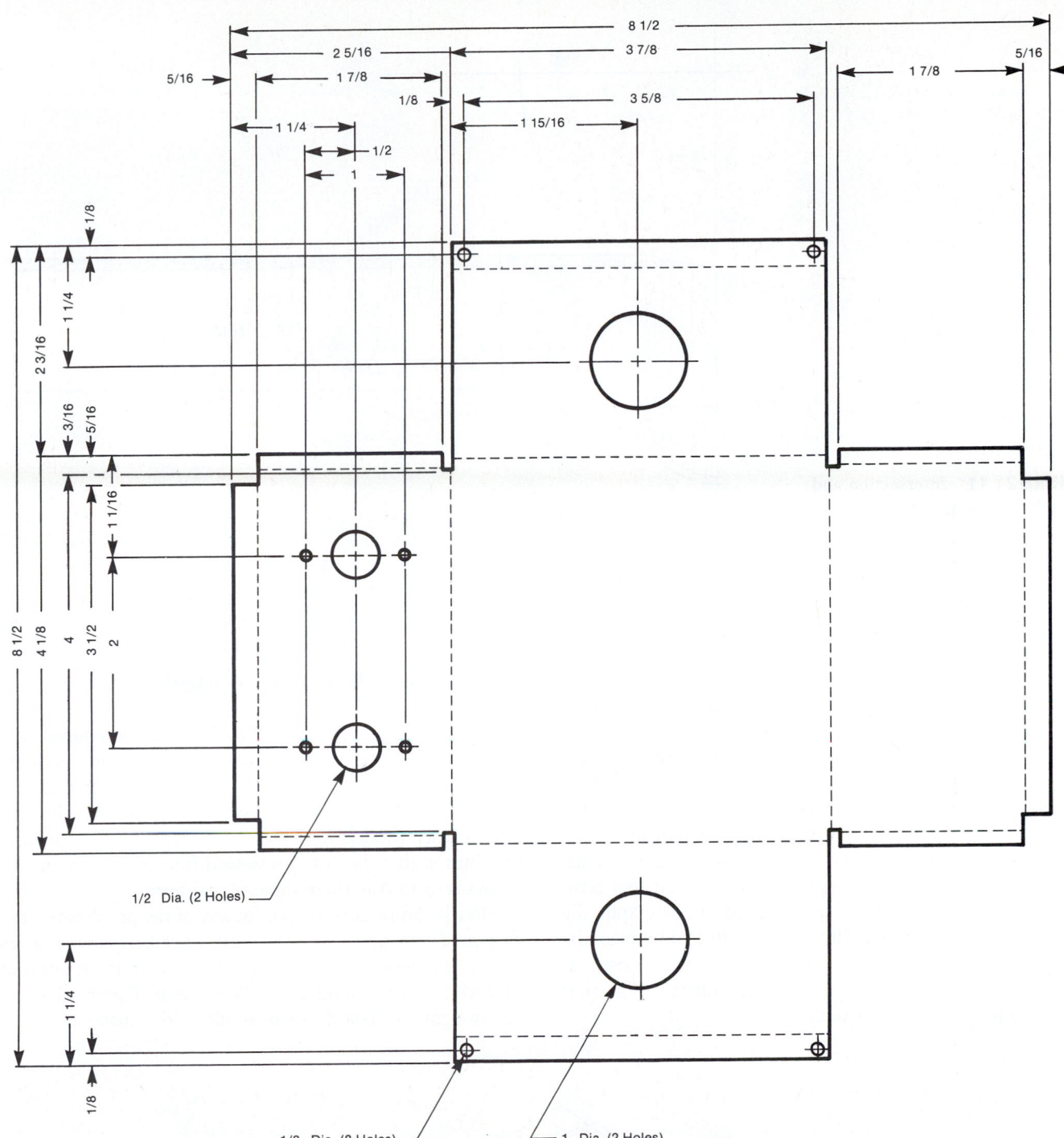

1/2 Dia. (2 Holes)

1/8 Dia. (8 Holes)

1 Dia. (2 Holes)

FIGURE 21.10   Pattern Development Used to Fabricate the Enclosure Shown in Figure 21.9

uses of patterns is given in Figure 21.11, where a pattern development has been drawn to serve as a pipe template. The template can be wrapped about the pipe to establish the shape to be cut.

21.2.2 Automated Flat Pattern Development

CAD software programs are available for flat pattern developments. Flat pattern development on a CAD system improves the speed and accuracy of transferring 3D part models into developed flat patterns. Such programs allow the designer to unfold the planes of the 3D part model on the screen of a graphics workstation. Figure 21.12 shows a 3D sheet metal design and the unfolded pattern.

The series of drawings in Figure 21.13 was generated on a CAD system. This software package includes dimensioning and programmed manufacturing. Figure 21.13 shows the sheet metal form as a 3D part model during the first stage of

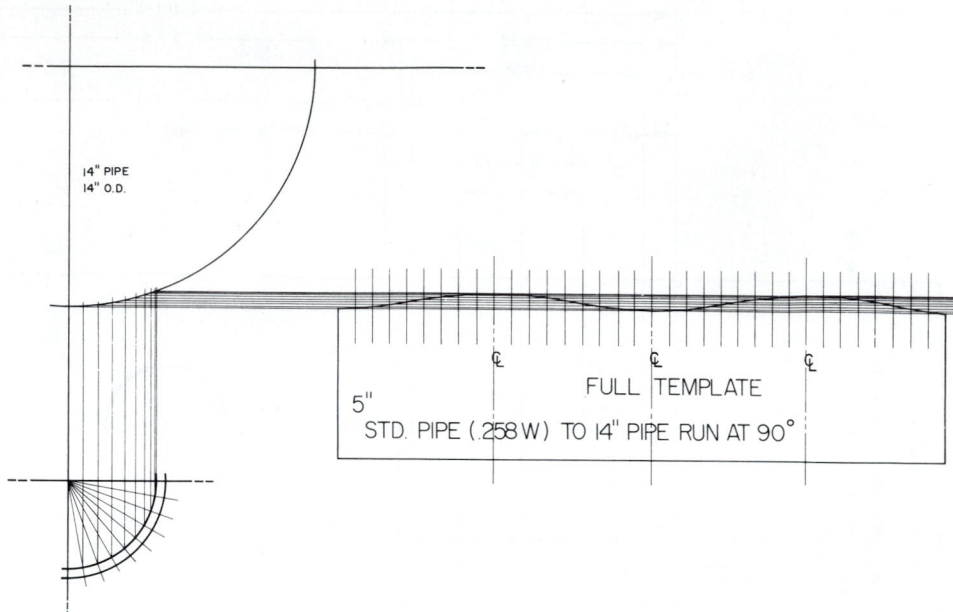

14" PIPE
14" O.D.

5"

FULL TEMPLATE

STD. PIPE (.258 W) TO 14" PIPE RUN AT 90°

FIGURE 21.11 Intersection and Template Pattern

unbending (originally a U-shape), as a finished flat pattern pictorial view, and as a dimensioned flat pattern shop drawing. The resulting flat pattern and punch tool configuration can be positioned in any orientation on the display screen. The pattern can be copied any number of times by means of a **nesting** technique. Nesting (see Chapter 17) allows the operator to create more parts with the best possible utilization of the sheet metal stock. This is done by repeating a flat pattern on the stock or by replicating the punch tool positions. Outlines of any stock size and shape can be graphically represented on the display. This nesting feature minimizes the percentage of excess scrap and reduces material costs. In Chapter 17, CAD software used for flat pattern design as it relates to packaging was covered.

21.2.3 Development of Models

Though a pattern is normally drawn full size, a reduced scale model is also made by the designer or drafter to check the design. Small-scale, accurate models are constructed for design analysis and to explain design variations to the fabricator or purchaser. Models have a distinct advantage over pictorial drawings in that they can be viewed from any angle and are always seen in true three-dimensional form.

Models can be constructed for any of the problems in this chapter. The pattern [Fig. 21.14(a)] is needed before a development and model is constructed. The pattern is cut out [Fig. 21.14(b)] and the model completed as in Figure 21.14(c). Lightweight cardboard, such as file folder material, works

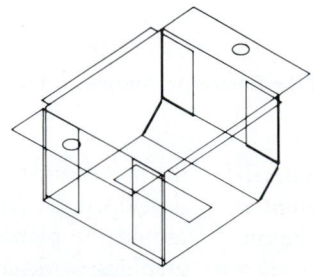

FOLDED 3-D SHEET METAL DESIGN

FIGURE 21.12 Sheet Metal Design on a CAD System

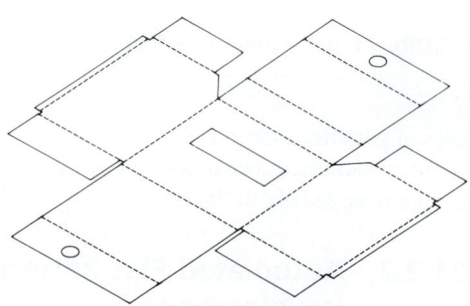

UNFOLDED SHEET METAL DESIGN

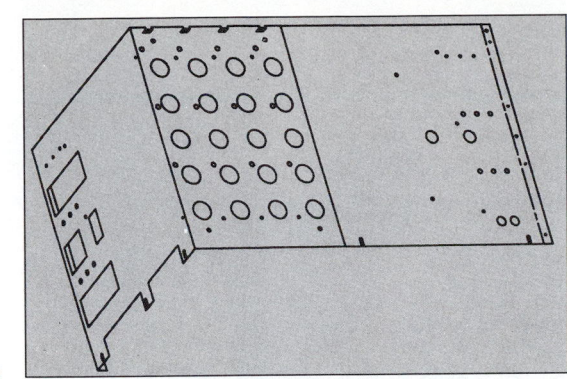

(a)

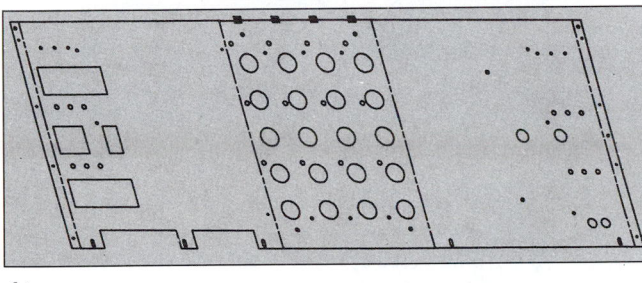

(b)

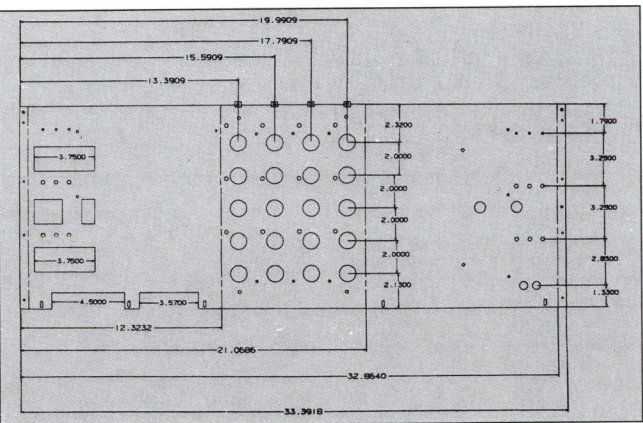

(c)

FIGURE 21.13   CAD Systems Allow the Designer/Drafter to Unfold the Design Automatically   (a) The first stage of unbending is complete. (b) The finished flat pattern can be displayed in an auxillary view. (c) The system automatically dimensions the flat pattern by incorporating the bending data.

well for making small models. The pattern outline and bend lines are easily transferred onto it, and it folds well, making sharp corners. Note that tabs were added along seam edges so as to join the form by gluing or taping [Fig. 21.14(a)]. Transfer the pattern onto the cardboard from a carefully executed projection by small pin pricks at controlling points (end points of edge/bend lines) or by the use of carbon paper. Transfer the pattern on the cardboard and cut along the outline. The resulting cardboard pattern is then folded along bend lines and joined along the tabs [Fig. 21.14(c)].

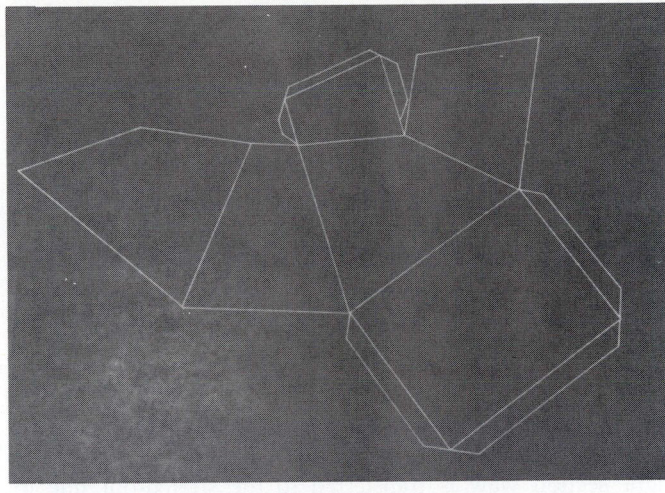

(a)

(b)

(c)

FIGURE 21.14   Development Model   (a) Cardboard model pattern drawing (b) Cutout pattern before gluing part in Figure 21.16 (c) Cardboard model

21.2.4   Development of a Truncated Right Prism

The first step in drawing a parallel line development is to find the true lengths of each edge line and the width of each face plane. A right section view shows the perimeter of the object. The length of the development is equal to the perimeter of the prism as measured in the right section view. A right section view is always taken perpendicular to the true length edge lines of a prism or the axis line of a cylinder (end view). The distance between each edge line/element is measured where they appear as points on the right section. The width of each lateral surface is equal to the distance between points on the right section and is transferred directly to the stretch-out line.

In Figure 21.15 the distance between points 1 and 2 in the right section view is transferred to the stretch-out line to establish the width of the first plane face. A **stretch-out line** is a construction line along which all perimeter dimensions are laid off. The prism is unfolded clockwise using the shortest edge as the seam when it is required. In Figure 21.15 edge line 1 is used as the seam line, not the shortest edge. The stretch-out line is drawn perpendicular to the edge lines as shown. The edge lengths are projected from the frontal view. The outline of the development is then completed by connecting the endpoints of the edge lines. Edge lines in both the front view and the development are true length. The development itself is made completely of true length lines. Therefore, each lateral surface (plane face) is true shape/size, as is the total development. The length of the development can be checked by measuring the perimeter of the prism (the distance around the right section view). The development length must equal the perimeter.

21.2.5   Development of a Prism (Top Face and Lower Base Included)

When one end face of a prism is perpendicular to edge lines, a true shape end view is a right section. The stretch-out line is projected parallel to the edge view of an end surface, if that surface is perpendicular to the edge lines of the prism. The stretch-out line forms one complete edge of the development outline.

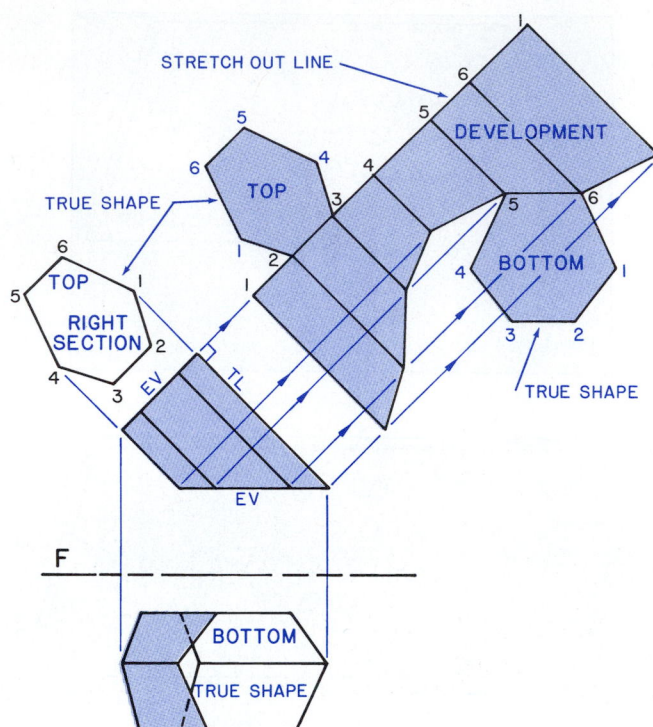

FIGURE 21.16   Prism Development Including End Surfaces

When the lower base and the upper face are required, a view showing these surfaces as true shape must be completed. The true shape of an end surface is established by projecting an auxiliary view perpendicular to the edge view of the base or top face. Each end surface is attached to an appropriate upper or lower border line of the development. A development's stretch-out line can be established at any convenient location on or off the paper. When this procedure is used, distances above and below the stretch-out line are transferred from the true length view to establish edge line (bend line) lengths on the development. The face widths are, as before, taken from the right section (or true shape end view).

In Figure 21.16 the development of the prism is required. The bottom surface and the top face are to be included as part of the development. Line 1 is used as the seam. The following steps were used to solve the problem:

1. The edge lines of the prism are frontal lines (true length in the frontal view). The prism is laid on its side. Therefore, draw the stretch-out line parallel to the edge view of the top face as shown. The bottom view is given instead of a top view for this example.
2. Project a true shape view of the top face (labeled "Right Section").
3. Transfer the face widths from the true shape/right section view and set off along the stretch-out line.
4. Project the edge line's end points to the development and connect them to form the outline. The stretch-out line is part of the outline on this development.
5. Attach the top face and the bottom base as shown. The base plane appears as true shape in the bottom view. The upper and lower surfaces can be attached along any related line on the development's outline.

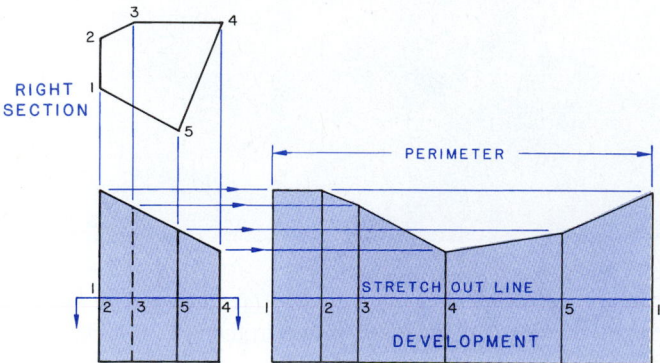

FIGURE 21.15   Development of a Right Truncated Prism

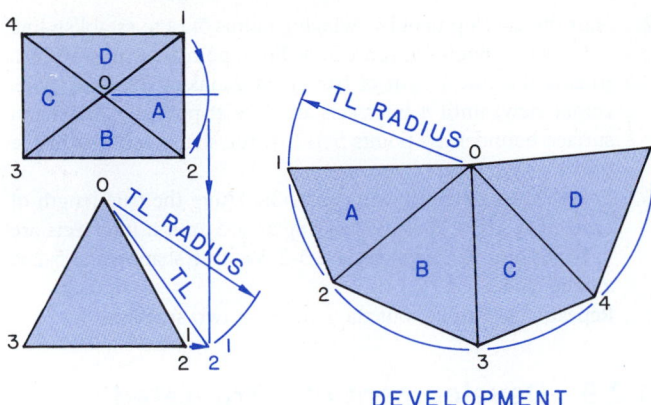

FIGURE 21.17 Development of a Right Pyramid

21.2.6 Development of a Right Pyramid

Developments of surfaces that are composed of triangular planes, such as pyramids, or that can be divided into small triangular areas, cones, are considered **radial line developments**. Each lateral edge of a pyramid, or element of a cone, *radiates* from the vertex point.

To develop a pyramid, it is necessary to establish the true length of each of its lateral edges and baselines. The development of a pyramid consists of laying out the true shape of each lateral surface in successive order. If the pyramid is a right pyramid, each of its lateral edges will be of equal length. Therefore, the true length of only one lateral edge is necessary.

In Figure 21.17 the perimeter of the base is true length in the horizontal (top) view. Revolve an edge line until parallel to the frontal plane to obtain its true length in the frontal view. Use this true length edge line as the **true length radius.**

To start the development, locate vertex point 0 at a convenient location. Swing an arc from point 0 using the TL radius. Starting with point 1, lay off the true length distances transferred from the base edges in the horizontal view. Lines 1-2, 2-3, 3-4, and 4-1 are true length in the top view. Connect each point with vertex point 0 and draw straight-line chords between the points to establish the base perimeter on the development.

21.2.7 Development of a Truncated Right Pyramid

In Figure 21.18 the frontal and horizontal views of a truncated right pyramid are given. A development, including its upper face (truncated surface), is required. The following steps were used in the solution:

1. Draw the F/A folding line parallel to the edge view of the truncated face and complete auxiliary view A. The upper/top face is true shape here.
2. Establish the true length of edge line 0-1 by revolution. The true length of 0-1 is equal to all other edge lines and is used as the TL radius.
3. Solve for the true length of the distances from vertex point 0 to where each edge line has been cut. Points 1^1, 2^1, 3^1, 4^1, etc., represent the points at which the lateral edge lines have been cut. True length distances $0-1^1$, $0-2^1$, $0-3^1$, etc., are used to establish the upper outline of the development.
4. Locate vertex point 0 at a convenient location. Swing the TL radius (radius 0-1) an indefinite length.
5. Line $1-1^1$ is the shortest edge. Therefore, it is used as the seam. Draw line 0-1 on the development and step off the baseline distances along the arc. Distances 1-2, 2-3, 3-4, 4-5, 5-6, 6-7, 7-8, and 8-1 (taken from the horizontal view) are laid off along

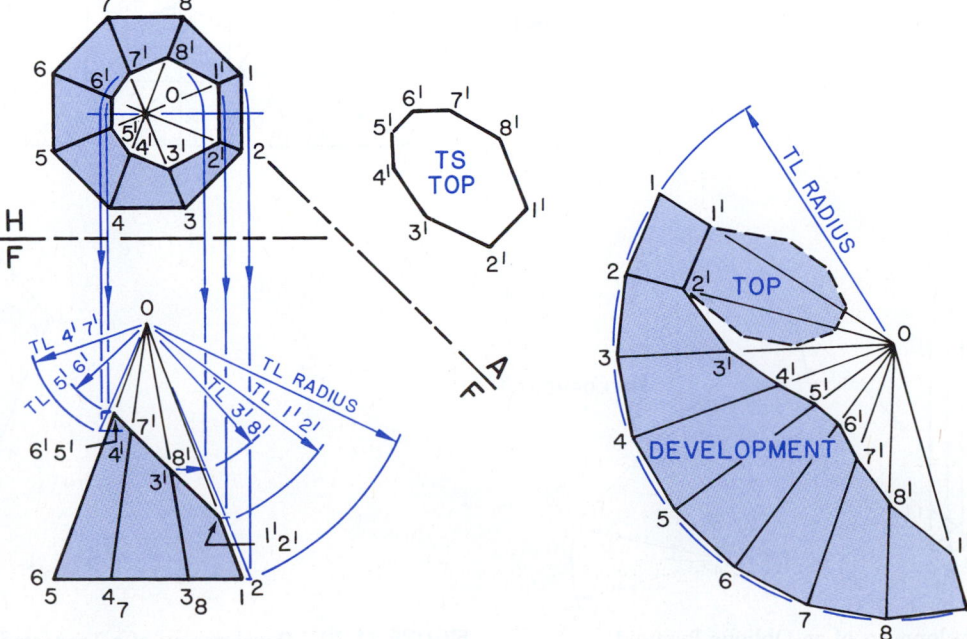

FIGURE 21.18 Truncated Pyramid Development

the arc. Each base length is equal since the base plane is an octagon. Therefore, distance 1-2 is used for the chord lengths.

6. Connect the base points to vertex point 0. Draw these lines as construction lines only. The actual bend lines include the distance from the base points to the cut points.

7. Connect the base points in sequence as straight-line chords to establish the lower outline of the development.

8. Transfer distance 0-1^1 to line 0-1 on the development. Repeat this procedure to locate the cut points on the development. Connect points 1^1, 2^1, 3^1, 4^1, etc., to form the development's upper outline.

9. Attach the true shape of the top surface to the development along a common line.

21.2.8   Development of an Oblique Pyramid

The development of an oblique pyramid is similar to that of a right pyramid, except that the lateral edges of an oblique pyramid are unequal. Hence, a radius cannot be used to speed the development process. The true length of each lateral edge must be determined separately. Two methods are commonly used: the true length diagram and the revolution method. In this section the revolution method has been employed.

The base plane normally appears as an edge in the frontal view and parallel to the horizontal plane. When this is the case, the true shape of the base plane shows in the horizontal view. A true shape view provides the true length of the base's perimeter. The development is constructed by drawing each triangular lateral surface as true shape with common edges joined. In Figure 21.19 the development of the oblique prism is required. The following steps were used to solve the problem:

1. Revolve each lateral edge line about vertex point 5 in the horizontal view and show in the frontal view as true length measurements. On the development each of these lines is used as a true length radius.

2. Start the development by swinging radius 5-1R to establish line 5-1. From point 5 swing arc 5-2R. From point 1, swing arc 1-2R (this is the true length of baseline 1-2, taken from the horizontal view) until it intersects arc 5-2R at point 2. The lateral surface bounded by points 5-1-2 is true shape, with its inside up.

3. From vertex point 5, swing arc 5-3R. Using the true length of baseline 2-3 as radius 2-3R, swing an arc until it intersects arc 5-3R at point 3. Lateral surface 5-2-3 is true shape. Line 5-2 is a bend line.

4. Repeat step 3 to lay out the remaining two surfaces.

21.2.9   Development of a Truncated Oblique Pyramid

A truncated oblique pyramid is easily developed when the vertex point can be established on the drawing. The true lengths of the edge lines from the vertex point to the base points must be determined first. In Figure 21.20 the frontal and horizontal views of the oblique prism are given. The following steps were used to develop the part:

1. Extend the lateral edge lines to establish vertex point 0.

2. Revolve each extended lateral edge line in the horizontal view and show as true length in the frontal view.

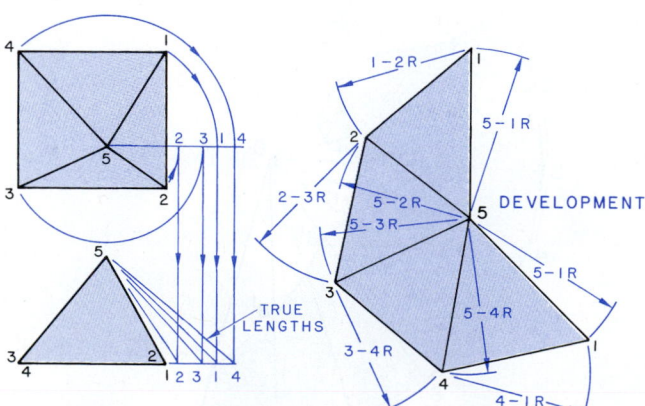

FIGURE 21.19   Development of an Oblique Pyramid

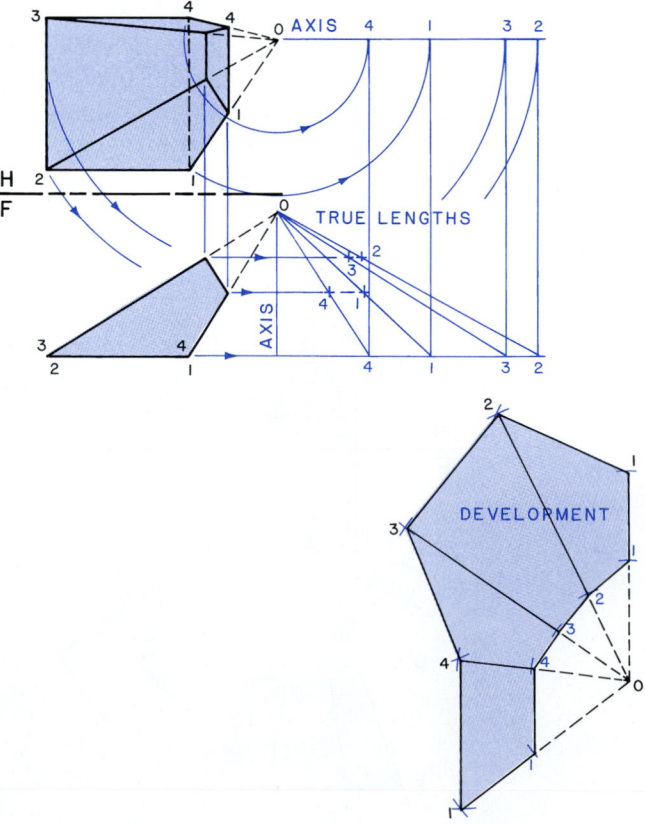

FIGURE 21.20   Development of a Truncated Oblique Pyramid

3. Establish the true lengths of the bend lines (cut edges) by projecting each cut point in the frontal view, perpendicular to the axis line until it intersects its related true length revolution.

4. Start the development by drawing edge line 0-1. Using baseline 1-2 as the radius, swing arc 1-2 from point 1. Swing an arc from vertex point 0 using line 0-2 as the radius, until it intersects arc 1-2 at point 2. Triangular plane 0-1-2 is one panel/face of the development. Complete the remaining triangular faces.

5. Complete the layout by establishing the cut edges to form the upper edge of the development as shown.

You May Complete Exercises 21.1 Through 21.4 at This Time

21.3 Curved Surfaces

In the preceding sections the developments of geometric forms were straight lines and plane surfaces. The development of forms whose surfaces are curved is also an important part of engineering design work. **Curved surfaces** fall into two basic categories: single-curved and double-curved.

A **single-curved surface** is a **ruled surface**, since it can be generated by the movement of a straight line. Cylinders, cones, and convolutes are the three types of single-curved surfaces. In Figure 21.6 the base support of the water tower is cylindrical. The wind tunnel in Figure 21.4 incorporates both cones and cylinders into its design. Single-curved surfaces are the most common and can be accurately developed.

A **double-curved surface** is generated by the movement of a curved line. The sphere, spheroid, torus, paraboloid, and hyperboloid are examples of double-curved surfaces. Double-curved surfaces can only be approximately developed. The water tank in Figure 21.6 is an example of a double-curved surface.

All curved surfaces are generated by the movement of a curved or straight line. The line that generates a surface is called a **generatrix**. Any one position of the generatrix is an **element** of the surface. The generatrix moves according to the **directrix**, which is a line or lines that define the direction and motion of the generatrix.

21.3.1 Development of Single-Curved Surfaces

Cylinders, cones, and convolutes are the three types of single-curved surfaces. A single-curved surface is generated by the movement of a straight line so that each of its two closest positions is in the same plane. Any two consecutive positions (elements) are parallel (as in a cylinder) or intersect (as in a cone or convolute).

A **cylinder** is generated by a straight-line generatrix moving around a curved directrix. The directrix is normally a closed curve (ellipse, circle, etc.). All positions of the generatrix (elements) are parallel to one another. A cylinder develops as a parallel-line development.

A **cone** is generated by the movement of one end of a straight-line element (generatrix) around a curved directrix (normally closed). The other end of the generatrix is fixed at one point: the vertex/apex. The positions of the generatrix establish elements on the surface of the cone. A development of a cone is a radial-line development since each of its elements radiates from the vertex point.

Convolutes are generated by a straight-line generatrix, which moves in accordance and tangent to a double-curved line (directrix). Two consecutive, but never three, elements intersect. Aircraft wings and fuselages, piping and ducting transition pieces, and automobile bodies are a few examples of the use of convolutes in industry.

21.3.2 Development of a Right Circular Cylinder

A cylinder is developed by unrolling its surface, normally inside-up. A right circular cylinder has a stretch-out line equal to its circumference: diameter × 3.141 (π), as in Figure 21.21. A right section (axis as a point) and a view showing the axis as true length are necessary to develop a cylinder. The edge view/right section determines the shape of the cylinder and provides a view where elements can be established on its surface. A true length view of the cylinder's axis shows all elements on its surface as true length. A development is made by rolling the lateral surface of the cylinder onto a plane.

In Figure 21.21 the right section of the cylinder is shown in the horizontal view. Elements are established along its surface by dividing the right section view into a number of equal parts. The elements are located by evenly dividing the circumference of the circular section as shown; 12, 16, or 24 radial divisions are commonly used. Each division is projected to the true length view (frontal view) to establish the elements on the lateral surface. The stretch-out line is drawn perpendicular to the true length view. The base perimeter may be used as the stretch-out line if it is perpendicular to the cylinder's axis as in the example. The stretch-out line is divided into the same number of equally spaced parts as the right section and labeled accordingly. The true length of each element is projected to the development, from the true length view, to establish its outline. In Figure 21.21 both bases are perpendicular to the axis. Therefore, all elements are the same length and the development unrolls as a rectangle, its height equaling the altitude of the cylinder and length equal to the circumference. Cylinders are a single surface; therefore, the elements are drawn as thin construction lines in all views and on the development.

21.3.3 Development of Intersecting Cylinders

In Figure 21.22 the development of two cylinders intersecting with a 90° **miter bend** is shown. The following steps were used to solve the problem:

1. Draw a half circle and divide into equal parts as shown. The half section corresponds to the end view (right section) of the cylinder. Label the intersection of the division lines from 1 to 7.
2. Project points 1 through 7 to the front view where they intersect the miter line.
3. Extend a stretch-out line perpendicular to the front view of the pipe (axis line) and lay off the length of the development using the calculated circumference (or set off the chord distances, 1-2, 2-3, etc.).
4. Divide the circumference into equal parts (12 here) along the stretch-out line and label as shown.
5. Project the height dimension of each element from the front view to the development.
6. Connect points on the development with a smooth curve.
7. The development can now be transferred to a pattern and cut out to use as a wrap-around template.

In Figure 21.23 two cylinders of different diameters are intersecting at 90° to form a tee. The following steps were used to solve the problem:

1. Draw the front and side views of the intersecting pipes (excluding the line of intersection).
2. Draw half circles (above each view) corresponding to the branch pipe circumference and divide it into equal parts.
3. Project the points into the views as shown. Where the points intersect the header (main larger pipe) in the side view, label the intersection points as shown and project to the front view.

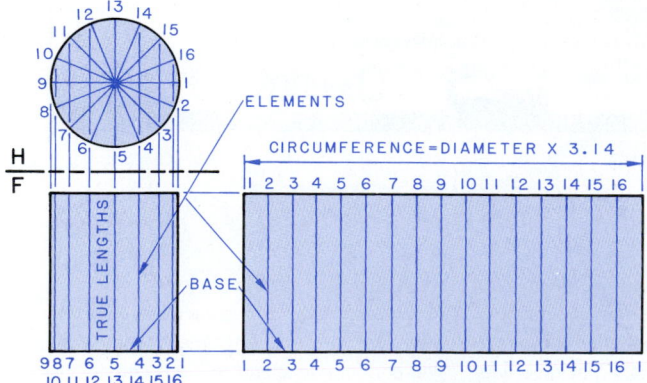

FIGURE 21.21   Development of a Right Cylinder

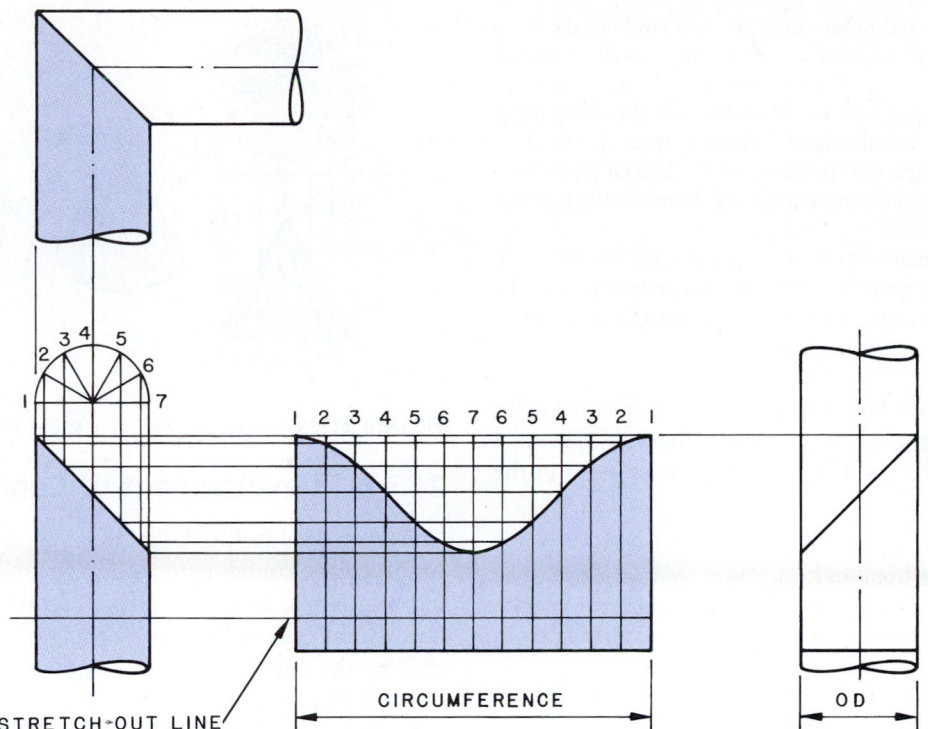

FIGURE 21.22   Development of a 90° Elbow

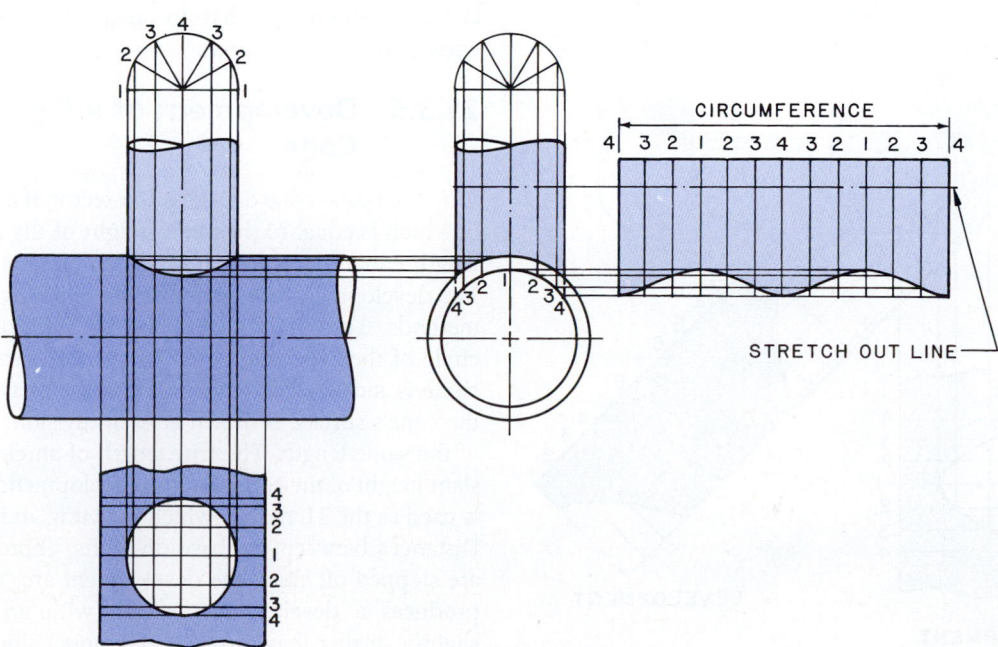

FIGURE 21.23   Development of a 90° Tee with Pipes of Differing Diameters

4. Project the numbered points from the half circle to the front view. Where they intersect corresponding points extended from the side view, points along the line of intersection are established. If the pipes are the same diameter the lowest point is established by calculating the distance from the header's centerline (2 × pipe wall thickness of the branch pipe). This method is used because the branch will fit inside the hole cut from the header.

5. Calculate the circumference of each pipe and establish the length of the developments. Divide the circumferences into 12 equal parts and establish the element lengths by projecting the points from the front view as shown.

Figure 21.24 describes how to establish a development for two pipes intersecting at something other than 90°. Here the pipes intersect at 45°. The following steps were used in the solution:

1. After drawing the front and side views, construct half-circle end sections and divide into equal parts as shown.
2. Project the end section divisions (points) to the front view to establish the line of intersection.
3. Draw the stretch-out lines perpendicular to the pipes and calculate their respective circumferences.
4. Divide the circumference length into 12 equal parts, project the related points to the development, and connect the points with a smooth curve.

You May Complete Exercises 21.5 Through 21.8 at This Time

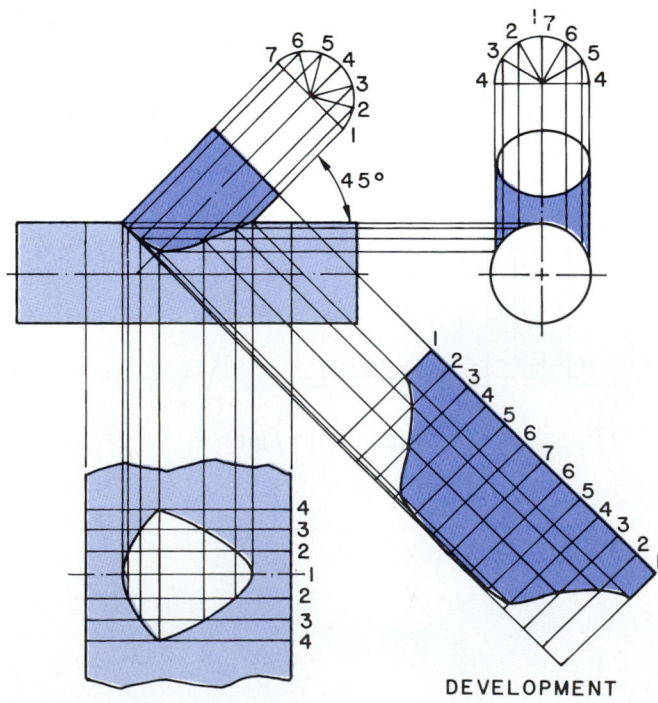

DEVELOPMENT

DEVELOPMENT

FIGURE 21.24 Pipe Lateral Pattern

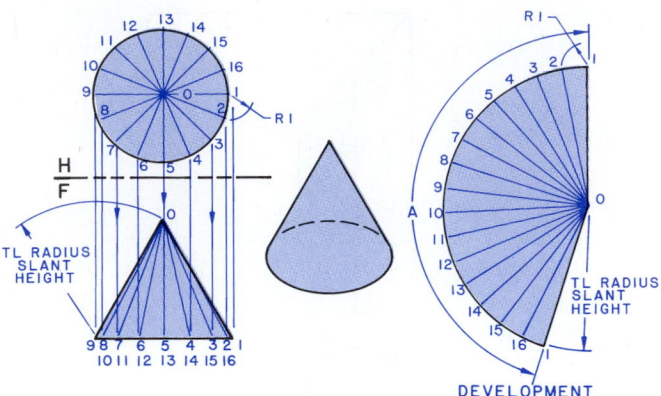

FIGURE 21.25 Development of a Right Circular Cone

21.3.4 Development of Cones

Cones are used in the design of a variety of industrial products, airplane configurations, storage tanks, ducting and piping transitions, and numerous structural, architectural, and mechanical designs. A **cone** is a single-curved surface generated by the movement of a straight-line generatrix, fixed at one end and intersecting a curved directrix. The fixed point is the vertex and the directrix is normally a closed curve (usually a circle or ellipse). Each position of the generatrix establishes an element on the surface of the cone. All elements of a cone terminate at the vertex point. Therefore, the development of a cone is a radial-line development. The generatrix of a cone is a straight line.

There are three general types of cones: right circular, oblique, and open. A **right circular cone** is a cone of revolution generated by revolving the generatrix about an axis line with a circle as a directrix and an axis perpendicular to the base plane (directrix plane). An **oblique cone** has an axis that is not perpendicular to its base plane. Its directrix is a closed curve. An **open cone** has an open single-curved or double-curved line as a directrix.

21.3.5 Development of a Right Circular Cone

A right circular cone develops as a sector of a circle, the radius of which is equal to the **slant height** of the cone with an arc length equal to the length of the circumference of the cone. The development of a right circular cone involves one of two methods. The graphical method involves dividing the base circle of the cone into equal parts. In Figure 21.25 the base circle is radially divided into 16 equal parts. An element on the cone's surface is drawn at each division. All elements are of the same length. The true length of an element equals the slant height of the cone. For the development, the slant height is used as the TL radius, which is swung an indefinite length. Distances between the base divisions, chord measurements, are stepped off along the development arc, R1. This method produces a development pattern with an arc length (A) slightly smaller than a true development since the chord distance between base divisions is smaller than the arc distance.

When an accurate development is required of a right circular cone, the arc angle (A) can be calculated. Angle (A) is the *sector angle* of the development. The sector angle (angle A) equals the radius of the cone's base divided by the slant height times 360° [angle A = radius (of base)/slant height × 360°]. The development is drawn using the computed sector angle to establish the length of the arc of the development.

21.3.6 Development of a Truncated Right Circular Cone

The development of a truncated right circular cone can be established by drawing the sector as in Figure 21.25. The upper outline of the development, corresponding to the truncated surface, is determined using the same general method as that for a truncated right pyramid. A right circular cone will have equal elements (Fig. 21.26).

In Figure 21.26 a development of the truncated right circular cone is required. The following steps were used to solve the problem:

1. Divide the cone's circular base into 12 evenly spaced parts to establish the surface elements and project to the F view.
2. Label the elements and the cut points along the elements as shown.
3. All elements are true length; therefore, the cut points (points A through G) may be moved perpendicular to the axis until they intersect element 1 or 7 (which appear true length in the frontal view). This procedure is simply the revolution of each cut point in the horizontal view and its true length projection in the frontal view.
4. Using element 0-1 as the slant height, swing an arc from vertex 0 to start the development. Establish the sector of the development by the graphical method, stepping off the cone's base chord distances on the sectors arc, 1-2, 2-3, 3-4, etc.

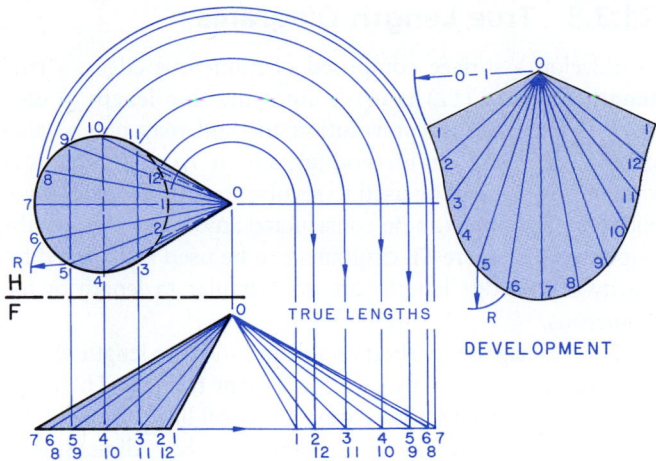

FIGURE 21.27   Development of an Oblique Cone

5. Transfer the true lengths of the upper portions of the elements to their related elements on the development and connect the cut points to form the upper outline. 0-A is transferred to element 0-1. 0-B is transferred to elements 0-2 and 0-12. 0-C is transferred to elements 0-3 and 0-11.

21.3.7 Development of an Oblique Cone

The development of an oblique cone is similar to the development of an oblique pyramid. Elements are established on the cone's surface by evenly dividing the base curve (Fig. 21.27). Since the cone is oblique, the elements are of different lengths. Therefore, the development is not a sector of a circle. Two adjacent elements and their corresponding **chordal distances** define a series of triangular planes on the cone's surface. The development of the cone involves laying out each successive triangle with common edges joined. The true length of each element is determined before the development is started. Revolution is used to establish the true length of the elements.

In Figure 21.27 a development of the oblique cone is required. The following steps were used in the solution:

1. Divide the cone's base in the horizontal view into 12 equal parts. Draw elements from vertex 0 to each point on the base. Show the frontal and horizontal views of the elements.
2. Determine the true length of each element.
3. Use the shortest element as the seam and draw the development inside-up. Start the development by drawing element 0-1.
4. From point 1 on the development, swing an arc (1-2) equal to the chordal distance R. All chords equal R.
5. Using the true length of element 0-2, swing an arc from vertex 0 until it intersects arc 1-2 (R) and locates point 2. Triangular plane 1-0-2 is the first of 12 successive planes representing the unrolled surface of the cone. Continue laying out the triangular planes as shown. Connect the end points of the elements with a smooth curve to complete the outline of the development.

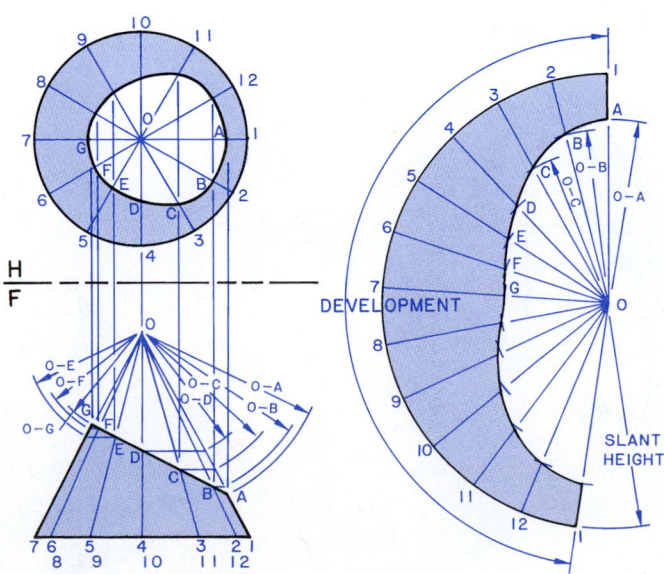

FIGURE 21.26   Development of a Truncated Cone

21.3.8   True Length Diagrams

To develop a surface composed of numerous edges, a **true length diagram** (TL) is used. Since the true length of each edge is necessary, the revolution method may not be adequate. The revolution method takes more room and requires that the given views be used to revolve the lines. A true length diagram, however, can be constructed anywhere on or off the paper. One or more TL diagrams can be used as required for clarity if the edge lengths are very similar in length or too numerous.

The TL diagram method establishes the true length of each edge surface element by creating a right triangle. The *height* dimension is drawn representing a vertical line dropped from the vertex point to the base plane. The *base* dimension is measured in the top view (H) as a straight line distance from the vertex (0) to one of the points on the curve's edge (0-8, 0-9, 0-10, etc.). The **hypotenuse** equals the true length of a corresponding edge line on the TL diagram, and is used to lay out the development (0-1, 0-2, etc.) (Fig. 21.28).

21.3.9   Development of a Conical Offset

A conical offset is sometimes used as a transition between two circular pipes of different diameters on different axes. This type of transition piece is actually a frustrum of an oblique cone. In order for the offset piece to be a frustrum, the upper and lower base planes must be parallel. Therefore, the two given pipes are intersected by parallel planes as shown in Figure 21.28.

In Figure 21.28 the frontal and horizontal views of the conical offset are given. Since the offset is symmetrical, only a half development needs to be drawn. The vertex is located by extending the edge lines of the offset until they intersect at vertex 0. Elements are established on the surface of the offset,

where it appears as a circle. The elements are drawn from the vertex through each division. The elements are then projected to the frontal view. A true length diagram is constructed in order to establish the true lengths and the frustrum (all points) of each element. Since the lower base of the offset is at an angle to the horizontal plane, the base end of the elements on the true length diagram will be at different elevations. The height dimensions can be projected from the frontal view.

The true length chordal distance between divisions on the offset's base cannot be determined in the given views. The lower base is revolved in the frontal view until parallel to the horizontal plane. A true shape view of the offset base is projected as shown. The true chordal distances, as represented by R, can now be used to lay out the approximate base outline of the development.

Start the development by locating the vertex point and drawing the shortest element 0-1 as shown. The lower leg of each thin triangular plane (representing the surface to be developed) is equal to the base divisions, e.g., 1-2, 2-3, 3-4, etc. Lay out the development using the true lengths from the TL diagram and the base divisions.

21.4   Transition Pieces

A general definition of a **transition piece** would include all shapes that connect two or more forms of different size. This broad definition would thus include types of developments already covered under cones and pyramids.

Transition pieces are developed by **triangulation**, dividing the surface of the piece into triangles. Triangulation has already been used to develop a variety of shapes in preceding sections. Elements are drawn on the surface of the form to be

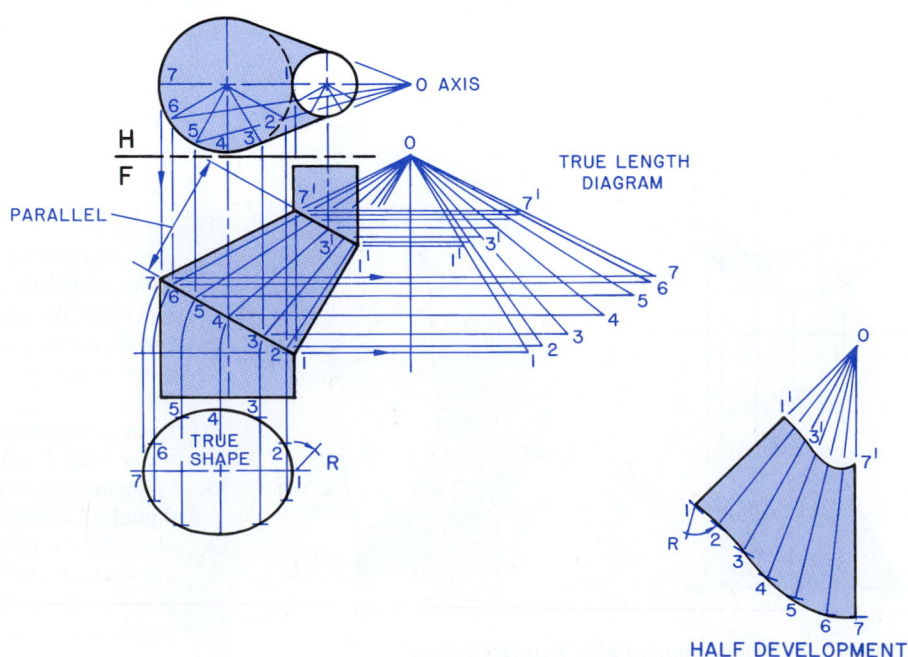

FIGURE 21.28 Development of
a Conical Offset

developed and connected by diagonals if adjacent elements do not intersect. The development is laid out as a series of joined triangular areas.

A transition piece joins two or more geometric forms. Therefore, each opening of the transition piece will be a different configuration. In general, transition pieces are designed to be formed from sheet metal or other materials and connected along a common seam. Transition pieces are used to join a variety of materials and objects. Pipe shapes and HVAC ducting utilize transition pieces throughout their design. Hoppers, warped funnels, and vessel bottoms of all types have transition pieces integrated into their design. The conical, convolute, or warped surface configuration of an aircraft's forward section is a transition piece between the nose and the fuselage.

In Figure 21.29, 11 possible variations of transition pieces are provided. The possibilities of shapes and sizes are limited only to the designer's imagination and the financial and production feasibilies. Types (a) and (b) are symmetrical square-to-round transitions. This type is one of the more

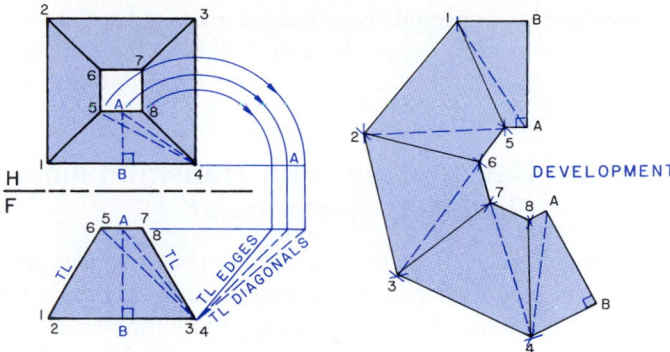

FIGURE 21.30 **Triangulation**

common variations; (c) is a rectangle-to-round transition and is developed with the same general method as (a) and (b); (d) is a square-to-rectangle transition. It is composed of plane surfaces and can therefore be accurately developed. Note that this type is really a frustrum of a right pyramid. Its given surfaces are developed by triangulation if the vertex is unavailable. The next three examples all involve the connecting of two or more circular or elliptical shapes: (e) is a conical offset connecting two separate pipes of differing diameters and axes; (f) is a *WYE* fitting, connecting two round pipes to one pipe of a larger diameter; and (g) is a three-stream transition into a single large-diameter pipe. The remainder are specialized variations of transition pieces: (h) round to oblong, (i) two square ducts to one round, (j) square-to-round transition at an angle, and (k) a hopper-type.

21.4.1 Triangulation

In Figure 21.30 the transition piece is developed using triangulation. The sheet metal hopper is an example of an industrial application of such a transition piece. The square to square form developed in Figure 21.30 has similarly shaped openings, and its edges can be extended to locate a vertex. Normally, when such a piece is to be developed, methods are used that utilize the vertex, and the development is constructed as a frustum of a pyramid. This form is used here only to provide a simple illustration of the triangulation of a surface. Each surface of the object is identical. Therefore, only one surface need be divided into a triangular area. A diagonal is drawn so as to divide one of the equal trapezoidal shapes into two triangular planes, 4-5. The true lengths of the hopper's edges and diagonals are established by revolution. The true lengths of the upper and lower openings appear in the horizontal view and can be transferred directly to the development.

To establish the shortest seam, divide the front surface in half. Line A-B will be used as the seam edge. This placement of the seam makes the joining method easier, quicker, and along the shortest line. This area must also be divided into triangles. Draw a diagonal from point A to point 4 and establish its true length by revolution.

Start the development by drawing line A-B longer than required. Using the true lengths of the edges, diagonals, and

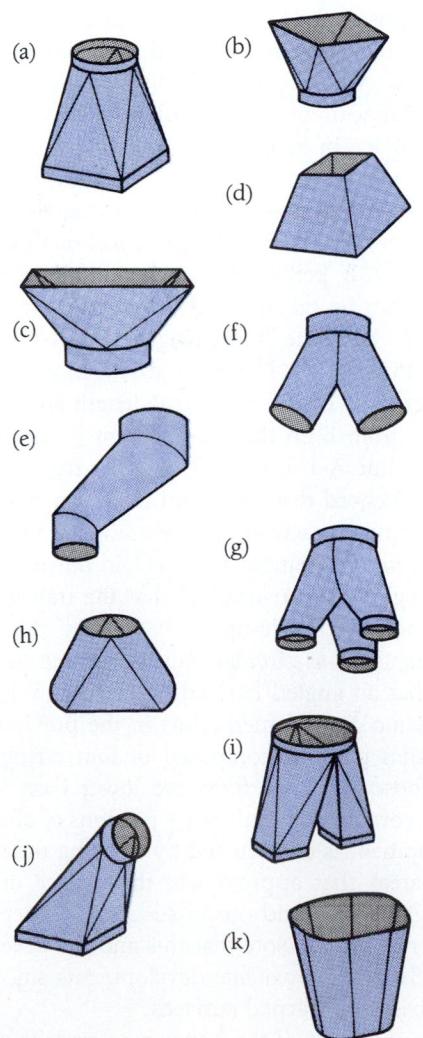

FIGURE 21.29 **Examples of Transition Pieces**

(a)
(b)
(c)
(d)
(e)
(f)
(g)
(h)
(i)
(j)
(k)

upper and lower opening edge lines as arc lengths, complete the development as shown. Triangle A-B-4 is a right triangle. Swing arc B-4 and 4-A to locate point A. Arcs A-8 and 4-8 intersect at point 8.

21.4.2 Development of a Transition Piece: Circular to Rectangular

A transition piece connecting a circular-to-rectangular geometric form is developed by dividing its surface as in Figure 21.31. The surface of the transition piece is composed of four isosceles triangles and four conical surfaces. The bases of the isosceles triangles form the lower base of the transition piece. The four conical surfaces are portions of an oblique cone. The first step in the development of a circular-to-rectangular transition is to divide the conical surfaces into triangular areas. In Figure 21.31 the circumference of the circular base is divided into 12 equal parts. Points 1, 4, 7, and 10 already exist as divisions since they correspond to the vertex points of the isosceles triangular areas of the piece's surface. All other points divide the conical surfaces into three separate areas. Since the transition piece is symmetrical, each of the four conical surfaces and their triangular divisions are identical. Therefore, the true lengths of only one set of elements need be established.

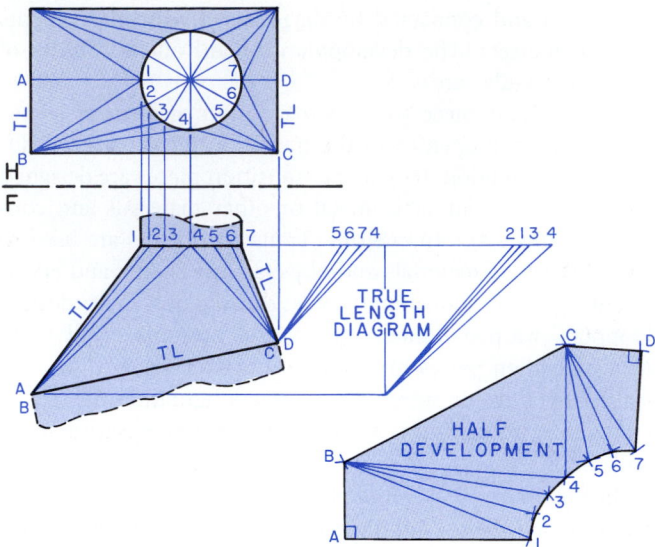

FIGURE 21.32 Transition Piece Development

A true length diagram is constructed as shown to establish the true lengths of the four elements. The true lengths of the lower rectangular base can be found in the horizontal view as can the chord distances between divisions on the upper circular base. The seam line is established by dividing the frontal triangular surface in half. Line 1-A will be used as the seam line.

Start the development by laying out triangle A-B-1. Draw line A-1 longer than the final length. Construct the triangle by drawing line A-B perpendicular to construction line A-1. Length A-B can be taken directly from the top view of the part, since the base line is true length here. A-B is one-half of base line B-E. Length B-1 and E-1 are the same, therefore use the TL diagram to establish the true length and swing an arc (radius B-1) from B on the development to where it crosses construction line A-1 at point 1. Use the true lengths of the elements, the chord distances, and the lower base lengths as arc lengths. Lay out each successive triangular surface to complete the drawing. Triangle 1-B-2 is laid out next. Each successive triangle is constructed so that the transition piece is unrolled clockwise inside-up.

The rectangular-to-circular transition piece shown in Figure 21.32 has an angled base edge. This figure is developed using the same general method as in the previous example. The transition piece is composed of four triangular lateral surfaces whose baselines form the lower base edge of the figure. The corners of the piece are portions of oblique cones. The development is constructed by dividing the surface into triangular areas that approximate the surface of the piece. Each triangle is then laid out in successive order with common elements joined. Note that this and the development in Figure 21.31 are *approximate* developments since the given forms are basically warped surfaces.

The circumference of the upper base circle is divided into equal parts. Elements that define triangular areas on the conical surface are drawn through the division points and con-

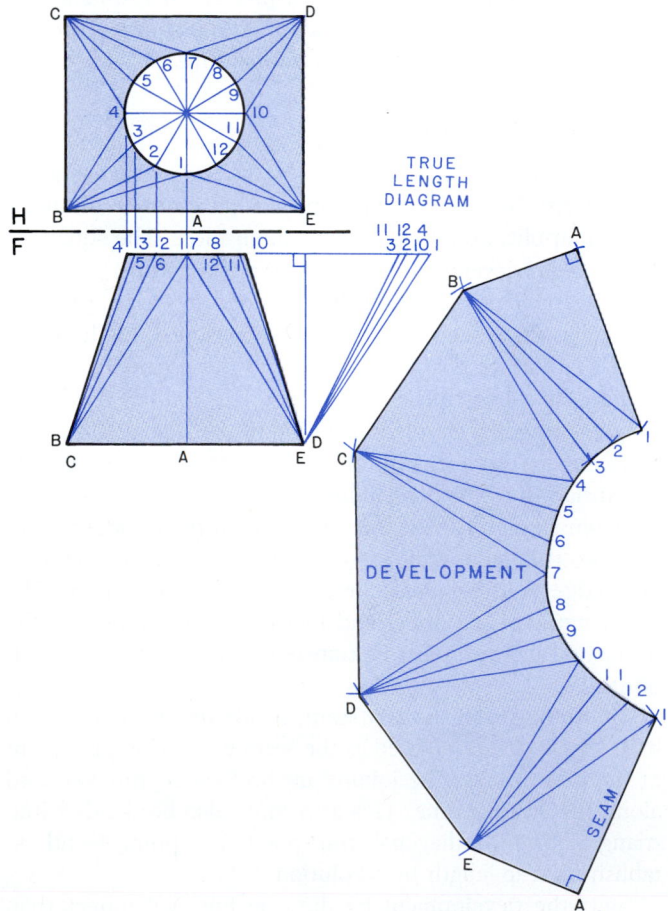

FIGURE 21.31 Transition Piece Development: Circular to Rectangular

nected to one of the lower base corners. The elements correspond to bend lines when the piece is formed by rolling a flat piece of sheet metal that was cut to the outline of the pattern. Since the lower base is at an angle and the circular base is not centered left to right, as was Figure 21.31, there will be a total of eight separate element lengths to establish before the development can be started. To avoid confusion, two true length diagrams are drawn as shown. Revolution could also have been used to determine the true lengths of the elements.

The true lengths of the lower base edges can be seen in the horizontal view for the right (C-D) and left (A-B) edges. The front (edge line B-C) and rear edge appear true length in the frontal view. The true length chord distances of the upper base are transferred directly from the horizontal view to the development.

In Figure 21.32 a half development is constructed, since the piece is symmetrical. The half development can be flipped over to complete the full pattern. Line D-7 is used as the seam edge line since it is the shortest line. The true lengths of the elements, baselines, and chord distances are used to lay out the development.

Start the development by drawing line A-1. Line A-B is drawn perpendicular to line A-1 to form the first triangular area, A-1-B. Triangle 1-B-2 is laid out next. Complete the half development by laying out each successive triangular area as shown.

21.4.3 Development of a Warped Transition Piece

A **warped surface** is considered to be theoretically nondevelopable. By dividing its surface into a series of small triangles, a warped transition piece can be adequately developed by approximation. The warped transition piece in Figure 21.33 connects a large circular shape to a smaller circular shape at an angle. The upper and lower base are divided into

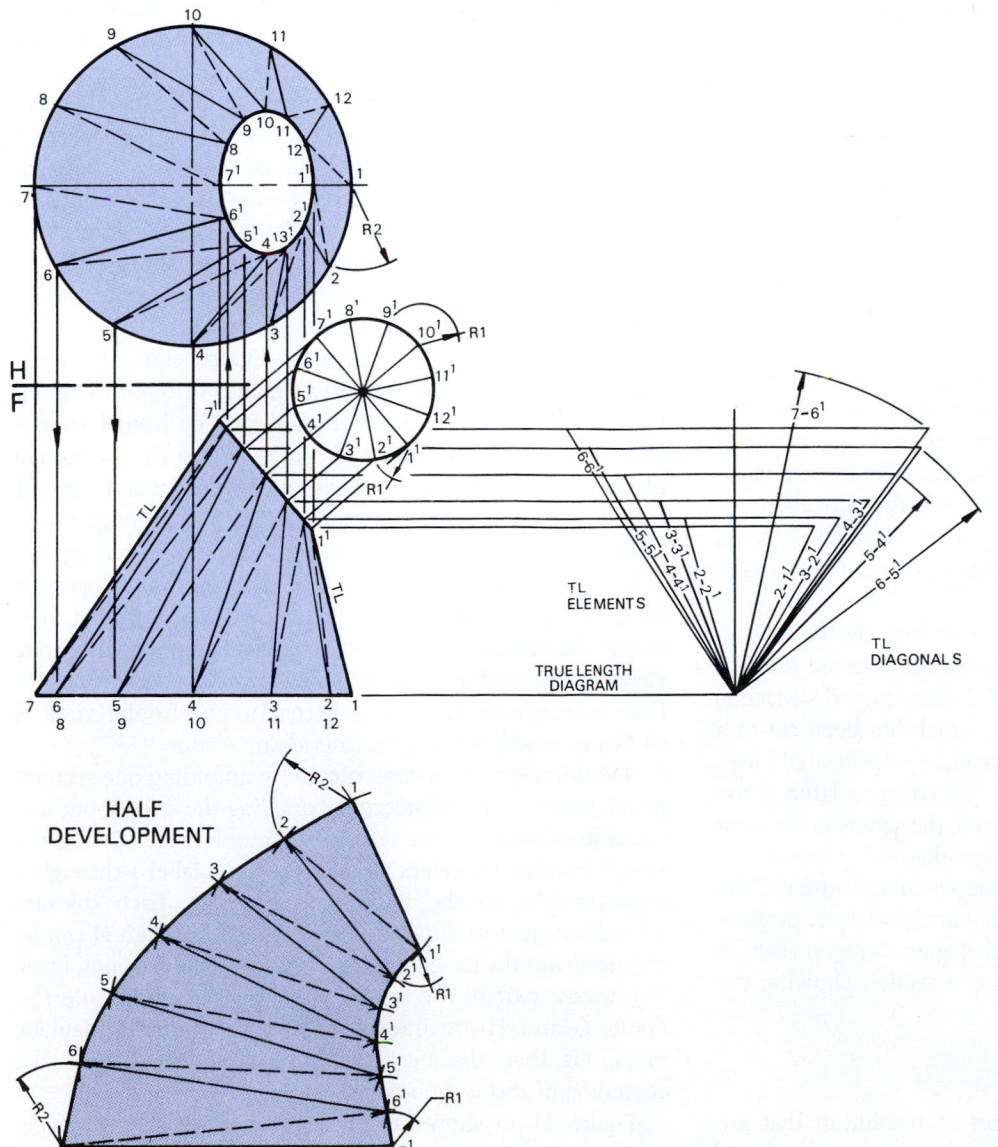

FIGURE 21.33 Development of a Warped Transition Piece

the same number of equal divisions and labeled in accordance with related points along the lower base. An auxiliary view showing the true shape of the upper base is projected in order to divide the circumference conveniently and to determine the true chord distances between divisions, R1. The chord distances on the circumference of the lower base appear as true length in the horizontal view, R2. Related points on the upper and lower bases are connected to establish elements. Diagonals are drawn between adjacent points on opposite bases, e.g., $7\text{-}6^1$. The true length of each element and diagonal is determined by constructing a true length diagram.

Using the true lengths of the elements, diagonals, and the upper and lower chord distances as true length arcs, lay out the development as shown. Line $1\text{-}1^1$ is used as the seam line since it is the shortest element. Draw line $1\text{-}1^1$ to start the development. Swing arc R2 from point 1 until it intersects arc $1^1\text{-}2$ at point 2. This will lay out triangle $1\text{-}1^1\text{-}2$. Continue to construct each successive triangular area unfolding the transition piece clockwise, inside-up. A half development is all that is necessary since the piece is symmetrical.

You May Complete Exercises 21.9 Through 21.12 at This Time

21.5   Double-Curved Surfaces

Double-curved surfaces are divided into two basic types: surfaces of revolution and double-curved surfaces of the general type. General types of double-curved surfaces are composed of curved lines or contours drawn at predetermined spacings. Contour maps, topographic models, and fairing surfaces of ships, airplanes, automobiles, and spacecraft are examples of the general type of double-curved surfaces. **Double-curved surfaces of revolution** are generated by the movement of a curved-line generatrix moving about a straight-line axis (directrix). A double-curved surface is composed solely of curved lines, therefore, it is theoretically non-developable. Approximate developments are constructed from double-curved surfaces by enclosing them in portions of cones and cylinders.

Double-curved surfaces of revolution include the following shapes: sphere, annular torus, spheroid/ellipsoid paraboloid, and the serpentine (spring). A double-curved surface is made by stretching flat sheet metal, which has been cut to a specific set of patterns, until it approximates the desired form. Surfaces of revolution can also be turned on a lathe if the finished piece is to be a solid. In general, the sphere is the most common form of double-curved surface that is developed.

There are no straight lines on a double-curved surface. The intersection of a plane and a double-curved surface, perpendicular to its axis line, cuts a curved element on its surface. A plane passed parallel to its axis cuts a section showing the outline of the piece.

21.5.1   Spheres

Spheres are double-curved surfaces of revolution that are generated by a revolving curved line (circle) generatrix about a straight-line axis (directrix). Spheres can be developed by many methods. The **gore method** (meridian method) divides the surface of the sphere into a number of meridians. A **meridian** is established by passing a plane through the axis of the sphere. Two adjacent radial meridians define a section/panel. Meridians are evenly spaced (radially) so that each panel of the development is identical. Since it can be used as a pattern for the remaining sections, only one panel need be established. A panel is really a section of a cylinder that encloses the sphere between two adjacent meridians.

The **zone method** of developing a sphere passes a series of evenly spaced parallel planes perpendicular to the axis. Two adjacent cutting planes establish a horizontal section. Each section approximates the surface of the sphere. A horizontal section can be thought of as a frustrum of a cone whose vertex is at the intersection of the extended chords that define the frustrum's sides.

21.5.2   Development of a Sphere (Gore Method)

The **gore method** of development divides the sphere into an equal number of sections (**gores**). Sections are established by passing equally spaced vertical planes through the axis. Each plane cuts a meridian on the sphere's surface. Two adjacent meridians form a section. Each section can be considered a section of a cylinder. Because it can be used as a pattern for the remaining sections, the development of one section is all that is necessary. The greater the number of sections, the more accurate the development and spherically perfect the final piece, but the number of sheet metal pieces to be cut and seams that need be joined will be increased.

In Figure 21.34 the sphere is divided into 16 evenly spaced sections by passing vertical planes through the point view of the axis in the horizontal view. The frontal view is similarly divided into equal divisions as shown. Horizontal planes are passed through divisions in the frontal view, 1 through 9. Each horizontal plane appears as an edge in the frontal view and projects as a small circle element on the sphere in the horizontal view. The chord distance between horizontal planes, dimension D, is equal for all frontal divisions. The vertical planes (meridian elements) and the circle elements intersect in the horizontal view, points A through N. Each intersection point is projected to the frontal view as shown to establish the gore (meridian) section.

The development is constructed by unfolding one section/panel. Start the development by drawing the stretch-out line equal to one-half of the sphere's circumference. Divide the stretch-out line into eight equal spaces and label 1 through 9 corresponding to the horizontal divisions. Each division should be equal to dimension D. Points A through N can be transferred to the development along related horizontal lines. The widest part of the section is at the equatorial line (5). Points G and H are transferred from the frontal view by measuring their distance from the axis line, which is the centerline of the section/panel.

Figure 21.35 shows a spherical tank constructed using gore sections. Because the spherical shape provides equal

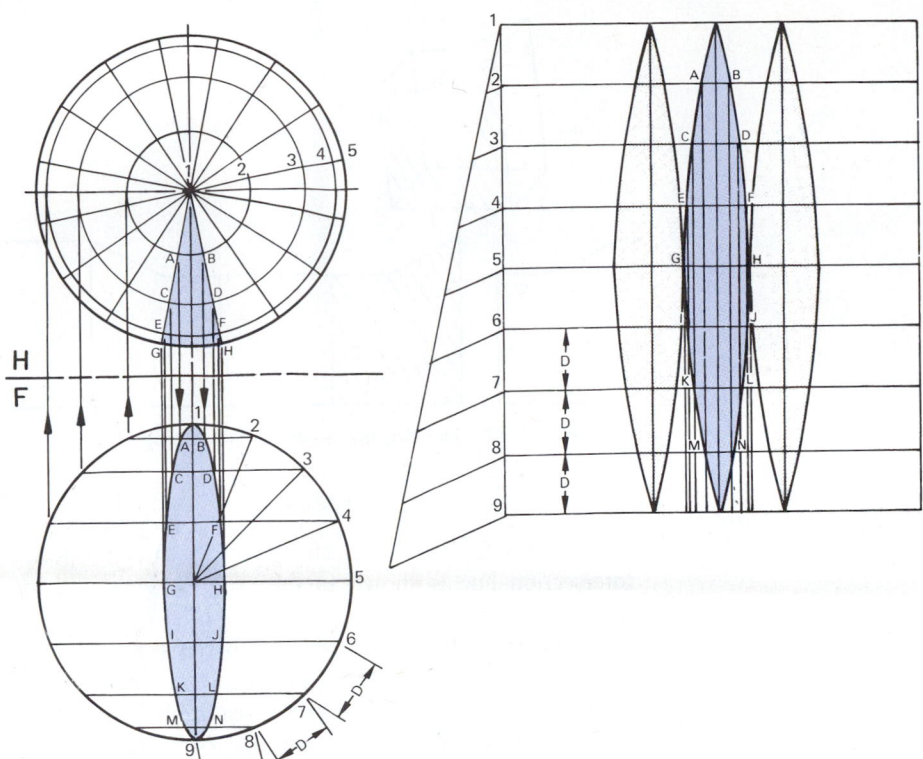

FIGURE 21.34   Sphere
Development Using the Gore
Method

pressure distribution of the vessel's contents, spheres are frequently used in the design of pressure vessels.

21.5.3   Development of a Sphere (Zone Method)

The **zone method** of developing a sphere divides the surface of the sphere into horizontal zones. This procedure approximates the surface of a sphere by enclosing each horizontal zone in a right circular cone. Each zone is really a frustrum of

FIGURE 21.35   Liquid Nitrogen Vessel Constructed of Welded Gore Sections

a cone. The development consists of developing successive frustrums.

In Figure 21.36 the sphere is divided into 16 equal spaces along its circumference. Horizontal planes are passed through the divisions to define the upper and lower bases of the frustrum. The horizontal projection of the plane sections are small circle elements on the sphere's surface. Two adjacent parallel plane sections define a zone. Dimension D is the chord distance between divisions. Related chords are extended to locate the vertex of their respective cones. R1, R2, R3, and R4 are the slant heights of the cones. Slant heights are used to swing a true length arc when drawing the development.

In the horizontal view the sphere is divided into equal parts by passing vertical cutting planes through the point view of the axis line. Each vertical plane cuts an element on the sphere's surface. The intersection of straight-line elements and the circle elements in the horizontal view determines dimensions D1, D2, D3, and D4.

Start this development by drawing the centerline from which all true length radii are swung. Swing arc R1 to locate the development outline for the largest frustrum (zone). Dimension D is used to establish the inside outline of the largest frustrum (zone). D1 and D2 are used to establish the true length of the zone's arc. Repeat this procedure drawing R2 tangent to the inside development line of the first zone. D2 and D3 are used to establish the second zone's development arc length. R3 is swung tangent to the inside of the second zone's outline and D3 and D4 are used to determine the total development arc length. R4 completes the development being swung so as to be tangent to the inside of the third zone's

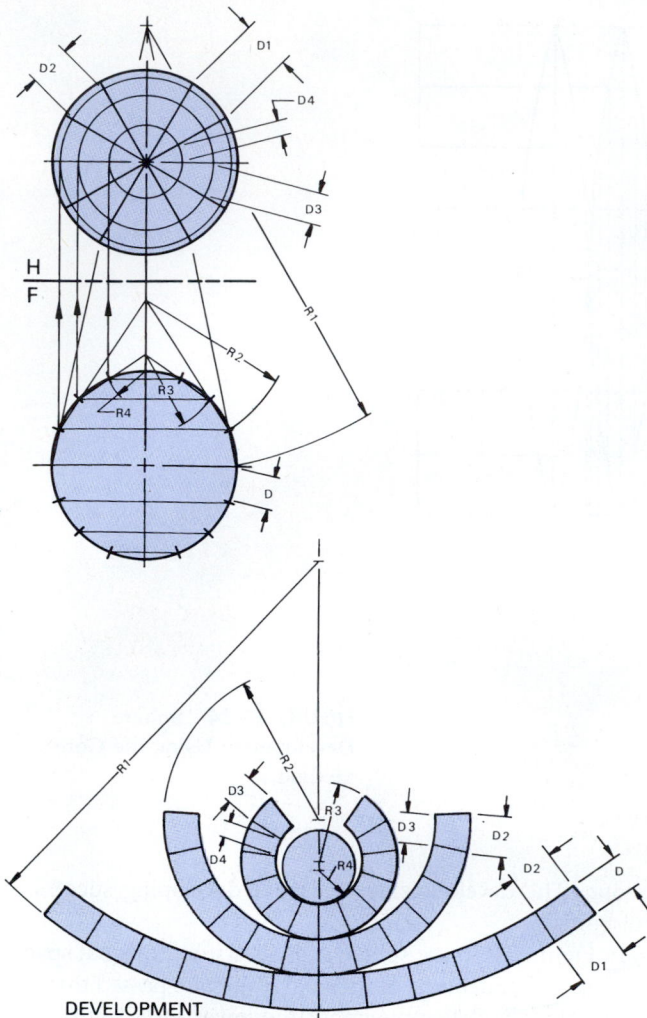

FIGURE 21.36 Development of a Sphere Using the Zone Method

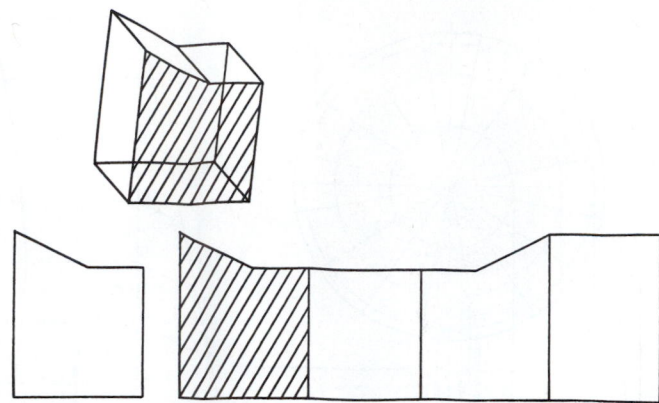

FIGURE 21.37 Development of a Prism Using CAD

In Figure 21.38 a truncated cylinder is developed. The intersection line is shown in the pictorial view and in the development pattern.

Two-dimensional development programs are also available but they either require the construction techniques found in manual drafting or the pattern is assembled from polygon elements. Both 2D and 3D CAD flat pattern programs can calculate bend allowances.

A development of a pyramid is shown in Figure 21.39. The model was unfolded by digitizing the surfaces to be developed after giving the **UNFOLD FLAT PATTERN** (Computervision) command.

The development of a transition piece is shown in Figure 21.40. The CAD solution simply required the inputting of the model coordinates giving the flat pattern command and digitizing the model edges in the pictorial view. The part could then be dimensioned using the system's commands.

outline. The fourth zone, as defined by R4, is a circle. Note dimension D is used as the thickness for all zones, $R1 - R2 = D$, $R2 - R3 = D$, and $R3 - R4 = D$.

21.6 CAD and the Development of Flat Patterns

CAD systems were originally limited to parallel line, radial line, and transition pieces requiring triangulation for development of flat patterns. Development programs now allow you to create a 3D model and to request the system to develop the piece automatically. In Figure 21.37, a prism was developed using a CAD system.

The design can be unfolded by one of two methods. One method allows you to unbend the 3D model, adding dimensions, title block, and border automatically. The other method requires each surface to be specified and unfolded. The drafter must then detail the pattern by adding dimensions.

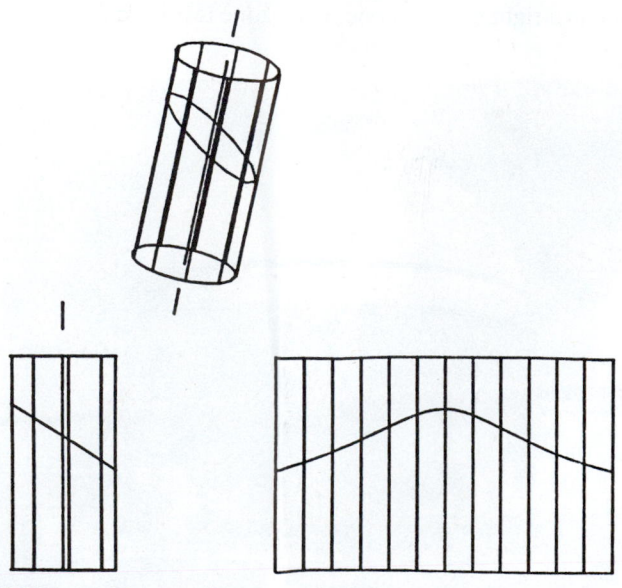

FIGURE 21.38 Development of a Truncated Cylinder Using CAD

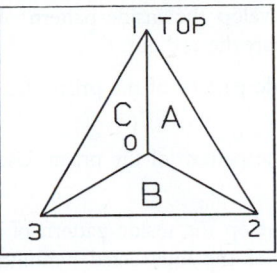

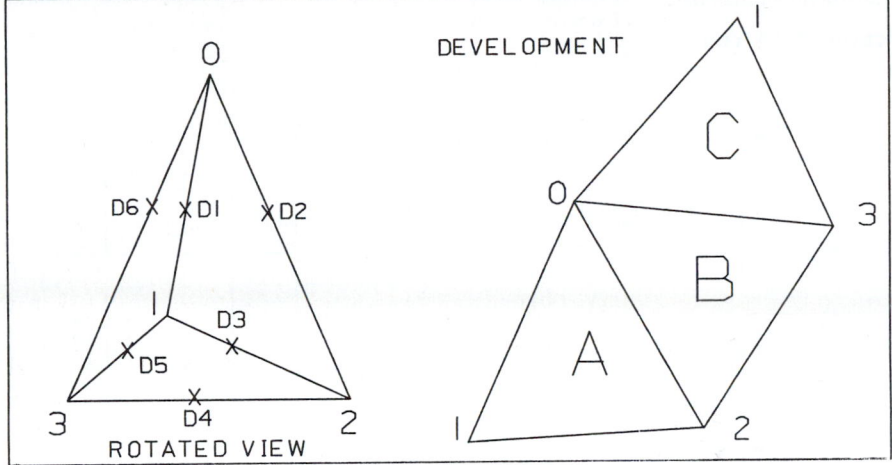

FIGURE 21.39 Unfolding a Flat Pattern using a CAD System

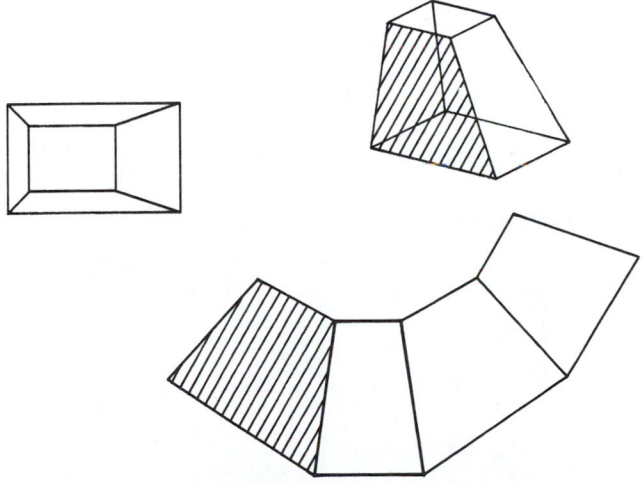

FIGURE 21.40 Development of a Right Pyramid Using CAD

QUIZ

True or False

1. The stretch-out line should always be drawn perpendicular to the object's lateral true length edges.
2. Developments of spheres and warped surfaces are true developments.
3. A pattern is composed of true length lines.
4. Cylinders and cones are considered single-curved surfaces.
5. An oblique cone has an axis that is perpendicular to its base.
6. Spheres are double-curved surfaces and must be approximately developed.
7. The Gore method divides the sphere into a number of zones used to lay out the development.
8. The first step in drawing a parallel line development is to find the true lengths of each face and edge.

Fill in the Blanks

9. Most developments should be unfolded with the _____ _____ .
10. The length of a cylindrical development is _____ to its _____ .
11. Transition pieces join _____ or _____ geometric forms of _____ _____ .
12. A cylinder is generated by a _____ _____ generatrix.
13. Curved surfaces fall into two general categories: _____ and _____ .
14. _____ surfaces are also considered ruled _____ .
15. The generatrix moves according to the _____ .
16. Sheet metal is designated by _____ _____ for sizes smaller than _____ .

Answer the Following

17. Name six different types of seams.
18. What types of shapes are developed using triangulation?
19. What is an approximate development?
20. What is a TL diagram?
21. What are the four types of developments?
22. Describe the difference between a double-curved and a single-curved surface.
23. What is a right section?
24. What is a transition piece?

EXERCISES

Exercises may be assigned as sketching, instrument, or CAD projects. Transfer the given information to an "A" size sheet of .25 in. grid paper. Complete all views and solve for proper visibility, including centerlines, object lines, and hidden lines. Exercises that are not assigned by the instructor can be sketched in the text to provide practice and understanding of the preceding instructional material.

After Reading the Chapter Through Section 21.2.9 You May Complete the Following Exercises

Exercises 21.1(A) and (B) Develop the inside pattern of the prism. Use the given element to start the roll out.

Exercise 21.2 Develop the inside pattern of the prism. Use the given element to start the roll out.

Exercise 21.3 Develop the inside pattern of the prism. Use the given element to start the roll out.

Exercises 21.4(A) and (B) Develop the inside pattern of each pyramid. Complete the top view of the intersected pyramid for Exercise 21.4(A).

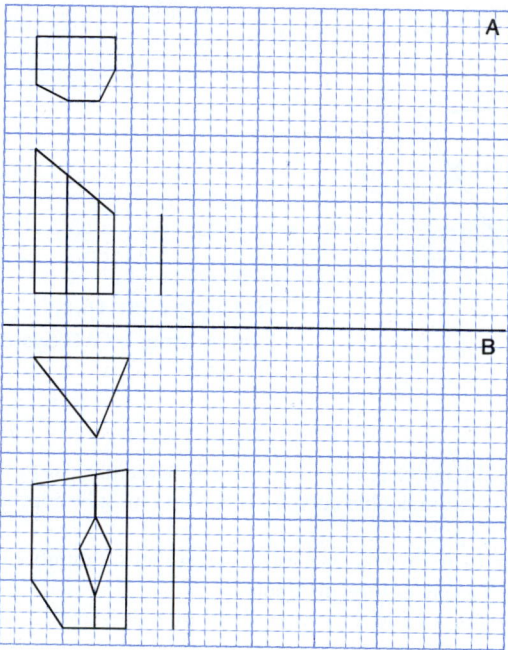

Exercise 21.1

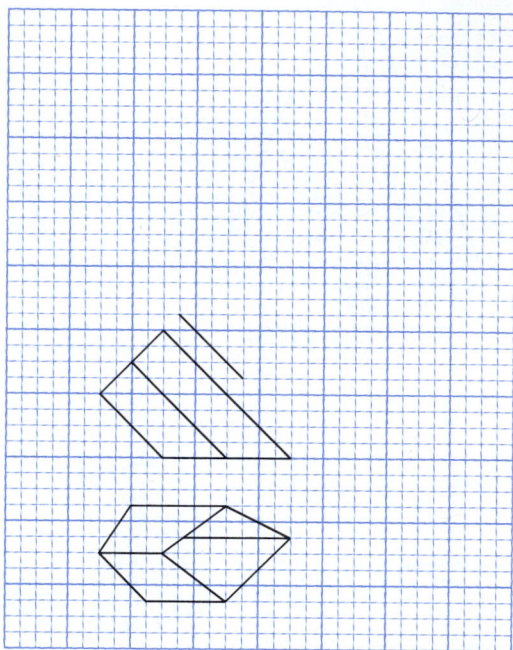

Exercise 21.3

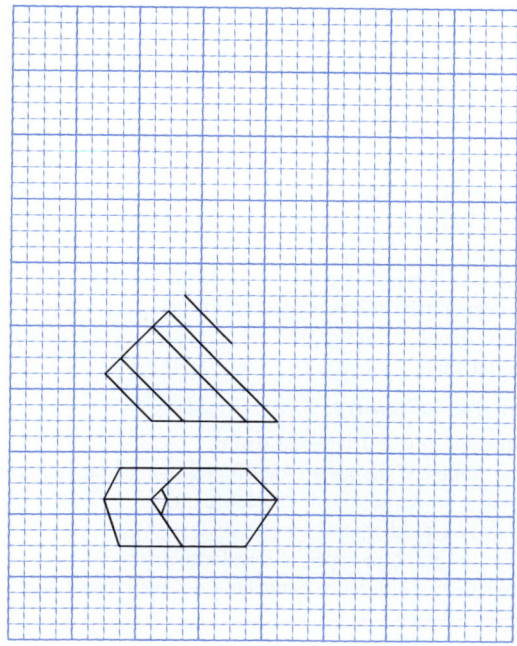

Exercise 21.2

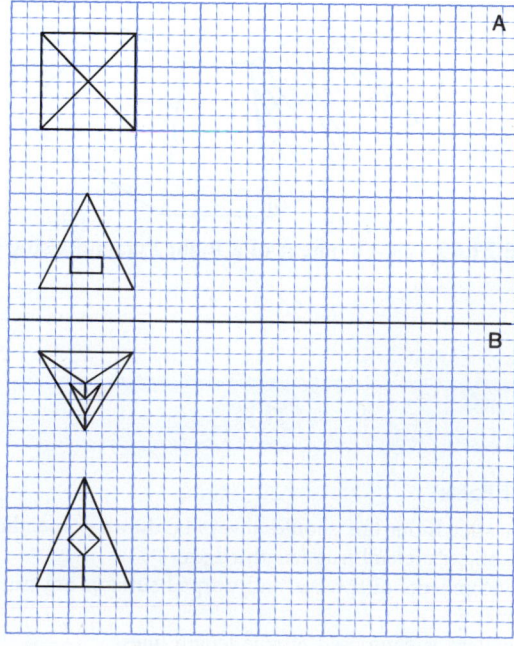

Exercise 21.4

After Reading the Chapter Through Section 21.3.3 You May Complete the Following Exercises

Exercises 21.5(A) and (B)   Develop the inside pattern of each pyramid. Complete the top view of Exercise 21.5(B).

Exercise 21.6(A)   Develop one-half of the inside pattern of the pyramid. Extend the edges to locate the vertex.

Exercise 21.6(B)   Develop the the inside pattern of the cylinder.

Exercise 21.7   Determine the intersection of the two cylinders on the given views and develop each of the two different patterns in the space provided.

Exercise 21.8(A)   Develop the inside pattern of the center piece of the mitered elbow.

Exercise 21.8(B)   Develop the inside pattern of the 45° WYE. Develop the header and one branch.

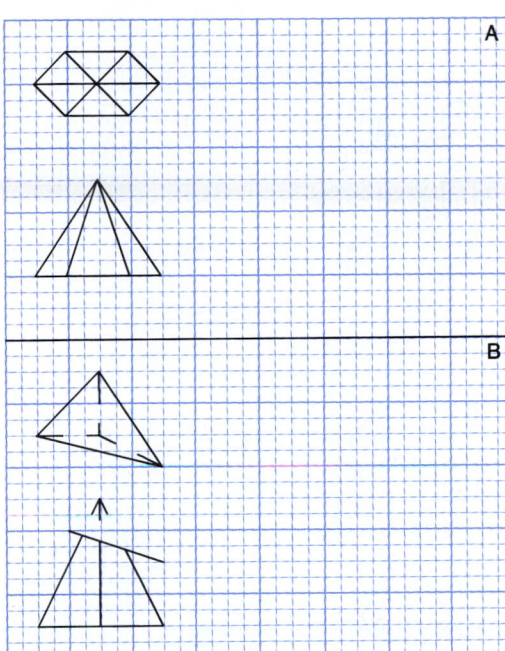

Exercise 21.5

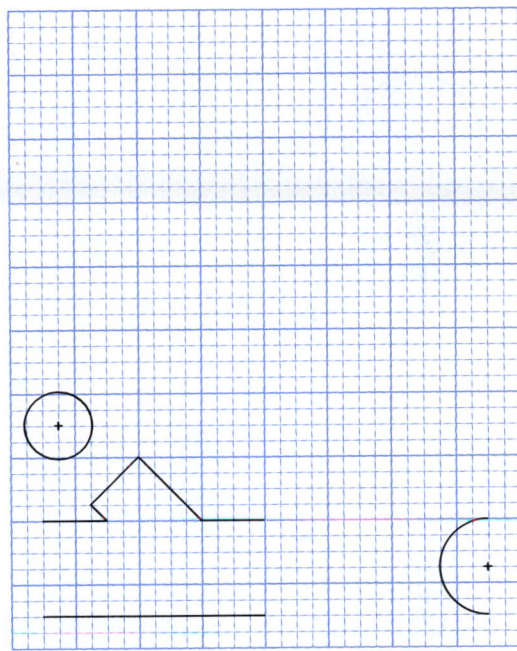

Exercise 21.7

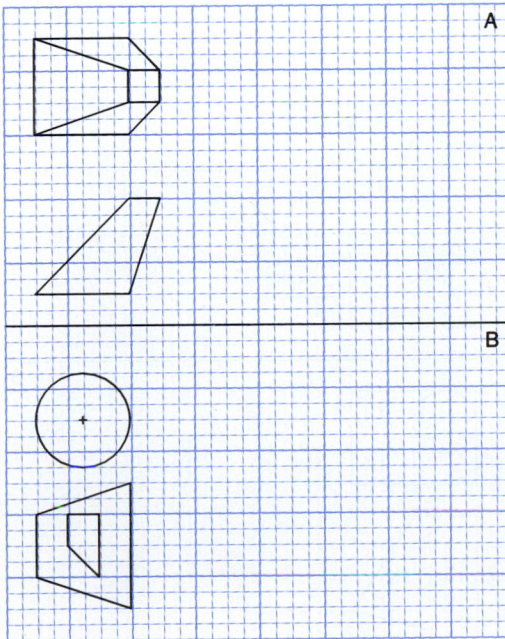

Exercise 21.6

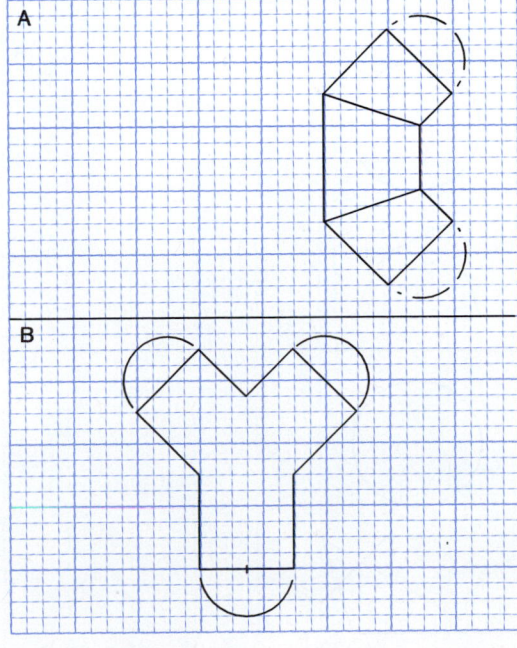

Exercise 21.8

After Reading the Chapter Through Section 21.4.3 You May Complete the Following Exercises

Exercise 21.9(A)   Develop one-half of the inside pattern of the oblique cone.

Exercise 21.9(B)   Establish the top view of the intersected cone and develop its inside pattern.

Exercise 21.10(A)   Develop the inside pattern of one-half of the truncated cone.

Exercise 21.10(B)   Complete the top view of the truncated oblique cone. Develop one-half of the inside pattern of the cone.

Exercise 21.11(A)   Develop the inside pattern of the conical offset.

Exercise 21.11(B)   Develop the inside pattern of the transition piece.

Exercise 21.12(A)   Develop one-half of the inside pattern of the transition piece.

Exercise 21.12(B)   Develop the inside pattern of the transition piece.

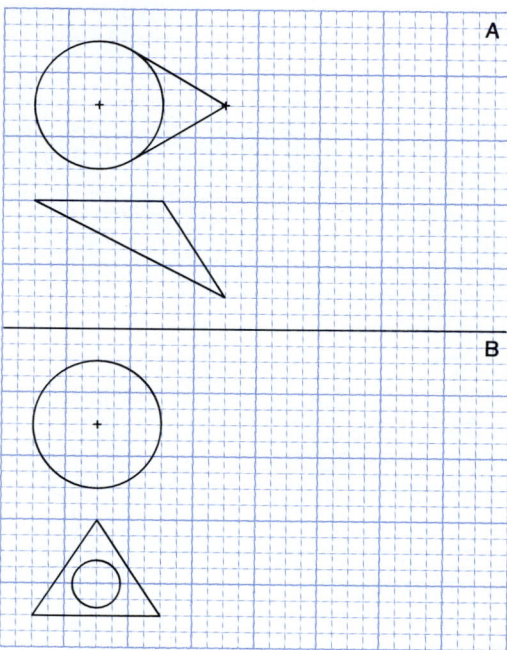

Exercise 21.9

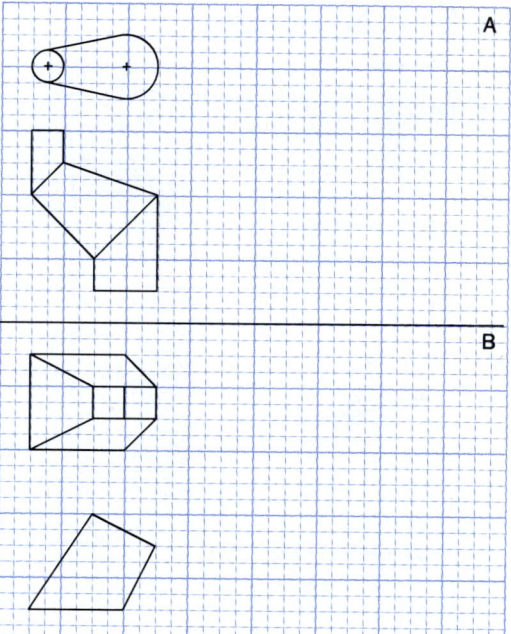

Exercise 21.11

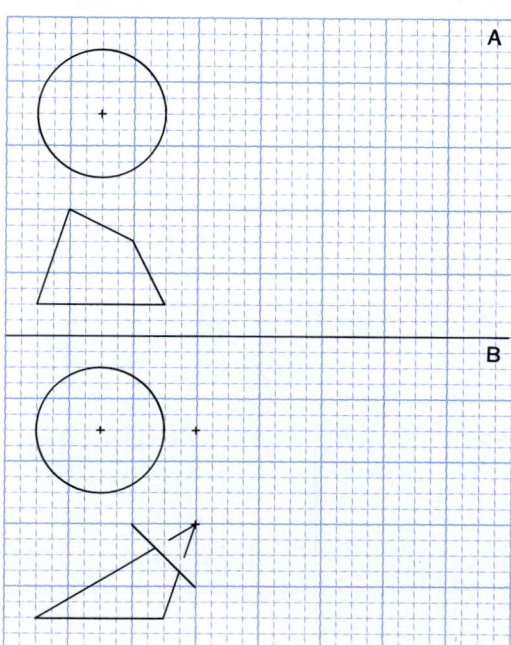

Exercise 21.10

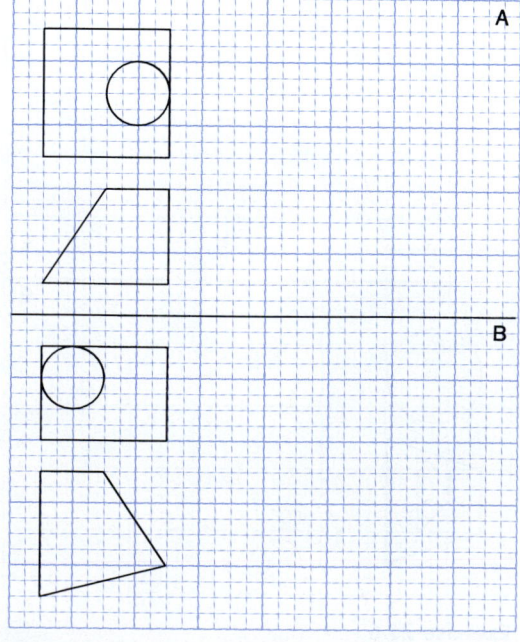

Exercise 21.12

PROBLEMS

Problems may be assigned as sketching, instrument, or CAD projects.

Problem 21.1   Transfer each problem to another sheet. All problems will fit on a "B" size sheet. Develop each part as an inside-up pattern. Instructor may assign some projects as half patterns. Models of any of the problems can also be completed as assigned.

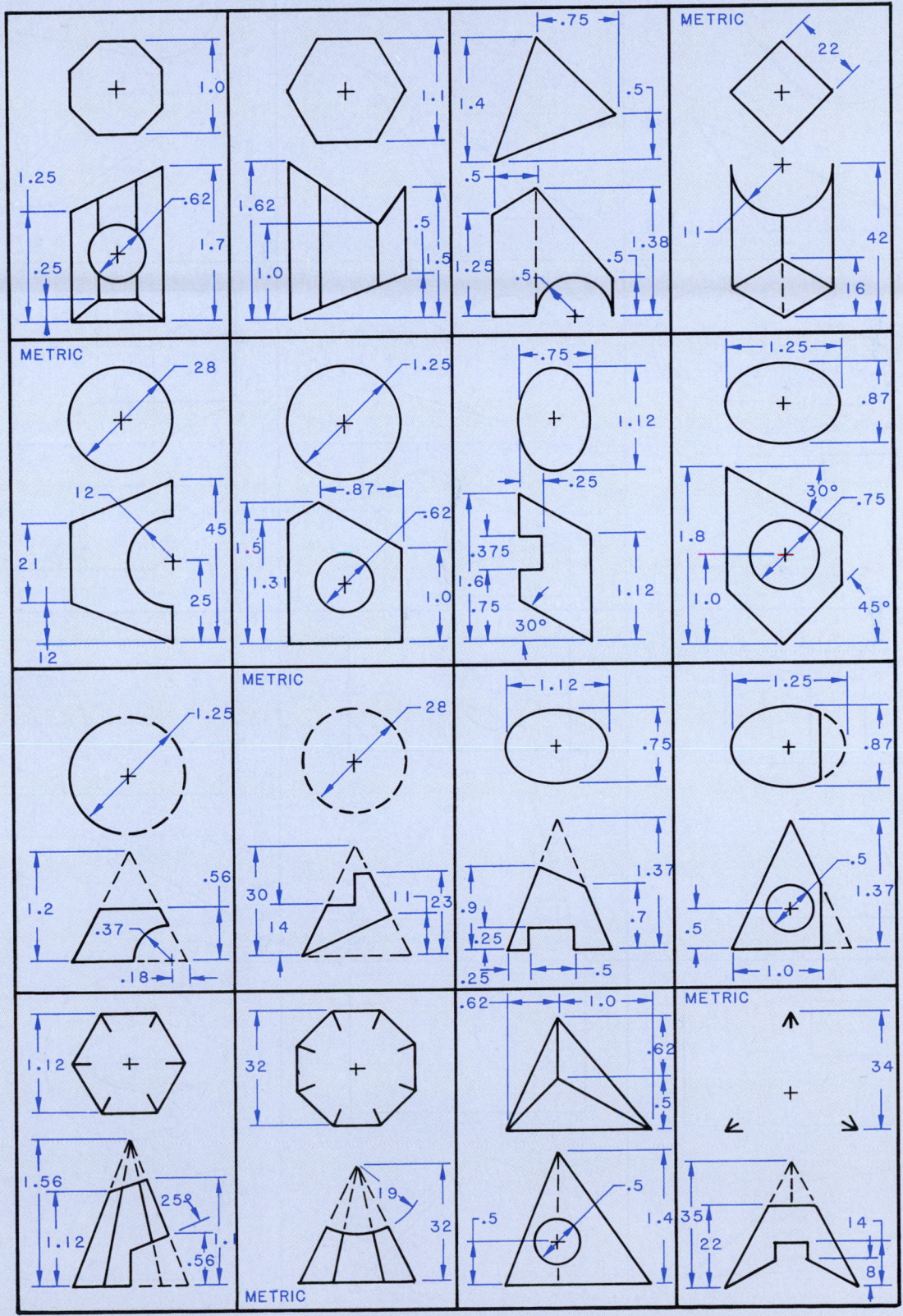

Problem 21.2 Transfer each problem to another sheet. All problems will fit on an "B" size sheet. Develop each part as an inside-up pattern. Instructor may assign some projects as half patterns. Models of any of the problems can also be completed as assigned.

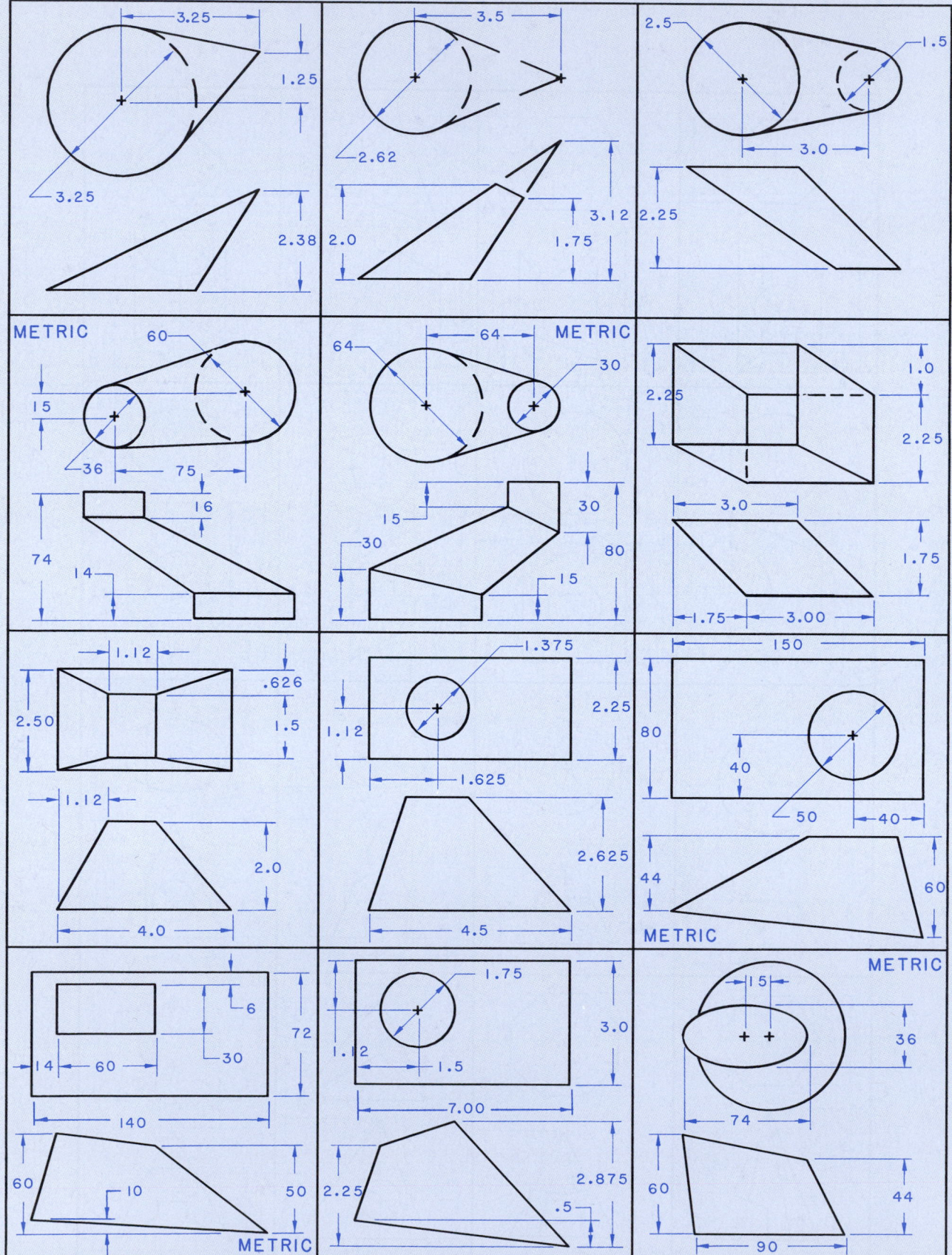

Problem 21.3 Draw and dimension the mounting bracket detail as shown. On a separate sheet layout and develop the part.

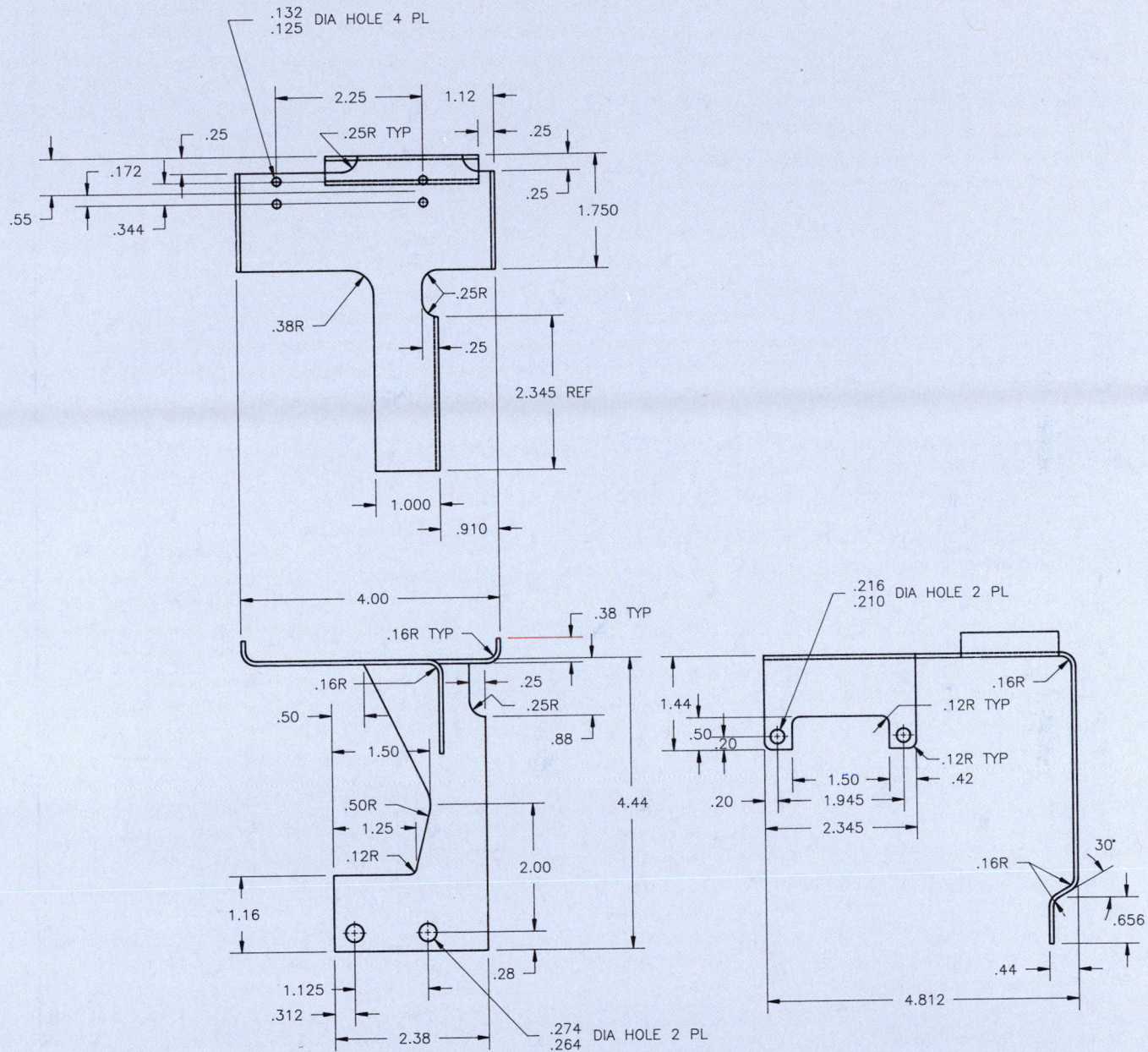

Problem 21.4 Develop the header and the branch for the following intersecting pipes:

1. 3 in. header and a 2 in. branch at 45°
2. 55 mm header and a 35 mm branch at 60°
3. 2.5 in. header and a 1.5 in. header at 40°
4. 45 mm header and a 38 mm branch at 90°

Problem 21.5 Develop a sphere with one of the following diameters:

1. 2.5 in. diameter using the gore method
2. 38 mm diameter using the zone method
3. 3.25 in. diameter using the zone method
4. 44 mm diameter using the gore method

PART V

Applications in Technical Drawing

859

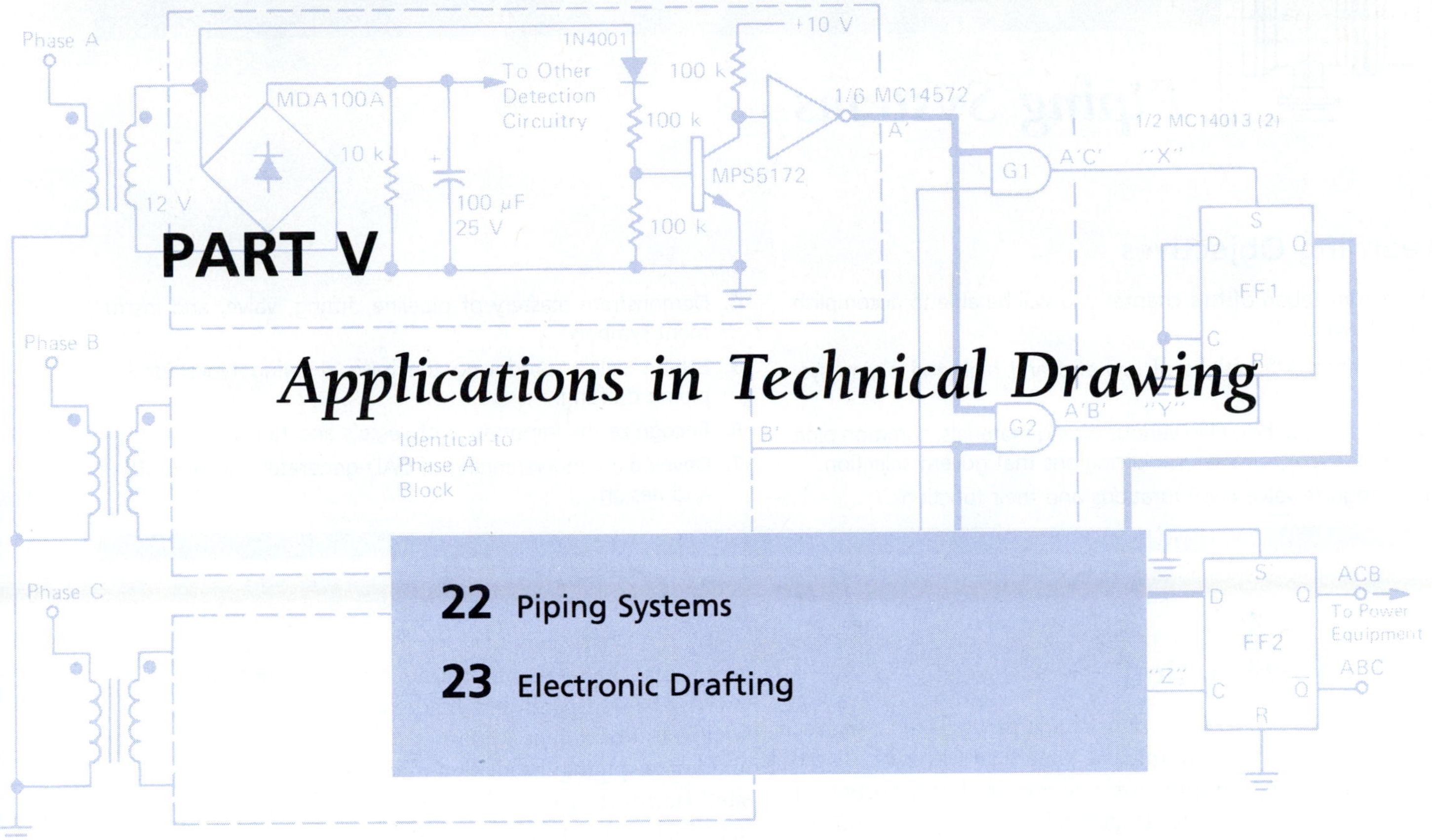

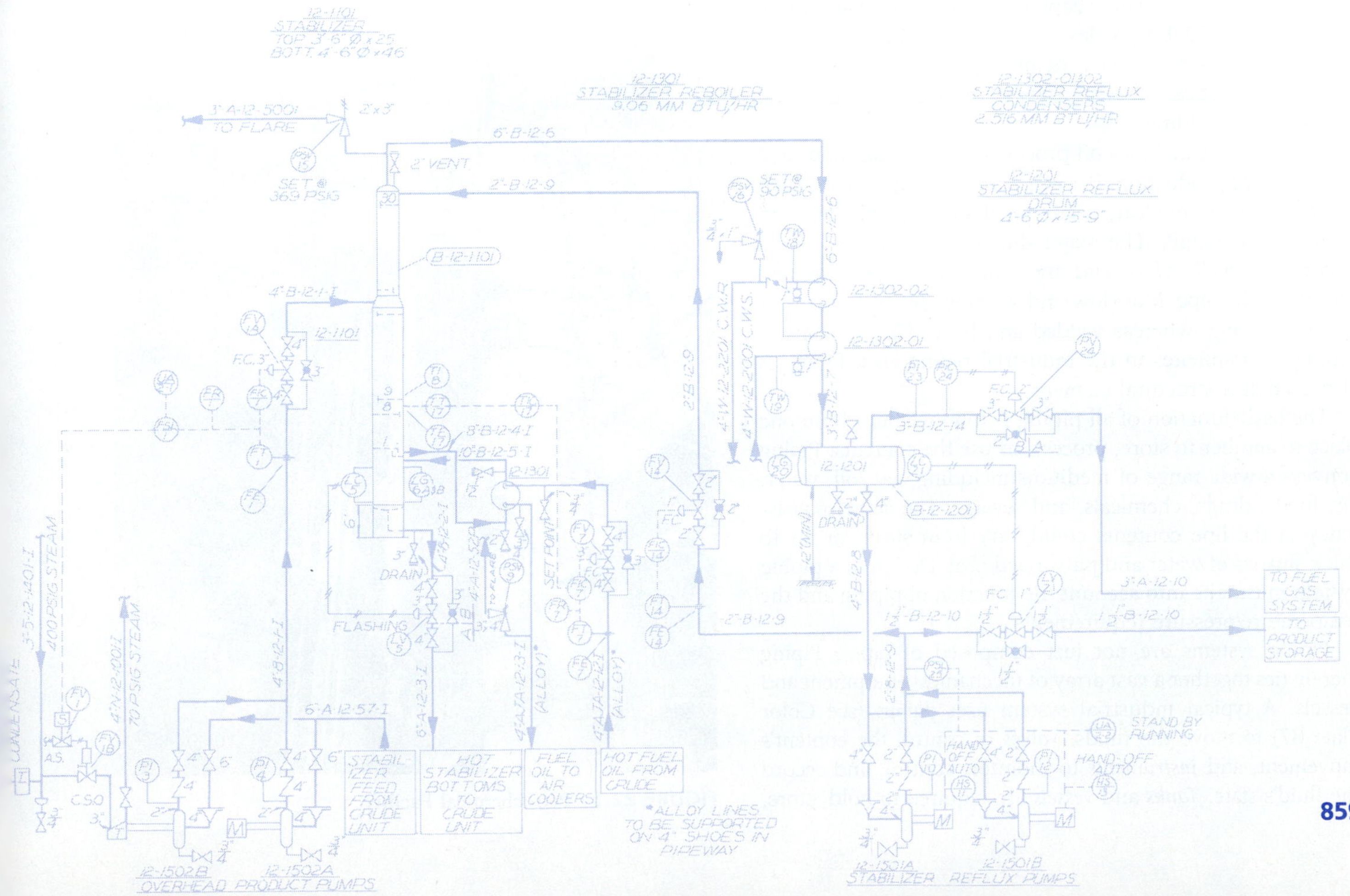

CHAPTER 22

Piping Systems

Learning Objectives

Upon completion of this chapter you will be able to accomplish the following:

1. Identify the functions of low-end and high-end piping systems.
2. Differentiate between various piping materials, common pipe fitting types, and service conditions that govern selection.
3. Recognize valve configurations and their functions.
4. Demonstrate mastery of pipeline, fitting, valve, and instrument symbols.
5. Exhibit skill in producing the basic drawing types used in piping drafting.
6. Recognize the importance of vessels and tanks.
7. Develop an understanding of CAD-generated piping drafting and design.

22.1 Introduction

Piping systems are used to transfer and process fluids, such as residential plumbing, municipal water, and sewage. These low-temperature, low-pressure systems are but a portion of the many uses for piping. In general, piping systems can be divided between the low-end residential and public utility systems, and the high-end process piping and power piping in industrial piping. This chapter concentrates on industrial piping. Figure 22.1 provides an example of a typical industrial piping system; a petrochemical plant is shown with a number of vertical vessels (towers), piping, and structural elements for building.

Process piping includes oil processing, chemicals, and food and beverage production. *Power generation* piping covers such diverse areas as nuclear, solar, fossil fuel, geothermal, and hydroelectric plants. The major differences between *low-end systems* and *high-end systems* are temperature, pressure, and the size of the pipe. Most low-end systems use small-diameter screwed piping, whereas welded and flanged large-diameter piping predominates in the industrial piping area. Piping is also used as a structural element.

The basic function of all piping is to move fluid from one place to another to store, process, or use the contents. Piping conveys a wide range of mediums including, gas, oil, water, air, foods, drugs, chemicals, and sewage. The actual consistency of the line contents could vary from steam or air to thick slurries of water and pulverized coal. Design of a piping system must take into account the function of piping and the temperature/pressure requirements.

Piping systems are not just composed of pipes. Piping merely ties together a vast array of mechanical equipment and vessels. A typical industrial system uses *pumps* (see Color Plate 87) to move the fluids, *valves* to control the content's movement, and *instruments* to monitor, control, and record the fluid's state. *Tanks* and *vessels* are required to hold, store,

or process the medium. *Structural elements* and *pipe supports* are used to suspend and hold the system in place. *Fittings* establish direction and connect different parts of the configuration. A piping installation also has a vast array of associated electrical, structural, HVAC, and utility (sewage, air, water, fuel) systems interconnected and complimenting the basic piping configuration.

FIGURE 22.1 **Petrochemical Facility**

FIGURE 22.2   Model of a Fin-Fan Section of a Petrochemical Plant

Two basic methods are employed in the design of a piping system: modeling and drafting. Both methods are integrated to gain optimum design effeciency. Drafting includes manual and CAD methods. Physical models (Fig. 22.2) are constructed of scaled plastic replicas of actual piping components, vessels, and structural elements. CAD models are 3D designs created on the system.

22.2   Piping Materials

The choice of material for a pipe is determined by the intended service of the piping system. Pipe is available in many materials including steel, cast iron, wrought iron, lead, aluminum, copper, brass, glass, wood, plastic, and clay. Because service conditions vary so widely regarding heat, strain, pressure, and chemical activity, the selection of the proper piping material is an important aspect of piping design. In general, steel and steel alloys, cast iron, and wrought iron are the most frequently specified piping materials.

Most pipes are manufactured from carbon steel. Normally Grade A and Grade B **steel pipe** is used although Grade C is used in a few cases. Other compositions include chrome, molybdenum steel, wrought iron, nickel steel, and stainless steel along with a number of nonferrous metals. Steel pipe is obtained in either black pipe form or is of the *galvanized* type, which is steel pipe that has been treated with molten zinc to prevent rust. Both varieties are available in smaller sizes in lengths up to 40 feet. Available lengths decrease with increasing wall thickness and diameter. Most pipes come in random (± 20 ft) or double random (± 40 ft) lengths.

Steel pipe is used throughout industry because it resists high temperatures and pressures. Fittings are also available in steel (see Appendix C). Standard steel pipe is specified by nominal diameter. **Nominal diameter** is less than the actual outside diameter of the pipe from $\frac{1}{8}$ in. to 12 in. sizes and equals the outside diameter (OD) for 14″ through 42″ pipe as shown in Table 22.1. To use common fittings, the OD of the different weights of pipe remains constant as the inside diameter (ID) varies to provide for various wall thicknesses.

Originally, steel pipe was available in three traditional designations to distinguish the different weights of pipe: standard wall (SW), extra strong wall (XS), and double extra strong wall (XXS). These designations are still in use (Table 22.1). ANSI has also established a range of wall thicknesses corresponding to designations called **Schedules** (SCH). Ten Schedules are available: 10, 20, 30, 40, 60, 80, 100, 120, 140, and 160. Schedule 10 is not shown in Table 22.1. To calculate the inside diameter of a pipe, subtract two times the wall thickness from the outside diameter.

Schedule numbers are indicative of approximate values of 1000 times the pressure/stress ratio and can be calculated by using the formula $1000 \times p/s$. Here p is equal to the internal pressure of the pipe and s is the allowable fiber stress, both in pounds per square inch. As pressure increases, so does the required wall thickness (Schedule number). The temperature of the fluid will put thermal stress on the system and thus also affect the pipe wall thickness. The s value is based on the pipe material, temperature, and pressure capabilities, and must be taken from tables provided by the piping manufacturer.

Cast iron pipe is used to transfer water and natural gas, and in some cases it is used for soil pipe (sewage pipe); these applications are used extensively in underground piping systems. The nominal size of cast iron pipe, unlike steel pipe, always indicates the inside diameter regardless of size. When designating cast iron pipe, specify the outside diameter, regular or heavy, wall thickness, and the nominal diameter. Cast iron pipe is available in a variety of standard sizes and weights. Most cast iron pipe is manufactured with push-on bell and spigot joints, although flanged and screwed joints are available in the smaller sizes.

Aluminum, because it weighs 66% less than steel, is used throughout the piping industry. Since temperature affects its strength, aluminum pipe design capabilities must be examined when specifying it for high-temperature/pressure service. **Lead pipe** or lead-lined pipe resists the chemical activity of acids; therefore, lead pipe is found in chemical work and in systems that transport acids. **Brass and copper pipe** are excellent for handling liquids containing salts. Because they are expensive, brass and copper are used only in special situations. Brass and copper pipes are manufactured in two weights: regular and extra strong. They are available in sizes of $\frac{1}{8}$ in. to 12 in. The outside diameters of brass and copper pipe are the same as the corresponding nominal sizes of steel pipe.

Glass pipe is limited to temperature services of 400° F and below and it is also vulnerable to vibration and high pressure. Glass pipe is excellent for resisting acids and chemicals and is used throughout the food, beverage, and chemical industries where corrosive contamination of the line contents is undesirable. **Plastic piping** is resistant to most corrosive chemicals including many acids, alkalies, and organic compounds. Major drawbacks

TABLE 22.1   Pipe Schedule Number, Nominal Pipe Size, and Wall Thickness

Nominal Pipe Size	O.D.	Nominal Wall Thickness for											
		Sched. 20	Sched. 30	SW	Sched. 40	Sched. 60	XS	Sched. 80	Sched. 100	Sched. 120	Sched. 140	Sched. 160	XXS
1/8	0.405	.....	.....	0.068	0.068	.....	0.095	0.095	.....	.....	.....	.....	.....
1/4	0.540	.....	.....	0.088	0.088	.....	0.119	0.119	.....	.....	.....	.....	.....
3/8	0.675	.....	.....	0.091	0.091	.....	0.126	0.126	.....	.....	.....		
1/2	0.840	.....	.....	0.109	0.109	.....	0.147	0.147	.....	.....	.....	0.187	0.294
3/4	1.050	.....	.....	0.113	0.113	.....	0.154	0.154	.....	.....	.....	0.218	0.308
1	1.315	.....	.....	0.133	0.133	.....	0.179	0.179	.....	.....	.....	0.250	0.358
1 1/4	1.660	.....	.....	0.140	0.140	.....	0.191	0.191	.....	.....	.....	0.250	0.382
1 1/2	1.900	.....	.....	0.145	0.145	.....	0.200	0.200	.....	.....	.....	0.281	0.400
2	2.375	.....	.....	0.154	0.154	.....	0.218	0.218	.....	.....	.....	0.343	0.436
2 1/2	2.875	.....	.....	0.203	0.203	.....	0.276	0.276	.....	.....	.....	0.375	0.552
3	3.5	.....	.....	0.216	0.216	.....	0.300	0.300	.....	.....	.....	0.438	0.600
3 1/2	4.0	.....	.....	0.226	0.226	.....	0.318	0.318	.....	.....	.....	.....	.....
4	4.5	.....	.....	0.237	0.237	.....	0.337	0.337	.....	0.438	.....	0.531	0.674
5	5.563	.....	.....	0.258	0.258	.....	0.375	0.375	.....	0.500	.....	0.625	0.750
6	6.625	.....	.....	0.280	0.280	.....	0.432	0.432	.....	0.562	.....	0.718	0.864
8	8.625	0.250	0.277	0.322	0.322	0.406	0.500	0.500	0.593	0.718	0.812	0.906	0.875
10	10.75	0.250	0.307	0.365	0.365	0.500	0.500	0.593	0.718	0.843	1.000	1.125	.....
12	12.75	0.250	0.330	0.375	0.406	0.562	0.500	0.687	0.843	1.000	1.125	1.312	.....
14 O.D.	14.0	0.312	0.375	0.375	0.438	0.593	0.500	0.750	0.937	1.093	1.250	1.406	.....
16 O.D.	16.0	0.312	0.375	0.375	0.500	0.656	0.500	0.843	1.031	1.218	1.438	1.593	.....
18 O.D.	18.0	0.312	0.438	0.375	0.562	0.750	0.500	0.937	1.156	1.375	1.562	1.781	.....
20 O.D.	20.0	0.375	0.500	0.375	0.593	0.812	0.500	1.031	1.281	1.500	1.750	1.968	.....
22 O.D.	22.0	.....	.....	0.375	.....	.....	0.500	.....	.....	.....	.....	.....	.....
24 O.D.	24.0	0.375	0.562	0.375	0.687	0.968	0.500	1.218	1.531	1.812	2.062	2.343	.....
26 O.D.	26.0	.....	.....	0.375	.....	.....	0.500	.....	.....	.....	.....	.....	.....
30 O.D.	30.0	0.500	0.625	0.375	.....	.....	0.500	.....	.....	.....	.....	.....	.....
34 O.D.	34.0	.....	.....	0.375	.....	.....	0.500	.....	.....	.....	.....	.....	.....
36 O.D.	36.0	.....	.....	0.375	.....	.....	0.500	.....	.....	.....	.....	.....	.....
42 O.D.	42.0	.....	.....	0.375	.....	.....	0.500	.....	.....	.....	.....	.....	.....

include deterioration in direct sunlight and confinement to low- and mid-temperature service. Plastic pipe is available in many iron pipe sizes and has low friction for water flow and many other liquids.

22.3 Pipe Fittings

Pipe fittings are used to connect pipe, valves, and equipment (see Color Plates 85, 86, and 87). Screwed, flanged, and welded fittings are the most common types of connections. Standard fittings come in the same range of materials as pipe and are specified by fitting type, nominal pipe size (NPS), and material. Fittings are joined to the system by welding, bolting, or screwing in most instances. Bell and spigot, flared, and soldered fittings are also used for special services.

The seven major joint variations used on piping systems are shown in Figure 22.3. One of the most common means of joining fittings to pipe is welding. **Welded systems** have many advantages over other types. They require less maintenance and they provide a permanent leakproof bond; in effect, the system becomes a closed container. *Butt welding fittings* are used for larger diameter pipes with *socket welding* confined to the smaller pipe sizes.

Flanged fittings are bolted together by means of screwed or welded flanges. Totally flanged systems are rare because of the cost, weight, and difficulty in supporting and insulating. In most cases, this type of joint is found on welded piping systems at points where the system must be dismantled and for valves. Flanged joints are used for 2″ diameter pipes and larger.

Bell and spigot fittings are used for low-temperature/pressure large-diameter piping on sewage, gas, and municipal water lines for underground services. Most bell and spigot fittings are made of cast iron. **Flared fittings** are used on copper and brass tubes.

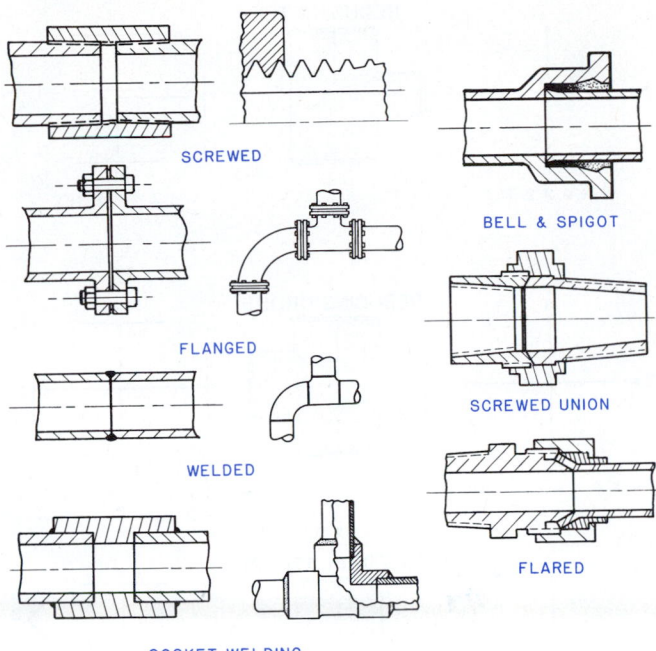

FIGURE 22.3   Pipe Joint Variations

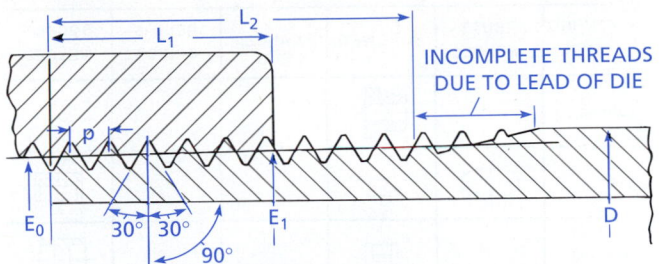

FIGURE 22.4   American Standard Pipe Taper Thread

Threaded or **screwed fittings** are normally limited to smaller sized piping. They are machined and threaded with standard pipe threads. The tapered thread is most common (Fig. 22.4). The screwed union is used where the pipe line must be disconnected frequently. Tapered threads have a 1:16 taper. American Standard Pipe Taper Thread (NPT) can be illustrated with or without showing the angle of threads. L2 in Figure 22.4 is the length of complete threads, whereas L1 shows the effective engagement by hand tightening.

In Figure 22.5 socket and butt welding fittings are shown. In most cases, these types are available in all joint variations.

Figure 22.6 gives the 20 most common fittings. **Bushings** are confined to screwed systems and are used to reduce the size of an opening in a fitting and are sometimes used in place of a reducer. **Caps** close the end of a pipe and come in welded and screwed types. **Couplings** enable two pieces of pipe to be joined. **Crosses** are available in all joint types and can be either straight or reducing. Straight crosses have four branch outlets of equal diameter. Reducing crosses have different size outlets (Fig. 22.7).

The primary purpose for most fittings is to change the direction of the pipe. **Elbows** are either short radius, long radius, or reducing. Elbows change direction at 45 or 90°. Short-radius elbows have a radius equal to the nominal diameter of the pipe. Long-radius elbows have a radius of $1\frac{1}{2}$ times the pipe diameter. Extra long radius elbows are also available and come with a radius of three times the nominal pipe diameter.

Laterals come in straight size and reducing types. Since they lack structural strength, they are confined to low-pressure applications. **Plugs** are used on screwed piping systems to close off the end of a line or fitting. **Reducers** are used to decrease the diameter of a pipe run. Eccentric reducers are

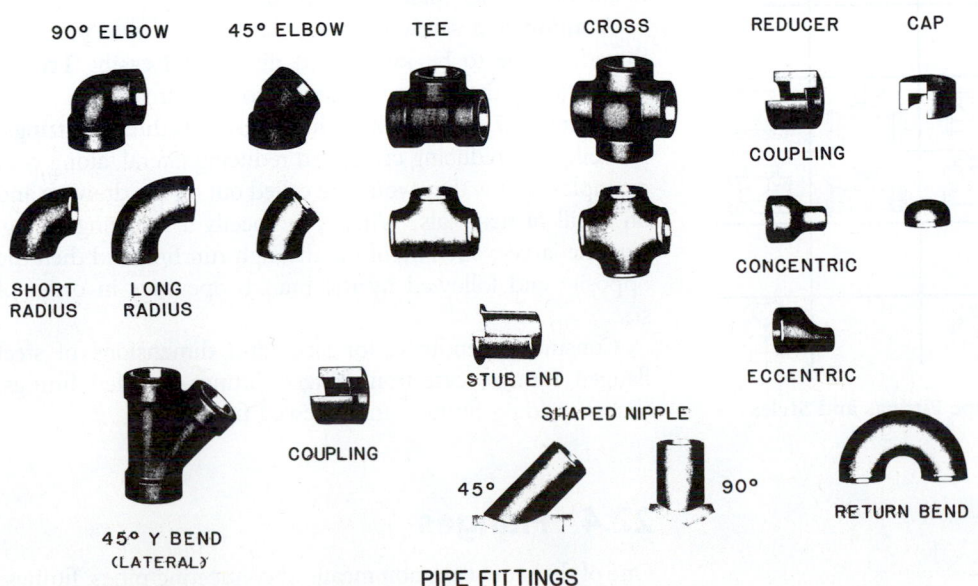

FIGURE 22.5   Welding Fittings

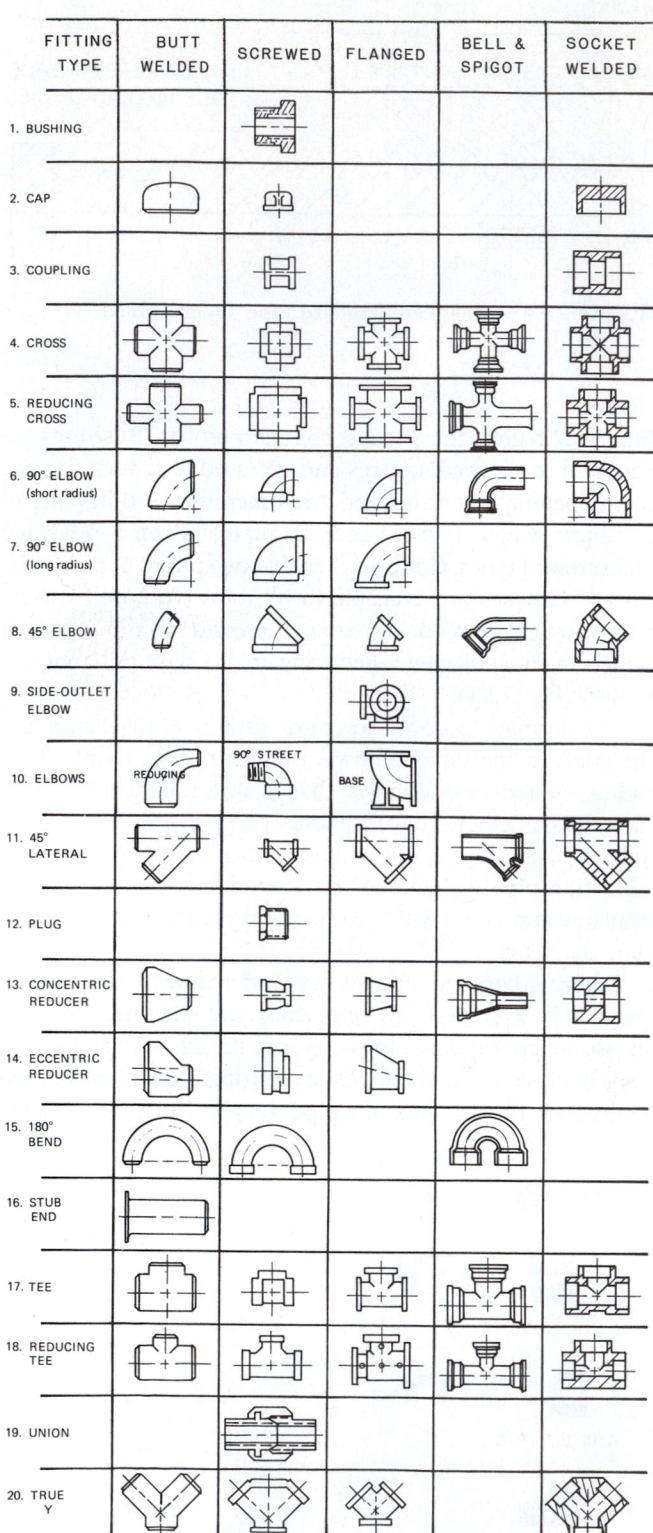

FIGURE 22.6 Common Types of Pipe Fittings and Styles

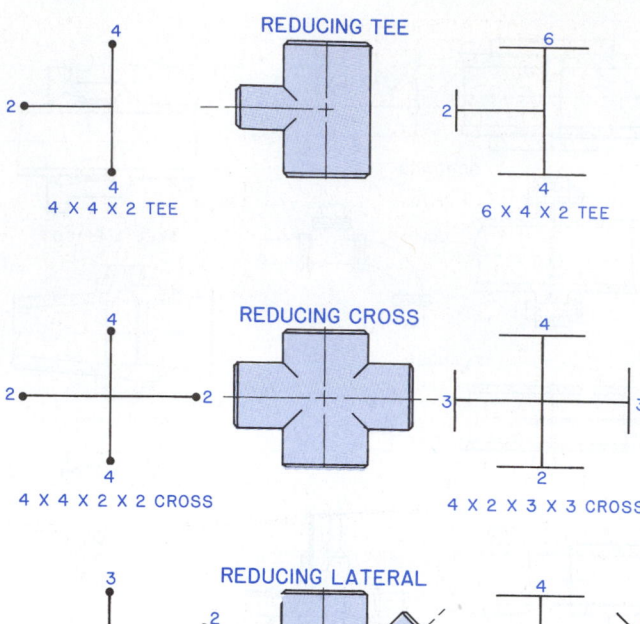

FIGURE 22.7 Designating Reducing Fittings

used where one line of pipe elevation must remain constant, but the diameter changes. The **180° bend** is used to change the direction of the pipe line and is found on heat exchangers and coils. **Stub ends** are used on butt-welded systems for lap flanges. A **tee** is a reinforced fitting that is branched to permit flow at 90° to the main run. Reducing tees come with branch diameters smaller than the main run.

A **union** is a screwed fitting that enables two pieces of threaded pipe to be joined and dismantled easily. **True Y** fittings allow the pipe to be split into two streams.

Figure 22.7 demonstrates three typical **reducing fittings**: reducing tee, reducing cross, and reducing lateral, along with examples of how they would be called out on the drawing and on a bill of materials. When you specify a reducing fitting, give the largest opening of the through run first and then the opposite end followed by the branch openings in order of size.

Consult Appendix C for sizes and dimensions of steel flanged fittings, cast iron flanged fittings, welded fittings, socket welding fittings, and screwed fittings.

22.4 Flanges

One of the more common means of connecting pipes, fittings, or valves is the **flange**. Flanged piping systems can be dismantled to repair, replace, or service valves, meters, and other

ITEMS OF INTEREST

Piping Systems

As far back as 400 B.C. man used pipe systems to transfer products in bulk form. The Chinese were probably the first to use pipelines. They used hollow bamboo to carry water and smaller diameter bamboo wrapped with waxed cloth to move marsh gas to various locations. Later, the Romans and Arab conquerors piped water through aqueducts of hollow stone. In approximately 600 A.D., the Japanese fashioned clay pipes by hand. Commercial production of pipe began about 200 years ago in Europe. These cast iron pipes were used for sewage, water, and gas.

In 1859 the first successful oil well was drilled in Pennsylvania. An effective method to transfer the crude oil to refineries was soon required. Because of their low cost, pipelines were the method of choice. Of course, railroads opposed this method and even refused to let pipelines cross under their tracks. Regardless, the use of pipelines proliferated after that time.

Improvements in metallurgy, construction, and equipment steadily reduced the cost of pipelines until the 1970s. Then, higher labor and material costs caused the prices to increase. Government regulations and the effort to protect the environment added to the total price.

Since the first pipelines were produced in the mid-1800s, several improvements to the systems have been made. One such improvement was lap-welded wrought iron pipe with threaded ends. Other improvements were made in the metallurgy of the pipe material. In the 1940s the maximum strength was 42,000 psi. Today the maximum strength is 70,000 psi, an increase that required about a 67% increase in the strength of the material.

Because of better equipment and materials, the total length possible for a pipeline increased. The 800-mile-long Trans-Alaska pipeline constructed in the 1970s illustrates the sophisticated technology used in modern pipelines. Because of the very low Arctic temperatures, the oil is heated to lower its viscosity and increase its ability to flow. The pipeline is encased in heavy insulation to prevent heat loss as the oil travels throughout the pipeline.

Bamboo Pipes

By the 1980s most countries had some pipeline system that carried refined products to their major cities. The United States was the first country to use "batching" of several products into one pipeline. This permits products to be conveyed together without any separation.

New technology continues to improve the pipelines that crisscross the United States and other parts of the world. Need seems to dictate how quickly advances are made to existing systems. Today, the need to protect our environment has become very important to us. This need will certainly play a key role in planning future pipelines.

Stone Aqueducts

types of equipment without disturbing the rest of the system. Flanges are normally used on systems larger than 2″ in diameter. Appendix C provides catalog pages for ordering flanges. Standard dimensions are given for 150#, 300#, and 400# forged steel flanges. In most cases, the flange thickness and outside diameter increase with the flange's pressure rating (150#, 300#, 400#, etc.).

Figure 22.8 shows the most common types of companion flanges. The **welding neck flange** (WN) comes in a regular and a long neck variation. This type of flange is butt-welded to the end of the pipe and is used in high-temperature/pressure applications. The long neck type is also used as a nozzle for vessels and pumps. **Slip-on flanges** are used on low-temperature/pressure, small-diameter pipelines. Here, the flange is slipped over the pipe. The **screwed** or **threaded flange** is similar to the slip-on flange except that the inside diameter is threaded. The threaded flange is ideal for $1\frac{1}{2}$ in. diameter piping and smaller and can be seal-welded for leak-proof service. **Blind flanges** are used to close off the end of a pipeline and can also be bored, drilled, or tapped for high reduction in pipe diameter for reduced flow. The **lap joint flange** slips over the pipe and is usually not fastened to the pipeline. Bolting pressure and a gasket maintain an adequate joint. **Socket welding flanges** are used on small-diameter piping where a screwed fitting is inadequate because of leakage. The flange is counterbored larger than the outside diameter of the matching pipe so the pipe can be inserted into the flange.

One of the most important aspects of a flange is its **facing**. Facings come in raised, ring, male and female, tongue and groove, and flat types. Raised facing is one of the most common. The faces are raised $\frac{1}{16}$ in. (1.6 mm) for 150# and 300# class flanges and $\frac{1}{4}$ in. (6.4 mm) for 400# and above. Weld neck raised face flanges are designated by giving the flange size and the abbreviation "WNRF."

Gaskets are used on all flanged connections to seal the system at bolted connections, fittings, valves, and equipment. The thickness of the gasket must be included when dimensioning the pipe with its attached valves and fittings. All flanged joints require bolting. Bolt patterns come in groups of four (4, 8, 12, and 16) and are equally spaced on the bolt circle.

22.5 Valves

Valves are mechanical devices that control the line contents. The four major functions of valves are:

1. starting and stopping flow
2. regulating or throttling flow
3. preventing backflow
4. relieving pressure

Starting and stopping flow is the service for which valves are most generally used. **Gate valves** and **ball valves** are the two primary valves for this service. Both types allow full-bore flow since the valve body ID is the same as the mating pipe ID. The

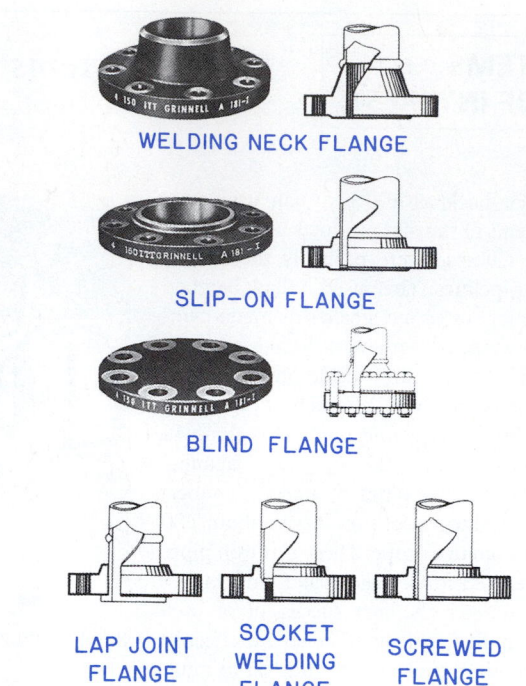

FIGURE 22.8   Flange Types

minimum restriction of flow prevents loss of pressure through the valve. Valves designed for on-off service are not suited for flow regulation or throttling. Figure 22.9 shows a variety of valve types including two gate valves: the split wedge (a) and the solid wedge (b). The split wedge valve shown here has welded ends and the solid wedge is a flanged valve (no bolt holes have been drilled in flanged ends). The ball valve in Figure 22.9(c) is also flanged. Ball and gate valves can be manufactured in almost any size.

Regulating or throttling flow is best accomplished using **globe valves**. In Figure 22.9(d), (e), and (f), three variations of globe valves are shown: straight globe, angle globe, and Y globe. The disk shape and material of a globe valve differs for various services. The disk seating for all globe valves causes a change of direction of flow through the valve body. This direction change causes a flow and pressure drop, which in turn enables a close regulation of line contents. Globe-type valves are limited to 12″ diameter and below. The **regular globe valve** [Fig. 22.9(d)] and the **Y globe** valve [Fig. 22.9(e)] are used in straight portions of a pipeline. Because of the Y globe's angle, the flow is less interrupted. The regular globe valve configuration causes the line material to change direction twice. The **angle globe valve** [Fig. 22.9(f)] is used in place of an elbow and a globe valve since it combines a change of direction (90° elbow) for the pipe along with the function of a globe valve.

Check valves are used to prevent the reversal of flow. Figure 22.9(g) and (h) show the two primary variations of a check valve. Flow keeps the valve open and gravity or flow reversal shuts the valve. **Swing checks** [Fig. 22.9(g)] are normally used with gate valves since their flow characteristics are

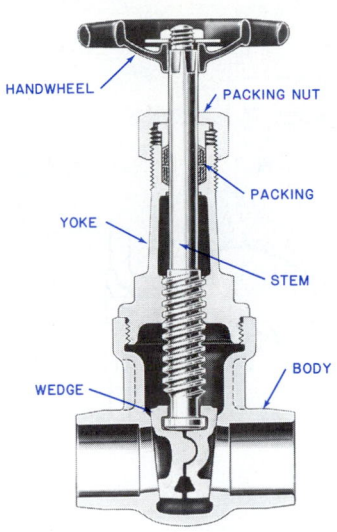

(a) Split wedge gate valve

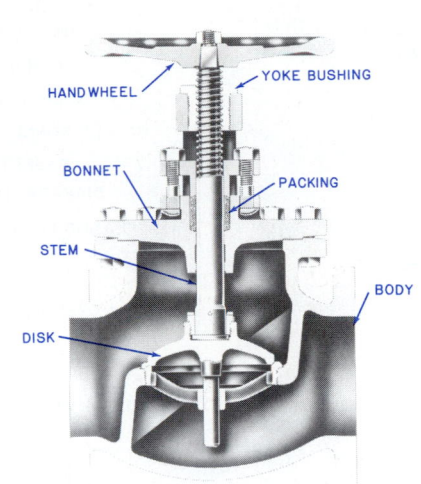

(d) Globe valve

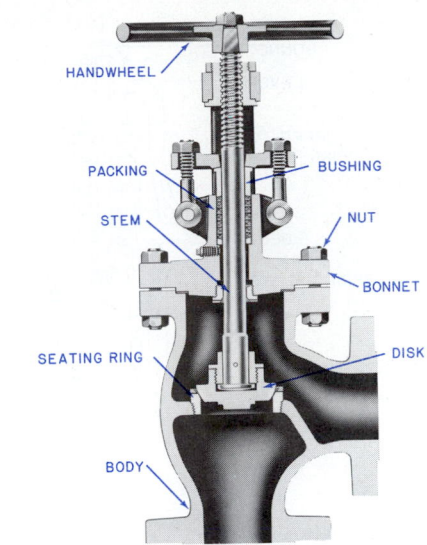

(f) Angle glove valve

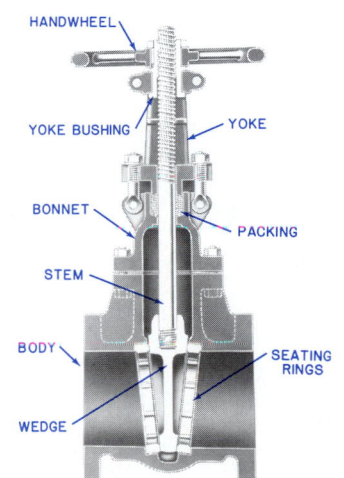

(b) Solid wedge gate valve

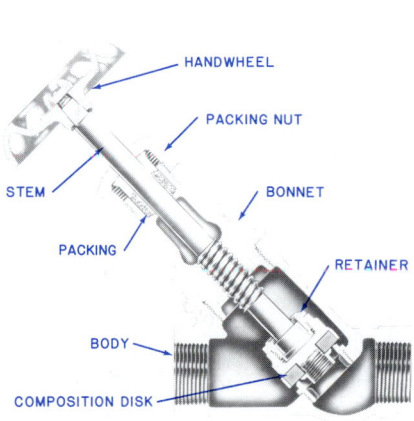

(e) Globe Y valve

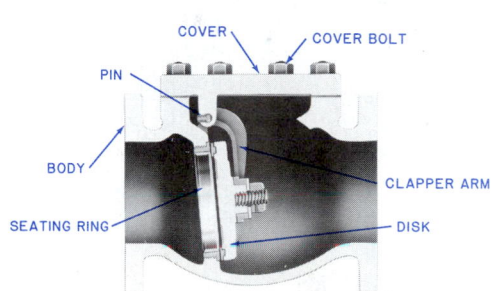

(g) Swing check valve

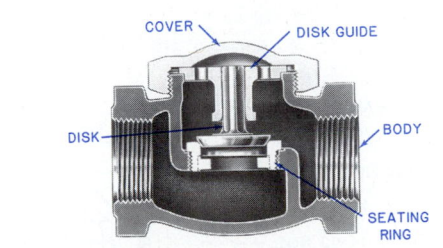

(h) Lift check valve

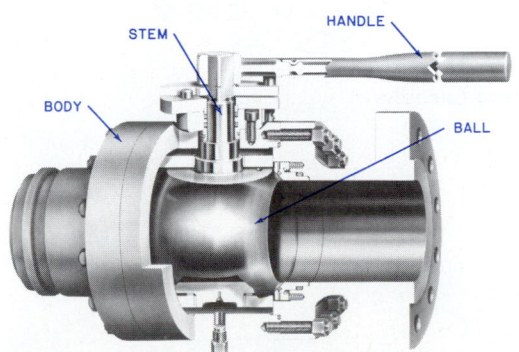

(c) Ball valve

FIGURE 22.9   Common Valves   (a) Split wedge gate valve (b) Solid wedge gate valve (c) Ball valve (d) Globe valve (e) Globe Y valve (f) Angle globe valve (g) Swing check valve (h) Lift check valve (i) Ball check valve

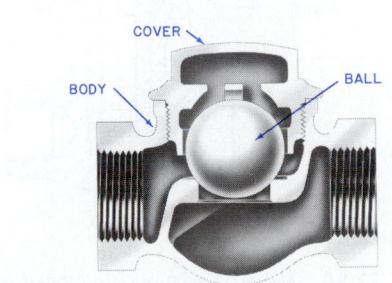

(i) Ball check valve

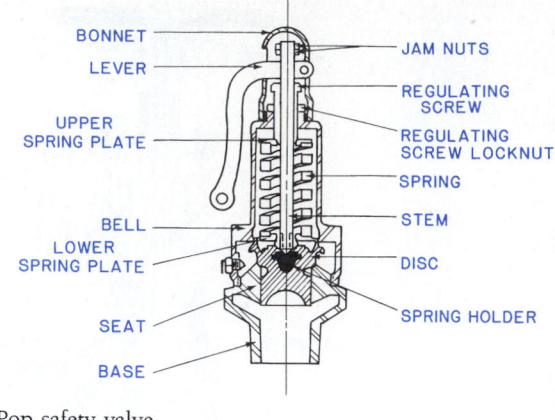

BONNET
LEVER
UPPER SPRING PLATE
BELL
LOWER SPRING PLATE
SEAT
BASE
JAM NUTS
REGULATING SCREW
REGULATING SCREW LOCKNUT
SPRING
STEM
DISC
SPRING HOLDER

(a) Pop safety valve

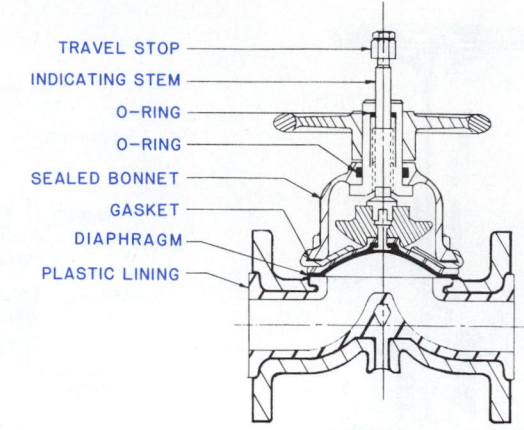

TRAVEL STOP
INDICATING STEM
O—RING
O—RING
SEALED BONNET
GASKET
DIAPHRAGM
PLASTIC LINING

(d) Diaphragm valve

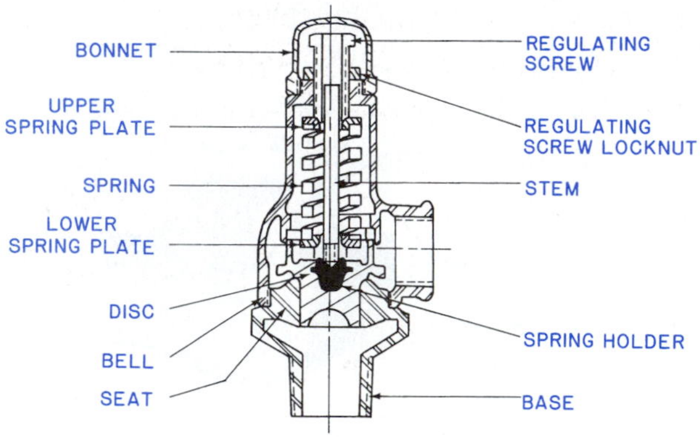

BONNET
UPPER SPRING PLATE
SPRING
LOWER SPRING PLATE
DISC
BELL
SEAT
REGULATING SCREW
REGULATING SCREW LOCKNUT
STEM
SPRING HOLDER
BASE

(b) Relief valve

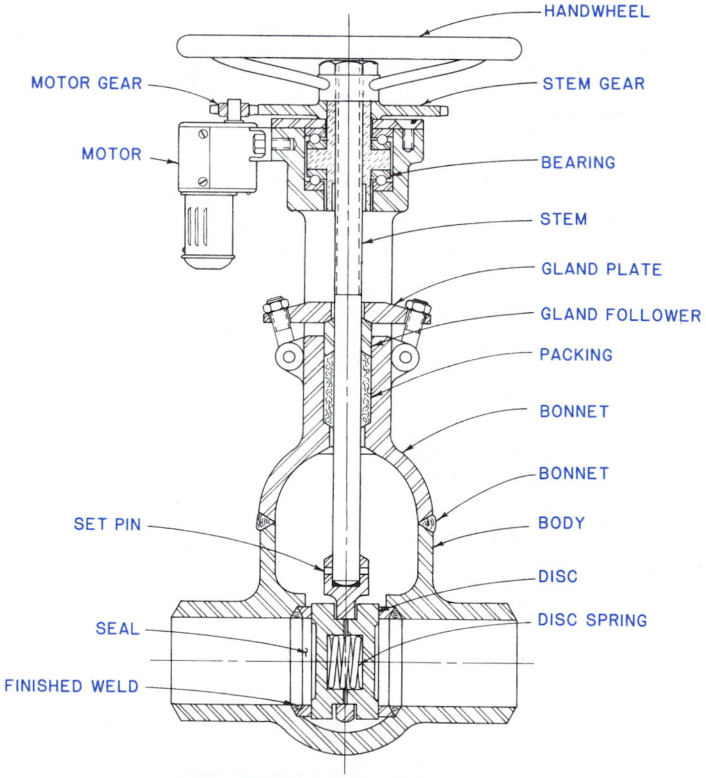

HANDWHEEL
MOTOR GEAR
MOTOR
STEM GEAR
BEARING
STEM
GLAND PLATE
GLAND FOLLOWER
PACKING
BONNET
BONNET
BODY
DISC
DISC SPRING
SET PIN
SEAL
FINISHED WELD

(e) Motor operated gate valve

HANDWHEEL
IDENTIFICATION PLATE
PACKING NUT
PACKING
BONNET
SEAT
HANDWHEEL NUT
STEM
GLAND FOLLOWER
PACKING NUT LOCK
UNION RING
BODY

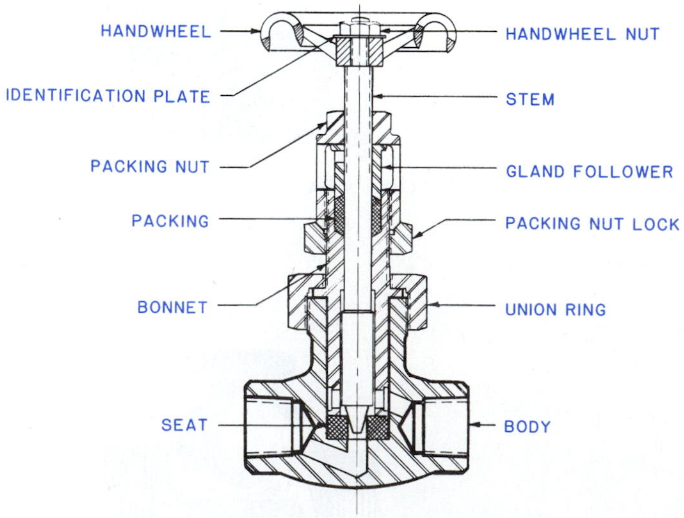

(c) Needle valve

FIGURE 22.10 **Valve Variations** (a) Relief valve (b) Pop safety valve (c) Needle valve (d) Diaphragm valve (e) Motor operated gate valve

similar (as is their body interior). **Lift check valves** [Fig. 22.9(h)] are usually used with globe or angle valves. Lift valves can use a solid disk or a ball as a disk [Fig. 22.9(i)].

Pressure relieving valves are used to prevent damage to equipment and for safety. **Safety valves** [Fig. 22.10(a)] are used on steam, air, and gas, while **relief valves** [Fig. 22.10(b)] are generally used for liquids.

Needle valves and diaphragm valves are two other valve variations intended for specific special services. **Needle valves** [Fig. 22.10(c)] are actually a type of globe valve, which are used on small-diameter high-pressure lines that require very close regulation. **Diaphragm valves** [Fig. 22.10(d)] are used where contamination of the line material must be prevented, such as in food and beverage production.

Valves can also be equipped with motors or cylinder-actuating devices for automatic and remote control of the valve [Fig. 22.10(e)].

22.6   Piping Drafting

Piping drafting and design uses a specialized language to transmit information for fabrication and construction. Pipeline, fitting, valve, and instrument symbols, along with special notations, are used on drawings to convey design and fabrication information unique to the piping field. Layout and dimensioning practices also differ from mechanical drafting, though quality linework and lettering are just as important.

Because piping projects represent *systems,* actual detail shown on the drawing must be kept to a minimum. Templates speed the drawing process for manual drawing (Fig. 22.11). CAD systems use menus and a library of preprogrammed piping symbols and notation for fast construction of drawings (Fig. 22.12). Piping components—fittings, valves, instruments, etc.—are almost always standard catalog items. Appendix D provides symbols used on piping drawings, and Appendix C provides a number of catalog pages to be used when drawing projects and completing exercises. Piping diagrams and pictorial spools are normally *not drawn to scale.* But dimensions for components are still necessary when providing measurements for dimensioning fabrication drawings. Multiview drawings (plan, elevation, and section) of piping systems are drawn to scale.

The six basic types of drawings for most piping projects are:

1. **flow diagram**
2. **plot plan**
3. **plan, elevation, and section**
4. **fabrication**
5. **pictorial spools**
6. **pipe support**

Flow diagrams include mechanical (P&ID) and utility diagrams. **Plot plans** may be preceded by site plan drawings for a project and are beyond the scope of this text. **Plan, elevation,** and **section drawings** show the total plant design to

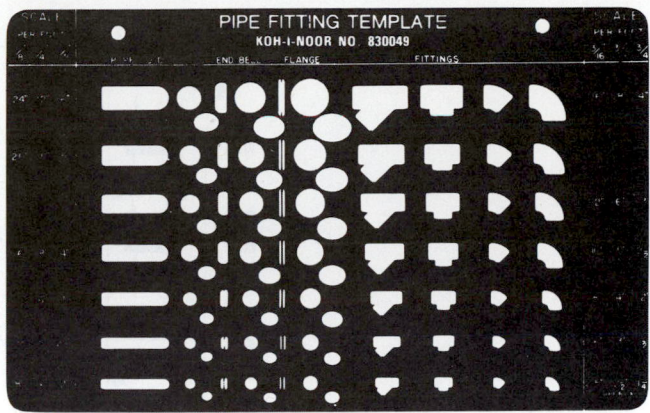

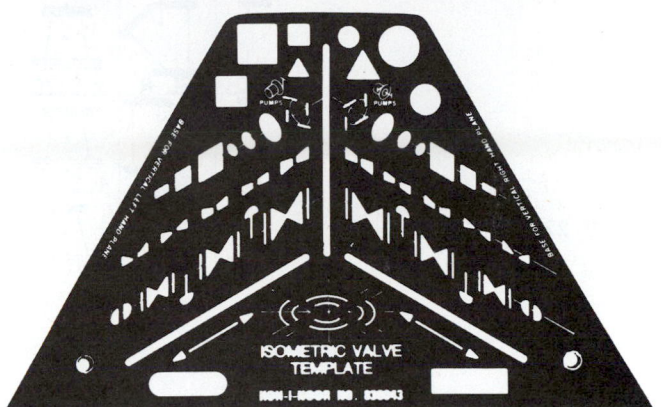

FIGURE 22.11   **Pipe Drafting Templates**

scale. **Fabrication drawings** include dimensioned portions of pipelines and vessel drawings. **Pictorial spools** are details of subsections of a pipe run. **Pipe supports** are location drawings and details of supports.

When manually drawn, the scale of most piping drawings is normally $\frac{3}{8}'' = 1'$; however, $\frac{1}{2}'' = 1'$ is often used in the power industry in order to provide more detail of the project. The $\frac{1}{2}'' = 1'$ scale is also used for modeling power plants. Most types of piping drawings, with the exception of plan, elevation, and section drawings (and CAD 3D models of the design), are not drawn to any scale.

Two methods are used to draw 2D piping projects: **double line** and **single line** (Fig. 22.13) (see Color Plates 83–87). Both double- and single-line drawings of 12″ pipe and larger are represented by a centerline and two thicker outside lines corresponding to the OD. Single-line drawings show only the centerline (as a solid thick line) and short marks representing the OD at the ends of the pipe for $1\frac{5}{8}$ in. pipe to 10″ pipe. Single-line drawings of $1\frac{1}{2}$ in. pipe and smaller only show the pipe's centerline as a thick solid line. Double-line drawings show all pipes with a thin centerline and solid object lines for the pipe's OD. Figure 22.14 shows three different ways of representing the pipe line and equipment: single line, double line, and pictorially.

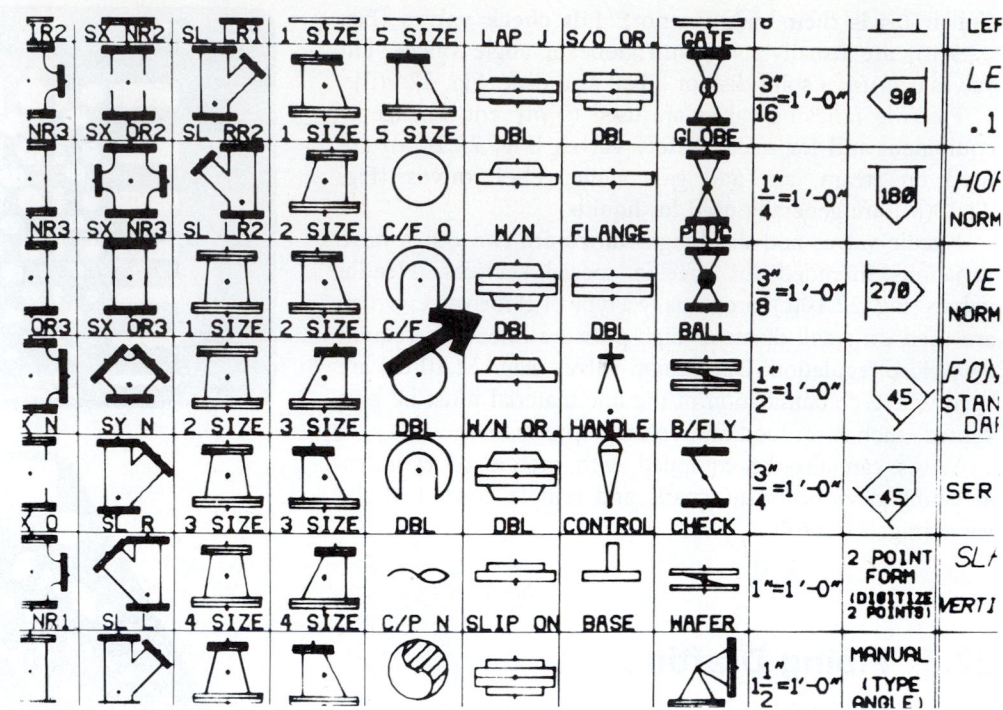

FIGURE 22.12   CAD Piping Menu

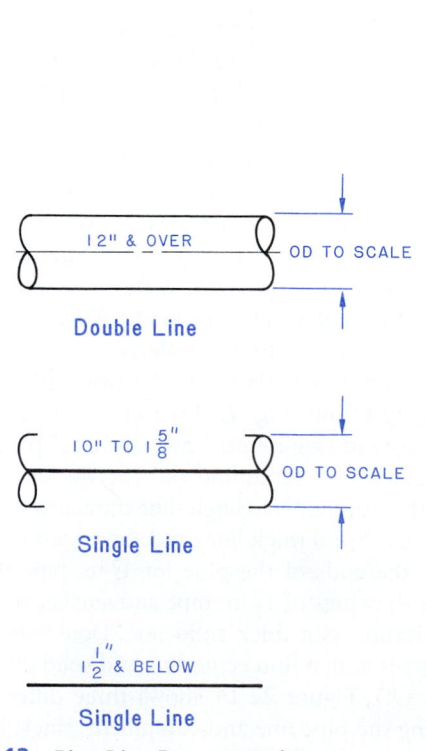

FIGURE 22.13   Pipe Line Representation

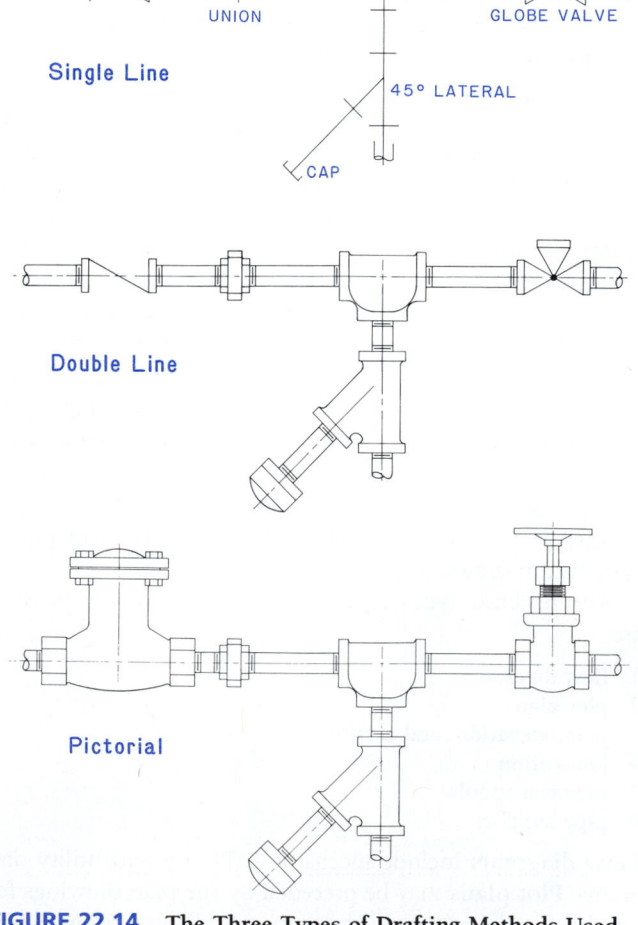

FIGURE 22.14   The Three Types of Drafting Methods Used for Piping Drawings: Single Line, Double Line, and Pictorial

22.6.1 Piping Symbols

Piping drafting uses symbols to represent the pipeline, fittings, valves, instruments, vessels, and mechanical equipment such as compressors and pumps. Figure 22.15 shows the types of lines that are found on piping drawings. Pipes are drawn with a thick, dense 0.7 mm line weight. Equipment

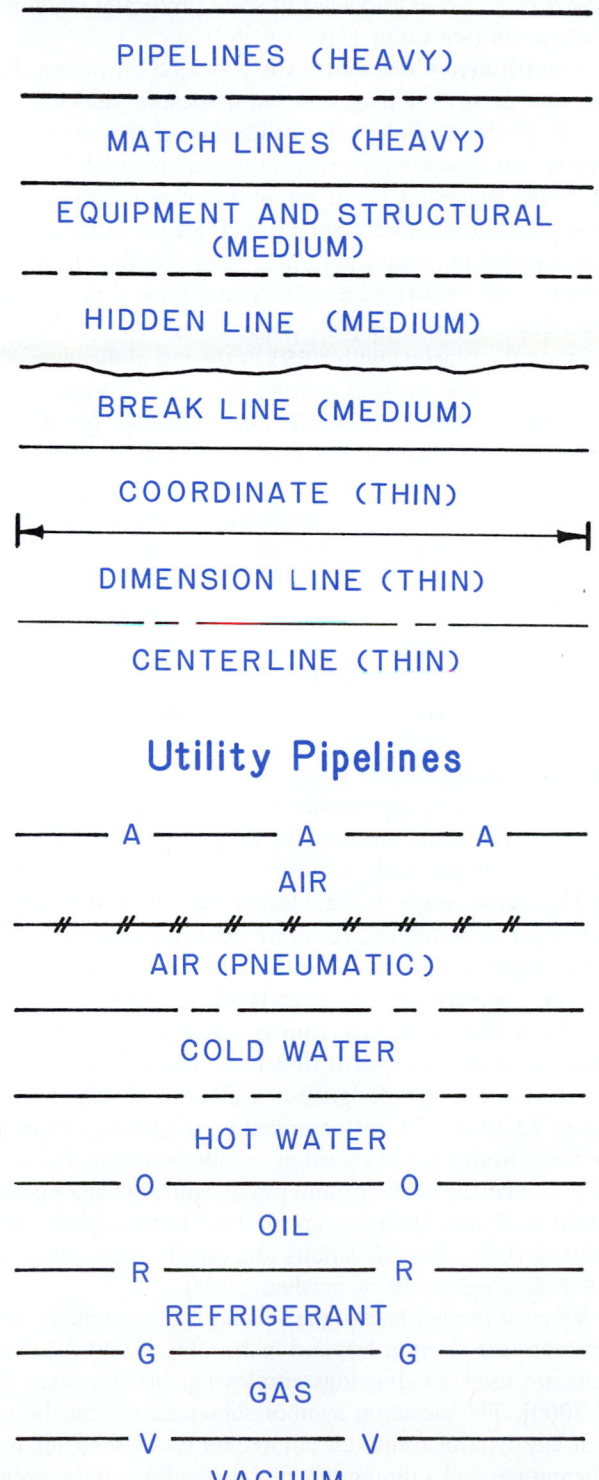

PIPELINES (HEAVY)

MATCH LINES (HEAVY)

EQUIPMENT AND STRUCTURAL (MEDIUM)

HIDDEN LINE (MEDIUM)

BREAK LINE (MEDIUM)

COORDINATE (THIN)

DIMENSION LINE (THIN)

CENTERLINE (THIN)

Utility Pipelines

A —— A —— A

AIR

AIR (PNEUMATIC)

COLD WATER

HOT WATER

O —— O

OIL

R —— R

REFRIGERANT

G —— G

GAS

V —— V

VACUUM

FIGURE 22.15   Piping Drafting Line Symbols

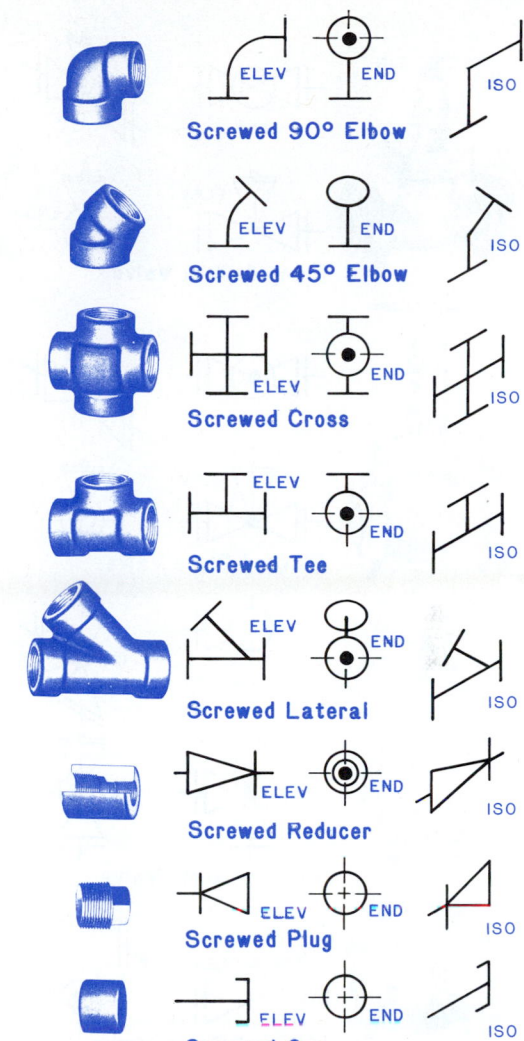

FIGURE 22.16   Pipe Fitting Symbols in Multiview and Isometric/Pictorial Projection

and structural lines are medium thickness (0.45 to 0.5 mm). Centerlines and dimension lines are drawn as in mechanical drafting—thin sharp lines approximately 0.3 to 0.35 mm thick. **Utility lines** are used primarily on flow diagrams and are normally represented symbolically.

Symbols are used to represent fittings and valves. Figure 22.16 shows the most common types of fittings. A photograph of each fitting is provided with the fitting as viewed in frontal and end view elevations (when drawn symbolically). An isometric view is also given. Only screwed fittings are shown in this figure. Figure 22.16 also shows the fitting as it looks from an end view. Notice that a large dot is shown when the fitting is turned *toward* you. Another method of representing this "end view" is shown in Figure 22.17. Here the four most typical types of valves are shown. The "turned toward" end view shows a symbolic shaded method of describing the position and direction of the line. Either method is acceptable.

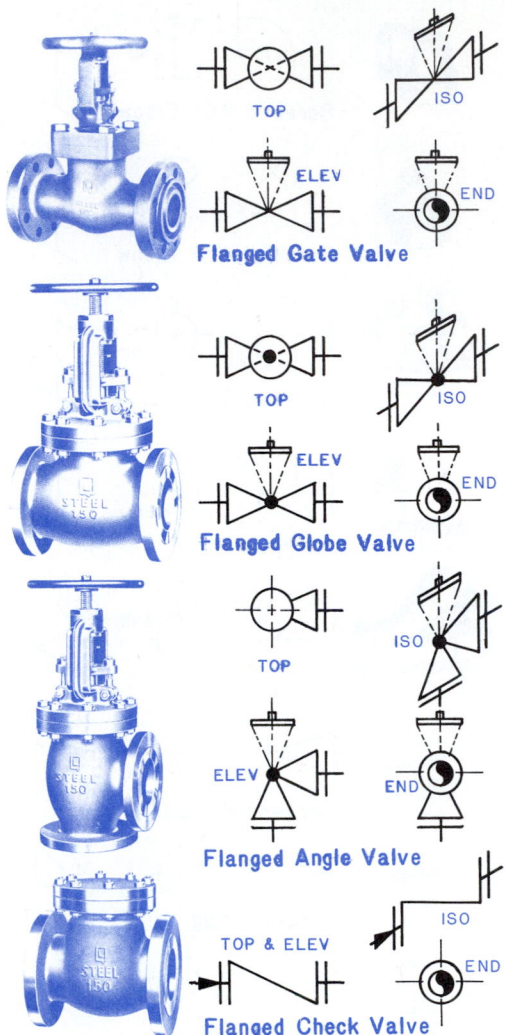

FIGURE 22.17 Valve Symbols in Multiview and Isometric/Pictorial Projection

In Figure 22.17 the top (plan), front elevation, and end elevation view of each valve are shown. An isometric view is also given. Flanged valves are shown in this figure. Figures 22.16 and 22.17 show the accepted size of fitting and valve symbols for all types of piping drawings. Dividers are used to transfer measurements for each symbol. Symbols for other types of fittings and valves are drawn by using these two figures as examples and consulting Appendixes C and D for the dimensions and shape. In other words, the end-to-end and the height measurements shown in these figures can be applied to all symbols. Note that isometric symbols of elbows use straight lines for the corners.

Handwheels of the valves in Figure 22.17 are symbolically represented. In many piping drawings the handwheel is not shown, as on flow diagrams. Flow diagram symbols are similar but slightly more simplified than symbols used on other piping drawings.

You May Complete Exercises 22.1 Through 22.4 at This Time

22.6.2 Multiview Piping Drawings

Multiview drawings for piping systems are called **plan, elevation**, and **section drawings**. In Figure 22.18 three elevation views of a piping and vessel installation are shown. This drawing is a portion of a plan, elevation, and section (the plan view is not shown). Plan, elevation, and section drawings are drawn to scale. The layout and design stage of a piping project may also be modeled to scale physically or on a 3D CAD system (see Color Plates 84–87).

A **north arrow orientation** is provided on piping drawings, except on flow diagrams and fabrication drawings. Figure 22.19 shows the standard direction of the north arrow. An alternate position places north in the upper left. In Figure 22.19 the suggested north arrow orientation and the three most common views are shown with an isometric view enclosed within the transparent box. View A is the **PLAN VIEW**, View B is the **FRONT ELEVATION**, and View C is the **RIGHT SIDE ELEVATION**. The plan (top) view, View A here, looks down on the pipeline with **WEST** at the top of the view. View B is an elevation view that looks **NORTH** and View C is an elevation view that looks **WEST**. Many drawings give location dimensions looking toward the north and east. In Figure 22.18 the front view lists coordinate dimensions from a specific point on the project (usually the battery limits or match line) toward the east, e.g., **E 5215'-3"**, **E 5239'-0"**, and **E 5228'-6"**. The left side view specifies coordinate dimensions looking north, e.g., **N 7703'-3"** and **N 7711'-2"**.

Besides specifying coordinate location dimensions (**X**, and **Y** or **X, Y**, and **Z**), piping drawings have elevation designations. **Elevations** are supplied for all horizontal runs of a pipe and may also be given to locate points along a sloping pipe. Pipelines that have small slopes are drawn as horizontal lines. Where the slope is appreciable, the pipe is drawn on an angle reflecting the slope amount. In Figure 22.20, methods for calling out slopes and elevation designations are provided: (a) The **slope angle** is established by giving the slope in inches per so many feet, (b) in **percent of slope**, or in (c) as **slope angle** in degrees. Elevations or **station points** could also be specified for both ends of a sloping pipe [Fig. 22.20(e)]. The **slope direction** is always given by an arrow pointing in the downward direction. The different types of elevation and slope designation callout methods shown in Figure 22.20 should not be mixed on a drawing. Elevations are taken from a grade elevation usually established as 10' or 100', so that any underground piping will still have a positive elevation. Some elevations are derived from a grade station point of 0'-0". Base elevations are usually established from **H.P.F.G.** (high point of finished grade).

When a project is designed using U.S. customary units, elevations are given in feet and inches [Fig. 22.20(d)]. Metric units are used on drawings employing the SI system [Fig. 22.20(e)]. The elevation symbol shown in (e) can be used with any type of units. Elevations are established for many different parts of a piping drawing depending on the projects needs: centerline of pipe, bottom of pipe (**BOP**), top of concrete (**TOC**), and top of steel (**TOS**) [Fig. 22.20(f)]. Slope and

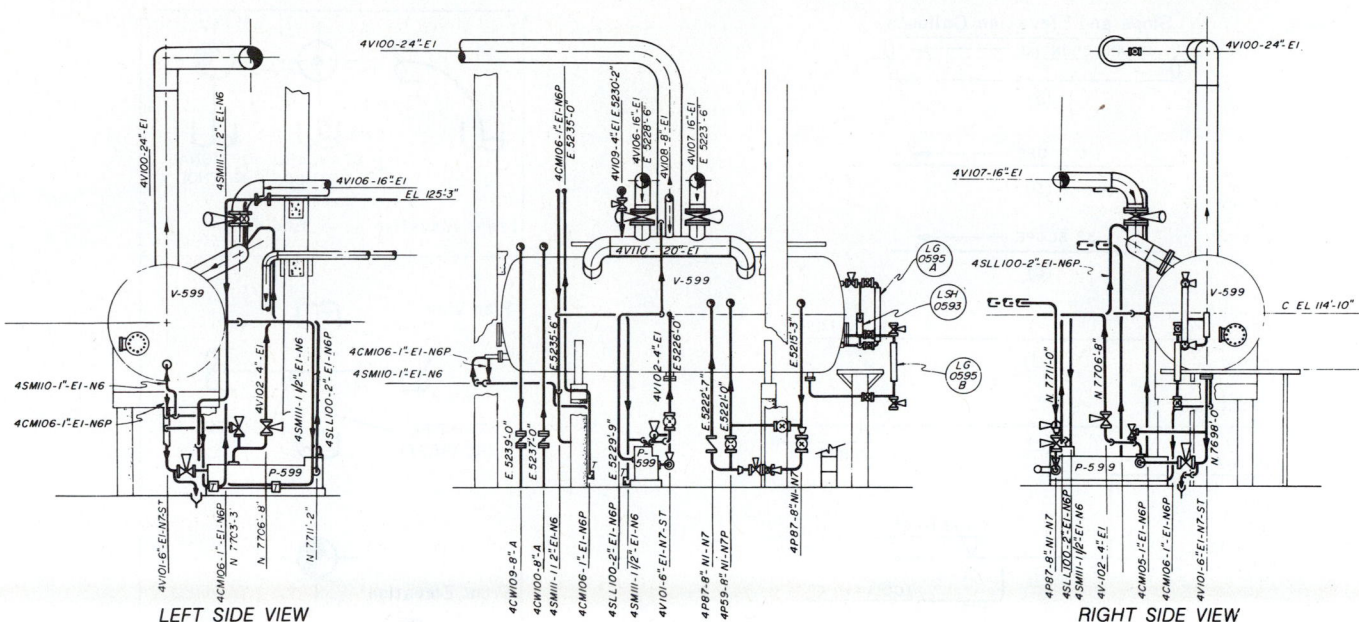

FIGURE 22.18   Elevation Views of Vessel and Associated Piping

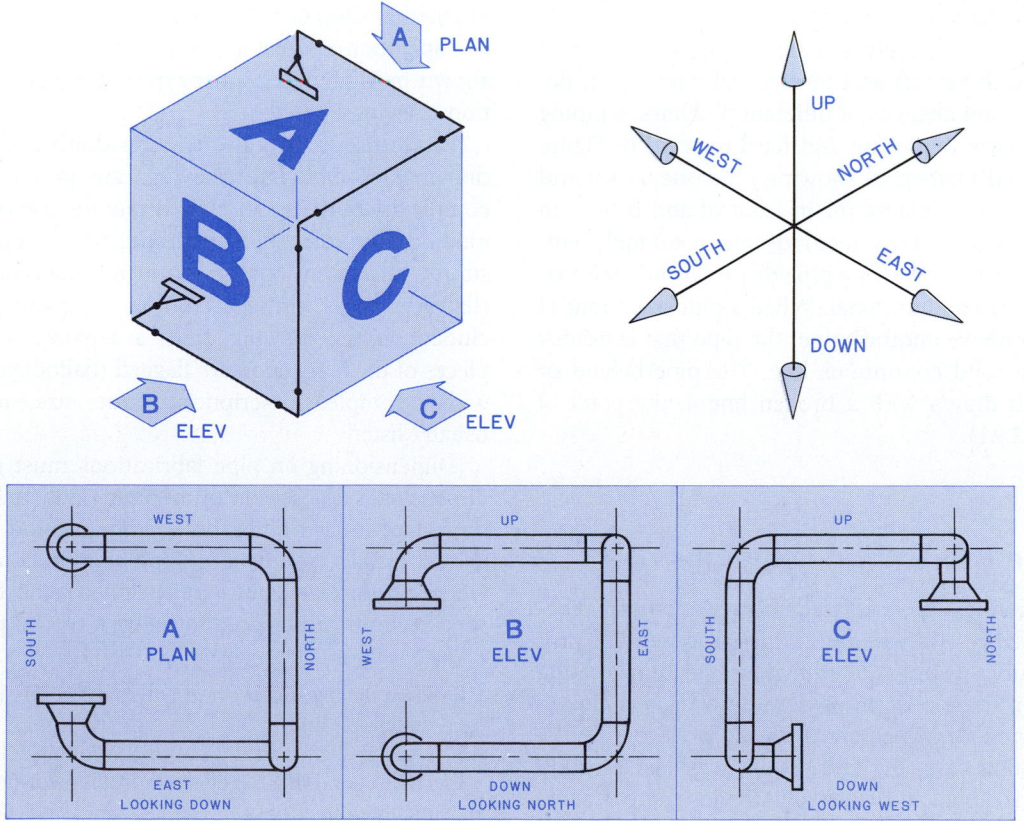

FIGURE 22.19   North Arrow Orientation and Views of a Piping System

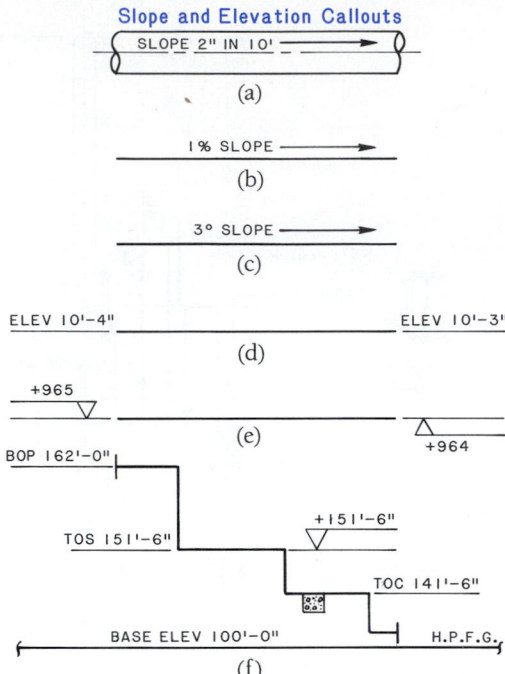

FIGURE 22.20 **Slope and Elevation Designations**

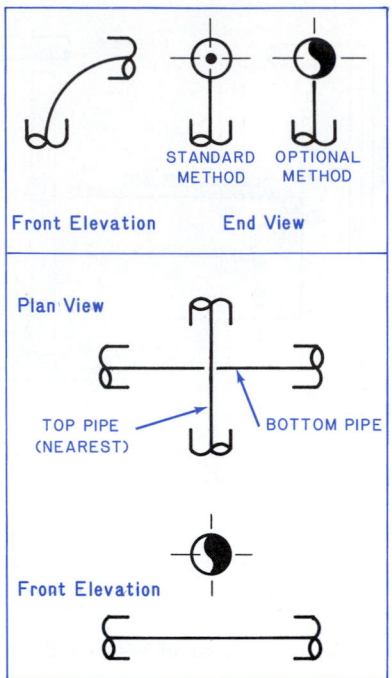

FIGURE 22.21 **Standard Drawing Practices for Piping Drawings**

elevation designations are also given on isometric spool sheets. Piping projects that are modeled physically or with the computer use elevations and coordinate dimensions to orientate the project in three-dimensional space. Elevations are tagged on the model when a physical model is constructed.

Piping projects are usually a maze of piping, steel, and concrete along with vessels and mechanical equipment. Because of the elevation changes of different pipelines, a piping drawing can become confusing and hard to read. In Figure 22.21 the accepted method of showing pipe orientation and which pipe is above or below (or in front of and behind in elevation) is provided. Two methods are commonly employed to show the end view of a pipe that is "turned toward" the viewer; standard and optional. When a pipe is in front of another pipe, or above another pipe, the pipe that is nearest is shown with a solid continuous line. The pipe behind or below another is drawn with a broken line at the point of crossing (Fig. 22.21).

22.6.3 Pipe Fabrication Drawings

Fabrication drawings are used to detail a section of a pipeline, including flanges, valves, and fittings that are to be produced as one unit. Fabrication drawings are drawn using either pictorial/isometric or multiview drawing techniques, although multiview drawings are normally preferred by the fabricator. In either case, the fabrication is termed a **spool.** Isometric/pictorial spool sheets usually provide more detailed location dimensions and callouts, such as pipe elevations and

pipe coordinate dimensions. Figure 22.22 is an example of a pipe fabrication. Units such as these are normally *shop fabricated* and then shipped to the construction site. *Field fabrication,* however, is common for large pipe sections. Regardless of whether shop or field fabrication is used, the actual assembly operation is done at the job site. Piping installations, as shown in Figure 22.23, are typical projects that use fabrication drawings.

Fabrication drawings are either double-line or single-line drawings. Double-line drawings are preferred, though the complexity of the spool may dictate the use of the single-line method. Regardless of the method, fabrication drawings must supply all dimensions necessary to locate component parts (flanges, valves, fittings, etc.). A complete parts list is included on the drawing or as a separate sheet. Individual pieces of the fabrication are flagged (ballooned) and provided with a complete description. Name, size, and material are usually listed.

Dimensioning on pipe fabrications must give a complete dimensional description of the unit. This includes lengths of pipe, face-to-face dimensions, and location dimensions for valves, fittings, and flanges. Pipe bend data and pipe angles, where appropriate, must be specified. The following list of specifications can be used to set up a typical pipe fabrication:

1. Place dimensions above the dimension line (do not break the dimension line).
2. Use the aligned method of dimensioning.
3. Use feet and inch marks for measurement units. Use standard metric units for SI drawings.

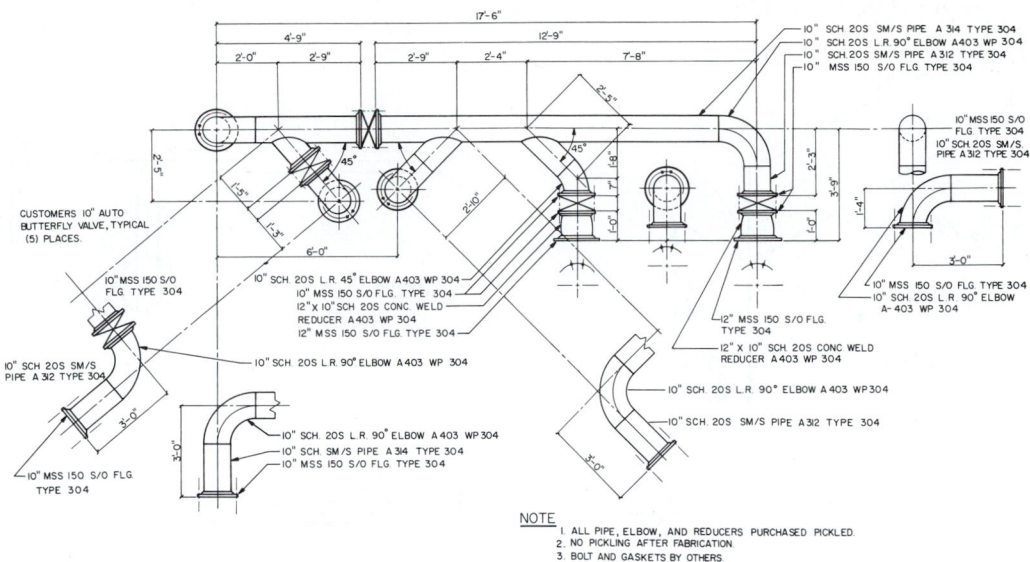

FIGURE 22.22 **Fabrication Drawing of Header Assembly**

4. Use balloons or flags to call out all individual parts of the unit: pipe, fittings, valves.
5. When using multiview drawings, show a sufficient number of views to describe the unit graphically.
6. Show rotation of valve stems and handwheel orientation.
7. Provide dimensions between valves and fittings and the end of the pipe where applicable.
8. Give face-to-face dimensions for valves.
9. Dimension each length of pipe.
10. Locate fittings from pipe ends where possible.
11. Dimension the distance between centerlines of pipes that are part of the same unit.
12. Use standard catalog dimensions for fittings and valve sizes.

Figure 22.24 shows the construction and detailing steps of a simple pipe fabrication:

1. Take the pipe, fitting, and valve information from the plan, elevation, and section views or from an existing project model. Using a sketch, note the general configuration and dimensions between elevations of the unit, and list the individual components.
2. Lightly lay out the centerlines of the spool using construction lines and establish the number and selection of views. In most cases, the spool is not drawn to any particular scale, though when possible an attempt is made to keep the parts and pipe lengths proportional.
3. Look up component sizes and dimensions in vendor catalogs. Fittings and valves are drawn and darkened first.
4. Draw the pipe using object lines and darken the centerlines.
5. Add dimension lines, measurements, leaders, and arrowheads. Provide callouts on individual spool parts.
6. Construct a bill of materials, parts list, or materials list on the drawing or on a separate sheet. This list includes item, quantity, and description. The description should include the part name, size, type, material, and the vendor and catalog number.

22.6.4 Flow Diagrams

Flow diagrams for piping projects graphically describe the system using simplified symbols for vessels, equipment, valves, and instrumentation. The flow diagram is not drawn to any scale and it does not show the actual configuration of the piping. Bends and change of direction fittings cannot be determined before the project is modeled or designed using the plan, elevation, and section method. Therefore, fittings are seldom shown on this drawing.

Flow diagrams are used to convey the system's process and what type of equipment is necessary for the project. In Figure 22.25 a typical mechanical [piping and instrumentation drawing (P&ID)] flow diagram of a petrochemical project is shown. Vessels are normally placed at the top of the sheet with the pumps (mechanical equipment) at the lower edge. Diagrams are constructed so that the flow process moves from the left to the right side of the sheet. Vessels, equipment, and

FIGURE 22.23 **Heat Exchanger Unit**

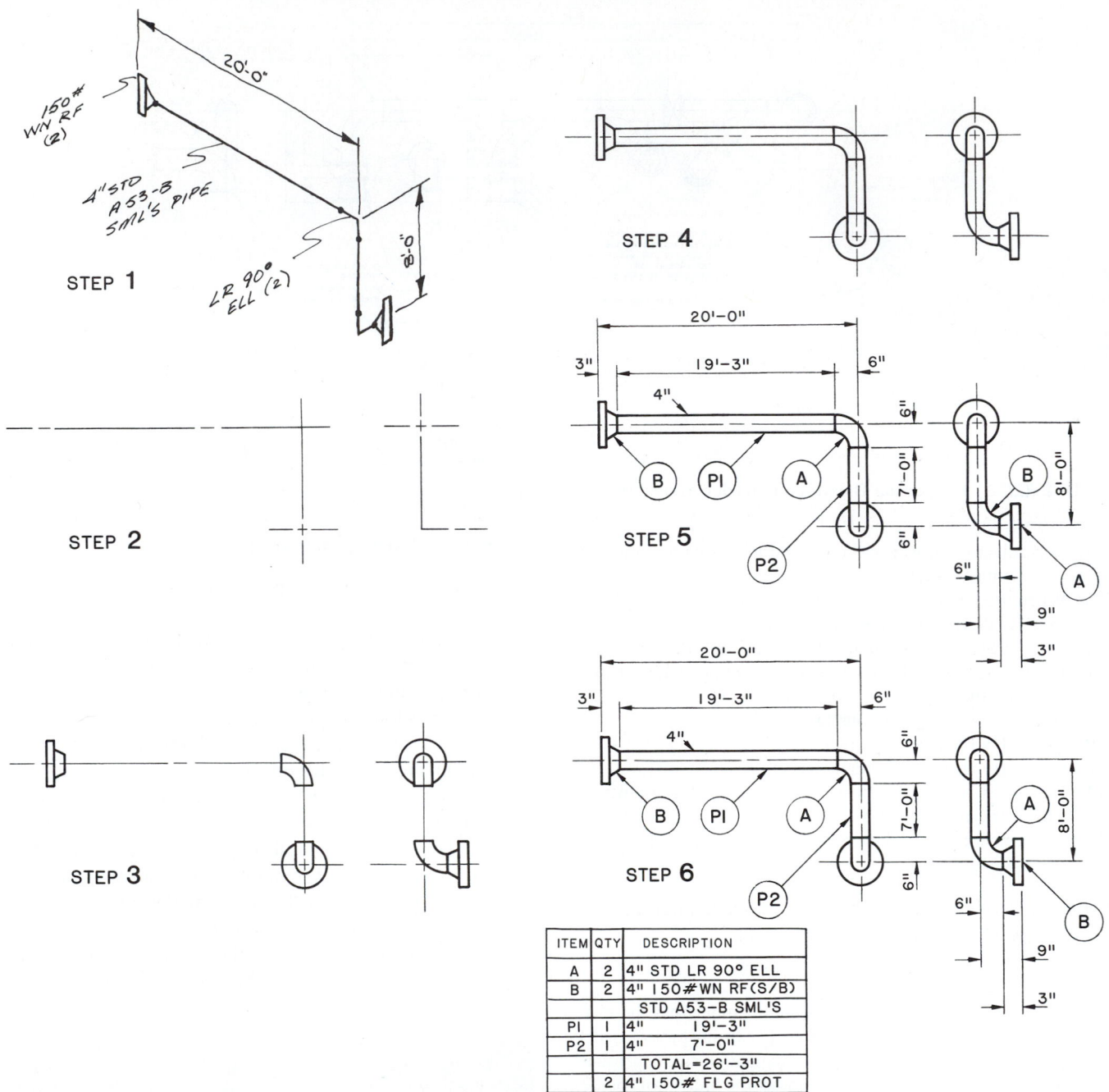

FIGURE 22.24 Steps for Detailing and Laying Out a Pipe Fabrication

valves are illustrated symbolically without concern for size or proportion. Pipes are labeled with a line number and a flow direction arrow. Instruments are ballooned and the type of instrument labeled with a standard abbreviation. Electrical and air lines are also drawn between related instruments.

Because flow diagrams do not have a particular scale, the size of the layout is determined by the complexity of the system. In general, short pipes should not be represented by long lines, and small equipment should be drawn in some way as to convey relative size in comparison to larger vessels and equipment. A sketch of the layout is made on grid paper

before starting the actual drawing. Line number, vessel codes, and equipment specifications are shown on this drawing. Line identification numbers are assigned for each pipe. In Figure 22.26 the CAD-generated P&ID shows each line number placed above the pipe. A **line identification number** specifies the line number, line size in inches, material classification of the line contents, and an insulation code. Many companies use their own version of a line identification number.

One of the most important parts of a flow diagram is the instrument callouts and notation. Instruments are used to monitor, sense, control, record, indicate, and transmit data

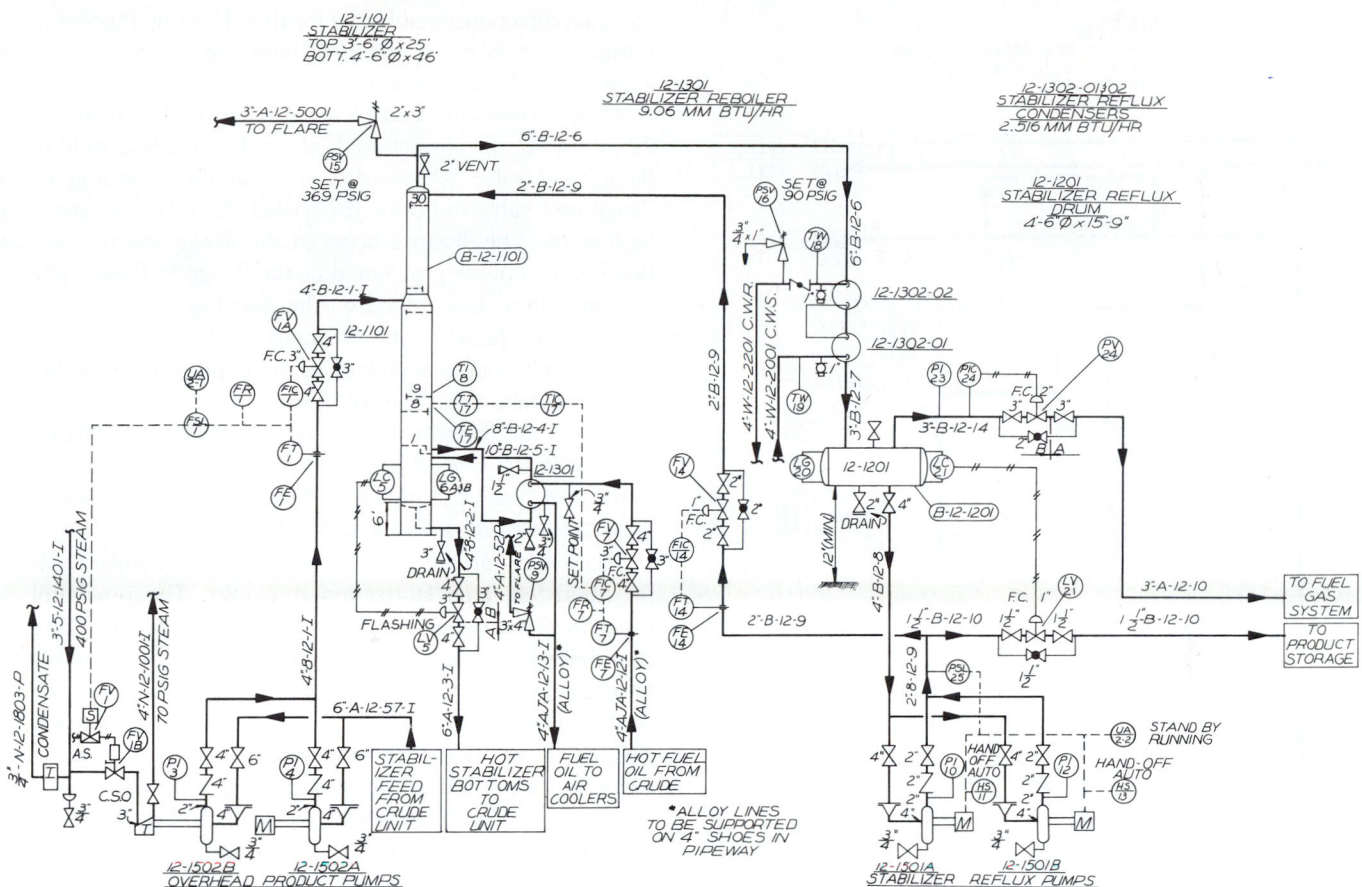

FIGURE 22.25   Mechanical Flow Diagram (P&ID)

about the process and the pipe contents. In Figures 22.25 and 22.26 balloons are used to enclose each standardized instrument designation. Figure 22.27 gives four examples of instrument callouts. **Instrumentation** falls into four distinct categories: temperature, pressure, flow, and level.

Instruments that are locally mounted, read, and operated are indicated by a balloon with an identification abbreviation. Instruments mounted, read, or operated on a board located on a control panel, away from the actual equipment, are called board-mounted instruments. Board instruments are represented with a balloon with a line drawn through its center and the abbreviation placed above the line. Line abbreviations include the instrument category: flow, pressure, level temperature, and its function. Figure 22.25 has a **LCV** (level control valve), **PSV** (pressure safety valve), and **FCV** (flow control valve). In Figure 22.25 a **TW** (temperature well), **PI** (pressure indicator), **FE** (flow element), **LC** (level controller), **LG** (level glass), and **TI** (temperature indicator) are shown along with a number of valve instruments.

You May Complete Exercises 22.5 Through 22.8 at This Time

22.6.5 Pictorial Spools

One of the most common drawings for a piping project is the **pictorial spool**, also known as an isometric spool when done manually. Construction techniques for this type of illustration are the same as for any isometrically drawn item when done manually. The dimensioning requirements are almost the same as for pipe fabrication drawings, and in many cases spool sheets are used by the fabricator. Figure 22.28 is an example of an undimensioned spool generated on a CAD system. A complete bill of materials is provided. A pictorial spool uses the single-line method for the pipe and symbols for fittings and valves.

The first step in detailing a pipe section is to select a north arrow orientation. The preferred direction is with north in the upper right (Fig. 22.29). The optional position can also be used. In addition to establishing the north arrow, some drawings need coordinate axes (**X, Y, Z**) indicated on the drawing. This is needed particularly when the spool is CAD generated because programming for a CAD system is based on a standard coordinate system. Pipe sections broken out of the plan, elevation, and section drawing are oriented according to the

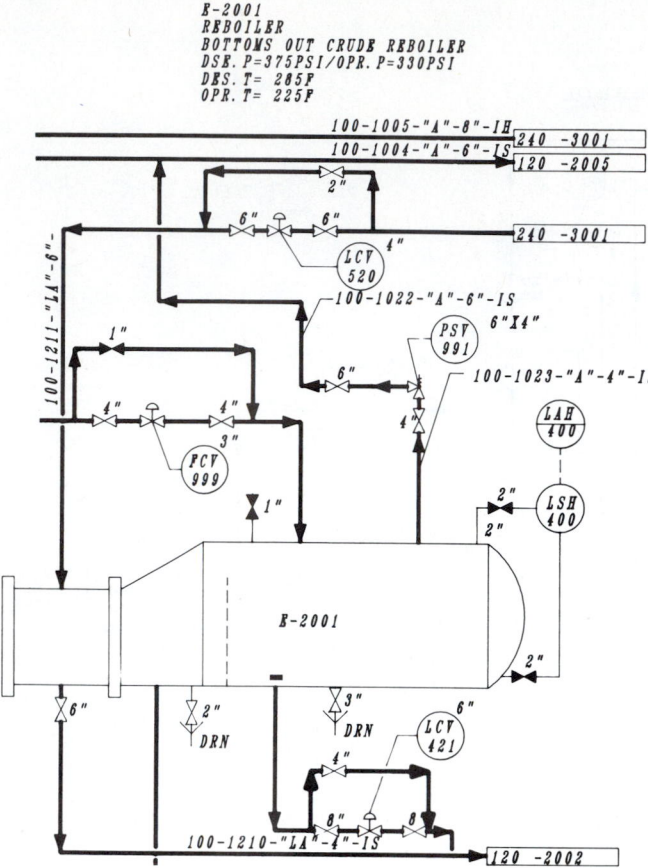

FIGURE 22.26   CAD-Generated P&ID Drawing

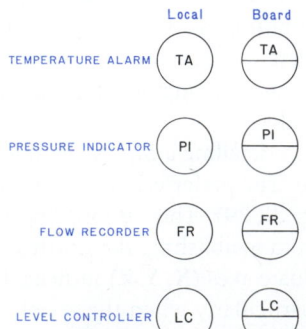

FIGURE 22.27   Instrumentation Board and Locally Mounted Instruments

compass directions established for that drawing. Pipe sections normally run north, south, east, west, up or down, or at an angle when the pipe is offset.

Flange orientation on a pictorial spool is shown in Figure 22.30. In (a), the correct method for illustrating a weld neck flange and valve is provided. Typical dimensioning for a flange and valve indicates the gasket thickness by showing *hash marks*. The distance between the flange and the nearest bend, or end of the pipe line plus the flange-to-flange dimension for valves, is included on the drawing.

In Figure 22.30(b) the accepted method of aligning the flange with the nearest change of direction of the pipe line is shown. When the pipe is in the horizontal plane [Fig. 22.30(c)], the flange is drawn with vertical lines. When the flange is in the vertical plane, the flange line is drawn at 30° to the horizontal and angled to the right or left depending on the orientation of the nearest bend (d).

Pictorial spools are constructed using steps similar to those for multiview pipe fabrication drawings. The pipe unit is taken from the design model or the plan, elevation, and section drawing by sketching the configuration and noting the fittings, flanges, and valves between two logical pipe breaks (*nodes*). Flanged joints, equipment connections, vessel nozzles, or valves are usually used as break points. Each spool represents a portion of the plant piping. Pictorial spools are usually not drawn to any particular scale. In Figure 22.31 the manual isometric construction of a spool is broken into four steps:

1. Using light construction lines, draw the pipe configuration. These lines represent the pipe's centerline.
2. Darken the pipeline and draw the fittings and valves using standard symbols.
3. Dimension and balloon the spool.
4. Complete the bill of materials.

22.6.6   Pipe Offsets

When a pipe must change direction in one or more planes, a **piping offset** is normally used. Simple offsets are based on the right triangle. The pipe changes from its first position to a parallel position by moving at an angle and then returning to the original direction. In Figure 22.32 the offset is in the horizontal plane, and is termed a **horizontal offset.** The plan (1) and elevation (2) views show that the pipe changes position in the horizontal plane. The distance that it moves along the pipe is called the **travel** and the amount it moves from the original position (at a right angle to the original line) is called the **offset.** This example is of a 45° offset in the horizontal plane. The (a), (b), and (c) views of Figure 22.32 show the offset in an isometric view: (a) gives the north arrow orientation, (b) shows the newest standard method for notating the offset, and (c) gives the most common method. In (c) the travel, offset, and degree of offset are shown. Figure 22.33 shows the same offset as it would appear in the vertical plane.

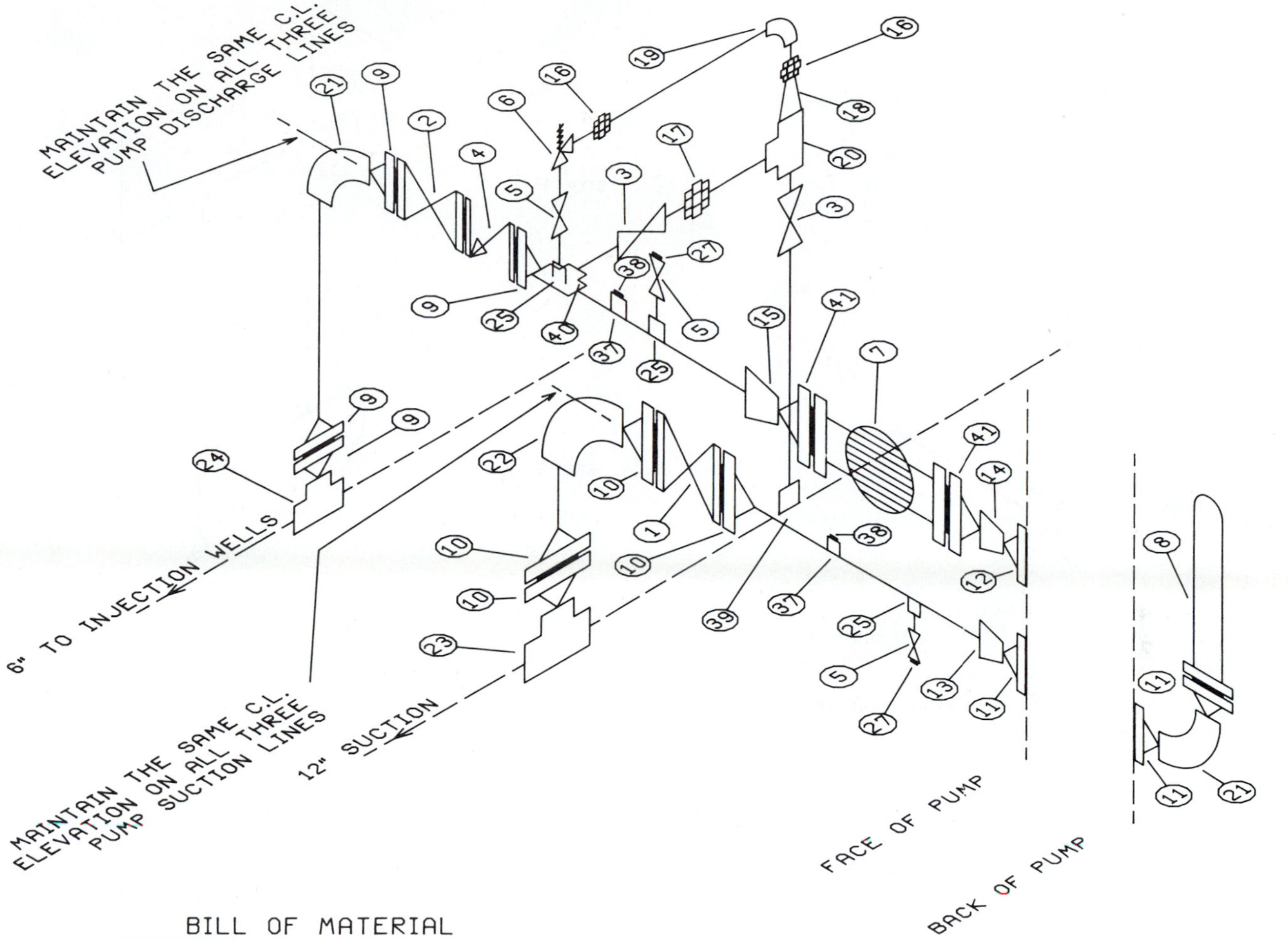

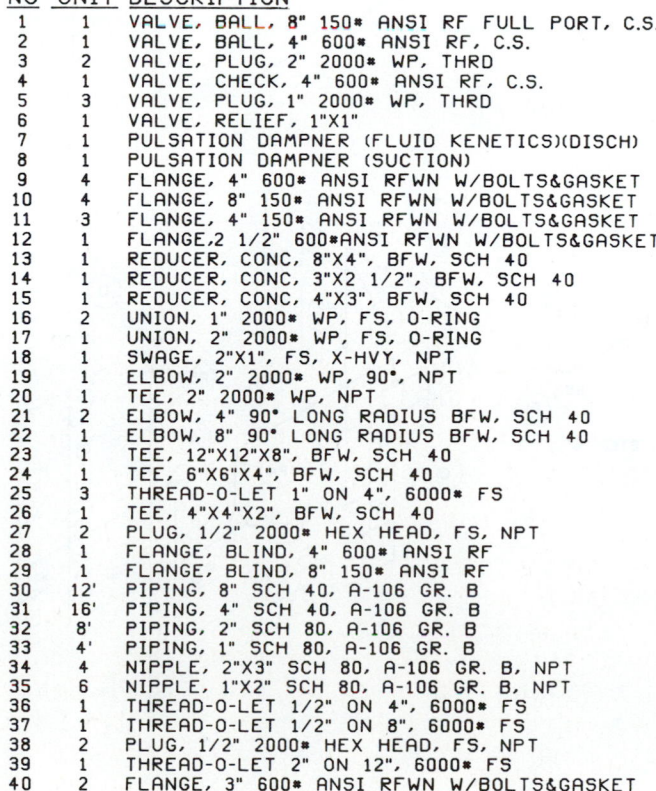

BILL OF MATERIAL

NO	UNIT	DESCRIPTION
1	1	VALVE, BALL, 8" 150# ANSI RF FULL PORT, C.S.
2	1	VALVE, BALL, 4" 600# ANSI RF, C.S.
3	2	VALVE, PLUG, 2" 2000# WP, THRD
4	1	VALVE, CHECK, 4" 600# ANSI RF, C.S.
5	3	VALVE, PLUG, 1" 2000# WP, THRD
6	1	VALVE, RELIEF, 1"X1"
7	1	PULSATION DAMPNER (FLUID KENETICS)(DISCH)
8	1	PULSATION DAMPNER (SUCTION)
9	4	FLANGE, 4" 600# ANSI RFWN W/BOLTS&GASKET
10	4	FLANGE, 8" 150# ANSI RFWN W/BOLTS&GASKET
11	3	FLANGE, 4" 150# ANSI RFWN W/BOLTS&GASKET
12	1	FLANGE,2 1/2" 600#ANSI RFWN W/BOLTS&GASKET
13	1	REDUCER, CONC, 8"X4", BFW, SCH 40
14	1	REDUCER, CONC, 3"X2 1/2", BFW, SCH 40
15	1	REDUCER, CONC, 4"X3", BFW, SCH 40
16	2	UNION, 1" 2000# WP, FS, O-RING
17	1	UNION, 2" 2000# WP, FS, O-RING
18	1	SWAGE, 2"X1", FS, X-HVY, NPT
19	1	ELBOW, 2" 2000# WP, 90°, NPT
20	1	TEE, 2" 2000# WP, NPT
21	2	ELBOW, 4" 90° LONG RADIUS BFW, SCH 40
22	1	ELBOW, 8" 90° LONG RADIUS BFW, SCH 40
23	1	TEE, 12"X12"X8", BFW, SCH 40
24	1	TEE, 6"X6"X4", BFW, SCH 40
25	3	THREAD-O-LET 1" ON 4", 6000# FS
26	1	TEE, 4"X4"X2", BFW, SCH 40
27	2	PLUG, 1/2" 2000# HEX HEAD, FS, NPT
28	1	FLANGE, BLIND, 4" 600# ANSI RF
29	1	FLANGE, BLIND, 8" 150# ANSI RF
30	12'	PIPING, 8" SCH 40, A-106 GR. B
31	16'	PIPING, 4" SCH 40, A-106 GR. B
32	8'	PIPING, 2" SCH 80, A-106 GR. B
33	4'	PIPING, 1" SCH 80, A-106 GR. B
34	4	NIPPLE, 2"X3" SCH 80, A-106 GR. B, NPT
35	6	NIPPLE, 1"X2" SCH 80, A-106 GR. B, NPT
36	1	THREAD-O-LET 1/2" ON 4", 6000# FS
37	1	THREAD-O-LET 1/2" ON 8", 6000# FS
38	2	PLUG, 1/2" 2000# HEX HEAD, FS, NPT
39	1	THREAD-O-LET 2" ON 12", 6000# FS
40	2	FLANGE, 3" 600# ANSI RFWN W/BOLTS&GASKET

FIGURE 22.28   CAD-Generated Piping Pictorial Spool

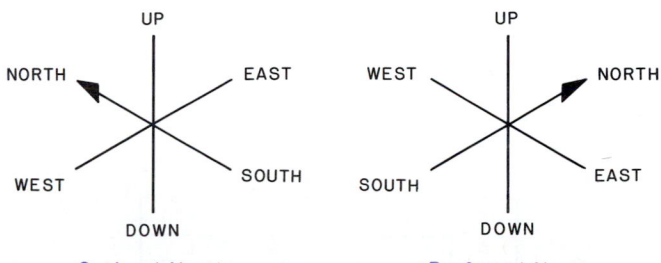

Optional North   Preferred North

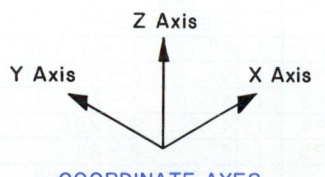

COORDINATE AXES

FIGURE 22.29   North Arrow Orientation and X, Y, Z
Coordinates

(a)

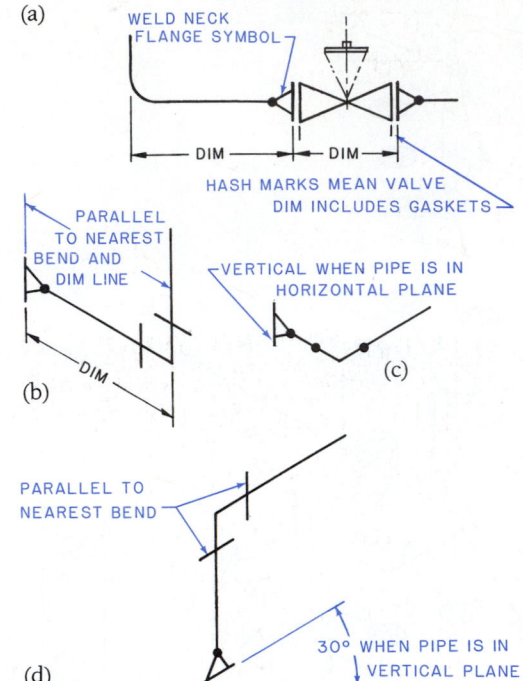

FIGURE 22.30 Flange Orientation on Isometric/Pictorial Spool Drawings

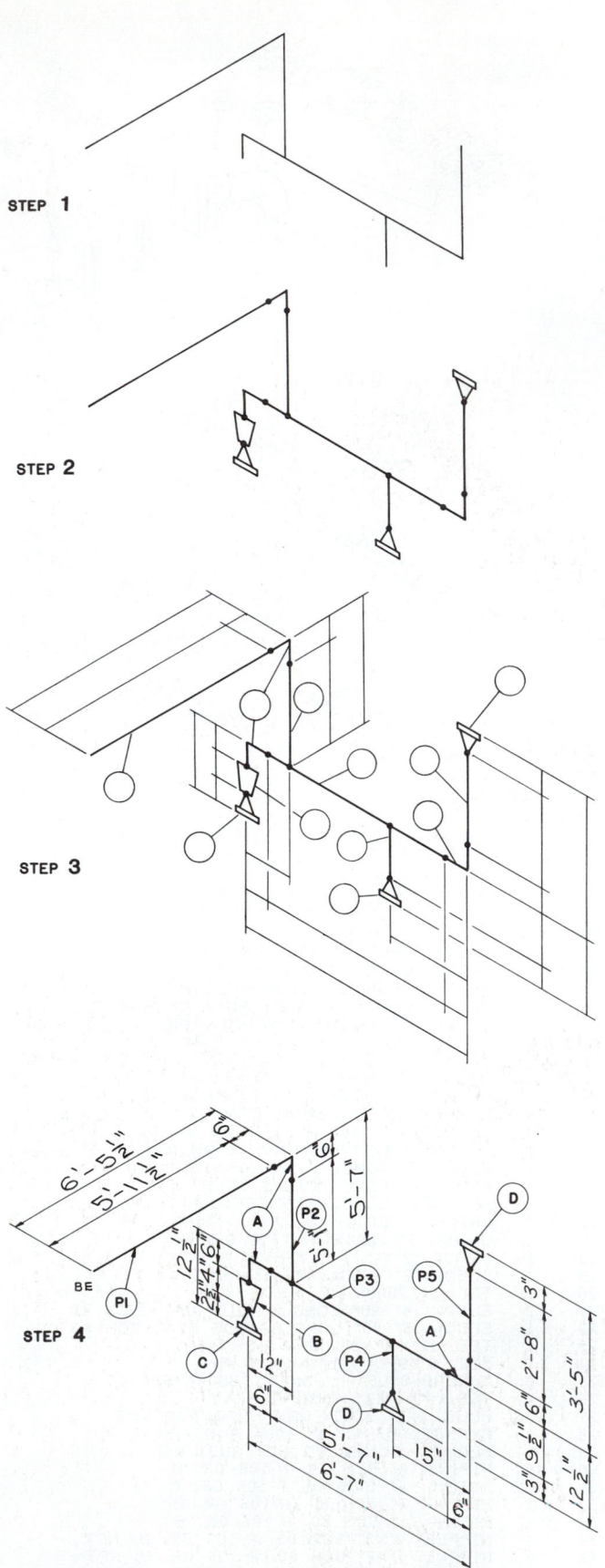

ITEM		DESCRIPTION
A	3	4" STD LR 90° ELL
B	1	4" X 2" STD CONC RED
C	1	2" 150# WN RF (S/B)
D	2	4" 150# WN RF (S/B)
		STD A53–B SML'S
P1	1	4" 5'–11 1/2"
P2	1	4" 2'–10 1/8"
P3	1	4" 5'–7"
P4	1	4" 9 1/2"
P5	1	4" 2'–8"
		TOTAL: 18'–0"

FIGURE 22.31 Steps for Isometric/Pictorial Spool Construction and Detailing

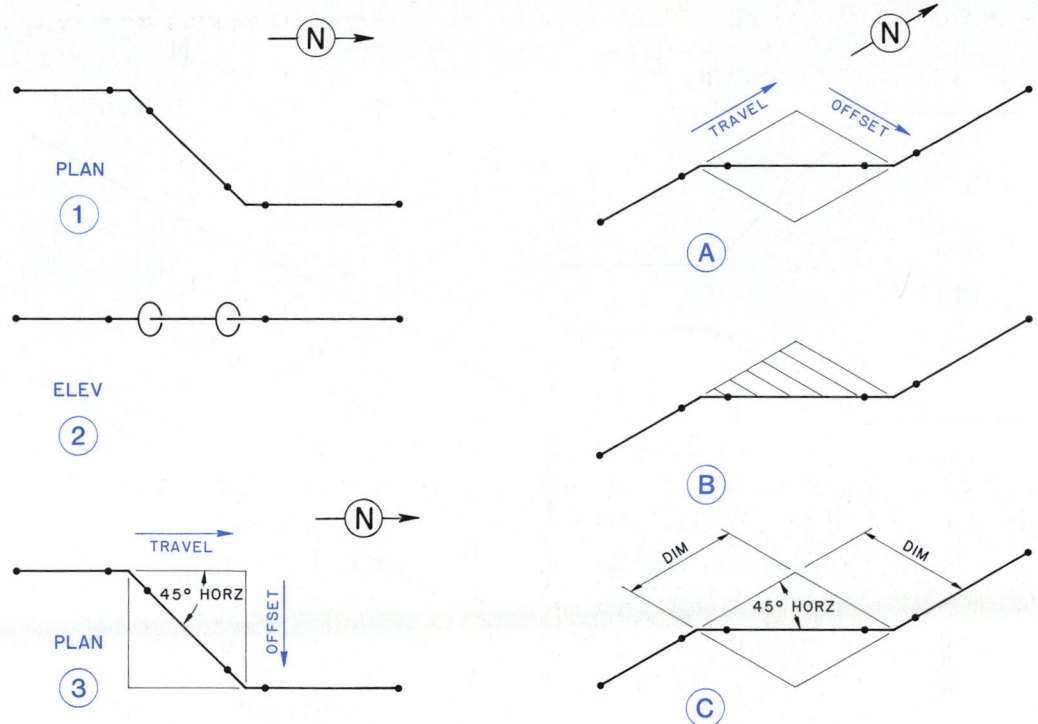

FIGURE 22.32   Horizontal Offset

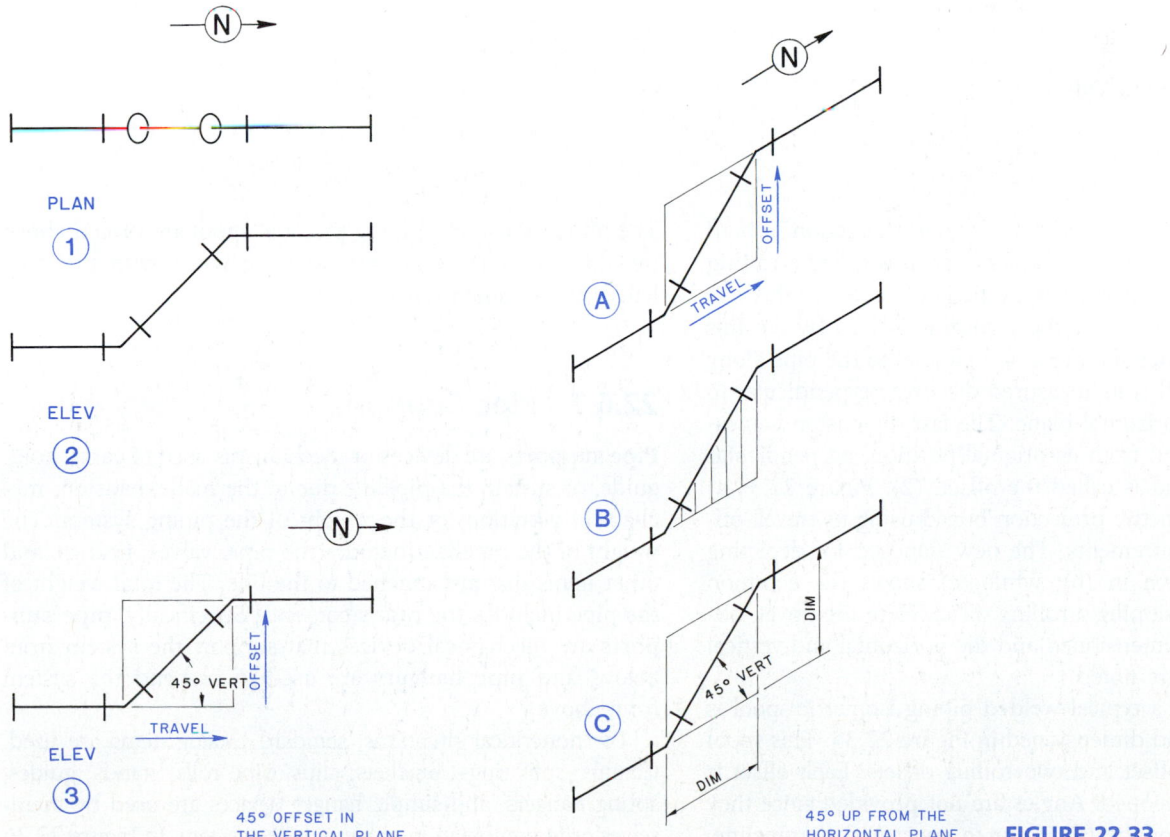

45° OFFSET IN
THE VERTICAL PLANE

45° UP FROM THE
HORIZONTAL PLANE   **FIGURE 22.33**   Vertical Offset

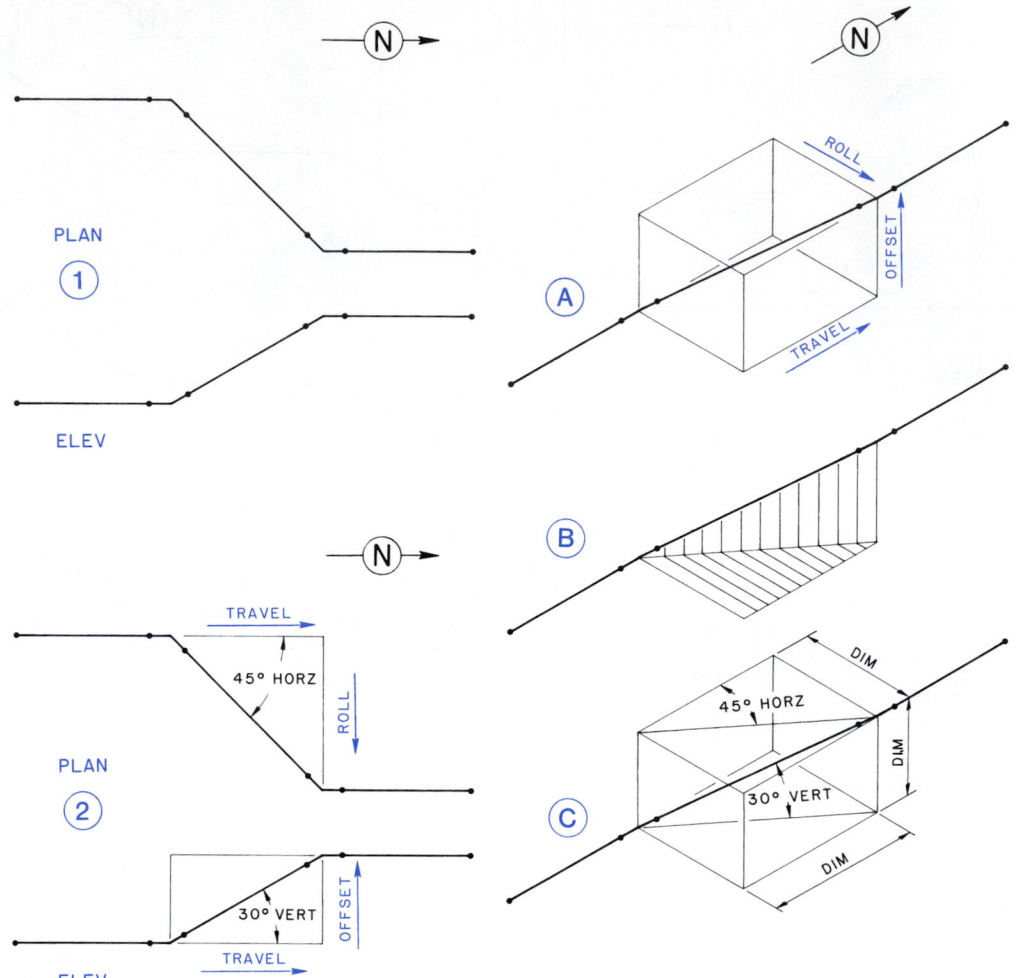

FIGURE 22.34   Rolling Offset

When the pipeline (Fig. 22.34) changes direction in both the vertical and the horizontal plane (1), it is called a **rolling offset**. This rolling offset changes direction at 45° in the horizontal plane and at 30° in the vertical plane. To lay out this offset, the travel must be measured parallel to the pipe along its length. The **roll** is its measured distance perpendicular to the pipe in the horizontal plane. The last dimension is measured up (or down) from its original position, perpendicular to the pipeline and is called the offset, (2). Figure 22.34(a) shows this in isometric projection boxed using its travel, offset, and roll measurements. The new standard for depicting the offset is shown in (b), while (c) shows the common method of dimensioning a rolling offset. Here the travel, offset, and roll are dimensioned and the horizontal and vertical angular changes are noted.

An example of a typical welded piping isometric spool is shown detailed and dimensioned in Figure 22.35. This spool has one vertical offset and two rolling offsets. Each offset is boxed and dimensioned. Angles are not provided since they are unnecessary for the fabricator to construct the pipeline.

The dimensions on a piping pictorial spool are placed above the dimension line and are usually aligned with the pipe length to be dimensioned.

22.6.7   Pipe Supports

Pipe supports are devices or mechanisms used to carry, hold, guide, or sustain the pipeline due to thermal expansion, mechanical vibration, or the weight of the piping system. The weight of the pipeline includes the pipe, valves, fittings, and other items that are attached to the line. The total weight of the pipe includes the pipe's contents. Specifically, **pipe supports** are mechanical devices that support the system from below, and **pipe hangers** are used to suspend the system from above.

For noncritical situations, standard catalog items are used. Clamps, split rings, brackets, clips, pipe rolls, stands, guides, spring hangers, and simple hanger devices are used by themselves or in combination to support the system. In Figure 22.36

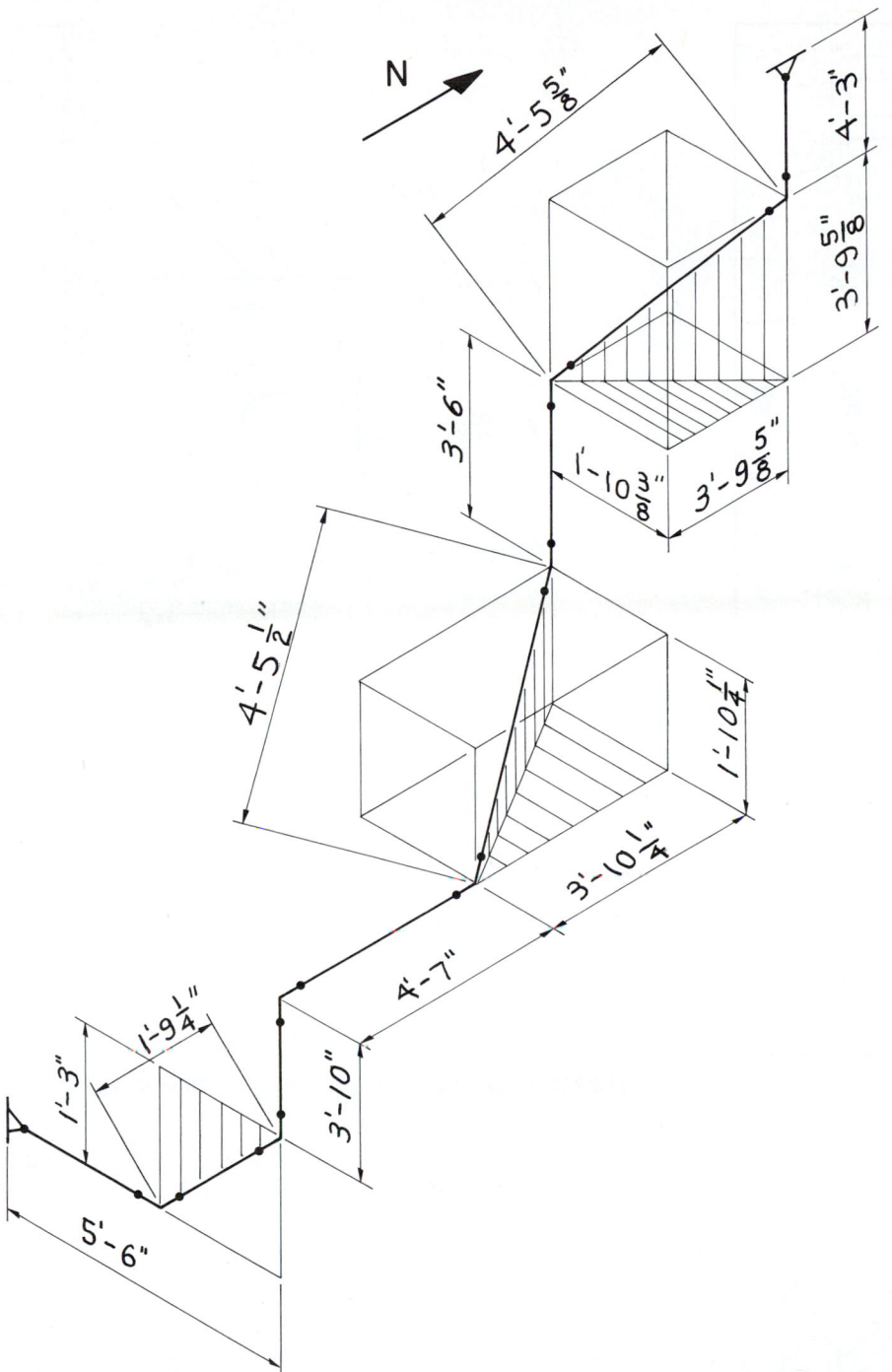

FIGURE 22.35   Piping Isometric Having Offsets

a variety of pipe supports and designs are shown. Welded structural steel shapes are also used to support pipelines.

For critical situations, standard items and fabricated assemblies (Fig. 22.37) are designed to withstand system stresses. **Pipe support details** are used to document, depict, design, and detail. In Figure 22.38 an example of a pipe support detail including a bill of materials is given. The detail provides all of the fabrication, setup, and purchasing requirements of the standard catalog items and the structural steel shapes. The **snubber** shown in this detail is used to suppress shock, vibration, and swaying. It does not support the pipe weight. Note that pipe support details are not drawn to scale. Welding specifications and pipe movement calculations are also shown on the detail drawing. (See Chapter 17 for more information on pipe support design.)

You May Complete Exercises 22.9 Through 22.12 at This Time

22.6.8   Vessels and Tanks

Vessels and **tanks** are the most important pieces of equipment in a piping system. Pipes connect equipment and transfer

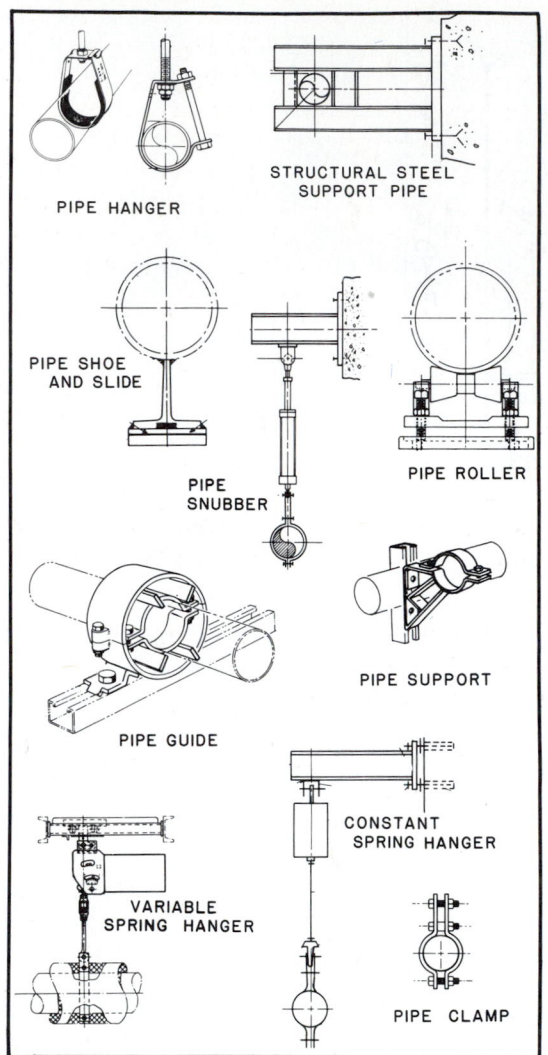

FIGURE 22.36   Standard Catalog Pipe Support Devices

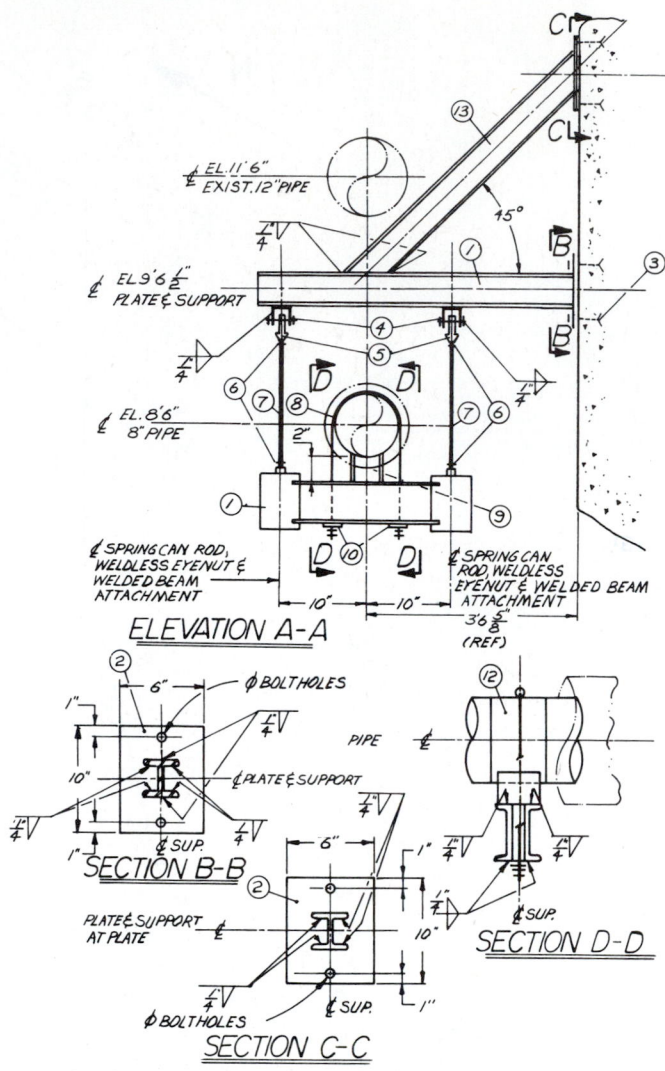

FIGURE 22.37   Variable-Spring Trapeze Pipe Hanger

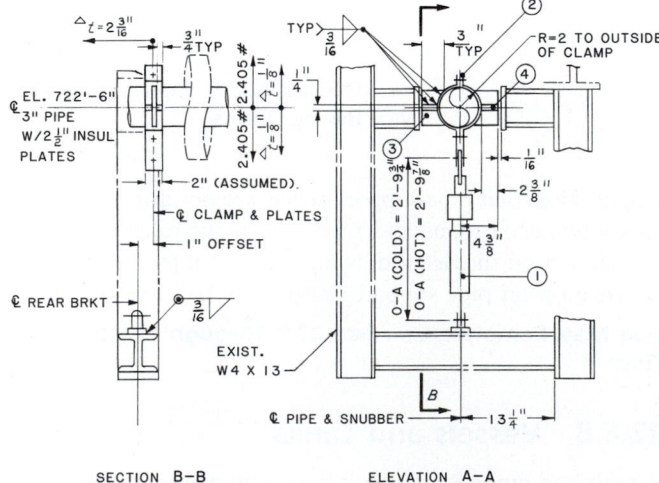

FIGURE 22.38   Pipe Support for a Pipe Snubber and Pipe Guide

FIGURE 22.39 Process Design Model

fluids from one point to another. Vessels and tanks are used to hold, store, mix, and process the line contents. **Pumps** and *head pressure* move the material between the vessels and tanks. In general, most vessels and tanks are nothing more than large-diameter pipes with enclosed ends.

The two categories of vessels and tanks are vertical and horizontal. **Vertical tanks** are manufactured in a wide range of sizes and diameters. Vertical tanks are used in the process industry for fractionation and distillation of petrochemical products. **Horizontal vessels** and **tanks** are limited in their size and capacity. Spherical and other odd-shaped vessels are also manufactured for specific uses (see Chapter 21 for an example of the layout of a spherical tank). In Figure 22.39 a portion of a piping process design model is shown. One knockout drum and two exchangers are shown. All parts of the model are made of plastic scaled replica parts and represent what the finished plant will look like when it is built. Models help the designer locate interferences between pipe,

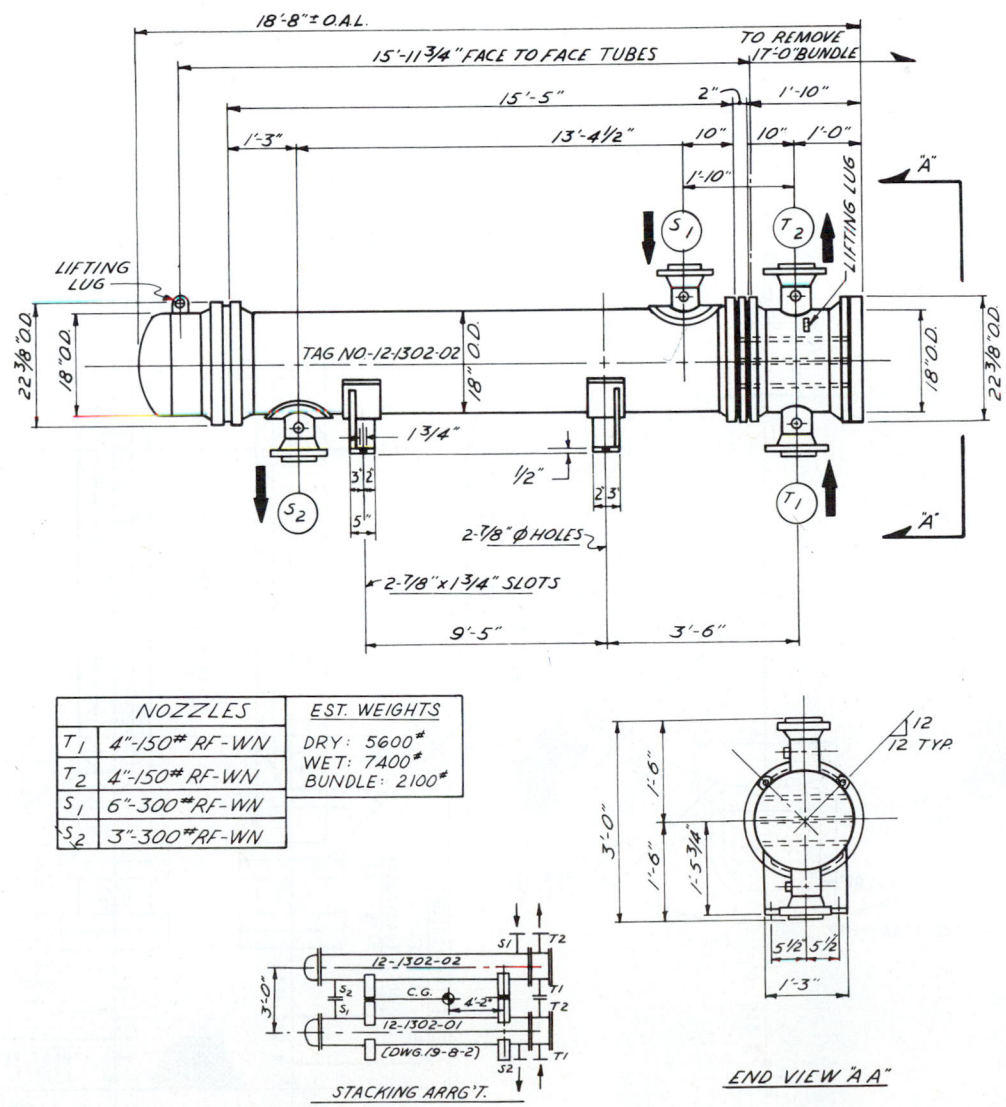

FIGURE 22.40 Vessel Detail for Stabilizer Reflux Condenser

vessels, supports, etc., and also establish the optimum placement of equipment for operation and construction.

Figure 22.40 shows an example of a horizontal vessel, a stabilizer reflux condenser. The detail provides sufficient information to fabricate and arrange the vessel. A small detail view shown in the lower left of the drawing gives the stacking arrangement dimensions. Nozzle and weight information is also provided as part of the detail. The large arrows show the flow direction for the two separate streams of fluids.

22.7   CAD for Piping Drafting and Design

CAD systems can be used to generate all forms of graphical documentation for a piping project, although some systems are limited to flow diagrams, piping isometrics, and other types of 2D views. Most systems will do these simple tasks along with construction of plan, elevation, and section layout drawings and allow modeling directly on the screen (see Color Plates 84–87). Figure 22.41 shows the plan view of a portion of a petrochemical plant. The plan, elevation, and section drawing is a scale computer model defined in 3D space through coordinates with specific piping and component data. You can automatically generate complete pictorial spools from the computer model. Some systems require that the spool be constructed via commands and a menu.

The piping menu shown in Figure 22.42 is used to generate piping drawings. The following list of commands is initiated using the digitizer and menu overlay. Though each CAD system has a different command structure, they generally have similar functions.

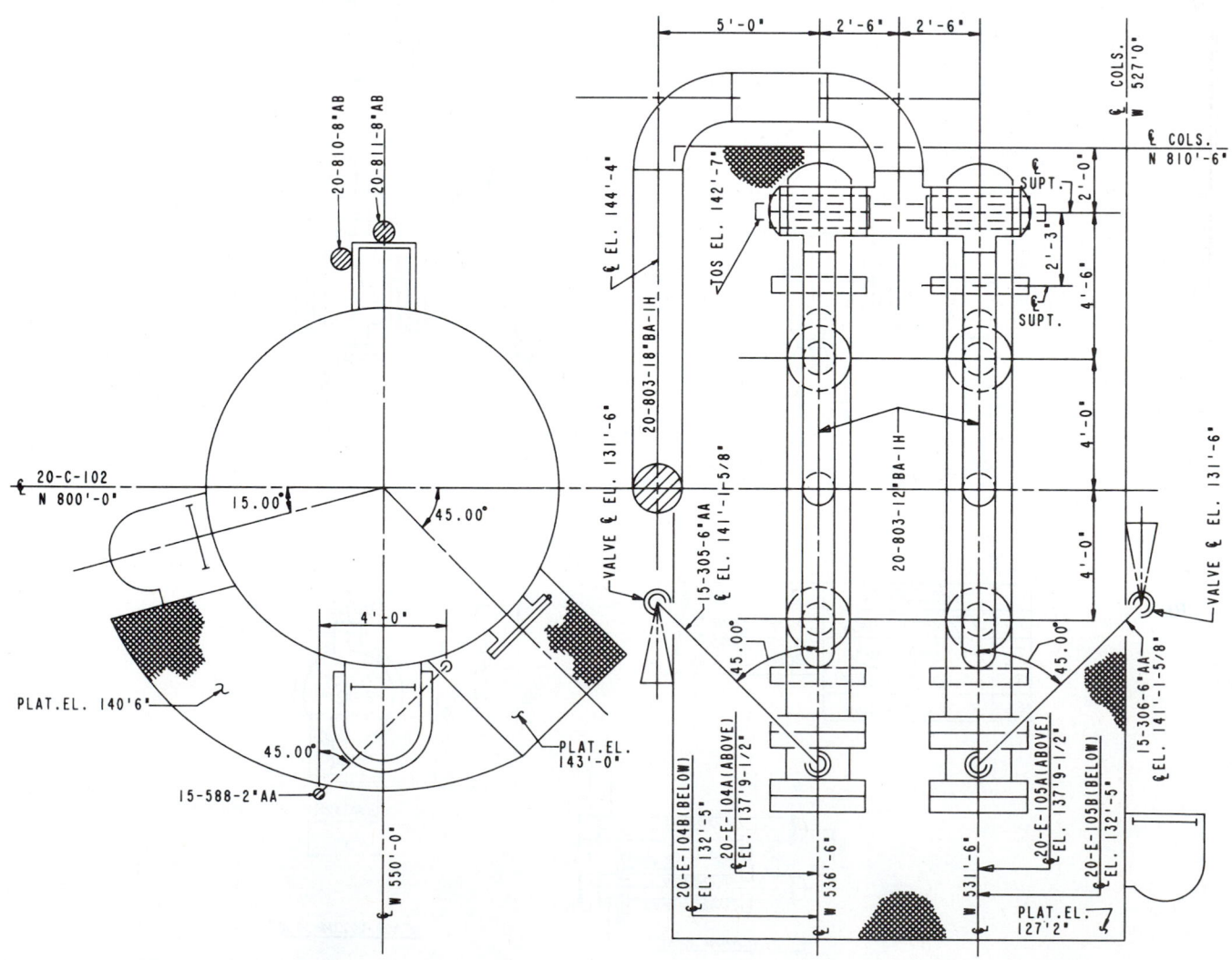

FIGURE 22.41   CAD-Generated Piping Layout

	1	2	3	4	5	6	7	8	9	10	11	12	13	14	15	16	17	18	19	20	21	22
A	MPNT	MELE	MLIN	STR	WIN	TRN	SLO	LBP	CRC	XHT	ORG	PON	DTL	GRP	TRM	PLT	DRW	MODEL ON	MODEL OFF	PROJECTION ON	PROJECTION OFF	AE&C MENU
B	MGNL	MDIM	MARC	MAG	TPO	WCS	PIC	TEXT START	NAME START	SYM	ALN	PVR	DEL	MBP	MIR	DUP	NUM		VFE	VFH	VFM	P&ID MENU
C	MTDI	MSYM	MANY	UPP	RTO	VPA	PER	GNT	GLB	RFN	TAN	PDG	TED	MVL	R	DR	VRL	VPP	ANG	PRP	PAR	PIPING MENU
D	ITM	CLS	ACT	DWN	CCW	ZWL	GRD	RVP	DAP	DMN	TXN	PND	MES	MHL	A	DA	0	.	—	+	CMP	STEEL MENU
E	DSP	SEL	PLY	SCF	RTN	ZTL	ONN	DMH	DMV	DMP	TXO	PIN	VER	MCR	X	DX	1	2	3	BACK-SPACE	REL	ELEC MENU
F	ADD	REL	ALL	PSF	RTP	ZTC	OFF	BDH	BDV	BDP	TAO	PCR	LPT	BLK	Y	DY	4	5	6	RE-START	ADD	EQUIP MENU
G	FNT	LWT	MOD	LCO	ROT	PIA	CLR	ODH	ODV	MDM	MTX	MRF	NER	UBK	Z	DZ	7	8	9	END		

Row H: STOP | FILE | REJECT | VIEW FILE REBUILD | REPAINT | C/C | HELP | MODEL MERGE | MODEL VERIFY | JOB SYSTEM | MISC OPERATIONS

	1	2	3	4	5	6	7	8	9	10	11	12	13	14	15	16	17	18	19	20	21	22
I	GRID ON	GRID OFF	ACT PLY	AXES	ZOOM	PAN	ZOOM ALL	ZOOM IN	ZOOM OUT	Z CLIP	VF PLOT		CHATR	CLOSE	CREATE	DELETE	INIT	LIST	OPEN	RENAME	SPOOL	TYPE
J	ROUTE		PIPE	STUB	TEE	CON RED	FLANGE		UPD PF	BREAK	NTS CS	REV DIR	LBL ITM	NORTH	CENTROID DISPLAY ON	OFF	CENTERLINE DISPLAY ON	OFF	MDV		HELP	
K	POINT		GEN PL	CAP	CROSS	ECC RED	BOLTS			MOD SET	MOD ANG		LBL LINE	DMP	DIRECTION DISPLAY ON	OFF	ALL LINES DISPLAYED ON	OFF	VER	UN DEF	START	
L	NORTH	DELTA NORTH	ELBOW	BRANCH	LAT	VALVE	GASKET	VER MAT	VER PROP	OFF SET	END PLN		LBL TOP	PIPE HS	SHRINK DISPLAY ON	OFF	HIDDEN LINES DASHED ON	OFF		DEF	GEN NTS	SET NTS
M	EAST	DELTA EAST	RET	UNION				LST MAT	LST PROP				LBL BOP	SYMBOL	POINT DISPLAY ON	OFF	HIDDEN LINES REMOVED ON	OFF	PI CHECK	POST PRO	BOX	PROCESS ISO
N	ELEV	DELTA ELEV	BEND	COUPLING				MOD MAT	MOD PROP		CHAIN PL		LBL ELV	JOINT SYM	ELEMENT DISPLAY ON	OFF	SIMPLIFIED CROSS-SECTION ON	OFF	PNT LST	VER POST	OPT	3D OPT
O	END	C/C	CON MEM	LINE DESG		AUTO FITTING	MANUAL FITTING	DEL MAT	DEL PROP	ADD NME	MOD NME	DEL NME	LBL SCN	AUTO SYM	JOINT DISPLAY ON	OFF	NOT TO SCALE CROSS-SECTION ON	OFF	BOM		SET FILES	DEFLT

Row P (symbols): PIPE | ELLLR | ELLSR | ELLRED | | ELLXLR | ELL45XLR | ELL45 XLR | RETSR | RETLR | RETXLR | BEND | TEE | RTEE | LAT | RLAT | CROSS | RCROSS | CON RED | ECC RED

Row Q (symbols): STUB | CAP | UNION | COUPLING | BRANCH | LATBR | | NIPPLE BRANCH | | GATE | ANG BLOWOFF | BLOWOFF-Y | GLOBE-Y | GLOBE | ANG GLOBE | STOP-Y | ANG STOP-Y | BUTTER FLY | DIAPH-Y | ANG STOP | CHECK | AUTO CONTROL

Row R (symbols): SAFETY SIDE | GATE WITH SEAL

Row S (symbols): SLIPON | THREADED | LAP JOINT | RAISED FACE | RING JOINT | WELD NECK | BLIND

Row T (symbols): BOLTS | GASKET | ENTER FITTING NUMBER | BUTT-WELDED | FLANGED | SOCKET WELDED | SCREWED

Rows U and V are blank grid cells.

FIGURE 22.42   Piping Layout and Design Menu

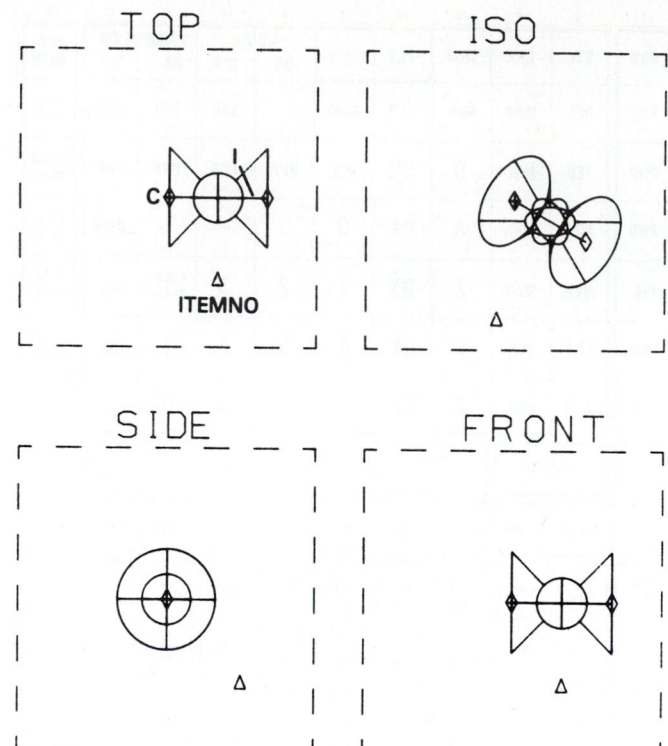

TOP ISO

SIDE FRONT

ITEMNO

PART PROPERTIES
COMPNAME : "BALV"
PNAME : "CVPD.BALV"
STOCKNO "   "

CVPD.&BCD.BALV
5-2-81 19:43:12

```
1!*
2!SHAPE = CYL,L = T1,D1 = T2
3!SHAPE = CONE,D1 = T3,D2 = 0,L = .5*T4-T1
4!*
5!SHAPE = CONE,D1 = 0,D2 = T3,L = .5*T4-T1
6!SHAPE = CYL,L = T1,D1 = T2
7!*
8!CLEARANCE
9!SHAPE = CYL,DI = T2,L = T4
```

FIGURE 22.43 Gate Valve Description from a Piping Database

Command	Function	Tablet
PLADDNME	Add names to piping items	0–10
PLAUTOSYM	Automatically display isometric symbols	0–14
PLBEND	Generate bends	N–3
PLBOM	Generate bill of materials	0–19
PLCROSS	Generate crosses	K–5
PLDMP	Generate parallel isometric dimensions	K–14
PLELBOW	Generate 45 and 90° elbows	L–3
PLFLANGE	Generate flanges	J–7
PLGENPL	Generate basic pipeline	K–7
PLLBLBOP	Generate labels for BOP elevations	M–13
PLNORTH	Place isometric north symbol on picture	J–14
PLSYMBOL	Display isometric symbols for fittings and valves	M–14
PLTEE	Generate tees	J–5
PLVALVE	Generate valves	L–6

Symbols on the menu are automatically placed on the drawing. The valve in Figure 22.43 is an example of a piping component that has been created and then saved in a library of parts and is available for instant recall. The valve has attributes (properties) imbedded within it. **Attributes** are information in the form of text that are attached to a symbol or other graphic entity. Attributes can be invisible on the drawing or displayed and plotted as part of the final illustration. In most cases, attributes are used to generate bills of materials or parts lists. In Figure 22.44 a set of steps in the creation of a piping spool is described along with the specific input structure. Commands and screen graphics are provided. Figure 22.45 provides a bill of materials generated from the spool in Figure 22.44.

In Figure 22.46 a complete pictorial spool is shown with a bill of materials. Attributes can also be used to generate other types of documentation. In Figure 22.47 a **from-to report** was created by the system using information imbedded in the pipe sections of the spool. Attributes are covered in more detail in Chapter 23.

The piping model is magnified to fill all four viewports.

AECZOOMALL C/C

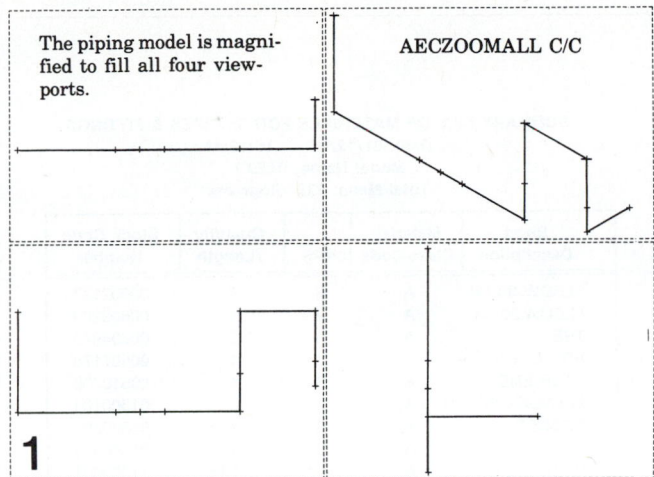

1

Isometric symbols representing the valves and the concentric reducer can be automatically inserted in the centerline model.

Isometric flange symbols and weld dots can be placed to indicate types of pipeline joints.

PLAUTOSYM C/C
5 C/C

PLJOINTSYM C/C
5 C/C
RPT

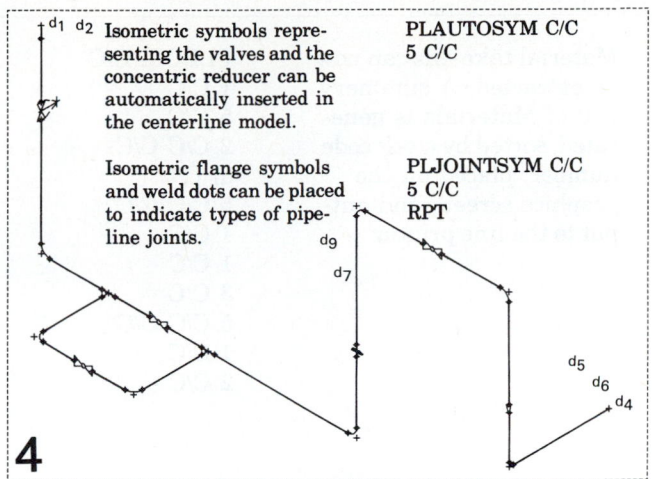

4

The isometric view is placed in the full screen layout.

SLO FULL C/C
WIN d *ISO1 C/C
RPT
AECZOOMALL C/C

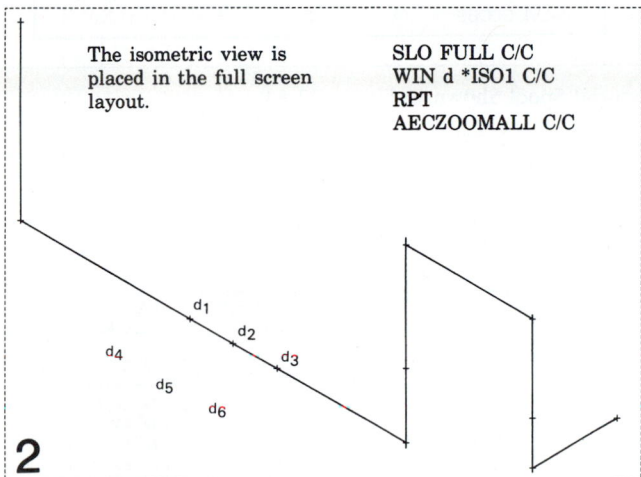

2

For demonstration purposes, weld neck flanges will be inserted on the vertical section of pipe located just before the last globe valve. The weld neck flange tablet symbol is touched, and the point location is digitized.

PLFLANGE C/C
d_1 C/C
RPT

(symbol)

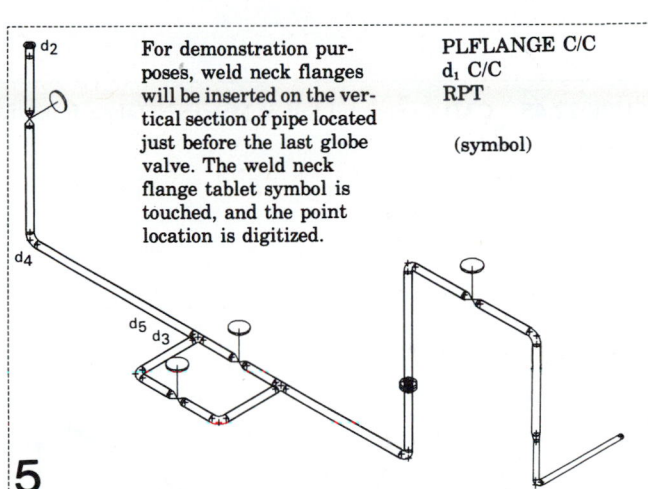

5

Fitting insertion can begin by touching the 90 degree LR elbow tablet symbol (ELLLR). Elbow properties and materials are automatically derived from the adjacent pipes. Insertion locations are digitized, and the elbows are generated.

PLELBOW C/C
d_1 d_2 d_3 d_4
d_5 d_6 C/C
RPT

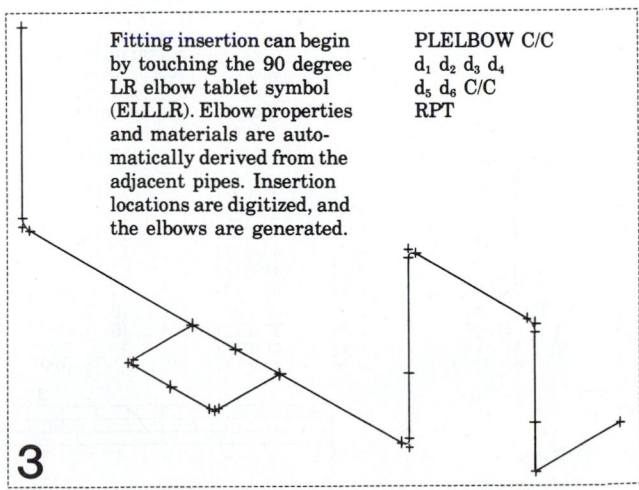

3

PLDMP is executed to dimension the pipeline. A point of alignment for the dimension lines is selected and then an axis establishing the extension line direction.

PLDMP C/C
d_1
1 C/C
d_2 d_3 d_4
C/C

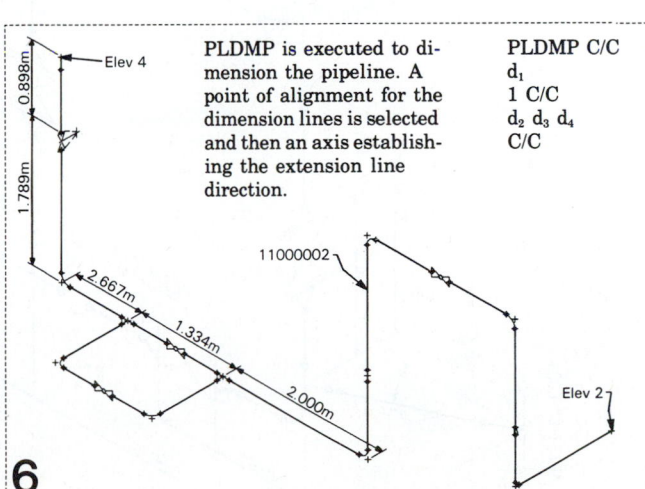

6

FIGURE 22.44   Pictorial Spool Created on a CAD System

Material take-offs can now be extracted. A summary Bill of Materials is generated, sorted by stock code number, placed on the graphics screen, and output to the line printer

PLBOM C/C
1 C/C
5 C/C
2 C/C C/C
d₁ C/C
5 C/C C/C
1 C/C
1 C/C
3 C/C
5 C/C C/C
1 C/C
2 C/C

SUMMARY BILL OF MATERIALS FOR 35 PIPES & FITTINGS
Date: 81/12/01   16:19:41
Model Name: PLEX1
Total Mass: 335 kilograms

Short Description	Material Class Code	NPS	Quantity /Length	Stock Code Number
ELBOW 90 LR	A	3	6	00602177
ELBOW 90 SR	A	2	1	00603209
TEE	A	3	2	00604942
RED CONC	A	3	1	00607176
STUB END	A	3	1	00610709
FLANGE WN	A	3	2	01300108
GASKET	A	3	1	01300300
BOLTS	A	3	1	01300310
PIPE	A	2	1.854	11000001
PIPE	A	3	14.852	11000002
VALVE GATE	A	3	1	11000031
VALVE GLOBE	A	3	3	11000034

FIGURE 22.45   CAD-Generated Bill of Materials Taken from the Pictorial Spool Shown in Figure 22.44

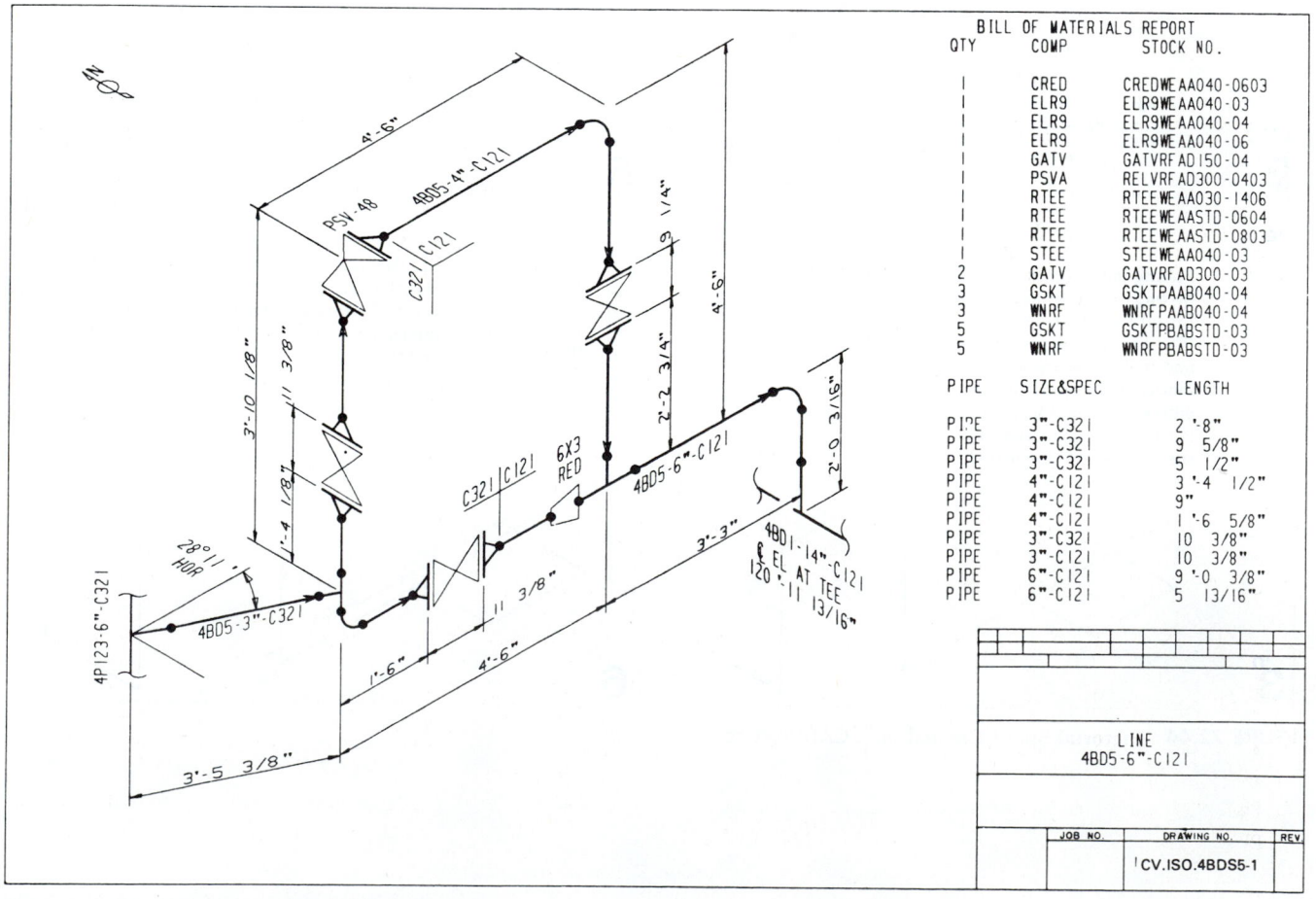

FIGURE 22.46   Spool and Bill of Materials Report

```
LINE                            FROM                    TO              PIPE
CW-26-24"-A6A                   A12                     B10             33'-4"
- - - - - - - - - - - - - - - - - - - - - - - - - - - - - - - - - - - - - - - - - -
    SPEC                        COMP                    STK*
    24"-A6A                     PIPE: 7'-0"
    24"-A6A                     ELR9                    ELR9WEAA010-24
    24"-A6A                     WNFF                    WNFFPAAB010-24
    24"-A6A                     GASKET                  GASKFFAG150-24
    24"-A6A                     GATV                    GATVRFAD150-24
    24"-A6A                     GASKET                  GASKFFAG150-24
    24"-A6A                     WNFF                    WNFFPAAB010-24
    24"-A6A                     PIPE: 8'-6"
    24"-A6A                     STEE                    STEEWEAA010-24
    24"-A6A                     ELR9                    ELR9WEAA010-24
    24"-A6A                     PIPE: 2'-0"
    24"-A6A                     ELR9                    ELR9WEAA010-24
    24"-A6A                     CRED                    CREDWEAA010-3024
    30"-A6A                     RTEE                    RTEEWEAA010-3018
    30"-A6A                     PIPE: 12'-7"
    30"-A6A                     ELR9                    ELR9WEAA010-30
    30"-A6A                     PIPE: 3'-3"

LINE                            FROM                    TO              PIPE
CW-27-24"-A6A                   CW-26-24"-A6A           D05             13'-8  3/16"
- - - - - - - - - - - - - - - - - - - - - - - - - - - - - - - - - - - - - - - - - -
    SPEC                        COMP                    STK*
    24"-A6A                     PIPE: 13'-8  3/16"

LINE                            FROM                    TO              PIPE
CW-28-18"-A6A                   CW-26-24"-A6A           C07             17'-0  1/2"
- - - - - - - - - - - - - - - - - - - - - - - - - - - - - - - - - - - - - - - - - -
    SPEC                        COMP                    STK*
    18"-A6A                     PIPE: 6'-1  1/2"
    18"-A6A                     ELR9                    ELR9WEAA010-18
    18"-A6A                     PIPE: 10'-11"
```

FIGURE 22.47   From-To Report Generated from a Piping Drawing Using CAD

QUIZ

True or False

1. Check valves allow the flow of fluids in only one direction.
2. The actual outside diameter of pipe in nominal sizes of $\frac{1}{8}$ in. to 12″ is larger than the nominal size.
3. Dimensioned single-line piping isometric spool drawings are always drawn to scale.
4. A reducing fitting has two or more ends with different size openings.
5. Globe valves are used for start-stop, on-off service.
6. A PI is used to indicate the temperature of a fluid.
7. Fabrication drawings are usually drawn with the double-line method.
8. Cast iron is the most common pipe material.

Fill in the Blanks

9. The main through run for a 5 × 4 × 3 reducing tee will be _____ .
10. A double-line piping drawing must have _____ lines if they are to be dimensioned.
11. Piping drawings are normally drawn at _____ . Most projects that are modeled use _____ or _____ scale.
12. Pipe is designated as OD pipe for nominal sizes of _____ and above.
13. Globe valves are used to _____ or _____ the flow of fluids in a piping system.
14. Screwed piping systems are normally limited to_____ diameter and below.
15. Cast iron piping is normally used for _____ and _____ systems and is usually placed _____ ground.
16. Flow diagrams do not show _____ or actual pipe _____ .

Answer the Following

17. What is a TI used for?
18. What type of valve is used to prevent backflow? Name three variations.
19. Give three parts of a piping system that normally have elevation callouts.
20. Single-line piping is usually shown up to what size on a piping plan and elevation view drawing?
21. What is the ID of a SCH 40, 10″ pipe?
22. What is the OD of a 14″ pipe?
23. What is the dimension of the raised face of a 6″ 300# RFWN flange?
24. What is the face-to-face dimension of a 6″ 150# flanged check valve?

EXERCISES

Exercises may be assigned as sketching, instrument, or CAD projects. Transfer the given information to an "A" size sheet of .25 in. grid paper. Complete all views and solve for proper visibility, including centerlines, object lines, and hidden lines. Exercises that are not assigned by the instructor can be sketched in the text to provide practice and understanding of the preceding instructional material.

After Reading the Chapter Through Section 22.6.1, You May Complete the Following Exercises

Exercise 22.1(A) Through (J)   Using the available centerlines, draw the requested fittings in double line, single line, and its corresponding end view: (A) 90° welded elbow, (B) flanged tee, (C) screwed cross, (D) 45° lateral, (E) 3 × 3 × 2″ screwed tee, (F) welded concentric reducer, (G) flanged 45° elbow, (H) screwed bushing, (I) soldered eccentric reducer, and (J) weld neck flanged joint.

Exercise 22.2(A) Through (F)   With the given valve outlines, fill in the interior configuration. Where appropriate show the disk, stem, bonnet, seating rings, body cavity, and packing: (A) flanged end diaphragm valve, (B) welded globe valve, (C) Y globe valve, (D) screwed ball check valve, (E) screwed split wedge gate valve, and (F) swing check valve.

Exercise 22.3(A) Through (D)   Complete the three views of each valve using single-line symbol representation. Insert the appropriate face-to-face dimension and the valve stem height where applicable: (A) 2″ Class 150# flanged check valve, (B) 8″ Class 600# flanged check valve, (C) bell and spigot plug valve, and (D) 8″ Class 1500# butt-welded gate valve.

Exercise 22.3(E) Through (H)   Draw three views of each valve in the given block using double-line symbols. Do not dimension the valve: (E) welded end ball valve, (F) soldered diaphragm valve, (G) screwed Y globe valve, and (H) 6″ Class 900# butt-welded globe angle valve.

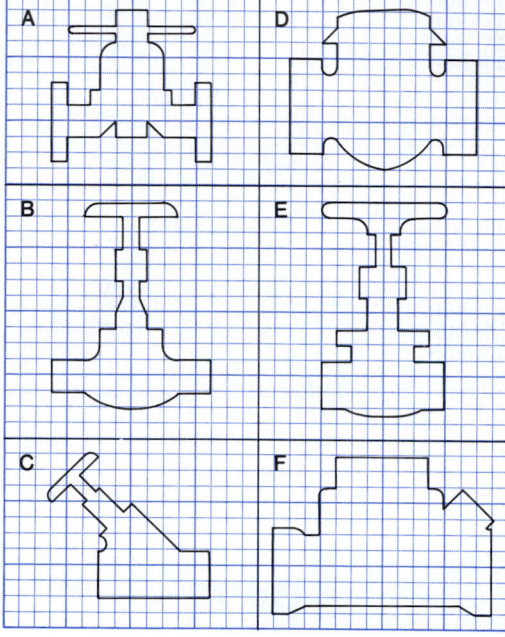

Exercise 22.2

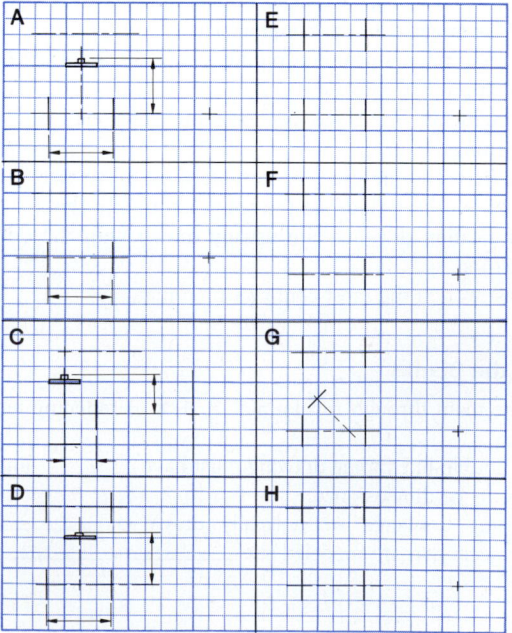

Exercise 22.1

Exercise 22.3

Exercise 22.4   Insert the requested symbol in each block. Use single-line symbols and show only the view required by the description. If the assignment is to be done on a CAD system, the student is to use the piping menu (if available) and simply insert the symbol in the block. The figures are to be inserted top to bottom starting with the left-hand column first.

First column 1–5:

Bell and spigot check valve
Flanged tee (outlet down)
Screwed bushing
Flanged check valve
Flanged 45° lateral

Second column 6–10:

90° welded elbow (end view)
Flanged 45° elbow (end view)
Soldered 6 × 4 reducing 90° elbow
Bell and spigot cap
Bell and spigot concentric reducer

Third column 11–15:

Screwed gate valve
Screwed cross (straight size)
Welded double sweep tee
Welded 4 × 4 × 3″ cross
Flanged long radius 90° elbow

Fourth column 16–20:

Soldered Y globe valve
Flanged bull plug
Soldered eccentric reducer
Welded plug valve
Screwed diaphragm valve

After Reading the Chapter Through Section 22.6.4 You May Complete the Following Exercises

Exercise 22.5(A) Through (C)   Complete the partial views for all exercises. Use single-line symbols.

Exercise 22.6(A)   Complete the given front view and draw the plan view of the pipe fabrication. Use the double-line method and show all dimension lines, leaders, and arrowheads. Using Appendix C, look up valve face-to-face measurements and elbow face-to-centerline dimensions. Do not calculate measurements for other dimensions. Balloon each separate piece. Fabrication includes the following parts: 6″ 300# WNRF flanges, welded fittings, STD LR elbows, 6″ flanged gate valve.

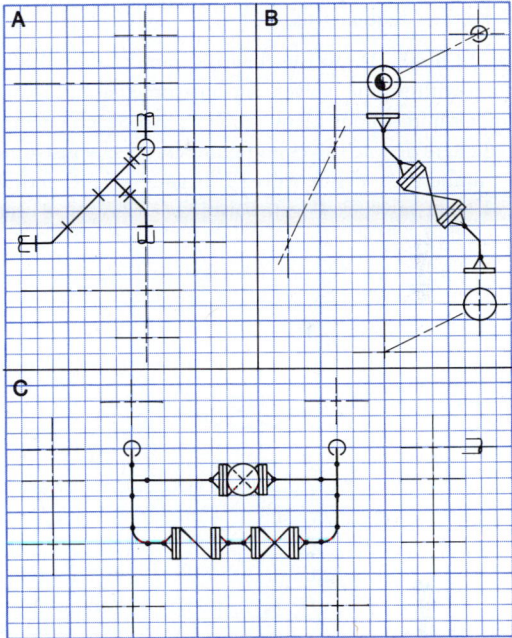

Exercise 22.5

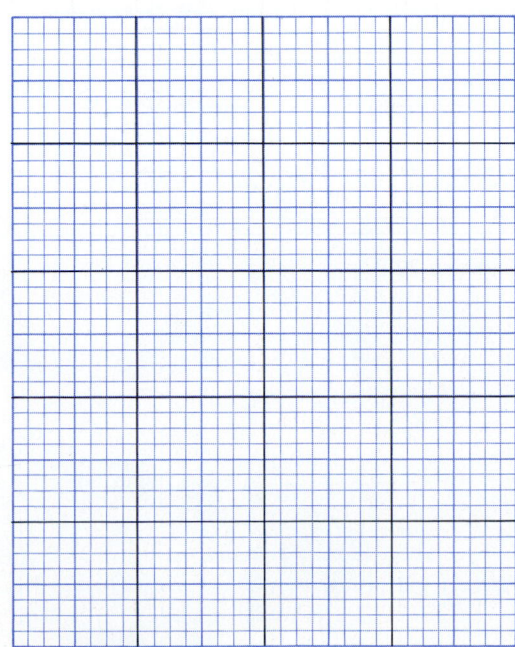

Exercise 22.4

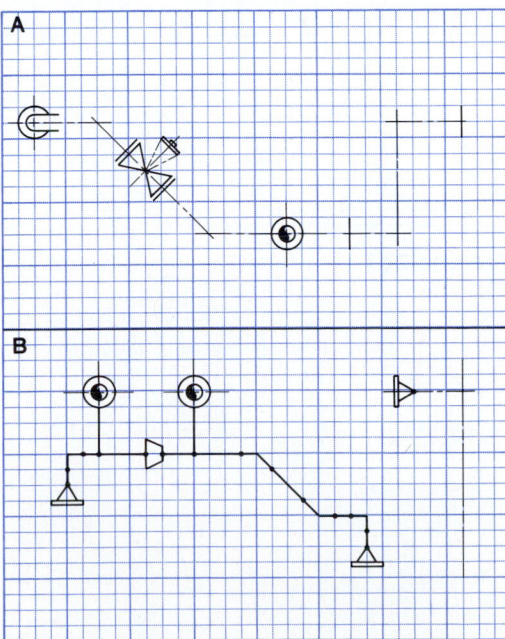

Exercise 22.6

Exercise 22.6(B)   Draw the front view of the pipe fabrication and complete the right view using the single-line method. Dimension the spool as required. Each grid division equals 6″ (except elbow, flange, and reducer lengths which must be taken from Appendix C) for pipe lengths. Balloon each part. Parts include one 8 × 6 concentric reducer and one 8″ and one 6″ 150# RFWN flange. The fabrication is an all-welded assembly.

Exercise 22.7   Complete the front elevation and right side view using the double-line method. Dimension completely. Each grid represents 6″ for pipe lengths only. All valve and fitting dimensions to be taken from Appendix C. Fabrication includes: 300# 6 and 8″ RFWN flanges, 8″ × 6″ reducing elbow, 300# 8″ and 6″ flanged gate valves, 300# 6″ flanged globe valve, 6″ TRC control valve, 8″ × 8″ × 6″ welding reducing tee.

Exercise 22.8(A)   Draw the flow diagram of the crude fraction tower along with piping, valves, and instrumentation. Show proper valve symbols and balloon all instruments. Note each line number as required. Letters denote valves and numbers specify instrumentation and line numbers. A: 4″ gate valve; B: 1″ gate valve; C and D: $\frac{3}{4}$″ gate valve; E: 1″ gate valve; F: 4″ gate valve; G: 4″ PSV; H: 8″ gate valve;

I: 4″ FCV; J: 8″ gate valve; K: 4″ gate valve; L: 2″ PCV; M: 4″ gate valve; N: 4″ gate valve; O: 4″ × 3″ reducer; P: 3″ check valve; Q: 3″ gate valve; 1: level controller; 2: level glass; 3: pressure indicator; 4: board pressure indicator; 5: temperature indicator; 6: pressure safety valve; 7: flow control valve; 8: flow element; 9: flow control valve; 10: 1001-A-12″-IH; 11: 1004-A-6″-IS; 12: 1101-A-8″-IH; 13: 1014-CA-3″-IS; 14: 1030-C-8″-IS; 15: 1013-C-3″-IS; 16: 1012-A-3″-IH.

Exercise 22.8(B)   Draw the crude knockout drum and associated piping, valves, fitting, and instruments. Show all valve symbols and note size. Insert instrument notation in balloons as required and place all pipeline numbers aligned with pipe. Use the following letters and numbers to determine the proper valves, instruments, and line numbers: A: 4″ × 6″ PSV; B: 3″ gate valve; C: 4″ gate valve; D: 14″ gate valve; E: 2″ gate valve; F: 12″ gate valve; G: 12″ level control valve; H: 12″ gate valve; I, J, K and L: $\frac{3}{4}$ in. gate valves; M: 2″ globe valve; N: 3″ gate valve; O: 4″ gate valve; P: 3″ globe valve; Q: 2″ gate valve; 1: pressure safety valve; 2: level control valve; 3: level controller; 4: level glass; 5: pressure valve; 6: 1012-A-4″-1H; 7: 1029-A-3″-IH; 8: drain; 9: 1011-A-3″-IH; 10: 1026-C-4″-IH; 11: 1027-A-4″-IS; 12: 1035-A-12″-IS; 13: 1028-C-14″-IH.

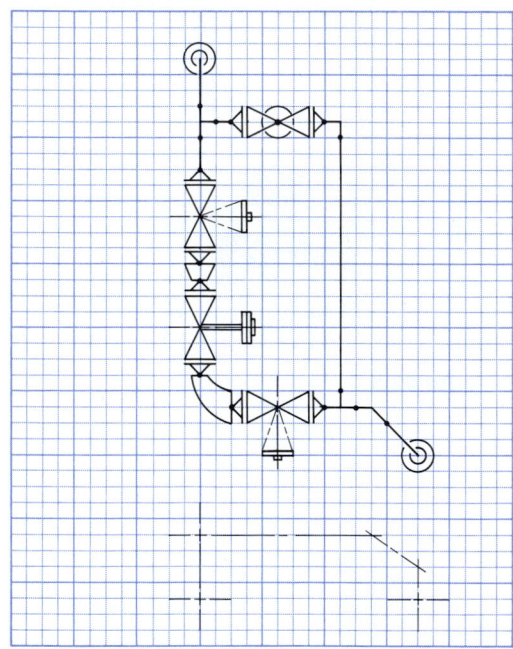

Exercise 22.7

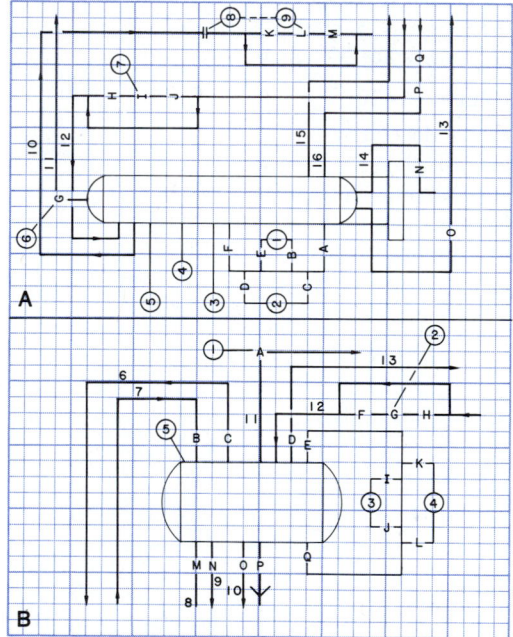

Exercise 22.8

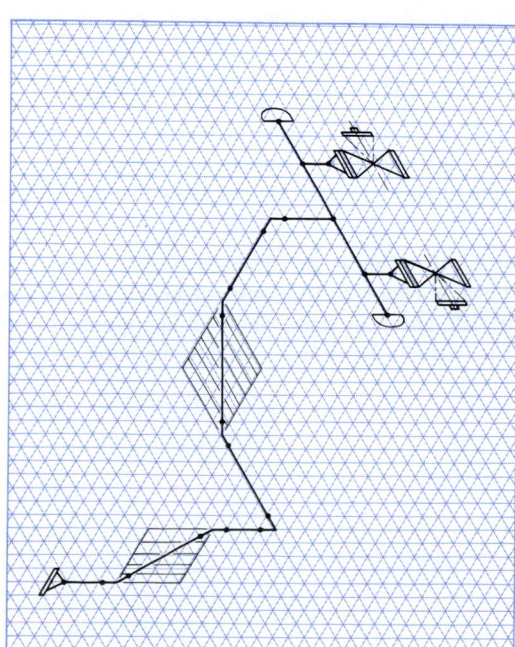

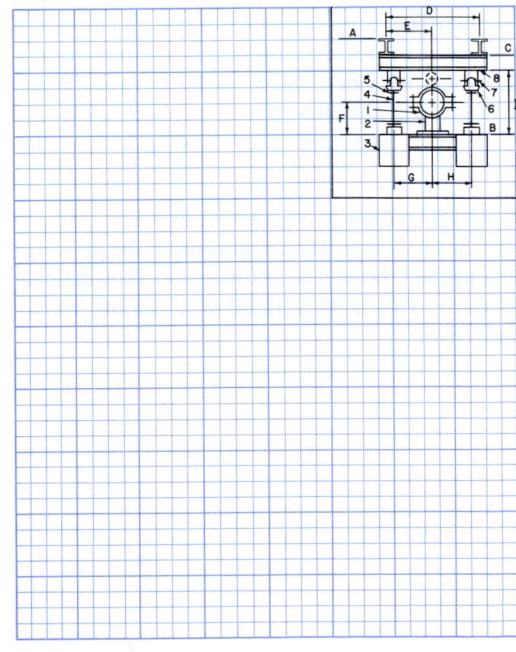

After Reading the Chapter Through Section 22.6.7 You May Complete the Following Exercises

Exercise 22.9   Complete the all-welded isometric spool. Dimension completely (use Appendix C as reference). Grid equals 1′ for all pipe lengths. Fittings to be 150# 6″ × 4″ welding concentric reducer and 150# WNRF 6″ and 4″ flanges.

Exercise 22.10   Dimension the given piping spool. Grid divisions equal 2′ for pipe lengths. Valves are 900# 16″ gates. Use double extra strong welding fittings. Both offsets are 45°. Dimension with box method.

Exercise 22.11   Dimension the screwed piping system spool. Use SCH 40 pipe, 2″ 100# screwed globe and gate valve with 2000# WOG fittings and a 6″ × 4″ concentric reducer.

Exercise 22.12   Redraw the pipe support detail using the following specifications: A: TOS. EL. 697′-2″; B: EL. 687′-8″; C: EL. 695′-10″; D: 6′-4″; E: 3′-2″; F: 2′-4″; G and H: 2′-6″; I: 6′-0″; 1: 10″ pipe clamp; 2: STD WT pipe stanchion type C; 3: #14 variable support, type GHL; 4: $1\frac{1}{8}$ in. steel rod by 5′-2″ length; 5: $1\frac{1}{8}$ in. hex nut; 6: $1\frac{1}{8}$ in. eye nut; 7: $1\frac{1}{8}$ in. steel attachment with pin and cotter pin; 8: structural element W 8″ × 20″ × 7′-4″. Make a complete parts list.

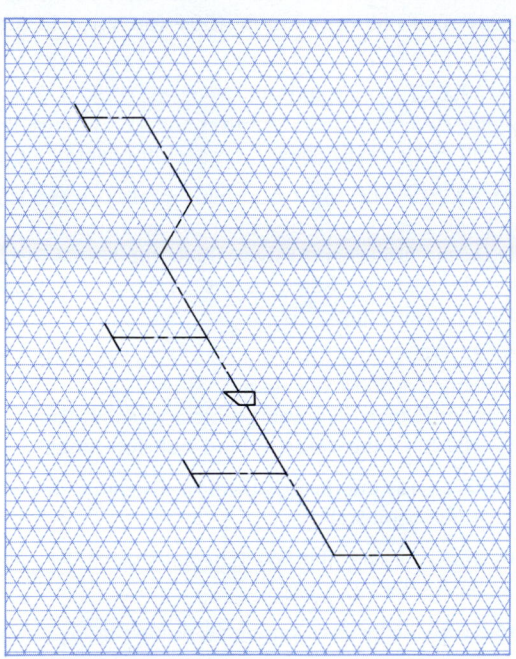

Exercise 22.9

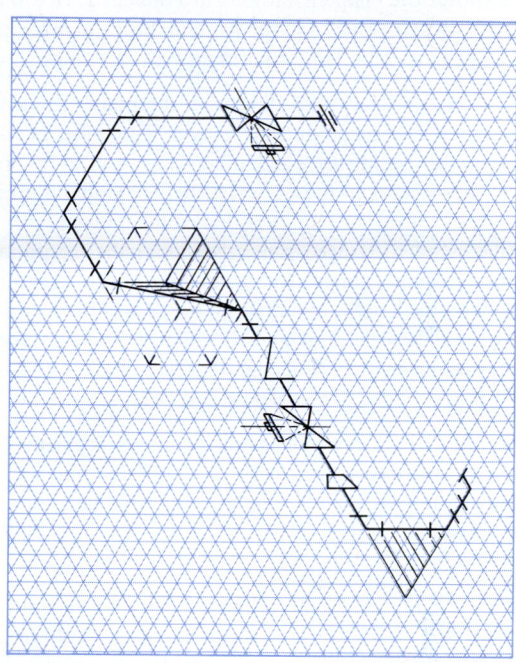

Exercise 22.11

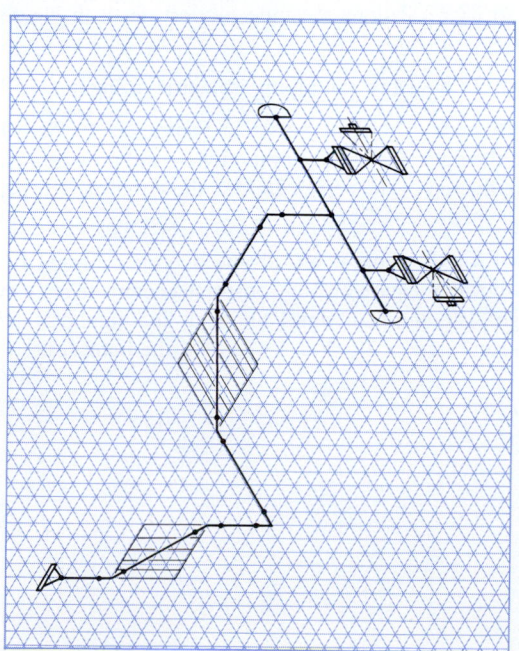

Exercise 22.10

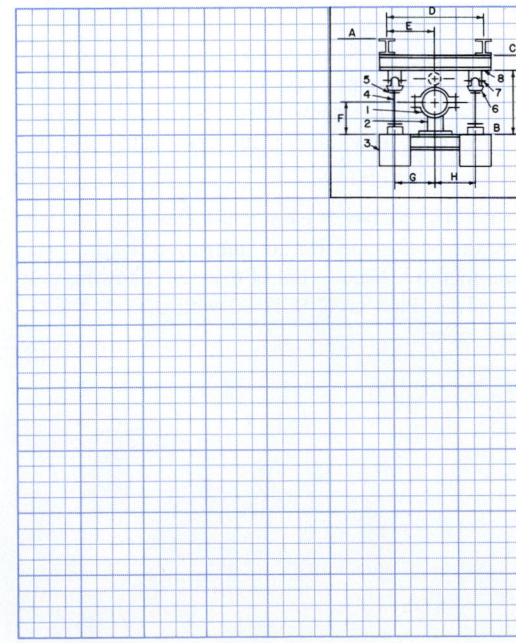

Exercise 22.12

PROBLEMS

Problems may be assigned as sketching, instrument, or CAD projects. The given drawing in Problems 22.1 and 22.2 may not be correctly dimensioned according to standard practice. The actual measurements are correct as is the configuration. Piping isometrics/pictorials and fabrication drawings are normally not drawn to scale, though they should be constructed as close to proportion as is realistic, given the shape and size of the system being detailed. All other projects for this chapter are taken from drawings provided as examples within the chapter. Projects in Problem 22.1 can also be assigned as isometric/pictorial spools, and Problem 22.2 projects may be assigned as pipe fabrication multiview drawings.

Problem 22.1(A) Draw and dimension the piping isometric as a multiview piping fabrication drawing. Provide a complete bill of materials. Look up the missing valve and fitting dimensions using Appendix C. Many of the dimensions must be calculated or found in Appendix C; only the overall dimensions are provided on the drawing.

The valve is an 8″ flanged gate valve. Draw the fabrication with double-line pipe and fittings. The fabrication can be constructed by estimating the pipe lengths and drawing the project proportionally or 5× or 6× the book scale. Show an N elevation, W elevation, and a plan view. The system uses 8″ SCH 60 pipe with Class 300# welded fittings and 150# 8″ weld neck flanges with raised faces.

Problem 22.1(B) Same general directions as Problem 22.1(A). This spool is composed of 6″ SCH 40 A-105 CS pipe with 400# RFWN flanges and 90° standard long-radius welding elbows. Show plan, W elevation, and N elevation views. Use the double-line method.

Problem 22.1(C) Same general directions as for Problem 22.1(A). Pipe section is 4″ SCH 80. Use 300# fittings with 300# slip-on welding flanges. Show plan, E elevation, N elevation, and S elevation views. Use single-line pipe and symbol representation. Draw 4× or 5× the book scale or lay out proportionally.

Problem 22.1(D) Same general directions as for Problem 22.1(A). Calculate or look up dimensions. The pipe section is composed of 3″ SCH 40 pipe, 2000# WOG screwed fittings and 3′ diameter vessels. Do not show vessels on the fabrication drawing. Draw the front (N elev) and plan views using the double-line method.

Problem 22.1(E) Draw N elevation, E elevation, and plan views, 4× or 5× the book scale. Do not dimension the drawing. Use the double-line method. Make a bill of materials showing only the fittings and valves. Pipe is 4″ SCH 80 with 3000# WOG screwed fittings and valves.

Problem 22.1(F) Draw N elevation, plan, and E elevation views using the double-line method. All fittings are 6000# WOG and pipe is $3\frac{1}{2}$ in. SCH 80. Construct 4× or 5× the book scale. Provide bill of materials for fittings.

Problem 22.2(A) Draw and dimension each problem as an isometric/pictorial spool. Provide a complete bill of materials using Appendix C for fitting and valve dimensions. Show north arrow orientation. Establish missing dimensions. Note that measurements that are provided are to be used for reference to establish proper spool layout and dimensions. Do not assume that the given dimensioning system is correct.

Draw an isometric/pictorial spool of the screwed piping system using 2000# WOG fittings and a 3″ 150# gate valve. Include a bill of materials.

Problem 22.2(B) Draw and dimension the 5″ SCH double extra strong piping system using 900# valves and steel fittings. Provide a complete bill of materials. Show the vessel in phantom lines.

Problem 22.2(C) Lay out the piping project as an isometric/pictorial spool. Draw 4× or 5× the book scale and make a bill of materials for the fittings and valves. Show the vessels in phantom lines. Do not dimension. System uses 4″ STD pipe and 300# valves with 3000# WOG fittings.

Problem 22.2(D) Draw and dimension the screwed $2\frac{1}{2}$ in. SCH 80 pipe system. Use 300# valves and 2000# WOG fittings throughout. Alternate: Change the given problem to an all-flanged system with 4″ SCH 120 piping, 600# valves, and steel fittings.

Problem 22.3 Lay out the existing flow diagram shown in Figure 22.25 4-5× the book scale.

Problem 22.4 Lay out the flow diagram shown in Figure 22.26 4-5× the book scale.

Problem 22.5 Redraw the piping fabrication in Figure 22.22.

Problem 22.6 Draw the pipe support detail shown in Figure 22.37 using an "A" size sheet.

Problem 22.7 Redraw the pipe support detail in Figure 22.38. Draw 4-5× the book scale.

Problem 22.8 Draw the piping isometric in Figure 22.35.

Problem 22.9 Draw the vessel in Figure 22.40. Place the end view on the right side of the elevation view and provide a plan view showing the top of the vessel. Do not show the stacked placement detail.

Problem 22.10 This is an advanced project. Draw the piping system shown in Figure 22.18. Construct a complete top view along with right, left, and plan views. Show all line numbers, elevations, and instrumentation. Draw at 3× or 4× the book scale.

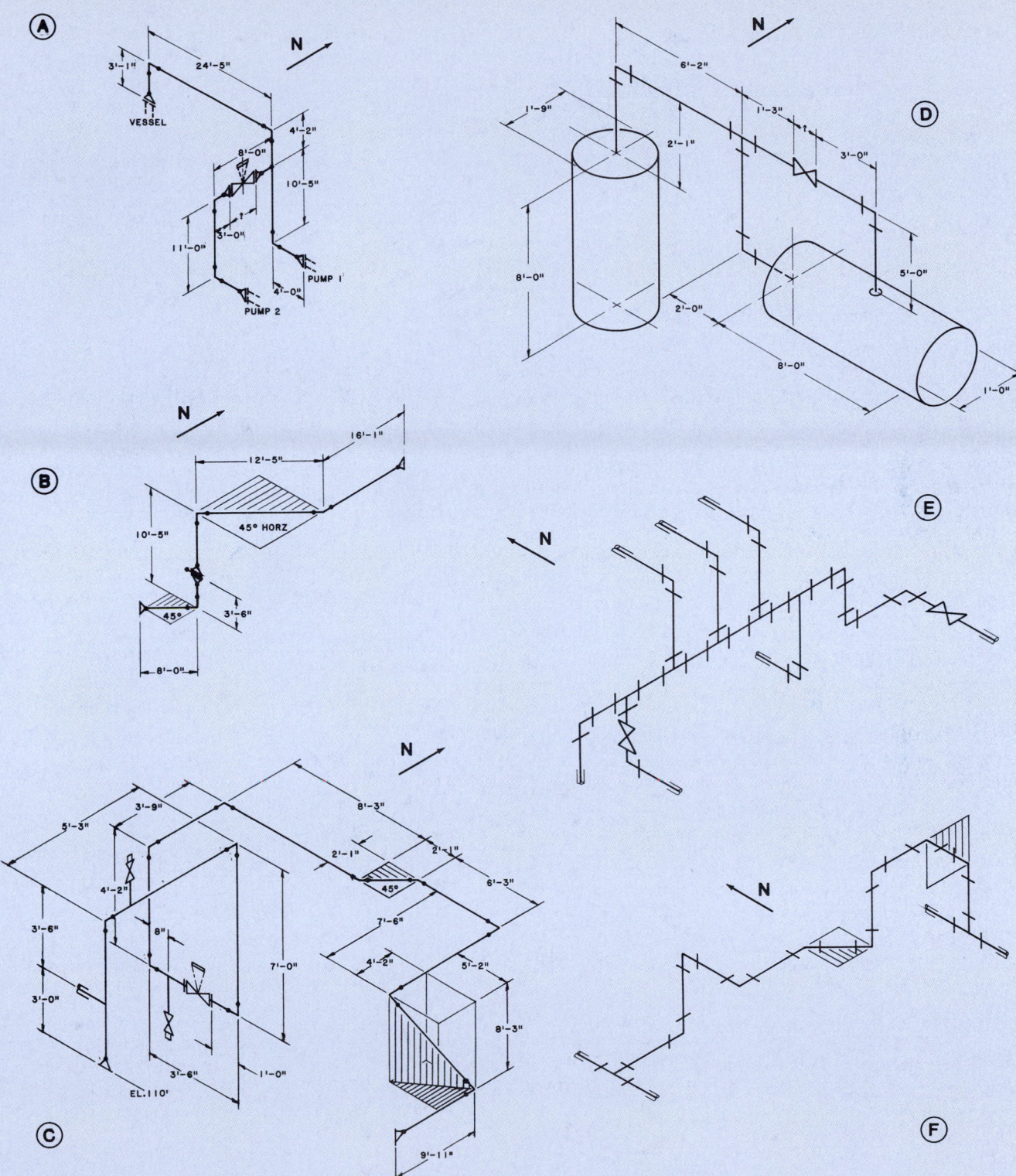

Problem 22.1

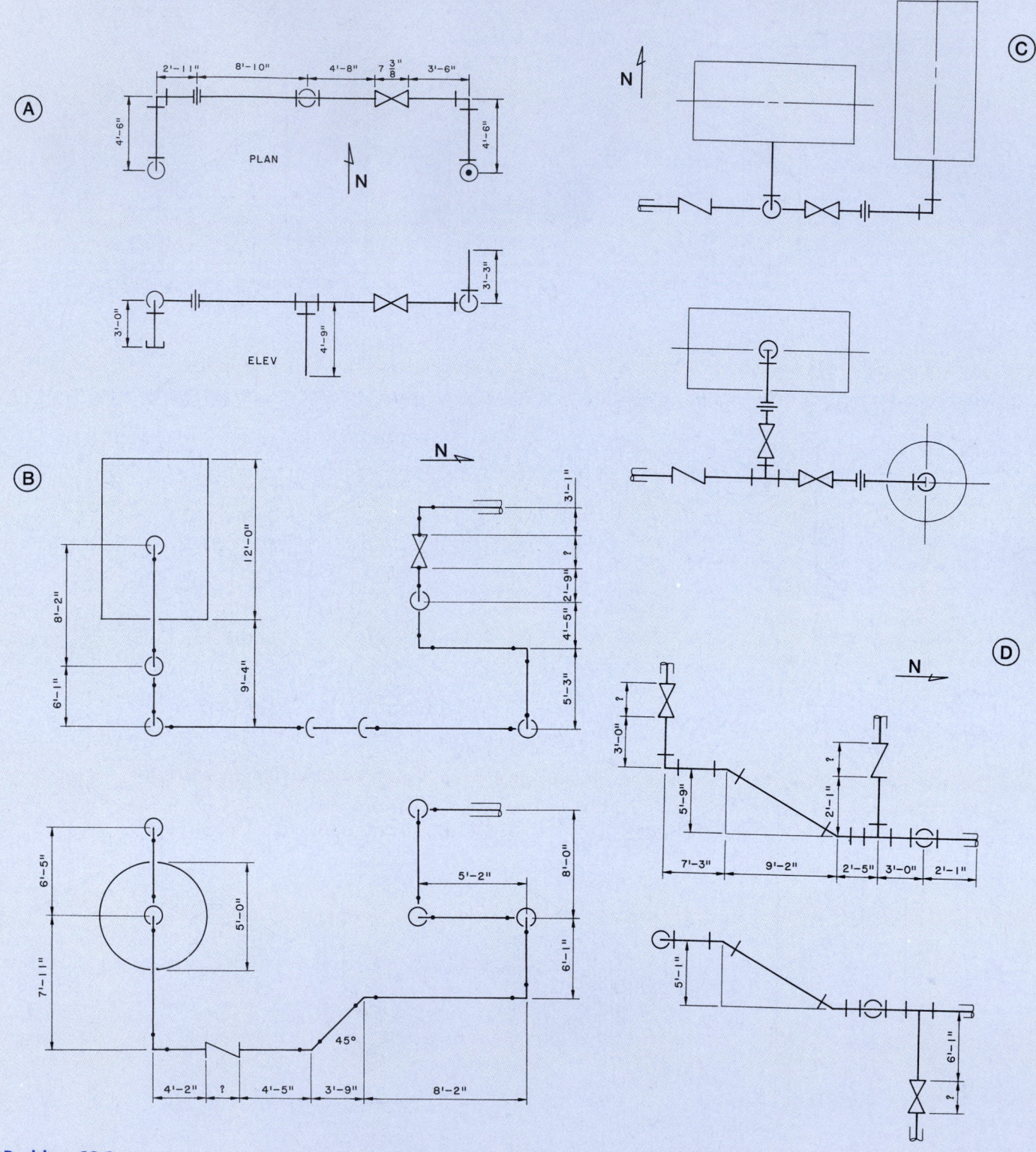

Problem 22.2

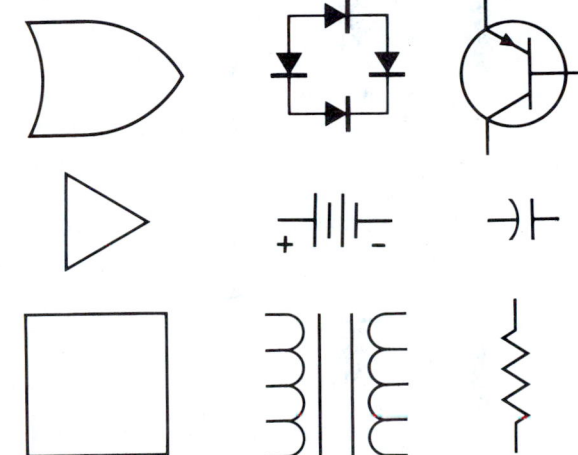

CHAPTER 23

Electronic Drafting

Learning Objectives

Upon completion of this chapter you will be able to accomplish the following:

1. Recognize electronic drafting's association with a wide range of electronic devices and systems.
2. Employ recommended line conventions and lettering for electronic drawings and diagrams.
3. Become proficient in the use of abbreviations, reference designations, components, and symbols.
4. Produce block, schematic, and logic diagrams.
5. Apply printed circuit board design and documentation criteria.
6. Develop familiarity with cable applications and harness and wiring diagrams.
7. Recognize and define CAD electronic drafting applications.

23.1 Introduction

Electronic drafting and design (Fig. 23.1) involves the creation of drawings associated with a wide range of electronic devices and systems. The information presented here serves as an introduction for the drafter who is relatively unfamiliar with the requirements for electronic design and layout. Appendix D provides a complete reference to electronic and electrical symbols and should be consulted while completing problems and exercises from this chapter.

Drafting tools used in electronic drafting and design are similar to those in other fields of engineering and design work. If a difference exists, it is in the level and complexity of drafting technology and the variety of drafting and design techniques available, which range from plastic tape and pre-printed transfer materials to the use of CAD. Every engineering department uses the tools described in this section, with varying degrees of sophistication, in the design process. When prepared manually, electronic drafting makes extensive use

FIGURE 23.2   Precut Stick-on Transfer Symbols

of transfer printed letters, numbers, electronic symbols, lines, and standard component shapes (Fig. 23.2). Printed component shapes are available in many configurations and are used for layout of printed circuit boards (Fig. 23.3). Electronic strips, component shapes, and slit shapes are used for lines and symbols in many instances, especially for printed circuit board artwork designs.

23.2 Lines on Electronic Drawings

The knowledge of lines and their symbolic meanings and usage is fundamental to the electronic drafter. One of the most important aspects of an electronic drafter's job is understanding the process, intent, and content of an electronic drawing. In electronics, most drawings are made up of single-line diagrams primarily composed of straight vertical and horizontal lines. Related drawings used for manufacturing electronics equipment include multiview dimensioned drawings,

FIGURE 23.1   Designer Examining a Plot of a Complex Circuit

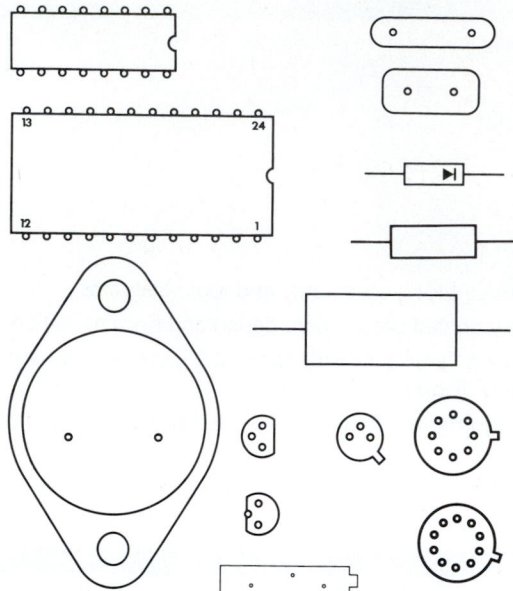

FIGURE 23.3   Component Assembly Outlines

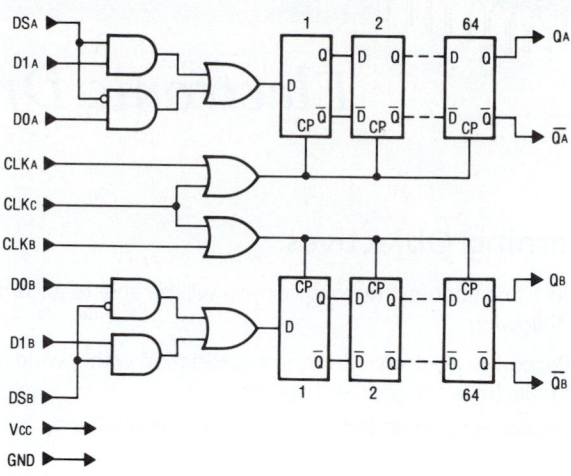

FIGURE 23.5   Logic Diagram

equipment drawings, sheet-metal enclosure layouts and developments, and component drawings. Graphs, charts, and tables are frequently used to represent tabulated and related data on electronic drawings.

Since most electronic drawings are used to describe a process, the single-line diagram is most frequently used to convey this information. Electronic drawings require mastery of the symbol meanings, as well as mastery of the actual symbol

and line usage. **Block diagrams** (Fig. 23.4), **logic diagrams** (Fig. 23.5), and **schematic diagrams** (Fig. 23.6), are single-line diagrams. Most diagrams are drawn with one line weight for the symbols' outline and for the lines representing the flow in the system. Printed circuit boards (see Fig. 23.37) are an exception, having in many cases lines of differing thicknesses. ANSI Standard Y32.2, "Graphic Symbols for Electrical and Electronic Diagrams," allows a degree of flexibility in choosing line weights. The width of a drawn line does not affect the meaning of a line or a symbol. In specific cases, a wider line may be used for emphasis (Fig. 23.7).

All electrical and electronic line weights should conform with ANSI Y14.2, "Line Conventions and Lettering." The selection of line thickness as well as letter size should take into account the drawing's reduction or enlargement. Figure 23.8

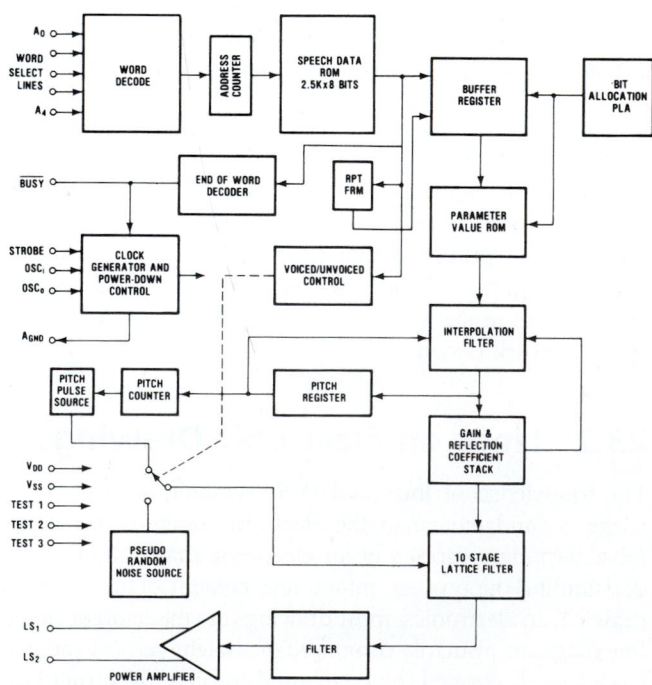

FIGURE 23.4   Block Diagram

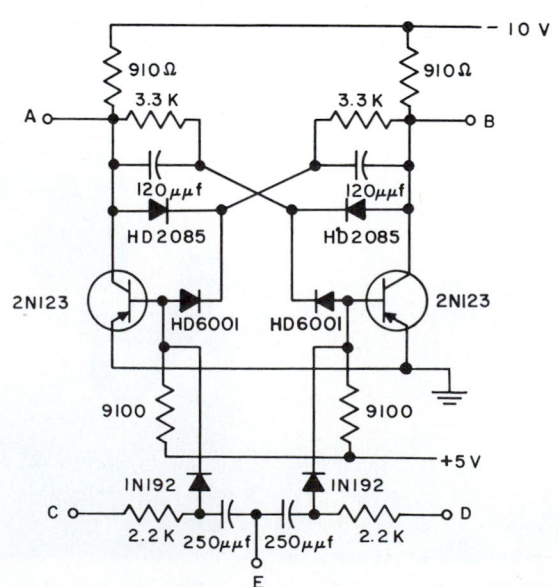

FIGURE 23.6   Schematic Diagram

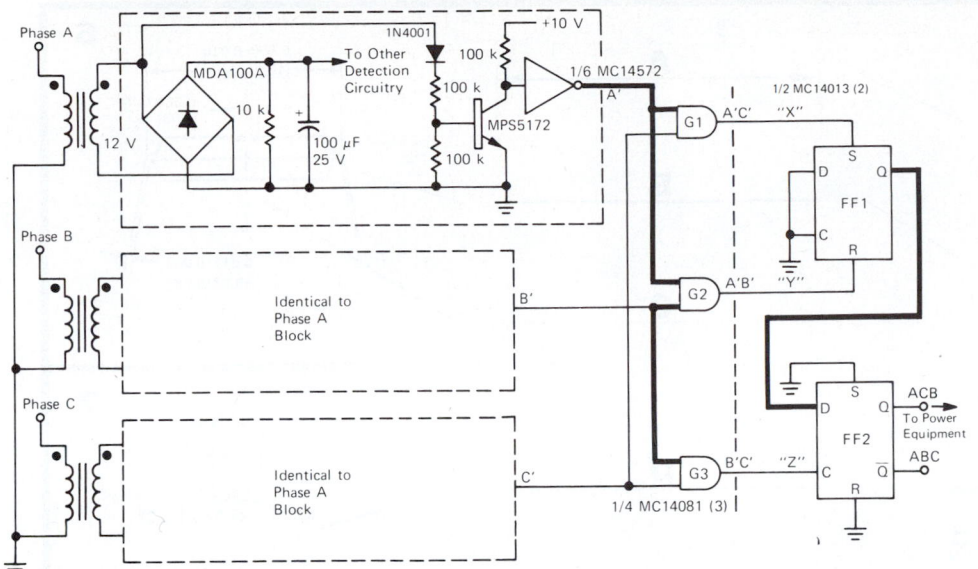

FIGURE 23.7 Schematic Diagram Showing Dashed, Emphasized, and Regular Solid Lines

illustrates recommended line weights for electronic drawings and diagrams:

A. *Dimension line*. Same as for mechanical convention; used on dimensioned production drawings, pictorial drawing (1), component multiview drawings (6), and sheet-metal details and layouts.

B. *Object line/visible line*. Same as for mechanical drawings; found on the same type of drawings as dimension lines (1 and 6).

C. *Centerline*. Same as for mechanical drawings (6).

D. *Component outline*. Can be drawn as thick as an object line though a medium to thin line is preferred depending on the reduction amount; used on PCB board layouts (7) and a variety of other electronic drawings.

E. *Phantom line*. Used to represent future or alternative arrangements, as on the wiring diagram (2).

F, G, H, I. *Diagram line*. The majority of all lines used in electronic drawing are this type. Diagram lines are not standard on block diagrams (3), logic diagrams (8), schematic diagrams (4 and 9), and wiring diagrams (2).

J, K. *Emphasis line*. A thicker line (10) used when a particular flow line (or symbol) on a diagram needs to be emphasized; also found on graphs (5).

L. *Dashed line*. Used on electronic diagrams; also used to indicate mechanical linkage or connection between components (10, foot control switch).

23.3 Designations, Standards, and Abbreviations

The American National Standards Institute (ANSI) and U.S. Department of Defense (DOD) set the standards for component symbols, reference designations, and abbreviations. These organizations work together and with other engineering groups to establish the criteria and distribution of standards to both commercial and military contractors.

Reference designations, standards, and abbreviations are used to define components, parts, and functions in electron-

ics. They are used in the preparation of all logic and schematic diagrams to communicate desired designs.

Abbreviations are used to identify quantities or units on electronic drawings. As an example, "microfarads" is not spelled out on a drawing, instead, the abbreviation "μf" is used (Fig. 23.9). Many times, reference designations and abbreviations are used on the same drawing.

Reference designations are letter symbols or the name of the component and are not to be confused with abbreviations on a drawing. Reference designations were developed using one- or two-letter symbols. Abbreviations are normally a brief version of words and are generally longer than a reference designation.

Components can be discussed, drawn, and identified by using an alphanumeric code. Designations are composed of two aspects; a component class letter and a sequence number. As an example, the letter "C" is used for capacitors, the number "1" would be the first capacitor on the schematic or logic diagram, the second would be written C2, until all of the capacitors on the diagram were identified (Fig. 23.9). Designations are located to the right, above, or below a component.

23.4 Components and Symbols

Because components are unique in size, function, and characteristics, they must have a special symbol to be quickly recognized. **Symbols** are used to represent the physical component when used on a diagram. *Color coding* and *tolerance* are used to identify specific components and to give value variation. The color code numbers range from 0 to 9; each number has a color. Components that use color coding also have a multiplier and a tolerance color. See Figures 23.10 and 23.11 for color coding of resistors. For example, if the first two significant figures are brown (1) and black (0) and the

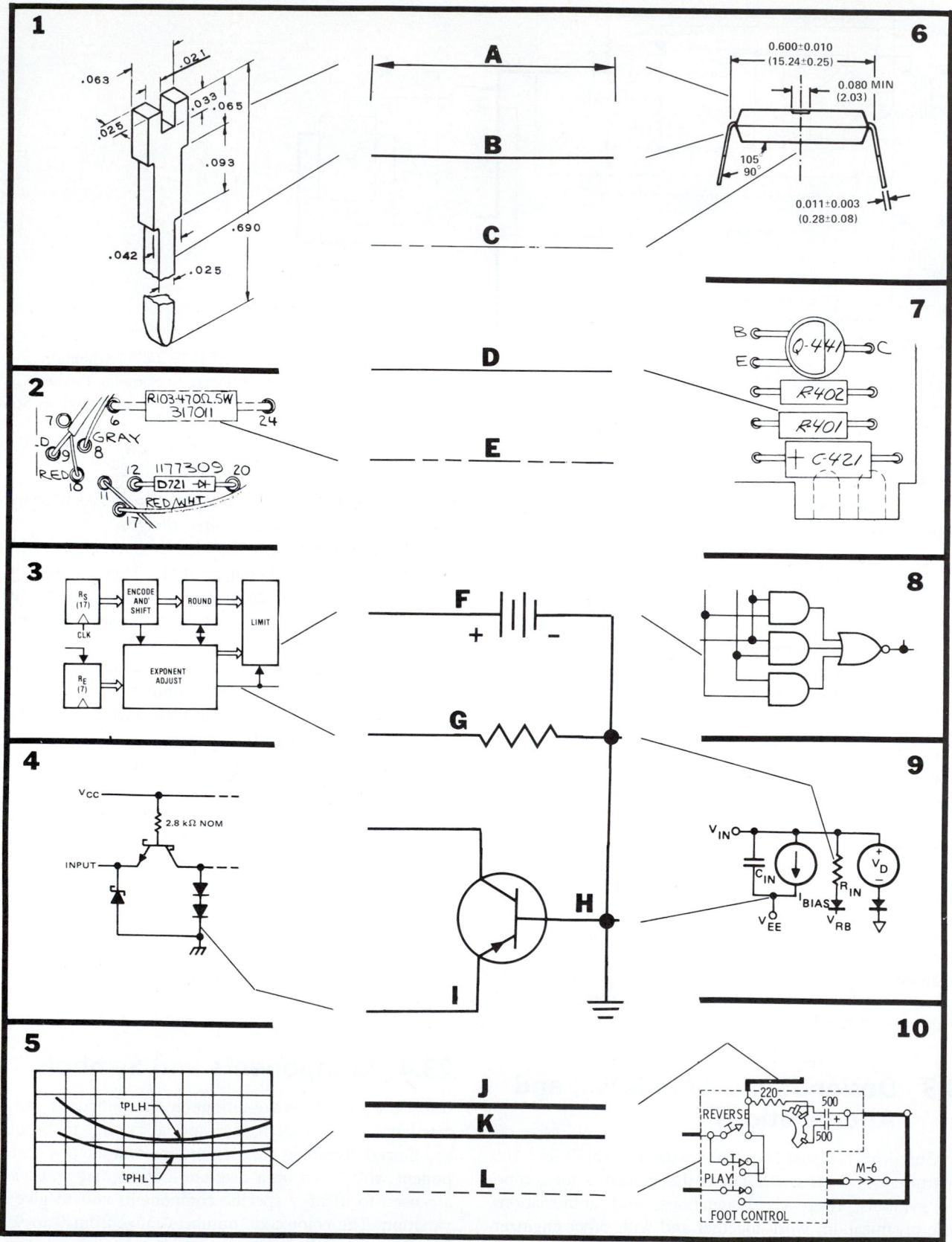

FIGURE 23.8   Line Key for Electronic Drawings

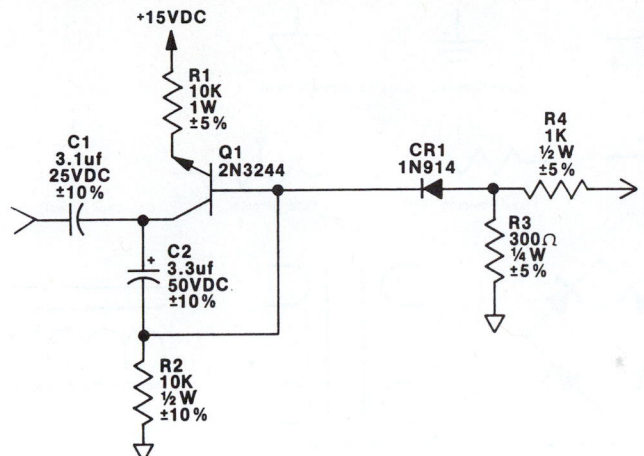

FIGURE 23.9   Reference Designation Values, Voltages, and Tolerances

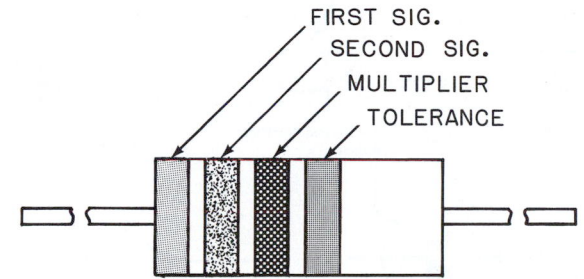

FIGURE 23.10   Color Stripes Showing a Number Code

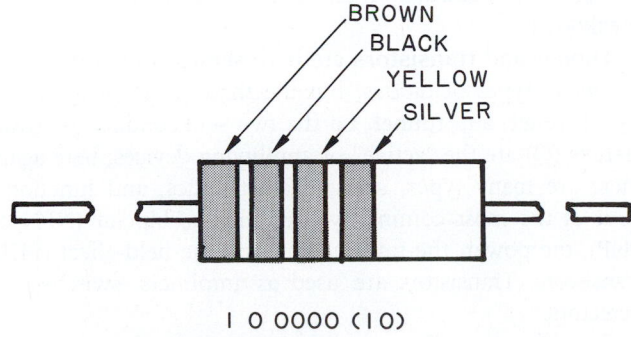

100,000 ohms ±10%

FIGURE 23.11   Brown, Black, Yellow, and Silver Bands, Showing Resistance of a 100 k Ω, ± 10%, Resistor

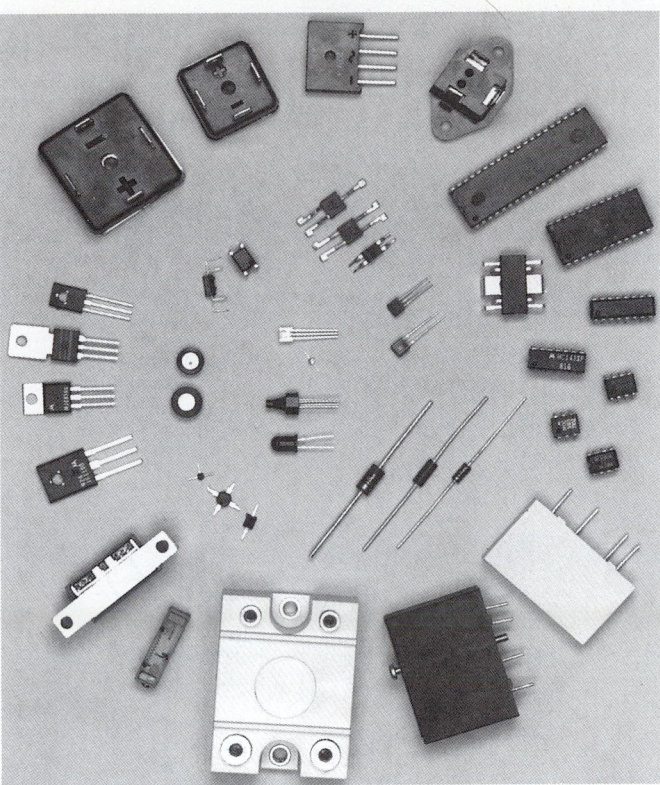

FIGURE 23.12   Typical Discrete and Integrated Component Packages

multiplier is (4) or 10,000, the third band on the resistor is yellow. The last or fourth band is silver (± 10%), making the resistor a 10 k Ω resistor with a ± 10% tolerance. A fifth band may be seen on the resistor; this could be for a reliability level or to indicate that the leads can be soldered. Some very small capacitors may also be color coded. Table 23.1 gives the standard color code for resistors. In Figure 23.12 one can see a few of the many different kinds of components used in electronics. In Figure 23.13 a few electronic component symbols are provided. Refer to Appendix D for a complete list of component symbols.

TABLE 23.1   Standard Color Code Used for Resistors

Color	Number	Multiplier	Tolerance
Black	0	1	
Brown	1	10	
Red	2	100	
Orange	3	1000	
Yellow	4	10,000	
Green	5	100,000	
Blue	6	1,000,000	
Violet	7	10,000,000	
Gray	8	100,000,000	
White	9	— — —	
Gold	—	.1	5%
Silver	—	.01	10%
body	—	— — —	20%

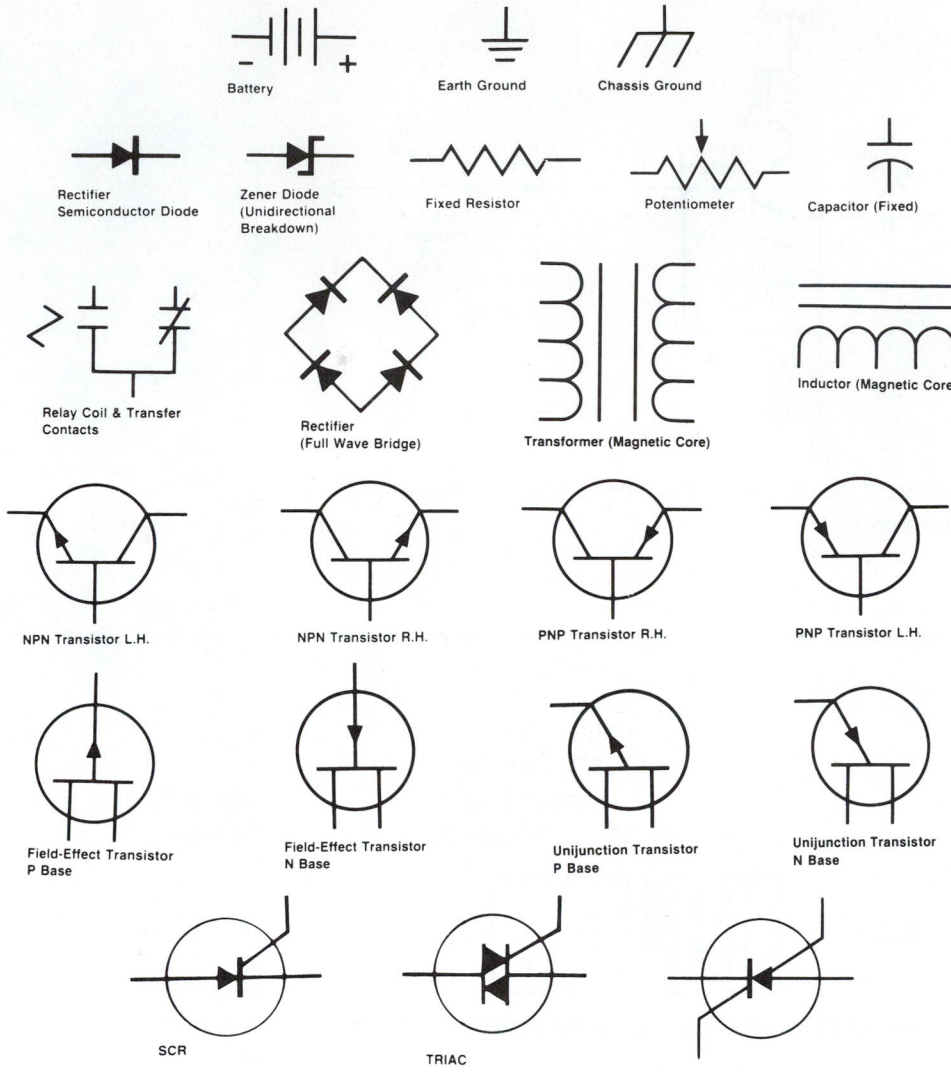

FIGURE 23.13   Dry Transfer
Stick-ons of Electronic Symbols

The most commonly used component is a **resistor** (R). The three basic types of resistors are fixed, variable, and rheostat. The resistance value is expressed in **ohms** (Ω), kilo-ohms (kΩ), or mega-ohms (MΩ); the resistance tolerance is expressed in a percentage (%) of component value, and the power rating is expressed in watts (W). For example, a drawing may call out 1 k, $\frac{1}{2}$ W, $\pm$10%, which refers to a 1000 Ω, $\frac{1}{2}$ watt resistor with a 10% tolerance (i.e., the actual resistance limits are 900 to 1100 Ω).

Capacitors (C) are components that also have three basic types; fixed, variable, and electrolytic (polarized). The functions of capacitors are to store energy or to block the flow of direct current and to permit the flow of alternating current. This flow of AC depends on the capacitance value and on the frequency. Capacitor characteristics are expressed on the drawing by capacitance value, *farads (F), microfarads (μF),* or *picofarads (pF)*, and a tolerance of capacitance is expressed as a ($\pm$ %) either $\pm$ 10% or $\pm$ 20%. Voltage rates may be called out on the drawing (F/D) or in notes, usually 10 to 200 VDC. The voltage controls the case size. Other characteristics may be considered when selecting a capacitor: temperature range, leakage, size construction, terminal arrangement, and voltage breakdown.

Diodes and **transistors** are both **semiconductors.** There are many types of diodes, but the three most common are signal, zener, and tunnel. Of the two semiconductors, **transistors** (Q) are the "active" or amplifying devices; here again there are many types, sizes, characteristics, and functions. Four of the most commonly used are the bipolar (NPN or PNP), the power, the unijunction, and the field-effect (FET) transistors. Transistors are used as amplifiers, switches, or detectors.

Transformers (T) are devices consisting of two or more coils that are coupled by magnetic induction. Transformers are used to transfer electric energy from one or more other circuits without change in frequency, but usually with changed values of voltage and current.

Another component is a **coil** or **inductor** (L). Coils consist of a number of turns of wire used to introduce inductance into an electric circuit to produce magnetic flux, or to react

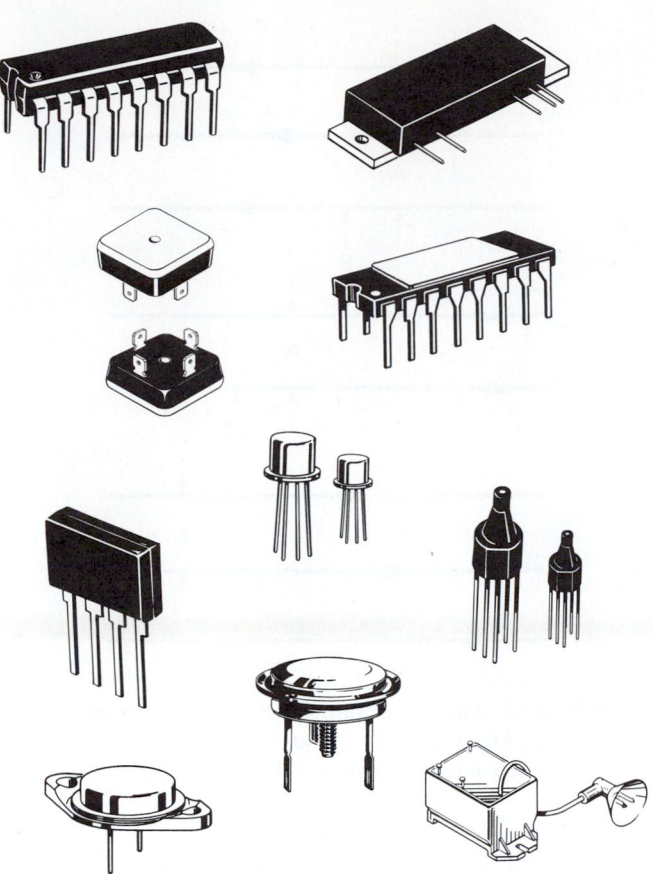

FIGURE 23.14   **Electronic Component Cases**

electrically to a changing magnetic flux. The electrical size of a coil is called its *inductance* and is expressed in *henrys*. The opposition that a coil offers to alternating current is called **impedance** and is expressed in ohms.

23.4.1   Integrated Circuits

Logic diagrams are composed of **integrated circuits** (ICs) or "logic chips." ICs are an interconnected array of active and passive elements integrated with a single semiconductor substrate or deposited on the substrate by a continuous series of compatible processes. ICs are capable of at least one or more complete electronic circuit functions. Normally, only the input, output, and supply terminations are accessible. When transistors or other discrete components are separately mounted and connected, it is a hybrid integrated circuit. ICs come in many physical configurations from flat paks, to TO-5 cans, to dual-in-line, and from 4-pin to 100-pin arrangements (Fig. 23.14). Integrated circuits have microcircuits consisting of diodes, transistors, and resistors, and are made up of silicon, aluminum, isolating barriers, and metal oxide.

23.5   Block Diagrams

A **block diagram** is a drawing in which the principal divisions of an electronic system, program, or process are indicated by rectangles or other geometric shapes, with signal paths represented by lines (Fig. 23.15). Block diagrams are the easiest

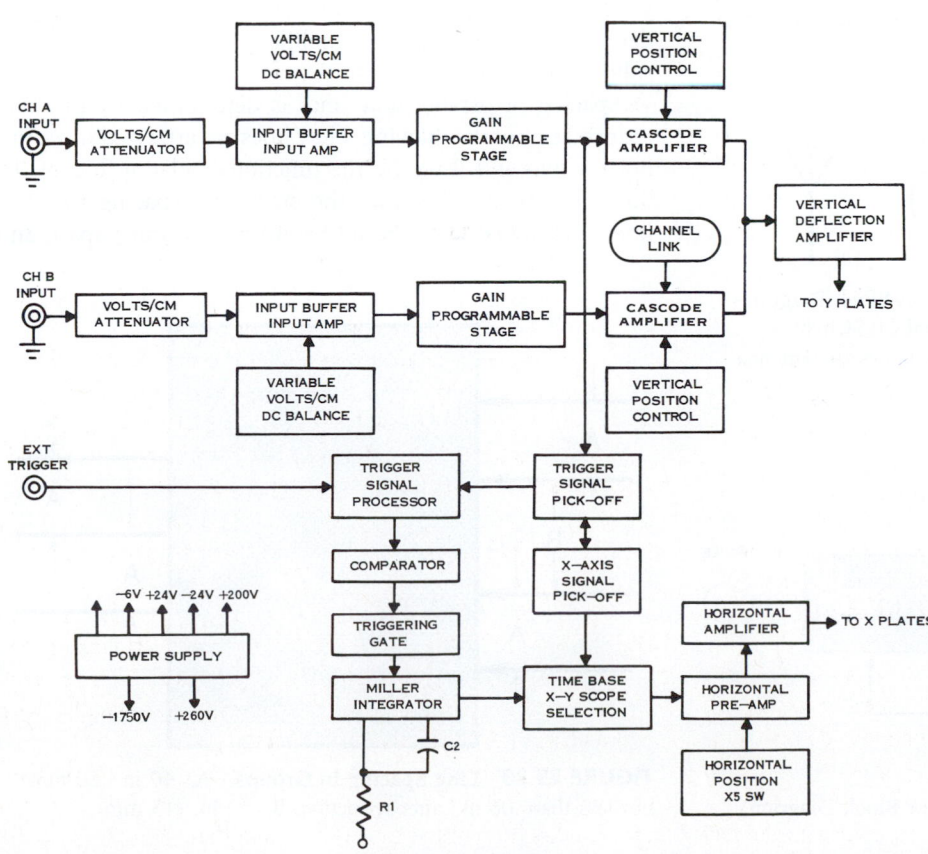

FIGURE 23.15   **Block Diagram for Oscilloscope**

form of diagram to draw and read, which makes them ideal for conveying information to people with limited technical knowledge.

Rectangles, diamonds, circles, and ellipses are used on block diagrams (Fig. 23.16). Electronic symbols are also used on some block diagrams. They are usually functional units in their own right and are normally depicted with aspects of their real-life configurations such as antennas, earphones, speakers, and switches (Fig. 23.17).

FIGURE 23.16   Common Flow Diagram and Block Diagram Geometric Shapes

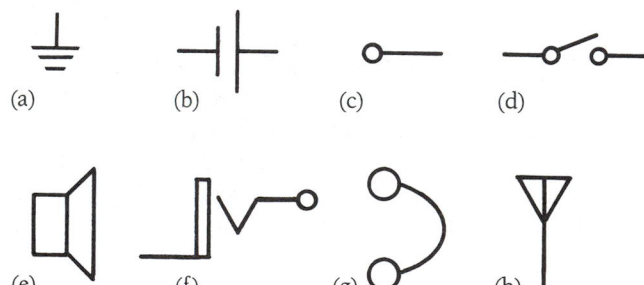

FIGURE 23.17   Common Symbols Used on Block Diagrams
(a) Ground (b) Single-cell battery (c) Terminal (d) Switch
(e) Speaker (f) Two conductor jacks (g) Earphones (h) Antenna

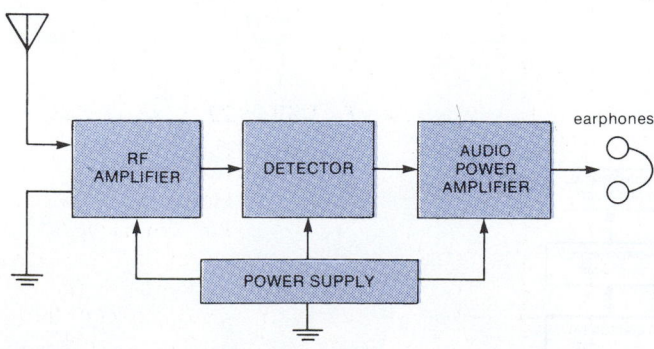

FIGURE 23.18   Tuned Frequency Receiver Block Diagram

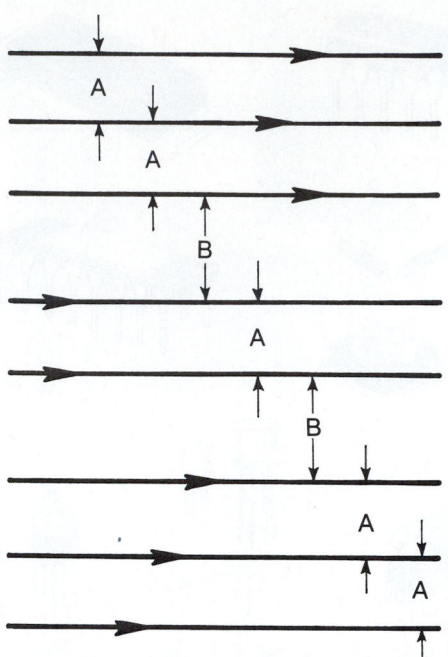

FIGURE 23.19   **Layout of Multiple (Parallel) Lines and Variations in Arrowhead Placement**   A: .40 in. (10 mm) minimum of .06 after reduction. B: .50 in. (13 mm).

Blocks and symbols are connected by flow lines according to the functional sequence of the system. In Figure 23.18, the signal depicted by the flow line goes from the power supply into each of the three units. The standard left-to-right flow sequence connects the antennas to the RF amplifier to the detector to the audio power amplifier. Flow lines are drawn as solid, medium-weight lines.

Spacing of parallel flow lines is determined by the final reduced size of the drawing. Flow lines are arranged in groupings of two and three by the functional relationship of the lines. Figure 23.19 shows the suggested spacing for flow lines. Individual lines should be .40 in. (10 mm) apart, and

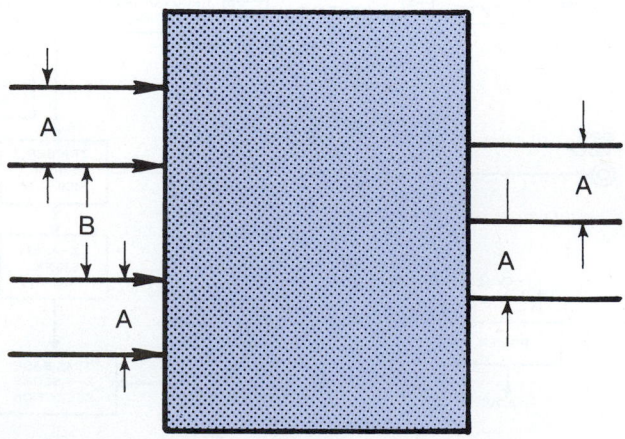

FIGURE 23.20   **Line Spacing in Groups**   A: .40 in. (10 mm), not less than .06 in.; after reduction. B: .50 in. (13 mm).

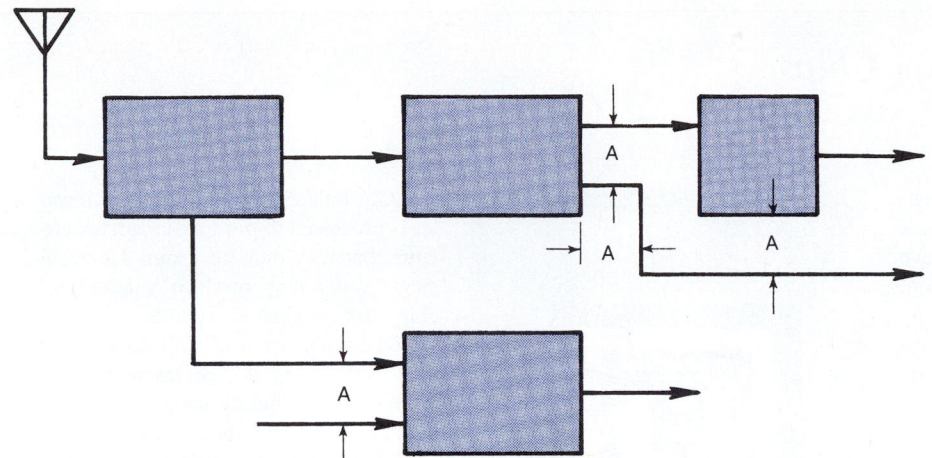

FIGURE 23.21 Line Spacing
A = .40 in. (10 mm).

.50 in. (13 mm) between groups of lines provides adequate reduction compatibility. The American Society of Mechanical Engineers (ASME) suggests a minimum of .06 in. (1.5 mm) spacing on the smallest reduction of the drawing. The suggested spacing dimensions for lines connecting symbols or block shapes is shown in Figures 23.20 and 23.21. The spacing of flow lines presented here is provided only as a general guideline for diagram construction. Besides block diagrams, *these specifications are used for drawing schematic diagrams, logic diagrams, and wiring diagrams, which are covered later in the chapter.*

Crossovers and connections of flow lines must be clearly presented for the drawing to be understood properly (Fig. 23.22). Connecting lines are drawn with a minimum number of changes in direction. When laying out the diagram, limit the amount of corners and crossovers to the absolute minimum. In Figure 23.22(a) a crossover is shown. In (b) an acceptable method of drawing a multiple connection is provided, but (c) and (d) are the preferred method for showing this form of connection or junction.

You can designate a connection by placing a dark solid dot about three line widths in diameter at the connecting point, as shown in Figure 23.22(f). When a line terminates at another line it is unnecessary to use the dot [Fig. 23.22(e)]. When an array or bank of parallel and perpendicular lines requires connection points, the dot method is used for multiple junctions [Fig. 23.22(g)]. When a line terminates at a perpendicular line in a single connection, the dot may be eliminated [Fig. 23.22(g)]. *Specifications for connections and crossovers and spacing can be applied to the layout and construction of schematic, logic, wiring, and other types of electrical and electronic diagrams.*

Lettering is the last step in the completion of any diagram. Lettering within blocks and other geometric shapes should conform to ANSI Y14.2. The height of the lettering is determined by the eventual reduction size. On block diagrams, most lettering is symmetrical and centered (Fig. 23.15).

Block diagrams are seldom hand lettered since they are used for printed manuals and sales literature. Most block diagrams are phototypeset or CAD generated. Freehand lettering is used for the original sketch and the layout sketch.

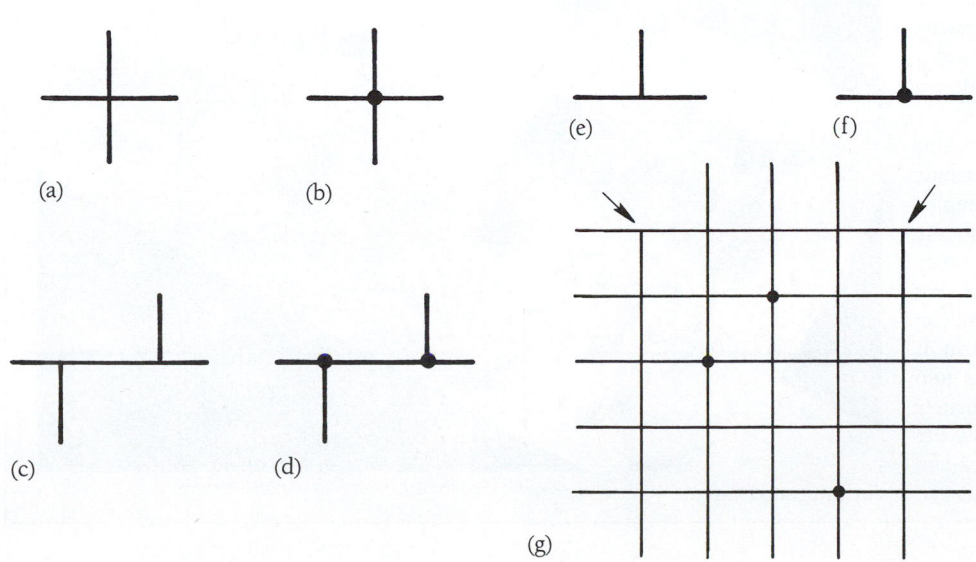

FIGURE 23.22 **Crossovers and Dashed Lines** (a) Crossover (b) Multiple connection (dot method) (c) Multiple connection (no dot) (d) Preferred multiple connection (dot method) (e) Single connection (no dot) (f) Single connection (dot method) (g) Using dots for array of lines (Note that single connections require no dots.)

Silicon Chips

Computers are amazing examples of technology at its best. Every year they get smaller and less expensive, but they have more memory, hold more information, and process it all faster. You can hardly keep up with the rapid pace of development! Today you can search an entire set of encyclopedias for a particular word on a CD-ROM on your home computer in a matter of seconds.

If you use your computer at home to do that search, you might want to look for the words *transistor, integrated circuit,* and *silicon.* Without those inventions, the computer revolution would not have been possible. A great deal of the technology for the microchip industry was developed for our defense industry, but today we use that technology and take it for granted (like other important inventions).

Integrated circuits and microprocessors are used to control our cars, dishwashers, microwave ovens, VCRs, and those ever frustrating video games. Industry uses them everywhere too. A visible example would be in a modern assembly line where robots are spray painting or welding car parts. Most of what you do involves integrated circuits of one form or another.

An integrated circuit is a complete circuit on a small piece of semiconductor material. Semiconductors are used because you can control the current needed for electronic devices on a very small scale. Silicon is "doped" with different materials to make the electrons go exactly where they are supposed to go. Usually, several integrated circuits are made on one small silicon wafer.

Processing the silicon so that it begins in a pure state and in the right electronic and mechanical state is a very complex process. Silicon comes from silica, the second most abundant material on earth. This is the same silica found in sand. For an integrated circuit, you need silicon that is 99.9999% pure. The silicon is transformed by a complex process into single-crystal rods that are approximately 4 inches by 24 inches. The long rods are sliced into "wafers" only $\frac{1}{2}$ mm thick and polished. After they are polished, you can

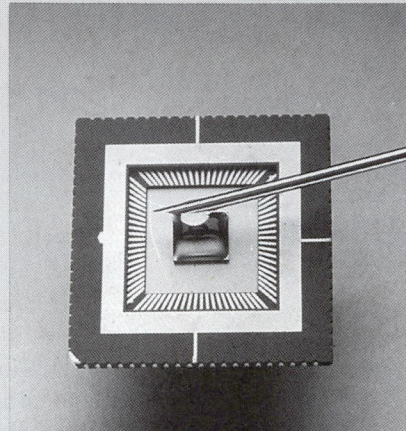

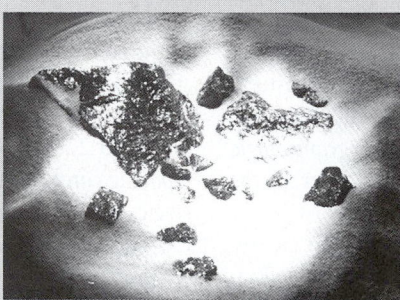

Various Silicon Products

see your reflection in the wafer. Each wafer is processed to produce integrated circuits that may only be 2 mm square. A single wafer may produce hundreds of chips for integrated circuits. All integrated circuits are made in a clean room in a very controlled environment. The workers wear "bunny suits" (so named because of the way they look) to protect the lab area from the contamination they might bring into it. A single hair would ruin the entire process. The more sophisticated the chip to be produced, the cleaner the environment has to be.

It's hard to imagine that our most sophisticated computer has components that start out as a simple grain of sand. It's also amazing that most of this technology was developed after the 1960s. Engineering graphics is used to lay out the circuits and to lay out the wiring on the microchips themselves. However, the development time and effort needed to make one of these amazing devices is enormous. This is something all of us have a hard time appreciating when we sit in front of our computer or use our microwave oven.

An Integrated Circuit

Regardless of the type or form of lettering, the size and style should be consistent.

You May Complete Exercises 23.1 and 23.2 at This Time

23.6 Schematic and Logic Diagrams

The **schematic diagram** is a drawing showing, by means of graphic symbols, the electrical connections and functions of a circuit arrangement. A schematic does not show the size, shape, or location of the component devices or parts. The **logic diagram** depicts logic symbols and supplementary no-

tations, the details of signal flow and control but not necessarily the point-to-point wiring existing in a system.

Spacing around each component and between components on electronic diagrams is important. Figure 23.23 shows different symbols and designations and their placement on a typical schematic diagram. If the component is placed horizontally, the letter designation, number sequence, component value, tolerance, and power rating may all be to the right side. Splitting the identifying information is also acceptable.

The drawing format, first sheet, or the last sheet of the diagram generally contains all tabulated information, notes, power and ground table, filter capacitor definitions, and the last reference designation used or not used table.

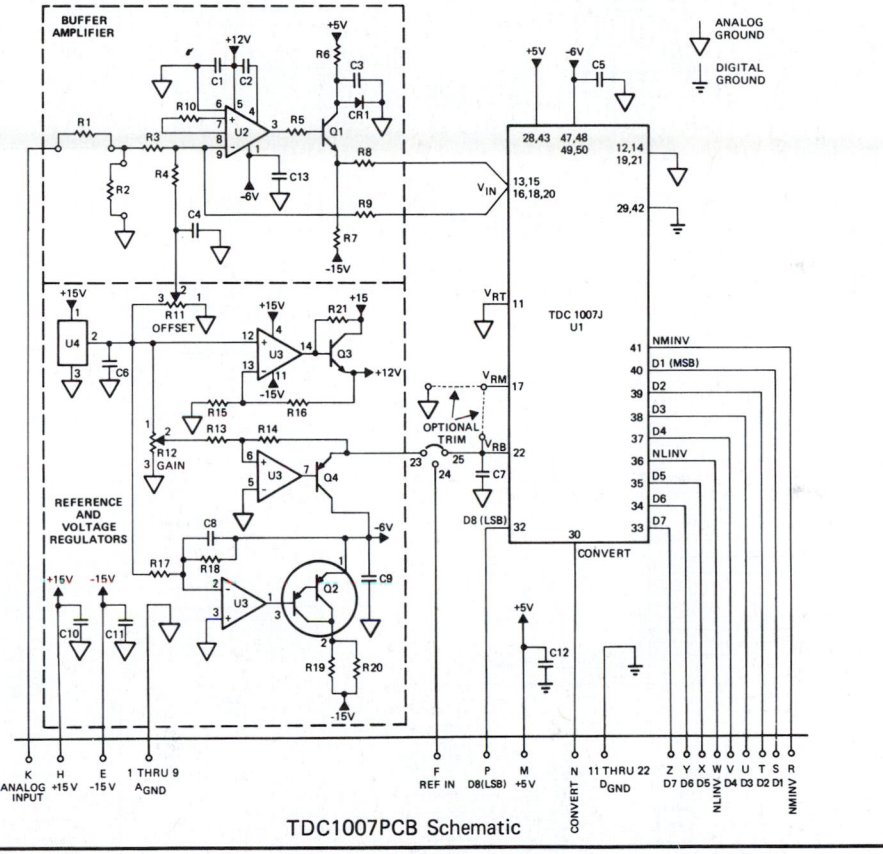

TDC1007PCB Schematic

PARTS LIST

RESISTORS			
R1	0Ω*	1/4W	2%
R2	80.6Ω*	1/4W	2%
R3	1.0KΩ	1/4W	2%
R4	4.2KΩ	1/4W	2%
R5	10Ω	1/4W	2%
R6	56Ω	1/4W	5%
R7	240Ω	2W	5%
R8	6.8Ω	1/2W	5%
R9	2.0KΩ	1/4W	2%
R10	†	1/4W	2%
R11	2.0KΩ	1/4W	Multiturn Cermet Pot
R12	2.0KΩ	1/4W	Multiturn Cermet Pot
R13	21.5KΩ	1/4W	2%
R14	21.5KΩ	1/4W	2%
R15	11.3KΩ	1/4W	2%
R16	42.2KΩ	1/4W	2%
R17	21.5KΩ	1/4W	2%
R18	51.5KΩ	1/4W	2%
R19	24Ω	2W	10%
R20	24Ω	2W	10%
R21	392Ω	1/4W	2%

CAPACITORS		
C1	0.1µF	50V
C2	2.0pF †	50V
C3	0.1µF	50V
C4	0.1µF	50V
C5	0.1µF	50V
C6	1.0µF	10V
C7	10.0µF	10V
C8	0.001µF	50V
C9	100.0µF	10V
C10	10.0µF	20V
C11	10.0µF	20V
C12	10.0µF	10V
C13	0.1µF	50V

INTEGRATED CIRCUITS

U1	TRW TDC1007J
U2	Plessey SL541C
U3	Motorola MC4741
U4	Motorola MC1403U

TRANSISTORS	
Q1	2N5836
Q2	2N6034
Q3	2N2222
Q4	2N2907

DIODE

CR1	1N4001

MISCELLANEOUS	
A1	Cambion 64 pin socket 704-4064-01-04-12 for U1**
A2	Thermalloy heat sink 60738 FOR Q2
A3	TRW Cinch edge connector 251 22 30 160
A4	Printed circuit board TRW TPC 1007
A5	Moore Systems stitch weld pins 700508 for R1, R2 (4 Required)

FIGURE 23.23 Schematic Diagram and Parts Lists for Printed Circuit Board

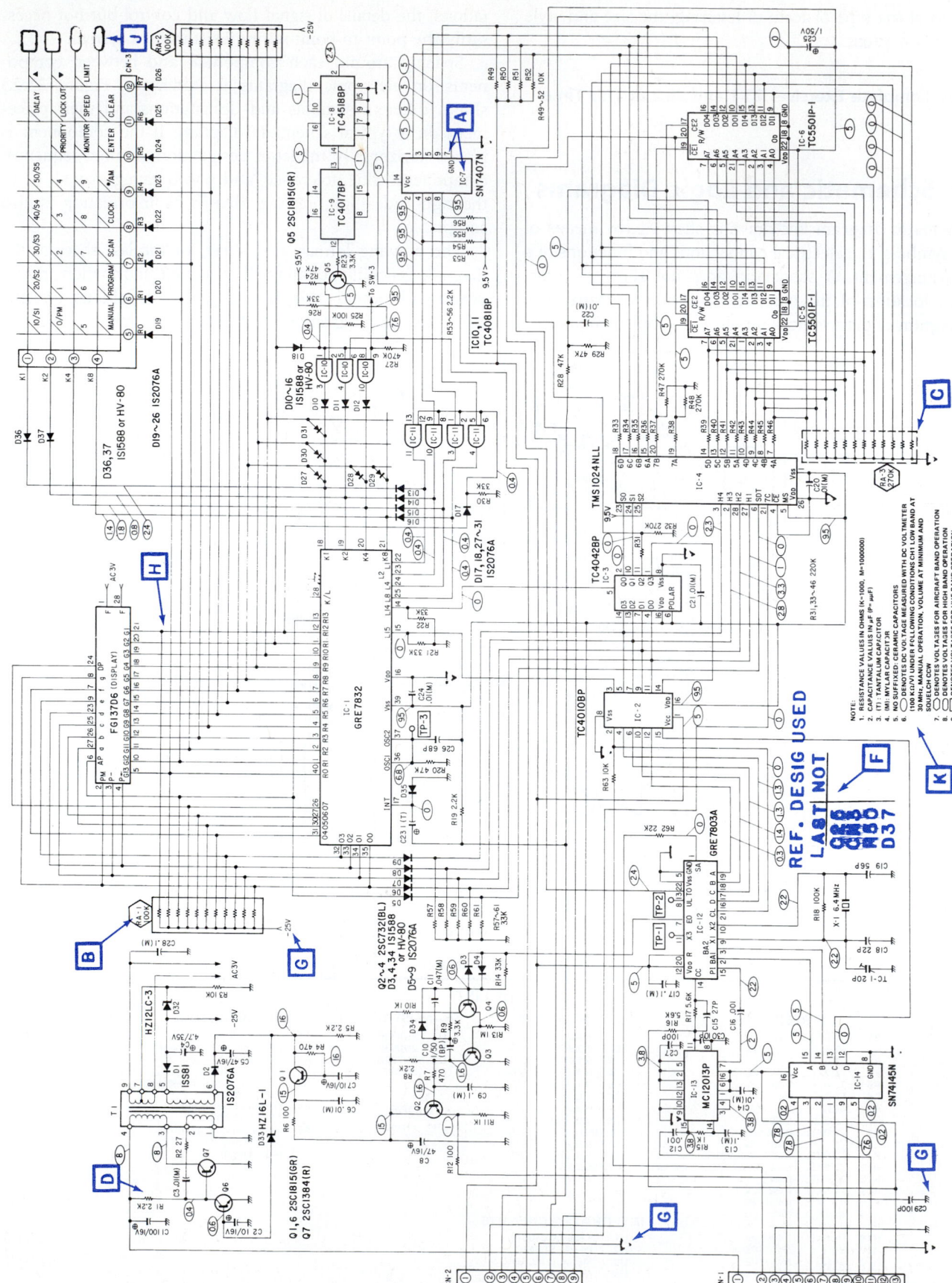

FIGURE 23.24 Complete Logic Circuit

23.6.1   Specifications for Drawing Electronic Diagrams

The layout of both schematic or logic diagrams is basically the same; the circuit flows with all inputs along the left and outputs along the right edge. If, and only if, additional input/output space is required for clarity, inputs enter along the top of the drawing and outputs exit along the bottom of the drawing.

Logic symbols are drawn according to ANSI Y32.14 with the size determined by nomenclature. When drawn manually, the preferred size on gates is half size using a RapiDesign template R 542. For electrical and electronics symbols, use ANSI Y32.2 with the .250 grid size preferred using RapiDesign template 315.

Figure 23.24 illustrates many of the standard specifications for a diagram layout. When the same device is repeated numerous times in the circuit on the same sheet, the detailed symbol labeling may be shown on only one device on that sheet. Reference designators and external pin numbers should be shown for each device on the sheet (A). Plan the circuit flow by determining the number of sheets required and dividing among several sheets. In general, both diagrams should be arranged so they can be read functionally from left to right. The more complex diagrams should be arranged to read either left to right or top to bottom and may be more than one sheet. Terminator resistors, etc., may be defined in the notes and only a simplified symbol need be shown on the field of the drawing (B). When groupings of parts are contained in a circuit, the grouping may be indicated by means of a phantom boundary line (C). Pull-up resistor nets are listed on the front sheets of all logic or schematic diagrams (D). Integrated circuits are listed in a table by reference designator, type number, voltage and ground specifications, and spare gates (if any). Spare gates are listed by reference designators and output of the spare gate. The reference designation table appears on both the schematic or logic diagrams and shows the *highest used* column and lists the highest reference designator number used for each category of components (F). The *not used* column lists all reference designations not used, due to their being passed over in the original design or deleted later by an engineering change order (ECO). All positive voltages ($+5$ V or VCC) should point toward and be near the top of the sheet and all negative voltages (-12 V) and/or grounds should point toward and be near the bottom of the sheet (G). When spacing the parts on the diagram, provide an even balance between blank spaces (open areas) and lines. Sufficient blank area should be provided in the vicinity of the symbols to avoid crowding of reference designation and value information. Connecting lines are drawn with as few bends, dog legs (zigzags), and crossovers as possible. Connecting lines and the symbols joined by them are drawn horizontally and vertically. Spacing between parallel lines is a minimum of .25 in. (6 mm). Lines should be in groups of three with a minimum of .25 in. (6 mm) to .30 in. (8 mm) between groups. For complex diagrams, the preferred method for depicting functions of connecting lines is the **dot** method (H).

Repetitive devices that have groups of signals that go from device to device, usually pin for pin such as in memory circuits, may use trunk lines in place of separate connecting lines. Trunk lines that go from sheet to sheet exit and enter the sheet at the outer edges of the diagram, labeled as the bus. Trunk lines are shown as thicker lines than individual connecting lines to provide contrast. They are drawn as $\frac{1}{10}$ grid size and are shaded.

Lines terminate with a connector symbol (J). Connector symbols must be labeled with connector and pin designations and signal name. Lines should terminate at the sheet edge, with the signal name on the line and are followed by sheet designation callouts. An output line going to several pages lists all of its destinations. Input designations list only the one sheet (K). Lettering is either freehand or completed with a lettering template, which is preferred. Lettering is a minimum of $\frac{5}{32}$ in. (4 mm) in height and is spaced far enough apart so that the lettering is distinct when the drawing is reduced. Spaces between lines of lettering is a minimum of .150 in. (4 mm).

Some general rules concerning logic or schematic diagram drawings are:

1. The position of a symbol on a drawing does not alter its meaning.
2. Electronically operated devices are shown in a position with the power off.
3. Parts of a symbol, such as a relay, may be separated on a circuit diagram provided designations are given to show the relationship of parts.
4. Switches are shown in a position with no operating force applied, or where switches are operated by a mechanical device, such as air pressure, a note is added to indicate the switch position.
5. All manually completed logic and schematic diagrams are drawn with templates (Figs. 23.25 and 23.26).
6. The coordinate location of logic elements is written directly above the element type. The coordinate location is usually underlined (Fig. 23.27).

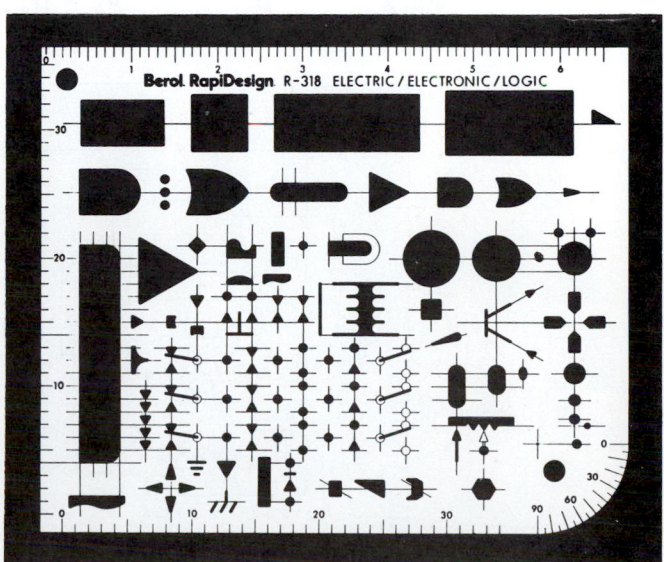

FIGURE 23.25   Logic and Schematic Template

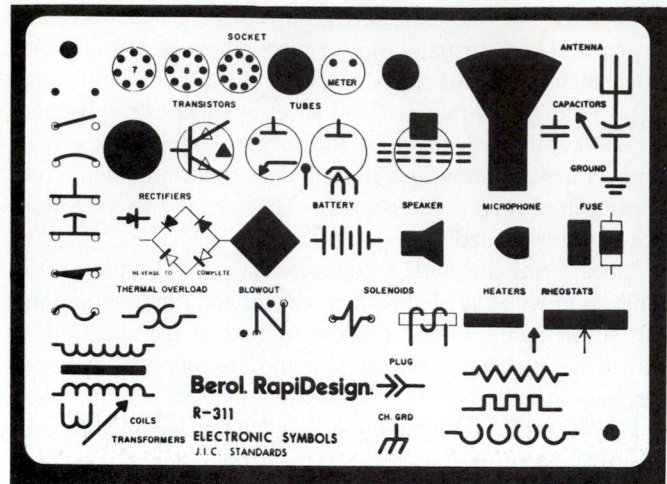

FIGURE 23.26 Template Used to Draw Electronic Symbols

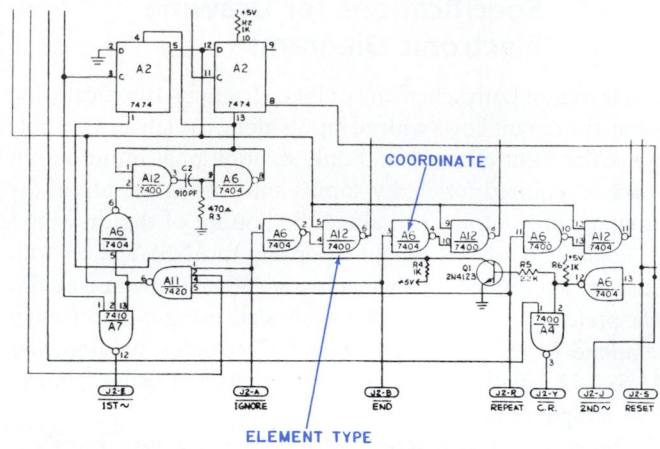

FIGURE 23.27 Logic Circuit

23.6.2 Layout of Electronic Diagrams

The first step in the layout of an electronic diagram is to sketch the circuit on grid paper to establish the tentative proportions. In Figure 23.28 the sketch was used to determine the logic diagram layout. Laying out a schematic or logic diagram involves placing the major components first. In Figure 23.29(a) the transistors were evenly spaced on grid paper. The second step placed the secondary components [Fig. 23.29(b)] where the resistors and capacitors are shown. Finally, the circuit flow lines, input-output, and ground and power sources were added [Fig. 23.29(c)].

You May Complete Exercises 23.3 Through 23.8 at This Time

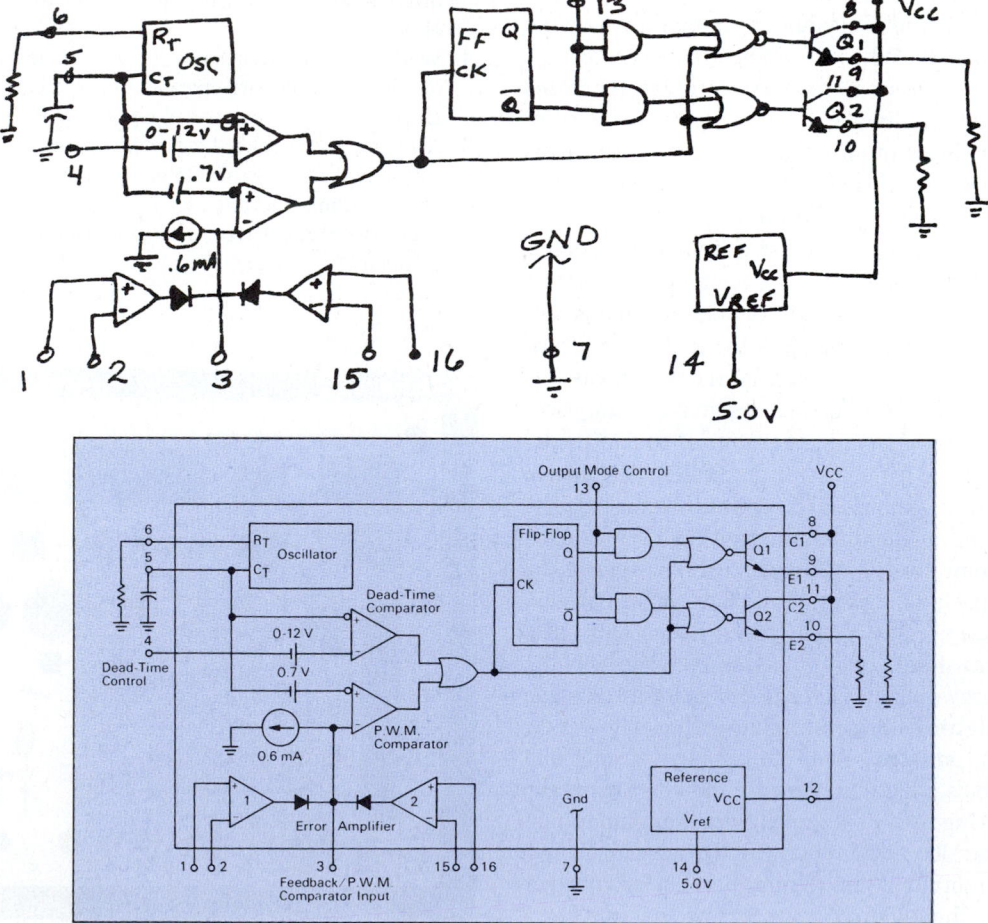

FIGURE 23.28 Engineering Sketch and Finalized Schematic Diagram

(a)

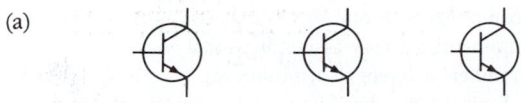

(b)

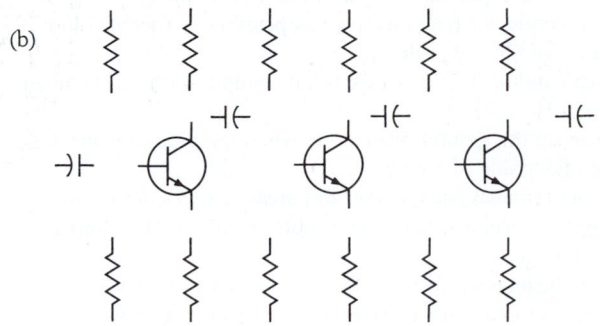

(c)

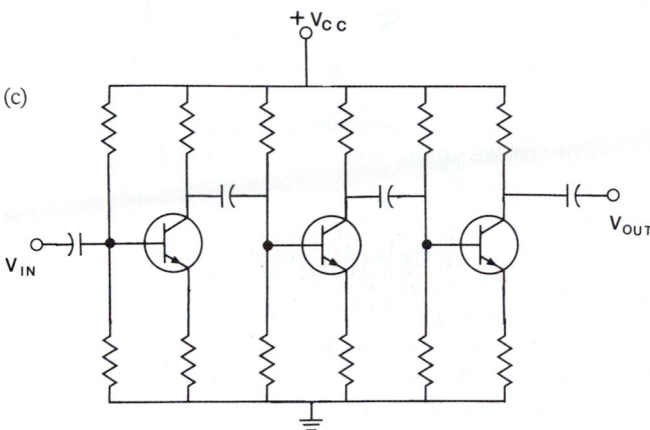

FIGURE 23.29   Component Placement (a) Transistor
(b) Resistor, capacitor (c) Flow line placement (completed
schematic diagram)

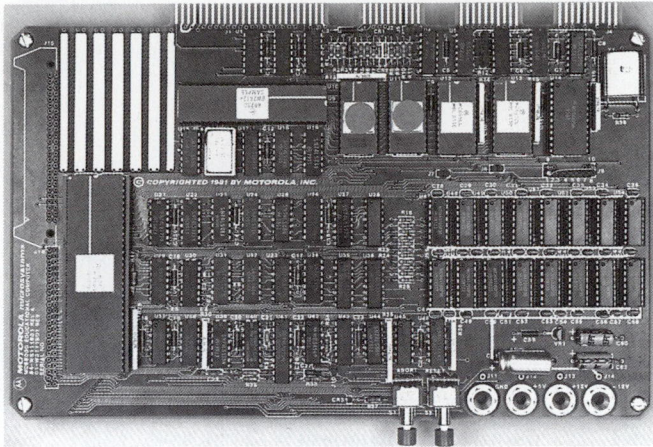

FIGURE 23.30   Microcomputer Printed Circuit Board

on the other (single-sided boards), or circuitry layered on a
number of bonded boards (multilayered boards). Components are sometimes mounted on both sides of the board,
although this practice is discouraged.

A PCB can be designed with manual or automated processes. Manual methods are frequently used for prototype
boards, or where the boards' tolerance and accuracy specifications are less stringent. Single-sided and double-sided
boards are more apt to be prepared manually than multilayered boards with their high density and critical alignment of
layers.

Regardless of whether a PCB is to be a one-of-a-kind prototype or a high-volume production article, it will require
graphic documentation. A PCB drawing package may include
the drawings shown in Figure 23.31. Exactly how much
documentation and how it should be prepared varies with
company practice, application, and method of generating the
documentation.

Adequate documentation conveys to the user the basic
electromechanical design concept, the type and quantity of
parts and materials required, special manufacturing instructions, and up-to-date revisions. Regardless of the number of
design steps, the method of design, or the types of documentation, the end result is the assembled functional PCB.

23.7.1   Printed Circuit Board Specifications

The following specifications can be used as a general guideline for PCB design and layout:

1. Keep the board design and component layout as simple as
   possible. Avoid odd-shaped boards and multiaxis component
   arrangements.
2. Keep the board outline dimensions simple and as nearly rectangular as possible.
3. Lay out the board on a toleranced grid medium.
4. Draw the artwork at an enlarged scale of at least 2:1; 4:1 or 10:1
   for greater tolerancing. CAD-generated art is usually 1:1.
5. Provide a minimum of two, preferably three, registration marks
   for artwork layering.
6. Lay out the board as viewed from the component side.

23.7   Printed Circuit Boards

Printed circuit board design is one of the primary functions of
electronic drafting. A **printed circuit board (PCB)** is a base-
board made of a laminated insulating material that contains
ICs or discrete components, along with the connections required to implement one or more electronic functions (Fig.
23.30); also see Color Plates 103, 104, 108, 109, and 110.
The connections of a PCB are a thin layer of conductor material. The **conductor pattern** is established on the board by
one of two main processes. The **additive process** involves
depositing the conductor material on the base in its required
conductor pattern. The **subtractive process** uses an etching
solution to eat away the nonconductor path areas on the
board after the conductor path pattern is coated or printed
with an etch-resisting paint or ink. A PCB may have all the
components on one side and the circuitry (conductor pattern)

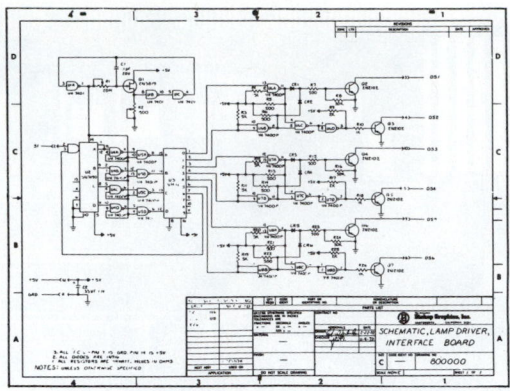

SCHEMATIC DIAGRAM: Consists of graphic symbols indicating the interconnections and functions of an electronic circuit. It is the basis for a printed circuit design. It is also used to test, evaluate and troubleshoot the completed circuit board.

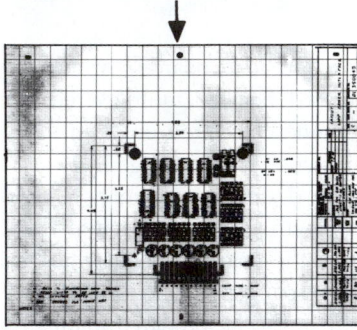

LAYOUT: The conceptual intermediate link between the schematic diagram and the master pattern.

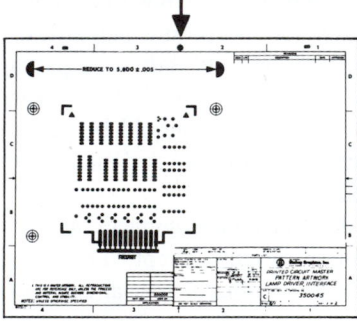

ARTWORK: Accurately scaled configuration of the printed circuit pattern from which the master pattern is photographically produced.

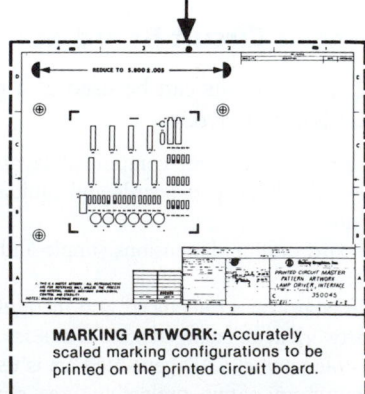

MARKING ARTWORK: Accurately scaled marking configurations to be printed on the printed circuit board.

FIGURE 23.31 **Printed Circuit Board Design and Fabrication Sequence**

7. Limit the components to one side of the board.
8. Locate components for easy assembly and servicing.
9. Keep the number of layers to a minimum.
10. Attempt to limit the number of axes for component placement to one or two. Keep components on an **X-Y** axis whenever possible.
11. Place IC DIP packages parallel to only one axis.
12. Keep conductor traces as short as possible and parallel to grid axes. Use 45° for angles.
13. Keep conductors .025 in. (0.6 mm) minimum from the board edge.
14. Break up the ground plane areas when the ground plane is on the solder side of board.
15. Locate terminal pads, lands, and areas at grid intersections.
16. Keep the terminal pads a minimum of .05 in. (1.3 mm) from board edge.
17. Keep the total number of different terminal area diameters, hole sizes, and pad configurations and conductor trace widths to a minimum.
18. Indicate polarity, component orientation, and reference designations.
19. Lay out adjustable components and test points where they are easily accessible.
20. Place heat sink components dissipating more than 2 W directly on the chassis (metal frame), and provide heat dissipators where necessary.

23.7.2 Master Pattern Artwork

The use of a grid system is essential in laying out and preparing the **master pattern artwork**. A grid will facilitate the placement of components, terminal areas, and conductor traces on the PC layout (Fig. 23.32). A grid system is essential if automated circuit board artwork preparation, manufacturing, or assembly techniques are being considered because the machines that perform these functions are coordinated to **X-Y** grid location systems. Most multiple lead components such as dual-in-line packages conform to standard grid increments.

A **terminal area** (pad) is a portion of a printed circuit used for making electrical connections between a component or wire and part of the conductive circuit pattern. The pad size is based on the hole diameter, and the hole diameter is determined from the lead diameter. Calculate the hole size first and then the pad size. The hole size can be found under the maximum lead diameter in the manufacturer's catalog. Terminal area shapes vary with designer preference. Certain

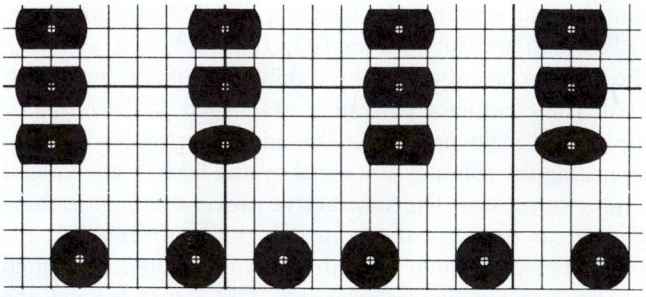

FIGURE 23.32 **Grid Pattern for Preparing and Laying Out Master Pattern Artwork**

shapes, however, have specific design advantages and disadvantages. Square or rectangular terminal areas provide maximum adhesion of the copper pad to the circuit board. They are useful when a large component hole is required and where there is a minimum of usable terminal area space. On the other hand, when terminal areas with straight sides such as squares, rectangles, and ovals are placed close to traces or other pads, they contribute to solder bridging during wave soldering. Round and elliptical pads reduce solder bridging under the same circumstances.

23.7.3   Component Mounting

Component mounting is one of the most important considerations in the design of a PCB. Component type, mounting style, and orientation on the board are all factors in the placement and layout of the board. In general, determining how to mount components involves the following steps:

1. Total the number of board-mounted components required as shown on the schematic diagram.
2. Calculate the amount of space needed for the components.
3. Determine the pad spacing needed for components.
4. Look up the hole sizes for the components.
5. Determine the component pad size.
6. Establish the heat sink and/or the heat dissipator requirements of the board and individual components.
7. Select the method of component insertion and board assembly.

When axial lead components are mounted vertically [Fig. 23.33(a)], they should be spaced a minimum of .105 in. (0.38 mm) above the board surface to allow for good solder joints and adequate cleaning (dimension D). The highest point of the top lead should not extend more than .550 in. (14 mm) above the board surface (dimension C). The bottom lead should be bent 180° around the component body and down into the board. The top lead should be insulated to prevent contact with other conductive elements (E), unless clearances are substantial. The straight portion of the lead should be a minimum of .0156 in. (0.4 mm) before the radius bend is formed. The minimum bend should be equal to the lead diameter.

Horizontally mounted axial lead components [Fig. 23.33(b)], should be attached so that the body of the part is in contact with the circuit board. However, components should not be placed in contact with more than one conductor unless the board surface is suitably protected from moisture traps. Components in transistor packages may be mounted vertically or horizontally.

23.7.4   PCB Design and Documentation

One of the primary considerations in PC board design is the selection of the board design and basic outline. Before **board geometry** is determined, the following considerations must be taken into account:

1. type of housing and packaging into which the board would fit
2. maximum amount of space available for the board
3. mounting, fastening, and clamping method to be used

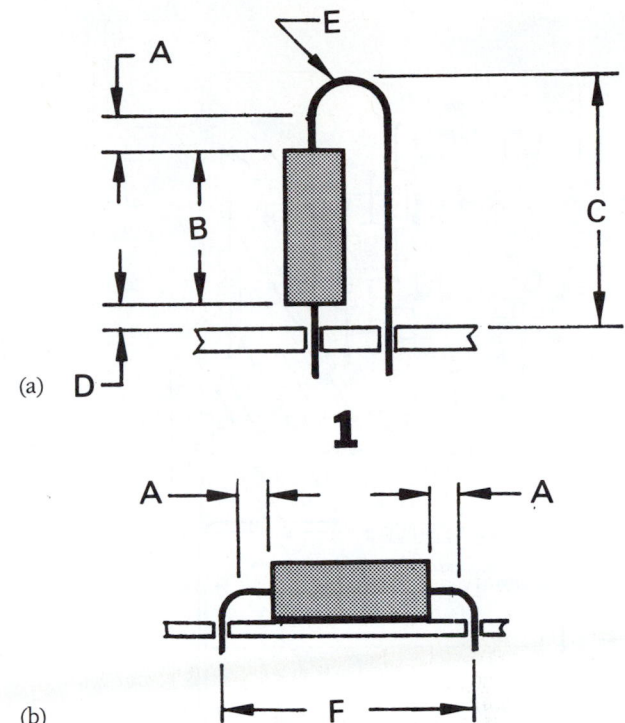

FIGURE 23.33   Axial Lead Component Mounting
A = minimum straight part
B = component body length
C = total height
D = minimum spacing
E = insulate top
F = pad (lead) spacing

4. electrical connection cable, connectors, terminals, and wiring requirements
5. type, thickness, and material to be used for the board
6. component mounting orientation (one side or both sides of the board)

The board outline (physical configuration) is determined after the above needs are assessed and the assembly, fabrication, and manufacturing methods available are determined. In general, a simple rectangular board with a connector strip is the easiest and most simple board geometry design. Boards designed with cutouts, curves, and irregular angles (Fig. 23.34) are more expensive to design, fabricate, and manufacture. The simple rectangular board geometry (Fig. 23.35) is the most common type of configuration.

Accurately registered PCB artwork is produced from pin-registered multisheet artwork techniques when done manually. With this method, a pad master base sheet is created on transparent, dimensionally stable drafting film. An accurate pattern of precisely sized locating holes punched into the sheet is used for pinning successive overlays in precise registration (Fig. 23.36). A PCB designer uses a light table and pin registration for manually laying out printed circuit artwork. The **LAYER** command can be used to separate different types of information when a CAD system is used.

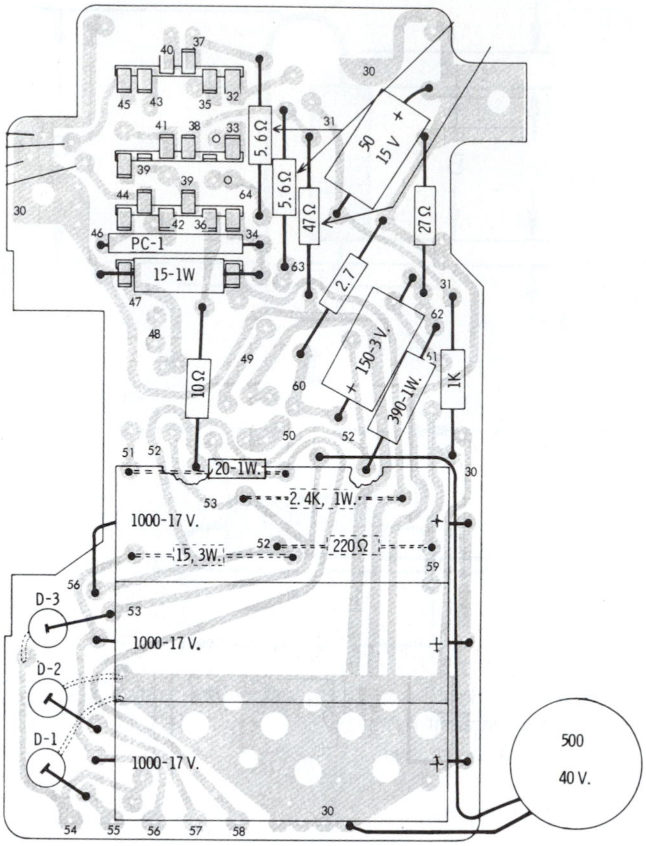

FIGURE 23.34   Irregularly Shaped Printed Circuit Board

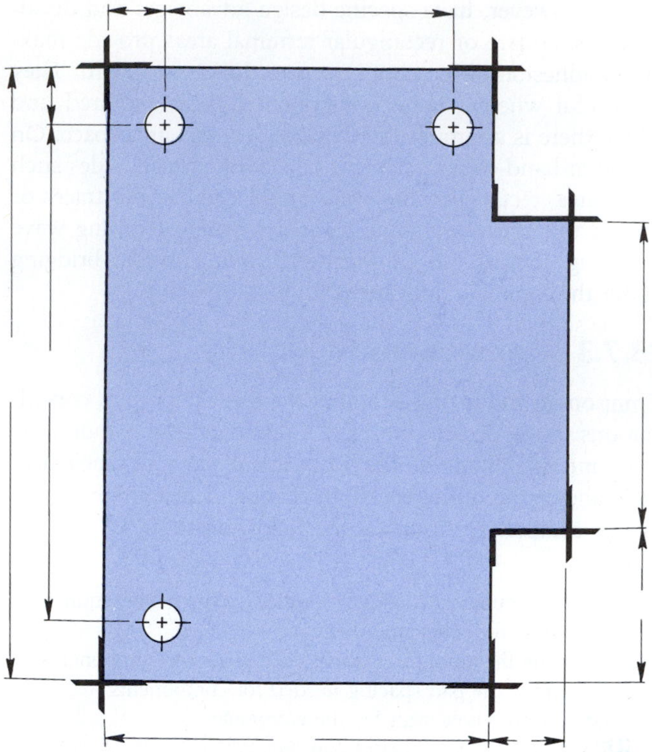

FIGURE 23.35   Board Geometry

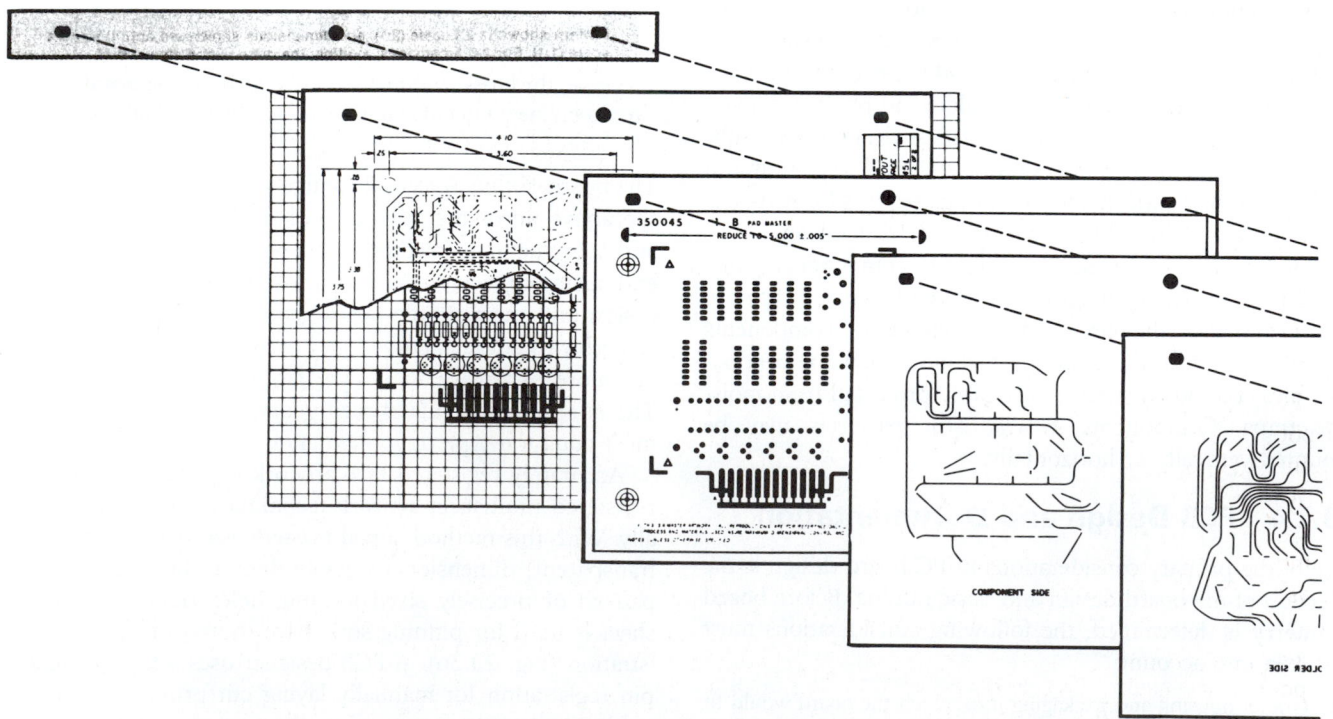

FIGURE 23.36   Pin Registration

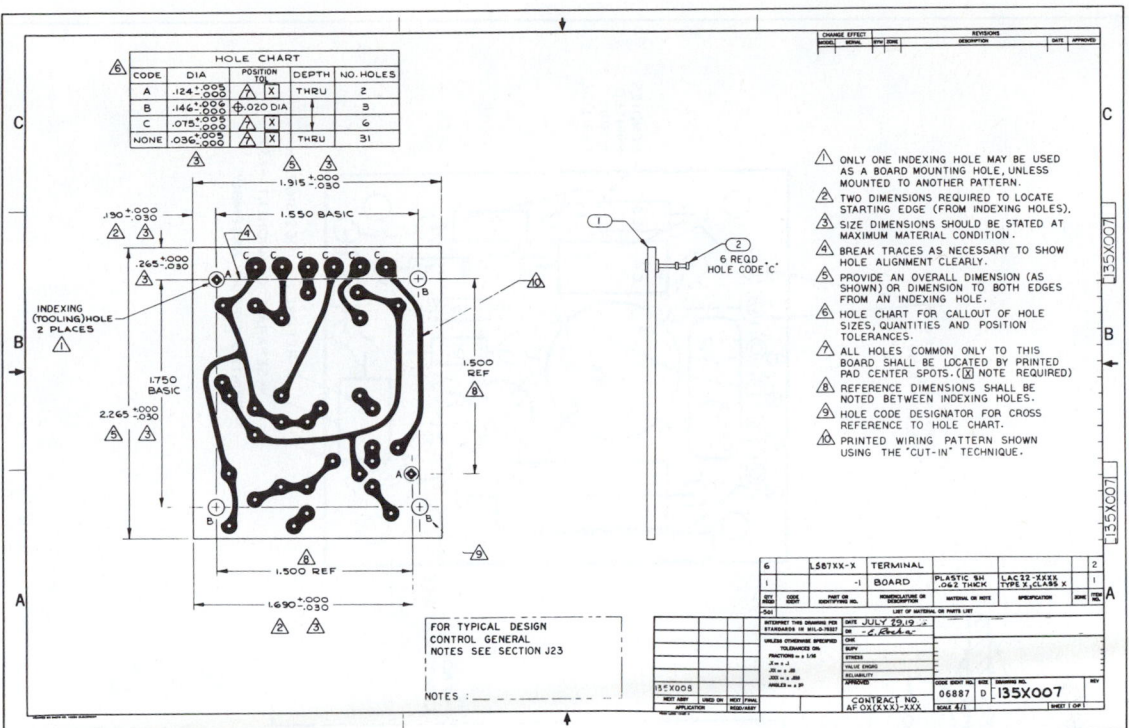

FIGURE 23.37   Printed Circuit Board Fabrication Drawing

A PCB **fabrication drawing** presents a complete engineering description of all design features. Information recurring from board to board is placed in the same location on the drawing to facilitate communications between departments and between the company and its outside vendors. The master fabrication drawing is normally drawn at the same scale as the film photomaster. It is viewed from the noncomponent side of the board if only one side is to be shown (Fig. 23.37).

The PCB **master drawing** (Fig. 23.38) normally includes the following information:

1. a reproduction of the conductor pattern image for the solder side of the board
2. the delineation of the board outline with dimensions and tolerances necessary for fabrication
3. the designation of the material, process, workmanship specifications, and plating requirements
4. hole identification information including type, finished size, and location (a hole chart may be used.)

The PCB **assembly drawing** is a complete engineering description of a PCB assembly (Fig. 23.39) including all components and parts mounted by fastening, soldering, or bolting. A parts list is included on the drawing or on a separate sheet. All parts, other than components, are ballooned on the assembly drawing and listed on the parts list. The assembly shows the board configuration, components, reference designation markings, mechanical parts (clamps, fasteners, and brackets), and dimensions required for accurate assembly and component orientation. The assembly drawing is drawn as viewed from the component side of the board and usually at the same scale as the artwork drawing. In general, the PCB

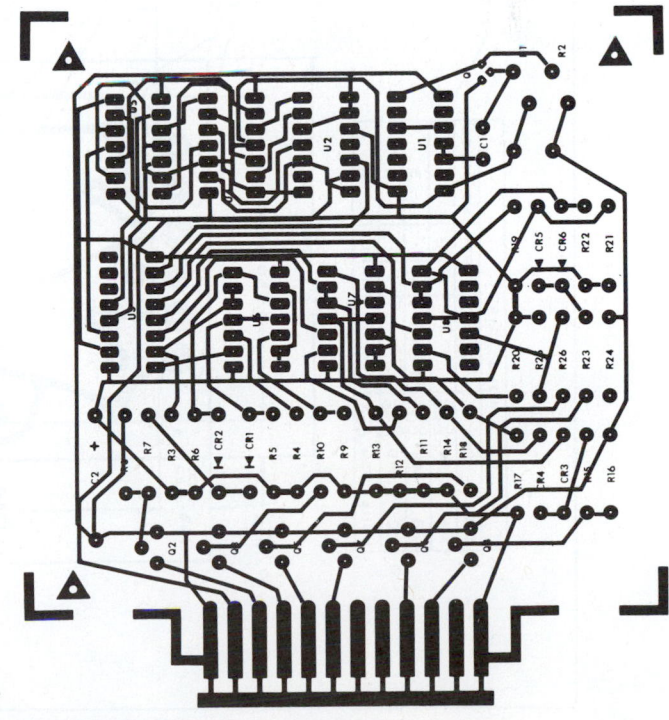

FIGURE 23.38   Printed Circuit Master Pattern

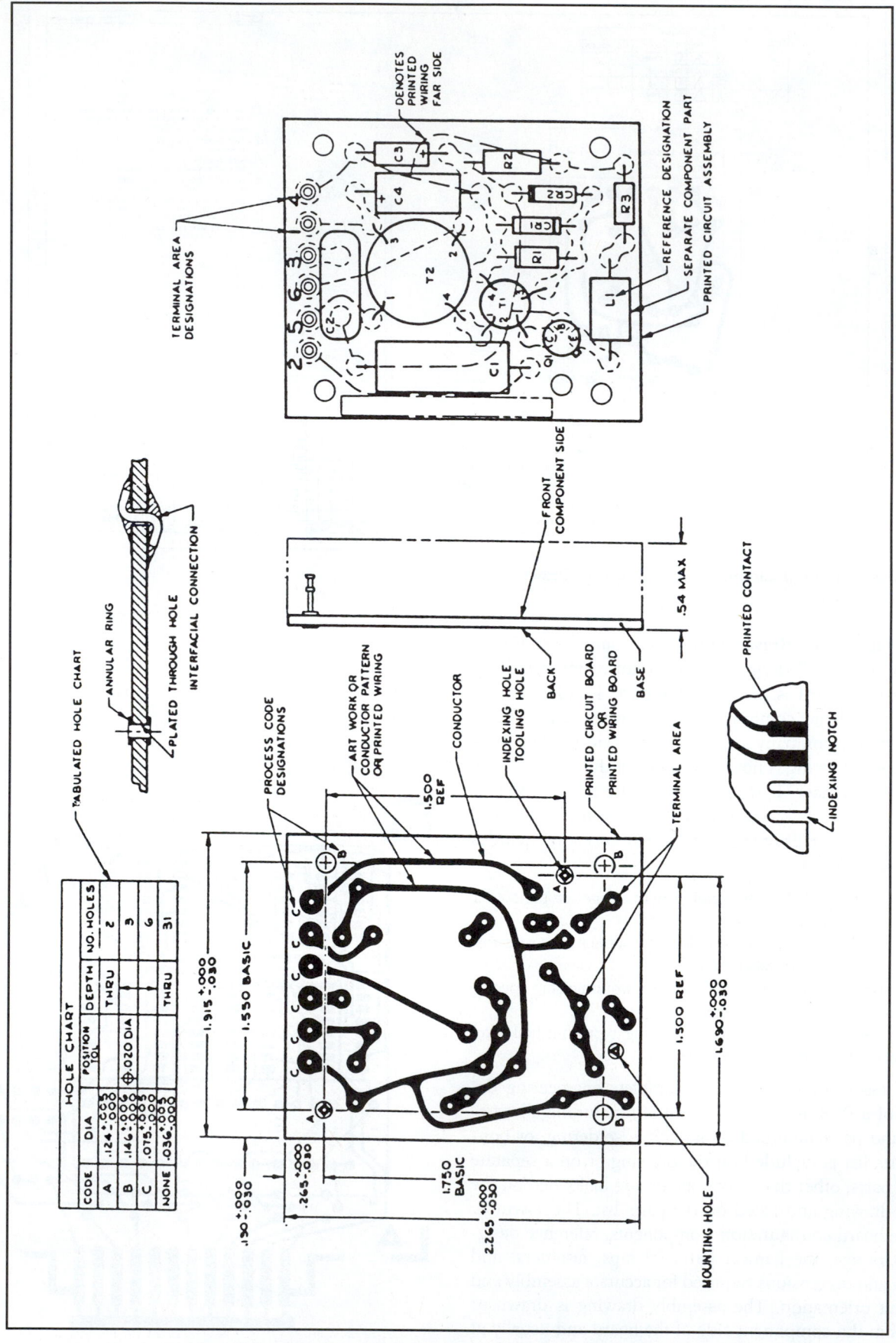

FIGURE 23.39   Board Assembly Drawing

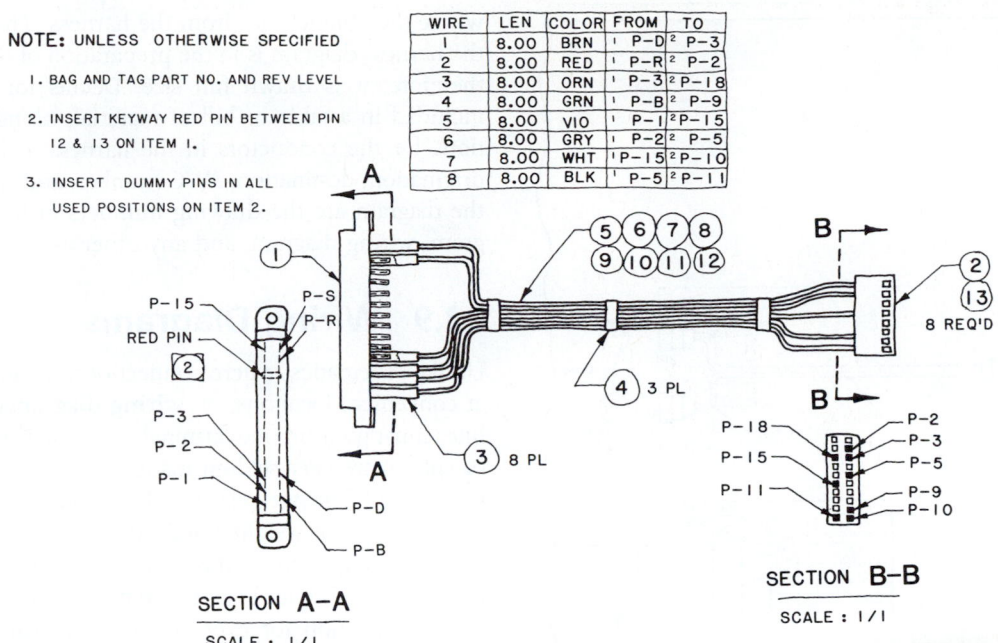

WIRE	LEN	COLOR	FROM	TO
1	8.00	BRN	¹ P-D	² P-3
2	8.00	RED	¹ P-R	² P-2
3	8.00	ORN	¹ P-3	² P-18
4	8.00	GRN	¹ P-B	² P-9
5	8.00	VIO	¹ P-1	² P-15
6	8.00	GRY	¹ P-2	² P-5
7	8.00	WHT	¹ P-15	² P-10
8	8.00	BLK	¹ P-5	² P-11

NOTE: UNLESS OTHERWISE SPECIFIED

1. BAG AND TAG PART NO. AND REV LEVEL

2. INSERT KEYWAY RED PIN BETWEEN PIN 12 & 13 ON ITEM 1.

3. INSERT DUMMY PINS IN ALL USED POSITIONS ON ITEM 2.

SECTION **A-A**
SCALE : 1/1

SECTION **B-B**
SCALE : 1/1

FIGURE 23.40   **Typical Harness Assembly**

assembly drawing is the same as any engineering assembly drawing. Parts, materials, and assembly instructions should appear on the drawing.

23.8   Cables and Harnesses

A **cable** is a group of two or more insulated conductors enclosed in the same outer protection. Generally, the conductors at either end terminate in the same approximate location. Frequently, a cable assembly terminates in a multiple connector. Typically, cable assemblies are used to connect one subassembly to another with mating connectors (Fig. 23.40). One common type of cable is the **flat ribbon cable**. The conductors on a flat cable are side by side and the assembly looks like a flat ribbon (Fig. 23.41). Although this type of cable is wide, it takes up very little routing space when used to interconnect subassemblies because it fits through small slots.

A **wiring harness** is shown in Figure 23.42. Unlike the cable, the wiring harness does not require a protective covering or coating over the bundled wires. A wiring harness may have some type of clear coating to protect it against environmental factors. The primary difference between a cable and a harness is that the cable includes the protective outer covering and a harness is simply a group of wires that for convenience have been bundled together. Also, harness wires can have many different lengths and can branch off at different locations (Fig. 23.42).

After the layout of the harness is complete, the **harness diagram assembly** can be prepared (Fig. 23.43). The overall outline of the harness is used rather than a drawing of individual conductors. The conductors are individually identified

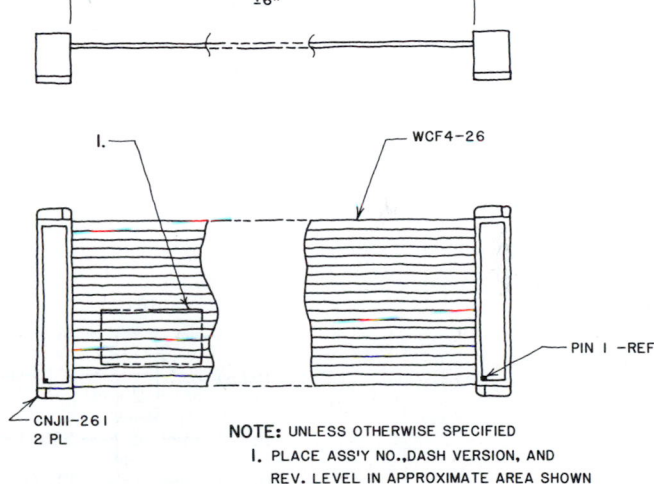

NOTE: UNLESS OTHERWISE SPECIFIED
1. PLACE ASS'Y NO., DASH VERSION, AND REV. LEVEL IN APPROXIMATE AREA SHOWN

FIGURE 23.41   **Typical Flat Ribbon Cable Assembly**

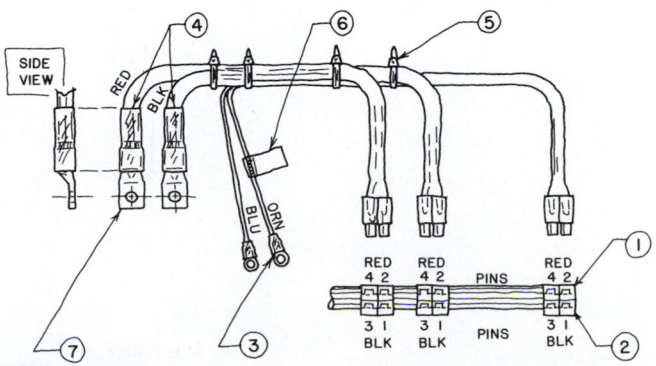

FIGURE 23.42   **Wire Harness Assembly Showing Location of Cable Ties**

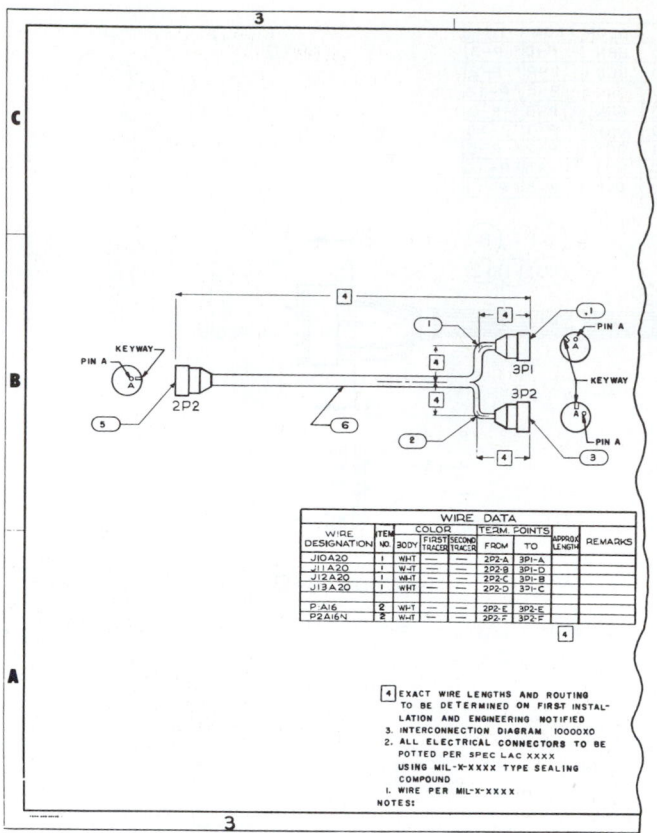

FIGURE 23.43 Harness Assembly with Wire Data and Notes

where they branch out from the harness. The primary use of the harness diagram is in the preparation of the harness itself; therefore, it is drawn full size. Details for conductors are included in a table or bill of materials along with specifications for the conductors in the harness: color, termination, origination, destination, AWG number, and type. Included on the diagram are the drawing numbers of the schematic diagram, wiring diagram, and any other associated diagrams.

23.9 Wiring Diagrams

Unlike schematics, where connections or junctions are made at convenient locations, on **wiring diagrams** the connecting lines must go from one terminal to another. Junctions, joints, or splices are very seldom made in electronic assemblies. In general, all line weights are the same on wiring diagrams (black, medium-weight lines). If necessary, use thin-weight lines for component outlines or symbols to avoid confusion. In addition to including some type of identification or reference designation for every component, each wire includes identification of all specifications. The lettering can be inclined or vertical and should be aligned to be read from no more than two sides. To avoid confusion, the wire identification lettering may be done with a break in the line representing the wire. The lettering is inserted in the break, as in the sketch of the control panel wiring diagram shown in Figure 23.44. This eliminates any doubt as to which line the identifying code accompanies.

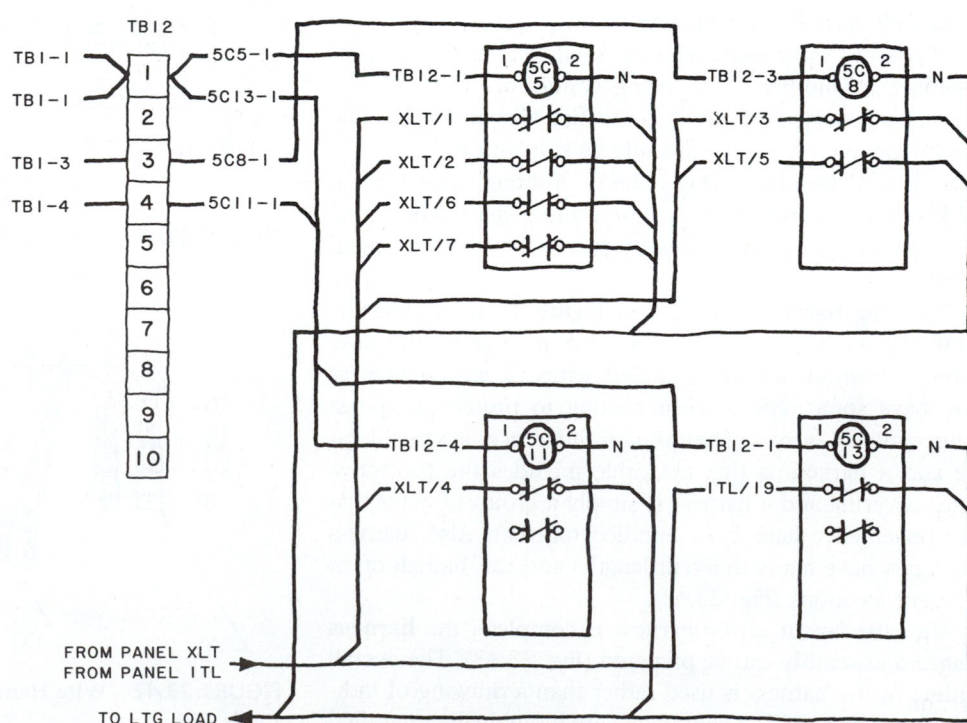

FIGURE 23.44 Wiring Diagram

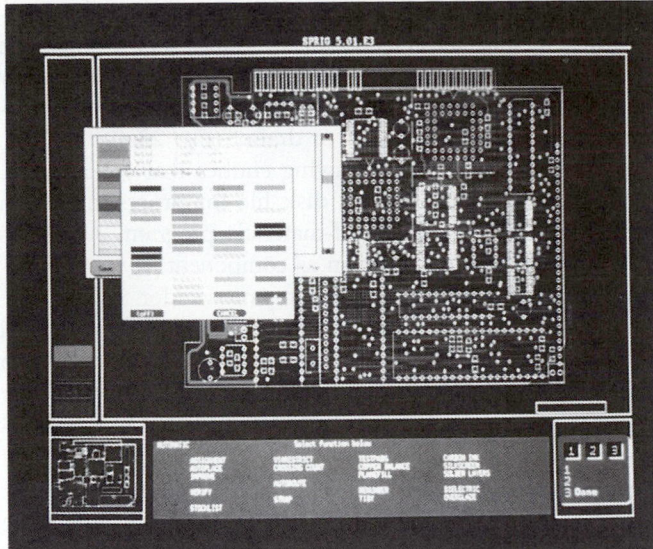

FIGURE 23.45   CAD-Generated PCB

23.10   CAD and Electronic Drawings

The production of electronic products involves many distinct but related operations: circuit design and development, PCB design (Fig. 23.45), IC layout (Fig. 23.46), mechanical design, manufacturing, assembly, and testing. Schematic, logic, and wiring diagrams can be drawn using predrawn symbols. PCB and IC design packages are also available that automate much of the design process in electronics.

23.10.1   Electronic Symbols

A **symbol** is a graphic representation of standard parts or items used repeatedly by the designer or drafter. Using traditional drafting methods, a template would be used to draw common features such as a resistor. With CAD, these symbols are drawn once and stored in memory or on disk. Once stored, these symbols can be recalled, scaled, rotated, or mirrored (Fig. 23.47). When symbols are created, information such as attributes and properties about the part can be included. This information can be used to create bills of materials or to do calculations. The collection of stored symbols is called the **symbol library** (Fig. 23.48).

23.10.2   Creating and Defining Symbols

Forming a symbol using CAD involves creating the graphics in the form of a block or subpart and storing the symbol for future use. Symbols are created using standard graphic commands. The connect nodes (base points) of a symbol must be created along with the other geometry. The nodes are created as permanent points; that is, handles that are used to place and position the symbol. The symbol node (origin) must be specified when the symbol is stored. The symbol origin (insertion point on some systems) is used as the reference point for future placement of the symbol. Attributes are added to

FIGURE 23.46   CAD-Generated IC Design

FIGURE 23.47   Constructing a Schematic Diagram with a CAD System

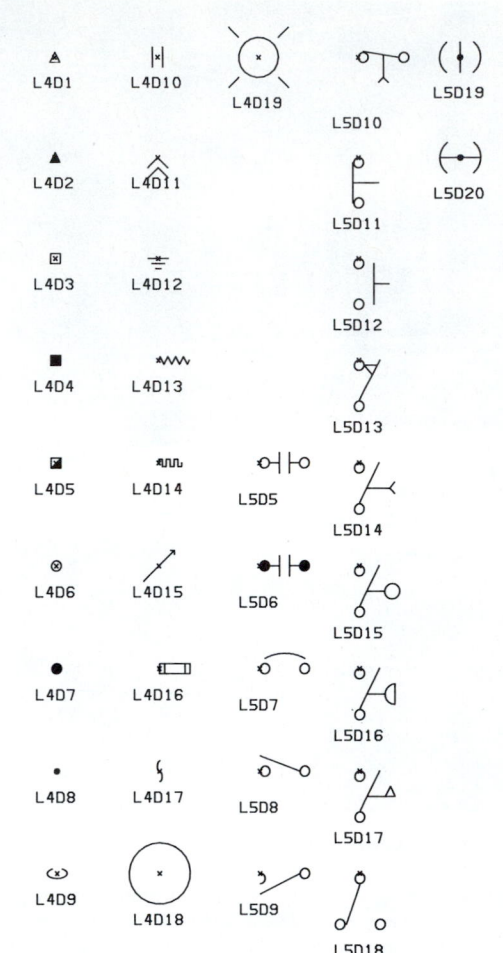

FIGURE 23.48 **Library of Symbols**

the block before saving the symbol. Symbols are the equivalent of a manual drafter's template. Libraries of symbols are easy to make and greatly aid productivity. The symbol library is programmed into a menu dedicated to a field of engineering required by the designer or drafter (Fig. 23.49).

Attributes are special drawing entities that contain text. You can collect them into a disk file for processing by an application such as a bill-of-materials program. Attributes may include such information as component, style, designation, capacity, code, cost, and company-vendor.

After the symbolic graphics have been constructed and attributes properly assigned, the symbol can be stored as a block or subpart. An invisible attribute is not displayed or plotted; however, information about it is stored in the drawing file and can be used for processing. Combinations of symbols nested together can be used to create new symbols.

A symbol can be altered by recalling the symbol and making the desired changes and restoring the symbol. A modified symbol can be stored with its old name, thereby replacing the old symbol, or stored under a new symbol name, creating a new symbol. The latter method is an easy way of forming a new symbol similar to an existing one. A new version of a symbol can be used to replace its old version on any drawing in which it appears by executing an update command. The old symbol is automatically replaced by the new version at every location at which it appears on the selected drawing. All other drawings where the old version appears are left unaltered.

23.10.3 CAD-Generated Diagrams

In general, the creation of an electronic diagram on a CAD system is not much different from preparing the diagram

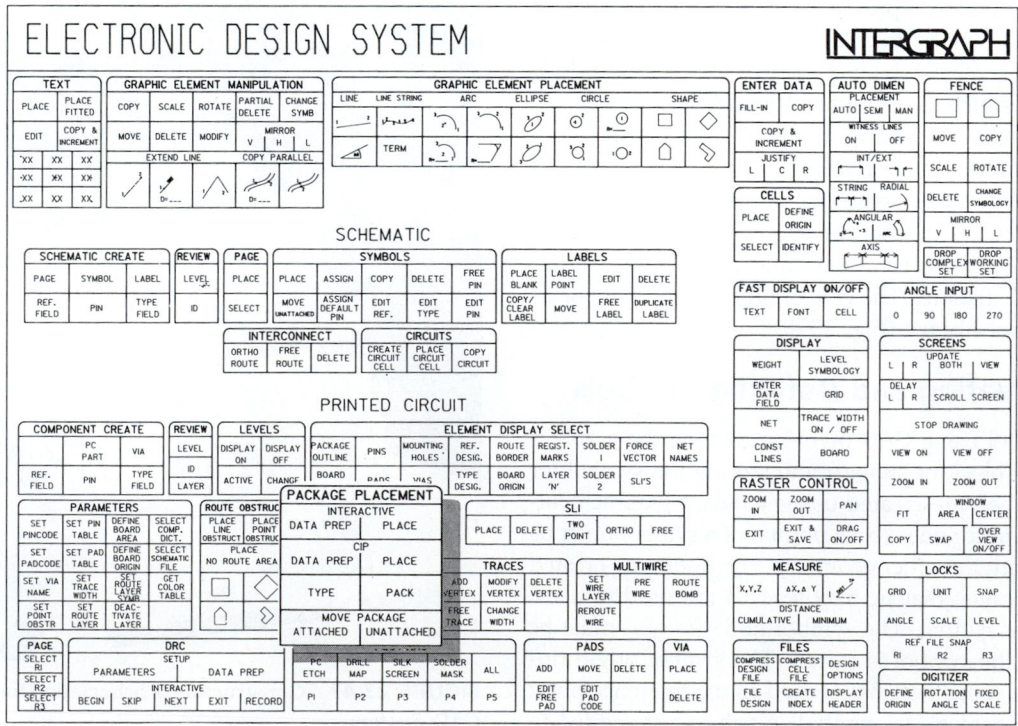

FIGURE 23.49 **Tablet Menu**

FIGURE 23.50   Digitizing a Schematic Sketch

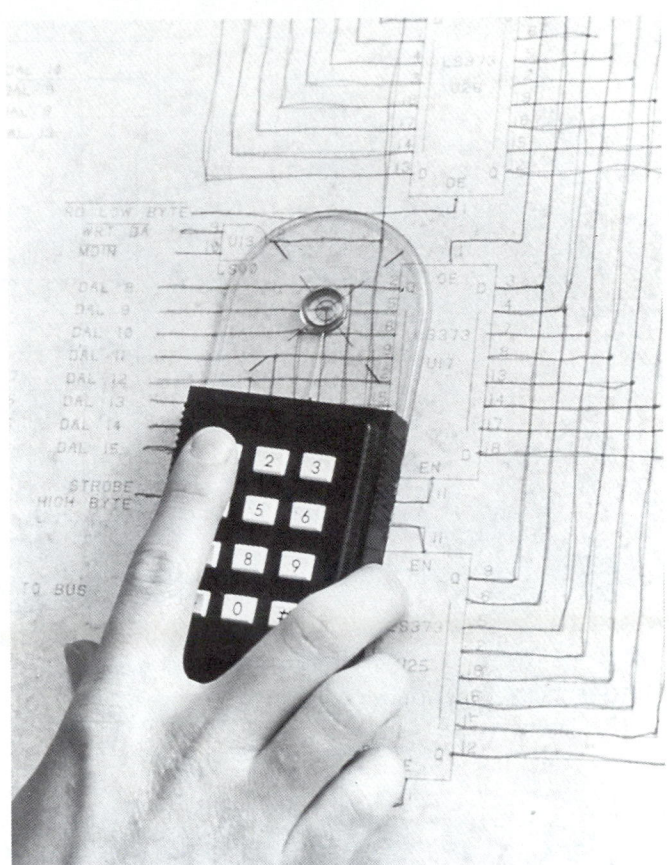

FIGURE 23.51   Inputting a Sketch Using a Digitizer

manually on a drafting board. The big difference, when using a CAD system, is the capability to recall instantly all the needed symbols from the library and to place them on the drawing at the desired location and position. A schematic diagram provides a means of capturing, concisely and accurately, all the data required to describe a particular circuit. As such, it forms an essential basis for any electronic design project and is used throughout the design process from development, through PCB layout, to inclusion in service handbooks.

Diagram symbols can be edited by using the standard editing commands of the CAD system. Symbols can be moved or reoriented if necessary. Symbol attribute text can also be added, deleted, or modified. Interconnects can be added, rerouted, or deleted as required. If two interconnects cross but are not intended to be electrically connected, a semicircular bridge can be added to one of the crossing interconnects. An interconnect may also be broken, if desired, without affecting its electrical continuity.

In some cases, a sketch of the circuit is made on a drafting board and later digitized by the drafter (Figs. 23.50 and 23.51). The logic diagram in Figure 23.52 and the schematic in Figure 23.53 are examples of electronic diagrams drawn directly on the CAD system using standard graphic commands and preprogrammed symbols.

23.10.4   PCB Diagram Data Retrieval

CAD systems provide the capability to extract the data from the drawing to generate a bill of materials automatically. Information such as part number, material, vendor, and cost are entered into the system when the part is used on a drawing. The information can then be tallied and a report generated by the system. The extracted data come from the attributes assigned to the parts or symbols used on the drawing.

If attributes are attached to the standard symbols, data can also be extracted to link a wide range of NC/CNC equipment, including drilling machines, board profilers, automatic component insertion machines, and automatic test equipment

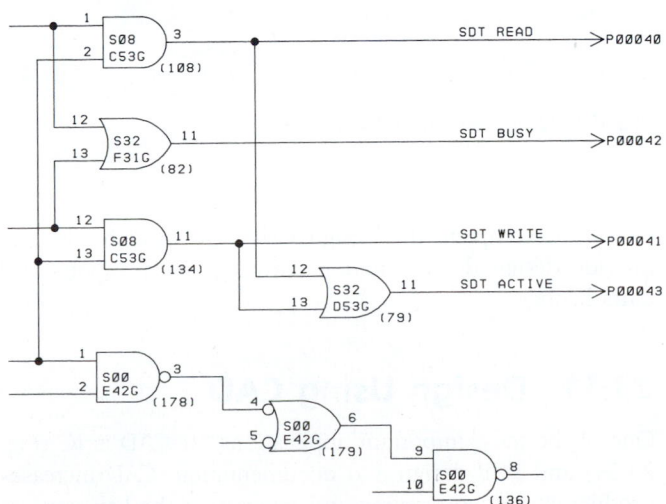

FIGURE 23.52   CAD-Generated Logic Diagram

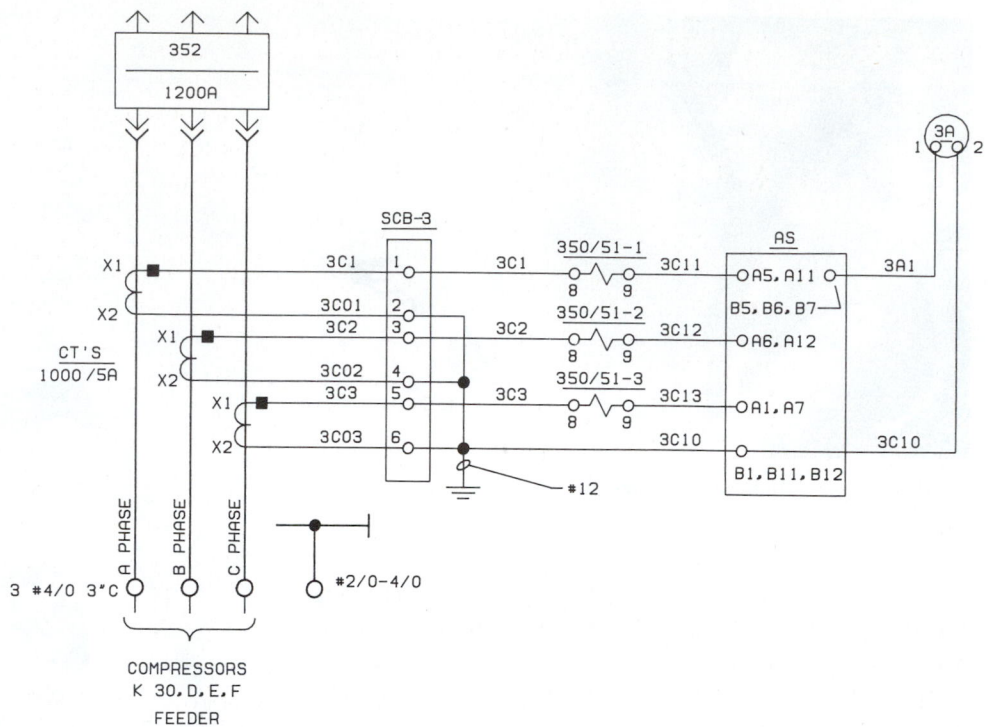

FIGURE 23.53 CAD-Drawn
Wiring Diagram

FIGURE 23.54 Integrated Circuit

(ATE). To complete the design cycle, the system can also provide design documentation with engineers' reports and parts listings.

23.11 Design Using CAD

One of the most important applications for CAD is IC (Fig. 23.54) and PCB design and documentation. CAD increases productivity by automating and integrating the key steps in the design and production of printed circuit boards. The typical PCB program uses automatic and manual editing modes to design the entire board from the drawing of the schematic to the final manufacturing and testing stages. Schematics, text, and board geometry are entered interactively into the system. Automatic assignment, placement, and routing routines are used to complete the design of the board. A variety of PC board sizes and types can be designed. Manual input can be used to override the automatic routines.

The **automatic routing** of PC boards is complemented by software to place components on the board. Because of the increasing density of boards and complexity of circuits, this is an important feature for development. The CAD program may also be used to generate control tapes for numerically controlled drilling and insertion machines.

A CAD system can also automate and integrate the key steps in the design, documentation, and design rules checking of wiring diagrams. It reduces the time and expense in capturing, checking, updating, and extracting design information. This capability is applied to many types of diagrams: elementary (ladder), schematic, wire harness, or interconnection. Designs are developed faster, with fewer errors, and with higher quality.

For the development department, there are special problems both in design and in preparing the necessary documentation for manufacturing. Each operation in development poses specific design problems: developing the circuit requires calculation of a theoretical solution, followed by breadboarding, testing, and refining; designing the printed board entails overcoming spatial restrictions and layout constraints; and designing the equipment housing requires consideration of cooling arrangements, protecting against shocks or vibrations, providing easy access for servicing and, at the same time, satisfying styling requirements. PCB and IC CAD design packages automate much of the design/drafting and layout of electronic systems, freeing the designer to develop and create new systems and products.

23.11.1   PCB Design—Case Study

Designing a PCB using manual drawing or taping methods is a very tedious and time-consuming task. Having first prepared all the necessary information for the layout, a skilled drafter finds a suitable component placement solution within spatial restrictions and design constraints. The drafter then creates a tracking pattern for hundreds, possibly thousands, of connections, all the time working to a high degree of accuracy to avoid dimensional spacing errors. The completed design is manually checked for spacing errors, for connectivity errors (by comparing it against the circuit diagram), and for artwork quality. Finally, when the board is ready to manufacture, drive tapes are programmed for any NC manufacturing and testing machines to be used.

When a CAD system is used, the schematic drawing package includes many aids to ensure fast schematic layout. The circuit layout is carried out at a design station. Automatic layout is available on some CAD systems; this allows for non-gridded input of symbols and nodal lines directly from an engineer's sketch (Fig. 23.55). Automatic layout aligns symbols and lines on the grid, producing the first document automatically (Fig. 23.56).

Schematic design symbols are called from the library and placed on the screen interactively. The designer moves and or rotates symbols as required. Subcircuits from previous work are stored and used in the same way, providing a good starting point for new schematics. The designer defines the point-to-point connection pattern of the symbols. The interconnections are made with a choice of line widths or choice of colors to enable easy differentiation between voltage, ground, and signal connections. Text, in various sizes, is added by typing. Once defined, the text is positioned as required. The designer reproduces repetitive areas of circuitry with ease, creating sections of circuitry only once, and then defines it as a subdrawing or block. The subdrawing is then positioned and replicated on the main drawing as required.

Once the schematic has been verified by the circuit engineer, data are transferred to a PCB application package. Data transfer includes full details on components and is correlated with the corresponding symbol or symbols on the schematic. More powerful systems allow you to verify the completed PCB against the schematic and automatically update the schematic drawing to ensure that both agree.

Routines are provided to move components interactively, rotate them, and fix them in position (Figs. 23.57 and 23.58). All associated connections move with the component to enable assessment of location and rotation. Text and component

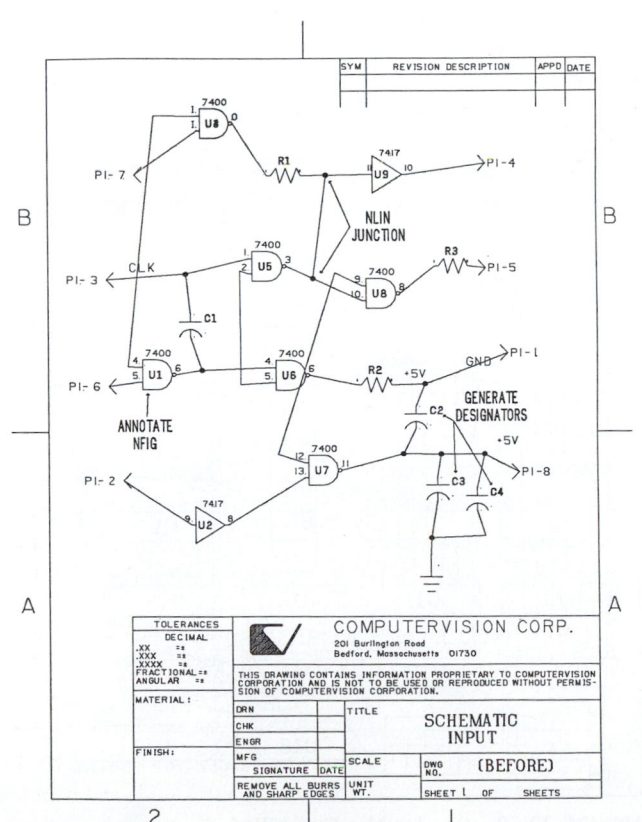

FIGURE 23.55   Schematic Input

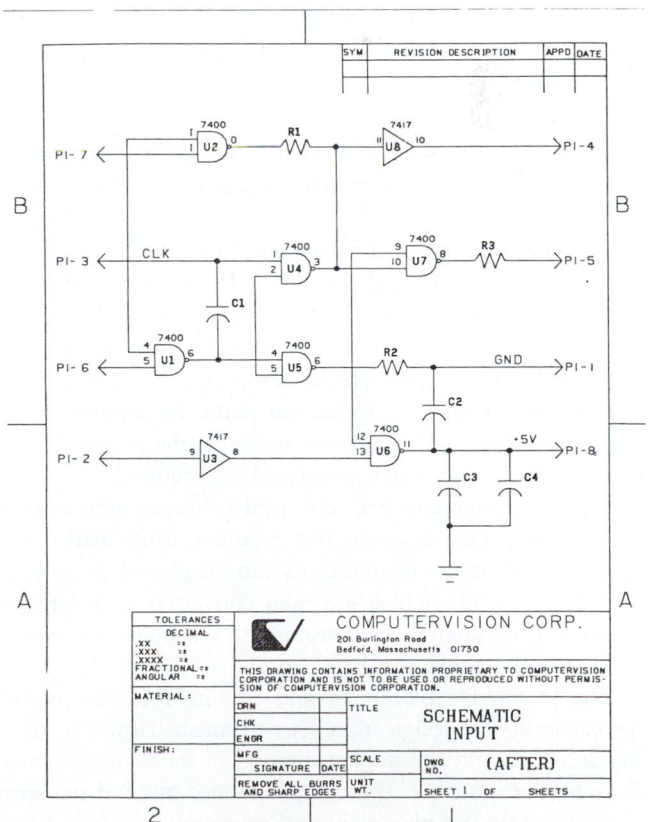

FIGURE 23.56   Finalized Schematic Diagram

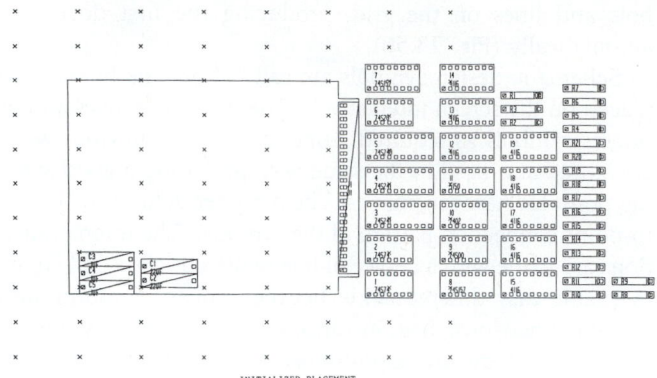

FIGURE 23.57   Initialized Component Placement

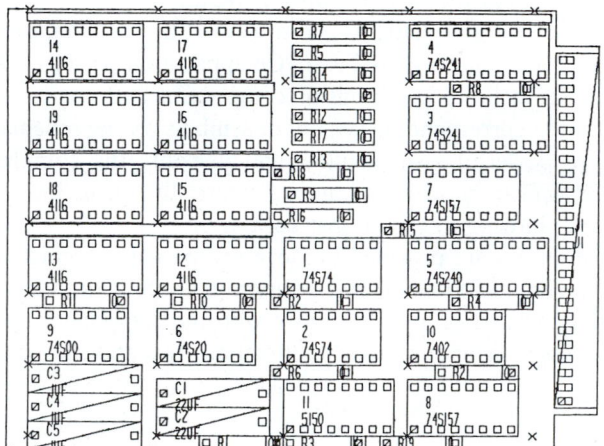

FIGURE 23.58   Component Placement with Keepouts

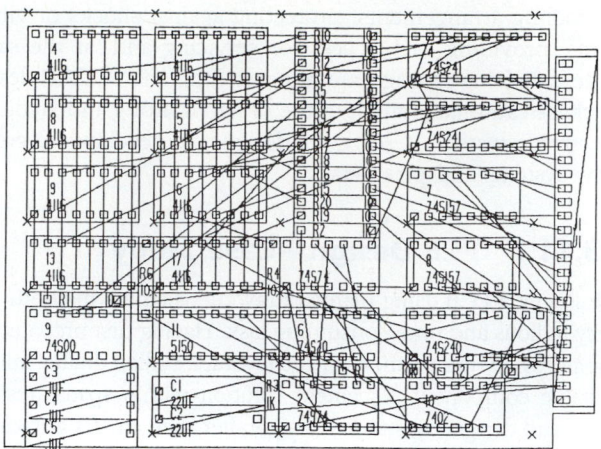

FIGURE 23.59   Component Placement with Ratsnest

names are manipulated in a manner similar to components; they are mirrored so the text will appear on either side of the board.

Automatic component placement allows the designer to lay out integrated circuits and discrete components on grids. Routines are provided to swap components to improve the connection scheme. The designer has flexibility in using the placement routines; he or she fixes certain components in position and restricts the routines to operate on particular sections of the board. In addition, the designer interrupts the automatic routines to place components interactively as required.

Circuit connections are converted to tracks with interactive routing. The designer also modifies route paths with interactive routing. Connections are displayed as straight lines (Fig. 23.59), which are then converted to a series of orthogonal or angled track segments. Via holes are created automatically where required.

·The interactive placement and routing routines provide the capability to design from start to finish. However, all of the decisions and the implementation of those decisions are done by the designer. The computer does most of the work required to do the placement and routing.

A pin-to-pin connection of all signals is used to verify connections or in conjunction with routing processes (Fig. 23.60). **Rubberbanding** allows the designer to move components to see the relative location of traces on the board. This aids in the placement of components in congested areas (Fig. 23.61).

The majority of circuit connections can also be converted to route automatically. Automatic routing includes routines for routing power and ground connections, memory arrays, and the remaining signal connections. More powerful systems include routers specifically designed for multilayer PCBs. The router minimizes the number of via holes and prevents the insertion of vias underneath integrated circuits. Automatic routing is further enhanced by routines to do automatic gate and pen swapping.

Assembly drawings (Fig. 23.62) and a 3D model (Fig. 23.63) are extracted and plotted from the original design

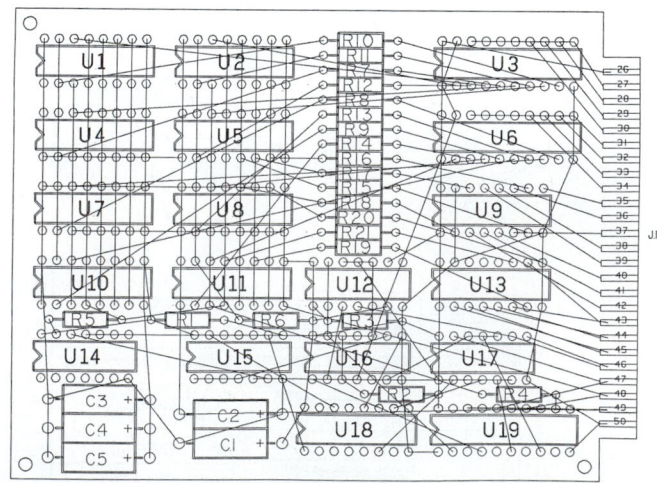

FIGURE 23.60   Display Net Capability

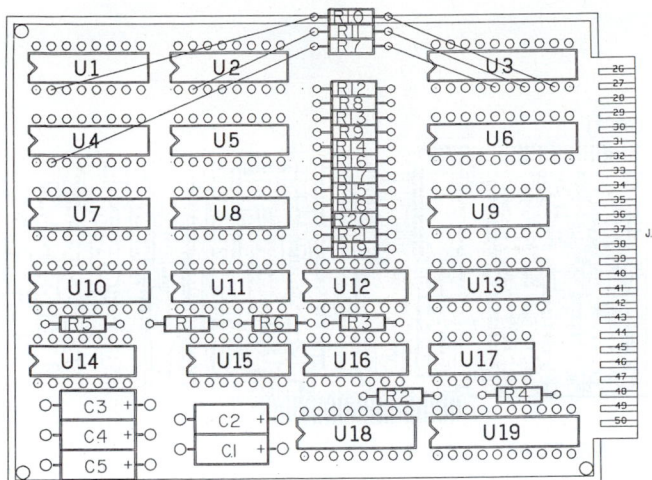

FIGURE 23.61   Rubberbanding of Components

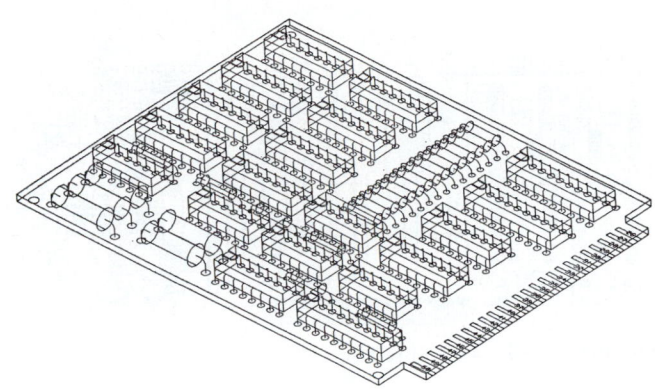

FIGURE 23.63   3D Design of PCB

database as the last step. Most systems include postprocessors to link to pen plotters, hardcopy units, and photoplotters. Pen plotters (Fig. 23.64) provide check plots quickly at any stage in the design. Photoplotters provide high-quality, one-to-one, or scaled artwork for manufacturing artwork.

Artwork masters, solder masks, component drawings, silk-screen masters, pad masters and drill drawings, and NC drill and NC automatic component placement tapes are all generated from the original PCB design data with much of the process automated. Figures 23.65–23.74 show a complete set of PCB documentation for a complex multilayered board. This project was designed and documented using a PC-based CAD system (Douglas CAD/CAM). To complete the design cycle, the system provides design documentation with engineering reports and parts listings.

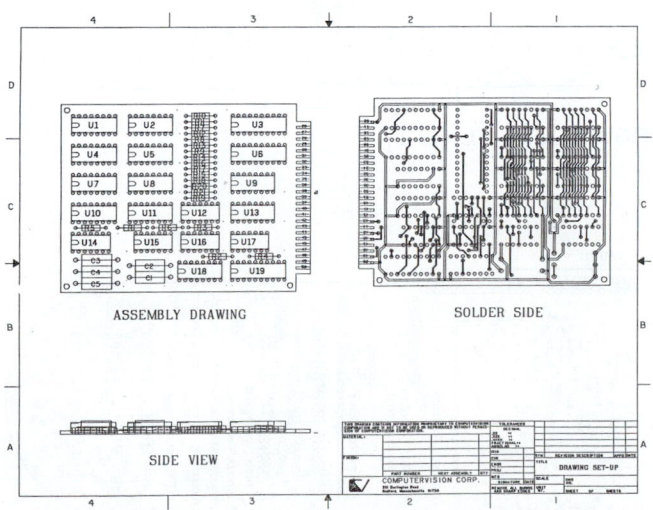

FIGURE 23.62   Assembly Drawing

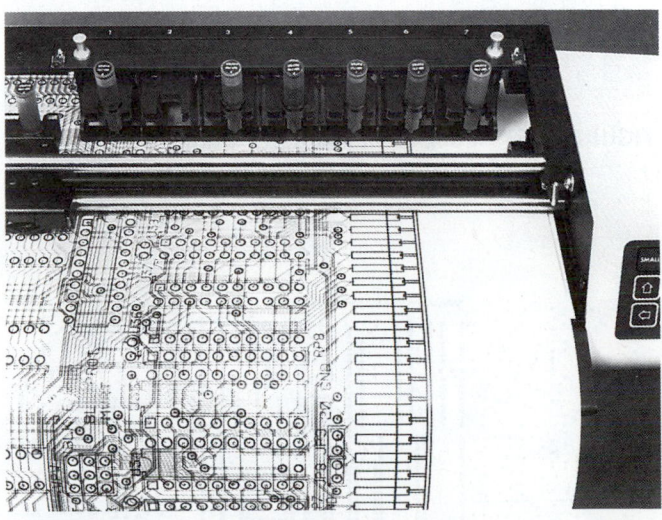

FIGURE 23.64   Pen Plotter Generating PCB Artwork

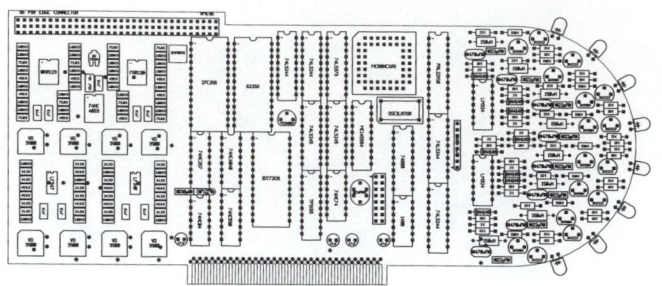

FIGURE 23.65 Assembly Plot

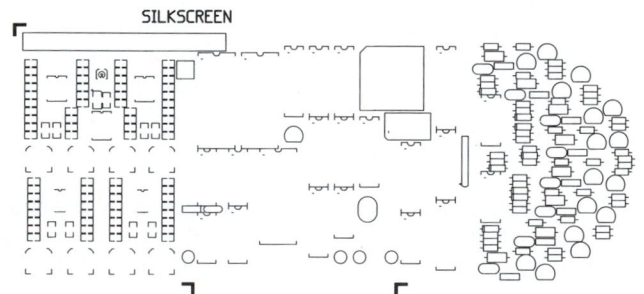

FIGURE 23.66 Silkscreen

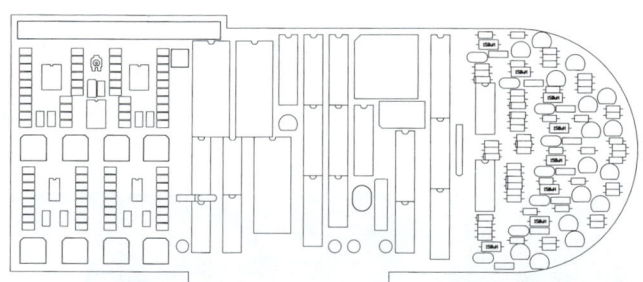

FIGURE 23.67 Component and Board Outline

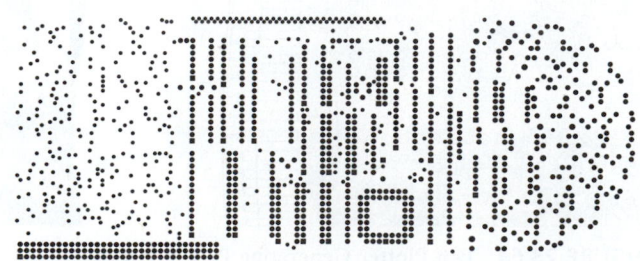

FIGURE 23.68 Drill Drawing

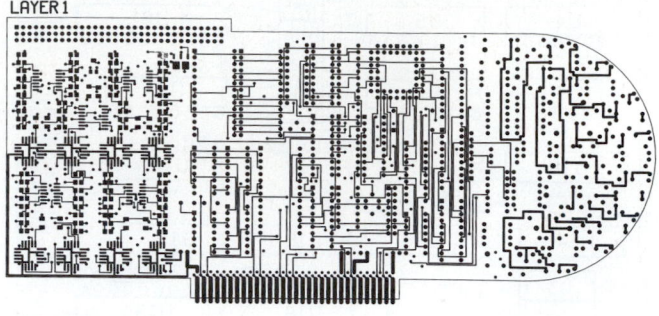

FIGURE 23.69 Layer 1

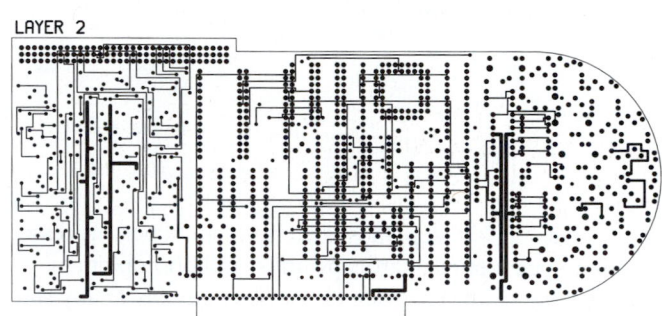

FIGURE 23.70 Layer 2

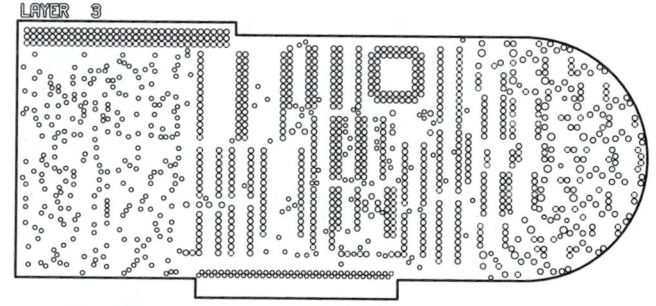

FIGURE 23.71 Layer 3

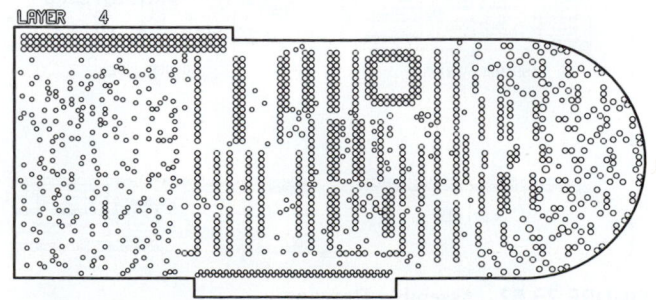

FIGURE 23.72 Layer 4

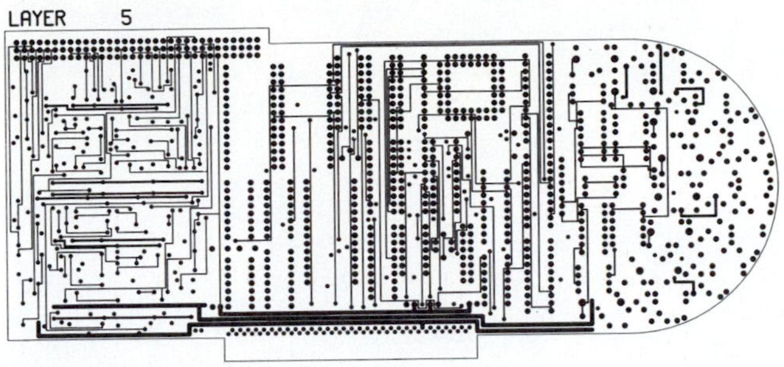

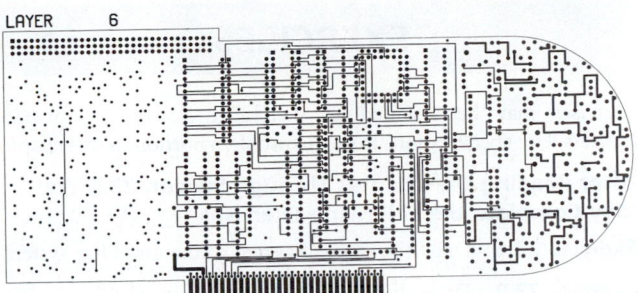

FIGURE 23.73   Layer 5

FIGURE 23.74   Layer 6

QUIZ

True or False

1. Many PCB CAD packages allow for autoplacement and auto-route of printed circuit boards.
2. Once stored in memory, symbols cannot be recalled.
3. Some systems can automatically generate a parts list.
4. Attributes are special drawing entities that contain text.
5. Once a symbol has been placed on a diagram it cannot be moved or reoriented.
6. A symbol is a graphical representation of a standard part.
7. Most electronic drafting and design is completed with a CAD system.
8. Logic diagrams are the first document used to design and lay out a printed circuit board.

Fill in the Blanks

9. The electronics industry does not make extensive use of _____ .
10. Diagram lines represent _____ on an electronic diagram.
11. In electronics, most drawings are made up of _____ .
12. Different line weights can also be used to _____ .
13. All electronic design software is designed to automatically place electronic _____ from a menu.
14. Automatic _____ _____ allows the designer to lay out the PCB on user-defined grid networks.
15. The placement of a previously created symbol onto a drawing is called a _____ _____ .
16. A _____ _____ does not require a _____ _____ in contrast to a cable.

Answer the Following

17. What is automatic routing and how does it help the PC designer?
18. Name four types of drawings that can be generated by CAD-printed circuit design software.
19. Explain how a symbol library can increase efficiency in the drawing task.
20. Explain how attributes are used to create a parts list.
21. Explain how a symbol library is created.
22. List the reference designations for the following components: resistors, capacitors, transistors, diodes, integrated circuits, transformers, inductors.
23. Name all the drawings that are normally a part of a PCB documentation package.
24. What is the primary use of a harness diagram?

EXERCISES

Exercises may be assigned as sketching, instrument, or CAD projects. Use specifications from the problem portion in this chapter.

After Reading the Chapter Through Section 23.5 You May Complete the Following Exercises

Exercise 23.1 Draw the block diagram of the amplifier system.

Exercise 23.2 Draw the functional block diagram.

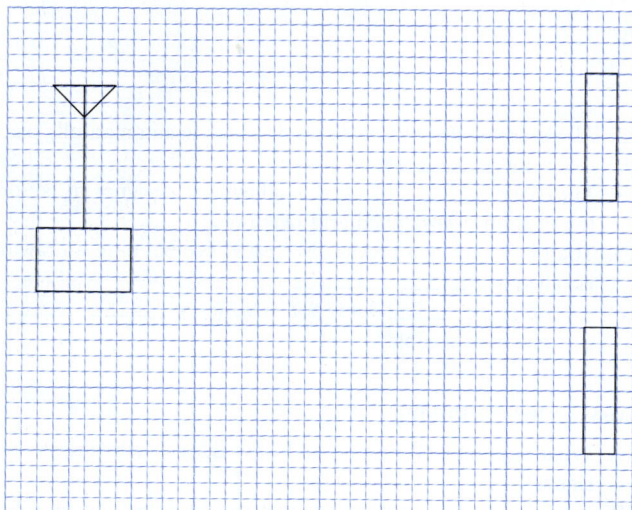

Exercise 23.1

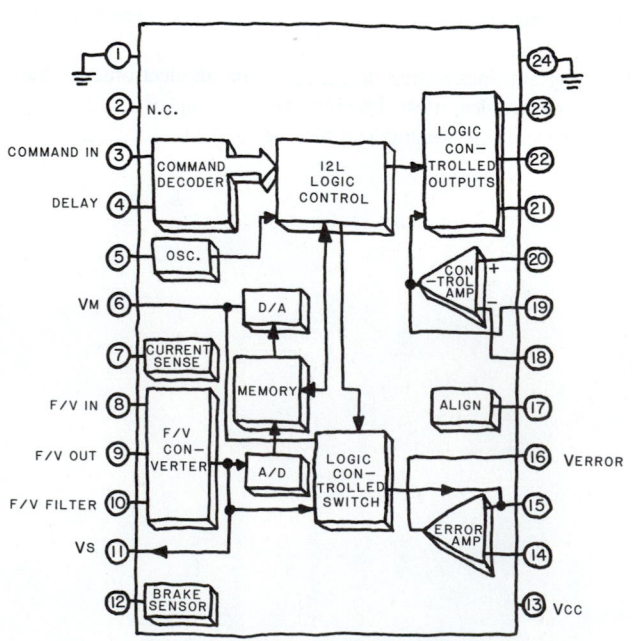

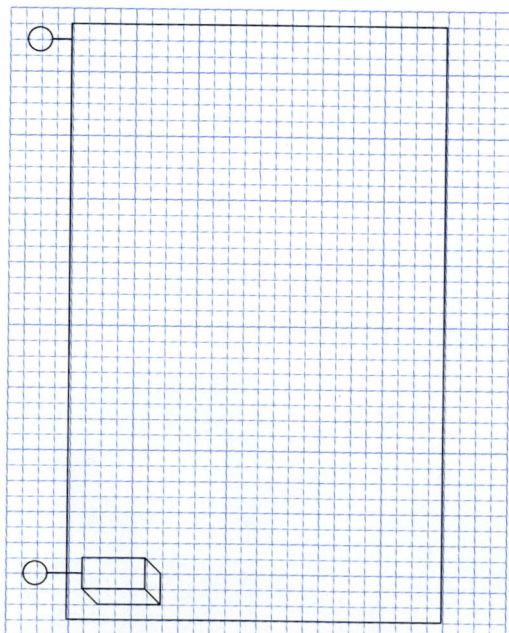

Exercise 23.2

After Reading the Chapter Through Section 23.6.2 You May Complete the Following Exercises

Exercise 23.3 Draw the shift register logic diagram.

Exercise 23.4 Draw the driver NAND gate logic diagram.

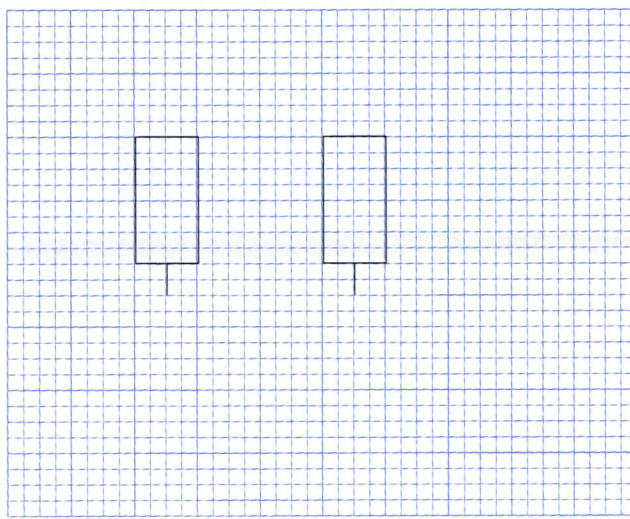

Exercise 23.3

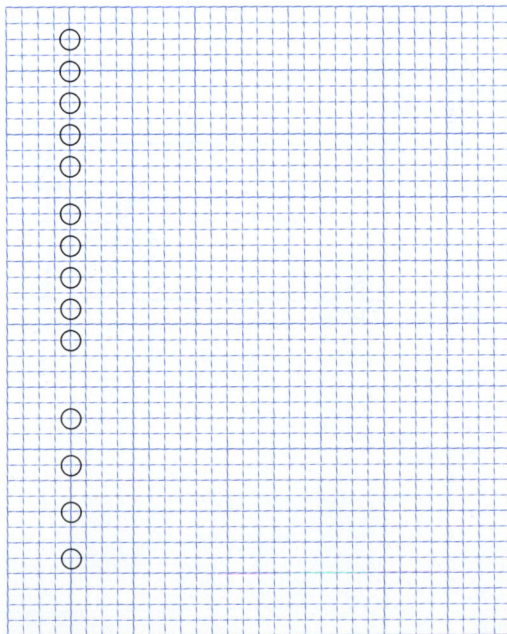

Exercise 23.4

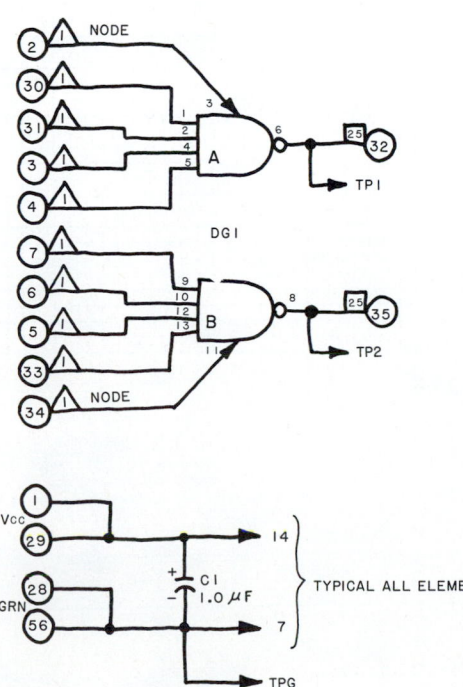

Exercise 23.5 Draw the diagram of the 16 bit random access memory.

Exercise 23.6 Draw the diagram for the line driver with three-wire complementary output—DTL.

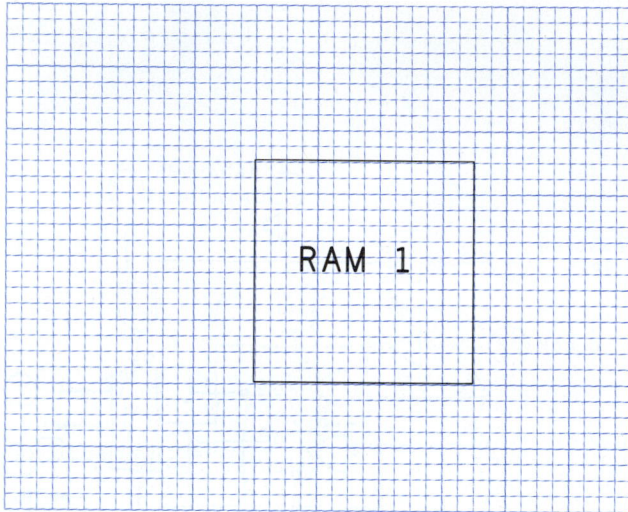

Exercise 23.5

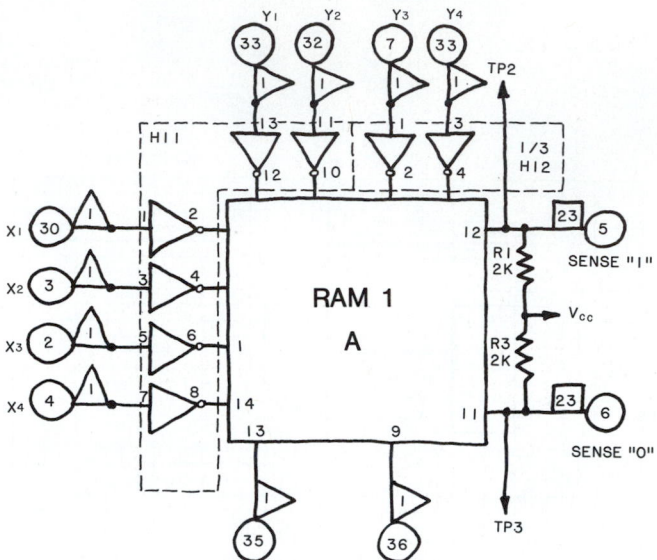

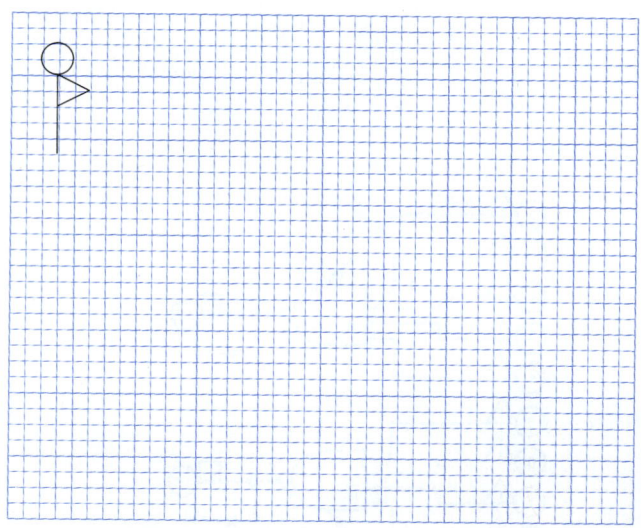

Exercise 23.6

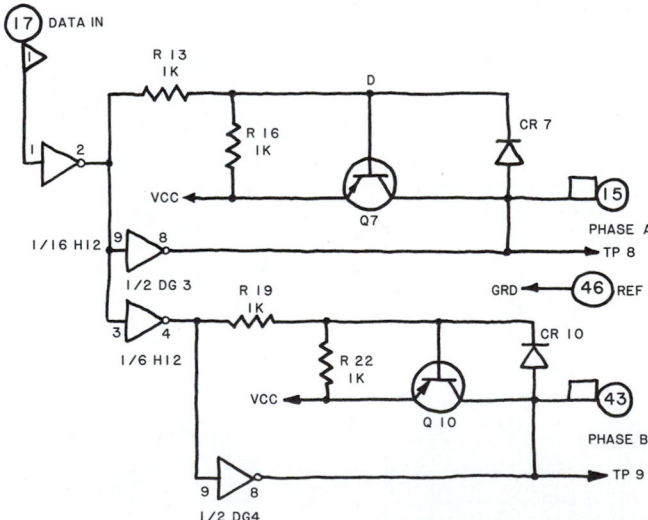

Exercise 23.7   Draw the key switch wiring diagram.

Exercise 23.8   Lay out the wiring diagram of the HV switch.

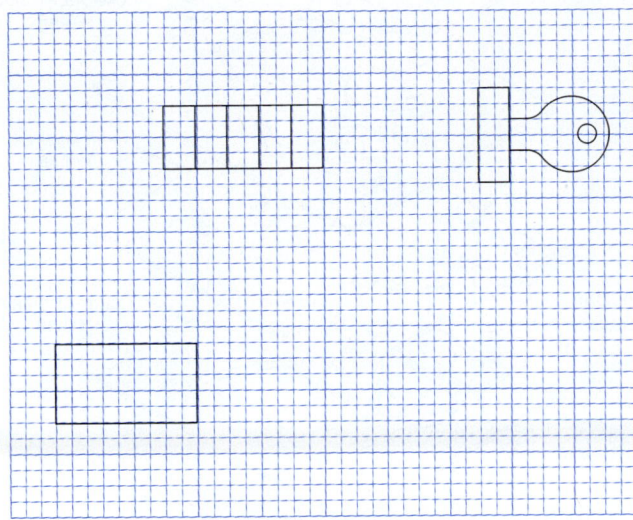

Exercise 23.7

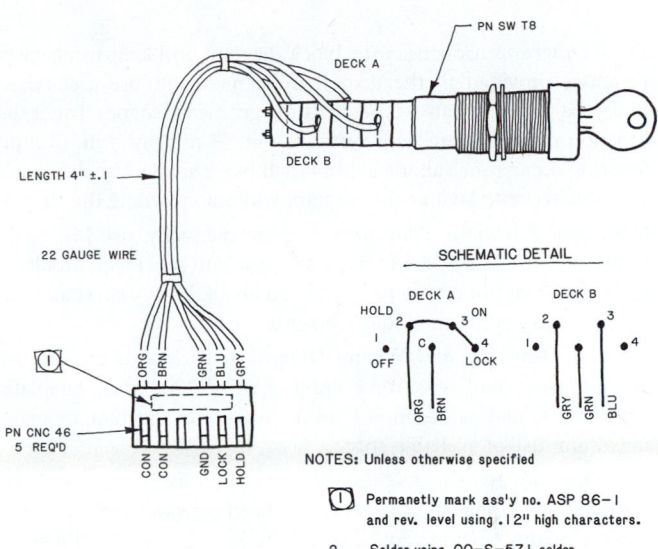

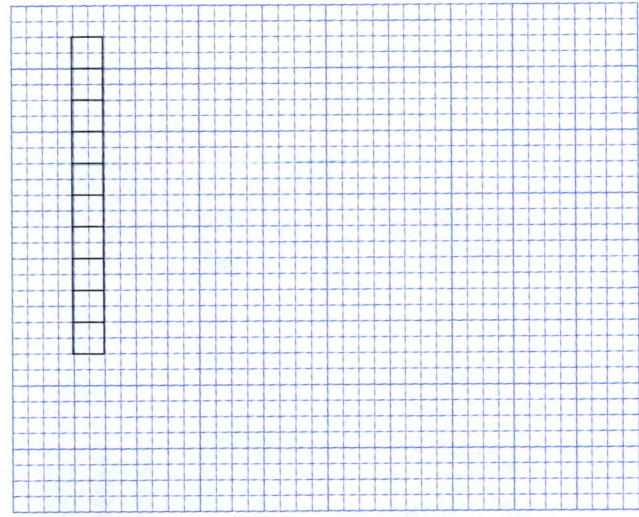

Exercise 23.8

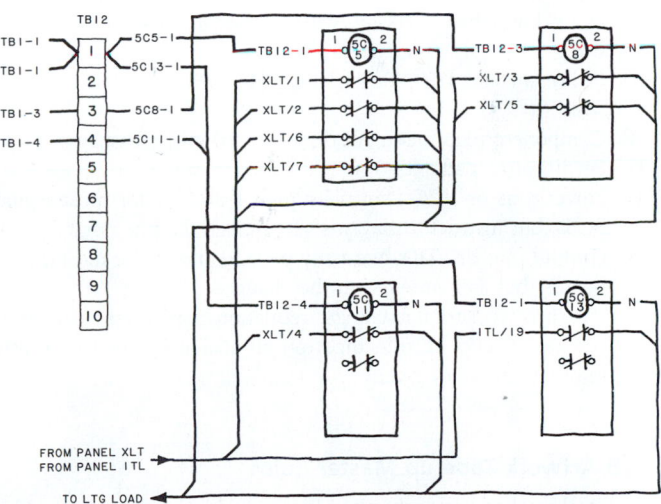

PROBLEMS

General Instructions

Problems may be assigned as sketching, instrument, or CAD projects.

Block Diagrams. Construct the block diagram problems using specifications provided in the text. If done manually, use a standard block diagram template to construct the geometric shapes. Letter the function nomenclature with vertical $\frac{5}{32}$ in. (4 mm) or $\frac{1}{8}$ in. (3 mm) lettering. Center the callouts within each block shape. Use the plate's available space to lay out the diagram without crowding the shapes.

Logic and Schematic Diagrams. If done manually, use MIL-STD-806C or ANSI STD Y32.14 template. Logic and schematic problems make excellent projects to be completed on a CAD system since each diagram has many repetitious elements.

Harness Drawings and Wiring Diagrams. If done manually, use an electrical and electronic ANSI Y32.2.200 grid template. Lettering should be $\frac{5}{32}$ in. (4 mm). Space the diagram to make maximum use of available space.

PCB Drawing and Documentation. Lay out the PCB represented by the diagrams. The board geometry has been provided for every PCB project in this section. For each of the boards use the following specifications:

A. Manual scale: 2/1; CAD scale: 1:1
B. Medium: 10 × 10 grid (nonreproducible)
C. Color code: Component side traces "blue" and solder side traces "red"
D. Trace widths: Signal lines—.015 in. wide; power/ground lines and primary bus—.100 in. wide; secondary bus lines—.050 in. wide
E. Pad diameters: .050, .062, .100, .150, .200, and .250 in. at 2/1 scale
F. Component placement: All on 10 × 10 grid crosshairs
G. Feedthrough pads: .050 in.
H. Power pins or VCC: Normally pins 1 and 31 for most digital PCBs, but instructor may wish to change the pin assignments
I. Ground pins or VDD: Normally pins 30 and 60 for most digital boards, but assignments can be changed
J. Put three registration targets, reduction marks, and reduction size (at ± .005 in. tolerance) on all analog boards where this information is not given.

PCB Artwork Tape-up Master Rules

1. Use the pad master as shown in Figure 23.75. Using prepunch .003, .005, or .007 clear film, align the film with registration pins. The film will be laid on top of the "RED" and "BLUE" layout drawing. If registration pins and prepunched film are not available, then use registration targets and register each layer of film to the layout. Place the correct size pads as required for the pad master.
2. All pads will be centered on the grid crosshairs. Apply reduction marks and dimensions as required. All reduction dimensions will have a ± .005 in. tolerance. Place three registration marks outside the board outline.
3. Put three tooling holes on each board when they are not already provided. For the following components use a square pad (Fig. 23.76): 1: transistor emitters; 2: pin 1 on all DIP packages (unless the given layout marks pin 1 with a dot or a different shape pad); 3: capacitors that are polarized (square pad for the plus

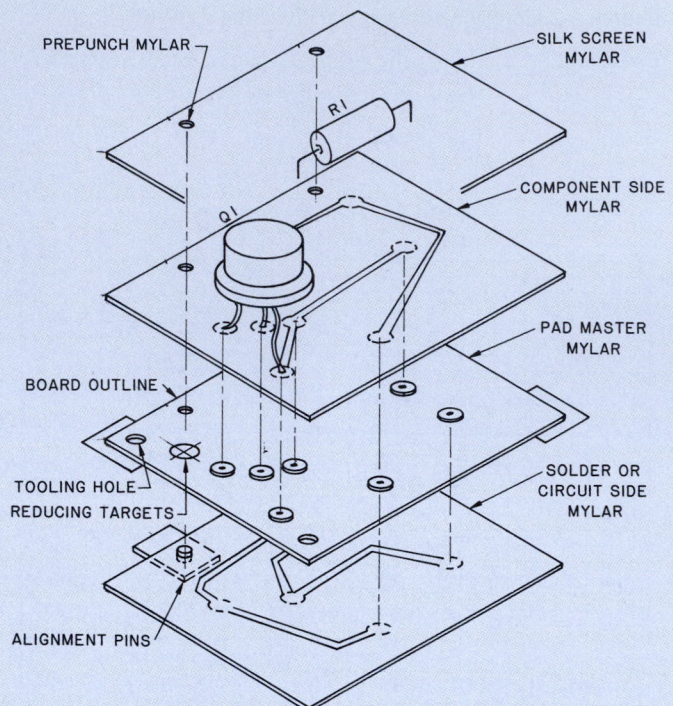

FIGURE 23.75   **Pad Master**

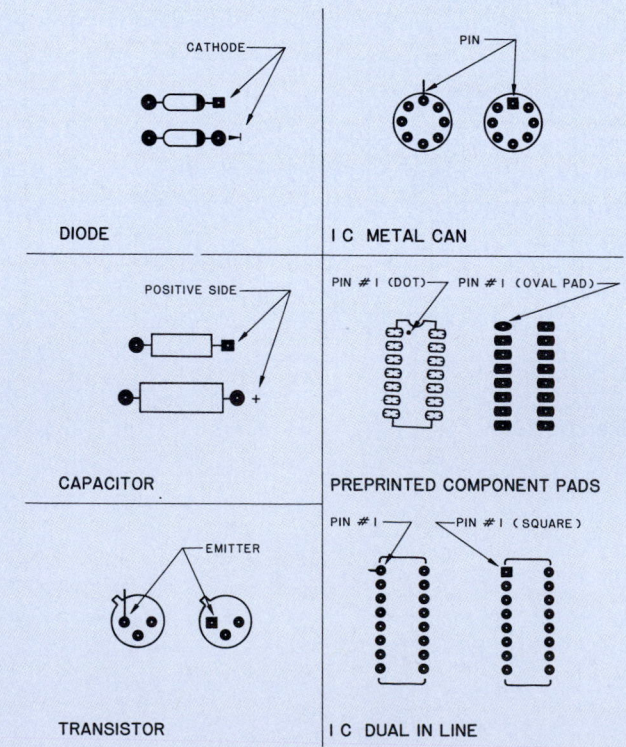

FIGURE 23.76   **Component Pads**

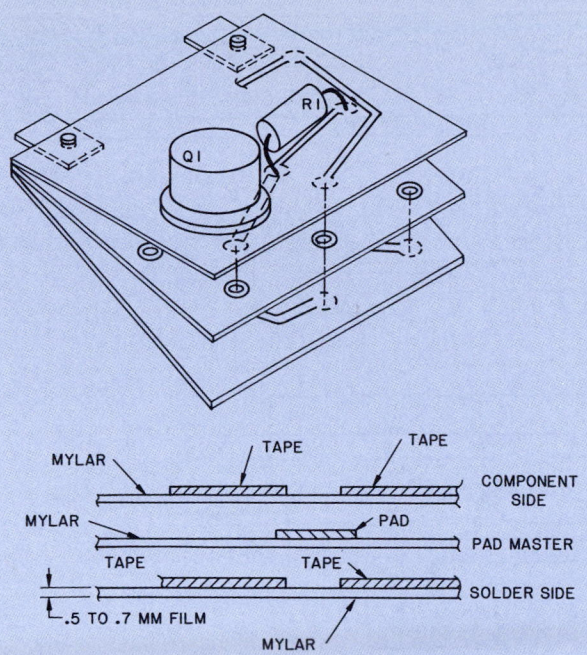

FIGURE 23.77 **PCB Tape-up**

5. **Component side** (Fig. 23.77): This is the next overlay that will be placed over the pad master. Show all "BLUE" traces that are on the layout. Show "COMPONENT SIDE" in large lettering along with the assembly number of the board if provided.
6. **Silkscreen** (Figs. 23.75 and 23.77): This will be the last overlay to be placed on the pad master. It will show the location of all components and reference designations.

Board Fabrication Rules

1. A board fabrication drawing shows the board geometry, dimensions, and tolerances.
2. Note the board material—G10 or G10-FR or another material.
3. A table showing hole diameters, tolerance, and number of holes should be included on the drawing. Code the holes so that they can be identified on the circuit side of the board.
4. Include the name and number and any other specifications that may apply to the part.
5. The circuit side pattern images should be shown with all traces and pads. Holes are drilled from the circuit side of the board.
6. If the board is multilayer, each layer should be indicated on a cross-section view of the board with thickness and tolerance given.

PCB Assembly Drawing Rules

1. The assembly drawing should show component placement and reference designation markings and assembly and test specifications. Include a list of materials to be ordered.
2. The assembly drawing is viewed from the component side of the board.
3. Orientation and indexing of all transistor tabs, polarized capacitors, diodes, variable resistors, DIP packages, and connector pin 1 and every tenth pin should be indicated.
4. All specifications should be included in the notes on this drawing.

Problem 23.1   Using the block diagram sketch of the telecommunications system, draw a finalized block diagram on a "B" size vellum.

side); 4: cathode end for diodes; 5: wiper side for variable resistors; 6: pin 1 on sips resistor packs; 7: jumper wires. The pad master will have the board geometry shown on it.
4. **Solder side** (Fig. 23.77): This is the next overlay that will be placed on or under the pad master. Show all "RED" traces on this overlay. Show the following on this layout: "SOLDER SIDE" in large letters, board part number, board revision letter, and serial number.

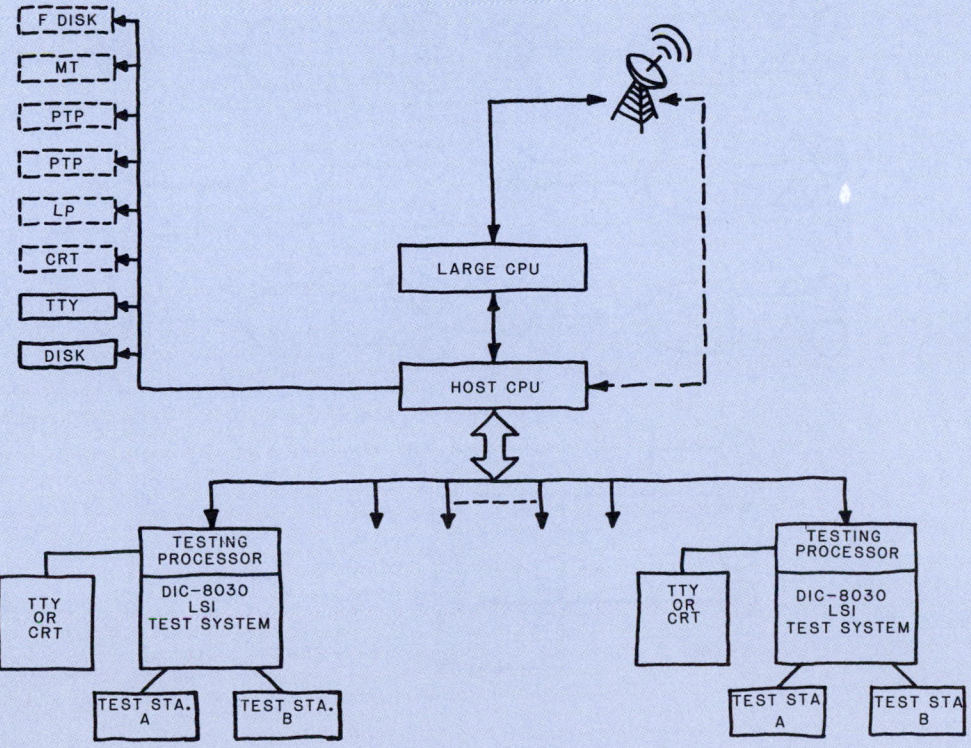

Problem 23.1

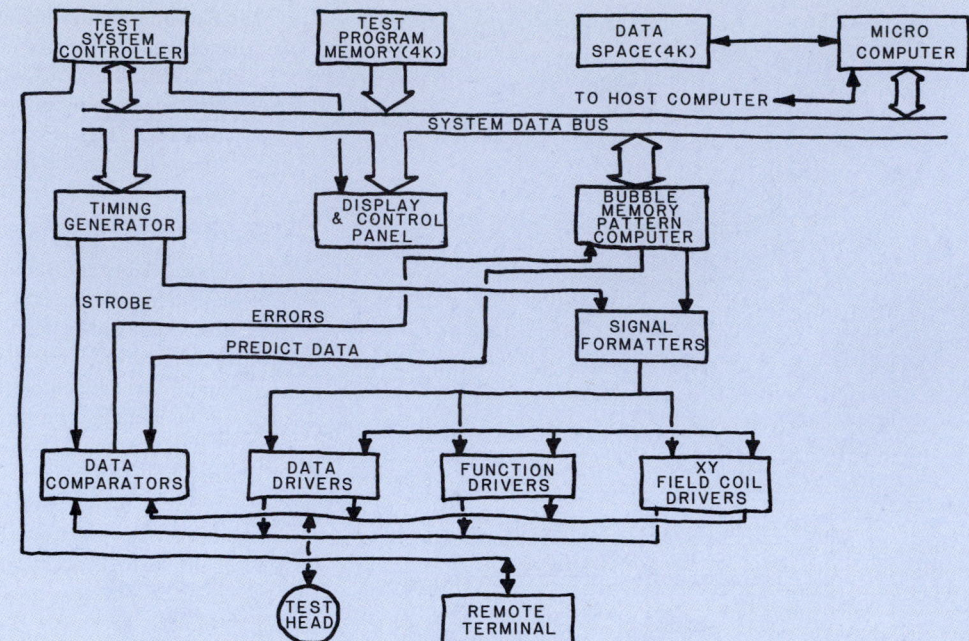

Problem 23.2 Draw the magnetic-bubble test system block diagram on a "B" size sheet.

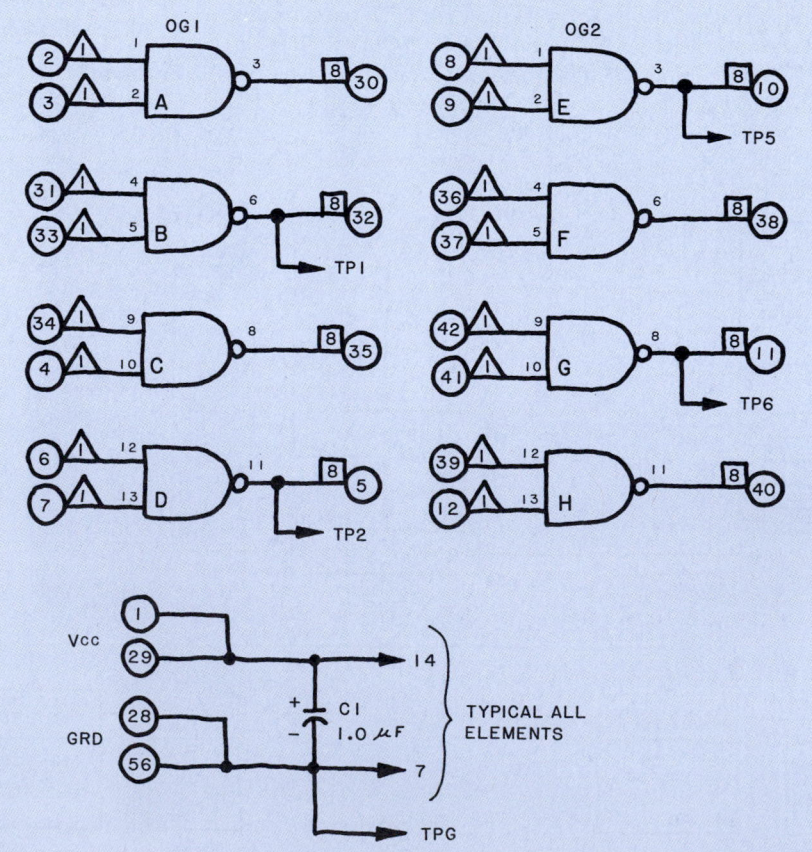

Problem 23.3 Draw the logic diagram using ANSI STD Y32.14 logic template on a "B" size sheet.

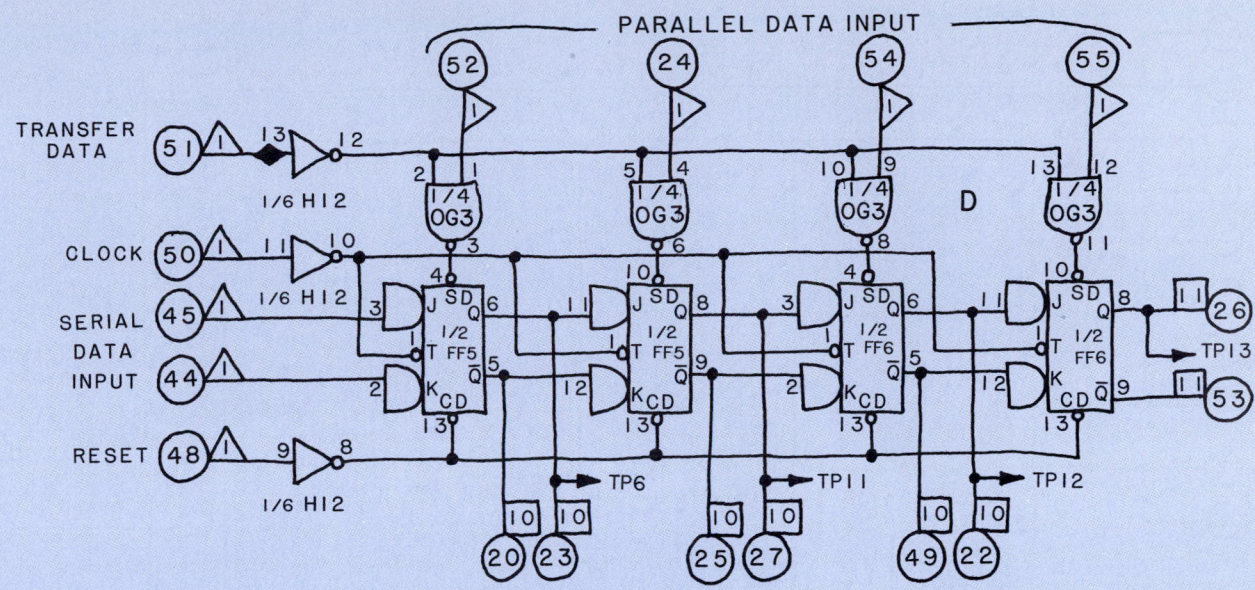

Problem 23.4   Complete the shift register logic diagram. Use a "B" size 10 × 10 fade-out grid vellum paper.

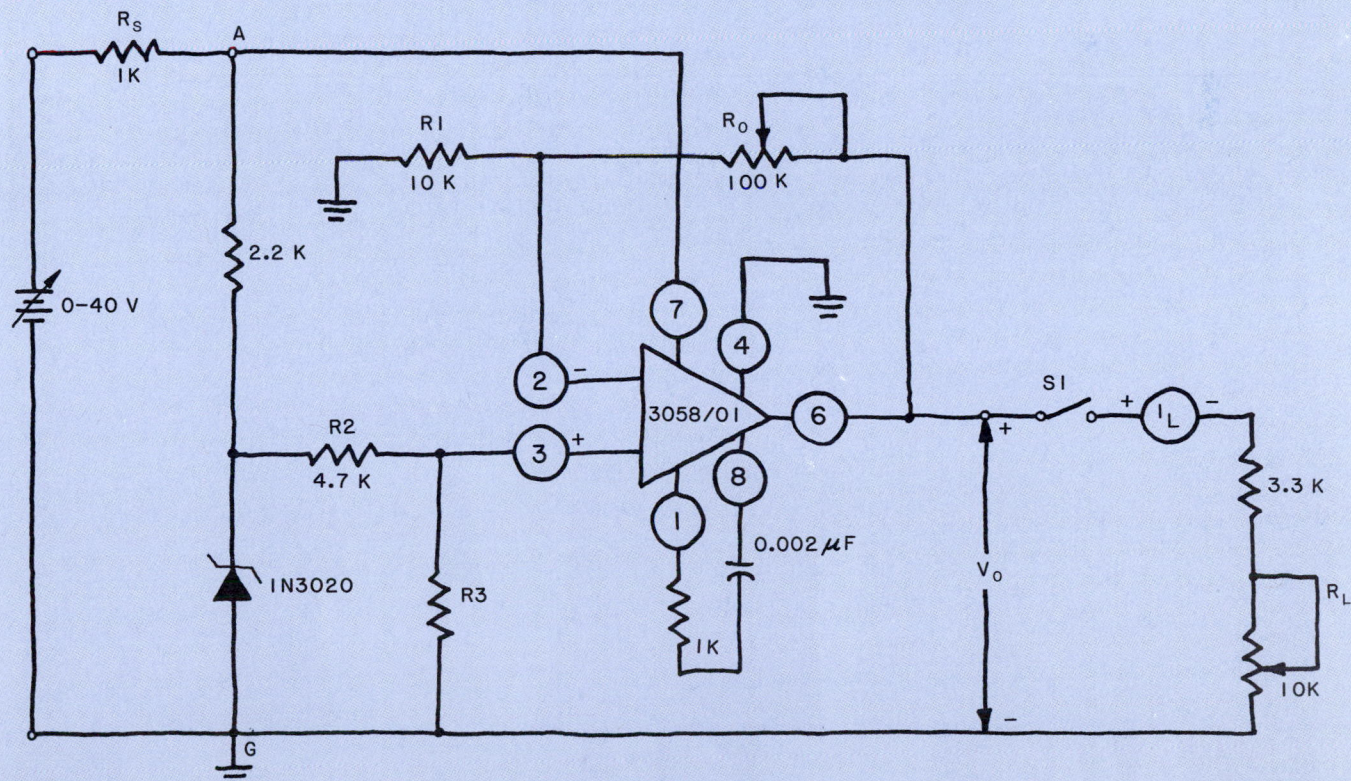

Problem 23.5   Using the ANSI STD Y32.2 electronic template, draw a finalized schematic diagram on "B" size 10 × 10 grid vellum.

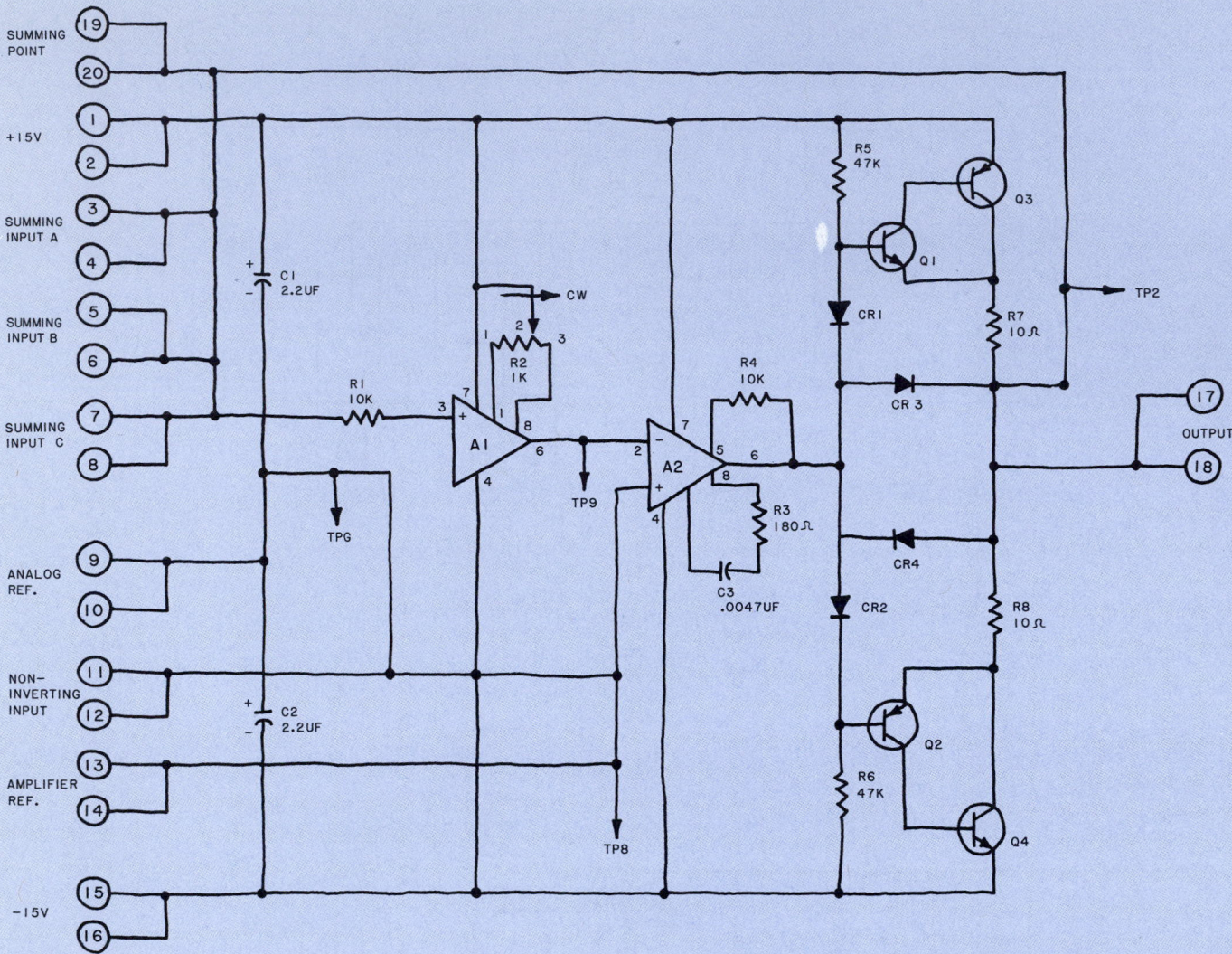

Problem 23.6   Using the sketch, draw the universal operational amplifier schematic diagram using a "C" size sheet.

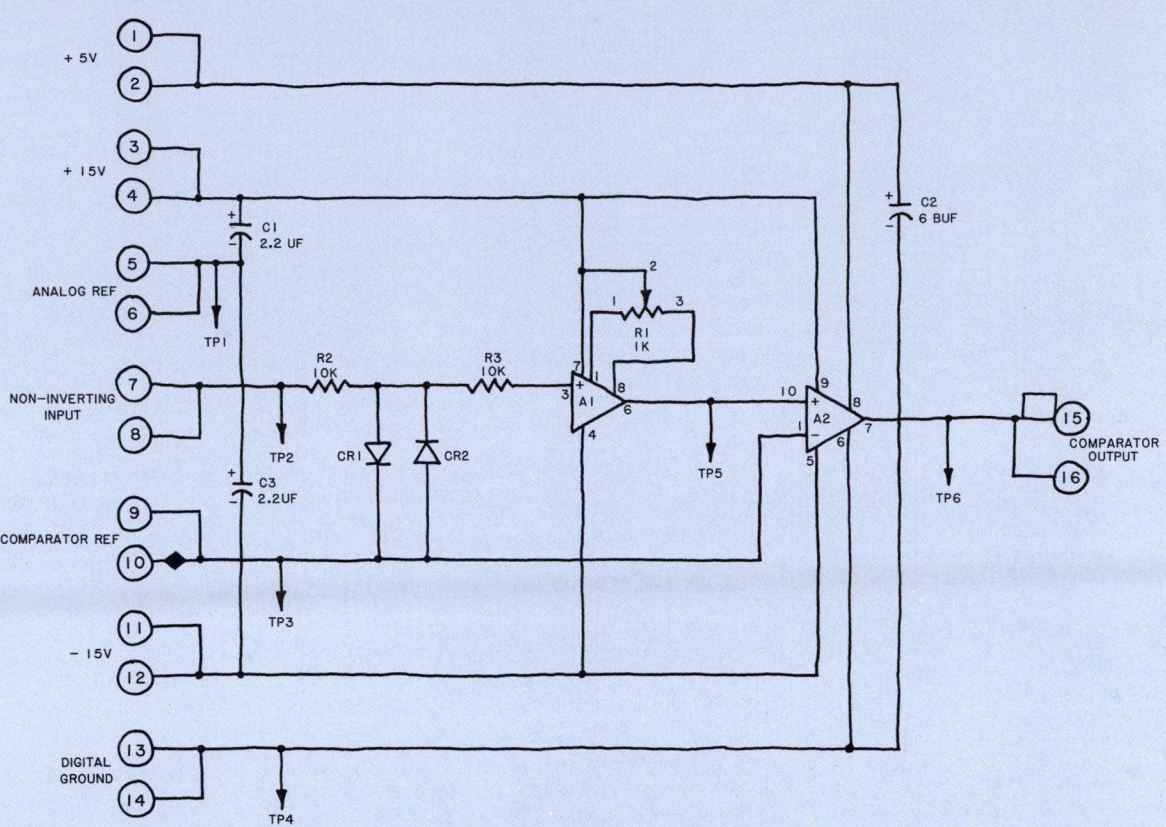

Problem 23.7 Finalize the high-speed analog comparator schematic using a "B" size sheet.

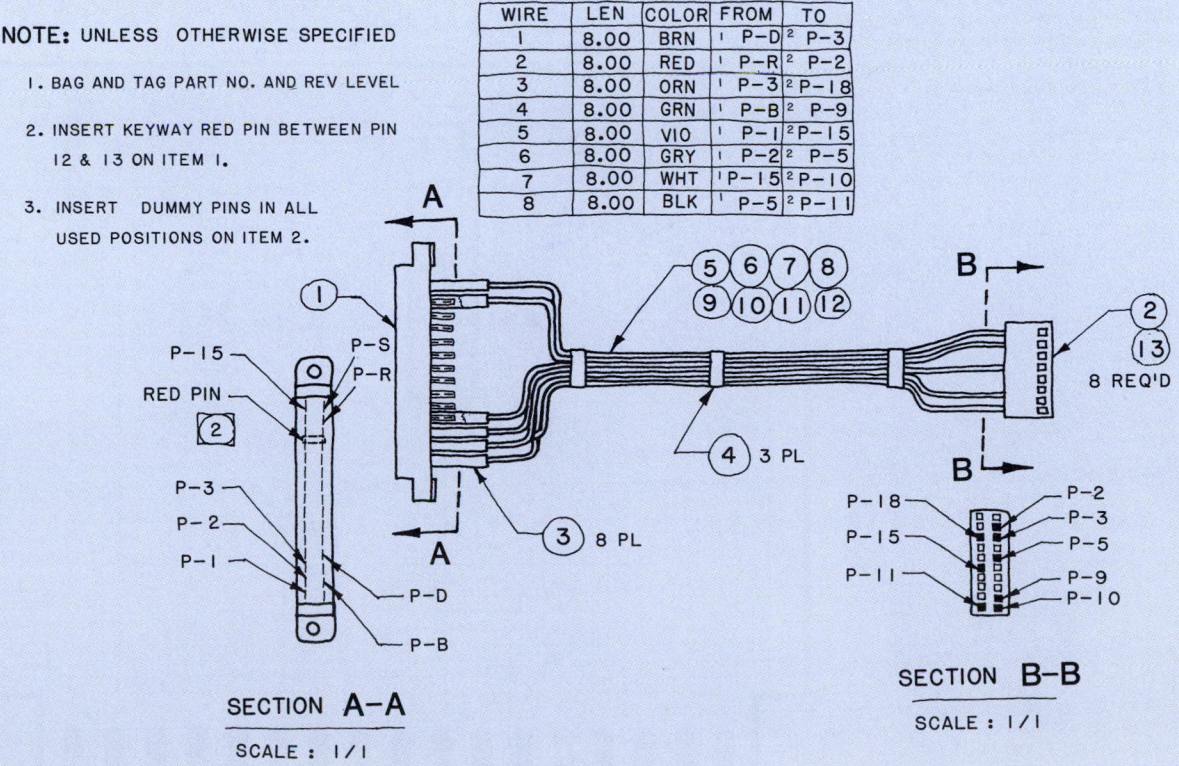

Problem 23.8 Redraw the harness assembly at 2:1 scale.

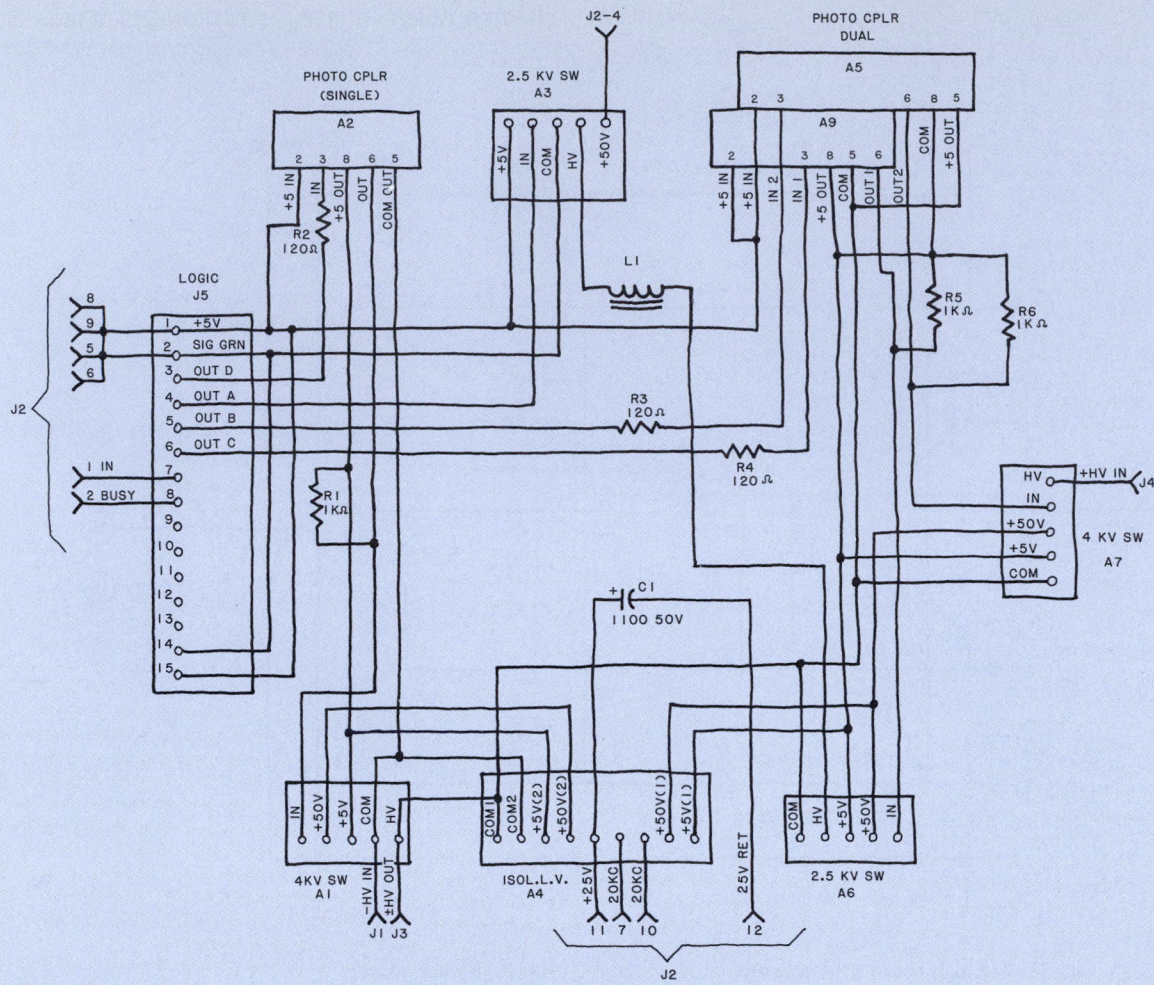

Problem 23.9   Lay out the wiring diagram on "C" size vellum.

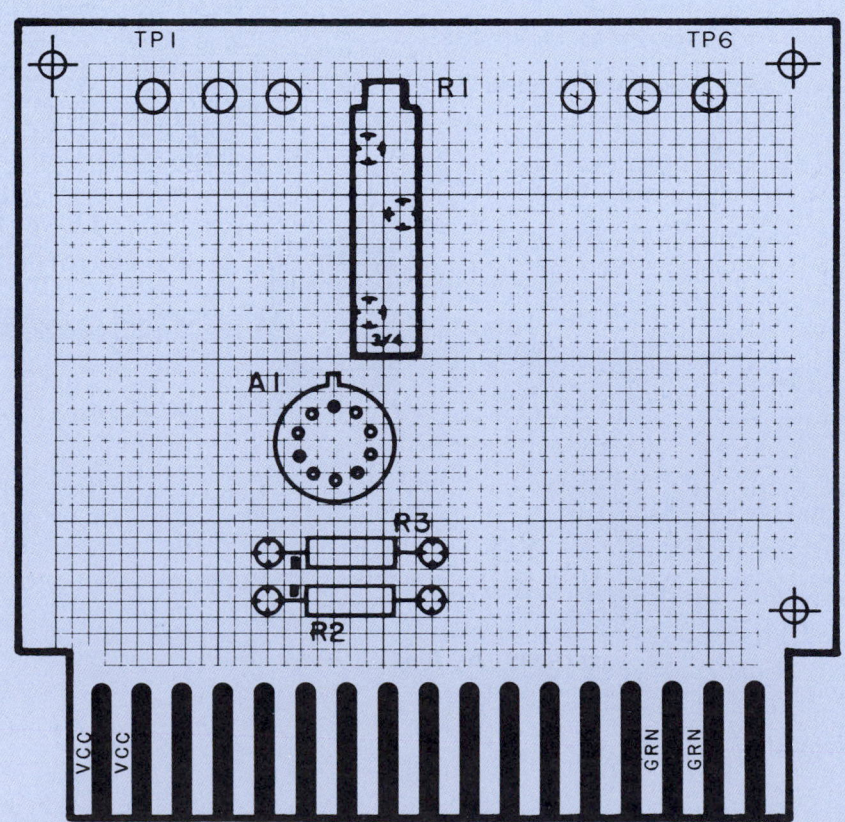

Problem 23.10   Using the schematic in Problem 23.7, create a layout of the printed circuit board.

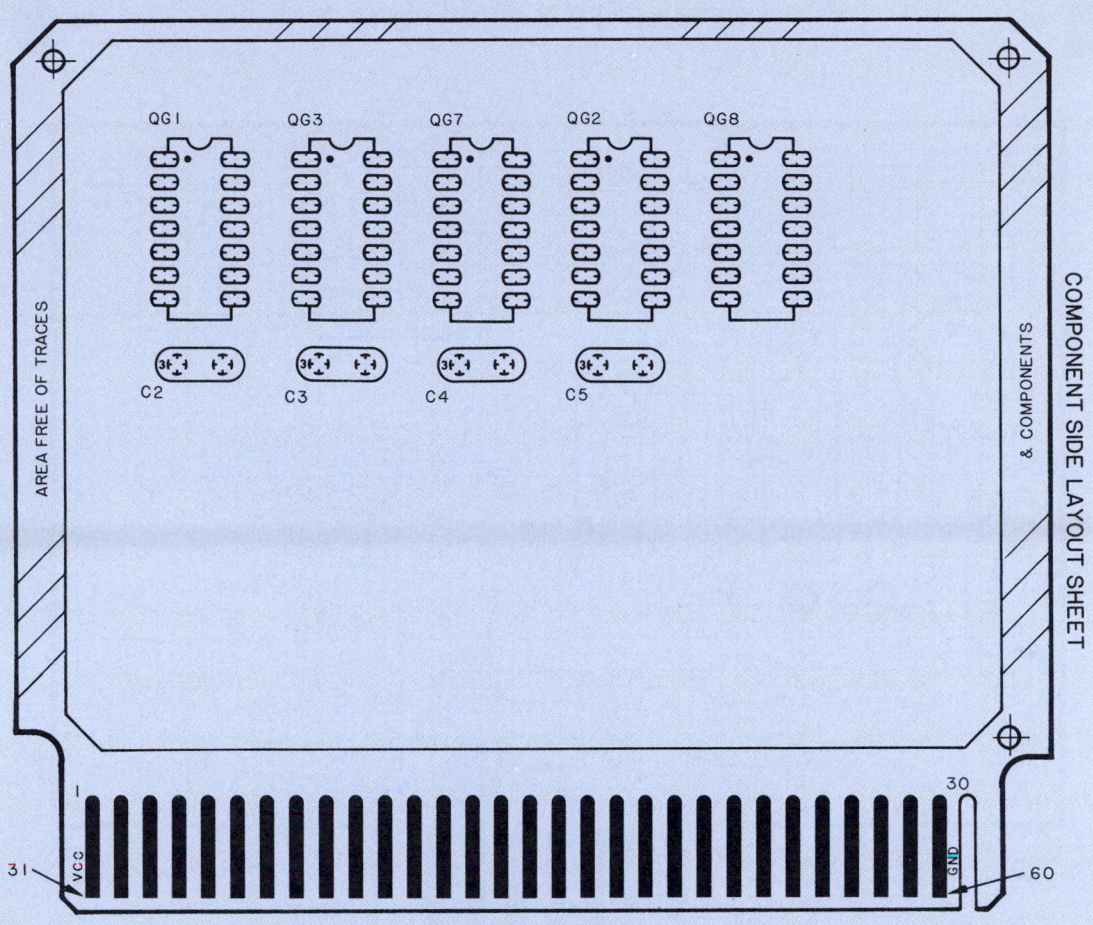

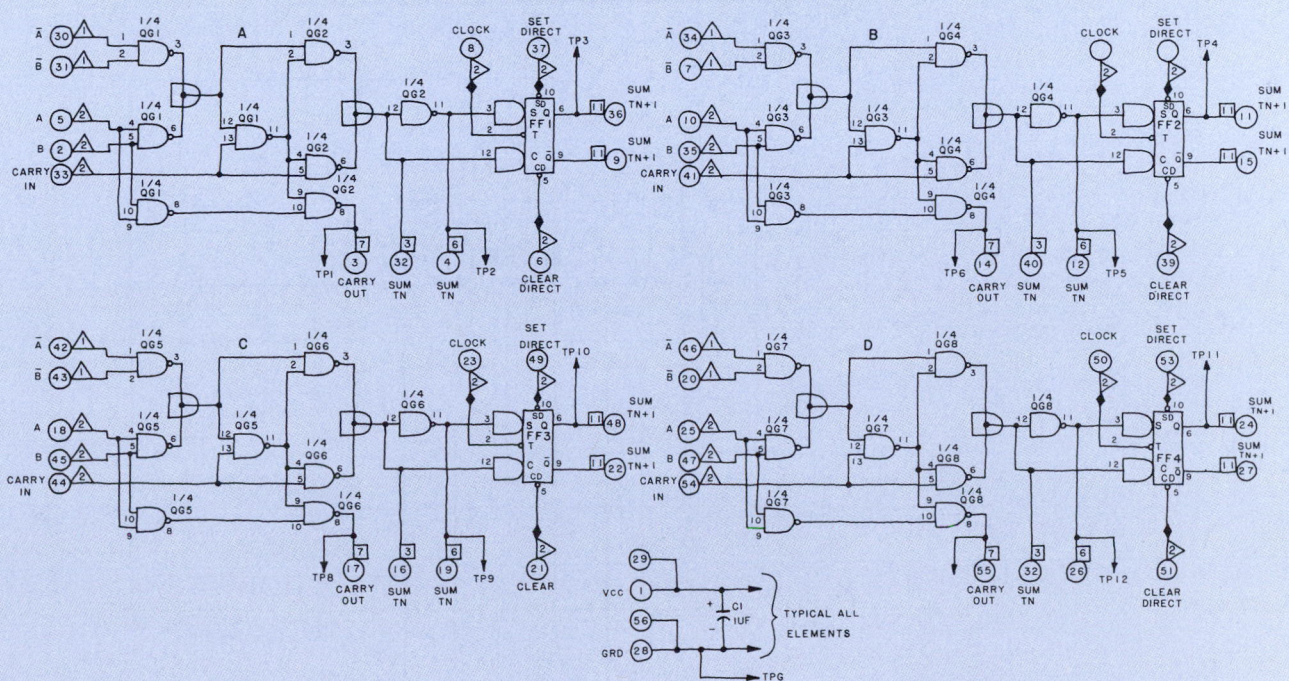

Problem 23.11 Clock storage

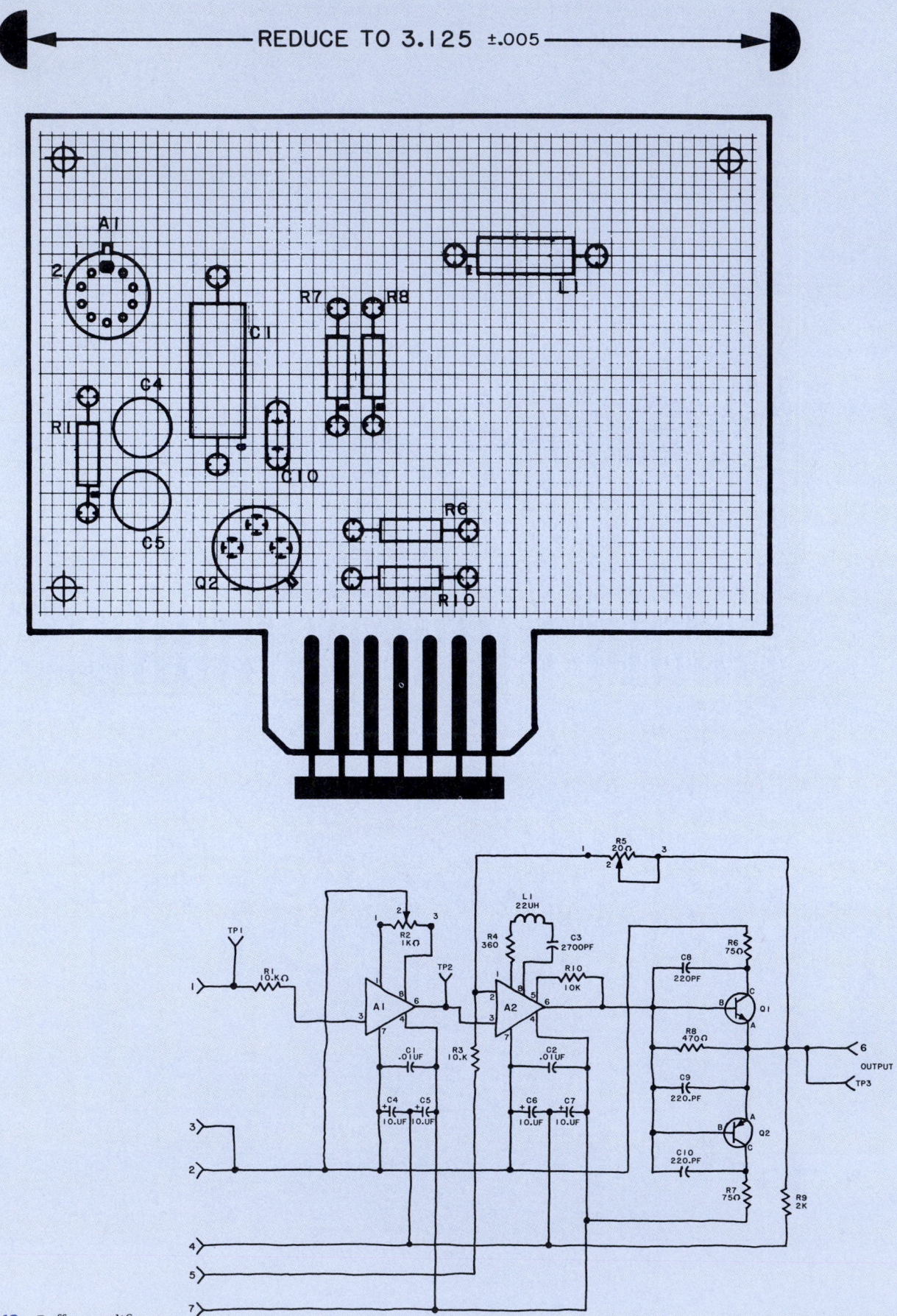

Problem 23.12 Buffer amplifier

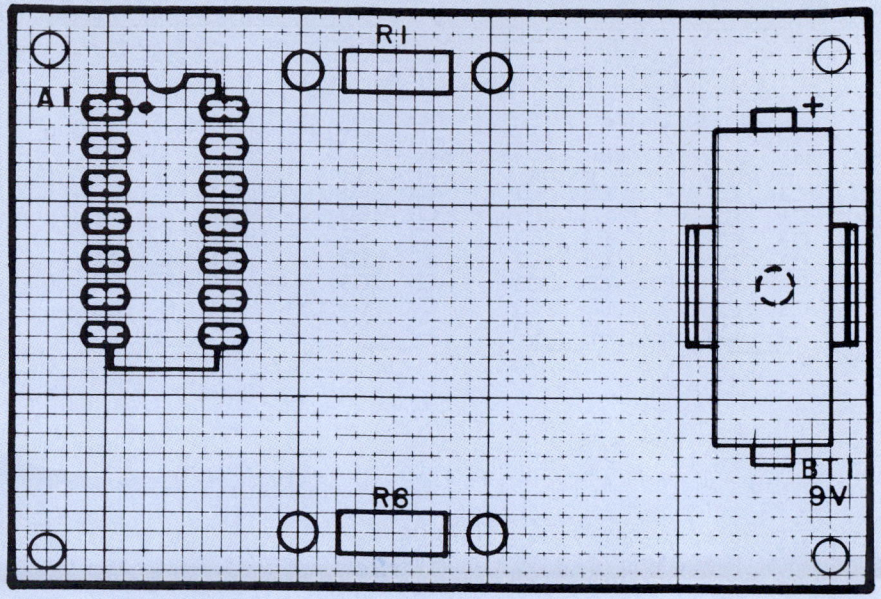

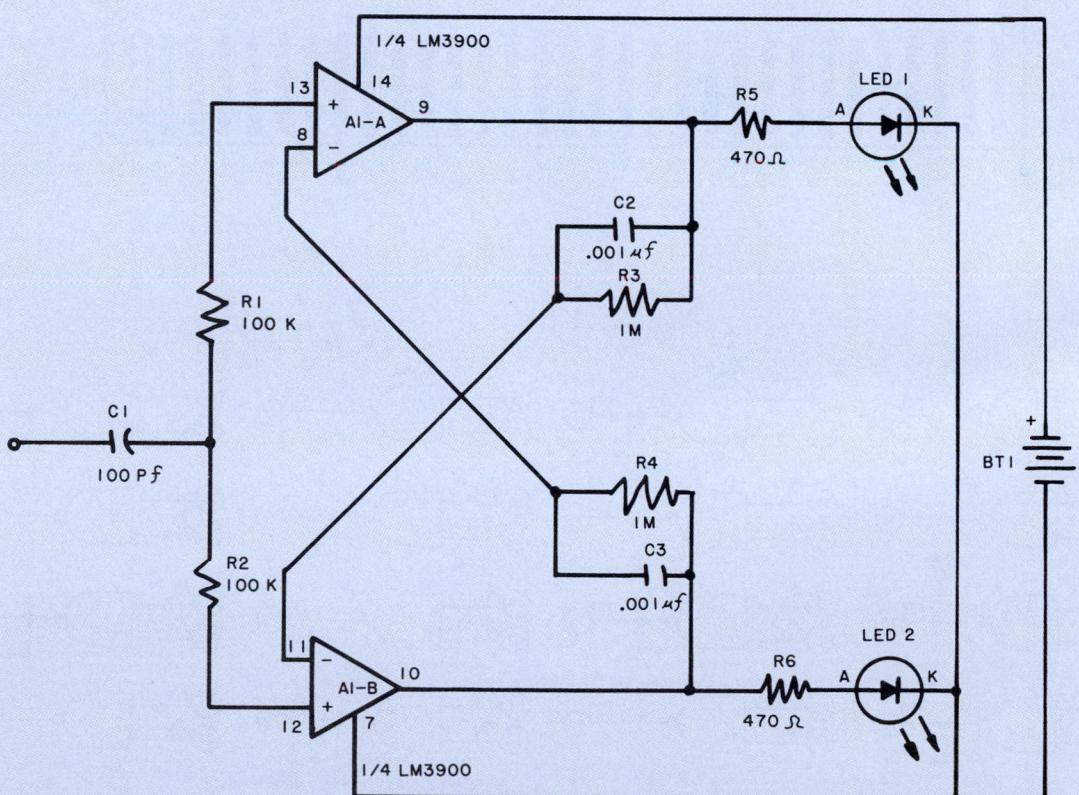

Problem 23.13 Flasher circuit

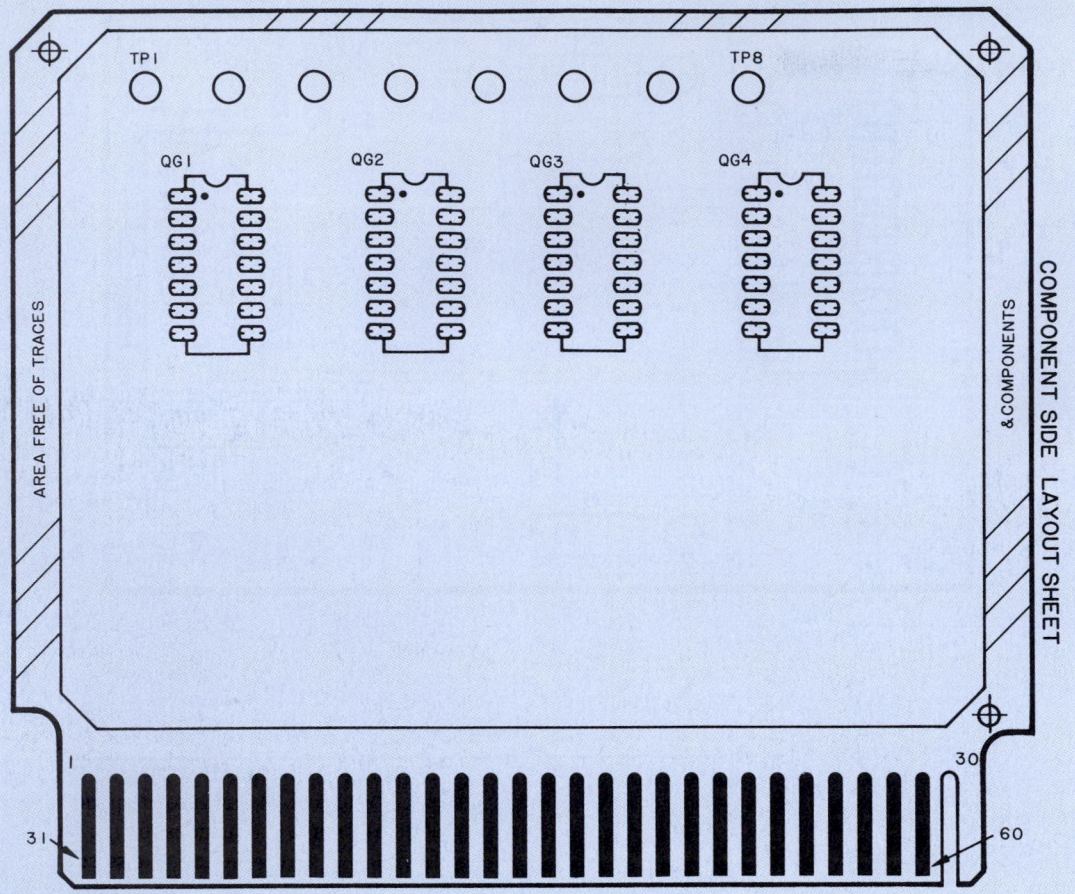

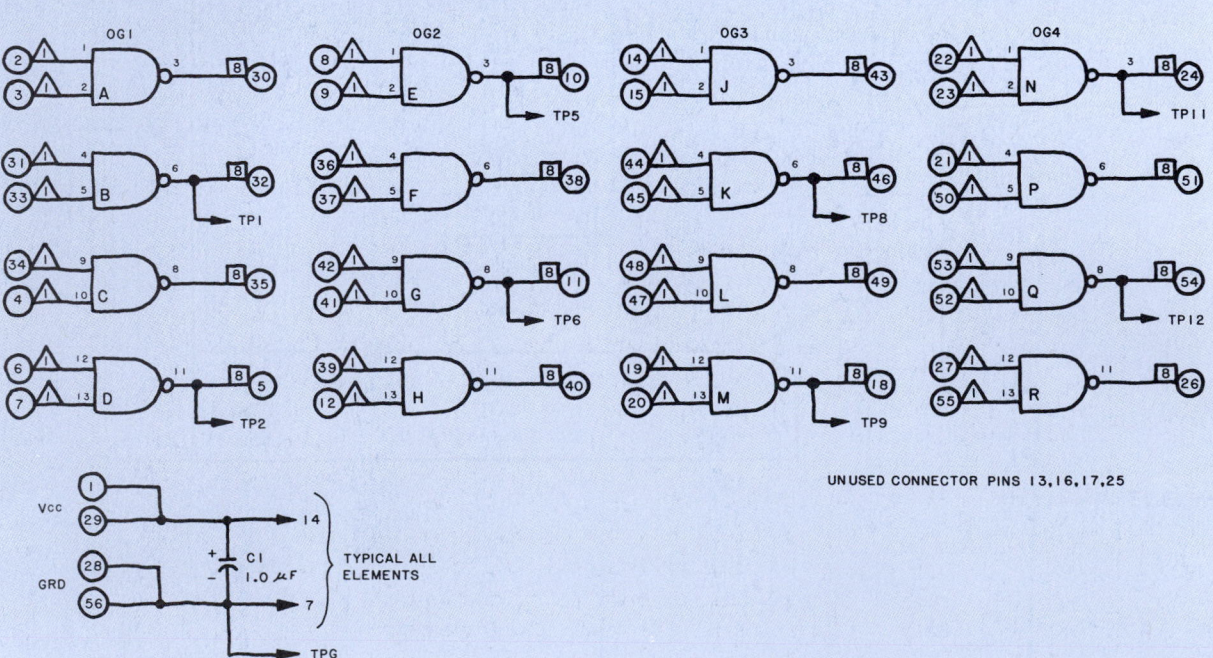

Problem 23.14 Input NAND gates—DTL

APPENDIX A

Glossaries

Mechanical Glossary

A

Accurate   Manufactured within the specified tolerances.

Acme thread   A screw thread similar to the square thread. The acme has in most cases replaced the square thread because it is stronger and easier to manufacture. It is widely used as a feed screw.

Acme thread

Addendum   The radial distance between the top of the tooth and the pitch circle of a gear.

Allen screw   Special set screw or cap screw with hexagon socket in head.

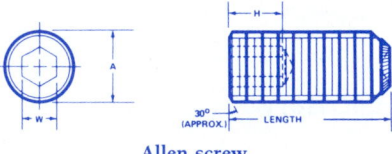

Allen screw

Allowance   The intentional difference between the MMC limits of size of mating parts; the minimum clearance (positive allowance) or maximum interference (negative allowance) between such parts.

Alloy   A mixture of two or more metals to obtain characteristics similar to the individual metals or different from any displayed by the individual components.

Aluminum   A lightweight but strong metal. Principle commercial source is bauxite ore.

Annealing   A process of heating steel above the critical range, holding it at that temperature until it is uniformly heated and the grain is refined, and then cooling it very slowly.

ANSI   American National Standards Institute. A nongovernmental organization that proposes, modifies, approves, and publishes drafting and manufacturing standards for voluntary use in the United States.

Arc   A continuous portion (as of a circle or ellipse) of a curved line.

Arc

Arc welding   A process of joining two or more metal parts together by fusing them with an electric arc. The arc melts the welding rod and fuses the parts together.

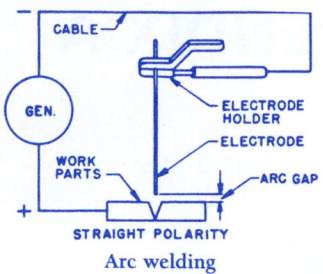

Arc welding

Assembly drawing   A drawing representing a group of parts constituting a major subdivision of the final product.

Auxiliary view   Any view that lies in a projection plane other than the horizontal (top), frontal (front), or profile (side) plane.

Axis   A straight line (centerline) about which a feature of revolution revolves; or about which opposite-hand features are symmetrical.

Axonometric   One of several forms of single-plane projections giving the pictorial effect of perspective with the possibility of measuring the principal planes directly.

B

Basic dimension   A numerical value used to describe the theoretically exact size, profile, orientation, or location of a feature or datum target. It is the basis from which permissible variations are established by tolerances on other dimensions, in notes, or in feature control frames.

Bearing   A machine part in which another part turns or slides.

Bend allowance   The amount of sheet metal required to make a bend of a specific radius.

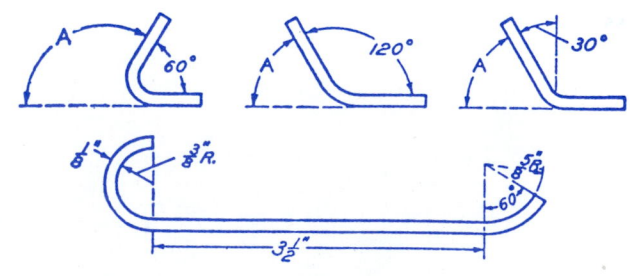

Bend allowance

Bevel   The angle that one surface or line makes with another when they are not at right angles.

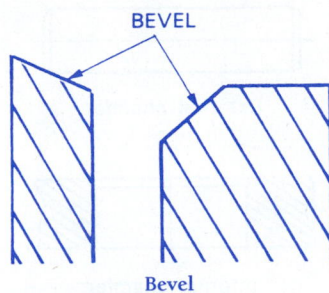

Bevel

Bilateral tolerance   A tolerance in which variation is permitted in both directions from the specified dimension.

Blanking   A punch press operation that consists of shearing from sheet metal stock a part having a definite contour determined by the punch and die.

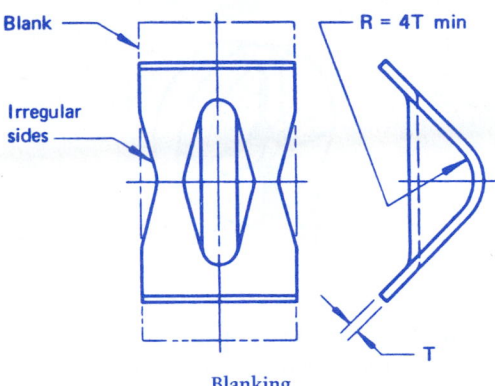

Blanking

Bolt   A headed and externally threaded mechanical device designed for insertion through holes in assembled parts. It mates with a nut and is normally intended to be tightened or released by turning that nut.

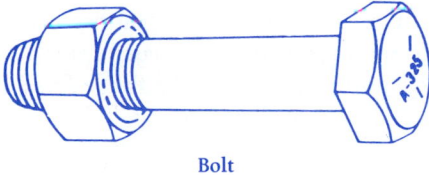

Bolt

Bolt circle   A circular centerline on a drawing; contains the centers of holes about a common center.

Bore   To enlarge a hole to a specified size by employing a point tool held in a boring bar operated by a lathe or a boring mill.

Boss   A circular raised portion of material added around holes in castings or forgings to give strength or bearing surface to the part.

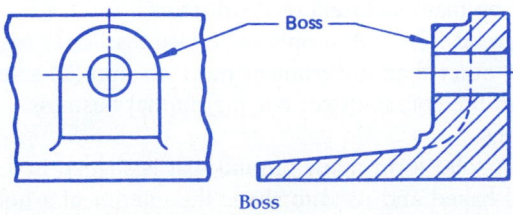

Boss

Brass   An alloy of copper and zinc.

Brazing   A group of welding processes wherein coalescence is produced by heating to a temperature above 800°F and by using a nonferrous filler metal (solder) having a melting point below that of the base metals (zinc or brass).

Brinell   A testing method to determine hardness of metal.

Broaching   To machine a hole to a desired shape by planing it with a transverse cutting tool moved in a straight line so that each tooth removes a definite amount of stock.

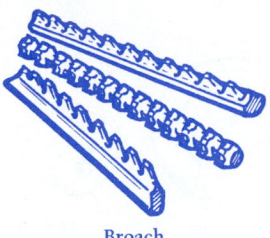

Broach

Bronze   An alloy of nine parts copper and one part tin.

Buffing   A polishing operation using a fine abrasive wheel made of discs of cotton or wool impregnated with very fine abrasive, bonded with wax or grease.

Burnishing   Smoothly finishing surfaces by compressing with the use of highly polished rolls or by the use of steel balls in rolling contact with the surface.

Burr   A rough edge raised on metal along the path of a cutting tool.

Bushing   A removable cylindrical sleeve used as a lining of low-friction material that provides a bearing surface. It is either press fitted or removable and provides accurate and quick location of the drilling operation when used in a drill jig.

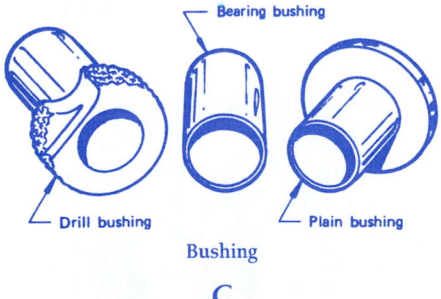

Bushing

C

Caliper   A measuring tool used for checking outside or inside measurements.

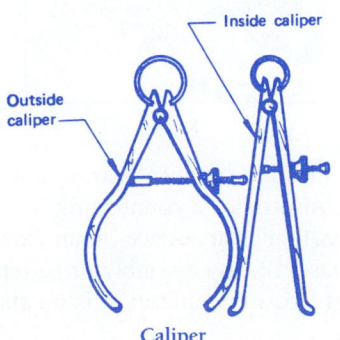

Caliper

Callout   A note on a drawing giving a dimension, specification, or manufacturing process.

Cam   A mechanical device used on a rotating shaft to transform rotary motion into lateral motion. A face cam is designed so that the follower travels in a groove cut in the face of the cam. A barrel cam is designed with a groove cut in the outer surface of a cylinder to give motion in a direction parallel to the axis of rotation. A disc cam is designed so that the follower travels along its periphery.

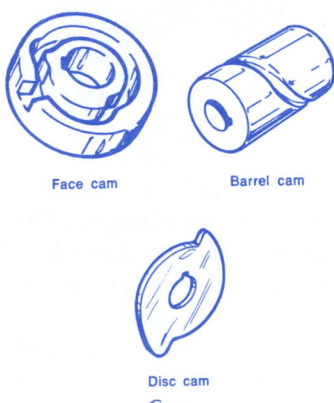

Face cam   Barrel cam

Disc cam
Cam

Carburize   To harden the surface of iron-based alloys by heating the metal below its melting point in contact with solids, liquids, or gases that have a high carbon content. Carburizing is best performed on steels containing less than 0.25% carbon content.

Case-harden   To harden a surface either by carburizing or through the use of potassium cyanide.

Cast   To produce parts by pouring molten material into a mold.

Cast

Center drill   A drill to produce bearing holes in the ends of a workpiece. Also called a countersink.

Chamfer   A small angular surface on an external edge or corner for purposes of easy assembly or to remove sharp edges. The most frequent application is on shafts and cylinders.

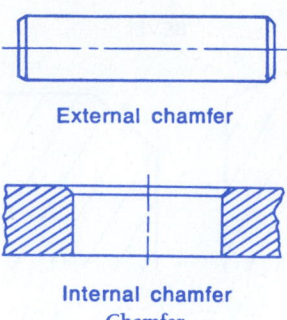

External chamfer

Internal chamfer
Chamfer

Chill   To harden the outer surface of a casting by quick cooling.

Chuck   A mechanism for holding a rotating tool or workpiece on a lathe.

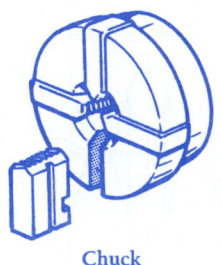

Chuck

Code identification number   A five-digit number, assigned to each design activity, used in conjunction with a part or identity number in a parts list [also referred to as a Federal Supply Code for Manufacturers (FSCM)].

Coining   A method of cold forging parts to desired size and shape by compressing them under heavy pressure between coining dies.

Cold-rolled steel (CRS)   Open hearth or Bessemer steel containing 0.12% to 0.20% carbon that has been rolled while cold to produce a smooth, accurate stock.

Collar   A cylindrical ring or round flange fitted on a shaft to prevent a sliding movement.

Collar

Commercial fastener   A fastener manufactured to the requirements of published standards or documents and stocked by manufacturers or distributors.

Commercial item   A supply or service that is (a) regularly used for other than government purposes and (b) sold or traded in the course of conducting normal business operations.

Core   A solid form made of sand that is shaped in a core box and baked and used to shape the interior of a hollow casting.

Core print A projection on a pattern that forms an opening in the sand to hold the end of a core.

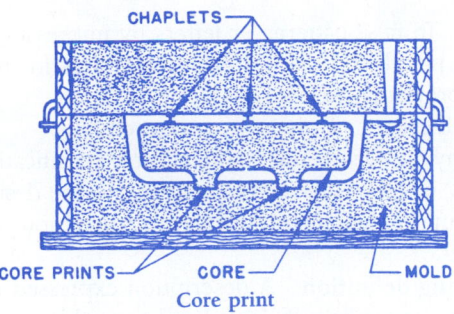

Core print

Cotter pin A half-round stock that is bent so as to have an eye at one end and forms a round split pin when compressed together (used to lock parts of an assembly together).

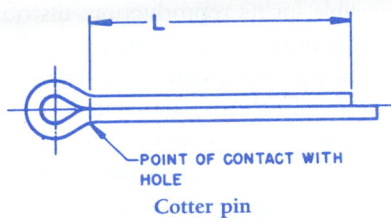

Cotter pin

Counterbore To enlarge the end of a cylindrical hole to a given depth with a flat shoulder; the name of the tool used to produce such a hole.

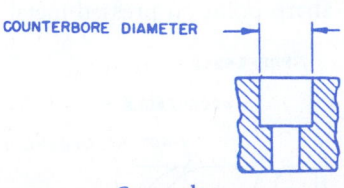

Counterbore

Counterdrill To form a conical shoulder in a drilled hole by enlarging it with a larger drill.

Countersink To recess a hole with a cone-shaped tool to provide a seat for a flathead screw or rivet; also the tool used to make such a hole.

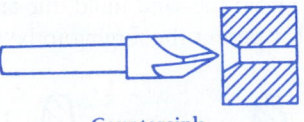

Countersink

Crosshatching Filling in an outline with a series of symbols to highlight part of a design.

Cyaniding Surface hardening of a ferrous alloy by heating at a suitable temperature in contact with a cyanide salt, followed by quenching.

D

Datum A theoretically exact point, axis, or plane derived from the true geometric counterpart of a specified datum feature. A datum is the origin from which the location or geometric characteristics of features of a part are established.

Dedendum Distance from pitch circle to bottom of tooth space on a gear.

Design activity An activity having responsibility for the design of an item; may be a government activity or a contractor, vendor, or others.

Detail drawing A drawing of a single part that provides all the information necessary in the production of that part.

Diameter The length of a straight line running through the center of a circle.

Diameter

Diametral pitch Number of gear teeth per inch of pitch diameter.

Die Hardened metal piece shaped to cut or form a required shape in a sheet of metal by pressing it against a mating die.

Die casting Part produced by forcing a molten alloy into a metal mold composed of two or more parts.

Die stamping A part that has been cut or formed from sheet metal by the use of dies.

Dimension, basic A numerical value used to describe the theoretically exact size, shape, or location of a feature or datum target. It is the basis from which permissible variations are established by tolerances on other dimensions, in notes, or by feature control symbols.

Dimension, coordinate Rectangular coordinate dimensioning is where all dimensions are measured from two or three mutually perpendicular datum planes.

Dog A small auxiliary clamp for preventing work from rotating in relation to the face plate of a lathe.

Dowel   A pin used to prevent sliding (and for location) between two contacting flat surfaces.

Draft   The taper used on the sides of a pattern so that it can be easily removed from the sand mold; the taper on the sides of a forging die that permit the forging to be removed easily.

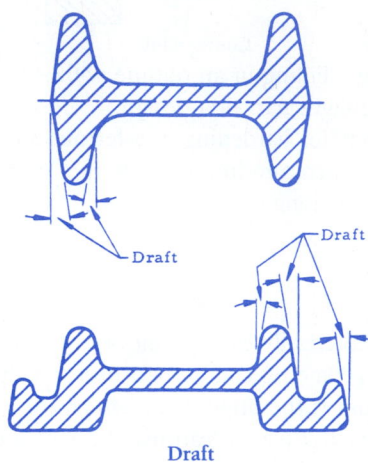

Draft

Draw   To form a metal, which may be either hot or cold, by distorting or stretching; to temper steel by gradual or intermittent quenching.

Drawing format   The standardized form, usually preprinted, on which various constant information (design activity identification, standard tolerance block, etc.) is provided together with spaces for variable information (drawing number, title, etc.).

Drawing number   Consists of letters, numbers, or combination of letters and numbers, which may or may not be separated by dashes. The number is assigned to a particular drawing for identification and file retrieval.

Drawing type   Name applied to a drawing, descriptive of its design and end use.

Drill   To form a cylindrical hole with a drill; one of a variety of revolving cutting tools designed for cutting at the point.

Drill press   A machine used for hole-forming operations.

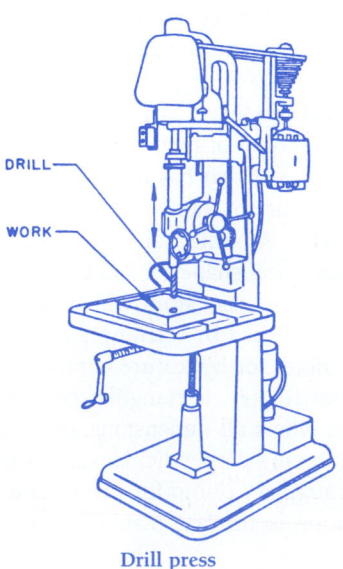

Drill press

Drop forge   To form a piece while hot by placing it between dies in a drop hammer.

E

Emboss   To raise patterns or letters by impressing with matching punch and die; to form projections in sheet metal prior to projection welding.

Engineering data   Drawings, associated lists, accompanying documents, manufacturer specifications, and standards, or other information relating to the design, manufacture, procurement, testing, or inspection of items or services.

Engineering definition   A description expressed in engineering terms in sufficient detail to enable meeting the requirements of design, development, engineering, production, procurement, or logistic support.

Engineering document release   The process of transferring custody of an engineering document, or change thereto, from the preparing activity to a control activity, which is responsible for its reproduction, distribution, storage, and the maintenance of history records.

Engineering drawing   An engineering document that discloses, by means of pictorial and/or textual presentations, the form and function of a part.

Extruding   To form a continuous cross section by forcing material through openings designed to a desired shape.

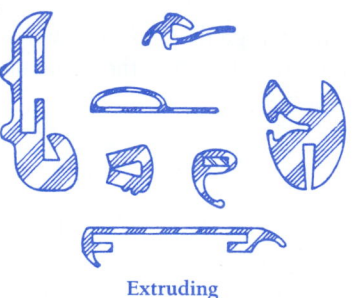

Extruding

F

Face   To machine a flat surface on a part using a lathe by turning the surface perpendicular to the axis of rotation.

Fastener   A mechanical device designed specifically to hold, join, couple, assemble, or maintain equilibrium of single or multiple components.

Feather   A rectangular sliding key that permits a pulley to move along the shaft parallel to its axis.

Feather edge   Sharp point on pressed metal stamping.

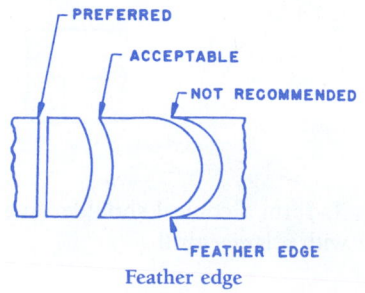

Feather edge

Feather key   A flat key, which is partly sunk in a shaft and partly in a hub, permitting the hub to slide lengthwise on the shaft.

Federal supply code for manufacturers (FSCM)   Five codes applicable to all activities that have produced or are producing items used by the federal government; also applies to government activities that control design or are responsible for the development of certain specifications, drawings, or standards that control the design of items.

File   To shape, finish, or trim with a fine-toothed metal cutting tool that is used in either a rotating arbor or done by hand.

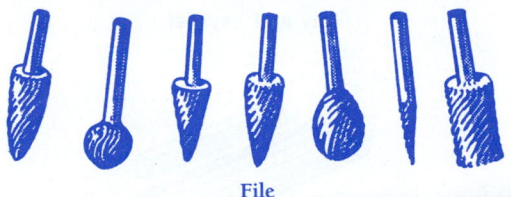

File

Fillet   A curved inside corner that increases the strength at the junction of two intersecting surfaces of a part.

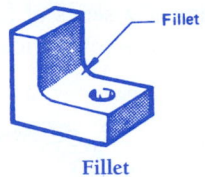

Fillet

Fin   A thin extrusion of metal at the intersection of dies or sand molds.

Finish   The degree of smoothness or roughness of a surface; the covering applied to a surface such as plating or painting.

Fit   Degree of tightness or looseness between two mating parts.

Fixture   A tool used for holding a part on which machining operations are being performed.

Flange   A rim extending from the main section of a part, such as the top and bottom members of a beam or a projecting rim added at the end of a pipe or fitting for making a connection.

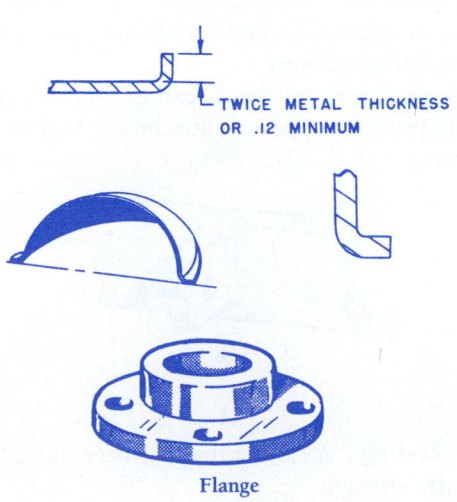

TWICE METAL THICKNESS OR .12 MINIMUM

Flange

Flask   The container in which sand molds are made; consists of two sections—the cope (upper section) and the drag (lower section). Any midsection is called a cheek.

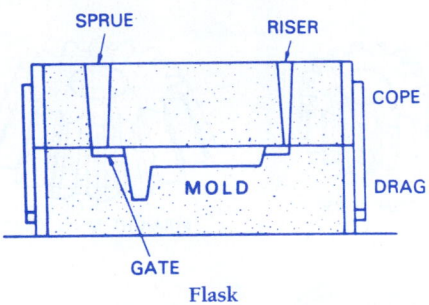

SPRUE   RISER   COPE   MOLD   DRAG   GATE

Flask

Flat pattern   A layout (development) showing true dimensions of a part before bending.

Flute   Groove, as on twist drills, reamers, and taps.

Forge   To force metal while it is hot to take on a desired shape by hammering or pressing.

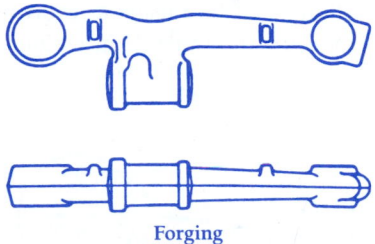

Forging

G

Gage   An instrument used for determining correctness of size or strength of manufactured parts within specified limits such as depth gage, dial gage, plug gage, ring gage, snap gage, surface gage, thread gage, and wire gage.

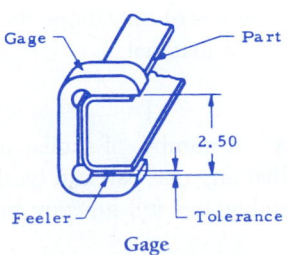

Gage   Part   2.50   Feeler   Tolerance

Gage

Galvanize   To coat metal parts by immersing in a zinc bath.

Gasket   A thin piece of metal, rubber, or other material placed between surfaces to make a tight joint.

Gate   The opening in a sand mold at the bottom of the sprue through which the molten metal passes to enter the cavity or mold.

Gears   Cylindrical or conical shaped parts having teeth and used in gear trains that transmit power between shafts such as spur gear, helical gear, herringbone gear, bevel gear, gear and rack, and internal spur gear.

Gears

Grinding   Finishing a surface using a revolving abrasive wheel. Abrasive wheels are available in various grades from fine to coarse.

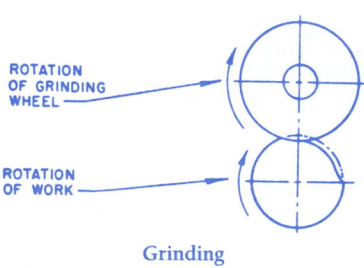

Grinding

Gusset   A small plate used in reinforcing assemblies.

H

Hardening   To heat steel or aluminum above a critical temperature and then quench in water or oil.

Heat treatment   A series of operations that improves the physical properties of a material.

I

Interchangeability   A number of similar parts manufactured so that any one part can be used in place of another in an assembly and still function properly.

J

Jig   A special type of fixture used to hold and accurately locate, as well as guide, the tools used in manufacture such as that used in drilling operations.

K

Key   A part used between a shaft and a hub to prevent movement of one relative to the other.

Keyseat or keyway   A groove cut parallel to the axis of a shaft or hub to receive the key. A key rests in a keyseat and slides in a keyway.

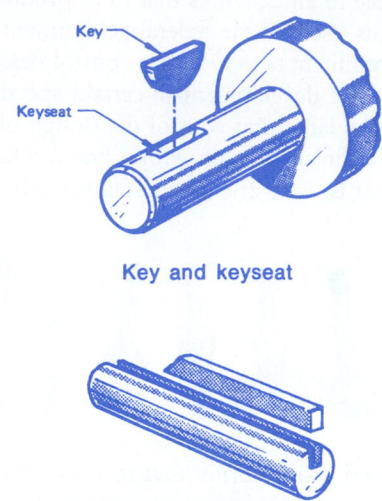

Key and keyseat

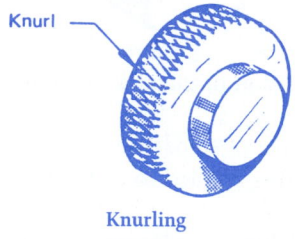

Keyseat or keyway

Knurling   The forming of a series of fine ridges to roughen a cylindrical surface to provide a firmer grip for the fingers.

Knurling

L

Lapping   To finish or polish a surface with a piece of soft metal, wood, or leather impregnated with abrasive compound.

Lead   The axial distance a point will travel on a screw thread when turned one complete revolution of the thread.

Limited production   Manufactured under model-shop conditions, as opposed to mass production under factory production line conditions.

Lug   A projection or ear that is cast or forged as a portion of a part to provide support or attachment facility with another part.

Lug

M

Malleable casting   A casting that has been annealed to provide extra strength.

Manufacturer A person or firm who owns, operates, or maintains a factory or establishment that produces on the premises the materials, supplies, articles, or equipment required under the contract or of the general character described by specifications, standards, and publications.

Matched parts Those parts, such as special application parts, which are machine matched, or otherwise mated, and for which replacement as a matched set or pair is essential.

Material allowance Extra material provided for machining to achieve close accuracy and smooth surfaces.

Material allowance

Micrometer caliper A caliper with a micrometer screw attached, used for making accurate measurements.

Micrometer caliper

Milling Removing material from a part by means of a revolving cutter. Various cutters are available: end mill, form cutter, straddle milling, and hollow cutter.

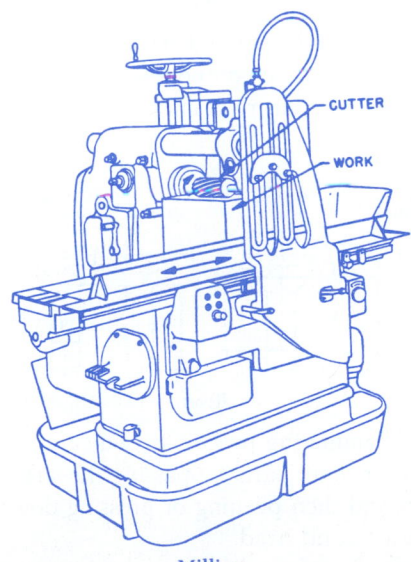

Milling

Mold The form provided for, or the act of forming by pouring molten metal into a hollow during a casting operation to give the part a desired shape when the material solidifies. A mold can be made of sand, plaster, or metal as long as the mold will withstand the temperature required for the material of the part.

N

Neck To cut a circular groove around a shaft to provide firm fitting between the shaft and its mating part in assembly.

Nesting The arrangement of sheet-metal parts on strip stock to provide the least scrap per blanks.

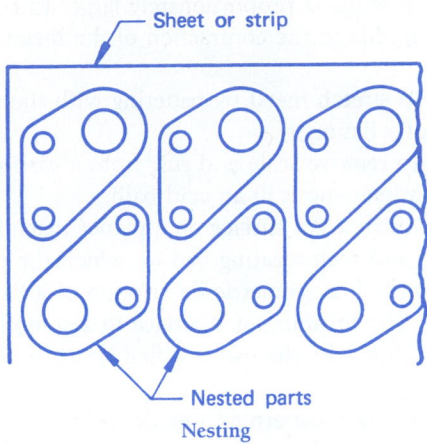

Nesting

Normalize To heat steel above its critical temperature and then cool it in air.

Nut A perforated block (usually of metal) possessing an internal, or female, screw thread, intended for use on an external, or male, screw thread such as a bolt for the purpose of tightening, adjusting, or holding two or more parts in definite relative positions.

P

Pack-harden To carburize, then to case-harden.

Pad A low projection surface, usually rectangular as contrasted with a boss.

Part drawing An engineering drawing that defines an item and assigns a part or control number to identify its configuration.

Part number A number (or combination of numbers and letters) assigned to uniquely identify a specific part. The part number includes the design activity drawing number.

Parting line The line along which the pattern is divided for molding; along the line where the sections of a mold or die separate.

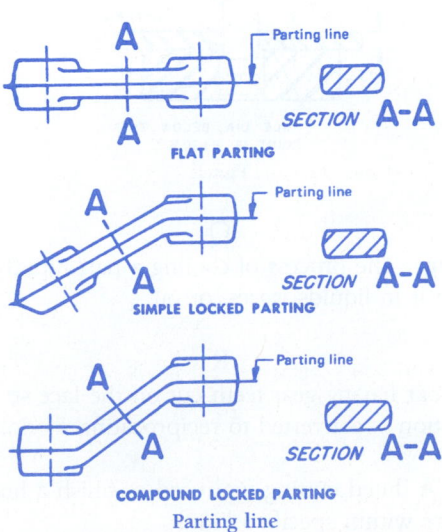

Parting line

Pattern   The form used to make the cavity in the mold and which duplicates the shape of the part to be cast, except that it is made proportionately larger to compensate for shrinkage due to the contraction of the metal when cooled.

Peening   To stretch metal by battering with the peen end (ball end) of a hammer.

Pickling   To remove scale and rust from a casting or forging by immersing it in an acid bath.

Plane   To finish a flat surface on a planer machine with a fixed cutter and reciprocating bed on which the part is securely attached; a geometric description of a flat surface.

Polishing   The finishing of a surface to a smooth and lustrous condition by the use of a fine abrasive as a basis for plating, etc.

Profiling   Using a pattern as a guide to make a similar part in a vertical milling machine operation in which the tool spindle is guided by the master plate made to the required shape of the part.

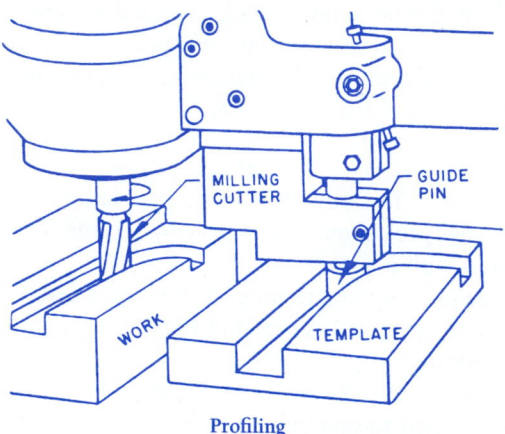

Profiling

Punch   That part of a tool that pierces holes in stock or shapes the inside contour of a part in a forming die.

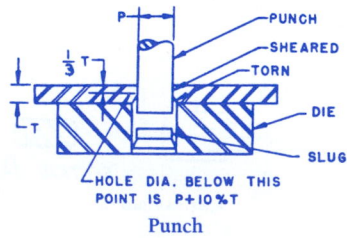

Punch

Q

Quenching   The process of cooling a part rapidly by immersing it in liquids, gases, or oil.

R

Rack   A bar having gear teeth cut on the face so that rotary motion is converted to reciprocating motion or vice versa.

Reamer   A fluted cutting tool used to finish a hole to a desired size within specified limits.

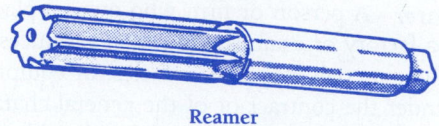

Reamer

Relief   A groove on a part such as a cut next to a shoulder.

Revision   Any change to an original drawing after that drawing has been released for use.

Revision authorization   A document such as a "Notice of Revision," "Engineering Change Notice," or "Revision Directive" that describes the revision in detail and is issued by the source having the authority to revise the drawing.

Revision symbol   A letter (which may be accompanied by a suffix number), used to identify particular revisions on the face of the drawing or in a revision description block.

Rib   A ridge cast into thin sections of a part to make it stronger.

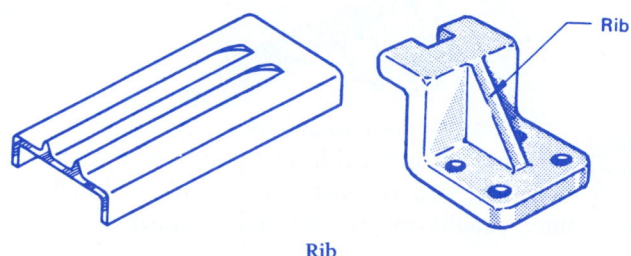

Rib

Rivet   A headed and unthreaded mechanical device used to assemble two or more components by an applied force, which deforms the plain rivet end to develop a completed mechanical joint.

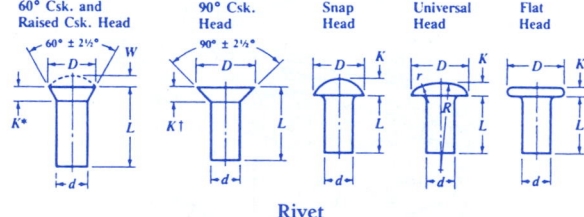

Rivet

Riveting   A hammering process by which a rivet is used to fasten two or more parts by passing the shank through mating holes and then peening or pressing down the plain end to form a second head.

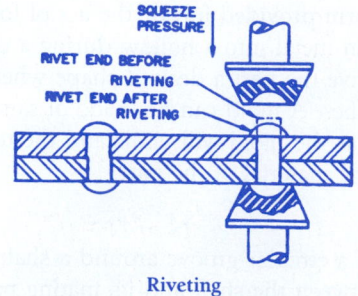

Riveting

Round   A rounded external corner on a casting or forging.

S

Sandblasting   The cleaning of the surface of a part by means of sand forced from a nozzle at high velocity.

Screw   A headed and externally threaded mechanical device possessing capabilities that permit it to be inserted into holes in assembled parts; it is meant to be mated with a preformed internal thread or form its own thread.

Set screw   A screw used in a hub which bottoms against a shaft to prevent relative motion between two parts. They are made either headless or with different types of heads as well as points.

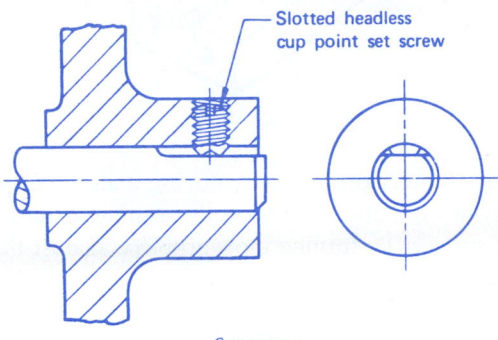

Set screw

Shaper   A machine tool with a sliding ram used to finish parts and flat surfaces. The workpiece is clamped in a stationary vise during the cutting stroke.

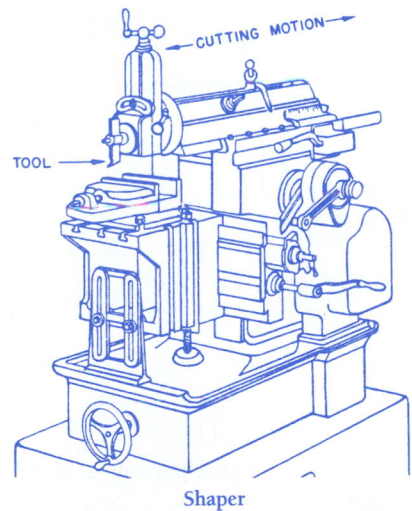

Shaper

Shear   To cut off sheet or bar metal with the shearing action of two blades.

Shim   A thin metal strip that is inserted between two parts for the purpose of adjustment.

Spline   A key for inserting in a slot in a shaft, or a rib that has been machined on the shaft and fits another part having a mating slot.

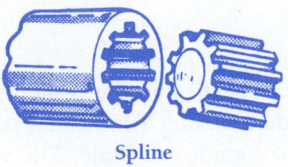

Spline

Spot weld   To weld two overlapping sheet-metal parts in spots by means of the heat generated by resistance to an electric current between a pair of electrodes.

Spotfacing   To finish the rough surface around a round hole using a counterbore tool to smooth and square the surface to allow a bolt or screw head to seat properly; a shallow counterbore.

Sprocket   A gear made for chain-driven rotating mechanisms.

Sprocket

Stamping   Any part made by pressed metal operations.

Staple   To assemble by use of a U-shaped fastener.

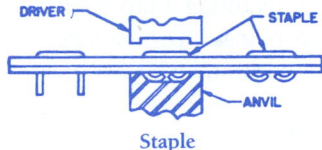

Staple

Stripper   The plate used in a die that strips the part from the die.

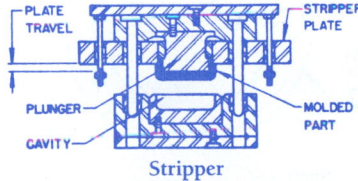

Stripper

Stud   A stationary shaft, one end of which is fastened to the body of the part and receives a nut for fastening on the other.

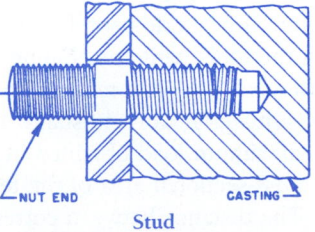

Stud

Surface gage   A flat block of steel carrying an adjustable, upright spindle with which a scriber is mounted for layout work or for use as an indicator for transfer readings.

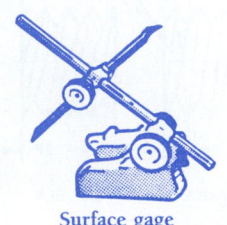

Surface gage

Surface plate   A plate with a flat surface used to check parts for flatness.

Surface plate

Swage   To form metal while cold by drawing or squeezing or by submitting to a number of blows sufficient to shape to desired form.

Sweat   To solder together by clamping the parts in contact with soft solder between them and heating.

T

Tack weld   The welding of short intermittent sections.

Tap   To cut an internal thread by screwing a fluted tapered cutting tool into the hole.

Taper   A gradual and uniform increase or decrease in size.

Taper pin   A pin requiring a taper reamed hole at assembly and depending only on a taper lock, which can totally disengage when minor displacement occurs.

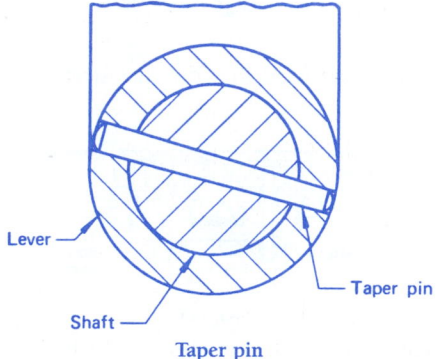

Taper pin

Temper   To reheat hardened steel to some temperature below critical temperature, followed by the desired rate of cooling; also called "drawing."

Template   A pattern or guide used for laying out duplicate parts or guiding the tools while machining.

Tensile strength (U.T.S.)   The maximum tensile load per square inch that a material can withstand. It is computed by dividing the maximum load obtained in a tensile tester by the original cross-sectional area of the test specimen.

Thread pitch   The distance between corresponding points on adjacent threads measured parallel to the axis.

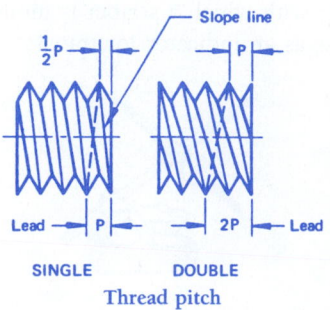

Thread pitch

Tolerance   The permissible variation from the basic dimension of a part, expressed either unilaterally (one side given) or bilaterally (a summation at both ends).

Truncate   To cut off a geometric solid at an angle to its base.

T-slot   A slot machined in a part having a sectional shape resembling the capital letter "T."

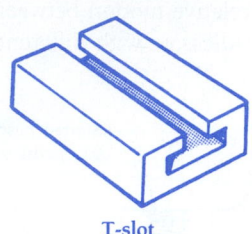

T-slot

Turning   A process used for removing material to produce relatively smooth and dimensionally accurate external and internal surfaces by turning the workpiece against the cutting tool as in a lathe.

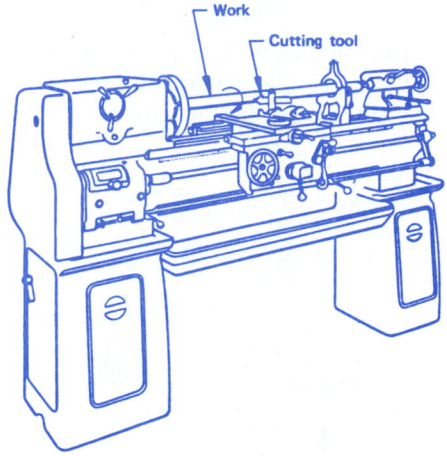

Lathe used for turning

U

Undercut   A recessed cut that permits a firm fitting of one part with another.

Union   Tube or pipe fitting used to connect lines that carry either gases or liquids at relatively high pressures and that are not subjected to excessive vibration or movement.

Upset   To increase the sectional area of a part to form a shoulder during forging.

V

Vernier caliper   A small movable scale used on measuring instruments for determining a fractional part of one of the equal divisions of a graduated scale. The vernier caliper yields high accuracy because it is, in effect, one scale on another scale.

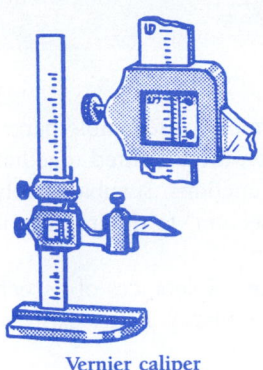

Vernier caliper

W

Washer A round piece of metal (usually steel), either flat or spring type, with a hole in the center and placed on the bolt or screw ahead of the nut to provide positive clamping, bearing surface, or to lock the nut in position.

Washer

Web A thin section of a casting between the ribs, bosses, and flanges to provide additional strength.

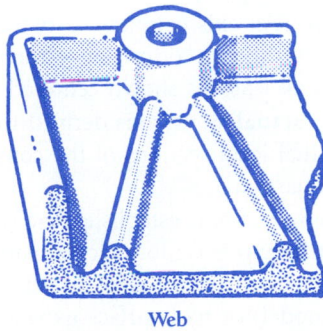

Web

Welding Any one of several methods of permanent assembly whereby parts are joined together by heating the joint to material fusion temperature, such as by arc welding, gas welding, projection welding, and spot welding.

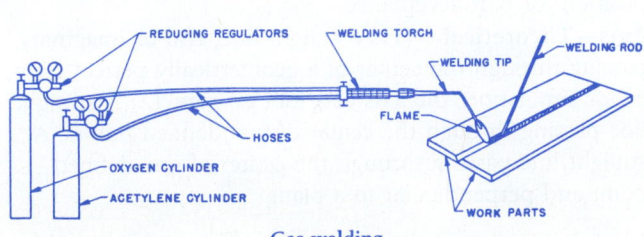

Gas welding

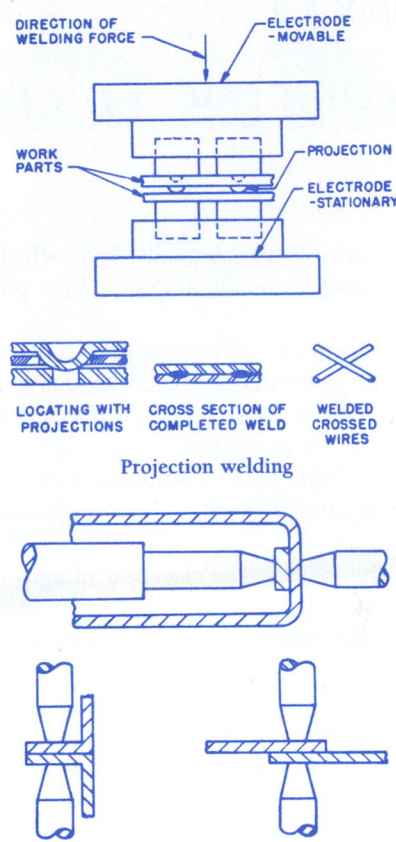

Projection welding

Spot welding

Wing nut Screw fastener especially designed with extensions on the internal threaded part for the convenience of hand tightening.

Wing nut

Worm A gear in the form of a screw used to transmit motion parallel to the axis of the shaft and that provides large reduction of velocity.

Worm wheel The gear that meshes with the worm in an installation, and may be combined with the worm; provides 90° transmission of revolving forces and increases torque and smoothness of action.

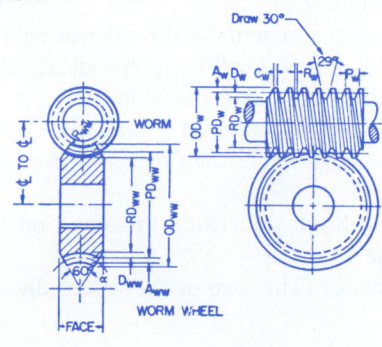

Worm and Worm wheel

Geometric Tolerancing Glossary

A

Acceptable quality level   A quality level which in a sampling plan corresponds to a specific high probability of acceptance.

Acceptance inspection   (1) Inspection to determine whether an item delivered or offered for delivery is acceptable. (2) The consent to accept or take a feature, part, assembly, or lot as offered.

Accuracy   The verification of a measurement when compared to an ultimate standard or true theoretical value. Also see precision.

Accuracy of the mean   The closeness of agreement between the true value and the mean result obtained by applying the experimental procedure numerous times.

Acronym   A word formed by the first (or first few) letters of a series of words, such as MMC from maximum material condition, RFS, LSC, MRS, etc.

Actual deviation   (1) The difference between the actual (measured size) and the specified (nominal or mean) size (*or for limits and fits*) (2) The algebraical difference between the maximum limit of size and the corresponding basic size.

Actual fit   The actual total clearance or interference between two parts at assembly.

Actual local size   The actual (measured) individual sizes (distances) at any cross section of a part.

Actual size   (1) The size determined from a number of actual local sizes of a dimension of an individual feature. It may be the smallest or largest, for an external or internal shape, respectively, perfect form that inscribes or envelopes the actual local sizes. The aforementioned perfect form refers to that which is specified or depicted. When the size dimension for this form is specified as being oriented, the actual size measurement must also be so oriented. (2) The measured size.

Alignment   The condition where features are coplanar, collinear, or coaxial.

Allowance   The intentional difference between the MMC limits of mating features.

Angle plate   A general term for the different right-angle irons used to establish a plane parallel or perpendicular to a surface plate, against which the part is placed in contact or clamped.

Angularity   The inclination of a surface or axis that is at a specified basic angle other than 0 or 90° from a datum plane or line.

Arc length   A linear dimension measured on (along) a curved outline.

Arithmetic mean   The sum of the values divided by their number.

Assembly   A number of separable parts or subassemblies or any combination thereof fitted together to perform one or more specific functions. A subassembly is sometimes referred to as a "section" to differentiate it from the main assembly for clarity.

Attitude tolerance   Tolerances of perpendicularity, parallelism, and angularity. Better expressed as (and see *orientation tolerance*.)

Auxiliary datum   A datum which has a tolerance relative to the part datum reference frame. A single datum, not related, which is generally erected by contact with a surface.

Auxiliary dimension   A reference dimension. A dimension in which size is given solely for information (see *reference dimension*).

Average diameter   (1) The diameter of an out-of-round feature in the free state found by averaging the diameter at various azimuths or more precisely by doubling the average radius from the least-squares center or by measuring the perimeter. If forces were applied to this feature constraining it round then, in that state, the average diameter (with its associated tolerance) should be the same as the rounded diameter on a constrained (round) part. (2) The diameter a free state part would assume if it were round; the perimeter (circumference) of the shape divided by π (Pi) or as measured with a Pi tape.

Axis—Common   An axis common to two or more coaxial features. The centerline on a drawing is the theoretical common axis of all features shown centered about it.

Axis—Derived (actual)   An axis derived from the center points of the actual local sections of the considered feature (such as least-squares axis).

Axis—Simulated   An axis established by (or from) a surface of adequately precise form (or a mathematical representation of same). In the RFS case the gage (mathematical model) or tool surface expands (to contact an internal feature) or contracts (to contact an external feature). In the MMC case the gage or mathematical representation is the MMC size of the considered feature thus allowing the tool or gage (datum) axis to "float" when the part feature departs from MMC. The philosophy is that the (MMC) axis must be positioned to the *ONE* best position for part acceptance.

Axis—Theoretical   (1) A straight line, real or imaginary, passing through the center of a geometrically perfect form, or for simulation, the axis of a tool or gage. (2) A straight line passing through the center of two defined points. A straight line passing through the center of one defined point and perpendicular to a plane.

Axis—True   The axis of revolution. (According to the classic definition in mathematical engineering—see Marks handbook or other source.)

B

Baseline dimensioning   Dimensioning from a common datum (specified or implied).

Basic angle   The basic dimension of an angle (shown enclosed in a rectangle).

Basic dimension   A dimension enclosed in a rectangle that is a numerical value used to describe the theoretically exact size, profile, orientation, or location of a feature or datum target. It is the basis from which permissible variations are established by tolerances in a feature control frame, by other dimensions, or by note.

Basic hole   In the ISO System of Limits and Fits wherein the hole lower deviation is always zero. In this case the symbol used is H (as in $\varnothing$ 40H11) and the minimum diameter of the hole is the basic specified size.

Basic note   "UNTOLERANCED DIMENSIONS LOCATING TRUE POSITION ARE BASIC," delineates basic dimensions by note rather than by symbol—nonpreferred.

Basic pattern   The theoretically exact interrelations of the considered features within the group.

Basic shaft   In the ISO System of Limits and Fits wherein the shaft upper deviation is always zero. In this case the symbol used is h (as in $\varnothing$ 040h8) and the maximum diameter of the shaft is the basic specified size.

Basic size   The basic size is that size from which the limits of size are derived by the application of allowances and tolerances. The common value of two mating features from which all limits of size are established.

Bilateral tolerance   A tolerance in which variation is permitted in both directions from the specified dimension (e.g., 1.500 ±.005).

Boundary of perfect form   An envelope of perfect form established by size limits, such as the boundary of perfect form at MMC (the true geometric form represented on the drawing), requirement for individual features.

C

Cartesian coordinate system   Three mutually perpendicular planes (**X, Y,** and **Z**) from which points are located in space. Used, especially, for robotic installation of components and CAM (computer-aided manufacturing) or on parts wherein relationships of features (originating from these three planes) are perfect at the maximum material conditions.

Centerlines   Theoretical lines, shown on a drawing, depicting an axis of revolution or representing two centerline/planes (at a true 90°) from which rectangular coordinate dimensions are given. Measurements cannot be taken from centerlines alone because they are not definitive—datums are specified for this purpose.

Center plane   The median plane of a feature such as a slot.

Center point   The center point of a circle, sphere, or other regular form.

Centers—machining   Formed shapes on an item (generally in the ends) dimensioned (ANSI B94.11M) to accommodate holding the part during manufacturing, such as on a lathe.

Chain dimensioning   Dimensioning in series from feature to feature as opposed to baseline or positional dimensioning. Generally allows a tolerance accumulation equal to the sum of the variances in each direction.

Circular runout   The independent measurement at a cross section or at a point on a surface oriented to the axis of circular elements on a solid of revolution when the part is rotated 360°. This composite control verifies out-of-roundness and position on cylindrical items and perpendicularity errors on faces.

Circularity   The condition wherein a circular element line is the same radial distance at all azimuths from a center point, independently taken in a plane normal to the axis of the considered feature.

Clearance   The algebraic difference between the sizes of the internal feature (hole) and the mating external feature, when the difference is positive.

Clearance fit   A fit having limits of size specified such that a clearance always results when mating parts are assembled.

Coaxiality   Collinear or coincident axis. Control of coaxiality may be specified as position, runout, or concentricity, as appropriate.

Collinear   The condition wherein the center lines or axes of features are in line.

Common axis   Axis of two or more coaxial features, which have a common tolerance or together shall act as a single datum.

Complex feature   A shape (generally an outline) composed of two or more simple individual features such as a square, rectangle, hexagon, etc.

Concentricity   The condition where the centers of all cross-sectional elements (such as the least-squares axis) of a surface of revolution (one or more feature axes) are collinear (or coaxial) with a datum axis.

Conditional tolerance   A tolerance or datum reference in a control frame with a modifier other than RFS (e.g., MMC, LMC).

Considered feature   The feature under consideration.

Constant   A term used with a dimension to indicate that a characteristic (e.g., section thickness, profile tolerance, etc.) is to have the same dimension and tolerance as depicted all over (or around) regardless of the shape of the considered feature.

Contour   The outline of a figure, generally a complex shape or portion of an arc. (See *profile of a line or surface.*)

Control drawing   A drawing that discloses configurations and configuration limitations; performance and test requirements; mass and space limitations; access clearances; pipe and cable attachments, to the extent necessary that an item can be developed and procured on the commercial market to meet standard requirements; or for the installation and functioning of an item to be installed with related items.

Coplanarity   The condition where axes, center planes, or all elements of a surface are in one plane. (Profile of a surface tolerance is used to control coplanarity.)

Cylindricity   The condition of a surface of revolution in which all points on the surface are equidistant from a common axis.

D

Datum   Theoretical geometrical reference (generally point, line, or plane) simulated by very precise manufacturing, tooling, or inspection equipment, from which the form, orientation, or position, of other features is established. (Common: the origin of measurement.)

Datum axis   The theoretically exact centerline of a true cylinder that would contact the extremities of a cylindrical feature. An axis or straight line established by two defined points such as the intersection of a diameter and a plane at each end of an object. When so specified, the centerline of an MMC cylindrical shape free to float when the feature is not at MMC. A mathematically derived axis such as the least-squares axis.

Datum—Compound   A datum established by more than one datum feature, the features being of equal importance/precedence.

Datum equalization   Orienting a datum feature relative to a manufacturing or inspection setup with tooling, inspection equipment, or by least-squares analysis.

Datum (identification) feature symbol   A rectangle containing the datum letter with a short dash on each side.

Datum letter   Any capital letter (preferably other than I, O, M, or Q) used to identify or refer to a datum feature.

Datum plane   A theoretically exact plane established by contacting the extremities of an actual feature surface with a simulator (such as a surface plate). In some cases a datum plane is established by the least-squares method.

Datum point   Has position in space on a plane but has no size or shape. In roundness measurements, for example, this point is normally the center from which radial measurements are taken. Mathematically the least-squares center is used as a datum point.

Datum reference frame   Three mutually perpendicular datum planes relative to which the part is oriented and measured. The datums involved are theoretical and are therefore simulated in manufacturing and inspection.

Datum, simulated   The plane, axis, or point established by, or from, a surface of adequately precise form contacting the datum feature. Simulated datums are used as practical embodiments of specified datums.

Datum, single   A datum established from one feature.

Datum, specified   An explicit datum that has been indicated in a note, datum identification, or feature control symbol.

Datum surface (or feature)   The actual (real) surface of the feature (part) from which the datum is established, by contact, simulation, or that which is used to establish the location or orientation of a datum.

Datum system   A system consisting of a group of features which are chosen to erect datums (mating of cofunctioning features) on each of two mating or cofunctioning components. A missile datum system may consist of a missile longitudinal axis, missile base, and azimuth datum planes. Generally a three-plane system.

Datum target   A specified point, line, or limited areas used to establish datums, especially useful for repeatability of orientation and location of as-forged or as-cast parts.

Derived axis   An axis established by a true form contacting the extremities of a feature, or by least-squares analysis.

Design size   Design size of a dimension is the size in relation to which the limits for that dimension are assigned. It is therefore usually the size specified on the drawing (especially for limits and fits), and is identical to the basic size when there is no allowance.

Detail assembly drawing   A drawing depicting an assembly on which one or more parts are detailed in the assembly view or on separate detail views.

Detail drawing   A drawing depicting end product requirements for the parts delineated on the drawing. Mono detail drawings delineate a single part or item.

Deviation   Algebraical difference between a size (actual, maximum, etc.) and the corresponding basic size.

Diagrammatic drawing (or diagram)   A drawing delineating by means of symbols and lines, characteristics and relationships of items forming an assembly or system.

Dimension   A numerical value expressed in appropriate units of measurement. A complete specification for a dimension must include (directly or by association) an origin, direction, magnitude, and allowable variation. Used with lines, symbols, and notes, dimensions are used to describe the size or geometrical characteristics of an object.

Direct dimensioning   Dimensions placed directly between functional features to avoid tolerance accumulation.

Drawing   A document presenting information pictorially and/or by textual matter. Note: A drawing is normally identified by a drawing number and title.

Dual dimensioning   Specifies dimensions in two sets of units (e.g., metric and customary). The primary set of units is specified in the conventional manner and the other is placed in square brackets (after the primary units in feature control frames and below the primary units in other areas). Where no equivalent exists (as for a thread) only the primary units are specified.

E

Eccentricity   Radial deviation from a centerline or axis. One half of concentricity.

Effective condition (or size)   The actual size to which a feature has been produced plus or minus (external or internal, respectively) the actual geometrical error [e.g., a shaft at .250 (measured) diameter with a measured straightness deviation on the axis of .007 has an effective size of .257]. Note: The effective condition is differentiated from the virtual condition in that the effective condition deals with actual (or measured) values.

End of full thread The point at which the thread profile ceases to be fully formed.

End product (or item) An item, either an individual part, assembly, structure, or product, in the condition in which it is to be used. It defines a piece ready for assembly or service or it may be the product of a foundry or forge supplied for further processing.

Enveloping boundary (elements) Profile tolerance boundary lines which are separated everywhere by a theoretical circle of the diameter of the specified tolerance centered on the basic (or mean) profile in one plane.

Enveloping boundary (surface) Profile tolerance boundaries which are separated everywhere by a theoretical sphere of the diameter of the specified tolerance centered on the basic (or mean) profile in all directions.

F

Feature A feature is a general term applied to a specific characteristic portion of a part, such as a surface, hole, slot, screw thread, radius, etc.

Feature control (symbol) frame A rectangular frame containing the geometric characteristic symbol, the applicable tolerance, required datums, and modifiers. This symbol describes allowable variations, datum relativity, zone shape information, and conditions under which the tolerances apply.

Feature of size Portion of an item such as (a) a single plane surface or (b) a single cylindrical surface or (c) a single spherical surface or (d) two parallel plane surfaces; each is associated with a size dimension.

Fit The general term used to signify the range of tightness or looseness that results from the application of a specific combination of allowances of two parts to be assembled. Examples of types of fits are: RC: running or sliding clearance; LC: locational clearance fit; LT: transition clearance or interference fit; LN: locational interference fit; and FN: force or shrink fit.

Fit system System of fits comprising shafts and holes belonging to a limit system.

Fixed fastener system The condition where the fastener is positively located (fixed) in one of the mating ports and passes through a clearance hole in the other (e.g., a clearance hole and tapped hole combination, or a press fit dowel hole and clearance hole combination).

Flatness The condition where element lines in all directions are in one plane.

Floating (free) fastener system Condition where a fastener is to be assembled with two or more parts, all of which contain clearance holes or features that do not positively locate (fix) the fastener.

Form tolerance Indicates how far individual surfaces (or elements of a single feature) can vary from the desired form or shape indicated on the drawing. Tolerances of form are straightness, flatness, roundness, cylindricity, and taper (flat or conical) and are not related to datums.

Free state variation (1) The condition where a part of the feature is distorted due to its own weight and geometrical configuration within the elastic limit [i.e., a large unsupported cylindrical shape of small cross section (thin) that is elliptical or oval until restrained round]. (2) The amount of distortion of a feature that occurs when manufacturing forces are removed.

Full indicator movement (FIM) The total movement of the indicator when transversing a surface. The absolute sum of the largest positive and largest negative indicator hand movement. FIM also refers to the total observed deviation with a dial indicator in contact with the part while the part is revolved about the datum axis.

Functional dimension A dimension that is essential to the function of a product.

Functional feature A feature that plays an essential part in the performance of serviceability of the piece to which it belongs. It may be a location feature, i.e., a spigot which serves to locate a component in an assembly, or a working surface, i.e., the bore of bearing.

Functional gage A gage with fixed elements (rather than readout). Provides a go/no-go type of verification. Uses some (generally 10%) percent of the part (feature) tolerance.

Fundamental deviation Defines the position of the tolerance zone relative to the zero line (basic size). This value when added to the basic size gives one limit of size. The fundamental deviation in the ISO system is designated by a letter, uppercase for internal features (holes) and lowercase for external features (shafts), e.g., ϕ 40H11.

G

Gage (a) *Direct measurement*—The gage is applied (probe, electronic beam, pneumatically, etc.) to the surface and the actual dimension is read on a graduated scale, digitally or from a chart or computer readout. (b) *Fixed limit*—Functional go/no-go type of gages that do not require the operator to make a decision. (c) *Paper or computer*—Actual dimensions from inspection machines or devices are plotted on paper or entered into a computer for mathematical simulation and/or analysis. Echelons of accuracy relative to gages are: International defining standard, National standard, National reference standard, Laboratory standard, Inspection gage, and Production or floor gage.

Gage dimension Theoretically exact (similar to basic dimension), not used on drawings.

Gage size A code number or designation used with cables, rods, sheets, and other materials, the actual dimensions of which are shown on the drawing. Gage or code numbers may be referenced (in parentheses) after the dimension.

General arrangement drawing   An arrangement drawing where the item depicted is the end product.

Geometric characteristic symbol   The symbols used to describe the type of tolerance (e.g., flat, parallel, etc.) in the tolerance frame.

Geometrical tolerance   The general term applied to the category of tolerances used to control maximum permissible variation of form, orientation, location, or runout specified on the drawing.

Go limit   The designation applied to the limit of size that corresponds to the maximum material condition, i.e., the upper limit of a shaft (ring gage is GO GAGE), and the lower limit of a hole (plug gage is GO GAGE).

Grade   The number symbol designating the tolerance as a function of the basic size (e.g., H8) in the ISO system of limits and fits.

Grade of tolerance   In a standardized system of limits and fits, a group of tolerances considered as corresponding to the same level of accuracy for all basic sizes.

H

Hole basis system   System of fits in which the different clearances and interferences are obtained by associating various shafts with a single hole (or, possibly, with holes of different grades, but always having the same fundamental deviation).

Hole depth   On a blind hole the depth specified is the depth of full-form diameter from the corresponding surface. Where the hole is countersunk, counterbored, or counterdrilled, the depth also applies from the outer surface.

Hole pattern   Any group of holes that function as a unit or group, regardless of differences in characteristics of the holes.

I

Implied datum   An unspecified (implicit) datum from which dimensions originate, the implied datums are used in any sequence (order of precedence). Implied datums are not recommended except where tolerances are extremely generous.

Interchangeability   Where two or more items possess such physical and functional characteristics as to be equivalent in performance and durability and capable of being exchanged one for the other without alteration of the items themselves or of adjoining items except for adjustment and without selection for fit or performance, the items are interchangeable.

Interference fit   Limits of size so prescribed such that an interference always results when mating parts are assembled.

International system of units   SI System International—An international system of units required to

be used by the EEC (European Economic Community) since December 1978. The standardized metric system used worldwide.

ISO   International Standards Organization.

L

Least material condition   The condition of a feature wherein it contains the least (minimum) amount of material (largest tolerance limit on an internal feature, such as a hole; smallest tolerance limit on an external feature, such as a shaft) within the specified limits of size.

Least material size   For an external feature, the minimum limit of size specified on the drawing. For an internal feature, the maximum limit of size specified on the drawing.

Limit dimension   A type of dimension wherein the maximum limit of size is expressed above or to the right of the minimum limit of size.

Limit system   System of standardized tolerances and deviations.

Limits and fits   Standardized fits for holes and shafts—ANSI B4.2 and ISO 286.

Limits of size   The two extreme allowable sizes (limits) within which the actual size should lie. For individual features of size the feature surface must lie within an MMC envelope of perfect form and the LMC size is verified by cross-sectional measurement.

Line fit   A fit having limits of size (or virtual conditions) so prescribed such that one limit on mating features is the same (line to line or surface to surface) and the other limit results in clearance.

Linear units   The units used on the drawing, i.e., metric or customary (inch).

Local size   Any individual measurement at a cross section of the feature of a part.

Location tolerance   The tolerances of concentricity and position.

Lower deviation   The algebraic difference between the minimum limit of size and the corresponding basic size.

M

Mating size   (a) *Holes*—The diameter of the largest perfect imaginary cylinder which can be inscribed within the hole so that it just contacts the extremities of the surface. (b) *Shafts*—The diameter of the smallest perfect imaginary cylinder which can be circumscribed about the shaft so that it just contacts the extremities of the surface. (It will be noted that this definition is unrelated to the position or attitude of the feature.)

Maximum clearance   The difference between the maximum specified size of an internal feature and the minimum specified size of the mating external feature.

Maximum dimension   The maximum dimension represents the largest acceptable value or the upper limit.

Maximum limit of size   The greater of the two limits of size.

Maximum material condition (MMC)   (1) The condition of a part or feature wherein it contains the maximum amount of material (within the limits of size). (2) The fit condition producing the smallest amount of clearance (i.e., maximum shaft size, minimum hole size).

Mean dimension   One-half of the sum of the limits of a dimension, not necessarily the nominal.

Median plane   The center plane of a square or rectangular feature. Median to two parallel planes that contact the extremities of the feature.

Minimum clearance   The difference between the minimum specified size of an internal feature and the maximum specified size of the mating external feature. Where geometric tolerances are involved, it is the difference between mating features at their virtual condition.

Minimum dimension   The smallest acceptable value or the lower limit.

Minimum limit of size   The smaller of the two limits of size.

Modifier   A symbol used in a feature control frame to modify the condition under which the tolerance applies. The modifiers are Ⓜ for maximum material condition, Ⓢ for regardless of feature size, Ⓛ for least material condition.

Multiple datum system   A system wherein more than one datum feature is used.

Murphy's law   A satirical law used in engineering; (does not recognize probability) assumes the worst possible situation will occur regardless of the nature of the data involved.

N

Nominal axis   See *derived axis.*

Nominal diameter step (limits and fits)   The principal range of limiting sizes, a set increment; the two (extreme) sizes in a given step (range).

Nominal dimension   The "ideal" dimension (used in "plus or minus" tolerancing).

Nominal size   The size by which an item is designated as a matter of convenience. Examples: M20 screw thread; 5-t crane; 10-kW motor.

Nonmandatory dimensions   Processing dimensions identified as "NONMANDATORY (MFG DATA)" such as shrink or finish allowance, etc.

Nonrigid part   A part that distorts (within the elastic range) in the free (nonrestrained) state due to its own weight or the release of internal stress buildup during fabrication.

Normal   Perpendicular, square.

Not go limit   Designation applied to that of the two limits of size which corresponds to the least material condition, i.e., the lower limit of a shaft or the upper limit of a hole.

O

Oblique projection   The projection of an object in which the lines of sight are parallel to each other but inclined to the plane of projection and where the object is oriented with the principal face parallel to the plane of projection, thus making this face and parallel faces show in true shape.

Orientation of a line   The orientation of a pair of parallel straight lines with the least separation which completely envelops an element or centerline (often found by the least-squares line method).

Orientation of a plane   The orientation of a pair of parallel planes with the least separation which completely envelops the actual surface or center plane (often found by the least-squares plane method).

Orientation tolerances   Tolerances of parallelism, perpendicularity, and angularity.

Origin of measurement   A dimension origin symbol (circle centered on an extension line as one end of a dimension line, the other end terminates with an arrowhead) indicates that the attendant tolerance applies to the feature on the arrow end.

Orthogonal projection   The projections of an object in which the lines of sight are perpendicular planes of projection and where the object is oriented so that its three principal axes are parallel to the planes of projection.

Overall dimension   The sum of the associated intermediate dimensions (often reference).

P

Parallelepiped   A rectangular prism-shaped tolerance zone. Used where a bidirectional tolerance is preferable for a feature of length as in the case of bidirectional position.

Parallelism   The condition where lines or planes extend in the same direction; in principle, the considered surface or axis is the same distance from a datum plane or axis at every point.

Part   One piece or member or two or more pieces or members joined together that cannot normally be separated without destruction or impairment of designed use. Note: A part is sometimes described as a component.

Pattern   Two or more features that are interdimensioned and located (relative to implied or specified datums) as a group.

Perpendicularity   The condition where primary surfaces, median planes, or axes are at exactly right angles to a datum.

Perspective projection   The projection of an object in which the lines of sight converge to a point of sight located at a finite distance in front of the plane of projection.

Polar dimensioning   Dimensioning by indicating the radius and azimuth (angle) with associated tolerances.

Position tolerance   (1) The total amount of variation permitted for the location of a feature in the group of which it is a member. (2) A numerical value describing the total zone (cylinder, two parallel planes, etc.) within which the (axis, median plane, surface, etc.) feature may be positioned (located). This zone is situated relative to a theoretically exact (basic) location or "true position."

Precision   Precise duplication traceable to an as-produced article or tooling rather than to a standard or theoretical model.

Primary datum   The first datum of a three-plane system; first in order of precedence.

Processing dimensions   See *nonmandatory dimensions.*

Profile of a line (element)   A uniform two-dimensional boundary along the true profile within which a surface element of an irregular shape, portion of an arc, or other established profile may lie.

Profile of a surface   A uniform three-dimensional boundary along the true profile within which the surface of an irregular shape, portion of an arc, or other established contour may lie.

Projected tolerance zone   A tolerance zone that extends beyond the fixing feature so that the projection of a fastener (or other feature) located from the fixing feature (thread, press fit hole, etc.) on installation will be controlled over its entire length. Projected zones control the angularity/perpendicularity of fixed fasteners to prevent interference.

R

Rectangular coordinate dimensioning   Dimensions giving location of features by abscissa and ordinate (*x, y* coordinates) from datums generally yielding a square or rectangular zone.

Reference dimension   A dimension usually without tolerance enclosed in parentheses (for information only) and not to be used to govern production or inspection. Generally used to orient a detail relative to a surface (repeating a dimension) or a value derived or calculated from other dimensions given on the drawing or related drawings.

Regardless of feature size   The condition wherein geometric tolerance must be met regardless of the size to which the considered feature, datum, or related features is produced.

Replaceability   An item that is a replacement for another item but is not interchangeable, in that the original item may not be interchanged for it.

Rounding   Linear units are rounded in accordance with ANSI Z210.1.

Roundness   The condition wherein a circular element line is the same radial distance at all azimuths from a center point at all cross sections independently taken normal to a derived axis (or the common center on a sphere) of the considered feature. (Circularity is the preferred term.)

Runout   Composite tolerance used to control the functional relationship of one or more features of a part to a datum axis.

Runout, circular   Composite two-dimensional tolerance departure of a circular element of the considered feature

with respect to a fixed point during one complete revolution about the datum axis, without axial movement of the part or measuring instrument.

Runout, total   Composite three-dimensional tolerance departure of a feature from a true geometric form, attitude, or position (as a composite), relative to a datum axis. The tolerance is applied to a zone that is verified over the entire considered feature as the part is rotated.

S

Section   The projection of the cut in an object made by a cutting plane.

Sectional view   A section of an object including features beyond the cutting plane.

Shaft basis system   A system wherein different clearances and interferences are obtained by associating various holes with a single shaft or with shafts of different grades having the same fundamental deviation. The basic shaft in this system generally has an upper deviation of zero.

Size   A generic term denoting magnitude of any kind.

Size tolerance   A "plus or minus" (unilateral or bilateral) or limit dimension, which designates magnitude and the allowable limits within which the size of the feature must lie.

Slope   The inclination of a surface expressed as the ratio of the difference in the heights (at each end) to the distance between the heights.

Specified datum   An explicit datum specified in a note, datum identification, or feature control frame.

Standard tolerance   Eighteen grades of tolerance (in the ISO system) called IT01, IT0, IT1 to IT16, the numerical values of which are given in tables or can be calculated for each nominal diameter step. For information on the U.S. system refer to ANSI B4.2.

Standard tolerance unit   In the ISO or U.S. System of Limits and Fits, a factor expressed only in terms of the basic size and used as a basis for the determination of the standard tolerances of the system. (Each tolerance is equal to the product of the value of the standard tolerance unit, for the considered basic size and a coefficient corresponding to each grade of tolerance.)

Stock   Items produced to established government or industry standards such as bars, sheets, tubing, etc., which prescribe dimensional and/or geometric tolerances. When "Stock" is specified on the drawing, the item remains in the as-furnished condition in the end item.

Straightness   Is that condition where an element of a surface or an axis is a straight line.

Subassembly   Two or more parts that form a portion of an assembly or a unit replaceable as a whole, but having a part or parts which are individually replaceable.

Surface texture   The finish on a surface generally specified in microinches, in standardized steps (e.g., 32, 63, 125). Applicable national standards are ANSI Y14.36 and ANSI B46.1.

Symbol   A mark, character, letter, or combination thereof that is nationally or internationally accepted for indicating an object, idea, or process. Geometric characteristic symbols represent a type of tolerance in lieu of words.

Symmetry (position)   Is that condition whereby a feature can be divided into two identical parts by an indicated line or plane.

System   A combination of parts and assemblies fitted together to perform a specific operational function or functions.

T

Tabulated assembly drawing   An assembly drawing showing similar configurations with the variations in assembly characteristics given in tabular form.

Tabulated drawing   A detail drawing showing similar configurations with variations in dimensions and features given in tabular form. Note: Sometimes referred to as a schedule.

Tangent plane, cylinder, or circle   A precise surface or mathematical model of ideal geometry that contacts the extremities (high points) of a surface or surface element.

Taper, conical or flat   The ratio of the difference in the height or diameter of the ends of a feature and the distance between the ends.

Tertiary datum   The third datum in the order of precedence in a three-plane system of three mutually perpendicular planes (datum reference frame). The datum feature from which the tertiary datum is located.

TIR   See *full indicator movement*.

Tolerance   The amount by which a specific dimension may vary. The difference between the maximum and the minimum limits. The allowable geometric variation of form, profile, orientation, position, or runout in the case of a geometric tolerance.

Tolerance diagram   The geometric reference frame with the tolerance zones superimposed on it.

Tolerance frame   A rectangular outline within which the geometric symbol, tolerances, datums, and other data are placed. This frame is used to specify geometric control to a feature.

Tolerance zone   The allowable boundaries within which the feature, surface element, center point, axis, or center plane must lie.

Total runout   Composite three-dimensional tolerance departure of an entire feature from a true geometrical form, attitude, or position (as a composite) as the part is rotated, relative to a datum axis, without axial movement of a part.

Transition fit   Limits of size so prescribed that either a clearance, line, or interference fit may result when mating parts are assembled.

True position   The theoretically exact (basic) location of a point, line, plane, or surface.

True position tolerance   The former name for positional tolerance.

U

Unilateral tolerance   A tolerance that has an allowable variation in only one direction from the nominal, (e.g., 28.00 + .02, 0; 28.00 0, − .02).

Unspecified angles   Features shown at 90° (implied); these are controlled by the tolerance block (or general note) for allowable angular variation.

Upper deviation   The algebraic difference (in the limit and fit system) between the maximum limit of size and the basic size of a considered feature.

V

Variation of fit   Arithmetical sum of the tolerances [and intentional slop (clearance) if designed in] of the two mating parts of a fit.

Verification equipment   The technical devices necessary for verification using a specific method.

Verification method   The verification methods are the practical applications of the verification principle through use of different equipment and operations.

Verification principle   The verification principle is a fundamental geometric basis for the verification of the considered geometrical characteristics.

Virtual condition   Of a feature—Limiting functional boundary permitted by the drawing data, which is generated by the collective effect of the maximum material size of the considered feature and the concerned form, orientation, runout, and/or location tolerance.

Of a group of features—Assembly of the virtual condition of all the features comprising the group in perfect geometric relationship as defined by the drawing data.

Virtual size   Dimension defining the actual virtual condition of a feature based on measured values.

Z

Zero line   In a graphical representation of limits and fits, straight line to which the deviations are referred, the zero line is the line of zero deviation and represents the basic size. By convention, when the zero line is drawn horizontally, positive deviations are shown above the line and negative deviations below it.

Zero tolerance at MMC   A tolerance specified as zero at MMC is dependent on the size of the feature involved. When the feature is at MMC the considered geometric tolerance is zero and may be increased an amount equal to the considered feature size departure from MMC.

CAD/CAM Glossary

A

Absolute coordinates The values of the X, Y, or Z coordinates with respect to the origin of the coordinate system.

Absolute data Values representing the absolute coordinates of a point or other geometric entity on a display surface. The values may be expressed in the units of the display or of the engineering drawing.

Acceptance test A test for evaluating newly purchased hardware or software. The hardware or software must conform to predefined specifications.

Access To retrieve and use a specific program or data.

Access time One measure of system response. The time interval between when data are requested from storage and when those data are displayed on the screen.

Accuracy Generally used to denote the number of digits to the right of the decimal point that can be used by a particular algorithm or system.

Acronym A word made from the first letters of words in a phrase (e.g., CAD is the acronym for computer-aided design).

Address The location of data or a program in storage.

Addressability A measure of picture resolution; the number of points that can be displayed on the screen.

Addressable point A position on the screen that can be specified by absolute coordinates.

Aiming device A pattern of light activated by a light pen on the display surface to assist positioning of the pen and to describe the pen's field of view. (See *cursor*.)

ALGOL ALGorithmic Oriented Language. A high-level programming language.

Algorithm A set of well-defined rules or procedures for solving a problem.

Aliasing Straight lines appear as jagged lines on a raster display if the display has low resolution.

Alphanumeric display A display that shows letters, numbers, and special characters. It allows the designer to enter commands and to receive messages from the system.

Alphanumeric keyboard A typewriterlike keyboard that allows a designer to communicate with the system.

Analog Data are represented by linear movement rather than the numbers 0 and 1 as with digital.

Annotation The process of adding text, notes, or identification to a drawing, map, or diagram.

ANSI American National Standards Institute. An association formed by industry and the U.S. government to produce and disseminate drafting and manufacturing standards.

Application software A computer program that assists a user performing a specific task.

APT (Automatically Programmed Tools) A computer language used to program numerically controlled machine tools.

Archive Placing infrequently used data in auxiliary storage.

Array A set of elements or components arranged in a pattern (e.g., a matrix).

Artificial intelligence The ability of a computer to perform tasks normally associated with human intelligence, such as reasoning, learning, and self-improvement.

Artwork A photoplot, photomask, pen plot, electrostatic copy, or positive or negative photographic transparency used to manufacture an IC, PC board, or other product.

ASCII American Standard Code for Information Interchange. A standard for representing characters in the computer.

Assembler The computer program that converts mnemonic instruction into equivalent machine language instructions.

Assembly language A computer-dependent language that corresponds one-to-one with the computer machine language instructions.

Associative dimensioning The means by which a CAD dimensioning program automatically updates the dimensions as the geometry changes.

Associativity The linking of parts, components, or elements with their attributes or with other geometric entities.

Attribute A nongraphic characteristic of a part, component, or element (e.g., length, diameter, name, volume, use, and creation date).

Automated Design System (ADS) Another term for computer-aided design system.

Automated drafting system Another term for computer-aided drafting system.

Automatic dimensioning The CAD system computes the dimensions and automatically places dimensions, extension lines, and arrowheads where required.

Autoplacement (TM) A Computervision software option that automatically packages IC elements and optimizes the layout of components on a PC board.

Autoroute (TM) A Computervision software option that automatically determines the placement of copper on the printed circuit board to connect part pins of the same signal.

Auxiliary storage Storage devices other than the main memory, also called peripheral storage (e.g., disk drives or magnetic tape).

B

Back annotation   Data are automatically extracted from a completed PC board and used to update the schematic. Information can also be back annotated into piping drawing and three-dimensional models.

Backup copy   A copy of a file that is kept for reference in case the original file is destroyed (e.g., safe keeping).

BASIC   Beginner's All-purpose Symbolic Instruction Code. A high-level algebraic programming language.

Batch processing   The running of a program or set of programs in a noninteractive mode.

Baud rate   A measure of the speed of signal transmission between the computer and the workstations. It is measured in bits per second.

Benchmark   A set of standards used in testing a software or hardware product or system from which a measurement can be made. Benchmarks are often run on a system to verify that it performs according to specifications.

Beta site   A CAD site selected for testing a new hardware or software enhancement before its sale to other customers of the vendor.

Bill of materials (BOM)   A listing of all the subassemblies, parts, materials, and quantities required to manufacture an assembly or to build a plant.

Binary code   The representation of all characters by using combinations of 0 and 1.

Bit   A binary digit. The smallest unit of information that can be stored and processed by a digital computer. It can only be a 0 or a 1. Computers are often classified by word size in bits, such as a 16-bit or 32-bit computer.

Bits per inch (BPI)   The number of bits of binary code that 1 in. of magnetic tape can store.

Boot up   To start up a computer.

Bootstrap   A routine whose first few instructions load the rest of the routine into the computer from storage.

Buffer   A software program or hardware device used to hold data, when transferring data from one device to another, if there is a difference in the time it takes the devices to process the data.

Bug   A flaw in a software program or hardware design that causes erroneous results or malfunctions.

Bus   A circuit or group of circuits that provides a communications path between two or more devices.

Byte   A sequence of 8 bits that are operated upon as a unit.

C

CAD (Computer-Aided Design)   A process whereby a computer assists in creating or modifying a design.

CAM (Computer-Aided Manufacturing)   A process employing computer technology to manage and control the operations of a manufacturing facility.

Cartesian coordinates   The distance of a point from any of three intersecting perpendicular planes; *X, Y, Z* coordinates.

Catalog   The directory of files contained in storage.

Cathode-ray tube (CRT)   A display device that creates images with a beam of electrons striking a screen.

Central Processing Unit (CPU)   The brain of a CAD system that controls the processing of information.

Character   A letter, number, or other symbol used to represent data. Symbols include the letters *A* through *Z*, numbers 0 through 9, punctuation marks, logical symbols, relational operators, and any other single symbol that may be interpreted by computer languages. A character is represented as a byte in the computer.

Characters per second (CPS)   The speed at which a device, such as a printer, can process data.

Chip   See *integrated circuit.*

CL file (cutter location file)   Output of an APT or graphics system that provides **X**, **Y**, and **Z** coordinates and NC information for machine tool processing.

COBOL   Common Business-Oriented Language. A high-level language oriented to business applications.

Code   A set of instructions that may be in machine language, assembly language, or a high-level language. Also may refer to an industry standard such as ANSI or ASCII.

COM   See *computer output microfilm.*

Command   An instruction given to a processor using a menu and tablet, stylus, or alphanumeric keyboard.

Command language   The language used by designers and drafters to operate a CAD system; it varies with each system.

Communication link   The physical connection, such as a telephone line, from one system to another or from one component to another.

Communications network   A number of systems linked together to exchange data.

Compatibility   The ability of a hardware module or software program to be used in a CAD system without modification.

Compiler   A program that translates high-level language instructions to machine language instructions that can be understood by the CPU.

Component   A subassembly or part that goes into higher level assemblies.

Computer   A data processor that can perform arithmetic and logical operations.

Computer architecture   The internal design of the parts of a computer system.

Computer graphics   A generic term applied to any discipline or activity that uses computers to generate, process, and display pictorial images.

Computer-Integrated Manufacturing (CIM)   A totally automated factory in which all manufacturing processes are integrated and controlled by a computer system.

Computer literacy   A basic understanding of computers and their use.

Computer network   Two or more interconnected computers.

Computer Numerical Control (CNC)   Using a computer to store numerical control instructions, generated by a CAD system, to control a machine.

Computer output microfilm   The image of a drawing plotted on 35-mm film at a small scale by a beam of light. Microfilm containing computer-generated data; also to place computer-generated data on microfilm.

Computer program   A set of software commands that instructs the computer to perform specific operations, often called a software program or software package.

Computer word   A sequence of bits or characters treated as a unit.

Configuration   A particular combination of computer software, hardware, and peripherals at a single installation.

Connect node   An attachment point for lines or text.

Connection   The lines between pins, components, contacts, or circuits in printed circuit board and writing diagram construction.

Construction plane   A predefined or operator-defined plane on which digitized points are projected.

Conversational mode   A mode of operation for a data processing system in which each unit of input entered by the user elicits a prompt response from the computer.

Coordinate dimensioning   A system of dimensioning in which points are defined as being a specified distance and direction from a reference point.

Copy   To reproduce a design in a different location on the screen or to duplicate a file and its contents.

CPU   See *central processing unit.*

Cross hairs   A horizontal line intersected by a vertical line to indicate a point on the display whose coordinates are desired.

Cursor   A special character, such as a small cross, on the screen that follows every movement of the stylus, light pen, or joystick.

Cut plane   A plane intersected with a three-dimensional object to derive a sectional view.

D

Data   Elements of information.

Data bank   The total collection of information used by an organization.

Data entry   Data entered by an operator from an input device such as a card reader, keyboard, or disk.

Data extract   The capability to obtain information from the database.

Data management   The control of access to information, information storage conventions, and the use of input and output devices.

Data processing system   A system that accepts information, processes it in a specific manner, and produces the desired results.

Data tablet   A graphical input device consisting of a board area capable of monitoring the position of a pen-shaped stylus.

Database   An organized collection of standard parts libraries, completed designs, documentation, and computer programs.

Debugging   Detecting and removing programming errors (bugs) from programs.

Dedicated   Assigned to a single function, such as a workstation used exclusively for engineering calculations.

Default   The predetermined value of a parameter that is automatically supplied by the system whenever that value is not specified by the user.

Delete   To erase information from the computer's memory or from storage.

Delimiter   A space, slash, asterisk, or other mark that separates data within a continuous string.

Design Automation (DA)   Using a computer to automate portions of the design process.

Design file   The information in a CAD database that relates to a design project.

Detail drawings   The drawing of a single part with all the dimensions and annotations necessary to define the part completely for manufacturing and inspection.

Device   A hardware item such as a cathode-ray tube, plotter, printer, or hardcopy unit.

Diagnostics   Computer programs that test a system or its key components to detect and isolate malfunctions.

Digit   Either 0 or 1 in binary notation; 0 through 9 in decimal notation.

Digital   The representation of data as combinations of the numbers 0 and 1.

Digitize   To convert lines and shapes into digital form.

Digitizer   A table or tablet on which the designer moves a puck or stylus to selected points and enters coordinates for lines and shapes by pressing down the input button on the puck or stylus.

Direct Numerical Control (DNC)   Using a shared computer to distribute part program data to remove machine tools.

Directory   The location on the disk where the names of files and information about them are stored.

Disk   A circular plate of magnetic media on which information is stored.

Disk drive   The device that reads data from or writes data on magnetic disks.

Disk storage   The use of magnetic disks as a storage device.

Display   The part of the workstation that shows the image of the data; usually refers to a cathode-ray tube.

Display elements   Points, line segments, and characters that are used to describe an object on the display.

Display group   A collection of display elements that can be manipulated as a unit and that may be further combined to form larger groups.

Display image   The collection of display elements shown together on the display device.

Display menu   A display option that allows an operator to select the next action by indicating one or more choices with an input device.

Display parameters   Data that control the appearance of graphics (e.g., choice of solid or dashed lines).

Display space   The usable area of the display surface that includes all addressable points.

Documentation   The general description, user's manual, and maintenance manual necessary to operate and maintain the system.

Down   The term used to describe a computer or device that is not working.

Drum plotter   An electromechanical pen plotter that draws a picture on paper or film mounted on a drum using a combination of plotting head movement and drum rotation.

Dumb terminal   A terminal that can only communicate with a host computer and cannot function in a stand-alone mode.

Dump   To transfer all the data accumulated on the system during a given period to permanent storage.

Dynamic movement   The ability to zoom, scroll, and rotate the image on the screen interactively.

E

Edit   To change, add, or delete data.

Electrical schematic   A diagram of the logical arrangement of hardware in an electrical system that uses standard component symbols.

Electrostatic plotter   Wire nibs, spaced 100 to 200 nibs per inch, that place dots where needed on a piece of paper to generate a drawing.

Element   The lowest level design entity with an identifiable logical, electrical, or mechanical function; a basic geometric unit (e.g., point, line, arc, or circle).

Emulation   The use of a computing system to execute programs written for another system.

Enhancements   Software or hardware improvements, additions, or updates.

Entity   The fundamental building blocks that a designer uses to represent a product (e.g., arc, circle, line, text, point, line, figure, nodal line).

Ergonomic   Designed with the needs of the user in mind.

Error file   File generated during data processing to retain information about errors during the process.

Execute   To carry out an instruction or perform a routine.

F

Family of parts   A collection of previously designed parts with similar geometric characteristics but differing in physical measurement.

Fetch   To locate data in storage and load it into the computer.

Field   A specific area in a string of characters or a record.

Figure   A symbol or a part that may contain other figures, attributes, and associations.

File   A name set of data on magnetic disk or tape; also to transfer the contents of working storage to permanent storage.

File management system   A software system that provides control of input, output, physical storage, and logical relationships for data files.

File protection   The control of access to a file without proper authority and prevention from accidental erasure of data within a file.

Fillet   A rounded corner or arc that blends together two intersection curves, lines, or surfaces.

Finite Element Analysis (FEA)   The determination of the structural integrity of a part by mathematic simulation of the part and the forces acting on the part.

Finite Element Modeling (also **Method**) **(FEM)**   The creation of a mathematical model of a part for input to a finite element analysis program.

Finite elements   The subdivision of a complex structure into small pieces.

Firmware   Sets of instructions built into user-modifiable hardware.

Flatbed plotter   An electromechanical pen plotter that draws a picture on paper, glass, or film mounted on a flat table. The plotting head moves in both axial directions.

Flicker   The flashing on and off of the image on the screen.

Flip   The same as mirror-image projection.

Floppy disk   A flexible magnetic disk used to store data.

Flowchart   A graphical representation of the solution of a problem in which symbols are used to represent operations, data flow, and equipment.

Font, line   Repetitive patterns used to make a line more easily recognized (e.g., a solid, dashed, or dotted line).

Font, text   An assortment of characters of a given size and style.

Form flash   To project a constant pattern such as a report form, grid, or map as background for a display; synonymous with form overlay.

Format   The specific arrangement of data for a list or report, a preprinted drawing border (i.e., title block and zones).

FORTRAN   FORmula TRANslation. A high-level language primarily for scientific applications that uses mathematical formulas.

Full frame   A display image scaled to maximize use of the viewing surface of the area of a display device.

Function key   An area on the digitizing tablet or a key on a box or terminal that is used to enter a command.

Function keyboard   A part of the workstation that contains a number of function keys.

Function menu   The display or list of commands that the user can use to perform a task.

G

Glitch   Minor, often temporary, malfunction of computer hardware or software.

Graphic primitives   Simple geometric shapes such as lines, circles, cones, cylinders, ellipses, and rectangles that can be used to construct more complex shapes.

Graphics   Pictorial data such as points, lines, shapes.

Graphics tablet   A surface through which coordinate points can be transmitted using a cursor or stylus; another term for a digitizing tablet.

Grid   A matrix of uniformly spaced points displayed on the screen for approximately locating and digitizing a position or placing symbols in the creation of a schematic.

H

Hard disk   A hard metal disk sealed in a disk drive and used for storage.

Hardcopy   A copy on paper of what is shown on the screen; generated with an on-line printer or plotter.

Hardware   The computer, disk, magnetic tape, cathode-ray tube, and other physical components that comprise a system.

Hidden lines   Line segments that would ordinarily be hidden from view in a three-dimensional display of a solid object because they are behind other items in the display.

Hierarchy   A data structure consisting of different levels where certain objects are subdivisions of an object on a higher level.

High-level language   A programming language that is independent of any given computer and permits the execution of a number of subroutines through a simple command (e.g., BASIC, FORTRAN, PASCAL, and COBOL).

Host computer   The computer attached to a network providing services such as computation, database management, and special programs; the primary computer in a multiple computer operation.

I

Inches per second (IPS)   The number of inches of magnetic tape that can be recorded or read per second or the speed of a pen plotter.

In-house   Within an organization or company.

Initialize computer   To set counters, switches, or addresses to 0 or to other starting values at the beginning of a program or routine.

Initialize disk   To prepare a disk to store information in the format of the particular operating system being used.

Input   To enter data or a program into the system.

Input device   Devices such as graphic tablets or keyboards that allow the user to input data into the CAD system.

Input/Output (I/O)   Communications devices and the process by which communication takes place in a CAD system.

Input/output channel   The path for transmitting data in and out of the central processing unit.

Inquiry   A request for information from the computer.

Insert   To enter entities, figures, or information into a design that is on the display.

Instruction   Line of computer programming telling the computer what to do.

Instruction set   All the commands to which a computer will respond.

Integrated circuit (IC)   An electronic component that may vary in complexity from a simple logic gate to a microprocessor. An IC is usually packaged in a single substrate as a slice of silicon; also called a chip.

Integrated system   A CAD system that integrates the entire product development cycle—analysis, design, and fabrication—into a single system.

Intelligent robot   A robot that can make decisions by using its sensing and recognizing capabilities.

Intelligent terminal   A terminal with local processing power whose characteristics can be changed under program control.

Interactive   Providing two-way instantaneous communication between a CAD system and its operators.

Interactive display terminal   A terminal consisting of one or more display devices and one or more input devices such as tablets, control balls, light pens, alphanumeric keyboards, function keys, and tape readers.

Interactive graphics   Capability to perform graphics operations directly on the computer with immediate feedback.

Interactive graphics system   A CAD system in which the workstations are used interactively for computer-aided design and drafting; often used synonymously with CAD.

Interconnection   The connection between one display entity or connection point on a component and another. On schematic drawings, interconnections are lines that connect elements.

Interface   A hardware or software link that enables two systems or a system and its peripherals to operate as a single, integrated system.

Interference checking   A CAD capability that allows plant or mechanical designers to examine a three-dimensional model and automatically pinpoint interfaces between pipes, equipment, structures, or machinery.

Interpreter   A software program that converts high-level language instructions to machine language instructions.

Isometric   A drawing in which the object is drawn from an oblique view so that it appears to be solid.

J

Jaggies   The jagged or sawtoothed appearance of lines on the screen when the screen has low resolution.

JCL   Job Control Language. A problem-oriented language used to express job requirements to an operating system.

Job   All necessary computer programs, linkages, files, and instructions for a unit of work.

Joystick   A CAD data entry device that uses a hand-controlled lever to move the cursor on the screen to enter coordinates' various points.

K

K   1,024, as in 1kbyte.

Keyboard   Resembles a typewriter and is used to enter instructions or coordinates into the computer.

Keypunch   A keyboard-actuated device that punches holes in cards.

Kinematics   A process for simulating the motion of mechanisms to study interference, acceleration, and forces.

L

Large-scale computer   A computer with large internal memory capacity and multiple input/output channels. Such computers can process many programs concurrently.

Layer   A logical concept used to distinguish subdividual groups of data within a given drawing, it may be thought of as a series of transparencies overlayed in any order without any depth.

Layer discrimination   The selective assignment of colors to a layer or the highlighting of entities to distinguish among data on different layers displayed on a screen.

Layout   A to-scale drawing of the physical components and the mechanical and electrical arrangements of a part, product, or plant.

Library   A collection of symbols, components, shapes, or parts stored in the CAD database as templates for future design work on the system.

Light pen   A penlike device used in conjunction with a vector-refresh screen that identifies displayed elements from the light sources on the screen.

Line printer   A peripheral device that prints alphanumeric data one line at a time.

Line speed   The rate at which signals can be transmitted over a communications line, usually measured in bauds or bits per second.

LIS (Large Interactive Surface)   An automated drafting table used to plot and/or digitize drawings; also called a digitizer table.

Load   To enter data into computer memory for later processing on the system.

Local Area Network (LAN)   A communications network in which all of the computers and workstations are in the same general area or building.

Log-off   To follow the procedure by which a user ends a workstation session.

Log-on   To follow the procedure by which a user begins a workstation session.

Loop   A sequence of instructions that is executed repeatedly in the computer until stopped by an operator or some predetermined condition.

M

Machine   A computer.

Machine instruction   An instruction that a computer can recognize and execute.

Machine language   The set of instructions, in combinations of the numbers 0 and 1, used directly by a computer.

Macro   A combination of commands executed as a single command.

Magnetic disk   A flat, circular plate with a magnetic surface on which data can be recorded and from which data can be read. The data can be randomly accessed.

Magnetic drum   A cylinder with a magnetic surface on which data can be recorded and from which data can be read.

Magnetic tape   A tape with a magnetic surface on which data can be recorded and from which data can be read. The data can only be sequentially accessed. The access speed is constrained by the location of the data on the tape, the speed of the tape drive, and the density of the data on the tape.

Main memory   The principal storage device of a computer-system—an integral part of the computer; generally, just called *memory*.

Main storage   The general-purpose storage of a computer, program addressable, from which instructions can be executed and from which data can be loaded directly into registers.

Mainframe   In general, the central processing unit of a large-scale computer configuration.

Management Information System (MIS)   A system that can store, retrieve, process, and output data to help management in its decision-making functions.

Mass storage device   Auxiliary or bulk memory that can store large amounts of data readily accessible to the computer (e.g., a disk or magnetic tape).

Matrix   A two- or three-dimensional rectangular array of identical symbols or entities.

Megabyte   Approximately one million bytes.

Menu   A table of available commands, either on a digitizing tablet or on the screen, that can be selected instead of using the keyboard.
one set.

Merge   To combine two or more sets of related data into

Microcomputer   A small, relatively low-cost computer that includes a microprocessor, memory, and all necessary interface circuits. Home or personal computers such as Apple, IBM-PC, and TRS-80 are examples of microcomputers.

Microprocessors   A single integrated circuit that is the central processing unit of a microcomputer.

Minicomputer   A computer that is between the mainframe computers and the microcomputers in size, power, complexity, and cost; generally, a 32-bit computer.

Mirror-image projection   In computer graphics, the reflection of display elements or groups with respect to a specific straight line or plane; synonymous with *flip* or *reflect*.

Mnemonic   Short words that represent complete sentences or phrases of instructions.

Model   An accurate three-dimensional representation of a part, assembly, or plant designed on a CAD system and stored in the database.

Modeling   Constructing a mathematical or analytical model of a physical object or system for analysis.

MODEM   MOdulator-DEModulator. A device that converts digital signals into analog signals for transmission over telephone lines. The analog signals are converted back to digital signals at the other end by another modem.

Modularity   The method of assembling a system by using components that can be replaced individually.

Monitor A display for computer output, either monochrome or full color, that is usually a cathode-ray tube.

Motherboard The large printed circuit board at the bottom of a computer to which chips, other boards, and components are attached.

Mouse A hand-held data entry device, about the size of a cigarette pack, that can be used without a digitizing pad. It can be used like a puck.

Multiprocessor Computer architecture that can execute one or more computer programs using two or more processing units simultaneously.

N

Nesting Embedding data in levels of other data so that certain routines or data can be executed or accessed continuously in loops.

Network Two or more central processing facilities that are interconnected.

Node A computer or workstation connected to a local area network.

Numeric keypad A calculator-type numeric input device that is generally part of the keyboard.

Numerical Control (NC) The control of machine tools, drafting machines, and plotters by punched paper or magnetic tape encoded with the proper information to cut a part or draw a figure.

O

Off-line Equipment or devices in a system that are not under direct control of the system's computer.

On-line Equipment or devices in a system that are directly connected to and under the control of the system's computer.

Operating system The software that controls the execution of computer programs and all hardware activity; also called system software.

Operation An action that a computer is instructed to perform, such as add, subtract, store, read, or write.

Operator The person who performs the input and output functions at a workstation.

Order To place in sequence according to rules or standards.

Origin An *X-Y,* or *X-Y-Z* coordinate from which all figures and entity locations are referenced.

Orthographic The method of making a layout, drawing, or map in which the projecting lines are perpendicular to the plane of the drawing or map.

Output The end result of a process or series of processes, such as artwork, hardcopy, reports, and drawings.

Output device Hardware, such as a printer or plotter, used to produce a copy of the results of the computer's processing operations.

Overlay To position one or more drawings on top of another and view them simultaneously on the screen.

P

Pad An area of plated copper on a PC board to which leads of components are soldered.

Paint To fill in a bounded figure on a display using a combination of repetitive patterns or line fonts.

Pan To scroll the view of an object on the screen.

Paper tape punch/reader A peripheral device that can read or punch perforated components.

Parallel interface An interface that transfers several signals at once.

Parameter A variable that controls the effect and usage of a command.

Part A product, assembly, subassembly, or component.

Part programming language A language that describes machining operations so that they are understood by computers or controllers.

Pascal A high-level programming language frequently preferred by computer scientists for its more logical structure and greater power.

Passive graphics The use of a display terminal in a noninteractive mode, usually through such items as plotters and microfilm viewers.

Passive mode A method of operating a display device that does not allow any on-line interaction or alteration.

Password A unique string of characters that a programmer, computer operator, or user must enter to gain access to data.

Path The route that an interconnection takes between connections in printed circuit board design.

Pattern generation The transformation of CAD integrated circuit design information into a format for use by photo-beam or electron-beam machines in producing a reticle.

PC Printed circuit or, more commonly, a personal computer.

Pen plotter An electromechanical CAD output device that draws a picture on paper or film using a ballpoint pen or liquid ink.

Perforated tape An input or output medium that uses punched holes along a continuous strip of nonmagnetic tape to record and store data.

Performance, CRT How well the cathode ray tube meets specifications such as screen resolution, display writing speed, internal intelligence, working area, accuracy, and precision.

Performance, system How well a system meets specifications such as speed, capacity, accuracy, and the productivity ratio of CAD versus manual methods.

Peripherals Devices connected to a computer such as tape drives, disks, workstations, and plotters.

Permanent storage The location, outside the central processing unit, where completed data are stored (e.g., a disk or tape).

Photoplotter A device used to generate artwork photographically for PC boards.

Pixels   PICture ELements. Individual dots on a display screen that are illuminated to create an image. Pixels are evenly spaced on the display.

PL/1   Programming Language/1. A high-level programming language used in a wide range of commercial and scientific applications.

Plot   Drawing by pen, pencil, or electrostatics of a design on paper film to create a drawing.

Plotter   An automated device used to produce accurate drawings. Plotters include electrostatic, photoplotter, and pen.

Point   An element that represents a single **X-Y-Z** coordinate.

Polar coordinates   The two numbers that locate a point by (1) its radial distance from the origin and (2) the angle that a line through this point makes with the *X*-axis.

Postprocessor   A software program or procedure that interprets graphical data and formats it for use by an NC machine or by other computer programs.

Power supply   A transformer that reduces voltage and changes AC to DC to provide electrical power to the computer.

Preprocessor   A method of converting data into computer-usable form for processing and output.

Processor   The hardware components that perform arithmetic and logic operations, often called the *computer*.

Program   The complete sequence of instructions to the computer to perform a task.

PROM   Programmable Read-Only Memory. A read-only integrated circuit that can be programmed.

Prompt   A message or symbol appearing on the screen that informs the user of a procedural error, incorrect input to the program being executed, or the next expected action.

Properties   Nongraphic entities that may be associated. Properties in electrical design may include component name and identification, color, wire size, pin number, lug type, and signal values.

Protocol   The format of signals between two computer systems or between a computer and its peripherals that allows them to communicate.

Puck   A hand-held device that enables the user to digitize a drawing placed on the digitizer surface.

Q

Quality control   The establishment and maintenance of standards to assure well-made products.

Quality engineering   The performance and interpretation of tests to measure product quality.

Queue   A waiting list of tasks to be performed or messages to be transmitted.

R

Random access memory (RAM)   A main memory storage unit that provides direct access to the stored information; memory from which data can be retrieved regardless of input sequence.

Raster   The geometric coordinate grid dividing the display area of a display device.

Raster display   A CAD workstation display in which the entire screen surface is a matrix of pixels and the image is scanned at a constant refresh rate. The bright, flicker-free image can be selectively written and erased.

Raster scan   A line-by-line sweep across the entire screen surface to generate the image. The device can display a large amount of information without flicker.

Rasterize   The process of converting an image into a corresponding pattern of dots.

Read-only memory (ROM)   A storage device (memory) generally used for control programs, the content of which is not alterable.

Real time   Immediate feedback to the user from tasks or functions executed by a CAD system. Immediate feedback through the workstation makes interactive operation of a CAD system possible.

Record   Related data processed as a unit.

Reflect   The same as mirror-image projection.

Refresh   CRT display technology requiring continuous redrawing of the display image.

Refresh rate   The rate at which the image on a screen is redrawn (e.g., 30 times/second or 30 Hz).

Reliability   The amount of time a system is running with no problems versus the downtime.

Remote terminal   An input or output peripheral located at a distance from the computer.

Repaint   Redraw a display image on a CRT to reflect its updated status.

Repeatability (of display device)   A measure of the hardware accuracy or the coincidence of successive retraces of a display element.

Replicate   To generate an exact copy of a design on the screen at any location or scale desired.

Resolution   The smallest spacing between points on a graphic device at which the points can be detected as distinct.

Response time   The elapsed time from the completing of a command at a workstation to the display of the results at that workstation.

Restart   To resume execution of an interrupted computer program.

Restore   To return a design to its original configuration after editing or modification.

Robotics   The use of computer-controlled robots to automate manufacturing processes such as welding, material handling, painting, and assembly.

Rotate   To turn a displayed image about an axis through a predefined angle.

Router   A program that automatically determines the routing path for the component connections on a PC board.

Routine   A computer program. A set of instructions arranged in proper sequence to cause a computer to perform a desired operation.

Routing   Placing the interconnects between components on a printed circuit board or integrated circuit.

Rubberbanding   A technique for displaying a straight line with one end fixed and the other end attached to the movable cursor.

Run   To execute a program.

S

Satellite   A remote system, connected to a host system, that contains processors, memory, and mass storage to operate independently from the host.

Save   To transfer the data created at the workstation to a storage device.

Scale   To enlarge or shrink an image without changing its shape.

Schematic   A not-to-scale diagram of an electrical circuit.

Scissor   To trim a drawing in the database so that it can be viewed on a CRT screen.

Screen   A computer display device, also called a *monitor* or *cathode-ray tube*.

Scroll   To roll up automatically on a screen, as on a spool, a message or drawing too large to be displayed all at once.

Section   To cut an object with an intersecting plane, then request generation and display of the total intersection geometry on a display surface.

Security   Safeguards and procedures that can be applied to computer hardware, programs, and data to assure that access to the system is controlled.

Selective erase   The deletion of portions of a design without repainting the entire screen.

Semiconductor   A material that conducts electricity and is used for the storage and transfer of computer data (e.g., silicon).

Serial interface   A connection that transfers data sequentially, one bit at a time.

Shape fill   The automatic shading of an area on the screen.

Silicon   The basic material used in the manufacturing of computer chips. See *semiconductor*.

Silk screen   Artwork used in print component placement and identification information on a printed circuit board.

Simulate   To imitate the behavior of a finished part under various structural and thermal loading conditions.

Software   The computer programs, procedures, rules, and instructions that control the use of the hardware.

Solid model   Solid models represent the mass and the boundary of a complete form.

Sort   To segregate items into groups according to specified criteria (e.g., to alphabetize).

Source   User-written instruction statements prior to translation by the computer into a form that can be executed by machine.

Spline   A smooth curve between a sequence of points in one place.

Storage   The physical device or location that contains all of the information on a CAD system.

Storage device or storage unit   A peripheral component in which data can be stored and later retrieved.

Storage tube   A CRT that retains an image for a considerable period of time without redrawing. It allows no selective editing or erasing.

String   A sequence of characters such as a word or sentence.

Stylus   A hand-held object that provides coordinate input to the display device.

Surface machining   The ability to output 3-, 4-, and 5-axis NC toolpaths using three-dimensional surface definition capabilities (e.g., ruled surfaces, tabulated cylinders, and surfaces of revolution).

Surface of revolution   Rotation of a curve around an axis through a specified angle.

Symbol   A set of primitive graphic entities, lines, points, arcs, circles, and text that are grouped together as a unit. Symbols may be combined or nested to form larger symbols or drawings.

Syntax   The set of rules that describes the structure of statements in a computer language.

System   All of the people, machines, and methods needed to perform a specific task.

T

Tablet   An input device that a designer can use to digitize coordinate data or enter commands into a CAD system by means of a stylus or puck, also called a *digitizing pad*.

Tape drive   The peripheral device that records and reads magnetic tape.

Telecommunications   The transmission of signals over long distances between a computing system and remotely located devices by telephone, microwave, infrared link, or coaxial cable.

Telewriter   A typewriterlike keyboard device used to enter commands or to print system messages.

Template   A commonly used component or part that serves as a design aid and can be subsequently traced instead of redrawn whenever needed. The CAD equivalent of a designer's template is a symbol in the symbol library.

Temporary storage   A location in memory for temporarily storing results of a program on the system until the results can be transferred to permanent storage; also called *working storage*.

Terminal   A device equipped with a keyboard and some kind of display that sends and receives information over a communication channel to and from a computer.

Text   Letters, numbers, and special characters.

Text editor   A program used to create and modify text on the system.

Text file   A file stored in the system that consists entirely of text.

Throughput   The work performed by a CAD system or workstation during a given period of time; a quantitative measure of system productivity.

Thumbwheels   A CAD input device that uses a manually controlled vertical wheel for locating a coordinate on the Y axis, and a horizontal wheel for locating a coordinate on the X axis.

Timesharing   The concurrent use of a computing system in which two or more users can execute computer programs simultaneously, usually from remote terminals.

Tolerance   The allowed variance from a given nominal dimension.

Tool path   A trace of the movement of the tip of a numerical control cutting tool that is used to guide or control machining equipment.

Tracking   Moving a cursor across the surface of the screen with a light pen, stylus, or puck.

Tracking symbol   A symbol such as a cross, dot, angle, or square used for indicating the position of a stylus.

Transistor   An electronic switch that transmits a signal of either 0 or 1 to communicate information in binary machine language. A semiconductor device often made of silicon.

Translate   To change data from one language to another.

Transportability   The ability to execute a program on different computers without major changes.

Tree   A method of file storage in which the file structure has a top level and one or more sublevels, which in turn may contain additional sublevels.

Turnaround time   The elapsed time between the start and finish of a task or project.

Turnkey system   A CAD system for which the vendor assumes total responsibility for building, installing, and testing all the hardware and software required to do a specific application or applications; a computer system sold in a ready-to-use state.

Tutorial   A message that is displayed to show the user how to perform a task.

U

Up   A term used to denote that the computer is working properly.

Updating   Changing a file by adding, modifying, or deleting information.

User-friendly   A CAD system (both hardware and software) that is easy to understand and operate.

Utility program   A specific system software program such as a diagnostic program, a plot program, or a sort program.

V

Vector   A directed line segment that has magnitude and direction.

Vector generation   The process that determines all intermediate points between two endpoints of a line segment.

Verification   The message feedback to a display device acknowledging that an input was detected (e.g., the brightening of a display element selected by a light pen).

Version   A configuration control identifier that is changed whenever there are modifications or enhancements.

Via   A hole in a printed circuit board through which a path from one layer or side is transferred to the other.

View port   A user-selected viewing area on the screen that frames the contents of a window.

W

Wafer   A slice of silicon from which a larger number of integrated circuit chips are produced.

Winchester drive   A combination of a disk drive and one or more hard disks permanently sealed in a case.

Window   A portion or view of a design that is framed by a view port.

Windowing   Proportionally enlarging a figure or portion of a figure so it fills the screen or view port.

Wire frame   A picture of a three-dimensional object displayed on the screen as a series of lines that represent the edges of its surfaces. This picture looks as if it were made from coat hangers.

Wiring diagram   A schematic representation of all circuits and devices that shows their interconnectivity.

Word processing (WP)   The use of a special program to create, edit, store, display, and print text.

Working drawing   A detailed layout of components with complete dimensions and notes.

Workstation   The hardware by which a designer interacts with the computer; also called a *terminal*.

Write   To copy information from main memory to a storage device.

Write protect   A security feature that prevents existing data from being erased by new data.

Z

Z clipping   The ability to specify depth parameter for a three-dimensional drawing such that all elements above or below the specified depth(s) become invisible. No change is made to the database of the part or drawing; useful in viewing cluttered or complex part geometry.

Zoom   The successive enlargement or shrinking of the image on the screen.

CAD–Manual Comparative Glossary

	Manual Definition	CAD Definition
Accuracy, design	Positional accuracy in critically tight areas determined graphically on large–scale study work-plot or manual calculations.	Positional accuracy in tight areas can be viewed graphically at any infinitely large scale and checked by requesting dimensional readout; used in interference checking.
Accuracy, drafting	Depending on scale of drawing, measure of positional accuracy of drawing elements. May be .01 inches (0.0254 mm) at best, if on dimensionally stable material.	Regardless of drawing scale, positional accuracy is plotted at .001 inches (0.0254 mm), while database coordinates are accurate to 14 decimal places.
Add	Arithmetic or design/drafting function.	To sum, by computer, like items or parts; augment a design or drafting image with further graphic, dimensional, or alphanumeric information.
Add text	Letter or type additional alphanumeric notation.	Type at workstation keyboard additional alphanumeric notation which is electronically placeable at preselected text nodes.
Algorithm	A predefined sequence of steps to be taken to solve problems of a particular type; a procedure attributed to an Uzbek mathematician: Al-Khwarizmi in ninth century.	A predefined program of steps to be followed by computer to solve problems of software furnished by CAD supplier to solve typical problems.
Align	Place in line, as in parallel to a reference or object line.	Automatically line up design features, shapes, symbols, text, etc., parallel to a reference or object line.
Annotate	Complement dimensioned drawing with explanatory text, labels, general notes, special notes, reference notes, subtitles, and titles.	Add explanatory text, labels, general notes, etc.; electronically copy and place repetitious notation common to many symbols, drawing segments, or drawings.
Array	In drafting, the alignment in X and Y of similar design entities or tabulated data.	Electronic alignment in **X**, **Y**, and **Z** of similar design entities or tabulated data.
Assemble	Place related units or parts into predetermined positions.	Electronically place related units or parts into predetermined positions as in arrangement and assembly drawings. Units or parts may be electronically copied from other drawings in the database.
Assign	Schedule or reserve a position for an activity or a drawing segment.	Schedule or reserve a position for an activity, data, symbol or drawing segment to a layer, drawing coordinate, model, or disk memory space.
Auto, revise		Revise all drawing segments, subtitles, titles, drawing numbers at each occurrence of faulty data in database; effect change with one command, on one or all drawings or documents of a set (see *Revise*).
Auxiliary view	See *View, auxiliary.*	See *View, auxiliary.*
Axis	One of a set of three lines intersecting at a common point in space in such a way that each axis is perpendicular to the plane containing the other two.	Same as manual definiton.
BASIC		A computer language: Beginners All-purpose Symbolic Instruction Code.
Batch process		Without benefit of interactivity by CRT; digitizer; tablet or keyboard; a means for creating alphanumeric and/or graphic output from data processed by any computer.
Baud		A unit of signaling speed equal to the number of discrete conditions or signal events per second.

	Manual Definition	CAD Definition
Bill of material	A listing of parts or items required to fabricate, assemble, or erect an engineering design. Also BOM or BOM list.	A computer listing (lettered on drawing or tabulated on printer) of parts or items represented on an engineering design, automatically derived from the database.
Blank, line	Erase line from drawing.	Electronically erase from view on screen, but leave in database for ultimate reuse or elimination.
Blank, model	Erase all views of a design feature on all drawings.	Electronically erase from view on screen, but leave in database for ultimate reuse, modification, or elimination.
Blank, screen		Electronically erase all data from view on screen, but leave in database for ultimate reuse, modification, or elimination.
Blank, submodel	Erase all views of a design on all drawings.	Electronically erase from view on screen, but leave in database for ultimate reuse, modification, or elimination.
CAD		Interchangeably: Computer-Aided Design or computer-aided drafting; a generic term used in the United States, Europe, and Japan.
COM		Computer-Output-Microfilm: an electromechanical system for transforming the digital version of an engineering design directly onto 35-mm microfilm or 105-mm microfiche images.
CPU		Central Processing Unit; that section of the computer that contains the control unit, the arithmetic unit, and memory.
Cartesian coordinates	A reference system similar to engineering LEFT-RIGHT, UP–DOWN, BACK–FORWARD, system for defining a point in three-dimensional space. Compares to projection planes: FRONTAL, HORIZONTAL, PROFILE.	A reference system along **X** (LEFT–RIGHT), **Y** (UP–DOWN), and **Z** (BACK–FORWARD); René Descartes' **X-Y-Z** system for defining a point in three-dimensional space.
Catalog	Compilation, in a printed book, of vendor's standard offerings; a reference document for designers.	Portion of the design database containing often-used vendor's or trade association's standard reference information, graphics, and dimensions.
Cathode-ray tube, refresh		Specialized type of CRT in which screen image is formed by continuously panning electron beam over phosphor-coated tube face, *rasterization*.
Cathode-ray tube, storage		Specialized type of CRT in which screen image is formed by electron-beam "stroking" phosphor-coated tube face.
Checking	Inspection or recalculation of engineering drawing data for compliance with original design, vendor's drawings, or catalog information.	Same as manual definition.
Class 1 drawing	A designation of drawing type: NONDIMENSIONED, NOT-TO-SCALE; usually schematic or diagrammatic.	Same as manual definition.
Class 2 drawing	A designation of drawing type: DIMENSIONED, NOT-TO-SCALE; usually with tabulated dimensions, but may be isometric (piping, etc.)	Same as manual definition, except designer has choice of electronically "rubberbanding" drawing to accurately reflect tabulated dimensions.
Class 3 drawing	A designation of drawing type: DIMENSIONED, TO SCALE.	Same as manual definition, except the three-dimensional model or submodel in database is source for two-dimensional (orthographic) views needed for working drawings.
Composite	A multilayered drawing; a series of special overlays viewable and reproducible with a base drawing to make a composite print.	Separable layers or overlays of graphic and/or alphanumeric data in the database; viewable on screen or plottable in any combination of base drawings or overlays.
Database	A collection of interrelated data items that must be assembled by each application thereby causing the "reinvention of the wheel" each time the database is needed.	A collection of interrelated data items organized by a consistent scheme that allows one or more applications to process the items without regard to physical storage locations.

	Manual Definition	**CAD Definition**
Delete	Remove from document.	Remove electronically from database; selectively remove portion of symbol or drawing segment, linework or text, and automatically remove all such occurrences on any drawing or document in the database.
Designer	Degreed or paraengineer who creates preliminary or working drawings and documentation from engineer's notes and sketches.	Operates input design workstations with interactive CAD processing system.
Digitize	Laborious scaling and recording X-Y-Z coordinates or drawing or map elements from an origin point.	Automatically recording by pointing—X-Y-Z coordinates as in manual definition; enters graphical data into a CAD system.
Digitizer		Old name for CAD drafters'/designers' input workstation; a computer-oriented device for automating graphic data reduction—process called *digitizing*.
Dimension	Annotate drawings with lettered dimensions to denote sizes of elemental shapes and areas as well as locations.	Automated placement of dimension lines—witness lines with typed or computer-supplied dimensions to denote size of elemental shapes and areas as well as locations.
Display	Show.	Command drawing or document to appear from database on the workstation screen.
Drafter	U.S. government-mandated term for man or woman performing engineering drafting; formerly draftsman, draughtsman, draftswoman, draftsperson.	An upgraded drafter; uses CAD input or output workstations interactively to conduct all drafting functions.
Drawing	Graphic representation with annotation of an engineered physical object; sketch.	Digital version of graphic and alphanumeric representation of an engineered physical object stored in database; electromechanically plotted graphic and alphanumeric representation of the object.
Drawing, layer	See *Composite*.	See *Composite*.
Drawing segment	A portion of complete drawing; may contain symbols and/or text.	A portion of complete drawing; a repeatable and electronically copied, reduced, or enlarged drawing segment for use on other drawings—with or without modification; a combination of symbols and/or text.
Drawing standards manual	Prepared by design/drafting management.	Same as manual definition, except for some special standards for CAD.
Drawings security	Method for protecting original documents (tracings) from theft or unauthorized alteration; usually by controlled access.	Method for protecting digital database from theft or unauthorized copying, alteration, or accidental erasure (see *Password*).
Edit	Review or proofread for possible revision.	Review or proofread on screen for possible revision; perform revision electronically.
Edit station–CAD		Workstation for inputting design or drafting changes to existing CAD drawing or document. Changes may be redesign, revision, construction ECO, or as-built data.
Enlarge	Make bigger than before.	Electronically causes the indicated portion of the picture to enlarge to fill screen. Operator can enlarge infinitely, until a decimal point, for example, is made to fill full 19-inch screen.
Erase	Rub out with abrasive material (erasure); remove with moist Q-tip as with water erasable ink on mylar; remove with No. 1 and No. 2 solution as on sepia print.	Remove electronically from database.
Font	A drafter's or printer's definition for unique sets of alphanumeric characters (e.g., Leroy lettering font, Futura type font).	Identifying name for lettering style or line characteristic (e.g., Leroy lettering font, dashed line font).
FORTRAN		FORmula TRANslation—a computer language universally used in engineering.
Graphics command language	May be instructions in design/drafting manual spelling out graphic procedures, drawing composition usage, text sizes, etc.	A CAD designer's "shorthand" for communicating desired graphic actions and responses to the system.

	Manual Definition	CAD Definition
Grid	A spaced array—graphical.	A design/drafting aid available as a placement background on the CRT screen. Grids may be square or stretch in **X**, **Y**, or **Z**.
Hidden line	A line on a drawing, usually shown dashed, representing an edge, contour, or surface that could be seen only if the object being drafted were transparent. May be omitted as well; must be constructed.	In three-dimensional work all hidden lines appear at first as object lines. Designer has option to "touch" each line with cursor, ask computer to make it dashed, or eliminate it from view.
Host computer or host CPU		Term usually given to a very large computer such as IBM-3081. May serve many minicomputers for data management and "number crunching."
Input/Output		Communication with processing system (computer). Facilities for "talking" to computer; give data, coordinates, instructions; receive answers, listings, drawings in readable form.
Interactive		A technique of designer communication in which the system immediately acknowledges and acts on requests entered by the designer at a workstation.
Isometric	A form of drawing projection in which three faces of an object or feature are shown on three major axes 120° apart and in which the angle the front edge makes with the vertical is 35°. True isometrics are to-scale drawings.	Same as manual definition.
Item	A component of a larger grouping or assembly; part of a design; a purchased unit under a single engineering specification used in fabrication, assembly, or erection.	A two-dimensional or three-dimensional symbol (cell), or submodel, an engineering database unit under a single specification; part; an elemental portion of a cell, submodel, or model.
Item select		A technique for selecting a symbol (cell) or submodel, including text, preparatory to executing a MOVE, COPY, or MIRROR command at the workstation.
Label	Hand-lettered note or "callout" identifying a drawing feature.	Computer-generated note or "callout" identifying a drawing feature.
Layer	See *Composite*.	See *Composite*.
Lettering, Leroy	See *Font*.	See *Font*.
Library	A cataloged collection of data.	Same as manual definition.
Line	A visible connection between two points in space.	Same as manual definition.
List		A command to request a list of items be printed by the system printer.
Macro		Directions that generate a known set of instructions. Used to eliminate the need to write a set of instructions that is used repeatedly.
Menu		An area of the digitizing tablet reserved for an array of commands. Allows choosing the commands with the stylus.
Metrication	The act of replacing, relettering, or recalculating nonmetric dimensions or values into SI units.	Automatic assignment and conversion of nonmetric dimensions or values into SI units, including roundoff.
Mirror	Create, by tracing back of drawing; an opposite-hand view of a portion of a design.	Electronically command, display, or plot an opposite-hand view of a portion of a design, wherein "mirrored" text remains right-reading.
Mirror, about line	Create opposite-hand view similar to or symmetrical about a line.	Electronically display or plot opposite-hand view; used in two-dimensional design only.
Mirror, about plane	Impossible to create without redrawing.	Electronically display or plot opposite-hand view; used in three-dimensional design only.
Model	A three-dimensional object used to obtain physical data for drawing information.	The three-dimensional object that is being constructed electronically in the computer.
MODEM	MODulator-DEModulator; device used to send and receive data in high-speed bulk mode over telephone lines.	Same as manual definition.

	Manual Definition	CAD Definition
Move	Completely erase and redraw or trace in a different location.	Electronically move a group of items without redrawing.
Orient	Line up with a known axis such as **X, Y,** or **Z.**	Line up working coordinating system to base coordinate system; in three-dimensional work line up item relative to submodel or submodel to model.
Orthogonal	At right angles to each other.	Same as manual definition.
Orthographic-projection	The projection of a point from one plane to another.	Same as manual definition.
Paint		Electronic drawing or lettering on the screen of a design.
Part	Elemental physical object or its symbolic representation; also, elemental portion of a drawing (i.e., point or line).	Same as manual definition; sometimes called *item*.
Password		A word or code required to gain access to the system.
Picture /	Any graphic representation.	The flat-plane (two-dimensional) view of a submodel or model, part of an engineering drawing to which dimensions, text, and titling will be added; a "window" portion of the complete design in database.
Plot		To get hardcopy output on a variety of plotters.
Plotter, belt		Upright high-speed pen (ballpoint or ink) plotter capable of handling drawings up to E size.
Plotter, electrostatic		A very high-speed plotter in which lines are formed by a matrix of dots.
Plotter, flatbed		Large tablelike pen (ballpoint or ink) plotter capable of handling very long drawings.
Plotter, microfilm		Computer-output microfilm (COM) recorder that converts mag tape version of a drawing or document from CAD database and records a miniature version on 35-mm microfilm or 105-mm microfilm.
Point	A visible dot to represent some coordinate in space.	Same as manual definition.
Process	An orderly method for attaining a given result.	A predesigned procedure for computer to aid in attaining a given design, drafting, or documentation result.
Process	To proceed, step-by-step, for attaining a given result.	Activate a predesigned software command(s) procedure to create a given result from data furnished by computer.
Repaint		Electronic "redraw or relettering" of latest status of a design, used right after a revision or edit has been executed, for designer to view corrections of revision or edit.
Revise	Alter existing tracing or document by erase-replace or redraw-retype.	Alter database—electronic erase and replace, seldom redraw.
Rubberband		Electronically "stretch" space between design components and have interconnected lines "stretch" also.
Ruler	Scale. A tool for linear measurement. May be architect's, engineer's, mechanical (machine), or metric.	A scalelike image with the ability to be placed electronically on screen, at any location or orientation as an aid for design layout at workstation. May be marked off as architect's, engineer's, mechanical (machine), or SI metric. English and metric units are interchangeable on command.
Save	Keep on file.	Same as manual definition.
Scale, architect's, USA	Measuring device marked off in units varying from 1/32 to 1/2 of an English inch.	Same as manual definition.
Scale, engineer's, USA	Measuring device marked off in units varying from 1/10 to 1/100 of an English inch.	Same as manual definition.
Scale, machine, USA	Measuring device marked off in equal units varying from 1/4 size to full size.	Same as manual definition.
Scale, metric, SI	Measuring device marked off in tenths of a millimeter or centimeter.	Same as manual definition.

	Manual Definition	CAD Definition
Screen	(Sometimes used to describe printers' Benday screen of dot patterns created photographically on a background site or structure drawings.)	TV-like picture tube; cathode-ray tube (CRT) may be storage, vector, or raster type.
Select	To choose.	Identify to the computer the portion of drawing to be acted on next.
Shift	To move.	Same as manual definition.
Skew	Place at an angle off plumb or level line.	Place at an angle off plumb, level, or depth line.
Smooth	Drafter's refinement of plotted-point spline using French curves.	Electronic refinement of known value point curve.
Space	Scale off on drawing positions for repetitive symbols, drawing segments.	Electronic scaling, positioning of repetitive points, symbols, or drawing segments by typing only the overall dimension and the number of units to be repetitively spaced and placed on the screen.
Spline curve	Cumbersome pliable metal strip used to draft varying radius curves through preplotted points on drawing or template (as in lofting).	Automatic curve-fit generator, with calculated offsets, through predetermined points for drawing or template plot (as in lofting, shipbuilding, or sheet metal).
Submodel	Portion of a three-dimensional object used to obtain physical data for drawing information.	Portion of a three-dimensional object that is being constructed geometrically.
Symbol library	Legend of symbols, names, and uses; key to symbols; may be plastic templates.	Digital version of symbols, by engineering discipline, instantly callable from symbol library database. Each symbol may contain associated text or preassigned space for varying text (see *Symbol transfer*).
Symbol template	Standard or custom, symbol cutout plastic template for tracing onto drawing; available by disciplines (e.g., piping, isometrics, electrical).	Not used (see *Symbol library*).
Symbol, transfer	"Rub-on" version of preprinted standard drafting symbols; used in photodrafting.	Digital version of standard or special symbol, library database. Electronically placeable, spaceable, or copyable anywhere on drawing in any orientation.
Tabular dimensioning	Listing of numerical values "keyed" to dimension letters. Used on typical details.	Same as manual definition.
Text node	Space reserved on drawing for later addition of alphanumeric characters, dimensions, etc.	A preselected space reserved on symbol (cell), drawing segment, or drawing for later addition, by keyboard typing of alphanumeric characters, dimensions, subtitles, and titles.
3D	Three-dimensional; relates to measurable volumes in engineering.	Three-dimensional; relates to measurable volumes X-Y-Z coordinates used to make orthographic views automatically.
2D	Two-dimensional; relates to measurable areas in engineering.	Two-dimensional; relates to measurable areas and symbols used for drawings (X-Y coordinates).
Trace	Recopy portion of repetitive drawing by tracing.	Electronically copy portion of repetitive drawing already in database.
View, auxiliary	Planar projection of a drawing portion not perpendicular to standard orthographic projection.	Same as manual definition.
Window		Portion of larger design area, filling the screen vertically and horizontally; the "distance" from which operator sees drawings or model; related to "scale."
Zoom	A photo technique for enlarging or reducing a portion of a drawing; a TV camera technique for enlarging or reducing field of view.	An electronic enlarge/reduce technique for changing scale on screen—infinitely, up or down.

A

ABS (acrylonitrile-butadiene-styrene) Plastic used in manufacturing drainage pipe and fittings.

Accumulator Container in which fluids or gases are stored under pressure. The term also refers to a holding tank used for temporary storage.

Actuator Any device that will operate a valve by remote control (fluid motor, air cylinder, hydraulic cylinder, electric motor).

Adjustability Ability of a pipe system and its support system to enable field installation and adequate functioning when the installation position differs from the design.

Alley, pipe Main bank of pipe headers located inside the limits of a structure; known as a pipe bridge when outside the limits.

Alloy steel Steel that owes its distinctive properties to elements other than carbon.

Anchor Rigid support that keeps the pipe from translation or rotation movement at one point along the piping system; also prevents transmission of forces and moments (thermal, shock, vibration) between both sides of the pipe.

Angle valve Valve designed so that the inlet and outlet are at a 90° angle to each other.

Annulus Doughnut-shaped duct or pipe.

Automatic valve Any valve whose position, as to degree of opening, is controlled by means other than manual.

B

Backflow Flow of a fluid in a pipe in the opposite direction to which it normally flows.

Backing ring Metal strip used to prevent melted metal from the welding process from entering a pipe when completing a butt-welded joint.

Ball valve Regulating valve that uses a ball with a hole through it to control the flow of fluid; normally has 90° open-and-shut operation.

Battery Group of similar reaction vessels or tanks.

Battery limit Lines used on a plot plan to determine the outside limits of a unit, usually established on the piping index drawing, plot plan, and site plan.

Bay line Line of structural steel columns that spans the width of a building; the "bay" is the space between two bay lines.

Bay of steel Steel surrounding a space bounded by the four nearest columns and the floor above.

Bell or hub Enlarged end of some types of pipe which fit over the next pipe section.

Bell and spigot joints Type of joint usually found in waste piping. The joint is sealed by some sort of packing.

Bend Vertical plane of steel structure that extends along a column row in a building; consists of two columns with horizontal connecting members. In a pipe rack, the bent is two columns and one or more horizontal connecting members which form a U shape.

Bend angle (pipe) Angle at the center of the bend between radial lines from the beginning and end of the bend to the center.

Black pipe Steel pipe that is not galvanized.

Blank flange Flange in which the bolt holes have not been drilled.

Blind flange Solid platelike fitting used to seal the end of a flanged-end pipeline; also known as dead end.

Blowdown tank Vessel into which line material or contents of another vessel can be emptied immediately in an emergency.

Boiler Vessel in which water is heated to generate steam under pressure.

Boiler, fire-tube Boiler system with heating tubes located within the shell. The use of tubes submerged in boiling water increases the area of contact between the water and the fire gases passing through the tubes.

Boiler, water-tube Reverse of the fire-tube boiler. Hot gases are in contact with the outside surface of the tubes and the water is inside.

Bonnet Upper portion of the gate valve body into which the disk of a gate valve rises when it is opened.

Branch Pipe, usually of small diameter, that enters into or exits from the main run pipe.

Branch tee Tee having multiple branches.

Braze weld or brazing Process of joining metals using a nonferrous filler metal or alloy, the melting point of which is higher than 800°F but lower than that of the metals to be joined.

Breakout flange Flanges placed in pipeline in order that that part of the line may be removed to facilitate maintenance work.

Bushing Tapped or threaded fitting (male outside, female inside) used to reduce the size of the end opening of a fitting or valve.

Butt weld Circumferential weld in pipe fusing the abutting pipe walls completely from inside wall to outside wall.

Butt-welded pipe Pipe welded along a seam, edge to edge and not scarfed or lapped.

Bypass Pipe loop that provides partial or full flow of material around a piece of equipment or valve station.

C

Cap   Fitting that seals the end of a pipe permanently.

Cap end   End enclosure of a vessel. Can be dished elliptical or flanged and bolted.

Carbon steel   Steel owing its distinctive properties chiefly to the various percentages of carbon (as distinguished from the other elements) that it contains.

Centrifugal pump   Impeller-type pump with suction at the center that discharges tangentially by the use of volutes.

Check valve   Valve that permits flow in one direction only.

Chemical plant   Plant that utilizes various hydrocarbon products from refineries to produce other products for consumer and industrial use.

Clevis   U-shaped or stirrup-shaped device used to connect two or more lifting members. Usually referred to as a shackle.

Close nipple   Shortest length of a given size pipe which can be threaded externally from both ends; used to connect closely two internally threaded pipe fittings.

Codes   Standards that provide industry with recognized specifications for convenience, safety, and uniform design.

Cold bending   Bending process for pipes with diameters (up to 42 in.) and walls (up to $\frac{3}{4}$ in.). Wrinkling, excessive thinning, and ovality can be avoided with proper equipment and fixtures.

Cold joint   Solder joint made with inadequate heat, or the two parts have been moved slightly as the solder is solidifying.

Column   Vertical vessel used for fractional distillation; also called tower or stanchion. Column also refers to vertical steel structural members for buildings, pipe racks, etc.

Column line   Straight row of steel columns represented on a model or drawing.

Companion flange   Any flange suited to connect with a flanged valve or fitting or with another flange to form a joint.

Compressor   Mechanical (piston and cylinder) device used to increase the pressure of air or gas.

Concentric reducer   Piping fitting used to reduce the size of pipe so that the pipe may be continued in a smaller size. The reducer's shape is such that the centerlines of the larger and smaller pipes are in a straight line.

Conduit   Structural covering for electrical lines made from a variety of materials (plastics, steel, aluminum). Conduit provides the strength needed to run electrical lines throughout an industrial installation.

Control valve   Automatic valve operated electrically, pneumatically, or hydraulically and used to regulate flow, temperature, pressure, etc.

Controller   Mechanism that operates a valve; it can be manual or automatic.

Coupling   Pipe fitting containing female threads on both ends. Couplings are used to join two or more lengths of pipe in a straight run or to join a pipe and a fixture.

Coupling, dresser   Coupling used for connecting plain-ended pipes.

Cross   Fitting the shape of a cross having four openings at 90° to each other.

Cross, straight   Fitting in which all outlets are of the same diameter.

D

Development, pipe   View on pipe fabrication drawing that shows the unfolding of pipe intersections in one plane. Developments are used for the construction of template drawings for pipe intersections.

Diaphragm valve   Valve whose port is sealed off by means of a flexible diaphragm.

Disk   Part of valve that initiates, shuts off, or regulates flow.

Double extra strong   Schedule of wrought pipe weights in common use.

Drainage system   All hubs, piping, fittings, connections, and holding tanks associated with the removal or relocation of unwanted materials that have been discharged from equipment; system includes runoff from rain or cleaning operations.

Dresser coupling   Coupling for connecting plain ended pipes.

Drip valve   Valve installed on drip legs for the removal of material from pipelines.

Dummy leg   Piece of pipe or rolled steel section that is welded to the pipe in order to support the line.

E

Eccentric reducer   Reducer that is flat on one side; used where trapped air in a line may cause problems.

Elbow   Standard fitting that creates a 90° or 45° bend; can be made for any degree bend. Used to change direction.

Elbow, long-radius   Elbow whose radius equals one and one-half pipe diameters.

Elbow, short-radius   Elbow whose radius equals the pipe diameter.

Elbowlet   Small fitting that is welded directly to an elbow to create a branch.

Ell, street   Elbow with male threads on one end and female threads on the other.

Expansion joint   Special type of joint in concrete or steel construction to permit expansion due to temperature changes. Also a piping specialty that allows for expansion and/or vibration in piping.

Expansion loop   Pipe bend designed to make the entire pipe more flexible to allow for its thermal expansion.

Extra strong   Pipe sizes corresponding to schedule 80.

Extruded nozzle   Nozzle or outlet formed by pulling hemispherically or conically shaped dies through a circular hole from inside the pipe.

F

Fabrication drawing Drawing used to represent pipeline configurations that must be made up in a shop or in the field.

Face Finished contact surface of flanged-end piping or components (valves).

Face-to-face Dimensions from the face of the outlet port to the face of the inlet port of a valve or fitting.

Facing Part of valve body that connects to a companion flange.

Female thread Internal thread in valves, fittings, and pipes for making screwed connections.

Field weld Weld performed at the construction site.

Fitting Wide range of piping components that enable pipe to change direction, change pipe size, provide branches for auxiliary lines, and provide connections.

Flange Rim on the end of a pipe, valve, or fitting for bolting to another piping element.

Flow indicator Linear indicator or dial that shows the flow rate. The indicator can be of the differential type or a direct hookup.

Flush bottom valve Special valve designed so that the valve seat is flush with the bottom of the tank when inserted in the nozzle.

Forming Method of pipe fabrication, including bending, swagging, lapping, extruding, expanding, and belling. Most forming is done in the shop.

Full-bore port Valve in which diameter of internal bore equals the inside diameter of pipe used on line.

G

Gage Any device used for measuring a quantity or value, such as steam pressure or temperature.

Gasket Thin piece of material, rubber, asbestos, etc., placed between two flanges to prevent leakage.

Gate valve Valve designed for open/shut operation. The controlling disk operates much like a gate.

Glass, sight Glass plate or tube inserted in a vessel or a pipe wall for observation of internal conditions.

Globe valve Valve whose design is such that it may be used for throttling.

H

Half coupling Similar to the coupling, but only one end is threaded; used to create small-diameter branches or to mount instruments.

Hanger Device used to suspend pipe from a ceiling or exposed steel.

Header Pipe to which two or more pipelines are joined to carry fluid from a common source to various points of use.

Heat exchanger Piece of equipment possessing two separate chambers or sets of coils that is used to transfer heat or cold from one liquid to another.

Heat pump Device used for heating or cooling by transferring heat via a mechanically driven thermodynamic process such as evaporation and condensation.

Hot bending Bending of pipe to a predetermined radius after heating to a suitable temperature.

Hub end End connection, caulked or leaded, used on valves, fittings, and pipe (mainly for water supply and sewage lines).

I

Increaser Coupling that has a larger opening at one end (used to increase size of pipe opening). See also *reducer*.

Indicator Type of gage or glass that permits visual readings of a certain variable, such as flow or temperature.

Instrument Device designed to sense, transmit, indicate, record, or control any number of variables within a piping system.

Instrumentation Application of industrial instruments to a process of manufacturing operation.

Insulation Material used to cover pipelines or vessels to maintain a constant temperature in the line; also used to prevent the transfer of heat between the atmosphere and the line fluid and to protect operators from burns.

Insulation, aluminum-armored Insulation made of calcium silicate and asbestos fiber and covered with a weatherproof aluminum jacket; used for steam and process lines which operate at temperatures up to 1200°F (650°C).

Insulation, antisweat Used to prevent cold water lines from sweating.

Insulation, asbestos-sponge felted Type of insulation applied to pipes, valves, and fittings with temperatures up to 700°F (370°C).

Insulation, cold Insulation applied to pipes, fittings, and valves in refrigeration services or to prevent heat penetration from local steam lines to the fluid in the insulated line.

Insulation, fiberglass Rigid structurally strong insulation for temperatures up to 600°F (315°C).

Insulation, hot Insulation applied to pipes, fittings, and valves in steam services.

Insulation, rock cork Mineral wool product bonded with a waterproof compound.

Insulation, vegetable cork Compressed cork granules baked into a mold and used for low thermal conductivity and high moisture resistance.

Insulation, wool felt Commonly used for both hot and cold water lines. It has a temperature range of 40° to 212°F (5° to 100°C) and is made up of layers of wool felt with an inner waterproof liner.

Insulation, 85 percent magnesia Durable, fireproof, molded insulation used for pipes at temperatures up to 600°F (315°C).

Insulation ring Steel ring used to support insulation attached to the outside of a vessel.

J

Jacketed Pipe or a vessel that is surrounded by another pipe or shell to provide a space to introduce heating or cooling mediums.

Joint Point of connection between two piping elements.

L

Lapp joint   Type of flanged joint used for joining pipe.

Lateral   Fitting that allows 45° angle entry into the main pipe run.

Latrolet   Small fitting welded directly to the pipe that creates a 45° angle entry into the run.

Lead joint   Joint made by pouring molten lead into the space between a bell and spigot.

Level gage   Device for measuring level in a vessel.

Level glass   Reading device directly connected to a vessel from the low to high points of a level variation. The liquid in the vessel finds its own level and may be observed through glass in the instrument.

Level indicating controller   Instrument that indicates a vessel's liquid level and regulates it by pneumatic signal to a control valve.

Level indicator   Dial or linear indicator that shows the level of liquid in the vessel.

Level recorder   Instrument that makes a permanent record of liquid level in a vessel by pneumatic signal from a displacement-type transmitter on the vessel.

Level recording controller   Instrument that has the same type of transmitter as the level recorder with a pneumatic signal to a control valve as well as a recorder.

Long radius   Elbow whose radius is $1\frac{1}{2}$ times the pipe's diameter.

M

Main   Primary piping; section of a piping system that contains the process fluid or a major service.

Male thread   External thread on pipes, fittings, and valves for making screwed connections.

Malleable fitting   Fitting made for malleable iron.

Malleable iron   Cast iron which has been heat-treated in an oven to relieve its brittleness, improve its tensile strength, and enable it to be pounded to a given shape.

Manifold   Main line pipe with several branch connections; also referred to as a header.

N

Nipple   Short length of pipe, threaded (male) on both ends, used for joining piping elements.

Nipple, close   Nipple that shows no unthreaded pipe between the threaded ends.

Nominal pipe size   Commercial designation of a pipe.

Nonrising stem valve   Valve whose stem does not rise on opening.

Nozzle   Any piece of pipe (stub-in) that is welded to a vessel or piece of equipment and has a flanged end onto which the pipeline with a similar flanged connection can be bolted. It is also possible to use a long-neck welded flange as a nozzle. Nozzles provide for the attachment of a piping system to a vessel, column, or tower. Also any device, fixed or adjustable, that controls a flow rate or discharge pattern from a pipe or line by means of special contour or size of an orifice.

O

Off plot   Area in the general vicinity of the project or on-plot area; battery limits determine what is on or off plot. Also refers to nonprocessing portion of plant, such as storage areas.

On plot   Area connected with a project and bounded by the battery limits. Any portion of the project or equipment which is on plot is drawn and constructed on the same set of drawings to provide a complete visual description of the system. Often the plot plan is divided into areas to provide a smaller drawing of individual sections; all are considered to be on plot. Also refers exclusively to processing area of plant.

On site   In the field; at the construction site. Any portion of the project that must be designed, constructed, or fabricated at the construction site is referred to as on-site production or construction.

Orifice   Device to produce differential pressures for flow measurement. Also used to increase the friction losses in pipelines. In this case, it is known as a restriction orifice.

P

Parallel piping   When several pieces of similar equipment have their inlet nozzles connected to one header and their outlet connected to another, the piping is in parallel.

Petrochemical   Chemicals derived from petroleum.

Pipe   Hollow cylinder used to carry fluids or gases.

Pipe alley   Main bank of headers.

Pipe bend   Directional change in pipeline obtained by bending the pipe. Normal bend radius is five pipe diameters.

Pipe bending   Forming the pipe sections into predetermined radii by hot or cold bending procedures. Pipe sections are often bent to a five-diameter radius, although sharper radii of three pipe diameters are sometimes required. Bending to the radius of 6, 10, or 15 times the diameter of the pipe can be accomplished.

Pipe coupling   Device for joining end of screwed pipe.

Pipe fabrication   Production of sections, configurations, or assemblies of pipe and various pipe components such as valves and fittings. Fabrication includes a variety of processing: welding, forming, shaping, heating, cleaning, machining.

Pipe rack   Structural steel framework used to carry pipe runs through a mill. The pipes are usually located above ground enough so that access is not obstructed under the pipe rack.

Pipe rack bent   Structure consisting of horizontal connecting members and two vertical columns (stanchions). The horizontal member is referred to as a strut when it connects two bents.

Pipe strap   Device used to hold lightweight pipe to wall or ceiling.

Pipe support   Devices that support piping.

Pipe support system   Complete arrangement of pipe supports (hangers, anchors, guides, snubbers) that (1) hold the weight of the system with a minimum safety factor of 3; (2) permit thermal and seismic movement; (3) dampen vibration caused by mechanical equipment; and (4) maintain a safe stress limit.

Pipe thimble   Sleeve used where pipes pass through walls or floors or are embedded in concrete or masonry.

Pipe volume   Total interior volume, expressed in cubic measurement, which a cylindrical object can hold. The volume can be found by multiplying pi times the inside radius squared by the length of pipe (area of cross section times length).

Piping, drains   Small valved pipes to drain main piping system on shutdown.

Piping, vents   Valved piping used for venting system on startup and shutdown.

Plug   Screwed fitting used for shutting off a tapped opening.

Plumbing   Piping system of small-diameter threaded pipe used for utility purposes.

Pocket   Low point in a pipe where liquids can be trapped, or high point where vapors may become trapped.

Port, inlet   Opening connected to the upstream side of a fluid system.

Pressure gage   Pressure in excess of atmospheric pressure.

Pressure vessel   Any vessel (container) designed to withstand the internal pressure of gases or liquids.

Pump   Piece of equipment, normally electrically powered, that draws a liquid from a source and propels it through pipe to a receiving point.

Q

Quick opening valve   Valve that can be opened quickly, usually by a pull chain.

R

Rebar   Steel rod used for reinforcing concrete.

Reducer   1. Coupling with a smaller opening at one end for reducing the size of the pipe opening (see *increaser*). 2. Fitting to reduce from one pipe size to a smaller one.

Reducing tee   Pipe fitting in which the side outlet is smaller than other outlets.

Reducing valve   Automatic valve to reduce pressure.

Refinery   Petrochemical complex that utilizes crude oil in its original form as the primary process medium, converting it to a variety of products, such as gasoline, tar, propane, fuel, oil, asphalt, and gas.

Regulator   Automatic valve that controls pressure of flow rate in a pipeline.

Relief valve   Automatic valve to relieve excess pressure.

Return bend   U-shaped fitting used to reverse the direction of a pipe run.

Ring joint   Type of flange joint for pipe.

Riser   Vertical pipe from a header. Also the vertical distance between stair treads.

Rising stem valve   Valve in which the stem rises when the valve is opened.

Rod hanger   Type of hanger used extensively to carry vertical downward loads. It allows limited horizontal pipe movement in all directions.

Rollers   Long pieces of round hardwood, or long pieces of pipe, used under heavy pieces of equipment to facilitate rolling along flat surface.

Run   Main line of piping that has branch connections and side outlets.

S

Saddle   U-shaped piece of metal that provides support or reinforcement to insulated pipelines. It can also be used to establish a sloped run. Horizontal vessels or other pieces of equipment are supported on pedestals by means of thick steel saddles welded to the vessel that allow for the anchoring of equipment of the concrete pedestal. Saddles may also be used with guides.

Saddle flange   Flange, usually curved and riveted or welded, to fit a boiler, tank, or other vessel and receive a threaded pipe. Also called a tank flange or boiler flange.

Safety valve   Rapid-opening valve designed to relieve buildups of excess gas or pressure within a vessel.

Sample connection   Valved spigot in a pipe or vessel to obtain process samples.

Schedule   Measure of the relation of the wall thickness of pipe to the inside diameter.

Schedule number   Approximate value of the expression 1000 times p/s, where p is the service pressure and s is the allowable stress (in psi).

Screwed end   Pipe or fitting joined by threaded connections.

Screwed fittings   Pipe fitting attached to pipes by means of threads.

Screwed flange   Flange attached to a pipe by a screwed connection.

Seamless   Piercing and rolling of a solid billet or cupping.

Service fitting   Street tee or street ell having a male thread at one end.

Shell   Outer wall of a vessel, whether horizontal or vertical.

Shoe   Metal piece attached (usually welded) to the underside of a pipe and resting on supporting steel. Used to reduce wear from sliding of lines subject to movement; also permits insulation to be applied to pipe and to provide elevation from the support to allow for a light slope of the pipeline.

Shop fabrication   Fabrication completed in a shop as opposed to field construction. Shop fabrication has many advantages over field construction, offering a wider variety of production methods in a controlled environment.

Short radius   Elbow pipe fitting whose radius equals one diameter of the pipe.

Short spring   Heavier spring than the medium type, giving 50 percent of the deflection a medium spring would provide under a given load.

Sight glass   Glass plate suitably inserted in a vessel or pipe for internal observation.

Slip-on flange   A flange that is slipped over the end of the pipe and welded in place.

Slope   Angle from the horizontal at which a pipe is placed for drainage reasons.

Snubber (shock suppressor, pipe arrestor)   Device, mechanical or hydraulic, that absorbs shock forces which could damage the pipe system. Snubbers do not resist slow thermal movement.

Socket fitting   Fitting used to join pipe in which the pipe is inserted into the fitting. A fillet weld is then made around the edge of the fitting and the outside wall of the pipe.

Socket weld   Type of weld performed when a piece of pipe is fitted into the socket of a fitting.

Socket-welded fitting or valve   Socket-end fitting or valve for low pressures and small diameters.

Socket-welding fittings   Pipe fittings in which the pipe is inserted in a socket.

Soldering   Method of joining metals using fusable alloys, usually tin and lead, having melting points under 700°F.

Spool   Assemblage of pipe and fittings normally welded in the fabricator's shop.

Spring hanger   Support that allows variations in pipe position due to changes in temperature; often used for vertical lines.

Standard   Designation of cast iron flanges, fittings, and valves suitable for a maximum working steam pressure of 125 psig.

Standard weight   Schedule of wrought iron pipe weights in common use.

Steam trap   Device that permits the passage of condensate but not steam.

Stem   Part of valve trim which moves the disk on and off the valve seat.

Straight cross   Cross pipe fitting in which all of the outlets are of the same diameter.

Straight tee   Tee pipe fitting in which all of the outlets are of the same diameter.

Street elbow   Threaded elbow pipe fitting with male thread on one end and female on the other.

Stub end   Ends welded on a pipe or into a vessel in order to make a Van Stone joint.

Stub-in   Connection or branch created when a small-diameter pipe is welded directly into a large one.

Subheader   Branch line from a large header or pipe.

Swagging   Process of reducing the ends of a pipe or tube section with rotating dies which are pressed intermittently or rotated against the pipe or tube end.

Swedged nipple   Pipe similar to a reducer in which the ends may have male threads if desired.

T

Tank   Basic process vessel used for the storage of raw materials, intermediates, and finished products. When modified, tanks can be used as dissolvers, precipitators, reactors, fermenters, and stills. Tanks are constructed in many sizes and shapes; the most common forms are vertical and horizontal right cylinders with end closures. Pressure tanks are fabricated as spheres or portions of spheres.

Tank, holding   Any tank or vessel in which material is stored before it goes through processing.

Tank, horizontal   Vessel, often cylindrical in shape, with closed ends. Head shapes are similar to those on vertical vessels or tanks. Usually supported below by saddles fastened to a foundation or floor or supported by slings hung from an overhead structure. Length of the horizontal tank should not be more than five times the diameter.

Tank, multicylinder   Vessel with cylindrical shell segments and internal diaphragms with heads which may be partial multispheres.

Tank, multisphere   Vessel used for storage of gas at pressures that would require prohibitive thickness in a single sphere.

Tank, pressure   Vessel used for storage of volatile materials. Can be constructed to withstand the maximum pressure developed in a process. Many shapes other than the upright cylinder are possible. A full spherical shape is sometimes used that is capable of withstanding higher pressures; for gasoline, the Horton spheroid is used. Ellipsoidal pressure tanks are available in large capacities. Cylindrical tanks with outward dished heads can serve for storage at medium and low pressures.

Tank, settling   Any vessel or tank that allows solids and liquids in the process material to separate gravitationally.

Tank, vertical (vertical vessel)   Vertical right cylinder, the most common tank. Can be built to virtually any size and capacity required. Tanks used for storage in the open are covered. The roof may be self-supporting, but it is often supported by a central column and radial rafter. Tanks built at grade are of the flat-bottom type; outdoor elevated tanks may be flat-bottomed, supported by a suitable structure, or suspended from the sides. Suspended bottoms may be hemispherical, hemiellipsoidal, conspherical, or conical. Outdoor flat-bottom tanks at grade may rest on a foundation of sand or both sand and a curbing of concrete slightly larger than the tank diameter. Indoor storage tanks are usually flat-bottomed. Pressurized tanks may have dished heads.

Tap   Tool used for forming female (internal) threads.

Tee   1. Three-way fitting shaped like the letter T.
2. Fitting that provides a branch of line size or smaller in the run pipe.

Tee joint   Joint between two members located at right angles to each other forming a T.

Temperature alarm   Temperature-sensitive device with an alarm that warns against rise or drop in the line or vessel temperature.

Temperature control valve   Control valve regulated by temperature fluctuations.

Temperature controller   Instrument that regulates pipeline or vessel temperature by a control valve which is actuated by pneumatic signals from a transmitter.

Temperature indicator   Device used for measuring temperature: (1) a locally mounted dial; (2) remote mounted dial capillary tubes; or (3) electric thermocouple.

Temperature recorder   Instrument that records a permanent continuous history of pipe or equipment temperature.

Thermocouple   Temperature-sensing device consisting of two dissimilar metals joined together.

Threader   Tool used for cutting male threads on the end of a pipe.

Threadolet   A fitting that is welded into the run pipe to provide a threaded branch connection.

Tower   Column or vertical vessel that increases the degree of separation that can be obtained during the fractionation and distillation of oil in a still.

Tower, forced-draft   Cooling tower that forces air through the water being cooled by utilizing a horizontal-shaft fan on the side of the tower.

Trap   Device that removes condensate, air, and gases from a steam line without releasing steam.

Tubing   System of small-diameter, lightweight (usually copper, brass, or plastic) pipes where OD always equals tubing size.

Turnbuckle   Simple position-adjustment device for use on pipe supports.

U

Union   Three-piece screwed fitting used to join lengths of pipe to permit easy opening of a line.

Unit fabrication   Pipe components formed, welded, and produced by a variety of methods to create assemblies that can be shipped and installed in a complete section (unit) in the field.

V

Valve   Mechanical device used to interrupt or regulate flow in a piping system.

Valve, control   Automatic valve.

Valve, flow-dividing   Valve that divides the flow from a single source into two or more branches.

Valve body   Main part of a valve into which the stem and other parts are installed.

Vessel   Any container used in conjunction with a piping system to hold, transform, or store the medium.

Volume of a pipe   Measurement of the space within the walls of the pipe. To find the volume of a pipe, multiply the length (or height) of the pipe by the product of the inside radius times the inside radius by 3.142.

W

Wedge   Disk shape for certain types of gate valves.

Weir port   Particular shape of a valve body interior.

Welded fitting   Forged or wrought steel elbow, tee, or similar piece for connection by welding to each other or to a pipe.

Welded joint   Union of two or more members produced by the application of a welding process.

Welding   Process of joining metals by heating until they are fused together, or by heating and applying pressure until there is a plastic joining action. Filler metal may or may not be used.

Welding end   End of a fitting, pipe, or valve that is joined to other piping elements by welding.

Weld-neck flange   Flange with integral extended neck for welding to pipe.

Weldolet   Small fitting welded directly to a pipe, creating a branch or connection for welded pipe smaller than the run.

Wrought pipe   Pipe worked as in the process of forming furnace-welded pipe from skelp; distinguished from cast pipe.

Y

Y-strainer   Y-shaped strainer for insertion into pipelines.

Y valve   Y-shaped globe valve.

Electronics and Electrical Glossary

A

AC-DC A device that will operate on alternating or direct current; an active device; a component that contains voltage or other current sources.

Air capacitor A capacitor that uses air as a dielectric.

Air gap The nonconductive air space between conductors, traces, pads, and so on.

Air inductor An inductor without a magnetic core.

Airline wiring diagram Connection diagram with a single horizontal or vertical line representing the cable location. Feeder lines branch off the main line.

Alternating current A current of electrons that move in one direction and then reverse and flow in the opposite direction at specific time intervals. The current has alternating positive and negative values.

Ampere Unit of current.

Amplifier A device that uses electron tubes or transistors to increase voltage, current, or power.

Analog A type of computer that uses numbers representing directly measurable quantities.

Analog circuit A circuit composed primarily of discrete components that produce data for physical variables such as resistance, voltage, and so on.

Annular ring The conductor width surrounding a hole in a PC board.

Anode A positive terminal capable of attracting negative charges.

Appliqués Electronic symbols, other graphical shapes, and lettering that are preprinted on sheets. They can be easily separated from mounting sheets and positioned on a drawing.

Armature The revolving part of a DC motor or generator. Also the vibrating or moving part of a buzzer or relay.

Artwork A precise scaled drawing used to produce the finished master pattern for a PC board, created by hand taping or plotting with a CAD system and photoplotter.

Auxiliary contacts In a switching device, supplements to the main-circuit contacts that function with movement.

Auxiliary device Any electrical device (other than motors and motor starters) necessary to operate the machine or equipment completely.

AWG American Wire Gauge. A standardized method for specifying a wire diameter. The larger the number, the smaller the corresponding wire diameter.

Axial leads Wire leads extending from the ends of various components, capacitors, resistors, and so on.

B

Bipolar A method of fabricating one type of IC by layering silicon that has two different electrical characteristics.

Block diagram A diagram showing the relationship of separate subunits (blocks) in the system.

Bonding conductor A transmitter that connects exposed metal surfaces.

Branch circuit The portion of a wiring system extending beyond the final overcurrent device protecting the circuit. (A device not approved for branch-circuit protection, such as a thermal cutout or motor overload protective device, is not considered the overcurrent device protecting the circuit.)

Breadboard Laying out an electronic circuit with components and wiring on a board for experimentation, testing, and designing.

Bridging When excess solder builds up during wave soldering, shorting out adjacent conductors by "bridging" the area between them.

Bus A conductive metal strip or trace used to distribute voltage, grounds, and so forth to smaller branch traces on a PC board.

Bus bar The main power distribution point of a circuit. The bus bar is connected to the primary power source.

Bypass capacitor A component that provides a comparatively low-impedance AC path around a circuit.

C

Capacitance A property of an electric circuit to oppose a change in voltage; also, an electric circuit's ability to store energy in an electrostatic field.

Capacitor A fixed or variable device providing capacitance. A simplified capacitor comprises two metal plates separated by an insulator.

Cathode The emitter of an electron tube, diode, semiconductor, and so on.

Chassis A sheet-metal box, frame, or simple plate on which electronic components and their associated circuitry can be mounted.

Circuit breaker A device to open and close a circuit nonautomatically, and to open the circuit automatically on a predetermined overload of current without injuring itself when properly applied within its rating.

Collector A conductor that maintains contact between moving and stationary parts of an electric circuit. Also, the portion of a transistor that attracts and collects electrons.

Component The smallest element of a circuit (i.e., resistor, capacitor, transistor, or integrated circuit package).

Conduit, flexible metal A flexible raceway of circular cross section specially constructed to pull in or withdraw wires or cables after the conduit and its fittings are in place.

Conduit, flexible nonmetallic A flexible raceway of circular cross section especially for pulling in or withdrawing wires or cables after the conduit and its fittings are in place.

Conduit, rigid metal A raceway specially constructed to pull in or wind wires or cables after the conduit is in place. Made of metal pipes, its standard weight and thickness permit cutting standard threads.

Connector A plug or receptacle for electrically interconnecting one or more cables or electronic circuits.

Connector tongue The edge of a PC board designed to mate with a receptacle that bridges (mechanically or electrically) the board and other circuitry.

Contactor A device for repeatedly establishing and interrupting an electric power circuit.

Control circuit The circuit of the control apparatus or system that carries the signals directing the controller's performance.

Control circuit transformer A voltage transformer that supplies a voltage suitable to operate control devices.

Control circuit voltage The voltage provided to operate shunt coil magnetic devices.

Controller, electronic A device or group of devices that governs in some predetermined manner the electronic signals delivered to the apparatus to which it is connected.

Current The flow of an electrical charge measured in amperes; also, the rate of that flow.

D

Device, input A device that initiates a signal that is a condition of the system.

Device, output A device that accepts a signal and executes a control function.

Dielectric A nonconductor of a direct electric current; also, the insulator material between plates of a capacitor.

Digital A discrete representation of a physical quantity, for example, devices, elements, or circuits that respond in discrete steps (i.e., pulses or "on/off" operation).

Digital circuit A circuit composed primarily of ICs that operates like a switch (i.e., it is either on or off).

Disconnect switch (motor circuit switch) A switch intended for use in a motor branch circuit. Rated in horsepower, it is also capable of interrupting the maximum operating overload current of a motor of the same rating at the rated voltage.

Discrete component A component fabricated prior to its installation, such as diodes, transistors, capacitors, and resistors.

E

Electrode A conductor that establishes electrical contact with a nonmetallic part of a circuit.

Electromechanical The term applied to any device in which electrical energy magnetically causes mechanical movement.

Electron An elementary particle of matter consisting of a charge of negative electricity.

Electronic control The term applied to electronic, static, precision, and associated equipment.

Elementary (schematic) diagram A wiring diagram that uses symbols and a plan of connections to illustrate the scheme of control simply. Also an electrical diagram containing components, logic elements, wire nets, bullets, miscellaneous graphic and nongraphic information, and text annotation.

Enclosure The case, box, or structure surrounding the electronic equipment that protects it from contamination. The degree of tightness is usually specified.

ES (Electrical Schematic) A diagram of a detailed arrangement of hardware, using conventional component symbols.

Eyelet The mechanism on printed circuit boards that makes electrical connections from one side of the board to the other side.

F

Farad The unit of measurement for capacitance.

Feedback Transferring voltage from the output of a circuit back to its input point.

Feeder The circuit conductors between the service equipment, or the generator switchboard of an isolated plant, and the branch circuit overcurrent device.

Feed-thru On a printed circuit board, a plated-thru hole used to provide an electrical connection between a trace on one side of a PC board and a trace on the other side. Normally the hole is small with a small pad size, since it is not used to mount a component lead.

Filter A circuit, device, or material designed to suppress or minimize waves or oscillations of certain electrical frequencies.

Frequency The number of complete cycles per second (cps) (hertz).

Fuse A safety device that opens an electric circuit when the circuit overloads. A current above the fuse rating will melt or break the fuse and open the circuit.

G

Gain The ratio of the output power, current, or voltage to the input power, current, or voltage.

Gate A circuit having two or more inputs and one output, the output depending on the combination of logic signals of the inputs.

Ground The common voltage reference point in a circuit. Also, a connection to earth using plates or rods. The chassis of electronic equipment is sometimes used as the ground.

Ground plane A condition on a PC board in which whole areas of the conductor material are left unetched and tied to the ground circuit throughout the board.

Grounded   Connected to the ground or to some conducting body that substitutes for the ground.

Grounded circuit   A circuit in which one conductor or point (usually the neutral or neutral point of the transformer or generator windings) is intentionally grounded (earthed), either solidly or through a grounding device.

Grounding conductor   A conductor that under normal conditions carries no current, but serves to connect exposed metal surfaces to an earth ground, to prevent hazards in case of a breakdown between current-carrying parts and exposed surfaces. The conductor, if insulated, is colored green, with or without a yellow stripe.

H

Henry   Unit of measurement of inductance.

I

Impedance   The total resistance to the flow of an alternating current.

Inductance   A circuit's ability to oppose a change in current and to store energy in a magnetic field.

Inductor   An apparatus such as a coil that acts on itself or another by induction.

IC (integrated circuit)   A tiny complex of electronic components and their connections on a slice of material such as silicon. A combination of inseparably interconnected active and passive circuit elements on or within a continuous substrate.

Interconnecting diagram   A diagram showing all terminal blocks in the complete system and identifying each terminal.

Interconnecting wire   A term referring to connections between subassemblies, panels, chassis, and remotely mounted devices; it does not necessarily apply to internal connections of these units.

Interconnection   Anything that connects one item to another. On PC boards, interconnections consist of copper runs connecting pads. On schematic drawings, interconnections are lines connecting elements.

Interrupting capacity   Interrupting capacity is the highest current at rated voltage that the device can interrupt.

Isolating transformer   A transformer that electrically isolates one circuit from another.

L

Lands   An enlarged portion of conductor material surrounding a component mounting hole.

LED (Light-Emitting Diode)   A PN junction that emits light when biased in the forward direction.

Limit switch   A switch operated by some part or motion of power-driven equipment to alter the equipment's electric or electronic circuits.

Logic control panel layout   The physical arrangement of the devices on a chassis or panel.

Logic design   Specifying the functions of various parts of a system in symbolic logic.

Logic diagram   A diagram showing the relationship of standard logic elements in a control system. No internal detail of the logic elements need be shown.

Logic element   A symbol with logical meaning; may also be called a logic symbol (e.g., gates, flip-flops, etc.).

M

Magnetic device   A device actuated electromagnetically.

Magnetic starter   A starter actuated electromagnetically.

Master pattern   A highly accurate scaled pattern that produces a PC board within a specified tolerance limit defined on the master drawing.

Motherboard   A relatively large PC board on which other PC boards, modules, connectors, and subassemblies are mounted and interconnected by traces.

N

Netlist   The list of names, symbols, and their connection points that are logically connected in a net.

Node   Also called a junction point or branch point, a terminal of any branch of a network or a terminal common to two or more branches.

Nominal voltage   The utilization voltage. See the appropriate NEMA standard for device voltage ratings.

O

Open circuit   A circuit that does not provide a complete path for signal flow.

Overcurrent   The current in an electric or electronic circuit that will cause an excessive or dangerous temperature in the conductor or conductor insulation.

Overcurrent protective device   A device operative on excessive current that causes and maintains power interruption in the circuit.

Overload relay   A device that provides overload protection for electrical equipment.

P

Panel   A subplate on which the control devices are mounted inside the control compartment or enclosure.

Panel layout   The physical position or arrangement of the components on a panel or chassis.

PCB (printed circuit board)   Insulated substrate (often plastic) on which interconnection wiring has been applied by photographic techniques.

Photoconductive   The ability of certain materials to increase in conductivity when exposed to a light source.

Photodiode   A two-terminal junction diode that conducts on exposure to light energy.

Plated-thru hole   A hole in the PC board in which metal is deposited on the wall to connect conductors electrically on each side of the board.

Plug-in device   A component or group of components and their circuitry that can be easily installed or removed from the equipment.

Power   The rate of doing work or expending energy. The watt is the unit of electric power.

Pressure connector   A conductor terminal applied with pressure to secure the connection mechanically and electrically.

Pulse   An abrupt change in voltage, either positive or negative, that conveys information to a circuit.

R

Radial lead   Lead of a component that extends from its side instead of its end.

Receptacle   A female connecting device into which a plug can be pushed or screwed to make electrical connections.

Rectifiers   A component or device that converts AC into a pulsating DC current (unidirectional current).

Registration   Alignment of a PC board pad with its mate pad on the opposite side. Alignment of graphic documentation when designing and laying out a PC board, using a CAD or manual layout system.

Relay   A device that a variation in the conditions of one electric circuit triggers to effect the operation of other devices in the same or another electrical circuit.

Resistance   The quality of an electrical circuit that opposes the flow of current passing through it.

Resistor   A component resisting or opposing flow of an electrical current.

Routing   Placement of interconnections on a PC board. Also, the sequence of steps in producing a part or assembly.

S

Schematic diagram   See *elementary diagram*.

Semiconductor   A device that can function either as a conductor or a nonconductor, depending on the polarity of the applied voltage (e.g., a rectifier or transistor with a variable conductance depending on the control signal applied).

Static device   For electronic and other control or information-handling circuits, the term refers to devices with switching functions that have no moving parts.

Subassembly   A portion of an assembly of electrical or electronic components, mounted on a panel or chassis, that forms a functional unit by itself.

Symbol   A sign, mark, or drawing representing an electrical or electronic device or component of it.

T

Terminal   A point of connection in an electronic circuit.

Terminal block   An insulating base or slab equipped with one or more terminal connectors to which electrical connections are made.

Tooling hole   Hole drilled through a PC board to aid in setting dimension, positioning, and manufacturing. Dimensions for the board geometry are normally established from tooling holes.

Transducer   A device to transfer one form of energy to another or one type of input to another.

Transformer   A device that uses electromagnetic induction to transfer energy from one circuit to another.

Triode   A three-electrode vacuum tube consisting of a grid, plate, and cathode.

V

Voltage   The force that causes free electrons to move in a conductor. The volt is the unit of measure.

W

Watt   The unit of power measurement.

Wave soldering   Also called flow soldering. A method of soldering a PC board by moving the board over a wave of flowing molten solder in a solder bath. Eliminates the need to hand solder each individual component lead.

Wire bond   The method by which very fine wires are attached to semiconductor chips for interconnection with package leads.

Wire list   Wire run list containing only two connections in each wire; also called a from-to list.

Wire net   Subset of electrical connections in a logical net having the same characteristics and common identifiers. No physical order of connection is implied.

Wire-wrapping   A technique to terminate conductors.

Wireway   Sheet metal troughs with hinged covers for housing and protecting electrical conductors and cable. Conductors are laid in place after the wireway has been installed as a complete system.

Wiring diagram   Diagram containing components, wire runs, wires, miscellaneous graphic and nongraphic information, and text annotation.

APPENDIX B

Abbreviations, Formulas, and Standards

General Abbreviations

Examples of Terms and Corresponding Abbreviations or Symbols

Term	Abbreviation or Symbol	Term	Abbreviation or Symbol
And	&	Liter	L
Across Flats	A/F	Machined	$\vee$ or √
American National Standards Institute	ANSI	Machine Steel	MS or MACH ST
		Material	MATL
Angular	ANG	Maximum	MAX
Approximate	APPROX	Maximum Material Condition	Ⓜ or MMC
Assembly	ASSY	Meter	m
Basic	BSC	Metric Thread	M
Bill of Material	B/M	Micrometer	μm
Bolt Circle	BC	Millimeter	mm
Brass	BR	Minimum	MIN
Brown and Sharpe Gage	B & S GA	Minute (Angle)	MIN
Bushing	BUSH	Newton	N
Canada Standards Institute	CSI	Nominal	NOM
Casting	CSTG	Not to Scale	____ or NTS
Cast Iron	CI	Number	NO
Centimeter	cm	On Center	OC
Center Line	₵	Outside Diameter	OD
Center to Center	C to C	Parallel	PAR
Chamfered	CHAM	Pascal	Pa
Circularity	CIR	Perpendicular	PERP
Cold-Rolled Steel	CRS	Pitch	P
Concentric	CONC	Pitch Circle Diameter	PCD
Counterbore	⌴ or CBORE	Pitch Diameter	PD
Countersink	∨ or CSK	Plate	PL
Cubic Centimeter	cm^3	Radian	rad
Cubic Meter	m^3	Radius	R
Datum	DATUM	Reference or Reference Dimension	( ) or REF
Deep	⊤	Regardless of Feature Size	Ⓢ or RFS
Degree (Angle)	° or DEG	Revolutions per Minute	rev/min
Diameter	⌀ or DIA	Right Hand	RH
Diametral Pitch	DP	Second (Arc)	(″)
Dimension	DIM	Second (Time)	SEC
Drawing	DWG	Section	SECT
Eccentric	ECC	Slotted	SLOT
Figure	FIG	Socket	SOCK
Finish All Over	FAO	Spherical	SPHER
Gage	GA	Spotface	⌴ or SFACE
Heat Treat	HT TR	Square	□ or SQ
Head	HD	Square Centimeter	cm^2
Heavy	HVY	Square Meter	m^2
Hexagon	HEX	Steel	STL
Hydraulic	HYD	Straight	STR
Inside Diameter	ID	Symmetrical	‡ or SYM
International Organization for Standardization	ISO	Thread	THD
		Through	THRU
Iron Pipe Size	IPS	Tolerance	TOL
Kilogram	kg	True Profile	TP
Kilometer	km	Undercut	UCUT
Large End	LE	U.S. Sheet-Metal Gage	USS GA
Least Material Condition	Ⓛ or LMC	Watt	W
Left Hand	LH	Wrought Iron	WI

ISO   ANSI
A   -A-

APPENDIX B.2

Piping Abbreviations

A

A Absolute
A Air
A Anchor
ABS Absolute
AC Air closes
AC Combustion air
ACCUM Accumulator
AFD Auxiliary feedwater
AGA American Gas Association
AI All iron
AI Instrument air
AISC American Institute of Steel Construction
Al Aluminum
ALY Alloy
AMER STD American Standard
ANSI American National Standards Institute
AO Air opens
AP Plant air
API American Petroleum Institute
APPROX Approximate
ARCH Architectural
AS Starting air
ASA American Standards Association
ASB Asbestos
ASHVE American Society of Heating and Ventilating Engineers
ASME American Society of Mechanical Engineers
ASNT American Society for Nondestructive Testing
ASSY Assembly
ASTE American Society of Testing Engineers
ASTM American Society for Testing and Materials
AUT Automatic vent trap
AUX Auxiliary
AV Average
AV Ventilation or cooling air
AWS American Welding Society
AWWA American Waterworks Association
AZ Azimuth

B

B Beveled
B & B Bell and bell
BB Bolted bonnet
BBE Bevel both ends
BBL Barrel
BC Between centers
BC Bolt cap
BC Bolt circle

BD Blowdown
BE Beveled end(s)
BF Blind flange
BF Bottom flat
BHN Brinell hardness number
BL Bottom level
BLDG Building
BLE Beveled large end
BLK Black
BLVD Beveled
BM Beam
B/M Bill of material
BOC Bottom of concrete
BOM Bill of materials
BOP Bottom of pipe
BOS Bottom of steel
BR Bronze
BRS Brass
B & S Bell and spigot
BTM Bottom
BTU British thermal unit
BUSH Bushing
BW Butt weld
BW Butt-welded
B/W Butt-weld pipe
BWG Birmingham wire gauge

C

C Center line
C Centigrade
C Channel or channel steel
C Condensate
°C Degrees centigrade
CAS Cast alloy steel
CBD Continuous blowdown
CtoC Center to center
CCW Component cooling water
CD Closed drain
CENT Centigrade
CFM Cubic feet per minute
CFS Cubic feet per second
CHG Change
CHKD Checked
CHO Chain-operated
CHO Chain operator
CHU Centigrade heat unit
CI Cast iron
CL Center line

A51

CL   Clearance
CM   Centimeter
CO   Chain operator
CO   Clean out
CO   Company
CO₂   Carbon dioxide
COL   Column
COMP   Compressor
CON   Concentric
CONC   Concentric
CONC   Concrete
COND   Condensate
CONN   Connection
CONSTR   Construction
CONT   Continuation
CORR   Corrosion
CP   Chemicals
CPLG   Coupling
CR   Conductivity recorder
Cr   Chromium
Cr13   Type 410 stainless steel
CS   Carbon steel
CS   Cast steel
CS   Cold spring
CSO   Car seal open
CTMT   Containment
CTR   Center
CTS   Containment spray
CU   Cubic
Cu   Copper
CVC   Chemical and volume control
CWP   Cold working pressure

D

DC   Density recorder
DC   Drain closed
DC   Drain connection
DD   Double disk
DEG   Degree
DEG(°)   Degree
DET   Detail
DF   Drain funnel
DI   Ductile iron
DIA   Diameter
DIM   Dimension
DIN   Deutsche Industrie Norm (German Standard)
DISCH   Discharge
DO   Drain open
DP   Process sewer
DPI   Differential pressure indicator
DRG   Drawing (not preferred)
DS   Sanitary sewer
DW   Storm sewer
DWG   Drawing
DWN   Drawn
DXS   Double extra strength

E

E   East
EA   Each
EBD   Emergency blowdown valve
ECC   Eccentric
ECN   Engineering change number
EF   Electric furnace
EFW   Electric fusion welded
EJMA   Expansion Joint Manufacturers Association
EL   Elevation
ELB   Elbowlet
ELEV   Elevation
ELL   Elbow
EMBED   Embedment
ENGR   Engineer
EP   Equipment piece
EQUIP   Equipment
ERW   Electric resistance welded
ESD   Emergency shutdown valve
EXCH   Exchanger
EXH   Exhaust
EX-HY   Extra heavy
EXIST   Existing
EXPJT   Expansion joint

F

°F   Fahrenheit
F   Furnished by others
FA   Flow alarm
FAB   Fabricate
FAHR   Fahrenheit
FBW   Furnace butt-welded
FCN   Field change number
FCV   Flow control valve
FD   Feedwater
F&D   Faced and drilled
FDS&F   Faced, drilled, and spot-faced
FE   Flanged end
FE   Flow element
F-F   Face to face
FtoF   Face to face
FF   Flange face
FF   Flat face(d)
FF   Full face (of gasket)
FH   Fixed hanger
FI   Flow indicator
FIC   Flow indicating controller
FICV   Flow indicating control valve
FIG   Figure or figure number
FL   Floor
FLD   Field
FLG(Flg.)   Flange or flanges
FLGD   Flanged
FMI   Displacement flowmeter
FO   Flow orifice

FOB   Flat on bottom
FOT   Flat on top
FPS   Feet per second
FR   Flow recorder
FR   From
FRC   Flow recording controller
FRCV   Flow recording control valve
FRP   Fiberglass-reinforced pipe
FS   Far side
FS   Flow switch
FS   Forged steel
FSD   Flat side down
FSS   Forged stainless steel
FSU   Flat side up
FT(′)   Foot or feet
FTG   Fitting
FW   Field weld

G

G   Gage or gauge
G   Gas
G   Grade
G   Gram
GA   Gage or gauge
GAL   Gallon
GALV   Galvanized
GEN   General
GEN   Generator
GF   Fuel gas
GG   Gauge glass
GJ   Ground joint
GN   Nitrogen or inert gas
GPH   Gallons per hour
GPM   Gallons per minute
GR   Grade
GRD   Ground
GRJT   Ground joint
GRV   Groove
GU   Guide
GV   Gate valve
GW   Waste gas

H

H   Horizontal
H   Hour
H   Hydrogen
HC   Hand (manual) controller
HC   Hose connection
HC   Hydrocarbon
HCV   Hand-operated control valve
HDR   Header
HEX   Hexagon
HF   Hard (stellite) face
Hg   Mercury
HGR   Hanger
HIC   Hand-actuated pneumatic controller

HOR   Horizontal
HP   High point
HPT   Hose-pipe thread
HR   Hour
HR   Hanger (rod)
HS   Hanger (spring)
HTR   Heater
HVAC   Heating, ventilating, and air conditioning
HVY   Heavy
HYD   Hydraulic

I

I
IBBM   Iron body bronze (or brass) mounted
IBD   Intermittent blowdown
ID   Inside diameter
ID   Inside depth of dish
IE   Invert elevation
IMP   Imperial (British unit)
IN(″)   Inch or inches
INS   Insulate or insulation
INT   Integral
INV   Invert (inside bottom of pipe)
IPS   Iron pipe size
IS   Inside screw (of valve stem)
ISA   Instrument Society of America
ISO   Isometric drawing
ISRS   Inside screw rising stem
IS&Y   Inside screw and yoke

J

JCT   Junction
JT   Joint

K

K   Kilo, times one thousand, ×1000
KG   Kilogram
KW   Kilowatt(s)

L

L   Angle (structural 4-in. angle shape)
L   Liquid
LA   Level alarm
LB, lb   Pound weight
LBS   Pounds
LC   Level controller
LC   Lock closed
LCR   Level control recorder
LCV   Level control valve
LG   Level glass
LI   Level indicator
LIC   Level indicating controller
LICV   Level indicating control valve
LLA   Liquid level alarm
LLC   Liquid level controller
LLI   Liquid level indicator

LLR   Liquid level recorder
LO   Lock opened
LOC   Location
L-O-L   Latrolet
LP   Low point
LR   Level recorder
LR   Long radius
LRC   Level recording controller
LS   Level switch
LW   Lap weld
L/W   Lapweld pipe

M

M   Mega, times one million
M   Meter
M   Miscellaneous shapes (steel)
M   Monel metal
MACH   Machined
MATL   Material
MAWP   Maximum allowable working pressure
MAX   Maximum
MB   Machine bolts
M/C   Machine
MCC   Motor control center
MECH   Mechanical
M&F   Male and female
MFG   Manufacturing
MFR   Manufacturer
MI   Malleable iron
MIN   Minimum
MIN   Minute (time)
MISC   Miscellaneous
MM   Millimeter
Mo   Molybdenum
MS   Mild steel
MSS   Manufacturers Standardization Society (valve and fittings industry)
MTD   Mounted
MW   Miter weld

N

N   North
NC   Normally closed
NEC   National Electric Code
NEG(−)   Negative
NEMA   National Electrical Manufacturers Association
NEWWA   New England Water Works Association
Ni   Nickel
NICU   Nickel-copper alloy
NIP   Nipple
NO   Normally opened
NO(#)   Number
NOM   Nominal
NOZ   Nozzle
NPS   National pipe size
NPS   Nominal pipe size

NPSH   Net positive suction head
NPT   National pipe thread
NPTF   National pipe thread female
NPTM   National pipe thread male
NS   Near side
NTS   Not to scale

O

OD   Open drain
OD   Outside diameter
OH   Heating oil or dowtherm
OH   Open hearth
OL   Lube oil
OPP   Opposite
ORIG   Original
OS   Seal oil
OS&Y   Outside screw and yoke
OV   Hydraulic oil
OWG   Oil, water, gas

P

P   Personnel protection
PA   Pressure alarm
PC   Pressure controller
PCV   Pressure control valve
PDC   Pressure differential controller
PDI   Pressure differential indicator
PDRC   Pressure differential recording controller
PE   Plain end (not beveled)
PE   Pressure test connection
PERP   Perpendicular
PF   Process fluid (no distinction)
PFI   Pipe Fabrication Institute
PI   Point of intersection
PI   Pressure indicator
PIC   Pressure indicator controller
PICV   Pressure indicator control valve
P&ID   Piping and instrument diagram
PIM   Pressure indicating manometer
PL   Plate
PL   Process liquid
PO   Pump out
POE   Plain one end
POS(+)   Positive
PR   Pair
PR   Pump
PR   Pressure recorder
PR   Pressure regulator
PRC   Pressure recording controller
PRESS   Pressure
PRI   Primary
PRV   Pressure-reducing valve
PS   Pipe support
PS   Pressure switch
PSD   Rupture disk
PSI (psi)   Pounds per square inch

PSIA   Pounds per square inch absolute
PSIG   Pounds per square inch gauge
PSV   Pressure safety valve or relief valve
PT   Point
PV   Process vapor
PVC   Polyvinyl chloride
PX   Process fluid special hazard

Q

QO   Quick opening
QTY   Quantity
QUAD   Quadrant

R

R   Radius
RA   Refrigerant ammonia
RB   Reactor building
RC   Reactor coolant
RE   Refrigerant (ethylene)
REAC   Reactor
RECD   Received
RED   Reducer (or reducing)
REF   Reference
REINF   Reinforce
REQ (REQ'D)   Required
REV   Revision
RF   Raised face
RF   Refrigerant (Freon)
RFC   Ratio flow controller
RFI   Ratio flow indicator
RHR   Residual heat removal
RJ (RTJ)   Ring-type joint
R/L   Random length
RP   Refrigerant (propane or propylene)
RPM (rpm)   Revolutions per minute
RR   Refrigerant (no distinction)
RS   Rising stem

S

S   South
S   Steam pressure
SA   Sludge acid
SA   Sulfuric acid
SAE   Society of Automotive Engineers
SC   Sample connection
SC   Steam condensate
SCD   Screwed
SCFH   Standard cubic feet per hour
SCFM   Standard cubic feet per minute
SCH   Schedule
SCHED   Schedule
SCR   Screwed ends
SCRD   Screwed
SD   Storm drain
SE   Steam exhaust
SECT   Section

SF   Semifinished
SG   Sight glass
SGA   Special gravity alarm
SGC   Special gravity controller
SGI   Special gravity indicator
SGR   Special gravity recorder
SH (SHT)   Sheet
SH   Steam-high pressure
SI   Safety injection
SJ   Solder joints
SK   Sketch
SL   Slip-on
SL   Steam-low pressure
SL FLG   Slip-on flange
SLOT   Slotted
SLV   Sleeve
SM   Steam-medium pressure
SMLS   Seamless
SNUB   Snubber
SO   Steam out
SOL   Sockolet
SP   Steam pressure
SPEC   Specification
SPG   Spring
SPI   Special
SQ   Square
SR   Short radius
SR   Speed recorder
SS   Stainless steel
SSP   Steam service pressure
STD   Standard
STIFF   Stiffener
STL   Steel
STM   Steam
STR (STRUCT)   Structure
SUCT   Suction
SUPT   Support
SW   Socket weld
SW   Socket-welded ends
SWG   Swag
SWP   Standard working pressure
SYS   System

T

T   Threaded
T   Steam trap
TA   Temperature alarm
TAN   Tangent
TBE   Threaded both ends
TC   Temperature controller
TC   Test connection
T & C   Threaded and coupled
TCV   Temperature control valve
TDC   Temperature differential controller
TDI   Temperature differential indicator
TDR   Temperature differential recorder

TE   Thread end
TE   Threaded end
TECH   Technical
TEF   Teflon
TEMP   Temperature
TENS   Tension
T & G   Tongue and groove
THD   Threaded
THRU   Through
TI   Temperature indicator
TIC   Temperature controller
TICV   Temperature-control valve
TK   Tank
TL   Top level
TLE   Thread large end
TOC   Top of concrete
TOE   Thread one end
TOG   Top of grating
T-O-L   Thread-o-let
TOP   Top of pipe
TOS (T/S)   Top of steel
TP   Equipment trim pumps
TP   Type
TPD   Tons per day
TR   Temperature recorder
TRANS   Transactions
TRC   Temperature recorder controller
TS   Temperature switch
TSE   Thread small end
TT   Equipment-exchanger tubes
T-T   Tangent to tangent
TURB   Turbine
TV   Temperature valve
TW   Temperature wall
TYP   Typical

U

UA   Unit alarm
UB   Union bonnet

V

VA   Valve
VB   Vortex breaker

VC   Vitrified clay
VERT   Vertical
VF   Vent to flare
VOL   Volume
VR   Viscosity recorder
VS   Vent to stack

W

W   West
W   Wide flange steel shape
W   Width
W/   With
WB   Welded bonnet
WC   Plant cooling water
WC   Water column
WE   Weld end
WF   Welded flange
WF   Wide flange
WH   Weep hole
WJ   Jacket or closed cycle water
WLD   Weld
WN   Weld neck
WN FLG   Weld neck flange
WOG   Water, oil, and gas (pressure)
W-O-L   Weld-o-let
WP   Potable water
WP   Working point
WR   Raw water
WR   Weight recorder
WS   Salt water
WSP   Working steam pressure
WT   Treated water
WT   Weight
WWP   Working water pressure

X

XH   Extra heavy
XS   Extra strong
XXH   Double extra heavy
XXS   Double extra strong

Reference Designations

Reference designations distinguish one graphic symbol from another and correlate these identifications with actual components on the parts lists and assembly drawings.

Reference designations identify electonic, electrical, and mechanical components as well as assemblies and subassemblies. These designations consist of a combination of letters and numbers identifying the component's class. The numerical designation following the class letter or letters always falls on the same line without a space or hyphen. When letters follow a numerical designation, they indicate a function separate from the designated component as a whole.

Reference designations may be placed above, below, or on either side of a graphic symbol. Other pertinent information, such as component value, tolerances or rating, terminal numbering, and other functional discriptions may be placed around the graphic symbols.

It is standard practice to number each class of components from left to right beginning with the upper left corner of the diagram and following horizontally and vertically across the sheet. This facilitates locating the symbols and related components on the schematic diagram.

When circuit changes are made, the schematic diagram is also changed by adding or deleting graphic symbols. The remaining symbols are not renumbered when a graphic symbol is deleted. Because of these changes, a reference designation table is often placed on the schematic diagram to avoid searching for a designation that may have been removed.

Class Designation Letters

This alphabetical listing of class designation letters is used in assigning reference designations for electrical and electronics parts and equipment as described in ANSI Y32.16-1968 and Y32.16a-1970.

Parts not specifically included in this list should be assigned a letter or class most similar in function.

Designations for general classes of parts are marked with an asterisk (*) to facilitate designation of parts not specifically included in this list.

A

accelerometer*
(1) assembly, separable or repairable (2)
circuit element, general
computer
divider, electronic

Provided Courtesy of Bishop Graphics, Inc. Westlake Village, California 91359

facsimile set
generator, electronic function
integrator
modulator
multiplier, electronic
recorder, sound
recording unit
reproducer, sound
servomechanism, positional
sensor (transducer to electric power)
subassembly, separable or reparable
telephone set
telephone station
teleprinter
teletypewriter

AR

amplifier (magnetic, operational, or summing)
repeater, telephone

AT

attenuator (fixed or variable)
bolometer
capacitive termination
inductive termination
isolator (nonreciprocal device)
pad
resistive termination

B

blower
fan
motor
synchro

BT

barrier photocell
battery
blocking layer cell
cell, battery
cell, solar
transducer, photovoltaic

C

capacitor
capacitor bushing

CB

circuit breaker

CP

adapter, connector
coupling (aperture, loop, or probe)
junction (coaxial or waveguide)

CR

absorber, overvoltage
current regulator (semiconductor device)
demodulator, diode-type ring
detector, crystal
diode (capacitive, storage, or tunnel)
modulator, diode-type ring
photodiode
rectifier (metallic or diode)
selenium cell (rectifier)
semiconductor device, diode
thyristor (semiconductor diode-type)
transducer, photoconductive
varactor
varistor, asymmetrical

DC

coupler, directional

DL

delay function
delay line
slow-wave structure

DS

alarm, visual
annunciator
audible signaling device
bell, electrical
buzzer
device, indicating (excluding meter or themometer)
flasher (circuit interrupter)
indicator (excluding meter or themometer)
lamp (cold cathode, fluorescent, glow, incandescent, indicating, pilot, signal, neon)
light source, general
ringer, telephone
signal light
siren
sounder, telegraph
vibrator, indicating
visual signaling device

E*

antenna, loop or radar
arrester, lighting
bimetallic strip
brush, electrical contact
carbon block
cell, aluminum or electrolytic
cell, conductivity

contact, electrical
core (adjustable tuning, electromagnetic, inductor, memory, transformer)
counterpoise, antenna
dipole antenna
ferrite bead rings
film element
gap (horn, protective, or sphere)
Hall element or generator
insulator
magnet, permanent
part, miscellaneous electrical
post, binding
protector (network, gap, telephone)
rotary joint (microwave)
shield (electrical or optical)
short (coaxial transmission)
spark gap
splice
terminal (individual)
terminal, circuit
termination, cable
valve element

EQ

equalizer
network, equalizing

F

fuse
fuse cutout
limiter, current (for power cable)

FL

filter

G

amplifier, rotating (regulating generator)
chopper, electronic
exciter (rotating machine)
frequency changer (rotating)
generator
magneto (ignition or telephone)
regulating generator
vibrator, interrupter

H*

hardware (common fasteners, etc.)

HP*

hydraulic part

HR

heater
lamp (heating or infrared)
resistor heating

HS

handset
operator's set

HT

earphone
headset, electrical
receiver (hearing-aid or telephone)

HY

circulator
hybrid coil (telephone usage)
junction, hybrid
magic T
network, hybrid circuit

J

connector, receptacle, electrical
disconnecting device (connector receptacle jack)
jack
receptacle (connector, stationary portion)
waveguide flange (choke)

K

contactor (magnetically operated)
relay (armature, solenoid, reed, thermal)

L

choke coil
coil (all not classified as transformers)
electromagnetic actuator
field (generator or motor)
inductor
inductor, shunt
reactor
saturable reactor
solenoid, electrical
winding

LS

horn, electrical
loudspeaker
loudspeaker-microphone
reproducer, sound
transducer, underwater sound

M

clock
coulomb accumulator
counter, electrical
gage
instrument
meter
oscillograph
oscilloscope
outdoor metering device

recorder, elapsed-time
strain gage
thermometer
timer, electric

MG

converter (rotating machine)
dynamotor
inverter (motor-generator)
motor-generator

MK

hydrophone
microphone
transmitter, telephone

MP*

brake
clutch
frame
gyroscope
interlock, mechanical
mechanical part
mounting (not electrical circuit, not a socket)
part, miscellaneous mechanical (bearing, coupling, gear, shaft)
part, structural
reed, vibration
tuning fork

MT

detector, primary
transducer (measuring or mode)

N(3)

subdivision, equipment

P

connector plug, electrical
disconnecting device (connector, plug)
plug (connector, movable portion)
waveguide flange (plain)

PS

inverter, static (DC to AC)
power supply
rectifier (complete power supply assembly)
thermogenerator

PU

eraser, magnetic
erasing head
head (with various modifiers)
pickup
recording head

Q

transistor
rectifier, semiconductor controlled
switch, semiconductor controlled
thyratron (semiconductor device)
thyristor (semiconductor triode)

R

magnetoresistor
potentiometer
resistor (adjustable, nonlinear, variable)
rheostat
shunt (instrument or relay)

RE

receiver, radio

RT

ballast (lamp or tube)
lamp, resistance
resistor (current-regulating or thermal)
temperature-sensing element
thermistor

RV

resistor, voltage-sensitive
varistor, symmetrical

S

contactor (manually, mechanically, or thermally operated)
dial, telephone
disconnecting device (switch)
governor (electrical contact type)
interlock, safety, electrical
key-switch (telephone usage)
key, telegraph
speed regulator (electrical contact type)
switch
switch (hook, interlock, reed)
thermal cutout (circuit interrupter)
thermostat

SQ

link (fusible or sensing)
squib (electric, explosive, igniter)

SR

slip ring
ring, electrical contact
rotating contact

T

autotransformer
coil (telephone induction or repeating)
coupler, linear
taper (coaxial or waveguide)
transformer (current or potential)

TB

block, connecting
strip, terminal
terminal board
test block

TC

thermocouple
thermopile

TP

testpoint

TR

transmitter, radio

U* (1)

integrated circuit package
microcircuit
micromodule
nonreparable assembly
photon-coupled isolator

V

cell (light-sensitive, photoemissive, photosensitive)
counter tube (Geiger-Muller or proportional)
detector, nuclear-radiation (gas filled)
electron tube
ion-diffusion device
ionization chamber
klystron
magnetron
phototube
photoelectric cell
resonator tube (cavity-type)
thyratron (electron tube)
traveline-wave-tube
voltage regulator (electron tube)

VR

diode, breakdown
regulator, voltage (excluding electron tube)
stabistor
voltage regulator (semiconductor device)

W

bus bar
cable
cable assembly (with connectors)
cable, coaxial
conductor
dielectric path
distribution line
Goubau line
transmission line

transmission line, strip-type
waveguide
wire

WT (5)

tiepoint, wiring

X

fuseholder
lampholder
socket

Y

crystal unit (piezoelectric or quartz)
oscillator (excluding electron tube)
oscillator, magnetostriction
resonator, tuning-fork

Z

artificial line (other than delay line)
balun
carrier-line trap
cavity, tuned
discontinuity (usually coaxial or waveguide transmission use)

gyrator
mode suppressor
network, general (where specific class letters do not fit)
network, phase-changing
resonator (tuned cavity)
shifter, directional phase (nonreciprocal)
shifter, phase
tuned circuit
tuner (E-H, multistub, slide-screw)

1. The class letter A indicates that the item is separable or reparable. The class letter U indicates that the item is inseparable or non-reparable.
2. For economic reasons, fundamentally separable or reparable assemblies may not be so provisioned but may be supplied as complete assemblies. However, the class letter A shall be retained.
3. Not a class letter, but used to identify a subdivision or equipment in the location numbering method.
4. Not a class letter, but commonly used to designate test points for maintenance purposes. See American National Standard Y14.15-1966.
5. Not a class letter, but commonly used to designate a tie-point on connection diagrams. See American National Standard Y14.15-1966.

ANSI and Canadian Standards

ANSI Standards

Column A	Column B	Column A	Column B
Abbreviations	Y1.1-1972	Mechanical and Acoustical Element as Used in Schematic Diagrams	Y32.18-1972(R1978)
American National Standard Drafting Practices		Pipe Fittings, Valves, and Piping	Z32.2.3-1949(R1953)
Size and Format	Y14.1-1980	Heating, Ventilating, and Air Conditioning	Z32.2.4-1949(R1953)
Line Conventions and Lettering	Y14.2M-1979	Heat Power Apparatus	Z32.2.6-1950(R1956)
Multi and Sectional View Drawings	Y14.3-1975(R1980)	Letter Symbols for:	
Pictorial Drawing	Y14.4-1957	Glossary of Terms Concerning Letter Symbols	Y10.1-1972
Dimensioning and Tolerancing	Y14.5M-1982	Hydraulics	Y10.2-1958
Screw Threads	Y14.6-1978	Quantities Used in Mechanics for Solid Bodies	Y10.3-1968
Screws Threads (Metric Supplement)	Y14.6aM-1981	Heat and Thermodynamics	Y10.4-1982
Gears and Splines		Quantities Used in Electrical Science and Electrical Engineering	Y10.5-1968
Spur, Helical, and Racks	Y14.7.1-1971	Aeronautical Sciences	Y10.7-1954
Bevel and Hyphoid	Y14.7.2-1978	Structural Analysis	Y10.8-1962
Forgings	Y14.9-1958	Meteorology	Y10.10-1953(R1973)
Springs	Y14.13M-1981	Acoustics	Y10.11-1953(R1959)
Electrical and Electronic Diagram	Y14.15-1966(R1973)	Chemical Engineering	Y10.12-1955(R1973)
Interconnection Diagrams	Y14.15a-1971	Rocket Propulsion	Y10.14-1959
Information Sheet	Y14.15b-1973	Petroleum Reservoir Engineering and Electric Logging	Y10.15-1958(R1973)
Fluid Power Diagrams	Y14.17-1966(R1980)	Shell Theory	Y10.16-1964(R1973)
Digital Representation for Communication of Product Definition Data	Y14.26M-1981	Guide for Selecting Greek Letters Used as Symbols for Engineering Mathematics	Y10.17-1961(R1973)
Computer-Aided Preparation of Product Definition Data Dictionary of Terms	Y14.26.3-1975	Illuminating Engineering	Y10.18-1967(R1977)
Digital Representation of Physical Object Shapes	Y14 Report	Mathematical Signs and Symbols for Use in Physical Sciences and Technology	Y10.20-1975
Guideline—User Instructions	Y14 Report No. 2	Unified Screw Threads	ANSI B1.1
Guideline—Design Requirements	Y14 Report No. 3	Square and Hex Bolts and Screws	ANSI B18.2.1
Ground Vehicle Drawing Practices	In Preparation	Square and Hex Nuts	ANSI B18.2.2
Chassis Frames	Y14.32.1-1974	Socket Cap, Shoulder, and Setscrews	ANSI B18.3
Parts Lists, Data Lists, and Index Lists	Y14.34M-1982	Slotted-Head Cap Screws, Square-Head Setscrews, Slotted-Headless Setscrews	ANSI B18.6.2
Surface Texture Symbols	Y14.36-1978	Machine Screws and Machine Screw Nuts	ANSI B18.6.3
Illustrations for Publication and Projection	Y15.1M-1979	Woodruff Key and Keyslot Dimensions	ANSI B17.2
Time Series Charts	Y15.2M-1979	Keys and Keyseats	ANSI B17.1
Process Charts	Y15.3M-1979	Lock Washers	ANSI B18.21.1
Graphic Symbols for:		Plain Washers	ANSI B27.2
Electrical and Electronics Diagrams	Y32.2-1975	Surface Texture	ANSI B46.1
Plumbing	Y32.4-1977		
Use on Railroad Maps and Profiles	Y32.7-1972(R1979)		
Fluid Power Diagrams	Y32.10-1967(R1974)		
Process Flow Diagrams in Petroleum and Chemical Industries	Y32.11-1961		

AMERICAN NATIONAL STANDARDS INSITUTE, INC.
1430 BROADWAY,
NEW YORK, N.Y. 10018
THE AMERICAN SOCIETY OF MECHANICAL ENGINEERS
UNITED ENGINEERING CENTER
345 EAST 47TH STREET,
NEW YORK, N.Y. 10017

CSA—Canadian Standards

Column A	Column B	Column A	Column B
Unified and American Screw Threads	CSA B1.1	Surface Texture	CSA B95
Plain Washers	CSA B19.1	Limits and Fits for Engineering and Manufacturing	CSA B97.1
Square and Hexagon Bolts and Nuts, Studs and Wrench Openings	CSA B33.1	Abbreviations for Scientific and Engineering Terms	CSA Z85
Machine Screws, Stove Bolts and Associated Nuts	CSA B35.1	Architectural Drawing Practices (National Research Council, Ottawa, Canada)	33-GP-7
Drawing Standard—General Principles	CSA B78.1		
Drawing Standard—Dimensioning and Tolerancing	CSA B78.2		

CANADIAN STANDARDS ASSOCIATION
178 REXDALE BOULEVARD
REXDALE, ONTARIO, CANADA, M9W 1R3

Formulas

Formulas for Circles

Circles

Area $A = \pi r^2$
$A = 3.141\, r^2$
$A = .7854\, d^2$

Radius $r = d/2$

Diameter $d = 2 \times r$

Circumference $C = \pi \times d$
$C = 3.141\, d$
$C = 2\,\pi\, r$

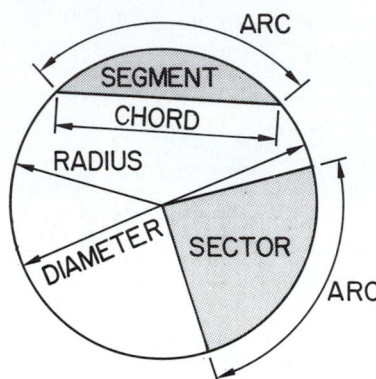

Sector of Circle

Area $A = \dfrac{3.141 \times r \times r \times \alpha}{360}$

Arc (length) $L = .01745 \times r \times \alpha$

Angle $\alpha = \dfrac{L}{.01745 \times r}$

Radius $r = \dfrac{L}{.01745 \times \alpha}$

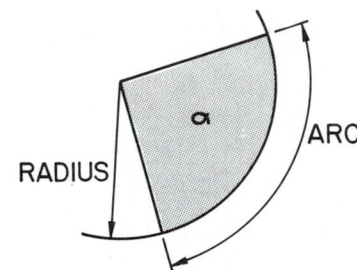

Segment of Circle

Area $A = 1/2\,[r \times L - c(r - h)]$

Arc (length) $L = .01745\, r\alpha$

Angle $\alpha = \dfrac{57.296\, L}{r}$

Height $h = r - 1/2\sqrt{4\,r^2 - c^2}$

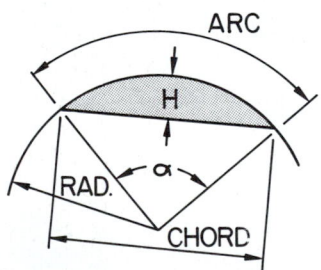

Circular Ring

Ring Area $A = .7854\,(\mathrm{OD}^2 - \mathrm{ID}^2)$

Ring Sector Area $a = .00873\,\alpha(\mathrm{OD}^2 - \mathrm{ID}^2)$

OD = outside diameter
ID = inside diameter
α = ring sector angle
OR = outside radius
IR = inside radius

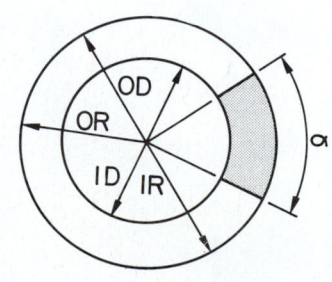

Formulas for Triangles

Equilateral Triangle

Area $A = a^2 \dfrac{\sqrt{3}}{4} = .433\,a^2$

$A = .577\,H^2$

$A = \dfrac{a^2}{2}$ or $\dfrac{a \times H}{2}$

Perimeter $P = 3a$

Height $H = \dfrac{a}{2}\sqrt{3} = .866\,a$

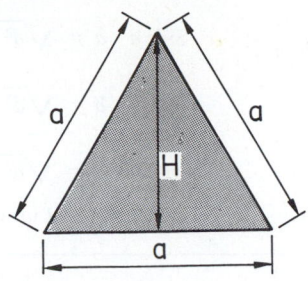

Right Triangle

Area $A = \dfrac{a \times b}{2}$

Perimeter $P = a + b + c$

Height $a = \sqrt{b^2 - c^2}$

Base $b = \sqrt{a^2 - c^2}$

Hypotenuse $c = \sqrt{a^2 + b^2}$

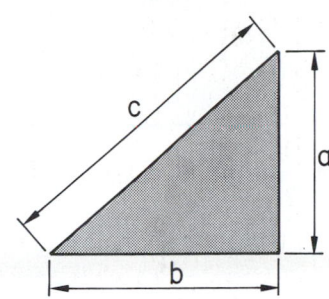

Acute Angle Triangle

Area $A = \dfrac{H \times b}{2}$

$A = \sqrt{S\,(S - a)\,(S - b)\,(S - c)}$
S is equal to $1/2\,(a + b + c)$

Perimeter $P = a + b + c$

Height $H = \dfrac{2}{b}\sqrt{S\,(S - a)\,(S - b)\,(S - c)}$

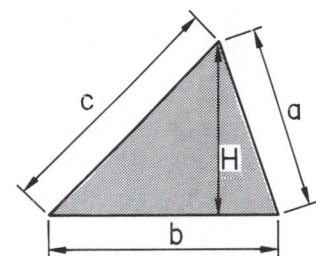

Obtuse Angle Triangle

Area $A = \dfrac{b \times H}{2}$

$A = \sqrt{S\,(S - a)\,(S - b)\,(S - c)}$

Perimeter $P = a + b + c$

Height $H = \dfrac{2}{b}\sqrt{S\,(S - a)\,(S - b)\,(S - c)}$

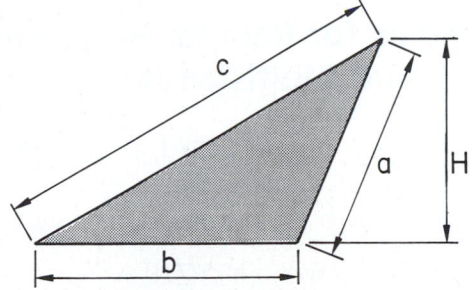

Formulas for Polygons (Four-Sided)

Squares

Area $A = s^2$
$A = .5\,d^2$

Side $s = .707\,d$

Diagonal $d = 1.414\,s$

Perimeter $P = 4\,s$

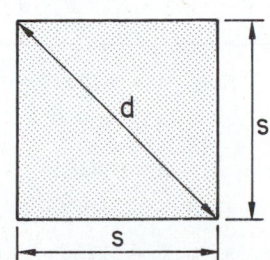

Rectangles

Area $A = ab$

Side a $a = \sqrt{d^2 - b^2}$

Side b $b = \sqrt{d^2 - a^2}$

Diagonal $d = \sqrt{a^2 + b^2}$

Perimeter $P = 2(a + b)$

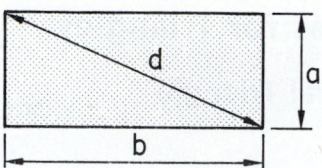

Parallelogram

Area $A = ab$

Height $a = \dfrac{A}{b}$

Base $b = \dfrac{A}{a}$

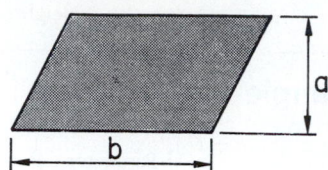

Trapezoid

Area $A = h \times \dfrac{a + b}{2}$

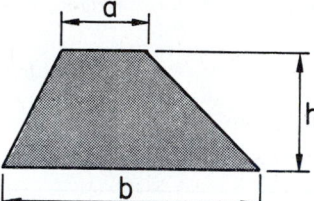

Trapezium

Area $A = \dfrac{(H + h) \times a + cH + dh}{2}$

Area $A =$ Divide the figure into two triangles. Compute the area of each. Add the areas together.

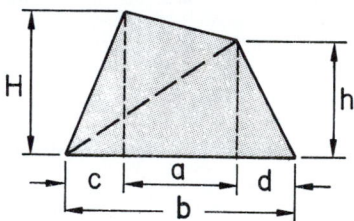

Formulas for Regular Polygons (Six, Eight, and Multisided)

Hexagon

Area $A = .866 f^2$ Flats $f = 1.732 s$

$A = .650 d^2$ $f = .866 d$

$A = 2.598 s^2$ Diagonal $d = 2 \times s$

Side $s = .577 f$ $d = 1.155 f$

$s = .5d$ Perimeter $P = 6 s$

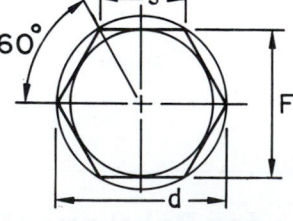

Octagon

Area $A = .828 f^2$ Flats $f = 2.414 s$

$A = .707 d^2$ $f = .924 d$

$A = 4.828 s^2$ Diagonal $d = 2.613 s$

Side $s = .414 f$ $d = 1.083 f$

$s = .383 d$ Perimeter $P = 8 s$

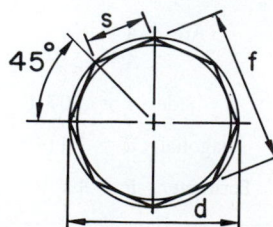

Regular Polygon (Multisided)

Area $A = \dfrac{n \times s \times 1/2\,f}{2}$

Angle $\alpha = \dfrac{360°}{n}$

Side $s = 2\sqrt{1/2\,d^2 - 1/2\,f^2}$

Perimeter $P =$ Sum of sides

$n =$ Number of sides

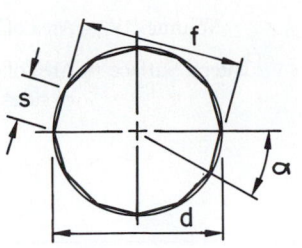

Formulas for Ellipses and Parabolas

Ellipse

Area $A = 3.142 \times a \times b$

$A = \pi \times a \times b$

Perimeter $P = 6.283 \times \dfrac{\sqrt{a^2 + b^2}}{2}$

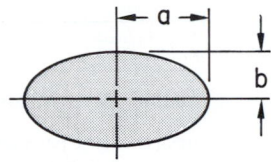

Parabola

Area $A = \dfrac{2}{3}\,a \times b$

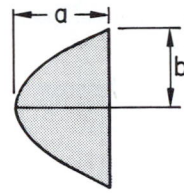

Formulas for Cubes, Prisms, Cones, and Pyramids

Cube

Volume $V = s^3$

Area $A = 6s$

Side $s = 3\sqrt{V}$

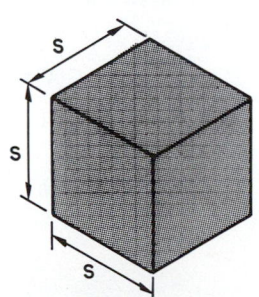

Rectangular Prism

Volume $V = l \times w \times h$

Area $A = 2 \times (lw + lh + wh)$

$l = \dfrac{V}{hw} \qquad w = \dfrac{V}{lh} \qquad h = \dfrac{V}{Lw}$

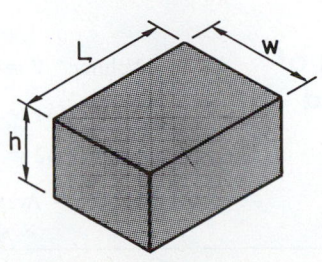

Prism

Volume V = Area of base × L

Lateral Surface = Area of each panel × number of sides

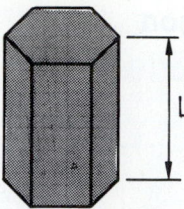

Frustrum

Volume V = Area of base × L

(L = average height)

Lateral Surface = Area of each panel × number of sides

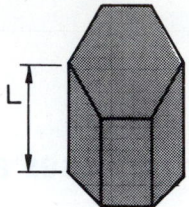

Cones

Volume V = 1/3 Area of base × h

Lateral Surface = 1/2 perimeter of base × slant height

= 1/2 × π × r × sh

(r = radius of base, sh = slant height)

Slant Height   sh = $\sqrt{r^2 + h^2}$

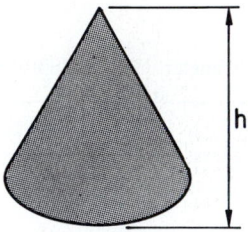

Frustrum of a Cone

Volume V = .262 × h ($D^2 + d^2 + Dd$)

(D = diameter of large base;

d = diameter of small base)

Lateral Surface   Average perimeter of base × slant height

Slant Height   sh = $\sqrt{(R - r)^2 + h^2}$

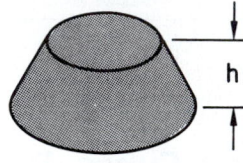

Pyramids

Volume V = 1/3 area of base × h

Lateral Surface = 1/2 perimeter of base × slant height

Slant Height   sh = $\sqrt{r^2 \times h^2}$

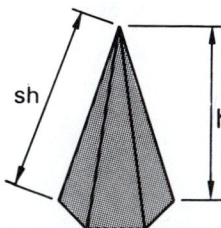

Frustrum of a Pyramid

Volume V = 1/3h ($A1 + A2 + \sqrt{A1 \times A2}$)

($A1$ = Area of large base;

$A2$ = Area of small base)

Lateral Surface = Average perimeter of bases × slant height

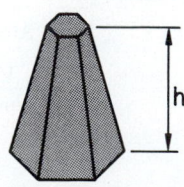

Formulas for Cylinders, Spheres, Torus, and Ellipsoids

Cylinders

Volume $V = \pi \times r^2 \times h$

$V = .7854 \times d^2 \times h$

Lateral Surface $= 6.2832 \times r \times h$

$= \pi \times d \times h$

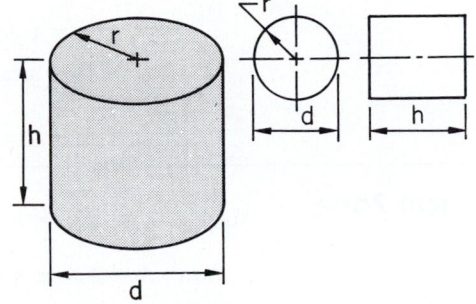

Frustrum of a Cylinder

Volume $V = 1.5708 \times r^2 \times (H + h)$

$V = .3927 \times d^2 \times (H + h)$

Lateral Surface $= \pi \times r \times (H + h)$

$= 1.5708 \times d \times (H + h)$

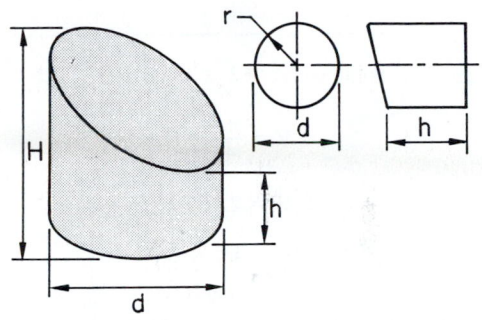

Elliptical Tanks

Volume $V = \pi \times a \times b \times h$

Lateral Surface $= \pi \times \sqrt{2 \times (a + b)} \times h$

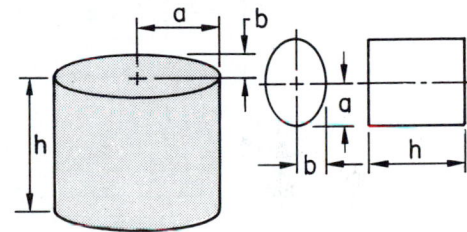

Sphere

Volume $V = 4.188 \times r^3$

$V = \dfrac{4 \times \pi \times r^3}{3}$

$V = \dfrac{\pi \times d^3}{6}$

Surface $= 4 \times \pi \times r^2$

$= 12.566 \times r^2$

$= \pi \times d^2$

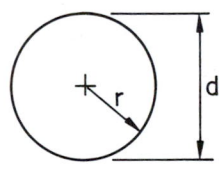

Spherical Sector

Volume $V = \dfrac{2 \times \pi \times r^2 \times h}{3}$

$V = 2.094 \times r^2 \times h$

Area $A = \pi \times r \times (2h + 1/2\, c)$

(A = area of spherical and conical surfaces)

$c = 2 \times \sqrt{h \times (2r - h)}$

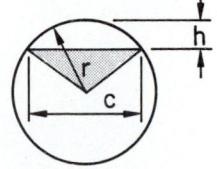

Spherical Segment

Volume $V = \pi \times h^2 \times \left(r - \dfrac{h}{3}\right)$

Area $A = 2 \times \pi \times r \times h$

$A = 6.283 \times r \times h$

(A = area of spherical surface)

$c = 2 \times \sqrt{h \times (2r - h)}$

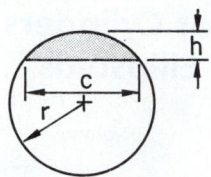

Spherical Zone

Volume $V = .532 \times h \times \left(\dfrac{3C^2}{4} + \dfrac{3c^2}{4} + h^2\right)$

Area $A = 2 \times \pi \times r \times h$

Area $A = 6.283 \times r \times h$

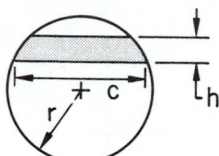

Torus

Volume $V = 2 \times \pi^2 \times R \times 1/2d^2$

$V = \dfrac{\pi^2}{4} \times D \times d^2$

$V = 2.467 \times D \times d^2$

Area $A = \pi^2 \times D \times d$

$A = 9.869 \times D \times d$

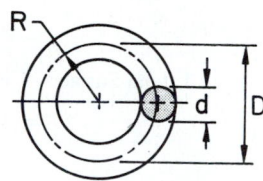

Ellipsoid

Volume $V = \dfrac{4 \times \pi}{3} \times a \times b \times x$

$V = 4.188 \times a \times b \times x$

Conversions

Conversion Factors

Multiply	by	To Obtain	Multiply	by	To Obtain
Absolute viscosity (poise)	1	Gram/second centimeter	BTU/Cu foot	8.89	Calories (Kg)/Cu meter at 32° F
Absolute viscosity (centipoise)	0.01	Poise	BTU/Hr/ft^2/°F/ft	0.00413	Cal (gm)/Sec/cm^2/°C/cm
Acceleration due to gravity (g)	32.174	Feet/second^2		1.49	Cal (Kg)/Hr/M^2/°C/ Meter
	980.6	Centimeters/second^2	BTU/minute	12.96	Foot pounds/second
Acres	0.4047	Hectares		0.02356	Horse power
	10	Square Chains		0.01757	Kilowatts
	43,560	Square Feet		17.57	Watts
	4047	Square Meters	BTU/pound	0.556	Calories (Kg)/Kilogram
	0.001562	Square Miles	Bushels	2150.4	Cubic inches
	4840	Square Yards		35.24	Liters
	160	Square Rods		4	Pecks
Acre-feet	43,560	Cubic Feet		32	Quarts (dry)
	325,851	Gallons (US)	Cables	120	Fathoms
	1233.49	Cubic Meters	Calories (gm)	0.003968	BTU
	1,233,490	Liters		0.001	Calories (Kg)
Acre-feet/hour	726	Cubic feet/Minute		3.088	Foot pounds
	5430.86	Gallons/Minute		1.558×10^{-6}	Horse power hours
Angstroms	10^{-10}	Meters		4.185	Joules
Ares	0.01	Hectares		0.4265	Kilogram meters
	1076.39	Square Feet		1.1628×10^{-6}	Kilowatt hours
	0.02471	Acres		0.0011628	Watt hours
Atmospheres	76.0	Cms of Hg at 32° F	Cal (gm)/sec/cm^2/°C/ cm	242.13	BTU/Hr/ft^2/°F/ft
	29.921	Inches of Hg at 32° F	Calories (Kg)	3.968	BTU
	33.94	Feet of Water at 62° F		1000	Calories (gm)
	10,333	Kgs/Square meter		3088	Foot pounds
	14.6963	Pounds/Square inch		0.001558	Horse power hours
	1.058	Tons/Square foot		4185	Joules
	1013.15	Millibars		426.5	Kilogram meters
	235.1408	Ounces/Square inch		0.0011628	Kilowatt hours
Bags of cement	94	Pounds of cement		1.1628	Watt hours
Barrels of oil	42	Gallons of oil (US)	Calories (Kg)/Cu meter	0.1124	BTU/Cu foot at 0° C
Barrels of cement	376	Pounds of cement	Cal (Kg)/Hr/M^2/°C/M	0.671	BTU/Hr/ft^2/°F/foot
Barrels (not legal)	31	Gallons (US)	Calories (Kg)/Kg	1.8	BTU/pound
or	31.5	Gallons (US)	Calories (Kg)/minute	51.43	Foot pounds/second
Board feet	144×1 in*	Cubic inches		0.09351	Horse power
Boiler horse power	33,479	BTU/hour		0.06972	Kilowatts
	9.803	Kilowatts	Carats (diamond)	200	Milligram
	34.5	Pounds of water evaporated/ hour at 212° F	Centares (Centiares)	1	Square meters
BTU	252.016	Calories (gm)	Centigram	0.01	Grams
	0.252	Calories (Kg)	Centiliters	0.01	Liters
	777.54	Foot pounds	Centimeters	0.3937	Inches
	0.0003927	Horse power hours		0.032808	Feet
	1054.2	Joules		0.01	Meters
	107.5	Kilogram meters		10	Millimeters
	0.0002928	Kilowatt hours			

*For thickness less than 1 in. use actual thickness in decimals of an inch.
Courtesy ITT Grinnell Corporation

Continued

Conversion Factors—Continued

Multiply	by	To Obtain	Multiply	by	To Obtain
Centimeters of Hg at 32° F	0.01316	Atmospheres	Cubic inches	16.387	Cubic centimeters
				0.0005787	Cubic feet
	0.4461	Feet of water at 62°F		1.639×10^{-5}	Cubic meters
	136	Kgs/Square meter		2.143×10^{-5}	Cubic yards
	27.85	Pounds/Square foot		0.004329	Gallons (US)
	0.1934	Pounds/Square inch		0.01639	Liters
Centimeters/second	1.969	Feet/minute		0.03463	Pints (liq. US)
	0.03281	Feet/second		0.01732	Quarts (liq. US)
	0.036	Kilometers/hour	Cubic meters	10^6	Cubic centimeters
	0.6	Meters/minute		35.31	Cubic feet
	0.02237	Miles/hour		61,023	Cubic inches
	0.0003728	Miles/minute		1.308	Cubic yards
Centimeters/second^2	0.03281	Feet/second^2		264.2	Gallons (US)
Centipoise	0.000672	Pounds/sec foot		1000	Liters
	2.42	Pounds/hour foot		2113	Pints (liq. US)
	0.01	Poise		1057	Quarts (liq. US)
Chains (Gunter's)	4	Rods	Cubic yards	764,600	Cubic centimeters
	66	Feet		27	Cubic feet
	100	Links		46,656	Cubic inches
Cheval-vapeur	1	Metric horsepower		0.7646	Cubic meters
	75	Kilogram meters/second		202	Gallons (US)
	0.98632	Horse power		764.6	Liters
Circular inches	10^6	Circular mils		1616	Pints (liq. US)
	0.7854	Square inches		807.9	Quarts (liq. US)
	785,400	Square mils	Cubic yards/minute	0.45	Cubic feet/second
Circular mils	0.7854	Square mils		3.367	Gallons (US)/second
	10^{-6}	Circular inches		12.74	Liters/second
	7.854×10^{-5}	Square inches	Cubit	18	Inches
Cubic centimeters	3.531×10^{-5}	Cubic feet	Days (mean)	1440	Minutes
	0.06102	Cubic inches		24	Hours
	10^{-6}	Cubic meters		86,400	Seconds
	1.308×10^{-6}	Cubic yards	Days (sidereal)	86,164.1	Solar seconds
	0.0002642	Gallons (US)	Decigrams	0.1	Grams
	0.001	Liters	Deciliters	0.1	Liters
	0.002113	Pints (liq. US)	Decimeters	0.1	Meters
	0.001057	Quarts (liq. US)	Degrees (angle)	60	Minutes
	0.0391	Ounces (fluid)		0.01745	Radians
Cubic feet	28,320	Cubic centimeters		3600	Seconds
	1728	Cubic inches	Degrees F [less 32]	0.5556	Degrees C
	0.02832	Cubic meters	Degrees F	1 [plus 460]	Degrees F above absolute 0
	0.03704	Cubic yards			
	7.48052	Gallons (US)	Degrees C	1.8 [plus 32]	Degrees F
	28.32	Liters		1 [plus 273]	Degrees C above absolute 0
	59.84	Pints (liq. US)			
	29.92	Quarts (liq. US)	Degrees/second	0.01745	Radians/second
	2.296×10^{-5}	Acre feet		0.1667	Revolutions/minute
	0.803564	Bushels		0.002778	Revolutions/second
Cubic feet of water	62.4266	Pounds at 39.2° F	Dekagrams	10	Grams
	62.3554	Pounds at 62° F	Dekaliters	10	Liters
Cubic feet/minute	472	Cubic centimeters/sec	Dekameters	10	Meters
	0.1247	Gallons (US)/second	Diameter (circle) (approx)	3.14159265359	Circumference
	0.472	Liters/second		3.1416	
	62.36	Pounds water/min at 62°F	(approx)	3.14	
	7.4805	Gallons (US)/minute	(approx)	$\frac{22}{7}$	
	10,772	Gallons/24 hours			
	0.033058	Acre feet/24 hours	Diameter (circle)	0.88623	Side of equal square
Cubic feet/second	646,317	Gallons (US)/24 hours		0.7071	Side of inscribed square
	448.831	Gallons/minute			
	1.98347	Acre feet/24 hours			

Continued

Conversion Factors—*Continued*

Multiply	by	To Obtain	Multiply	by	To Obtain
Diameter³ (sphere)	0.5236	Volume (sphere)	Gallons (Imperial)	277.42	Cubic inches
Diam (major) × diam				4.543	Liters
(minor)	0.7854	Area of ellipse		1.20095	Gallons (US)
Diameter² (circle)	0.7854	Area (circle)	Gallons (US)	3785	Cubic centimeters
Diameter² (sphere)	3.1416	Surface (sphere)		0.13368	Cubic feet
Diam (inches) × RPM	0.262	Belt speed ft/minute		231	Cubic inches
Digits	0.75	Inches		0.003785	Cubic meters
Drams (avoirdupois)	27.34375	Grains		0.004951	Cubic yards
	0.0625	Ounces (avoir.)		3.785	Liters
	1.771845	Grams		8	Pints (liq. US)
Fathoms		Feet		4	Quarts (liq. US)
Feet	30.48	Centimeters		0.83267	Gallons (Imperial)
	12	Inches		3.069×10^{-6}	Acre feet
	0.3048	Meters	Gallons (US) of water		
	$\frac{1}{3}$	Yards	at 62°F	8.3357	Pounds of water
	0.06061	Rods	Gallons (US) of water/		
Feet of water at 62	0.029465	Atmospheres	minute	6.0086	Tons of water/24 hours
	0.88162	Inches of Hg at 32° F	Gallons (US)/minute	0.002228	Cubic feet/second
	62.3554	Pounds/square foot		0.13368	Cubic feet/minute
	0.43302	Pounds/square inch		8.0208	Cubic feet/hour
	304.44	Kilogram/sq meter		0.06309	Liters/second
Feet/minute	0.5080	Centimeters/second		3.78533	Liters/minute
	0.01667	Feet/second		0.0044192	Acre feet/24 hours
	0.01829	Kilometers/hour	Grains	1	Grains (avoirdupois)
	0.3048	Meters/minute		1	Grains (apothecary)
	0.01136	Miles/hour		1	Grains (troy)
Feet/second	30.48	Centimeters/second		0.0648	Grams
	1.097	Kilometers/hour		0.0020833	Ounces (troy)
	0.5921	Knots		0.0022857	Ounces (avoir.)
	18.29	Meters/minute	Grains/gallon (US)	17.118	Parts/million
	0.6818	Miles/hour		142.86	Pounds/million gallons
	0.01136	Miles/minute			(US)
Feet/second²	30.48	Centimeters/second²	Grams	980.7	Dynes
	0.3048	Meters/second²		15.43	Grains
Flat of a hexagon	1.155	Distance across corners		0.001	Kilograms
Flat of a square	1.414	Distance across corners		1000	Milligrams
Foot pounds	0.0012861	BTU		0.03527	Ounces (avoir.)
	0.32412	Calories (gm)		0.03215	Ounces (troy)
	0.0003241	Calories (Kg)		0.002205	Pounds
	5.05×10^{-7}	Horse power hours	Grams/centimeter	0.0056	Pounds/inch
	1.3558	Joules	Grams/cubic centimeter	62.43	Pounds/cubic foot
	0.13826	Kilogram meters		0.03613	Pounds/cubic inch
	3.766×10^{-7}	Kilowatt hours		4.37	Grains/100 cubic ft
	0.0003766	Watt hours	Grams/liter	58.417	Grains/gallon (US)
Foot pounds/minute	0.001286	BTU/minute		8.345	Pounds/100 gallons (US)
	0.01667	Foot pounds/second		0.062427	Pounds/cubic foot
	3.03×10^{-5}	Horse power		1000	Parts/million
	0.0003241	Calories (Kg)/minute	Gravity (g)	32.174	Feet/second²
	2.26×10^{-5}	Kilowatts		980.6	Centimeters/second²
Foot pounds/second	0.07717	BTU/minute	Hand	4	Inches
	0.001818	Horse power		10.16	Centimeters
	0.01945	Calories (Kg)/minute	Hectares	2.471	Acres
	0.001356	Kilowatts		107,639	Square feet
Furlong	40	Rods		100	Ares
	220	Yards	Hectograms	100	Grams
	660	Feet	Hectoliters	100	Liters
	0.125	Miles	Hectometers	100	Meters
	0.2042	Kilometers	Hectowatts	100	Wattsi

Continued

Conversion Factors—*Continued*

Multiply	by	To Obtain	Multiply	by	To Obtain
Hogshead	63	Gallons (US)	Kilogram meters	3.653×10^{-6}	Horse power hours
	238.4759	Liters		9.806	Joules
Horse power	42.44	BTU/minute		2.724×10^{-6}	Kilowatt hours
	33,000	Foot pounds/minute		0.002724	Watt hours
	550	Foot pounds/second	Kilograms/cubic meter	0.06243	Pounds/cubic foot
	1.014	Metric horse power (Cheval vapeur)	Kilograms/meter	0.6720	Pounds/foot
	10.7	Calories (Kg)/min	Kilograms/sq centimeter	14.223	Pounds/sq inch
	0.7457	Kilowatts		1	Metric atmosphere
	745.7	Watts	Kilogram/sq meter	9.678×10^{-5}	Atmospheres
Horse power (boiler)	33,479	BTU/hour		0.003285	Feet of water at 62° F
	9.803	Kilowatts		0.002896	Inches of Hg at 32° F
	34.5	Pounds of water evaporated/ hour at 212° F		0.2048	Pounds/square foot
				0.001422	Pounds/square inch
Horse power hours	2546.5	BTU		0.007356	Centimeters of Hg at 32° F
	641,700	Calories (gm)			
	641.7	Calories (Kg)	Kiloliters	1000	Liters
	1,980,000	Foot pounds	Kilometers	100,000	Centimeters
	2,684,500	Joules		1000	Meters
	273,740	Kilogram meters		3281	Feet
	0.7455	Kilowatt hours		0.6214	Miles
	745.5	Watt hours		1094	Yards
Inches	2.54	Centimeters	Kilometers/hour	27.78	Centimeters/second
	0.08333	Feet		54.68	Feet/minute
	1000	Mils		0.9113	Feet/second
	12	Lines		16.67	Meters/minute
	72	Points		0.6214	Miles/hour
Inches of Hg at 32° F	0.03342	Atmospheres		0.5396	Knots
	345.3	Kilograms/square meter	Kilometers/hr/sec	27.78	Centimeters/sec/sec
	70.73	Pounds/square foot		0.9113	Feet/sec/sec
	0.49117	Pounds/square inch		0.2778	Meters/sec/sec
	1.1343	Feet of water at 62° F	Kilowatts	56.92	BTU/minute
	13.6114	Inches of water at 62° F		44,250	Foot pounds/minute
	7.85872	Ounces/square inch		737.6	Foot pounds/second
Inches of water at 62° F	0.002455	Atmospheres		1.341	Horse power
	25.37	Kilograms/square meter		14.34	Calories (Kg)/min
	0.5771	Ounces/square inch		1000	Watts
	5.1963	Pounds/square foot	Kilowatt hours	3413	BTU
	0.03609	Pounds/square inch		860,500	Calories (gm)
	0.07347	Inches of Hg at 32° F		860.5	Calories (Kg)
Joules	0.00094869	BTU		2,655,200	Foot pounds
	0.239	Calories (gm)		1.341	Horse power hours
	0.000239	Calories (Kg)		3,600,000	Joules
	0.73756	Foot pounds		367,100	Kilogram meters
	3.72×10^{-7}	Horse power hours		1000	Watt hours
	0.10197	Kilogram meters	Knots	1	Nautical miles/hour
	2.778×10^{-7}	Kilowatt hours		1.1516	Miles/hour
	0.0002778	Watt hours		1.8532	Kilometers/hour
	1	Watt second	Leagues	3	Miles
Kilograms	980,665	Dynes	Lines	0.08333	Inches
	2.205	Pounds	Links	7.92	Inches
	0.001102	Tons (short)	Liters	1000	Cubic centimeters
	1000	Grams		0.03531	Cubic feet
	35.274	Ounces (avoir.)		61.02	Cubic inches
	32.1507	Ounces (troy)		0.001	Cubic meters
Kilogram meters	0.009302	BTU		0.001308	Cubic yards
	2.344	Calories (gm)		0.2642	Gallons (US)
	0.002344	Calories (Kg)		0.22	Gallons (Imp)
	7.233	Foot pounds			

Continued

Conversion Factors—*Continued*

Multiply	by	To Obtain	Multiply	by	To Obtain
Liters	2.113	Pints (liq. US)	Miner's inches	1.5	Cubic feet/minute
	1.057	Quarts (liq. US)	Minutes (angle)	0.0002909	Radians
	8.107×10^{-7}	Acre Feet	Nautical miles	6080.2	Feet
	2.2018	Pounds of water at 62° F		1.1516	Miles
Liters/minute	0.0005886	Cubic feet/second	Ounces (avoirdupois)	16	Drams (avoir.)
	0.004403	Gallons (US)/second		437.5	Grains
	0.26418	Gallons (US)/minute		0.0625	Pounds (avoir.)
Meters	100	Centimeters		28.349527	Grams
	3.281	Feet		0.9115	Ounces (troy)
	39.37	Inches	Ounces (fluid)	1.805	Cubic inches
	1.094	Yards		0.02957	Liters
	0.001	Kilometers		29.57	Cubic centimeters
	1000	Millimeters		0.25	Gills
Meters/minute	1.667	Centimeters/second	Ounces (troy)	480	Grains
	3.281	Feet/minute		20	Pennyweights (troy)
	0.05468	Feet/second		0.08333	Pounds (troy)
	0.06	Kilometers/hour		31.103481	Grams
	0.03728	Miles/hour		1.09714	Ounces (avoir.)
Meters/second	196.8	Feet/minute	Ounces/square inch	0.0625	Pounds/square inch
	3.281	Feet/second		1.732	Inches of water at 62° F
	3.6	Kilometers/hour		4.39	Centimeters of water at 62° F
	0.06	Kilometers/minute			
	2.237	Miles/hour		0.12725	Inches of Hg at 32° F
	0.03728	Miles/minute		0.004253	Atmospheres
Microns	10^{-6}	Meters	Palms	3	Inches
	0.001	Millimeters	Parts/million	0.0584	Grains/gallon (US)
	0.03937	Mils		0.07016	Grains/gallon (Imp)
Mils	0.001	Inches		8.345	Pounds/million gal (US)
	0.0254	Millimeters	Pennyweights (troy)	24	Grains
	25.4	Microns		1.55517	Grams
Miles	160,934	Centimeters		0.05	Ounces (troy)
	5280	Feet		0.0041667	Pounds (troy)
	63,360	Inches	Pints (liq. US)	4	Gills
	1.609	Kilometers		16	Ounces (fluid)
	1760	Yards		0.5	Quarts (liq. US)
	80	Chains		28.875	Cubic inches
	320	Rods		473.1	Cubic centimeters
	0.8684	Nautical miles	Pipe	126	Gallons (US)
Miles/hour	44.70	Centimeters/second	Points	0.01389	Inches
	88	Feet/minute	Poise	0.0672	Pounds/sec foot
	1.467	Feet/second		242	Pounds/hour foot
	1.609	Kilometers/hour		100	Centipoise
	0.8684	Knots	Poncelots	100	Kilogram meters/second
	26.82	Meters/minute		1.315	Horse power
Miles/minute	2682	Centimeters/second	Pounds (avoirdupois)	16	Ounces (avoir.)
	88	Feet/second		256	Drams (avoir.)
	1.609	Kilometers/minute		7000	Grains
	60	Miles/hour		0.0005	Tons (short)
Millibars	0.000987	Atmosphere		453.5924	Grams
Milliers	1000	Kilograms		1.21528	Pounds (troy)
Milligrams	0.001	Grams		14.5833	Ounces (troy)
	0.01543	Grains	Pounds (troy)	5760	Grains
Milligrams/liter	1	Parts/million		240	Pennyweights (troy)
Milliliters	0.001	Liters		12	Ounces (troy)
Million gals/24 hours	1.54723	Cubic feet/second		373.24177	Grams
Millimeters	0.1	Centimeters		0.822857	Pounds (avoir.)
	0.03937	Inches		13.1657	Ounces (avoir.)
	39.37	Mils		0.00036735	Tons (long)
	1000	Microns			

Continued

Conversion Factors—*Continued*

Multiply	by	To Obtain	Multiply	by	To Obtain
Pounds (troy)	0.00041143	Tons (short)	Revolutions	360	Degrees
	0.00037324	Tons (metric)		4	Quadrants
Pounds of water at 62° F	0.01604	Cubic feet		6.283	Radians
	27.72	Cubic inches	Revolutions/minute	6	Degrees/second
	0.120	Gallons (US)		0.1047	Radians/second
Pounds of water/min at				0.01667	Revolutions/second
62° F	0.0002673	Cubic feet/second	Revolutions/minute^2	0.001745	Radians/second^2
Pounds/cubic foot	0.01602	Grams/cubic centimeter		0.0002778	Revolutions/second^2
	16.02	Kilograms/cubic meter	Revolutions/second	360	Degrees/second
	0.0005787	Pounds/cubic inch		6.283	Radians/second
Pounds/cubic inch	27.68	Grams/cubic centimeter		60	Revolutions/minute
	27,680	Kilograms/cubic meter	Revolutions/second^2	6.283	Radians/second^2
	1728	Pounds/cubic foot		3600	Revolutions/minute^2
Pounds/foot	1.488	Kilograms/meter	Rods	16.5	Feet
Pounds/inch	178.6	Grams/centimeter		5.5	Yards
Pounds/hour foot	0.4132	Centipoise	Seconds (angle)	4.848×10^{-6}	Radians
	0.004132	Poise grams/sec cm	Sections	1	Square miles
Pounds/sec foot	14.881	Poise grams/sec cm	Side of a square	1.4142	Diameter of inscribed circle
	1488.1	Centipoise		1.1284	Diameter of circle with
Pounds/square foot	0.016037	Feet of water at 62° F			equal area
	4.882	Kilograms/square meter	Span	9	Inches
	0.006944	Pounds/square inch	Square centimeters	0.001076	Square feet
	0.014139	Inches of Hg at 32° F		0.1550	Square inches
	0.0004725	Atmospheres		0.0001	Square meters
Pounds/square inch	0.068044	Atmospheres		100	Square millimeters
	2.30934	Feet of water at 62° F	Square feet	2.296×10^{-5}	Acres
	2.0360	Inches of Hg at 32° F		929.0	Square centimeters
	703.067	Kilograms/square meter		144	Square inches
	27.912	Inches of water at 62° F		0.0929	Square meters
Quadrants (angular)	90	Degrees		3.587×10^{-8}	Square miles
	5400	Minutes		0.1111	Square yards
	324,000	Seconds	Square inches	6.452	Square centimeters
	1.751	Radians		0.006944	Square feet
Quarts (dry)	67.20	Cubic inches		645.2	Square millimeters
Quarts (liq. US)	2	Pints (liq. US)		1.27324	Circular inches
	0.9463	Liters		1,273,239	Circular mils
	32	Ounces (fluid)		1,000,000	Square mils
	57.75	Cubic inches	Square kilometers	247.1	Acres
	946.3	Cubic centimeters		10,760,000	Square feet
Quintal, Argentine	101.28	Pounds		1,000,000	Square meters
Brazil	129.54	Pounds		0.3861	Square miles
Castile, Peru	101.43	Pounds		1,196,000	Square yards
Chile	101.41	Pounds	Square meters	0.0002471	Acres
Metric	220.46	Pounds		10.764	Square feet
Mexico	101.47	Pounds		1.196	Square yards
Quires	25	Sheets		1	Centares
Radians	57.30	Degrees	Square miles	640	Acres
	3438	Minutes		27,878,400	Square feet
	206,625	Seconds		2.590	Square kilometers
	0.637	Quadrants		259	Hectares
			3,097,600	Square yards
			102,400	Square rods
Radians/second	57.30	Degrees/second		1	Sections
	0.1592	Revolutions/second	Square millimeters	0.01	Square centimeters
	9.549	Revolutions/minute		0.00155	Square inches
Radians/second^2	573.0	Revolutions/minute^2		1550	Square mils
	0.1592	Revolutions/second^2		1973	Circular mils
Reams	500	Sheets			

Continued

Conversion Factors—*Continued*

Multiply	by	To Obtain	Multiply	by	To Obtain
Square mils	1.27324	Circular mils	Watts	0.05692	BTU/minute
	0.0006452	Square millimeters		44.26	Foot pounds/minute
	10^{-6}	Square inches		0.7376	Foot pounds/second
Square yards	0.0002066	Acres		0.001341	Horsepower
	9	Square feet		0.01434	Calories (Kg)/minute
	0.8361	Square meters		0.001	Kilowatts
	3.228×10^{-7}	Square miles		1	Joule/second
Stere	1	Cubic meters	Watt hours	3.413	BTU
Stone	14	Pounds		860.5	Calories (gm)
	6.35029	Kilograms		0.8605	Calories (Kg)
Tons (long)	1016	Kilograms		2655	Foot pounds
	2240	Pounds		0.001341	Horsepower hours
	1.12	Tons (short)		3600	Joules
Tons (metric)	1000	Kilograms		367.1	Kilogram meters
	2205	Pounds		0.001	Kilowatt hours
	1.1023	Tons (short)	Watts/square inch	8.2	BTU/square foot/ minute
Tons (short)	2000	Pounds		6373	Foot pounds/sq ft/ minute
	32,000	Ounces		0.1931	Horsepower/square foot
	907.185	Kilograms	Yards	91.44	Centimeters
	0.90718	Tons (metric)		3	Feet
	0.89286	Tons (long)		36	Inches
Tons of refrigeration	12,000	BTU/hour		0.9144	Meters
	288,000	BTU/24 hours		0.1818	Rods
Tons of water/24 hours at 62° F			Year (365 days)	8760	Hours
	83.33	Pounds of water/hour			
	0.16510	Gallons (US)/minute			
	1.3263	Cubic feet/hour			

Reference Tables
Geometric Formulas

A

Area of a circle = half diameter × half circumference

Area of a circle = square of diameter × 0.7854

Area of a circle = square of circumference × 0.07958

Area of a sector of circle = length of arc × one-half radius

Area of a segment of circle = area of sector of equal radius minus area of triangle, when the segment is less, and plus area of triangle, when segment is greater than the semicircle

Area of ellipse = product of the two diameters × 0.7854

Area of a parabola = base × two-thirds of the altitude

Area of parallelogram = base × altitude

Area of a regular polygon = sum of its sides × perpendicular from its center to one of its sides divided by 2

Area of a rectangle = length × breadth or height

Area of circular ring = sum of the diameter of the two circles × difference of the diameter of the two circles and that product × 0.7854

Area of a square = length × breadth or height

Area of trapezium = divide into two triangles, total their areas

Area of trapezoid = altitude × one-half of the sum of parallel sides

Area of a triangle = base × one-half of the altitude

C

Circumference of circle = diameter × 3.1416

Circumference of circle = radius × 6.283185

Circumference of sphere = square root of surface × 1.772454

Circumference of sphere = cube root of solidity × 3.8978

Contents of pyramid or cone = area of base × one-third of the altitude

Contents of frustum of pyramid or cone = sum of circumference at both ends × one-half of the slant height plus area of both ends

Contents of frustum of pyramid or cone = multiply areas of two ends together and extract square root; add to this root the two areas and × one-third of the altitude

Contents of a sphere = diameter × 0.5236

Contents of segment of sphere = (height squared plus three times the square of radius of base) × (height × 0.5236)

Contents of a wedge = area of base × one-half of the altitude

D

Diameter of circle = circumference × 0.3183

Diameter of circle = square root of area × 1.12838

Diameter of circle that shall contain area of a given square = side of square × 1.1284

Diameter of sphere = cube root of solidity × 1.2407

Diameter of sphere = square root of surface × 0.56419

R

Radius of a circle = circumference × 0.0159155

S

Side of inscribed cube of sphere = radius × 1.1547

Side of inscribed cube of sphere = square root of diameter

Side of inscribed square = diameter × 0.7071

Side of inscribed square = circumference × 0.225

Side of square that shall equal area of circle = diameter × 0.8862

Side of square that shall equal area of circle = circumference × 0.2821

Side of inscribed equilateral triangle = diameter × 0.86

Surface of cylinder or prism = area of both ends plus length and × circumference

Surface of pyramid or cone = circumference of base × one-half of the slant height plus area of base

Surface of sphere = diameter × circumference

V

Volume of sphere = surface × one-sixth of the diameter

Volume of sphere = cube of diameter × 0.5236

Volume of sphere = cube of radius × 4.1888

Volume of sphere = cube of circumference × 0.016887

US Weights and Measures

Weights

Apothecaries' 20 grains (gr)	1 scruple (s ap. or ℈)
3 scruples	1 dram (dr ap. or ʒ)
8 drams	1 ounce (oz ap. or ℥)
12 ounces	1 pound (lb ap. or ℔)
Avoirdupois 27–11/32 grains (gr)	1 dram (dr)
16 drams	1 ounce (oz)
16 ounces	1 pound (lb)
25 pounds	1 quarter
4 quarters	1 hundredweight (cwt)
20 hundredweights or 2,000 pounds	1 ton (tn or t) or short ton (s.t.)
2,240 pounds	1 long ton (l.t.)
Troy 24 grains (gr)	1 pennyweight (dwt)
20 pennyweights	1 ounce (oz t.)
12 ounces	1 pound (lb t.)

Measures

Circular 60 seconds (″)	1 minute (′)
60 minutes	1 degree (°)
30 degrees	1 sign
3 signs	1 quadrant or 90 degrees
4 quadrants	1 circle or 1 circumference or 360 degrees
Cubic 1,728 cubic inches (cu in.)	1 cubic foot (cu ft)
27 cubic feet	1 cubic yard (cu yd)
128 cubic feet	1 cord (cd)
Dry 2 pints (pt)	1 quart (qt)
8 quarts	1 peck (pk)
4 pecks	1 bushel (bu) or 2,150.42 cubic inches (cu in.)
Linear or Long 12 inches (in.)	1 foot (ft)
3 feet	1 yard (yd)
5 1/2 yards	1 rod (rd) or pole (p) or perch (p)
40 rods	1 furlong (fur.)
8 furlongs or 1,760 yards or 5,280 feet	1 mile (mi)
3 miles	1 league
Liquid 8 fluid drams (f ʒ)	1 fluid ounce (f ℥)
4 fluid ounces	1 gill (gi)
4 gills	1 pint (pt)
2 pints	1 quart (qt)
4 quarts	1 gallon (gal) or 231 cubic inches (cu in.)
31 ½ gallons	1 barrel (bbl)
Mariners' or Nautical 6 feet (ft)	1 fathom (f or fm)
100 fathoms	1 cable's length (ordinary)
10 cables' lengths	1 nautical mile or 6,080.20 feet
1 nautical mile	1.1516 statute miles
1 knot	a speed of 1 nautical mile, or 1.1516 statute miles per hour
Paper 24 sheets (sh)	1 quire (qr)
20 quires	1 ream (rm)
2 reams	1 bundle (bdl)
5 bundles	1 bale (B/-)
Square 144 square inches (sq in.)	1 square foot (sq ft)
9 square feet	1 square yard (sq yd)
30¼ square yards	1 square rod (sq rd) or square pole (sq p) or square perch (sq p)
160 square rods or 4,840 square yards	1 acre (A)
640 acres	1 square mile (sq mi)
36 square miles	1 township (tp)

APPENDIX C

Standard Catalog Parts and Reference Material

APPENDIX C.1

Threads

TABLE C.1.1 Standard Unified Thread Series[a]

Present Unified Thread Nominal Size—diameter			Coarse (NC) (UNC)		Fine (NF) (UNF)		Extra-fine (NEF) (UNEF)	
Inch		Metric Equiv.	Threads per inch	Tap drill[b]	Threads per inch	Tap drill[b]	Threads per inch	Tap drill[b]
.060	0	1.52	—	—	80	3/64	—	—
.073	1	1.85	64	No. 53	72	No. 53	—	—
.086	2	2.18	56	No. 50	64	No. 50	—	—
.099	3	2.51	48	No. 47	56	No. 45	—	—
.112	4	2.84	40	No. 43	48	No. 42	—	—
.125	5	3.17	40	No. 38	44	No. 37	—	—
.138	6	3.50	32	No. 36	40	No. 33	—	—
.164	8	4.16	32	No. 29	36	No. 29	—	—
.190	10	4.83	24	No. 25	32	No. 21	—	—
.216	12	5.49	24	No. 16	28	No. 14	32	No. 13
.250	1/4	6.35	20	No. 7	28	No. 3	32	No. 2
.3125	5/16	7.94	18	F	24	I	32	K
.375	3/8	9.52	16	5/16	24	O	32	S
.4375	7/16	11.11	14	U	20	25/64	28	Y
.500	1/2	12.70	13	27/64	20	29/64	28	15/32
.5625	9/16	14.29	12	31/64	18	33/64	24	17/32
.625	5/8	15.87	11	17/32	18	37/64	24	19/32
.6875	11/16	17.46	—	—	—	—	24	41/64
.750	3/4	19.05	10	21/32	16	11/16	20	45/64
.8125	13/16	20.64	—	—	—	—	20	49/64
.875	7/8	22.22	9	49/64	14	13/16	20	53/64
.9375	15/16	23.81	—	—	—	—	20	57/64
1.000	1	25.40	8	7/8	12	59/64	20	61/64
1.0625	1 1/16	26.99	—	—	—	—	18	1
1.125	1 1/8	28.57	7	63/64	12	1 3/64	18	1 5/64
1.1875	1 3/16	30.16	—	—	—	—	18	1 9/64
1.250	1 1/4	31.75	7	1 7/64	12	1 11/64	18	1 13/64
1.3125	1 5/16	33.34	—	—	—	—	18	1 17/64
1.375	1 3/8	34.92	6	1 13/64	12	1 19/64	18	1 5/16
1.4375	1 7/16	36.51	—	—	—	—	18	1 3/8
1.500	1 1/2	38.10	6	1 21/64	12	1 27/64	18	1 29/64
1.5625	1 9/16	39.69	—	—	—	—	18	1 1/2
1.625	1 5/8	41.27	—	—	—	—	18	1 9/16
1.6875	1 11/16	42.86	—	—	—	—	18	1 5/8
1.750	1 3/4	44.45	5	1 35/64	—	—	16	1 11/16
2.000	2	50.80	4 1/2	1 25/32	—	—	16	1 15/16
2.250	2 1/4	57.15	4 1/2	2 1/32	—	—	—	—
2.500	2 1/2	63.50	4	2 1/4	—	—	—	—
2.750	2 3/4	69.85	4	2 1/2	—	—	—	—
3.000	3	76.20	4	2 3/4	—	—	—	—
3.250	3 1/4	82.55	4	3	—	—	—	—
3.500	3 1/2	88.90	4	3 1/4	—	—	—	—
3.750	3 3/4	95.25	4	3 1/2	—	—	—	—
4.000	4	101.60	4	3 3/4	—	—	—	—

[a]Adapted from ANSI B1.1-1960.
Bold type indicates Unified threads. To be designated UNC or UNF.
Unified Standard—Classes 1A, 2A, 3A, 1B, 2B, and 3B.
For recommended hole-size limits before threading, see Tables 38 and 39, ANSI B1.1-1960.
[b]Tap drill for a 75% thread (not Unified—American Standard).
Bold-type sizes smaller than 1/4 in. are accepted for limited applications by the British, but the symbols NC or NF, as applicable, are retained.

TABLE C.1.2   Thread Sizes and Dimensions: Fraction/Decimal/Metric

Nominal Size		Diameter (Major)		(Minor)		Tap Drill (For 75% Th'd.)			Threads Per Inch		Pitch (mm)		T.P.I. (Approx.)	
Inch	mm	Inch	mm	Inch	mm	Drill	Inch	mm	UNC	UNF	Coarse	Fine	Coarse	Fine
—	M1.4	.055	1.397	—	—	—	—	—	—	—	.3	.2	85	127
0	—	.060	1.524	.0438	1.092	3/64	.0469	1.168	—	80	—	—	—	—
—	M1.6	.063	1.600	—	—	—	—	—	—	—	.35	.2	74	127
1	—	.073	1.854	.0527	1.320	53	.0595	1.499	64	—	—	—	—	—
1	—	.073	1.854	.0550	1.397	53	.0595	1.499	—	72	—	—	—	—
—	M.2	.079	2.006	—	—	—	—	—	—	—	.4	.25	64	101
2	—	.086	2.184	.0628	1.587	50	.0700	1.778	56	—	—	—	—	—
2	—	.086	2.184	.0657	1.651	50	.0700	1.778	—	64	—	—	—	—
—	M2.5	.098	2.489	—	—	—	—	—	—	—	.45	.35	56	74
3	—	.099	2.515	.0719	1.828	47	.0785	1.981	48	—	—	—	—	—
3	—	.099	2.515	.0758	1.905	46	.0810	2.057	—	58	—	—	—	—
4	—	.112	2.845	.0795	2.006	43	.0890	2.261	40	—	—	—	—	—
4	—	.112	2.845	.0849	2.134	42	.0935	2.380	—	48	—	—	—	—
—	M3	.118	2.997	—	—	—	—	—	—	—	.5	.35	51	74
5	—	.125	3.175	.0925	2.336	38	.1015	2.565	40	—	—	—	—	—
5	—	.125	3.175	.0955	2.413	37	.1040	2.641	—	44	—	—	—	—
6	—	.138	3.505	.0975	2.464	36	.1065	2.692	32	—	—	—	—	—
6	—	.138	3.505	.1055	2.667	33	.1130	2.870	—	40	—	—	—	—
—	M4	.157	3.988	—	—	—	—	—	—	—	.7	.35	36	51
8	—	.164	4.166	.1234	3.124	29	.1360	3.454	32	—	—	—	—	—
8	—	.164	4.166	.1279	3.225	29	.1360	3.454	—	36	—	—	—	—
10	—	.190	4.826	.1359	3.429	26	.1470	3.733	24	—	—	—	—	—
10	—	.190	4.826	.1494	3.785	21	.1590	4.038	—	32	—	—	—	—
—	M5	.196	4.978	—	—	—	—	—	—	—	.8	.5	32	51
12	—	.216	5.486	.1619	4.089	16	.1770	4.496	24	—	—	—	—	—
12	—	.216	5.486	.1696	4.293	15	.1800	4.572	—	28	—	—	—	—
—	M6	.236	5.994	—	—	—	—	—	—	—	1.0	.75	25	34
1/4	—	.250	6.350	.1850	4.699	7	.2010	5.105	20	—	—	—	—	—
1/4	—	.250	6.350	.2036	5.156	3	.2130	5.410	—	28	—	—	—	—
5/16	—	.312	7.938	.2403	6.096	F	.2570	6.527	18	—	—	—	—	—
5/16	—	.312	7.938	.2584	6.553	I	.2720	6.908	—	24	—	—	—	—
—	M8	.315	8.001	—	—	—	—	—	—	—	1.25	1.0	20	25
3/8	—	.375	9.525	.2938	7.442	5/16	.3125	7.937	16	—	—	—	—	—
3/8	—	.375	9.525	.3209	8.153	Q	.3320	8.432	—	24	—	—	—	—
—	M10	.393	9.982	—	—	—	—	—	—	—	1.5	1.25	17	20
7/16	—	.437	11.113	.3447	8.738	U	.3680	9.347	14	—	—	—	—	—
7/16	—	.437	11.113	.3726	9.448	25/64	.3906	9.921	—	20	—	—	—	—
—	M12	.471	11.963	—	—	—	—	—	—	—	1.75	1.25	14.5	20
1/2	—	.500	12.700	.4001	10.162	27/64	.4219	10.715	13	—	—	—	—	—
1/2	—	.500	12.700	.4351	11.049	29/64	.4531	11.509	—	20	—	—	—	—
—	M14	.551	13.995	—	—	—	—	—	—	—	2	1.5	12.5	17
9/16	—	.562	14.288	.4542	11.531	31/64	.4844	12.3031	12	—	—	—	—	—
9/16	—	.562	14.288	.4903	12.446	33/64	.5156	13.096	—	18	—	—	—	—
5/8	—	.625	15.875	.5069	12.852	17/32	.5312	13.493	11	—	—	—	—	—
5/8	—	.625	15.875	.5528	14.020	37/64	.5781	14.684	—	18	—	—	—	—
—	M16	.630	16.002	—	—	—	—	—	—	—	2	1.5	12.5	17
—	M18	.709	18.008	—	—	—	—	—	—	—	2.5	1.5	10	17
3/4	—	.750	19.050	.6201	15.748	21/32	.6562	16.668	10	—	—	—	—	—
3/4	—	.750	19.050	.6688	16.967	11/16	.6875	17.462	—	16	—	—	—	—
—	M20	.787	19.990	—	—	—	—	—	—	—	2.5	1.5	10	17
—	M22	.866	21.996	—	—	—	—	—	—	—	2.5	1.5	10	17
7/8	—	.875	22.225	.7307	18.542	49/64	.7656	19.446	9	—	—	—	—	—
7/8	—	.875	22.225	.7822	19.863	13/16	.8125	20.637	—	14	—	—	—	—
—	M24	.945	24.003	—	—	—	—	—	—	—	3	2	8.5	12.5
1	—	1.000	25.400	.8376	21.2598	7/8	.8750	22.225	8	—	—	—	—	—
1	—	1.000	25.400	.8917	22.632	59/64	.9219	23.415	—	12	—	—	—	—
—	M27	1.063	27.000	—	—	—	—	—	—	—	3	2	8.5	12.5

TABLE C.1.3 Unified Screw Thread Standard Series

Nominal Size		Basic Major Diameter	Graded Pitch Series*			Constant Pitch Series*								Nominal Size
Primary	Secondary		Coarse UNC	Fine UNF	Extra Fine UNEF	4 UN	6 UN	8 UN	12 UN	16 UN	20 UN	28 UN	32 UN	
						Threads Per Inch								
0		0.0600	—	80	—	—	—	—	—	—	—	—	—	0
	1	0.0730	64	72	—	—	—	—	—	—	—	—	—	1
2		0.0860	56	64	—	—	—	—	—	—	—	—	—	2
	3	0.0990	48	56	—	—	—	—	—	—	—	—	—	3
4		0.1120	40	48	—	—	—	—	—	—	—	—	—	4
5		0.1250	40	44	—	—	—	—	—	—	—	—	—	5
6		0.1380	32	40	—	—	—	—	—	—	—	—	UNC	6
8		0.1640	32	36	—	—	—	—	—	—	—	—	UNC	8
10		0.1900	24	32	—	—	—	—	—	—	—	—	UNC	10
	12	0.2160	24	28	32	—	—	—	—	—	—	UNF	UNEF	12
1/4		0.2500	20	28	32	—	—	—	—	—	UNC	UNF	UNEF	1/4
5/16		0.3125	18	24	32	—	—	—	—	—	20	28	UNEF	5/16
3/8		0.3750	16	24	32	—	—	—	—	UNC	20	28	UNEF	3/8
7/16		0.4375	14	20	28	—	—	—	—	16	UNF	UNEF	32	7/16
1/2		0.5000	13	20	28	—	—	—	—	16	UNF	UNEF	32	1/2
9/16		0.5625	12	18	24	—	—	—	UNC	16	20	28	32	9/16
5/8		0.6250	11	18	24	—	—	—	12	16	20	28	32	5/8
	11/16	0.6875	—	—	24	—	—	—	12	16	20	28	32	11/16
3/4		0.7500	10	16	20	—	—	—	12	UNF	UNEF	28	32	3/4
	13/16	0.8125	—	—	20	—	—	—	12	16	UNEF	28	32	13/16
7/8		0.8750	9	14	20	—	—	—	12	16	UNEF	28	32	7/8
	15/16	0.9375	—	—	20	—	—	—	12	16	UNEF	28	32	15/16
1		1.0000	8	12	20	—	—	UNC	UNF	16	UNEF	28	32	1
	1-1/16	1.0625	—	—	18	—	—	8	12	16	20	28	—	1-1/16
1-1/8		1.1250	7	12	18	—	—	8	UNF	16	20	28	—	1-1/8
	1-3/16	1.1875	—	—	18	—	—	8	12	16	20	28	—	1-3/16
1-1/4		1.2500	7	12	18	—	—	8	UNF	16	20	28	—	1-1/4
	1-5/16	1.3125	—	—	18	—	—	8	12	16	20	28	—	1-5/16
1-3/8		1.3750	6	12	18	—	UNC	8	UNF	16	20	28	—	1-3/8
	1-7/16	1.4375	—	—	18	—	6	8	12	16	20	28	—	1-7/16
1-1/2		1.5000	6	12	18	—	UNC	8	UNF	16	20	28	—	1-1/2
	1-9/16	1.5625	—	—	18	—	6	8	12	16	20	—	—	1-9/16
1-5/8		1.6250	—	—	18	—	6	8	12	16	20	—	—	1-5/8
	1-11/16	1.6875	—	—	18	—	6	8	12	16	20	—	—	1-11/16
1-3/4		1.7500	5	—	—	—	6	8	12	16	20	—	—	1-3/4
	1-13/16	1.8125	—	—	—	—	6	8	12	16	20	—	—	1-13/16
1-7/8		1.8750	—	—	—	—	6	8	12	16	20	—	—	1-7/8
	1-15/16	1.9375	—	—	—	—	6	8	12	16	20	—	—	1-15/16
2		2.0000	$4\frac{1}{2}$	—	—	—	6	8	12	16	20	—	—	2
	2-1/8	2.1250	—	—	—	—	6	8	12	16	20	—	—	2-1/8
2-1/4		2.2500	$4\frac{1}{2}$	—	—	—	6	8	12	16	20	—	—	2-1/4
	2-3/8	2.3750	—	—	—	—	6	8	12	16	20	—	—	2-3/8
2-1/2		2.5000	4	—	—	UNC	6	8	12	16	20	—	—	2-1/2
	2-5/8	2.6250	—	—	—	4	6	8	12	16	20	—	—	2-5/8
2-3/4		2.7500	4	—	—	UNC	6	8	12	16	20	—	—	2-3/4
	2-7/8	2.8750	—	—	—	4	6	8	12	16	20	—	—	2-7/8
3		3.0000	4	—	—	UNC	6	8	12	16	20	—	—	3
	3-1/8	3.1250	—	—	—	4	6	8	12	16	—	—	—	3-1/8
3-1/4		3.2500	4	—	—	UNC	6	8	12	16	—	—	—	3-1/4
	3-3/8	3.3750	—	—	—	4	6	8	12	16	—	—	—	3-3/8
3-1/2		3.5000	4	—	—	UNC	6	8	12	16	—	—	—	3-1/2
	3-5/8	3.6250	—	—	—	4	6	8	12	16	—	—	—	3-5/8
3-3/4		3.7500	4	—	—	UNC	6	8	12	16	—	—	—	3-3/4
	3-7/8	3.8750	—	—	—	4	6	8	12	16	—	—	—	3-7/8

Continued

TABLE C.1.3   Unified Screw Thread Standard Series—*Continued*

Nominal Size		Basic Major Diameter	Graded Pitch Series*			Constant Pitch Series*								Nominal Size
Primary	Secondary		Coarse UNC	Fine UNF	Extra Fine UNEF	4 UN	6 UN	8 UN	12 UN	16 UN	20 UN	28 UN	32 UN	
						Threads Per Inch								
4		4.0000	4	—	—	4	6	8	12	16	—	—	—	4
	4-1/8	4.1250	—	—	—	4	6	8	12	16	—	—	—	4-1/8
4-1/4		4.2500	—	—	—	4	6	8	12	16	—	—	—	4-1/4
	4-3/8	4.3750	—	—	—	4	6	8	12	16	—	—	—	4-3/8
4-1/2		4.5000	—	—	—	4	6	8	12	16	—	—	—	4-1/2
	4-5/8	4.6250	—	—	—	4	6	8	12	16	—	—	—	4-5/8
4-3/4		4.7500	—	—	—	4	6	8	12	16	—	—	—	4-3/4
	4-7/8	4.8750	—	—	—	4	6	8	12	16	—	—	—	4-7/8
5		5.0000	—	—	—	4	6	8	12	16	—	—	—	5
	5-1/8	5.1250	—	—	—	4	6	8	12	16	—	—	—	5-1/8
5-1/4		5.2500	—	—	—	4	6	8	12	16	—	—	—	5-1/4
	5-3/8	5.3750	—	—	—	4	6	8	12	16	—	—	—	5-3/8
5-1/2		5.5000	—	—	—	4	6	8	12	16	—	—	—	5-1/2
	5-5/8	5.6250	—	—	—	4	6	8	12	16	—	—	—	5-5/8
5-3/4		5.7500	—	—	—	4	6	8	12	16	—	—	—	5-3/4
	5-7/8	5.8750	—	—	—	4	6	8	12	16	—	—	—	5-7/8
6		6.0000	—	—	—	4	6	8	12	16	—	—	—	6

*For series symbols applying to a particular thread, see dimensional tables for Unified Screw Threads.
Courtesy of American National Standards.

TABLE C.1.4   Drill and Counterbore Sizes for Socket Head Cap Screws (1960 Series)

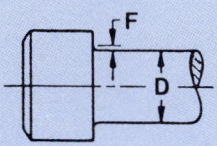 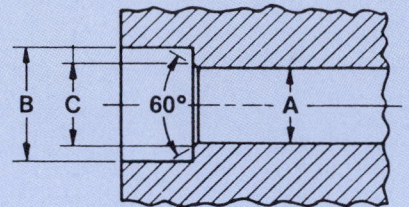 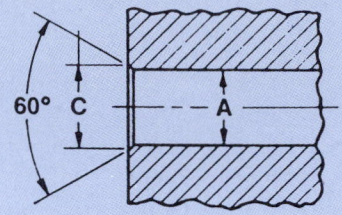

Nominal Size or Basic Screw Diameter		A				B	C
		Nominal Drill Size				Counterbore Diameter	Countersink Diameter D (Max) + 2F (Max)
		Close Fit		Normal Fit			
		Number or Fractional Size	Decimal Size	Number or Fractional Size	Decimal Size		
0	0.0600	51	0.067	49	0.073	1/8	0.074
1	0.0730	46	0.081	43	0.089	5/32	0.087
2	0.0860	3/32	0.094	36	0.106	3/16	0.102
3	0.0990	36	0.106	31	0.120	7/32	0.115
4	0.1120	1/8	0.125	29	0.136	7/32	0.130
5	0.1250	9/64	0.141	23	0.154	1/4	0.145
6	0.1380	23	0.154	18	0.170	9/32	0.158
8	0.1640	15	0.180	10	0.194	5/16	0.188
10	0.1900	5	0.206	2	0.221	3/8	0.218
1/4	0.2500	17/64	0.266	9/32	0.281	7/16	0.278
5/16	0.3125	21/64	0.328	11/32	0.344	17/32	0.346
3/8	0.3750	25/64	0.391	13/32	0.406	5/8	0.415
7/16	0.4375	29/64	0.453	15/32	0.469	23/32	0.483
1/2	0.5000	33/64	0.516	17/32	0.531	13/16	0.552
5/8	0.6250	41/64	0.641	21/32	0.656	1	0.689
3/4	0.7500	49/64	0.766	25/32	0.781	1 3/16	0.828
7/8	0.8750	57/64	0.891	29/32	0.906	1 3/8	0.963
1	1.0000	1 1/64	1.016	1 1/32	1.031	1 5/8	1.100
1 1/4	1.2500	1 9/32	1.281	1 5/16	1.312	2	1.370
1 1/2	1.5000	1 17/32	1.531	1 9/16	1.562	2 3/8	1.640
1 3/4	1.7500	1 25/32	1.781	1 13/16	1.812	2 3/4	1.910
2	2.0000	2 1/32	2.031	2 1/16	2.062	3 1/8	2.180

Metric Twist Drills

TABLE C.2.1 American National Standard Combined Drills and Countersinks—Plain and Bell Types (ANSI B94.11M-1979)

PLAIN TYPE

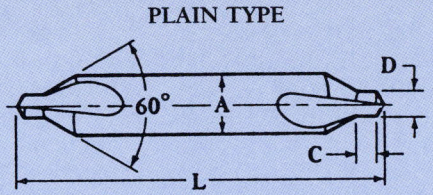

BELL TYPE

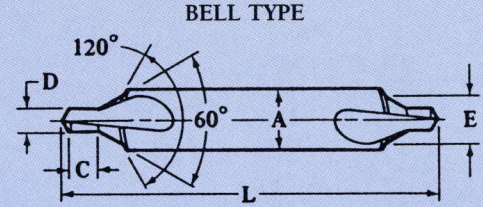

	Plain Type							
	Body Diameter		**Drill Diameter**		**Drill Length**		**Overall Length**	
Size Designation	**A**		**D**		**C**		**L**	
	Inches	Millimeters	Inches	Millimeters	Inches	Millimeters	Inches	Millimeters
00	⅛	3.18	.025	0.64	.030	0.76	1⅛	29
0	⅛	3.18	¹⁄₃₂	0.79	.038	0.97	1⅛	29
1	⅛	3.18	³⁄₆₄	1.19	³⁄₆₄	1.19	1¼	32
2	³⁄₁₆	4.76	⁵⁄₆₄	1.98	⁵⁄₆₄	1.98	1⅞	48
3	¼	6.35	⁷⁄₆₄	2.78	⁷⁄₆₄	2.78	2	51
4	⁵⁄₁₆	7.94	⅛	3.18	⅛	3.18	2⅛	54
5	⁷⁄₁₆	11.11	³⁄₁₆	4.76	³⁄₁₆	4.76	2¾	70
6	½	12.70	⁷⁄₃₂	5.56	⁷⁄₃₂	5.56	3	76
7	⅝	15.88	¼	6.35	¼	6.35	3¼	83
8	¾	19.05	⁵⁄₁₆	7.94	⁵⁄₁₆	7.94	3½	89

TABLE C.2.2   Twist Drill Sizes: Decimal/Metric

Number Sizes								Letter sizes			
No. Size	Decimal Equivalent	Metric Equiavalent	Closest Metric Drill (mm)	No. Size	Decimal Equivalent	Metric Equivalent	Closest Metric Drill (mm)	Size Letter	Decimal Equivalent	Metric Equivalent	Closest Metric Drill (mm)
1	.2280	5.791	5.80	41	.0960	2.438	2.45	A	.234	5.944	5.90
2	.2210	5.613	5.60	42	.0935	2.362	2.35	B	.238	6.045	6.00
3	.2130	5.410	5.40	43	.0890	2.261	2.25	C	.242	6.147	6.10
4	.2090	5.309	5.30	44	.0860	2.184	2.20	D	.246	6.248	6.25
5	.2055	5.220	5.20	45	.0820	2.083	2.10	E	.250	6.350	6.40
6	.2040	5.182	5.20	46	.0810	2.057	2.05	F	.257	6.528	6.50
7	.2010	5.105	5.10	47	.0785	1.994	2.00	G	.261	6.629	6.60
8	.1990	5.055	5.10	48	.0760	1.930	1.95	H	.266	6.756	6.75
9	.1960	4.978	5.00	49	.0730	1.854	1.85	I	.272	6.909	6.90
10	.1935	4.915	4.90	50	.0700	1.778	1.80	J	.277	7.036	7.00
11	.1910	4.851	4.90	51	.0670	1.702	1.70	K	.281	7.137	7.10
12	.1890	4.801	4.80	52	.0635	1.613	1.60	L	.290	7.366	7.40
13	.1850	4.699	4.70	53	.0595	1.511	1.50	M	.295	7.493	7.50
14	.1820	4.623	4.60	54	.0550	1.397	1.40	N	.302	7.671	7.70
15	.1800	4.572	4.60	55	.0520	1.321	1.30	O	.316	8.026	8.00
16	.1770	4.496	4.50	56	.0465	1.181	1.20	P	.323	8.204	8.20
17	.1730	4.394	4.40	57	.0430	1.092	1.10	Q	.332	8.433	8.40
18	.1695	4.305	4.30	58	.0420	1.067	1.05	R	.339	8.611	8.60
19	.1660	4.216	4.20	59	.0410	1.041	1.05	S	.348	8.839	8.80
19	.1610	4.089	4.10	60	.0400	1.016	1.00	T	.358	9.093	9.10
21	.1590	4.039	4.00	61	.0390	0.991	1.00	U	.368	9.347	9.30
22	.1570	3.988	4.00	62	.0380	0.965	0.95	V	.377	9.576	9.60
23	.1540	3.912	3.90	63	.0370	0.940	0.95	W	.386	9.804	9.80
24	.1520	3.861	3.90	64	.0360	0.914	0.90	X	.397	10.084	10.00
25	.1495	3.797	3.80	65	.0350	0.889	0.90	Y	.404	10.262	10.50
26	.1470	3.734	3.75	66	.0330	0.838	0.85	Z	.413	10.491	10.50
27	.1440	3.658	3.70	67	.0320	0.813	0.80				
28	.1405	3.569	3.60	68	.0310	0.787	0.80				
29	.1360	3.454	3.50	69	.0292	0.742	0.75				
30	.1285	3.264	3.25	70	.0280	0.711	0.70				
31	.1200	3.048	3.00	71	.0260	0.660	0.65				
32	.1160	2.946	2.90	72	.0250	0.635	0.65				
33	.1130	2.870	2.90	73	.0240	0.610	0.60				
34	.1110	2.819	2.80	74	.0225	0.572	0.55				
35	.1100	2.794	2.80	75	.0210	0.533	0.55				
36	.1065	2.705	2.70	76	.0200	0.508	0.50				
37	.1040	2.642	2.60	77	.0180	0.457	0.45				
38	.1015	2.578	2.60	78	.0160	0.406	0.40				
39	.0995	2.527	2.50	79	.0145	0.368	0.35				
40	.0980	2.489	2.50	80	.0135	0.343	0.35				

*Fraction-size drills range in size from one-sixteenth—4 in. and over in diameter—by sixty-fourths.

Bolts, Nuts, and Screws

Socket Flat Countersunk Head Cap Screws (ANSI/ASME B18.3, 1986)

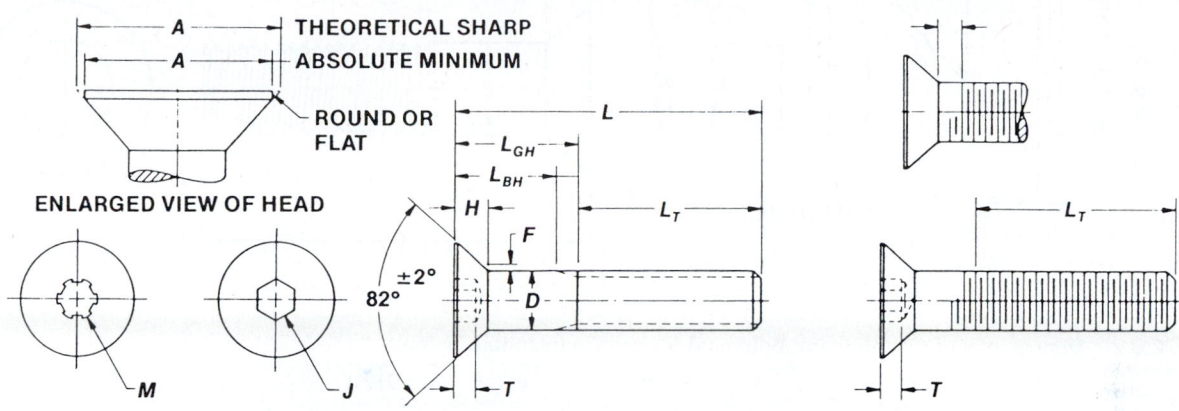

TABLE C.3.1 Dimensions of Hexagon and Spline Socket Flat Countersunk Head Cap Screws

Nominal Size or Basic Screw Diameter	D			A Head Diameter		H Head Height		M Spline Socket Size	J Hexagon Socket Size	T Key Engagement	F Fillet Extension Above D Max
		Body Diameter		Theoretical Sharp Max	Abs Min	Reference	Flushness Tolerance				
		Max	Min						Nom	Min	Max
0	0.0600	0.0600	0.0568	0.138	0.117	0.044	0.006	0.048		0.035	0.025	0.006
1	0.0730	0.0730	0.0695	0.168	0.143	0.054	0.007	0.060		0.050	0.031	0.008
2	0.0860	0.0860	0.0822	0.197	0.168	0.064	0.008	0.060		0.050	0.038	0.010
3	0.0990	0.0990	0.0949	0.226	0.193	0.073	0.010	0.072	1/16	0.062	0.044	0.010
4	0.1120	0.1120	0.1075	0.255	0.218	0.083	0.011	0.072	1/16	0.062	0.055	0.012
5	0.1250	0.1250	0.1202	0.281	0.240	0.090	0.012	0.096	5/64	0.078	0.061	0.014
6	0.1380	0.1380	0.1329	0.307	0.263	0.097	0.013	0.096	5/64	0.078	0.066	0.015
8	0.1640	0.1640	0.1585	0.359	0.311	0.112	0.014	0.111	3/32	0.094	0.076	0.015
10	0.1900	0.1900	0.1840	0.411	0.359	0.127	0.015	0.145	1/8	0.125	0.087	0.015
1/4	0.2500	0.2500	0.2435	0.531	0.480	0.161	0.016	0.183	5/32	0.156	0.111	0.015
5/16	0.3125	0.3125	0.3053	0.656	0.600	0.198	0.017	0.216	3/16	0.188	0.135	0.015
3/8	0.3750	0.3750	0.3678	0.781	0.720	0.234	0.018	0.251	7/32	0.219	0.159	0.015
7/16	0.4375	0.4375	0.4294	0.844	0.781	0.234	0.018	0.291	1/4	0.250	0.159	1.015
1/2	0.5000	0.5000	0.4919	0.938	0.872	0.251	0.018	0.372	5/16	0.312	0.172	0.015
5/8	0.6250	0.6250	0.6163	1.188	1.112	0.324	0.022	0.454	3/8	0.375	0.220	0.015
3/4	0.7500	0.7500	0.7406	1.438	1.355	0.396	0.024	0.454	1/2	0.500	0.220	0.015
7/8	0.8750	0.8750	0.8647	1.688	1.604	0.468	0.025	. . .	9/16	0.562	0.248	0.015
1	1.0000	1.0000	0.9886	1.938	1.841	0.540	0.028	. . .	5/8	0.625	0.297	0.015
1 1/8	1.1250	1.1250	1.1086	2.188	2.079	0.611	0.031	. . .	3/4	0.750	0.325	0.031
1 1/4	1.2500	1.2500	1.2336	2.438	2.316	0.683	0.035	. . .	7/8	0.875	0.358	0.031
1 3/8	1.3750	1.3750	1.3568	2.688	2.553	0.755	0.038	. . .	7/8	0.875	0.402	0.031
1 1/2	1.5000	1.5000	1.4818	2.938	2.791	0.827	0.042	. . .	1	1.0000	0.435	0.031

Countersunk Bolts and Slotted Countersunk Bolts (ANSI/ASME B18.5, 1978)

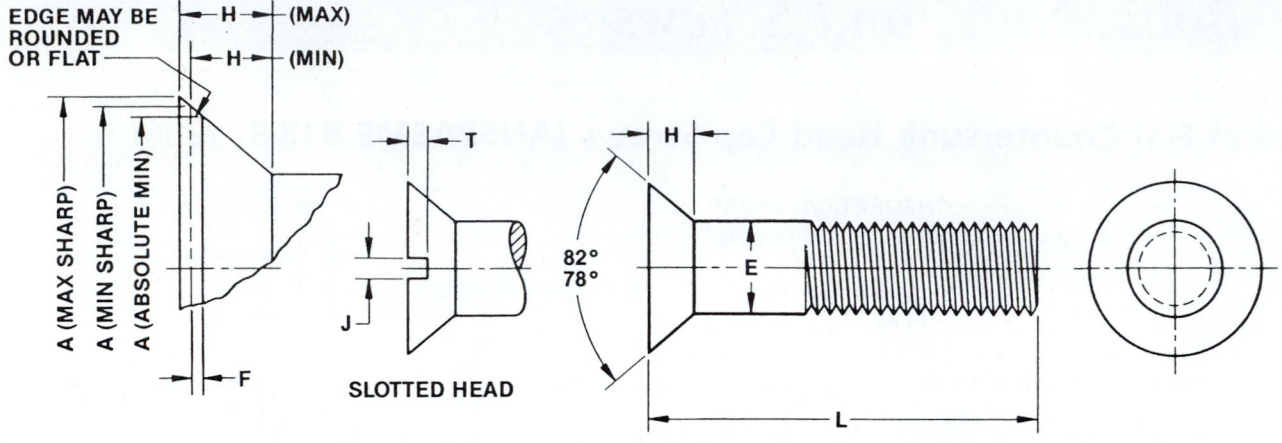

TABLE C.3.2   Dimensions of Countersunk Bolts and Slotted Countersunk Bolts

Nominal Size or Basic Bolt Diameter		E Body Diameter		A Head Diameter			F Flat on Min Dia Head	H Head Height		J Slot Width		T Slot Depth	
		Max	Min	Max Edge Sharp	Min Edge Sharp	Absolute Min Edge Rounded or Flat	Max	Max	Min	Max	Min	Max	Min
1/4	0.2500	0.260	0.237	0.493	0.477	0.445	0.018	0.150	0.131	0.075	0.064	0.068	0.045
5/16	0.3125	0.324	0.298	0.618	0.598	0.558	0.023	0.189	0.164	0.084	0.072	0.086	0.057
3/8	0.3750	0.388	0.360	0.740	0.715	0.668	0.027	0.225	0.196	0.094	0.081	0.103	0.068
7/16	0.4375	0.452	0.421	0.803	0.778	0.726	0.030	0.226	0.196	0.094	0.081	0.103	0.068
1/2	0.5000	0.515	0.483	1.935	1.905	0.845	0.035	0.269	0.233	0.106	0.091	0.103	0.068
5/8	0.6250	0.642	0.605	1.169	1.132	1.066	0.038	0.336	0.292	0.133	0.116	0.137	0.091
3/4	0.7500	0.768	0.729	1.402	1.357	1.285	0.041	0.403	0.349	0.149	0.131	0.171	0.115
7/8	0.8750	0.895	0.852	1.637	1.584	1.511	0.042	0.470	0.408	0.167	0.147	0.206	0.138
1	1.0000	1.022	0.976	1.869	1.810	1.735	0.043	0.537	0.466	0.188	0.166	0.240	0.162
1 1/8	1.1250	1.149	1.098	2.104	2.037	1.962	0.043	0.604	0.525	0.196	0.178	0.257	0.173
1 1/4	1.2500	1.277	1.223	2.337	2.262	2.187	0.043	0.671	0.582	0.211	0.193	0.291	0.197
1 3/8	1.3750	1.404	1.345	2.571	2.489	2.414	0.043	0.738	0.641	0.226	0.208	0.326	0.220
1 1/2	1.5000	1.531	1.470	2.804	2.715	2.640	0.043	0.805	0.698	0.258	0.240	0.360	0.244

Hex Cap Screws (Finished Hex Bolts) (ANSI/ASME B18.2.1, 1981)

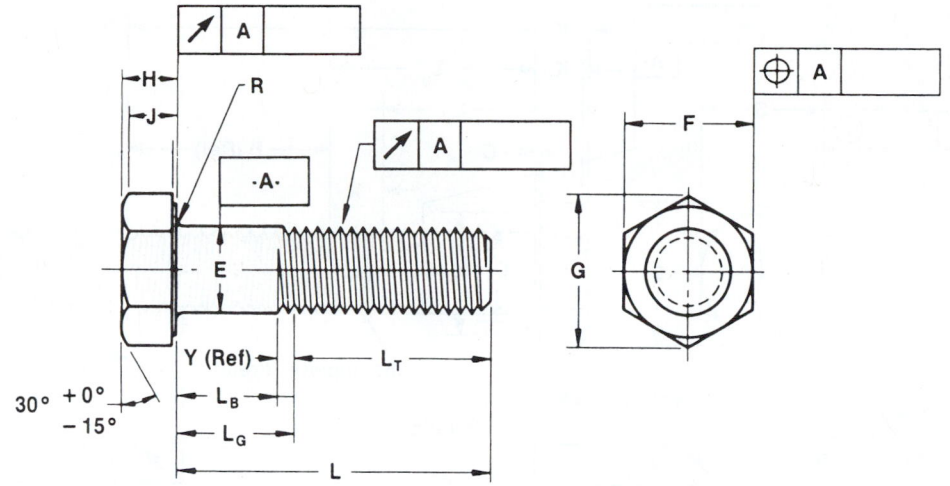

TABLE C.3.3 Dimensions of Hex Cap Screws

		E		F			G			H			J	L_T		Y	Runout
Nominal Size or Basic Product Dia		Body Diameter		Width Across Flats			Width Across Corners			Height			Wrenching Height	Thread Length For Screw Lengths		Transition Thread Length	Runout of Bearing Surface FIM
		Max	Min	Basic	Max	Min	Max	Min	Basic	Max	Min	Min	6 in. and Shorter	Over 6 in.	Max	Max
													Basic	Basic		
1/4	0.2500	0.2500	0.2450	7/16	0.438	0.428	0.505	0.488	5/32	0.163	0.150	0.106	0.750	1.000	0.250	0.010
5/16	0.3125	0.3125	0.3065	1/2	0.500	0.489	0.577	0.557	13/64	0.211	0.195	0.140	0.875	1.125	0.278	0.011
3/8	0.3750	0.3750	0.3690	9/16	0.562	0.551	0.650	0.628	15/64	0.243	0.226	0.160	1.000	1.250	0.312	0.012
7/16	0.4375	0.4375	0.4305	5/8	0.625	0.612	0.722	0.698	9/32	0.291	0.272	0.195	1.125	1.375	0.357	0.013
1/2	0.5000	0.5000	0.4930	3/4	0.750	0.736	0.866	0.840	5/16	0.323	0.302	0.215	1.250	1.500	0.385	0.014
9/16	0.5625	0.5625	0.5545	13/16	0.812	0.798	0.938	0.910	23/64	0.371	0.348	0.250	1.375	1.625	0.417	0.015
5/8	0.6250	0.6250	0.6170	15/16	0.938	0.922	1.083	1.051	25/64	0.403	0.378	0.269	1.500	1.750	0.455	0.017
3/4	0.7500	0.7500	0.7410	1-1/8	1.125	1.100	1.299	1.254	15/32	0.483	0.455	0.324	1.750	2.000	0.500	0.020
7/8	0.8750	0.8750	0.8660	1-5/16	1.312	1.285	1.516	1.465	35/64	0.563	0.531	0.378	2.000	2.250	0.556	0.023
1	1.0000	1.0000	0.9900	1-1/2	1.500	1.469	1.732	1.675	39/64	0.627	0.591	0.416	2.250	2.500	0.625	0.026
1-1/8	1.1250	1.1250	1.1140	1-11/16	1.688	1.631	1.949	1.859	11/16	0.718	0.658	0.461	2.500	2.750	0.714	0.029
1-1/4	1.2500	1.2500	1.2390	1-7/8	1.875	1.812	2.165	2.066	25/32	0.813	0.749	0.530	2.750	3.000	0.714	0.033
1-3/8	1.3750	1.3750	1.3630	2-1/16	2.062	1.994	2.382	2.273	27/32	0.878	0.810	0.569	3.000	3.250	0.833	0.036
1-1/2	1.5000	1.5000	1.4880	2-1/4	2.250	2.175	2.598	2.480	1-5/16	0.974	0.902	0.640	3.250	3.500	0.833	0.039
1-3/4	1.7500	1.7500	1.7380	2-5/8	2.625	2.538	3.031	2.893	1-3/32	1.134	1.054	0.748	3.750	4.000	1.000	0.046
2	2.0000	2.0000	1.9880	3	3.000	2.900	3.464	3.306	1-7/32	1.263	1.175	0.825	4.250	4.500	1.111	0.052
2-1/4	2.2500	2.2500	2.2380	3-3/8	3.375	3.262	3.897	3.719	1-3/8	1.423	1.327	0.933	4.750	5.000	1.111	0.059
2-1/2	2.5000	2.5000	2.4880	3-3/4	3.750	3.625	4.330	4.133	1-17/32	1.583	1.479	1.042	5.250	5.500	1.250	0.065
2-3/4	2.7500	2.7500	2.7380	4-1/8	4.125	3.988	4.763	4.546	1-11/16	1.744	1.632	1.151	5.750	6.000	1.250	0.072
3	3.0000	3.0000	2.9880	4-1/2	4.500	4.350	5.196	4.959	1-7/8	1.935	1.815	1.290	6.250	6.500	1.250	0.079

Metric Hex Cap Screws (ANSI B18.2.3.1M, 1979)

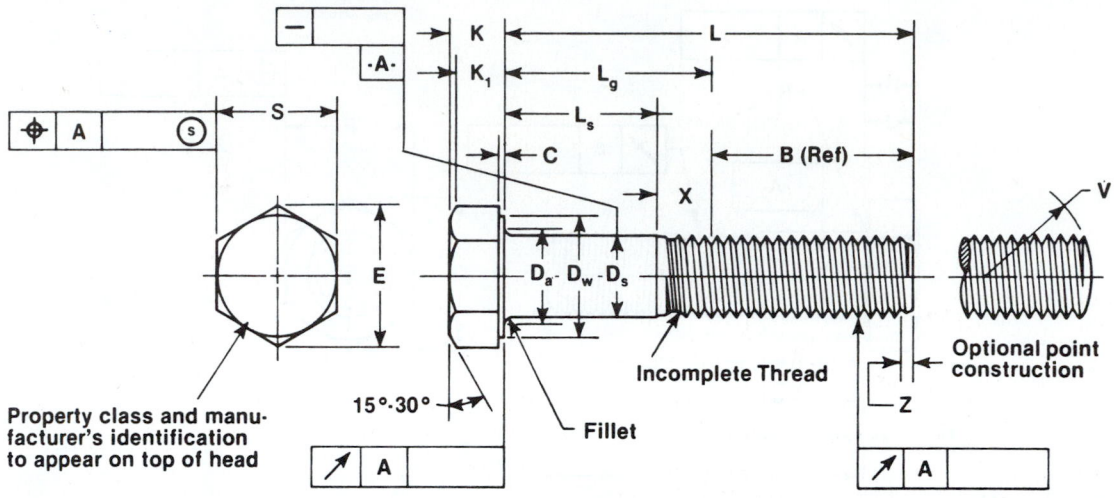

TABLE C.3.4 Dimensions of Hex Cap Screws

D	D_S		S		E		K		K_1	C		D_W	Runout of
Nom Screw Dia and Thread Pitch	Body Diameter		Width Across Flats		Width Across Corners		Head Height		Wrenching Height	Washer Face Thickness		Washer Face Dia	Bearing Surface FIM
	Max	Min	Max	Min	Max	Min	Max	Min	Min	Max	Min	Min	Max
M5 × 0.8	5.00	4.82	8.00	7.78	9.24	8.79	3.65	3.35	2.4	0.5	0.2	6.9	0.22
M6 × 1	6.00	5.82	10.00	9.78	11.55	11.05	4.15	3.85	2.8	0.5	0.2	8.9	0.25
M8 × 1.25	8.00	7.78	13.00	12.73	15.01	14.38	5.50	5.10	3.7	0.6	0.3	11.6	0.28
M10 × 1.5	10.00	9.78	16.00	15.73	18.48	17.77	6.63	6.17	4.5	0.6	0.3	14.6	0.32
M12 × 1.75	12.00	11.73	18.00	17.73	20.78	20.03	7.76	7.24	5.2	0.6	0.3	16.6	0.35
M14 × 2	14.00	13.73	21.00	20.67	24.25	23.35	9.09	8.51	6.2	0.6	0.3	19.6	0.39
M16 × 2	16.00	15.73	24.00	23.67	27.71	26.75	10.32	9.68	7.0	0.8	0.4	22.5	0.43
M20 × 2.5	20.00	19.67	30.00	29.16	34.64	32.95	12.88	12.12	8.8	0.8	0.4	27.7	0.53
M24 × 3	24.00	23.67	36.00	35.00	41.57	39.55	15.44	14.56	10.5	0.8	0.4	33.2	0.63
M30 × 3.5	30.00	29.67	46.00	45.00	53.12	50.85	19.48	17.92	13.1	0.8	0.4	42.7	0.78
M36 × 4	36.00	35.61	55.00	53.80	63.51	60.79	23.38	21.62	15.8	0.8	0.4	51.1	0.93
M42 × 4.5	42.00	41.38	65.00	62.90	75.06	71.71	26.97	25.03	18.2	1.0	0.5	59.8	1.09
M48 × 5	48.00	47.38	75.00	72.60	86.60	82.76	31.07	28.93	21.0	1.0	0.5	69.0	1.25
M56 × 5.5	56.00	55.26	85.00	82.20	98.15	93.71	36.20	33.80	24.5	1.0	0.5	78.1	1.47
M64 × 6	64.00	63.26	95.00	91.80	109.70	104.65	41.32	36.68	28.0	1.0	0.5	87.2	1.69
M72 × 6	72.00	71.26	105.00	101.40	121.24	115.60	46.45	43.55	31.5	1.2	0.6	96.3	1.91
M80 × 6	80.00	79.26	115.00	111.00	132.72	126.54	51.58	48.42	35.0	1.2	0.6	105.4	2.13
M90 × 6	90.00	89.13	130.00	125.50	150.11	143.07	57.74	54.26	39.2	1.2	0.6	119.2	2.41
M100 × 6	100.00	99.13	145.00	140.00	167.43	159.60	63.90	60.10	43.4	1.2	0.6	133.0	2.69
*M10 × 1.5	10.00	9.78	15.00	14.73	17.32	16.64	6.63	6.17	4.5	0.6	0.3	13.6	0.31

Socket Head Cap Screws (1960 Series) (ANSI/ASME B 18.3, 1986)

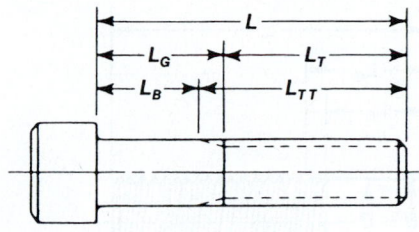

TABLE C.3.5   Screws Beyond Sizes in Table 1C

Nom Size or Basic Screw Dia		L_T Thread Length Min	L_{TT} Total Thread Length Max	Nom Size or Basic Screw Dia		L_T Thread Length Min	L_{TT} Total Thread Length Max
0	0.0600	0.50	0.62	7/8	0.8750	2.25	3.69
1	0.0730	0.62	0.77	1	1.0000	2.50	4.12
2	0.0860	0.62	0.80	1 1/8	1.1250	2.81	4.65
3	0.0990	0.62	0.83	1 1/4	1.2500	3.12	5.09
4	0.1120	0.75	0.99	1 3/8	1.3750	3.44	5.65
5	0.1250	0.75	1.00	1 1/2	1.5000	3.75	6.08
6	0.1380	0.75	1.05	1 3/4	1.7500	4.38	7.13
8	0.1640	0.88	1.19	2	2.0000	5.00	8.11
10	0.1900	0.88	1.27	2 1/4	2.2500	5.62	8.99
1/4	0.2500	1.00	1.50	2 1/2	2.5000	6.25	10.00
5/16	0.3125	1.12	1.71	2 3/4	2.7500	6.88	10.87
3/8	0.3750	1.25	1.94	3	3.0000	7.50	11.75
7/16	0.4375	1.38	2.17	3 1/4	3.2500	8.12	12.63
1/2	0.5000	1.50	2.38	3 1/2	3.5000	8.75	13.50
5/8	0.6250	1.75	2.82	3 3/4	3.7500	9.38	14.37
3/4	0.7500	2.00	3.25	4	4.0000	10.00	15.25

Metric Socket Head Cap Screws (ANSI/ASME B18.3.1M, 1982)

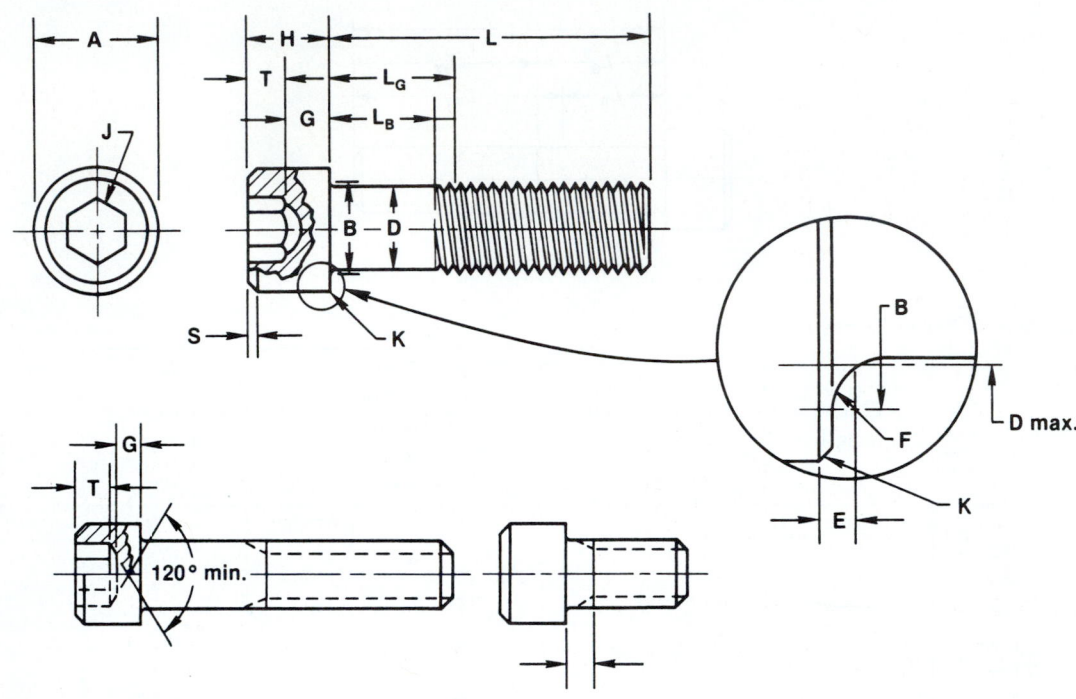

TABLE C.3.6   Dimensions of Metric Socket Head Cap Screws

Nom Screw Dia and Thread Pitch	D Body Diameter		A Head Diameter		H Head Height		S Cham-fer or Radius	J Hex-agon Socket Size	T Key En-gage ment	G Wall Thick-ness	B Under Head Fillet Transi-tion Diameter		E Under Head Fillet Transi-tion Length	F Under Head Fillet Junc-ture Radius	K Cham-fer or Radius
	Max	Min	Max	Min	Max	Min	Max	Nom	Min	Min	Max	Min	Max	Min	Max
M1.6 × 0.35	1.60	1.46	3.00	2.87	1.60	1.52	0.16	1.5	0.80	0.54	2.0	1.8	0.34	0.10	0.08
M2 × 0.4	2.00	1.86	3.80	3.65	2.00	1.91	0.20	1.5	1.00	0.68	2.6	2.2	0.51	0.10	0.08
M2.5 × 0.45	2.50	2.36	4.50	4.33	2.50	2.40	0.25	2.0	1.25	0.85	3.1	2.7	0.51	0.10	0.08
M3 × 0.5	3.00	2.86	5.50	5.32	3.00	2.89	0.30	2.5	1.50	1.02	3.6	3.2	0.51	0.10	0.13
M4 × 0.7	4.00	3.82	7.00	6.80	4.00	3.88	0.40	3.0	2.00	1.52	4.7	4.4	0.60	0.20	0.13
M5 × 0.8	5.00	4.82	8.50	8.27	5.00	4.86	0.50	4.0	2.50	1.90	5.7	5.4	0.60	0.20	0.13
M6 × 1	6.00	5.82	10.00	9.74	6.00	5.85	0.60	5.0	3.00	2.28	6.8	6.5	0.68	0.25	0.20
M8 × 1.25	8.00	7.78	13.00	12.70	8.00	7.83	0.80	6.0	4.00	3.20	9.2	8.8	1.02	0.40	0.20
M10 × 1.5	10.00	9.78	16.00	15.67	10.00	9.81	1.00	8.0	5.00	4.00	11.2	10.8	1.02	0.40	0.20
M12 × 1.75	12.00	11.73	18.00	17.63	12.00	11.79	1.20	10.0	6.00	4.80	14.2	13.2	1.87	0.60	0.25
(1)M14 × 2	14.00	13.73	21.00	20.60	14.00	13.77	1.40	12.0	7.00	5.60	16.2	15.2	1.87	0.60	0.25
M16 × 2	16.00	15.73	24.00	23.58	16.00	15.76	1.60	14.0	8.00	6.40	18.2	17.2	1.87	0.60	0.25
M20 × 2.5	20.00	19.67	30.00	29.53	20.00	19.73	2.00	17.0	10.00	8.00	22.4	21.6	2.04	0.80	0.40
M24 × 3	24.00	23.67	36.00	35.48	24.00	23.70	2.40	19.0	12.00	9.60	26.4	25.6	2.04	0.80	0.40
M30 × 3.5	30.00	29.67	45.00	44.42	30.00	29.67	3.00	22.0	15.00	12.00	33.4	32.0	2.89	1.00	0.40
M36 × 4	36.00	35.61	54.00	53.37	36.00	35.64	3.60	27.0	18.00	14.40	39.4	38.0	2.89	1.00	0.40
M42 × 4.5	42.00	41.61	63.00	62.31	42.00	41.61	4.20	32.0	21.00	16.80	45.6	44.4	3.06	1.20	0.40
M48 × 5	48.00	47.61	72.00	72.27	48.00	47.58	4.80	36.0	24.00	19.20	52.6	51.2	3.91	1.60	0.40

Socket Head Shoulder Screws (ANSI/ASME B18.3, 1986)

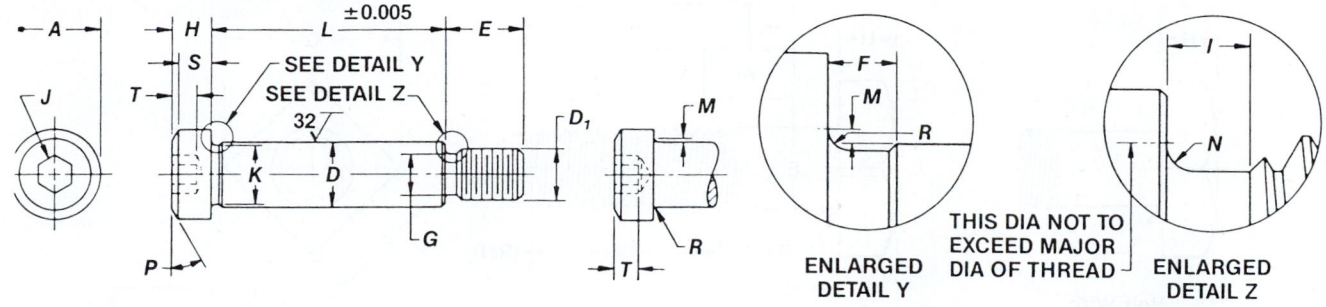

TABLE C.3.7 Dimensions of Hexagon Socket Head Shoulder Screws

Nominal Size or Basic Shoulder Diameter		D Shoulder Diameter		A Head Diameter		H Head Height		S Head Side Height	J Hexagon Socket Size		T Key Engagement	M Head Fillet Extension Above D	R Head Fillet Radius
		Max	Min	Max	Min	Max	Min	Min	Nom		Min	Max	Min
1/4	0.250	0.2480	0.2460	0.375	0.357	0.188	0.177	0.157	1/8	0.125	0.094	0.014	0.009
5/16	0.312	0.3105	0.3085	0.438	0.419	0.219	0.209	0.183	5/32	0.156	0.117	0.017	0.012
3/8	0.375	0.3730	0.3710	0.562	0.543	0.250	0.240	0.209	3/16	0.188	0.141	0.020	0.015
1/2	0.500	0.4980	0.4960	0.750	0.729	0.312	0.302	0.262	1/4	0.250	0.188	0.026	0.020
5/8	0.625	0.6230	0.6210	0.875	0.853	0.375	0.365	0.315	5/16	0.312	0.234	0.032	0.024
3/4	0.750	0.7480	0.7460	1.000	0.977	0.500	0.490	0.421	3/8	0.375	0.281	0.039	0.030
1	1.000	0.9980	0.9960	1.312	1.287	0.625	0.610	0.527	1/2	0.500	0.375	0.050	0.040
1 1/4	1.250	1.2480	1.2460	1.750	1.723	0.750	0.735	0.633	5/8	0.625	0.469	0.060	0.050
1 1/2	1.500	1.4980	1.4960	2.125	2.095	1.000	0.980	0.842	7/8	0.875	0.656	0.070	0.060
1 3/4	1.750	1.7480	1.7460	2.375	2.345	1.125	1.105	0.948	1	1.000	0.750	0.080	0.070
2	2.00	1.9980	1.9960	2.750	2.720	1.250	1.230	1.054	1 1/4	1.250	0.937	0.090	0.080

Nominal Size or Basic Shoulder Diameter		K Shoulder Neck Diameter	F Shoulder Neck Width	D₁ Nominal Thread Size or Basic Thread Diameter		Threads per in.	G Thread Neck Diameter		I Thread Neck Width	N Thread Neck Fillet		E Thread Length
		Min	Max				Max	Min	Max	Max	Min	Basic
1/4	0.250	0.227	0.093	10	0.1900	24	0.142	0.133	0.083	0.023	0.017	0.375
5/16	0.312	0.289	0.093	1/4	0.2500	20	0.193	0.182	0.100	0.028	0.022	0.438
3/8	0.375	0.352	0.093	5/16	0.3125	18	0.249	0.237	0.111	0.031	0.025	0.500
1/2	0.500	0.477	0.093	3/8	0.3750	16	0.304	0.291	0.125	0.035	0.029	0.625
5/8	0.625	0.602	0.093	1/2	0.5000	13	0.414	0.397	0.154	0.042	0.036	0.750
3/4	0.750	0.727	0.093	5/8	0.6250	11	0.521	0.502	0.182	0.051	0.045	0.875
1	1.000	0.977	0.125	3/4	0.7500	10	0.638	0.616	0.200	0.055	0.049	1.000
1 1/4	1.250	1.227	0.125	7/8	0.8750	9	0.750	0.726	0.222	0.062	0.056	1.125
1 1/2	1.500	1.478	0.125	1 1/8	1.1250	7	0.964	0.934	0.286	0.072	0.066	1.500
1 3/4	1.750	1.728	0.125	1 1/4	1.2500	7	1.089	1.059	0.286	0.072	0.066	1.750
2	2.000	1.978	0.125	1 1/2	1.5000	6	1.307	1.277	0.333	0.102	0.096	2.000

Square Bolts (ANSI/ASME B18.2.1, 1981)

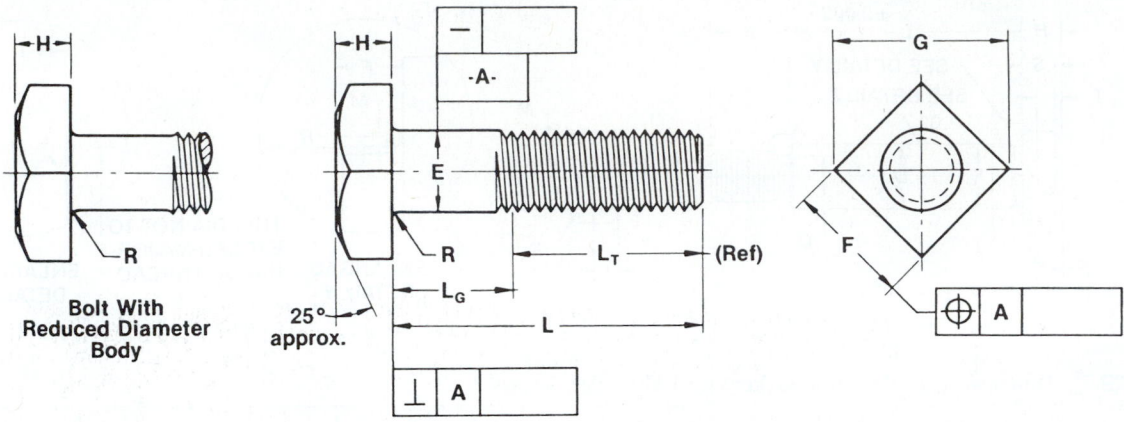

Bolt With
Reduced Diameter
Body

25°
approx.

TABLE C.3.8   Dimensions of Square Bolts

Nominal Size or Basic Product Dia		E	F			G		H			R		L_T	
		Body Dia	Width Across Flats			Width Across Corners		Height			Radius of Fillet		Thread Length For Bolt Lengths	
													6 in. and shorter	over 6 in.
		Max	Basic	Max	Min	Max	Min	Basic	Max	Min	Max	Min	Basic	Basic
1/4	0.2500	0.260	3/8	0.375	0.362	0.530	0.498	11/64	0.188	0.156	0.03	0.01	0.750	1.000
5/16	0.3125	0.324	1/2	0.500	0.484	0.707	0.665	13/64	0.220	0.186	0.03	0.01	0.875	1.125
3/8	0.3750	0.388	9/16	0.562	0.544	0.795	0.747	1/4	0.268	0.232	0.03	0.01	1.000	1.250
7/16	0.4375	0.452	5/8	0.625	0.603	0.884	0.828	19/64	0.316	0.278	0.03	0.01	1.125	1.375
1/2	0.5000	0.515	3/4	0.750	0.725	1.061	0.995	21/64	0.348	0.308	0.03	0.01	1.250	1.500
5/8	0.6250	0.642	15/16	0.938	0.906	1.326	1.244	27/64	0.444	0.400	0.06	0.02	1.500	1.750
3/4	0.7500	0.768	1-1/8	1.125	1.088	1.591	1.494	1/2	0.524	0.476	0.06	0.02	1.750	2.000
7/8	0.8750	0.895	1-5/16	1.312	1.269	1.856	1.742	19/32	0.620	0.568	0.06	0.02	2.000	2.250
1	1.0000	1.022	1-1/2	1.500	1.450	2.121	1.991	21/32	0.684	0.628	0.09	0.03	2.250	2.500
1-1/8	1.1250	1.149	1-11/16	1.688	1.631	2.386	2.239	3/4	0.780	0.720	0.09	0.03	2.500	2.750
1-1/4	1.2500	1.277	1-7/8	1.875	1.812	2.652	2.489	27/32	0.876	0.812	0.09	0.03	2.750	3.000
1-3/8	1.3750	1.404	2-1/16	2.062	1.994	2.917	2.738	29/32	0.940	0.872	0.09	0.03	3.000	3.250
1-1/2	1.5000	1.531	2-1/4	2.250	2.175	3.182	2.986	1	1.036	0.964	0.09	0.03	3.250	3.500

Socket Button Head Cap Screws (ANSI/ASME B18.3, 1986)

General Note: This product is designed and recommended for light fastening applications such as guards, hinges, etc. It is not suggested for use in critical high strength applications where socket head cap screws should normally be used.

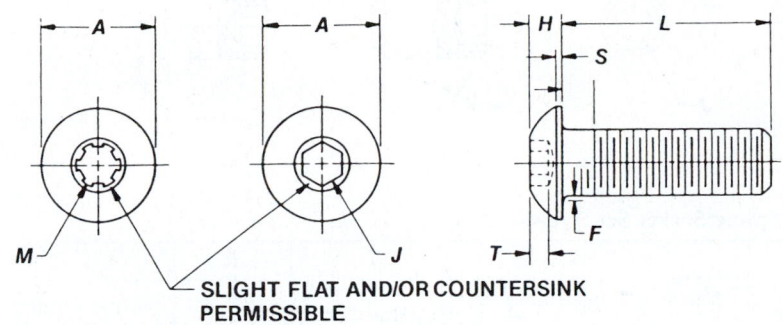

SLIGHT FLAT AND/OR COUNTERSINK PERMISSIBLE

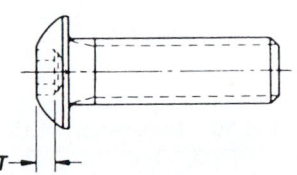

TABLE C.3.9 Dimensions of Hexagon and Spline Socket Button Head Cap Screws

Nominal Size or Basic Screw Diameter		A Head Diameter		H Head Height		S Head Side Height	M Spline Socket Size	J Hexagon Socket Size		T Key Engagement	F Fillet Extension		L Max Standard Length
		Max	Min	Max	Min	Ref	Nom		Nom	Min	Max	Min	Nom
0	0.0600	0.114	0.104	0.032	0.026	0.010	0.048		0.035	0.020	0.010	0.005	0.50
1	0.0730	0.139	0.129	0.039	0.033	0.010	0.060		0.050	0.028	0.010	0.005	0.50
2	0.0860	0.164	0.154	0.046	0.038	0.010	0.060		0.050	0.028	0.010	0.005	0.50
3	0.0990	0.188	0.176	0.052	0.044	0.010	0.072	1/16	0.062	0.035	0.010	0.005	0.50
4	0.1120	0.213	0.201	0.059	0.051	0.015	0.072	1/16	0.062	0.035	0.010	0.005	0.50
5	0.1250	0.238	0.226	0.066	0.058	0.015	0.096	5/64	0.078	0.044	0.010	0.005	0.50
6	0.1380	0.262	0.250	0.073	0.063	0.015	0.096	5/64	0.078	0.044	0.010	0.005	0.63
8	0.1640	0.312	0.298	0.087	0.077	0.015	0.111	3/32	0.094	0.052	0.015	0.010	0.75
10	0.1900	0.361	0.347	0.101	0.091	0.020	0.145	1/8	0.125	0.070	0.015	0.010	1.00
1/4	0.2500	0.437	0.419	0.132	0.122	0.031	0.183	5/32	0.156	0.087	0.020	0.015	1.00
5/16	0.3125	0.547	0.527	0.166	0.152	0.031	0.216	3/16	0.188	0.105	0.020	0.015	1.00
3/8	0.3750	0.656	0.636	0.199	0.185	0.031	0.251	7/32	0.219	0.122	0.020	0.015	1.25
1/2	0.5000	0.875	0.851	0.265	0.245	0.046	0.372	5/16	0.312	0.175	0.030	0.020	2.00
5/8	0.6250	1.000	0.970	0.331	0.311	0.062	0.454	3/8	0.375	0.210	0.030	0.020	2.00

Socket Set Screws (ANSI/ASME B18.3, 1986)

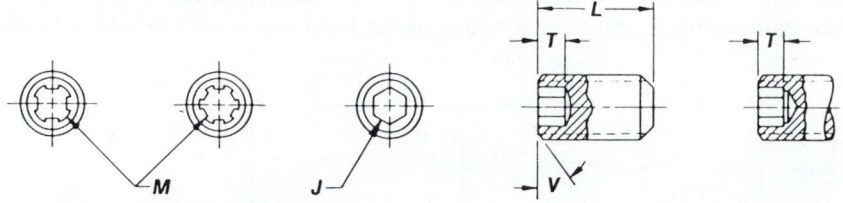

TABLE C.3.10   Dimensions of Hexagon and Spline Socket Set Screws

Nominal Size or Basic Screw Diameter		J Hexagon Socket Size		M Spline Socket Size	T Min Key Engagement to Develop Functional Capability of Key		C Cup and Flat Point Diameters		R Oval Point Radius	Y Cone Point Angle 90 deg ±2 deg for These Nominal Lengths or Longer; 118 deg ±2 deg for Shorter Nominal Lengths
			Nom	Nom	Hex Socket T_H Min	Spline Socket T_S Min	Max	Min	Basic	
0	0.0600			0.028	0.033	0.050	0.026	0.033	0.027	0.045	0.09
1	0.0730			0.028	0.033	0.060	0.035	0.040	0.033	0.055	0.09
2	0.0860			0.035	0.048	0.060	0.040	0.047	0.039	0.064	0.13
3	0.0990			0.050	0.048	0.070	0.040	0.054	0.045	0.074	0.13
4	0.1120			0.050	0.060	0.070	0.045	0.061	0.051	0.084	0.19
5	0.1250	1/16	0.062	0.072	0.080	0.055	0.067	0.057	0.094	0.19
6	0.1380	1/16	0.062	0.072	0.080	0.055	0.074	0.064	0.104	0.19
8	0.1640	5/64	0.078	0.096	0.090	0.080	0.087	0.076	0.123	0.25
10	0.1900	3/32	0.094	0.111	0.100	0.080	0.102	0.088	0.142	0.25
1/4	0.2500	1/8	0.125	0.145	0.125	0.125	0.132	0.118	0.188	0.31
5/16	0.3125	5/32	0.156	0.183	0.156	0.156	0.172	0.156	0.234	0.38
3/8	0.3750	3/16	0.188	0.216	0.188	0.188	0.212	0.194	0.281	0.44
7/16	0.4375	7/32	0.219	0.251	0.219	0.219	0.252	0.232	0.328	0.50
1/2	0.5000	1/4	0.250	0.291	0.250	0.250	0.291	0.270	0.375	0.57
5/8	0.6250	5/16	0.312	0.372	0.312	0.312	0.371	0.347	0.469	0.75
3/4	0.7500	3/8	0.375	0.454	0.375	0.375	0.450	0.425	0.562	0.88
7/8	0.8750	1/2	0.500	0.595	0.500	0.500	0.530	0.502	0.656	1.00
1	1.0000	9/16	0.562	...	0.562	...	0.609	0.579	0.750	1.13
1 1/8	1.1250	9/16	0.562	...	0.562	...	0.689	0.655	0.844	1.25
1 1/4	1.2500	5/8	0.625	...	0.625	...	0.767	0.733	0.938	1.50
1 3/8	1.3750	5/8	0.625	...	0.625	...	0.848	0.808	1.031	1.63
1 1/2	1.5000	3/4	0.750	...	0.750	...	0.926	0.886	1.125	1.75
1 3/4	1.7500	1	1.000	...	1.000	...	1.086	1.039	1.312	2.00
2	2.0000	1	1.000	...	1.000	...	1.244	1.193	1.500	2.25

Metric Socket Set Screws (ANSI B18.3.6M, 1979)

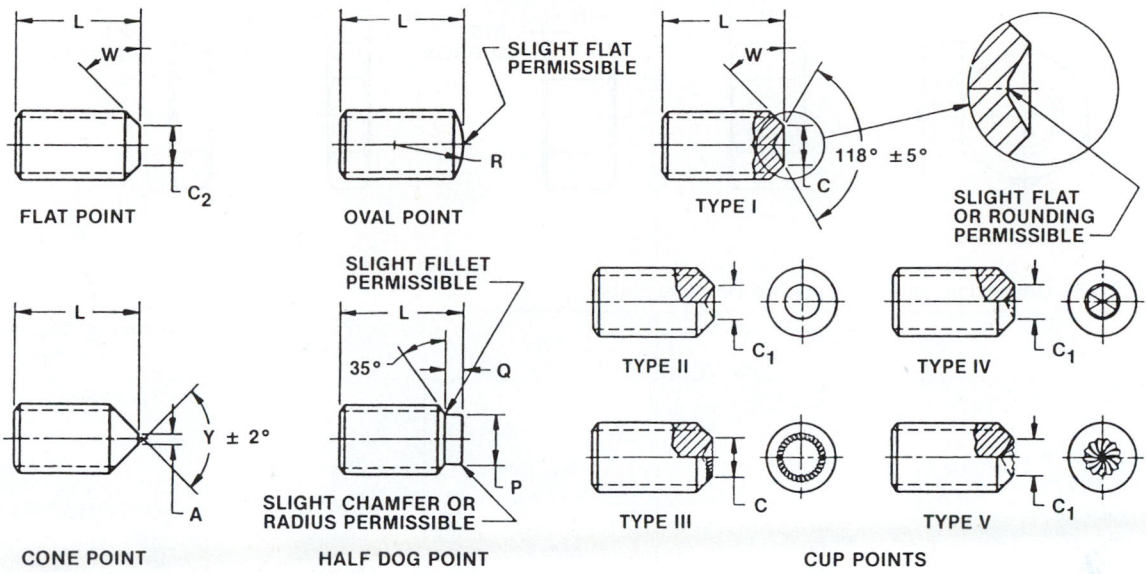

FLAT POINT · OVAL POINT · TYPE I · CONE POINT · HALF DOG POINT · TYPE II · TYPE IV · TYPE III · TYPE V · CUP POINTS

TABLE C.3.11 Dimensions of Points for Metric Socket Set Screws

D	C		C_1		C_2		R		Y	A		P		Q	
Nominal Size of Basic Screw Diameter	Cup Point Diameter For Types I and III		Cup Point Diameter For Types II, IV and V		Flat Point Diameter		Oval Point Radius		Cone Point Angle 90° For These Lengths And Over; 118° For Shorter Lengths	Flat of Truncation on Cone Point		Half Dog Point			
												Diameter		Length	
	Max	Min	Max	Min	Max	Min	Max	Min		Max	Min	Max	Min	Max	Min
1.6	0.80	0.55	0.80	0.64	0.80	0.55	1.60	1.20	3	1.16	0	0.80	0.55	0.53	0.40
2	1.00	0.75	1.00	0.82	1.00	0.75	1.90	1.50	3	0.2	0	1.00	0.75	0.64	0.50
2.5	1.20	0.95	1.25	1.05	1.50	1.25	2.28	1.88	4	0.25	0	1.50	1.25	0.78	0.63
3	1.40	1.15	1.50	1.28	2.00	1.75	2.65	2.25	4	0.3	0	2.00	1.75	0.92	0.75
4	2.00	1.75	2.00	1.75	2.50	2.25	3.80	3.00	5	0.4	0	2.50	2.25	1.20	1.00
5	2.50	2.25	2.50	2.22	3.50	3.20	4.55	3.75	6	0.5	0	3.50	3.20	1.37	1.25
6	3.00	2.75	3.00	2.69	4.00	3.70	5.30	4.50	8	1.5	1.2	4.00	3.70	1.74	1.50
8	5.00	4.70	4.00	3.65	5.50	5.20	6.80	6.00	10	2.0	1.6	5.50	5.20	2.28	2.00
10	6.00	5.70	5.00	4.60	7.00	6.64	8.30	7.50	12	2.5	2.0	7.00	6.64	2.82	2.50
12	8.00	7.64	6.00	5.57	8.50	8.14	9.80	9.00	16	3.0	2.4	8.50	8.14	3.35	3.00
16	10.00	9.64	8.00	7.50	12.00	11.57	12.80	12.00	20	4.0	3.2	12.00	11.57	4.40	4.00
20	14.00	13.57	10.00	9.44	15.00	14.57	15.80	15.00	25	5.0	4.0	15.00	14.57	5.45	5.00
24	16.00	15.57	12.00	11.39	18.00	17.57	18.80	18.00	30	6.0	4.8	18.00	17.57	6.49	6.00

Hex Nuts and Hex Jam Nuts (ANSI/ASME B18.2.2, 1986)

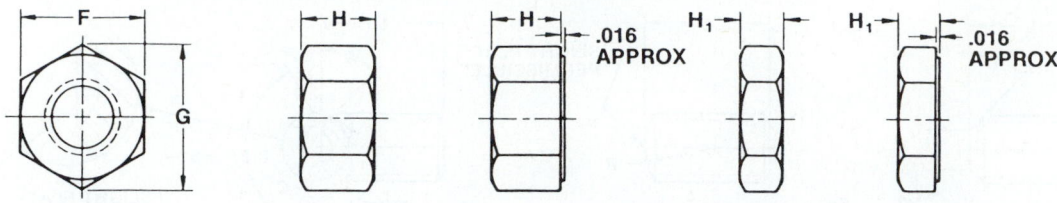

TABLE C.3.12   Dimensions of Hex Nuts and Hex Jam Nuts

Nominal Size or Basic Major Dia of Thread		F Width Across Flats			G Width Across Corners		H Thickness Hex Nuts			H₁ Thickness Hex Jam Nuts			Runout of Bearing Face, FIM		
													Hex Nuts Specified Proof Load		Hex Jam Nuts
		Basic	Max	Min	Max	Min	Basic	Max	Min	Basic	Max	Min	Up to 150,000 psi	150,000 psi and Greater	All Strength Levels
													Max		
1/4	0.2500	7/16	0.438	0.428	0.505	0.488	7/32	0.226	0.212	5/32	0.163	0.150	0.015	0.010	0.015
5/16	0.3125	1/2	0.500	0.489	0.577	0.557	17/64	0.273	0.258	3/16	0.195	0.180	0.016	0.011	0.016
3/8	0.3750	9/16	0.562	0.551	0.650	0.628	21/64	0.337	0.320	7/32	0.227	0.210	0.017	0.012	0.017
7/16	0.4375	11/16	0.688	0.675	0.794	0.768	3/8	0.385	0.365	1/4	0.260	0.240	0.018	0.013	0.018
1/2	0.5000	3/4	0.750	0.736	0.866	0.840	7/16	0.448	0.427	5/16	0.323	0.302	0.019	0.014	0.019
9/16	0.5625	7/8	0.875	0.861	1.010	0.982	31/64	0.496	0.473	5/16	0.324	0.301	0.020	0.015	0.020
5/8	0.6250	15/16	0.938	0.922	1.083	1.051	35/64	0.559	0.535	3/8	0.387	0.363	0.021	0.016	0.021
3/4	0.7500	1 1/8	1.125	1.088	1.299	1.240	41/64	0.665	0.617	27/64	0.446	0.398	0.023	0.018	0.023
7/8	0.8750	1 5/16	1.312	1.269	1.516	1.447	3/4	0.776	0.724	31/64	0.510	0.458	0.025	0.020	0.025
1	1.0000	1 1/2	1.500	1.450	1.732	1.653	55/64	0.887	0.831	35/64	0.575	0.519	0.027	0.022	0.027
1 1/8	1.1250	1 11/16	1.688	1.631	1.949	1.859	31/32	0.999	0.939	39/64	0.639	0.579	0.030	0.025	0.030
1 1/4	1.2500	1 7/8	1.875	1.812	2.165	2.066	1 1/16	1.094	1.030	23/32	0.751	0.687	0.033	0.028	0.033
1 3/8	1.3750	2 1/16	2.062	1.994	2.382	2.273	1 11/64	1.206	1.138	25/32	0.815	0.747	0.036	0.031	0.036
1 1/2	1.5000	2 1/4	2.250	2.175	2.598	2.480	1 9/32	1.317	1.245	27/32	0.880	0.808	0.039	0.034	0.039

Square Nuts (ANSI/ASME B18.2.2, 1986)

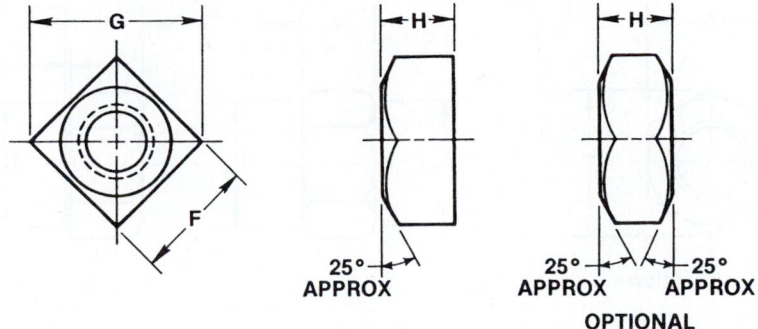

TABLE C.3.13   Dimensions of Square Nuts

Nominal Size or Basic Major Dia of Thread		F Width Across Flats			G Width Across Corners		H Thickness		
		Basic	Max	Min	Max	Min	Basic	Max	Min
1/4	0.2500	7/16	0.438	0.425	0.619	0.554	7/32	0.235	0.203
5/16	0.3125	9/16	0.562	0.547	0.795	0.721	17/64	0.283	0.249
3/8	0.3750	5/8	0.625	0.606	0.884	0.802	21/64	0.346	0.310
7/16	0.4375	3/4	0.750	0.728	1.061	0.970	3/8	0.394	0.356
1/2	0.5000	13/16	0.812	0.788	1.149	1.052	7/16	0.458	0.418
5/8	0.6250	1	1.000	0.969	1.414	1.300	35/64	0.569	0.525
3/4	0.7500	1 1/8	1.125	1.088	1.591	1.464	21/32	0.680	0.632
7/8	0.8750	1 5/16	1.312	1.269	1.856	1.712	49/64	0.792	0.740
1	1.0000	1 1/2	1.500	1.450	2.121	1.961	7/8	0.903	0.847
1 1/8	1.1250	1 11/16	1.688	1.631	2.386	2.209	1	1.030	0.970
1 1/4	1.2500	1 7/8	1.875	1.812	2.652	2.458	1 3/32	1.126	1.062
1 3/8	1.3750	2 1/16	2.062	1.994	2.917	2.708	1 13/64	1.237	1.169
1 1/2	1.5000	2 1/4	2.250	2.175	3.182	2.956	1 5/16	1.348	1.276

Metric Hex Nuts, Style 1 (ANSI B18.2.4.1M, 1979)

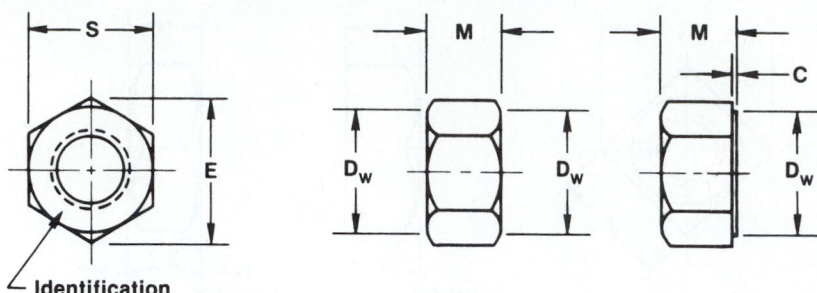

Identification

TABLE C.3.14 Dimensions of Hex Nuts, Style 1

Nominal Nut Dia and Thread Pitch	S Width Across Flats		E Width Across Corners		M Thickness		D_W Bearing Face Dia	C Washer Face Thickness		Total Runout of Bearing Surface FIM
	Max	Min	Max	Min	Max	Min	Min	Max	Min	Max
M1.6 × 0.35	3.20	3.02	3.70	3.41	1.30	1.05	2.4	—	—	—
M2 × 0.4	4.00	3.82	4.62	4.32	1.60	1.35	3.1	—	—	—
M2.5 × 0.45	5.00	4.82	5.77	5.45	2.00	1.75	4.1	—	—	—
M3 × 0.5	5.50	5.32	6.35	6.01	2.40	2.15	4.6	—	—	—
M3.5 × 0.6	6.00	5.82	6.93	6.58	2.80	2.55	5.1	—	—	—
M4 × 0.7	7.00	6.78	8.08	7.66	3.20	2.90	5.9	—	—	—
M5 × 0.8	8.00	7.78	9.24	8.79	4.70	4.40	6.9	—	—	0.30
M6 × 1	10.00	9.78	11.55	11.05	5.20	4.90	8.9	—	—	0.33
M8 × 1.25	13.00	12.73	15.01	14.38	6.80	6.44	11.6	—	—	0.36
M10 × 1.5	16.00	15.73	18.48	17.77	8.40	8.04	14.6	—	—	0.39
M12 × 1.75	18.00	17.73	20.78	20.03	10.80	10.37	16.6	—	—	0.42
M14 × 2	21.00	20.67	24.25	23.35	12.80	12.10	19.6	—	—	0.45
M16 × 2	24.00	23.67	27.71	26.75	14.80	14.10	22.5	—	—	0.48
M20 × 2.5	30.00	29.16	34.64	32.95	18.00	16.90	27.7	0.8	0.4	0.56
M24 × 3	36.00	35.00	41.57	39.55	21.50	20.20	33.2	0.8	0.4	0.64
M30 × 3.5	46.00	45.00	53.12	50.85	25.60	24.30	42.7	0.8	0.4	0.76
M36 × 4	55.00	53.80	63.51	60.79	31.00	29.40	51.1	0.8	0.4	0.89
*M10 × 1.5	15.00	14.73	17.32	16.64	9.1	8.7	13.6	—	—	0.39

APPENDIX C.4

Washers

Plain Washers (ANSI/ASME B18.22.1 1965, (1981)

TABLE C.4.1   Dimensions of Preferred Sizes of Type A Plain Washers

Nominal Washer Size			A Inside Diameter			B Outside Diameter			C Thickness		
			Basic	Tolerance Plus	Tolerance Minus	Basic	Tolerance Plus	Tolerance Minus	Basic	Max	Min
—	—		0.078	0.000	0.005	0.188	0.000	0.005	0.020	0.025	0.016
—	—		0.094	0.000	0.005	0.250	0.000	0.005	0.020	0.025	0.016
—	—		0.125	0.008	0.005	0.312	0.008	0.005	0.032	0.040	0.025
No. 6	0.138		0.156	0.008	0.005	0.375	0.015	0.005	0.049	0.065	0.036
8	0.164		0.188	0.008	0.005	0.438	0.015	0.005	0.049	0.065	0.036
10	0.190		0.219	0.008	0.005	0.500	0.015	0.005	0.049	0.065	0.036
3/16	0.188		0.250	0.015	0.005	0.562	0.015	0.005	0.049	0.065	0.036
12	0.216		0.250	0.015	0.005	0.562	0.015	0.005	0.065	0.080	0.051
1/4	0.250	N	0.281	0.015	0.005	0.625	0.015	0.005	0.065	0.080	0.051
1/4	0.250	W	0.312	0.015	0.005	0.734	0.015	0.007	0.065	0.080	0.051
5/16	0.312	N	0.344	0.015	0.005	0.688	0.015	0.007	0.065	0.080	0.051
5/16	0.312	W	0.375	0.015	0.005	0.875	0.030	0.007	0.083	0.104	0.064
3/8	0.375	N	0.406	0.015	0.005	0.812	0.015	0.007	0.065	0.080	0.051
3/8	0.375	W	0.438	0.015	0.005	1.000	0.030	0.007	0.083	0.104	0.064
7/16	0.438	N	0.469	0.015	0.005	0.922	0.015	0.007	0.065	0.080	0.051
7/16	0.438	W	0.500	0.015	0.005	1.250	0.030	0.007	0.083	0.104	0.064
1/2	0.500	N	0.531	0.015	0.005	1.062	0.030	0.007	0.095	0.121	0.074
1/2	0.500	W	0.562	0.015	0.005	1.375	0.030	0.007	0.109	0.132	0.086
9/16	0.562	N	0.594	0.015	0.005	1.156	0.030	0.007	0.095	0.121	0.074
9/16	0.562	W	0.625	0.015	0.005	1.469	0.030	0.007	0.109	0.132	0.086
5/8	0.625	N	0.656	0.030	0.007	1.312	0.030	0.007	0.095	0.121	0.074
5/8	0.625	W	0.688	0.030	0.007	1.750	0.030	0.007	0.134	0.160	0.108
3/4	0.750	N	0.812	0.030	0.007	1.469	0.030	0.007	0.134	0.160	0.108
3/4	0.750	W	0.812	0.030	0.007	2.000	0.030	0.007	0.148	0.177	0.122
7/8	0.875	N	0.938	0.030	0.007	1.750	0.030	0.007	0.134	0.160	0.108
7/8	0.875	W	0.938	0.030	0.007	2.250	0.030	0.007	0.165	0.192	0.136
1	1.000	N	1.062	0.030	0.007	2.000	0.030	0.007	0.134	0.160	0.108
1	1.000	W	1.062	0.030	0.007	2.500	0.030	0.007	0.165	0.192	0.136
1-1/8	1.125	N	1.250	0.030	0.007	2.250	0.030	0.007	0.134	0.160	0.108
1-1/8	1.125	W	1.250	0.030	0.007	2.750	0.030	0.007	0.165	0.192	0.136
1-1/4	1.250	N	1.375	0.030	0.007	2.500	0.030	0.007	0.165	0.192	0.136
1-1/4	1.250	W	1.375	0.030	0.007	3.000	0.030	0.007	0.165	0.192	0.136
1-3/8	1.375	N	1.500	0.030	0.007	2.750	0.030	0.007	0.165	0.192	0.136
1-3/8	1.375	W	1.500	0.045	0.010	3.250	0.045	0.010	0.180	0.213	0.153
1-1/2	1.500	N	1.625	0.030	0.007	3.000	0.030	0.007	0.165	0.192	0.136
1-1/2	1.500	W	1.625	0.045	0.010	3.500	0.045	0.010	0.180	0.213	0.153

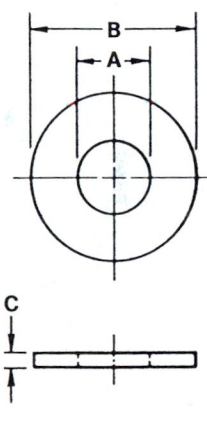

Continued

TABLE C.4.1   Dimensions of Preferred Sizes of Type A Plain Washers—*Continued*

Nominal Washer Size		A Inside Diameter			B Outside Diameter			C Thickness		
		Basic	Tolerance		Basic	Tolerance		Basic	Max	Min
			Plus	Minus		Plus	Minus			
1-5/8	1.625	1.750	0.045	0.010	3.750	0.045	0.010	0.180	0.213	0.153
1-3/4	1.750	1.875	0.045	0.010	4.000	0.045	0.010	0.180	0.213	0.153
1-7/8	1.875	2.000	0.045	0.010	4.250	0.045	0.010	0.180	0.213	0.153
2	2.000	2.125	0.045	0.010	4.500	0.045	0.010	0.180	0.213	0.153
2-1/4	2.250	2.375	0.045	0.010	4.750	0.045	0.010	0.220	0.248	0.193
2-1/2	2.500	2.625	0.045	0.010	5.000	0.045	0.010	0.238	0.280	0.210
2-3/4	2.750	2.875	0.065	0.010	5.250	0.065	0.010	0.259	0.310	0.228
3	3.000	3.125	0.065	0.010	5.500	0.065	0.010	0.284	0.327	0.249

Metric Plain Washers (ANSI B18.22M, 1981)

TABLE C.4.2   Dimensions of Metric Plain Washers (General Purpose)

Nom Washer Size	Washer Series	A Inside Dia		B Outside Dia		C Thickness	
		Max	Min	Max	Min	Max	Min
1.6	Narrow	2.09	1.95	4.00	3.70	0.70	0.50
	Regular	2.09	1.95	5.00	4.70	0.70	0.50
	Wide	2.09	1.95	6.00	5.70	0.90	0.60
2	Narrow	2.64	2.50	5.00	4.70	0.90	0.60
	Regular	2.64	2.50	6.00	5.70	0.90	0.60
	Wide	2.64	2.50	8.00	7.64	0.90	0.60
2.5	Narrow	3.14	3.00	6.00	5.70	0.90	0.60
	Regular	3.14	3.00	8.00	7.64	0.90	0.60
	Wide	3.14	3.00	10.00	9.64	1.20	0.80
3	Narrow	3.68	3.50	7.00	6.64	0.90	0.60
	Regular	3.68	3.50	10.00	9.64	1.20	0.80
	Wide	3.68	3.50	12.00	11.57	1.40	1.00
3.5	Narrow	4.18	4.00	9.00	8.64	1.20	0.80
	Regular	4.18	4.00	10.00	9.64	1.40	1.00
	Wide	4.18	4.00	15.00	14.57	1.75	1.20
4	Narrow	4.88	4.70	10.00	9.64	1.20	0.80
	Regular	4.88	4.70	12.00	11.57	1.40	1.00
	Wide	4.88	4.70	16.00	15.57	2.30	1.60
5	Narrow	5.78	5.50	11.00	10.57	1.40	1.00
	Regular	5.78	5.50	15.00	14.57	1.75	1.20
	Wide	5.78	5.50	20.00	19.48	2.30	1.60
6	Narrow	6.87	6.65	13.00	12.57	1.75	1.20
	Regular	6.87	6.65	18.80	18.37	1.75	1.20
	Wide	6.87	6.65	25.40	24.88	2.30	1.60
8	Narrow	9.12	8.90	18.80	18.37	2.30	1.60
	Regular	9.12	8.90	25.40	24.48	2.30	1.60
	Wide	9.12	8.90	32.00	31.38	2.80	2.00

Continued

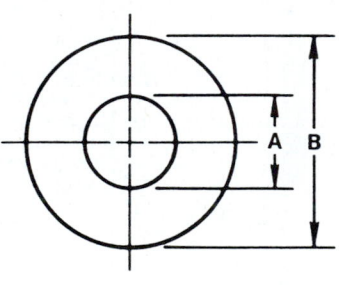

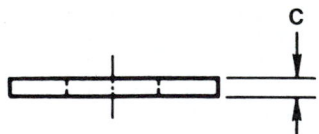

TABLE C.4.2 Dimensions of Metric Plain Washers (General Purpose)—*Continued*

Nom Washer Size	Washer Series	A Inside Dia		B Outside Dia		C Thickness	
		Max	Min	Max	Min	Max	Min
10	Narrow	11.12	10.85	20.00	19.48	2.30	1.60
	Regular	11.12	10.85	28.00	27.48	2.80	2.00
	Wide	11.12	10.85	39.00	38.38	3.50	2.50
12	Narrow	13.57	13.30	25.40	24.88	2.80	2.00
	Regular	13.57	13.30	34.00	33.38	3.50	2.50
	Wide	13.57	13.30	44.00	43.38	3.50	2.50
14	Narrow	15.52	15.25	28.00	27.48	2.80	2.00
	Regular	15.52	15.25	39.00	38.38	3.50	2.50
	Wide	15.52	15.25	50.00	49.38	4.00	3.00
16	Narrow	17.52	17.25	32.00	31.38	3.50	2.50
	Regular	17.52	17.25	44.00	43.38	4.00	3.00
	Wide	17.52	17.25	56.00	54.80	4.60	3.50
20	Narrow	22.32	21.80	39.00	38.38	4.00	3.00
	Regular	22.32	21.80	50.00	49.38	4.60	3.50
	Wide	22.32	21.80	66.00	64.80	5.10	4.00
24	Narrow	26.12	25.60	44.00	43.38	4.60	3.50
	Regular	26.12	25.60	56.00	54.80	5.10	4.00
	Wide	26.12	25.60	72.00	70.80	5.60	4.50
30	Narrow	33.02	32.40	56.00	54.80	5.10	4.00
	Regular	33.02	32.40	72.00	70.80	5.60	4.50
	Wide	33.02	32.40	90.00	88.60	6.40	5.00
36	Narrow	38.92	38.30	66.00	64.80	5.60	4.50
	Regular	38.92	38.30	90.00	88.60	6.40	5.00
	Wide	38.92	38.30	110.00	108.60	8.50	7.00

NOTES:
1. Nominal washer sizes are intended for use with comparable nominal screw or bolt sizes.
2. See 4.3 for maximum permissible I.D. at the punch exit side.
3. See 4.2 for closeness of fit with coated or plated products.
4. The 18.80/18.37 and 25.40/24.88 mm outside diameters avoid washers which could be used in coin operated devices.

Lock Washers (ANSI/ASME B18.21.1, 1972, R1983)

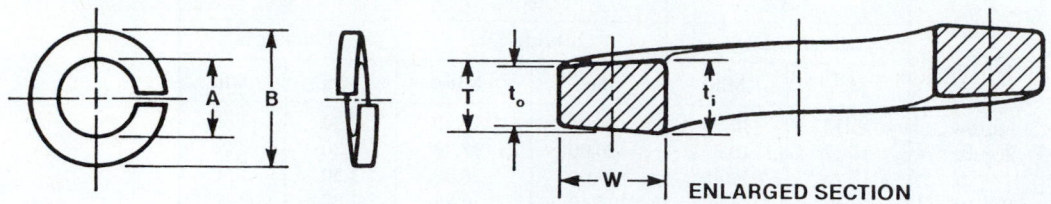

ENLARGED SECTION

TABLE C.4.3   Dimensions of Regular Helical Spring Lock Washers

Nominal Washer Size		A Inside Diameter		B Outside Diameter	T Mean Section Thickness $\left(\dfrac{t_i + t_o}{2}\right)$	W Section Width
		Max	Min	Max[2]	Min	Min
No. 2	0.086	0.094	0.088	0.172	0.020	0.035
No. 3	0.099	0.107	0.101	0.195	0.025	0.040
No. 4	0.112	0.120	0.114	0.209	0.025	0.040
No. 5	0.125	0.133	0.127	0.236	0.031	0.047
No. 6	0.138	0.148	0.141	0.250	0.031	0.047
No. 8	0.164	0.174	0.167	0.293	0.040	0.055
No. 10	0.190	0.200	0.193	0.334	0.047	0.062
No. 12	0.216	0.227	0.220	0.377	0.056	0.070
1/4	0.250	0.262	0.254	0.489	0.062	0.109
5/16	0.312	0.326	0.317	0.586	0.078	0.125
3/8	0.375	0.390	0.380	0.683	0.094	0.141
7/16	0.438	0.455	0.443	0.779	0.109	0.156
1/2	0.500	0.518	0.506	0.873	0.125	0.171
9/16	0.562	0.582	0.570	0.971	0.141	0.188
5/8	0.625	0.650	0.635	1.079	0.156	0.203
11/16	0.688	0.713	0.698	1.176	0.172	0.219
3/4	0.750	0.775	0.760	1.271	0.188	0.234
13/16	0.812	0.843	0.824	1.367	0.203	0.250
7/8	0.875	0.905	0.887	1.464	0.219	0.266
15/16	0.938	0.970	0.950	1.560	0.234	0.281
1	1.000	1.042	1.017	1.661	0.250	0.297
1-1/16	1.062	1.107	1.080	1.756	0.266	0.312
1-1/8	1.125	1.172	1.144	1.853	0.281	0.328
1-3/16	1.188	1.237	1.208	1.950	0.297	0.344
1-1/4	1.250	1.302	1.271	2.045	0.312	0.359
1-5/16	1.312	1.366	1.334	2.141	0.328	0.375
1-3/8	1.375	1.432	1.398	2.239	0.344	0.391
1-7/16	1.438	1.497	1.462	2.334	0.359	0.406
1-1/2	1.500	1.561	1.525	2.430	0.375	0.422

Lock Washers (ANSI/ASME B18.21.1 1972, R1983)

TABLE C.4.4   Dimensions of Internal Tooth Lock Washers

Nominal Washer Size		A Inside Diameter		B Outside Diameter		C Thickness	
		Max	Min	Max	Min	Max	Min
No. 2	0.086	0.095	0.089	0.200	0.175	0.015	0.010
No. 3	0.099	0.109	0.102	0.232	0.215	0.019	0.012
No. 4	0.112	0.123	0.115	0.270	0.255	0.019	0.015
No. 5	0.125	0.136	0.129	0.280	0.245	0.021	0.017
No. 6	0.138	0.150	0.141	0.295	0.275	0.021	0.017
No. 8	0.164	0.176	0.168	0.340	0.325	0.023	0.018
No. 10	0.190	0.204	0.195	0.381	0.365	0.025	0.020
No. 12	0.216	0.231	0.221	0.410	0.394	0.025	0.020
1/4	0.250	0.267	0.256	0.478	0.460	0.028	0.023
5/16	0.312	0.332	0.320	0.610	0.594	0.034	0.028
3/8	0.375	0.398	0.384	0.692	0.670	0.040	0.032
7/16	0.438	0.464	0.448	0.789	0.740	0.040	0.032
1/2	0.500	0.530	0.512	0.900	0.867	0.045	0.037
9/16	0.562	0.596	0.576	0.985	0.957	0.045	0.037
5/8	0.625	0.663	0.640	1.071	1.045	0.050	0.042
11/16	0.688	0.728	0.704	1.166	1.130	0.050	0.042
3/4	0.750	0.795	0.769	1.245	1.220	0.055	0.047
13/16	0.812	0.861	0.832	1.315	1.290	0.055	0.047
7/8	0.875	0.927	0.894	1.410	1.364	0.060	0.052
1	1.000	1.060	1.019	1.637	1.590	0.067	0.059
1-1/8	1.125	1.192	1.144	1.830	1.799	0.067	0.059
1-1/4	1.250	1.325	1.275	1.975	1.921	0.067	0.059

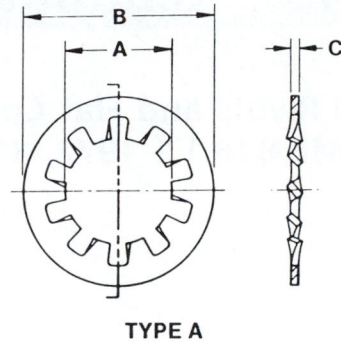

TYPE A

TABLE C.4.5   Dimensions of Heavy Internal Tooth Lock Washers

Nominal Washer Size		A Inside Diameter		B Outside Diameter		C Thickness	
		Max	Min	Max	Min	Max	Min
1/4	0.250	0.267	0.256	0.536	0.500	0.045	0.035
5/16	0.312	0.332	0.320	0.607	0.590	0.050	0.040
3/8	0.375	0.398	0.384	0.748	0.700	0.050	0.042
7/16	0.438	0.464	0.448	0.858	0.800	0.067	0.050
1/2	0.500	0.530	0.512	0.924	0.880	0.067	0.055
9/16	0.562	0.596	0.576	1.034	0.990	0.067	0.055
5/8	0.625	0.663	0.640	1.135	1.100	0.067	0.059
3/4	0.750	0.795	0.768	1.265	1.240	0.084	0.070
7/8	0.875	0.927	0.894	1.447	1.400	0.084	0.075

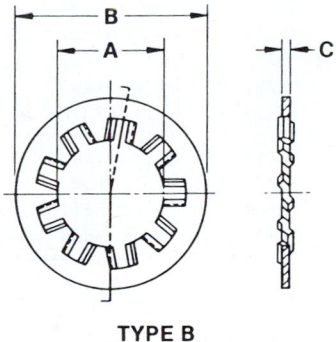

TYPE B

Rivets, Retaining Rings

Flat Head Rivets and Flat Countersunk Head Rivets (ANSI/ASME B18.1.1 1972, R1981)

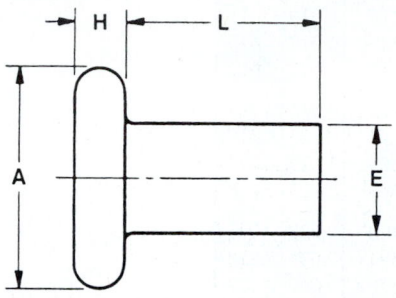

TABLE C.5.1 Dimensions of Flat Head Rivets

Nominal Size or Basic Shank Diameter		E Shank Diameter		A Head Diameter		H Head Diameter	
		Max	Min	Max	Min	Max	Min
1/16	0.062	0.064	0.059	0.140	0.120	0.027	0.017
3/32	0.094	0.096	0.090	0.200	0.180	0.038	0.026
1/8	0.125	0.127	0.121	0.260	0.240	0.048	0.036
5/32	0.156	0.158	0.152	0.323	0.301	0.059	0.045
3/16	0.188	0.191	0.182	0.387	0.361	0.069	0.055
7/32	0.219	0.222	0.213	0.453	0.427	0.080	0.065
1/4	0.250	0.253	0.244	0.515	0.485	0.091	0.075
9/32	0.281	0.285	0.273	0.579	0.545	0.103	0.085
5/16	0.312	0.316	0.304	0.641	0.607	0.113	0.095
11/32	0.344	0.348	0.336	0.705	0.667	0.124	0.104
3/8	0.375	0.380	0.365	0.769	0.731	0.135	0.115
13/32	0.406	0.411	0.396	0.834	0.790	0.146	0.124
7/16	0.438	0.443	0.428	0.896	0.852	0.157	0.135

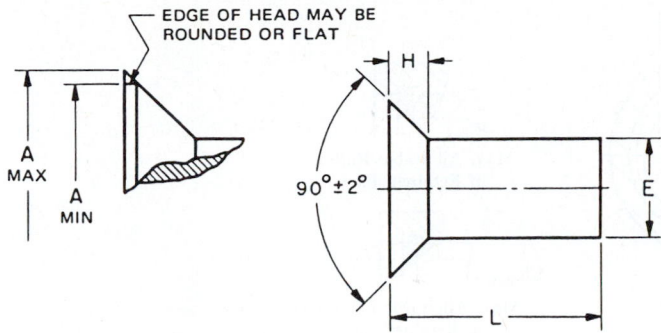

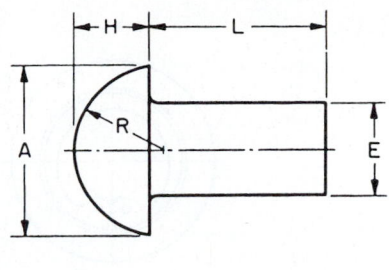

TABLE C.5.2   Dimensions of Flat Countersunk Head Rivets

Nominal Size[1] or Basic Shank Diameter		E		A		H
		Shank Diameter		Head Diameter		Head Height
		Max	Min	Max[2]	Min[3]	Ref[4]
1/16	0.062	0.064	0.059	0.118	0.110	0.027
3/32	0.094	0.096	0.090	0.176	0.163	0.040
1/8	0.125	0.127	0.121	0.235	0.217	0.053
5/32	0.156	0.158	0.152	0.293	0.272	0.066
3/16	0.188	0.191	0.182	0.351	0.326	0.079
7/32	0.219	0.222	0.213	0.413	0.384	0.094
1/4	0.250	0.253	0.244	0.469	0.437	0.106
9/32	0.281	0.285	0.273	0.528	0.491	0.119
5/16	0.312	0.316	0.304	0.588	0.547	0.133
11/32	0.344	0.348	0.336	0.646	0.602	0.146
3/8	0.375	0.380	0.365	0.704	0.656	0.159
13/32	0.406	0.411	0.396	0.763	0.710	0.172
7/16	0.438	0.443	0.428	0.823	0.765	0.186

TABLE C.5.3   Dimensions of Button Head Rivets

Nominal Size[1] or Basic Shank Diameter		E		A		H		R
		Shank Diameter		Head Diameter		Head Height		Head Radius
		Max	Min	Max	Min	Max	Min	Approx
1/16	0.062	0.064	0.059	0.122	0.102	0.052	0.042	0.055
3/32	0.094	0.096	0.090	0.182	0.162	0.077	0.065	0.084
1/8	0.125	0.127	0.121	0.235	0.215	0.100	0.088	0.111
5/32	0.156	0.158	0.152	0.290	0.268	0.124	0.110	0.138
3/16	0.188	0.191	0.182	0.348	0.322	0.147	0.133	0.166
7/32	0.219	0.222	0.213	0.405	0.379	0.172	0.158	0.195
1/4	0.250	0.253	0.244	0.460	0.430	0.196	0.180	0.221
9/32	0.281	0.285	0.273	0.518	0.484	0.220	0.202	0.249
5/16	0.312	0.316	0.304	0.572	0.538	0.243	0.225	0.276
11/32	0.344	0.348	0.336	0.630	0.592	0.267	0.247	0.304
3/8	0.375	0.380	0.365	0.684	0.646	0.291	0.271	0.332
13/32	0.406	0.411	0.396	0.743	0.699	0.316	0.294	0.358
7/16	0.438	0.443	0.428	0.798	0.754	0.339	0.317	0.387

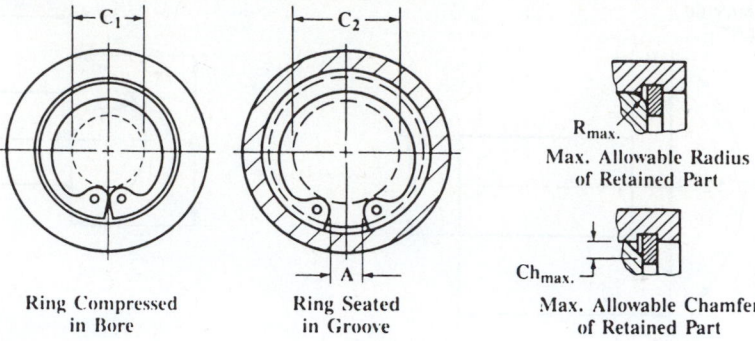

Ring Compressed in Bore Ring Seated in Groove Max. Allowable Radius of Retained Part Max. Allowable Chamfer of Retained Part

Ring Series and Size No.	Clearance Diam.		Gaging Diameter*	Allowable Thrust Loads Sharp Corner Abutment		Maximum Allowable Corner Radii and Chamfers	
	Ring in Bore	Ring in Groove					
₃BM₁	C_1	C_2	A min	P_r†	P_g‡	R max	Ch max
No.	mm	mm	mm	kN	kN	mm	mm
−8	4.4	4.8	1.40	2.4	1.0	0.4	0.3
−9	4.6	5.0	1.50	4.4	1.2	0.5	0.35
−10	5.5	6.0	1.85	4.9	1.5	0.5	0.35
−11	5.7	6.3	1.95	5.4	2.0	0.6	0.4
−12	6.7	7.3	2.25	5.8	2.4	0.6	0.4
−13	6.8	7.5	2.35	8.9	2.6	0.7	0.5
−14	6.9	7.7	2.65	9.7	3.2	0.7	0.5
−15	7.9	8.7	2.80	10.4	3.7	0.7	0.5
−16	8.8	9.7	2.80	11.0	4.2	0.7	0.5
−17	9.8	10.8	3.35	11.7	4.9	0.75	0.6
−18	10.3	11.3	3.40	12.3	5.5	0.75	0.6
−19	11.4	12.5	3.40	13.1	6.0	0.8	0.65
−20	11.6	12.7	3.8	13.7	6.6	0.9	0.7
−21	12.6	13.8	4.2	14.5	7.3	0.9	0.7
−22	13.5	14.8	4.3	22.5	8.3	0.9	0.7
−23	14.5	15.9	4.9	23.5	8.9	1.0	0.8
−24	15.5	16.9	5.2	24.8	9.7	1.0	0.8
−25	16.5	18.1	6.0	25.7	11.6	1.0	0.8
−26	17.5	19.2	5.7	26.8	12.7	1.2	1.0
−27	17.4	19.2	5.9	33	14.0	1.2	1.0
−28	18.2	20.0	6.0	34	14.6	1.2	1.0
−30	20.0	21.9	6.0	37	16.5	1.2	1.0
−32	22.0	23.9	7.3	39	17.6	1.2	1.0
−34	24.0	26.1	7.6	42	20.6	1.2	1.0
−35	25.0	27.2	8.0	43	22.3	1.2	1.0
−36	26.0	28.3	8.3	44	23.9	1.2	1.0
−37	27.0	29.3	8.4	45	24.6	1.2	1.0
−38	28.0	30.4	8.6	46	26.4	1.2	1.0
−40	29.2	31.6	9.7	62	27.7	1.7	1.3
−42	29.7	32.2	9.0	65	30.2	1.7	1.3
−45	32.3	34.9	9.6	69	33.8	1.7	1.3
−46	33.3	36.0	9.7	71	36	1.7	1.3
−47	34.3	37.1	10.0	72	38	1.7	1.3
−48	35.0	37.9	10.5	74	40	1.7	1.3
−50	36.9	40.0	12.1	77	45	1.7	1.3
−52	38.6	41.9	11.7	99	50	2.0	1.6
−55	40.8	44.2	11.9	105	54	2.0	1.6
−57	42.2	45.7	12.5	109	58	2.0	1.6

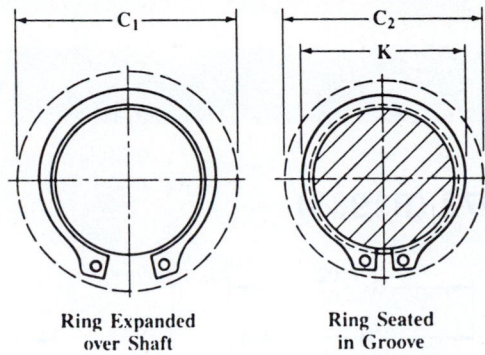

Ring Expanded
over Shaft

Ring Seated
in Groove

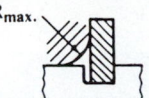

Max. Allowable Radius
of Retained Part

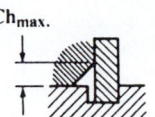

Max. Allowable Chamfer
of Retained Pa:

Ring Series and Size No.	Clearance Diam.		Gaging Diameter*	Allowable Thrust Loads Sharp Corner Abutment		Maximum Allowable Corner Radii and Chamfers		Allowable Assembly Speed§
	Ring Over Shaft	Ring in Groove						
$_3$AM$_1$	C_1	C_2	K max	P_r†	P_g‡	R max	Ch max	...
No.	mm	mm	mm	kN	kN	mm	mm	rpm
−4*	7.0	6.8	4.90	0.6	0.2	0.35	0.25	70 000
−5*	8.2	7.9	5.85	1.1	0.3	0.35	0.25	70 000
−6*	9.1	8.8	6.95	1.4	0.4	0.35	0.25	70 000
−7	12.3	11.8	8.05	2.6	0.7	0.45	0.3	60 000
−8	13.6	13.0	9.15	3.1	1.0	0.5	0.35	55 000
−9	14.5	13.8	10.35	3.5	1.2	0.6	0.35	48 000
−10	15.5	14.7	11.50	3.9	1.5	0.7	0.4	42 000
−11	16.4	15.6	12.60	4.3	1.8	0.75	0.45	38 000
−12	17.4	16.6	13.80	4.7	2.0	0.8	0.45	34 000
−13	19.7	18.8	15.05	7.5	2.2	0.8	0.5	31 000
−14	20.7	19.7	15.60	8.1	2.6	0.9	0.5	28 000
−15	21.7	20.6	17.20	8.7	3.2	1.0	0.6	27 000
−16	22.7	21.6	18.35	9.3	3.5	1.1	0.6	25 000
−17	23.7	22.6	19.35	9.9	4.0	1.1	0.6	24 000

Pins

Clevis Pins ANSI/ASME B18.8.1 1972 (R1983)

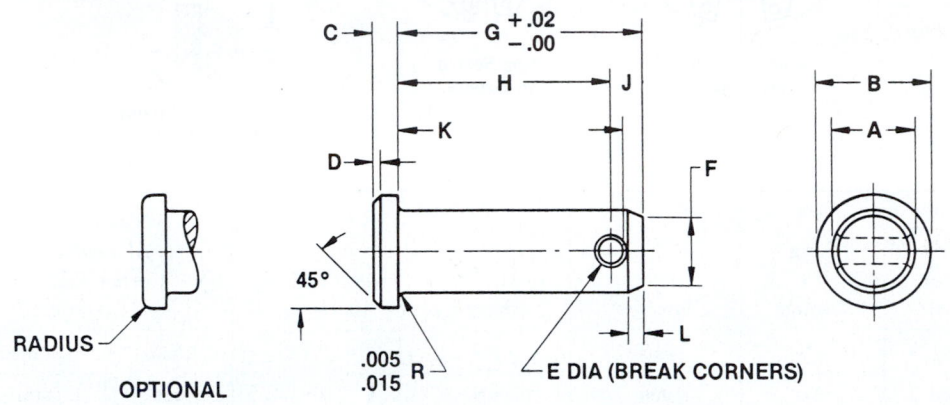

TABLE C.6.1 Dimensions of Clevis Pins

Nominal Size or Basic Pin Diameter		A Shank Diameter		B Head Diameter		C Head Height		D Head Chamfer	E Hole Diameter		F Point Diameter		G Pin Length	H Head to Center of Hole		J End to Center Ref	K Head to Edge of Hole Ref		L Point Length		Recommended Cotter Pin Nominal Size	
		Max	Min	Max	Min	Max	Min	±0.01	Max	Min	Max	Min	Basic	Max	Min	Basic	Max	Min	Max	Min		
3/16	0.188	0.186	0.181	0.32	0.30	0.07	0.05	0.02	0.088	0.073	0.15	0.14	0.58	0.504	0.484	0.09	0.548	0.520	0.055	0.035	1/16	0.062
1/4	0.250	0.248	0.243	0.38	0.36	0.10	0.08	0.03	0.088	0.073	0.21	0.20	0.77	0.692	0.672	0.09	0.736	0.708	0.055	0.035	1/16	0.062
5/16	0.312	0.311	0.306	0.44	0.42	0.10	0.08	0.03	0.119	0.104	0.26	0.25	0.94	0.832	0.812	0.12	0.892	0.864	0.071	0.049	3/32	0.093
3/8	0.375	0.373	0.368	0.51	0.49	0.13	0.11	0.03	0.119	0.104	0.33	0.32	1.06	0.958	0.938	0.12	1.018	0.990	0.071	0.049	3/32	0.093
7/16	0.438	0.436	0.431	0.57	0.55	0.16	0.14	0.04	0.119	0.104	0.39	0.38	1.19	1.082	1.062	0.12	1.142	1.114	0.071	0.049	3/32	0.093
1/2	0.500	0.496	0.491	0.63	0.61	0.16	0.14	0.04	0.151	0.136	0.44	0.43	1.36	1.223	1.203	0.15	1.298	1.271	0.089	0.063	1/8	0.125
5/8	0.625	0.621	0.616	0.82	0.80	0.21	0.19	0.06	0.151	0.136	0.56	0.55	1.61	1.473	1.453	0.15	1.548	1.521	0.089	0.063	1/8	0.125
3/4	0.750	0.746	0.741	0.94	0.92	0.26	0.24	0.07	0.182	0.167	0.68	0.67	1.91	1.739	1.719	0.18	1.830	1.802	0.110	0.076	5/32	0.156
7/8	0.875	0.871	0.866	1.04	1.02	0.32	0.30	0.09	0.182	0.167	0.80	0.79	2.16	1.989	1.969	0.18	2.080	2.052	0.110	0.076	5/32	0.156
1	1.000	0.996	0.991	1.19	1.17	0.35	0.33	0.10	0.182	0.167	0.93	0.92	2.41	2.239	2.219	0.18	2.330	2.302	0.110	0.076	5/32	0.156

Cotter Pins ANSI/ASME B18.8.1 1972 (R1983)

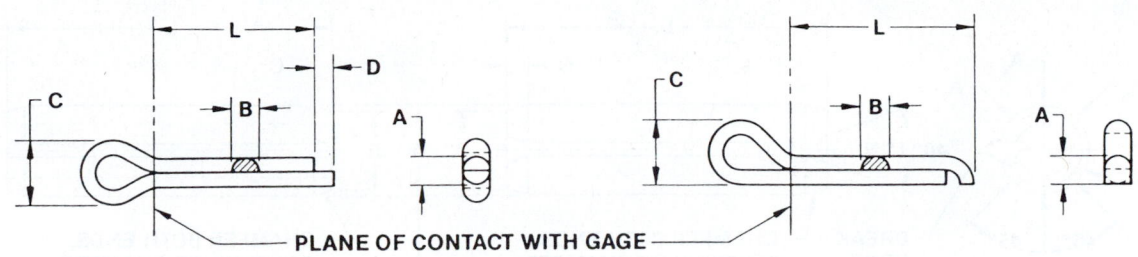

EXTENDED PRONG
SQUARE CUT TYPE

HAMMER LOCK TYPE

TABLE C.6.2   Dimensions of Cotter Pins

Nominal Size[1] or Basic Pin Diameter		A Total Shank Diameter		B Wire Width		C Head Diameter	D Extended Prong Length	Recommended Hole Size
		Max	Min	Max	Min	Min	Min	
1/32	0.031	0.032	0.028	0.032	0.022	0.06	0.01	0.047
3/64	0.047	0.048	0.044	0.048	0.035	0.09	0.02	0.062
1/16	0.062	0.060	0.056	0.060	0.044	0.12	0.03	0.078
5/64	0.078	0.076	0.072	0.076	0.057	0.16	0.04	0.094
3/32	0.094	0.090	0.086	0.090	0.069	0.19	0.04	0.109
7/64	0.109	0.104	0.100	0.104	0.080	0.22	0.05	0.125
1/8	0.125	0.120	0.116	0.120	0.093	0.25	0.06	0.141
9/64	0.141	0.134	0.130	0.134	0.104	0.28	0.06	0.156
5/32	0.156	0.150	0.146	0.150	0.116	0.31	0.07	0.172
3/16	0.188	0.176	0.172	0.176	0.137	0.38	0.09	0.203
7/32	0.219	0.207	0.202	0.207	0.161	0.44	0.10	0.234
1/4	0.250	0.225	0.220	0.225	0.176	0.50	0.11	0.266
5/16	0.312	0.280	0.275	0.280	0.220	0.62	0.14	0.312
3/8	0.375	0.335	0.329	0.335	0.263	0.75	0.16	0.375
7/16	0.438	0.406	0.400	0.406	0.320	0.88	0.20	0.438
1/2	0.500	0.473	0.467	0.473	0.373	1.00	0.23	0.500
5/8	0.625	0.598	0.590	0.598	0.472	1.25	0.30	0.625
3/4	0.750	0.723	0.715	0.723	0.572	1.50	0.36	0.750

Spring Pins ANSI/ASME B18.8.2 1978

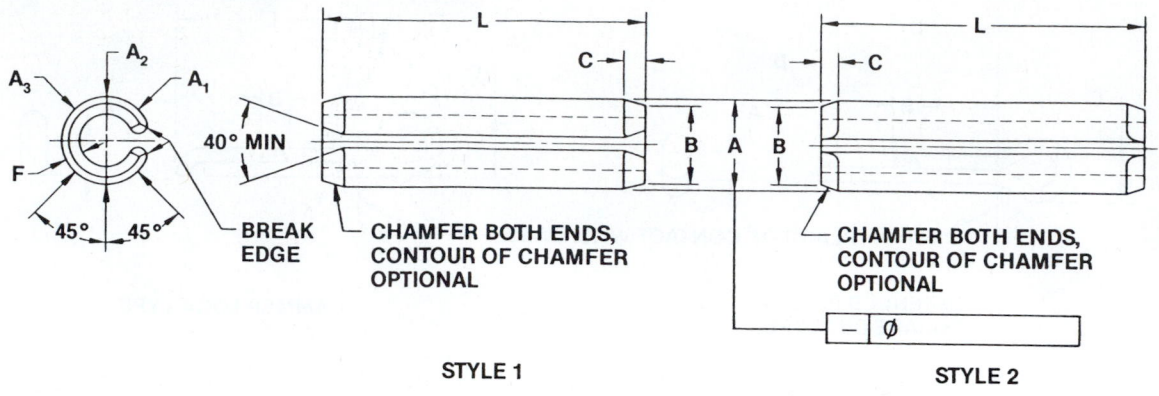

STYLE 1

STYLE 2

OPTIONAL CONSTRUCTIONS

TABLE C.6.3   Dimensions of Slotted Type Spring Pins

Nominal Size or Basic Pin Diameter		A Pin Diameter		B Chamfer Diameter	C Chamfer Length		F Stock Thickness	Recommended Hole Size		Double Shear Load, Min, lb Material		
		Max	Min	Max	Max	Min	Basic	Max	Min	AISI 1070-1095 and AISI 420	AISI 302	Beryllium Copper
1/16	0.062	0.069	0.066	0.059	0.028	0.007	0.012	0.065	0.062	425	350	270
5/64	0.078	0.086	0.083	0.075	0.032	0.008	0.018	0.081	0.078	650	550	400
3/32	0.094	0.103	0.099	0.091	0.038	0.008	0.022	0.097	0.094	1,000	800	660
1/8	0.125	0.135	0.131	0.122	0.044	0.008	0.028	0.129	0.125	2,100	1,500	1,200
9/64	0.141	0.149	0.145	0.137	0.044	0.008	0.028	0.144	0.140	2,200	1,600	1,400
5/32	0.156	0.167	0.162	0.151	0.048	0.010	0.032	0.160	0.156	3,000	2,000	1,800
3/16	0.188	0.199	0.194	0.182	0.055	0.011	0.040	0.192	0.187	4,400	2,800	2,600
7/32	0.219	0.232	0.226	0.214	0.065	0.011	0.048	0.224	0.219	5,700	3,550	3,700
1/4	0.250	0.264	0.258	0.245	0.065	0.012	0.048	0.256	0.250	7,700	4,600	4,500
5/16	0.312	0.328	0.321	0.306	0.080	0.014	0.062	0.318	0.312	11,500	7,095	6,800
3/8	0.375	0.392	0.385	0.368	0.095	0.016	0.077	0.382	0.375	17,600	10,000	10,100
7/16	0.438	0.456	0.448	0.430	0.095	0.017	0.077	0.445	0.437	20,000	12,000	12,200
1/2	0.500	0.521	0.513	0.485	0.110	0.025	0.094	0.510	0.500	25,800	15,500	16,800
5/8	0.625	0.650	0.640	0.608	0.125	0.030	0.125	0.636	0.625	46,000[+]	18,800	. . .
3/4	0.750	0.780	0.769	0.730	0.150	0.030	0.150	0.764	0.750	66,000[+]	23,200	. . .

Metric Spring Pins IFI 512-S 1982

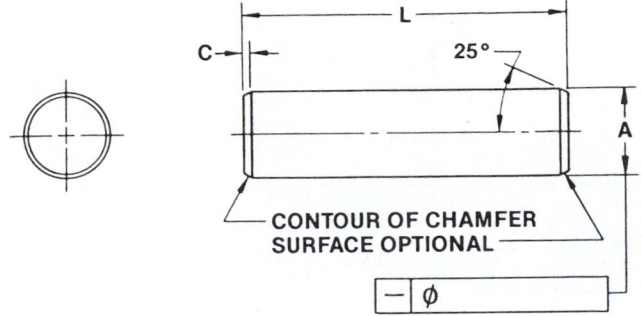

CONTOUR OF CHAMFER
SURFACE OPTIONAL

TABLE C.6.4		Slotted Spring Pin Dimensions								
Nom Pin Size	**D**		**B** Chamfer Dia	**C** Chamfer Length		**S** Stock Thickness	**Recommended Hole Size**			
	Dia									
	Max	Min	Max	Max	Min	Nom	Max	Min		
1.5	1.68	1.60	1.4	0.7	0.15	0.3	1.60	1.50		
2	2.20	2.12	1.9	0.8	0.2	0.4	2.10	2.00		
2.5	2.72	2.63	2.4	0.9	0.2	0.5	2.60	2.50		
3	3.25	3.15	2.9	1.0	0.2	0.6	3.10	3.00		
4	4.28	4.15	3.9	1.2	0.3	0.8	4.12	4.00		
5	5.33	5.17	4.8	1.4	0.3	1.0	5.12	5.00		
6	6.36	6.20	5.8	1.6	0.4	1.2	6.12	6.00		
8	8.40	8.22	7.8	2.0	0.4	1.6	8.15	8.00		
10	10.43	10.25	9.7	2.4	0.5	2.0	10.15	10.00		
12	12.48	12.28	11.7	2.8	0.6	2.5	12.18	12.00		

Dowel Pins ANSI/ASME B18.8.2 1978

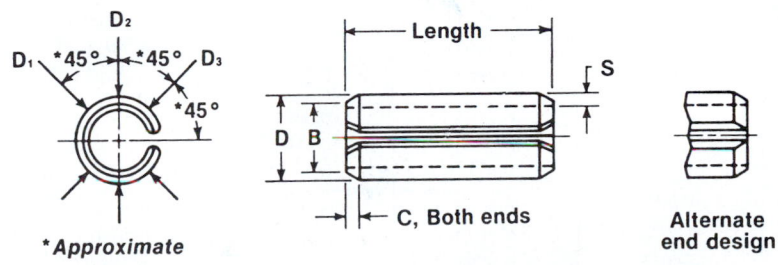

*Approximate

C, Both ends

Alternate end design

TABLE C.6.5	Dimensions of Unhardened Ground Dowel Pins						
Nominal Size or Nominal Pin Diameter		**A** Pin Diameter		**C** Chamfer Length		**Double Shear Load Min, lb** Material	
		Max	Min	Max	Min	Carbon Steel	Brass
1/16	0.0625	0.0600	0.0595	0.025	0.005	350	220
3/32	0.0938	0.0912	0.0907	0.025	0.005	820	510
*7/64	0.1094	0.1068	0.1063	0.025	0.005	1,130	710
1/8	0.1250	0.1223	0.1218	0.025	0.005	1,490	930
5/32	0.1562	0.1535	0.1530	0.025	0.005	2,350	1,470
3/16	0.1875	0.1847	0.1842	0.025	0.005	3,410	2,130
7/32	0.2188	0.2159	0.2154	0.025	0.005	4,660	2,910
1/4	0.2500	0.2470	0.2465	0.025	0.005	6,120	3,810
5/16	0.3125	0.3094	0.3089	0.040	0.020	9,590	5,990
3/8	0.3750	0.3717	0.3712	0.040	0.020	13,850	8,650
7/16	0.4375	0.4341	0.4336	0.040	0.020	18,900	11,810
1/2	0.5000	0.4964	0.4959	0.040	0.020	24,720	15,450
5/8	0.6250	0.6211	0.6206	0.055	0.035	38,710	24,190
3/4	0.7500	0.7548	0.7453	0.055	0.035	55,840	34,900
7/8	0.8750	0.8705	0.8700	0.070	0.050	76,090	47,550
1	1.0000	0.9952	0.9947	0.070	0.050	99,460	62,160

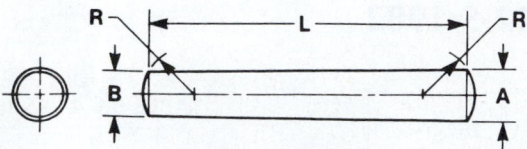

TABLE C.6.6 Dimensions of Taper Pins

Pin Size Number and Basic Pin Diameter		A				R	
		Major Diameter (Large End)				End Crown Radius	
		Commercial Class		Precision Class			
		Max	Min	Max	Min	Max	Min
7/0	0.0625	0.0638	0.0618	0.0635	0.0625	0.072	0.052
6/0	0.0780	0.0793	0.0773	0.0790	0.0780	0.088	0.068
5/0	0.0940	0.0953	0.0933	0.0950	0.0940	0.104	0.084
4/0	0.1090	0.1103	0.1083	0.1100	0.1090	0.119	0.099
3/0	0.1250	0.1263	0.1243	0.1260	0.1250	0.135	0.115
2/0	0.1410	0.1423	0.1403	0.1420	0.1410	0.151	0.131
0	0.1560	0.1573	0.1553	0.1570	0.1560	0.166	0.146
1	0.1720	0.1733	0.1713	0.1730	0.1720	0.182	0.162
2	0.1930	0.1943	0.1923	0.1940	0.1930	0.203	0.183
3	0.2190	0.2203	0.2183	0.2200	0.2190	0.229	0.209
4	0.2500	0.2513	0.2493	0.2510	0.2500	0.260	0.240
5	0.2890	0.2903	0.2883	0.2900	0.2890	0.299	0.279
6	0.3410	0.3423	0.3403	0.3420	0.3410	0.351	0.331
7	0.4090	0.4103	0.4083	0.4100	0.4090	0.419	0.399
8	0.4920	0.4933	0.4913	0.4930	0.4920	0.502	0.482
9	0.5910	0.5923	0.5903	0.5920	0.5910	0.601	0.581
10	0.7060	0.7073	0.7053	0.7070	0.7060	0.716	0.696
11	0.8600	0.8613	0.8593	*	*	0.870	0.850
12	1.0320	1.0333	1.0313	*	*	1.042	1.022
13	1.2410	1.2423	1.2403	*	*	1.251	1.231
14	1.5210	1.5223	1.5203	*	*	1.531	1.511

Bushings

TABLE C.7.1   Jig Bushings

Range of Hole Sizes in Renewable Bushings	Inside Diameter A			Body Diameter B	Unfinished		Finished		Over-all Length C	Radius D	Head Diam. E	Head Thick. F Max	Number
	Nom	Max	Min	Nom	Max	Min	Max	Min					
0.0135 to 0.1562	0.312	0.3129	0.3126	0.500	0.520	0.515	0.5017	0.5014	0.312 0.500 0.750 1.000	0.047	0.625	0.094	HL-32-5 HL-32-8 HL-32-12 HL-32-16
0.1570 to 0.3125	0.500	0.5005	0.5002	0.750	0.770	0.765	0.7518	0.7515	0.312 0.500 0.750 1.000 1.375 1.750	0.062	0.875	0.094	HL-48-5 HL-48-8 HL-48-12 HL-48-16 HL-48-22 HL-48-28
0.3160 to 0.5000	0.750	0.7506	0.7503	1.000	1.020	1.015	1.0018	1.0015	0.500 0.750 1.000 1.375 1.750 2.125	0.062	1.125	0.125	HL-64-8 HL-64-12 HL-64-16 HL-64-22 HL-64-28 HL-64-34
0.5156 to 0.7500	1.000	1.0007	1.0004	1.375	1.395	1.390	1.3772	1.3768	0.500 0.750 1.000 1.375 1.750 2.125 2.500	0.094	1.500	0.125	HL-88-8 HL-88-12 HL-88-16 HL-88-22 HL-88-28 HL-88-34 HL-88-40
0.7656 to 1.0000	1.375	1.3760	1.3756	1.750	1.770	1.765	1.7523	1.7519	0.750 1.000 1.375 1.750 2.125 2.500	0.094	1.875	0.188	HL-112-12 HL-112-16 HL-112-22 HL-112-28 HL-112-34 HL-112-40
1.0156 to 1.3750	1.750	1.7512	1.7508	2.250	2.270	2.265	2.2525	2.2521	1.000 1.375 1.750 2.125 2.500 3.000	0.094	2.375	0.188	HL-144-16 HL-144-22 HL-144-28 HL-144-34 HL-144-40 HL-144-48
1.3906 to 1.7500	2.250	2.2515	2.2510	2.750	2.770	2.765	2.7526	2.7522	1.000 1.375 1.750 2.125 2.500 3.000	0.125	2.875	0.188	HL-176-16 HL-176-22 HL-176-28 HL-176-34 HL-176-40 HL-176-48

All dimensions are in inches.

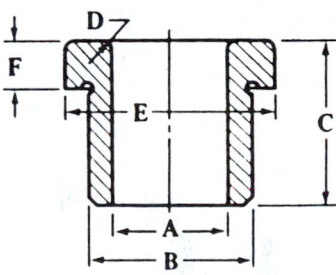

TABLE C.7.2   Headless Type Press Fit Wearing Bushings Type-P

Range of Hole Sizes A	Body Diameter B					Body Length C	Radius D	Number
	Nom	Unfinished		Finished				
		Max	Min	Max	Min			
0.0135 Up To And Including 0.0625	0.156	0.166	0.161	0.1578	0.1575	0.250 0.312 0.375 0.500	0.016	P-10-4 P-10-5 P-10-6 P-10-8
0.0630 To 0.0995	0.203	0.213	0.208	0.2046	0.2043	0.250 0.312 0.375 0.500 0.750	0.016	P-13-4 P-13-5 P-13-6 P-13-8 P-13-12
0.1015 To 0.1405	0.250	0.260	0.255	0.2516	0.2513	0.250 0.312 0.375 0.500 0.750	0.016	P-16-4 P-16-5 P-16-6 P-16-8 P-16-12
0.1406 To 0.1875	0.312	0.327	0.322	0.3141	0.3138	0.250 0.312 0.375 0.500 0.750 1.000	0.031	P-20-4 P-20-5 P-20-6 P-20-8 P-20-12 P-20-16
0.1890 To 0.2500	0.406	0.421	0.416	0.4078	0.4075	0.250 0.312 0.375 0.500 0.750 1.000 1.375 1.750	0.031	P-26-4 P-26-5 P-26-6 P-26-8 P-26-12 P-26-16 P-26-22 P-26-28
0.2570 To 0.3125	0.500	0.520	0.515	0.5017	0.5014	0.312 0.375 0.500 0.750 1.000 1.375 1.750	0.047	P-32-5 P-32-6 P-32-8 P-32-12 P-32-16 P-32-22 P-32-28

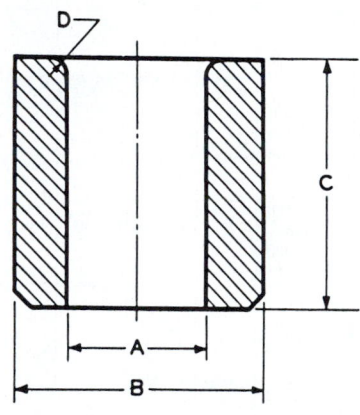

Woodruff Keys

Keys and Keyseats

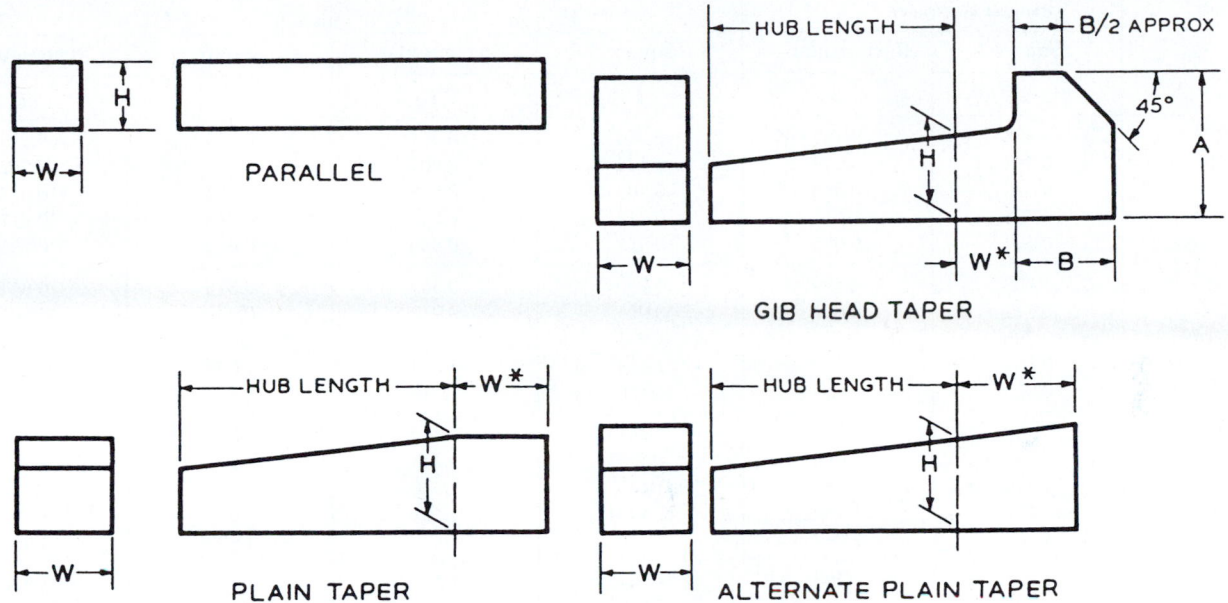

GIB HEAD TAPER

PARALLEL

PLAIN TAPER

ALTERNATE PLAIN TAPER

Plain and Gib Head Taper Keys Have a 1/8″ Taper in 12″

TABLE C.8.1 Key Dimensions and Tolerances

KEY			NOMINAL KEY SIZE		TOLERANCE	
			Width, W		Width, W	Height, H
			Over	To (Incl)		
Parallel	Square	Bar Stock	—	3/4	+0.000 −0.002	+0.000 −0.002
			3/4	1-1/2	+0.000 −0.003	+0.000 −0.003
			1-1/2	2-1/2	+0.000 −0.004	+0.000 −0.004
			2-1/2	3-1/2	+0.000 −0.006	+0.000 −0.006
		Keystock	—	1-1/4	+0.001 −0.000	+0.001 −0.000
			1-1/4	3	+0.002 −0.000	+0.002 −0.000
			3	3-1/2	+0.003 −0.000	+0.003 −0.000
	Rectangular	Bar Stock	—	3/4	+0.000 −0.003	+0.000 −0.003
			3/4	1-1/2	+0.000 −0.004	+0.000 −0.004
			1-1/2	3	+0.000 −0.005	+0.000 −0.005
			3	4	+0.000 −0.006	+0.000 −0.006
			4	6	+0.000 −0.008	+0.000 −0.008
			6	7	+0.000 −0.013	+0.000 −0.013
		Keystock	—	1-1/4	+0.001 −0.000	+0.005 −0.005
			1-1/4	3	+0.002 −0.000	+0.005 −0.005
			3	7	+0.003 −0.000	+0.005 −0.005
Taper	Plain or Gib Head Square or Rectangular		—	1-1/4	+0.001 −0.000	+0.005 −0.000
			1-1/4	3	+0.002 −0.000	+0.005 −0.000
			3	7	+0.003 −0.000	+0.005 −0.000

*For locating position of dimension H. Tolerance does not apply.
All dimensions given in inches.

TABLE C.8.2 Depth Control Values Table 3 Values for *S* and *T*

Nominal Shaft Diameter	Parallel and Taper		Parallel		Taper	
	Square	Rectangular	Square	Rectangular	Square	Rectangular
	S	S	T	T	T	T
1/2	0.430	0.445	0.560	0.544	0.535	0.519
9/16	0.493	0.509	0.623	0.607	0.598	0.582
5/8	0.517	0.548	0.709	0.678	0.684	0.653
11/16	0.581	0.612	0.773	0.742	0.748	0.717
3/4	0.644	0.676	0.837	0.806	0.812	0.781
13/16	0.708	0.739	0.900	0.869	0.875	0.844
7/8	0.771	0.802	0.964	0.932	0.939	0.907
15/16	0.796	0.827	1.051	1.019	1.026	0.994
1	0.859	0.890	1.114	1.083	1.089	1.058
1-1/16	0.923	0.954	1.178	1.146	1.153	1.121
1-1/8	0.986	1.017	1.241	1.210	1.216	1.185
1-3/16	1.049	1.080	1.304	1.273	1.279	1.248
1-1/4	1.112	1.144	1.367	1.336	1.342	1.311
1-5/16	1.137	1.169	1.455	1.424	1.430	1.399
1-3/8	1.201	1.232	1.518	1.487	1.493	1.462
1-7/16	1.225	1.288	1.605	1.543	1.580	1.518
1-1/2	1.289	1.351	1.669	1.606	1.644	1.581
1-9/16	1.352	1.415	1.732	1.670	1.707	1.645
1-5/8	1.416	1.478	1.796	1.733	1.771	1.708
1-11/16	1.479	1.541	1.859	1.796	1.834	1.771
1-3/4	1.542	1.605	1.922	1.860	1.897	1.835
1-13/16	1.527	1.590	2.032	1.970	2.007	1.945
1-7/8	1.591	1.654	2.096	2.034	2.071	2.009
1-15/16	1.655	1.717	2.160	2.097	2.135	2.072
2	1.718	1.781	2.223	2.161	2.198	2.136
2-1/16	1.782	1.844	2.287	2.224	2.262	2.199
2-1/8	1.845	1.908	2.350	2.288	2.325	2.263
2-3/16	1.909	1.971	2.414	2.351	2.389	2.326
2-1/4	1.972	2.034	2.477	2.414	2.452	2.389
2-5/16	1.957	2.051	2.587	2.493	2.562	2.468
2-3/8	2.021	2.114	2.651	2.557	2.626	2.532
2-7/16	2.084	2.178	2.714	2.621	2.689	2.596
2-1/2	2.148	2.242	2.778	2.684	2.753	2.659
2-9/16	2.211	2.305	2.841	2.748	2.816	2.723
2-5/8	2.275	2.369	2.905	2.811	2.880	2.786
2-11/16	2.338	2.432	2.968	2.874	2.943	2.849
2-3/4	2.402	2.495	3.032	2.938	3.007	2.913
2-13/16	2.387	2.512	3.142	3.017	3.117	2.992
2-7/8	2.450	2.575	3.205	3.080	3.180	3.055
2-15/16	2.514	2.639	3.269	3.144	3.244	3.119
3	2.577	2.702	3.332	3.207	3.307	3.182
3-1/16	2.641	2.766	3.396	3.271	3.371	3.246
3-1/8	2.704	2.829	3.459	3.334	3.434	3.309

All dimensions given in inches.

Woodruff Keys and Keyseats

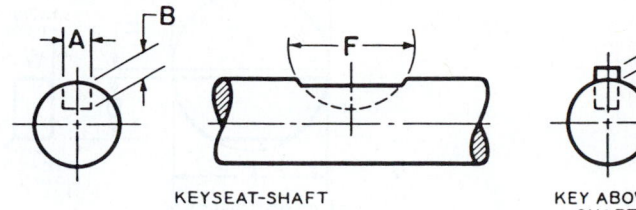

KEYSEAT-SHAFT

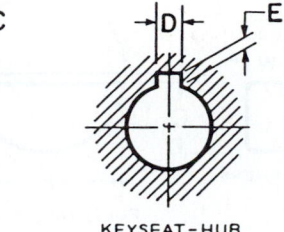

KEY ABOVE SHAFT

KEYSEAT-HUB

TABLE C.8.3   Keyseat Dimensions

Key Number	Nominal Size Key	Keyseat—Shaft					Key Above Shaft	Keyseat—Hub	
		Width A*		Depth B	Diameter F		Height C	Width D	Depth E
		Min	Max	+0.005 −0.000	Min	Max	+0.005 −0.005	+0.002 −0.000	+0.005 −0.000
202	¹⁄₁₆ × ¼	0.0615	0.0630	0.0728	0.250	0.268	0.0312	0.0635	0.0372
202.5	¹⁄₁₆ × ⁵⁄₁₆	0.0615	0.0630	0.1038	0.312	0.330	0.0312	0.0635	0.0372
302.5	³⁄₃₂ × ⁵⁄₁₆	0.0928	0.0943	0.0882	0.312	0.330	0.0469	0.0948	0.0529
203	¹⁄₁₆ × ⅜	0.0615	0.0630	0.1358	0.375	0.393	0.0312	0.0635	0.0372
303	³⁄₃₂ × ⅜	0.0928	0.0943	0.1202	0.375	0.393	0.0469	0.0948	0.0529
403	⅛ × ⅜	0.1240	0.1255	0.1045	0.375	0.393	0.0625	0.1260	0.0685
204	¹⁄₁₆ × ½	0.0615	0.0630	0.1668	0.500	0.518	0.0312	0.0635	0.0372
304	³⁄₃₂ × ½	0.0928	0.0943	0.1511	0.500	0.518	0.0469	0.0948	0.0529
404	⅛ × ½	0.1240	0.1255	0.1355	0.500	0.518	0.0625	0.1260	0.0685
305	³⁄₃₂ × ⅝	0.0928	0.0943	0.1981	0.625	0.643	0.0469	0.0948	0.0529
405	⅛ × ⅝	0.1240	0.1255	0.1825	0.625	0.643	0.0625	0.1260	0.0685
505	⁵⁄₃₂ × ⅝	0.1553	0.1568	0.1669	0.625	0.643	0.0781	0.1573	0.0841
605	³⁄₁₆ × ⅝	0.1863	0.1880	0.1513	0.625	0.643	0.0937	0.1885	0.0997
406	⅛ × ¾	0.1240	0.1255	0.2455	0.750	0.768	0.0625	0.1260	0.0685
506	⁵⁄₃₂ × ¾	0.1553	0.1568	0.2299	0.750	0.768	0.0781	0.1573	0.0841
606	³⁄₁₆ × ¾	0.1863	0.1880	0.2143	0.750	0.768	0.0937	0.1885	0.0997
806	¼ × ¾	0.2487	0.2505	0.1830	0.750	0.768	0.1250	0.2510	0.1310
507	⁵⁄₃₂ × ⅞	0.1553	0.1568	0.2919	0.875	0.895	0.0781	0.1573	0.0841
607	³⁄₁₆ × ⅞	0.1863	0.1880	0.2763	0.875	0.895	0.0937	0.1885	0.0997
707	⁷⁄₃₂ × ⅞	0.2175	0.2193	0.2607	0.875	0.895	0.1093	0.2198	0.1153
807	¼ × ⅞	0.2487	0.2505	0.2450	0.875	0.895	0.1250	0.2510	0.1310
608	³⁄₁₆ × 1	0.1863	0.1880	0.3393	1.000	1.020	0.0937	0.1885	0.0997
708	⁷⁄₃₂ × 1	0.2175	0.2193	0.3237	1.000	1.020	0.1093	0.2198	0.1153
808	¼ × 1	0.2487	0.2505	0.3080	1.000	1.020	0.1250	0.2510	0.1310
1008	⁵⁄₁₆ × 1	0.3111	0.3130	0.2768	1.000	1.020	0.1562	0.3135	0.1622
1208	⅜ × 1	0.3735	0.3755	0.2455	1.000	1.020	0.1875	0.3760	0.1935
609	³⁄₁₆ × 1⅛	0.1863	0.1880	0.3853	1.125	1.145	0.0937	0.1885	0.0997
709	⁷⁄₃₂ × 1⅛	0.2175	0.2193	0.3697	1.125	1.145	0.1093	0.2198	0.1153
809	¼ × 1⅛	0.2487	0.2505	0.3540	1.125	1.145	0.1250	0.2510	0.1310
1009	⁵⁄₁₆ × 1⅛	0.3111	0.3130	0.3228	1.125	1.145	0.1562	0.3135	0.1622

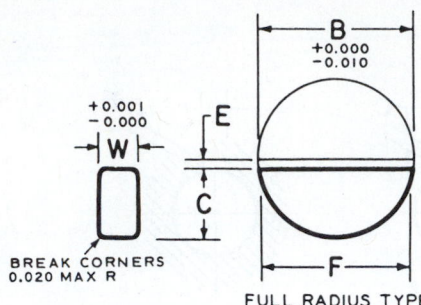

FULL RADIUS TYPE

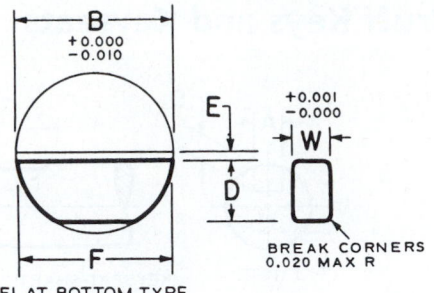

FLAT BOTTOM TYPE

TABLE C.8.4   Woodruff Keys

Key No.	Nominal Key Size W × B	Actual Length F +0.000-0.010	Height of Key				Distance Below Center E
			C		D		
			Max	Min	Max	Min	
202	1/16 × 1/4	0.248	0.109	0.104	0.109	0.104	1/64
202.5	1/16 × 5/16	0.311	0.140	0.135	0.140	0.135	1/64
302.5	3/32 × 5/16	0.311	0.140	0.135	0.140	0.135	1/64
203	1/16 × 3/8	0.374	0.172	0.167	0.172	0.167	1/64
303	3/32 × 3/8	0.374	0.172	0.167	0.172	0.167	1/64
403	1/8 × 3/8	0.374	0.172	0.167	0.172	0.167	1/64
204	1/16 × 1/2	0.491	0.203	0.198	0.194	0.188	3/64
304	3/32 × 1/2	0.491	0.203	0.198	0.194	0.188	3/64
404	1/8 × 1/2	0.491	0.203	0.198	0.194	0.188	3/64
305	3/32 × 5/8	0.612	0.250	0.245	0.240	0.234	1/16
405	1/8 × 5/8	0.612	0.250	0.245	0.240	0.234	1/16
505	5/32 × 5/8	0.612	0.250	0.245	0.240	0.234	1/16
605	3/16 × 5/8	0.612	0.250	0.245	0.240	0.234	1/16
406	1/8 × 3/4	0.740	0.313	0.308	0.303	0.297	1/16
506	5/32 × 3/4	0.740	0.313	0.308	0.303	0.297	1/16
606	3/16 × 3/4	0.740	0.313	0.308	0.303	0.297	1/16
806	1/4 × 3/4	0.740	0.313	0.308	0.303	0.297	1/16
507	5/32 × 7/8	0.866	0.375	0.370	0.365	0.359	1/16
607	3/16 × 7/8	0.866	0.375	0.370	0.365	0.359	1/16
707	7/32 × 7/8	0.866	0.375	0.370	0.365	0.359	1/16
807	1/4 × 7/8	0.866	0.375	0.370	0.365	0.359	1/16
608	3/16 × 1	0.992	0.438	0.433	0.428	0.422	1/16
708	7/32 × 1	0.992	0.438	0.433	0.428	0.422	1/16
808	1/4 × 1	0.992	0.438	0.433	0.428	0.422	1/16
1008	5/16 × 1	0.992	0.438	0.433	0.428	0.422	1/16
1208	3/8 × 1	0.992	0.438	0.433	0.428	0.422	1/16
609	3/16 × 1 1/8	1.114	0.484	0.479	0.475	0.469	5/64
709	7/32 × 1 1/8	1.114	0.484	0.479	0.475	0.469	5/64
809	1/4 × 1 1/8	1.114	0.484	0.479	0.475	0.469	5/64
1009	5/16 × 1 1/8	1.114	0.484	0.479	0.475	0.469	5/64

APPENDIX C.9

Pipe and Fitting Sizes

American Standard Straight Threads

Information abstracted from American Standard Pipe Threads ANSI.B2.1

■ Straight thread gages are used to gage mechanical joint straight pipe threads.

The actual pitch diameters of the tapped hole will be slightly smaller than the values given.
basic dimensions (inches)

◆ American Standard taper pipe thread plug gages are used to gage straight pipe threads in couplings with the gaging notch coming flush with the edge of the thread or with the bottom of chamfer, if chamfered, allowing a tolerance of one and one half turns large or small.

TABLE C.9.1 American Standard Straight Pipe Threads

| Nominal Pipe Size | Threads Per Inch | Pitch of Thread | Straight Pipe Threads ◆ in Pipe Couplings (Pressure Tight Joints) Internal | | Straight Pipe Threads for Mechanical Joints ■ (Free Fitting) | | | | Straight Pipe Threads for Locknut Connections (Loose Fitting Mechanical Joints) | | | |
| | | | | | External | | Internal | | External | | Internal | |
			Max	Min	Max	Min	Max	Min	Max	Min	Max	Min
⅛	27	0.0370	0.3782	0.3713	0.3748	0.3713	0.3782	0.3748	0.3840	0.3805	0.3898	0.3863
¼	18	0.0556	0.4951	0.4847	0.4899	0.4847	0.4951	0.4899	0.5038	0.4986	0.5125	0.5073
⅜	18	0.0556	0.6322	0.6218	0.6270	0.6218	0.6322	0.6270	0.6409	0.6357	0.6496	0.6444
½	14	0.0714	0.7851	0.7717	0.7784	0.7717	0.7851	0.7784	0.7963	0.7896	0.8075	0.8008
¾	14	0.0714	0.9956	0.9822	0.9889	0.9822	0.9956	0.9889	1.0067	1.0000	1.0179	1.0112
1	11½	0.0870	1.2468	1.2305	1.2386	1.2305	1.2468	1.2386	1.2064	1.2523	1.2739	1.2658
1¼	11½	0.0870	1.5915	1.5752	1.5834	1.5752	1.5915	1.5834	1.6051	1.5970	1.6187	1.6106
1½	11½	0.0870	1.8305	1.8142	1.8223	1.8142	1.8305	1.8223	1.8441	1.8360	1.8576	1.8495
2	11½	0.0870	2.3044	2.2881	2.2963	2.2881	2.3044	2.2963	2.3180	2.3099	2.3315	2.3234
2½	8	0.1250	2.7739	2.7505	2.7622	2.7505	2.7739	2.7622	2.7934	2.7817	2.8129	2.8012
3	8	0.1250	3.4002	3.3768	3.3885	3.3768	3.4002	3.3885	3.4198	3.4081	3.4393	3.4276
3½	8	0.1250	3.9005	3.8771	3.8888	3.8771	3.9005	3.8888	3.9201	3.9084	3.9396	3.9279
4	8	0.1250	4.3988	4.3754	4.3871	4.3754	4.3988	4.3871	4.4184	4.4067	4.4379	4.4262
5	8	0.1250			5.4493	5.4376	5.4610	5.4493	5.4805	5.4688	5.5001	5.4884
6	8	0.1250			6.5060	6.4943	6.5177	6.5060	6.5372	6.5255	6.5567	6.5450
8	8	0.1250							8.5313	8.5196	8.5508	8.5391
10	8	0.1250							10.6522	10.6405	10.6717	10.6600
12	8	0.1250							12.6491	12.6374	12.6686	12.6569

Reprinted courtesy of Crane Company.

TABLE C.9.2   American National Standard Taper Pipe Threads (NPT)

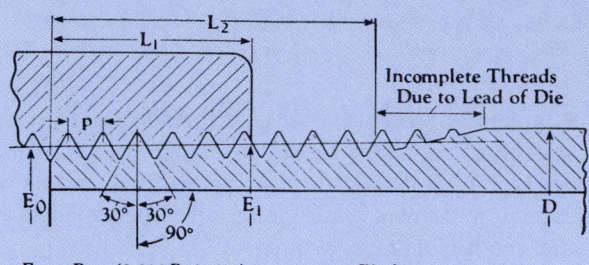

$E_0 = D - (0.050D + 1.1)p$
$\cdot E_1 = E_0 + 0.0625\ L_1$
$L_2 = (0.80D + 6.8)p$

p = Pitch
Depth of thread = $0.80p$
Total Taper ¾-inch per Foot

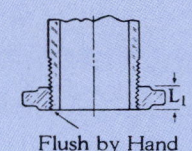

Tolerance on Product
One turn large or small
from notch on plug gauge
or face of ring gauge.

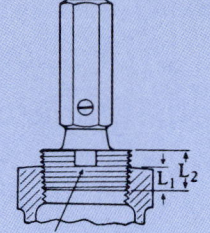

Notch flush with face of
fitting. If chamfered, notch
flush with bottom of chamfer

Nominal Pipe Size	D Outside diameter of pipe	Number of threads per inch	p Pitch of thread	E_o Pitch diameter at end of external thread	E_1† Pitch diameter at end of internal thread	L_1◐ Normal engagement by hand between external and internal threads	L_2§ Length of effective external thread	Height of thread
1/16	0.3125	27	0.03704	0.27118	0.28118	0.160	0.2611	0.02963
1/8	0.405	27	0.03704	0.36351	0.37360	0.1615	0.2639	0.02963
1/4	0.540	18	0.05556	0.47739	0.49163	0.2278	0.4018	0.04444
3/8	0.675	18	0.05556	0.61201	0.62701	0.240	0.4078	0.04444
1/2	0.840	14	0.07143	0.75843	0.77843	0.320	0.5337	0.05714
3/4	1.050	14	0.07143	0.96768	0.98887	0.339	0.5457	0.05714
1	1.315	11.5	0.08696	1.21363	1.23863	0.400	0.6828	0.06957
1¼	1.660	11.5	0.08696	1.55713	1.58338	0.420	0.7068	0.06957
1½	1.900	11.5	0.08696	1.79609	1.82234	0.420	0.7235	0.06957
2	2.375	11.5	0.08696	2.26902	2.29627	0.436	0.7565	0.06957
2½	2.875	8	0.12500	2.71953	2.76216	0.682	1.1375	0.10000
3	3.500	8	0.12500	3.34062	3.38850	0.766	1.2000	0.10000
3½	4.000	8	0.12500	3.83750	3.88881	0.821	1.2500	0.10000
4	4.500	8	0.12500	4.33438	4.38712	0.844	1.3000	0.10000
5	5.563	8	0.12500	5.39073	5.44929	0.937	1.4063	0.10000
6	6.625	8	0.12500	6.44609	6.50597	0.958	1.5125	0.10000
8	8.625	8	0.12500	8.43359	8.50003	1.063	1.7125	0.10000
10	10.750	8	0.12500	10.54531	10.62094	1.210	1.9250	0.10000
12	12.750	8	0.12500	12.53281	12.61781	1.360	2.1250	0.10000
14 O.D.	14.000	8	0.12500	13.77500	13.87262	1.562	2.2500	0.10000
16 O.D.	16.000	8	0.12500	15.76250	15.87575	1.812	2.4500	0.10000
18 O.D.	18.000	8	0.12500	17.75000	17.87500	2.000	2.6500	0.10000
20 O.D.	20.000	8	0.12500	19.73750	19.87031	2.125	2.8500	0.10000
24 O.D.	24.000	8	0.12500	23.71250	23.86094	2.375	3.2500	0.10000

Dimensions in inches.
†Also pitch diameter at gauging notch.
§Also length of plug gauge.
¶Also length of ring gauge, and length from gauging notch to small end of plug gauge.
*For the 1/8-27 and 1/4-18 sizes . . . E_1 approx. $= D - (0.05D + 0.827)\,p$
Above information extracted from American National Standard for Pipe Threads, ANSI B2.1.
Reprinted courtesy of ITT-Grinnell.

TABLE C.9.3   Schedule Numbers and Pipe Sizes for Steel and Stainless Steel Pipe

The following formulas are used in the computation of the values shown in the table:

$$\dagger\text{weight of pipe per foot (pounds)} = 10.6802t(D-t)$$
$$\text{weight of water per foot (pounds)} = 0.3405d^2$$
$$\text{square feet outside surface per foot} = 0.2618D$$
$$\text{square feet inside surface per foot} = 0.2618d$$
$$\text{inside area (square inches)} = 0.785d^2$$
$$\text{area of metal (square inches)} = 0.785(D^2-d^2)$$
$$\text{moment of inertia (inches}^4) = 0.0491(D^4-d^4)$$
$$= A_m R_g^2$$
$$\text{section modulus (inches}^3) = \frac{0.0982(D^4-d^4)}{D}$$
$$\text{radius of gyration (inches)} = 0.25\sqrt{D^2+d^2}$$

A_m = area of metal (square inches)
d = inside diameter (inches)
D = outside diameter (inches)
R_g = radius of gyration (inches)
t = pipe wall thickness (inches)

†The ferritic steels may be about 5% less, and the austenitic stainless steels about 2% greater than the values shown in this table which are based on weights for carbon steel.

*schedule numbers

Standard weight pipe and schedule 40 are the same in all sizes through 10-inch; from 12-inch through 24-inch, standard weight pipe has a wall thickness of ⅜-inch.

Extra strong weight pipe and schedule 80 are the same in all sizes through 8-inch; from 8-inch through 24-inch, extra strong weight pipe has a wall thickness of ½-inch.

Double extra strong weight pipe has no corresponding schedule number.

a: ANSI B36.10 steel pipe schedule numbers

b: ANSI B36.10 steel pipe nominal wall thickness designation

c: ANSI B36.19 stainless steel pipe schedule numbers

Nominal Pipe Size Outside Diameter. In.	Schedule Number* a	b	c	Wall Thick-ness, In.	Inside Diam-eter, In.	Inside Area, Sq. In.	Metal Area, Sq. In.	Sq Ft Outside Surface, Per Ft	Sq Ft Inside Surface, Per Ft	Weight Per Ft, Lb†	Weight of Water Per Ft, Lb	Moment of Inertia, In.⁴	Section Modu-lus, In.³	Radius Gyra-tion, In.
⅛ 0.405			10S	0.049	0.307	0.0740	0.0548	0.106	0.0804	0.186	0.0321	0.00088	0.00437	0.1271
	40	Std	40S	0.068	0.269	0.0568	0.0720	0.106	0.0705	0.245	0.0246	0.00106	0.00525	0.1215
	80	XS	80S	0.095	0.215	0.0364	0.0925	0.106	0.0563	0.315	0.0157	0.00122	0.00600	0.1146
¼ 0.540			10S	0.065	0.410	0.1320	0.0970	0.141	0.1073	0.330	0.0572	0.00279	0.01032	0.1694
	40	Std	40S	0.088	0.364	0.1041	0.1250	0.141	0.0955	0.425	0.0451	0.00331	0.01230	0.1628
	80	XS	80S	0.119	0.302	0.0716	0.1574	0.141	0.0794	0.535	0.0310	0.00378	0.01395	0.1547
⅜ 0.675			SS	0.065	0.710	0.396	0.1582	0.220	0.1859	0.538	0.1716	0.01197	0.0285	0.2750
			10S	0.065	0.545	0.2333	0.1246	0.177	0.1427	0.423	0.1011	0.00586	0.01737	0.2169
	40	Std	40S	0.091	0.493	0.1910	0.1670	0.177	0.1295	0.568	0.0827	0.00730	0.02160	0.2090
	80	XS	80S	0.126	0.423	0.1405	0.2173	0.177	0.1106	0.739	0.0609	0.00862	0.02554	0.1991
½ 0.840			5S	0.065	0.710	0.3959	0.1583	0.220	0.1859	0.538	0.171	0.0120	0.0285	0.2750
			10S	0.083	0.674	0.357	0.1974	0.220	0.1765	0.671	0.1547	0.01431	0.0341	0.2692
	40	Std	40S	0.109	0.622	0.304	0.2503	0.220	0.1628	0.851	0.1316	0.01710	0.0407	0.2613
	80	XS	80S	0.147	0.546	0.2340	0.320	0.220	0.1433	1.088	0.1013	0.02010	0.0478	0.2505
	160			0.187	0.466	0.1706	0.383	0.220	0.1220	1.304	0.0740	0.02213	0.0527	0.2402
		XXS		0.294	0.252	0.0499	0.504	0.220	0.0660	1.714	0.0216	0.02425	0.0577	0.2192
¾ 1.050			5S	0.065	0.920	0.665	0.2011	0.275	0.2409	0.684	0.2882	0.02451	0.0467	0.349
			10S	0.083	0.884	0.614	0.2521	0.275	0.2314	0.857	0.2661	0.02970	0.0566	0.343
	40	Std	40S	0.113	0.824	0.533	0.333	0.275	0.2157	1.131	0.2301	0.0370	0.0706	0.334
	80	XS	80S	0.154	0.742	0.432	0.435	0.275	0.1943	1.474	0.1875	0.0448	0.0853	0.321
	160			0.218	0.614	0.2961	0.570	0.275	0.1607	1.937	0.1284	0.0527	0.1004	0.304
		XXS		0.308	0.434	0.1479	0.718	0.275	0.1137	2.441	0.0641	0.0579	0.1104	0.2840

Continued

TABLE C.9.3   Schedule Numbers and Pipe Sizes for Steel and Stainless Steel Pipe—*Continued*

Nominal Pipe Size Outside Diameter, In.	Schedule Number*			Wall Thickness, In.	Inside Diameter, In.	Inside Area, Sq. In.	Metal Area, Sq. In.	Sq Ft Outside Surface, Per Ft	Sq Ft Inside Surface, Per Ft	Weight Per Ft, Lb†	Weight of Water Per Ft, Lb	Moment of Inertia, In.^{4}	Section Modulus, In.^{3}	Radius Gyration, In.
	a	b	c											
1 1.315			5S	0.065	1.185	1.103	0.2553	0.344	0.310	0.868	0.478	0.0500	0.0760	0.443
			10S	0.109	1.097	0.945	0.413	0.344	0.2872	1.404	0.409	0.0757	0.1151	0.428
	40	Std	40S	0.133	1.049	0.864	0.494	0.344	0.2746	1.679	0.374	0.0874	0.1329	0.421
	80	XS	80S	0.179	0.957	0.719	0.639	0.344	0.2520	2.172	0.311	0.1056	0.1606	0.407
	160			0.250	0.815	0.522	0.836	0.344	0.2134	2.844	0.2261	0.1252	0.1903	0.387
		XXS		0.358	0.599	0.2818	1.076	0.344	0.1570	3.659	0.1221	0.1405	0.2137	0.361
1¼ 1.660			5S	0.065	1.530	1.839	0.326	0.434	0.401	1.107	0.797	0.1038	0.1250	0.564
			10S	0.109	1.442	1.633	0.531	0.434	0.378	1.805	0.707	0.1605	0.1934	0.550
	40	Std	40S	0.140	1.380	1.496	0.669	0.434	0.361	2.273	0.648	0.1948	0.2346	0.540
	80	XS	80S	0.191	1.278	1.283	0.881	0.434	0.335	2.997	0.555	0.2418	0.2913	0.524
	160			0.250	1.160	1.057	1.107	0.434	0.304	3.765	0.458	0.2839	0.342	0.506
		XXS		0.382	0.896	0.631	1.534	0.434	0.2346	5.214	0.2732	0.341	0.411	0.472
1½ 1.900			5S	0.065	1.770	2.461	0.375	0.497	0.463	1.274	1.067	0.1580	0.1663	0.649
			10S	0.109	1.682	2.222	0.613	0.497	0.440	2.085	0.962	0.2469	0.2599	0.634
	40	Std	40S	0.145	1.610	2.036	0.799	0.497	0.421	2.718	0.882	0.310	0.326	0.623
	80	XS	80S	0.200	1.500	1.767	1.068	0.497	0.393	3.631	0.765	0.391	0.412	0.605
	160	—	—	0.281	1.338	1.406	1.429	0.497	0.350	4.859	0.608	0.483	0.508	0.581
	—	XXS	—	0.400	1.100	0.950	1.885	0.497	0.288	6.408	0.412	0.568	0.598	0.549
	—	—	—	0.525	0.850	0.567	2.267	0.497	0.223	7.710	0.246	0.6140	0.6470	0.5200
	—	—	—	0.650	0.600	0.283	2.551	0.497	0.157	8.678	0.123	0.6340	0.6670	0.4980
2 2.375	—	—	5S	0.065	2.245	3.96	0.472	0.622	0.588	1.604	1.716	0.315	0.2652	0.817
	—	—	10S	0.109	2.157	3.65	0.776	0.622	0.565	2.638	1.582	0.499	0.420	0.802
	40	Std	40S	0.154	2.067	3.36	1.075	0.622	0.541	3.653	1.455	0.666	0.561	0.787
	80	XS	80S	0.218	1.939	2.953	1.477	0.622	0.508	5.022	1.280	0.868	0.731	0.766
	160	—	—	0.343	1.689	2.240	2.190	0.622	0.442	7.444	0.971	1.163	0.979	0.729
	—	XXS	—	0.436	1.503	1.774	2.656	0.622	0.393	9.029	0.769	1.312	1.104	0.703
	—	—	—	0.562	1.251	1.229	3.199	0.622	0.328	10.882	0.533	1.442	1.2140	0.6710
	—	—	—	0.687	1.001	0.787	3.641	0.622	0.262	12.385	0.341	1.5130	1.2740	0.6440
2½ 2.875	—	—	5S	0.083	2.709	5.76	0.728	0.753	0.709	2.475	2.499	0.710	0.494	0.988
	—	—	10S	0.120	2.635	5.45	1.039	0.753	0.690	3.531	2.361	0.988	0.687	0.975
	40	Std	40S	0.203	2.469	4.79	1.704	0.753	0.646	5.793	2.076	1.530	1.064	0.947
	80	XS	80S	0.276	2.323	4.24	2.254	0.753	0.608	7.661	1.837	1.925	1.339	0.924
	160	—	—	0.375	2.125	3.55	2.945	0.753	0.556	10.01	1.535	2.353	1.637	0.894
	—	XXS	—	0.552	1.771	2.464	4.03	0.753	0.464	13.70	1.067	2.872	1.998	0.844
	—	—	—	0.675	1.525	1.826	4.663	0.753	0.399	15.860	0.792	3.0890	2.1490	0.8140
	—	—	—	0.800	1.275	1.276	5.212	0.753	0.334	17.729	0.554	3.2250	2.2430	0.7860
3 3.500	—	—	5S	0.083	3.334	8.73	0.891	0.916	0.873	3.03	3.78	1.301	0.744	1.208
	—	—	10S	0.120	3.260	8.35	1.274	0.916	0.853	4.33	3.61	1.822	1.041	1.196
	40	Std	40S	0.216	3.068	7.39	2.228	0.916	0.803	7.58	3.20	3.02	1.724	1.164
	80	XS	80S	0.300	2.900	6.61	3.02	0.916	0.759	10.25	2.864	3.90	2.226	1.136
	160	—	—	0.437	2.626	5.42	4.21	0.916	0.687	14.32	2.348	5.03	2.876	1.094
	—	XXS	—	0.600	2.300	4.15	5.47	0.916	0.602	18.58	1.801	5.99	3.43	1.047
	—	—	—	0.725	2.050	3.299	6.317	0.916	0.537	21.487	1.431	6.5010	3.7150	1.0140
	—	—	—	0.850	1.800	2.543	7.073	0.916	0.471	24.057	1.103	6.8530	3.9160	0.9840
3½ 4.000	—	—	5S	0.083	3.834	11.55	1.021	1.047	1.004	3.47	5.01	1.960	0.980	1.385
	—	—	10S	0.120	3.760	11.10	1.463	1.047	0.984	4.97	4.81	2.756	1.378	1.372
	40	Std	40S	0.226	3.548	9.89	2.680	1.047	0.929	9.11	4.28	4.79	2.394	1.337
	80	XS	80S	0.318	3.364	8.89	3.68	1.047	0.881	12.51	3.85	6.28	3.14	1.307
	—	XXS	—	0.636	2.728	5.845	6.721	1.047	0.716	22.850	2.530	9.8480	4.9240	1.2100

Continued

TABLE C.9.3   Schedule Numbers and Pipe Sizes for Steel and Stainless Steel Pipe—*Continued*

Nominal Pipe Size Outside Diameter, In.	Schedule Number*			Wall Thickness, In.	Inside Diameter, In.	Inside Area, Sq. In.	Metal Area, Sq. In.	Sq Ft Outside Surface, Per Ft	Sq Ft Inside Surface, Per Ft	Weight Per Ft, Lb†	Weight of Water Per Ft, Lb	Moment of Inertia, In.^{4}	Section Modulus, In.^{3}	Radius Gyration, In.
	a	b	c											
4 4.500	—	—	5S	0.083	4.334	14.75	1.152	1.178	1.135	3.92	6.40	2.811	1.249	1.562
	—	—	10S	0.120	4.260	14.25	1.651	1.178	1.115	5.61	6.17	3.96	1.762	1.549
	—	—	—	0.188	4.124	13.357	2.547	1.178	1.082	8.560	5.800	5.8500	2.6000	1.5250
	40	Std	40S	0.237	4.026	12.73	3.17	1.178	1.054	10.79	5.51	7.23	3.21	1.510
	80	XS	80S	0.337	3.826	11.50	4.41	1.178	1.002	14.98	4.98	9.61	4.27	1.477
	120	—	—	0.437	3.626	10.33	5.58	1.178	0.949	18.96	4.48	11.65	5.18	1.445
	—	—	—	0.500	3.500	9.621	6.283	1.178	0.916	21.360	4.160	12.7710	5.6760	1.4250
	160	—	—	0.531	3.438	9.28	6.62	1.178	0.900	22.51	4.02	13.27	5.90	1.416
	—	XXS	—	0.674	3.152	7.80	8.10	1.178	0.825	27.54	3.38	15.29	6.79	1.374
	—	—	—	0.800	2.900	6.602	9.294	1.178	0.759	31.613	2.864	16.6610	7.4050	1.3380
	—	—	—	0.925	2.650	5.513	10.384	1.178	0.694	35.318	2.391	17.7130	7.8720	1.3060
5 5.563	—	—	5S	0.109	5.345	22.44	1.868	1.456	1.399	6.35	9.73	6.95	2.498	1.929
	—	—	10S	0.134	5.295	22.02	2.285	1.456	1.386	7.77	9.53	8.43	3.03	1.920
	40	Std	40S	0.258	5.047	20.01	4.30	1.456	1.321	14.62	8.66	15.17	5.45	1.878
	80	XS	80S	0.375	4.813	18.19	6.11	1.456	1.260	20.78	7.89	20.68	7.43	1.839
	120	—	—	0.500	4.563	16.35	7.95	1.456	1.195	27.04	7.09	25.74	9.25	1.799
	160	—	—	0.625	4.313	14.61	9.70	1.456	1.129	32.96	6.33	30.0	10.80	1.760
	—	XXS	—	0.750	4.063	12.97	11.34	1.456	1.064	38.55	5.62	33.6	12.10	1.722
	—	—	—	0.875	3.813	11.413	12.880	1.456	0.998	43.810	4.951	36.6450	13.1750	1.6860
	—	—	—	1.000	3.563	9.966	14.328	1.456	0.933	47.734	4.232	39.1110	14.0610	1.6520

Reprinted courtesy of ITT-Grinnell.

TABLE C.9.4 Dimensions of Steel-Welding Fittings (Based on ASA B16.9 except as noted) All dimensions in inches

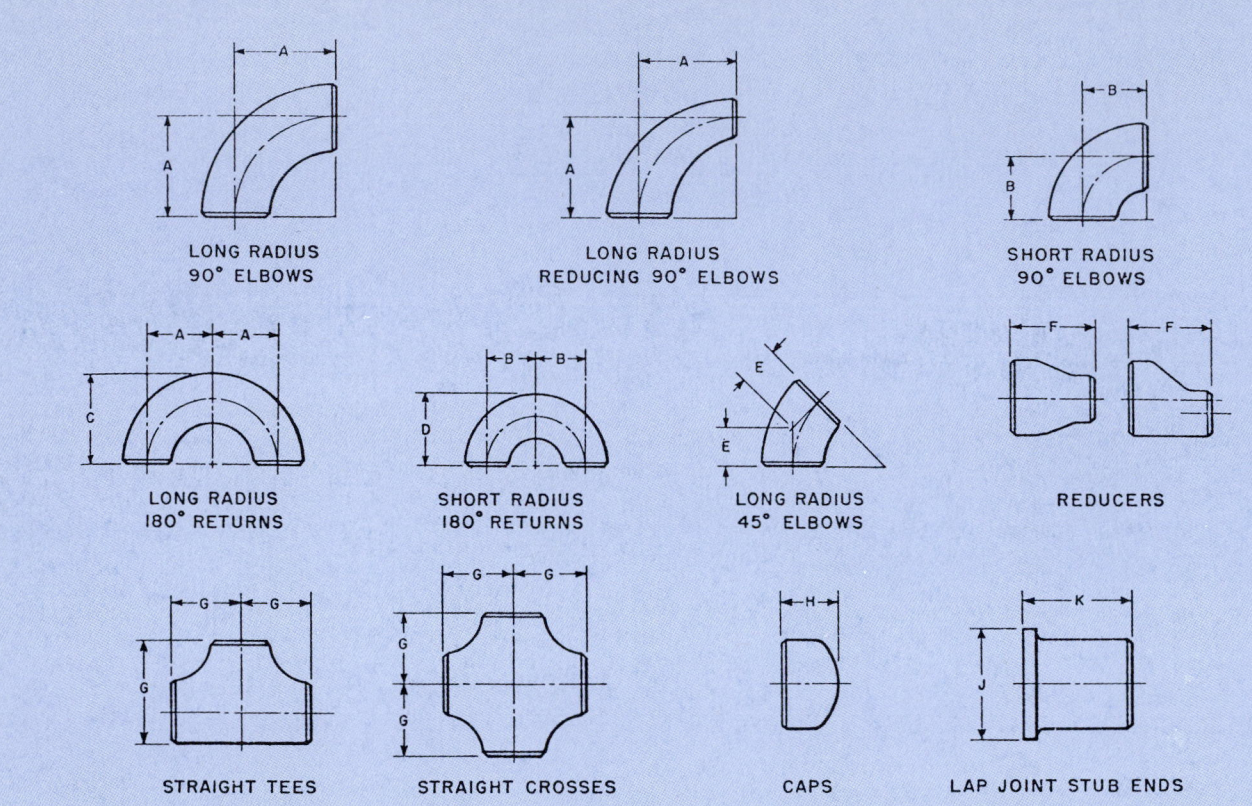

Nominal Pipe Size	A	B	C	D	E	F	G	H[5]	J	K
1		1½	2³⁄₁₆	1⅝	⅞	2	1½	1½	2	4
1½		2¼	3¼	2⁷⁄₁₆	1⅛	2½	2¼	1½	2⅞	4
2		3	4³⁄₁₆	3³⁄₁₆	1⅜	3	2½	1½	3⅝	6
3		4½	6¼	4¾	2	3½	3⅜	2	5	6
4	(1.5)(Nominal Pipe Size)	6	8¼	6¼	2½	4	4⅛	2½	6³⁄₁₆	6
6		9	12⁵⁄₁₆	9⁵⁄₁₆	3¾	5½	5⅝	3½	8½	8
8		12	16⁵⁄₁₆	12⁵⁄₁₆	5	6	7	4	10⅝	8
10		15	20⅜	15⅜	6¼	7	8½	5	12¾	10
12		18	24⅜	18⅜	7½	8	10	6	15	10
14		21	28	21	8¾	13	11[4]	6½	16¼	12
16	Same as Nominal Pipe Size	24	32	23	10	14	12[4]	7	18½	12
18		27	36	25½	11¼	15	13½[4]	8	21	12
20		30	40	30½	12½	20	15[4]	9	23	12
24		36	48	34	15	20	17[4]	10½	27¼	12

[1] Dimensions for these fittings not an ASA standard but common commercial practice.

[2] For reducing tees, see ASA B16.9.

[3] For sizes larger than 24", see MSS-SP-48.

[4] Center to end dimensions for outlet are not standardized in 14" and larger. Dimensions given are in common use.

[5] For standard weight and extra strong. See ASA B16.9 for dimensions of other thicknesses.

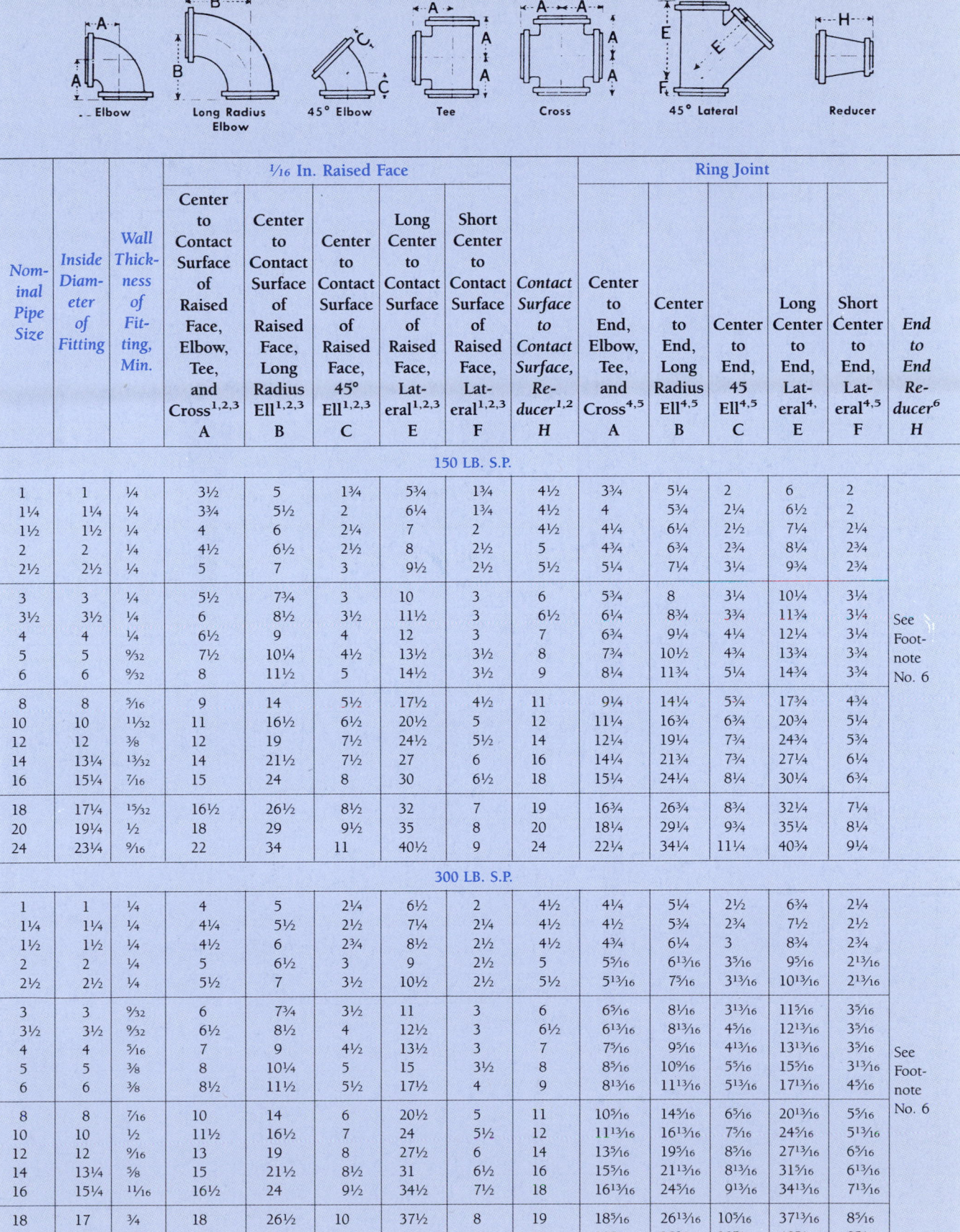

Elbow — Long Radius Elbow — 45° Elbow — Tee — Cross — 45° Lateral — Reducer

Nominal Pipe Size	Inside Diameter of Fitting	Wall Thickness of Fitting, Min.	1/16 In. Raised Face						Ring Joint					End to End Reducer[6] H
			Center to Contact Surface of Raised Face, Elbow, Tee, and Cross[1,2,3] A	Center to Contact Surface of Raised Face, Long Radius Ell[1,2,3] B	Center to Contact Surface of Raised Face, 45° Ell[1,2,3] C	Long Center to Contact Surface of Raised Face, Lateral[1,2,3] E	Short Center to Contact Surface of Raised Face, Lateral[1,2,3] F	Contact Surface to Contact Surface, Reducer[1,2] H	Center to End, Elbow, Tee, and Cross[4,5] A	Center to End, Long Radius Ell[4,5] B	Center to End, 45 Ell[4,5] C	Long Center to End, Lateral[4,] E	Short Center to End, Lateral[4,5] F	
150 LB. S.P.														
1	1	¼	3½	5	1¾	5¾	1¾	4½	3¾	5¼	2	6	2	
1¼	1¼	¼	3¾	5½	2	6¼	1¾	4½	4	5¾	2¼	6½	2	
1½	1½	¼	4	6	2¼	7	2	4½	4¼	6¼	2½	7¼	2¼	
2	2	¼	4½	6½	2½	8	2½	5	4¾	6¾	2¾	8¼	2¾	
2½	2½	¼	5	7	3	9½	2½	5½	5¼	7¼	3¼	9¾	2¾	
3	3	¼	5½	7¾	3	10	3	6	5¾	8	3¼	10¼	3¼	
3½	3½	¼	6	8½	3½	11½	3	6½	6¼	8¾	3¾	11¾	3¼	See Foot-note No. 6
4	4	¼	6½	9	4	12	3	7	6¾	9¼	4¼	12¼	3¼	
5	5	9/32	7½	10¼	4½	13½	3½	8	7¾	10½	4¾	13¾	3¾	
6	6	9/32	8	11½	5	14½	3½	9	8¼	11¾	5¼	14¾	3¾	
8	8	5/16	9	14	5½	17½	4½	11	9¼	14¼	5¾	17¾	4¾	
10	10	11/32	11	16½	6½	20½	5	12	11¼	16¾	6¾	20¾	5¼	
12	12	3/8	12	19	7½	24½	5½	14	12¼	19¼	7¾	24¾	5¾	
14	13¼	13/32	14	21½	7½	27	6	16	14¼	21¾	7¾	27¼	6¼	
16	15¼	7/16	15	24	8	30	6½	18	15¼	24¼	8¼	30¼	6¾	
18	17¼	15/32	16½	26½	8½	32	7	19	16¾	26¾	8¾	32¼	7¼	
20	19¼	½	18	29	9½	35	8	20	18¼	29¼	9¾	35¼	8¼	
24	23¼	9/16	22	34	11	40½	9	24	22¼	34¼	11¼	40¾	9¼	
300 LB. S.P.														
1	1	¼	4	5	2¼	6½	2	4½	4¼	5¼	2½	6¾	2¼	
1¼	1¼	¼	4¼	5½	2½	7¼	2¼	4½	4½	5¾	2¾	7½	2½	
1½	1½	¼	4½	6	2¾	8½	2½	4½	4¾	6¼	3	8¾	2¾	
2	2	¼	5	6½	3	9	2½	5	5 5/16	6 13/16	3 5/16	9 5/16	2 13/16	
2½	2½	¼	5½	7	3½	10½	2½	5½	5 13/16	7 5/16	3 13/16	10 13/16	2 13/16	
3	3	9/32	6	7¾	3½	11	3	6	6 5/16	8 1/16	3 13/16	11 5/16	3 5/16	
3½	3½	9/32	6½	8½	4	12½	3	6½	6 13/16	8 13/16	4 5/16	12 13/16	3 5/16	
4	4	5/16	7	9	4½	13½	3	7	7 5/16	9 5/16	4 13/16	13 13/16	3 5/16	See Foot-note No. 6
5	5	3/8	8	10¼	5	15	3½	8	8 5/16	10 9/16	5 5/16	15 5/16	3 13/16	
6	6	3/8	8½	11½	5½	17½	4	9	8 13/16	11 13/16	5 13/16	17 13/16	4 5/16	
8	8	7/16	10	14	6	20½	5	11	10 5/16	14 5/16	6 5/16	20 13/16	5 5/16	
10	10	½	11½	16½	7	24	5½	12	11 13/16	16 13/16	7 5/16	24 5/16	5 13/16	
12	12	9/16	13	19	8	27½	6	14	13 5/16	19 5/16	8 5/16	27 13/16	6 5/16	
14	13¼	5/8	15	21½	8½	31	6½	16	15 5/16	21 13/16	8 13/16	31 5/16	6 13/16	
16	15¼	11/16	16½	24	9½	34½	7½	18	16 13/16	24 5/16	9 13/16	34 13/16	7 13/16	
18	17	¾	18	26½	10	37½	8	19	18 5/16	26 13/16	10 5/16	37 13/16	8 5/16	
20	19	13/16	19½	29	10½	40½	8½	20	19 7/8	29 3/8	10 7/8	40 7/8	8 7/8	
24	23	15/16	22½	34	12	47½	10	24	22 15/16	34 7/16	12 7/16	47 15/16	10 7/16	

TABLE C.9.6 Forged Steel Screwed Fittings Dimensions, in Inches

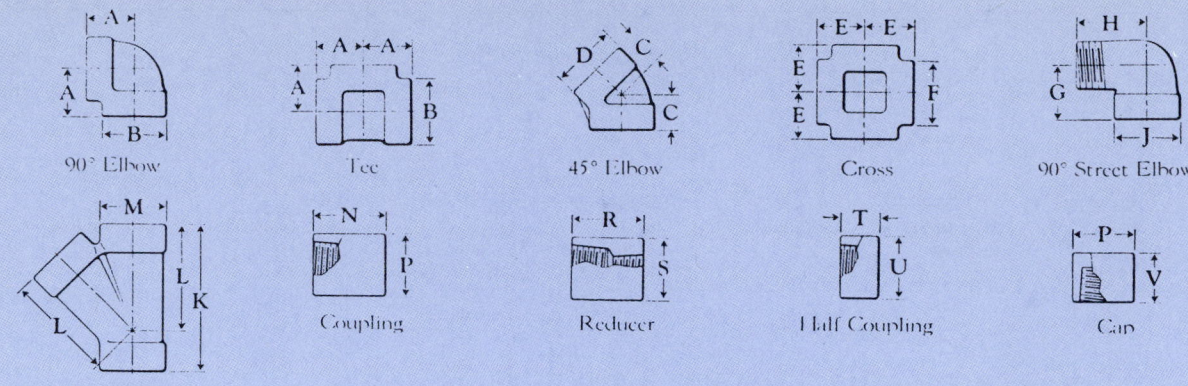

90° Elbow   Tee   45° Elbow   Cross   90° Street Elbow

45° Y-Bend   Coupling   Reducer   Half Coupling   Cap

Dimensions of reducing sizes are the same as those of the straight size corresponding to the largest opening.

Size	A	B	C	D	E	F	G	H	J	K	L	M	N	P	R	S	T	U	V
2000-Pound W.O.G. Fittings																			
1/8	13/16	29/32	11/16	15/16	31/32	1													
1/4	13/16	29/32	3/4	1 1/32	31/32	1				2 5/16	1 5/8	13/16							
3/8	31/32	1 1/32	3/4	1 1/32	31/32	1				2 11/16	1 7/8	1							
1/2	1 1/8	1 5/16	7/8	1 5/16	1 1/8	1 5/16				3	2 1/8	1 5/16							
3/4	1 5/16	1 1/2	1	1 1/2	1 5/16	1 1/2				3 9/16	2 9/16	1 1/2							
1	1 1/2	1 13/16	1 1/8	1 13/16	1 1/2	1 13/16				4 1/8	3	1 13/16							
1 1/4	1 3/4	2 7/32	1 5/16	2 7/32	1 3/4	2 3/16				4 13/16	3 1/2	2 3/16							
1 1/2	2	2 15/32	1 7/16	2 15/32	2	2 7/16				5 3/8	3 15/16	2 7/16							
2	2 3/8	3	1 11/16	3	2 3/8	2 31/32				6 7/16	4 3/4	2 31/32							
2 1/2	3	3 5/8	2 1/16	4	3 1/4	4													
3	3 3/8	4 5/16	2 1/2	4 5/8	3 3/8	4 5/8													
4	4 3/16	5 3/4	3 1/8	5 3/4	4 3/16	5 3/4													
3000-Pound W.O.G. Fittings																			
1/8	13/16	29/32	5/8	7/8	31/32	1							1 1/8	19/32		3/4	5/8	3/4	1/2
1/4	31/32	1 1/32	3/4	1 1/32	31/32	1	7/8	1 1/4	1				1 3/8	3/4	1 3/8	3/4	11/16	3/4	11/16
3/8	1 1/8	1 5/16	7/8	1 5/16	1 1/8	1 5/16	1	1 1/2	1 1/4				1 5/8	15/16	1 1/2	7/8	3/4	7/8	3/4
1/2	1 5/16	1 1/2	1	1 1/2	1 5/16	1 1/2	1 1/4	1 5/8	1 1/2	3 9/16	2 9/16	1 1/2	1 7/8	1 1/8	1 7/8	1 1/8	15/16	1 1/8	1 1/4
3/4	1 1/2	1 13/16	1 1/8	1 13/16	1 1/2	1 13/16	1 3/8	1 7/8	1 3/4	4 1/8	3	1 13/16	2 1/8	1 3/8	2	1 3/8	1	1 3/8	1 1/4
1	1 3/4	2 7/32	1 5/16	2 7/32	1 3/4	2 3/16	1 3/4	2 1/4	2	4 13/16	3 1/2	2 3/16	2 3/8	1 3/4	2 3/8	1 3/4	1 3/16	1 3/4	1 1/2
1 1/4	2	2 15/32	1 7/16	2 15/32	2	2 7/16	2	2 5/8	2 7/16	5 3/8	3 15/16	2 7/16	2 7/8	2 1/4	2 5/8	2 1/4	1 5/16	2 1/4	1 5/8
1 1/2	2 3/8	3	1 11/16	3	2 3/8	2 31/32	2 1/8	2 13/16	2 3/4	6 7/16	4 3/4	2 31/32	2 7/8	2 1/2	3 1/8	2 1/2	1 9/16	2 1/2	1 5/8
2	2 1/2	3 9/16	1 23/32	3 5/16	2 1/2	3 5/16	2 1/2	3 5/16	3 5/16				3 3/8	3	3 3/8	3	1 11/16	3	2
2 1/2	3 3/8	4 3/8	2 1/16	4	3 1/4	4							3 5/8	3 5/8	3 5/8	3 5/8	1 13/16	3 5/8	2 3/8
3	3 3/4	4 3/4	2 1/2	4 5/8	3 3/8	4 5/8							4 1/4	4 1/4	4 1/4	4 1/4	2 1/8	4 1/4	2 9/16
3 1/2	4 1/2	6	3 1/8	5 3/4	4 3/16	5 3/4							4 1/2	4 3/4	4 1/2	4 3/4	2 1/4	4 3/4	2 5/8
4	4 1/2	6	3 1/8	5 3/4	4 3/16	5 3/4							4 3/4	5 1/2	4 3/4	5 1/2	2 3/8	5 1/2	2 11/16
5														6 1/2					3 1/16
6														8					3 3/16
6000-Pound W.O.G. Fittings																			
1/8	31/32	1 1/32	3/4	1 1/16	31/32	1							1 1/4	7/8			5/8		3/4
1/4	1 1/8	1 5/16	7/8	1 5/16	1 1/8	1 5/16	1	1 1/2	1 1/4				1 3/8	1	1 3/8	1	11/16	1	
3/8	1 5/16	1 1/2	1	1 1/2	1 5/16	1 1/2	1 1/8	1 5/8	1 1/2	3 9/16	2 9/16	1 1/2	1 1/2	1 1/4	1 1/2	1 1/4	3/4		1 1/4
1/2	1 1/2	1 13/16	1 1/8	1 13/16	1 1/2	1 13/16	1 3/8	1 7/8	1 3/4	4 1/8	3	1 13/16	1 7/8	1 1/2	1 7/8	1 1/2	15/16		1 1/2
3/4	1 3/4	2 7/32	1 5/16	2 7/32	1 3/4	2 3/16	1 3/4	2 1/4	2	4 13/16	3 1/2	2 3/16	2	1 3/4	2	1 3/4	1		1 3/4
1	2	2 15/32	1 7/16	2 15/32	2	2 7/16	2	2 5/8	2 7/16	5 3/8	3 15/16	2 7/16	2 3/8	2 1/4	2 3/8	2 1/4	1 3/16		2 1/4
1 1/4	2 3/8	3	1 11/16	2 31/32	2 3/8	2 31/32	2 1/8	2 13/16	2 3/4	6 7/16	4 3/4	2 31/32	2 5/8	2 1/2	2 5/8	2 1/2	1 5/16		2 1/2
1 1/2	2 1/2	3 9/16	1 23/32	3 5/16	2 1/2	3 5/16	2 1/2	3 5/16	3 5/16				3 1/8	3	3 1/8	3	1 9/16		3
2	3 3/8	4 3/8	2 1/16	4	3 1/4	4							3 3/8	3 5/8	3 3/8	3 5/8	1 11/16		3 5/8
2 1/2	3 3/4	4 3/4	2 1/2	4 5/8	3 3/8	4 5/8							3 5/8	4 1/4	3 5/8	4 1/4	1 13/16		4 1/4
3	4 3/16	5 3/4	3 1/8	5 3/4	4 3/16	5 3/4							4 1/4	5	4 1/4	5	2 1/8		5
3 1/2	4 1/2	6	3 1/8	5 3/4	4 3/16	5 3/4							4 1/2	5 3/4	4 1/2	5 3/4	2 1/4		5 3/4
4													4 3/4	6 1/4	4 3/4	6 1/4	2 3/8		6 1/4

TABLE C.9.7 Forged Steel Socket-Welding Fittings Dimensions, in Inches

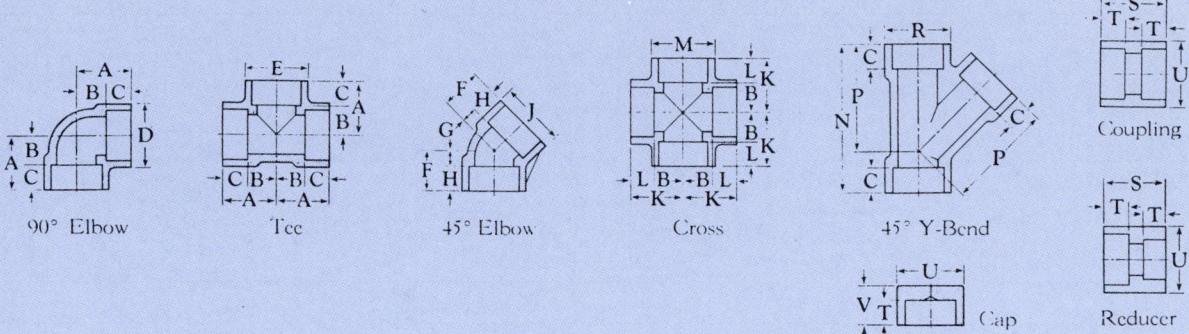

90° Elbow Tee 45° Elbow Cross 45° Y-Bend Coupling Cap Reducer

Dimensions of reducing sizes are the same as those of the straight size corresponding to the largest opening.

Size	A	B	C	D	E	F	G	H	J	K	L	M	N	P	R	S	T	U	V
2000-Pound W.O.G. Fittings, for use with Schedule 40 or Standard Pipe																			
	13/16	7/16	3/8	15/16	7/8	11/16	5/16	3/8	15/16	31/32	17/32	1				1	3/8	3/4	5/8
1/4	13/16	7/16	3/8	29/32	29/32	3/4	5/16	7/16	1 1/32	31/32	17/32	1	2 5/16	1 5/8	13/16	1	3/8	3/4	5/8
3/8	31/32	17/32	7/16	1 1/32	1 1/32	3/4	5/16	7/16	1 1/32	31/32	7/16	1	2 11/16	1 7/8	1	1 1/8	7/16	1	11/16
1/2	1 1/8	5/8	1/2	15/16	15/16	7/8	7/16	7/16	15/16	1 1/8	1/2	15/16	3	2 1/8	1 1/4	1 3/8	1/2	1 1/4	3/4
3/4	1 5/16	3/4	9/16	1 1/2	1 1/2	1	1/2	1/2	1 1/2	1 5/16	9/16	1 1/2	3 9/16	2 9/16	1 1/2	1 1/2	9/16	1 1/2	13/16
1	1 1/2	7/8	5/8	1 13/16	1 13/16	1 1/8	9/16	9/16	1 13/16	1 1/2	5/8	1 13/16	4 1/8	3	1 13/16	1 3/4	5/8	1 3/4	1
1 1/4	1 3/4	1 1/16	11/16	2 7/32	2 7/32	1 5/16	11/16	5/8	2 7/32	1 3/4	11/16	2 3/16	4 13/16	3 1/2	2 3/16	1 7/8	11/16	2 1/4	1 1/16
1 1/2	2	1 1/4	3/4	2 15/32	2 15/32	1 7/16	13/16	5/8	2 15/32	2	3/4	2 7/16	5 3/8	3 15/16	2 7/16	2	3/4	2 1/2	1 3/16
2	2 3/8	1 1/2	7/8	3	3	1 11/16	1	11/16	3	2 3/8	7/8	2 31/32	6 7/16	4 3/4	2 31/32	2 1/2	7/8	3	1 3/8
2 1/2	3	1 5/8	1 3/8	3 5/8	3 5/8	2 1/16	1 1/8	15/16	4	3 1/4	1 5/8	4				2 1/2	7/8	3 5/8	1 1/2
3	3 3/8	2 1/4	1 1/8	4 5/16	4 5/16	2 1/2	1 1/4	1 1/4	4 5/8	3 3/8	1 1/8	4 5/8				2 3/4	1	4 1/8	1 5/8
4	4 3/16	2 5/8	1 9/16	5 3/4	5 3/4	3 1/8	1 5/8	1 1/2	5 3/4	4 3/16	1 9/16	5 3/4				3	1 1/8	5 1/4	1 7/8
3000-Pound W.O.G. Fittings, for use with Schedule 80 or Extra Strong Pipe																			
1/4	13/16	7/16	3/8	29/32	29/32	3/4	5/16	7/16	1 1/32	31/32	17/32	1	2 5/16	1 5/8	13/16	1	3/8	7/8	11/16
3/8	31/32	17/32	7/16	1 1/32	1 1/32	3/4	5/16	7/16	1 1/32	31/32	7/16	1	2 11/16	1 7/8	1	1 1/8	7/16	1	3/4
1/2	1 1/8	5/8	1/2	15/16	15/16	7/8	7/16	7/16	15/16	1 1/8	1/2	15/16	3	2 1/8	1 1/4	1 3/8	1/2	1 1/4	7/8
3/4	1 5/16	3/4	9/16	1 1/2	1 1/2	1	1/2	1/2	1 1/2	1 5/16	9/16	1 1/2	3 9/16	2 9/16	1 1/2	1 1/2	9/16	1 1/2	1
1	1 1/2	7/8	5/8	1 13/16	1 13/16	1 1/8	9/16	9/16	1 13/16	1 1/2	5/8	1 13/16	4 1/8	3	1 13/16	1 3/4	5/8	1 3/4	1 1/16
1 1/4	1 3/4	1 1/16	11/16	2 7/32	2 7/32	1 5/16	11/16	5/8	2 7/32	1 3/4	11/16	2 3/16	4 13/16	3 1/2	2 3/16	1 7/8	11/16	2 1/4	1 3/16
1 1/2	2	1 1/4	3/4	2 15/32	2 15/32	1 7/16	13/16	5/8	2 15/32	2	3/4	2 7/16	5 3/8	3 15/16	2 7/16	2	3/4	2 1/2	1 1/4
2	2 3/8	1 1/2	7/8	3	3	1 11/16	1	11/16	3	2 3/8	7/8	2 31/32	6 7/16	4 3/4	2 31/32	2 1/2	7/8	3	1 1/2
2 1/2	3	1 5/8	1 3/8	3 5/8	3 5/8	2 1/16	1 1/8	15/16	4	3 1/4	1 5/8	4				2 1/2	7/8	3 5/8	1 1/2
3	3 3/8	2 1/4	1 1/8	4 5/16	4 5/16	2 1/2	1 1/4	1 1/4	4 5/8	3 3/8	1 1/8	4 5/8				2 3/4	1	4 1/4	1 3/4
4	4 3/16	2 5/8	1 9/16	5 3/4	5 3/4	3 1/8	1 5/8	1 1/2	5 3/4	4 3/16	1 9/16	5 3/4				3	1 1/8	5 1/2	1 7/8

Continued

TABLE C.9.7 Forged Steel Socket-Welding Fittings Dimensions, in Inches—*Continued*

Size	*A*	*B*	*C*	*D*	*E*	*F*	*G*	*H*	*J*	*K*	*L*	*M*	*N*	*P*	*R*	*S*	*T*	*U*	*V*
4000-Pound W.O.G. Fittings, for use with Schedule 160 Pipe																			
1/2	1 5/16	3/4	9/16	1 1/2	1 1/2	1	1/2	1/2	1 1/2	1 5/16	9/16	1 1/2	3 9/16	2 9/16	1 1/2	1 3/8	1/2	1 1/2	7/8
3/4	1 1/2	7/8	5/8	1 13/16	1 13/16	1 1/8	9/16	9/16	1 13/16	1 1/2	5/8	1 13/16	4 1/8	3	1 13/16	1 1/2	9/16	1 3/4	15/16
1	1 3/4	1 1/16	11/16	2 3/16	2 3/16	1 5/16	11/16	5/8	2 3/16	1 3/4	11/16	2 3/16	4 13/16	3 1/2	2 3/16	1 3/4	5/8	2 1/4	1 1/8
1 1/4	2	1 1/4	3/4	2 7/16	2 7/16	1 11/32	13/16	17/32	2 7/16	2	3/4	2 7/16	5 3/8	3 15/16	2 7/16	1 7/8	11/16	2 1/2	1 3/16
1 1/2	2 3/8	1 1/2	7/8	2 31/32	2 31/32	1 11/16	1	11/16	2 31/32	2 3/8	7/8	2 31/32	6 7/16	4 3/4	2 31/32	2	3/4	3	1 3/8
2	2 1/2	1 5/8	7/8	3 5/16	3 5/16	1 23/32	1 1/8	19/32	3 5/16	2 1/2	7/8	3 5/16				2 1/2	7/8	3 5/8	1 1/2
2 1/2	3 1/4	2 1/4	1	4	4	2 1/16	1 1/4	13/16	4	3 1/4	1	4				2 1/2	7/8	4 1/8	1 5/8
3	3 3/4	2 1/2	1 1/4	4 3/4	4 3/4	2 1/2	1 3/8	1 1/8	4 5/8	3 3/8	7/8	4 5/8				2 3/4	1	4 5/8	1 3/4
4	4 3/16	2 5/8	1 9/16	5 3/4	5 3/4	3 1/8	1 5/8	1 1/2	5 3/4	4 3/16	1 9/16	5 3/4				3	1 1/8	6	2
6000-Pound W.O.G. Fittings, for use with Double Extra Strong Pipe																			
3/8	1 1/8	17/32	19/32	1 5/16	1 5/16	7/8	3/8	1/2	1 5/16	1 1/8	19/32	1 5/16	3	2 1/8	1 1/4	1 1/8	7/16	1 5/16	15/16
1/2	1 5/16	5/8	11/16	1 1/2	1 1/2	1	3/8	5/8	1 1/2	1 5/16	11/16	1 1/2	3 9/16	2 9/16	1 1/2	1 3/8	1/2	1 1/2	1
3/4	1 1/2	3/4	3/4	1 13/16	1 13/16	1 1/8	7/16	11/16	1 13/16	1 1/2	3/4	1 13/16	4 1/8	3	1 13/16	1 1/2	9/16	1 3/4	1 1/16
1	1 3/4	7/8	7/8	2 3/16	2 3/16	1 5/16	1/2	13/16	2 3/16	1 3/4	7/8	2 3/16	4 13/16	3 1/2	2 3/16	1 3/4	5/8	2 1/4	1 1/4
1 1/4	2	1 1/16	15/16	2 7/16	2 7/16	1 11/32	5/8	23/32	2 7/16	2	15/16	2 7/16	5 3/8	3 15/16	2 7/16	1 7/8	11/16	2 1/2	1 5/16
1 1/2	2 3/8	1 1/4	1 1/8	2 31/32	2 31/32	1 11/16	19/32	1 3/32	2 31/32	2 3/8	1 1/8	2 31/32	6 7/16	4 3/4	2 31/32	2	3/4	3	1 3/8
2	2 1/2	1 1/2	1	3 5/16	3 5/16	1 23/32	7/8	27/32	3 5/16	2 1/2	1	3 5/16				2 1/2	7/8	3 5/8	1 5/8
2 1/2	3 1/4	1 3/4	1 1/2	4	4	2 1/16	1	1 1/16	4	3 1/4	1 1/2	4				2 1/2	7/8	4 1/4	1 5/8
3	3 3/4	2 1/8	1 5/8	4 3/4	4 3/4	2 1/2	1 1/4	1 1/4	4 5/8	3 3/8	1 1/4	4 5/8				2 3/4	1	5	1 7/8
4	4 1/2	2 5/8	1 7/8	6	6	3 1/8	1 5/8	1 1/2	5 3/4	4 3/16	1 9/16	5 3/4				3	1 1/8	6 1/4	2 1/8

TABLE C.9.8 150 lb. Flanges

welding neck

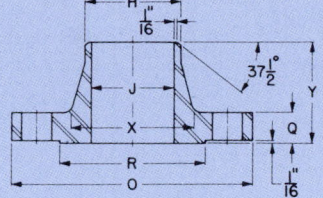

threaded

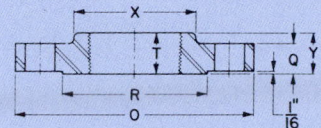

manufacture: ★150 lb flanges are carbon steel furnished to ASTM specifications A 181 grade 1. ASTM A181 is the same as Boiler Construction Code Specification SA181. Flanges furnished faced, drilled, and spot faced or back faced. For standard flange facings, see page wff-85. For ring joint type details, see pages wff-86 to wff-88.

dimensions: All dimensions are in inches and in accordance with ANSI B16.5 where applicable. 22 inch is an interpolated dimension as given in MSS-SP-44. Sizes 26″ to 42″ have same flange drilling dimensions as 125 lb class cast iron flanges, ANSI B16.1. For dimensional tolerances see page wff-81.

pressure-temperature ratings: See page wff-89.

footnotes: ▪Bolt holes are ⅛ inch larger than bolt diameter.

◆Flanges bored to dimensions shown, unless otherwise specified. Dimensions shown correspond to ANSI B36.10 inside diameter of standard wall pipe. The smallest bores to which forgings for these flanges may be machined are listed on page wff-82.

✛ Thread lengths for 150 lb flanges are ANSI for Pipe Threads ANSI B2.1. Add depths or height of facing to thread length.

✛ Lengths of alloy steel and stud bolts include the thickness of two nuts, but do not include height of points.

✛ Length shown does not include thickness of lap. For lapped to lapped, add thickness of both laps; for lapped to ¹⁄₁₆ inch raised face add on thickness of lap; for lapped to any other facing, add amount that such facing and one lap will cause the flanges to be separated.

Nominal Pipe Size	Outside Diam. of Flange O	Thickness of Flange Q (Min.)	Diam. of Raised Face R	Diam. of Hub at Base X	No. of Bolt Holes	Diam. of Bolts▪	Diam. of Bolt Circle	Length of Bolts			Length Thru Hub		
								Stud		Machine	Welding Neck Y	Slip-On, Th'rd, Socket Y	Lap Joint Y
								¹⁄₁₆″ raised face	ring joint	¹⁄₁₆″ raised face			
½	3½	⁷⁄₁₆	1⅜	1³⁄₁₆	4	½	2⅜	2¼	—	1¾	1⅞	⅝	⅝
¾	3⅞	½	1¹¹⁄₁₆	1½	4	½	2¾	2¼	—	2	2¹⁄₁₆	⅝	⅝
1	4¼	⁹⁄₁₆	2	1¹⁵⁄₁₆	4	½	3⅛	2½	3	2	2³⁄₁₆	¹¹⁄₁₆	¹¹⁄₁₆
1¼	4⅝	⅝	2½	2⁵⁄₁₆	4	½	3½	2½	3	2¼	2¼	¹³⁄₁₆	¹³⁄₁₆
1½	5	¹¹⁄₁₆	2⅞	2⁹⁄₁₆	4	½	3⅞	2¾	3¼	2¼	2⁷⁄₁₆	⅞	⅞
2	6	¾	3⅝	3⁷⁄₁₆	4	⅝	4¾	3	3½	2¾	2½	1	1
2½	7	⅞	4⅛	3⁹⁄₁₆	4	⅝	5½	3¼	3¾	3	2¾	1⅛	1⅛
3	7½	¹⁵⁄₁₆	5	4¼	4	⅝	6	3½	4	3	2¾	1³⁄₁₆	1³⁄₁₆
3½	8½	¹⁵⁄₁₆	5½	4¹³⁄₁₆	8	⅝	7	3½	4	3	2¹³⁄₁₆	1¼	1¼
4	9	¹⁵⁄₁₆	6³⁄₁₆	5⁵⁄₁₆	8	⅝	7½	3½	4	3	3	1⁵⁄₁₆	1⁵⁄₁₆
5	10	¹⁵⁄₁₆	7⁵⁄₁₆	6⁷⁄₁₆	8	¾	8½	3¾	4¼	3¼	3½	1⁷⁄₁₆	1⁷⁄₁₆
6	11	1	8½	7⁹⁄₁₆	8	¾	9½	3¾	4¼	3¼	3½	1⁹⁄₁₆	1⁹⁄₁₆
8	13½	1⅛	10⅝	9¹¹⁄₁₆	8	¾	11¾	4	4½	3½	4	1¾	1¾
10	16	1³⁄₁₆	12¾	12	12	⅞	14¼	4½	5	3¾	4	1¹⁵⁄₁₆	1¹⁵⁄₁₆
12	19	1¼	15	14⅜	12	⅞	17	4½	5	4	4½	2³⁄₁₆	2³⁄₁₆
14	21	1⅜	16¼	15¾	12	1	18¾	5	5½	4¼	5	2¼	3⅛
16	23½	1⁷⁄₁₆	18½	18	16	1	21¼	5¼	5¾	4½	5	2½	3⁷⁄₁₆
18	25	1⁹⁄₁₆	21	19⅞	16	1⅛	22¾	5¾	6¼	4¾	5½	2¹¹⁄₁₆	3¹³⁄₁₆
20	27½	1¹¹⁄₁₆	23	22	20	1⅛	25	6	6½	5¼	5¹¹⁄₁₆	2⅞	4¹⁄₁₆
22	29½	1¹³⁄₁₆	25¼	24	20	1¼	27¼	6½	7	5½	5⅞	3⅛	4¼
24	32	1⅞	27¼	26⅛	20	1¼	29½	6¾	7¼	5¾	6	3¼	4⅜

Continued

TABLE C.9.8   150 lb. Flanges—*Continued*

Nominal Pipe Size	Outside Diam. of Flange O	Thickness of Flange Q (Min.)	Diam. of Raised Face R	Diam. of Hub at Base X	No. of Bolt Holes	Diam. of Bolts	Diam. of Bolt Circle	Length of Bolts			Length Thru Hub		
								Stud		Machine	Welding Neck Y	Slip-On, Th'rd, Socket Y	Lap Joint Y
								1/16" raised face	ring joint	1/16" raised face			
26	34¼	2	29¼	28½	24	1¼	31¾	7	—	6	5	3⅜	—
28	36½	2 1/16	31¼	30¾	28	1¼	34	7	—	6	5 1/16	3 7/16	—
30	38¾	2⅛	33¾	32¾	28	1¼	36	7¼	—	6¼	5⅛	3½	—
32	41¾	2¼	35¾	35	28	1½	38½	8	—	6¾	5¼	3⅝	—
34	43¾	2 5/16	37¾	37	32	1½	40½	8	—	7	5 5/16	3 11/16	—
36	46	2⅜	40¼	39¼	32	1½	42¾	8¼	—	7	5⅜	3¾	—
42	53	2⅝	47	46	36	1½	49½	8¾	—	7½	5⅜	4	—

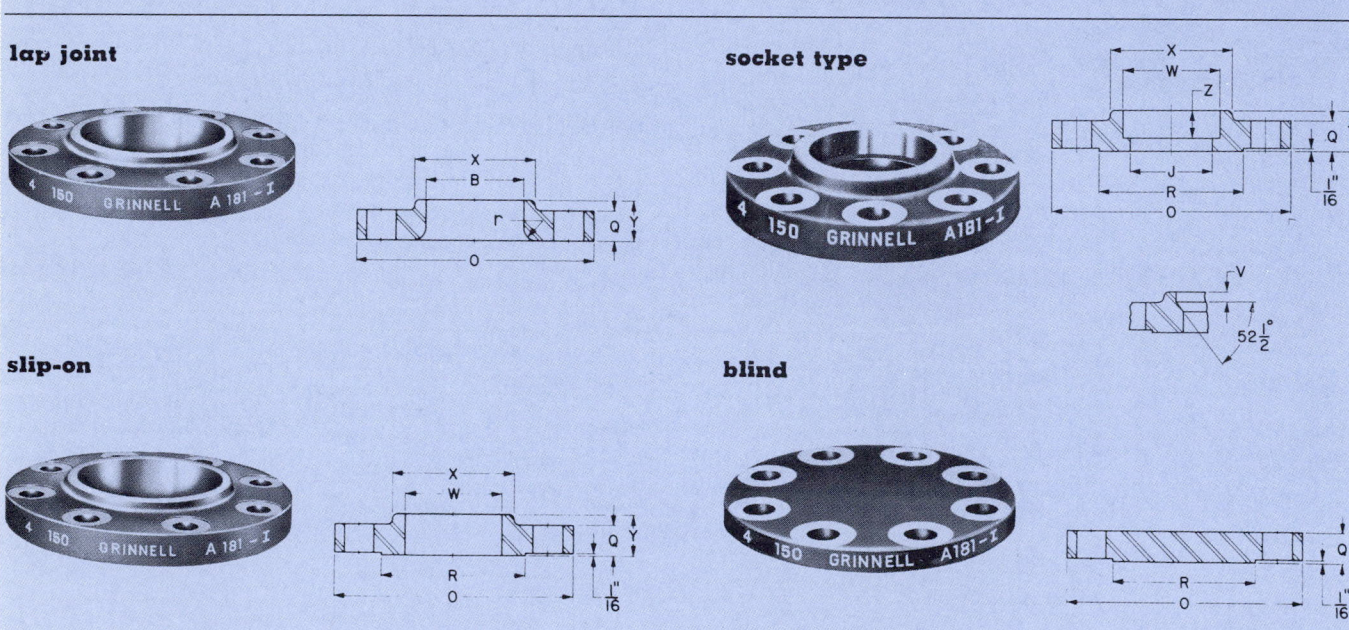

lap joint

socket type

slip-on

blind

Nominal Pipe Size	Diameter of Bore			Minimum Thread Length T	Diam. of Hub at Point of Welding H	Radius R	Depth of Socket Z	Depth of Socket V	Weight (Approx.) Lb				
	Lap Joint B	Slip-On, Socket W	Welding Neck, Socket J						Welding Neck	Slip-On and Threaded	Lap Joint	Blind	Socket
½	.90	.88	.62	⅝	.84	⅛	⅜	3/16	2	2	2	2	2
¾	1.11	1.09	.82	⅝	1.05	⅛	7/16	⅛	2	2	2	2	2
1	1.38	1.36	1.05	11/16	1.32	⅛	½	1/18	2½	2	2	2	2
1¼	1.72	1.70	1.38	13/16	1.66	3/16	9/16	3/16	2½	3	3	3	3
1½	1.97	1.95	1.61	⅞	1.90	¼	⅝	3/16	4	3	3	3	3
2	2.46	2.44	2.07	1	2.38	5/16	11/16	¼	6	5	5	4	5
2½	2.97	2.94	2.47	1⅛	2.88	5/16	¾	¼	10	7	7	7	7
3	3.60	3.57	3.07	1 3/16	3.50	⅜	13/16	¼	11¼	8	8	9	8
3½	4.10	4.07	3.55	1¼	4.00	⅜	⅞	5/16	12	11	11	13	11
4	4.60	4.57	4.03	1 5/16	4.50	7/16	15/16	⅜	15	13	13	17	13
5	5.69	5.66	5.05	1 7/16	5.56	7/16	15/16	½	19	15	15	20	15
6	6.75	6.72	6.07	1 9/16	6.63	½	1 1/16	9/16	24	19	19	26	19

Continued

Nominal Pipe Size	Diameter of Bore			Minimum Thread Length T	Diam. of Hub at Point of Welding H	Radius R	Depth of Socket Z	Depth of Socket V	Weight (Approx.) Lb				
	Lap Joint B	Slip-On, Socket W	Welding Neck, Socket J◆						Welding Neck	Slip-On and Threaded	Lap Joint	Blind	Socket
8	8.75	8.72	7.98	1¾	8.63	½	1¼	⅝	39	30	30	45	30
10	10.92	10.88	10.02	1¹⁵⁄₁₆	10.75	½	1⁵⁄₁₆	¾	52	43	43	70	43
12	12.92	12.88	12.00	2³⁄₁₆	12.75	½	1⁹⁄₁₆	¹⁵⁄₁₆	80	64	64	110	64
14	14.18	14.14	13.25	2¼	14.00	½	1⅝	⅞	120	85	99	131	85
16	16.19	16.16	15.25	2½	16.00	½	1¾	1¹⁄₁₆	127	93	128	170	93
18	18.20	18.18	17.25	2¹¹⁄₁₆	18.00	½	1¹⁵⁄₁₆	1⅛	140	120	146	209	120
20	20.25	20.20	19.25	2⅞	20.00	½	2⅛	1³⁄₁₆	170	155	185	272	155
22	22.25	22.22	21.25	3⅛	22.00	½	2⅜	—	224	159	245	333	185
24	24.25	24.25	23.25	3¼	24.00	½	2½	1⅜	260	210	260	411	210
26	—	26.25	as specified by purchaser	—	26.00	—	—	—	300	250	—	525	—
28	—	28.25		—	28.00	—	—	—	315	285	—	620	—
30	—	30.25		—	30.00	—	—	—	360	315	—	720	—
32	—	32.25		—	32.00	—	—	—	435	395	—	870	—
34	—	34.25		—	34.00	—	—	—	465	420	—	990	—
36	—	36.25		—	36.00	—	—	—	520	480	—	1125	—
42	—	42.25		—	42.00	—	—	—	750	680	—	1625	—

150. LB. CAST STEEL SWING CHECK VALVES

BOLTED CAP

For Pressure-Temperature Ratings, See Page 210

Fig. 1572, Flanged Ends

Fig. 1573, Butt-Weld Ends

Lunkenheimer 150 lb. Steel Swing Check Valves are exceptionally sturdy and have many quality features usually found only in valves with higher pressure-temperature ratings.

See page 224 for complete description.

Design—The body and cap are made with heavy metal sections to assure safe, dependable service. Streamlined flow areas reduce turbulence and pressure drop. The valve may be used in either a horizontal line, or in a vertical line to prevent downward flow. For vertical line installations, a stop-lug in the body prevents cocking of the disc in the open position.

Materials—The carbon steel used in these valves has

been selected to provide good casting properties, mechanical strength and safe weldability.

Castings are made by the electric furnace process using modern foundry equipment.

Body-Cap Connections are male-female joints with profile corrugated gaskets. Bolting consists of through-studs with a nut on each end.

Disc Assembly—The disc is fastened securely to the disc carrier by *a locknut*. Wear is eliminated on the disc as it is designed to swivel free.

Seat Rings are rectangular bottom seating construction to resist distortion. This also assures a tight seat ring joint. Seat rings are available in various trims.

DIMENSIONS, IN INCHES AND WEIGHTS, IN POUNDS

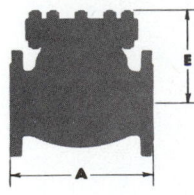

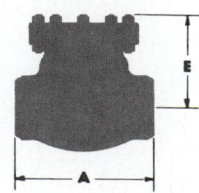

Size	1½	2	2½	3	3½	4	5	6	8	10	12
A	6½	8	8½	9½	10½	11½	13	14	19½	24½	27½
E	4⅝	5¹¹⁄₁₆	6⅛	6⅝	7⅛	7½	8¹¹⁄₁₆	9⅜	11⅛	13¹¹⁄₁₆	15¼
Fig. 1572, Wts.	20	38	44	63	70	92	120	162	304	793	—
Fig. 1573, Wts.	16	30	35	51	56	74	96	130	240	632	

"KING-CLIP" GATE VALVES

IRON BODY BRONZE MOUNTED OR ALL-IRON

Screwed ¼ to 2 in., 150 LB. S.P. 450°F. — 225 LB. W.O.G.

Screwed 2½ to 4 in., 125 LB., S.P. 450°F. — 175 LB. W.O.G.

Flanged 1 to 4 in., 125 LB. S.P. 450°F. — 175 LB. W.O.G.

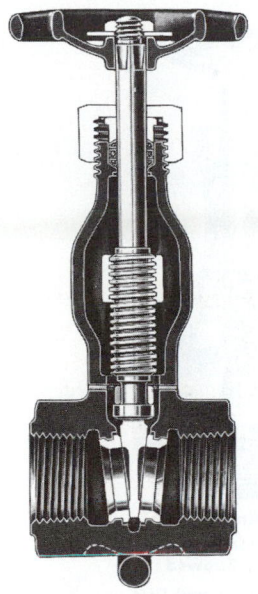

Bronze Mounted "Stemalloy" Stem Fig. 1640

Flanged I.B.B.M., Fig. 1641 All-Iron, Fig. 1645

Screwed OS&Y I.B.B.M., Fig. 1681 All-Iron, Fig 1683

Flanged, OS&Y I.B.B.M., Fig. 1682 All-Iron, Fig. 1684

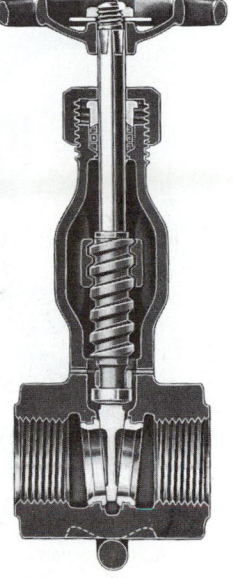

All-Iron Steel Stem Fig. 1644

The "King-clip" Gate Valve is the modern version of the clip valve developed and patented by Lunkenheimer years ago. It is rugged, exceptionally rigid, and can be readily disassembled by removing the two U-bolt nuts. It is built to do rough jobs where lighter valves fail.

Bronze Mounted valves are for general service on steam, water, gas, air, oil, and gasoline lines. Seat rings, discs, and bonnet bushings are bronze.

Stems are "Stemalloy," a bronze alloy highly resistant to stem thread wear.

Drain Channels, of ample size, provide for bonnet drainage—preventing damage to that part by freezing of trapped water.

All-Iron Valves handle solutions which attack bronze but not iron. Seats are integral in 2½ inch and larger sizes, tubular steel in smaller sizes. Discs are iron in larger sizes, forged steel in 1½ inch and smaller sizes.

Bodies and Bonnets are of close grained Lunkenheimer Cast Iron (A.S.T.M. A-126), more corrosion resistant than the average cast iron. See page 45.

Stems are steel which are chemically treated with phosphate to inhibit rust, with coarse loose fittings threads—to prevent seizing due to corrosive action.

Drain Channels in bonnet are for the purpose of clearing space above stem threads of media when draining pipe lines.

DIMENSIONS, IN INCHES

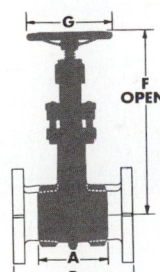

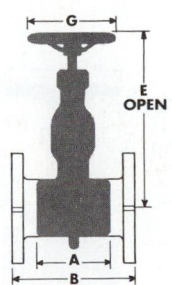

Size (inches)	¼	⅜	½	¾	1	1¼	1½	2	2½	3	4
A	1⅞	2 1/16	2¼	2⅝	2 15/16	3 5/16	3 7/16	4 1/16	4⅝	4 15/16	6 13/16
B	—	—	—	—	3 3/16	3½	6	7	7½	8	9
E	4⅞	4⅞	5⅝	6 13/16	7 15/16	8 15/16	10 5/16	12¾	15¼	17⅞	24 1/16
F	—	—	6¾	7 11/16	8 11/16	9½	11	13½	15 15/16	18⅝	—
G	2½	2½	2½	3	3½	4⅛	4⅝	5⅛	5½	7	8

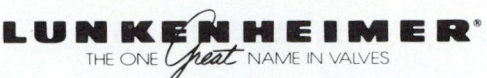

LUNKENHEIMER®
THE ONE *Great* NAME IN VALVES

300 LB. BRONZE "RENEWO" GLOBE VALVE
350 LB. BRONZE "RENEWO" ANGLE VALVE

Globe Screwed: 300 LB. S.P. 550°F. — 600 LB. W.O.G.
Angle Screwed: 350 LB. S.P. 550°F. — 1000 LB. W.O.G.

RENEWABLE REGULAR AND PLUG TYPE SEAT AND DISC

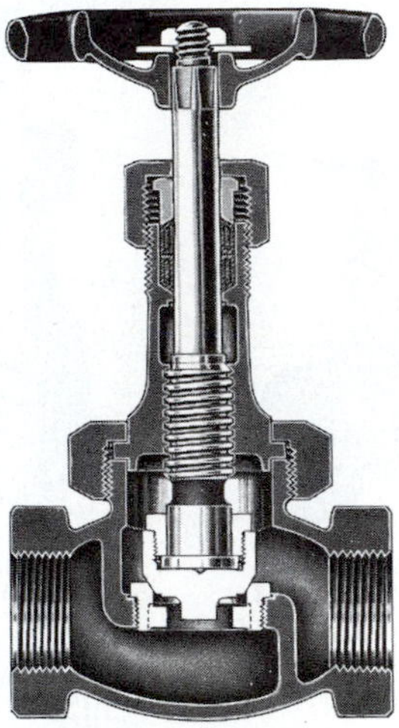

Globe
Regular Type Seat and Disc
"NT4" Nickel Alloy
Union Bonnet
Fig. 16, Screwed

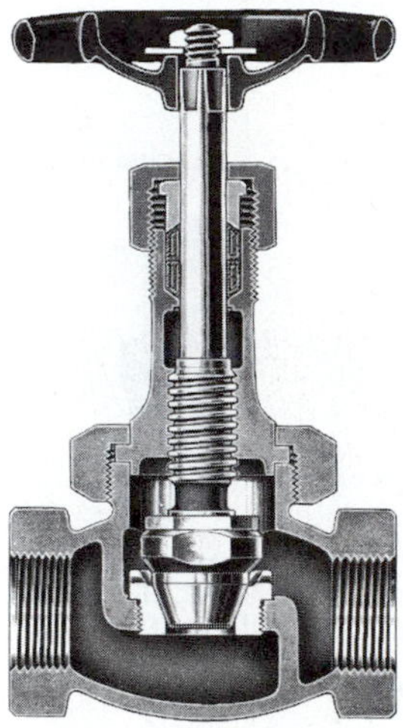

Globe
Plug Type Seat and Disc
500 Brinell Stainless Steel
Union Bonnet
Fig. 16-PS, Screwed

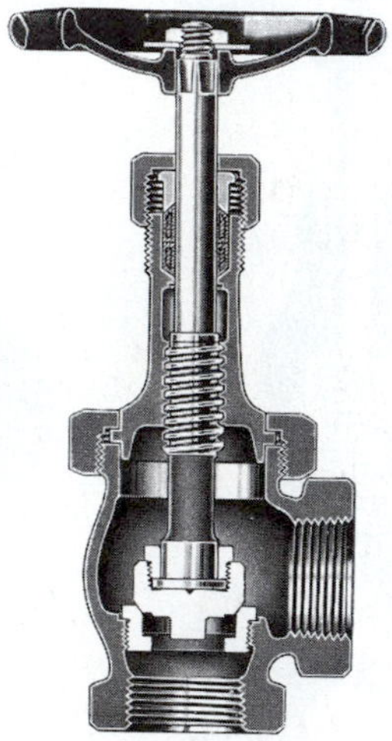

Angle
Regular Type Seat and Disc
Fig. 17, Screwed
Plug Type Seat and Disc
Fig. 17-PS, Screwed

Lunkenheimer 300 and 350 lb. "Renewo" globe and angle valves offer two distinct types of Seat-Disc combination.

Plug Type 500 Brinell Stainless Steel Seats and Discs—recommended for service demanding high resistance to destructive action on seat bearings. Valves are recommended for throttling, drain, drip, water column blow down and other severe services. Stainless Steel, heat treated to extreme hardness affords maximum resistance to severe erosive service.

Regular Type "NT4" Seats and Discs—Economical for numerous general service installations, including steam, water, oil and gas lines. For use where full flow is desired. "NT4" Nickel Alloy seating material is hard and resists wear.

Bodies and Bonnets are of Lunkenheimer S-1 Steam Bronze (A.S.T.M. B61).

Renewability—As the name "Renewo" implies, all parts including the seats and discs are renewable and interchangeable.

Handwheels are malleable iron, "Non Slip" design.

Stems of "Stemalloy" provide maximum resistance to thread wear, corrosion, and embrittlement.

Repacking is easily done while valve is wide open under pressure. Stuffing boxes are deep for extra packing. Hexagon head gland provides wrench hold to loosen gland without prying.

Wrenches for removing and inserting seat rings are shown on page 201

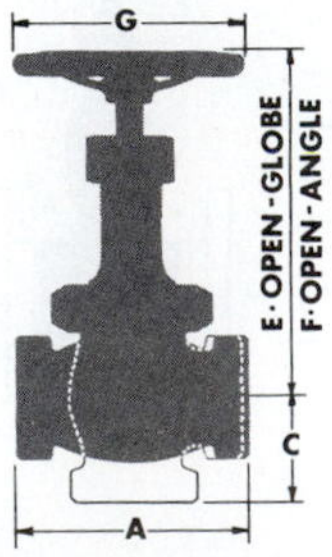

DIMENSIONS, IN INCHES AND WEIGHTS, IN POUNDS

Size	¼	⅜	½	¾	1	1¼	1½	2	2½	3
A	2 5/16	2½	2⅞	3 17/32	4⅛	4 23/32	5¼	6⅜	7⅜	8⅜
C	1 3/32	1 5/32	1⅜	1⅝	1 29/32	2 7/32	2 7/16	3	3 19/32	4⅛
E	4⅝	4⅝	5 3/16	6⅛	6⅞	7 13/16	8⅜	9½	11⅛	12 11/16
F	4⅝	4⅝	5 3/16	6⅛	6⅞	7 13/16	8⅜	9½	11⅛	12 11/16
G	2½	2½	3	3½	4⅛	4⅝	5⅛	5½	8	10
Fig. 16 Wt.	1.2	1.3	2.0	3.4	5.2	7.3	10.0	17.0	30.0	43.0
Fig. 16 PS Wt.	1.2	1.4	2.0	3.4	5.2	7.3	10.0	17.0	30.0	43.0
Fig. 17 Wt.	1.2	1.3	1.9	3.2	5.0	7.0	9.2	15.0	28.0	—
Fig. 17 PS Wt.	1.2	1.3	1.9	3.2	4.8	7.2	9.3	16.0	26.0	—

150 LB. CAST STEEL GLOBE AND ANGLE VALVES

BOLTED BONNET

For Pressure-Temperature Ratings, See Page 210

**Globe, Flanged Ends
Fig. 1542, Plug Disc**

**Angle, Flanged Ends
Fig. 1552, Spherical Disc**

**Globe, Butt-Weld Ends
Fig. 1543, Plug Disc**

**Angle, Butt-Weld Ends
Fig. 1563, Plug Disc**

**Globe, Flanged Ends
Fig. 1532, Spherical Disc**

**Angle, Flanged Ends
Fig. 1562, Plug Disc**

Lunkenheimer 150 lb. Steel Globe and Angle Valves have many quality features usually found only in valves with higher-pressure temperature ratings. See page 218 for complete description.

Bonnet Joints are self centering male-female type connections. Bonnet bolting consists of through studs with nut on each end.

Discs are furnished in full-way design. In the 150 and 300 lb. pressure classes, a long swivel nut coupled with small clearances between the swivel nut and stem is utilized to accurately guide the disc to its seat. Trim "U" full-way valves are similarly guided. *Seats* are shoulder seated and threaded.

Stem is heavy acme threads with liberal thread engagement with the yoke bushing, assuring long life of these parts.

Materials of bodies and bonnets are heavy shell-thickness to afford maximum safety. Long tapered fillets eliminate danger of casting defects at critical points.

Design. Available with either spherical or plug type discs. Adjustable to a wide variety of service requirements.

For material specifications, modifications and accessories, see page 218.

Note: Face-to-face dimension of flanged valves include 1/16-inch raised faces.
Drilling Templates and Flange Dimensions.................. page 304.
Butt Welding end valves same dimensions as flanged end.

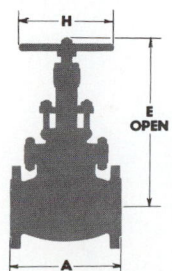

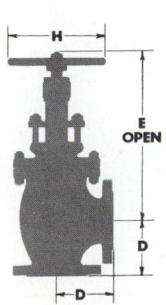

DIMENSIONS, IN INCHES AND WEIGHTS, IN POUNDS

Size	2	2½	3	3½	4	5	6	8
A	8	8½	9½	10½	11½	14	16	19½
D	4	4½	4¾	5¼	5¾	7	8	9¾
E	13¹³/₁₆	14⁹/₁₆	16²³/₃₂	17¹³/₃₂	20¹/₃₂	22½	23¹⁵/₁₆	27¹³/₁₆
H	8	8	9	9	10	12	12	16
Fig. 1532, 1542, Wts.	48	62	83	98	120	169	210	352
Fig. 1543, Wts.	37	50	66	78	103	146	191	280
Fig. 1552, 1562, Wts.	46	61	77	97	120	168	210	338
Fig. 1563, Wts.	37	50	62	77	96	132	168	267

Standard Sheet Metal Gauges

Gauge	Thickness		Wt. Per Sq. Ft.		Gauge
10	.1406 in.	3.571 mm	5.625 lbs	2.551 kg	10
11	.1250 in.	3.175 mm	5.000 lbs	2.267 kg	11
12	.1094 in.	2.778 mm	4.375 lbs	1.984 kg	12
13	.0938 in.	2.383 mm	3.750 lbs	1.700 kg	13
14	.0781 in.	1.983 mm	3.125 lbs	1.417 kg	14
15	.0703 in.	1.786 mm	2.813 lbs	1.276 kg	15
16	.0625 in.	1.588 mm	2.510 lbs	1.134 kg	16
17	.0563 in.	1.430 mm	2.250 lbs	1.021 kg	17
18	.0500 in.	1.270 mm	2.000 lbs	0.907 kg	18
19	.0438 in.	1.111 mm	1.750 lbs	0.794 kg	19
20	.0375 in.	0.953 mm	1.500 lbs	0.680 kg	20
21	.0344 in.	0.877 mm	1.375 lbs	0.624 kg	21
22	.0313 in.	0.795 mm	1.250 lbs	0.567 kg	22
23	.0280 in.	0.714 mm	1.125 lbs	0.510 kg	23
24	.0250 in.	0.635 mm	1.000 lbs	0.454 kg	24
25	.0219 in.	0.556 mm	0.875 lbs	0.397 kg	25
26	.0188 in.	0.478 mm	0.750 lbs	0.340 kg	26
27	.0172 in.	0.437 mm	0.687 lbs	0.312 kg	27
28	.0156 in.	0.396 mm	0.625 lbs	0.283 kg	28
29	.0141 in.	0.358 mm	0.563 lbs	0.255 kg	29
30	.0120 in.	0.318 mm	0.500 lbs	0.227 kg	30

Structural Shapes and Sizes

Structural Steel Shapes

Structural steel shapes are manufactured in a wide variety of shapes, sizes and weights per linear foot. Steel mills roll these sections in six basic steel materials. The following are most common materials.

American Standard Beams (S) Generally called I-beams because of their resemblance to that capital letter. Used as columns and struts.

American Standard Channels (C) Used as struts and in trusses when light loadings are required. They are often used for steel platforming load-bearing members.

Wide-Flange Shapes (W) Used as both beams and columns and are furnished with constant thickness flanges.

Miscellaneous Shapes (M) Similar in shape to W shapes.

Structural Tees (WT, MT, and ST) Made by splitting S, W, and M shapes, usually at mid-distance of their webs. Most structural steel fabricators order S, W, and M shapes and cut the webs themselves to form Tees.

Angles (L) Used for struts, platforms, to add framing strength and for many other items. They have two legs set at right angles to each other. These legs may be equal or unequal widths.

Flat Bars (Bar) Have a rectangular cross section, and are rolled in many widths and thicknesses, but widths are normally limited to 6″ or 8″ depending on the thickness. If wider bars are needed a sheet of plate is cut to form it.

Plate (PL or PL) Rectangular in cross section and comes in varied widths and thicknesses, but in larger pieces than bars. Plate widths start at 10″ and are rolled up to 200″ wide depending on thickness. Lengths are as long as shipping will allow.

Common Structural Steel Shapes Used on Pipe Supports

TYPE OF COMPONENT

GRAPHIC REPRESENTATION

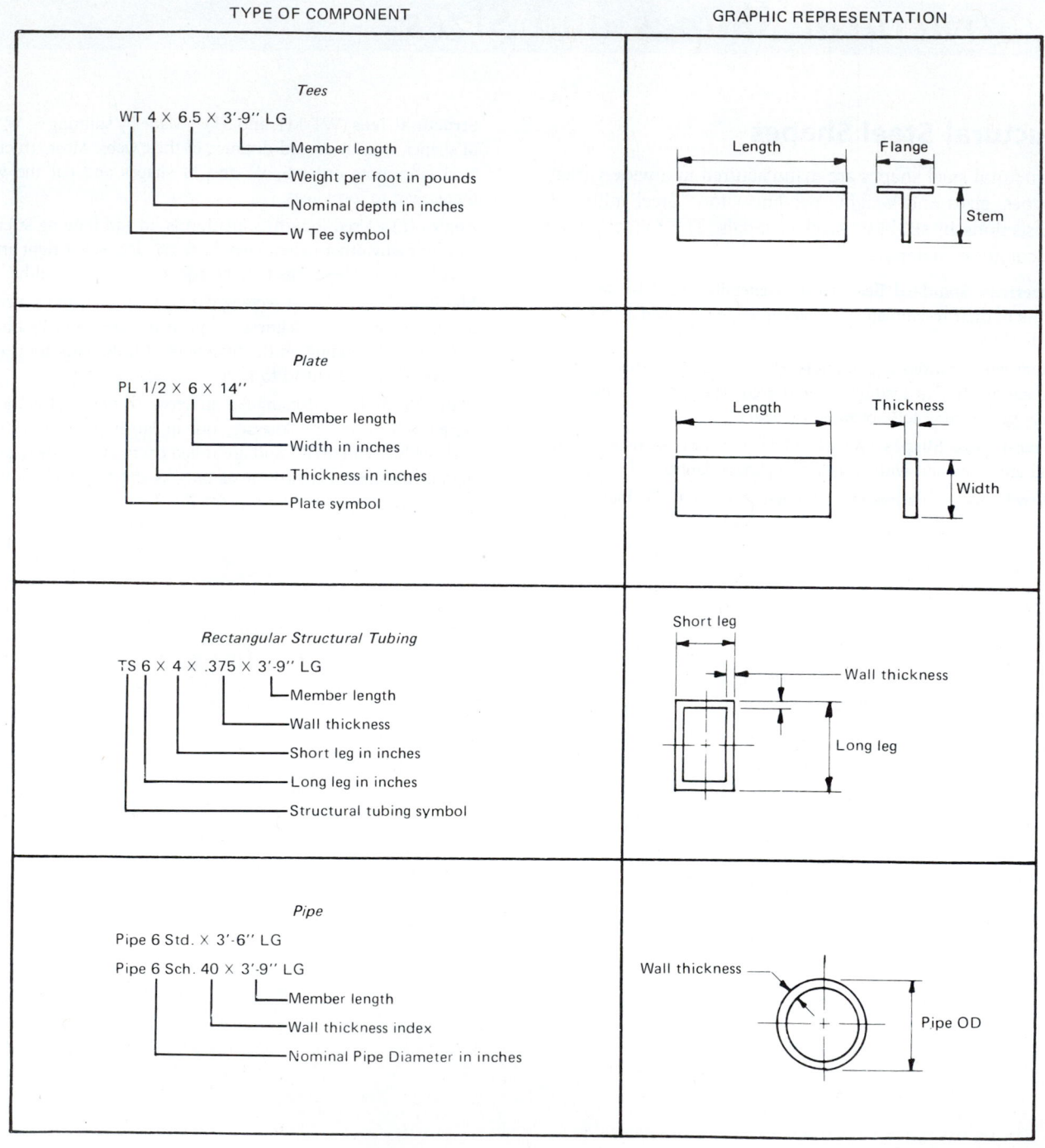

Tees

WT 4 × 6.5 × 3'-9" LG

— Member length
— Weight per foot in pounds
— Nominal depth in inches
— W Tee symbol

Length   Flange   Stem

Plate

PL 1/2 × 6 × 14"

— Member length
— Width in inches
— Thickness in inches
— Plate symbol

Length   Thickness   Width

Rectangular Structural Tubing

TS 6 × 4 × .375 × 3'-9" LG

— Member length
— Wall thickness
— Short leg in inches
— Long leg in inches
— Structural tubing symbol

Short leg   Wall thickness   Long leg

Pipe

Pipe 6 Std. × 3'-6" LG
Pipe 6 Sch. 40 × 3'-9" LG

— Member length
— Wall thickness index
— Nominal Pipe Diameter in inches

Wall thickness   Pipe OD

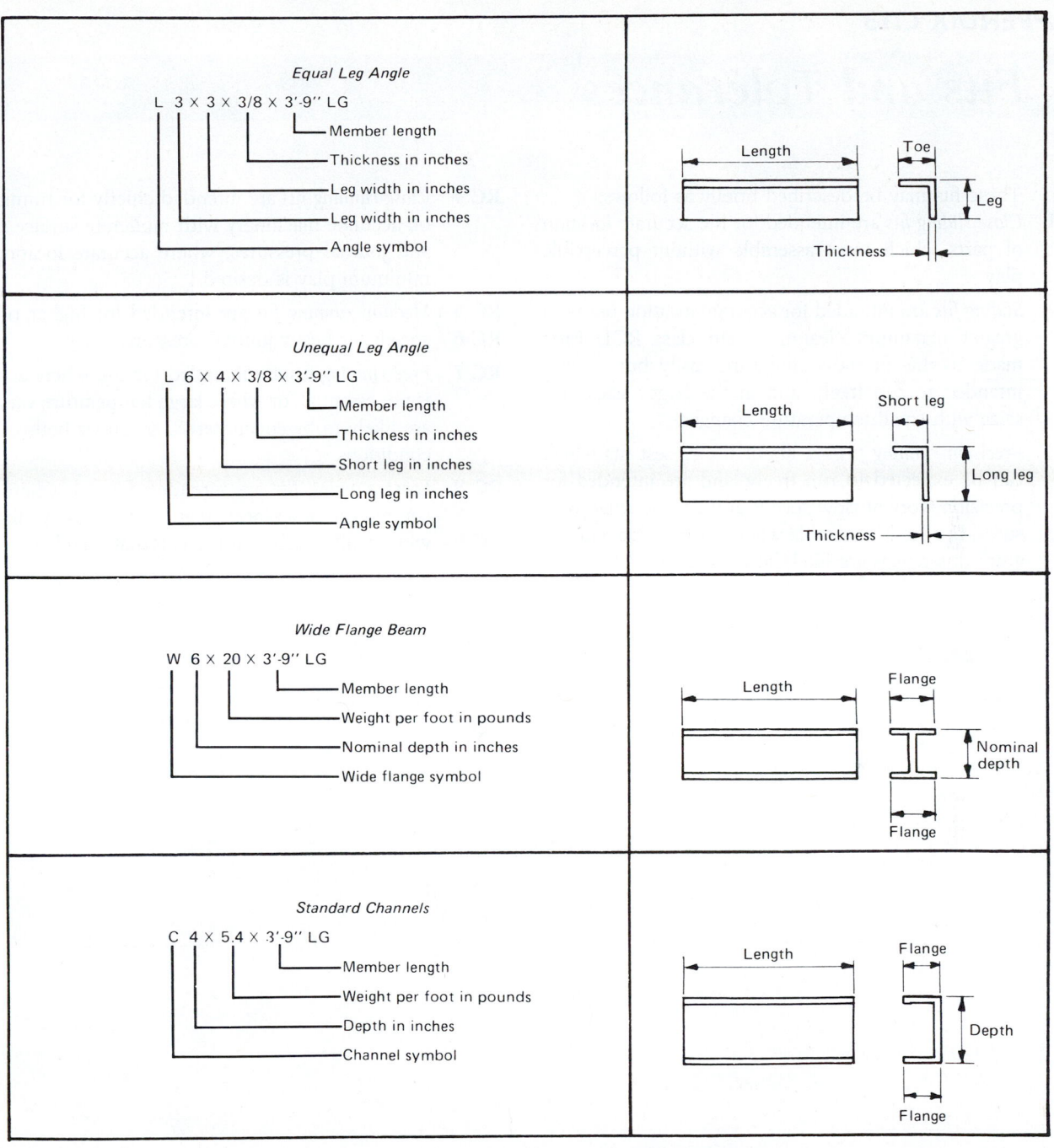

Equal Leg Angle

L 3 × 3 × 3/8 × 3'-9'' LG
- Member length
- Thickness in inches
- Leg width in inches
- Leg width in inches
- Angle symbol

Length Toe Leg Thickness

Unequal Leg Angle

L 6 × 4 × 3/8 × 3'-9'' LG
- Member length
- Thickness in inches
- Short leg in inches
- Long leg in inches
- Angle symbol

Length Short leg Long leg Thickness

Wide Flange Beam

W 6 × 20 × 3'-9'' LG
- Member length
- Weight per foot in pounds
- Nominal depth in inches
- Wide flange symbol

Length Flange Nominal depth Flange

Standard Channels

C 4 × 5.4 × 3'-9'' LG
- Member length
- Weight per foot in pounds
- Depth in inches
- Channel symbol

Length Flange Depth Flange

Fits and Tolerances

These fits may be described briefly as follows:

RC 1 *Close sliding fits* are intended for the accurate location of parts which must assemble without perceptible play.

RC 2 *Sliding fits* are intended for accurate location but with greater maximum clearance than class RC1. Parts made to this fit move and turn easily but are not intended to run freely, and in the larger sizes may seize with small temperature changes.

RC 3 *Precision running fits* are about the closest fits which can be expected to run freely, and are intended for precision work at slow speeds and light journal pressures, but are not suitable where appreciable temperature differences are likely to be encountered.

RC 4 *Close running fits* are intended chiefly for running fits on accurate machinery with moderate surface speeds and journal pressures, where accurate location and minimum play is desired.

RC 5 *Medium running fits* are intended for higher running
RC 6 speeds, or heavy journal pressures, or both.

RC 7 *Free running fits* are intended for use where accuracy is not essential, or where large temperature variations are likely to be encountered, or under both of these conditions.

RC 8 *Loose running fits* are intended for use where wide
RC 9 commercial tolerances may be necessary, together with an allowance, on the external member.

TABLE C.13.1 Running and Sliding Fits

Limits are in thousandths of an inch. Limits for hole and shaft are applied algebraically to the basic size to obtain the limits of size for the parts. Date in bold face are in accordance with ABC agreements. Symbols H5, g5, etc., are Hole and Shaft designations used in ABC System.

Nominal Size Range Inches Over — To	Class RC 1 Limits of Clearance	Class RC 1 Standard Limits Hole H5	Class RC 1 Standard Limits Shaft g4	Class RC 2 Limits of Clearance	Class RC 2 Standard Limits Hole H6	Class RC 2 Standard Limits Shaft g5	Class RC 3 Limits of Clearance	Class RC 3 Standard Limits Hole H7	Class RC 3 Standard Limits Shaft f6	Class RC 4 Limits of Clearance	Class RC 4 Standard Limits Hole H8	Class RC 4 Standard Limits Shaft f7
0 — 0.12	0.1 0.45	+0.2 0	−0.1 −0.25	0.1 0.55	+0.25 0	−0.1 −0.3	0.3 0.95	+0.4 0	−0.3 −0.55	0.3 1.3	+0.6 0	−0.3 −0.7
0.12 — 0.24	0.15 0.5	+0.2 0	−0.15 −0.3	0.15 0.65	+0.3 0	−0.15 −0.35	0.4 1.12	+0.5 0	−0.4 −0.7	0.4 1.6	+0.7 0	−0.4 −0.9
0.24 — 0.40	0.2 0.6	0.25 0	−0.2 −0.35	0.2 0.85	+0.4 0	−0.2 −0.45	0.5 1.5	+0.6 0	−0.5 −0.9	0.5 2.0	+0.9 0	−0.5 −1.1
0.40 — 0.71	0.25 0.75	+0.3 0	−0.25 −0.45	0.25 0.95	+0.4 0	−0.25 −0.55	0.6 1.7	+0.7 0	−0.6 −1.0	0.6 2.3	+1.0 0	−0.6 −1.3
0.71 — 1.19	0.3 0.95	+0.4 0	−0.3 −0.55	0.3 1.2	+0.5 0	−0.3 −0.7	0.8 2.1	+0.8 0	−0.8 −1.3	0.8 2.8	+1.2 0	−0.8 −1.6
1.19 — 1.97	0.4 1.1	+0.4 0	−0.4 −0.7	0.4 1.4	+0.6 0	−0.4 −0.8	1.0 2.6	+1.0 0	−1.0 −1.6	1.0 3.6	+1.6 0	−1.0 −2.0
1.97 — 3.15	0.4 1.2	+0.5 0	−0.4 −0.7	0.4 1.6	+0.7 0	−0.4 −0.9	1.2 3.1	+1.2 0	−1.2 −1.9	1.2 4.2	+1.8 0	−1.2 −2.4
3.15 — 4.73	0.5 1.5	+0.6 0	−0.5 −0.9	0.5 2.0	+0.9 0	−0.5 −1.1	1.4 3.7	+1.4 0	−1.4 −2.3	1.4 5.0	+2.2 0	−1.4 −2.8
4.73 — 7.09	0.6 1.8	+0.7 0	−0.6 −1.1	0.6 2.3	+1.0 0	−0.6 −1.3	1.6 4.2	+1.6 0	−1.6 −2.6	1.6 5.7	+2.5 0	−1.6 −3.2
7.09 — 9.85	0.6 2.0	+0.8 0	−0.6 −1.2	0.6 2.6	+1.2 0	−0.6 −1.4	2.0 5.0	+1.8 0	−2.0 −3.2	2.0 6.6	+2.8 0	−2.0 −3.8
9.85 — 12.41	0.8 2.3	+0.9 0	−0.8 −1.4	0.8 2.9	+1.2 0	−0.8 −1.7	2.5 5.7	+2.0 0	−2.5 −3.7	2.5 7.5	+3.0 0	−2.5 −4.5
12.41 — 15.75	1.0 2.7	+1.0 0	−1.0 −1.7	1.0 3.4	+1.4 0	−1.0 −2.0	3.0 6.6	+ 0	−3.0 −4.4	3.0 8.7	+3.5 0	−3.0 −5.2
15.75 — 19.69	1.2 3.0	+1.0 0	−1.2 −2.0	1.2 3.8	+1.6 0	−1.2 −2.2	4.0 8.1	+1.6 0	−4.0 −5.6	4.0 10.5	+4.0 0	−4.0 −6.5
19.69 — 30.09	1.6 3.7	+1.2 0	−1.6 −2.5	1.6 4.8	+2.0 0	−1.6 −2.8	5.0 10.0	+3.0 0	−5.0 −7.0	5.0 13.0	+5.0 0	−5.0 −8.0
30.09 — 41.49	2.0 4.6	+1.6 0	−2.0 −3.0	2.0 6.1	+2.5 0	−2.0 −3.6	6.0 12.5	+4.0 0	−6.0 −8.5	6.0 16.0	+6.0 0	−6.0 −10.0
41.49 — 56.19	2.5 5.7	+2.0 0	−2.5 −3.7	2.5 7.5	+3.0 0	−2.5 −4.5	8.0 16.0	+5.0 0	−8.0 −11.0	8.0 21.0	+8.0 0	−8.0 −13.0
56.19 — 76.39	3.0 7.1	+2.5 0	−3.0 −4.6	3.0 9.5	+4.0 0	−3.0 −5.5	10.0 20.0	+6.0 0	−10.0 −14.0	10.0 26.0	+10.0 0	−10.0 −16.0
76.39 — 100.9	4.0 9.0	+3.0 0	−4.0 −6.0	4.0 12.0	+5.0 0	−4.0 −7.0	12.0 25.0	+8.0 0	−12.0 −17.0	12.0 32.0	+12.0 0	−12.0 −20.0
100.9 — 131.9	5.0 11.5	+4.0 0	−5.0 −7.5	5.0 15.0	+6.0 0	−5.0 −9.0	16.0 32.0	+10.0 0	−16.0 −22.0	16.0 36.0	+16.0 0	−16.0 −26.0
131.9 — 171.9	6.0 14.0	+5.0 0	−6.0 −9.0	6.0 19.0	+8.0 0	−6.0 −11.0	18.0 38.0	+8.0 0	−18.0 −26.0	18.0 50.0	+20.0 0	−18.0 −30.0
171.9 — 200	8.0 18.0	+6.0 0	−8.0 −12.0	8.0 22.0	+10.0 0	−8.0 −12.0	22.0 48.0	+16.0 0	−22.0 −32.0	22.0 63.0	+25.0 0	−22.0 −38.0

Continued

TABLE C.13.1   Running and Sliding Fits—Continued

	Class RC 5			Class RC 6			Class RC 7			Class RC 8			Class RC 9		Nominal Size Range Inches	
	Limits of Clearance	Standard Limits		Limits of Clearance	Standard Limits		Limits of Clearance	Standard Limits		Limits of Clearance	Standards Limits		Limits of Clearance	Standard Limits			
		Hole H8	Shaft e7		Hole H9	Shaft e8		Hole H9	Shaft d8		Hole H10	Shaft c9		Hole H11	Shaft	Over	To
	0.6 / 1.6	+0.6 / −0	−0.6 / −1.0	0.6 / 2.2	+1.0 / −0	−0.6 / −1.2	1.0 / 2.6	+1.0 / 0	−1.0 / −1.6	2.5 / 5.1	+1.6 / 0	−2.5 / −3.5	4.0 / 8.1	+2.5 / 0	−4.0 / −5.6	0−	0.12
	0.8 / 2.0	+0.7 / −0	−0.8 / −1.3	0.8 / 2.7	+1.2 / −0	−0.8 / −1.5	1.2 / 3.1	+1.2 / 0	−1.2 / −1.9	2.8 / 5.8	+1.8 / 0	−2.8 / −4.0	4.5 / 9.0	+3.0 / 0	−4.5 / −6.0	0.12−	0.24
	1.0 / 2.5	+0.9 / −0	−1.0 / −1.6	1.0 / 3.3	+1.4 / −0	−1.0 / −1.9	1.6 / 3.9	+1.4 / 0	−1.6 / −2.5	3.0 / 6.6	+2.2 / 0	−3.0 / −4.4	5.0 / 10.7	+3.5 / 0	−5.0 / −7.2	0.24−	0.40
	1.2 / 2.9	+1.0 / −0	−1.2 / −1.9	1.2 / 3.8	+1.6 / −0	−1.2 / −2.2	2.0 / 4.6	+1.6 / 0	−2.0 / −3.0	3.5 / 7.9	+2.8 / 0	−3.5 / −5.1	6.0 / 12.8	+4.0 / −0	−6.0 / −8.8	0.40−	0.71
	1.6 / 3.6	+1.2 / −0	−1.6 / −2.4	1.6 / 4.8	+2.0 / −0	−1.6 / −2.8	2.5 / 5.7	+2.0 / 0	−2.5 / −3.7	4.5 / 10.0	+3.5 / 0	−4.5 / −6.5	7.0 / 15.5	+5.0 / 0	−7.0 / −10.5	0.71−	1.19
	2.0 / 4.6	+1.6 / −0	−2.0 / −3.0	2.0 / 6.1	+2.5 / −0	−2.0 / −3.6	3.0 / 7.1	+2.5 / 0	−3.0 / −4.6	5.0 / 11.5	+4.0 / 0	−5.0 / −7.5	8.0 / 18.0	+6.0 / 0	−8.0 / −12.0	1.19−	1.97
	2.5 / 5.5	+1.8 / −0	−2.5 / −3.7	2.5 / 7.3	+3.0 / −0	−2.5 / −4.3	4.0 / 8.8	+3.0 / 0	−4.0 / −5.8	6.0 / 13.5	+4.5 / 0	−6.0 / −9.0	9.0 / 20.5	+7.0 / 0	−9.0 / −13.5	1.97−	3.15
	3.0 / 6.6	+2.2 / −0	−3.0 / −4.4	3.0 / 8.7	+3.5 / −0	−3.0 / −5.2	5.0 / 10.7	+3.5 / 0	−5.0 / −7.2	7.0 / 15.5	+5.0 / 0	−7.0 / −10.5	10.0 / 24.0	+9.0 / 0	−10.0 / −15.0	3.15−	4.73
	3.5 / 7.6	+2.5 / −0	−3.5 / −5.1	3.5 / 10.0	+4.0 / −0	−3.5 / −6.0	6.0 / 12.5	+4.0 / 0	−6.0 / −8.5	8.0 / 18.0	+6.0 / 0	−8.0 / −12.0	12.0 / 28.0	+10.0 / 0	−12.0 / −18.0	4.73−	7.09
	4.0 / 8.6	+2.8 / −0	−4.0 / −5.8	4.0 / 11.3	+4.5 / 0	−4.0 / −6.8	7.0 / 14.3	+4.5 / 0	−7.0 / −9.8	10.0 / 21.5	+7.0 / 0	−10.0 / −14.5	15.0 / 34.0	+12.0 / 0	−15.0 / −22.0	7.09−	9.85
	5.0 / 10.0	+3.0 / 0	−5.0 / −7.0	5.0 / 13.0	+5.0 / 0	−5.0 / −8.0	8.0 / 16.0	+5.0 / 0	−8.0 / −11.0	12.0 / 25.0	+8.0 / 0	−12.0 / −17.0	18.0 / 38.0	+12.0 / 0	−18.0 / −26.0	9.85−	12.41
	6.0 / 11.7	+3.5 / 0	−6.0 / −8.2	6.0 / 15.5	+6.0 / 0	−6.0 / −9.5	10.0 / 19.5	+6.0 / 0	−10.0 / 13.5	14.0 / 29.0	+9.0 / 0	−14.0 / −20.0	22.0 / 45.0	+14.0 / 0	−22.0 / −31.0	12.41−	15.75
	8.0 / 14.5	+4.0 / 0	−8.0 / −10.5	8.0 / 18.0	+6.0 / 0	−8.0 / −12.0	12.0 / 22.0	+6.0 / 0	−12.0 / −16.0	16.0 / 32.0	+10.0 / 0	−16.0 / −22.0	25.0 / 51.0	+16.0 / 0	−25.0 / −35.0	15.75−	19.69
	10.0 / 18.0	+5.0 / 0	−10.0 / −13.0	10.0 / 23.0	+8.0 / 0	−10.0 / −15.0	16.0 / 29.0	+8.0 / 0	−16.0 / −21.0	20.0 / 40.0	+12.0 / 0	−20.0 / −28.0	30.0 / 62.0	+20.0 / 0	−30.0 / −42.0	19.69−	30.09
	12.0 / 22.0	+6.0 / 0	−12.0 / −16.0	12.0 / 28.0	+10.0 / 0	−12.0 / −18.0	20.0 / 36.0	+10.0 / 0	−20.0 / −26.0	25.0 / 51.0	+16.0 / 0	−25.0 / −35.0	40.0 / 81.0	+25.0 / 0	−40.0 / −56.0	30.09−	41.49
	16.0 / 29.0	+8.0 / 0	−16.0 / −21.0	16.0 / 36.0	+12.0 / 0	−16.0 / −24.0	25.0 / 45.0	+12.0 / 0	−25.0 / −33.0	30.0 / 62.0	+20.0 / 0	−30.0 / −42.0	50.0 / 100	+30.0 / 0	−50.0 / −70.0	41.49−	56.19
	20.0 / 36.0	+10.0 / 0	−20.0 / −26.0	20.0 / 46.0	+16.0 / 0	−20.0 / −30.0	30.0 / 56.0	+16.0 / 0	−30.0 / −40.0	40.0 / 81.0	+25.0 / 0	−40.0 / −56.0	60.0 / 125	+40.0 / 0	−60.0 / −85.0	56.19−	76.39
	25.0 / 45.0	+12.0 / 0	−25.0 / −33.0	25.0 / 57.0	+20.0 / 0	−25.0 / −37.0	40.0 / 72.0	+20.0 / 0	−40.0 / −52.0	50.0 / 100	+30.0 / 0	−50.0 / −70.0	80.0 / 160	+50.0 / 0	−80.0 / −110	76.39−	100.9
	30.0 / 56.0	+16.0 / 0	−30.0 / −40.0	30.0 / 71.0	+25.0 / 0	−30.0 / −46.0	50.0 / 91.0	+25.0 / 0	−50.0 / −66.0	60.0 / 125	+40.0 / 0	−60.0 / −85.0	100 / 200	+60.0 / 0	−100 / −140	100.9−	131.9
	35.0 / 67.0	+20.0 / 0	−35.0 / −47.0	35.0 / 85.0	+30.0 / 0	−35.0 / −55.0	60.0 / 110.0	+30.0 / 0	−60.0 / −80.0	80.0 / 160	+50.0 / 0	−80.0 / −110	130 / 260	+80.0 / 0	−130 / −180	131.9−	171.9
	45.0 / 86.0	+25.0 / 0	−45.0 / −61.0	45.0 / 110.0	+40.0 / 0	−45.0 / −70.0	80.0 / 145.0	+40.0 / 0	−80.0 / −105.0	100 / 200	+60.0 / 0	−100 / −140	150 / 310	+100 / 0	−150 / −210	171.9−	200

TABLE C.13.2 Locational Clearance Fits

Limits are in thousandths of an inch. Limits for hole and shaft are applied algrebraically to the basic size to obtain the limits of size for the parts. Data in bold face are in accordance with ABC agreements. Symbols H6, h5, etc., are Hole and Shaft designations used in ABC System.

Nominal Size Range Inches (Over — To)	Class LC 1 Limits of Clearance	Class LC 1 Hole H6	Class LC 1 Shaft h5	Class LC 2 Limits of Clearance	Class LC 2 Hole H7	Class LC 2 Shaft h6	Class LC 3 Limits of Clearance	Class LC 3 Hole H8	Class LC 3 Shaft h7	Class LC 4 Limits of Clearance	Class LC 4 Hole H10	Class LC 4 Shaft h9	Class LC 5 Limits of Clearance	Class LC 5 Hole H7	Class LC 5 Shaft g6
0 — 0.12	0 / 0.45	+0.25 / −0	+0 / −0.2	0 / 0.65	+0.4 / −0	+0 / −0.25	0 / 1	+0.6 / −0	+0 / −0.4	0 / 2.6	+1.6 / −0	+0 / −1.0	0.1 / 0.75	+0.4 / −0	−0.1 / −0.35
0.12 — 0.24	0 / 0.5	+0.3 / −0	+0 / −0.2	0 / 0.8	+0.5 / −0	+0 / −0.3	0 / 1.2	+0.7 / −0	+0 / −0.5	0 / 3.0	+1.8 / −0	+0 / −1.2	0.15 / 0.95	+0.5 / −0	−0.15 / −0.45
0.24 — 0.40	0 / 0.65	+0.4 / −0	+0 / −0.25	0 / 1.0	+0.6 / −0	+0 / −0.4	0 / 1.5	+0.9 / −0	+0 / −0.6	0 / 3.6	+2.2 / −0	+0 / −1.4	0.2 / 1.2	+0.6 / −0	−0.2 / −0.6
0.40 — 0.71	0 / 0.7	+0.4 / −0	+0 / −0.3	0 / 1.1	+0.7 / −0	+0 / −0.4	0 / 1.7	+1.0 / −0	+0 / −0.7	0 / 4.4	+2.8 / −0	+0 / −1.6	0.25 / 1.35	+0.7 / −0	−0.25 / −0.65
0.71 — 1.19	0 / 0.9	+0.5 / −0	+0 / −0.4	0 / 1.3	+0.8 / −0	+0 / −0.5	0 / 2	+1.2 / −0	+0 / −0.8	0 / 5.5	+3.5 / −0	+0 / −2.0	0.3 / 1.6	+0.8 / −0	−0.3 / −0.8
1.19 — 1.97	0 / 1.0	+0.6 / −0	+0 / −0.4	0 / 1.6	+1.0 / −0	+0 / −0.6	0 / 2.6	+1.6 / −0	+0 / −1	0 / 6.5	+4.0 / −0	+0 / −2.5	0.4 / 2.0	+1.0 / −0	−0.4 / −1.0
1.97 — 3.15	0 / 1.2	+0.7 / −0	+0 / −0.5	0 / 1.9	+1.2 / −0	+0 / −0.7	0 / 3	+1.8 / −0	+0 / −1.2	0 / 7.5	+4.5 / −0	+0 / −3	0.4 / 2.3	+1.2 / −0	−0.4 / −1.1
3.15 — 4.73	0 / 1.5	+0.9 / −0	+0 / −0.6	0 / 2.3	+1.4 / −0	+0 / −0.9	0 / 3.6	+2.2 / −0	+0 / −1.4	0 / 8.5	+5.0 / −0	+0 / −3.5	0.5 / 2.8	+1.4 / −0	−0.5 / −1.4
4.73 — 7.09	0 / 1.7	+1.0 / −0	+0 / −0.7	0 / 2.6	+1.6 / −0	+0 / −1.0	0 / 4.1	+2.5 / −0	+0 / −1.6	0 / 10	+6.0 / −0	+0 / −4	0.6 / 3.2	+1.6 / −0	−0.6 / −1.6
7.09 — 9.85	0 / 2.0	+1.2 / −0	+0 / −0.8	0 / 3.0	+1.8 / −0	+0 / −1.2	0 / 4.6	+2.8 / −0	+0 / −1.8	0 / 11.5	+7.0 / −0	+0 / −4.5	0.6 / 3.6	+1.8 / −0	−0.6 / −1.8
9.85 — 12.41	0 / 2.1	+1.2 / −0	+0 / −0.9	0 / 3.2	+2.0 / −0	+0 / −1.2	0 / 5	+3.0 / −0	+0 / −2.0	0 / 13	+8.0 / −0	+0 / −5	0.7 / 3.9	+2.0 / −0	−0.7 / −1.9
12.41 — 15.75	0 / 2.4	+1.4 / −0	+0 / −1.0	0 / 3.6	+2.2 / −0	+0 / −1.4	0 / 5.7	+3.5 / −0	+0 / −2.2	0 / 15	+9.0 / −0	+0 / −6	0.7 / 4.3	+2.2 / −0	−0.7 / −2.1
15.75 — 19.69	0 / 2.6	+1.6 / −0	+0 / −1.0	0 / 4.1	+2.5 / −0	+0 / −1.6	0 / 6.5	+4 / −0	+0 / −2.5	0 / 16	+10.0 / −0	+0 / −6	0.8 / 4.9	+2.5 / −0	−0.8 / −2.4
19.69 — 30.09	0 / 3.2	+2.0 / −0	+0 / −1.2	0 / 5.0	+3 / −0	+0 / −2	0 / 8	+5 / −0	+0 / −3	0 / 20	+12.0 / −0	+0 / −8	0.9 / 5.9	+3.0 / −0	−0.9 / −2.9
30.09 — 41.49	0 / 4.1	+2.5 / −0	+0 / −1.6	0 / 6.5	+4 / −0	+0 / −2.5	0 / 10	+6 / −0	+0 / −4	0 / 26	+16.0 / −0	+0 / −10	1.0 / 7.5	+4.0 / −0	−1.0 / −3.5
41.49 — 56.19	0 / 5.0	+3.0 / −0	+0 / −2.0	0 / 8.0	+5 / −0	+0 / −3	0 / 13	+8 / −0	+0 / −5	0 / 32	+20.0 / −0	+0 / −12	1.2 / 9.2	+5.0 / −0	−1.2 / −4.2
56.19 — 76.39	0 / 6.5	+4.0 / −0	+0 / −2.5	0 / 10	+6 / −0	+0 / −4	0 / 16	+10 / −0	+0 / −6	0 / 41	+25.0 / −0	+0 / −16	1.2 / 11.2	+6.0 / −0	−1.2 / −5.2
76.39 — 100.9	0 / 8.0	+5.0 / −0	+0 / −3.0	0 / 13	+8 / −0	+0 / −5	0 / 20	+12 / −0	+0 / −8	0 / 50	+30.0 / −0	+0 / −20	1.4 / 14.4	+8.0 / −0	−1.4 / −6.4
100.9 — 131.9	0 / 10.0	+6.0 / −0	+0 / −4.0	0 / 16	+10 / −0	+0 / −6	0 / 26	+16 / −0	+0 / −10	0 / 65	+40.0 / −0	+0 / −25	1.6 / 17.6	+10.0 / −0	−1.6 / −7.6
131.9 — 171.9	0 / 13.0	+8.0 / −0	+0 / −5.0	0 / 20	+12 / −0	+0 / −8	0 / 32	+20 / −0	+0 / −12	0 / 8	+50.0 / −0	+0 / −30	1.8 / 21.8	+12.0 / −0	−1.8 / −9.8
171.9 — 200	0 / 16.0	+10.0 / −0	+0 / −6.0	0 / 26	+16 / −0	+0 / −10	0 / 41	+25 / −0	+0 / −16	0 / 100	+60.0 / −0	+0 / −40	1.8 / 27.8	+16.0 / −0	−1.8 / −11.8

Continued

TABLE 13.2 Locational Clearance Fits—Continued

Class LC 6			Class LC 7			Class LC 8			Class LC 9			Class LC 10			Class LC 11			Nominal Size Range Inches	
Limits of Clearance	Standard Limits		Limits of Clearance	Standard Limits		Limits of Clearance	Standard Limits		Limits of Clearance	Standard Limits		Limits of Clearance	Standard Limits		Limits of Clearance	Standard Limits			
	Hole H9	Shaft f8		Hole H10	Shaft e9		Hole H10	Shaft d9		Hole H11	Shaft c10		Hole H12	Shaft		Hole H13	Shaft	Over	To
0.3 / 1.9	+1.0 / 0	−0.3 / −0.9	0.6 / 3.2	+1.6 / 0	−0.6 / −1.6	1.0 / 3.6	+1.6 / −0	−1.0 / −2.0	2.5 / 6.6	+2.5 / −0	−2.5 / −4.1	4 / 12	+4 / −0	−4 / −8	5 / 17	+6 / −0	−5 / −11	0 −	0.12
0.4 / 2.3	+1.2 / 0	−0.4 / −1.1	0.8 / 3.8	+1.8 / 0	−0.8 / −2.0	1.2 / 4.2	+1.8 / −0	−1.2 / −2.4	2.8 / 7.6	+3.0 / −0	−2.8 / −4.6	4.5 / 14.5	+5 / −0	−4.5 / −9.5	6 / 20	+7 / −0	−6 / −13	0.12 −	0.24
0.5 / 2.8	+1.4 / 0	−0.5 / −1.4	1.0 / 4.6	+2.2 / 0	−1.0 / −2.4	1.6 / 5.2	+2.2 / −0	−1.6 / −3.0	3.0 / 8.7	+3.5 / −0	−3.0 / −5.2	5 / 17	+6 / −0	−5 / −11	7 / 25	+9 / −0	−7 / −16	0.24 −	0.40
0.6 / 3.2	+1.6 / 0	−0.6 / −1.6	1.2 / 5.6	+2.8 / 0	−1.2 / −2.8	2.0 / 6.4	+2.8 / −0	−2.0 / −3.6	3.5 / 10.3	+4.0 / −0	−3.5 / −6.3	6 / 20	+7 / −0	−6 / −13	8 / 28	+10 / −0	−8 / −18	0.40 −	0.71
0.8 / 4.0	+2.0 / 0	−0.8 / −2.0	1.6 / 7.1	+3.5 / 0	−1.6 / −3.6	2.5 / 8.0	+3.5 / −0	−2.5 / −4.5	4.5 / 13.0	+5.0 / −0	−4.5 / −8.0	7 / 23	+8 / −0	−7 / −15	10 / 34	+12 / −0	−10 / −22	0.71 −	1.19
1.0 / 5.1	+2.5 / 0	−1.0 / −2.6	2.0 / 8.5	+4.0 / 0	−2.0 / −4.5	3.0 / 9.5	+4.0 / −0	−3.0 / −5.5	5 / 15	+6 / −0	−5 / −9	8 / 28	+10 / −0	−8 / −18	12 / 44	+16 / −0	−12 / −28	1.19 −	1.97
1.2 / 6.0	+3.0 / 0	−1.2 / −3.0	2.5 / 10.0	+4.5 / 0	−2.5 / −5.5	4.0 / 11.5	+4.5 / −0	−4.0 / −7.0	6 / 17.5	+7 / −0	−6 / −10.5	10 / 34	+12 / −0	−10 / −22	14 / 50	+18 / −0	−14 / −32	1.97 −	3.15
1.4 / 7.1	+3.5 / 0	−1.4 / −3.6	3.0 / 11.5	+5.0 / 0	−3.0 / −6.5	5.0 / 13.5	+5.0 / −0	−5.0 / −8.5	7 / 21	+9 / −0	−7 / −12	11 / 39	+14 / −0	−11 / −25	16 / 60	+22 / −0	−16 / −38	3.15 −	4.73
1.6 / 8.1	+4.0 / 0	−1.6 / −4.1	3.5 / 13.5	+6.0 / 0	−3.5 / −7.5	6 / 16	+6 / −0	−6 / −10	8 / 24	+10 / −0	−8 / −14	12 / 44	+16 / −0	−12 / −28	18 / 68	+25 / −0	−18 / −43	4.73 −	7.09
2.0 / 9.3	+4.5 / 0	−2.0 / −4.8	4.0 / 15.5	+7.0 / 0	−4.0 / −8.5	7 / 18.5	+7 / −0	−7 / −11.5	10 / 29	+12 / −0	−10 / −17	16 / 52	+18 / −0	−16 / −34	22 / 78	+28 / −0	−22 / −50	7.09 −	9.85
2.2 / 10.2	+5.0 / 0	−2.2 / −5.2	4.5 / 17.5	+8.0 / 0	−4.5 / −9.5	7 / 20	+8 / −0	−7 / −12	12 / 32	+12 / −0	−12 / −20	20 / 60	+20 / −0	−20 / −40	28 / 88	+30 / −0	−28 / −58	9.85 −	12.41
2.5 / 12.0	+6.0 / 0	−2.5 / −6.0	5.0 / 20.0	+9.0 / 0	−5 / −11	8 / 23	+9 / −0	−8 / −14	14 / 37	+14 / −0	−14 / −23	22 / 66	+22 / −0	−22 / −44	30 / 100	+35 / −0	−30 / −65	12.41 −	15.75
2.8 / 12.8	+6.0 / 0	−2.8 / −6.8	5.0 / 21.0	+10.0 / 0	−5 / −11	9 / 25	+10 / −0	−9 / −15	16 / 42	+16 / −0	−16 / −26	25 / 75	+25 / −0	−25 / −50	35 / 115	+40 / −0	−35 / −75	15.75 −	19.69
3.0 / 16.0	+8.0 / 0	−3.0 / −8.0	6.0 / 26.0	+12.0 / −0	−6 / −14	10 / 30	+12 / −0	−10 / −18	18 / 50	+20 / −0	−18 / −30	28 / 88	+30 / −0	−28 / −58	40 / 140	+50 / −0	−40 / −90	19.69 −	30.09
3.5 / 19.5	+10.0 / 0	−3.5 / −9.5	7.0 / 33.0	+16.0 / −0	−7 / −17	12 / 38	+16 / −0	−12 / −22	20 / 61	+25 / −0	−20 / −36	30 / 110	+40 / −0	−30 / −70	45 / 165	+60 / −0	−45 / −105	30.09 −	41.49
4.0 / 24.0	+12.0 / 0	−4.0 / −12.0	8.0 / 40.0	+20.0 / −0	−8 / −20	14 / 46	+20 / −0	−14 / −26	25 / 75	+30 / −0	−25 / −45	40 / 140	+50 / −0	−40 / −90	60 / 220	+80 / −0	−60 / −140	41.49 −	56.19
4.5 / 30.5	+16.0 / 0	−4.5 / −14.5	9.0 / 50.0	+25.0 / −0	−9 / −25	16 / 57	+25 / −0	−16 / −32	30 / 95	+40 / −0	−30 / −55	50 / 170	+60 / −0	−50 / 110	70 / 270	+100 / −0	−70 / −170	56.19 −	76.39
5.0 / 37.0	+20.0 / 0	−5 / −17	10.0 / 60.0	+30.0 / −0	−10 / −30	18 / 68	+30 / −0	−18 / −38	35 / 115	+50 / −0	−35 / −65	50 / 210	+80 / −0	−50 / −130	80 / 330	+125 / −0	−80 / −205	76.39 −	100.9
6.0 / 47.0	+25.0 / 0	−6 / −22	12.0 / 67.0	+40.0 / −0	−12 / −27	20 / 85	+40 / −0	−20 / −45	40 / 140	+60 / −0	−40 / −80	60 / 260	+100 / −0	−60 / −160	90 / 410	+160 / −0	−90 / −250	100.9 −	131.9
7.0 / 57.0	+30.0 / 0	−7 / −27	14.0 / 94.0	+50.0 / −0	−14 / −44	25 / 105	+50 / −0	−25 / −55	50 / 180	+80 / −0	−50 / −100	80 / 330	+125 / −0	−80 / −205	100 / 500	+200 / −0	−100 / −300	131.9 −	171.9
7.0 / 72.0	+40.0 / 0	−7 / −32	14.0 / 114.0	+60.0 / −0	−14 / −54	25 / 125	+60 / −0	−25 / −65	50 / 210	+100 / −0	−50 / −110	90 / 410	+160 / −0	−90 / −250	125 / 625	+250 / −0	−125 / −375	171.9 −	200

TABLE C.13.3   Locational Transition Fits

Limits are in thousandths of an inch. Limits for hole and shaft are applied algebraically to the basic size to obtain the limits of size for the mating parts. Data in bold face are in accordance with ABC agreements. "Fit" represents the maximum interference (minus values) and the maximum clearance (plus values). Symbols H7, js6, etc., are Hole and Shaft designations used in ABC System.

Nominal Size Range Inches — Over	To	LT 1 Fit	LT 1 Hole H7	LT 1 Shaft js6	LT 2 Fit	LT 2 Hole H8	LT 2 Shaft js7	LT 3 Fit	LT 3 Hole H7	LT 3 Shaft k6	LT 4 Fit	LT 4 Hole H8	LT 4 Shaft k7	LT 5 Fit	LT 5 Hole H7	LT 5 Shaft n6	LT 6 Fit	LT 6 Hole H7	LT 6 Shaft n7
0	0.12	−0.10 / +0.50	+0.4 / −0	+0.10 / −0.10	−0.2 / +0.8	+0.6 / −0	+0.2 / −0.2							−0.5 / +0.15	+0.4 / −0	+0.5 / +0.25	−0.65 / +0.15	+0.4 / −0	+0.65 / +0.25
0.12	0.24	−0.15 / +0.65	+0.5 / −0	+0.15 / −0.15	−0.25 / +0.95	+0.7 / −0	+0.25 / −0.25							−0.6 / +0.2	+0.5 / −0	+0.6 / +0.3	−0.8 / +0.2	+0.5 / −0	+0.8 / +0.3
0.24	0.40	−0.2 / +0.8	+0.6 / −0	+0.2 / −0.2	−0.3 / +1.2	+0.9 / −0	+0.3 / −0.3	−0.5 / +0.5	+0.6 / −0	+0.5 / +0.1	−0.7 / +0.8	+0.9 / −0	+0.7 / +0.1	−0.8 / +0.2	+0.6 / −0	+0.8 / +0.4	−1.0 / +0.2	+0.6 / −0	+1.0 / +0.4
0.40	0.71	−0.2 / +0.9	+0.7 / −0	+0.2 / −0.2	−0.35 / +1.35	+1.0 / −0	+0.35 / −0.35	−0.5 / +0.6	+0.7 / −0	+0.5 / +0.1	−0.8 / +0.9	+1.0 / −0	+0.8 / +0.1	−0.9 / +0.2	+0.7 / −0	+0.9 / +0.5	−1.2 / +0.2	+0.7 / −0	+1.2 / +0.5
0.71	1.19	−0.25 / +1.05	+0.8 / −0	+0.25 / −0.25	−0.4 / +1.6	+1.2 / −0	+0.4 / −0.4	−0.6 / +0.7	+0.8 / −0	+0.6 / +0.1	−0.9 / +1.1	+1.2 / −0	+0.9 / +0.1	−1.1 / +0.2	+0.8 / −0	+1.1 / +0.6	−1.4 / +0.2	+0.8 / −0	+1.4 / +0.6
1.19	1.97	−0.3 / +1.3	+1.0 / −0	+0.3 / −0.3	−0.5 / +2.1	+1.6 / −0	+0.5 / −0.5	−0.7 / +0.9	+1.0 / −0	+0.7 / +0.1	−1.1 / +1.5	+1.6 / −0	+1.1 / +0.1	−1.3 / +0.3	+1.0 / −0	+1.3 / +0.7	−1.7 / +0.3	+1.0 / −0	+1.7 / +0.7
1.97	3.15	−0.3 / +1.5	+1.2 / −0	+0.3 / −0.3	−0.6 / +2.4	+1.8 / −0	+0.6 / −0.6	−0.8 / +1.1	+1.2 / −0	+0.8 / +0.1	−1.3 / +1.7	+1.8 / −0	+1.3 / +0.1	−1.5 / +0.4	+1.2 / −0	+1.5 / +0.8	−2.0 / +0.4	+1.2 / −0	+2.0 / +0.8
3.15	4.73	−0.4 / +1.8	+1.4 / −0	+0.4 / −0.4	−0.7 / +2.9	+2.2 / −0	+0.7 / −0.7	−1.0 / +1.3	+1.4 / −0	+1.0 / +0.1	−1.5 / +2.1	+2.2 / −0	+1.5 / +0.1	−1.9 / +0.4	+1.4 / −0	+1.9 / +1.0	−2.4 / +0.4	+1.4 / −0	+2.4 / +1.0
4.73	7.09	−0.5 / +2.1	+1.6 / −0	+0.5 / −0.5	−0.8 / +3.3	+2.5 / −0	+0.8 / −0.8	−1.1 / +1.5	+1.6 / −0	+1.1 / +0.1	−1.7 / +2.4	+2.5 / −0	+1.7 / +0.1	−2.2 / +0.4	+1.6 / −0	+2.2 / +1.2	−2.8 / +0.4	+1.6 / −0	+2.8 / +1.2
7.09	9.85	−0.6 / +2.4	+1.8 / −0	+0.6 / −0.6	−0.9 / +3.7	+2.8 / −0	+0.9 / −0.9	−1.4 / +1.6	+1.8 / −0	+1.4 / +0.2	−2.0 / +2.6	+2.8 / −0	+2.0 / +0.2	−2.6 / +0.4	+1.8 / −0	+2.6 / +1.4	−3.2 / +0.4	+1.8 / −0	+3.2 / +1.4
9.85	12.41	−0.6 / +2.6	+2.0 / −0	+0.6 / −0.6	−1.0 / +4.0	+3.0 / −0	+1.0 / −1.0	−1.4 / +1.8	+2.0 / −0	+1.4 / +0.2	−2.2 / +2.8	+3.0 / −0	+2.2 / +0.2	−2.6 / +0.6	+2.0 / −0	+2.6 / +1.4	−3.4 / +0.6	+2.0 / −0	+3.4 / +1.4
12.41	15.75	−0.7 / +2.9	+2.2 / −0	+0.7 / −0.7	−1.0 / +4.5	+3.5 / −0	+1.0 / −1.0	−1.6 / +2.0	+2.2 / −0	+1.6 / +0.2	−2.4 / +3.3	+3.5 / −0	+2.4 / +0.2	−3.0 / +0.6	+2.2 / −0	+3.0 / +1.6	−3.8 / +0.6	+2.2 / −0	+3.8 / +1.6
15.75	19.69	−0.8 / +3.3	+2.5 / −0	+0.8 / −0.8	−1.2 / +5.2	+4.0 / −0	+1.2 / −1.2	−1.8 / +2.3	+2.5 / −0	+1.8 / +0.2	−2.7 / +3.8	+4.0 / −0	+2.7 / +0.2	−3.4 / +0.7	+2.5 / −0	+3.4 / +1.8	−4.3 / +0.7	+2.5 / −0	+4.3 / +1.8

TABLE C.13.4 Locational Interference Fits

Limits are in thousandths of an inch. Limits for hole and shaft are applied algebraically to the basic size to obtain the limits of size for the parts. Data in bold face are in accordance with ABC agreements, Symbols H7, p 6, etc., are Hole and Shaft designations used in ABC System.

Nominal Size Range Inches (Over – To)	Class LN 1 Limits of Intolerance	Class LN 1 Standard Limits Hole H6	Class LN 1 Standard Limits Shaft n5	Class LN 2 Limits of Tolerance	Class LN 2 Standard Limits Hole H7	Class LN 2 Standard Limits Shaft p6	Class LN 3 Limits of Intolerance	Class LN 3 Standard Limits Hole H7	Class LN 3 Standard Limits Shaft r6
0 – 0.12	0 / 0.45	+0.25 / −0	+0.45 / +0.25	0 / 0.65	+0.4 / −0	+0.65 / +0.4	0.1 / 0.75	+0.4 / −0	+0.75 / +0.5
0.12 – 0.24	0 / 0.5	+0.3 / −0	+0.5 / +0.3	0 / 0.8	+0.5 / −0	+0.8 / +0.5	0.1 / 0.9	+0.5 / 0	+0.9 / +0.6
0.24 – 0.40	0 / 0.65	+0.4 / −0	+0.65 / +0.4	0 / 1.0	+0.6 / −0	+1.0 / +0.6	0.2 / 1.2	+0.6 / −0	+1.2 / +0.8
0.40 – 0.71	0 / 0.8	+0.4 / −0	+0.8 / +0.4	0 / 1.1	+0.7 / −0	+1.1 / +0.7	0.3 / 1.4	+0.7 / −0	+1.4 / +1.0
0.71 – 1.19	0 / 1.0	+0.5 / −0	+1.0 / +0.5	0 / 1.3	+0.8 / −0	+1.3 / +0.8	0.4 / 1.7	+0.8 / −0	+1.7 / +1.2
1.19 – 1.97	0 / 1.1	+0.6 / −0	+1.1 / +0.6	0 / 1.6	+1.0 / −0	+1.6 / +1.0	0.4 / 2.0	+1.0 / −0	+2.0 / +1.4
1.97 – 3.15	0.1 / 1.3	+0.7 / −0	+1.3 / +0.7	0.2 / 2.1	+1.2 / −0	+2.1 / +1.4	0.4 / 2.3	+1.2 / −0	+2.3 / +1.6
3.15 – 4.73	0.1 / 1.6	+0.9 / −0	+1.6 / +1.0	0.2 / 2.5	+1.4 / −0	+2.5 / +1.6	0.6 / 2.9	+1.4 / −0	+2.9 / +2.0
4.73 – 7.09	0.2 / 1.9	+1.0 / −0	+1.9 / +1.2	0.2 / 2.8	+1.6 / −0	+2.8 / +1.8	0.9 / 3.5	+1.6 / −0	+3.5 / +2.5
7.09 – 9.85	0.2 / 2.2	+1.2 / −0	+2.2 / +1.4	0.2 / 3.2	+1.8 / −0	+3.2 / +2.0	1.2 / 4.2	+1.8 / −0	+4.2 / +3.0
9.85 – 12.41	0.2 / 2.3	+1.2 / −0	+2.3 / +1.4	0.2 / 3.4	2.0 / −0	+3.4 / +2.2	1.5 / 4.7	+2.0 / −0	+4.7 / +3.5
12.41 – 15.75	0.2 / 2.6	+1.4 / −0	+2.6 / +1.6	0.3 / 3.9	+2.2 / −0	+3.9 / +2.5	2.3 / 5.9	+2.2 / −0	+5.9 / +4.5
15.75 – 19.69	0.2 / 2.8	+1.6 / −0	+2.8 / +1.8	0.3 / 4.4	+2.5 / −0	+4.4 / +2.8	2.5 / 6.6	+2.5 / −0	+6.6 / +5.0
19.69 – 30.09		+2.0 / −0		0.5 / 5.5	+3 / −0	+5.5 / +3.5	4 / 9	+3 / −0	+9 / +7
30.09 – 41.49		+2.5 / −0		0.5 / 7.0	+4 / −0	+7.0 / +4.5	5 / 11.5	+4 / −0	+11.5 / +9
41.49 – 56.19		+3.0 / −0		1 / 9	+5 / −0	+9 / +6	7 / 15	+5 / −0	+15 / +12
56.19 – 76.39		+4.0 / −0		1 / 11	+6 / −0	+11 / +7	10 / 20	+6 / −0	+20 / +16
76.39 – 100.9		+5.0 / −0		1 / 14	+8 / −0	+14 / +9	12 / 25	+8 / −0	+25 / +20
100.9 – 131.9		+6.0 / −0		2 / 18	+10 / −0	+18 / +12	15 / 31	+10 / −0	+31 / +25
131.9 – 171.9		+8.0 / −0		4 / 24	+12 / −0	+24 / +16	18 / 38	+12 / −0	+38 / +30
171.9 – 200		+10.0 / −0		4 / 30	+16 / −0	+30 / +20	24 / 50	+16 / −0	+50 / +40

TABLE C.13.5   Force and Shrink Fits

Limits are in thousandths of an inch. Limits for hole and shaft are applied algebraically to the basic size to obtain the limits of size for the parts. Data in bold face are in accordance with ABC agreements. Symbols H7, s6, etc., are Hole and Shaft designations used in ABC System.

Nominal Size Range Inches		Class FN 1			Class FN 2			Class FN 3			Class FN 4			Class FN 5		
		Limits of Interference	Standard Limits		Limits of Interference	Standard Limits		Limits of Interference	Standard Limits		Limits of Interference	Standard Limits		Limits of Interference	Standard Limits	
Over	To		Hole H6	Shaft		Hole H7	Shaft s6		Hole H7	Shaft t6		Hole H7	Shaft u6		Hole H8	Shaft ×7
0	0.12	0.05 0.5	+0.25 −0	+0.5 +0.3	0.2 0.85	+0.4 −0	+0.85 +0.6				0.3 0.95	+0.4 −0	+0.95 +0.7	0.3 1.3	+0.6 −0	+1.3 +0.9
0.12	0.24	0.1 0.6	+0.3 −0	+0.6 +0.4	0.2 1.0	+0.5 −0	+1.0 +0.7				0.4 1.2	+0.5 −0	+1.2 +0.9	0.5 1.7	+0.7 −0	+1.7 +1.2
0.24	0.40	0.1 0.75	+0.4 −0	+0.75 +0.5	0.4 1.4	+0.6 −0	+1.4 +1.0				0.6 1.6	+0.6 −0	+1.6 +1.2	0.5 2.0	+0.9 −0	+2.0 +1.4
0.40	0.56	0.1 0.8	−0.4 −0	+0.8 +0.5	0.5 1.6	+0.7 −0	+1.6 +1.2				0.7 1.8	+0.7 −0	+1.8 +1.4	0.6 2.3	+1.0 −0	+2.3 +1.6
0.56	0.71	0.2 0.9	+0.4 −0	+0.9 +0.6	0.5 1.6	+0.7 −0	+1.6 +1.2				0.7 1.8	+0.7 −0	+1.8 +1.4	0.8 2.5	+1.0 −0	+2.5 +1.8
0.71	0.95	0.2 1.1	+0.5 −0	+1.1 +0.7	0.6 1.9	+0.8 −0	+1.9 +1.4				0.8 2.1	+0.8 −0	+2.1 +1.6	1.0 3.0	+1.2 −0	+3.0 +2.2
0.95	1.19	0.3 1.2	+0.5 −0	+1.2 +0.8	0.6 1.9	+0.8 −0	+1.9 +1.4	0.8 2.1	+0.8 −0	+2.1 +1.6	1.0 2.3	+0.8 −0	+2.3 +1.8	1.3 3.3	+1.2 −0	+3.3 +2.5
1.19	1.58	0.3 1.3	+0.6 −0	+1.3 +0.9	0.8 2.4	+1.0 −0	+2.4 +1.8	1.0 2.6	+1.0 −0	+2.6 +2.0	1.5 3.1	+1.0 −0	+3.1 +2.5	1.4 4.0	+1.6 −0	+4.0 +3.0
1.58	1.97	0.4 1.4	+0.6 −0	+1.4 +1.0	0.8 2.4	+1.0 −0	+2.4 +1.8	1.2 2.8	+1.0 −0	+2.8 +2.2	1.8 3.4	+1.0 −0	+3.4 +2.8	2.4 5.0	+1.6 −0	+5.0 +4.0
1.97	2.56	0.6 1.8	+0.7 −0	+1.8 +1.3	0.8 2.7	+1.2 −0	+2.7 +2.0	1.3 3.2	+1.2 −0	+3.2 +2.5	2.3 4.2	+1.2 −0	+4.2 +3.5	3.2 6.2	+1.8 −0	+6.2 +5.0
2.56	3.15	0.7 1.9	+0.7 −0	+1.9 +1.4	1.0 2.9	+1.2 −0	+2.9 +2.2	1.8 3.7	+1.2 −0	+3.7 +3.0	2.8 4.7	+1.2 −0	+4.7 +4.0	4.2 7.2	+1.8 −0	+7.2 +6.0
3.15	3.94	0.9 2.4	+0.9 −0	+2.4 +1.8	1.4 3.7	+1.4 −0	+3.7 +2.8	2.1 4.4	+1.4 −0	+4.4 +3.5	3.6 5.9	+1.4 −0	+5.9 +5.0	4.8 8.4	+2.2 −0	+8.4 +7.0
3.94	4.73	1.1 2.6	+0.9 −0	+2.6 +2.0	1.6 3.9	+1.4 −0	+3.9 +3.0	2.6 4.9	+1.4 −0	+4.9 +4.0	4.6 6.9	+1.4 −0	+6.9 +6.0	5.8 9.4	+2.2 −0	+9.4 +8.0
4.73	5.52	1.2 2.9	+1.0 −0	+2.9 +2.2	1.9 4.5	+1.6 −0	+4.5 +3.5	3.4 6.0	+1.6 −0	+6.0 +5.0	5.4 8.0	+1.6 −0	+8.0 +7.0	7.5 11.6	+2.5 −0	+11.6 +10.0
5.52	6.30	1.5 3.2	+1.0 −0	+3.2 +2.5	2.4 5.0	+1.6 −0	+5.0 +4.0	3.4 6.0	+1.6 −0	+6.0 +5.0	5.4 8.0	+1.6 −0	+8.0 +7.0	9.5 13.6	+2.5 −0	+13.6 +12.0
6.30	7.09	1.8 3.5	+1.0 −0	+3.5 +2.8	2.9 5.5	+1.6 −0	+5.5 +4.5	4.4 7.0	+1.6 −0	+7.0 +6.0	6.4 9.0	+1.6 −0	+9.0 +8.0	9.5 13.6	+2.5 −0	+13.6 +12.0
7.09	7.88	1.8 3.8	+1.2 −0	+3.8 +3.0	3.2 6.2	+1.8 −0	+6.2 +5.0	5.2 8.2	+1.8 −0	+8.2 +7.0	7.2 10.2	+1.8 −0	+10.2 +9.0	11.2 15.8	+2.8 −0	+15.8 +14.0
7.88	8.86	2.3 4.3	+1.2 −0	+4.3 +3.5	3.2 6.2	+1.8 −0	+6.2 +5.0	5.2 8.2	+1.8 −0	+8.2 +7.0	8.2 11.2	+1.8 −0	+11.2 +10.0	13.2 17.8	+2.8 −0	+17.8 +16.0
8.86	9.85	2.3 4.3	+1.2 −0	+4.3 +3.5	4.2 7.2	+1.8 −0	+7.2 +6.0	6.2 9.2	+1.8 −0	+9.2 +8.0	10.2 13.2	+1.8 −0	+13.2 +12.0	13.2 17.8	+2.8 −0	+17.8 +16.0
9.85	11.03	2.8 4.9	+1.2 −0	+4.9 +4.0	4.0 7.2	+2.0 −0	+7.2 +6.0	7.0 10.2	+2.0 −0	+10.2 +9.0	10.0 13.2	+2.0 −0	+13.2 +12.0	15.0 20.0	+3.0 −0	+20.0 +18.0

Continued

TABLE C.13.5   Force and Shrink Fits—Continued

Nominal Size Range Inches (Over – To)	Class FN 1 Limits of Interference	Class FN 1 Standard Limits Hole H6	Class FN 1 Shaft	Class FN 2 Limits of Interference	Class FN 2 Standard Limits Hole 17	Class FN 2 Shaft s6	Class FN 3 Limits of Interference	Class FN 3 Standard Limits Hole H7	Class FN 3 Shaft t6	Class FN 4 Limits of Interference	Class FN 4 Standard Limits Hole H7	Class FN 4 Shaft u6	Class FN 5 Limits of Interference	Class FN 5 Standard Limits Hole H8	Class FN 5 Shaft ×7
11.03 – 12.41	2.8 / 4.9	+ 1.2 / − 0	+ 4.9 / + 4.0	5.0 / 8.2	+ 2.0 / − 0	+ 8.2 / + 7.0	7.0 / 10.2	+ 2.0 / − 0	+ 10.2 / + 9.0	12.0 / 15.2	+ 2.0 / − 0	+ 15.2 / + 14.0	17.0 / 22.0	+ 3.0 / − 0	+ 22.0 / + 20.0
12.41 – 13.98	3.1 / 5.5	+ 1.4 / − 0	+ 5.5 / + 4.5	5.8 / 9.4	+ 2.2 / − 0	+ 9.4 / + 8.0	7.8 / 11.4	+ 2.2 / − 0	+ 11.4 / + 10.0	13.8 / 17.4	+ 2.2 / − 0	+ 17.4 / + 16.0	18.5 / 24.2	+ 3.5 / + 0	+ 24.2 / + 22.0
13.98 – 15.75	3.6 / 6.1	+ 1.4 / − 0	+ 6.1 / + 5.0	5.8 / 9.4	+ 2.2 / − 0	+ 9.4 / + 8.0	9.8 / 13.4	+ 2.2 / − 0	+ 13.4 / + 12.0	15.8 / 19.4	+ 2.2 / − 0	+ 19.4 / + 18.0	21.5 / 27.2	+ 3.5 / − 0	+ 27.2 / + 25.0
15.75 – 17.72	4.4 / 7.0	+ 1.6 / − 0	+ 7.0 / + 6.0	6.5 / 10.6	+ 2.5 / − 0	+ 10.6 / + 9.0	9.5 / 13.6	+ 2.5 / − 0	+ 13.6 / + 12.0	17.5 / 21.6	+ 2.5 / − 0	+ 21.6 / + 20.0	24.0 / 30.5	+ 4.0 / − 0	+ 30.5 / + 28.0
17.72 – 19.69	4.4 / 7.0	+ 1.6 / − 0	+ 7.0 / + 6.0	7.5 / 11.6	+ 2.5 / − 0	+ 11.6 / + 10.0	11.5 / 15.6	+ 2.5 / − 0	+ 15.6 / + 14.0	19.5 / 23.6	+ 2.5 / − 0	+ 23.6 / + 22.0	26.0 / 32.5	+ 4.0 / − 0	+ 32.5 / + 30.0
19.69 – 24.34	6.0 / 9.2	+ 2.0 / − 0	+ 9.2 / + 8.0	9.0 / 14.0	+ 3.0 / − 0	+ 14.0 / + 12.0	15.0 / 20.0	+ 3.0 / − 0	+ 20.0 / + 18.0	22.0 / 27.0	+ 3.0 / − 0	+ 27.0 / + 25.0	30.0 / 38.0	+ 5.0 / − 0	+ 38.0 / + 35.0
24.34 – 30.09	7.0 / 10.2	+ 2.0 / − 0	+ 10.2 / + 9.0	11.0 / 16.0	+ 3.0 / − 0	+ 16.0 / + 14.0	17.0 / 22.0	+ 3.0 / − 0	+ 22.0 / + 20.0	27.0 / 32.0	+ 3.0 / − 0	+ 32.0 / + 30.0	35.0 / 43.0	+ 5.0 / − 0	+ 43.0 / + 40.0
30.09 – 35.47	7.5 / 11.6	+ 2.5 / − 0	+ 11.6 / + 10.0	14.0 / 20.5	+ 4.0 / − 0	+ 20.5 / + 18.0	21.0 / 27.5	+ 4.0 / − 0	+ 27.5 / + 25.0	31.0 / 37.5	+ 4.0 / − 0	+ 37.5 / + 35.0	44.0 / 54.0	+ 6.0 / − 0	+ 54.0 / + 50.0
35.47 – 41.49	9.5 / 13.6	+ 2.5 / − 0	+ 13.6 / + 12.0	16.0 / 22.5	+ 4.0 / − 0	+ 22.5 / + 20.0	24.0 / 30.5	+ 4.0 / − 0	+ 30.5 / + 28.0	36.0 / 43.5	+ 4.0 / − 0	+ 43.5 / + 40.0	54.0 / 64.0	+ 6.0 / − 0	+ 64.0 / + 60.0
41.49 – 48.28	11.0 / 16.0	+ 3.0 / − 0	+ 16.0 / + 14.0	17.0 / 25.0	+ 5.0 / − 0	+ 25.0 / + 22.0	30.0 / 38.0	+ 5.0 / − 0	+ 38.0 / + 35.0	45.0 / 53.0	+ 5.0 / − 0	+ 53.0 / + 50.0	62.0 / 75.0	+ 8.0 / − 0	+ 75.0 / + 70.0
48.28 – 56.19	13.0 / 18.0	+ 3.0 / − 0	+ 18.0 / + 16.0	20.0 / 28.0	+ 5.0 / − 0	+ 28.0 / + 25.0	35.0 / 43.0	+ 5.0 / − 0	+ 43.0 / + 40.0	55.0 / 63.0	+ 5.0 / − 0	+ 63.0 / + 60.0	72.0 / 85.0	+ 8.0 / − 0	+ 85.0 / + 80.0
56.19 – 65.54	14.0 / 20.5	+ 4.0 / − 0	+ 20.5 / + 18.0	24.0 / 34.0	+ 6.0 / − 0	+ 34.0 / + 30.0	39.0 / 49.0	+ 6.0 / − 0	+ 49.0 / + 45.0	64.0 / 74.0	+ 6.0 / − 0	+ 74.0 / + 70.0	90.0 / 106	+ 10.0 / − 0	+ 106 / + 100
65.54 – 76.39	18.0 / 24.5	+ 4.0 / − 0	+ 24.5 / + 22.0	29.0 / 39.0	+ 6.0 / − 0	+ 39.0 / 35.0	44.0 / 54.0	+ 6.0 / − 0	+ 54.0 / + 50.0	74.0 / 84.0	+ 6.0 / − 0	+ 84.0 / + 80.0	110 / 126	+ 10.0 / − 0	+ 126 / + 120
76.39 – 87.79	20.0 / 28.0	+ 5.0 / − 0	+ 28.0 / + 25.0	32.0 / 45.0	+ 8.0 / − 0	+ 45.0 / + 40.0	52.0 / 65.0	+ 8.0 / − 0	+ 65.0 / + 60.0	82.0 / 95.0	+ 8.0 / − 0	+ 95.0 / + 90.0	128 / 148	+ 12.0 / − 0	+ 148 / + 140
87.79 – 100.9	23.0 / 31.0	+ 5.0 / − 0	+ 31.0 / + 28.0	37.0 / 50.0	+ 8.0 / − 0	+ 50.0 / + 45.0	62.0 / 75.0	+ 8.0 / − 0	+ 75.0 / + 70.0	92.0 / 105	+ 8.0 / − 0	+ 105 / + 100	148 / 168	+ 12.0 / − 0	+ 168 / + 160
100.9 – 115.3	24.0 / 34.0	+ 6.0 / − 0	+ 34.0 / + 30.0	40.0 / 56.0	+ 10.0 / − 0	+ 56.0 / + 50.0	70.0 / 86.0	+ 10.0 / − 0	+ 86.0 / + 80.0	110 / 126	+ 10.0 / − 0	+ 126 / + 120	164 / 190	+ 16.0 / − 0	+ 190 / + 180
115.3 – 131.9	29.0 / 39.0	+ 6.0 / − 0	+ 39.0 / + 35.0	50.0 / 66.0	+ 10.0 / − 0	+ 66.0 / + 60.0	80.0 / 96.0	+ 10.0 / − 0	+ 96.0 / + 90.0	130 / 146	+ 10.0 / − 0	+ 146 / + 140	184 / 210	+ 16.0 / − 0	+ 210 / + 200
131.9 – 152.2	37.0 / 50.0	+ 8.0 / − 0	+ 50.0 / + 45.0	58.0 / 78.0	+ 12.0 / − 0	+ 78.0 / + 70.0	88.0 / 108	+ 12.0 / − 0	+ 108 / + 100	148 / 168	+ 12.0 / − 0	+ 168 / + 160	200 / 232	+ 20.0 / − 0	+ 232 / + 220
152.2 – 171.9	42.0 / 55.0	+ 8.0 / − 0	+ 55.0 / + 50.0	68.0 / 88.0	+ 12.0 / − 0	+ 88.0 / + 80.0	108 / 128	+ 12.0 / − 0	+ 128 / + 120	168 / 188	+ 12.0 / − 0	+ 188 / + 170	230 / 262	+ 20.0 / − 0	+ 262 / + 250
171.9 – 200	50.0 / 66.0	+ 10.0 / − 0	+ 66.0 / + 60.0	74.0 / 100	+ 16.0 / − 0	+ 100 / + 90	124 / 150	+ 16.0 / − 0	+ 150 / + 140	184 / 210	+ 16.0 / − 0	+ 210 / + 200	275 / 316	+ 2.5 / − 0	+ 316 / + 300

TABLE C.13.6   Preferred Metric Hole Basis Clearance Fits

BASIC SIZE		LOOSE RUNNING			FREE RUNNING			CLOSE RUNNING			SLIDING			LOCATIONAL CLEARANCE		
		Hole H11	Shaft c11	Fit	Hole H9	Shaft d9	Fit	Hole H8	Shaft f7	Fit	Hole H7	Shaft g6	Fit	Hole H7	Shaft h6	Fit
1	MAX	1.060	0.940	0.180	1.025	0.980	0.070	1.014	0.994	0.030	1.010	0.998	0.018	1.010	1.000	0.016
	MIN	1.000	0.880	0.060	1.000	0.955	0.020	1.000	0.984	0.006	1.000	0.992	0.002	1.000	0.994	0.000
1.2	MAX	1.260	1.140	0.180	1.225	1.180	0.070	1.214	1.194	0.030	1.210	1.198	0.018	1.210	1.200	0.016
	MIN	1.200	1.080	0.060	1.200	1.155	0.020	1.200	1.184	0.006	1.200	1.192	0.002	1.200	1.194	0.000
1.6	MAX	1.660	1.540	0.180	1.625	1.580	0.070	1.614	1.594	0.030	1.610	1.598	0.018	1.610	1.600	0.016
	MIN	1.600	1.480	0.060	1.600	1.555	0.020	1.600	1.584	0.006	1.600	1.592	0.002	1.600	1.594	0.000
2	MAX	2.060	1.940	0.180	2.025	1.980	0.070	2.014	1.994	0.030	2.010	1.998	0.018	2.010	2.000	0.016
	MIN	2.000	1.880	0.060	2.000	1.955	0.020	2.000	1.984	0.006	2.000	1.992	0.002	2.000	1.994	0.000
2.5	MAX	2.560	2.440	0.180	2.525	2.480	0.070	2.514	2.494	0.030	2.510	2.498	0.018	2.510	2.500	0.016
	MIN	2.500	2.380	0.060	2.500	2.455	0.020	2.500	2.484	0.006	2.500	2.492	0.002	2.500	2.494	0.000
3	MAX	3.060	2.940	0.180	3.025	2.980	0.070	3.014	2.994	0.030	3.010	2.998	0.018	3.010	3.000	0.016
	MIN	3.000	2.880	0.060	3.000	2.955	0.020	3.000	2.984	0.006	3.000	2.992	0.002	3.000	2.994	0.000
4	MAX	4.075	3.930	0.220	4.030	3.970	0.090	4.018	3.990	0.040	4.012	3.996	0.024	4.012	4.000	0.020
	MIN	4.000	3.855	0.070	4.000	3.940	0.030	4.000	3.978	0.010	4.000	3.988	0.004	4.000	3.992	0.000
5	MAX	5.075	4.930	0.220	5.030	4.970	0.090	5.018	4.990	0.040	5.012	4.996	0.024	5.012	5.000	0.020
	MIN	5.000	4.855	0.070	5.000	4.940	0.030	5.000	4.978	0.010	5.000	4.988	0.004	5.000	4.992	0.000
6	MAX	6.075	5.930	0.220	6.030	5.970	0.090	6.018	5.990	0.040	6.012	5.996	0.024	6.012	6.000	0.020
	MIN	6.000	5.855	0.070	6.000	5.940	0.030	6.000	5.978	0.010	6.000	5.988	0.004	6.000	5.992	0.000
8	MAX	8.090	7.920	0.260	8.036	7.960	0.112	8.022	7.987	0.050	8.015	7.995	0.029	8.015	8.000	0.024
	MIN	8.000	7.830	0.080	8.000	7.924	0.040	8.000	7.972	0.013	8.000	7.986	0.005	8.000	7.991	0.000
10	MAX	10.090	9.920	0.260	10.036	9.960	0.112	10.022	9.987	0.050	10.015	9.995	0.029	10.015	10.000	0.024
	MIN	10.000	9.830	0.080	10.000	9.924	0.040	10.000	9.972	0.013	10.000	9.986	0.005	10.000	9.991	0.000
12	MAX	12.110	11.905	0.315	12.043	11.950	0.136	12.027	11.984	0.061	12.018	11.994	0.035	12.018	12.000	0.029
	MIN	12.000	11.795	0.095	12.000	11.907	0.050	12.000	11.966	0.016	12.000	11.983	0.006	12.000	11.989	0.000
16	MAX	16.110	15.905	0.315	16.043	15.950	0.136	16.027	15.984	0.061	16.018	15.994	0.035	16.018	16.000	0.029
	MIN	16.000	15.795	0.095	16.000	15.907	0.050	16.000	15.966	0.016	16.000	15.983	0.006	16.000	15.989	0.000
20	MAX	20.130	19.890	0.370	20.052	19.935	0.169	20.033	19.980	0.074	20.021	19.993	0.041	20.021	20.000	0.034
	MIN	20.000	19.760	0.110	20.000	19.883	0.065	20.000	19.959	0.020	20.000	19.980	0.007	20.000	19.987	0.000

Continued

TABLE C.13.6   Preferred Metric Hole Basis Clearance Fits—*Continued*

BASIC SIZE	LOOSE RUNNING			FREE RUNNING			CLOSE RUNNING			SLIDING			LOCATIONAL CLEARANCE		
	Hole H11	Shaft c11	Fit	Hole H9	Shaft d9	Fit	Hole H8	Shaft f7	Fit	Hole H7	Shaft g6	Fit	Hole H7	Shaft h6	Fit
25 MAX	25.130	24.890	0.370	25.052	24.935	0.169	25.033	24.980	0.074	25.021	24.993	0.041	25.021	25.000	0.034
MIN	25.000	24.760	0.110	25.000	24.883	0.065	25.000	24.959	0.020	25.000	24.980	0.007	25.000	24.987	0.000
30 MAX	30.130	29.890	0.370	30.052	29.935	0.169	30.033	29.980	0.074	30.021	29.993	0.041	30.021	30.000	0.034
MIN	30.000	29.760	0.110	30.000	29.883	0.065	30.000	29.959	0.020	30.000	29.980	0.007	30.000	29.987	0.000
40 MAX	40.160	39.880	0.440	40.062	39.920	0.204	40.039	39.975	0.089	40.025	39.991	0.050	40.025	40.000	0.041
MIN	40.000	39.720	0.120	40.000	39.858	0.080	40.000	39.950	0.025	40.000	39.975	0.009	40.000	39.984	0.000
50 MAX	50.160	49.870	0.450	50.062	49.920	0.204	50.039	49.975	0.089	50.025	49.991	0.050	50.025	50.000	0.041
MIN	50.000	49.710	0.130	50.000	49.858	0.080	50.000	49.950	0.025	50.000	49.975	0.009	50.000	49.984	0.000
60 MAX	60.190	59.860	0.520	60.074	59.900	0.248	60.046	59.970	0.106	60.030	59.990	0.059	60.030	60.000	0.049
MIN	60.000	59.670	0.140	60.000	59.826	0.100	60.000	59.940	0.030	60.000	59.971	0.010	60.000	59.981	0.000
80 MAX	80.190	79.850	0.530	80.074	79.900	0.248	80.046	79.970	0.106	80.030	79.990	0.059	80.030	80.000	0.049
MIN	80.000	79.660	0.150	80.000	79.826	0.100	80.000	79.940	0.030	80.000	79.971	0.010	80.000	79.981	0.000
100 MAX	100.220	99.830	0.610	100.087	99.880	0.294	100.054	99.964	0.125	100.035	99.988	0.069	100.035	100.000	0.057
MIN	100.000	99.610	0.170	100.000	99.793	0.120	100.000	99.929	0.036	100.000	99.966	0.012	100.000	99.978	0.000
120 MAX	120.220	119.820	0.620	120.087	119.880	0.294	120.054	119.964	0.125	120.035	119.988	0.069	120.035	120.000	0.057
MIN	120.000	119.600	0.180	120.000	119.793	0.120	120.000	119.929	0.036	120.000	119.966	0.012	120.000	119.978	0.000
160 MAX	160.250	159.790	0.710	160.100	159.855	0.345	160.063	159.957	0.146	160.040	159.986	0.079	160.040	160.000	0.065
MIN	160.000	159.540	0.210	160.000	159.755	0.145	160.000	159.917	0.043	160.000	159.961	0.014	160.000	159.975	0.000
200 MAX	200.290	199.760	0.820	200.115	199.830	0.400	200.072	199.950	0.168	200.046	199.985	0.090	200.046	200.000	0.075
MIN	200.000	199.470	0.240	200.000	199.715	0.170	200.000	199.904	0.050	200.000	199.956	0.015	200.000	199.971	0.000
250 MAX	250.290	249.720	0.860	250.115	249.830	0.400	250.072	249.950	0.168	250.046	249.985	0.090	250.046	250.000	0.075
MIN	250.000	249.430	0.280	250.000	249.715	0.170	250.000	249.904	0.050	250.000	249.956	0.015	250.000	249.971	0.000
300 MAX	300.320	299.670	0.970	300.130	299.810	0.450	300.081	299.944	0.189	300.052	299.983	0.101	300.052	300.000	0.084
MIN	300.000	299.350	0.330	300.000	299.680	0.190	300.000	299.892	0.056	300.000	299.951	0.017	300.000	299.968	0.000
400 MAX	400.360	399.600	1.120	400.140	399.790	0.490	400.089	399.938	0.208	400.057	399.982	0.111	400.057	400.000	0.093
MIN	400.000	399.240	0.400	400.000	399.650	0.210	400.000	399.881	0.062	400.000	399.946	0.018	400.000	399.964	0.000
500 MAX	500.400	499.520	1.280	500.155	499.770	0.540	500.097	499.932	0.228	500.063	499.980	0.123	500.063	500.000	0.103
MIN	500.000	499.120	0.480	500.000	499.615	0.230	500.000	499.869	0.068	500.000	499.940	0.020	500.000	499.960	0.000

TABLE C.13.7   Preferred Metric Hole Basis Transition and Interference Fits

BASIC SIZE		LOCATIONAL TRANSN.			LOCATIONAL TRANSN.			LOCATIONAL INTERF.			MEDIUM DRIVE			FORCE		
		Hole H7	Shaft k6	Fit	Hole H7	Shaft n6	Fit	Hole H7	Shaft p6	Fit	Hole H7	Shaft s6	Fit	Hole H7	Shaft u6	Fit
1	MAX	1.010	1.006	0.010	1.010	1.010	0.006	1.010	1.012	0.004	1.010	1.020	−0.004	1.010	1.024	−0.008
	MIN	1.000	1.000	−0.006	1.000	1.004	−0.010	1.000	1.006	−0.012	1.000	1.014	−0.020	1.000	1.018	−0.024
1.2	MAX	1.210	1.206	0.010	1.210	1.210	0.006	1.210	1.212	0.004	1.210	1.220	−0.004	1.210	1.224	−0.008
	MIN	1.200	1.200	−0.006	1.200	1.204	−0.010	1.200	1.206	−0.012	1.200	1.214	−0.020	1.200	1.218	−0.024
1.6	MAX	1.610	1.606	0.010	1.610	1.610	0.006	1.610	1.612	0.004	1.610	1.620	−0.004	1.610	1.624	−0.008
	MIN	1.600	1.600	−0.006	1.600	1.604	−0.010	1.600	1.606	−0.012	1.600	1.614	−0.020	1.600	1.618	−0.024
2	MAX	2.010	2.006	0.010	2.010	2.010	0.006	2.010	2.012	0.004	2.010	2.020	−0.004	2.010	2.024	−0.008
	MIN	2.000	2.000	−0.006	2.000	2.004	−0.010	2.000	2.006	−0.012	2.000	2.014	−0.020	2.000	2.018	−0.024
2.5	MAX	2.510	2.506	0.010	2.510	2.510	0.006	2.510	2.512	0.004	2.510	2.520	−0.004	2.510	2.524	−0.008
	MIN	2.500	2.500	−0.006	2.500	2.504	−0.010	2.500	2.506	−0.012	2.500	2.514	−0.020	2.500	2.518	−0.024
3	MAX	3.010	3.006	0.010	3.010	3.010	0.006	3.010	3.012	0.004	3.010	3.020	−0.004	3.010	3.024	−0.008
	MIN	3.000	3.000	−0.006	3.000	3.004	−0.010	3.000	3.006	−0.012	3.000	3.014	−0.020	3.000	3.018	−0.024
4	MAX	4.012	4.009	0.011	4.012	4.016	0.004	4.012	4.020	0.000	4.012	4.027	−0.007	4.012	4.031	−0.011
	MIN	4.000	4.001	−0.009	4.000	4.008	−0.016	4.000	4.012	−0.020	4.000	4.019	−0.027	4.000	4.023	−0.031
5	MAX	5.012	5.009	0.011	5.012	5.016	0.004	5.012	5.020	0.000	5.012	5.027	−0.007	5.012	5.031	−0.011
	MIN	5.000	5.001	−0.009	5.000	5.008	−0.016	5.000	5.012	−0.020	5.000	5.019	−0.027	5.000	5.023	−0.031
6	MAX	6.012	6.009	0.011	6.012	6.016	0.004	6.012	6.020	0.000	6.012	6.027	−0.007	6.012	6.031	−0.011
	MIN	6.000	6.001	−0.009	6.000	6.008	−0.016	6.000	6.012	−0.020	6.000	6.019	−0.027	6.000	6.023	−0.031
8	MAX	8.015	8.010	0.014	8.015	8.019	0.005	8.015	8.024	0.000	8.015	8.032	−0.008	8.015	8.037	−0.013
	MIN	8.000	8.001	−0.010	8.000	8.010	−0.019	8.000	8.015	−0.024	8.000	8.023	−0.032	8.000	8.028	−0.037
10	MAX	10.015	10.010	0.014	10.015	10.019	0.005	10.015	10.024	0.000	10.015	10.032	−0.008	10.015	10.037	−0.013
	MIN	10.000	10.001	−0.010	10.000	10.010	−0.019	10.000	10.015	−0.024	10.000	10.023	−0.032	10.000	10.028	−0.037
12	MAX	12.018	12.012	0.017	12.018	12.023	0.006	12.018	12.029	0.000	12.018	12.039	−0.010	12.018	12.044	−0.015
	MIN	12.000	12.001	−0.012	12.000	12.012	−0.023	12.000	12.018	−0.029	12.000	12.028	−0.039	12.000	12.033	−0.044
16	MAX	16.018	16.012	0.017	16.018	16.023	0.006	16.018	16.029	0.000	16.018	16.039	−0.010	16.018	16.044	−0.015
	MIN	16.000	16.001	−0.012	16.000	16.012	−0.023	16.000	16.018	−0.029	16.000	16.028	−0.039	16.000	16.033	−0.044
20	MAX	20.021	20.015	0.019	20.021	20.028	0.006	20.021	20.035	−0.001	20.021	20.048	−0.014	20.021	20.054	−0.020
	MIN	20.000	20.002	−0.015	20.000	20.015	−0.028	20.000	20.022	−0.035	20.000	20.035	−0.048	20.000	20.041	−0.054

Continued

TABLE C.13.7 Preferred Metric Hole Basis Transition and Interference Fits—*Continued*

BASIC SIZE	LOCATIONAL TRANSN.			LOCATIONAL TRANSN.			LOCATIONAL INTERF.			MEDIUM DRIVE			FORCE		
	Hole H7	Shaft k6	Fit	Hole H7	Shaft n6	Fit	Hole H7	Shaft p6	Fit	Hole H7	Shaft s6	Fit	Hole H7	Shaft u6	Fit
25 MAX	25.021	25.015	0.019	25.021	25.028	0.006	25.021	25.035	−0.001	25.021	25.048	−0.014	25.021	25.061	−0.027
MIN	25.000	25.002	−0.015	25.000	25.015	−0.028	25.000	25.022	−0.035	25.000	25.035	−0.048	25.000	25.048	−0.061
30 MAX	30.021	30.015	0.019	30.021	30.028	0.006	30.021	30.035	−0.001	30.021	30.048	−0.014	30.021	30.061	−0.027
MIN	30.000	30.002	−0.015	30.000	30.015	−0.028	30.000	30.022	−0.035	30.000	30.035	−0.048	30.000	30.048	−0.061
40 MAX	40.025	40.018	0.023	40.025	40.033	0.008	40.025	40.042	−0.001	40.025	40.059	−0.018	40.025	40.076	−0.035
MIN	40.000	40.002	−0.018	40.000	40.017	−0.033	40.000	40.026	−0.042	40.000	40.043	−0.059	40.000	40.060	−0.076
50 MAX	50.025	50.018	0.023	50.025	50.033	0.008	50.025	50.042	−0.001	50.025	50.059	−0.018	50.025	50.086	−0.045
MIN	50.000	50.002	−0.018	50.000	50.017	−0.033	50.000	50.026	−0.042	50.000	50.043	−0.059	50.000	50.070	−0.086
60 MAX	60.030	60.021	0.028	60.030	60.039	0.010	60.030	60.051	−0.002	60.030	60.072	−0.023	60.030	60.106	−0.057
MIN	60.000	60.002	−0.021	60.000	60.020	−0.039	60.000	60.032	−0.051	60.000	60.053	−0.072	60.000	60.087	−0.106
80 MAX	80.030	80.021	0.028	80.030	80.039	0.010	80.030	80.051	−0.002	80.030	80.078	−0.029	80.030	80.121	−0.072
MIN	80.000	80.002	−0.021	80.000	80.020	−0.039	80.000	80.032	−0.051	80.000	80.059	−0.078	80.000	80.102	−0.121
100 MAX	100.035	100.025	0.032	100.035	100.045	0.012	100.035	100.059	−0.002	100.035	100.093	−0.036	100.035	100.146	−0.089
MIN	100.000	100.003	−0.025	100.000	100.023	−0.045	100.000	100.037	−0.059	100.000	100.071	−0.093	100.000	100.124	−0.146
120 MAX	120.035	120.025	0.032	120.035	120.045	0.012	120.035	120.059	−0.002	120.035	120.101	−0.044	120.035	120.166	−0.109
MIN	120.000	120.003	−0.025	120.000	120.023	−0.045	120.000	120.037	−0.059	120.000	120.079	−0.101	120.000	120.144	−0.166
160 MAX	160.040	160.028	0.037	160.040	160.052	0.013	160.040	160.068	−0.003	160.040	160.125	−0.060	160.040	160.215	−0.150
MIN	160.000	160.003	−0.028	160.000	160.027	−0.052	160.000	160.043	−0.068	160.000	160.100	−0.125	160.000	160.190	−0.215
200 MAX	200.046	200.033	0.042	200.046	200.060	0.015	200.046	200.079	−0.004	200.046	200.151	−0.076	200.046	200.265	−0.190
MIN	200.000	200.004	−0.033	200.000	200.031	−0.060	200.000	200.050	−0.079	200.000	200.122	−0.151	200.000	200.236	−0.265
250 MAX	250.046	250.033	0.042	250.046	250.060	0.015	250.046	250.079	−0.004	250.046	250.169	−0.094	250.046	250.313	−0.238
MIN	250.000	250.004	−0.033	250.000	250.031	−0.060	250.000	250.050	−0.079	250.000	250.140	−0.169	250.000	250.284	−0.313
300 MAX	300.052	300.036	0.048	300.052	300.066	0.018	300.052	300.088	−0.004	300.052	300.202	−0.118	300.052	300.382	−0.298
MIN	300.000	300.004	−0.036	300.000	300.034	−0.066	300.000	300.056	−0.088	300.000	300.170	−0.202	300.000	300.350	−0.382
400 MAX	400.057	400.040	0.053	400.057	400.073	0.020	400.057	400.098	−0.005	400.057	400.244	−0.151	400.057	400.471	−0.378
MIN	400.000	400.004	−0.040	400.000	400.037	−0.073	400.000	400.062	−0.098	400.000	400.208	−0.244	400.000	400.435	−0.471
500 MAX	500.063	500.045	0.058	500.063	500.080	0.023	500.063	500.108	−0.005	500.063	500.292	−0.189	500.063	500.580	−0.477
MIN	500.000	500.005	−0.045	500.000	500.040	−0.080	500.000	500.068	−0.108	500.000	500.252	−0.292	500.000	500.540	−0.580

TABLE C.13.8   Preferred Metric Shaft Basis Clearance Fits

BASIC SIZE		LOOSE RUNNING Hole C11	Shaft h11	Fit	FREE RUNNING Hole D9	Shaft h9	Fit	CLOSE RUNNING Hole F8	Shaft h7	Fit	SLIDING Hole G7	Shaft h6	Fit	LOCATIONAL CLEARANCE Hole H7	Shaft h6	Fit
1	MAX	1.120	1.000	0.180	1.045	1.000	0.070	1.020	1.000	0.030	1.012	1.000	0.018	1.010	1.000	0.016
	MIN	1.060	0.940	0.060	1.020	0.975	0.020	1.006	0.990	0.006	1.002	0.994	0.002	1.000	0.994	0.000
1.2	MAX	1.320	1.200	0.180	1.245	1.200	0.070	1.220	1.200	0.030	1.212	1.200	0.018	1.210	1.200	0.016
	MIN	1.260	1.140	0.060	1.220	1.175	0.020	1.206	1.190	0.006	1.202	1.194	0.002	1.200	1.194	0.000
1.6	MAX	1.720	1.600	0.180	1.645	1.600	0.070	1.620	1.600	0.030	1.612	1.600	0.018	1.610	1.600	0.016
	MIN	1.660	1.540	0.060	1.620	1.575	0.020	1.606	1.590	0.006	1.602	1.594	0.002	1.600	1.594	0.000
2	MAX	2.120	2.000	0.180	2.045	2.000	0.070	2.020	2.000	0.030	2.012	2.000	0.018	2.010	2.000	0.016
	MIN	2.060	1.940	0.060	2.020	1.975	0.020	2.006	1.990	0.006	2.002	1.994	0.002	2.000	1.994	0.000
2.5	MAX	2.620	2.500	0.180	2.545	2.500	0.070	2.520	2.500	0.030	2.512	2.500	0.018	2.510	2.500	0.016
	MIN	2.560	2.440	0.060	2.520	2.475	0.020	2.506	2.490	0.006	2.502	2.494	0.002	2.500	2.494	0.000
3	MAX	3.120	3.000	0.180	3.045	3.000	0.070	3.020	3.000	0.030	3.012	3.000	0.018	3.010	3.000	0.016
	MIN	3.060	2.940	0.060	3.020	2.975	0.020	3.006	2.990	0.006	3.002	2.994	0.002	3.000	2.994	0.000
4	MAX	4.145	4.000	0.220	4.060	4.000	0.090	4.028	4.000	0.040	4.016	4.000	0.024	4.012	4.000	0.020
	MIN	4.070	3.925	0.070	4.030	3.970	0.030	4.010	3.988	0.010	4.004	3.992	0.004	4.000	3.992	0.000
5	MAX	5.145	5.000	0.220	5.060	5.000	0.090	5.028	5.000	0.040	5.016	5.000	0.024	5.012	5.000	0.020
	MIN	5.070	4.925	0.070	5.030	4.970	0.030	5.010	4.988	0.010	5.004	4.992	0.004	5.000	4.992	0.000
6	MAX	6.145	6.000	0.220	6.060	6.000	0.090	6.028	6.000	0.040	6.016	6.000	0.024	6.012	6.000	0.020
	MIN	6.070	5.925	0.070	6.030	5.970	0.030	6.010	5.988	0.010	6.004	5.992	0.004	6.000	5.992	0.000
8	MAX	8.170	8.000	0.260	8.076	8.000	0.112	8.035	8.000	0.050	8.020	8.000	0.029	8.015	8.000	0.024
	MIN	8.080	7.910	0.080	8.040	7.964	0.040	8.013	7.985	0.013	8.005	7.991	0.005	8.000	7.991	0.000
10	MAX	10.170	10.000	0.260	10.076	10.000	0.112	10.035	10.000	0.050	10.020	10.000	0.029	10.015	10.000	0.024
	MIN	10.080	9.910	0.080	10.040	9.964	0.040	10.013	9.985	0.013	10.005	9.991	0.005	10.000	9.991	0.000
12	MAX	12.205	12.000	0.315	12.093	12.000	0.136	12.043	12.000	0.061	12.024	12.000	0.035	12.018	12.000	0.029
	MIN	12.095	11.890	0.095	12.050	11.957	0.050	12.016	11.982	0.016	12.006	11.989	0.006	12.000	11.989	0.000
16	MAX	16.205	16.000	0.315	16.093	16.000	0.136	16.043	16.000	0.061	16.024	16.000	0.035	16.018	16.000	0.029
	MIN	16.095	15.890	0.095	16.050	15.957	0.050	16.016	15.982	0.016	16.006	15.989	0.006	16.000	15.989	0.000
20	MAX	20.240	20.000	0.370	20.117	20.000	0.169	20.053	20.000	0.074	20.028	20.000	0.041	20.021	20.000	0.034
	MIN	20.110	19.870	0.110	20.065	19.948	0.065	20.020	19.979	0.020	20.007	19.987	0.007	20.000	19.987	0.000

Continued

TABLE C.13.8   Preferred Metric Shaft Basis Clearance Fits—*Continued*

BASIC SIZE		LOOSE RUNNING			FREE RUNNING			CLOSE RUNNING			SLIDING			LOCATIONAL CLEARANCE		
		Hole C11	Shaft h11	Fit	Hole D9	Shaft h9	Fit	Hole F8	Shaft h7	Fit	Hole G7	Shaft h6	Fit	Hole H7	Shaft h6	Fit
25	MAX	25.240	25.000	0.370	25.117	25.000	0.169	25.053	25.000	0.074	25.028	25.000	0.041	25.021	25.000	0.034
	MIN	25.110	24.870	0.110	25.065	24.948	0.065	25.020	24.979	0.020	25.007	24.987	0.007	25.000	24.987	0.000
30	MAX	30.240	30.000	0.370	30.117	30.000	0.169	30.053	30.000	0.074	30.028	30.000	0.041	30.021	30.000	0.034
	MIN	30.110	29.870	0.110	30.065	29.948	0.065	30.020	29.979	0.020	30.007	29.987	0.007	30.000	29.987	0.000
40	MAX	40.280	40.000	0.440	40.142	40.000	0.204	40.064	40.000	0.089	40.034	40.000	0.050	40.025	40.000	0.041
	MIN	40.120	39.840	0.120	40.080	39.938	0.080	40.025	39.975	0.025	40.009	39.984	0.009	40.000	39.984	0.000
50	MAX	50.290	50.000	0.450	50.142	50.000	0.204	50.064	50.000	0.089	50.034	50.000	0.050	50.025	50.000	0.041
	MIN	50.130	49.840	0.130	50.080	49.938	0.080	50.025	49.975	0.025	50.009	49.984	0.009	50.000	49.984	0.000
60	MAX	60.330	60.000	0.520	60.174	60.000	0.248	60.076	60.000	0.106	60.040	60.000	0.059	60.030	60.000	0.049
	MIN	60.140	59.810	0.140	60.100	59.926	0.100	60.030	59.970	0.030	60.010	59.981	0.010	60.000	59.981	0.000
80	MAX	80.340	80.000	0.530	80.174	80.000	0.248	80.076	80.000	0.106	80.040	80.000	0.059	80.030	80.000	0.049
	MIN	80.150	79.810	0.150	80.100	79.926	0.100	80.030	79.970	0.030	80.010	79.981	0.010	80.000	79.981	0.000
100	MAX	100.390	100.000	0.610	100.207	100.000	0.294	100.090	100.000	0.125	100.047	100.000	0.069	100.035	100.000	0.057
	MIN	100.170	99.780	0.170	100.120	99.913	0.120	100.036	99.965	0.036	100.012	99.978	0.012	100.000	99.978	0.000
120	MAX	120.400	120.000	0.620	120.207	120.000	0.294	120.090	120.000	0.125	120.047	120.000	0.069	120.035	120.000	0.057
	MIN	120.180	119.780	0.180	120.120	119.913	0.120	120.036	119.965	0.036	120.012	119.978	0.012	120.000	119.978	0.000
160	MAX	160.460	160.000	0.710	160.245	160.000	0.345	160.106	160.000	0.146	160.054	160.000	0.079	160.040	160.000	0.065
	MIN	160.210	159.750	0.210	160.145	159.900	0.145	160.043	159.960	0.043	160.014	159.975	0.014	160.000	159.975	0.000
200	MAX	200.530	200.000	0.820	200.285	200.000	0.400	200.122	200.000	0.168	200.061	200.000	0.090	200.046	200.000	0.075
	MIN	200.240	199.710	0.240	200.170	199.885	0.170	200.050	199.954	0.050	200.015	199.971	0.015	200.000	199.971	0.000
250	MAX	250.570	250.000	0.860	250.285	250.000	0.400	250.122	250.000	0.168	250.061	250.000	0.090	250.046	250.000	0.075
	MIN	250.280	249.710	0.280	250.170	249.885	0.170	250.050	249.954	0.050	250.015	249.971	0.015	250.000	249.971	0.000
300	MAX	300.650	300.000	0.970	300.320	300.000	0.450	300.137	300.000	0.189	300.069	300.000	0.101	300.052	300.000	0.084
	MIN	300.330	299.680	0.330	300.190	299.870	0.190	300.056	299.948	0.056	300.017	299.968	0.017	300.000	299.968	0.000
400	MAX	400.760	400.000	1.120	400.350	400.000	0.490	400.151	400.000	0.208	400.075	400.000	0.111	400.057	400.000	0.093
	MIN	400.400	399.640	0.400	400.210	399.860	0.210	400.062	399.943	0.062	400.018	399.964	0.018	400.000	399.964	0.000
500	MAX	500.880	500.000	1.280	500.385	500.000	0.540	500.165	500.000	0.228	500.083	500.000	0.123	500.063	500.000	0.103
	MIN	500.480	499.600	0.480	500.230	499.845	0.230	500.068	499.937	0.068	500.020	499.960	0.020	500.000	499.960	0.000

TABLE C.13.9 Preferred Metric Shaft Basis Transition and Interference Fits

BASIC SIZE		LOCATIONAL TRANSN. Hole K7	Shaft h6	Fit	LOCATIONAL TRANSN. Hole N7	Shaft h6	Fit	LOCATIONAL INTERF. Hole P7	Shaft h6	Fit	MEDIUM DRIVE Hole S7	Shaft h6	Fit	FORCE Hole U7	Shaft h6	Fit
1	MAX	1.000	1.000	0.006	0.996	1.000	0.002	0.994	1.000	0.000	0.986	1.000	−0.008	0.982	1.000	−0.012
	MIN	0.990	0.994	−0.010	0.986	0.994	−0.014	0.984	0.994	−0.016	0.976	0.994	−0.024	0.972	0.994	−0.028
1.2	MAX	1.200	1.200	0.006	1.196	1.200	0.002	1.194	1.200	0.000	1.186	1.200	−0.008	1.182	1.200	−0.012
	MIN	1.190	1.194	−0.010	1.186	1.194	−0.014	1.184	1.194	−0.016	1.176	1.194	−0.024	1.172	1.194	−0.028
1.6	MAX	1.600	1.600	0.006	1.596	1.600	0.002	1.594	1.600	0.000	1.586	1.600	−0.008	1.582	1.600	−0.012
	MIN	1.590	1.594	−0.010	1.586	1.594	−0.014	1.584	1.594	−0.016	1.576	1.594	−0.024	1.572	1.594	−0.028
2	MAX	2.000	2.000	0.006	1.996	2.000	0.002	1.994	2.000	0.000	1.986	2.000	−0.008	1.982	2.000	−0.012
	MIN	1.990	1.994	−0.010	1.986	1.994	−0.014	1.984	1.994	−0.016	1.976	1.994	−0.024	1.972	1.994	−0.028
2.5	MAX	2.500	2.500	0.006	2.496	2.500	0.002	2.494	2.500	0.000	2.486	2.500	−0.008	2.482	2.500	−0.012
	MIN	2.490	2.494	−0.010	2.486	2.494	−0.014	2.484	2.494	−0.016	2.476	2.494	−0.024	2.472	2.494	−0.028
3	MAX	3.000	3.000	0.006	2.996	3.000	0.002	2.994	3.000	0.000	2.986	3.000	−0.008	2.982	3.000	−0.012
	MIN	2.990	2.994	−0.010	2.986	2.994	−0.014	2.984	2.994	−0.016	2.976	2.994	−0.024	2.972	2.994	−0.028
4	MAX	4.003	4.000	0.011	3.996	4.000	0.004	3.992	4.000	0.000	3.985	4.000	−0.007	3.981	4.000	−0.011
	MIN	3.991	3.992	−0.009	3.984	3.992	−0.016	3.980	3.992	−0.020	3.973	3.992	−0.027	3.969	3.992	−0.031
5	MAX	5.003	5.000	0.011	4.996	5.000	0.004	4.992	5.000	0.000	4.985	5.000	−0.007	4.981	5.000	−0.011
	MIN	4.991	4.992	−0.009	4.984	4.992	−0.016	4.980	4.992	−0.020	4.973	4.992	−0.027	4.969	4.992	−0.031
6	MAX	6.003	6.000	0.011	5.996	6.000	0.004	5.992	6.000	0.000	5.985	6.000	−0.007	5.981	6.000	−0.011
	MIN	5.991	5.992	−0.009	5.984	5.992	−0.016	5.980	5.992	−0.020	5.973	5.992	−0.027	5.969	5.992	−0.031
8	MAX	8.005	8.000	0.014	7.996	8.000	0.005	7.991	8.000	0.000	7.983	8.000	−0.008	7.978	8.000	−0.013
	MIN	7.990	7.991	−0.010	7.981	7.991	−0.019	7.976	7.991	−0.024	7.968	7.991	−0.032	7.963	7.991	−0.037
10	MAX	10.005	10.000	0.014	9.996	10.000	0.005	9.991	10.000	0.000	9.983	10.000	−0.008	9.978	10.000	−0.013
	MIN	9.990	9.991	−0.010	9.981	9.991	−0.019	9.976	9.991	−0.024	9.968	9.991	−0.032	9.963	9.991	−0.037
12	MAX	12.006	12.000	0.017	11.995	12.000	0.006	11.989	12.000	0.000	11.979	12.000	−0.010	11.974	12.000	−0.015
	MIN	11.988	11.989	−0.012	11.977	11.989	−0.023	11.971	11.989	−0.029	11.961	11.989	−0.039	11.956	11.989	−0.044
16	MAX	16.006	16.000	0.017	15.995	16.000	0.006	15.989	16.000	0.000	15.979	16.000	−0.010	15.974	16.000	−0.015
	MIN	15.988	15.989	−0.012	15.977	15.989	−0.023	15.971	15.989	−0.029	15.961	15.989	−0.039	15.956	15.989	−0.044
20	MAX	20.006	20.000	0.019	19.993	20.000	0.006	19.986	20.000	−0.001	19.973	20.000	−0.014	19.967	20.000	−0.020
	MIN	19.985	19.987	−0.015	19.972	19.987	−0.028	19.965	19.987	−0.035	19.952	19.987	−0.048	19.946	19.987	−0.054

Continued

TABLE C.13.9 Preferred Metric Shaft Basis Transition and Interference Fits—*Continued*

BASIC SIZE	LOCATIONAL TRANS.			LOCATIONAL TRANSN.			LOCATIONAL INTERF.			MEDIUM DRIVE			FORCE		
	Hole K7	Shaft h6	Fit	Hole N7	Shaft h6	Fit	Hole P7	Shaft h6	Fit	Hole S7	Shaft h6	Fit	Hole U7	Shaft h6	Fit
25 MAX	25.006	25.000	0.019	24.993	25.000	0.006	24.986	25.000	−0.001	24.973	25.000	−0.014	24.960	25.000	−0.027
MIN	24.985	24.987	−0.015	24.972	24.987	−0.028	24.965	24.987	−0.035	24.952	24.987	−0.048	24.939	24.987	−0.061
30 MAX	30.006	30.000	0.019	29.993	30.000	0.006	29.986	30.000	−0.001	29.973	30.000	−0.014	29.960	30.000	−0.027
MIN	29.985	29.987	−0.015	29.972	29.987	−0.028	29.965	29.987	−0.035	29.952	29.987	−0.048	29.939	29.987	−0.061
40 MAX	40.007	40.000	0.023	39.992	40.000	0.008	39.983	40.000	−0.001	39.966	40.000	−0.018	39.949	40.000	−0.035
MIN	39.982	39.984	−0.018	39.967	39.984	−0.033	39.958	39.984	−0.042	39.941	39.984	−0.059	39.924	39.984	−0.076
50 MAX	50.007	50.000	0.023	49.992	50.000	0.008	49.983	50.000	−0.001	49.966	50.000	−0.018	49.939	50.000	−0.045
MIN	49.982	49.984	−0.018	49.967	49.984	−0.033	49.958	49.984	−0.042	49.941	49.984	−0.059	49.914	49.984	−0.086
60 MAX	60.009	60.000	0.028	59.991	60.000	0.010	59.979	60.000	−0.002	59.958	60.000	−0.023	59.924	60.000	−0.057
MIN	59.979	59.981	−0.021	59.961	59.981	−0.039	59.949	59.981	−0.051	59.928	59.981	−0.072	59.894	59.981	−0.106
80 MAX	80.009	80.000	0.028	79.991	80.000	0.010	79.979	80.000	−0.002	79.952	80.000	−0.029	79.909	80.000	−0.072
MIN	79.979	79.981	−0.021	79.961	79.981	−0.039	79.949	79.981	−0.051	79.922	79.981	−0.078	79.879	79.981	−0.121
100 MAX	100.010	100.000	0.032	99.990	100.000	0.012	99.976	100.000	−0.002	99.942	100.000	−0.036	99.889	100.000	−0.089
MIN	99.975	99.978	−0.025	99.955	99.978	−0.045	99.941	99.978	−0.059	99.907	99.978	−0.093	99.854	99.978	−0.146
120 MAX	120.010	120.000	0.032	119.990	120.000	0.012	119.976	120.000	−0.002	119.934	120.000	−0.044	119.869	120.000	−0.109
MIN	119.975	119.978	−0.025	119.955	119.978	−0.045	119.941	119.978	−0.059	119.899	119.978	−0.101	119.834	119.978	−0.166
160 MAX	160.012	160.000	0.037	159.988	160.000	0.013	159.972	160.000	−0.003	159.915	160.000	−0.060	159.825	160.000	−0.150
MIN	159.972	159.975	−0.028	159.948	159.975	−0.052	159.932	159.975	−0.068	159.875	159.975	−0.125	159.785	159.975	−0.215
200 MAX	200.013	200.000	0.042	199.986	200.000	0.015	199.967	200.000	−0.004	199.895	200.000	−0.076	199.781	200.000	−0.190
MIN	199.967	199.971	−0.033	199.940	199.971	−0.060	199.921	199.971	−0.079	199.849	199.971	−0.151	199.735	199.971	−0.265
250 MAX	250.013	250.000	0.042	249.986	250.000	0.015	249.967	250.000	−0.004	249.877	250.000	−0.094	249.733	250.000	−0.238
MIN	249.967	249.971	−0.033	249.940	249.971	−0.060	249.921	249.971	−0.079	249.831	249.971	−0.169	249.687	249.971	−0.313
300 MAX	300.016	300.000	0.048	299.986	300.000	0.018	299.964	300.000	−0.004	299.850	300.000	−0.118	299.670	300.000	−0.298
MIN	299.964	299.968	−0.036	299.934	299.968	−0.066	299.912	299.968	−0.088	299.798	299.968	−0.202	299.618	299.968	−0.382
400 MAX	400.017	400.000	0.053	399.984	400.000	0.020	399.959	400.000	−0.005	399.813	400.000	−0.151	399.586	400.000	−0.378
MIN	399.960	399.964	−0.040	399.927	399.964	−0.073	399.902	399.964	−0.098	399.756	399.964	−0.244	399.529	399.964	−0.471
500 MAX	500.018	500.000	0.058	499.983	500.000	0.023	499.955	500.000	−0.005	499.771	500.000	−0.189	499.483	500.000	−0.477
MIN	499.955	499.960	−0.045	499.920	499.960	−0.080	499.892	499.960	−0.108	499.708	499.960	−0.292	499.420	499.960	−0.580

APPENDIX D

Symbols

Welding Symbols

Welding Symbols and Processes—American Welding Society Standard (ANSI/AWS A2.4-79.)

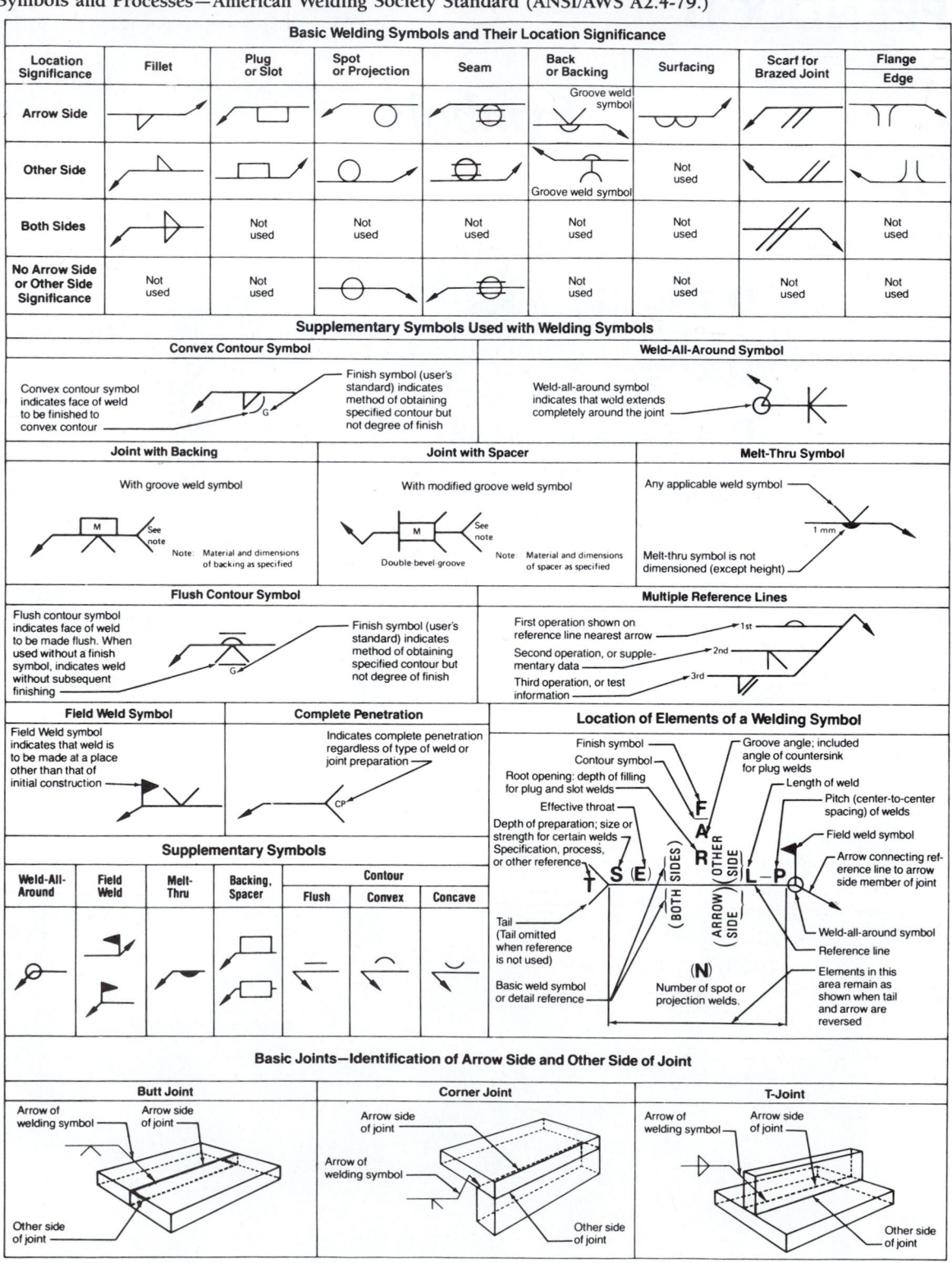

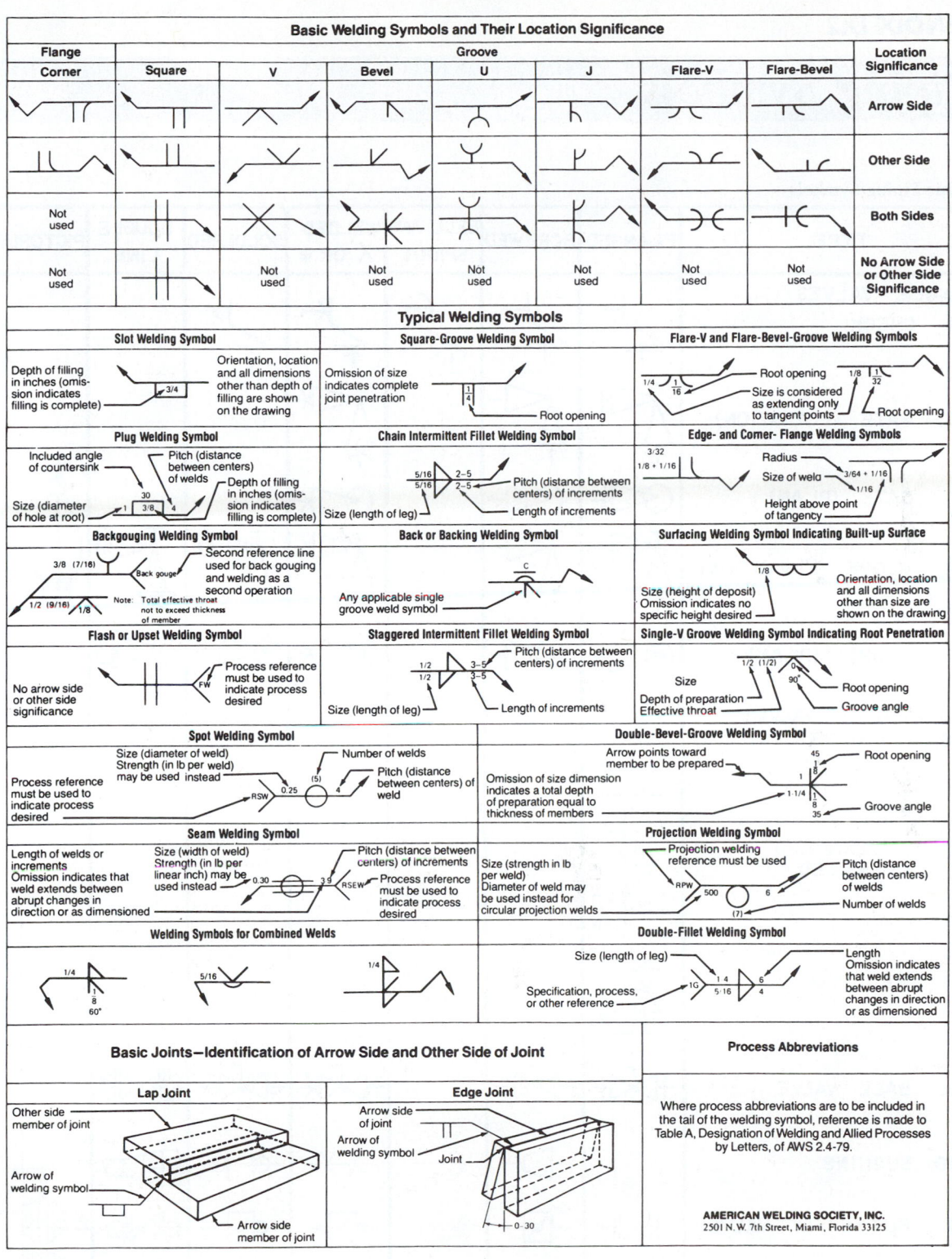

Piping Symbols

Orthographic Piping Symbols

TYPE	FLANGED	SCREWED	BELL AND SPIGOT	WELDED X OR ●	SOLDERED	DOUBLE LINE	PICTORIAL
ANGLE VALVES 1. CHECK							
2. GATE (ELEVATION)							
3. GATE (PLAN)							
4. GLOBE (ELEVATION)							
5. GLOBE (PLAN)							
AUTOMATIC VALVES 6. BY-PASS							
7. GOVERNORED OPERATED							
8. REDUCING							
9. BALL VALVE							
10. BUSHING							
11. BUTTERFLY VALVE							
CHECK VALVES 12. STRAIGHTWAY							
13. COCK OR PLUG VALVE							
14. CAP							

TYPE	FLANGED	SCREWED	BELL AND SPIGOT	WELDED X OR ●	SOLDERED	DOUBLE LINE	PICTORIAL
15. COUPLING							
16. CROSS, STRAIGHT							
17. CROSS, REDUCING							
18. CROSS							
19. DIAPHRAGM VALVE							
ELBOWS 20. 45°							
21. 90°							
22. TURNED DOWN							
23. TURNED UP							
24. BASE							
25. DOUBLE BRANCH							
26. LONG RADIUS							
27. REDUCING							
28. SIDE OUTLET (TURNED DOWN)							
29. SIDE OUTLET (TURNED UP)							
30. ELBOWLET							
FLANGES 31. BLIND							

TYPE	FLANGED	SCREWED	BELL AND SPIGOT	WELDED X OR ●	SOLDERED	DOUBLE LINE	PICTORIAL
32. ORIFICE							
33. REDUCING							
34. SOCKET WELD							
35. WELD NECK							
36. FLOAT VALVE							
37. GATE VALVE							
38. MOTOR OPERATED GATE VALVE							
39. GLOBE VALVE							
40. MOTOR OPERATED GLOBE VALVE							
HOSE VALVE 41. ANGLE							
42. GATE							
43. GLOBE							
JOINTS 44. CONNECTING PIPE							
45. EXPANSION							
46. LATERAL							
47. LOCKSHIELD VALVE							
48. MOTOR CONTROL VALVE							
PLUGS 49. BULL							
50. PIPE							

TYPE	FLANGED	SCREWED	BELL AND SPIGOT	WELDED X OR ●	SOLDERED	DOUBLE LINE	PICTORIAL
51. QUICK OPENING							
REDUCERS							
52. CONCENTRIC							
53. ECCENTRIC							
54. SOLENOID VALVE							
55. RELIEF VALVE							
56. SAFETY VALVE							
57. SLEEVE							
58. STRAINER							
TEES							
59. STRAIGHT SIZE							
60. OUTLET UP							
61. OUTLET DOWN							
62. DOUBLE SWEEP							
63. REDUCING							
64. SINGLE SWEEP							
65. SIDE OUTLET DOWN							
66. SIDE OUTLET UP							
67. UNION							
68. Y-VALVE							

Electronic Symbols

Typical Graphic Symbols for Electronic Diagrams with Basic Device Designations

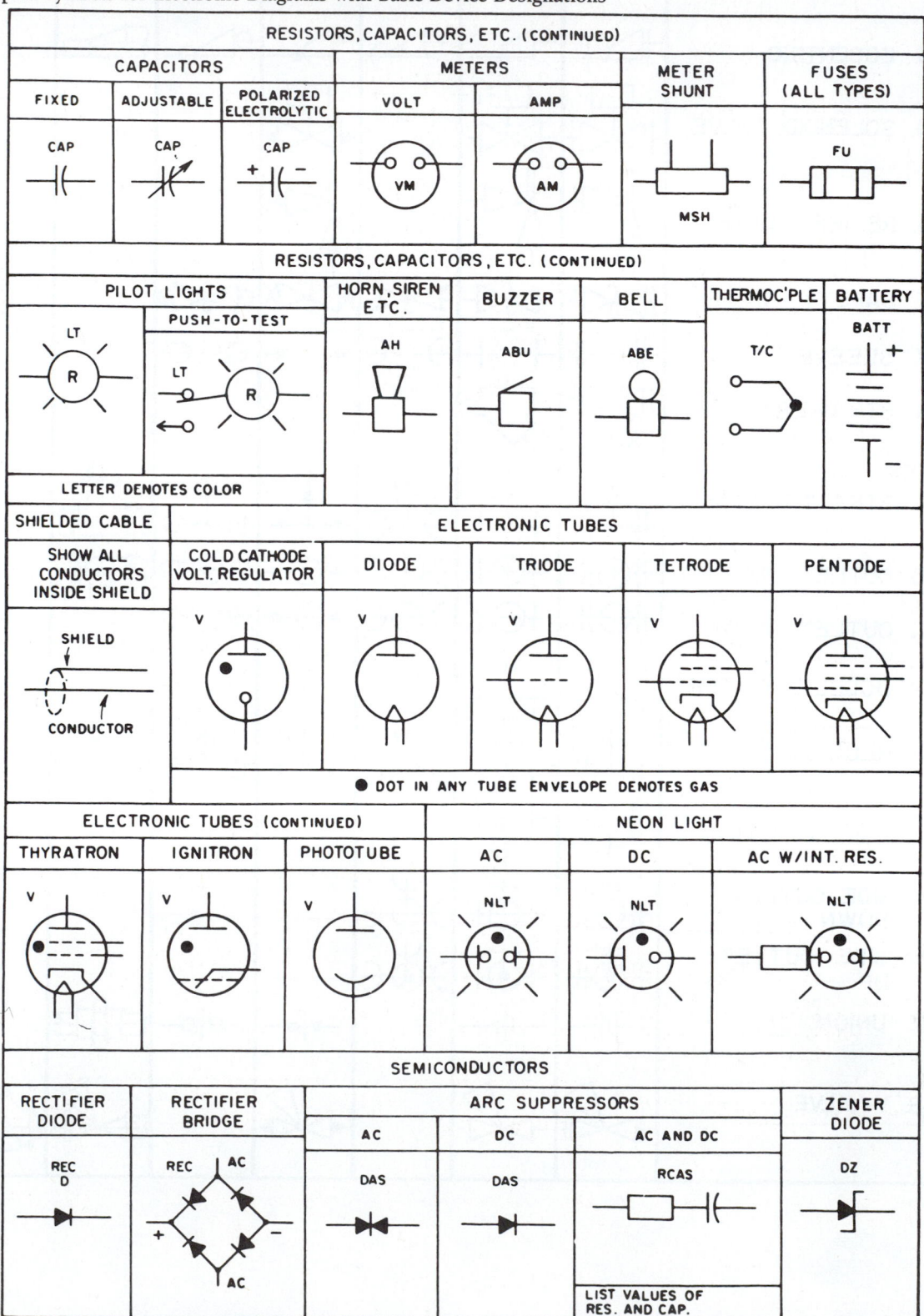

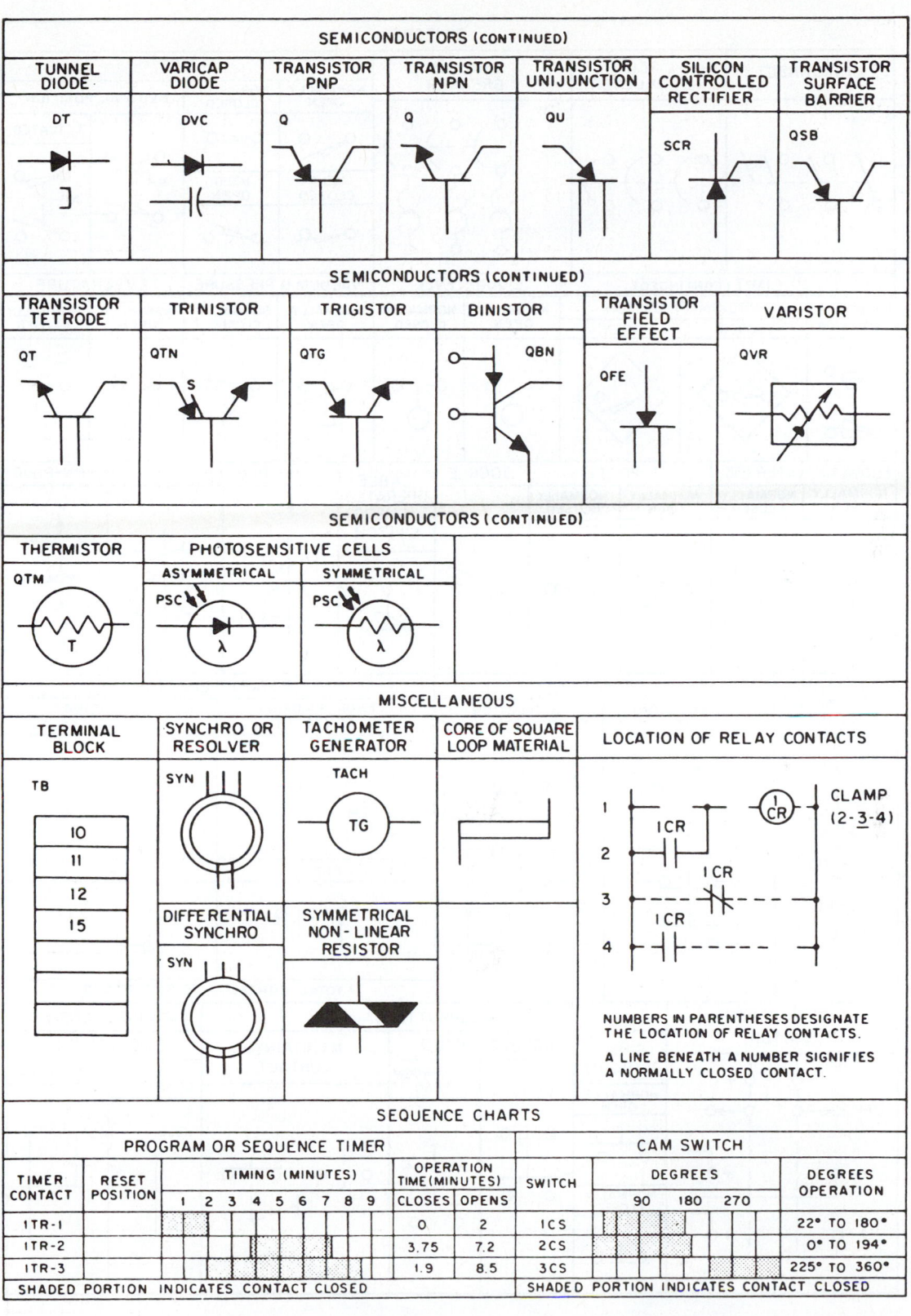

SEMICONDUCTORS (CONTINUED)

TUNNEL DIODE	VARICAP DIODE	TRANSISTOR PNP	TRANSISTOR NPN	TRANSISTOR UNIJUNCTION	SILICON CONTROLLED RECTIFIER	TRANSISTOR SURFACE BARRIER
DT	DVC	Q	Q	QU	SCR	QSB

SEMICONDUCTORS (CONTINUED)

TRANSISTOR TETRODE	TRINISTOR	TRIGISTOR	BINISTOR	TRANSISTOR FIELD EFFECT	VARISTOR
QT	QTN (S)	QTG	QBN	QFE	QVR

SEMICONDUCTORS (CONTINUED)

THERMISTOR	PHOTOSENSITIVE CELLS	
QTM (T)	ASYMMETRICAL — PSC (λ)	SYMMETRICAL — PSC (λ)

MISCELLANEOUS

TERMINAL BLOCK	SYNCHRO OR RESOLVER	TACHOMETER GENERATOR	CORE OF SQUARE LOOP MATERIAL	LOCATION OF RELAY CONTACTS
TB — 10, 11, 12, 15	SYN	TACH — TG		CLAMP (2-3-4)
	DIFFERENTIAL SYNCHRO — SYN	SYMMETRICAL NON-LINEAR RESISTOR		

NUMBERS IN PARENTHESES DESIGNATE THE LOCATION OF RELAY CONTACTS.

A LINE BENEATH A NUMBER SIGNIFIES A NORMALLY CLOSED CONTACT.

SEQUENCE CHARTS

PROGRAM OR SEQUENCE TIMER							CAM SWITCH			
TIMER CONTACT	RESET POSITION	TIMING (MINUTES) 1 2 3 4 5 6 7 8 9		OPERATION TIME (MINUTES) CLOSES	OPENS	SWITCH	DEGREES 90 180 270			DEGREES OPERATION
1TR-1				0.	2	1CS				22° TO 180°
1TR-2				3.75	7.2	2CS				0° TO 194°
1TR-3				1.9	8.5	3CS				225° TO 360°
SHADED PORTION INDICATES CONTACT CLOSED						SHADED PORTION INDICATES CONTACT CLOSED				

Table of electrical switch symbols including: SWITCHES (Disconnect, Circuit Interrupter, Circuit Breaker, Limit — Normally Open, Normally Closed, Neutral Position, Actuated, Held Closed, Held Open); Limit (continued) — Maintained Position, Proximity Switch (Closed, Open); Liquid Level (Normally Open, Normally Closed); Vacuum & Pressure (Normally Open, Normally Closed); Temperature (Normally Open, Normally Closed); Flow (Air, Water etc.) (Normally Open, Normally Closed); Foot (Normally Open, Normally Closed); Toggle; Cable Operated (Emerg.) Switch; Plugging; Non-Plug; Plugging w/Lock-out Coil; Selector (2-Position, 3-Position); Rotary Selector (Non-Bridging Contacts, Bridging Contacts), † Total Contacts to Suit Needs; Thermocouple Switch; Pushbuttons (Single Circuit — Normally Open, Normally Closed; Double Circuit, Mushroom Head; Maintained Contact); Connections, etc. — Conductors (Not Connected, Connected).

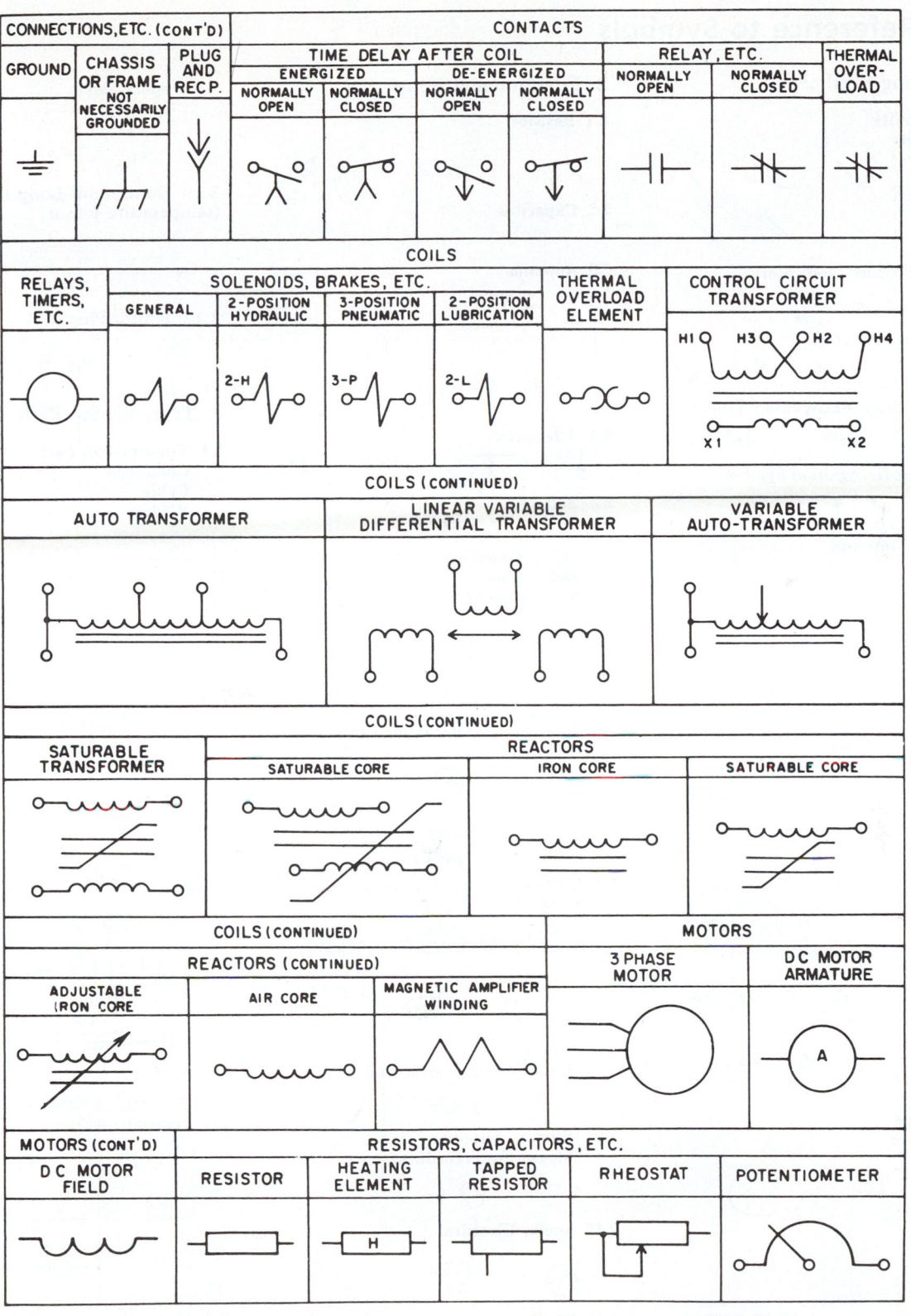

Quick Reference to Symbols

1. Qualifying Symbols

1.1 Adjustability
Variability
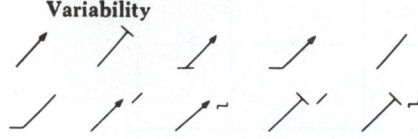

1.2 Special-Property Indicators

1.3 Radiation Indicators
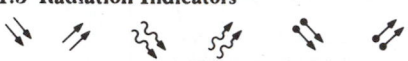

1.4 Physical State Recognition Symbols
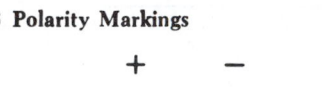

1.5 Test-Point Recognition Symbol
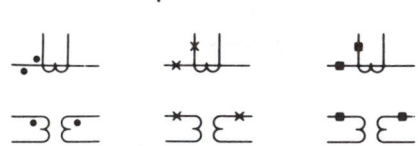

1.6 Polarity Markings
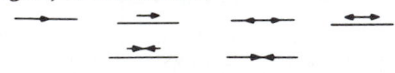

1.7 Direction of Flow of Power, Signal, or Information
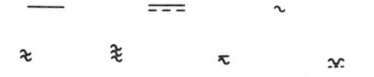

1.8 Kind of Current

1.9 Connection Symbols

1.10 Envelope
Enclosure

1.11 Shield
Shielding
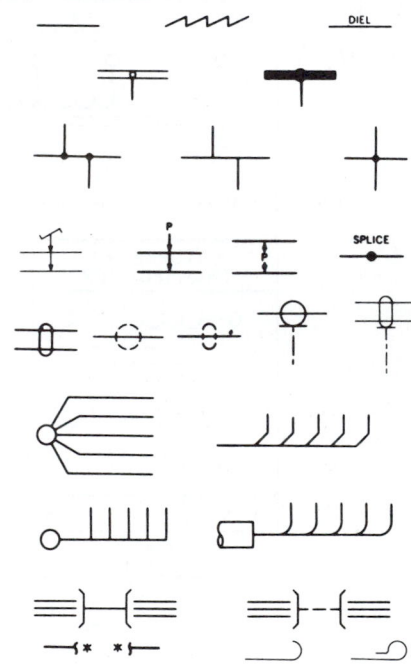

1.12 Special Connector or Cable Indicator

1.13 Electret

2. Fundamental Items

2.1 Resistor

2.2 Capacitor
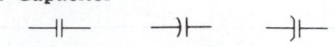

2.3 Antenna
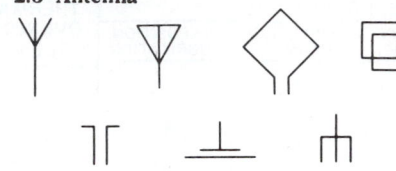

2.4 Attenuator
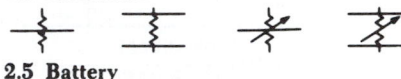

2.5 Battery

2.6 Delay Function
Delay Line
Slow-Wave Structure
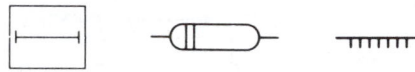

2.7 Oscillator
Generalized Alternating-Current Source

2.8 Permanent Magnet

2.9 Pickup
Head
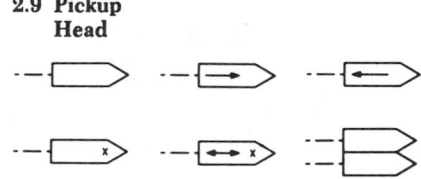

2.10 Piezoelectric Crystal Unit

2.11 Primary Detector
Measuring Transducer

2.12 Squib, Electrical
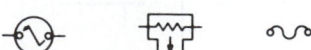

2.13 Thermocouple

2.14 Thermal Element
Thermomechanical Transducer

2.15 Spark gap
Igniter gap

2.16 Continuous Loop Fire Detector
(temperature sensor)

2.17 Ignitor Plug
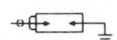

3. Transmission Path

3.1 Transmission Path
Conductor
Cable
Wiring

3.2 Distribution lines
Transmission lines

F	S	T	V

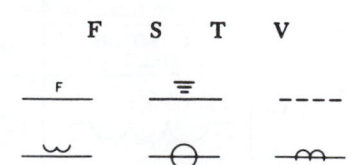

3.3 Alternative or Conditioned Wiring

3.4 Associated or Future

3.5 Intentional Isolation of Direct-Current Path in Coaxial or Waveguide Applications

3.6 Waveguide

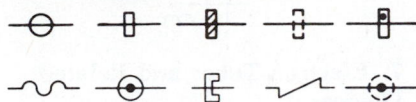

3.7 Strip-Type Transmission Line

3.8 Termination

3.9 Circuit Return

3.10 Pressure-Tight Bulkhead Cable Gland
Cable Sealing End

4. Contacts, Switches, Contactors, and Relays

4.1 Switching Function

4.2 Electrical Contact

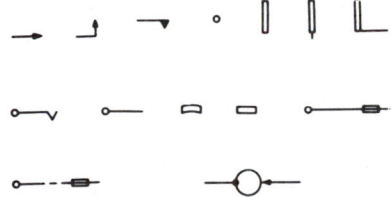

4.3 Basic Contact Assemblies

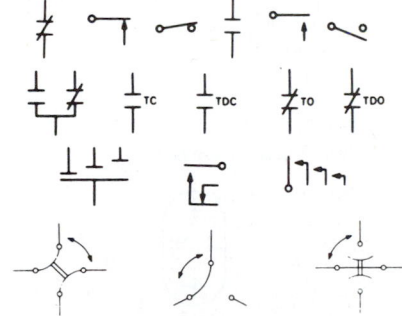

4.4 Magnetic Blowout Coil

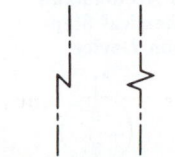

4.5 Operating Coil
Relay Coil

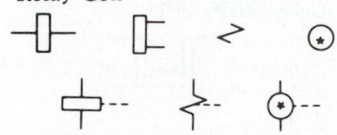

4.6 Switch

4.7 Pushbutton, Momentary or Spring-Return

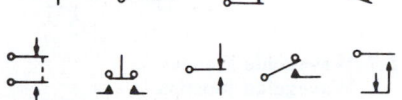

4.8 Two-Circuit, Maintained or Not Spring-Return

4.9 Nonlocking Switch, Momentary or Spring-Return

4.10 Locking Switch

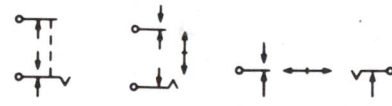

4.11 Combination Locking and Nonlocking Switch

4.12 Key-Type Switch
Lever Switch

4.13 Selector or Multiposition Switch

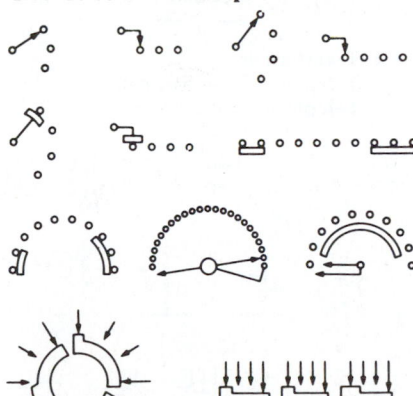

4.14 Limit Switch
Sensitive Switch

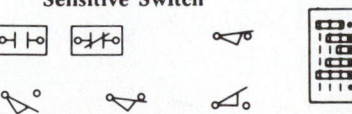

4.15 Safety Interlock

4.16 Switches with Time-Delay Feature

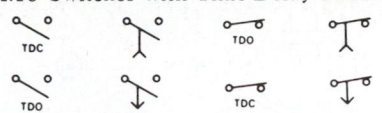

4.17 Flow-Actuated Switch

4.18 Liquid-Level-Actuated Switch

4.19 Pressure- or Vacuum-Actuated Switch

4.20 Temperature-Actuated Switch

4.21 Thermostat

4.22 Flasher
Self-interrupting switch

4.23 Foot-Operated Switch
Foot Switch

4.24 Switch Operated by Shaft Rotation and Responsive to Speed or Direction

4.25 Switches with Specific Features

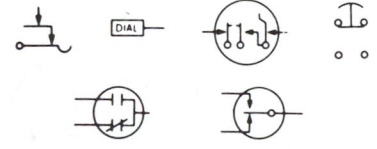

4.26 Telegraph Key

4.27 Governor
Speed Regulator

4.28 Vibrator
Interrupter

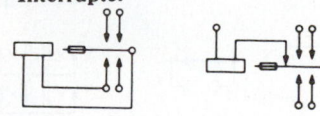

4.29 Contactor

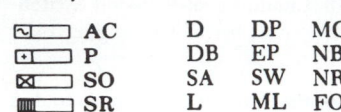

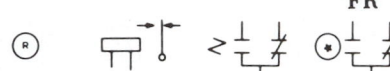

4.30 Relay

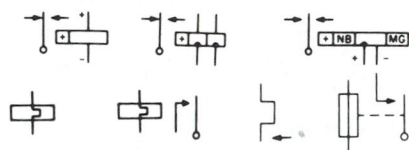

AC	D	DP	MG	
P	DB	EP	NB	
SO	SA	SW	NR	
SR	L	ML	FO	
			FR	

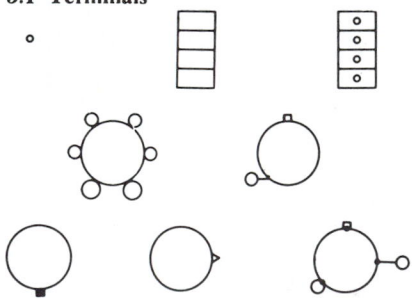

4.31 Inertia Switch

4.32 Mercury Switch

4.33 Aneroid Capsule

5. Terminals and Connectors

5.1 Terminals

5.2 Cable Termination

5.3 Connector
Disconnecting Device

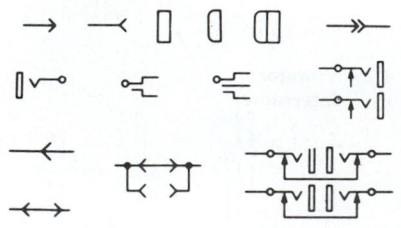

5.4 Connectors of the Type Commonly Used for Power-Supply Purposes

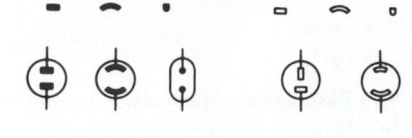

5.5 Test Blocks

5.6 Coaxial Connector

5.7 Waveguide Flanges
Waveguide junction

6. Transformers, Inductors, and Windings

6.1 Core

6.2 Inductor
Winding
Reactor
Radio frequency coil
Telephone retardation coil

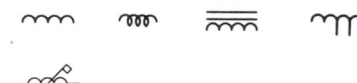

6.3 Transductor

6.4 Transformer
Telephone induction coil
Telephone repeating coil

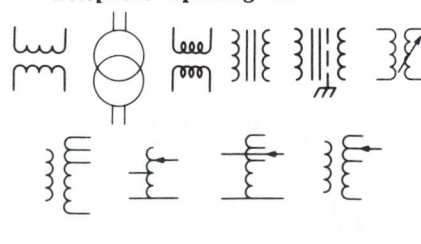

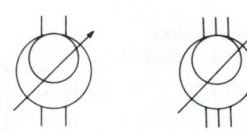

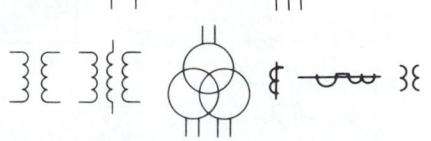

6.5 Linear Coupler

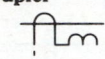

7. Electron Tubes and Related Devices

7.1 Electron Tube

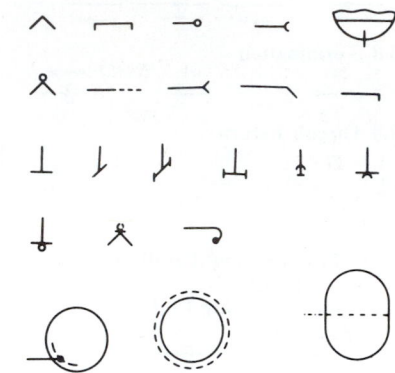

7.2 General Notes

7.3 Typical Applications

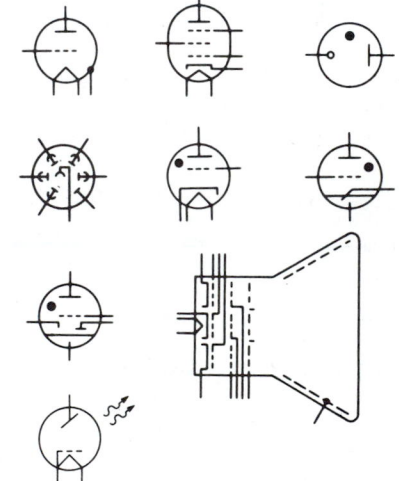

7.4 Solion
Ion-Diffusion Device

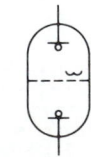

7.5 Coulomb Accumulator
Electrochemical Step-Function Device

7.6 Conductivity cell

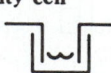

7.7 Nuclear-Radiation Detector
Ionization Chamber
Proportional Counter Tube
Geiger-Müller Counter Tube

8. Semiconductor Devices

8.1 Semiconductor Device
Transistor
Diode

8.2 Element Symbols

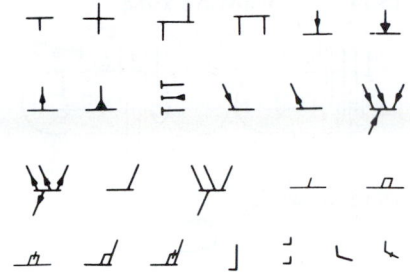

8.3 Special Property Indicators

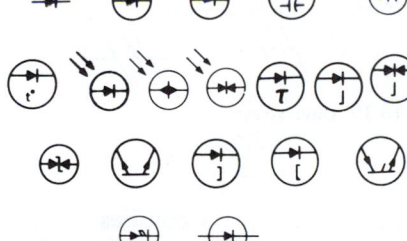

8.4 Rules for Drawing Style 1 Symbols

8.5 Typical Applications: Two-Terminal
Devices

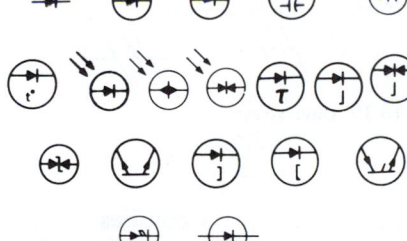

8.6 Typical Applications: Three- (or
More) Terminal Devices

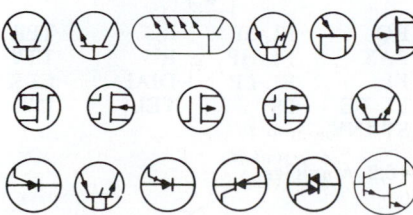

8.7 Photosensitive Cell

8.8 Semiconductor Thermocouple

8.9 Hall Element
Hall Generator

8.10 Photon-coupled isolator

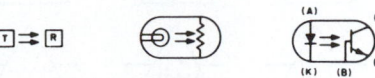

8.11 Solid-state-thyratron

9. Circuit Protectors

9.1 Fuse

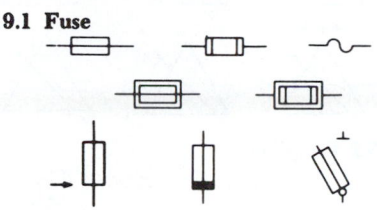

9.2 Current Arrester

9.3 Lightning Arrester
Arrester
Gap

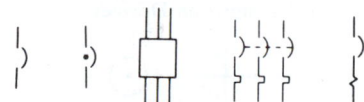

9.4 Circuit Breaker

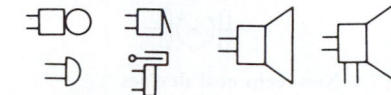

9.5 Protective Relay

C	F	φ	S	V
Z	GP	W	T	

10. Acoustic Devices

10.1 Audible-Signaling Device

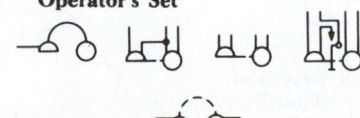

10.2 Microphone

10.3 Handset
Operator's Set

10.4 Telephone Receiver
Earphone
Hearing-Aid Receivers

11. Lamps and Visual-Signaling Devices

11.1 Lamp

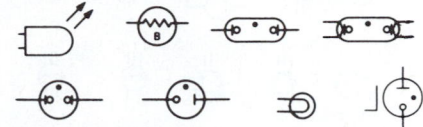

11.2 Visual-Signaling Device

12. Readout Devices

12.1 Meter
Instrument

A	DB	I	OP	RF	VA
AH	DBM	INT	OSCG	SY	VAR
C	DM	μA	PH	TLM	VARH
CMA	DTR	UA	PI	t°	VI
CMC	F	MA	PF	THC	VU
CMV	G	NM	RD	TT	W
CRO	GD	OHM	REC	V	WH

12.2 Electromagnetically Operated
Counter
Message Register

13. Rotating Machinery

13.1 Rotating Machine

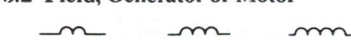

13.2 Field, Generator or Motor

13.3 Winding Connection Symbols

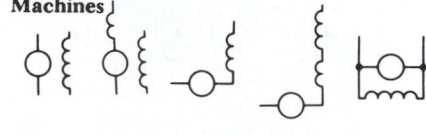

13.4 Applications: Direct-Current
Machines

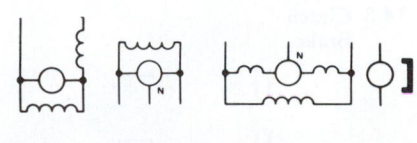

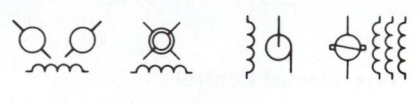

13.5 Applications: Alternating-Current Machines

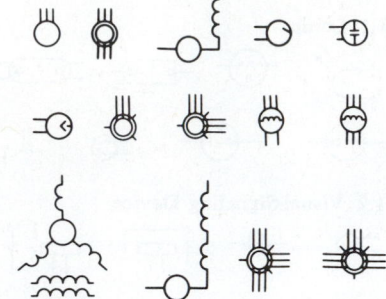

13.6 Applications: Alternating-Current Machines with Direct-Current Field Excitation

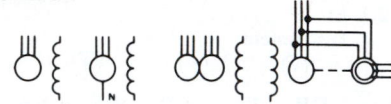

13.7 Applications: Alternating- and Direct-Current Composite

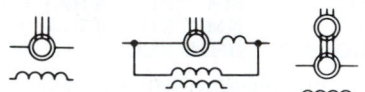

13.8 Synchro

CDX	TDX
CT	TR
CX	TX
TDR	RS

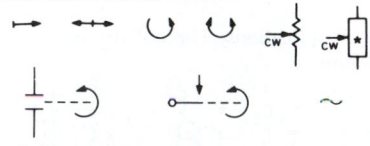

14. Mechanical Functions

**14.1 Mechanical Connection
Mechanical Interlock**

- - - - -   - -ʌ- -   ════

14.2 Mechanical Motion

**14.3 Clutch
Brake**

14.4 Manual Control

15. Commonly Used in Connection with VHF, UHF, SHF Circuits

15.1 Discontinuity

15.2 Coupling

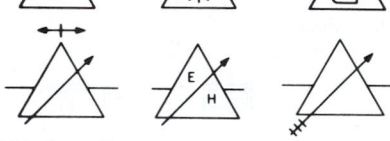

15.3 Directional Coupler

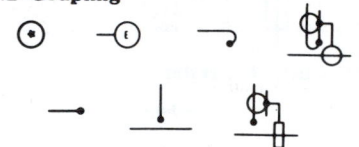

**15.4 Hybrid
Directionally Selective
Transmission Devices**

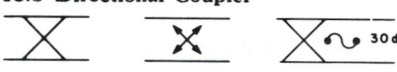

15.5 Mode Transducer

15.6 Mode Suppression

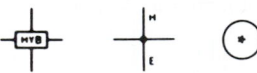

15.7 Rotary Joint

15.8 Non-reciprocal devices

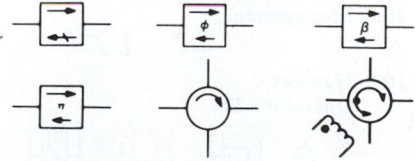

**15.9 Resonator
Tuned Cavity**

15.10 Resonator (Cavity Type) Tube

15.11 Magnetron

15.12 Velocity-Modulation (Velocity-Variation) Tube

15.13 Transmit-Receive (TR) Tube

15.14 Traveling-Wave-Tube

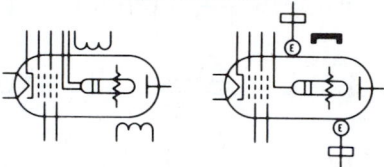

15.15 Balun

15.16 Filter

15.17 Phase shifter

15.18 Ferrite bead rings

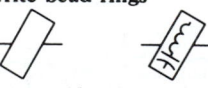

15.19 Line stretcher

16. Composite Assemblies

**16.1 Circuit assembly
Circuit subassembly
Circuit element**

EQ	FL-BP	RG	TPR
FAX	FL-HP	RU	TTY
FL	FL-LP	DIAL	CLK
FL-BE	PS	TEL	IND
ST-INV			

16.2 Amplifier

BDG	EXP	PRE
BST	LIM	PWR
CMP	MON	TRQ
DC	PGM	

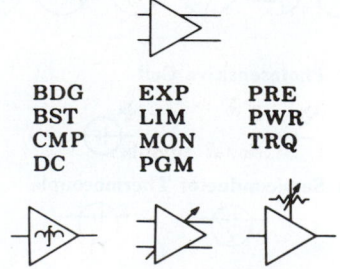

16.3 Rectifier

16.4 Repeater

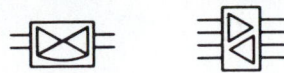

16.5 Network

16.6 Phase Shifter
Phase-Changing Network

16.7 Chopper
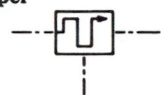

16.8 Diode-type ring demodulator
Diode-type ring modulator

16.9 Gyro
Gyroscope
Gyrocompass

16.10 Position Indicator

16.11 Position Transmitter
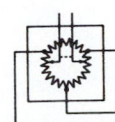

16.12 Fire Extinguisher Actuator Head

17. Analog Functions
17.1 Operational Amplifier
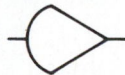

17.2 Summing Amplifier
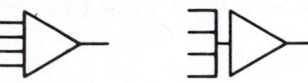

17.3 Integrator
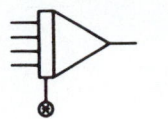 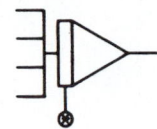

17.4 Electronic Multiplier

17.5 Electronic Divider

17.6 Electronic Function Generator

17.7 Generalized Integrator

17.8 Positional Servo-mechanism
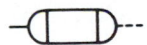

17.9 Function Potentiometer

18. Digital Logic Functions
18.1 Digital Logic Functions
(See cross references)

19. Special Purpose Maintenance Diagrams
19.1 Data flow code signals
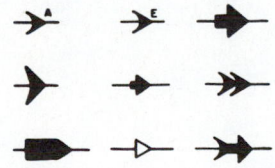

19.2 Functional Circuits
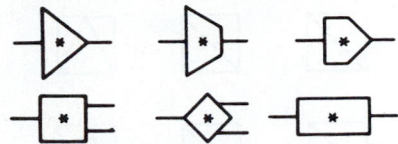

20. System Diagrams, Maps and Charts
20.1 Radio station

20.2 Space station

20.3 Exchange equipment
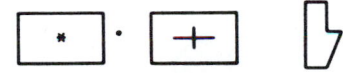

20.4 Telegraph repeater
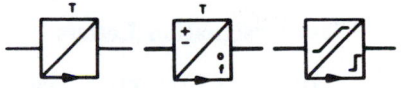

20.5 Telegraph equipment
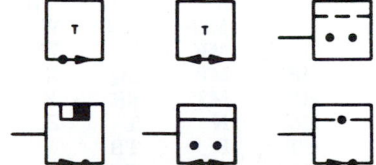

20.6 Telephone set

21. System Diagrams, Maps and Charts
21.1 Generating station

21.2 Hydroelectric generating station

21.3 Thermoelectric generating station

21.4 Prime mover

21.5 Substation

22. Class Designation Letters

A	DS	J	PU	TP
AR	E	K	Q	TR
AT	EQ	L	R	U
B	F	LS	RE	V
BT	FL	M	RT	VR
C	G	MG	RV	W
CB	H	MK	S	WT
CP	HP	MP	SQ	X
CR	HR	MT	SR	Y
D	HS	N	T	Z
DC	HT	P	TB	
DL	HY	PS	TC	

Index

A page number in *italics* indicates that a photograph or an illustration appears on that page.

Credits

Chapter 1

1.1 Lockheed-California Co.; 1.2 Hewlett-Packard Co.; 1.4 Computervision; 1.5 and 1.6 Engineering Model Associates, Inc.; 1.7 Evolution Computing; 1.9 NASA; 1.13 Lockheed-California Co.; 1.15 Macola, Inc.; 1.16 J.I. CASE; 1.18 Evolution Engineering; 1.19 Chicago Bridge and Iron Co.; 1.21 Pacific Pipe Co.; 1.22 ISICAD, Inc.; 1.23 NASA; 1.26 Adage, Inc.; 1.27 AUTODESK; 1.28 Hampton Roads Naval Museum; 1.29 Evolution Engineering; 1.31 AUTODESK.

Chapter 2

2.1 Teledyne Post; 2.2 and 2.3 Hamilton; 2.4 through 2.6 3M; 2.7 Pickett; 2.8 through 2.10 Keuffel & Esser/Kratos; 2.12 Berol RapiDesign; 2.13 Koh-I-Noor; 2.15 and 2.16 Berol RapiDesign; 2.17 Koh-I-Noor; 2.21 Hearlihy & Co.; 2.24 Hearlihy & Co.; 2.25 Keuffel & Esser/Kratos; 2.26 Teledyne Post; 2.27 Hearlihy & Co.; 2.32 Staedtler; 2.34 Hearlihy & Co.; 2.35 and 2.36 Berol RapiDesign; 2.37 Hearlihy & Co.; 2.38 Keuffel & Esser/Kratos; 2.39 Berol RapiDesign; 2.40 and 2.41 VEMCO; 2.42 Keuffel & Esser/Kratos; 2.45 through 2.47 Keuffel & Esser/Kratos; 2.48 and 2.49 Koh-I-Noor; 2.55 and 2.56 ANSI; 2.69 Koh-I-Noor.

Chapter 3

3.1 Hewlett-Packard Co.; 3.2 Cincinnati Milacron; 3.3 CADKEY, Inc.; 3.4 Cincinnati Milacron; 3.5 CADKEY, Inc.; 3.6 Apple Computer, Inc.; 3.7 and 3.8 Hewlett-Packard Co.; 3.9 Apple Computer, Inc.; 3.10 Computervision; 3.11 and 3.12 Hewlett-Packard Co.; 3.14 CADKEY, Inc.; 3.15 ISICAD, Inc.; 3.17 CADAM; 3.18 Logitech, Inc.; 3.19 Hewlett-Packard Co.; 3.20 Computervision; 3.21 Bausch & Lomb; 3.22 through 3.26 Hewlett-Packard Co.; 3.27 PCAD; 3.28 Computervision; 3.29 Intergraph Corp.; 3.30 through 3.32 AUTODESK; 3.33 Drawn using American Small Business Computers' DesignCAD 2D; 3.34 McDonnell Douglas; 3.35 Drawn using American Small Business Computers' DesignCAD 2D; 3.36a Vector Automation; 3.36b Macola, Inc.; 3.37 Drawn using American Small Business Computers' DesignCAD 3D; 3.38 Hewlett-Packard Co.; 3.39 Drawn using American Small Business Computers' DesignCAD 3D; 3.40 CADAM; 3.41 Drawn using American Small Business Computers' DesignCAD 3D; 3.42 CADKEY, Inc. 3.43a Drawn using American Small Business Computers' DesignCAD 3D; 3.43b CADKEY, Inc.; 3.44 CAMAX Systems, Inc.; 3.45 through 3.47 Cincinnati Milacron; 3.48 Ford Motor Co.; 3.49 Computervision; 3.50 Evans & Sutherland Computer Corp.

Chapter 4

4.9 Koh-I-Noor; 4.23 Hearlihy & Co.; 4.25 Keuffel & Esser/Kratos; 4.27 Lettering Guide; 4.28 Varigraph, Inc.; 4.30 Graphic Products; 4.31 and 4.32 Kroy, Inc.; 4.34 NASA; 4.36 Lockheed-California Co.; 4.37 AUTODESK and CADplus Products; Items of Interest The Bettmann Archive.

Chapter 6

6.1 NASA; 6.52 through 6.53 IBM; 6.54 Computervision; Items of Interest The Bettmann Archive.

Chapter 7

7.1 Auto-trol Technology; Items of Interest Outboard Marine Co.

Chapter 8

8.2 through 8.5 ANSI; 8.22 Rachel Svit; 8.24 David Cunningham; 8.25 ANSI; 8.29 Rachel Svit; 8.31 NASA; 8.42 Rachel Svit; 8.44 Rachel Svit; 8.45 ANSI; 8.49 Lunkenheimer Co.; 8.50 Rachel Svit; 8.52 Rachel Svit; 8.55 Evans & Sutherland Computer Corp.; 8.80 Rachel Svit; Items of Interest The Bettmann Archive.

Chapter 9

9.1 Lunkenheimer Co.; 9.6 ANSI; 9.25 ANSI; 9.44 AUTODESK; 9.45 Control Data Corp.; 9.47 AUTODESK; Items of Interest Techsonic Industries, Inc., Humminbird's TCR Color 1, 8-color liquid crystal TFT screen with over 114,000 pixels.

Chapter 10

Items of Interest Johnson & Johnson.

Chapter 11

11.1 Lockheed-California Co.; 11.50 Control Data Corp.; 11.53 and 11.54 CAMAX Systems, Inc.; 11.57 Evans & Sutherland Computer Corp.; Items of Interest Ford Motor Co.

Chapter 12

12.1 VersaCAD; 12.51 ANSI; 12.53 ANSI; 12.99 Computervision; 12.101 Computervision; Items of Interest The Bettmann Archive.

Chapter 14
Items of Interest   Cincinnati Milacron.

Chapter 15
15.33   Sandia National Laboratories; 15.35   American National Pipe Thread; 15.37   Federal Screw Products, Inc.; 15.42   CARR LANE Manufacturing; 15.43   General Motors Corp.; 15.45   General Motors Corp.; 15.49   Great Lakes Screw; 15.51   Holo-Krome; 15.87   Koh-I-Noor; 15.88   House of Fasteners; 15.107   Associated Spring, Barnes Grouping.

Chapter 16
16.1   FAG Bearing Corp.; 16.3   David Cunningham; 16.23   AUTODESK; 16.45   Hewlett-Packard Co.; 16.48   FAG Bearing Corp.; 16.50   Boston Gear, INCOM International, Inc.; 16.51 and 16.52   The Timken Company; 16.53 through 16.57   FAG Bearing Corp.; 16.59   Commercial Cam Co., Inc.; 16.61   CARR LANE Manufacturing; 16.63   AUTODESK.

Chapter 17
17.4   CADKEY, Inc.; 17.5   Logitech, Inc.; 17.8 and 17.9   NASA; 17.10   Engineering Model Associates, Inc.; 17.11   Heathkit; 17.14 and 17.15   Engineering Model Associates, Inc.; 17.17 and 17.18   NASA; 17.22   Engineering Model Associates, Inc.; 17.28 and 17.29   Grove Valve & Regulator Co.; 17.31   David Cunningham; 17.34   Johns-Manville Co.; 17.35 and 17.36   NASA; 17.37   Engineering Model Associates, Inc.; 17.38   Magee-Bralla, Inc.; 17.41   Engineering Model Associates, Inc.; 17.45   Bergen-Paterson Pipe Support Group; 17.46 through 17.48   ANSI; 17.50   ANSI; 17.52   Strux Corp.; 17.54   NASA; 17.56 through 17.58   NASA; 17.59   Silverscreen; 17.61 and 17.62   NASA; 17.64   NASA; 17.65   The Scale Model Makers; 17.67   Magee-Bralla, Inc.; 17.68   Megatek Corp.; 17.69   Gerber Systems Technology; 17.70   Evans & Sutherland Computer Corp.; 17.71   Megatek Corp.; 17.72   CADAM; 17.74   Calma, a division of Prime Computer; 17.75   Computervision; 17.79   Evans & Sutherland Computer Corp.; 17.81   Computervision; 17.83   Innovative Design Systems Corp.; 17.84   Logitech, Inc.

Chapter 18
18.1   Hewlett-Packard Co.; 18.6   Grove Valve & Regulator Co.; 18.9   FAG Bearing Corp.; 18.11   Evans & Sutherland Computer Corp.; 18.13   Drawn by P. Jenkins; 18.23   Teledyne Corp.; 18.24   3M; 18.28   CADKEY, Inc.; 18.29   Computervision; 18.30   Lockheed-California Co.; 18.33   Silverscreen; 18.36   Gerber Systems Technology; 18.38   CARR LANE Manufacturing; 18.39 and 18.40   Wedge Innovations.

Chapter 19
19.42 and 19.43   NASA.

Chapter 20
20.2   CADKEY, Inc.; 20.10   Megatek Corp.; 20.13   NASA; 20.16   Evans & Sutherland Computer Corp.; 20.29 and 20.30   CADKEY, Inc.; 20.37 through 20.46   Drawn by Che Rangle.

Chapter 21
21.4   NASA; 21.6   Bonestroo, Rosene, Anderlik & Assoc.; 21.12   Computervision; 21.13   Auto-trol Technology; Items of Interest   General Mills.

Chapter 22
22.1   Chicago Bridge and Iron Co.; 22.28   Sigma; 22.41   California Computer Products, Inc.; Items of Interest   The Bettmann Archive.

Chapter 23
23.1   American Microsystems, Inc.; 23.2   Bishop Graphics, Inc.; 23.9   Jerry Rye; 23.12   Motorola, Inc., Semiconductor Products Sector; 23.13   Bishop Graphics, Inc.; 23.14   Motorola, Inc., Semiconductor Products Sector; 23.23   TRW LSI Products; 23.24   Motorola, Inc., Semiconductor Products Sector; 23.25 and 23.26   Berol RapiDesign; 23.30   Motorola, Inc., Semiconductor Products Sector; 23.31 and 23.32   Bishop Graphics, Inc.; 23.36   Bishop Graphics, Inc.; 23.42   Motorola, Inc., Semiconductor Products Sector; 23.46   Calma, a division of Prime Computer; 23.54   AMI; 23.55   Computervision; 23.57 through 23.60   DOUGLAS CAD/CAM.

Color Plates
1 through 15   Control Data Corp.; 16 and 17   Hewlett-Packard Co.; 18 through 22   AUTODESK; 23   Hewlett-Packard Co.; 24   CADKEY, Inc.; 25 through 29   AUTODESK; 30   Hewlett-Packard Co.; 31   CADKEY, Inc.; 32   AUTODESK; 33 and 34   Calma, a division of Prime Computer; 35 through 43   Control Data Corp.; 44 and 45   Cincinnati Milacron; 46 through 54   Calma, a division of Prime Computer; 55   CADKEY, Inc.; 56 through 59   AUTODESK; 60   Megatek Corp.; 61 through 63   PATRAN, a division of PDA Engineering; 64   Evans & Sutherland Computer Corp.; 65   PATRAN, a division of PDA Engineering; 66   IBM; 67   Evans & Sutherland Computer Corp.; 68   Megatek Corp.; 69 through 76   PATRAN, a division of PDA Engineering; 77 and 78   AUTODESK; 79 and 80   Evans & Sutherland Computer Corp.; 81   AUTODESK; 82   Lockheed-California Co.; 83   PATRAN, a division of PDA Engineering; 84   McDonnell Douglas Automation Co.; 85 through 87   Macola, Inc.; 88 through 90   McDonnell Douglas Automation Co.; 91   Megatek Corp.; 92 through 94   AUTODESK; 95 through 97   McDonnell Douglas Automation Co.; 98   AUTODESK; 99   Evans & Sutherland Computer Corp.; 100 through 102   McDonnell Douglas Automation Co.; 103   Intergraph Corp.; 104 through 106   Calma, a division of Prime Computer; Plate 107   Versatec; 108 and 109   Intergraph Corp.; 110   AUTODESK.

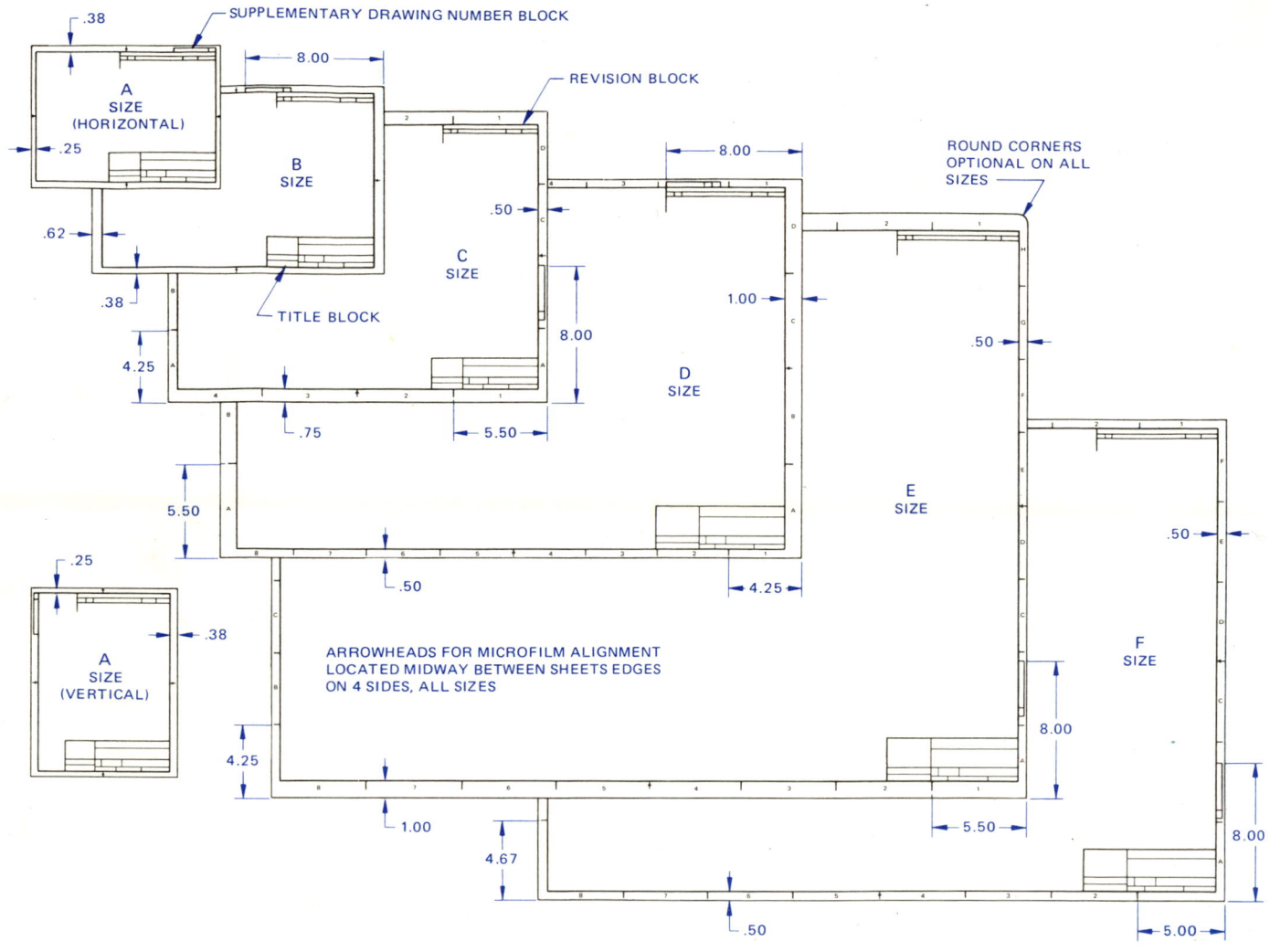

SUPPLEMENTARY DRAWING NUMBER BLOCK

.38

A
SIZE
(HORIZONTAL)

.25

8.00

REVISION BLOCK

.62

B
SIZE

ROUND CORNERS
OPTIONAL ON ALL
SIZES

8.00

.38

.50

4.25

C
SIZE

TITLE BLOCK

8.00

1.00

.50

D
SIZE

.75

5.50

5.50

.50

A
SIZE
(VERTICAL)

.25

.38

ARROWHEADS FOR MICROFILM ALIGNMENT
LOCATED MIDWAY BETWEEN SHEETS EDGES
ON 4 SIDES, ALL SIZES

E
SIZE

4.25

F
SIZE

.50

8.00

4.25

1.00

5.50

4.67

8.00

.50

5.00